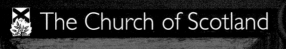 The Church of Scotland

HOUSING & LOAN FUND
for Retired Ministers and Widows and Widowers of Ministers

The Church of Scotland Housing and Loan Fund exists to support ministers and manse families with housing on retirement.

Because of the requirement to live in a tied house whilst they are in a charge, many ministers are unable to provide their own house for retirement. Ministers and their widows or widowers, or bereaved civil partners may be assisted by the provision of a house to rent, or a loan to allow them to purchase a house themselves. Estranged spouses of ministers may also be eligible to apply for assistance.

Donations, legacies and gift aid contributions will be welcomed and greatly support the Fund's ongoing work.

The Secretary of the Fund is also happy to give talks and presentations about the work of the Fund.

For further information please contact:
The Secretary,
The Church of Scotland,
121 George Street,
Edinburgh, EH2 4YN

Tel: 0131 225 5722

Scottish Charity Number: SC011353

www.churchofscotland.org.uk

The
Scottish
Law
Directory
2022

The Scottish Law Directory 2022

The Directory
of the
Law Society of Scotland

ONE HUNDRED AND THIRTY FIRST EDITION

THE LAW SOCIETY
of SCOTLAND
www.lawscot.org.uk

LexisNexis®

LexisNexis® UK & Worldwide

United Kingdom	*RELX (UK) Limited, trading as LexisNexis ®, 1–3 Strand, London WC2N 5JR*
LNUK Global Partners	*LexisNexis® encompasses authoritative legal publishing brands dating back to the 19th century including: Butterworths® in the United Kingdom, Canada and the Asia-Pacific region; Les Editions du Juris Classeur® in France; and Matthew Bender® worldwide. Details of LexisNexis® locations worldwide can be found at www.lexisnexis.com*

© 2022 RELX (UK) Ltd

Published by LexisNexis®

This is a Butterworths® title

A CIP Catalogue record for this book is available from the British Library.

ISBN for the Scottish Law Directory 131st Edition: 978 1 474 32114 3

Printed and bound by CPI Group (UK) Limited, Croydon CR0 4YY

Typeset by Letterpart Ltd, Caterham, Surrey

Visit LexisNexis® UK at www.lexisnexis.co.uk

Contents

Introduction

The Official List of Certificated Solicitors for 2022

The Scottish Law Directory contains a list of those qualified to practice as a solicitor in Scotland. The list is provided by the Law Society of Scotland, the professional body for solicitors, at the start of the practising year and contains all solicitors with a practising certificate at that time. A more up to date reference for practising solicitors at any given time during the year can be found at www.lawscot.org.uk/find-a-solicitor

Publishers' Note

The list of certificated solicitors published in *The Scottish Law Directory 2022* is dated **2nd December 2021**. The publishers have included all other information available to them at 1st April 2022 and, where possible, changes occurring after that date. At the time of going to press various appointments were in the offing but not confirmed and have therefore not been included.

Editor's note: The Alphabetical List of Law Firms in Scotland is now arranged by surname e.g. law firm 'A B Crow' will fall under 'C' as opposed to 'A'.

The Scottish Law Directory Fees Supplement 2022

The 2022 Fees Supplement will be published later this year at a price of £99.99, copies can be purchased from LexisNexis®.

Disclaimer

The publishers have taken all reasonable measures to ensure the accuracy of the information contained in this Directory but cannot accept responsibility or liability for errors in or omissions from any information given or any consequences arising.

The Supreme Court

Parliament Square, London SW1P 3BD Tel: (020) 7960 1500 DX: 157230 Parliament Sq 4 Email: enquiries@supremecourt.uk Website: www.supremecourt.uk

Justices of the Supreme Court
(in order of seniority)

The Right Hon The Lord Reed of Allermuir (President)
The Right Hon Lord Hodge (Deputy President)
The Right Hon Lord Lloyd-Jones
The Right Hon Lord Briggs of Westbourne
The Right Hon Lady Arden of Heswall DBE
The Right Hon Lord Kitchin
The Right Hon Lord Sales
The Right Hon Lord Hamblen of Kersey
The Right Hon Lord Leggatt
The Right Hon Lord Burrows
The Right Hon Lord Stephens of Creevyloughgare
The Right Hon Lady Rose of Colmworth
Registrar: Louise di Mambro OBE
Deputy Registrar: Ian Sewell
Chief Executive: Vicky Fox
Director of Corporate Services: Sam Clark

Judicial Committee of the Privy Council

Parliament Square, London SW1P 3BD Tel: (020) 7960 1500 DX: 157230 Parliament Sq 4 Email: enquiries@supremecourt.uk Website: www.jcpc.uk

Members of the Judicial Committee
The Judicial Committee of the Privy Council is the highest court of appeal for many Commonwealth countries, as well as the United Kingdom's overseas territories, crown dependencies, and military sovereign base areas. It also hears very occasional appeals from a number of ancient and ecclesiastical courts. These include the Church Commissioners, the Arches Court of Canterbury, the Chancery Court of York, prize courts and the Court of Admiralty of the Cinque Ports.

Justices
The Right Hon Lord Reed of Allermuir (President)
The Right Hon Lord Hodge (Deputy President)
The Right Hon Lord Lloyd-Jones
The Right Hon Lord Briggs of Westbourne
The Right Hon Lady Arden of Heswall DBE
The Right Hon Lord Kitchin
The Right Hon Lord Sales
The Right Hon Lord Hamblen of Kersey
The Right Hon Lord Leggatt
The Right Hon Lord Burrows
The Right Hon Lord Stephens of Creevyloughgare
The Right Hon Lady Rose of Colmworth
Chief Executive: Vicky Fox
Registrar: Louise di Mambro
Director of Corporate Services: Sam Clark

The Privy Council Office
The Privy Council dates back to Norman times and is one of the oldest parts of Government. These days, however, the Privy Council is simply the mechanism through which interdepartmental agreement is reached on those items of Government business which, for historical or other reasons, fall to Ministers as Privy Counsellors rather than as Departmental Ministers. Although members of the Privy Council are appointed for life, only Ministers of the current Government participate in its day-to-day business and they are accountable to Parliament for all matters conducted through the Privy Council. The Ministerial head of the Privy Council Office is the Lord President of the Council.
The Right Honourable Jacob Rees-Mogg (Lord President)
Richard Tilbrook (Clerk of the Council)

Court of Session

Parliament House, Parliament Square, Edinburgh EH1 1RQ Tel: (0131) 225 2595
Fax: (0131) 240 6711 DX: 549306 Edinburgh 36 Email: supreme.courts@scotcourts.gov.uk Website: www.scotcourts.gov.uk
The Rolls of Court can be found at website: www.scotcourts.gov.uk

THE COURT OF SESSION, which is the highest civil tribunal in Scotland, consists of thirty-five judges. The Lord President and five other judges sit in the First Division, and the Lord Justice-Clerk and five other judges sit in the Second Division, the two divisions together comprising the Inner House. The remaining judges officiate in the Outer House as Lords Ordinary.

The terms of the court during 2022 are fixed as follows:
From Wednesday 5 January to Saturday 9 March
From Monday 22 April to Saturday 23 December

Inner House Judges

Bar	Bench	First Division
1997	2000	The Rt Hon Lord Carloway (Colin J M Sutherland) (Lord President and Lord Justice General)
1982	2006	The Rt Hon Lord Turnbull (A D Turnbull)
1991	2002	The Rt Hon Lord Pentland (Paul B Cullen)
1991	2002	The Rt Hon Lord Pentland (Paul B Cullen)
1987	2010	The Rt Hon Lord Tyre (Colin J Tyre)
1983	2012	The Rt Hon Lord Boyd of Duncansby (Colin Boyd)
1993	2013	The Hon Lady Wise (Morag B Wise

Bar	Bench	Second Division
1981	2005	The Rt Hon Lady Dorrian (Leeona J Dorrian)(Lord Justice Clerk)
1977	2000	The Rt Hon Lady Paton (Ann Paton)
1976	2001	The Rt Hon Lord Woolman (Stephen E Woolman)
1977	2007	The Rt Hon Lord Malcolm (C M Campbell)
1992	2005	The Hon Lord Doherty (J Raymond Doherty)
1979	2007	The Hon Lord Matthews (Hugh Matthews)

Outer House Judges

Bar	Bench	
1981	2006	The Hon Lord Brailsford (S N Brailsford)
1987	2009	The Hon Lady Stacey (Valerie E Stacey)
1991	2012	The Hon Lady Scott (Margaret E Scott)
1986	2013	The Hon Lord Armstrong (Iain Gillies Armstrong)
1993	2016	The Hon Lord Beckett (John Beckett)
1994	2016	The Hon Lord Clark (Alistair Clark)
1996	2016	The Hon Lord Ericht (Andrew F Stewart)
1993	2016	The Hon Lady Carmichael (Ailsa Carmichael)
2008	2016	The Hon Lord Mulholland (Frank Mulholland)
1994	2017	The Hon Lord Summers (Alan A. Summers)
1991	2017	The Hon Lord Arthurson(Paul A. Arthurson)
1999	2020	The Hon Lord Fairley (Douglas Fairley)
1998	2020	The Hon Lady Poole (Anna Poole)

Bar	Bench	
1999	2020	The Hon Lord Harrower (Sean Smith)
1995	2020	The Hon Lord Weir (Robert Weir)
1995	2020	The Hon Lord Braid (Peter Braid)
1996	2021	The Hon Lord Sandison (Craig Sandison)
1996	2021	The Hon Lady Haldane (Shona Haldane)
2003	2021	The Hon Lord Richardson (Martin Richardson)
1994	2014	The Hon Lord Minginish (Roderick John MacLeod)

Intellectual Property Judges: The Hon Lords Clark ,Ericht, Braid and Harrower
Commercial Judges: The Hon Lords Clark, Ericht, Braid and Harrower
Employment Appeal Tribunal Judges: The Hon Lord Summers and Hon Lord Fairley (reserve)
Parole Board Judge: The Hon Lord Mulholland
Court of Exchequer: The Hon Lord Doherty
Insolvency Judges: The Hon Lords Clark, Ericht, Braid and Harrower
Registration Appeal Court: The Rt Hon Lady Paton, Rt Hon Lord Pentland, and the Hon Lord Matthews
Lands Valuation Appeal Court: The Lord Justice Clerk, Rt Hon Lords Malcolm, Woolman and Tyre, and the Hon Lord Doherty

Principal Clerk of Session and Justiciary:
Mrs P McFarlane

Personal Secretary to the Principal Clerk:
Ms V A Arthur

Keeper of the Rolls:
P Fiddes

Deputy Principal Clerk of Session:
Mrs D Machin

Depute in Charge:
C Anderson (Acting)
Senior Assistant Clerk: J Hutchison (Acting)
Superintendents, Court Buildings: F Crawford, Mrs E Cameron

High Court of Justiciary

Justiciary Office, Parliament House, 11 Parliament Square, Edinburgh EH1 1RQ Tel: (0131) 225 2595
Fax: (0131) 240 6746 (Civil)
Fax: (0131) 240 6915 (Criminal) DX: 549306 Edinburgh-36 Email: supreme.courts@scotcourts.gov.uk
(The Rolls of Court can be found at website:
www.scotcourts.gov.uk/current-business/court-rolls/high-court)

THE HIGH COURT OF JUSTICIARY is the supreme criminal court in Scotland, having exclusive
jurisdiction in certain crimes. It sits as a court of first instance in Edinburgh, and on circuit throughout
Scotland as may be required. Acting in an appellate capacity, the court disposes of appeals against
convictions and sentences on indictment under the provisions of the Criminal Procedure (Scotland)
Act 1995 and also appeals from courts of summary jurisdiction and under the Courts-Martial
(Appeals) Act 1968.

Lord Justice-General: The Rt Hon Lord Carloway
Lord Justice-Clerk: The Rt Hon Lady Dorrian
Lords Commissioners of Justiciary: All the other Judges of the Court of Session, in terms of the Criminal
Procedure (Scotland) Act 1995, s 1(2).

Principal Clerk of Justiciary: Mrs P McFarlane
Deputy Principal Clerk of Justiciary: R Martin
Appeal Clerks: A McKay, D Morrison
Depute in Charge: Mrs L Glasgow
Senior Assistant Clerk: Miss E Cranston

CRIMINAL COURT RULES COUNCIL The Lord Justice General; The Lord Justice Clerk (Chairperson);
The Clerk of Justiciary (Mrs P McFarlane); Sheriff Alastair Brown; Sheriff William Gilchrist; Anthony
McGeehan (Crown Office and Procurator Fiscal Service); Professor James Chalmers (University of
Glasgow); Ian Dickson (Scottish Legal Aid Board); The Hon. Lord Matthews; Peter Lockhart (Solicitor);
Willie Cowan (Scottish Government); Sheriff Norman McFadyen (Appeal Sheriff); Stuart Fair (Justice
of the Peace); Kate Wallace (Victim Support Scotland); Gail Smith (Sheriff Clerk); Shelagh McCall
QC (Faculty of Advocates); John Scullion QC (Faculty of Advocates); Ruth McQuaid (Crown Office
and Procurator Fiscal Service); The Hon. Lord Beckett; Stuart Munro (Solicitor)
Secretary: Mr E McHugh, Deputy Legal Secretary to the Lord President

Courts Administration

Scottish Government Justice Directorate

2nd Floor West, St Andrew's House, Regent Road, Edinburgh EH1 3DG Tel: (0300) 244 4000 Email: ceu@gov.scot Website: www.gov.scot
Director General Education and Justice: Joe Griffin
Director Justice: Neil Rennick
CabinetSecretary for Justice and Veterans: Cabinet Keith Brown MSP
Minister for Community Safety: Ash Regan MSP

Judicial Appointments Board for Scotland

Thistle House, 91 Haymarket Terrace, Edinburgh EH12 5HE Tel: 0131 528 5101 Website: www.judicialappointments.scot
Interim Chair of the Board: Deirdre Fulton
Board Members: Professor Stephen Tierney, Ms Neelam Bakshi, The Honourable Lady Wise QC, The Honourable Lord Minginish QC, Mrs Elizabeth Burnley CBE, Sheriff Principal Lewis, Ms Morag Ross QC, Sheriff David Young QC
Business Management Unit: Chief Executive, Head of the Business Management Unit, Court Appointments Manager and Board Secretary, Business Support Officer, Appointments Administrator

Scottish Courts & Tribunals Service Headquarters

Saughton House, Broomhouse Drive, Edinburgh EH11 3XD Tel: 0131 444 3300 Fax: 0131 443 2610 Email: enquiries@scotcourts.gov.uk Website: www.scotcourts.gov.uk DX: 545309 Edinburgh 39
Chief Executive: Eric McQueen
Interim Deputy Chief Executive: Noel Rehfisch
Executive Director Court Operations: David Fraser
Executive Director Tribunals and OPG: Tim Barraclough
Chief Finance Officer: Richard Maconachie
Executive Director Judicial Office: Kay McCorquodale
Executive Director Change & Digital Innovation: Mike Milligan
Scottish Courts & Tribunals Service Board:
Lord President (Chairman of the Board) – The Rt Hon Lord Carloway, Lord Justice Clerk –The Rt Hon Lady Dorrian, President of the Scottish Tribunals – The Rt Hon Lord Woolman, Chief Executive of the Scottish Courts and Tribunals Service – Eric McQueen
Judicial Members: Sheriff Principal Craig Turnbull, Sheriff Olga Pasportnikov, Sheriff Jillian Martin-Brown, Anne Scott, Morna Rae JP
Advocate Member: Dr Kirsty J Hood
Solicitor Member: Mr Simon J D Catto
Members from Outside the Justice System: Mr Joseph Martin Al-Gharabally, Colonel (Retired) John David McIlroy, BSc CEng FICE, Dr Sophie Flemig

Scottish Civil Justice Council

Parliament House, Edinburgh EH1 1RQ Tel: 0131 240 6776 Email: scjc@scotcourts.gov.uk Website: www.scottishciviljusticecouncil.gov.uk
Chair: The Rt. Hon. Lord Carloway (Colin John MacLean Sutherland) Lord President and Lord Justice General
Ex Officio Members: Eric McQueen – Chief Executive, Scottish Courts and Tribunal Service, Colin Lancaster – Chief Executive, Scottish Legal Aid Board, Denise Swanson – Scottish Ministers' appointee
Judicial Members: The Hon. Lady Carmichael (Ailsa Carmichael QC), The Right Hon. Lord Boyd of Duncansby (Colin Boyd), Sheriff Principal Duncan L Murray, Sheriff Thomas Hughes (Dundee), Sheriff George Way
Advocate Members: Lynda Brabender QC, Catherine Smith QC
Solicitor Members: Jacqueline Harris, Joel Conn
Consumer Representative Members: Thomas Docherty
Lord President Members: Employment Judge Joseph d'Inverno, Brandon Malone
Observers: Cameron Stewart, Director of Development and Innovation, Scottish Courts and Tribunals Service, Nicola Anderson, Legislation Implementation Team, Scottish Courts and Tribunals Service, Diane Machin, Deputy Principal Clerk of Session, Scottish Courts and Tribunals Service

Lord President's Private Office

Parliament House, Edinburgh EH1 1RQ
Tel: (0131) 240 6701
Fax: (0131) 240 6704 Email: lppo@scotcourts.gov.uk Website: www.scotcourts.gov.uk
Legal Secretary to the Lord President: A Campbell
Head of the Legal Secretariat: Ms S Campbell and Ms C Marshall
Deputy Legal Secretaries: E McHugh, Ms M Kaney, Ms A Pitcairn, Ms K Kelman, I Vicherstaff, Ms C Whyte
Private Secretary to the Lord President: Mr P Gilmour
Law Clerk to the Lord President: Ms Y Middleton
Personal Secretary to the Lord President: Mrs D Laidlaw
Information about the Judiciary of Scotland can be found at www.scotland-judiciary.org.uk

Other Court Personnel

Head of Administration: Mrs E Reid
Administration Manager: Miss D Fleming

Personal Secretary to the Lord Justice-Clerk: Mrs L Scott
Law Clerk to Lord Justice-Clerk: Ms A McGinley

Librarian: Miss J Findlay
Cashier: Mrs E Hunter

Other Courts and Tribunals

The Scottish Sentencing Council

Parliament House, Edinburgh EH1 1RQ
Tel: (0300) 790 0006 Email:
sentencingcouncil@scotcourts.gov.uk Website:
https://www.scottishsentencingcouncil.org.uk/
The Scottish Sentencing Council was established
in October 2015 under The Criminal Justice and
Licensing (Scotland) Act 2010. The Council's
responsibilities include preparing sentencing
guidelines for the Scottish courts, publishing
guideline judgments issued by the Scottish
courts, and publishing information about
sentences imposed by the courts.
It also has powers to publish information about,
and conduct research into, sentencing and to
provide advice and guidance of a general nature
on sentencing matters.
Chair: Rt. Hon. Lady Dorrian, the Lord Justice
Clerk
Senator member: Rt. Hon Lord Matthews
Sheriff member: Sheriff Iain Fleming
Summary Sheriff member: Vacant
Justice of the peace member: Susan Fallone JP
Sheriff Principal member: Sheriff Principal Craig
Turnbull
Prosecutor member: Lindsey Miller (October
2026)
Advocate member: Vacant
Solicitor member: Krista Johnston
Constable member: DCC Will Kerr
Victims expert member: Lesley Weber
Lay member: Dr Hannah Graham

The Accountant of Court

Hadrian House, Callendar Business Park,
Callendar Road, Falkirk FK1 1XR Tel: (01324)
678300
Fax: (01324) 678365 DX: 550360 Falkirk 3
Email: accountantofcourt@scotcourts.gov.uk
Website:
www.scotcourts.gov.uk/the-courts/more/the-accountant-of-court
Accountant of Court: Mrs Fiona Brown Tel: 01324
678323
Deputy Accountant of Court: Mrs Carrie Diggins
Tel: 01324 678303
Consignations/Children Scotland Act – Directions:
Mrs Anne Fulton Tel: 01324 677742, Mr
Matthew Clarkson Tel: 01324 678381
Judicial Factors and Enforcement Administrators:
Mr Raish Allan Tel: 01324 677740

Valuation Appeal Court

The Lord Justice Clerk, Rt Hon Lords Malcolm,
Woolman and Tyre, and the Hon Lord Doherty

This Court consists of 3 judges whose purpose is
to hear appeals against decisions of the Valuation
Appeal Committee in the matter of valuation of
lands for rating.

Office of the Public Guardian

Hadrian House, Callendar Business Park,
Callendar Road, Falkirk FK1 1XR Tel: (01324) 678
300
Fax: (01324) 678 301
/ (Twit-
ter:) Public Guardian@OPGScotland DX: 550360
Falkirk 3 Email: opg@scotcourts.gov.uk Website:
www.publicguardian-scotland.gov.uk/
Public Guardian: Fiona Brown
Deputy Public Guardians: Carrie Diggins, Danielle
Rose (Acting), Debra Allison

Insolvency Judge

The Hon Lords Clark, Ericht, Braid and Harrower.

The insolvency judge is nominated by the Lord
President to deal with proceedings under the
Insolvency Act 1986 or under the Company
Directors Disqualification Act 1986.

Council Tax Reduction Review Panel

Glasgow Tribunals Centre, 20 York Street,
Glasgow G2 8GT Tel: (0141) 302 5840
Fax: (0141) 302 5901 DX: 551943 GLASGOW
42 Email: ctrrpadmin@scotcourtstribunals.gov.uk
Website: counciltaxreductionreview.scot
The United Kingdom Welfare Reform Act 2012
abolished Council Tax Benefit from April 2013,
removing support for council tax from the
benefits system. In Scotland, providing support
now falls to the Scottish Government. Local
authorities administer applications for Council
Tax Reductions and Housing Benefit separately
from April 2013.
The Scottish Government's Council Tax
Reduction scheme creates a schedule of means
tested reductions to an individual's council tax
liability.
The Council Tax Reduction Review Panel was
established by The Council Tax Reduction
(Scotland) Amendment (No.2) Regulations 2013
from 1 October 2013. Supported by the Scottish
Courts and Tribunals Service, it provides an
additional review service to safeguard an
individual's rights to administrative justice when
assessing an individual's Council Tax Reduction
The CTRRP cannot accept appeal requests for
Council Tax Benefit, only Council Tax Reduction
review applications.

Additional Support Needs Tribunals for Scotland

Glasgow Tribunals Centre, 20 York Street, Glasgow G2 8GT Tel: (0141) 302 5860 Email: ASNTribunal@scotcourtstribunals.gov.uk Website: https://www.healthandeducationchamber.scot/
The Additional Support Needs Tribunals for Scotland (ASNTS) transferred into the Health and Education Chamber of the First-tier Tribunal for Scotland on 12 January 2018, and became the Additional Support Needs jurisdiction within the Chamber.
President's Office:
HEChamberPresident@scotcourtstribunals.gov.uk
Tel: 0141 302 5863

Court of the Lord Lyon

HM New Register House, Edinburgh EH1 3YT / Twitter: LyonCourt Email: lyonoffice@gov.scot Website: www.courtofthelordlyon.scot
Lord Lyon King of Arms: Dr Joseph J. Morrow CBE, QC, LLD, DL, FRSE
Lyon Clerk and Keeper of the Records:
Russell Hunter Esq
Herald Painter: Ms Clare McCrory
Procurator-Fiscal: Alexander Green Esq
Lyon Macer: David Walker Esq
Office Manager: Ms Jacqueline Higginson
Ceremonial & Development Officer: Fiona Mackay
Honorary Vexillologist: Philip Tibbetts Esq
Honorary Photographer: Edward Mallinson Esq

Employment Appeal Tribunal

George House, 126 George Street, Edinburgh EH2 4HH Tel: (0131) 225 3963 Fax: (01264) 785 030 Email: edinburgheat@justice.gov.uk
The EAT is responsible for handling appeals against decisions made by the Employment Tribunal where a legal mistake may have been made in the case. This might be because the Employment Tribunal:
got the law wrong
didn't apply the correct law
didn't follow the correct procedures and this affected the decision
had no evidence to support its decision
was unfairly biased towards the other party
The EAT also hears appeals and applications about decisions made by the Certification Officer and the Central Arbitration Committee.

Employment Tribunals (Scotland)

General Enquiries Scotland:
Employment Tribunal Customer Contact Centre, PO Box 27105, Glasgow G2 9JR
Tel: 0300 790 6234
President of Employment Tribunals (Scotland):
Judge Simon
Vice President of Employment Tribunals (Scotland):
Judge Walker
Employment Tribunal Judges (salaried):

Employment Judge d'Inverno, Employment Judge Doherty, Employment Judge Eccles, Employment Judge Gall, Employment Judge Hendry, Employment Judge Hoey, Employment Judge Hosie, Employment Judge Jones, Employment Judge Kearns, Employment Judge Kemp, Employment Judge MacLean, Employment Judge McFatridge, Employment Judge McManus, Employment Judge McPherson, Employment Judge Macleod, Employment Judge O'Donnell, Employment Judge Porter, Employment Judge Robison, Employment Judge Sangster, Judge Simon – President, Michelle Sutherland, Judge Walker – Vice-President, Employment Judge Whitcombe, Employment Judge Wiseman
Employment Tribunal Judges (fee paid):
Employment Judge Beyzade, Employment Judge Bradley, Employment Judge Brewer, Employment Judge Buzzard, Employment Judge Campbell, Employment Judge Cowen, Employment Judge Kearns, Employment Judge King, Employment Judge MacKay, Employment Judge Mannion, Employment Judge McCluskey, Employment Judge McMahon, Employment Judge McManus, Employment Judge McPherson, Employment Judge Meiklejohn, Employment Judge Murphy, Employment Judge Neilson, Employment Judge O'Dempsey, Employment Judge Shepherd, Employment Judge Smith, Employment Judge Sorrell, Employment Judge Strain, Employment Judge Sutherland, Employment Judge Tinnion, Employment Judge Young

Glasgow Office:
Glasgow Tribunals Centre, 20 York Street, Glasgow G2 8GT
Tel: 0141 204 0730 Fax: 01264 785 177
E-mail: glasgowet@justice.gov.uk

Edinburgh Office:
54-56 Melville Street, Edinburgh EH3 7HF
Tel: 0131 226 5584 Fax: 0131 220 6847
E-mail: edinburghet@justice.gov.uk

Aberdeen Office:
Ground floor, AB1, 48 Huntly Street, Aberdeen AB10 1SH
Tel: 01224 593 137 Fax: 0870 761 7766 DX: AB77 Aberdeen
E-mail: aberdeenet@justice.gov.uk

Dundee Office:
Ground Floor, Endeavour House, 1 Greenmarket, Dundee DD1 4QB
Tel: 01382 221578 Fax: 01382 227136
E-mail: dundeeet@justice.gov.uk

Inverness Office:
Hearing Venue Only: Highland Rail House, First Floor, Station Square, Academy Street, Inverness IV1 1LE
Contact the Glasgow Office

First-tier Tribunal for Scotland Health and Education Chamber

Glasgow Tribunal Centre, 20 York Street, Glasgow G2 8GT Tel: (0141) 302 5860 Email: ASNTribunal@scotcourtstribunals.gov.uk Website: https://www.healthandeducationchamber.scot The Tribunals (Scotland) Act 2014 creates two new tribunals – the First-tier Tribunal for Scotland and the Upper Tribunal for Scotland – and makes the Lord President the Head of the Scottish Tribunals; and creates the post of President of the Scottish Tribunals (who is presently Lord Stephen Woolman). The 2014 Act brings tribunal appointments under the remit of the Judicial Appointments Board for Scotland (JABS) and transfers administrative support of tribunals to the Scottish Courts and Tribunals Service (SCTS). Appeals are heard in the Upper Tribunal. There are a number of Chambers within the First-tier Tribunal for Scotland. The Additional Support Needs Tribunals for Scotland (ASNTS) transferred into the Health and Education Chamber of the First-tier Tribunal for Scotland on 12 January 2018, and became the Additional Support Needs jurisdiction within the Chamber.

Housing and Property Chamber

First-tier Tribunal for Scotland, Glasgow Tribunals Centre, 20 York Street, Glasgow G2 8GT Tel: (0141) 302 5900 Fax: (0141) 302 5901 DX: DX551943 Glasgow 42 Website: www.housingandpropertychamber.scot Thefunctions of both prhp and hohp were transferred to The First-tier Tribunal for Scotland (Housing and Property Chamber) on 1 December 2016 as part of the changes introduced by the Tribunals (Scotland) Act 2014. On 1 December 2017, the jurisdiction of the First-tier Tribunal for Scotland (Housing and Property Chamber) expanded further, with new legislation introducing applications in respect of Private Sector Rented Cases and Private Residential Tenancies. Civil cases relating to the private rented sector will no longer be dealt with as a Summary Cause Action raised within the Sheriff Court. These cases will transfer to the First-tier Tribunal for Scotland (Housing and Property Chamber). Landlords will be able to apply to the Tribunal for eviction and repossession orders where they consider that they have ground(s) for eviction. Former tenants will be able to apply to the Tribunal if they consider that their tenancy has been terminated unlawfully. Any actions presented to the courts prior to 1 December 2017 will continue before the Sheriff until conclusion. The Private Housing (Tenancies) (Scotland) Act 2016 creates a new Private Residential Tenancy for the private rented sector in Scotland. Applications may be made to the Tribunal by tenants and landlords where the terms of the new Private Residential Tenancy are not being met, or where there is disagreement with the rent that has been set for the property by the Rent Officer. The

Immigration and Asylum – Reserved

General Enquiries:
PO Box 6987, Leicester LE1 6ZX
Tel: 0300 123 1711
Email: customer.service@justice.gov.uk
Urgent Appeals:
Expedite Requests The First-Tier Tribunal Office of the Duty Judge, Expedited Appeal Hearing Requests
First-tier Tribunal (Immigration and Asylum Chamber), PO Box 6987, Leicester LE1 6ZX
Email: customer.service@justice.gov.uk Fax: 0870 739 5895
Chamber President: Judge Clements

Lands Tribunal for Scotland

George House, 126 George Street, Edinburgh EH2 4HH Tel: (0131) 271 4350
Fax: (0131) 271 4399 DX: ED259 Email: LTS_Mailbox@scotcourtstribunals.gov.uk Website: www.lands-tribunal-scotland.org.uk
President: Hon. Lord Minginish
Members: Ralph A Smith QC, Andrew Oswald FRICS, Charles Craigie Marwick FRICS.
Clerk: Neil Tainsh
Deputy Clerk: Douglas Ballantyne
Administrative Officer: Eli Do Rego

Mental Health Tribunal for Scotland

Bothwell House, First Floor, Hamilton Business Park, Caird Park, Hamilton ML3 0QA Tel: (01698) 390 000 (Mental Health Professionals)
Fax: (0800) 345 7060 (Patients, Carers, General Public) Website: www.mhtscotland.gov.uk
President: Laura Dunlop QC
Panel Members:
The Tribunal discharges its functions through panels of three members: a legal member (who acts as Convener), a medical member and a general member. The judicial arm of the Tribunal is supported in its functions by the staff of the Scottish Courts and Tribunals Service (SCTS).

Pensions Appeal Tribunals for Scotland

George House, 126 George Street, Edinburgh EH2 4HH Tel: (0131) 271 4340
Fax: (0131) 271 4398 Email: PAT_Info_Mailbox@scotcourtstribunals.gov.uk
Website: www.patscotland.org.uk/
President: Marion Caldwell QC

Scottish Charity Appeals Panel

George house, 126 George Street, Edinburgh EH2 4HH Tel: (0131) 271 4340 Email: Charityappeals@scotcourtstribunals.gov.uk
Website: www.generalregulatorychamber.scot/
Chair:

Aileen Devanny, Solicitor, Motherwell
Gary McIlravey, Solicitor, Dundee
John Walker, Solicitor, Ayr
Member:
Asif Haseeb, Senior Manager, Audit Scotland, Glasgow
Catriona Whitfield, Chartered Accountant, Helmsdale
Charlotte Barbour
John Blackwood
Asif Haseeb
Jane Happenstall
Ashan Khan
Mary Lyden
Catriona Whitfield

Scottish Land Court

George House, 126 George Street, Edinburgh
EH2 4HH Tel: (0131) 271 4360
Fax: (0131) 271 4399 DX: ED259 Email:
SLCourtMailbox@scotcourtstribunals.gov.uk
Website: www.scottish-land-court.org.uk/
Chairman: Lord Minginish
Deputy Chairman: Iain F Maclean
Members: John Smith, Tom Campbell

Social Security & Child Support Tribunal (SSCS) – Reserved

Part of the Social Entitlement Chamber, one of 7 chambers of the First-tier Tribunal which settles legal disputes and is structured around particular areas of law.

Scottish Offices:
By post: The Glasgow Tribunals Centre, 20 York Street, Glasgow G2 8GT
In person: Riverside House, 2nd Floor, 502 Gorgie Road, Edinburgh EH11 3AF
Tel: 0300 790 6234 Email:
sscsa-glasgow@justice.gov.uk DX: 551940
Chamber President: Judge Markus QC

Tax Tribunals for Scotland

George House, 126 George Street, Edinburgh
EH2 4HH Tel: (0131) 271 4385 DX: ED 259
Email: taxchamber@scotcourtstribunals.gov.uk
Website: www.taxtribunals.scot/
President: Mrs Anne Scott
Legal Members: Mr Paul Doyle, Miss Katrina Louise Lumsdaine
Ordinary Members: Mrs Charlotte Mary Barbour

The Upper Tribunal

The Glasgow Tribunals Centre, 20 York Street, Glasgow G2 8GT Tel: (0141) 302 5880 Email: uppertribunalforscotland@scotcourtstribunals.gov.uk
President of Scottish Tribunals: The Rt Hon Lord Woolman

Criminal Justice Committee

CRIMINAL JUSTICE COMMITTEE

The Committee was established in June 2021. It focuses on the Criminal Justice system in Scotland, including:

Police Scotland and the Scottish Fire and Rescue Service

Courts, including the Scottish Courts and Tribunals Service

Prosecution and the work of the Crown Office and Procurator Fiscal Service

The Scottish Prison Service and community sentencing

Stephen Imrie, Clerk
Address: Scottish Parliament, Edinburgh, EH99 1SP
Tel: 0131 348 6241
Email: justice.committee@parliament.scot
Twitter: @SP_Justice
Members: Audrey Nicoll, Russell Findlay, Katy Clark, Jamie Green, Fulton MacGregor, Rona Mackay, Pauline McNeill, Collette Stevenson, Donald Cameron, Jackie Dunbar, Daniel Johnson

Sheriffdoms

Alphabetical List of Sheriff Court Districts

Aberdeen Sheriff Court District	Grampian, Highland & Islands
Airdrie Sheriff Court District	South Strathclyde, Dumfries & Galloway
Alloa Sheriff Court District	Tayside, Central & Fife
Ayr Sheriff Court District	South Strathclyde, Dumfries & Galloway
Banff Sheriff Court District	Grampian, Highland & Islands
Campbeltown Sheriff Court District	North Strathclyde
Dumbarton Sheriff Court District	North Strathclyde
Dumfries Sheriff Court District	South Strathclyde, Dumfries & Galloway
Dundee Sheriff Court District	Tayside, Central & Fife
Dunfermline Sheriff Court District	Tayside, Central & Fife
Dunoon Sheriff Court District	North Strathclyde
Edinburgh Sheriff Court District	Lothian and Borders
Elgin Sheriff Court District	Grampian, Highland & Islands
Falkirk Sheriff Court District	Tayside, Central & Fife
Forfar Sheriff Court District	Tayside, Central & Fife
Fort William Sheriff Court District	Grampian, Highland & Islands
Glasgow and Strathkelvin Sheriff Court District	Glasgow and Strathkelvin
Greenock Sheriff Court District	North Strathclyde
Hamilton Sheriff Court District	South Strathclyde, Dumfries & Galloway
Inverness Sheriff Court District	Grampian, Highland & Islands
Jedburgh Sheriff Court District	Lothian and Borders
Kilmarnock Sheriff Court District	North Strathclyde
Kirkcaldy Sheriff Court District	Tayside, Central & Fife
Kirkwall Sheriff Court District	Grampian, Highland & Islands
Lanark Sheriff Court District	South Strathclyde, Dumfries & Galloway
Lerwick Sheriff Court District	Grampian, Highland & Islands
Livingston Sheriff Court District	Lothian and Borders
Lochgilphead Sheriff Court District	North Strathclyde
Lochmaddy Sheriff Court District	Grampian, Highland & Islands
Oban Sheriff Court District	North Strathclyde
Paisley Sheriff Court District	North Strathclyde
Perth Sheriff Court District	Tayside, Central & Fife
Peterhead Sheriff Court District	Grampian, Highland & Islands
Portree Sheriff Court District	Grampian, Highland & Islands
Selkirk Sheriff Court District	Lothian and Borders
Stirling Sheriff Court District	Tayside, Central & Fife
Stornoway Sheriff Court District	Grampian, Highland & Islands
Stranraer Sheriff Court District	South Strathclyde, Dumfries & Galloway
Tain Sheriff Court District	Grampian, Highland & Islands
Wick Sheriff Court District	Grampian, Highland & Islands

SHERIFFDOM OF SOUTH STRATHCLYDE, DUMFRIES AND GALLOWAY

Sheriff Principal's Chambers, Beckford Street, Hamilton ML3 0BT Tel: (01236) 439170 DX: HA2 Hamilton Email: spsecretaryssdg@scotcourts.gov.uk
Sheriff Principal: Aisha Y Anwar
Sheriffdom Business Manager: Ms L Pettigrew
Sheriff Principal's Executive Support: Mrs S Doherty

Airdrie Sheriff Court District

Sheriff Court House, Graham Street, Airdrie ML6 6EE Tel: (01236) 751121
Fax: (01236) 747497 DX: 570416 Airdrie Email: airdrie@scotcourts.gov.uk
The district comprises part of North Lanarkshire.
Criminal Court Holidays 2022

1 and 3 January; 2, 15 and 18 April; 2 May; 2 and 3 June; 18 July; 26 September; 5, 26 and 27 December
Sheriffs: M M Shankland, P Collins, D O'Carroll, F Thomson, Summary Sheriff Mercer WMD
Sheriff Clerk: Ms Lauren Young

Sheriff Clerk Deputes: Mrs C Sharkey, Mrs C McPartlin , Miss M McGlynn, Miss V Anderson, Mrs L Murnin, Mrs A McGhee, Miss K Obrien, Miss L Aitchison, Mr A MacLeod, Mr C McKenna
Auditor of Court: C MacKinnon

CIVIL COURT
Each Thursday at 10.00am

SUMMARY CAUSE COURT
Alternate Tuesdays at 10.00am

Ayr Sheriff and Justice of the Peace Court District

Sheriff Court House, Wellington Square, Ayr
KA7 1EE Tel: (01292) 292200
Fax: (01292) 292249 DX: AY16 Ayr Email:
ayr@scotcourts.gov.uk
The area of South Ayrshire and, in the area of East Ayrshire, wards 21-30.
Court Holidays 2022
3 and 4 January; 15 and 18 April; 2 May; 2 and 3 June; 19 September; 10 October; 5, 26 and 27 December
Sheriffs: John Montgomery, Desmond Leslie, Mhari Mactaggart
Summary Sheriff: Siobhan Connelly
Honorary Sheriffs: JShaw, CB Miller J
Sheriff Clerk: Mrs P Meiklejohn
Sheriff Clerk Deputes: Mrs L Clelland, J Wilson, L Currie, M Clark, A Brown, A Shannon
Auditors of Court: Ms Catherine MacKinnon
Legal Advisor: Mr J Mortimer

ORDINARY COURT/OPTIONS HEARINGS
Alternate Thursdays 10.00am

SUMMARY CAUSES COURT/ SMALL CLAIMS COURT/SIMPLE PROCEDURE
Alternate Thursdays at 10.00am

Dumfries Sheriff and Justice of the Peace Court

Sheriff Court House, Buccleuch Street, Dumfries
DG1 2AN Tel: (01387) 262334
Fax: (01387) 262357 DX: 580617 Dumfries
Email: dumfries@scotcourts.gov.uk
The district of Nithsdale and the district of Annandale and Eskdale and the district of Stewartry.
Criminal Court Holidays 2022
3 and 4 January; 15 and 18 April; 2 May; 2 and 3 June; 7 June; 5 September; 10 October; 5, 26 and 27 December
Sheriffs: Summary Sheriff Colm Dempsey, Brian Mohan
Honorary Sheriffs: J Findlay, B Kearney, R Hulley, C Lawrie, N Cavers, R Ireland, A Stannett, M Stryjewski
Sheriff Clerk: Miss E S O Young
Sheriff Clerk Deputes: L Biggar, S Cree, J McMillan, K Clark, K Leask
Legal Advisor to JP's: Miss F Ross

CIVIL COURT/OPTIONS HEARING
Every second Thursday at 10.00am

SUMMARY CAUSES/SIMPLE PROCEDURE COURT
Every fourth Friday at 10.00am

Hamilton Sheriff Court District

Sheriff Court House, 4 Beckford Street, Hamilton
ML3 0BT Tel: (01698) 282957
Fax: (01698) 201366 DX: HA2 Hamilton Email:
hamilton@scotcourts.gov.uk
Civil Office, Birnie House, Caird Street, Hamilton
ML3 0AL
DX: HA16 Hamilton
Justice of the Peace Court, Campbell Street, Hamilton, ML3 6AS
Criminal Court Holidays 2022
3 and 4 January; 15 and 18 April; 2 May; 2 and 3 June; 18 July; 26 September; 5, 26 and 27 December
Sheriffs: C Dunipace, L Gallacher, A L MacFadyen, A McIntyre, M Mackenzie, H K Small, L Nicolson, R MacFarlane, T S Millar;,L Murphy, J Speir
Sheriff Clerk: Jean Flanagan
Sheriff Clerk Deputes: C Blair, G Megan, G Mehmood, J Barrowman, L Blackburn, M Cannon, N Chalmers, V Coventry, S Foran, L Galbraith, S Hamilton, L Houston, P Hughes, N Hutchieson, C Keegan, A Kennedy, K Laird, G Loughlan, I Main, V McConville, S McGinley, S McLeod, D Muircroft, L Munro, M Robb, J Pullen, B Swinburne, A Watson
Auditor of Court: Jim Hamilton
Legal Advisors: A Kinsella, J Donnelly, M Neville, A Livingstone, J Mortimer , C Thomson

ORDINARY COURT
Every Wednesday at 10.00am

ORDINARY PROOFS
Every Monday, Tuesday, Wednesday and Thursday at 10.00am

SUMMARY CAUSE & SIMPLE PROCEEDURE
Every Thursday at 10.00am

HERITABLE CASES
Every Monday at 10.00am

SUMMARY COURT PROOFS AND SIMPLE PROCEDURE
Every Thursday at 12.00am and every 2nd Friday at 11.00am

Lanark Sheriff Court and Justice of the Peace Court

Sheriff Court House, 24 Hope Street, Lanark
ML11 7NE Tel: (01555) 661531
Fax: (01555) 664319 DX: 570832 Lanark Email:
lanarksc@scotcourtstribunals.gov.uk
The district of South Lanarkshire.
Criminal Court Holidays 2022

3 and 4 January; 15 and 18 April; 2 May; 2 and 3 June; 18 July; 26 September; 5, 26 and 27 December
Sheriff: Nikola C Stewart, QC
Honorary Sheriffs: D Fanshawe, T McCallum, D Forrest, J Robertson, J Wilson, W Steele, R Milligan
Sheriff Clerk: Mrs Wendy Robertson
Sheriff Clerk Deputes: Mrs Nicola G Small, Mr Alasdair Watson

ORDINARY COURT
Every second Tuesday at 11.00am

SUMMARY CAUSES COURT
Every second Tuesday at 10.00am
Same day and time as Ordinary Court

JP COURT
Every Wednesday at 10.00am (Except Sheriff and Jury Sitting Weeks)

Stranraer Sheriff & Justice of the Peace Court District
Sheriff Court House, Lewis Street, Stranraer DG9 7AA Tel: (01776) 702138

Fax: (01776) 706792 DX: 581261 Stranraer
Email: stranraer@scotcourts.gov.uk
The district of Wigtown.
Criminal Court Holidays 2022
3 and 4 January; 15 and 18 April; 2 May; 2 and 3 June; 1 August; 12 September; 5, 25 and 26 December
Sheriff: Anthony McGlennan
Honorary Sheriffs: Kenneth Patterson, Charles Lawrie, Ross Ireland, William Adam, Johan Findlay, David Ferguson, Stephen Stables, Elizabeth Sykes
Sheriff Clerk and Auditor of Court: Vacant
Sheriff Clerk Depute: D Munro

ORDINARY COURT, SIMPLE PROCEDURE, SUMMARY CAUSES AND SMALL CLAIMS COURT
Every alternate Friday at 10.00am

SHERIFFDOM OF TAYSIDE, CENTRAL AND FIFE
Sheriff Principal's Chambers, Sheriff Court House, Tay Street, Perth PH2 8NL Tel: (01738) 492931
DX: PE20 Perth Website: www.scotcourts.gov.uk
Sheriff Principal: Marysia Lewis
Sheriff Principal's Assistant: David Heitler (Email: dheitler@scotcourts.gov.uk)

Court Sessions
Vacation Courts: Ordinary, Simple Procedure Courts will be held during vacation on the same days as during session.

Alloa Sheriff Court and Justice of the Peace Court
47 Drysdale Street, Alloa FK10 1JA Tel: (01259) 722734
Fax: (01259) 219470 DX: 560433 Alloa Email: alloa@scotcourts.gov.uk
The district of Clackmannanshire.
Court Holidays 2022
3 and 4 January; 15 and 18 April; 2 May; 2 and 3 June; 1 August; 12 September; 5, 26 and 27 December
Sheriff: N Bowie
Sheriff Clerk: J Bicket
Sheriff Clerk Depute: J Hamilton

ORDINARY COURT
Every First Friday at 10.00am

SIMPLE PROCEDURE COURT
Every Second Tuesday at 10.00am

SUMMARY CAUSES COURT
Every Second Tuesday at 10.00am

SMALL CLAIMS COURT
Every Second Tuesday at 10.00am

Dundee Sheriff Court and Justice of the Peace Court
Sheriff Court House, 6 West Bell Street, Dundee DD1 9AD Tel: (01382) 229961
Fax: (01382) 318222 DX: DD33 Dundee Email: dundee@scotcourts.gov.uk
The district of the City of Dundee.
Court Holidays 2022
3 and 4 January; 15 and 18 April; 2 May; 2 and 3 June; 18 July; 3 October; 5, 26 and 27 December
Sheriffs: P Brown, A Carmichael, L Drummond, QC, G Murray, G A Way
Summary Sheriffs: J Rafferty
Sheriff Clerk: Gillian Stewart
Sheriff Clerk Deputes: Ross McParland, Emma Wheelan
Auditor of Court: A Pirie

ORDINARY COURT

Every Tuesday and Thursday at 10.00am

SUMMARY CAUSE/SMALL CLAIMS/SIMPLE
PROCEDURE COURT
Every Wednesday at 10.00am

Dunfermline Sheriff & Justice of the Peace Court

Sheriff Court House, 1/6 Carnegie Drive,
Dunfermline KY12 7HJ Tel: (01383) 724666
Fax: (01383) 621205 DX: DF17 Dunfermline
Email: dunfermline@scotcourts.gov.uk
The district of Dunfermline (West Fife).
Court Holidays 2022
3 and 4 January; 2 May; 2 and 3 June; 18 July; 3
October; 5, 26 and 27 December
Sheriffs: C N Macnair QC, S Duff
Sheriff Clerk: G Smith
Sheriff Clerk Deputes: R Campbell, M Lawson, K
Smith, S Vass, L Reid
Auditor of Court: A Pirie

ORDINARY COURT
Wednesdays at 10.00am once every 4 weeks

SUMMARY CAUSE COURT
Fridays at 10.00am once every 4 weeks

SIMPLE PROCEDURE COURT
Fridays at 10.00am once every 4 weeks

Falkirk Sheriff Court and Justice of the Peace Court

Sheriff Court House, Main Street, Camelon,
Falkirk FK1 4AR Tel: (01324) 620822
Fax: (01324) 678238 DX: 55207 Falkirk 4 Email:
falkirk@scotcourts.gov.uk
The district of Falkirk.
Civil & Criminal Court Holidays 2022
3 and 4 January; 15 and 18 April; 2 May; 2 and
3 June; 1 August; 12 September; 5, 26 and 27
December
Sheriffs: C Shead, S G Collins, C Harris
Summary Sheriff: D Livingston
Sheriff Clerk: K McCall
Sheriff Clerk Deputes: A Ure, E Thomson, L Ainslie,
P Gillan, P Harold
Legal Advisers to the Justice of the Peace Court:
Amanda Inglis, Tracey Scott

ORDINARY COURT
Every Wednesday at 10.30am

SUMMARY CAUSES COURT
Every Tuesday every 4 weeks at 10.00am

SUMMARY CAUSE HERITABLE COURT
Every Tuesday every 4 weeks at 10.00am

SIMPLE PROCEDURE COURT
Every Thursday every 4 weeks at 10.00am

Forfar Sheriff Court and Justice of the Peace Court

Sheriff Court House, Market Street, Forfar
DD8 3LA Tel: (01307) 462186
Fax: (01307) 462268 DX: 530674 Forfar Email:
forfar@scotcourts.gov.uk
The district of Angus
Criminal Court Holidays 2022
3 and 4 January; 15 and 18 April; 2 May; 2 and
3 June; 18 July; 3 October; 5, 26 and 27
December
Sheriff: Sheriff J Martin-Brown and Summary
Sheriff D Reekie
Honorary Sheriffs: G Couston, C Garvie
Sheriff Clerk: Kay Hendry
Sheriff Clerk Deputes: Sarah Carabine, Lisa
Henderson, Stephanie Watson
Legal Advisor: L Stewart

FAMILY/ORDINARY COURT
Every second Wednesday at 10.00 am

ORDINARY COURT
Every alternate Wednesday at 10.00am

FAMILY COURT
Every other alternate Wednesday at 10.00am

SUMMARY CAUSES/SMALL CLAIMS/SIMPLE
PROCEDURE COURT
One Friday a month

SUMMARY CAUSE
Once per month on a Tuesday at 10.00am

SIMPLE PROCEDURE
Every alternate Friday at 10.00am

Kirkcaldy Sheriff Court and Justice of the Peace Court

Sheriff Court House, Whytescauseway, Kirkcaldy
KY1 1XQ Tel: (01592) 260171
Fax: (01592) 642361 DX: KY17 Kirkcaldy Email:
Civil business: Kirkcaldycivil@scotcourts.gov.uk
Email: kirkcaldy@scotcourts.gov.uk
In the area of Fife, old wards 35-74.
Civil Vacation Court Days 2022
Civil courts held during vacation on the same
days as during session.
Court Holidays 2022
3 and 4 January; 15 and 18 April; 2 May; 2 and
3 June; 18 July; 3 October; 5, 26 and 27
December
Jury Trials and Custody/ Summary procedural
business is held at: The Sheriff Court Annexe, St.
Brycedale Avenue, Kirkcaldy KY1 1EU
Sheriffs: JH Williamson, J Gilchrist, A McKay, E
McFarlane, T Niven-Smith
Sheriff Clerk: N Rawlings
Sheriff Clerk Deputes: D Graham, C Watson, LA
Proudfoot, L McPhee, L Murray, P Soutar, H
Joyce, A Duff, A Scott, K Fargie
Auditor of Court: A Pirie

ORDINARY COURT
Every Tuesday at 10.00am

SUMMARY CAUSES, SUMMARY CAUSE HERITABLE, SIMPLIFIED PROCEDURE COURT
Every alternate Thursday at 10.00am

Perth Sheriff Court and Justice of the Peace Court

Sheriff Court House, Tay Street, Perth PH2 8NL
Tel: (01738) 620546
Fax: (01738) 623601 DX: PE20 Perth Email: perth@scotcourts.gov.uk
The district of Perth and Kinross.
Court Holidays 2022
3 and 4 January; 15 and 18 April; 2 May; 2 and 3 June; 12 September; 3 October; 5, 26 and 27 December
Sheriffs: Lindsay D R Foulis, G A Wade, W M Wood
Honorary Sheriffs: H Cruickshank, R A Hunter, R Heeps, R R McIntyre, D A O Edward, QC, D P McDonald, Mrs H G Murray, MBE
Sheriff Clerk: Lee Allan
Depute Sheriff Clerk: L Mahoney
Sheriff Clerk Deputes: G Ringland, B Patterson, L Digney, S Thomas
Legal Advisor L Stewart

ORDINARY COURT
Every Alternate Wednesday at 10.00am

SIMPLE PROCEDURE COURT
Monthly on Wednesday at 10.00am

Stirling Sheriff Court and Justice of the Peace Court

Sheriff Court House, Viewfield Place, Stirling FK8 1NH Tel: (01786) 462191
Fax: (01786) 470456 DX: ST15 Stirling Email: stirling@scotcourts.gov.uk
The district of Stirling.
Court Holidays 2022
3 and 4 January; 15 and 18 April; 2 May; 2 and 3 June; 1 August; 12 September; 5, 25 and 26 December
Sheriffs: D J Hamilton, K O'Mahony
Sheriff Clerk: L Mahoney
Office Manager: L Smith
Sheriff Clerk Deputes: S Mathers, P Mackie
Auditorof Court: Auditor A Pirie
Legal Advisor: T Scott
Business Manager: D Blue

ORDINARY COURT
Every alternate Tuesday at 10.00am

SUMMARY CAUSES/SMALL CLAIMS COURT
Every alternate Tuesday at 10.00am

SHERIFFDOM OF LOTHIAN AND BORDERS

Sheriff Principal's Chambers, Sheriff Court House, 27 Chambers Street, Edinburgh EH1 1LB Tel: (0131) 225 2525 DX: 550308 Edinburgh 37
Sheriff Principal: M M Stephen, QC (until end April)
Sheriff Principal's Secretary: Miss J Scott (until end April)

Selkirk Sheriff Court District & Justice of the Peace Court

Sheriff Court House, Ettrick Terrace, Selkirk TD7 4LE Tel: (01750) 721269
Fax: (01750) 722884 DX: 581011 Selkirk Email: selkirk@scotcourts.gov.uk
The district of Ettrick and Lauderdale.
Criminal Court Holidays 2022
3 and 4 January; 15 and 18 April; 3 May; 2, 3 and 17 June; 19 September; 5, 26 and 27 December
Sherrif: Sheriff Paterson
Legal Advisor: Covered by Edinburgh
Sheriff Clerk: Gail Edwards

ORDINARY COURT
Every alternate Wednesday

SUMMARY CAUSES COURT
Every alternate Wednesday

SIMPLE PROCEDURE COURT
Every alternate Wednesday

Edinburgh Sheriff Court and Justice of the Peace Court

Sheriff Court House, 27 Chambers Street, Edinburgh EH1 1LB Tel: (0131) 225 2525 Email: edinburgh@scotcourts.gov.uk
Administration:
Tel: 0131 247 2560
Civil Dept:
Tel: 0131 247 2847 DX: ED550312 Edinburgh 37
Small Claims/Summary Cause/Simple Procedure:
Tel: 0131 225 2525
Email: edinburghsummcause@scotcourts.gov.uk
Edinburgh Ordinary Court:
Email: edinburghordinary@scotcourts.gov.uk
Edinburgh Family Court:
Email: edinburghfamily@scotcourts.gov.uk
Criminal Dept:
Tel: 0131 247 2571 DX: ED550308 Edinburgh 37
Commissary Dept:

Tel: 0131 225 2525 DX: ED550313 Edinburgh 37
Email: cru@scotcourts.gov.uk
All Scotland Sheriff Personal Injury Court:
Tel: 0131 225 2525 DX: ED550311 Edinburgh 37
Email: nationalpicourt@scotcourts.gov.uk
The areas of City of Edinburgh and Midlothian and East Lothian.
Criminal Court Holidays 2022
3 and 4 January; 11, 15 and 18 April; 2 May; 2 and 3 June; 19 September; 5, 26 and 27 December
Sheriffs: D S Corke, W Holligan, J Mundy, N McFayden, A W Noble, N Ross, W A Sheehan, T Welsh, QC, F Tait, A N Stirling, RDM Fife, C Dickson, D Keir, K Campbell, D Kelly
Summary Sheriffs: J P Cook, P McCormack, R W Flinn, A Fraser M Auchincloss
Lothian and Borders Business Manager and Sheriff Clerk at Edinburgh: Les McIntosh
Principal Sheriff Clerk Depute (Civil): Elaine Wilson
Principal Sheriff Clerk Depute (Criminal): David Young
Principal Sheriff Clerk Depute (Administration): James Parkinson
Auditors of Court: Alan Pirie SCTS Auditor Team

SUMMARY CAUSE, SMALL CLAIMS & SIMPLE PROCEDURE COURT
every Thursday at 10.00am

HERITABLE COURT
every Friday at 10.00am

CIVIL COURT INCLUDING MOTIONS
Ordinary Court every Tuesday & Thursday at 10.00am

FAMILY COURT
every Monday, Tuesday, Wednesday & Friday and every 4th Thursday at 10.00am and 12.00pm

ADULTS WITH INCAPACITY HEARINGS
every Thursday at 10.00am and 2.00pm

ALL SCOTLAND SHERIFF PERSONAL INJURY COURT
Procedural hearings every Monday at 10.00am

CHILDREN'S' REFERRALS

Referrals Court every Friday at 10.00am

Jedburgh Sheriff Court and Justice of the Peace Court

Sheriff Court House, Castlegate, Jedburgh TD8 6AR Tel: (01835) 863231
Fax: (01835) 864110 DX: 581222 Jedburgh
Email: jedburgh@scotcourts.gov.uk
The district of Roxburgh.
Criminal Court Holidays 2022
3 and 4 January; 15 and 18 April; 3 May; 2 and 3 June; 8 July; 19 September; 5, 26 and 27 December
Sheriff: P Paterson
Sheriff Clerk: G Edwards
Legal Advisor: Covered by Edinburgh

ORDINARY COURT
Every alternate Wednesday

SUMMARY CAUSES AND SIMPLE PROCEDURE COURT
Every alternate Wednesday

Livingston Sheriff Court & Justice of the Peace Court

The Civic Centre, Howden South Road, Livingston EH54 6FF Tel: (01506) 402400
Fax: (01506) 415262 DX: 552062 Livingston-7
Email: livingston@scotcourts.gov.uk
The area of West Lothian.
Court Holidays 2022
3 and 4 January; 11, 15 and 18 April; 2 May; 2 and 3 June; 19 September; 5, 26 and 27 December
Sheriffs: D Kinloch, S A Craig, P Hammond, J Farquharson
Summary Sheriff: J A MacRitchie
Sheriff Clerk: Lorna McPhee
Auditor of Court: Gillian Gray
Sheriff Clerk Deputes: C Howley, A Nimmo, J Adlington, A Reynolds, F Birch, J McKay, J Dominick, M Jany
Sheriffdom Legal Advisor: Francesca Liddle
Business Manager: Les McIntosh

ORDINARY COURT
Every Wednesday at 10.00a.m.

SUMMARY CAUSES COURT
Every Thursday at 10.00a.m.

SHERIFFDOM OF GRAMPIAN, HIGHLAND AND ISLANDS

Sheriff Principal's Chambers, Sheriffdom Management Team, The Inverness Justice Centre, Longman Road, Inverness IV1 1AH Tel: (01463) 251965
Sheriff Principal: Derek Colin Wilson Pyle
Sheriff Principal's Executive Support: Vacant
Email: SMTGrampianHighlandandIsland@scotcourts.gov.uk
Interim Sheriffdom Business Manager: Ms P Meiklejohn
Tel: 01463 251960

Inverness Sheriff & Justice of the Peace Court

The Inverness Justice Centre, Longman Road, Inverness IV1 1AH Tel: (01463) 230782 Fax: (01463) 710602 DX: IN25 Inverness Email: inverness@scotcourts.gov.uk
The districts of Badenoch and Strathspey, Inverness and Nairn; the District of Ross and Cromarty except that part comprised in the Sheriff Court District of Tain; the District of Skye and Lochalsh, and the parishes of Lochalsh, Glenshiel and Kintail.
Criminal Court Holidays 2022
3 and 4 January; 15 and 18 April; 2 May; 2 and 3 June; 22 August; 3 October; 5, 26 and 27 December
Sheriffs: S Matheson, E Macdonald, G Aitken, I Cruickshank, R Frazer
Floating Sheriffs: R McDonald
Honorary Sheriffs: C Graham, N Ramsay, G McWilliam, R Skelton, D Somerville, J Stewart
Sheriff Clerk: Mrs. R Thomson
Sheriff Clerk Deputes: Mr S McDines, Ms T O'Connor, Mr K Kerr, Ms S Amarnath, Mr I Dunbar, Miss J Fraser, Miss D Jack, Mr R Wells, Miss J Lindsay, Mr R Grant, Ms H MacDonald
Sheriffdom Auditor of Court: Mr R Cantwell
ORDINARY COURT Every Wednesday at 10.30am
SUMMARY CAUSES COURT Every Wednesday at 10.00am
SIMPLE PROCEDURE COURT Every second Thursday at 10.00am

Kirkwall Sheriff Court District

Sheriff Court House, Watergate, Kirkwall KW15 1PD Tel: (01856) 872110 Email: kirkwall@scotcourts.gov.uk
The islands area of Orkney.
Criminal Court Holidays 2022
3 and 4 January; 15 and 18 April; 2 May; 2 and 3 June; 1 August; 26 September; 5, 26 and 27 December
Sheriff: Robert McDonald
Honorary Sheriffs: Lieutenant E M Gibson, Dr Margaret Cant, Bryan Clark, Eric Green, Cpt William Spence, Janette Park, Duncan Hill, Barbara Foulkes, Robert Sclater, Tim Wright
Sheriff Clerk Depute: Laura-Beth Macvie
Auditors of Court: Richard Cantwell

SUMMARY CAUSES/SMALL CLAIMS & ORDINARY COURT
Every second Tuesday at 10.00am

CRIMINAL COURT
Every second Wednesday at 10.00am

SUMMARY TRIALS
Every fourth Monday, Thursday and Friday and every second Wednesday at 12:00 noon

Lerwick Sheriff Court

District Sheriff Court House, King Erik Street, Lerwick ZE1 0HD Tel: (01595) 693914
Fax: (01595) 693340 Email: lerwick@scotcourts.gov.uk Website: www.scotcourts.gov.uk
The islands area of Shetland.
Criminal Court Holidays 2022
3 and 4 January; 2 and 15 and 18 April; 2 May; 2 and 3 June; 5, 26 and 27 December
Sheriff: Sheriff Cruickshank
Honorary Sheriffs: Eric Peterson, Arnold Duncan, Willie Shannon, Malcolm Bell, Susan Brunton
Sheriff Clerk Depute: Terri Tollan

ORDINARY/CIVIL COURT
Every second Friday

PROOFS COURT
Every second week Monday and Tuesday

Lochmaddy Sheriff Court District

Sheriff Court House, Lochmaddy HS6 5AE Tel: (01478) 612191
Fax: (01478) 613203 Email: lochmaddy@scotcourts.gov.uk
In the area of Western Isles, wards 24-30.
Criminal Court Holidays 2022
3 and 4 January; 15 and 18 April; 2 May; 2 and 3 June; 1 August; 12 September; 5, 25 and 26 December
Sheriff: Gordon Lamont
Honorary Sheriffs: N M Johnson, A McIlwraith, I G MacDonald, I Marr, C Gillies, A MacKenzie
Sheriff Clerk Depute and Auditor of Court: Vacant

CIVIL AND CRIMINAL COURT
Every fourth Tuesday at 10.30am and every fourth Wednesday at 09.30am

Peterhead Sheriff Court and Justice of the Peace Court

Sheriff Court House, Queen Street, Peterhead AB42 1TP Tel: (01779) 476676 DX: 521376 Peterhead Email: peterhead@scotcourts.gov.uk
That part of the district of Banff and Buchan comprising the parishes of Aberlour, Crimond, Cruden, Lonmay, New Deer, Old Deer, Peterhead, Pitsligo, Rathen, St Fergus, Strichen and Tyrie.
Court Holidays 2022
3 and 4 January; 15 and 18 April; 2 May; 2 and 3 June; 4 July; 29 August; 5, 26 and 27 December
Sheriff: Christine McCrossan
Sheriff Clerk: Donald Hossack
Sheriff Clerk Deputes: Cherry Kelman, Stacey Beaumont

Portree Sheriff Court District

Sheriff Court House, Somerled Square, Portree IV51 9EH Tel: (01478) 612191
Fax: (01478) 613203 Email: portree@scotcourts.gov.uk
The district of Skye and Lochalsh except the parishes of Lochalsh, Glenshiel and Kintail.

Criminal Court Holidays 2022
3 and 4 January; 15 and 18 April; 2 May; 2 and 3 June; 1 August; 12 September; 5, 25 and 26 December
Sheriff: Robert Frazer (from 1st May 2022)
Honorary Sheriffs: D A MacLeod, I Marr, C Gillies, A MacKenzie, I G MacDonald, I G Peppe, D A MacDonald
Sheriff Clerk Depute and Auditor of Court: Vacant

ORDINARY COURT
Every fourth Tuesday at 2.00pm

SUMMARY CAUSES COURT
Every fourth Tuesday at 2.00pm

CRIMINAL DIET COURT
Every fourth Tuesday at 10.00am

Stornoway Sheriff Court District

Sheriff Court House, 9 Lewis Street, Stornoway HS1 2JF Tel: (01851) 702231
Fax: (01851) 704296 Email:
stornoway@scotcourts.gov.uk
The islands area of Western Isles except that part comprised in the sheriff court district of Lochmaddy.
Criminal Court Holidays 2021
3 and 4 January; 15 and 18 April; 2 May; 2 and 3 June; 22 August; 26 September; 5, 26 and 27 December
Sheriff: Gordon Lamont
Honorary Sheriffs: Iain Macleod, Roddie MacKay
Sheriff Clerk: Kenneth Finnie

ORDINARY COURT
Every alternate Monday at 10.00am

SUMMARY CAUSES COURT
Every alternate Monday at 10.00am

Tain Sheriff and Justice of the Peace Court District

Sheriff Court House, High Street, Tain IV19 1AB
Tel: (01862) 892518 Email:
tain@scotcourts.gov.uk
The district of Sutherland and that part of the district of Ross and Cromarty comprising the parishes of Alness, Edderton, Fearn, Kilmuir Easter, Logie Easter, Nigg, Rosskeen, Tarbat and Tain.
Court Holidays 2022
3 and 4 January; 15 and 18 April; 2 May; 2 and 3 June; 22 August; 3 October; 5, 26 and 27 December
Sheriff: G Aitken
Honorary Sheriffs: J S Moore, L Keir
Sheriff Clerk: Christina Phiri
Sheriffdom Auditor of Court: Mr R Cantwell

ORDINARY COURT Every fourth Tuesday at 10.30am

SUMMARY CAUSE COURT Every fourth Tuesday at 10.00am

SIMPLE PROCEDURE COURT Every fourth Tuesday at 10.00am

Wick Sheriff Court

Sheriff Court House, Bridge Street, Wick KW1 4AJ
Tel: (01955) 602846
The district of Caithness.
Criminal Court Holidays 2022
3 and 4 January; 15 and 18 April; 2 May; 2 and 3 June; 18 July; 3 October; 5, 26 and 27 December
Sheriff: Vacant
Honorary Sheriffs: Elaine M. Robertson, Bruce de Wert, J W Farquar McGregor, Alexander Manson, Robert Silverwood, Alistair Burnett, Isabell Blumfield, Leisa Swanson, John A Clasper
Sheriff Clerk: Peta Donachie
Business Manager Patricia Meiklejohn (Temporary)

ORDINARY COURT
Every fourth Thursday at 10.00am

SUMMARY CAUSES COURT
Every fourth Thursday at 10.00am

Aberdeen Sheriff Court and Justice of the Peace Court

Sheriff Court House, Castle Street, Aberdeen AB10 1WP Tel: (01224) 657200
Fax: (01224) 657234 DX: AB61 Aberdeen Email:
Criminal Team Email:
aberdeencriminalteam@scotcourts.gov.uk Email:
aberdeen@scotcourts.gov.uk
Aberdeen Sheriff Court Annex & High Court of Justiciary: 53 Castle Street, Aberdeen AB11 5BB
The districts of City of Aberdeen.

OPENING TIMES
Mon – Fri 09:00 – 13:00, 14:00- 16:30
Court Holidays 2022
3 and 4 January; 15 and 18 April; 2 May; 2 and 3 June; 11 July; 26 September; 5, 26 and 27 December
Sheriffs: G Buchanan, W Summers, G Napier, J A Brown, A Miller, P Mann, M McLaughlin
Summary Sheriffs: M Hodge, I Wallace
Sheriff Clerk: Fiona Flemming (01224 657200)
Sheriff Clerk Deputes: Mrs I Morgan, Mrs F Fleming, N Wilson, Mr J Paterson, Mrs P Brock, Miss S MacPherson, M Pithie, R Henderson, K Bain, J Bywalec, D Park, Mrs J Munro, Mrs J Campbell, D Milne, J Gawthorpe, G Henderson, R Thomson, J Pickard
Auditor of Court: Mr R Cantwell

Aberdeen Civil Justice Centre and Commercial Courts

This complex, located in the former Justice of the Peace Court is a specialist centre designed to hear civil and commercial cases:

Queen Street, Aberdeen AB10 1AQ
Fax: 01224 657223 DX: AB61 ABERDEEN
Email: aberdeen@scotcourts.gov.uk
Civil Team Email:
aberdeencivilteam@scotcourts.gov.uk
Court Holidays 2022
3 and 4 January; 15 and 18 April; 2 May; 2 and
3 June; 11 July; 26 September; 5, 26 and 27
December
Sheriff Clerk: Fiona Flemming

OPENING TIMES
Mon – Fri 09:00 – 13:00, 14:00- 16:30

Banff Sheriff and Justice of the Peace Court

Sheriff Court House, Low Street, Banff AB45 1AU
Tel: (01261) 812140
Fax: (01261) 818394 DX: 521325 Banff Email:
banff@scotcourts.gov.uk
The district of Banff and Buchan except that part
comprised in the sheriff court district of
Peterhead and parishes of Fraserburgh, Pitsligo,
Aberdour, Rathen and Tyrie.
Criminal Court Holidays 2022
3 and 4 January; 15 and 18 April; 2 May; 2 and
3 June; 4 July; 29 August; 5, 26 and 27
December
Sheriff: Robert McDonald
Sheriff Clerk Depute: Bruce Graham
Auditor of Court: Richard Cantwell
Legal Advisor: Nicola Cunningham
Business Manager: Patricia Meiklejohn

ORDINARY COURT
Alternate Fridays at 10.00am

SUMMARY CAUSES AND SIMPLE PROCEDURE
COURT
Alternate Fridays at 11.00am

Elgin Sheriff Court and Justice of the Peace Court

Sheriff Court House, High Street, Elgin IV30 1BU
Tel: (01343) 542505
Fax: (01343) 559517 DX: 520652 Elgin Email:
elgin@scotcourts.gov.uk
The district of Moray.
Criminal Court Holidays 2022
3 and 4 January; 15 and 18 April; 2 May; 2 and
3 June; 22 August; 3 October; 5, 26 and 27
December
Sheriff: O Pasportnikov, R McDonald
Honorary Sheriffs: W P Mennie, I Cameron, C M
Murray, A Campbell, J Smith, M Mackay
Sheriff Clerk: Iain MacArthur
Sheriff Clerk Deputes: Barry Reid, Zoe Antley
Legal Advisor: Nicola Cunningham

ORDINARY COURT
Alternate Fridays at 10.30am

SIMPLE PROCEDURE AND SMALL CLAIMS
COURT
Alternate Fridays at 10.00am

Fort William Sheriff and Justice of the Peace Court

Sheriff Court House, High Street, Fort William
PH33 6EE Tel: (01397) 702087
Fax: (01397) 706214 DX: 531405 Fort William
Email: fortwilliam@scotcourts.gov.uk
The district of Lochaber.
Court Holidays 2022
3 and 4 January; 15 and 18 April; 2 May; 2 and
3 June; 1 August; 26 September; 5, 26 and 27
December
Sheriff: Robert Frazer
Sheriff Clerk Depute: Vacant

ORDINARY COURT
Every fourth Wednesday of the month

SUMMARY CAUSES COURT
Every fourth Wednesday of the month

SHERIFFDOM OF GLASGOW AND STRATHKELVIN

Sheriff Principal's Chambers, Sheriff Court House, 1 Carlton Place, Glasgow G5 9DA Tel: (0141) 429
8888 DX: 551022 Glasgow
Sheriff Principal: Craig D Turnbull
Sheriff Clerk: Neil Christie
Sheriff Principal's Secretary: Miss Healy
Criminal Court Holidays 2022
3 and 4 January; 15 and 18 April; 2 May; 2 and 3 June; 18 July; 26 September; 5, 26 and 27
December

Glasgow and Strathkelvin Sheriff and Justice of the Peace Court

Sheriff Court House, PO Box 23, 1 Carlton Place,
Glasgow G5 9DA Tel: (0141) 429 8888

Fax: (0141) 418 5270 (Criminal Solemn)
Fax: (0141) 418 5244 (Fines Enforcement Office)
Fax: (0141) 418 5185 (Criminal Summary)
Fax: (0141) 418 5248 (Civil) DX: 551020 (Sheriff
Clerk) DX: 551021 (Criminal) DX: 551022

(Sheriffs) DX: 551023 Email: glasgow@scotcourts.gov.uk Website: www.scotcourts.gov.uk

The area of City of Glasgow and Strathkelvin.
Sheriff Principal: Craig D Turnbull
Sheriffs: I H L Miller, L M Ruxton, L Wood, J Platt, M H Liddell, M Jones QC, A.R Mackenzie, S Murphy QC, A Mackie, J McCormick, J Johnston QC, A Swanson, A Cubie, A Miller, S Reid, P V Crozier, A Y Anwar, J Kerr, I Fleming, T Kelly, P Reid
Summary Sheriffs: A Findlay, B Cameron, M Shields, G Bonnar, B Divers, S Gilroy, D McConnell, D Kelly, P Brown, V Mays, P Pryce, C Lugton
Sheriff Clerk Glasgow & Sheriffdom Business Manager (SBM): Neil Christie
Support Manager to SBM: Eileen Kenmuir
Principal Depute Criminal (Solemn): Karen McCall
Principal Deputes (Civil): Maureen Davidson/Elaine McLeod
Principal Depute (Criminal): Andrea Dyer (Summary)
Principal Depute (Administration): Grace Carthy/Joe Margey
Sheriff Clerk Deputes: Nadine Neil, Karen Carroll, Lorraine Craig, Anne Grubb, Marianne Harvey, Christina Herriot, Elaine Donnelly, Nicola Martin, Rona Nixon, Eveline Mullen, Victoria O'Hara

SUMMARY CAUSES COURT
Heritable: Each Wednesday at 10.00am and 2.00pm

SUMMARY CAUSE PAYMENTS AND SMALL CLAIMS
Payments (including Incidental Applications and Minutes for Recall) and Miscellaneous: Every Tuesday at 10.00am.

SIMPLE PROCEDURE COURT PROCEDURAL BUSINESS (INCLUDING CASE MANAGEMENT DISCUSSIONS, TIME TO PAY HEARINGS): Every day at 10.00am

APPEAL COURT
Thursday at 10.00am

DEBTORS (SCOTLAND) ACT COURT
Every alternate Monday at 10.00am

MISCELLANEOUS CIVIL COURT
Every alternative Monday at 11.00am

OPTIONS HEARING
Family: Tuesday 9:30am, Commercial: Wednesday 10.00am and 2.00pm; Ordinary: Friday 10.00am; Motions: 12.00pm

CHILD WELFARE HEARING COURT
Monday & Thursday 10.00am

HIGH COURT OF JUSTICIARY COURT
High Court, 1 Mart Street, Glasgow; Tel: 0141 552 3795

SHERIFFDOM OF NORTH STRATHCLYDE

Sheriff Principal's Chambers, Sheriff Court House, St James Street, Paisley PA3 2HW Tel: (0141) 847 6746 Fax: (0141) 887 6702 DX: PA48 Paisley
Sheriff Principal: D L Murray
Sheriffdom Business Manager: Jackie Powell
Sheriff Principal's Assistant: Mrs R Johnstone (Email: rjohnstone@scotcourts.gov.uk)
Sheriff Clerk: Fiona Smith

Greenock Sheriff and Justice of the Peace Court

Sheriff Court House, 1 Nelson Street, Greenock PA15 1TR Tel: (01475) 787073
Fax: (01475) 729746 DX: GR16 Greenock Email: greenock@scotcourts.gov.uk
The district of Inverclyde.
Criminal Court Holidays 2022
3 and 4 January; 15 and 18 April; 2 May; 2 and 3 June; 1 August; 26 September; 5, 26 and 27 December
Sheriffs: JC Hughes, M Higgins, Summary Sheriff S. Fraser
Sheriff Clerk: Nadine Neil
Sheriff Clerk Deputes: J Borris, L McCloy, D McMunagle, F Doak, J Docherty, J Moore
Auditor of Court: C McKinnon

Office Manager: Jonathan Robin

ORDINARY COURT
Every Thursday at 10.00am

SUMMARY CAUSES/SIMPLE PROCEDURE COURT
Every alternate Monday at 10.00am

Kilmarnock Sheriff Court and Justice of the Peace Court

Sheriff Court House, St Marnock Street, Kilmarnock KA1 1ED Tel: (01563) 550024
Fax: (01563) 543568 DX: KK20 Kilmarnock Email: kilmarnock@scotcourts.gov.uk
The area of North Ayrshire and that part of East Ayrshire formerly Kilmarnock and Loudoun district.

Criminal Court Holidays 2022
3 and 4 January; 15 and 18 April; 2 May; 2 and 3 June; 4 July; 19 September; 5, 26 and 27 December
Sheriffs: A G Watson, George Jamieson, Murdoch Mactaggart, Colin Bissett
Summary Sheriff: M Hanlon
Sheriff Clerk: C McShane
Sheriff Clerk Deputes: A Kerr, T McLellan, M Rosamond, J Caldwell, F Clover, J Fergusson, M Hannah, J McBlain, C McGill, B Moran, R Murphy, S Stevenson, S Wilkinson-Gurney
Auditors of Court: C McKinnon
Legal Advisors: K Walsh, A Livingstone, J Scott

ORDINARY COURT
Every Wednesday at 10.00am

SUMMARY CAUSES AND SIMPLE PROCEDURE COURT
Every Second Friday at 10.00am

Oban Sheriff Court District & Justice of the Peace Court

Sheriff Court House, Albany Street, Oban PA34 4AL Tel: (01631) 562414
Fax: (01631) 562037 DX: OB8 Oban Email: oban@scotcourts.gov.uk
That part of the district of Argyll and Bute comprising the parishes of Ardchattan, Muckairn, Coll, Colonsay and Oronsay, Craignish, Glenorchy and Innishael, Kilbrandon and Kilchattan, Kilchrenan and Dalavich, Kilfinochen and Kilvickeon, Kilmore and Kilbride, Kilninian and Kilmore, Kilninver and Kilmelford, Lismore and Appin, Tiree, Torosay and that part of Jura consisting of the islands North of the Gulf of Corrievreckan.
Criminal Court Holidays 2022
3 and 4 January; 15 and 18 April; 2 May; 2 and 3 June; 25 July; 5 September; 5, 26 and 27 December
Sheriff: P Hughes
Honorary Sheriffs: G Pagan, T Macnair, K MacKinnon, K McMahon, G Seaton, F Black, J MacGregor, J MacKenzie, K Moncrieff, L Stewart, M Kupris, J Hoey, F Llanos, G Innes
Sheriff Clerk: Andrea Dyer, Dumbarton Tel: 01389 763266
Sheriff Clerk Deputes: Caroline Brady, Allison Black
Auditor of Court: Graham Whitelaw
Business Manager: Jackie Powell
Legal Advisors: Julie Scott, David Watt

ORDINARY COURT
Every fourth Thursday at 10.00am

SUMMARY CAUSES COURT
Every fourth Thursday at 10.00am

Paisley Sheriff and Justice of the Peace Court District

Sheriff Court House, St James Street, Paisley PA3 2HW Tel: (0141) 887 5291

Fax: (0141) 887 6702 DX: PA48 Paisley Email: Electronic submissions for civil business: paisleycivil@scotcourts.gov.uk Email: paisley@scotcourts.gov.uk
The districts of Renfrewshire and East Renfrewshire.
Criminal Court Holidays 2022
3 and 4 January; 15 and 18 April; 2 May; 2 and 3 June; 1 August; 26 September; 5 December; 26 and 27 December
Sheriffs: T McCartney, B Mohan, B Erroch QC, G Craig, H McGinty
Summary Sheriffs: L Kooner, S Gill, L Mundell
Sheriff Clerk: Fiona Smith
Auditor of Court: C MacKinnon
Sheriff Clerk Deputes: J Dunnett, G Docherty, A Hendry, M Ijaz, D Gladstone, K McEvoy, H Fleming, A Brady, G Stewart, A McNab, L Nobbs, C Prentice
Sheriffdom Business Manager: Jackie Powell
Sheriffdom Legal Advisor: Julie Scott (Acting)
Legal Advisors: V Lindsay, E Burns, A Devine, K Walsh, A Livingstone

ORDINARY COURT
Docketed cases, assigned and case managed by a Sheriff

SIMPLE PROCEDURE COURT
Every Wednesday at 10.00am

SUMMARY CAUSE COURT
Every Friday at 9.30am

Campbeltown Sheriff and Justice of the Peace Court

Sheriff Court House, Castlehill, Campbeltown PA28 6AN Tel: (01586) 552503
Fax: (01586) 554967 Email: campbeltown@scotcourts.gov.uk
The district of Argyll and Bute except the parts thereof comprised in the sheriff court districts of Dunoon, Oban and Rothesay.
Criminal Court Holidays 2022
3 and 4 January; 15 and 18 April; 2 May; 2 and 3 June; 19 September; 3 October; 5, 26 and 27 December
Sheriff: Patrick Hughes
Honarary Sheriffs: D A H Cousin, P L M Stewart, I Henderson, C M O'Neill, A G T Walker, J Stewart, J Morrison
Sheriff Clerk: Louise Taylor
Auditor of Court: Graham Whitelaw
Legal Advisor: David Watt

ORDINARY COURT
Every fourth Friday at 10.00am

SUMMARY CAUSES COURT
Every fourth Friday at 10.00am

Dumbarton Sheriff & Justice of the Peace Court

Sheriff Court House, Church Street, Dumbarton G82 1QR Tel: (01389) 763266
Fax: (01389) 764085 DX: 500597 Dumbarton
Email: dumbarton@scotcourts.gov.uk
The local authority areas of West Dunbartonshire and parts of East Dunbartonshire and Argyll and Bute.
Criminal Court Holidays 2022
3 and 4 January; 15 and 18 April; 2 May; 2 and 3 June; 18 July; 26 September; 5, 26 and 27 December
Sheriffs: W Gallacher, M Hendry, F McCartney, Summary Sheriff Hamilton
Sheriff Clerk: Andrea Dyer
Auditor of Court: Catherine MacKinnon
Sheriff Clerk Deputes: L Young, J Hutchison, G Ross, C Calderwood, L Griffiths, A Dunsmuir, M Sayers, E Harvey ,J Margey
Legal Advisor: Mairi MacNeil

ORDINARY COURT
Every Tuesday at 10.00am

SIMPLE PROCEDURE COURT
Every second Wednesday at 10.00am
Due to Covid 19 there are teleconferences every day in all actions.

Dunoon Sheriff Court and Justice of the Peace Court

Sheriff Court House, George Street, Dunoon PA23 8BQ Tel: (0300) 7900049
Fax: (01369) 702191 DX: 591655 Dunoon
Email: dunoon@scotcourts.gov.uk
That part of the district of Argyll and Bute, comprising the parishes of Dunoon and Kilmun, Inveraray, Inverchaolain, Kilfinan, Kilmichael-Glassary, Kilmodan, Lochgoilhead and Kilmorich, North Knapdale, Strachur and Strathlachlan and that part of the parish of South Knapdale north of the line of the B8024 road from Clachbreck on Loch Caolisport in the west to the junction of the B8024 road with the A83 road in the east.
Criminal Court Holidays 2022
3 and 4 January; 15 and 18 April; 2 May; 2 and 3 June; 1 August; 26 September; 5, 26 and 27 December
Sheriff: Nicola Patrick
Sheriff Clerk: Nadine Neil
Sheriff Clerk Depute: Kim Wilson

ORDINARY COURT
Every alternate Tuesday at 10.00am

SUMMARY CAUSES COURT
Every alternate Tuesday at 10.00am

COMMISSARY BUSINESS

Commissary business may be carried out at the commissariots of the undernoted sheriffdoms:

Grampian, Highland and Islands: Aberdeen, Banff, Elgin, Wick, Inverness, Peterhead, Kirkwall and Lerwick
Tayside, Central and Fife: Forfar, Dundee, Perth, Alloa, Falkirk, Stirling, Dunfermline and Kirkcaldy
Lothian and Borders: Edinburgh, Linlithgow, Selkirk, Jedburgh
Glasgow and Strathkelvin: Glasgow
North Strathclyde: Dumbarton, Greenock, Kilmarnock and Paisley
South Strathclyde, Dumfries and Galloway: Dumfries, Stranraer, Airdrie, Ayr, Hamilton and Lanark

PROCURATOR FISCAL'S OFFICES

AB1, Crimon Place, ABERDEEN AB10 1BJ; Tel: 0300 020 3000 Email: PFAberdeensummary@copfs.gov.uk
Procurator Fiscal: Andy Shanks
87A Graham Street, AIRDRIE ML6 6DE; Tel: 0300 020 3000 Email: PFOAirdrie@copfs.gov.uk
Procurator Fiscal: Les Brown
Sheriff Court, 47 Drysdale Street, ALLOA FK10 1HR; Tel: 0300 020 3000 Email: PFOAlloa@copfs.gov.uk

Procurator Fiscal: Sineidin Corrins
Sheriff Court, Low Street, BANFF AB45 1AU; Tel: 0300 020 3000 Email: PFOBanff@copfs.gov.uk
Procurator Fiscal: Andy Shanks
Sheriff Court, Castlehill, CAMPBELTOWN PA28 6AN; Tel: 0300 020 3000 Email: PFOCampbeltown@copfs.gov.uk
Procurator Fiscal: Katie Stewart
Crown Office, 25 Chambers Street, EDINBURGH EH1 1LA Tel: 0300 020 3000
1st Floor, St Mary's Way, DUMBARTON G82 1NL; Tel: 0300 020 3000 Email: PFODumbarton@copfs.gov.uk
Procurator Fiscal: Katie Stewart
44 Buccleuch Street, DUMFRIES DG1 2AP; Tel: 0300 020 3000 Email: PFODumfries@copfs.gov.uk
Procurator Fiscal: Les Brown
West Port House, 144 West Marketgait, DUNDEE DD1 1NJ; Tel: 0300 020 3000 Email: pfodundee@copfs.gov.uk
Procurator Fiscal: Sineidin Corrins
Sheriff Court House, Carnegie Drive, DUNFERMLINE KY12 7HW; Tel: 0300 020 3000 Email: PFDunfermline@copfs.gov.uk

Procurator Fiscal: Sineidin Corrins
Procurator Fiscal's Office, Sheriff Court, 29
Chambers Street, EDINBURGH EH1 1LB Tel:
0300 020 3000 Email:
PFOEdinburgh@copfs.gov.uk
Procurator Fiscal: Laura Buchan
48 South Street, ELGIN, Moray IV30 1JX; Tel:
0300 020 3000 Email: PFOElgin@copfs.gov.uk
Procurator Fiscal: Andy Shanks
Mansionhouse Road, Camelon, FALKIRK FK1
4LW; Tel: 0300 020 3000 Email:
PFOFalkirk@copfs.gov.uk
Procurator Fiscal: Sineidin Corrins
Sheriff Court, FORFAR DD8 3LA; Tel: 0300 020
3000
Procurator Fiscal: Sineidin Corrins
c/o Police Scotland, Blar Mhor, FORT WILLIAM
PH33 7GA; Tel: 0300 020 3000 Email:
PFOFortWilliam@copfs.gov.uk
Procurator Fiscal: Alison Young
10 Ballater Street, GLASGOW G5 9PS; Tel: 0300
020 3000 Email: PFOGlasgow@copfs.gov.uk
Procurator Fiscal: Moira Orr
Greenock Sheriff Court, 1 Nelson Street
GREENOCK PA15 1TR; Tel: 0300 020 3000
Email: PFOGreenock@copfs.gov.uk
Procurator Fiscal: Katie Stewart
Cameronian House, 3/5 Almada Street,
HAMILTON ML3 0HG; Tel: 0300 020 3000
Email: PFOHamilton@copfs.gov.uk
Procurator Fiscal: Les Brown
The Inverness Justice Centre, Longman Road,
INVERNESS IV1 1AH; Tel: 0300 020 3000 Email:
PFOInverness@copfs.gov.uk
Procurator Fiscal: Andy Shanks
Sheriff Court, Castlegate, JEDBURGH TD8 6AR;
Tel: 0300 020 3000 Email:
PFOJedburgh@copfs.gov.uk
Procurator Fiscal: Fraser Matheson
St Marnock Street, KILMARNOCK KA1 1DZ; Tel:
0300 020 3000 Email:
PFOKilmarnock@copfs.gov.uk
Procurator Fiscal: Katie Stewart
Carlyle House, Carlyle Road, KIRKCALDY KY1
1DB; Tel: 0300 020 3000
Procurator Fiscal: Sineidin Corrins
Sheriff Court, Watergate, KIRKWALL KW15 1PD;
Tel: 0300 020 3000
Procurator Fiscal: Sue Foard
Sheriff Court, 24 Hope Street, LANARK ML11
7NE; Tel: 0300 020 3000 Email:
PFOLanark@copfs.gov.uk
Procurator Fiscal: Les Brown
Sheriff Court, King Erik Street, LERWICK ZE1
0HD; Tel: 0300 020 3000 Email:
PFOLerwick@copfs.gov.uk
Procurator Fiscal: Sue Foard
West Lothian Civic Centre, Howden South Road,
LIVINGSTON EH54 6FF; Tel: 0300 020 3000
Procurator Fiscal: Laura Buchan
Sheriff Court, Lochmaddy, ISLE OF NORTH UIST
HS6 5AE; Tel: 0300 020 3000 Email:
PFOLochmaddy@copfs.gov.uk

Procurator Fiscal: Andy Shanks
Sheriff Court House, Albany Street, OBAN PA34
4AL; Tel: 0300 020 3000 Email:
PFOOban@copfs.gov.uk
Procurator Fiscal: Katie Stewart
1 Love Street, PAISLEY PA3 2DA; Tel: 0300 020
3000 Email: PFOPaisley@copfs.gov.uk
Procurator Fiscal: Katie Stewart
82 Tay Street, PERTH PH2 8NN; Tel: 0300 020
3000
Procurator Fiscal: Sineidin Corrins
70 St Peter Street, PETERHEAD AB42 1QB; Tel:
0300 020 3000 Email:
PFOPeterhead@copfs.gov.uk
Procurator Fiscal: Andy Shanks
Ettrick Terrace, Sheriff Court, SELKIRK TD7 4LE;
Tel: 0300 020 3000 Email:
PFOSelkirk@copfs.gov.uk
Procurator Fiscal: Fraser Matheson
Sheriff Court, Lewis Street, STORNOWAY HS1
2JF; Tel: 0300 020 3000 Email:
PFOStornoway@copfs.gov.uk
Procurator Fiscal: Andy Shanks
Sheriff Court, Lewis Street, STRANRAER DG9
7AA; Tel: 0300 020 3000 Email:
PFOStranraer@copfs.gov.uk
Procurator Fiscal: Les Brown
11 Stafford Street, TAIN IV19 1BP; Tel: 0300 020
3000 Email: PFOTain@copfs.gov.uk
Procurator Fiscal: Andy Shanks
Sheriff Court, Bridge Street, WICK KW1 4AJ; Tel:
0300 020 3000 Email: PFOWick@copfs.gov.uk
Procurator Fiscal: Andy Shanks

COPFS Specialist Units
Appeals Unit: Wendy Barr
Criminal Allegations Against the Police Unit:
Justin Farrell
Health & Safety Investigations Unit:
Alistair Duncan
International Co-Operation Unit: Vacant
National Procurator Fiscal for Domestic Abuse:
Moira Price
National Sexual Crimes Unit: Fraser Gibson
Proceeds of Crime Unit: Brian Duffy
Scottish Fatalities Investigation Unit: Katrina Parkes
Covid Deaths Investigation Team: Lorraine Almond
Serious and Organised Crime Unit: Lynne Barrie
Wildlife and Environmental Crime Unit:
Fiona Caldwell
Homicide & Major Crime: David Green

Civil Online
You can use Civil Online to make or respond to
a simple procedure claim You can make a claim:
for payment of a sum of money you are due
   where the value of the claim is £5000 or less;
for the return or delivery of goods, but only
   where there is an alternative claim for
   payment of a sum of money of £5000 or less;
if you want the court to order the person you
   are making a claim against to do something
   (for example to complete or perform a

service), but only where there is an alternative claim for payment of a sum of money of £5000 or less.

The value of your claim cannot be more than £5000.

You can use Civil Online to track the progress of your case or submit a document.
Civil Online can be accessed here:
https://www.scotcourts.gov.uk/taking-action/civil-online-gateway/welcome2

SHERIFFS' AND SUMMARY SHERIFFS' ASSOCIATION

President: Sheriff Wendy Sheehan
Vice-President: Sheriff Gillian Wade
Secretary: Sheriff Tony Kelly
Glasgow Sheriff Court, 1 Carlton Place, Glasgow G5 9TW

Members of Council:
President – Sheriff Wendy Sheehan, Edinburgh, Vice-President – Sheriff Gillian Wade QC, Perth, , Vice President (Summary Sheriff) – Summary Sheriff James Macdonald, Honorary Secretary and Treasurer – Sheriff Tony Kelly, Glasgow, Sheriff Brian Cameron (Sheriffdom of Glasgow & Strathkelvin), Sheriff Fergus Thomson (Sheriffdom of South Strathkelvin Dumfries and Galloway), Sheriff Jillian Martin-Brown (Sheriffdom of Tayside, Central and Fife), Sheriff Christine McCrossan Sheriffdom of Grampian, Highland and Islands, Sheriff Brian Mohan (Sheriffdom of North Strathclyde), Sheriff Kenneth Campbell QC (Sheriffdom of Lothian and Borders), Sheriff Colin Dunipace (Any Sheriffdom Member), Summary Sheriff John Hamilton QC (Any-Sheriffdom Member), Sumamry Sheriff Margaret Hodge (Any-Sheriffdom Member), Sheriff Susan Craig (Co-opted member Judical Institute for Scotland

SCOTTISH JUSTICES ASSOCIATION

SCOTTISH JUSTICES ASSOCIATION Correspondence to Secretary SJA, Email: secretary@scottishjustices.org, Web: www.scottishjustices.org
Members: Ashley Ward (Tayside, Central and Fife), David Caddick (Grampian, Highlands and Islands), David Donaldson (Tayside Central and Fife), Dennis Barr (Glasgow and Strathkelvin), Gary Watson (Lothian and Borders), Gordon Hunter (South Strathclyde Dumfries and Galloway), Grace MacLeod (North Strathclyde), John Lawless (Glasgow and Strathkelvin), Martin Morley (Grampian Highlands and Islands), Phil Cropper (Grampian Highland and Islands), Richard Scott (North Strathclyde), Robert Walsh (South Strathclyde Dumfries and Galloway), Sean Connor (Glasgow and Strathkelvi), Stephen Stables (South Strathclyde Dumfries and Galloway), Stuart Fair (Tayside, Central and Fife), Sue Cook (Lothian and Borders), Susan Fallone (Lothian and Borders), Tom Finnigan (North Strathclyde)

Stand Alone Justice of the Peace Courts

Lochgilphead Justice of the Peace Court
C/o Dunoon Sheriff Court
George Street, Dunoon PA23 3BQ Tel: (0300) 7900049
Fax: (01369) 702191 DX: 591655 Email: dunoon@scotcourts.gov.uk
Clerk: Kim Wilson

Hamilton Justice of the Peace Court
4 Beckford Street, Hamilton ML3 0BT
Tel: (01698) 282957

Fax: (01698) 201365 (Criminal)
Fax: (01698) 201366 (Admin) DX: HA2 Email: hamilton@scotcourts.gov.uk
Clerk: Jackie Powell

Inverness Justice Centre
Longman Road, Inverness IV1 1AH Tel: (01463) 230782
Fax: (01463) 710602 DX: IN25 Email: inverness@scotcourts.gov.uk
Clerk: Ruth Thomson

Sheriff Appeal Courts

Sheriff Appeal Court – Civil

Parliament House, Parliament Square, Edinburgh EH1 1RQ Tel: (0131) 240 6945 DX: 549306 Edinburgh 36 Email: SAC.civil@scotcourts.gov.uk Website: www.scotcourts.gov.uk/the-courts/sheriff-appeal-court/sheriff-appeal-court–civil

Email is the default method for lodging motions in the court. To be able to use this facility, a single email address, to be registered with the Court, must be provided to SACmotions@scotcourts.gov.uk.

Part 1 of Schedule 4 to the Coronavirus (Scotland) Act 2020 enables the use of electronic signatures and electronic transmission of court documents. Where a document requires to be signed, electronic signature will be accepted by the Court in accordance with Schedule 4. Part 1 of Schedule 4 also suspends the requirement for physical attendance at court unless the Court directs otherwise. Under these provisions all civil hearings in the Sheriff Appeal Court will be conducted remotely until further notice. All current and new documents, including all new notes of appeal should be lodged by e-mail to SAC.civil@scotcourts.gov.uk

Sheriff Appeal Court – Criminal

Justiciary Office, Parliament House, Parliament Square, Edinburgh EH1 1RQ Tel: (0131) 240 6912 DX: 549306 Edinburgh 36 Email: summaryappeals@scotcourts.gov.uk

The Sheriff Appeal Court (SAC) was established on 22 September 2015, as part of Lord Gill's Scottish Civil Courts Reforms, to deal with criminal appeals.

It hears appeals against summary criminal proceedings from both the sheriff and justice of the peace courts. The Bench generally comprises two or three appeal sheriffs depending on the type of appeal to be considered.

The Court also hears appeals against bail decisions made by a sheriff or a justice of the peace. These hearings are presided over by a single appeal sheriff. The criminal Court sits in the courthouse at Lawnmarket, Edinburgh.

Legal Secretariat to the Lord Advocate

Crown Office & Procurator Fiscal Service, 25 Chamber Street, Edinburgh EH1 1LA

Lord Advocate: Rt. Hon. Dorothy Bain, QC
Solicitor General for Scotland: Ruth Charteris, QC

Crown Office

25 Chambers Street, Edinburgh EH1 1LA
Tel: 0300 020 3000 DX: 540310 Edinburgh 38
Email: _EnquiryPoint@copfs.gsi.gov.uk Website:
www.copfs.gov.uk
Lord Advocate: Rt. Hon. Dorothy Bain, QC
Solicitor General: Ruth Charteris, QC
Private Secretary to the Lord Advocate:
Holly Garland
Private Secretary to the Solicitor General:
Dawn Andrews
Crown Agent/Chief Executive: David Harvie
Personal Secretary to the Crown Agent: Ann Marie
Henderson

Operational Support (Policy & Engagement & Business Services)
Deputy Crown Agent: Lindsey Miller

Serious Casework (High Court & Specialist Casework)
Deputy Crown Agent: Stephen McGowan

Local Court
Deputy Crown Agent: John Logue

Crown Counsel
Principal Crown Counsel: Ashley Edwards QC
Deputy Crown Counsel: Richard Goddard QC

Queen's and Lord Treasurer's Remembrancer Office

Scottish Government Building, 1F North, Victoria Quay, Edinburgh EH6 6QQ Tel: (0300) 0203512
Email: enquiries@qltr.gov.uk Website:
www.qltr.gov.uk

Chief Solicitor:
Robert Sandeman
Administrator:
Julia McNamara

The Scottish Criminal Cases Review Commission

Portland House, 17 Renfield Street, Glasgow G2 5AH Tel: (0141) 270 7030
Fax: (0141) 270 7040 Email: info@sccrc.org.uk Website: www.sccrc.co.uk

THE SCOTTISH CRIMINAL CASES REVIEW COMMISSION'S, role is to review and investigate cases where it is alleged that a miscarriage of justice may have occurred in relation to conviction, sentence or both. It can only review cases where the conviction and sentence was imposed by a Scottish court and can review both solemn and summary cases.

Chair: Mr Bill Matthews
Board Members: Professor Jim Fraser, Mrs Elaine Noad, Mr Raymond McMenamin, Dr Alex Quinn, Mrs Laura Reilly, Ms Jacqueline Fordyce, Mrs Gillian Mawdsley
Chief Executive: Mr Michael Walker BSc (Hons), LLB, Dip L.P. LLM
Director of Corporate Services: Mr Chris Reddick CMIIA
Senior Legal Officers: Mr Daniel Fenn LLB (Hons) Dip L.P. N.P., Mrs Fiona Govan LLB (Hons), BSc (Hons), DipFMS

Scottish Children's Reporter Administration

Head Office
Ochil House, Springkerse Business Park, Stirling FK7 7XE Tel: (0131) 244 8600 Email: communcations@scra.gov.uk Website: www.scra.gov.uk
Principal Reporter/Chief Executive Officer: Neil Hunter
Chair: Michelle Miller
Board Members: Anela Anwar, Martin Toye, Suzanne Vestri, James Edgar, Tam Baillie, Kay Barton, Lorraine Moore
Human Resources Manager: Susan Deery
Head of Practice and Policy: Alistair Hogg
Head of Finance and Resources: Ed Morrison
Head of Strategy & Organisational Development: Lisa Bennett
Senior Operational Manager: Helen Etchells
Senior Operational Manager: Paul Mulvanny

Aberdeen (Aberdeenshire & Aberdeen City)
The Exchange No.2, 62-104 Market Street, Aberdeen AB11 5PJ Tel: 0131 244 8720
Email: grampianmailbox@scra.gov.uk

Alloa (Alloa team)
Town Hall Lodge, Alloa FK10 1AB Tel: 0131 244 8700 Email: StirlingMailbox@scra.gov.uk

Arbroath (Angus team)
Merrin House, 50 East Abbey Street, Arbroath DD11 1EN Tel: 0131 244 5700
Email: AngusMailbox@scra.gov.uk

Ayr (Ayrshire Locality)
35 Carrick Street, Ayr KA7 1NS Tel: 0131 244 8777 Email: Ayrshiremailbox@scra.gov.uk

Bellshill (North Lanarkshire team)
70 North Rd, Bellshill ML4 1EN Tel: 0131 244 8701 Email: NorthLanarkshireMailbox@scra.gov.uk

Dalkeith (South East team)
29 Elmfield Court, Dalkeith EH22 1DY Tel: 0131 244 4111 Email: southeastmailbox@scra.gov.uk

Dumbarton (West Dumbartonshire team)
55 Church Court, Dumbarton G82 1SU Tel: 0131 244 8540
Email: WestDunbartonshireMailbox@scra.gov.uk

Dumfries (Dumfries & Galloway team)
99 George Street, Dumfries DG1 1EA Tel: 0131 244 8550 Email: DumfriesMailbox@scra.gov.uk

Dundee (Dundee, Angus, Perth & Kinross team)
6 Commercial Street, Dundee DD1 3EH Tel: 0131 244 5700 Email: AngusMailbox@scra.gov.uk
(Angus) DundeeMailbox@scra.gov.uk (Dundee)

Edinburgh (Edinburgh, Mid/East Lothian & Scottish Borders)
1 Fountainhall Road, Edinburgh EH9 2NL Tel: 0131 244 4111 Email: southeastmailbox@scra.gov.uk

Elgin (Moray team)
Phoenix House, 1 Wards Road, Elgin, Moray IV30 1QL Tel: 0131 244 8716
Email: MorayMailbox@scra.gov.uk

Falkirk (Falkirk team)
Campfield House, Wellside Place, Falkirk FK1 5RL Tel: 0131 244 8700
Email: FalkirkMailbox@scra.gov.uk

Fraserburgh (Aberdeenshire team)
   10 Commerce Street, Fraserburgh AB43 9AQ Tel: 0131 244 8720
   Email: AberdeenshireMailbox@scra.gov.uk

Glasgow (Glasgow teams)
   Merchant Exchange, 10/20 Bell Street, Candleriggs, Glasgow G1 1LG Tel: 0131 244 2100
   Email: GlasgowMailbox@scra.gov.uk

Glenrothes (Fife team)
   Albany House, 3 North Street, Glenrothes KY7 5NA Tel: 0131 244 4106
   Email: PerthandKinrossMailbox@scra.gov.uk (Perth & Kinross team) FifeMailbox@scra.gov.uk (Fife
   team)

Greenock (Inverclyde team)
   1/3 Brisbane Street, Greenock PA16 8LH Tel: 0131 244 8560 Email: InverclydeMailbox@scra.gov.uk

Hamilton (North & South Lanarkshire team)
   Hamilton House, Hamilton Business Park, Caird Park, Hamilton ML3 0QA Tel: 0131 244 8701
   Email: SouthLanarkshireMailbox@scra.gov.uk (South Lanarkshire team)
   NorthLanarkshireMailbox@scra.gov.uk (North Lanarkshire team)

Inverness (Highland team)
   6 Castle Wynd, Inverness IV2 3EB Tel: 0131 244 8788 Email: InvernessMailbox@scra.gov.uk

Irvine (Ayrshire)
   Sovereign House, Academy Road, Irvine KA12 8RL Tel: 0131 244 8777
   Email: Ayrshiremailbox@scra.gov.uk

Kilmarnock (Ayrshire teams)
   21 West Langlands Street, Kilmarnock KA1 2PY Tel: 0131 244 8777
   Email: Ayrshiremailbox@scra.gov.uk

Kirkwall (Orkney team)
   Eastbank, East Road, Kirkwall KW15 1LX 0131 244 8379 Email: OrkneyMailbox@scra.gov.uk

Lerwick (Shetland team)
   13 Hill Lane, Lerwick ZE1 0HA Tel: 0131 244 3780 Email: ShetlandMailbox@scra.gov.uk

Livingston (West Lothian team)
   West Lothian Civic Centre, Howden Road South, Livingstone EH54 6FF Tel: 0131 244 3130
   Email: WestLothianMailbox@scra.gov.uk

Lochgilphead (Argyll & Bute team)
   Kilbrandon House, Manse Brae, Lochgilphead PA31 8QX Tel: 0131 244 8400
   Email: ArgyllandButeMailbox@scra.gov.uk

Paisley (Renfrewshire/East Renfrewshire & East Dumbartonshire teams)
   10 Glen Lane, Paisley PA3 2HU Tel: 0131 244 8201 Email: RenfrewshireMailbox@scra.gov.uk

Perth (Perth & Kinross teams)
   Bellshaven House, Marshall Place, Perth PH2 8NS Tel: 0131 244 5700
   Email: PerthandKinrossMailbox@scra.gov.uk

Selkirk (Scottish Borders team)
   12 Ettrick Terrace, Selkirk TD7 4LE Tel: 0131 244 4111 Email: southeastmailbox@scra.gov.uk

Stirling (Stirling, Clackmannanshire & Falkirk teams)
   Ochil House, Springkerse Business Park, Stirling FK7 7XE Tel: 0131 244 8700
   Email: FalkirkMailbox@scra.gov.uk/StirlingMailbox@scra.gov.uk

Stornoway (Western Isles team)
   Unit 9, James Square, Stornoway HS1 2QN Tel: 0131 244 8391
   Email: EileanSiarMailbox@scra.gov.ukStranraer (Stranraer, Dumfries & Galloway teams)
   10 Market Street, Stranraer DG9 7RF Tel: 0131 244 8561 Email: StranraerMailbox@scra.gov.uk

Thurso (Thurso team)
  23 Swanson Street, Thurso KW14 8AP Tel: 0131 244 8386 Email: ThursoMailbox@scra.gov.uk

Tranent (East Lothian team)
  1 Loch Road, Tranent EH33 2JX Tel: 0131 244 4111 Email: southeastmailbox@scra.gov.uk

The Scottish Parliament

The Scottish Parliament, Edinburgh EH99 1SP
Tel: (0131) 348 5000 / 0800 092 7500 Email:
info@parliament.scot Website:
www.parliament.scot

Members of the Scottish Parliament

MSPs may be contacted by telephone using the
number given above, by letter at the above
address or by e-mail (addresses available from
Public Information on the telephone numbers
above).

Key to party abbreviations:

Con – Conservative
Ind – Independent
Green – Scottish Green Party
Lab – Labour
LD – Liberal Democrat
SNP – Scottish National Party
Ref – Reform UK
NPA – No Party Affiliation

Adam, George (SNP – Paisley)
Adam, Karen (SNP – Banffshire and Buchan Coast)
Adamson, Clare (SNP – Motherwell and Wishaw)
Allan, Alasdair (SNP – Na h-Eileanan an Iar)
Arthur, Tom (SNP – Renfrewshire South)
Baillie, Jackie (Lab – Dumbarton)
Baker, Claire (Lab – Mid Scotland and Fife)
Balfour, Jeremy (Con – Lothian)
Beattie, Colin (SNP – Midlothian North and Musselburgh)
Bibby, Neil (Lab – West Scotland)
Boyack, Sarah (Lab – Lothian)
Briggs, Miles (Con – Lothian)
Brown, Keith (SNP – Clackmannanshire and Dunblane)
Brown, Siobhian (SNP – Ayr)
Burgess, Ariane (Green – Highlands and Islands)
Burnett, Alexander (Con – Aberdeen West)
Callaghan, Stephanie (SNP – Uddingston and Bellshill)
Cameron, Donald (Con – Highlands and Islands)
Carlaw, Jackson (Con – Eastwood)
Carson, Finlay (Con – Galloway and West Dumfries)
Chapman, Maggie (SNP – North East Scotland)
Choudray, Foysol (Lab – Lothian)
Clark, Katy (Lab – West Scotland)
Coffey, Willie (SNP – Kilmarnock and Irvine Valley)
Cole-Hamilton, Alex (LD – Edinburgh West)
Constance, Angela (SNP – Almond Valley)
Dey, Graeme (SNP – Angus South)
Don, Natalie (SNP – Renfrewshire North and West)

Doris, Bob (SNP – Glasgow Maryhill and Springburn)
Dornan, James (SNP – Glasgow Cathcart)
Dowey, Sharon (Con – South Scotland)
Dunbar, Jackie (SNP – Aberdeen Donside)
Duncan-Glancy, Pam (Lab – Glasgow)
Ewing, Annabelle (SNP – Cowdenbeath)
Ewing, Fergus (SNP – Inverness and Nairn)
Fairlie, Jim (SNP – Perthshire South and Kinross-shire)
Findlay, Russell (Con – West Scotland)
FitzPatrick, Joe (SNP – Dundee City West)
Forbes, Kate (SNP – Skye, Lochaber and Badenoch)
Fraser, Murdo (Con – Mid Scotland and Fife)
Gallacher, Meghan (Con – Central Scotland)
Gibson, Kenneth (SNP – Cunninghame North)
Gilruth, Jenny (SNP – Mid Fife and Glenrothes)
Golden, Maurice (Con – West Scotland)
Gosal, Pam (Con – West Scotland)
Gougeon, Mairi (SNP – Angus North and Mearns)
Grahame, Christine (SNP – Midlothian South, Tweeddale and Lauderdale)
Grant, Rhoda (Lab – Highlands and Islands)
Gray, Neil (SNP – Airdrie and Shotts)
Greene, Jamie (Con – West Scotland)
Greer, Ross (Green – West Scotland)
Griffin, Mark (Lab – Central Scotland)
Gulhane, Dr. Sandesh (Con -Glasgow)
Halcro Johnston, Jamie (Con – Highlands and Islands)
Hamilton, Rachael (Con – Ettrick, Roxburgh and Berwickshire)
Harper, Emma (SNP – South Scotland)
Harvie, Patrick (Green – Glasgow)
Haughey, Clare (SNP – Rutherglen)
Hepburn, Jamie (SNP – Cumbernauld and Kilsyth)
Hoy, Craig (Con – South Scotland)
Hyslop, Fiona (SNP – Linlithgow)
Johnson, Daniel (Lab – Edinburgh Southern)
Johnstone, Alison (NPA – Lothian)
Kerr, Liam (Con – North East Scotland)
Kerr, Stephen (Con – Central Scotland)
Kidd, Bill (SNP – Glasgow Anniesland)
Lennon, Monica (Lab – Central Scotland)
Leonard, Richard (Lab – Central Scotland)
Lochhead, Richard (SNP – Moray)
Lockhart, Dean (Con – Mid Scotland and Fife)
Lumsden, Douglas (Con – North East Scotland)
MacDonald, Gordon (SNP – Edinburgh Pentlands)
MacGregor, Fulton (SNP – Coatbridge and Chryston)
Mackay, Gillian (Green – Central Scotland)
Mackay, Rona (SNP – Strathkelvin and Bearsden)

Macpherson, Ben (SNP – Edinburgh Northern and Leith)
Maguire, Ruth (SNP – Cunninghame South)
Marra, Michael (Lab – North East Scotland)
Martin, Gillian (SNP – Aberdeenshire East)
Mason, John (SNP – Glasgow Shettleston)
Matheson, Michael (SNP – Falkirk West)
McAllan, Mairi (SNP – Clydesdale)
McArthur, Liam (LD – Orkney Islands)
McDonald, Mark (Ind – Aberdeen Donside)
McKee, Ivan (SNP – Glasgow Provan)
McKelvie, Christina (SNP – Hamilton, Larkhall & Stonehouse)
McLennan, Paul (SNP -East Lothian)
McMillan, Stuart (SNP – Greenock and Inverclyde)
McNair, Marie (SNP – Clydebank and Milngavie)
McNeill, Pauline (Lab – Glasgow)
Minto, Jenni (SNP – Argyll and Bute)
Mochan, Carol (Lab – South Scotland)
Mountain, Edward (Con – Highlands and Islands)
Mundell, Oliver (Con – Dumfriesshire)
Nicoll, Audrey (SNP – Aberdeen South and North Kincardine)
O'Kane, Paul (Lab – West Scotland)
Regan, Ash (SNP – Edinburgh Eastern)
Rennie, Willie (LD – North East Fife)
Robertson, Angus (SNP – Edinburgh Central)
Robison, Shona (SNP – Dundee City East)
Roddick, Emma (SNP – Highlands and Islands)
Ross, Douglas (Con – Highlands and Islands)
Rowley, Alex (Lab – Mid Scotland and Fife)
Ruskell, Mark (Green – Mid Scotland and Fife)
Sarwar, Anas (Lab – Glasgow)
Simpson, Graham (Con – Central Scotland)
Slater, Lorna (Green – Lothian)
Smith, Liz (Con – Mid Scotland and Fife)
Smyth, Colin (Lab – South Scotland)
Somerville, Shirley-Anne (SNP – Dunfermline)
Stevenson, Collette (SNP – East Kilbride)
Stewart, Alexander (Con – Mid Scotland and Fife)
Stewart, Kaukab (SNP – Glasgow Kelvin)
Stewart, Kevin (SNP – Aberdeen Central)
Sturgeon, Nicola (SNP – Glasgow Southside)
Sweeney, Paul (Lab – Glasgow)
Swinney, John (SNP – Perthshire North)
Thomson, Michelle (SNP – Falkirk East)
Todd, Maree (SNP – Caithness, Sutherland and Ross)
Torrance, David (SNP – Kirkcaldy)
Tweed, Evelyn (SNP – Stirling)
Villalba, Mercedes (Lab – North East Scotland)
Webber, Sue (Con – Lothian)
Wells, Annie (Con – Glasgow)
White, Tess (Con -North East Scotland)
Whitfield, Martin (Lab – South Scotland)
Witham, Elena (SNP – Carrick, Cumnock and Doon Valley)
Whittle, Brian (Con – South Scotland)
Wishart, Beatrice (LD – Shetland Islands)
Yousaf, Humza (SNP – Glasgow Pollock)

Presiding Officer: Alison Johnstone MSP
Deputy Presiding Officers: Annabelle Ewing, Liam McArthur

Committees
COVID-19 RECOVERY
Convener: Siobhian Brown
Deputy Convener: Murdo Fraser
Committee Remit: Committee covers: the Scottish Government's response to COVID-19 and actions to recover from the pandemic; Government legislation introduced in response to the pandemic; legislation or policies aiming to help Scotland recover from the pandemic; how Government departments work together to respond and recover from the pandemic.
Members: Jim Fairlie, John Mason, Alex Rowley, Brian Whittle
Committee Substitutes: Jackie Baillie, James Dornan, Dr. Sandesh Gulhane
Clerk: Sigrid Robinson (0131 348 6226)
E-mail: Covid19.Committee@parliament.scot

CITIZEN PARTICIPATION AND PUBLIC PETITIONS
Convener: Jackson Carlaw
Deputy Convener: David Torrance
Committe Remit: Committee covers: all public petitions submitted to the Parliament and determines if they meet the rules; deciding what actions should be taken for all public petitions which meet the rules; reviewing the operation of the public petitions system; any other forms of public engagement the committee decides to undertake.
Members: Ruth Maguire, Alexander Stewart, Paul Sweeney
Committee Substitutes: Sharon Dowey, Marie McNair, Carol Mochan
Clerk: Pauline McIntyre (0131 348 5254)
E-mail: petitions.committee@parliament.scot

CONSTITUTION, EUROPE, EXTERNAL AFFAIRS AND CULTURE
Convener: Clare Adamson
Deputy Convener: Donald Cameron
Committee Remit: Committee covers: the Scottish Government's EU and international policy; the constitution including policy on the UK's exit from the EU; culture, including the creative industries.
Members: Alasdair Allan, Sarah Boyack, Maurice Golden, Jenni Minto, Mark Ruskell
Committee Substitutes: Clare Baker, Fergus Ewing, Graham Simpson
Clerk: James Johnston (0131 348 5215)
E-mail: ceeac.committee@parliament.scot

CRIMINAL JUSTICE COMMITTEE
Convener: Audrey Nicoll
Deputy Convener: Russell Findlay
Committee Remit: Committee covers: Police Scotland and the Scottish Fire and Rescue

Service; Courts, including the Scottish Courts and Tribunals Service; Prosecution and the work of the Crown Office and Procurator Fiscal Service; The Scottish Prison Service and community sentencing.
Members: Katy Clark, Jamie Greene, Fulton MacGregor, Rona Mackay, Pauline McNeill, Collette Stevenson
Committee Substitutes: Donald Cameron, Jackie Dunbar, Daniel Johnson
Clerk: Stephen Imrie (0131 348 6241)
E-mail: justice.committee@parliament.scot

DELEGATED POWERS AND LAW REFORM
Convener: Stuart McMillan
Deputy Convener: Bill Kidd
Committee Remit: Committee covers: checking secondary legislation coming before the Parliament for legal and technical accuracy; checking whether proposed secondary legislation in Bills is appropriate; reporting its findings to the Parliament so all laws and proposals for laws get proper oversight from MSPs; looking at certain Bills which are based on reports from the Scottish Law Commission. The Commission recommends changes to the law so it keeps pace with the way we live and work.
Members: Craig Hoy, Graeme Simpson, Paul Sweeney
Committee Substitutes: Maurice Golden, Rhoda Grant, Jenni Minto
Clerk: Andrew Proudfoot
E-mail: dplr.committee@parliament.scot

ECONOMY AND FAIR WORK
Convener: Clare Baker
Deputy Convener: Colin Beattie
Committee Remit: Commitee covers: the Scottish Government's economic policy and strategy; employment, procurement, investment and trade policies; support for business, industry, tourism and manufacturing; broadband connectivity and the digital economy; the Scottish National Investment Bank
Members: Alexander Burnett, Maggie Chapman, Jamie Halcro Johnston, Fiona Hyslop, Gordon MacDonald, Colin Smyth, Michelle Thomson
Committee Substitutes: John Mason, Liz Smith, Paul Sweeney
Clerk: Anne Peat
E-mail: economyandfairwork@parliament.scot

EDUCATION, CHILDREN AND YOUNG PEOPLE
Convener: Stephen Kerr
Deputy Convener: Kaukab Stewart
Committee Remit: Committe covers: schools, colleges and universities; additional support for learning; early years and childcare; Children's Hearings child protection; and; the Scottish Child Abuse Inquiry
Members: Callaghan, Stephanie, Bob Doris, James Dornan, Fergus Ewing, Ross Greer, Michael Marra, Oliver Mundell, Willie Rennie

Committee Substitutes: Alex Cole-Hamilton, Natalie Don, Meghan Gallacher, Martin Whitfield
Clerk: Stephen Herbert (0131 348 6225)
E-mail: ecyp.committee@parliament.scot

EQUALITIES AND HUMAN RIGHTS AND CIVIL JUSTICE
Convener: Joe Fitzpatrick
Deputy: Maggie Chapman
Committee Remit: Committee covers: equal opportunities matters; human rights matters; civil justice matters including debt, evictions and family law
Committee Members: Karen Adam, Pam Duncan-Glancy, Pam Gosal, Fulton MacGregor, Alexander Stewart
Committee Substitutes: Jeremy Balfour, Paul O'Kane, Kaukab Stewart
Clerk: Katrina Venters Tel: (0131 348 6244)
E-mail: ehrcj.committee@parliament.scot

FINANCE AND PUBLIC ADMINISTRATION
Convener: Kenneth Gibson
Deputy: Damiel Johnson
Committee Remit: Committee covers: Scotland's public finances; public service reform; the National Performance Framework; public administration in government.
Committee Members: Ross Greer, Douglas Lumsden, John Mason, Liz Smith, Michelle Thomson
Committee Substitutes: Alasdair Allan, Jamie Halcro Johnston, Colin Smyth
Clerk: Joanne McNaughton
Email: fpa.committee@parliament.scot

HEALTH SOCIAL CARE AND SPORT
Convener: Gillian Martin
Deputy: Paul O'Kane
Committee Remit: Committee covers: health services in Scotland – including performance, staffing and funding; primary care – including dentistry, GPs, and pharmacy services; public health including mental health and wellbeing, and tackling drugs misuse;; social care; sport and physical activity.
Committee Members: Stephanie Callaghan, Dr. Sandesh Gulhane, Emma Harper, Gillian Mackay, Carol Mochan, David Torrance, Evelyn Tweed, Sue Webber
Committee Substitutes: Jackie Baillie, Russell Findlay, Marie McNair
Clerk: Alex Bruce
E-mail: hscs.committee@parliament.scot

LOCAL GOVERNMENT HOUSING AND PLANNING
Convener: Ariane Burgess
Deputy: Miles Briggs
Committee Remit: Committee covers: local government (including councils); the third sector

and social economy (like charities and non-profits); housing and housing strategy; building standards
Committee Members: Willie Coffey, Graeme Dey, Meghan Gallacher, Mark Griffin, Paul McLennan
Committee Substitutes: Sarah Boyack, Murdo Fraser, Emma Roddick
Clerk: Euan Donald
E-mail: localgov.committee@parliament.scot

NET ZERO, ENERGY AND TRANSPORT
Convener: Dean Lockhart
Deputy Convener: Fiona Hyslop
Committee Remit: Committee covers: Scrutinising the Scottish Government's policies and progress towards meeting climate change targets across all government departments; Transport; Energy; Net zero and circular economy; Aspects of environmental policy.
Committee Members: Natalie Don, Jackie Dunbar, Liam Kerr, Monica Lennon, Mark Ruskell
Committee Substitutes: Collette Stevenson, Mercedes Villalba, Brian Whittle
Clerk: Peter McGrath (0131 348 6039)
E-mail: netzero.committee@parliament.scot

PUBLIC AUDIT
Convener: Richard Leonard
Deputy Convener: Sharon Dowey
Committee Remit: Committee covers: the Scottish Government, and; other public bodies (including colleges, police and fire services and the NHS).
Committee Members: Colin Beattie, Willie Coffey, Craig Hoy
Substitute Members: Alexander Burnett, Katy Clark, Bill Kidd
Clerk: Lynn Russell (Tel: 0131 348 5186)
E-mail: publicaudit.committee@parliament.scot

RURAL AFFAIRS, ISLANDS AND NATURAL ENVIRONMENT
Convener: Finlay Carson
Deputy: Beatrice Wishart
Committee Remit: Committee covers: farming; food and drink supply; animal welfare; fisheries and aquaculture; crofting; issues relevant to the Islands (Scotland) Act 2018.
Committee Members: Karen Adam, Alasdair Allan, Ariane Burgess, Jim Fairlie, Rachael Hamilton, Jenni Minto, Mercedes Villalba
Committee Substitutes: Emma Harper, Liam McArthur, Edward Mountain, Colin Smyth
Clerk: Emma Johnston
E-mail: rural.committee@parliament.scot

SOCIAL JUSTICE AND SOCIAL SECURITY
Convener: Natalie Don
Deputy Convener: Jeremy Balfour
Committee Remit: Committee covers: the Scottish Government's policies on welfare, poverty and homelessness; the social security system in Scotland; violence against women and girls and domestic violence; social justice (looking at ways to create a fairer Scotland).
Committee Members: Miles Briggs, Foysol Choudhury, Pam Duncan-Glancy, Marie McNair, Emma Roddick, Elena Whitham
Substitute Members: Mark Griffin, Rachael Hamilton, Evelyn Tweed
Clerk: Clare Menzies (0131 348 5320)
E-mail: sjss.commitee@parliament.scot

STANDARDS, PROCEDURES AND PUBLIC APPOINTMENTS
Convener: Martin Whitfield
Deputy Convener: Bob Doris
Committee Remit: Committee covers: the Parliament's procedures rules for MSPs' behaviour and conduct; rules on lobbying; and elections and referendums.
Committee Members: Edward Mountain, Collette Stevenson, Tess White
Substitute Members: Rhoda Grant, Rhona Mackay, Sue Webber
Clerk: Katy Orr (0131 348 6924)
E-mail: sppa.commitee@parliament.scot

Parliamentary Bureau

The Bureau proposes the Parliament's business programme. Membership of the Bureau includes: the Presiding Officer (chair), a member of parties or groupings with 5 or more MSPs.
Current Members: Alison Johnstone – Convener (NPA), George Adam (SNP), Neil Bibby (Lab), Stephen Kerr (Con), Gillian Mackay (Green)
Clerk: Catherine Fergusson (Tel: 0131 348 5176)
E-mail: business.team@parliament.scot

Scottish Parliamentary Corporate Body (SPCB)

The Scottish Parliament Corporate Body makes sure the Parliament: has everything it needs to run; provides support to MSPs to enable them to carry out their parliamentary duties. This includes property, services and staff. It makes decisions on: budgets; staffing; accommodation; security. It is chaired by the Presiding Officer and includes 4 elected members. Each of the elected members takes a lead interest in specific issues.
Elected Members: Maggie Chapman MSP: Business support and Officeholders, Jackson Carlaw MSP: Finance and organisation governance, Claire Baker MSP: Digital services, resilience and sustainability, Christine Grahame MSP: Engagement and communications
Members:
Alison Johnstone, Claire Baker, Jackson Carlaw, Maggie Chapman, Christine Grahame
Clerk: SPCB Secretariat (0131 348 5307)
Email: SPCBsecretariat@parliament.scot

Leadership Group

The Leadership Group (LG) is the Scottish Parliament's senior management group. It advises the Clerk/Chief Executive on how to achieve the Parliament's strategic objectives. LG members share their expertise and knowledge and contribute to running the Parliament.

Officeholders

Commissioner for Ethical Standards in Public Life in Scotland – Ian Bruce
Scottish Biometrics Commissioner
Scottish Commissioner for Children and Young People – Bruce Adamson
Scottish Human Rights Commission – Judith Robertson (Chair)
Scottish Information Commissioner – Daren Fitzhenry
Scottish Public Services Ombudsman – Rosemary Agnew
Standards Commission for Scotland – Paul Walker (Convener)

Management

David McGill – Clerk/Chief Executive
Alison Johnstone MSP – Presiding Officer (PO)
Annabelle Ewing, Liam McArthur – Deputy Presiding Officers

Advisory Audit Board

The Advisory Audit Board (AAB) gives advice to the Scottish Parliamentary Corporate Body (SPCB) and the Clerk/Chief Executive on how the organisation is managed. Its advice is based on: reports from internal and external auditors; SPCB annual reports and accounts financial policies and management practices set by Leadership Group; compliance with legal matters, where relevant to its work. The AAB currently has 5 members. Three are independent external members, for objectivity, and 2 are from the SPCB:
Current Membership: Andy Shaw (Chair), Jackson Carlaw MSP – SPCB member, Claire Baker MSP – SPCB member, Claire Robertson, David Watt

Scottish Commission for Public Audit (SCPA)

The Scottish Commission for Public Audit (SCPA) is made up of 5 Members of the Scottish Parliament. The SCPA is not a parliament committee. The Commission is responsible for: looking at Audit Scotland's proposals for the use of resources and spend, then reporting on them to the Parliament; appointing a qualified person to audit the accounts of Audit Scotland; presenting and publishing a copy of Audit Scotland's accounts and the auditor's report on them; appointing 3 of the 5 members of Audit Scotland under terms and conditions agreed by the SCPA appointing 1 of these 3 members to be the chair of Audit Scotland. It was set up under the Public Finance and Accountability (Scotland) Act 2000 (Section 12).

Scottish Ministers

First Minister: Nicola Sturgeon
As head of the Scottish Government, the First Minister is responsible for the overall development, implementation and presentation of the administration's policies and for promoting and representing Scotland at home and overseas.

Deputy First Minister and Cabinet Secretary for Covid Recovery: John Swinney
The Cabinet Secretary is responsible for cross-government co-ordination of Covid Recovery policies and cross-government co-ordination on COVID-19 recovery and COVID-19 strategic reviews

Cabinet Secretary for Justice and Veterans: Keith Brown MSP
Responsibilities include: police, Emergency Services Mobile Communications Programme (ESMCP), miner's strike pardons, Sheku Bayoh public inquiry, courts and sentencing, justice system and criminal law procedure, violence reduction, prison reform and prisoner policy, reducing reoffending, criminal justice social work, offender services, security, youth justice, victim/witness support, Criminal Injuries Compensation, Scottish Courts and Tribunals Service, Bairn's Hoose, justice reform, National Community Justice Strategy, veterans, anti-racism, anti-sectarianism, serious organised crime, CashBack for Communities.

Cabinet Secretary for Health and Social Care: Humza Yousaf MSP
Responsibilities include: NHS remobilisation, NHS primary care, community care and acute services, National Care Service, NHS performance, staff and pay, patient services and patient safety, health and social care integration, GPs and primary care, dentistry, community pharmacy, community optometry, community audiology, mobile healthcare, health improvement and protection, quality and improvement, person-centred care, Pharmacy First, National Pharmaceutical Agency, COVID-19 vaccinations, shielding, pandemic preparedness, eHealth, MyNHS Digital, NHS estate, Centre of excellence for rural and remote medicine and social care

Cabinet Secretary for Finance and Economy: Kate Forbes MSP
Responsibilities include: Scottish budget, budgetary monitoring and reporting, fiscal policy and taxation, exchequer and the public, finances, economic strategy, National Strategy for Economic Transformation and Council for Economic Transformation, wellbeing economy, enterprise agencies, employment policy, four-day working week, Just Transition (with CS Net Zero), Scottish National Investment Bank, Scottish Futures Trust (SFT), trade and inward investment, Office of the Chief Economic Adviser, City and Regional Growth Deals, Scottish Fiscal Commission, enterprise, innovation and increasing productivity, government investments (Prestwick, Fergusons, BiFab), digital economy, strategy, participation and connectivity (inc, 100% broadband and Connecting Scotland), Revenue Scotland, Green Jobs Fund, Women's Business Centre, Rural Entrepreneur Fund.

Cabinet Secretary for Net Zero, Energy and Transport: Michael Matheson MSP
Responsibilities include: cross-government co-ordination of Net Zero policy, climate crisis and environmental protection, COP26 delivery, biodiversity, sustainable development, circular economy, including implementation of the Deposit Return Scheme, cross-government co-ordination of infrastructure (policy, investment and commission), cross-government delivery of 20-minute neighbourhoods, renewable energy industries, energy and energy consents, energy efficiency, National Public Energy Agency, heating and domestic energy transformation, heat networks, fuel poverty, physical and marine environment, flood prevention and coastal erosion, Scottish Environment Protection Agency, NatureScot, Zero Waste Scotland, water quality and Scottish Water, Strategic Transport Projects Review.

Cabinet Secretary for the Rural Affairs and Islands: Mairi Gougeon MSP
Responsibilities include: cross-government co-ordination on islands, Islands Bond, carbon-neutral islands, food and drink supply chain, Scottish Food Agency, agriculture, fisheries and aquaculture, animal welfare, crofting.

Cabinet Secretary for the Constitution, External Affairs and Culture: Angus Robertson MSP
Responsibilities include: independence, cross-government co-ordination of European and external relations, policy in relation to UK's exit from the EU, post-Brexit relations, migration, Scottish diaspora, Global Affairs Network, Scottish Cities of Refuge, National Records of

Scotland, New Scot strategy, culture policy, broadcasting and screen, British Irish Council, royal and ceremonial.

Cabinet Secretary for Education and Skills: Shirley-Anne Somerville MSP
Responsibilities include: COVID-19 Education and Development recovery, school standards, quality and improvement, school infrastructure and staffing, attainment, and closing the attainment gap, reform of the curriculum, National Improvement Framework, teaching profession, removing barriers to education and supporting digital inclusion, behaviour and measures to combat bullying, protection of vulnerable groups, Education Scotland (ES), school learning and support, education analytical services, education strategy and performance, additional support for learning, lifelong learning, cross-government support for learning disabilities, autism and neurodiversity, learning difficulties, National Digital Academy, Scotland's languages, include Gaelic, Scots and BSL.

Cabinet Secretary for Social Justice, Housing and Local Government: Shona Robison MSP
Responsibilities include: welfare policy and social security, social justice, local government, child poverty, housing and housing strategy, homelessness and rough sleeping, building standards, tackling inequalities, violence against women and girls and domestic violence, poverty action measures, third sector and social economy, mainstreaming equality, human rights, kinship carers, minimum income guarantee, equalities, refugees and asylum, Office of the Scottish Charity Regulator.

Minister for Parliamentary Business: George Adam MSP

Minister for Environment and Land Reform: Mairi McAllan MSP

Minister for Community Safety: Ash Regan MSP

Minister for Children and Young People: Clare Haughey MSP

Minister for Further Education, Higher Education, Youth Employment and Training: Jamie Hepburn MSP

Minister for Social Security and Local Government: Ben Macpherson MSP

Minister for Business, Trade, Tourism and Enterprise: Ivan McKee MSP

Minister for Public Health, Women's Health and Sport: Maree Todd MSP

Minister for Drugs Policy: Angela Constance MSP

Minister for Mental Wellbeing and Social Care: Kevin Stewart MSP

Minister for Older People and Equalities: Christina McKelvie MSP

Minister for Green Skills, Circular Economy and Biodiversity: Lorna Slater MSP

Minister for Zero Carbon Buildings, Active Travel and Tenants' Rights: Patrick Harvie MSP

Minister for Culture, Europe and International Development: Awaiting Appointment

Minister for Just Transition, Employment and Fair Work: Richard Lochhead MSP

Minister for Public Finance, Planning and Community Wealth: Tom Arthur MSP

Minister for Transport: Jenny Gilruth MSP

Law Officers:
Lord Advocate: The Rt Hon Dorothy Bain QC
Solicitor General: Ruth Charteris QC

The Scottish Government

THE SCOTTISH GOVERNMENT
St Andrew's House, Regent Road, Edinburgh
EH1 3DG Tel: (0300) 2444000 Email:
ceu@gov.scot Website: www.gov.scot

First Minister: Nicola Sturgeon

Deputy First Minister and Cabinet Secretary for Covid Recovery:
John Swinney MSP

Permanent Secretary: John-Paul Marks

Directorate – Advanced Learning and Science
Director-General Education and Justice: Joe Griffin
Minister for Further Education, Higher Education, Youth Employment and Training: Jamie Hepburn MSP
Cabinet Secretary for Education and Skills: Shirley-Anne Somerville MSP

Directorate – Agriculture and Rural Economy
Director-General Economy: Elinor Mitchell
Chief Veterinary Officer for Scotland: Shiela Voas
Cabinet Secretary for Rural Affairs and Islands: Mairi Gougeon MSP
Minister for Environment and Land Reform: Mairi McAllan MSP

Directorate – Budget and Public Spending
Cabinet Secretary for Finance and the Economy: Kate Forbes
Minister for Public Finance, Planning and Community Wealth: Tom Arthur MSP
Director – Budget and Public Spending: Andrew Watson
Director-General Scottish Exchequer: Alyson Stafford CBE

Directorate – Chief Economist
Director-General Economy: Elinor Mitchell
Chief Economic Adviser: Gary Gillespie
Cabinet Secretary for Finance and the Economy: Kate Forbes MSP
Minister for Business, Trade, Tourism and Enterprise: Ivan McKee MSP
Minister for Just Transition, Employment and Fair Work: Richard Lochhead MSP
Minister for Public Finance, Planning and Community Wealth: Tom Arthur MSP

Directorate – Chief Medical Officer
Chief Executive NHS Scotland and Director-General Health and Social Care: Caroline Lamb
Chief Medical Officer: Professor Sir Gregor Smith
Cabinet Secretary for Health and Social Care: Humza Yousaf MSP
Minister for Mental Wellbeing and Social Care: Kevin Stewart MSP
Minister for Public Health, Women's Health and Sport: Maree Todd MSP

Directorate – Chief Nursing Officer
Chief Executive NHS Scotland and Director-General Health and Social Care: Caroline Lamb
Chief Healthcare Science Professions Officer: Catherine Ross
Chief Allied Health Professions Officer: Carolyn McDonald
Cabinet Secretary for Health and Social Care: Humza Yousaf MSP
Minister for Mental Wellbeing and Social Care: Kevin Stewart MSP
Minister for Public Health, Women's Health and Sport: Maree Todd MSP

Directorate – Children and Families
Director-General Education and Justice: Joe Griffin
Director, Children and Families: Michael Chalmers
Cabinet Secretary for Education and Skills: Shirley-Anne Somerville MSP
Minister for Children and Young People: Clare Haughey MSP

Directorate – Communications and Ministerial Support
Director-General Corporate: Lesley Fraser
Director, Communications and Ministerial Support: Andy Bruce
Cabinet Secretary for the Constitution, External Affairs and Culture: Angus Robertson MSP
Minister for Parliamentary Business: George Adam MSP

Directorate – Constitution and Cabinet
Director General Constitution and External Affairs: Ken Thomson
Director for Constitution and Cabinet: David Rogers
Cabinet Secretary for the Constitution, External Affairs and Culture: Angus Robertson MSP
Minister for Parliamentary Business: George Adam MSP

Directorate – Covid Coordination
Director General Constitution and External Affairs: Ken Thomson

Interim Director of Covid Coordination and Director of Culture and Major Events: Penelope Cooper
Deputy First Minister and Cabinet Secretary for Covid Recovery: John Swinney MSP

Directorate – Culture and Major Events
Director General Constitution and External Affairs: Ken Thomson
Interim Director of Covid Coordination and Director of Culture and Major Events: Penelope Cooper
Cabinet Secretary for the Constitution, External Affairs and Culture: Angus Robertson MSP
Minister Culture, Europe and International Development: Awaiting Appointment

Directorate – Digital
Director-General Corporate: Lesley Fraser
Director, Digital: Colin Cook
Minister for Public Finance, Planning and Community Wealth: Tom Arthur MSP

Directorate – Digital Health and Care
Chief Executive NHS Scotland and Director-General Health and Social Care: Caroline Lamb
Interim Director of Digital Health and Care: Jonathan Cameron
Cabinet Secretary for Health and Social Care: Humza Yousaf MSP
Cabinet Secretary for Rural Affairs and Islands: Mairi Gougeon MSP

Directorate -EU
Director General Constitution and External Affairs: Ken Thomson
Director EU Directorate: Martin Johnson
Cabinet Secretary for the Constitution, External Affairs and Culture: Angus Robertson MSP
Minister Culture, Europe and International Development: Awaiting Appointment

Directorate – Early Learning and Childcare
Director General Education and Justice: Joe Griffin
Cabinet Secretary for Education and Skills: Shirley-Anne Somerville MSP
Minister for Children and Young People: Clare Haughey MSP

Directorate – Economic Development
Director-General Economy: Elinor Mitchell
Director, Economic Development: Mary McAllan
Cabinet Secretary for Finance and the Economy: Kate Forbes MSP
Minister for Business, Trade, Tourism and Enterprise: Ivan McKee MSP
Minister for Just Transition, Employment and Fair Work: Richard Lochhead MSP
Minister for Public Finance, Planning and Community Wealth: Tom Arthur MSP

Directorate – Energy and Climate Change
Director General Economy: Elinor Mitchell
Director Energy and Climate Change: Kersti Berge
Cabinet Secretary for Finance and the Economy: Kate Forbes MSP
Minister for Business, Trade, Tourism and Enterprise: Ivan McKee MSP

Directorate – Environment and Forestry
Director-General Economy: Elinor Mitchell
Director, Environment and Forestry
Cabinet Secretary for Net Zero, Energy and Transport: Michael Matheson MSP
Cabinet Secretary for Rural Affairs and Islands: Mairi Gougeon MSP
Minister for Environment and Land Reform: Mairi McAllan MSP

Directorate – Equality, Inclusion and Human Rights
Director General Communities: Paul Johnston
Minister for Equalities and Older People: Christina McKelvie MSP

Directorate – External Affairs
Director-General Constitution and External Affairs: Ken Thomson
Director, External Affairs: Scott Wightman
Cabinet Secretary for the Constitution, External Affairs and Culture: Angus Robertson MSP
Minister Culture, Europe and International Development: Awaiting Appointment

Directorate – Fair Work, Employability and Skills
Director-General Economy: Elinor Mitchell
Director, Fair Work: Dominic Munro
Interim Director Fair Work, Employability and Skills: David Wilson
Deputy First Minister: John Swinney MSP
Minister for Business, Trade, Tourism and Enterprise: Ivan McKee MSP
Minister for Just Transition, Employment and Fair Work: Richard Lochhead MSP

Directorate – Financial Management
Director-General Corporate: Lesley Fraser
Chief Financial Officer: Jackie McAllister
Cabinet Secretary for Finance and the Economy: Kate Forbes MSP
Minister for Public Finance, Planning and Community Wealth: Tom Arthur MSP

Directorate – Health Finance, Corporate Governance and Value
Chief Executive NHS Scotland and Director-General Health and Social Care: Caroline Lamb
Director of Health Finance and Governance: Richard McCallum

Cabinet Secretary for Health and Social Care:
Humza Yousaf MSP
Minister for Mental Wellbeing and Social Care:
Kevin Stewart MSP
Minister for Public Health, Women's Health and Sport: Maree Todd MSP

Directorate – Health Performance and Delivery

Chief Executive NHS Scotland and Director-General Health and Social Care: Caroline Lamb
Cabinet Secretary for Health and Social Care:
Humza Yousaf MSP
Minister for Mental Wellbeing and Social Care:
Kevin Stewart MSP
Minister for Public Health, Women's Health and Sport: Maree Todd MSP

Directorate – Health Workforce, Leadership and Service Reform

Chief Executive NHS Scotland and Director-General Health and Social Care: Caroline Lamb
Director of Health Workforce: Gillian Russell
Cabinet Secretary for Health and Social Care:
Humza Yousaf MSP
Minister for Mental Wellbeing and Social Care:
Kevin Stewart MSP
Minister for Public Health, Women's Health and Sport: Maree Todd MSP

Directorate – Healthcare Quality and Improvement

Chief Executive NHS Scotland and Director-General Health and Social Care: Caroline Lamb
National Clinical Director of Healthcare Quality and Strategy: Professor Jason Leitch
Interim Director of Healthcare Quality and Improvement: Linda Pollock
Cabinet Secretary for Health and Social Care:
Humza Yousaf MSP
Minister for Mental Wellbeing and Social Care:
Kevin Stewart MSP
Minister for Public Health, Women's Health and Sport: Maree Todd MSP

Directorate – Housing and Social Justice

Director-General Communities: Paul Johnston
Director of Housing and Social Justice:
Shirley Laing
Minister for Public Finance, Planning and Community Wealth: Tom Arthur MSP
Minister for Equalities and Older People:
Christina McKelvie MSP
Cabinet Secretary for Social Justice, Housing and Local Government: Shona Robison MSP
Minister for Social Security and Local Government:
Ben Macpherson MSP

Directorate – Internal Audit and Assurance

Director-General Scottish Exchequer:
Alyson Stafford CBE
Director, Internal Audit: Sharon Fairweather

Directorate – International Trade and Investment

Director-General Economy: Elinor Mitchell
Cabinet Secretary for Finance and the Economy:
Kate Forbes MSP
Minister for Business, Trade, Tourism and Enterprise: Ivan McKee MSP
Cabinet Secretary for Rural Affairs and Islands:
Mairi Gougeon MSP

Directorate – Justice

Director-General Education and Justice: Joe Griffin
Director, Justice: Neil Rennick
Cabinet Secretary for Justice and Veterans:
Keith Brown MSP
Minister for Community Safety: Ash Regan MSP

Directorate – Learning

Director-General Education and Justice: Joe Griffin
Director, Learning: Graeme Logan
Cabinet Secretary for Education and Skills:
Shirley-Anne Somerville MSP
Minister for Further Education, Higher Education, Youth Employment and Training: Jamie Hepburn MSP

Legal Services (Solicitor to the Scottish Government)

Director-General Constitution and External Affairs:
Ken Thomson
Director of Legal Directorate: Ruaraidh Macniven
Lord Advocate: The Rt Hon Dorothy Bain QC
Solicitor General: Ruth Charteris QC

Directorate – Local Government and Communities

Director-General Communities: Paul Johnston

Directorate – Marine Scotland

Director-General Economy: Elinor Mitchell
Director, Marine Scotland: Annabel Turpie
Cabinet Secretary for Rural Affairs and Islands:
Mairi Gougeon MSP
Minister for Environment and Land Reform:
Mairi McAllan MSP
Cabinet Secretary for Net Zero, Energy and Transport: Michael Matheson MSP

Directorate – Mental Health and Social Care

Chief Executive of NHS Scotland and Director General Health and Social Care: Caroline Lamb
Director of Mental Health, Learning Disability,

Neurodiversity and Dementia: Donna Bell
Cabinet Secretary for Health and Social Care:
Humza Yousaf MSP
Minister for Mental Wellbeing and Social Care:
Kevin Stewart MSP

Office of the Chief Executive NHS Scotland

*Chief Executive of NHS Scotland and Director
General Health and Social Care:* Caroline Lamb

Directorate – Organisational Readiness

Director-General Constitution and External Affairs:
Ken Thomson
Deputy First Minister: John Swinney

Directorate – Parliamentary Counsel

Director-General Constitution and External Affairs:
Ken Thomson
Director, Parliamentary Counsel Office:
Andy Beattie
*Cabinet Secretary for the Constitution, External
Affairs and Culture:* Angus Robertson MSP
Minister for Parliamentary Business: George Adam
MSP

Directorate – People

Director-General Corporate: Lesley Fraser
Director, People: Nicola Richards
*Cabinet Secretary for the Constitution, External
Affairs and Culture:* Angus Robertson MSP
Minister for Parliamentary Business: George Adam
MSP

Directorate – Performance and Strategic Outcomes

Director for Performance and Strategic Outcomes:
Jenny Barogu
Director-General Scottish Exchequer:
Alyson Stafford CBE
Cabinet Secretary for Finance and the Economy:
Kate Forbes MSP
First Minister: Nicola Sturgeon MSP

Directorate – Population Health

*Chief Executive of NHS Scotland and Director
General Health and Social Care:* Caroline Lamb
Director of Population Health: Michael Kellet
Cabinet Secretary for Health and Social Care:
Humza Yousaf MSP
Minister for Mental Wellbeing and Social Care:
Kevin Stewart MSP
*Minister for Public Health, Women's Health and
Sport:* Maree Todd MSP

Directorate – Primary Care

*Chief Executive of NHS Scotland and Director
General Health and Social Care:* Caroline Lamb
Director of Primary Care: Tim Mcdonnell
Cabinet Secretary for Health and Social Care:

Humza Yousaf MSP

Directorate – Safer Communities

Director-General Education and Justice: Joe Griffin
Cabinet Secretary for Justice and Veterans:
Keith Brown MSP
Minister for Community Safety: Ash Regan MSP

Directorate – Scottish Procurement and Property

Director-General Corporate: Lesley Fraser
Director, Procurement and Property: Nick Ford
Cabinet Secretary for Finance and the Economy:
Kate Forbes MSP
*Minister for Business, Trade, Tourism and
Enterprise:* Ivan McKee MSP

Directorate – Social Security

Director-General Communities: Paul Johnston
Director, Social Security: Stephen Kerr
Minister for Older People and Equalities:
Christina McKelvie MSP

Directorate – Taxation and Fiscal Sustainability

Director-General Scottish Exchequer:
Alyson Stafford CBE
Director of Taxation and Fiscal Sustainability:
Lucy O'Carroll
Cabinet Secretary for Finance and the Economy:
Kate Forbes MSP
*Minister for Public Finance, Planning and
Community Wealth:* Tom Arthur MSP

Scottish Cabinet

Nicola Sturgeon – First Minister
John Swinney MSP – Deputy First Minister and
    Cabinet Secretary for Covid Recovery
Shirley-Anne Somerville MSP – Cabinet Secretary
    for Education and Skills
Humza Yousaf MSP – Cabinet Secretary for
    Health and Social Care
Kate Forbes MSP – Cabinet Secretary for Finance
    and the Economy
Keith Brown MSP – Cabinet Secretary for Justice
    and Veterans
Mairi Gougeon MSP – Cabinet Secretary for
    Rural Affairs and Islands
Angus Robertson MSP – Cabinet Secretary for
    the Constitution, External Affairs and Culture
Michael Matheson MSP – Cabinet Secretary for
    Net Zero, Energy and Transport
Shona Robison MSP – Cabinet Secretary for
    Social Justice, Housing and Local Government

The Civil Service

John-Paul Marks – Permanent Secretary
Lesley Fraser – Director-General Corporate
Elinor Mitchell – Director-General Economy

Joe Griffin – Director-General Education and Justice

Alyson Stafford CBE – Director-General Scottish Exchequer

Caroline Lamb – Chief Executive of NHS Scotland and Director-General Health and Social Care

Ken Thomson – Director-General Constitution and External Affairs

Paul Johnston – Director-General Communities

Roy Brannen – Director-General Net Zero

Non-Executive Directors Nichola Clyde, Annie Gunner Logan, Ronnie Hinds, Hugh McKay, Linda McKay MBE, Ben McKendrick, Neil Richardson, Jim Robertson, Fiona Ross, Jayne Scott

Ministers

Angela Constance MSP – Minister for Drugs Policy

George Adam MSP – Minister for Parliamentary Business

Richard Lochhead – Minister for Just Transition, Employment and Fair Work

Ivan McKee MSP – Minister for Business, Trade, Tourism and Enterprise

Tom Arthur MSP – Minister for Public Finance, Planning and Community Wealth

Maree Todd MSP – Minister for Public Health, Women's Health and Sport

Kevin Stewart MSP – Minister for Mental Wellbeing and Social Care

Clare Haughey MSP – Minister for Children and Young People

Jamie Hepburn MSP – Minister for Higher Education, Further Education, Youth Employment and Training

Mairi McAllan MSP – Minister for Environment and Land Reform

Jenny Gilruth MSP – Minister for Transport

Ash Regan MSP – Minister for Community Safety

Christina McKelvie MSP – Minister for Older People and Equalities

Ben Macpherson MSP – Minister Social Security and Local Government

Awaiting Appointment – Minister for Culture, Europe and International Development

Patrick Harvie MSP – Minister for Zero Carbon Buildings, Active Travel and Tenants' Rights

Lorna Slater MSP – Minister for Green Skills, Circular Economy and Biodiversity

Rt Hon Dorothy Bain QC – Lord Advocate

Ruth Charteris – Solicitor General

Scottish Government Legal Directorate

Victoria Quay, Edinburgh EH6 6QQ Tel: (0131) 244 0815 DX: 557000 Edinburgh 20 Email: GLSenquiries@gov.scot

Director & Solicitor: Mr R Macniven

Divisional Solicitors: Ms C Beattie, Ms A Coull, Ms S E Ferguson, M C French, K Hannaway, Ms R Inglis, Mrs D McKay, J S Paterson, Ms J Bartlett, Mr G Fisher

Legal Staff: McLean R (Rachael) (SOLS); Rayner R (Rachel); Barekat A (Afson); Blair E (Elizabeth); Bonellie S (Susan); Boyd M (Magdalene); Cullen CF (Claire); Darvishzadeh A (Arezo); Gaston B (Ben); Grant G (Gemma); Guild N (Nicola); Kerr A (Aisha); Mackintosh C (Caroline); Main M (Margaret); McCaffrey B (Barry); McKenzie-Juetten N (Nico); Morton V (Victoria); Munro A (Anna); O'Malley C (Carolyn); Burnet F (Fiona); Carey M (Michael); Evans M (Mari); Forman A (Adrienne); Galloway LM (Lucy); Hughes M (Michael); Jackson S (Stephen); Jamieson K (Kirsty); Macleod NT (Norman); Manson I (Inez); Paton R (Rudi); Reay CA (Christine)(SOLS); Reilly A (Anna); Richards M (Mark); Saddler B (Beth); Singerman J (Jennifer); Smith E (Eilidh) (Legal); Stevens K (Kirsty); Stutley V (Vuyi); Williams Boylston E (Emily); Bowman J (Jamie); Brown MB (Martin); Gilchrist C (Colin); Luton E (Emma); Maclennan D (David); MacQueen J (Jamie); Matheson S (Scott); Mcclure H (Heather); Morton F (Francesca); Nicholson C (Chris); Reid R (Rebecca); Ross CR (Calum); Thomson J (John) (SGLD); Tinto J (Jo-Anne); Walkinshaw L (Lorraine); Duffy N (Nicholas); Dunlop A (Amanda); Hughes M (Martin); Joiner I (Isobel); Kerr D (Douglas); Kubala C (Caroline); Lindsay R (Rosemary); Mcgarvey K (Katherine); McGuffie C (Craig); McKinlay C (Clare); Miller L (Louise); Thomson E (Emma); Boemer I (Ivan); Caitlin Kinloch; Campbell L (Louise) (LS); Catt P (Pita); Davidson J (Julie); Davies AD (Ann) (Solicitors Office); Dyce H (Holly); Garland A (Ailsa); Irvine J (Johanna); MacQueen R (Rosie); Magill C (Carolyn); Mathie A (Anne); McCullough C (Cecilia); McGill C (Claire); McGrory J (Jordan); Mcleod A (Alison); Mojee N (Neel); Murphy N (Nadine); Neal K (Kate); Nicol T (Thomas); Orren L (Lucy); Pantony J (Jacqueline); Richards K (Katy); Walker K (Kate); Whaley RCM (Rosemary) (Sols); Beck F (Frances); Campbell S (Sinead); Clark H (Heather); Davidson M (Morven); Fitzgerald C (Caitlin); Freeland R (Robert); Hepburn J (Jasmin); Kennedy L (Laura); Lavelle B (Brian); Livingstone P (Peter); Lyle H (Helen-Anne); Marshall C (Catriona); Marshall K (Katherine); Meikle C (Claire); Murdoch D (David); Newlands L (Lewis); Nimmo A (Aileen); Sharif F (Francesca); Stevenson E (Emma); Swanson R (Ruth); Toledo A (Alison); Vezza R (Rachel); Walls L (Louisa); Arredondo C (Camilo); Blaikie D (Daniel); Blair K (Kayleigh); Brown CD (Colin); Callaghan E (Emily); Christie N (Ninian); Clelland J (James); Hamilton J (James); Nicholson R (Rachel) (SGLD); Reid M (Mhairi); Robb S (Susan); Simonnet-Lefevre K (Kirsten); St Clair JB (John); Stewart N (Natalie); Virlogeux S (Stephanie); West M (Micheila); Anderson L

(Lindsay); Anderson V (Veronika); Archer D
(Dawn); Banks P (Philip); Blair D (Deborah);
Burgham Pearson J (Julia); Cairns A (Anne);
Cohen D (Dorothy); Conroy S (Susan); De Rosa
D (Darren); Dingwall J (Joanna) (Dr); Fraser A
(Andrea) (SGLD); Gibson K (Kevin); Grace A
(Ania); Hodges J (Jonathan); Hogarth A (Amy);
Martin AK (Alison); McClean F (Fiona);
McHutchison J (Joan); McIntyre E (Elise);
McMichael L (Lucy); McNeil S (Sandy); Moffat D
(David); Munro N (Norman); Penman M (Marie);
Phillips E (Emma); Reilly H (Hazel); Simpson J
(Jane); Slee K (Kirsty); Spy J (Jan); Turnbull J (Jill);
Wood R (Rosalind); Brown J (Judith); Coutts R
(Rachel); Crawley A (Andrew); Cunningham S
(Stewart); Foulis R (Ruth); Freeman E (Emily);
Heine A (Ailsa); Kerr L (Lewis); Lawson A
(Angela); MacLeod N (Neil) (DLSSSG); Mclarty G
(Grant); O'Brien M (Megan); O'Neill E (Euan);
Pedreschi L (Luigi); Scott C (Catherine); Simpson
S (Susan); White K (Keith)

Standing Junior Counsel for Scottish Government Departments
First Standing Junior Counsel:
Paul Reid
Second Standing Junior Counsel:
Lesley Irvine

Standing Juniors
Stephen Donnelly
Dennis Edwards
Tim Haddow
David McLean (Suspended as taking AD duties)
Dominic Scullion
Timothy Young
Daniel Byrne
Ewen Campbell
Miranda Hamilton
Bryan Heaney
Wojciech Jajdelski (Suspended as taking AD duties)
Leigh Lawrie (Suspended as taking AD duties)
Kenneth McGuire
Julie McKinlay Hastie
Niall McLean
Susan Ower
Chris Paterson
Laura Thomson
Michael Way
David Welsh
Jennifer Nicholson-White
Ranald McPherson
Ewen Brown
Euan Scott
Fiona Drysdale
Ross McClelland

National Public Bodies

NON-MINISTERIAL OFFICES
ENVIRONMENTAL STANDARDS SCOTLAND
FOOD STANDARDS SCOTLAND

NATIONAL RECORDS OF SCOTLAND
OFFICE OF THE SCOTTISH CHARITY REGULATOR
REGISTERS OF SCOTLAND
REVENUE SCOTLAND
SCOTTISH COURTS AND TRIBUNALS SERVICE
SCOTTISH FISCAL COMMISSION
SCOTTISH HOUSING REGULATOR

EXECUTIVE NDPBs
ACCOUNTS COMMISSION FOR SCOTLAND
ARCHITECTURE AND DESIGN SCOTLAND
BORD NA GAIDHLIG
CAIRNGORMS NATIONAL PARK AUTHORITY
CARE INSPECTORATE
CHILDREN'S HEARING'S SCOTLAND
COMMUNITY JUSTICE SCOTLAND
CREATIVE SCOTLAND
CROFTING COMMISSION
DAVID MACBRAYNE LTD
FERGUSON MARINE (PORT GLASGOW) LTD
HIGHLANDS & ISLANDS AIRPORTS LTD
HIGHLANDS & ISLANDS ENTERPRISE
HISTORIC ENVIRONMENT SCOTLAND
INDEPENDANT LIVING FUND SCOTLAND
LOCH LOMOND AND THE TROSSACHS
   NATIONAL PARK AUTHORITY
NATIONAL GALLERIES OF SCOTLAND
NATIONAL LIBRARY OF SCOTLAND
NATIONAL MUSEUMS OF SCOTLAND
POLICE INVESTIGATIONS & REVIEW
   COMMISSIONER
QUALITY MEAT SCOTLAND
RISK MANAGEMENT AUTHORITY
ROYAL BOTANIC GARDEN, EDINBURGH
SCOTTISH AGRICULTURAL WAGES BOARD
SCOTTISH CANALS
SCOTTISH CHILDREN'S REPORTER
   ADMINISTRATION
SCOTTISH CRIMINAL CASES REVIEW
   COMMISSION
SCOTTISH ENTERPRISE
SCOTTISH ENVIRONMENT PROTECTION
   AGENCY
SCOTTISH FUNDING COUNCIL
SCOTTISH FUTURES TRUST
SCOTTISH LAND COMMISSION
SCOTTISH LEGAL AID BOARD
SCOTTISH LEGAL COMPLAINTS COMMISSION
SCOTTISH NATIONAL INVESTMENT BANK
NATURESCOT
SCOTTISH QUALIFICATIONS AUTHORITY
SCOTTISH SOCIAL SERVICES COUNCIL
SKILLS DEVELOPMENT SCOTLAND
SOUTH OF SCOTLAND ENTERPRISE AGENCY
SPORT SCOTLAND
VISIT SCOTLAND
WATER INDUSTRY COMMISSION FOR
   SCOTLAND

ADVISORY NDPBs
JUDICIAL APPOINTMENTS BOARD FOR
   SCOTLAND

BOUNDARIES SCOTLAND
MOBILITY AND ACCESS COMMITTEE FOR
SCOTLAND
POVERTY AND INEQUALITY COMMISSION FOR
SCOTLAND
SCOTTISH ADVISORY COMMITTEE ON
DISTINCTION AWARDS
SCOTTISH COMMISSION ON SOCIAL SECURITY
SCOTTISH LAW COMMISSION
SCOTTISH LOCAL AUTHORITIES
REMUNERATION COMMITTEE (STOOD
DOWN IN 2013)

TRIBUNALS
FIRST TIER TRIBUNAL FOR SCOTLAND
PAROLE BOARD FOR SCOTLAND
UPPER TRIBUNAL FOR SCOTLAND

PUBLIC CORPORATIONS
CALEDONIAN MARITIME ASSETS LTD
GLASGOW PRESTWICK AIRPORT
SCOTTISH WATER
CROWN ESTATE SCOTLAND

HEALTH BODIES
NHS AYRSHIRE & ARRAN
NHS BORDERS
NHS DUMFRIES & GALLOWAY
NHS FIFE
NHS FORTH VALLEY
NHS GRAMPIAN
NHS GREATER GLASGOW & CLYDE
NHS HIGHLAND
NHS LANARKSHIRE
NHS LOTHIAN
NHS ORKNEY
NHS SHETLAND
NHS TAYSIDE
NHS WESTERN ISLES
HEALTHCARE IMPROVEMENT SCOTLAND
MENTAL WELFARE COMMISSION FOR
SCOTLAND
NATIONAL WAITING TIMES CENTRE BOARD
NHS 24
NHS EDUCATION FOR SCOTLAND
NHS NATIONAL SERVICES SCOTLAND
PUBLIC HEALTH SCOTLAND
SCOTTISH AMBULANCE SERVICE BOARD
STATE HOSPITAL BOARD FOR SCOTLAND

For more detailed information on Agencies
please see the Government in Scotland website.

EXECUTIVE AGENCIES
ACCOUNTANT IN BANKRUPTCY
DISCLOSURE SCOTLAND
EDUCATION SCOTLAND
FORESTRY AND LAND SCOTLAND
SCOTTISH FORESTRY
SCOTTISH PRISON SERVICE
SCOTTISH PUBLIC PENSIONS AGENCY

SOCIAL SECURITY SCOTLAND
STUDENT AWARDS AGENCY FOR SCOTLAND
TRANSPORT SCOTLAND

COMMISSIONERS & OMBUDSMEN
COMMISSIONER FOR ETHICAL STANDARDS IN
PUBLIC LIFE
SCOTTISH BIOMETRICS COMMISSIONER
SCOTLAND'S COMMISSIONER FOR CHILDREN
& YOUNG PEOPLE
SCOTTISH HUMAN RIGHTS COMMISSION
SCOTTISH INFORMATION COMMISSIONER
SCOTTISH PUBLIC SERVICES OMBUDSMAN
STANDARDS COMMISSION FOR SCOTLAND

OTHER SIGNIFICANT NATIONAL BODIES
AUDIT SCOTLAND
CONVENER OF SCHOOL CLOSURE REVIEW
PANELS
COURT OF LORD LYON
DRINKING WATER QUALITY REGULATOR
HM INSPECTOR OF CONSTABULARY IN
SCOTLAND
HM CHIEF INSPECTOR OF PRISONS IN
SCOTLAND
HM CHIEF INSPECTOR OF PROSECUTION IN
SCOTLAND
HM FIRE SERVICE INSPECTORATE IN SCOTLAND
JUSTICES OF THE PEACE ADVISORY COMMITTEE
OFFICE OF THE QUEENS PRINTER
SCOTTISH FIRE AND RESCUE SERVICE
SCOTTISH POLICE AUTHORITY
SCOTTISH ROAD WORKS COMMISSIONER

Education and Training
Education Scotland
Denholm House, Almondvale Business Park,
Almondvale Way, Livingston EH54 6GA
Tel: (0131) 244 4330 Email:
enquiries@educationscotland.gsi.gov.uk Website:
www.education.gov.scot

Chief Executive: Gayle Gorman
Strategic Director, Scrutiny: Janie McManus
Strategic Director, Scrutiny (interim): Gill Ritchie
*Strategic Director, Corporate Services and
Governance and Professional Learning and
Leadership:* Gillian Hamilton
Strategic Director, Regional: Patricia Watson
*Strategic Director, Curriculum Innovation, Design
and Pedagogy:* Ollie Bray
*Strategic Director, Regional Locality Performance
and Improvement:* Craig Clement
Board: John Fyffe (appointed November 2017),
David Gemmell (appointed July 2019), Kevin
Kelman (appointed November 2019), Ray
McCowan (appointed July 2019), Lyndsay
McRoberts (appointed November 2019), Aileen
Ponton (appointed July 2019)

Director General Health and Chief Executive NHS Scotland

St Andrew's House, Regent Road, Edinburgh EH1 3DG

Ministers:
Cabinet Secretary for Health and and Social Care: Humza Yousaf MSP
Minister for Mental Wellbeing and Social Care: Kevin Stewart MSP
Minister for Public Health, Women's Health and Sport: Maree Todd MSP

Chief Executive of NHS Scotland and Director General of Health and Social Care: Caroline Lamb
Director, Health Finance and Governance: Richard McCallum
Director, Health Workforce, Leadership and Service Reform: Gillian Russell
Clinical Director, Healthcare Quality and Strategy: Professor Jason Leitch

Health and Social Care Directorates:
Chief Medical Officer: Professor Sir Gregor Smith
Chief Allied Health Professions Officer: Carolyn McDonald
Chief Healthcare Science Professions Officer: Catherine Ross

Chief Professional Officers:
Chief Dental Officer: Tom Ferris
Chief Pharmaceutical Officer: Alison Strath
Chief Scientist: Professor Andrew Morris
Chief Scientific Adviser (Scotland): Professor Julie Fitzpatrick OBE

Directorate General Learning and Justice

St Andrew's House, Regent Road, Edinburgh EH1 3DG

Director-General Education and Justice: Joe Griffin

Director, Justice: Neil Rennick
Minister for Community Safety: Ash Regan MSP
Cabinet Secretary for Justice and Veterans: Keith Brown MSP

Director, Learning: Graeme Logan
Cabinet Secretary for Education and Skills: Shirley- Anne Somerville MSP
Minister for Further Education, Higher Education, Youth Employment and Training: Jamie Hepburn MSP

Director General Local Government & Communities

St Andrews House, Regent Road, Edinburgh EH1 3DG

Director-General Communities: Paul Johnston

Director – Economic Development

St Andrew's House, Regent Road, Edinburgh EH1 3DG

Director-General Economy: Elinor Mitchell
Director, Economic Development: Mary McAllan

Cabinet Secretary for Finance and the Economy: Kate Forbes MSP
Minister for Business, Trade, Tourism and Enterprise: Ivan McKee MSP
Minister for Just Transition, Employment and Fair Work: Richard Lochhead MSP
Minister for Public Finance, Planning and Community Wealth: Tom Arthur MSP

Scottish Agricultural Science Agency

(Division of the Agriculture and Rural Economy Directorate)
Roddinglaw Road, Edinburgh EH12 9FJ Tel: 0131 244 8890 Fax: 0131 244 8940 Email: info@sasa.gov.scot Website: www.sasa.gov.uk
Chief Plant Health Officer for Scotland and Head of SASA: Gerry Sadler
Head of Agricultural Science Delivery: Jacqueline Hughes
Chief Officer, Official Seed Testing Station for Scotland: Gillian Musgrove
Head of Diagnostics, Wildlife & Molecular Biology: David Kenyon
Head of Seed Certification: Mike Parker
Head of Virology & Zoology: Jon Pickup
Head of Genotyping: Alex Reid
Head of Chemistry: Katie Viezens

Marine Scotland

1A South, Victoria Quay, Edinburgh EH6 6QQ
Tel: 0300 244 4000 Web: www.marine.gov.scot
Email: marinescotland@gov.scot
Director, Marine Scotland: Annabel Turpie
Management:
Director-General Economy: Elinor Mitchell
Cabinet Secretary for Environment and Land Reform: Mairi McAllan MSP
Cabinet Secretary Rural Affairs and Islands: Mairi Gougeon MSP
Cabinet Secretary for Net Zero, Energy and Transport: Michael Matheson MSP

Crown Office and Procurator Fiscal Service

25 Chambers Street, Edinburgh EH1 1LA
Tel: (0300) 020 3000 DX: 540310 Edinburgh 37
Email: _EnquiryPoint@copfs.gsi.gov.uk Website: www.copfs.gov.uk/

Chief Executive/Crown Agent: David Harvie
Deputy Chief Executive/Business Services: Ian Walford

Deputy Crown Agent, High Court Function/Specialist Casework: Stephen McGowan
Deputy Crown Agent, Local Court Function: John Logue
Deputy Crown Agent, Operational Support: Lindsay Miller
Procurator Fiscal for High Court: Ruth McQuaid
Procurator Fiscal Policy & Engagement:

Kenny Donnelly
Procurator Fiscal Specialist Casework:
Anthony McGeehan
Deputy Head of Local Court: Jennifer Harrower

Lord Advocate: Rt. Hon. Dorothy Bain, QC
Solicitor General: Ruth Charteris, QC
Principal Crown Counsel: Ashley Edwards, QC

Area Procurator Fiscals
Glasgow & Strathkelvin: Moira Orr
Grampian, Highland and Islands: Andy Shanks
Lothian & Borders: Laura Buchan
North Strathclyde: Katie Stewart
South Strathclyde, Dumfries & Galloway:
Les Brown
Tayside, Central & Fife: Sineidin Corrins
Shetland & Orkney: Sue Foard

Director General Constitution and Cabinet

St Andrews House, Regent Road, Edinburgh
EH1 3DG

Director-General Constitution and External Affairs:
Ken Thomson
Director for Constitution and Cabinet:
David Rogers

Cabinet Secretary for the Constitution, External Affairs and Culture: Angus Robertson MSP
Minister for Parliamentary Business: George Adam MSP

Director General Financial Management

St Andrews House, Regent Road, Edinburgh
EH1 3DG

Director-General Corporate: Lesley Fraser
Chief Financial Officer: Jackie McAllister
Cabinet Secretary for Finance and the Economy:
Kate Forbes MSP
Minister for Public Finance, Planning and Community Wealth: Tom Arthur MSP

The Scotland Office

Queen Elizabeth House, Edinburgh EH8 8FT
Tel: (0131) 244 9010 Email:
enquiries@scotlandoffice.gsi.gov.uk Website:
https://www.gov.uk/government/organisations/
office-of-the-secretary-of-state-for-scotland
Secretary of State for Scotland: The Rt Hon Alister
Jack MP
*Parliamentary Under Secretary of State (Minister
for Scotland):* Iain Stewart MP
Parliamentary Under Secretary of State:
Lord Offord of Garvel
The Office of the Secretary of State for Scotland
supports the Secretary of State in promoting
the best interests of Scotland within a stronger
United Kingdom. It ensures Scottish interests
are fully and effectively represented at the
heart of the UK Government, and the UK
Government's responsibilities are fully and
effectively represented in Scotland.
Director of Scotland Office:
Laurence Rockey
Principal Private Secretary to the Secretary of State:
Craig Chalcraft
*Deputy Director, Policy Delivery and Relationship
Management:*
Kris Krasnowski
Deputy Director, Communications:
Anna Macmillan
Deputy Director, Constitutional Policy:
Rachel Irvine
Joint Deputy Directors, Corporate Services:
Laura Crawforth, Alison Evans

Advocate General for Scotland

Queen Elizabeth House, Edinburgh EH8 8FT
Tel: (0131) 244 0359 Email:
enquiries@advocategeneral.gov.uk Website:
https://www.gov.uk/government/organisations/
office-of-the-advocate-general-for-scotland

The Office of the Advocate General (OAG) is the UK government's Scottish legal team. They provide legal advice, drafting and litigation services to the UK government in relation to Scotland. They also support the Advocate General in his role as a Law Officer.

HM Advocate General for Scotland: Lord Stewart of Dirleton QC
Director and Solicitor to the Advocate General: Neil Taylor
Head of HMRC Division: Shona Bathgate
Head of Litigation Division: Fiona Robertson
Legal Secretary to the Advocate General: Paul Scullion
Head of Advisory and Legislation Division: Victoria MacDonald

Standing Junior Counsel for Scottish Government Departments

First Standing Junior Counsel:
Paul Reid
Second Standing Junior Counsel:
Lesley Irvine

Standing Juniors
Stephen Donnelly
Dennis Edwards
Tim Haddow
David McLean (Suspended as taking AD duties)
Dominic Scullion
Timothy Young
Daniel Byrne
Ewen Campbell
Miranda Hamilton
Bryan Heaney
Wojciech Jajdelski (Suspended as taking AD duties)
Leigh Lawrie (Suspended as taking AD duties)
Kenneth McGuire
Julie McKinlay Hastie
Niall McLean
Susan Ower
Chris Paterson
Laura Thomson
Michael Way
David Welsh
Jennifer Nicholson-White
Ranald McPherson
Ewen Brown
Euan Scott
Fiona Drysdale
Ross McClelland

Prisons and Other Institutions

Scottish Prison Service Headquarters
Calton House, 5 Redheughs Rigg, Edinburgh
EH12 9HW Tel: (0131) 330 3500 Email:
gaolinfo@sps.pnn.gov.uk Website:
www.sps.gov.uk
Interim Chief Executive: Teresa Medhurst
Director of Corporate Services (Interim):
Caroline Johnston
*Director of Strategy & Stakeholder Engagement
(Interim):* Sue Brooks
Director of Operations (Interim): Allister Purdie
Non-Executive Directors: Gill Stillie, Kay Hampton,
Ann McKechin, Ian Hartley, Lynne Clow, Stephen
Upton

Addiewell
9 Station Road, Addiewell EH55 8QA
Tel: (01506) 874500
Director: Fraser Munro
Deputy Director: John Joyce

Barlinnie
HM Prison, Barlinnie, 81 Lee Avenue, Riddrie,
Glasgow G33 2QX Tel: (0141) 770 2000
Governor: Michael Stoney
Deputy Governor: Lorraine Roughan

Castle Huntly
HM Prison, Castle Huntly, Longforgan, Dundee
DD2 5HL Tel: (01382) 319333
Governor: Paul Yarwood (Acting)
Deputy Governor: Lillian Burns (Acting)

Cornton Vale
Cornton Road, Stirling FK9 5NU Tel: (01786)
832591
(for female offenders for both remand and
convicted prisoners)
Governor: Jacqueline Clinton
Deputy Governor: Tony Martin

Dumfries
HM Prison, Terregles Street, Dumfries DG2 9AX
Tel: (01387) 261218
Governor: Andy Hunstone
Deputy Governor: Alan Easton (Acting)

Edinburgh
HM Prison, 33 Stenhouse Road, Edinburgh
EH11 3LN Tel: (0131) 444 3000
Governor: David Abernethy
Deputy Governor: Gillian Walker

Glenochil
HM Prison, King O'Muir Road, Tullibody
FK10 3AD Tel: (01259) 760471
Governor: Natalie Beal
Deputy Governor: Malcolm Smith

Grampian
South Road, Peterhead AB42 2YY Tel: (01779)
485 600
Governor: Mike Hebden
Deputy Governor: George Peden

Greenock
HM Prison, Old Inverkip Road, Greenock
PA16 9AJ Tel: (01475) 787 801
Governor: Karen Smith
Deputy Governor: Gerry Watt

Inverness
HM Prison, Duffy Drive, Inverness IV2 3HH
Tel: (01463) 229 000
Governor: Brian McKirdy
Deputy Governor: Mark Halloway

Kilmarnock
HM Prison, Mauchline Road, Kilmarnock
KA1 5AA Tel: (01563) 548800
Director: Craig Thomson
Deputy Director: Pamela Swan

Low Moss
HM Prison, Crosshill Road, Bishopbriggs,
Glasgow G64 2QB Tel: (0141) 7629500
Governor: Paula Arnold (Acting)
Deputy Governor: Morag Stirling

Perth
HM Prison, 3 Edinburgh Road, Perth PH2 8AT
Tel: (01738) 622293
Governor: Andy Hodge
Deputy Governor: Forbes McKillop

Polmont
Polmont, Brightons, Falkirk FK2 0AB Tel: (01324)
711558
Governor: Gerald Michie
Deputy Governor: Tony Martin

Shotts
HM Prison, Canthill Road, Shotts ML7 4LE
Tel: (01501) 824000
Governor: William Stuart (Acting)
Deputy Governor: Calum Kincaid (Acting)

Police

Police Scotland

Headquarters, Tullialllan Castle, Kincardine on Forth FK10 4BE Tel: (01786) 289 070 Website: www.scotland.police.uk/
Police Scotland was formally established on 1 April 2013. The non-emergency number for local police in Scotland is 101. In an emergency call 999.

Further information can be found here http://www.scotland.police.uk/
Any written correspondence should be sent to: PO Box 2460, Dalmarnock, Glasgow G40 9BA

Public Offices and Others

ACAS
151 West George Street, Glasgow G2 2JJ
Tel: 0300 123 1150 (Customer Services) Website: www.acas.org.uk
Chair (ACAS Council): Clare Chapman
Chief Executive Officer/Accounting Officer:
Susan Clews
Chief Operations Officer: Tony Cooper
Director of People: Dan Ellis
Director of Finance, Estates and Procurement:
Rob Mackintosh
Director of Strategic Planning, Performance and Change: Kate Nowicki
Director of Digital, Data and Technology:
James Vincent
Director of Strategy: Ian Wood
Council Members:
Neil Carberry, Chief Executive of the Recruitment and Employment Confederation
Mike Clancy, General Secretary and Chief Executive of Prospect
Anne Davies, Dean of the Oxford Faculty of Law and Professor of Law and Public Policy
Jayne Haines, Senior Vice President of Talent, Learning and Organisation Development at GlaxoSmithKline
Christina McAnea, Assistant General Secretary at Unison
Matthew Percival, People and Skills Policy Director of the CBI
Roy Rickhuss, General Secretary of Community
Ben Summerskill, Director of the Criminal Justice Alliance

Accountant in Bankruptcy
1 Pennyburn Road, Kilwinning KA13 6SA
Tel: 0300 200 2600 DX: 552090 KILWINNING 2
Email: aib@aib.gov.uk Website: www.aib.gov.uk
Accountant in Bankruptcy/Chief Executive:
Dr. Richard Dennis
Executive Director of Case Operations/Depute Accountant in Bankruptcy: John Cook
Head of Efficiencies and Technology:
Brian Kennedy
Head of Policy Development: Alex Reid
Head of Operational Policy and Compliance:
Graeme Perry
Head of Finance: Amanda Dowse
Non-Executive Board Members: Bryan Jackson, Mike Norris, Christine Sinclair, Laura Murphy, Almira Broome

Accounts Commission for Scotland
4th Floor, 102 West Port, Edinburgh EH3 9DN
Tel: 0131 625 1500 Email:
info@audit-scotland.gov.uk Website:
www.audit-scotland.gov.uk
Chair of the Accounts Commission: Dr William Moyes
Interim Deputy Chair: Tim McKay
Members of the Accounts Commission:
Andrew Burns, Andrew Cowie, Dr Sophie Flemig, Sheila Gunn, Christine Lester, Stephen Moore, Sharon O'Connor, Geraldine Wooley

AFA (Adoption and Fostering Alliance Scotland)
Foxglove offices/GF2, 14 Links Place, Edinburgh
EH6 7EZ Tel: (0131) 322 8490 Email:
info@afascotland.com Website:
www.afascotland.com
Executive Director: Robin Duncan
Legal Consultant: Rhona Pollock
Business Support & Finance Manager:
Brenda Reilly
Trainer Consultants: Ravinder Kaur, Jane Steele, Angie Gillies
Research Associate: Maggie Grant

Audit Scotland
4th Floor, 102 West Port, Edinburgh EH3 9DN
Tel: 0131 625 1500 Email:
info@audit-scotland.gov.uk Website:
www.audit-scotland.gov.uk

Other Audit Scotland offices:
4th Floor, South Suite, The Athenaeum Building, 8 Nelson Mandela Place, Glasgow G2 1BT
1st Floor, Room 03, The Green House, Beech Wood Business Park, Inverness IV2 3BL
Chair of Audit Scotland Board: Professor Alan Alexander OBE
Auditor General and Accountable Officer:
Stephen Boyle
Independent, non-executive directors of the Audit Scotland Board: Jackie Mann, Colin Crosby
Interim Director of Performance Audit and Best Value: Antony Clark
Director of Audit Services: Fiona Kordiak

Auditor General for Scotland
4th Floor, 102 West Port, Edinburgh EH3 9DN
Tel: 0131 625 1500 Email:
info@audit-scotland.gov.uk Website:
www.audit-scotland.gov.uk
Auditor General: Stephen Boyle

Auditor of the Court of Session
Parliament House, Parliament Square, Edinburgh
EH1 1RQ Tel: (0131) 240 6789 DX: 549304
Edinburgh 36 Email:
auditorcos@scotcourts.gov.uk Website:
www.auditorcos.org.uk
Auditor of the Court of Session (Temporary):

Robin Macpherson

Bank of England Agency for Scotland
2 West Regent Street, Glasgow G2 1RW
Tel: (0141) 433 7165 Email:
scotland@bankofengland.co.uk Website:
www.bankofengland.co.uk
Agent: William Dowson
Deputy Agents: Iain Duff, Raakhi Odedra

Boundary Commission for Scotland
Thistle House, 91 Haymarket Terrace, Edinburgh
EH12 5HD Tel: (0131) 244 2001 Email:
bcs@scottishboundaries.gov.uk Website:
www.bcomm-scotland.independant.gov.uk
Chairman: The Rt Sir Lindsay Hoyle (Speaker of
the House of Commons)
Deputy Chair: The Hon Lord Matthews (Hugh
Matthews)
Commissioners: Alisa Henderson, Sue Walker

British and Irish Legal Information Institute
Institute of Advanced Legal Studies, Charles
Clore House, 17 Russell Square, London
WC1B 5DR Tel: (020) 7862 5806
Fax: (020) 7862 5770 Website:
https://www.bailii.org/databases.html#scot
Chair: Sir Ross Cranston
Chief Executive: Andrea Coomber
Director: Prof Carl Stychin IALS

British Broadcasting Corporation (BBC)
Website: www.bbc.co.uk/

BBC Scotland Sites:
Aberdeen: Broadcasting House, Beechgrove
Terrace, Aberdeen AB15 5ZT
Tel: 01224 625 233
Dumfries: Queen of the South Arena, Lochfield
Road, Dumfries DG2 9BA
Tel: 01387 268 008
Dundee: Nethergate Centre, 66 Nethergate,
Dundee DD1 4ER
Tel: 01382 202481
Edinburgh: The Tun, Holyrood Road, Edinburgh
EH8 8JF
Tel: 0131 557 5888
Glasgow: 40 Pacific Quay, Glasgow G51 1DA
Tel: 0141 422 6000
Inverness: 7 Culduthel Road, Inverness IV2 4AD
Tel: 01463 720 720
Orkney: Castle Street, Kirkwall, Orkney KW15
1DF
Tel: 01856 873 939
Portree: Somerled Square, Portree, Isle of Skye
IV51 9EH
Tel: 01478 612 005
Selkirk: Unit 5, Ettrick Riverside, Dunsdale Rd,
Selkirk TD7 5EB
Tel: 01750 724567
Shetland: Pitt Lane, Lerwick, Shetland ZE1 0DW

Tel: 01595 694 747
Stornoway: 54 Seaforth Road, Stornoway, Isle of
Lewis HS1 2SD
Tel: 01851 705 000

General enquiries BBC Audience Services, PO
Box 1922, Darlington, DL3 0UR, Tel: 03700 100
222
Director, BBC Scotland: Stephen Carson
Scotland Committee Chair: Steve Morrison
Director, Nations: Rhodri Talfan Davies
Head of Policy and Corporate Affairs: Ian Small
Member for Scotland: Muriel Gray

Chancery and Judicial Registers
Meadowbank House, 153 London Road,
Edinburgh EH8 7AU Tel: (0800) 169 9391
DX: 555400 Edinburgh 15 Website:
https://www.ros.gov.uk
Glasgow Office:
St Vincent Plaza, 319 St Vincent Street, Glasgow
G2 5LP
Tel: 0800 169 9391 DX: 555400 Edinburgh 15
*Keeper of the Registers of Scotland (Chief
Executive):* Jennifer Henderson
Accountable Officer: Janet Egdell
Corporate Director: Billy Harkness
Business Development Director: Kenny Crawford
Registration and Policy Director: Chris Kerr

Children's Hearings Scotland
3rd Floor, Thistle House, 91 Haymarket Terrace,
Edinburgh EH12 5HE Tel: (0131) 244 3696
Email: enquiries@chs.gov.scot Website:
www.chscotland.gov.uk
National Convener and Chief Executive:
Elliot Jackson
*Head of Area Support and Community
Improvement:* Carol Wassell
Head of Learning: Christine Mullen
Finance Director (SCRA shared services role):
Ed Morrison
*Head of Strategy and Development and Depute
Chief Executive:* Lynne Harrison
Head of Practice and Policy: Stephen Bermingham
*Head of Human Resources (SCRA shared services
role)* Susan Deery

The Church of Scotland
121 George Street, Edinburgh EH2 4YN
Tel: (0131) 225 5722 DX: ED144 EDINBURGH
Email: lawdept@churchofscotland.org.uk Website:
www.churchofscotland.org.uk
Solicitor of the Church: Mary Macleod

Citizens Advice Scotland
1st Floor, Broadside, 2 Powderhall Road,
Edinburgh EH7 4GB Tel: (0131) 550 1000
Fax: (0131) 550 1001 Email: info@cas.org.uk
Website: www.cas.org.uk

North Area office
Citizens Advice Scotland, 1st Floor, David Whyte House, 57 Church Street Inverness IV1 1DR

West Area office
Citizens Advice Scotland, 5th Floor, Tara House, 46 Bath Street Glasgow G2 1HG
Chief Executive Officer: Derek Mitchell
Chair: Rory Mair
Deputy Chair: Graeme Bissett
Deputy Chief Executive Officer: Anne Lavery
Director of Impact: Polly Tolley
Director of Advice Services: George Eckton
Head of Bureau Services: David Brownlee
Head of Finance: Frances Donnelly
Head of HR: Vikki Shelton
Head of IT: Iain Forrester

Client Protection Fund
Solicitor to the Client Protection Fund, Atria 1, 144 Morrison Street, Edinburgh EH3 8EX Email: clientprotectionfund@lawscot.org.uk Website: https://www.lawscot.org.uk/for-the-public/client-protection/client-protection-fund/

Community Justice Scotland
Saughton House, Broomhouse Drive, Edinburgh EH11 3XD Tel: (0300) 244 8420 Email: info@communityjustice.scot Website: www.communityjustice.scot
Chair: Catherine Dyer CBE
Board Members: Glenys Watt, Alec Spencer, Adam Burley, Linda Bendle, Steve Kirkwood, Sheriff Katherine Mackie, Graham Macneil Bell, Linda de Caestecker, Pauline Aylesbury
Chief Executive: Karyn McCluskey
Director of Operations: Bill Fitzpatrick
Head of People: Nina Rogers
Advisory Officer: James Docherty
Business Manager: Dorothy Smith
Head of Analysis and Improvement: Keith Gardner
HR and Finance Officer: Denise Huntridge

Companies House (Scotland)
4th Floor, Edinburgh Quay 2, 139 Fountainbridge, Edinburgh EH3 9FF Tel: (0303) 1234 500 DX: ED235 Edinburgh 1 Email: enquiries@companieshouse.gov.uk Website: https://www.gov.uk/government/organisations/companies-house
Registrar of Companies, Chief Executive: Louise Smyth
Registrar for Scotland: Lisa Davis

Convention of Scottish Local Authorities (COSLA)
Verity House, 19 Haymarket Yards, Edinburgh EH12 5BH Tel: (0131) 474 9200
Fax: (0131) 474 9292 Email: info@cosla.gov.uk
Website: www.cosla.gov.uk
Glasgow Office:

COSLA (Glasgow), Floor 3, 49 Bath Street, Glasgow G2 2DL
Tel: 0131 474 9200 Fax: 0131 474 9292 Email: info@cosla.gov.uk
Brussels Office:
COSLA (Brussels), COSLA Brussels Office, House of Municipalities, 1 Square de Meeus, Brussels B-1000 Belgium
Tel: 00 322 2138 121 Fax: 00 322 2138 129
Head of Brussels Office: Serafin Pazos-Vidal
EU Policy Officer: Judith Macgregor
Chief Executive: Sally Louden
Director of People Policy: Nicola Dickie
Director of Integration and Development: James Fowlie
Director of Membership and Resources: Sarah Watters

Criminal Injuries Compensation Authority
Alexander Bain House, Atlantic Quay, 15 York Street, Glasgow G2 8JQ Tel: (0300) 003 3601 DX: GW379 Glasgow Website: https://www.gov.uk/government/organisations/criminal-injuries-compensation-authority
Chief Executive, CICA: Linda Brown
Second Permanent Secretary: Jo Farrar

Crofting Commission
Great Glen House, Leachkin Road, Inverness IV3 8NW Tel: (01463) 663439 Email: info@crofting.gov.scot Website: www.crofting.scotland.gov.uk
Chief Executive: Bill Barron
Head of Digital & Improvements Services: Aaron Ramsay
Solicitor: David Finlay
Head of Policy: John Toal
Head of Regulatory Support: Joseph Kerr
Head of Business Support and Compliance: Jane Thomas
Temporary Head of Operations & Workforce: Mary Ross
Head of Crofting Development: Heather Mack
Head of Finance: Neil MacDonald

Crown Estate Scotland
Quartermile Two, 2nd Floor, 2 Lister Square, Edinburgh EH3 9GL Tel: (0131) 260 6070 Email: enquiries@crownestatescotland.com Website: www.crownestatescotland.com

Glenlivet Estate Office, Main Street, Tomintoul, Banffshire AB37 9EX
Tel: 01479 870 070 Email: info@glenlivetestate.co.uk
Chief Executive: Simon Hodge
Director of Corporate Operations: Esther Black
Chair Crown Estate Scotland: Amanda Bryan
Director of Property: Oster Milambo
Director of Finance and Business Services: Alastair Milloy
Director of Marine: Colin Palmer
Investment and Sales Programme Director:

Andy Wells
Governance Manager: Helen Howden

Edinburgh Gazette

PO BOX 3584, Norwich NR7 7WD Tel: (0333) 200 2434
Fax: (0333) 202 5080 Email: edinburgh@thegazette.co.uk Website: www.thegazette.co.uk
The Gazette is formally the combination of three publications: The London Gazette, The Belfast Gazette and The Edinburgh Gazette. The Gazettes are official journals of record.
As a publication, The Gazette consists largely of statutory notices. This means that there is some legal requirement for the notice placer to advertise an event or proposal in The Gazette.
Price lists for 2022 are available here: https://www.thegazette.co.uk/place-notice/pricing
There are over 450 different types of notice that are advertised in The Gazette, including:
242 notice types required by law to be published in The Gazette
82 notice types required by law to be published in The Gazette, as well as somewhere else (for example, a newspaper)
54 notice types required by law to be published, but the law doesn't specify where
36 notice types that may be published in The Gazette
41 notice types that are optional publication, so are not required by law to be published

ENABLE Scotland

Inspire House, 3 Renshaw Place, Eurocentral Lanarkshire, Lanark ML1 4UF Tel: (0300) 0200 101 Email: enabledirect@enable.org.uk Website: www.enable.org.uk
CEO: Theresa Shearer
Director of ENABLE Scotland: Jan Savage
Director of ENABLE Works: Ashley Ryan
Director of ENABLE Cares: Howard Elliott
Chair ENABLE Scotland: Paul Jukes
Vice Chair: Paul McMahon

The Government Legal Service for Scotland

GLSS, 1-G North, Victoria Quay, Edinburgh EH6 6QQ Tel: (0300) 244 4000 Email: GLSSResourcing@gov.scot Website: https://www.gov.scot/groups/government-legal-service-for-scotland

The GLSS member offices are:

Scottish Government Legal Directorate
Office of the Advocate General
Scottish Law Commission
Civil Recovery Unit, Crown Office and Procurator Fiscal Service
Lord President's Private Office
Revenue Scotland

Edinburgh Tram Inquiry
Crofting Commission
Director-General Education and Justice: Joe Griffin
Director Justice: Neil Rennick
Director-General Constitution and External Affairs: Ken Thomson
Director of Legal Services and Solicitor to the Scottish Government: Ruaraidh Macniven

Health and Safety Executive

Queen Elizabeth House, 1 Sibbald Walk, Edinburgh EH8 8FT Tel: (0300) 790 6787
Website: www.hse.gov.uk
Edinburgh Office covers: Borders, Lothian, Central Perth, Kinross, Fife and Dundee
GLASGOW, Cornerstone, 107 West Regent Street, Glasgow, G2 2BA
Covers: West Scotland
ABERDEEN, Field Operations Division, Buliding 2, Level 1, Aberdeen International Business Park, Dyce Drive, Dyce, Aberdeen AB21 0BR
Covers: Angus, Aberdeenshire, Moray and Shetland
ABERDEEN, Energy Division, Buliding 2, Level 1, Aberdeen International Business Park, Dyce Drive, Dyce, Aberdeen AB21 0BR
Covers: Aberdeen
INVERNESS, Longman House, 28 Longman Road, Longman Industrial Estate, Inverness IV1 1SF
Covers: Highlands and Orkney
Chief Executive: Sarah Albon
Chair: Sarah Newton
Director of Planning, Finance and Procurement: David Murray
Director of Science and Commercial: Karen Russ
Director of Engagement and Policy: Peter Brown
Director of Regulation: Philip White
Director of Transformation: Angela Storey
Chief Inspector of Buildings – Health and Safety Executive: Peter Baker
Director of Human Resources: Clare Millington-Hume
Chief Technology Officer: James Anderson
Legal Director: Katy Shrimplin

Highlands and Islands Enterprise

An Lochran, 10 Inverness Campus, Inverness IV2 5NA Tel: (01463) 245245 Website: www.hie.co.uk
Chief Executive: Stuart Black
Deputy Chief Executive: Carroll Buxton
Director Communities and Place: Douglas Cowan
Director Business Improvement and Internal Audit: Sandra Dunbar
Director Service Delivery: Rachel Hunter
Director Strategy and Regional Economy: Martin Johnson
Director Human Resources: Karen Moncrieff
Director Finance and Corporate Services: Nick Kenton
Director Strategic Projects: David Oxley
Chair: Alistair Dodds CBE

Historic Environment Scotland

Longmore House, Salisbury Place, Edinburgh
EH9 1SH Tel: (0131) 668 8600 Website:
https://www.historicenvironment.scot/
John Sinclair House, 16 Bernard Terrace,
Edinburgh EH8 9NX
Chief Executive: Alex Paterson
Director of Heritage: Elizabeth McCrone
Director of Conservation: Dr David Mitchell
Director of Commercial and Tourism:
Stephen Duncan
Project Director: Gary Love
Director of Finance and Corporate Services:
Donella Steel
Director of External Relations and Partnerships:
Alison Turnbull
Director of People: Lindsey Ross

The Institute and Faculty of Actuaries

Level 2 Exchange Crescent, 7 Conference
Square, Edinburgh EH3 8RA Tel: (020) 7632
2100
Fax: (0131) 240 1313 Website:
www.actuaries.org.uk
Scottish Board Leader: Mark Chadwick (RBS)
Deputy Leader: Caitlin Stronach (Royal London)
Scottish Board:
Email: Engagement.team@actuaries.org.uk
Chief Executive: Stephen Mann

Institute of Chartered Foresters

59 George Street, Edinburgh EH2 2JG Tel: (0131)
240 1425 Email: icf@charteredforesters.org
Website: www.charteredforesters.org
Executive Director: Shireen Chambers MBE FICFor
President: Sharon Durdant-Hollamby FICFor
Vice President: Geraint Richards MVO FICFor
Member Services Director: Dr Stuart Glen
Finance Manager: Denise Camilleri
Development Director: Louise Simpson
Policy Manager: Jemima Cooper BA(Hons) MA
Member Services Manager: Ben Summers-McKay
BA(Hons) MA
Marketing and Communications Manager:
Mark Goodwin BA(Hons) MA
Events Manager: Nathaniel Jackson BA(Hons)
Marketing and Communications Officer:
Alice Hancock BA(Hons)
Education and Outreach Officer: Dr Rob Hawkins
Member Services Administrator: Dawn Elliot

Judicial Office for Scotland

Parliament House, Edinburgh EH1 1RQ
Tel: (0131) 2406930 Email:
judicialinstitute@scotcourts.gov.uk Website:
www.judiciary.scot
Members of the Advisory Council of the Judicial
Institute:
President of the Judicial Institute for Scotland:
The Rt Hon Lord Carloway
Chairman, Senator of the College of Justice:
The Hon Lord Armstrong

Vice Chairman, Senator of the College of Justice:
The Hon Lord Beckett
Interim Director, Judicial Institute for Scotland:
Sheriff Susan Craig
*President of the Tax and Social Security Chambers
of the First-tier Tribunal for Scotland:* Anne Scott

Maritime and Coastguard Agency
Aberdeen Coastguard Operations Centre

4th Floor, Marine House, Blaikies Quay,
Aberdeen AB11 5PB Tel: 01224 592 334
Website:
https://www.gov.uk/government/organisations/
maritime-and-coastguard-agency
Chief Executive: Brian Johnson
Director, Her Majesty's Coastguard: Claire Hughes
Director of UK Maritime Services: Katy Ware

Mental Health Foundation

McLellan Works, 1st Floor, Suites 1-4, 274
Sauchiehall St, Glasgow G2 3EH Email:
scotland@mentalhealth.org.uk Website:
www.mentalhealth.org.uk/scotland
Director Scotland & Northern Ireland: Lee Knifton
Associate Director Scotland & Northern Ireland:
Julie Cameron
Head of Evidence and Impact: Shari McDaid
Head of Communications and Fundraising:
Chris O'Sullivan

Mental Welfare Commission for Scotland

Thistle House, 91 Haymarket Terrace, Edinburgh
EH12 5HE Tel: (0131) 313 8777 Email:
mwc.enquiries@nhs.scot Website:
www.mwcscot.org.uk
Chairman: Sandy Riddell
Chief Executive: Julie Paterson
Head of Corporate Services: Alison McRae
Executive Director (Medical): Dr Arun Chopra
Executive Director (Nursing): Alison Thomson
Executive Director (Social Work):
Suzanne McGuiness
Board Members: Safaa Baxter, Gordon Johnston,
Mary Twaddle, Cindy Mackie, David Hall,
Nichola Brown, Alison White

National Library of Scotland

92 Cowgate, Edinburgh EH1 1JN Tel: (0131) 623
3700 Email: enquiries@nls.uk Website:
www.nls.uk
National Librarian and Chief Executive:
Amina Shah
Director of Business Support: Anthony Gillespie
Associate Director of Access: John Coll
Interim Associate Director of Digital: Gill Hamilton
*Interim Associate Director of Collections and
Research:* Alison Stevenson
Associate Director of External Relations:
Jackie Cromarty
Associate Director of Collections Management:
Joseph Marshall

National Records of Scotland

HM General Register House, 2 Princes Street, Edinburgh EH1 3YY Tel: (0131) 334 0380 Email: customerservices@scotlandspeople.gov.uk Website: www.nrscotland.gov.uk
Chief Executive/Registrar General and Keeper:
Paul Lowe
Director of Information and Records Services, and Deputy Keeper: Laura Mitchell
Director of Corporate Services and Accountable Officer: Linda Sinclair
Director of Operations and Customer Services:
Anne Slater
Director of Statistical Services: Peter Whitehouse
Director of IT Services: Laura Lucas
Chief Finance Office: Claire Gillespie
Delivery Director: Carla McHendry

The National Trust for Scotland

Hermiston Quay, 5 Cultins Road, Edinburgh EH11 4DF Tel: (0131) 458 0200
Fax: (0131) 458 0201 Website: www.nts.org.uk
Chief Executive Officer: Philip Long
Chief Operating Officer: Katerina Brown
Director of Customer & Cause: Mark Bishop
People Director: Carol-Anne Boyter
Head of Conservation and Policy: Stuart Brooks
Head of Heritage and Consultancy Services:
Michael Terwey
General Manager South and West: Ian McLelland
General Manager Highlands and Islands:
Clea Warner
General Manager North East: Iain Hawkins
General Manager Edinburgh and East:
Stuart Maxwell
Operational Manager Mar Lodge Estate:
David Frew

National Ultimus Haeres Unit

Procurator Fiscal Office, Cameronian House, 3/5 Almada Street, Hamilton ML3 0HG Tel: (0300) 0204196 Email:
_NationalUltimusHaeresUnit@copfs.gov.uk
Website:
https://www.qltr.gov.uk/content/estates-ultimus-haeres

NatureScot

Great Glen House, Leachkin Road, Inverness IV3 8NW Tel: (01463) 725000 Email: enquiries@nature.scot Website:
https://www.nature.scot
Chair: Dr Mike Cantlay OBE
Deputy Chair: Cath Denholm
Chief Executive: Francesca Osowska
Director for Nature and Climate Change:
Nick Halfhide
Director of Sustainable Growth: Robbie Kernahan
Director of Business Services and Transformation:
Jane Macdonald
Deputy Director for Nature and Climate Change:
Eileen Stuart

Deputy Director of Sustainable Growth:
Claudia Rowse
Deputy Director of Business Services and Transformation: Stuart MacQuarrie
Head of External Affairs: Jason Ormiston

NHS National Services Scotland
Central Legal Office

Anderson House, Breadalbane Street, Bonnington Road, Edinburgh EH6 5JR DX: ED154 Email: nhs.feedback@nhs.scot Website:
https://www.nss.nhs.scot
Chief Executive: Mary Morgan
Medical Director: Dr Lorna Ramsay
Director Central Legal Office: Norma Shippin

Northern Lighthouse Board

84 George Street, Edinburgh EH2 3DA Tel: (0 131) 473 3100 Email: enquiries@nlb.org.uk Website: www.nlb.org.uk
Operating Base (Oban): Gallanach Road, Oban, Argyll PA34 4LS
Tel: +44(0) 1631 562146
Email: enquiries@nlb.org.uk
Chief Executive: Mike Bullock
Director of Business Services: Mairi Rae
Director of Operations: Phil Day

Office of the Public Guardian (Scotland)

Hadrian House, Callendar Business Park, Callendar Road, Falkirk FK1 1XR Tel: (01324) 678300
Fax: (01324) 678301 DX: 550360 Falkirk 3
Email: opg@scotcourts.gov.uk Website:
www.publicguardian-scotland.gov.uk
Public Guardian: Fiona Brown
Deputy Public Guardian: Carrie Diggins
Acting Deputy Public Guardian: Danielle Rose
Special Projects Deputy Public Guardian:
Debra Allison

Parole Board for Scotland

Saughton House, Broomhouse Drive, Edinburgh EH11 3XD Tel: (0131) 244 8373 Email: enquiries@paroleboard.scot Website:
https://www.scottishparoleboard.scot/
Chairman: John Watt
Chief Executive: Colin Spivey
Chief Executive of the Legal Defence Union:
Professor David O'Donnell

Public Defence Solicitors' Office

9 York Place, Edinburgh EH1 3EB Tel: (0131) 557 1222
Fax: (0131) 557 2212 Email:
edinburgh@pdso.org.uk Website:
www.pdso.org.uk
PDSO Ayr, 17 Wellington Square, Ayr KA7 1EZ
Tel: 01292 269 139 Fax: 01292 265 253 Email: ayr@pdso.org.uk
Head of Office and Solicitor: Hugh Duncan
Solicitor: Louise Craig, Ashley Kane

PDSO Dundee, 152 West Marketgait, Dundee DD1 1NJ
Tel: 01382 226 051 Fax: 01382 225 992 Email: dundee@pdso.org.uk
Head of Office and Solicitor: Nicky Brown
Solicitors: David Sinclair
PDSO Edinburgh, 9 York Place, Edinburgh EH1 3EB
Tel: 0131 557 1222 Fax: 0131 557 2212 Email: Edinburgh@pdso.org.uk
Acting Director: Paul Haran
Acting Head of Office: Andrew Docherty
Solicitors: Charles Morrison, Paul Cannavan, Gillian Koren, Lesley Cunningham, Julie Torley
PDSO Falkirk, 47-49 West Bridge Street, Falkirk FK1 5AZ
Tel: 01324 631 475 Fax: 01324 632 389 Email: falkirk@pdso.org.uk
Head of Office and Solicitor: Laura Jackson
Solicitors: Stan Quirk, Nuala Devlin
PDSO Glasgow, 120-124 Saltmarket, Glasgow G1 5LB
Tel: 0141 553 0794 Fax: 0141 548 1486 Email: glasgow@pdso.org.uk
Head of Office: Claire McCarron
Solicitors: Pauline McKenzie, Greg Cunningham, Marco Buonaccorsi, James Irvine
PDSO Inverness, 2 Castle Wynd, Inverness IV2 3EB
Tel: 01463 709680 Fax: 01463 709682 Email: inverness@pdso.org.uk
Acting Head of Office and Solicitor: Patrick O'Dea
PDSO Kirkwall, Room7, Scottish Government Building, Tankerness Lane, Kirkwall, Orkney KW15 1AQ
Tel: 01856 870 100 Fax: 01856 870 116 Email: kirkwall@pdso.org.uk
Senior Solicitor: Cheryl Beattie

Queen's and Lord Treasurer's Remembrancer
Scottish Government Building, 1F North, Victoria Quay, Edinburgh EH6 6QQ Tel: (0300) 0203512
Tel: (0131) 2433210 Email: enquiries@qltr.gov.uk
Website: www.qltr.gov.uk
Chief Solicitor: Robert Sandeman
Administrator: Julia McNamara

Register of Births, Deaths and Marriages (Scotland)
See National Records of Scotland

Registers of Scotland
Public registers of land, property, and other legal documents in Scotland
Meadowbank House, 153 London Road, Edinburgh EH8 7AU Tel: (0800) 169 9391
DX: 555400 Edinburgh 15 Website: www.ros.gov.uk
Keeper of the Registers of Scotland (Chief Executive): Jennifer Henderson
Accountable Officer: Janet Egdell

Corporate Director: Billy Harkness
Business Development Director: Kenny Crawford
Registration and Policy Director: Chris Kerr

Glasgow:
St Vincent Plaza, 319 St Vincent Street, Glasgow G2 5LP
Tel: 0800 169 9391 DX: 555400 Edinburgh 15

Edinburgh:
Meadowbank House, 153 London Road, Edinburgh EH8 7AU
Tel: 0800 169 9391 DX: 555400 Edinburgh 15

Knowledge Base:
www.kb.ros.gov.uk

Relationships Scotland
18 York Place, Edinburgh EH1 3EP Tel: (0345) 119 2020
Fax: (0345) 119 6089 Email: enquiries@relationships-scotland.org.uk Website: www.relationships-scotland.org.uk
Chief Executive: Stuart Valentine
Head of Practice for Family Mediation and Relationship Counselling: Rosanne Cubitt
Head of Corporate Services: Mike Reid
Head of Network Services: Heather Lickley
Head of Practice for Contact Centres: Vacant

Royal Incorporation of Architects in Scotland
15 Rutland Square, Edinburgh EH1 2BE
Tel: (0131) 229 7545 Email: info@rias.org.uk
Website: www.rias.org.uk/
President: Christina Gaiger PRIAS
Director of Policy and Development: Karen Stevenson
Practice Committee Chair: Peter Drummond
Planning Committee Chair: Hugh Crawford

Royal Institution of Chartered Surveyors in Scotland
3rd Floor, 125 Princes Street, Edinburgh EH2 4AD Tel: (024) 7686 8555 Email: contactrics@rics.org Website: www.rics.org
Chair: Richard S Burnett MA FRICS FIRPM
Board: Alastair Wallace FRICS, David Mitchell FRICS IRRV MCMI RICS, Les McAndrew BLE MRICS, Craig Kecheran MRICS, Susan Hanley FRICS, Nick Rowan MRICS, Nial Milner MRICS FAAV, Matthew D. Moggach

SACRO
National Office, 29 Albany Street, Edinburgh EH1 3QN Tel: (0131) 624 7270
Fax: (0131) 624 7269 Email: info@sacro.org.uk
Website: www.sacro.org.uk
Honorary President: Lord Carloway
Chair: Jim Crighton
Depute Chair: Eric Fraser CBE
Chief Executive: Annie Mauger-Thompson
Chief Operating Officer: Gerry Milne

Director of Justice: Sharon Stirrat
Director of Care and Housing: Cary Tamm
Director of Public Protection and Community Safety: John Kennedy

Scottish Assessors Association Website:
www.saa.gov.uk/
President: Gary Bennett BSc MSc MRICS IRRV(Hons) AEA(Cert-Scotland)
Vice President: Pete Wildman BSc MRICS IRRV (Hons) AEA (Dip)
Secretary: Heather Honeyman BSc (Hons) MBA MRICS
Past President: Alastair Kirkwood BSc MRICS Dip Rating IRRV (Hons) AEA
Local Contacts can be found here:
https://www.saa.gov.uk/contactlists/

Scottish Chambers of Commerce
Strathclyde Business School, 199 Cathedral Street, Glasgow G4 0QU Tel: (0141) 444 7500 Email: admin@scottishchambers.org.uk Website: www.scottishchambers.org.uk
President, SCC: Stephen Leckie (Chairman & Chief Executive Crieff Hydro Ltd)
Chief Executive & Director: Dr Liz Cameron OBE
Deputy Chief Executive: Charandeep Singh BEM

Office of the Scottish Charity Regulator
2nd Floor, Quadrant House, 9 Riverside Drive, Dundee DD1 4NY Tel: (01382) 220446 Email: info@oscr.org.uk Website: www.oscr.org.uk
Chief Executive: Maureen Mallon
Interim Chair: George Walker

The Scottish Council of Law Reporting
7 Rosemount Place, Perth PH2 7EH Website: www.scottishlawreports.org.uk
Chair: Angela Grahame QC
Vice Chair: Christine McLintock

Scottish Enterprise
Atrium Court, 50 Waterloo Street, Glasgow G2 6HQ Tel: (0300) 013 3385 DX: GW170 GLASGOW Website: www.scottish-enterprise.com
Chief Executive: Adrian Gillespie
Managing Director Scottish Economic Development: Linda Hanna
Managing Director Business Services and Advice: Jane Martin
Chief People Officer: Carolyn Stewart
Interim Managing Director International Development: Neil Francis
Chief Financial Officer: Douglas Colquhoun
Chair: Lord Smith of Kelvin

The Scottish Environment Protection Agency
Strathallan House, Castle Business Park, Stirling FK9 4TZ Tel: (01786) 457 700 Fax: (01786) 446 855 Website: www.sepa.org.uk
Acting Chief Executive: Jo Green

Chair: Bob Downes
Clerk to the Board: Jennifer McWhirter

Scottish Forestry
Silvan House, 231 Corstorphine Road, Edinburgh EH12 7AT Tel: (0131) 370 5250 Email: Scottish.Forestry@forestry.gov.scot Website: www.forestry.gov.scot

Conservancies

Highlands and Islands:
Woodlands, Fodderty Way, Dingwall Ross-shire IV15 9XB

Grampian:
Portsoy Road, Huntly AB54 4SJ

Central Scotland:
Bothwell House, Hamilton Business Park, Caird Park, Hamilton ML3 0QA

Perth and Argyll:
Upper Battleby, Redgordon, Perth PH1 3EN

South Scotland:
55/57 Moffat Road, Dumfries DG1 1NP
Weavers Court, Forest Mill Selkirk TD7 5NY
Chief Executive: Dave Signorini
Chief Forester for Scotland: Dr Helen McKay OBE
Head of Operational Delivery: Doug Howieson
Head of Operational Services and Transformation: Zahid Deen
Head of Scottish Forestry Executive Office: Jonathan Taylor
Head of Finance and Business Support: Ross MacHardie
Head of Policy and Practice: Alan Hampson

Scottish Law Commission
140 Causewayside, Edinburgh EH9 1PR Tel: (0131) 668 2131 Email: info@scotlawcom.gov.uk Website: www.scotlawcom.gov.uk
Chair: The Rt Hon Lady Paton
Commissioners: David Bartos, Professor Gillian Black, Kate Dowdalls QC, Professor Frankie McCarthy
Interim Chief Executive: Charles Garland
Legal staff – Government Legal Service for Scotland: Stephen Crilly, Alison Fraser, Graham McGlashan, Alastair Smith, Lorraine Stirling
Legal Assistants: Daniel Buchan, Rebecca Gale, Hannah Renneboog, Lucy Robertson
Library and Information Services: Emma McLarty
Office Manager: Helen Stevenson
General Office: Gordon Speirs
Executive Assistants: Wilma Campbell, Scott Macdonald

Scottish Legal Aid Board (SLAB)
91 Haymarket Terrace, Edinburgh EH12 5HE Tel: (0131) 226 7061 DX: 555250 Edinburgh 30 Email: general@slab.org.uk Website: www.slab.org.uk

Chief Executive: Colin Lancaster
Director of Corporate Services and Accounts:
Graeme Hill
Director of Operations: Marie-Louise Fox
Director of Strategic Development: TBC
Principal Legal Advisor: Ian Dickson
Acting Director PDSO: Paul Haran
Internal Audit: Nicola Johnston
Chair: Ray Macfarlane

Scottish Legal Complaints Commission

The Stamp Office, 10-14 Waterloo Place,
Edinburgh EH1 3EG Tel: (0131) 201 2130 Email:
enquiries@scottishlegalcomplaints.org.uk
Website: www.scottishlegalcomplaints.org.uk
Chief Executive: Neil Stevenson
Chair: Jim Martin
Lawyer Members: Richard McMeeken
Lay Members: Morag Sheppard, Prof June
Andrews OBE, Niki Mclean, Jean Grier, John
Stevenson

Scottish Police College

Tulliallan Castle, Fife, Kincardine on Forth
FK10 4BE Tel: (01786) 289 070 Website:
www.scotland.police.uk
Chief Constable: Iain Livingstone QPM
Deputy Chief Constable – Local Policing: Will Kerr
OBE
*Deputy Chief Constable – Crime and Operational
Support:* Malcolm Graham
Deputy Chief Constable – People and Development:
Jude Helliker
*Deputy Chief Officer – Corporate Services, People
and Strategy:* David Page

Scottish Prison Service

Communications Branch Room G20, Calton
House, 5 Redheughs Rigg, Edinburgh EH12 9HW
Tel: (0131) 330 3500 Email:
gaolinfo@sps.pnn.gov.uk Website:
www.sps.gov.uk
Interim Chief Executive: Teresa Medhurst
Director of Operations (interim): Alistair Purdie
Director of Corporate Services (Interim):
Caroline Johnston
*Director of Strategy & Stakeholder Engagement
(Interim):* Sue Brookes

Scottish Public Services Ombudsman

Bridgeside House, 99 McDonald Road,
Edinburgh EH7 4NS Tel: (0131) 225 5300
Fax: (0800) 377 7331 Website:
www.spso.org.uk/spso
Scottish Public Services Ombudsman:
Rosemary Agnew
Director: Niki Maclean
Head of Improvement, Standards and Engagement:
Andrew Sheridan

Scottish Safeguarders Panel

Children 1st, 83 Whitehouse Loan, Edinburgh
EH9 1AT Tel: (0131) 446 2300
Fax: (0131) 446 2339 Email:
cfs@children1st.org.uk Website:
www.children1st.org.uk
Chief Executive: Mary Glasgow
Director of Children and Family Services:
Linda Jardine
Director of Fundraising: Gary Kernahan
Chair: Ken Cunningham
Vice Chair: Stella Everingham
Honorary Law Agent: Caroline Gilchrist

Scottish Solicitors' Discipline Tribunal

Unit 3.5, The Granary Business Centre, Coal
Road, Cupar KY15 5YQ Tel: (01334) 659088
Fax: (01334) 659099 Email:
enquiries@ssdt.org.uk Website: www.ssdt.org.uk
Chairman: Colin Bell
Vice Chair: Beverley Atkinson, Benjamin Kemp,
Kenneth Paterson, Catherine Hart
Members: David Dickinson, Mark Hastings,
Thomas Hempleman, Deborah Lovell, Chris
Mackay, Vincent McGovern, Sally Swinney

Scottish Water

Castle House, 6 Castle Drive, Carnegie Campus,
Dunfermline KY11 8GG Tel: (0800) 0778 778
Email: help@scottishwater.co.uk Website:
www.scottishwater.co.uk
Chief Executive: Douglas Millican
Chair: Dame Susan Rice DBE
Director of Capital Investment: Mark Dickson
Director for People: Shirley C. Campbell
Director of Digital: Rob Mustard
Chief Operating Officer: Peter Farrer
Director of Strategic Customer Service Planning:
Simon Parsons
Strategy and Commercial Director: Alan Scott
Director of Finance: Brian Strathie
Director of Corporate Affairs: Brian Lironi

Shelter Scotland

4th Floor, Scotiabank House, 6 South Charlotte
Street, Edinburgh EH2 4AW Tel: (0808) 800
4444 Website: scotland.shelter.org.uk/

Community Hubs:
Aberdeen: 29 Crown Street, Aberdeen, AB11 6HA
Dundee: 4 South Ward Road, Dundee, DD1 1PN
(drop-in Mon, Tues, Fri) Scotty Centre, 163
Albert Street, Dundee, DD4 6PX (drop-in Wed)
Edinburgh: 4th Floor, Scotiabank House, 6 South
Charlotte Street, Edinburgh, EH2 4AW
Glasgow: 116 Osborne Street, Glasgow, G1 5QH
Director: Alison Watson
Assistant Director Operations: Gillian Reid
Chair: Kezia Dugdale
Assistant Director Communications and Advocacy:
Gordon MacRae

Strathclyde Partnership for Transport
131 St Vincent Street, Glasgow G2 5JF
Tel: (0141) 332 6811 Email: enquiry@spt.co.uk
Website: www.spt.co.uk
Chief Executive: Valerie Davidson
Director of Finance: Neil Wylie
Director of Subway: Antony Smith
Chair: Dr Martin Bartos
Vice Chair: Alan Moir, David Wilson

STV Group Plc
Pacific Quay, Glasgow G51 1PQ Tel: (0141) 300
3000 Email: enquiries@stv.tv Website:
www.stvplc.tv

STV Offices
STV (Aberdeen):
Television Centre, Craigshaw Business Park, West
Tullos, Aberdeen AB12 3QH
Tel: +44 1224 848848 Fax: +44 1224 848800
STV (Dundee):
Seabraes, Greenmarket, Dundee DD1 4QB
Tel: 01382 591000 Fax: 01382 591010
STV (Edinburgh):
Edinburgh Quay, 133 Fountainbridge, Edinburgh
EH3 9QG
Tel: 0131 2008000 Fax: 0131 2008008
STV (Inverness):
Suite 1, Ground Floor, Barony House, Stoneyfield
Business Park, Inverness IV2 7PA
Tel: 01463 256170 Fax: 01463 715384
STV (London):
9 Savoy Street , London WC2E 7AE
Tel: 0203 931 0445
Chair: Paul Reynolds
Chief Executive: Simon Pitts
Legal Director: Helen Arnot
Chief Financial Officer: Lindsay Dixon

The Accountant of Court
Hadrian House, Callendar Business Park,
Callendar Road, Falkirk FK1 1XR Tel: (01324) 678
300
Fax: (01324) 678 365 DX: 550360 Falkirk 3
Email: accountantofcourt@scotcourts.gov.uk
Website:
https://www.scotcourts.gov.uk/the-courts/more/
the-accountant-of-court
Accountant of Court: Fiona Brown Tel: 01324
678323
Deputy Accountant of Court: Carrie Diggins Tel:
01324 678303

Specific Enquiries:
Consignations:
Mrs Anne Fulton, Funds Administration Manager,
Tel: 01324 677742
Mr Matthew Clarkson, Funds Administration
Manager, Tel: 01324 678381
Email: funds@scotcourts.gov.uk
Judicial Factors & Enforcement Administrators:
Mr Raish Allan, Judicial Factory Case Manager,
Tel: 01324 677740

Email: judicialfactories@scotcourts.gov.uk
Children Scotland Act – Directions:
Mrs Anne Fulton Funds Administration Manager,
Tel: 01324 677742
Mr Matthew Clarkson Funds Administration
Manager, Tel: 01324 678381
Email: funds@scotcourts.gov.uk

The Law Society of Scotland
Atria One, 144 Morrison Street, Edinburgh
EH3 8EX Tel: (0131) 226 7411
Fax: (0131) 225 2934 DX: ED 1 Edinburgh
Email: lawscot@lawscot.org.uk Website:
www.lawscot.org.uk/
Chief Executive: Diane McGiffen
President: Ken Dalling
Vice President: Murray Etherington
Treasurer: Graham Watson

The Scottish Child Law Centre
The Melting Pot, 15 Calton Road, Edinburgh
EH8 8DL Tel: (0131) 667 6333 (Advice)
Tel: (0131) 668 4400 (Admin) Email:
advice@sclc.org.uk Website: www.sclc.org.uk
Administrator: Denise Chalmers
Solicitors: Sadia Arshad, Amerdeep Dhami
Office Manager: Evelyn Hay
Chair: Ewan MacDonald-Russell
Interim Chair: Maria Joanna Galli
Treasurer: Jennifer Law

The Scottish Paralegal Association
c/o The Law Society of Scotland, Atria One, 144
Morrison Street, Edinburgh EH3 8EX Website:
www.scottish-paralegal.org.uk
President: Sandra Reid

The SSC Library
11 Parliament Square, Edinburgh EH1 1RF
Tel: (0131) 225 6268
Fax: (0131) 225 2270 DX: ED209 Edinburgh 1
Email: enquiries@ssclibrary.co.uk Website:
www.ssclibrary.co.uk
President: Douglas Thomson
Vice-President: Sarah Erskine
Treasurer: Donald Skinner-Reid
Secretary: Robert Shiels
Head Librarian: Christine Wilcox
Keeper of the Library: Ann Ogg
Council Members: Robert Carr, Raymond
Fairgrieve, Lynn Harrison, Douglas Mill, Jackie
McRae, Sean Lynch

The W.S. Society
Parliament Square, Edinburgh EH1 1RF
Tel: (0131) 220 3249 DX: 549300 Edinburgh 36
Website: www.wssociety.co.uk/
Keeper of the Signet: Lord Mackay of Clashfern,
KT
Deputy Keeper of the Signet: Amanda Laurie WS
(Burness Paull LLP)

Office Bearers: Jim Cormack QC, WS (Pinsent Masons), Treasurer, Reema Mannah WS (Titlesolv), Rachel Wood WS (The Law Society of Scotland), Anthony Jones QC, WS (Brodies), Fiscal
Clerk: Sarah Booth, WS
Chief Executive: Robert Pirrie WS
Deputy Chief Executive: Anna Bennett WS

Traffic Commissioner for Scotland

Level 6, The Stamp Office, 10 Waterloo Place, Edinburgh EH1 3EG Tel: 0300 123 9000 Email: enquiries@otc.gov.uk Website: https://www.gov.uk/government/organisations/traffic-commissioners
Traffic Commissioner for Scotland: Claire Gilmore

TSO Scotland

18 Central Avenue, St Andrews Business Park, Norwich NR7 0HR Tel: (0333) 202 5070 Email: esupport@tso.co.uk Website: www.tsoshop.co.uk
Parent: Williams Lea Tag

VisitScotland

Ocean Point One, 94 Ocean Drive, Edinburgh EH6 6JH Tel: (0131) 472 2222
Fax: (0131) 554 4583 Email: info@visitscotland.com Website: www.visitscotland.com (consumer) Website: www.visitscotland.org (corporate)
Chairman: Lord John Thurso
Chief Executive: Malcolm Roughead, OBE
Corporate Communications: Carolyn Churchill
Human Resources: Lynn Jack
Insight: Susan Dickie

Law Societies

THE LAW SOCIETY OF SCOTLAND

Atria 1, 144 Morrison Street, Edinburgh EH3 8EX Tel: (0131) 226 7411
Fax: (0131) 225 2934 DX: ED 1 Edinburgh Email: lawscot@lawscot.org.uk Website:
www.lawscotjobs.co.uk Website: www.journalonline.co.uk Website: www.lawscot.org.uk
Brussels Office: Avenue de Nerviens, 1040 Brussels, Belgium
E-mail: brussels@lawsociety.org.uk

Council of the Society 2021-2022

President: Ken Dalling
Vice President: Murray Etherington
Past President: Amanda Millar
Treasurer: Graham Watson

Elected Members: David Mair, Paul Gostelow,
Sheila Webster, Susan Murray, Jennifer Livingston
(Co-opted member), Diane McGiffen (Chief
Executive), David Gordon (Observer member)

Senior Leadership Team

Chief Executive: Diane McGiffen
*Executive Director of Education, Training and
Qualifications:* Liz Campbell
Executive Director of External Relations: Kevin Lang
Executive Director of Finance and Operations:
Loraine Strachan
Executive Director of Regulation: Rachel Wood
Executive Director of Member Services:
Paul Mosson

THE LAW SOCIETY OF ENGLAND AND WALES

The Law Society's Hall, 113 Chancery Lane, London WC2A 1PL Tel: (020) 7242 1222
Fax: (020) 7831 0344 DX: 56 Lon/Chancery Lane Website: www.lawsociety.org.uk
Law Society Office in Wales, Capital Tower, Greyfriars Road, Cardiff CF10 3AG
DX: 33080 Cardiff
Email: wales@lawsociety.org.uk
Brussels, Avenue des Nerviens, 85, Box 10, B-1040 Brussels, Belgium
Tel: +322 743 85 85
Email: brussels@lawsociety.org.uk
President: I. Stephanie Boyce
Vice President: Lubna Shuja
Deputy Vice President: Nick Emmerson
Interim Chief Executive: Gerry Walsh
Chair: Robert Bourns

THE LAW SOCIETY OF NORTHERN IRELAND

96 Victoria Street, Belfast BT1 3GN Tel: (028) 9023 1614
Fax: (028) 9023 2606 DX: 422NR Belfast 1 Website: www.lawsoc-ni.org
President: Brigid Napier
Senior Vice-President: Rowan White
Junior Vice-President: Brian Archer
Treasurer: Brian H. Speers
Chief Executive: David A. Lavery CB
Deputy Chief Executive (Practice): Peter O'Brien
Deputy Secretary: Catherine McKay
Head of Practice & Procedure: Ann McMahon
Head of Professional Development: Darren Patterson
Head of Non Contentious Business: Brian Carson
Head of Finance: Christopher Houston
Head of Library and Information Services: Heather Semple
Head of Professional Conduct: John Mackell
Head of Communications: Paul O'Connor

National Legal Societies

Association of Pension Lawyers

Ground Floor, 4 Victoria Aquare, St. Albans AL1 3TF Tel: (0845) 680 9889 Email: membership@apl.org.uk Website: www.apl.org.uk

Scottish Group

Chairman: Edwin Mustard, Shepherd & Wedderburn LLP
Secretary: James Keith, MacRoberts LLP
Email: james.keith@macroberts.com
Scottish Committee Members:
Juliet Bayne, Brodies LLP
Mairi Carlin, Brodies LLP
Mathew Boyle, White & Case LLP
Colin Greig, Treasurer, DWF LLP
Cameron McCulloch, Pinsent Masons LLP
Sarah Phillips, Burness Paull LLP
Regular seminars, an annual dinner and conferences are held in Scotland and are open to non-members of the Association.

CALM

MSM Solicitors, 51 Moss Street, Paisley PA1 1DR Tel: (0141) 889 6244 Email: ns@msmlaw.co.uk Website: www.calmscotland.co.uk

(Comprehensive Accredited Lawyer Mediators)

Office Bearers

Chair: Helen Hughes
Email: h.hughes-paisley@btconnect.com
Vice-Chair: Morag Fraser
morag@frasershepherd.co.uk
Secretary & Treasurer: Nicos Scholarios
Email: ns@msmlaw.co.uk
Online & Strategy: Awaiting Appointment

The Chartered Society of Forensic Sciences

Office 40, Flexspace, Harrogate HG3 2XA Tel: (01423) 534 646 Email: info@csofs.org Website: www.csofs.org
Chief Executive Officer: Dr Anya Hunt
President: Dr Sheila Willis
Vice President: Marce Lee-Gorman
Honorary Treasurer: Dr Ben Jones
Honorary Secretary: Adam Long
Honorary Editor: Dr Rachel Bolton-King
Honorary Chair of Quality Standards: Brian Rankin
Quality and Competency Manager: David Bellamy
Quality and Competency Co-ordinator: Dannie Williams
Training Manager: April Robson
Finance Administrator: Suzanne Solly
Events – Conference Administration Membership Administrator: Jean Lewis

Educational Quality Standards Administrator (covering accreditation, recognition and endorsement): Katharine Sowerby

In 2004, the Society became a professional body and the voice for forensic practitioners both in the UK and abroad. It was in 2014 that the Society was granted a Royal Charter and became The Chartered Society of Forensic Sciences. It is a registered charity, not for profit, whose structure is clearly laid out in the Charter and Bye laws.

Family Law Association

Web: www.familylawassociation.org
Chair: Lesley Anderson, Lesley Anderson Law, 5 Manse Place, Falkirk, FK1 1JN
Tel: 01324 278565
Email: la@lesleyandersonlaw.co.uk
Vice Chair: Karen Wylie, Gibson Kerr, 6 Randolph Crescent, Edinburgh EH3 7TH
Tel: 0131 3858821
Email: karen.wylie@gibsonkerr.co.uk
Secretary: Cheryl Wallace, Thorntons Law LLP, 49 Bonnygate, Cupar, KY15 4BY
Tel: 01334 652285
Email: cherylwallace@thorntons-law.co.uk
Treasurer: Rachael Macdonald, Harper MacLeod, Citypoint, 65 Haymarket Terrace, Edinburgh, EH12 5HD
Tel: 0131 247 2500
Email: rachael.macdonald@harpermacleod.co.uk
Committee Members: Judith Meil, Susan Oswald, Richard Frenz, Rachael Noble, Jamie Foulis, Danielle Stevenson

The Legal Defence Union

Walkend, Aldbar, Brechin DD9 6SW Tel: (07739) 486 369 Email: david.odonnell@ldu.org.uk
Website: www.ldu.org.uk
Chairman: William Macreath
Chief Executive: Professor David O'Donnell
Company Secretary: Fiona O'Donnell
Advice Line: 07739 486369
Solicitor Directors: James McCann, David M Burnside, Ian Ferguson, Johnston P Clark
Panel Solicitors: John Macmillan, Nicola Irvine

Scottish Law Agents Society
Tel: (07858) 254501 Email: scottishlawagentssociety@gmail.com
President: John Stirling, Hamilton, Email: stirling.j@outlook.com
Vice-President: David P.H. MacLennan, Edinburgh, Email: david@maclennan.org.uk
Secretary: Andrew Stevenson, 14, The Firs, Millholm Road, Cathcart, Glasgow G44 3YB, Tel:

07858 254501, Email:
scottishlawagentssociety@gmail.com
Members: James Hotchkis, Ian C Ferguson, Grant McLennan, Darren Murdoch, Rod Maclean, Dorothy McGhie, Claire Maguire, Kenneth Swinton, John Flanagan

The Scottish Law Agents Society (SLAS) is a company incorporated by a Royal Charter granted by Queen Victoria in 1883. Initially it was named the Incorporation of Law Agents in Scotland. A Supplementary Charter of 1925 amended the name to the Scottish Law Agents' Society and a further change was made by another Royal Charter in 2006. It is the oldest and the largest national voluntary association of solicitors in Scotland.

Scottish Parliamentary Agents

The following firms are firms with one or more "Roll A" Parliamentary Agent who can act for the promoters of private legislation or assist in opposing it in Parliament. Copies of private bills may be purchased from the particular Parliamentary Agent responsible for each bill (whose name is given at the end of the text of the bill).

Bexley Beaumont Limited
Centurion House, 129 Deansgate, Manchester M3 3WR
Email: richardbull@bexleybeaumont.com
Website: www.bexleybeaumont.com
Roll A Agent – Richard Bull

Bryan Cave Leighton Paisner LLP
Adelaide House, London Bridge, London EC4R 9HA
Tel: 020 3400 1000
Email: Helen.kemp@bclplaw.com
Website: www.bclplaw.com
Roll A Agent – Ms Helen Kemp

BDB Pitmans LLP
One Bartholomew Close, London EC1A 7BL
Tel: 020 7227 7080
Email: pamthompson@bdbpitmans.com
Website: www.bdbpitmans.com
Roll A Agent – Ian H McCulloch, E N (Nick) W Brown, David Mundy, Nicholas Evans
Roll C Parliamentary Clerk – Mrs Pam J Thompson

Eversheds Sutherland (International) LLP
1 Wood Street, London EC2V 7WS
Tel: 020 7497 9797
Website: www.eversheds-sutherland.com
E-mail: stephencollings@eversheds-sutherland.com
Roll A Agent – Joe A Durkin (consultant), Miss Monica A R Peto, Stephen Collings, James O'Connor
Roll C Parliamentary Clerk – Mr Darren C White, Mr David Slevin – 020 79194878

Pinsent Masons LLP
30 Crown Place, Earl Street, London EC2A 4ES
Tel: 020 7418 7000
Website: www.pinsentmasons.com
Email: robbie.owen@pinsentmasons.com
Roll A Agent – Robbie J V Owen
Roll C Parliamentary Clerk – Frances Ellis – 020 7667 0164

Sharpe Pritchard LLP
Elm Yard, 13-16 Elm Street, London WC1X 0BJ
Tel: 020–7405 4600
Website: www.sharpepritchard.co.uk
E-mail: alewis@sharpepritchard.co.uk
Roll A Agent – W A (Alastair) Lewis, Emyr Rh Thomas

Veale Wasbrough Vizards LLP
Barnards Inn, 86 Fetter Lane, London EC4A 1AD
Tel: 020-7405 1234
Website: www.vwv.co.uk
E-mail: rperry@vwv.co.uk
Roll A Agent – Ron E Perry

Winckworth Sherwood LLP
Minerva House , 5 Montague Close, London SE1 9BB
Tel: 020–7593 5000
Website: www.wslaw.co.uk
E-mail: agorlov@wslaw.co.uk
Roll A Agent – Paul M C F Irving, Mrs Alison M H Gorlov, H S (Stephen) Wiggs
Roll C Parliamentary Clerk – Mr David Walker

City Remembrancer
Paul Double
Deputy: Paul Wright
City Remembrancer's Office
PO Box 270, London EC2P 2EJ
Tel: 020–7332 1200
Email: CityRemembrancer@TheGuildhall.org/ RemParliamentary@cityoflondon.gov.uk

Scottish Society for Computers & Law

5th Floor, Quartermile Two, 2 Lister Square, Edinburgh EH3 9GL Email: mail@sscl.org
Website: www.scl.org

The Society exists for legal professionals who advise and practice in the IT sector – including data protection and e-commerce. IT law issues are covered on both the Society's website and in their magazine. Established originally in 1988 as a branch of the Society for Computers and Law, the SSCL provides a programme of events, seminars and conferences throughout the year. Members enjoy the full benefits of membership of the UK national Society, including the Society's journal 'Computers & Law' and access to the Society's website (www.scl.org) which has a separate Scottish section.
President: Prof Richard Susskind OBE FRSE
Vice President: Mark O'Conor
Chair: Patricia Shaw

Vice Chair: Sue McLean
Chief Executive: Caroline Gould
Trustees: Toby Crick, Matthew Lavy, Mark
Lumley, Cynthia O'Donoghue, Katherine Ramo,
Fernando Barrio, Shelley Thomas, Andy Crystal

Scottish Young Lawyers Association (SYLA)

Email: mail@syla.co.uk
Website: www.syla.co.uk
President: Chiara Pieri
Vice-President: Laila Kennedy
Secretary: Patricia Taylor
Treasurer: Maddie Thomas
Past President: Ayla Iridag
Honorary President: Kenneth Norrie
Committee Members: Anna Hills, Matthew
McGovern, Kerri Montgomery, Brianella Scott,
Robyn Canning, Marsaili Van Looy, Amina Amin

Society of Solicitor Advocates

52a Kettil'stoun Mains, Linlithgow EH49 6SL
Tel: (01506) 846587 Email:
contact@solicitoradvocates.org Website:
www.solicitoradvocates.org
President: John Scott QC
Vice-President – Criminal: Ross Yuill
Vice-President – Civil: Laura McMillan
Treasurer: Lesley Anderson
Secretary: Fiona Mundy
Administrator: Ellen Wilson
The Society of Solicitor Advocates exists to
promote the interests of Solicitor Advocates in
Scotland. The Society is committed to facilitating
and enhancing the training of Scottish Solicitor
Advocates.

SSC Society

SSC Library, 11 Parliament Square, Edinburgh
EH1 1RF Tel: (0131) 225 6268
Fax: (0131) 225 2270 DX: ED 209 Edinburgh 1
Email: enquiries@ssclibrary.co Website:
www.ssclibrary.co.uk
President: Douglas Thomson

Vice-President: Sarah Erskine
Treasurer: Donald Skinner-Reid
Keeper of the Library: Ann Ogg
Expert in Sourcing Material: Joanne Bennett
Secretary: Robert Shiels
Head Librarian: Christine Wilcox
Members of Council: Robert Carr, Raymond
Fairgrieve, Lynn Harrison, Douglas Mill, Jackie
McRae, Sean Lynch

Trainee and Newly Qualified Society

Royal Faculty of Procurators in Glasgow, 12
Nelson Mandela Place, Glasgow G2 1BT
Tel: (0141) 332 3593
Fax: (0141) 332 4714 DX: GW 197 Glasgow
Email: tanq@rfpg.org Website:
www.rfpg.org/tanq
Committee Members:
Danielle Connell, Thorntons
Annie Hwang, BLM
Ruairidh Leishman,Shepherd & Wedderburn
Alan Ritchie
Zenab Saheel-Ikram, Watt Law Solicitors
Jennifer Sillars, COPFS
Alasdair Schreiber, Miller Hendry
Emily Wood, NHS Scotland

The WS Society

The Signet Library, Parliament Square, Edinburgh
EH1 1RF Tel: (0131) 220 3249 Email:
library@wssociety.co.uk Website:
www.wssociety.co.uk
Keeper of the Signet: Lord Mackay of Clashfern,
KT
Deputy Keeper: Amanda Laurie WS (Burness Paull
LLP)
Office Bearers: Jim Cormack QC, WS (Pinsent
Masons), Treasurer, Reema Mannah WS
(Titlesolv), Rachel Wood WS (Law Society of
Scotland), Anthony Jones QC, WS (Brodies),
Fiscal, Sarah Booth WS, Clerk
Chief Executive: Robert Pirrie WS
Email: rpirrie@wssociety.co.uk
Council: Deputy Keeper, Office Bearers, Clerk

Local Societies and Faculties

Aberdeen Bar Association
Ayr Faculty of Solicitors
Dundee CPD Group
Dunfermline District Society of Solicitors
Dunoon Faculty of Procurators
East Lothian Faculty of Procurators
Edinburgh Bar Association
Faculty of Procurators and Solicitors in Dundee
Faculty of Procurators for the Stewartry of Kirkcudbright
Faculty of Procurators in Paisley
Faculty of Procurators of Berwickshire
Faculty of Procurators of Caithness
Faculty of Procurators of Dumfriesshire
Faculty of Procurators of Greenock
Faculty of Solicitors at Lanark and District
Faculty of Solicitors for the Western Isles
Faculty of Solicitors in Bute
Faculty of Solicitors in Roxburghshire
Faculty of Solicitors in Shetland
Faculty of Solicitors of Dunbartonshire
Faculty of Solicitors of Kincardine and Deeside
Faculty of Solicitors of Ross-shire and Sutherland
Faculty of Solicitors of the Highlands
Faculty of West Lothian Solicitors
Falkirk and District Faculty of Solicitors
Glasgow Bar Association

Kilmarnock Faculty of Solicitors
Kirkcaldy Law Society
Lochaber Faculty of Solicitors
Moray Faculty of Solicitors
North CPD Group
Oban Faculty of Solicitors
Royal Faculty of Procurators in Glasgow
Society of Procurators and Solicitors in the City and County of Perth
Society of Procurators and Solicitors of Angus
Society of Scottish Lawyers in London
Society of Solicitors and Procurators for the Eastern District of Fife
Society of Solicitors and Procurators of Stirling
Society of Solicitors in Orkney
Society of Solicitors in Peterhead and Fraserburgh
Society of Solicitors in the Shires of Galashiels, Selkirk and Peebles
Society of Solicitors of Banffshire
Society of Solicitors of Clackmannanshire
Society of Solicitors, Airdrie
The Campbeltown Faculty of Solicitors
The Society of Advocates in Aberdeen
The Society of Solicitors of Hamilton
Wick Faculty
Wigtown District Faculty of Solicitors

Law Centres

Castlemilk Law & Money Advice Centre
155 Castlemilk Drive, Glasgow G45 9UG Tel: (0141) 634 0313
Fax: (0141) 634 1944 Email: mail@castlemilklawcentre.co.uk Website: www.castlemilklawcentre.co.uk

Gorbals Law and Money Advice Centre 6 St Ninian Terrace, Glasgow G5 0RJ Tel: 0141 418 1010

Toryglen Law and Money Advice Centre 179 Prospecthill Circus, Glasgow G42 0LA Tel: 0141 647 4333

Castlemilk Citizens Advice Bureau 27 Dougrie Drive, Glasgow G45 9AD Tel: 0141 634 0338
Senior Principal Solicitor: Angus McIntosh
Principal Solicitors: Gerry Loughery, Simon Hodge
Advice Worker: Lynn Smillie
Senior Solicitor: Maureen Smith
Assistant Solicitors: Peter Benham, Angela Duncan, Shazia Akhtar, Judith Stevenson

Clan Child Law
Norton Park, 57 Albion Road, Edinburgh EH7 5QY Tel: (0808) 129 0522 Email: info@clanchildlaw.org
Website: www.clanchildlaw.org
Glasgow Office: First Floor, 11 & 13 at Wellpark Enterprise Centre, 20 Sydney St, Glasgow G31 1JF
Board: Cathy Asante, Neil Collar, Sue Grant, Tom Harvie-Clark (Chair), Peter Hastie, Mandy Young
Principal Solicitor and Chief Executive: Alison Reid
Deputy Principal Solicitor: Julia Donnelly
Managing Solicitors: Lucy Frazer, Rebecca Scott

Dundee Law Centre
163 Albert Street, Dundee DD4 6PX Tel: (01382) 918230 Email: enquiries@dundeelaw.org Website:
www.dundeelaw.org
Principal Solicitor: Joyce Horsman
Solicitor: Rebecca Menzies
Administrator: Angela Jones
Finance and Operations Manager: Linda McDonald
Legal Secretary: Teresa Wilkinson, Jodie Muir
Receptionist: Kay Lizanec

Ethnic Minorities Law Centre
41 St Vincent Place, Glasgow G1 2ER Tel: (0141) 204 2888 Email: admin@emlc.org.uk Website:
www.emlc.org.uk
Principal Solicitor: Brzoom Kadirgolam
Solicitors: Gurjeet Singh, Michael Ross, Daljit Singh
Operations Manager: Shahzad Moughal
Development Officer: Lazarous Chisela
Projects and Finance: Ajmal Yamin

Fife Law Centre
Ore Valley Business Centre, 93 Main Street, Lochgelly KY5 9AF Tel: (01592) 786710 Email:
info@fifelawcentre.co.uk Website: www.fifelawcentre.co.uk
Leven Outreach Service: Citizen's Advice and Rights Fife (CARF), Greig Institute, Fourth Street, Leven
KY8 4PF Appointments only. Tel: 0345 140 0095
Dunfermline Advice Hub: 31 Chapel St, Dunfermline, KY12 7AW Tel: 01383 432 483
Board: Peter Wilson – Chair, Alison Denton – Vice Chair, John Barnett – Treasurer, Anne MacIntyre,
Callum Macinnes, Abby McMurtrie, Thomas Docherty, John Macmillan, Tom Marshall, Dianne
Williamson

Govan Law Centre

Orkney Street Enterprise Centre, Units 4 & 6, 18-20 Orkney Road, Glasgow G51 2BZ Tel: (0800) 043 0306 Email: m@govanlc.com Website: https://govanlawcentre.org/

Govanhill Law Centre Samaritan House, Lower Ground Floor, 79 Coplaw Street, Glasgow G42 7JG Tel: 0141 433 2665

Education Law Unit See Govan Law Centre Tel: 0141 440 2503

Govan Office
Senior Management team:
Solicitor Advocate & Principal Solicitor: Mike Dailly
Service Manager: Candy Walker
Senior Project Manager: Alistair Sharp
Senior Solicitor/Legal Services Manager (partner): Lorna Walker
Legal team: Christine McKellar, Laura Simpson, Jennifer Barr, Agnes Maxwell-Ferguson, Anna Considine, Holly Sloey, Chloe Minto, Lynda Nouar, Sophie Berry, Charis Brooks

Govanhill Office:
Senior Solicitor/Legal Services Manager: Rachel Moon
Solicitor: Claire Cochrane
Vulnerable Persons Case Worker: Donna Alexander
Welfare Rights Caseworker: Jitka Perinova

Lanarkshire Community Law Centre

61A Stirling Street, Airdrie ML6 0AS Tel: (01236) 758 620 Email: office@lclc.org.uk

Legal Services Agency Ltd

Fleming House, 134 Renfrew Street, Glasgow G3 6ST Tel: (0141) 353 3354 DX: GW12 Email: mail@lsa.org.uk Website: www.lsa.org.uk

Greenock: 9 Sir Michael Street, Greenock PA15 1PQ DX: GR3 Tel: 01475 725665 Email: greenock@lsa.org.uk
Convener: Barrie Levine
Company Secretary: GarryBurns Garry
Treasurer/Vice Convenor: Willie Croft
Trustees: Grant Carson, Kirstie Cusick, Mhairi Reid, Paul Brown, Peter Beckett

Scottish Child Law Centre

91 George Street, Edinburgh EH2 3ES Tel: (0131) 667 6333 Email: advice@sclc.org.uk Website: www.sclc.org.uk
Solicitors: Amerdeep Dhami, Sadia Arshad
Administrator: Denise Chalmers
Board of Trustees: Maria Joanna Galli (Interim Chair), Jennifer Law (Treasurer), Ewan MacDonald-Russell, Joel Meekison, Katy Macfarlane, Alan Inglis, Stewart McLachlan, Rachael MacDonald, Sarah Drummond

Universities

University of Aberdeen
School of Law
School of Law, Taylor Building
Aberdeen AB24 3UB Tel: (01224) 274260 Email:
law430@abdn.ac.uk Website:
www.abdn.ac.uk/law/
Head of School: Professor G Gordon
Intellectual Property Law: Titilayo Adebola, Abbe
E. L Brown, Catherine Ng
Civil Law: John Ford
Criminal Justice: Graeme Brown, Peter Duff, Susan
Stokeld, Elizabeth Shaw
Criminal Law and Evidence: Isla Callander
Commercial Law: Chike Emedosi, Claudio
Lombardi, Alisdair MacPherson, Scott Styles
Energy Law: Tomilola Akanle Eni-ibukun, John
Paterson, Daria Shapovalova
Energy Transition Law: Thomas Muinzer
Legal History and Private Law: Jonathan Ainslie
International Comparative Law: Roy Partain
International Dispute Resolution: Gloria Alvarez,
Patricia Živković
International Economic Law: Edouard Fromageau
*International Trade Law and Private International
Law:* Burcu Yüksel Ripley
IT Law and Regulation: Rossana Ducato
Oil and Gas Law and Scots Private Law:
Greg Gordon, Mark Igiehon
Offshore Energy Risk Governance: Eddy Wifa
Planning and Environmental Law:
Anne-Michelle Slater
Public International Law: Irène Couzigou, Zeray
Yihdego, Katarina Trimmings
Public Law: Tamas Gyorfi, Mike Radford, Robert
Taylor
*Public Law, Medical Law, Sales Law and Legal
History:* Adelyn Wilson
Dispute Process Law: Derek Auchie
Private International Law: Justin Borg-Barthet,
Onyoja Momoh
Tax Law: Qiang (John) Cai
Senior Scots Law and Family Law: Ilona Cairns
Scots Law: Roderick Paisley, Euan West
Solicitors: Fiona Stuart

University of Aberdeen
Diploma in Legal Practice
Director: Jamie Hunter
Professional Programmes Secretary: Ms Jackie
Ewen
Advanced Civil Litigation: Stephen McLaren
Business Environment and Ethics: Jamie Hunter
Contracts: Stuart Robson
Conveyancing: Gregor Sim
Corporate Finance and Acquisition: Fiona Kindness
Dispute Resolution: Professor Derek Auchie
Employment Law: Annika Neukirch

Energy Law: Laura Petrie
Family Law: Fiona Barker, Susan Purvis
Litigation: Shane Campbell (Criminal and
Advanced Criminal), Dean Purdie (Civil)
Private Client: Jamie Hunter
Public Law and Administration: Martin Ingram

Abertay University
The Dundee Business School
Law Division, Bell Street
Dundee DD1 1HG Tel: (01382) 308401 308527
Fax: (01382) 308000 Email: dbs@abertay.ac.uk
Head of School: Professor Mohamed Branine
Head of Division: Professor Annelize McKay
Business law: Professor Nicholas Grier
Company law: Professor Nicholas Grier
Competition Law: Dr Maria O'Neill
Contract Law: Dr Vanessa Constant LaForce
Criminal law: Mr Jamie Taylor
Delict: Vacant
Employment law: Dr Michelle Weldon-Johns
EU law: Dr Vanessa Constant LaForce
Family law: Ms Tracy Lelei
International Private Law: Dr Michelle
Weldon-Johns, Ms Tracy Lelei
EU Security, Justice and Home Affairs: Dr Maria
O'Neill
Justice and Home Affairs: Jade Kouletakis
Public law: Jade Kouletakis
Succession: Ms Tracy Lelei
Intellectual Property: Jade Kouletakis
Property Law: Vacant
Medical Law and Bioethics: Prof Annelize McKay
Pubic International Law: Prof Annelize McKay

University of Dundee
School of Law
Scrymgeour Building, Park Place
Dundee DD1 4HN Tel: (01382) 384461
Fax: (01382) 386737
Commercial Law: Mr S Abboud, Prof A Belcher,
Ms E Lecchi, Ms M Malone, Dr B Xie
Criminal Law: Prof PR Ferguson, Dr T Giddens
Energy Law: See Centre for Energy, Petroleum
and Mineral Law and Policy
English Private Law: Mr S Abboud, Dr L Eldridge,
Dr T Giddens, Dr L Silquini-Cinelli, Mr A
Simmonds
Environmental Law: Mr A Allan, Dr S Hendry, Prof
CT Reid, Professor A Ross, Dr S Whittaker
Healthcare Law: Ms M Malone, Prof PR Ferguson,
Prof A Belcher
Human Rights: Dr S El Droubi, Dr J Hartmann, Dr
S Hendry, Dr C Methven O'Brien, Dr T Olcay
Legal History and Roman Law: Mr D Adam, Mr B
Dempsey, Dr L Eldridge, Mrs S King, Dr L
Silquini-Cinelli

Legal Theory: Dr T Giddens, Dr L Silquini-Cinelli
Private International Law: Ms A Fiorini, Dr E
Jueptner, Prof P McEleavy
Public Law: Dr T Olcay, Prof CT Reid, Prof A Ross,
Dr S Whittaker
Public International Law: Dr S El Droubi, Dr J
Hartmann, Dr C Methven O'Brien
Scots Private Law: Mr D Adam, Ms E Comerford,
Mr B Dempsey, Ms Y Evans, Mrs S King, Mrs N
Tully
Technology and Cyberlaw: Prof S Cross, Prof A
Daly, Ms M Malone
Solicitors: Claire McGinnis, Eloise Robb, Umran
Sarwar, Jaclyn Suttie

University of Dundee
Diploma in Legal Practice

Diploma in Professional Legal Practice
Director of Diploma in Professional Legal Practice:
Ms E Comerford
Deputy Director: Ms Y Evans
Conveyancing: Mr S Drake
Criminal court practice: Mr J Laverty
Civil court practice: Mr I MacRae
Professional Practice: Ms E Comerford
Private client: Ms Y Evans
Business and Financial Services: Mr R Smith

University of Edinburgh
School of Law
Old College, South Bridge
Edinburgh EH8 9YL Tel: (0131) 650 2008
Fax: (0131) 650 2005 Email: law@ed.ac.uk
Website: www.law.ed.ac.uk
Dr Arianna Andreangeli: Senior Lecturer in
European Law
Dr Andy Aydin-Aitchison: Senior Lecturer in
Criminology
Professor Christine Bell: Professor of Constitutional
Law
Professor Nehal Bhuta: Professor of Public
International Law
Professor Gillian Black: Professor of Scots Private
Law
Dr Michelle Burgis-Kasthala: Senior Lecturer in
Public International Law
Professor David Cabrelli: Professor of Labour Law
Professor John W. Cairns: Professor of Civil Law
Dr Daniel J. Carr: Senior Lecturer in Private Law
Dr Elisenda Casanas Adam: Lecturer in Public Law
and Human Rights
Dr Paolo Cavaliere: Lecturer in Digital Media & IT
Law
Anna L Christie: Lecturer in Banking, Corporate
and Financial Law
Dr Andrew Cornford: Senior Lecturer in Criminal
Law
Ms Jane Cornwell: Senior Lecturer in Intellectual
Property Law
Professor Sharon Cowan: Professor of Feminist
and Queer Legal Studies

Dr Ana Maria Daza Vargas: Lecturer in
International Law
Dr Deval Desai: Lecturer in International
Economic Law
Dr Edward Dove: Lecturer in Health Law and
Regulation
Professor Paul J. du Plessis: Professor of Roman
Law
Professor Luís Duarte d'Almeida: Professor of
Jurisprudence
Professor Anne-Maree Farrell: Professor of Medical
Jurisprudence
Dr Filippo Fontanelli: Senior Lecturer in
International Economic Law
Professor David Fox: Professor of Common Law
Dr Agomoni Ganguli Mitra: Lecturer and
Chancellor's Fellow in Bioethics and Global
Health Ethics
Mr Navraj Singh Ghaleigh: Senior Lecturer in
Climate Law
Dr Jonathan Hardman: Lecturer in International
Commercial Law
Professor James Harrison: Professor of
Environmental Law
Dr Alistair Henry: Senior Lecturer in Criminology
Dr Parker Hood: Lecturer in Commercial Law
Dr Richard Jones: Senior Lecturer in Criminology
Dr Martin David Kelly: Lecturer in Legal Theory
Dr Chloë Kennedy: Senior Lecturer in Criminal
Law
Dr Smita Kheria: Senior Lecturer in Intellectual
Property Law
Dr Simone Lamont-Black: Senior Lecturer in
International Trade Law
Dr Robert Lane: Senior Lecturer in EU Law
Professor Andrew Lang: Professor of International
Law and Global Governance
Dr Amy Lawton: Lecturer in Tax Law
Dr Longjie Lu: Lecturer in Banking, Corporate and
Financial Law
Dr Cormac Mac Amhlaigh: Senior Lecturer in
Public Law
Dr Euan MacDonald: Senior Lecturer in
Jurisprudence
Professor Laura Macgregor: Chair of Scots Law
Dr John Macleod: Senior Lecturer in Private Law
Professor Gerry Maher QC: Professor of Criminal
Law
Dr Leandro Mancano: Senior Lecturer in European
Union Law
Professor Lesley McAra: Professor of Penology
Dr Kasey McCall-Smith: Senior Lecturer in Public
International Law
Professor Susan McVie: Professor of Quantitative
Criminology
Professor Claudio Michelon: Professor of
Philosophy of Law
Professor Stephen Neff: Professor of War and
Peace
Professor Niamh Nic Shuibhne: Professor of
European Union Law
Dr Alasdair Peterson: Lecturer in Private Law

Dr Emmanuel Oke: Lecturer in International Intellectual Property Law
Mr Gerard Porter: Lecturer in Medical Law and Ethics
Ms Judith Rauhofer: Senior Lecturer in IT Law
Ms Lorna Richardson: Senior Lecturer in Commercial Law
Dr Veronica Ruiz Abou-Nigm: Senior Lecturer in International Private Law
Professor Burkhard Schafer: Professor of Computational Legal Theory
Professor Andrew R C Simpson: Professor of Scottish Legal History
Ms Annie Sorbie: Lecturer in Law (Medical Law and Ethics)
Dr Anna Souhami: Senior Lecturer in Criminology
Professor Richard Sparks: Professor of Criminology
Professor Andrew J. M. Steven: Professor of Property Law
Professor Stephen Tierney: Professor of Constitutional Theory
Dr Milena Tripkovic: Lecturer in Criminology
Dr Lachlan D. Urquhart: Lecturer in Technology Law
Dr Remus Valsan: Senior Lecturer in Corporate Law
Dr Asanga Welikala: Lecturer in Public Law
Mr Scott Wortley: Lecturer in Commercial Law
Dr Raphaële Xenidis: Lecturer in EU Law
Dr Ruiqiao Zhang: Lecturer in Corporate Finance, Corporate and Commercial Law
Solicitors (Old College) Graham Ayres, Fiona Campbell, Leigh Suzanne Chalmers, Anna Crilly, Louise Susan Cullum, Nicholas Donald Day, Esther Mary Duncan, David Louis Faith, Lindsay Hampton, Nora Alison Kellock, Joanne Christina MacConnell, David Malcolm Matheson
Solicitors (The Data Lab) Kristina Elizabeth Mutch
Solicitors (School of Law): Rebecca Samaras
Solicitors (Edinburgh Research Office): Elizabeth Ann Greybe, Allan David Shanks, María Del Mar Val Fernández

University of Edinburgh
Diploma in Professional Legal Practice
Diploma in Professional Legal Practice Office: Tel: +44 (0)131 651 4254/650 2004
Email: law.diploma@ed.ac.uk
Edinburgh Law School, 9B Holyrood Road, Holyrood Campus, Edinburgh EH8 8FQ

Glasgow Caledonian University
Glasgow School for Business and Society
Dept Economics and Law
70 Cowcaddens Road
Glasgow G4 0BA Tel: (0141) 331 3000 Email: ukroenquiries@gcu.ac.uk Website: www.gcu.ac.uk
Head of Department of Economics and Law: Ben Middleton
Professor of Healthcare and Medical Law: Prof Alison Britton

Director Wise Centre for Economic Justice: Prof Sara Cantillon
Senior Lecturers in Law: James P Connolly, Dr Manos Maganaris, Dr Eleanor J Russell
Law Lecturers: William A M Henderson, Dr Tracy Kirk, Dr Karla Perez Portilla, Dr Andrew Tickell
Academic Director – The Law Clinic/Lecturer in Law: Claire McFadzean
Solicitor – Law Division Paul Brown

University of Glasgow
School of Law
Stair Building
Glasgow G12 8QQ Tel: (0141) 330 3583 Email: law-enquiries@glasgow.ac.uk Website: www.gla.ac.uk
Head of College of Social Sciences: Professor Sara Carter
Head of School: Professor Jane Mair
Commercial: Dr Catriona Cannon, Dr Katarzyna Chalaczkiewicz-Ladna, Professor Irene- marié Esser, Dr Obiora Ezike, Dr Livashnee Naidoo, Professor Andreas Rahmatian, Professor Konstantinos Sergakis, Dr Javier Solana, Professor George Walker, Dr Chi Zhang
Company: Dr Katarzyna Chalaczkiewicz-Ladna, Professor Irene-marié Esser, Professor Iain MacNeil, Professor Konstantinos Sergakis
Comparative: Dr Antonio Marzal, Professor Andreas Rahmatian
Competition: Dr Magali Eben, Dr Florence Thepot
Criminal: Professor James Chalmers, Professor Lindsay Farmer, Mr Eamon Keane, Dr Louise Kennefick, Professor Fiona Leverick, Dr Rachel McPherson, Dr Micheál Ó Floinn
European: Ms Maria Fletcher, Dr Florence Thepot
Family: Dr Lesley-Anne Barnes Macfarlane, Ms Felicity Belton, Professor Janeen Carruthers, Professor Jane Mair, Professor Frankie McCarthy, Dr Dot Reid
Human rights: Professor Nicole Busby, Professor Jim Murdoch
Intellectual Property: Dr Elena Cooper, Dr Ula Furgal, Dr Marta Iljadica, Professor Martin Kretschmer, Dr Luis Porangaba, Professor Andreas Rahmatian, Ms Amy Thomas
International private law: Professor Janeen Carruthers, Dr Bobby Lindsay, Dr Antonio Marzal, Professor Andreas Rahmatian
Labour law: Professor Nicole Busby, Professor Ruth Dukes, Professor Jane Mair, Dr Vera Pavlou
Legal education: Dr Jacqueline Kingham
Legal history: Dr Stephen Bogle, Professor Ruth Dukes, Professor John Finlay, Professor Mark Godfrey, Professor Ernest Metzger, Dr Dot Reid
Legal theory: Professor Emilios Christodoulidis, Dr Gregor Clunie, Professor Ruth Dukes, Professor Lindsay Farmer, Dr Marco Goldoni, Dr Lilian Moncrieff, Professor George Pavlakos, Dr Akbar Rasulov
Medical law and ethics: Ms Sarah J Elliston, Ms Joanne Ramsey, Ms Shanti Williamson

Private law: Ms Felicity Belton, Dr Stephen Bogle, Dr Alan Brown, Professor Nicole Busby, Dr Mat Campbell, Professor Janeen Carruthers, Dr Graeme Cunningham, Professor Ruth Dukes, Professor Mark Godfrey, Dr Bobby Lindsay, Professor Jane Mair, Dr Antonio Marzal, Professor Frankie McCarthy, Professor Andreas Rahmatian, Dr Dot Reid, Dr Adam Reilly, Dr Jill Robbie
Property: Professor Frankie McCarthy, Dr Dot Reid
Public international: Dr Anna Chadwick, Mr Joseph Crampin, Dr James Devaney, Dr Mohamed Janaby, Dr Giedre Jokubauskaite, Dr Henry Lovat, Dr Charlotte Peevers, Dr Anni Pues, Dr Akbar Rasulov, Dr Rebecca Sutton, Professor Christian Tams, Professor Jörg Terhechte, Dr Andrea Varga
Public law: McCarthy, Dr Dot Reid Public international law: Dr Anna Chadwick, Mr Joseph Crampin, Dr James Devaney, Dr Mohamed Janaby, Dr Giedre Jokubauskaite, Dr Henry Lovat, Dr Charlotte Peevers, Dr Anni
Roman Law: Dr Graeme Cunningham, Professor Ernest Metzger
Succession: Dr Dot Reid

Diplomain Legal Practice Diploma
Director: Ms Kerry Trewern
Tel: 0141 330 7159
Depute Director: Ms Rona McNair
Tel: 0141 330 8197

Heriot-Watt University
School of Social Sciences
Edinburgh Campus
Edinburgh EH14 4AS Tel: (0131) 449 5111
Email: enquiries@ebs.hw.ac.uk Website: www.hw.ac.uk
Commercial Law: Ms Yvonne McLaren, Ms Jill Stirling
Consumer Law: Ms Yvonne McLaren, Ms Jill Stirling
Contract Law: Ms Yvonne McLaren, Ms Jill Stirling
Discrimination Law: Ms Yvonne McLaren
Employment Law: Ms Yvonne McLaren
Company Law: Ms J Bisacre
Delict: Ms Yvonne McLaren, Ms Jill Stirling
International Trade Law/International Business Law: Josephine Bisacre
Law of Property: Ms Yvonne McLaren
Solicitors: Derek Brown, Iain McClure, Angus McGuire

Edinburgh Napier University
Department of Law
Craiglockhart Campus
Edinburgh EH14 1DJ Tel: (0131) 455 4522
Fax: (0131) 455 0369
Law Staff/Lecturers:
Prof Richard Whitecross (Head of Law)
Mr Kenneth Dale-Risk
Dr Lorna Gillies
Dr Leslie Dodd

Prof Paul Hutton
Mr James McDougall
Dr Clare Frances Moran
Dr Katrina Morrison
Mr Zhongdong Nui
Elizabeth Speakman
Prof Jill Stavert

University of the West of Scotland
School of Business and Enterprise
Paisley PA1 2BE Tel: (0141) 848 3000 Website: www.uws.ac.uk
Dean of School: Dominic Elliott
Administrative law: Dale McFadzean
Arbitration & ADR: Carolynn Gray, Dale McFadzean
Company law: Colin McFadyen
Commercial law: Colin McFadyen
Constitutional law: Dale McFadzean
Contract law: Clive Mitchell, Muriel Finnigan
Criminal law: Colin Macintosh
Delict: Clive Mitchell
Employment law: Colin Macintosh
Environmental law: Clive Mitchell
Equality law: Carolynn Gray
Family law: Carolynn Gray
Human Rights law: Dale McFadzean
Information Technology law: Clive Mitchell
Legal Research: Dale McFadzean
Legal Education: Dale McFadzean
Medical law: Colin Macintosh, Carolynn Gray
Property law: Colin McFadyen
Solicitors: Emma Louise Cuckow, Alison Jane Niven

Robert Gordon University
Law School
Garthdee Road
Aberdeen AB10 7QE Tel: (01224) 263800 Email: m.downie@rgu.ac.uk Website: www.rgu.ac.uk
Head of Law: John Clifford
Property Law and Conveyancing: Craig Anderson
Employment Law and Delict: Sarah Arnell
Human rights: Dr Paul Arnell
Tax Law: Jonathan Brown
Criminal law: Dr Sarah Christie, Laura Sharp
Academic Strategic Lead: Margaret Downie
Construction Law and Arbitration: Bukola Faturoti, Joseph Mante
Law and Management: Lisa Gibbons-Wood, Jennifer Richmond
Private International Law: David Hill
Learning Enhancement Coordinator: Thorsten Lauterbach
European Union Law: Carole Lyons
Oil and Gas: Nicholas Maulet, Leon Moller
Constitutional Law: Gerry McGee

University of Stirling
School of Law
Stirling FK9 4LA Tel: (01786) 473171 Website: www.stir.ac.uk

Senior Lecturer, Head of Law: Dr David McArdle
Professor of Private International Law:
Professor Paul Beaumont
Lecturer in Private International Law: Dr Jayne
Holliday
Professor of Environmental and Public Law:
Professor Gavin McLeod Little
Professor of Child and Family Law: Professor Elaine
Sutherland
Professors: Dr Katie Boyle, Professor Alison Green,
Professor Simon Marsden, Dr Guido Noto La
Diega, Professor Hong-Lin Yu, Fraser Davidson,
Professor Francis McManus
Law Lecturers: Dr Wisam Abboud, Dr Sarah
Carrick, Dr Michelle Donnelly, Dr Mo Egan, Dr
Damian Etone, Mrs Tikus Little, Dr Pontian Okoli,
Dr Annalisa Savaresi, Dr Domenico Carolei, Dr
Zoi Krokida, Dr Geoffrey Wood, Dr Edit Frenyo,
Dr Tracy Kirk, Dr Amber Dar, Dr Elizabeth
Brandon, Ms Ziyana Mohamed Nazeemudeen,
Dr Katie Boyle, Ms Maria Fonseca Paim

University of Strathclyde
The Law School
Lord Hope Building, 141 St James Road
Glasgow G4 0LT Tel: (0141) 548 3738
DX: GW23 Glasgow Email:
hass-courses-law@strath.ac.uk Website:
www.strath.ac.uk/
Head of School: Professor Claire McDiarmid
Access to Justice & Legal Aid: Mr Aidan ODonnell,
Professor Alan Paterson, Professor Cyrus Tata
Administrative: Dr Chris McCorkindale, Dr
Michael Foran, Dr Pablo Grez

Artificial Intelligence, Algorithms & Data Privacy:
Dr Birgit Schippers
Business Law: Mr Aidan ODonnell, Professor Barry
Rodger
Childhood and Crime: Dr Michelle Donnelly,
Professor Claire McDiarmid
Childrens Rights: Dr Michelle Donnelly
Clinical Legal Education: Mr Malcolm Combe, Dr
Rhonda Wheate
Commercial: Dr Jonathan Brown, Mr Malcolm
Combe, Prof The Hon Lady Wolffe QC, Dr
Rebecca Zahn
Competition: Dr Oles Andriychuk, Professor Barry
Rodger, Dr Jing Wang
Constitutional: Dr Michael Foran, Dr Pablo Grez,
Dr Douglas Jack, Dr Chris McCorkindale, Dr
Elaine Webster
Contract: Professor Douglas Brodie, Dr Jonathan
Brown, Dr Rebecca Zahn
Counter-terrorism: Dr Genevieve Lennon
Criminal: Mr Stuart Kelly, Dr James MacLean,
Professor Claire McDiarmid, Professor Cyrus Tata,
Dr Rhonda Wheate
Criminal Justice: Dr Genevieve Lennon, Professor
Claire McDiarmid, Dr James MacLean, Professor
Cyrus Tata, Dr Rhonda Wheate
Criminology: Dr James MacLean

Delict: Professor Douglas Brodie, Dr Jonathan
Brown, Professor Kenneth Norrie, Professor Barry
Rodger, Dr Rebecca Zahn
Disaster Law: Ms Therese O'Donnell
English Contract Law: Professor Douglas Brodie,
Dr Mel Kenny, Dr Jing Wang
English Criminal Law: Dr Genevieve Lennon, Dr
James MacLean, Dr Rhonda Wheate
English Tort: Professor Douglas Brodie, Dr
Michael Randall
Environmental: Dr Antonio Cardesa-Salzmann,
Professor Elisa Morgera, Dr Maria Ntona, Dr
Francesco Sindico, Dr Stephanie Switzer, Dr
Saskia Vermeylen, Dr Rebecca Williams
European: Dr Oles Andriychuk, Dr Antonio
Cardesa-Salzmann, Dr Sylvie da Lomba, Professor
Elisa Morgera, Dr Maria Ntona, Mr Michael
Randall, Dr Rebecca Zahn
Evidence: Mr Donald Campbell, Dr Rhonda
Wheate
Financial/Banking Law: Dr Michael Randall
Family: Dr Michelle Donnelly, Professor Kenneth
Norrie
Healthcare and Ethics: Dr Jonathan Brown, Dr
Mary Neal
Housing: Professor Peter Robson
Human Rights: Dr Douglas Jack, Dr Genevieve
Lennon, Dr Sylvie da Lomba, Professor Alan
Miller, Ms Maria Ntona, Dr Birgit Schippers, Ms
Therese O'Donnell, Dr Elaine Webster
Immigration and Asylum: Dr Sylvie da Lomba
Indigenous People's Rights: Dr Saskia Vermeylen
Information Technology: Dr Oles Andriychuk, Dr
Conor Heaney, Dr Birgit Schippers
International Criminal Law: Dr James MacLean
International Migration Law: Dr Sylvie da Lomba
International Private Law: Professor Barry Rodger
IT and Internet Law: Dr Oles Andriychuk, Dr Birgit
Schippers
Judges: Professor Alan Paterson, Mr Aidan
ODonnell, Professor Cyrus Tata
Jurisprudence: Dr Oles Andriychuk, Professor
Cyrus Tata
Justice & Penal Decision Making: Professor Cyrus
Tata
Labour: Professor Douglas Brodie, Mr Aidan
ODonnell, Dr Emily Rose, Dr Rebecca Zahn
Land Reform: Mr Malcolm Combe
Law and Film: Mr Stuart Kelly, Dr Michael
Randall, Professor Peter Robson; Dr Conor
Heaney
Law and Gender: Dr Lynsey Mitchell, Professor
Jane Scoular
Law and Literature: Dr Lynsey Mitchell, Dr Saskia
Vermeylen
Law and Society: Professor Paul James Cardwell,
Dr James MacLean, Professor Alan Paterson, Mr
Douglas Jack, Dr Emily Rose, Professor Jane
Scoular, Professor Cyrus Tata, Dr Saskia
Vermeylen
Law, Justice and Society: Dr Antonio
Cardesa-Salzmann, Dr James MacLean, Dr Lynsey
Mitchell, Professor Alan Paterson, Dr Douglas

Jack, Dr Emily Rose, Professor Jane Scoular, Professor Cyrus Tata, Dr Saskia Vermeylen, Dr Conor Heaney
Law and Time: Dr Conor Heaney
Law, Justice and Society: Dr Antonio Cardesa-Salzmann, Dr James MacLean, Dr Birgit Schippers Professor Cyrus Tata, Dr Saskia Vermeylen, Dr Rhonda Wheate, Dr Conor Heaney, Ms Maria Ntona
Law of Business Associations: Dr Mel Kenny
Law of Trusts: Dr Jonathan Brown, Dr Genevieve Lennon
Lawyers' Ethics: Mr Stuart Kelly, Professor Alan Paterson, Dr Rhonda Wheate
Legal Education: Mr Stuart Kelly, Dr Rhonda Wheate
Legal History: Professor Kenneth Norrie
Legal Practice: Mr Stuart Kelly, Ms Frances Murray
Legal Process: Mr Charlie Irvine, Mr Aidan ODonnell, Professor Cyrus Tata
Legal Profession: Mr Malcolm Combe, Mr Stuart Kelly, Professor Alan Paterson
Legal Theory: Dr Oles Andriychuk, Dr James MacLean, Dr Lynsey Mitchell, Dr Mary Neal, Dr Emily Rose, Dr Birgit Schippers, Professor Jane Scoular, Professor Cyrus Tata, Dr Saskia Vermeylen, Dr Conor Heaney
Media and Entertainment: Dr Oles Andriychuk, Dr Conor Heaney
Mediation and Conflict Resolution: Mr Charlie Irvine, Prof The Hon Lady Wolffe QC
Medical: Dr Jonathan Brown, Dr Mary Neal, Dr Rhonda Wheate
Obligations: Professor Douglas Brodie, Dr Jonathan Brown, Professor Kenneth Norrie, Professor Barry Rodger, Dr Rebecca Zahn
Outer Space Law: Dr Saskia Vermeylen
Policing: Dr Genevieve Lennon, Dr Rhonda Wheate
Policing (Industrial Policy): Dr Jing Wang
Professional Ethics: Professor Alan Paterson
Property: Dr Jonathan Brown, Mr Malcolm Combe, Dr Mary Neal
Public International Law: Dr Antonio Cardesa-Salzmann, Dr Lynsey Mitchell, Professor Elisa Morgera, Dr Maria Ntona, Ms Therese O'Donnell, Dr Francesco Sindico, Dr Stephanie Switzer
Refugee: Dr Sylvie da Lomba
Regulation: Dr Francesco Sindico
Sentencing: Professor Cyrus Tata

Sexuality: Professor Kenneth Norrie
Social Security: Professor Peter Robson
Socio Legal Studies: Dr Lynsey Mitchell, Professor Alan Paterson, Dr Emily Rose, Professor Jane Scoular
Sports Law: Mr Stuart Kelly
Succession: Mr Stuart Kelly
Surveillance: Dr Conor Heaney
The Sociology of Law: Dr James MacLean, Dr Emily Rose, Professor Jane Scoular, Professor Cyrus Tata
Tax Law: Dr Michael Randall
Transitional Justice: Dr James MacLean
World Trade Law: Dr Francesco Sindico, Dr Stephanie Switzer

Diplomain Professional Legal Practice Diploma
Acting Co-Directors: Mr Stuart Kelly, Ms Frances Murray
Administrator: Ms Kirsty Doyle
Professional Practice and Ethics: Mr Brendan Cameron, Ms Jacqueline Fox
Business and Financial Awareness: Mr Donald Munro
Conveyancing: Mr Richard Leggett
Private Client: Ms Elspeth Talbot
Civil Litigation: Ms Jacqueline Fox
Criminal Litigation: Ms Pauline MacKenzie
Personal Injury Claim Handling: Ms Marie Donald
Advanced Criminal Advocacy: Mr Stuart Hamilton
Company Law: Mr Craig McKerracher
Practical Public Admin: Mr Christopher Anderson
Family Business: Mr Donald Munro
Family Law: Ms Fiona Carey, Ms Janice Jones
Mediation and Mediation Advocacy: Ms Kathleen Bolt
Employment Law: Ms Gillian Mair
Commercial Conveyancing: Mr Richard Leggett
Commercial Contracts and IP: Mr Andrew MacKenzie

Work-Based Learning in a Legal Environment: Mr Stuart Kelly
Advanced Private Client: Ms Elspeth Talbot
Tomorrow's Legal Industry: Mr Iain Sim

General Practice – Problem Based Learning: Professor Scott Slorach
Solicitors: Louise Catherine McKean, Verity Elizabeth Watson, Gavin Stewart Grant, Andrew William MacKenzie, David Peter Robertson Reid, Ms Jill Gwendoline Scott, Gillian Carol Melville

European Parliament Liaison Office

EUROPEAN PARLIAMENT LIAISON OFFICE IN EDINBURGH

The Tun, 4 Jackson's Entry, Holyrood Road, Edinburgh EH8 8PJ Tel: (0131) 557 7866
Fax: (0131) 557 4977 Email: epedinburgh@europarl.europa.eu Website:
https://www.europarl.europa.eu/unitedkingdom/en/edinburgh-office.html

United Kingdom Office:

London, Europe House, 32 Smith Square, London SW1P 3EU
Tel: +44 (0)20 7227 4300 (UK)
Fax: +44 (0) 20 7227 4302 (UK)
Email: eplondon@europarl.europa.eu
Head of UK Office: Susanne Oberhauser

Local Government

Aberdeen City Council

Business Hub 1, Lower Ground Floor West, Marischal College, Broad Street, Aberdeen AB10 1AB Tel: (03000) 200292 DX: AB529450 Aberdeen (Legal Services) Website: www.aberdeencity.gov.uk
The area comprises: the area of Aberdeen City Council
Solicitors: Mr Malcolm Fraser Bell, Mr Scott James Duncan Connor, Mrs Deirdre Anne Nicolson, Mr Robert James Templeton, Mrs Sharon Mary Wares, Mrs Karen Wilkie
Solicitors (Commercial & Procurement Services): Mrs Suzanne Claire Douglas, Mrs Janey Elizabeth Martyniuk, Mrs Keri Lyn Morrison, Mrs Dawn Michele Pittendreigh, Mrs Pamela Ross Wheadon
Solicitors (Legal Services, Governance): Mrs Jessica Maria Anderson, Mr Ross Grant Campbell, Mr Graham Richard Chandler, Mrs Lisa Jane Christie, Mrs Sarah Clubley, Mr Craig Brian Donald, Mrs Elizabeth Ann Falconer, Mr John Simpson Forsyth, Miss Caragh Meriel Gilhooly, Mrs Carolyn Harrison, Mr Steven Stewart Inglis, Mrs Kate Anne Johnstone, Miss Vicki Johnstone, Mrs Catriona Margaret Campbell Kelly, Mrs Jennifer Louise Lawson, Mrs Gwen McEwen, Mr Grant John Milne, Mr Alexander Munro, Mr Alan Douglas Thomson, Mrs Sarah Anne Walkden
Solicitors (Legal and Democratic Services): Miss Judith Katy Forbes

Aberdeenshire Council

Woodhill House, Westburn Road, Aberdeen AB16 5GB Tel: (03456) 081208 Website: www.aberdeenshire.gov.uk
The area comprises: Banff and Buchan; Formartine; Garioch; Kincardine and Mearns; Marr
Solicitors (Banff) Mr James McKay, Ms Fiona Mary Stewart
Solicitors (Legal and People): Mr Alan Robert Adam, Miss Leigh Anderson, Ms Laura Jane Bremner, Mrs Lauren Jacquelene Cowie, Mr Christopher Martin De Villiers, Mrs Donna Marie Elrick, Mrs Sheila Margaret Forbes, Mrs Geraldine Margaret Fraser, Mrs Arlene Louise Gibbs, Mrs Nicola Henderson, Mr Tristan James Horsburgh, Mr Martin Ingram, Mrs Patricia Jericevich, Mrs Claire Elizabeth Kent, Ms Lynsey Jane Martin Kimmitt, Mr John Allan Scott Mackenzie, Mr Robert McIntosh, Mrs Jennifer Isobel Cruickshank McKearney, Miss Catherine Rose Mullen, Mrs Ruth Elizabeth O'Hare, Miss Sheereen Razaq, Mrs Moira Simpson Reid, Mr Alistair James Stobie, Miss Kirsty Ann Street, Mrs Kirsten Frances Sutherland-George, Mr Robin George Taylor, Miss Laurel Ann Wheatley, Mrs Karen Frances Wiles

Solicitors (Law and Admin): Mrs Fiona Margaret Binnie, Miss Amanda Jane de Candia, Mr Brian Holden, Miss Anna Ziarkowska
Solicitors (Legal & Governance Inverurie): Mrs Jill Maria Joss, Miss Suzanne Victoria Ward

Angus Council

Angus House, Orchardbank Business Park, Orchardbank, Forfar DD8 1AN Tel: (03452) 777778 Website: www.angus.gov.uk
The area comprises: Angus; Tayside electoral divisions 30 (Monifieth) and 31 (Sidlaw – part)
Solicitors (Legal and Democratic Services): Mrs Jacqueline Margaret Buchanan, Ms Jennifer Burns, Miss Marie Pauline Callander, Mrs Lesley Law, Miss Elaine Longwill, Miss Tina Magson, Miss Lynsey Isabel McLeod, Mr John Gary Munro, Mrs Claire Lynn Richardson, Mr Akemkar Singh, Mr David Joseph Thompson, Mrs Ngozi Elizabeth Vincent-Eloagu, Mrs Alison Watson, Mr Andrew George Wyse

Argyll and Bute Council

Kilmory, Lochgilphead PA31 8RT Tel: (01546) 605522 DX: 599700 Lochgilphead Email: enquiries@argyll-bute.gov.uk Website: www.argyll-bute.gov.uk
The area comprises: Argyll and Bute District Council; Strathclyde electoral divisions 7 (Helensburgh) and 8 (Vale of Leven – part)
Solicitors (Quality Assurance Unit Community Services): Mr Douglas MacNicol Hendry, Mrs Anne Elizabeth MacColl-Smith
Solicitors (Legal and Regulatory Support): Mr Gordon Paul Dagleish, Mr Iain Alexander Jackson, Mrs Emma Christina Ledsom, Mr David McDiarmid Logan, Mrs Moira Catherine Logan, Mrs Sheila Margaret MacFadyen, Miss Susan Catherine Mair, Mr Graeme James McMillan, Miss Annette Christiona Weaver
Solicitors (Procurement & Contract Management): Mr Michael John Nicol
Solicitors (Democratic Services & Governance): Ms Fiona Theresa Campbell MacDonald

Clackmannanshire Council

Kilncraigs, Greenside Street, Alloa FK10 1EB Tel: (01259) 450000 Email: customerservice@clacks.gov.uk Website: www.clacks.gov.uk
The area comprises: The County of Clackmannanshire
Solicitors: Mr Dale Brian Bell, Mrs Heather Anne Buchanan, Mr Saul Morgan Milne, Mrs Lee Elizabeth Robertson, Mr Richard John Thompson

Comhairle nan Eilean Siar

Sandwick Road, Stornoway HS1 2BW
Tel: (01851) 600 501 Email:
enquiries@cne-siar.gov.uk Website:
www.cne-siar.gov.uk

Council Offices:
Balivanich, Isle of Benbecula HS7 5LA; Tel: 01870
602425 Email: enquiries@cne-siar.gov.uk
Old Primary School, West Tarbert, Isle of Harris
HS3 3BG; Tel: 01859 502367 Email:
enquiries@cne-siar.gov.uk
Castlebay, Isle of Barra HS9 5XD; Tel: 01871
810431 Email: enquiries@cne-siar.gov.uk

The area comprises The Western Isles: Isle of
Lewis, Isle of Harris, Isle of Benbecula, Isle of
Barra
Solicitors: Mr Malcolm Burr, Mr Timothy Isaac
Langley, Mr Allan Joseph MacDonald, Mr Iain
Ronald Maclean, Miss Sheekha Saha

Dumfries and Galloway Council

Council HQ, English Street, Dumfries DG1 2DD
Tel: 030 33 33 3000 DX: 580642 Dumfries
Email: contact@dumgal.gov.uk Website:
www.dumgal.gov.uk

The area comprises: Dumfries and Galloway
Solicitors: Mrs Carolyn Frances Cowan, Mr Robin
Ian Douglas Fletcher, Mr John Angus
MacEachern, Mrs Kirsteen Yvonne Macintyre, Mr
Marcus Robert Parham, Miss Julie Shannon, Ms
Caroline Anne Treanor, Mrs Laura Currie Caldwell
Whitelaw, Mr Vladimir Ernesto Bujanda-Valiente,
Mrs Jacqueline Holland, Miss Lucy Wenda
Irons-Young

Dundee City Council

Dundee House, 50 North Lindsay Street, Dundee
DD1 1QE Tel: (01382) 434000 Email:
customerservices@dundeecity.gov.uk Website:
www.dundeecity.gov.uk
Solicitors: Miss Aysha Anwar, Mrs Jacqueline Bell,
Mrs Pauline Carena, Ms Marjory Elizabeth
Geddes, Mr Kenneth James McKaig, Mr Roger
William Hunter Mennie, Mrs Gemma Elizabeth
Miller, Miss Maureen Moran, Miss Mary Elizabeth
Morrissey, Mr James Alexander Murray, Mrs Julie
Ellen Murray, Mrs Sarah Jane O'Connor, Mrs
Jennifer Elaine Ritchie, Mrs Karen Jane Scouller,
Mr Graeme Samuel Smillie, Mr Brian Woodcock

East Ayrshire Council

Council Headquarters, London Road, Kilmarnock
KA3 7BU Tel: (01563) 554400 DX: KK23
Kilmarnock (Receipt only) Website:
www.east-ayrshire.gov.uk
The area comprises: former Kilmarnock and
Loudoun, Cumnock and Doon Valley Districts
Solicitors: Mr Gordon James Anderson, Mr
Richard Alasdair Crawford, Miss Rosemary

Dornan Duffy, Miss Avril Agnes Elizabeth Forrest,
Mrs Claire Linda Gregory, Mr Stuart McCall, Mrs
Tamara Elizabeth Mae McQuade, Mr David John
Mitchell, Ms Michelle Audrey Mooney, Miss Julie
Anne Nicholson, Miss Donna Ann Phelps, Miss
Sarah Leanne Thomson, Mr Alexander Craig
Young

East Dunbartonshire Council

12 Strathkelvin Place, Kirkintilloch G66 1TJ
Tel: (0300) 1234510 Email:
customerservices@eastdunbarton.gov.uk Website:
www.eastdunbarton.gov.uk
The area comprises: in the County of Dumbarton
the burghs of Bearsden, Kirkintilloch, Milngavie
and those parts of the electoral divisions of
Twechar and Waterside lying outwith the
designated area of Cumbernauld New Town; in
the County of the Barony and Regality of
Glasgow the burgh of Bishopbriggs; in the
county of Stirling the Western No3 district.
Solicitors: Mr Thomas Bissett, Mrs Lynsey Clare
Brown, Mrs Mhairi Casey, Miss Karen Marie
Donnelly, Ms Roslyn MacDonald, Miss Eilidh
MacQuarrie, Mrs Caroline Magowan, Mr Andrew
Kenneth McLaughlin, Mr George McLaughlin,
Miss Cecilia Miller, Mrs Ann Marie Minty, Mrs
Jane Mai O'Connell, Miss Justine Jennifer Porter,
Mr Craig William Smith, Mr Andrew Patrick
Kearns Walker

East Lothian Council

John Muir House, Brewery Park, Haddington
EH41 3HA Tel: (01620) 827827 Email:
customerservices@eastlothian.gov.uk Website:
www.eastlothian.gov.uk
The area comprises: Dunbar, Musselburgh, North
Berwick, Prestonpans, Tranent
Dunbar area office: The Bleachfield Centre,
Countess Crescent EH42 1DX
Musselburgh area office: Brunton Hall, Ladywell
Way EH21 6AF
North Berwick area office: North Berwick Shared
Facility, School Road EH39 4JU
Prestonpans area office: Aldhammer House, High
Street EH32 9SH
Tranent area office: The George Johnstone
Centre, 35 Winton Place EH33 1AE
Solicitors: Mr Donald Malcolm Campbell, Miss
Keren Louise Conway, Mrs Morag Ferguson, Mr
Ian Alexander Forrest, Mr Carlo Domenico Grilli,
Miss Fariha Haque, Miss Marielle Elizabeth
Hunter, Ms Catherine Mary Molloy, Mrs Louise
Shearer

East Renfrewshire Council

Council Headquarters, Eastwood Park, Rouken
Glen Road, Giffnock G46 6UG Tel: (0141) 577
3000 DX: 501600 Giffnock Email:
customerservices@eastrenfrewshire.gov.uk
Website: www.eastrenfrewshire.gov.uk

The area comprises: the former Eastwood District Council; Strathclyde electoral division 79 (Barrhead)
Solicitors: Mr Joseph George Abrami, Miss Apryl Chalmers, Mrs Janice Mackay, Mr Gerard James Mahon, Mrs Jacqueline McCusker, Mrs Marie Julie Paterson, Miss Katherine Jane Robb, Miss Siobhan Wilson

City of Edinburgh Council

Council Headquarters, City Chambers, High Street, Edinburgh EH1 1YJ Tel: (0131) 200 2000 Email: myedinburgh@edinburgh.gov.uk Website: www.edinburgh.gov.uk
The area comprises: Edinburgh, Currie, Ratho, Balerno, Kirkliston, Dalmeny, Newbridge, South Queensferry.

Administrative Headquarters:
4 East Market Street, Edinburgh EH8 8BG
Solicitors (Legal & Risk): Miss Amy Meadows Alexander, Ms Caitlin Janina Allan, Mr Euan George Bathgate, Mr Matthew Robert Clarke, Mrs Morven Kirsty Coulter, Miss Ailsa McLaren Cunningham, Miss Margaret Catherine Deane, Mrs Abigail Laura Drummond, Miss Alison Falconer, Mrs Shabnam Faqir, Mrs Charlotte Mary Todd Fleming, Miss Charlotte Louise Flood, Mr Nicholas Jonathan Fraser, Miss Amy Mairead Hitchin Hood, Mr Alexander Hugh Richard Irvine, Mr Keith Brian Irwin, Mrs Morag Anne Leck, Miss Sheila Jane Mackintosh, Mr Stephen Michael McCaig, Miss Anna Rose McKay, Mr Kevin Joseph McKee, Miss Margaret Jean Elizabeth McLaren, Ms Nicola Dee McLaren, Mrs Jennifer Anne Moir, Mr Graham Douglas Nelson, Mr Kevin Scott Paterson, Mrs Judith Jane Peacock, Miss Fiona Emma Ross, Mrs Hannah Beverley Ross, Mr Craig Scott Russell, Mr Nicholas Scott Smith, Mrs Stefanie Thomson, Mr Simon Daniel Todd, Mrs Julia Claire Donnetta Walker, Mr Iain Andrew Wallace

Falkirk Council

Municipal Buildings, West Bridge Street, Falkirk FK1 5RS Tel: (01324) 506070 Email: contact.centre@falkirk.gov.uk Website: www.falkirk.gov.uk
The area comprises: former Falkirk District Council Area

Solicitors (Corporate and Housing Services):
Ms Wendy Margaret Barber, Mr Douglas Blyth, Mrs Eilean Margaret Anne Duncan, Mr Peter James Farquhar, Miss Claire Gillan, Mr Iain Wallace Henderson, Ms Rose Mary Hoey, Miss Jessica Alice Knight, Mrs Frances Mary Kobiela, Mr Colin Douglas Moodie, Mr Alexander Joseph Muir, Mr Alan Peebles, Mrs Karen Anne Quin, Miss Iona Joyce Bell Rodgers, Mr Alistair George Steel, Mrs Julie Anne White

Fife Council

Fife House, North Street, Glenrothes KY7 5LT Tel: (03451) 550000 DX: 561502 Glenrothes 3 Email: fife.council@fife.gov.uk Website: www.fife.gov.uk
Fife Comprises the former County of Fife
Solicitors: Mrs Sarah Louise Goldberg
Solicitors (Finance and Corporate Services):
Mrs June Anne Barrie, Miss Lynda Anne Batchelor, Mr Philip Robert Blair, Mr Christopher William Glendinning, Miss Alison Elizabeth Higgins, Miss Rebecca Louise Jeynes, Mrs Kimberley Patricia Langley, Mr Neil Iain Macdonald, Mrs Alison Clare Marr, Mr William McDonald, Mrs Margaret Josephine Bannon McFadden, Mrs Kerry McLaren, Miss Mary Elizabeth Ritchie McLean, Mr Steven John Paterson, Mr Ewen Graham Robertson, Miss Sheila Rodger, Mr Calum Morrison Ross, Ms Lindsay Margaret Thomson, Mrs Uzma Yasir

Glasgow City Council

City Chambers, George Square, Glasgow G2 1DU Tel: (0141) 287 2000 DX: GW145 Glasgow Website: www.glasgow.gov.uk
The area comprises: City of Glasgow District Council except Strathclyde electoral divisions 37 (Rutherglen/Fernhill), 38 (Cambuslang/Halfway) and 35 (King's Park/Toryglen – part)
Solicitors (Corporate Services): Ms Pauline Marie Bradshaw, Miss Sarah Shirley Douglas Davidson, Miss Victoria Mary Hyndman, Miss Lauren Margaret Anne Reid
Solicitors (Chief Executives Department):
Miss Judith Sharon Abrahamson, Mr Stephen David Annis, Miss Shahana Andaleeb Arshad, Miss Ikra Kausar Bhatti, Miss Lee Cormack, Miss Fiona Elizabeth Coulter, Mr Ronan James Cunning, Ms Amanda Mary Cunningham, Miss Victoria Eve Curran, Ms Maria-Claire Cushley, Mr Patrick Daniel Docherty, Mr Raymond Farrell, Mrs Jennifer Gail Forsyth, Miss Elaine Clare Galletly, Mrs Heather Margaret George, Miss Clare Marie Gribbon, Miss Zara Amber Heaney, Mrs Irene Kyle Hemfrey, Ms Deborah Elise Henderson, Miss Gillian Ingram, Miss Yvonne Jackson, Mr Paul Latta, Mrs Ruth Denise MacColl, Mrs Gillian Elizabeth MacEachen, Mr Roderick William Maciver, Mr David John Mair, Miss Tracey Ann McAleese, Mr Martin Fitzgerald McColgan, Mr Kenneth McDonald, Mrs Anne Janet McFarlane, Mr Kevin McGinnes, Miss Louise Elizabeth McHugh, Ms Christine Helen McInnes, Mr Peter Grant McKechnie, Miss Mary Josephine McKelvie, Mrs Eileen McLaughlin, Miss Jennifer Ann McMartin, Miss Gillian McNaught, Mr Donald Andrew McPartlin, Dr Kenneth Alastair Meechan, Mr James Alexander Meneely, Ms Mairi Davidson Millar, Mr Iain Lindsay Miller, Miss Michelle Murphy, Ms Annemarie O'Donnell, Mrs Gillian O'Neil, Miss Shirley-Ann Rhynd, Mrs Eleanor Ramage Macdonald Richards, Miss Becky

Elizabeth Robertson, Miss Kristine Elizabeth Robinson, Ms Jillian Amanda Rodgers, Miss Sanaa Shahid, Miss Gurnish Kaur Sidhu, Ms Fiona May Simpson, Mrs Iulia Toch, Ms Lauren Towie, Miss Fiona Jane Traill, Mrs Samerah Ul-Hassan, Mr Mark Farrel Wallace, Mr Alan Martin Wright, Mr Andrew Wright

Highland Council

The Highland Council Headquarters, Glenurquhart Road, Inverness IV3 5NX Tel: (01463) 702000 Website: www.highland.gov.uk
The area comprises: Highland Council, and the districts of Badenoch and Strathspey, Caithness, Inverness, Lochaber, Nairn, Ross and Cromarty, Skye and Lochalsh and Sutherland
Solicitors (Chief Executives Department): Mrs Karen Lyons, Mr Jonathan Paul Harper Nevin
Solicitors (Council Offices): Miss Claire Margaret McArthur, Mr Iain Paul Meredith, Mrs Shona Ann Pottinger
Solicitors (Townhouse): Mr David Milton Haas
Solicitors (Corporate Governance): Miss Nicola Bain, Ms Theresa Alison Batchelor, Miss Rhoda Nyaaba Banfro, Miss Jane Elizabeth Davey, Miss Anne Fearon David, Mrs Sarah Lucia Duncan, Mr Stewart David Fraser, Mrs Tessa Iona Arbuthnot Gall, Mrs Emma Anne Linn, Mrs Fiona Janine Malcolm, Miss Amy Rebecca Noble, Miss Alison Mary Scullion, Ms Kirsty Jane Shaw, Mrs Nicola Edna Underdown

Inverclyde Council

Municipal Buildings, Clyde Square, Greenock PA15 1LY Tel: (01475) 717171 Email: customerservice@inverclyde.gov.uk Website: www.inverclyde.gov.uk
This area comprises: Inverclyde
Solicitors: Mr Jonathan Philip Hamilton, Mr Martin Francis Hughes, Mr David Douglas Keenan, Mr James Kerr, Mr Peter John MacDonald, Miss Siobhan MacMaster, Mrs Denese O'Donnell, Miss Emma Peacock, Miss Victoria Mary Pollock, Miss Anne Margaret Sinclair, Mr Iain David Strachan, Mr Grant Kyle Walker

Midlothian Council

Midlothian House, 40-46 Buccleuch Street, Dalkeith EH22 1DN Tel: (0131) 270 7500 Email: enquiries@midlothian.gov.uk Website: www.midlothian.gov.uk
The area comprises: Midlothian Council
Buccleuch House:
1 – 7 White Hart Street, Dalkeith Midlothian EH22 1AE Tel: 0131 270 7500
Fairfield House:
8 Lothian Road, Dalkeith, Midlothian EH22 3AA Tel: 0131 270 7500
Solicitors: Miss Holy Lewis, Mrs Jane Scott McLeish, Miss Emma Marguerite Padden, Miss

Suzanne Anderson Ross, Mr Lindsay George Thomson, Mr Alan Leonard Turpie, Mr William Venters

Moray Council

High Street, Elgin IV30 1BX Tel: (01343) 543451 DX: 520666 Elgin Email: access.point@moray.gov.uk Website: www.moray.gov.uk
The area comprises: The Moray Council – Buckie, Elgin, Forres, Keith.
Buckie: 13 Cluny Square, Buckie AB56 1AJ Tel: 01343 543451
Elgin: High Street, Elgin IV30 1BX Tel: 01343 543451
Forres: Forres Library, Forres House, High Street, Forres IV36 1BU Tel: 01343 543451
Keith: The Resource Centre, 26 Mid Street, Keith AB55 5AH Tel: 01542 885102
Solicitors: Mrs Georgina Ann Anderson, Mr Sean Andrew Hoath, Mr Alasdair John Stewart McEachan, Mr Neil Lachlan McGlinchey, Miss Sana Sarwar, Mrs Aileen Scott, Miss Jennifer Fiona Smith, Ms Morag Jane Smith

North Ayrshire Council

Cunninghame House, Irvine KA12 8EE Tel: (01294) 310000 DX: IR 11 Irvine Email: contactus@north-ayrshire.gov.uk Website: www.north-ayrshire.gov.uk
The area comprises: Cunninghame District Council
Customer Service Centres:
Bridgegate House, Irvine KA12 8BD
The Town Hall, Saltcoats KA21 5HW
Brooksby Medical & Resource Centre, 31 Brisbane Road, Largs KA30 8LH
Solicitors (Corporate Services): Miss Rosemary Conner, Mrs Jennifer Claire Coyne, Mrs Aileen Mary Craig, Mr David Robert Grier, Mrs Lauren Marie Ingram, Miss Claire Bernadette Kierney, Miss Jean Hamilton Law, Mr David McDowall, Mrs Kris Reid McDowall, Mrs Jennifer Linda Niven, Mr William Henry O'Brien, Miss Madeleine Jane Pender, Miss Nicola Carson Shearer, Ms Linda Joyce Taylor, Mrs Carolyn Anne Wallace, Mrs Ruth Mary Wilson

North Lanarkshire Council

Civic Centre (Council headquarters), Windmillhill Street, Motherwell ML1 1AB Tel: (01698) 403200 DX: 571701 Motherwell 2 Website: www.northlanarkshire.gov.uk
This area comprises: Cumbernauld and Kilsyth, Motherwell and Monklands District Councils; Strathclyde electoral division 46 (Chryston-part)
Northline Contact Centre, 52-60 Merry Street, Motherwell ML1 1LZ
Municipal Buildings, (Learning and Leisure Services), Kildonan Street, Coatbridge ML5 3BT

Fleming House, (Regeneration and Environmental Services), 2 Tryst Road, Cumbernauld G67 1JW
Scott House, (Housing and Social Work Services), 73-77 Merry Street, Motherwell ML1 1JE
Solicitors (Corporate Services): Mr Archibald Henry Aitken, Miss Raksana Akhtar, Miss Gillian Emma Allan, Mrs Rachel Elizabeth McLeod Blair, Mrs Colette Anne Cameron, Mr James Paul Kennedy Corrigan, Mrs Heather Elizabeth Cox, Mrs Fiona Sinclair Nicolson Ekinli, Miss Alison Mary Gallacher, Mr Paul Gerard Guidi, Mr Mark Thomas Henderson, Ms Leanne Claire Joss, Miss Jane Baxter Kirkhope, Mrs Nicola Lauchlan, Mrs Isabel Graham Lawton, Mrs Maud Cecilia Lithgow, Mr John Anthony McCluskey, Miss Collette Frances McFarlane, Miss Shafana Raza, Miss Jill Rogerson, Miss Evelyn Ross, Mrs Joanne Saunders, Miss Jillian Deborah Spilg, Ms Fiona Ann Stewart, Mrs Caley Jane Toner

Orkney Islands Council

Council Offices, School Place, Kirkwall KW15 1NY Tel: (01856) 873535 Email: customerservice@orkney.gov.uk Website: www.orkney.gov.uk
The area comprises: Orkney Islands Council
Solicitors (Legal Services): Ms Karen Frankish Bevilacqua, Mrs Emma Louise Findlay, Miss Georgette Herd, Mr Paul Dominic Maxton, Miss Katharine Elizabeth Seymour McKerrell, Mr Gavin Rattray Mitchell, Mr Michael Sydney William Scott, Mr Peter Francis Trodden, Ms Sheila Mary Tulloch

Perth and Kinross Council

Pullar House, 35 Kinnoull Street, Perth PH1 5GD Tel: (01738) 475000 DX: PE28 Perth Website: www.pkc.gov.uk
The area comprises: Perth and Kinross District Council and Tayside electoral division 31 (Sidlaw – part)
Solicitors: Miss Lynne Sarah Clark, Mr Lee Donald Coulter, Mr Colin David Elliott, Mr Geoffrey David Fogg, Mr Adam James Heath, Miss Helen Mary Anne Johnstone, Mr Bernard MacFarlane, Mr Patrick Guermont Mair, Mrs Moina Kassandra McLaren, Mr Stuart Alan McQueen, Mrs Deborah Alison Robertson, Mrs Sarah-Louise Rodger, Miss Lisa Simpson, Mr Andrew William Thomson

Renfrewshire Council

Customer Service Centre, Renfrewshire House, Cotton Street, Paisley PA1 1AN Tel: (0300) 300 0300 DX: 590702 Paisley 3 (Legal Services) Email: customerservices.contact@renfrewshire.gov.uk Website: www.renfrewshire.gov.uk
The area comprises: Renfrew District Council except Strathclyde electoral division 79 (Barrhead)

Solicitors (Chief Executive Services): Mrs Barbara Margaret Ellen Walker
Solicitors (Finance and Resources): Mrs Christine Murray Adam, Mrs Allison Elizabeth Black, Mrs Dorothy Anne Chalmers Briggs, Mrs Gemma Frances Cameron, Miss Eilidh Clements, Mr Mark John Conaghan, Mrs Amy Jane Frances Cook, Mrs Margaret Robins Craig, Miss Lesley Ann Currie, Mr Ross Calum Graham, Mrs Irene Margaret Halpin, Ms Laura-Ann Claire Michelle Lilburn, Mr Declan MacAskill, Miss Emma Margaret Mary McBride, Mr Ross Kenneth McGinness, Miss Lynn Catherine Mitchell, Ms Bernadette O'Neill, Mrs Christine Anne Panton, Miss Evelyn Margaret Pinkerton, Mrs Veronika Prag, Ms Gemma Rose Macgregor Thomson, Mr Nairn Robert Young

Scottish Borders Council

Council Headquarters, Newtown St Boswells, Melrose TD6 0SA Tel: (0300) 100 1800 Email: customeradvice@scotborders.gov.uk Website: www.scotborders.gov.uk
The area comprises: the area of the former Borders Regional Council
Solicitors: Mr Scott Michael Archibald, Mr Iain Finlay Davidson, Miss Christina Donald, Mr Ronald Adam Kirk, Mrs Hannah Elizabeth MacLeod, Mrs Rebecca Helen McDonald, Mrs Nuala Bernadette McKinlay, Miss Lauren Margaret Mitchell, Mr Fraser Donald Moore Rankine, Mrs Gillian Christine Sellar, Mrs Sarah Marie Thompson, Ms Diane Margaret Jane Webster

Shetland Islands Council

Town Hall, Lerwick ZE1 0HB Tel: (01595) 693535 Email: info@shetland.gov.uk Website: www.shetland.gov.uk
The area comprises: Shetland Islands Council
Solicitors (Governance and Law): Mr David Keith Adam, Miss Joanna Margaret Belford, Mr Michael James Hodgson, Mrs Kristen Jane Johnston, Miss Charlotte Stephen McAuley Jones, Ms Caroline Margaret Laing, Mr Jan-Robert Riise, Mrs Karen Emily Simmons, Mr Paul Edward Ferguson Wishart

South Ayrshire Council

County Buildings, Wellington Square, Ayr KA7 1DR Tel: (0300) 123 0900 Email: customerservices@south-ayrshire.gov.uk Website: www.south-ayrshire.gov.uk
The area comprises: the former Kyle and Carrick District Council
Solicitors (Legal and Licensing Services): Mrs Karen Boyd Briggs, Miss Ruth Alexandra Burley, Mrs Wynne Stewart Carlaw, Mrs Catriona Jane Caves, Mrs Morag Simpson Douglas, Mrs Margaret Anne Horsley, Miss Simone Mairi Lucas-Broadley, Miss Deirdre Victoria Una Mackintosh, Miss Laura Anne McChristie, Miss Christine McMenamin,

Mrs Lorraine McPartlin, Mrs Claire Helen Neillie, Miss Fiona Campbell Ross of Ross, Miss Emma Victoria Louise Stevenson, Miss Margaret Agnes Jamieson Vance, Mr Gavin Thomas Whyte

South Lanarkshire Council
Council Offices, Almada Street, Hamilton ML3 0AA Tel: (0303) 1231015 DX: HA35
Website: www.southlanarkshire.gov.uk
The area comprises: Clydesdale, Hamilton, East Kilbride, Cambuslang and Rutherglen.
Solicitors: Mrs Mary Geraldine McCann
Solicitors (Administration and Legal Services):
Mr Michael John Barrett, Mrs Monica Eleanor Cannon, Mr Alan Bryce Cox, Mr Kevin John McInnes Goldie, Mrs Gillian Gray, Mr Harry David Horsburgh, Miss Marie Clare Lunny, Mr Donald Patrick McLardy, Mr Graham Stewart Murray, Mr Sean Adam O'Neill, Miss Jennifer Elizabeth Margaret Wallace
Solicitors (Legal Services): Mrs Susan Christie, Mrs Daryle Anne Dickson, Mr William Alexander Dunn, Mr Gerard Charles Mays, Miss Elaine Alexandria Paton, Mrs Claire Margaret Rogers, Miss Maria Therese Sharkey, Mr Gordon John Stewart, Mrs Avril Elaine Watkins, Mrs Nicola Jane Weir, Mrs Margaret Mary Wilson

Stirling Council
Viewforth, 14-20 Pitt Terrace, Stirling FK8 2ET
Tel: (01786) 404040 Website:
https://www.stirling.gov.uk/
The area comprises: the District of Stirling
Solicitors (Legal Services): Mr Mark Alexander Easton, Mrs Claire Louise Ferguson, Mr Graeme Bruce Forrester, Mr Ewan Alastair Grant, Mr Charles John Haggerty, Mrs Julia Anne McAfee, Mr Paul McCandlish, Mrs Julia Rose Mountford, Ms Carla Joy Roth

West Dunbartonshire Council
Council Offices, 16 Church Street, Dumbarton G82 1QL Tel: (01389) 738282 Website:
www.west-dunbarton.gov.uk
The area comprises: Clydebank District Council; Strathclyde electoral divisions 6 (Dumbarton) and 8 (Vale of Leven – part)
Clydebank Office: Clydebank Town Centre Office, 10 Sylvania Way South, Clydebank, G81 1EA
Solicitors (Legal Services, Regulatory and Regeneration): Mr Christopher Edward Anderson, Mr Alan Shaw Douglas, Mr Nigel William Ettles, Mrs Maureen Teresa Hastings, Mr Peter David Hessett, Miss Valerie Love, Mr Raymond James Lynch, Mrs Kimberley McCallum, Mrs Sally Jane Michael, Miss Heather Lorna Campbell Milne, Mr John Paul Mitchell, Mr Gavin Walsh

West Lothian Council
West Lothian Civic Centre, Howden South Road, Livingston EH54 6FF Tel: (01506) 280000

Website: www.westlothian.gov.uk
The area comprises: West Lothian
Solicitors (Corporate/Support/Legal Services):
Mrs Eleanor Ann Campbell, Miss Jessica Sen Tin Chan, Ms Catherine Margaret Crowe, Ms Eileen Cameron Grant, Miss Nicola Marianne Hogg, Miss Carol Grant Johnston, Miss Sarah-Jane Kissock, Mr Gary James McMullan, Mr James David Millar, Mrs Lesley Mary Montague, Miss Kerri Ann Murphy, Mrs Wendy Margaret Richardson, Mrs Audrey Frances Watson

Western Isles Council
See Comhairle nan Eilean Siar

Licensing Boards

Aberdeen City Licensing Board
Legal Services Aberdeen City Council, Business Hub 6 L1S, Marischal College, Broad Street, Aberdeen AB10 1AB Tel: (01224) 522449 DX: AB529450 Aberdeen-9 Email: licensing@aberdeencity.gov.uk Website: https://www.aberdeencity.gov.uk/services/business-and-licensing/licences-and-permits/licensing-board
Solicitors: John Simpson Forsyth, Karen Wilkie, Alexander Munro

Aberdeenshire Licensing Board
Woodhill House, Westburn Road, Aberdeen AB16 5GB Tel: (03456) 08 12 08 Email: licensing@aberdeenshire.gov.uk Website: www.aberdeenshire.gov.uk/licensing
Solicitors: Geraldine Margaret Fraser, , Ruth Elizabeth O'Hare, Martin Ingram, Lauren Jacquelene Cowie, Aberdeenshire Council, Woodhill House, Westburn Road, Aberdeen AB16 5GB

North and Central Board Areas – Banff Town House, Low Street, Banff AB45 1AU Tel: 01261 813530 Buchan House, St. Peter Street, Peterhead AB42 1DA

Central Board Area – Gordon House, Blackhall Road, Inverurie AB51 3WA Tel: 01467 628436

South Board Area – Viewmount, Arduthie Road, Stonehaven AB39 2DQ Tel: 01569 768223

Angus Licensing Board
Angus Council, Angus House, Orchardbank Business Park, Forfar DD8 1AN Tel: (03452) 777 778 Email: LAWLicensing@angus.gov.uk Website: www.angus.gov.uk
Solicitors: Andrew George Wyse, John Gary Munro, Lynsay Isabel McLeod, Anne Janette McKeown

Argyll and Bute Licensing Board
Governance and Law, Argyll and Bute Council, Kilmory, Lochgilphead PA 31 8RT Tel: (01546) 604128 Email: licensing@argyll-bute.gov.uk Website: www.argyll-bute.gov.uk/law-and-licensing/argyll-and-bute-licensing-board-0
Solicitors: Douglas MacNicol Hendry, Sheila Margaret MacFadyen

Clackmannanshire Licensing Board
Development & Environment Services, Kilncraigs, Greenside Street, Alloa FK10 1EB Tel: (01259) 452093 / 450000
Fax: (01259) 452230 DX: 560436 Alloa Email: licensing@clacks.gov.uk Website: www.clacks.gov.uk/regulation/

Comhairle nan Eilean Siar Licensing Board
Sandwick Road, Stornoway HS1 2BW
Tel: (01851) 600501
Fax: (01851) 705349 Email: enquiries@cne-siar.gov.uk Website: www.cne-siar.gov.uk

Dumfries and Galloway Licensing Boards
Municipal Chambers, Buccleuch Street, Dumfries DG1 2AD Tel: 030 33 33 3000 Email: licensing@dumgal.gov.uk Website: www.dumgal.gov.uk
Solicitors: Mr Vladimir Ernesto Bujanda-Valiente

Dundee Licensing Board
The Licensing Section, Dundee City Council, 20 City Square, Dundee DD1 3BY Tel: (01382) 434499 Email: licensing.board@dundeecity.gov.uk Website: www.dundeecity.gov.uk
Solicitors: Jacqueline Bell, Brian Woodcock

East Ayrshire Licensing Board
London Road, Kilmarnock KA3 7BU Tel: (01563) 576005 DX: KK23 Kilmarnock (receipt only) Email: licensing@east-ayrshire.gov.uk Website: www.east-ayrshire.gov.uk/LawAndLicensing/Law-and-licensing.aspx
Solicitors: David John Mitchell

East Dunbartonshire Licensing Board
12 Strathkelvin Place, Kirkintilloch G66 1TJ
Tel: (0141) 578 8319
Fax: (0141) 578 8468 DX: 500832 KIRKINTILLOCH Email: liquor.licensing@eastdunbarton.gov.uk Website: www.eastdunbarton.gov.uk/content/law_and_licensing/licences_permits_permissions/licensing_board.aspx
Solicitors: Karen Marie Donnelly

East Lothian Licensing Board
John Muir House, Brewery Park, Haddington EH41 3HA Tel: (01620) 827867
Fax: (01620) 827253 Email: licensing@eastlothian.gov.uk Website: www.eastlothian.gov.uk/meetings/committee/53/east_lothian_licensing_board
Solicitors: Morag Ferguson

East Renfrewshire Licensing Board

Council Headquarters, Eastwood Park, Rouken Glen Road, Giffnock G46 6UG Tel: (0141) 577 3005 DX: 501600 Giffnock Email: customerservices@eastrenfrewshire.gov.uk Website: www.eastrenfrewshire.gov.uk/article/2074/Licensing-Board
Solicitors: Jacqueline McCusker, Siobhan Wilson

Edinburgh Licensing Board

249 High Street, Edinburgh EH1 1YJ Tel: (0131) 529 4208
Fax: (0131) 529 4207 Email: licensing@edinburgh.gov.uk Website: www.edinburgh.gov.uk/info/20023/licences_and_permits/960/licensing_board
Solicitors: Nicholas Jonathan Fraser, Graham Douglas Nelson

Falkirk Licensing Board

District Court Offices, Municipal Buildings, West Bridge Street, Falkirk FK1 5RS Tel: (01324) 501575 Email: licensing@falkirk.gov.uk Website: www.falkirk.gov.uk/services/law-licensing/licensing/alcohol/licensing-board/
Solicitors: Frances Mary Kobiela

Fife Licensing Board

Fife House, North Street, Glenrothes KY7 5LT Tel: (03451) 551177 Email: glenrothesarea.lsc@fife.gov.uk Website: www.fifedirect.org.uk/news/index.cfm?fuseaction=committee.detail&servid=1F953986-FE8E-5E82-0B9A03ADFCA643DC
Solicitors: June Anne Barrie, William McDonald

City of Glasgow Licensing Board

Licensing Section, City Chambers, Glasgow G2 1DU Tel: (0141) 287 5354
Fax: (0141) 287 5357 DX: GW145 Glasgow Email: LicensingBoard@glasgow.gov.uk Website: www.glasgow.gov.uk
Solicitors: Gillian Elizabeth MacEachen, Mairi Davidson Millar, Iain Lindsay Miller, Patrick Daniel Docherty, Lee Cormack

Highland Licensing Board

The Highland Council Headquarters, Glenurquhart Road, Inverness IV3 5NX Tel: (01349) 886609 Email: licensing@highland.gov.uk Website: https://www.highland.gov.uk/info/1125/licences_permits_and_permissions/304/licensing_offices
Solicitors: Claire Margaret McArthur, Ian Paul Meredith
Caithness, Sutherland and Easter Ross – Council Offices, Caithness House, Market Place, Wick KW1 4AB
Sutherland and Easter Ross – Main Street, Golspie KW10 6RB

Ross Area – High Street, Dingwall IV15 9QN
Skye Area – Tigh Na Sgire, Park Lane, Portree IV51 9GP
Lochaber – Lochaber House, High Street, Fort William PH33 6EL
South – Town House, Inverness IV1 1JJ

Inverclyde Licensing Board

Customer Service Centre, Municipal Buildings, Clyde Square, Greenock PA15 1LY Tel: (01475) 717171 Email: licensing.section@inverclyde.gov.uk Website: www.inverclyde.gov.uk/law-and-licensing/licensing

Midlothian Licensing Board

Midlothian House, Buccleuch Street, Dalkeith EH22 1DN Tel: (0131) 2707500 Email: licensing@midlothian.gov.uk Website: www.midlothian.gov.uk/info/200269/licences_and_permits/404/licensing_board
Solicitors: William Venters

Moray Licensing Board

Moray Council, Council Office, High Street, Elgin IV30 1BX Tel: (01343) 563030
Fax: (01343) 540183 DX: 520666 Elgin Email: licensing@moray.gov.uk Website: www.moray.gov.uk/moray_standard/page_67620.html
Solicitors: Sean Andrew Heath

North Ayrshire Licensing Board

Licensing Section, Legal Services, North Ayrshire Council, Cunninghame House, Irvine KA12 8EE Tel: (01294) 324305 Email: licensing@north-ayrshire.gov.uk Website: www.north-ayrshire.gov.uk/business/licences-and-permits/food-alcohol-gambling-licences/licensing-board.aspx
Solicitors: Ruth Mary Wilson, William Henry O'Brian

North Lanarkshire Licensing Board

Civic Centre, Windmillhill Street, Motherwell ML1 1AB Tel: (01698) 302459
Fax: (01698) 302211 DX: 571702 MOTHERWELL 2 Email: wortonj@northlan.gov.uk Website: www.northlanarkshire.gov.uk/index.aspx?articleid=20112
Solicitors: John Anthony McCluskey

Orkney Islands Area Licensing Board

Licensing Team, Council Offices, Kirkwall KW15 1NY Tel: (01856) 873535 Email: licensing@orkney.gov.uk Website: www.orkney.gov.uk/Service-Directory/L/Law-and-Licensing.htm
Solicitors: Georgette Herd

Perth and Kinross Licensing Board

Pullar House, 35 Kinnoull Street, Perth PH1 5GD
Tel: (01738) 475167 Email:
liquorlicensing@pkc.gov.uk Website:
www.pkc.gov.uk/article/1658/
Licences-permits-and-permissions
Solicitors: Sarah-Louise Rodger, Colin David
Elliott, Stuart Alan McQueen

Renfrewshire Licensing Board

Licensing Section, Renfrewshire House, Cotton
Street, Paisley PA1 1TT Tel: (0300) 300 0300
DX: 590702 Paisley-3 Email:
licensing.cs@renfrewshire.gov.uk Website:
www.renfrewshire.gov.uk
Solicitors: Mark John Conaghan, Lara Macaulay
Stimpson, Douglas John Campbell, Ross Calum
Graham

Scottish Borders Licensing Board

Council Headquarters, Newtown St Boswells,
Melrose TD6 0SA Tel: (01835) 826662
Fax: (01835) 826693 Website:
www.scotborders.gov.uk/info/1125/
licences_permits_and_permissions/88/licences
Solicitors: Ronald Adam Kirk

Shetland Islands Area Licensing Board

Governance & Law, c/o Town Hall, Lerwick
ZE1 0HB Tel: (01595) 744067 / 744091 Email:
legal.services@shetland.gov.uk Website:
www.shetland.gov.uk
Solicitors: Paul Edward Ferguson Wishart

South Ayrshire Licensing Board

Licensing, County Buildings, Wellington Square,
Ayr KA7 1DR Tel: (01292) 617683 DX: AY72 Ayr
Email: licensing@south-ayrshire.gov.uk Website:
www.south-ayrshire.gov.uk/licensing
Solicitors: Morag Simpson Douglas, Emma
Victoria Louise Stevenson, Karen Boyd Briggs

South Lanarkshire Licensing Divisions

Town House, 102 Cadzow Street, Hamilton
ML3 6HH Tel: (0303) 123 1015
Fax: (01698) 452195 Email:
licensing@southlanarkshire.gov.uk Website:
www.southlanarkshire.gov.uk

Licensing & Registration Offices:

Floor 13, Council Offices, Almada Street,
Hamilton ML3 0AA
102 Cadzow Street, Hamilton ML3 6HH
Town Hall, 139 Main Street, Rutherglen, G73 2JJ
Solicitors: Mary Geraldine McCann, Gerard
Charles Mays

Stirling District Licensing Board

Licensing Team, Municipal Buildings, Corn
Exchange Road, Stirling FK8 2HU Tel: (01786)
233612 Email: licensing@stirling.gov.uk Website:
www.stirling.gov.uk/licensing
Solicitors: Charles John Haggerty, Mark Alexander
Easton, Paul McCandlish, Graeme Bruth Forrester

West Dunbartonshire Licensing Board

Legal, Democratic and Regulatory Services,
Municipal Buildings, College Street, Dumbarton
G82 1NR Tel: (01389) 738741
Fax: (01389) 738674 Email:
licensing@west-dunbarton.gov.uk Website:
www.west-dunbarton.gov.uk/council/
west-dunbartonshire-licensing-forum/
Solicitors: Alan Shaw Douglas, Raymond James
Lynch, Nigel William Ettles

West Lothian Licensing Board

West Lothian Civic Centre, Howden Road South,
Livingston EH54 6FF Tel: (01506) 281632
DX: 552560 Livingston 7 Email:
licensingboard@westlothian.gov.uk Website:
www.westlothian.gov.uk/licensing
Solicitors: Gary James McMullen, Carol Grant
Johnston, Audrey Frances Watson

Western Isles Licensing Board

See Comhairle nan Eilean Siar Licensing Board

Faculty of Advocates

Advocates Library, Parliament Square, Edinburgh, EH1 1RF
Tel: 0131 226 5071
DX: 549302 Edinburgh-36
Email: info@advocates.org.uk
Web: www.advocates.org.uk
The following Members of the Faculty, Queen's Counsel, Advocate Stables and Advocate Clerks lists are provided by the Faculty of Advocates and are dated February 2022. At the time of going to press various appointments were in the offering but not confirmed and have therefore not been included. Any inaccuracies in the following lists should be updated with the Faculty of Advocates to ensure such changes are reflected in the lists provided for future editions of the Scottish Law Directory.
Dean of Faculty: Roddy Dunlop, Q.C.
Vice-Dean: Ronnie Renucci, Q.C.
Treasurer: Ruth Crawford, Q.C.
Clerk of Faculty: Richard Pugh
Keeper of the Library: Vacant
Chairman of Faculty Services Limited: Anthony Graham, Q.C.
Chief Executive: Iain Reid

Members of the Faculty
Please note:
Only those Advocates who have a clerk should be contacted at the Advocates Library. The date following the name refers to the year of admission to the Faculty. Members of Faculty who practice at the English Bar are denoted with a *. Those who are admitted to, but do not practice at the English Bar are denoted with a †. The names within the brackets are those of the clerks.

The names within the brackets are those of the Stables and Clerks.

ABERCROMBIE, Sheriff Principal I.R., Q.C., LL.B. (Hons) (1981)
ADAM, Bill R., LL.B.
　[Optimum Advocates] (2003)
ADAMS, David P., LL.B(Hons), Dip LP
　[Compass Chambers] (2018)
AGNEW OF LOCHNAW, Sir Crispin, Bt., Q.C. (1982)
AITKEN, Julian GF., LL.B(Hons), Dip LP
　[Optimum Advocates] (2014)
ALLAN, G.J.G., Q.C., LL.B. (Hons)
　Optimum Advocates (1994)
ALLARDICE, C.T., LL.B. (1990)
ALONZI, Lorenzo, LL.B.
　[Black Chambers] (1990)
ANCRAM, M.A.F.J., B.A., LL.B. (1970)
ANDERSON, David D., LL.B (Hons)
　[Westwater Advocates] (2014)
ANDERSON, G.J., LL.B. (Hons),
　[Compass Chambers] (2001)
ANDERSON, I, LL.B.(Hons), LL.M., LL.B. (1973)
ANDERSON, M.T., LL.B.(Hons) (1997)
ANDERSON, Michael D., LL.B. (Hons),
　[Black Chambers] (2006)
ANDERSON, R.N.M., # C.A., LL.B. (Hons) (1987)
ANDERSON, Rory W.J., Q.C., M.A., LL.B. (1989)
ANDERSON, Ross G., LL.B., Ph.D.,
　[Ampersand] (2013)

ANDERSON, Sheriff Ruth A., Q.C., M.A., M.Phil. (1991)
ANGIOLINI, Q.C., The Rt. Hon. Dame Elish F, D.B.E, Q.C., LL.B. (Hons), (2008)
ANTHONY, R.B., Q.C., LL.B. (1988)
ARDREY, Adam, LL.B. (Hons)
　[Optimum Advocates] (1990)
ARMSTRONG, Donna, BA, LL.B
　[Optimum Advocates] (2014)
ARMSTRONG, Miss Morag E., M.A., LL.B. (1995)
ARMSTRONG, R. Douglas, * Q.C., LL.B. (Hons)
　[Terra Firma Chambers] (1990)
ARMSTRONG, The Hon. Lord Iain G., Q.C., LL.B. (1986)
ARNOTT, Victoria M., LL.B. (Hons) Dip LP
　[Axiom Advocates] (2020)
ARROL, Louise M., LL.B.,
　[Optimum Advocates] (2005)
ARTHURSON, The Hon. Lord (1991)
BAHRAMI Faryma. LL.B (Hons) Dundee, Dip LP (Dundee) LL.M (Glasgow)
　[Terra Firma Advocates] (2015)
BAILLIE, Patricia M., LL.B (Hons)., Dip LP., LL.M
　[Optimum Advocates] (2021)
BAIN, D.K., C.B.E., T.D., LL.B. (1973)
BAIN, Miss Dorothy R., Q.C., LL.B. (1994)
BAIN, Mrs. Jennifer S., B.Sc. (Hons), LL.B.
　[Black Chambers] (2002)
BAIRD, J.A., LL.B.(Hons) (1986)

BALFOUR, G.S., B.A. (Hons), LL.B.,
[Compass Chambers] (2002)
BALLANTYNE, D.F., LL.B.
[Themis Advocates] (1992)
BANNATYNE, The Hon. Lord (1979)
BARBOUR, Melanie J., LL.B. (Hons) Dip LP
[Westwater Advocates] (2020)
BARCLAY, P.G.S., LL.B.
[Arnot Manderson Advocates] (1995)
BARNE, J.M., B.A. Q.C., (Hons), LL.B.,
[Axiom Advocates] (2003)
BARR, J.A., LL.B.
[Optimum Advocates] (1999)
BARRON, Miss Margaret J., LL.B. (Hons),
[Black Chambers] (2006)
BARTOS, David, LL.B. (Hons) (1993)
BEARDMORE, N.J., M.A. (Hons), LL.B.
[Optimum Advocates] (1998)
BECKETT, The Hon. Lord (1993)
BELL, A.M., B.L. (1975)
BELL, M.J., LL.B. (Hons)
[Themis Advocates] (1992)
BELL, S.A., LL.B. (Hons)
[Ampersand] (1996)
BENNETT, Kate L., B.Soc.Sc(Hons), LL.B
[Compass Chambers] (2014)
BENNIE, Anne., LL.B.(Hons), Dip LP
[Westwater Advocates] (2015)
BERGIN, Andrew J., LL.B. (Hons)., Dip LP
[Compasss Chambers] (2021)
BEVAN, J.S., M.A., LL.B. (1990)
BEYNON, N.E., B.A. (Oxon) (Hons), LL.B.
[Terra Firma Chambers] (1990)
BLACK, Adam., LL.B. (Hons) Dip LP
[Compass Chambers] (2020)
BLAIR, David R., LL.B. (Hons)., Dip LP
[Axiom Advocates] (2021)
BLAIR, Scott, LL.B. (Hons)
[Terra Firma Chambers] (2000)
BLESSING, M.A., LL.B.,
[Arnot Manderson Advocates] (2002)
BONI, Mark S., LL.B. (Hone) Dip LP
[Ampersand] (2020)
BONOMY, The Hon. Lord (1984)
BORLAND, G.C., QC LL.B. (Hons), B.C.L.
[Axiom Advocates] (2000)
BORTHWICK, S.C., LL.B. (Hons),
[Black Chambers] (2002)
BOVEY, Mungo, Q.C., LL.B.
[Themis Advocates] (1984)
BOWEN, A.J., Q.C., * B.A.(Oxon), LL.M.(London)
[Terra Firma Chambers] (1997)
BOWIE, S.D.R., Q.C., LL.B. (Hons), LL.M.
[Ampersand] (1995)
BOYD OF DUNCANSBY, The Right Hon. Lord
(1983)
BRABENDER, Lynda J. Q.C., LL.B. (Hons),
[Westwater Advocates] (2005)
BRACADALE, The Rt. Hon. Lord (1985)
BRADBURY, Emily J., B.A (Hons)., Graduate
Diploma in Law,
[Westwater Advocates] (2021)
BRADLEY, J. Russell, M.A., LL.B, Dip L.P.

[Ampersand] (2012)
BRADY, Scott, * Q.C., LL.B.
[Terra Firma Chambers] (1987)
BRAILSFORD, The Hon. Lord (1981)
BRANNIGAN, John., LL.B. (Hons)., Dip LP
[Black Chambers] (2021)
BREMNER, Jonathan S, G., Q.C., B.A., BCL.,
BVC.,
[Axiom Advocates] (2021)
BRESLIN, Ms. Margaret, LL.B.,
BRODIE, P. Jonathan, Q.C., LL.B. (Hons)
[Arnot Manderson Advocates] (1994)
BRODIE, The Rt. Hon. Lord (1976)
BROOME, Jonathan, LL.B. (Hons), Dip L.P.
[Axiom Advocates] (2012)
BROWN, A.L., Q.C., LL.B. (Hons)
[Themis Advocates] (1995)
BROWN, Eric C., * LL.B. (Hons) (1987)
BROWN, Ewen D., LL.B(Hons), Dip LP
[Terra Firma Chambers] (2018)
BROWN, J.A., B.A. (Hons), LL.B.
[Axiom Advocates] (2000)
BROWN, Paul J., LL.B. (Hons) (2009)
BROWN, Sheriff A. N., LL.B (Hons) PhD (2010)
BROWN, Tracey., M.A(Hons), M.Phil, LL.B, Dip
LP
[Themis Advocates] (2019)
BROWNE of Ladyton, The Rt. Hon. The Lord,
LL.B. (Hons) (1993)
BROWNLEE, Thomas R., LL.B. (Hons)., Dip LP
[Compass Chambers] (2021)
BRUCE LOCKHART, Miss Karen, LL.B., M.Sc.
(2004)
BUCHANAN, S.P.J., LL.B. (Hons), (2001)
BURNET, A.J., B.A. (Hons), LL.B.,
[Terra Firma Chambers] (2006)
BURNS, The Hon. Lord (1977)
BURR, D. Frank M., B.A. (Hons), LL.B.,
[Arnot Manderson Advocates] (2006)
BYRNE, Daniel E., LL.B. (Hons)
[Axiom Advocates] (2010)
CAHILL, W. Joe, LL.B., (2006)
CALDWELL, Miss Marion, # Q.C., LL.B. (Hons),
Dip. L.P. (1986)
CAMERON, Donald, B.A. (Hons), (2005)
CAMPBELL, Ewen M., LL.B. (Hons), Dip.L.P.,
[Axiom Advocates] (2013)
CAMPBELL, H.H., QC, B.A. (Hons), LL.B. (Hons),
F.C.I.Arb. (1969)
CAMPBELL, J.D., Q.C., LL.B. (Hons)
[Themis Advocates] (1981)
CAMPBELL, J.R., Q.C., LL.B, (1984)
CAMPBELL, John P., M.A. (Hons), LL.B., (2005)
CAMPBELL, Sheriff K.J., Q.C., LL.B., LL.M. (1996)
CAMPBELL, Roderick A.M., B.A., LL.M.,
[Ampersand] (2008)
CARLOWAY, The Rt. Hon Lord, Lord President
and Lord Justice General (1977)
CARMICHAEL, Miss Heather-Mairi R., LL.B.
(Hons) (2004)
CARMICHAEL, The Hon. Lady (1993)
CARTWRIGHT, Julianna F., LL.B (Hons),
[Westwater Advocates] (2011)

CASEY, Miss Juliette M., B.C.L. (Hons), LL.B. (Hons), Ph.D., Dip.L.P.,
[Fees-Only FSL Subscribers] (2006)
CASKIE, Alan B., B.A. (Hons),
[Themis Advocates] (2006)
CATHCART, Sheriff S., LL.B. (1989)
CHARTERIS, Miss Ruth B., Q.C. (Mrs. R.M. Morrison), LL.B. (Hons) (2000)
CHERRY, Miss Joanna C., Q.C., LL.B. (Hons), LL.M.
[Arnot Manderson Advocates] (1995)
CHEYNE, D.P., M.A., LL.B.
[Westwater Advocates] (1986)
CHRISTINE, K.M., B.A. (Hons), LL.B.
[Compass Chambers] (2000)
CLANCY, R.G., Q.C., LL.B. (Hons), LL.M. (1990)
CLARK OF CALTON, The Hon. Lady (1977)
CLARK, G.M., LL.B. (1972)
CLARK, Mrs. Marie H., (Mrs. H. Clark), LL.B.
[Arnot Manderson Advocates] (1996)
CLARK, The Hon. Lord (1994)
CLARKE, Mrs. Maria A., # (Mrs. M.M. Clarke), B.A., LL.B., LL.M.
[Themis Advocates] (1986)
CLELAND, R.G., LL.B. (Hons),
[Compass Chambers] (2005)
CLIVE, A.M.M., LL.B., (1994)
CLOGGIE, Kenneth W., LL.B. (Hons) Dip LP
[Black Chambers] (2020)
CLOUGH, Miss Pamela, # (Mrs. I.S. Fraser) (1980)
COBB, David W., LL.B. (Hons)
[Arnot Manderson Advocates] (1997)
COLL, G.F., LL.B., LL.M.,
[Themis Advocates] (2000)
COLLAR, Mrs. Paula M.I., LL.B. (Hons), (2002)
COLLINS, Sheriff Petra M., LL.B. (Hons) (1997)
COLQUHOUN, Fergus A.M., M.A., LL.B. Dip LP
[Terra Firma Chambers] (2020)
COMISKEY, Miss Patricia B., B.Sc. (Hons), M.Sc., Ph.D., LL.B.
[Arnot Manderson Advocates] (2001)
CONNELLY, Ms Clare E., M.A. (Hons), LL.B., Dip.L.P.,
[Compass Chambers] (2013)
CONNOR, Miss Frances C., LL.B.,
[Optimum Advocates] (2002)
CONVERY, Sheriff D., M.A. (1980)
CONWAY, D.H.S., B.A., LL.B., M.Phil. (1991)
CORKE, D.S., Sheriff, B.A., LL.B. (1988)
COSGROVE, The Rt. Hon. Lady H.J., CBE QC (1968)
COWAN, A.J., LL.B (Hons), Dip LP
[Ampersand] (2017)
COWAN, Sheriff A.M., LL.B., M.Sc. (1987)
COWIE, C.R.R., LL.B. (Hons) (1998)
CRABB, Simon P., LL.B(Hons), Magister, Dip LP
[Arnot Manderson Advocates] (2017)
CRADDOCK, F.E., LL.B. (1987)
CRAIG, Susan Ann. LL.B (2015)
CRAIK, R.G., Q.C., M.A., LL.B. (1966)
CRAWFORD, Martin R. L., LL.B. (Hons), Dip.L.P.,
[Arnot Manderson Advocates] (2013)

CRAWFORD, Miss Ruth, Q.C., LL.B. (Hons)
[Axiom Advocates] (1993)
CREALLY, Eugene P., Q.C., LL.B. (Hons), Ph.D.
[Eugene Creally] (1993)
CROOK Brian, M.A (Hons) St Andrews, LL.B (Glasgow)
[Terra Firma Chambers] (2015)
CROSBIE, Andrew J., LL.B. (Hons) Dip LP
[Arnot Manderson Advocates] (2020)
CROWE, Jonathan, LL.B.
[Black Chambers] (2000)
CRUICKSHANK, S.M., LL.B. (Hons) (2000)
CULLEN OF WHITEKIRK, The Rt. Hon. The Lord, KT, LL.D. (1960)
CUNNINGHAM, L. G., M.A., LL.B., LL.M.,
[Westwater Advocates] (1997)
DALGLEISH, G.A., LL.B. (Hons),
[Fees-Only FSL Subscribers] (2005)
DAVIDSON, Donald, B.A. (Hons), LL.B.
[Themis Advocates] (1995)
DAVIDSON, The Lord of Glen Clova, * Q.C.
[Axiom Advocates] (1979)
DAVIE, Isla R., Q.C., LL.B.(Hons), Diplome de Droit Francais
[Ampersand] (2004)
DAVIES, P.G., B.Sc., LL.B.
[Arnot Manderson Advocates] (1995)
DAWSON, James T., Q.C., B.A. (Oxon), LL.B.
[Ampersand] (2004)
DELIBEGOVIC-BROOME, Mrs. Almira, Q.C., LL.B. (Hons), LL.M.
[Axiom Advocates] (2003)
DEMPSEY, Michael., B.A.(Hons), LL.B, Dip LP
[Themis Advocates] (2017)
DEVANEY, Miss Catherine E., LL.B. (Hons), (2006)
DEVLIN, A.W., LL.B.
[Themis Advocates] (1998)
DEWAR, A.R., Q.C. LL.B. (Hons)
[Ampersand] (1989)
DEWAR, Gavin A., LL.B. (Hons), Dip.L.P.,
[Arnot Manderson Advocates] (2013)
DI EMIDIO, P.E.G., LL.B. (Hons), LL.M. (1994)
DI ROLLO, Simon R., Q.C. LL.B. (Hons)
[Ampersand] (1987)
DIVERS, Sheriff Barry, LL.B. (Hons) (1999)
DOHERTY, Miss Una F., Q.C.,(Mrs. D. Fairley), LL.B. (Hons),
[Ampersand] (1999)
DOHERTY, The Hon. Lord (1984)
DONACHIE, Amy J., LL.B(Hons), Dip LP
[Westwater Advocates] (2018)
DONNELLY Stephen P. LL.B (Hons) Glasgow, Dip LP (Glasgow)
[Arnot Manderson Advocates] (2015)
DORRIAN, The Rt. Hon. Lady, Lord Justice Clerk of the Court of Session (1981)
DOW, E.A., LL.B. (Hons),
[Optimum Advocates] (2006)
DOW, Mrs. Victoria J., LL.B. (Hons),
[Black Chambers] (2013)
DOWDALLS, Miss Catherine, Q.C., LL.B. (Hons) (2000)
DRUMMOND YOUNG, The Rt. Hon. Lord

[Axiom Advocates] (1976)

DRUMMOND, Mrs Lorna A., Q.C., LL.B. (Hons), Ph.M. (1998)

DRUMMOND, Sheriff T.A.K., LL.B (1974)

DRYSDALE, FIONA, C LL.B. (Hons) and Diplome De Droit Francais
[Ampersand] (2002)

DUFF, Sheriff Susan M., LL.B. (2003)

DUGUID, I.M., Q.C., LL.B. (Hons)
[Black Chambers] (1988)

DULING, Kelly M., BA, LL.B, Dip LP, LL.M
[Black Chambers] (2012)

DUNCAN, A.J., Q.C., LL.B. (Hons), LL.M.
[Axiom Advocates] (1999)

DUNDAS, Shane P., LL.B, Dip LP
[Ampersand] (2019)

DUNLOP, Graham A., B.A. (Hons), LL.B., LL.M.,
[Terra Firma Chambers] (2009)

DUNLOP, Miss Laura J., (Mrs. R.I. McLeod), Q.C. LL.B. (Hons)
[Themis Advocates] (1989)

DUNLOP, R.W., Q.C., LL.B. (Hons)
[Axiom Advocates] (1998)

DUNLOP, Sheriff Principal R. Alastair, Q.C., LL.B. (1978)

DUNLOP, Sheriff W, Q.C., LL.B. (1985)

DUNN, V.J., LL.B. (Hons) (2000)

DUTHIE, Sheriff C. Euan, Q.C., M.A. (Hons), LL.B. (2006)

DYCKHOFF, Mrs Cecilia M., M.A., LL.B., Dip.Const.Law (2001)

EASSIE, R.D., The Rt. Hon. Lord (1972)

EDWARD, Colin K., M.A. (Hons), LL.B.,
[Westwater Advocates] (2010)

EDWARD, The Rt. Hon. Prof. Sir David, K.C.M.G., Q.C., LL.D., F.R.S.E. (1962)

EDWARDS, Denis J., # LL.B. (Hons), LL.M.
[Terra Firma Chambers] (2012)

EDWARDS, Miss Ashley A. Q.C., B.Sc. (Hons)(Pharmacology), LL.B.
[Black Chambers] (2000)

EDWARDSON, Miss Jo M., LL.B. (2008)

ELLIS, Nicholas St.John, Q.C., LL.B.
[Westwater Advocates] (1990)

EMSLIE, The Rt. Hon. Lord (1972)

ENNIS, Miss Isabella R., LL.B. (Hons)
[Westwater Advocates] (1993)

ERICHT, The Hon. Lord (1996)

ERROCH, Sheriff B.A., Q.C., LL.B. (Hons) (1998)

FACENNA, Gerald C., * B.A. (Hons), M.A., LL.B.
[Gerry Facenna] (2006)

FAIRLEY, The Hon. Lord (1999)

FALLONE, Susan., LL.B., Dip LP., LL.M.,
[Themis Advocates] (2021)

FARQUHARSON, Sheriff Jane C., Q.C (Mrs. Christopher Cowdy), LL.B. (Hons) (2002)

FARRELL, F.J., LL.B. (2003)

FARRELL, Gregory D., M.A. (Hons), LL.B. (Dinstinction), Dip.L.P.,
[Optimum Advocates] (2013)

FARRELL, J.A., Q.C., M.A., LL.B. (1974)

FERGUSON, Charles., LL.B. (Hons) Dip LP., LL.M.
[Black Chambers] (2020)

FERGUSON, Iain W.F. Q.C., LL.B. (Hons)
[Axiom Advocates] (1987)

FERGUSON, Peter W., Q.C., LL.B. (Hons), M.Sc.
[Terra Firma Chambers] (1987)

FINDLATER, Craig, LL.B (Hons)
[Black Chambers] (2012)

FINDLAY, D.R., QC, LL.B. (Hons), M.Phil., F.R.S.A.
[Optimum Advocates] (1975)

FINDLAY, James d.C. * Q.C., M.A. (Hons)
[Terra Firma Chambers] (2008)

FITZPATRICK, Brian, LL.B. (Hons),
[Ampersand] (1993)

FITZPATRICK, M.J., # M.A., LL.B.
[Ampersand] (1985)

FLEMING, Sheriff G.R., M.A., LL.B. (1976)

FLETCHER, Robin I.D., LL.B. (Hons), B.C.L., (2007)

FORBES Dana M. LL.B (Hons)
[Ampersand] (2015)

FORBES, Alyson V., LL.B, MSc
[Alyson Forbes] (2014)

FORBES, Geoffrey, LL.B.,
[Optimum Advocates] (2002)

FORDYCE, Jacqueline., LL.B., Dip LP., LL.M
[Axiom Advocates] (2016)

FORREST, K.H., LL.B. (Hons)
[Themis Advocates] (2000)

FORREST, Miss Edith F.D., Ll.B. (Hons), Dip. F.M.S.,
[Edith Forrest] (2007)

FORRESTER, I.S., * Q.C., LL.D., M.A., LL.B., M.C.L.
[Ampesand] (1972)

FORSYTH, A.C. (Sandy), LL.B. (Hons), BD, MTh (1999)

FORSYTH, A.J.M., # OstJ, M.Th., LL.B., A.C.I.I.
[Alistair Forsyth] (1995)

FOSTER, A.J.E., B.A., LL.B. (1975)

FRAIN-BELL, W.J., * M.A., LL.B., F.C.I. Arb.,
[Terra Firma Chambers] (1999)

FRANCIS, D.R.L., # LL.B.
[Terra Firma Chambers] (1985)

FRASER, Carla R., LL.B. (Hons) Dip LP
[Compass Chambers] (2020)

FRASER, Sheriff Sheena M., LL.B. (2003)

FRAZER, Sheriff Robert W., LL.B, Dip L.P. (2012)

GALBRAITH, Amber, LL.B. (Hons),
[Compass Chambers] (2005)

GALE, W. Stuart, Q.C., LL.B. (Hons), LL.M.
[Terra Firma Chambers] (1980)

GAMBLE, A.J., LL.B., LL.M., (1978)

GARDINER, Jamie R., BA (Hons), GDL, BVC
[Ampersand] (2016)

GARDINER, N.J.L., M.A. (Hons), LL.B.
[Arnot Manderson Advocates] (2001)

GARRITY, Denis J., LL.B(Hons), Dip LP
[Terra Firma Chambers] (2014)

GEARY, M.C., R.D., M.A., LL.B. (1980)

GEBBIE, G.C., LLB. (Hons)
[Black Chambers] (1987)

GHOSH, I. Julian, Q.C. * (QC England & Wales) LL.B., LL.M. D.Phil.,
[Axiom Advocates] (1999)

GIANNI, Mrs. Gail I., LL.B.,
[Black Chambers] (2001)
GIBSON, D.Q., LL.B. (1983)
GIBSON, Kenneth J.S., B.A. (Hons), LL.B.,
Dip.L.P.,
[Themis Advocates] (2008)
GILBRIDE, S.J., M.A., LL.B.
[Anne Gilbride] (1995)
GILCHRIST, Jamie, Q.C., M.A., LL.B. (1994)
GILCHRIST, Mrs. June M., (Mrs. James Gilchrist),
LL.B. (1993)
GILCHRIST, Nicola J., MA (Hons), LL.B
[Arnot Manderson Advocates] (2011)
GILL, B.J., B.A. (Hons), LL.B., LL.M.
[Arnot Manderson Advocates] (2006)
GILL, The Rt. Hon. Lord, (1967)
GILLESPIE, Lisa J., LL.B. (Hons),
[Black Chambers] (2005)
GILMORE, Mrs. Marian L.B.G., Q.C., LL.B.
(Hons), D.E.S.U
[Arnot Manderson Advocates] (1992)
GLANCY, Lorraine M., LL.B.,
[Optimum Advocates] (2005)
GLENNIE, The Rt. Hon. Lord
[Axiom Advocates] (1992)
GRAHAM, A.J. Q.C., LL.B.
[Optimum Advocates] (2002)
GRAHAME, Miss Angela T., Q.C., LL.B. (Hons)
[Compass Chambers] (1995)
GRANT-HUTCHISON, P.A., M.A. (Hons), LL.B.
[Terra Firma Chambers] (1988)
GRAY, P.L., # Q.C. LL.B. (Hons)
[Compass Chambers] (1992)
GREEN, Miss Janice, LL.B. (Hons),
[Optimum Advocates] (2009)
GROSSART, Sir A.M.M., Q.C., C.A., M.A., LL.B.,
LL.D. (1963)
GUILD, D.W.A, M.A. (1999)
GUINNANE, Miss Rosemary M., LL.B. (Hons)
[Optimum Advocates] (1994)
HADDOW, Christopher, Q.C., LL.B. (1971)
HADDOW, Timothy R., B.Eng., LL.B., Dip LP
[Themis Advocates] (2016)
HAJDUCKI, A.M., # Q.C., M.A. (1979)
HALDANE, The Hon. Lady, (Mrs. T.J. Edward),
LL.B. (1996)
HALLEY, John, M.A., LL.B.
[Arnot Manderson Advocates] (1997)
HAMILTON, A.J., LL.B.(Hons) (1990)
HAMILTON, Duncan G., Q.C., M.A. (Hons), LL.B.
[Arnot Manderson Advocates] (2006)
HAMILTON, J.R.A., Q.C., LL.B. (1998)
HAMILTON, Miranda I.H., M.A. (Hons), LL.B.,
[Axiom Advocates] (2007)
HAMILTON, The Rt. Hon. Lord,
[Axiom Advocates] (1968)
HAMMOND, Sheriff P.G.L., LL.B. (1992)
HANRETTY, G.F., Q.C. LL.B. (1990)
HARDIE, The Rt. Hon. the Lord (1973)
HARDMAN, Alasdair, LL.B.
[Themis Advocates] (2000)
HARRIS, C.J., B.A., LL.B. (1979)
HARROWER, The Hon. Lord (1999)

HARVEY, P.G., LL.B(Hons), GDL, PhD, BVC
[Arnot Manderson Advocates] (2017)
HASTIE, J.B., LL.B. (Hons)
[Compass Chambers] (2004)
HAVENGA, H.L., Dip. Law (Rand), LL.B. (1989)
HAWKES, G.I., Q.C., LL.B. (Hons),
[Ampersand] (2003)
HAWTHORN, Ewan G., LL.B., B.Sc., M.Sc., B.A.
[Themis Advocates] (2010)
HAWTHORNE, Mrs. S.M.E. Gail, (Mrs. Robin E.
Whealing), M.A., LL.B., (2013)
HAY, David, J.P., LL.B. (Hons),
[Westwater Advocates] (2008)
HAY, Ms. Wendy L., M.A. (Hons), LL.B., Dip.L.P.,
[Optimum Advocates] (2013)
HAYHOW, Robert, LL.B. (Hons)
[Westwater Advocates] (1997)
HEANEY, B.J., LL.B. (Hons)
[Westwater Advocates] (1999)
HENDERSON, Graeme M., B.A., LL.B.
[Themis Advocates] (1987)
HENDERSON, Miss Lisa M. * Q.C., (Mrs. B.
Davidson), LL.B.
[Ampersand] (1995)
HENDERSON, Richard S., LL.B. (Hons),
[Compass Chambers] (2009)
HENRY, Kevin J., LL.B(Hons), Dip LP
[Optimum Advocates] (2018)
HIGGINS, Miss Roisin A., Q.C., LL.B. (Hons)
[Axiom Advocates] (2000)
HILLER, Callum A., B.A. (Hons)., LL.B., Dip LP
[Optimum Advocates] (2021)
HODGE, Miss Margaret F.H., B.A. (Oxon), LL.B.
(1996)
HODGE, The Rt. Hon. Lord (1983)
HOFFORD, Leo, B.A., LL.B., Q.C.
[Themis Advocates] (1990)
HOLROYD, N.W., LL.B., B.C.L.(Oxon), T.E.P.,
F.S.A. Scot,
[Terra Firma Chambers] (1992)
HOOD, Miss Kirsty J., Q.C., LL.B. (Hons),
[Themis Advocates] (2001)
HOPE OF CRAIGHEAD, The Right Hon. The Lord,
K.T., P.C., LL.D., (1965)
HOVEY, Robert S., BSc (Hons)., LL.B., Dip LP
[Themis Advocates] (2020)
HOWIE, R.B.M., Q.C., LL.B. (Hons)
[Ampersand] (1986)
HOWLIN, M.P., # Q.C., B.A. (Hons), M.A.
[Terra Firma Chambers] (1996)
HUGHES, Dale W.A., LL.B. (Hons)
[Optimum Advocates] (1993)
HUGHES, Maggie, M.A., LL.B.
[Westwater Advocates] (1991)
HUGHES, S.J., M.A.(Hons), LL.B.
[Arnot Manderson Advocates] (1997)
ILLIUS, Mrs. Dinah D., (Mrs. A.W. Illius), M.A.,
LL.B. (1991)
INGLIS, Alan., B.A., M.A., CQSW., LL.M
[Arnot Manderson Advocates] (2009)
INNES, Ruth M., Q.C.,LL.B. (Hons),
[Westwater Advocates] (2005)
IRVINE, Ms Lesley, LL.B. (Hons), LL.M.

[Axiom Advocates] (2012)
IRVINE, Ms. Jeya L., LL.B. (Hons), LL.M. (2007)
IVEY, R. Gilmour, Q.C., LL.B. (1985)
JACK, D.M., B.A., LL.B. (1993)
JACK, Mrs. Morag A.F., B.A. (2000)
JACKSON, Sheriff M.D.QC, LL.B. (Hons) (2000)
JACKSON, W.Gordon, * Q.C., LL.B.
[Arnot Manderson Advocates] (1979)
JAJDELSKI, Wojciech, LL.B
[Arnot Manderson Advocates] (2014)
JAMIESON, Maurice, # LL.B. (Hons), LL.M. (Dist)
[Arnot Manderson Advocates] (1993)
JOHNSTON, D.E.L., Q.C., M.A., Ph.D., LL.D.,
[Axiom Advocates] (1992)
JOHNSTON, Sheriff Johanna M., Q.C., LL.B.
(1992)
JONES, Christopher D., LL.B (Hons), Dip LP
[Themis Advocates] (2014)
JONES, Gareth E., * LL.B. (Hons)
[Black Chambers] (2011)
JONES, Sheriff Martin, Q.C., LL.B., M.Phil. (1994)
JOUGHIN, Miss Gail, (Mrs. I.F. Smith), M.A., LL.B.
(1989)
JUNOR, G.J., LL.B. (Hons), (1993)
KEANE, L A, LL.B. (1988)
KEANE, M.F., LL.B. (1997)
KEEN, The Rt. Hon The Lord of Elie R.S., * Q.C.,
LL.B. (Hons)
[Axiom Advocates] (1980)
KELLY, Christopher, M.A. (Hons), LL.B.
[Fees-Only FSL Subscribers] (2003)
KENNEDY, Laurence C., LL.B.
[Ampersand] (2000)
KENNEDY, Lewis K., M.A., LL.B., LL.M,
[Optimum Advocates] (2000)
KERRIGAN, H.A., * Q.C., M.A., LL.B. (Hons)
[Black Chambers] (1970)
KHURANA, Vinit, * Q.C., M.B., Ch.B., LL.B.
[Ampersand] (1999)
KIDDIE, Jonathan., LL.B. (Hons) Dip LP
[Terra Firma Chambers] (2020)
KINCLAVEN, The Hon. Lord (1978)
KINLOCH, Sheriff D.A., LL.B. (Hons) (1989)
KINNEAR, N.C., LL.B.
[Terra Firma Chambers] (1994)
KINROY, Alastair J., Q.C., LL.B. (Hons) (1987)
KIRK, S.P., M.A., M.A., LL.B. (1989)
KOMOROWSKI, Julius M., LL.B. (Hons) (2008)
LABAKI, Sheriff Maryam, LL.B. B.A. (Hons) (2010)
LAING, S.A., LL.B. (Hons),
[Compass Chambers] (2002)
LAKE, J.C., Q.C., LL.B.
[Axiom Advocates] (1994)
LAMB, A.J., Q.C., LL.B.
[Black Chambers] (1984)
LAMONT, Sheriff G.W., LL.B. (Hons) (1999)
LANGLANDS, Bruce T., LL.B(Hons), Dip LP
[Compass Chambers] (2019)
LAWRIE, Leigh, D. LL.B, LL.M,
[Black Chambers] (2010)
LAYDEN, P.J., T.D., Q.C., LL.B. (1973)
LAZAROWICZ, M.J., M.A. (Hons), LL.B.

[Terra Firma Chambers] (1996)
LEIGHTON, D.N., LL.B.
[Themis Advocates] (2003)
LENEHAN, Tony, B.Eng. (Hons), LL.B.,
[Black Chambers] (2005)
LIDDLE, Sheriff G.W.M., LL.B. (1988)
LINDHORST, G.J.S., LL.B. (Hons), LL.M.
[Westwater Advocates] (1995)
LINDSAY, M.S.H., Q.C., LL.B. (Hons), Dip.L.P.
[Axiom Advocates] (1996)
LIVINGSTONE, Miss Sarah M., LL.B. (Hons)
[Optimum Advocates] (1999)
LLOYD, Preston, M.A. (Hons), LL.B. (Hons)
[Compass Chambers] (1996)
LOCKE, Miss M. Luise S., B.A., M.B.A.
[Terra Firma Chambers] (2000)
LOGAN, D.J.T., LL.B. (Hons)
[Terra Firma Chambers] (2000)
LOTHIAN, Miss Amanda J.C., M.A., LL.B., Dip.L.P.
(1998)
LOVE, S.A. Q.C., LL.B.
[Compass Chambers] (2001)
LUGTON, Charles H.G., LL.B., Dip.L.P. (2012)
LUNNY, Sheriff Vincent T., LL.B (Hons), LL.M
(2015)
MACAULAY, C.J., Q.C., LL.B. (Hons)
[Arnot Manderson Advocates] (1977)
MACBRIDE, Caroline F., B.A. (Hons), LL.B.
[Optimum Advocates] (2006)
MACCOLL, Catherine, (Mrs. G.L. MacColl), B.A.,
LL.B., M.Sc.,
[Themis Advocates] (2008)
MACCOLL, G.L. Q.C., B.A. (Hons), M.A., LL.B.
[Themis Advocates] (2000)
MACDONALD, Miss Lynsey J., LL.B. (Hons),
[Optimum Advocates] (2008)
MACDONALD, Peter M., LL.B. (Hons) (1987)
MacDONALD, Sheriff James, LL.B. (Hons) (2005)
MACDOUGALL, Neil, LL.B (Hons)
[Westwater Advocates] (2011)
MACFARLANE, Sheriff R.P. Q.C., LL.B. (1994)
MACGREGOR, J.N.M., Q.C., LL.B. (Hons), B.C.L.
[Axiom Advocates] (2007)
MACIVER, G.M., LL.B. (Hons),
[Ampersand] (2007)
MACKAY, Alan A., LL.B. (Hons)
[Optimum Advocates] (1990)
MACKAY, D.I., Q.C., LL.B.
[Compass Chambers] (1980)
MACKENZIE, E.G. Q.C., LL.B. (Hons)
[Ampersand] (1999)
MACKENZIE, N.R., QC, LL.B. (Hons)
[Arnot Manderson Advocates] (1999)
MACKENZIE, Sheriff Alan R., LL.B. (1993)
MACKENZIE, Sheriff Moira C., LL.B. (Hons)
(1991)
MACKIE, Sheriff D.N., LL.B. (Hons) (1991)
MACKINNON, Sheriff N.J., LL.B.(Hons) (1984)
MACKINTOSH, Fred, QC, M.A. (Hons), LL.B.
[Terra Firma Chambers] (2000)
MACLEAN, Eoghainn C.M., LL.B. (Hons)
[Ampersand] (1995)

MACLEAN, Iain F., LL.B. (Hons), LL.M., M.Sc.
(1994)
MACLEAN, Lorna M., LL.B. (2004)
MACLEAN, The Rt. Hon. Lord (1964)
MACLEOD, Allan, LL.B. (Hons)
[Optimum Advocates] (2004)
MACLEOD, Catriona LL.B. (Hons),
[Terra Firma Chambers] (2007)
MACLEOD, Ceit-Anna., LL.B (Hons), Dip LP
[Arnot Manderson Advocates] (2012)
MACLEOD, David Ross, B.A., LL.B., LL.M. Dip.L.P.
[Optimum Advocates] (2000)
MACLEOD, M.A., Q.C., LL.B. (Hons)
[Compass Chambers] (1994)
MACLEOD, Roderick A.S., LL.B (Hons)
[Terra Firma Chambers] (2016)
MACMILLAN, A.K., LL.B. (Hons)
[Westwater Advocates] (1995)
MACNAIR, Sheriff C.N., Q.C. LL.B. (1988)
MACNEILL, Ann., LL.B, PhD, MSc, MBA, Dip LP
[Themis Advocates] (2018)
MACNEILL, C.H.S., Q.C., LL.B. (Hons)
[Westwater Advocates] (1992)
MACPHERSON, John, B.Sc. (Hons), LL.B.
[Arnot Manderson Advocates] (2016)
MACPHERSON, Ranald I., MA(Hons), LL.B, Dip
LP
[Compass Chambers] (2019) MACQUEEN,
Catriona J., LL.B (Hons)., LL.M (Hons)., Dip Lp
[Arnot Manderson Advocates] (2021)
MACSPORRAN, Archibald, Q.C., M.A. (Hons),
LL.B.
[Ampersand] (1992)
MAGUIRE, Miss Maria B., (Mrs. G.R. Nicholson),
Q.C. LL.B.
[Ampersand] (1987)
MAGUIRE, Ms Katariina S., LL.B. (Hons)
[Black Chambers] (2003)
MAHER, G, Q.C., LL.B., B.Litt. (1987)
MALCOLM, Miss Kirsty, LL.B. (Hons),
[Westwater Advocates] (2007)
MALCOLM, The Hon. Lord (1977)
MANSON, Scott G., LL.B (Hons)
[Axiom Advocates] (2014)
MARKIE, Grant D., LL.B(Hons)
[Compass Chambers] (2014)
MARNEY, C.D., LL.B. (Hons)
[Ampersand] (1998)
MARSH, Miss Linda R. Dip. Ed., Dip Lp., BA
(Hons) M.B.A., LL.B. (2002)
MARTIN-BROWN, Sheriff Jillian, LL.B. (Hons)
(2010)
MASON, A.D.K., B.A. (Hons), LL.B.,
[Andrew Mason] (2007)
MASON, Ms. Leigh A., B.A. (Hons), LL.B., (2002)
MASTERS, Hugh L., M.A. (Hons)., LL.B., Dip LP.,
[Compass Chambers] (2021)
MATTHEWS, The Hon. Lord (1979)
MAY, D.J., LL.B. (1971)
MCALPINE, Scott, LL.B. (Hons), Dip.L.P.,
Dip.F.M.S.
[Westwater Advocates] (2012)
MCANDREW, Nicholas A., LL.B. (Hons) Dip LP

[Ampersand] (2020)
MCBREARTY, Kenneth, Q.C., LL.B. (Hons)
[Axiom Advocates] (2000)
MCCAFFERY, E. Kevin, LL.B. (Hons),
[Arnot Manderson Advocates] (2003)
MCCALL SMITH, Rodney Alexander, L.L.B.
(Hons), PhD. (2010)
MCCALL, Miss Jan, (Mrs. G.J.G. MacKinnon)
LL.B. (Hons)
[Compass Chambers] (1999)
MCCALL, Ms. Shelagh M., Q.C., LL.B. (Hons),
LL.M.
[Black Chambers] (2000)
MCCALLUM, K.F., LL.B. (Hons)
[Black Chambers] (2000)
MCCLELLAND, Ross D., LL.B (Hons), LL.M
(Cantab)
[Axiom Advocates] (2011)
MCCLOY, S.F., LL.B. (Hons), C.A.,
[Arnot Manderson Advocates] (2007)
MCCLUSKEY, Niall R., LL.B.
[Optimum Advocates] (1995)
MCCONNACHIE, Brian, Q.C., LL.B.
[Black Chambers] (1994)
MCCONNELL, James, LL.B. (Hons)
[Ampersand] (2006)
MCCORMACK, Sheriff Peter, M.A., LL.B. (1992)
MCCREADIE, Sheriff R.A., Q.C., LL.B. (Hons),
Ph.D. (1992)
MCEACHRAN, C.N., Q.C., B.A., LL.B., J.D. (1968)
MCELROY, John P., LL.B., Dip. L.P., Dip.F.M.S.,
[Optimum Advocates] (2013)
MCFARLANE, Margaret B., LL.B., Dip.L.P., LL.M.,
[Margaret McFarlane] (2013)
MCFARLANE, Sheriff C.W., LL.B. (1976)
MCGHIE, The Hon. Lord (1969)
MCGREGOR, M.B., LL.B. (Hons)
[Compass Chambers] (1998)
MCGUIRE, Kenneth, LL.B. (Hons)
[Westwater Advocates] (2010)
MCMILVRIDE, R.R. QC, LL.B. (Hons)
[Terra Firma Chambers] (2005)
MCINTOSH OF PICKERING, Lady Anne., LL.B.,
M.P. (1982)
MCKAY, Allan, Ll.B. (Hons), LL.M., (2007)
MCKAY, M.E. Q.C., LL.B. (Hons)
[Ampersand] (2000)
MCKENDRICK, John, LL.B. (Hons), LL.M.,
M.Sc.(Oxon) (2008)
MCKENNA, Shirley, LL.B.
[Optimum Advocates] (2005)
MCKENZIE, Alasdair N., LL.B. (Hons),
[Axiom Advocates] (2009)
MCKENZIE, Drew, M.A. (Hons), LL.B.
[Black Chambers] (1992)
MCKINLAY, Adam J., LL.B(Hons), Dip LP
[Axiom Advocates] (2018)
MCKINLAY, Julie, LL.B. (Hons), Dip.L.P.
[Themis Advocates] (2013)
MCLAUGHLIN, J.A., LL.B. (1993)
MCLEAN, A.W.D., Q.C., M.A., LL.B.
[Themis Advocates] (1993)
MCLEAN, David H., LL.B. (Hons), Dip L.P., LL.M

[Themis Advocates] (2012)
MCMENAMIN, Miss Frances J., Q.C., B.A., LL.B., D.Univ.
[Black Chambers] (1985)
MCNAUGHTAN, David, LL.B. (Hons)
[Compass Chambers] (2003)
MCNEILL, Lachlan, LL.B. (2000)
MCPHIE, D. H., LL.B. (Hons), M.Sc., M.B.A.,
[Optimum Advocates] (1996)
MCSHANE, F.M., LL.B. (Hons), Ph.D.,
[Themis Advocates] (2001)
MCSHERRY, Sheriff J.C.C., LL.B. (Hons) (1993)
MCTAGGART, Rosalyn J., LL.B., Dip LP
[Optimum Advocates] (2021)
MCWHIRTER, Andrew J., LL.B (Hons)., Dip LP
[Axiom Advocates] (2021)
MEEHAN, M.E.A., QC, LL.B.
[Black Chambers] (2003)
MELVIN-FARR, A.N., LL.B. (Hons), LL.M.
[Optimum Advocates] (2002)
MENZIES, The Rt. Hon. Lord (1978)
MERCER, Sheriff W.M.D., LL.B. (Hons), LL.M. (2000)
MIDDLETON, G.S., LL.B. (Hons),
[Compass Chambers] (2003)
MIDDLETON, Graham R., MA(Hons), LL.B
[Themis Advocates] (2014)
MILLER, Christopher., LL.B. (Hons) LL.M. Dip LP
[Themis Advocates] (2020)
MILLER, Sheriff I.H.L., M.A.(Hons), LL.B. (1992)
MILLIGAN, Miss Louise J., (Mrs. J.C. Adams), LL.B. (Hons), M.B.A.
[Ampersand] (1993)
MILLIGAN, P.G., M.A. (1992)
MILLIGAN, R.G., Q.C., B.A. (Hons), LL.B.
[Compass Chambers] (1995)
MINGINISH, The Hon. Lord (1994)
MITCHELL, Geoffrey D., Q.C., LL.B. (Hons)
[Ampersand] (1992)
MITCHELL, I.G., Q.C., LL.B. (Hons)
[Arnot Manderson Advocates] (1976)
MITCHELL, John L., Q.C., LL.B. (Hons) (1974)
MITCHELL, Jonathan J., Q.C., B.A., LL.B.
[Arnot Manderson Advocates] (1979)
MITCHELL, Miss Claire M., QC, LL.B. (Hons)
[Compass Chambers] (2003)
MITCHELL, Sheriff J.K., LL.B. (1979)
MOGGACH, D.J., LL.B.
[Black Chambers] (1999)
MOHAMMED, Mark C., LL.B (Hons)
[Terra Firma Chambers] (2011)
MOIR, J.A.P., LL.B.
[Themis Advocates] (1993)
MOIR, M.D., LL.B., B.A.,
[Optimum Advocates] (2000)
MOLL, Louis, * LL.B. (Hons) (2006)
MOORE, Ms. Di, LL.B. (Hons), Dip.L.P., (2013)
MORI, Valentina., LL.B. (Hons) Dip LP., LL.M.
[Optimum Advocates] (2020)
MORRIS, Sheriff J.C., LL.B. (1985)
MORRISON, Sheriff N M P, Q.C. (1975)
MORROW, J.J., Q.C., B.D., D.Min, LL.B. (2000)
MOYNIHAN, G.J.B., Q.C., LL.B., D.Phil.

[Axiom Advocates] (1985)
MULHOLLAND, The Hon. Lord (2008)
MULLAN, Owen, LL.B (Hons), LL.M
[Optimum Advocates] (2011)
MULLIN, J.C., LL.B. (1978)
MUNDY, Sheriff John K., LL.B. (1987)
MUQIT, Miss Piya D., * LL.B. (Hons), LL.M., (2005)
MURE, J.D.McF.H., Q.C., M.A., LL.B.
[Axiom Advocates] (1995)
MURPHY, Andrew J., * M.A., LL.B.
[Andrew Murphy] (1970)
MURPHY, Jonathan., B.A. (Hons) LL.B. Dip LP
[Arnot Manderson Advocates] (2020)
MURPHY, Laurence, Q.C., M.A., LL.B. (1990)
MURPHY, P.O.V., M.Th., LL.B., F.S.A. Scot. (1990)
MURPHY, Sheriff S.F., Q.C., M.A. (Hons), LL.B. (1992)
MURRAY, Craig M., LL.B. (Hons), LL.M.,
[Compass Chambers] (2008)
MURRAY, N.D., Q.C., M.A., LL.B.
[Optimum Advocates] (1979)
NAPIER, B.W., * Q.C. LL.B., M.A., Ph.D.(Cantab)
[Themis Advocates] (1986)
NELSON, Derick, LL.B.
[Black Chambers] (1999)
NELSON, P.M., LL.B. (Hons)
[Optimum Advocates] (2004)
NICHOLSON-WHITE, Jennifer B., LL.B. (Hons), Dip L.P.,
[Ampersand] (2013)
NICOL, A.M., M.A. (Hons), LL.B., D.F.M., FSA Scot., (1993)
NICOL, D.E., LL.B.(Hons) (1989)
NICOLL, S.D.D., LL.B. (Hons)
[Stuart Nicoll] (1988)
NICOLSON, David, LL.B.,
[Compass Chambers] (2005)
NIVEN-SMITH, Timothy, B.A., LL.B. (2000)
NOBLE, Sheriff A.W., LL.B. (1978)
O'BRIEN, Miss Susan J., Q.C., B.A. (Hons), B.Phil, LL.B. (1987)
O'BRIEN, Paul R., Q.C., LL.B. (Hons)
[Axiom Advocates] (2004)
O'CARROLL, Maurice, * LL.B. (Hons)
[Terra Firma Chambers] (1995)
O'CARROLL, Sheriff Derek, LL.B. (Hons), Dip.L.P., (2000)
O'GRADY, Sheriff M.G., QC, M.A., LL.B. (1988)
OLIVER, Charles J.C., LL.B. (Hons) Dip LP
[Arnot Manderson Advocates] (2020)
OLSON, H.J., LL.B. (Hons)
[Arnot Manderson Advocates] (1996)
O'NEILL, A.M., * Q.C., LL.B. (Hons), LL.M. (Hons), LL.M., LL.D.
[Ampersand] (1987)
OWER, Miss Susan P., LL.B. (Hons),
[Axiom Advocates] (2009)
PATERSON, Christopher J., LL.B. (Hons)
[Axiom Advocates] (2010)
PATON, The Rt. Hon. Lady (1977)

PATRICK, Miss Jane E. (Mrs. M.B. Holmes), LL.B.
  (1994)
PENROSE, The Rt. Hon. Lord (1964)
PENTLAND, The Hon. Lord (1982)
PEOPLES, J.A., Q.C., LL.B.
  [Westwater Advocates] (1979)
PICKARD, Kathryn, M, B.A, M.A. BLL (2014)
PIERI, Sheriff Frank, LL.B. (1994)
PIKE, Mrs. Linda, LL.B. (Hons), (2008)
PILKINGTON, Ross, LL.B.
  [Themis Advocates] (1999)
PIRIE, Christopher J., LL.B. (Hons)
  [Themis Advocates] (2004)
POOLE, I.A., LL.B. (1964)
POOLE, The Hon. Lady (1998)
PORTER, Miss Jane M.,LL.B. (Hons) (1994)
PORTER, Mrs. Margaret T., (Mrs. K.J. Porter)
  LL.B.(Hons) (1987)
PRAIS, Lili, LL.B. (Hons)
  [Black Chambers] (2010)
PRESTON, N.J.H. * B.A., M.A. (1999)
PRICE-MARMION, Alexandra R. G.,* M.A. (Hons)
  (Oxon)
  [Arnot Manderson Advocates] (2011)
PRIMROSE, G.S., Q.C., LL.B.
  [Ampersand] (1993)
PUGH, Richard J., LL.B. (Hons)
  [Compass Chambers] (2008)
RADCLIFFE, Laura Anne., BA., LL.B. Dip LP
  [Optimum Advocates] (2020)
RAE, D.C., LL.B. (Hons) (1989)
RAE, The Hon. Lady (1982)
RAEBURN, Sheriff S.A.O., LL.B. (1977)
RALSTON, Miss Mary F., M.A. (Hons), LL.B.
  (1986)
RASHID, Safeena, LL.B. (Hons), Dip.L.P., (2013)
RATTRAY, Jane D., LL.B (Hons), LL.M
  [Westwater Advocates] (2015)
REED, The Hon. Lord (1983)
REEKIE, Derek R., LL.B. (2005)
REID Giles C. B.A. (Hons) Cambridge, MPhil
  (Cambridge), LL.B
  [Ampersand] (2015)
REID, P., LL.B. (Hons)
  [Ampersand] (2011)
REILLY, Laura M., LL.B. (Hons) (2006)
REITH, Sheriff F.L., LL.B. (1983)
RENUCCI, R.A., Q.C., LL.B.
  [Black Chambers] (2001)
REVIE, Kenneth M., LL.B. (Hons), (2008)
REVILLE, Miss Nancy M., B.Sc. (Hons), LL.B.,
  (2003)
RICHARDS, Mhairi R., Q.C., LL.B. (Hons),
  Dip.F.M.,
  [Mhairi Richards] (1988)
RICHARDSON, The Hon. Lord, LL.B. (Hons),
  LL.M. (Dist) (2004)
RITCHIE, Sheriff Norman C., Q.C., LL.B. (1990)
ROBERTSON, E.W., LL.B. (Hons)
  [Arnot Manderson Advocates] (1994)
ROBERTSON, J. Graham, # B.Sc., LL.B.
  [Robertson] (1983)
ROBERTSON, J.P., LL.B. (Hons) (1994)

ROLFE, Gregor., LL.B, Dip LP
  [Compass Chambers] (2019)
RONNIE, S.P., LL.B.
  [Optimum Advocates] (1996)
ROSS, Barney A. R., LL.B. (Hons), Dip.L.P.,
  [Compass Chambers] (2013)
ROSS, D.B. Q.C., LL.B. (Hons), LL.M.
  [Ampersand] (1998)
ROSS, Miss Gillian, LL.B. (Hons)
  [Optimum Advocates] (2009)
ROSS, Miss Morag V. Q.C., B.A. (Hons), LL.B.
  [Axiom Advocates] (2003)
ROSS, Sheriff N.A., LL.B. (Hons), (1991)
ROSS, T.L. Q.C., LL.B.
  [Thomas Ross] (2000)
ROXBURGH, Elisabeth, LL.B. (Hons), Dip.L.P.,
  [Axiom Advocates] (2013)
RUSSELL, Elaine J., MA (Hons), LL.B. Dip LP
  [Compass Chambers] (2020)
RUSSELL, J.A., B.Sc., Ph.D. (1985)
SANDERS, C.G., LL.B., Dip.F.M.
  [Westwater Advocates] (2001)
SANDERSON, Mrs. Celia L., LL.B. (1994)
SANDISON, The Hon. Lord, LL.B. (Hons), LL.M.
  (Hons), Ph.D. (1996)
SCOTT, Euan D.N. M.A. (Hons) LL.B. Dip LP
  [Ampersand] (2020)
SCOTT, I.M., LL.B. (Hons) (1990)
SCOTT, M.C.N., Q.C., B.A., LL.B. (1978)
SCOTT, Mrs. Janys M., (Mrs. K.F. Scott), Q.C.,
  M.A.
  [Westwater Advocates] (1992)
SCOTT, Sheriff Principal C.A.L., Q.C., LL.B.
  (1986)
SCOTT, The Hon. Lady (1991)
SCULLION, Dominic., LL.B. (Hons) Dip LP
  [Compass Chambers] (2020)
SCULLION, J.J. QC, LL.B. (Hons),
  [Compass Chambers] (2002)
SELLAR Gavin, A., LL.B, LL.B (Hons), LLM, BPTC
  (2015)
SELLAR, David P. Q.C., M.A. (Hons), LL.B.
  [Ampersand] (1995)
SHAND, Miss Lesley M., (Mrs. T.G. Reid), Q.C.,
  LL.B. (Hons)
  [Compass Chambers] (1990)
SHAND, Neil G., LL.B (Hons)
  [Optimum Advocates] (2015)
SHARPE, Ian, B.A., LL.B (Hons), LL.M.
  [Westwater Advocates] (1992)
SHARPE, Miss Mary, M.A., LL.B., (1990)
SHEAD, C.M., LL.B. (Hons) (1996)
SHELDON, D.H., Q.C., LL.B. (Hons)
  [Compass Chambers] (1998)
SHEWAN, Rachel I.M., LL.B (Hons)
  [Westwater Advocates] (2014)
SIMPSON, P.J.D., * QC, LL.B. (Hons), LL.M.,
  [Terra Firma Chambers] (2001)
SINCLAIR, Miss Susan M., (Mrs. D.R. Adie),
  M.A.(Hons), LL.B., Dip.L.P. (1988)
SKINNER, Robert G., LL.B. (Hons)
  [Terra Firma Chambers] (1987)
SMALL, David H., LL.B. (Hons), B.C.L., LL.B.

[Arnot Manderson Advocates] (2004)

SMALL, Sheriff H.K.(Ray), LL.B. (Hons) (1992)

SMART, D.A., B.A., LL.B. (1980)

SMART, Michael B., LL.B. (1990)

SMART, Miss Astrid E., QC, M.A. (Hons), LL.B.
  [Compass Chambers] (1999)

SMART, Sheriff Marie T., (Mrs. T.K. Smart), M.A.,
  LL.B. (1995)

SMITH, Andrew, * Q.C., LL.B. (Hons)
  [Compass Chambers] (1988)

SMITH, B.T., Q.C., LL.B. (Hons), LL.M.,
  [Compass Chambers] (2005)

SMITH, Cameron N., LL.B. (Hons) LL.M. Dip LP
  [Compass Chambers] (2020)

SMITH, Catherine A., LL.B., M.A. (Hons),
  [Compass Chambers] (2007)

SMITH, Iain A., LL.B(Hons)
  [Black Chambers] (2014)

SMITH, R.A., Q.C., LL.B. (1985)

SMITH, S, LL.B. (1990)

SMITH, S.C., Q.C., LL.B. (Hons) (1999)

SMITH, The Rt. Hon. Lady (1980)

SPEIR, Sheriff John, LL.B. (1993)

SPIERS, D.A., M.A. (1997)

SPRINGHAM, Ms. Kay M. Q.C., LL.B. (Hons),
  D.E.A.
  [Compass Chambers] (1999)

SPY, Sheriff J, LL.B. (1979)

ST. CLAIR, J.B., LL.B. (1987)

STACEY, The Hon. Lady (1987)

STALKER, A.G., LL.B. (Hons)
  [Westwater Advocates] (2007)

STEEL, Murray., LL.B, DIP LP, LL.M
  [Axiom Advocates] (2019)

STEELE, G.R., Q.C., LL.B.
  [Terra Firma Chambers] (1981)

STEIN, Katerina, M.A., M.Sc., Ph.D., LL.B.,
  Dip.L.P.,
  [Themis Advocates] (2013)

STEPHEN, Mhairi M., B.A., LL.B, Sheriff Principal
  of Lothian & Borders (2014)

STEPHENSON, D.A., Q.C., LL.B. (Hons)
  [Ampersand] (1991)

STEWART, A.L., B.A., LL.B. (1963)

STEWART, J.B., M.A., LL.B. (1969)

STEWART, M.L., Q.C., M.A., LL.B.
  [Compass Chambers] (1988)

STEWART, Mary Ellen., M.A.(Hons)., LL.B.
  (Hons).,Dip LP.
  [Ampersand] (2021)

STEWART, Miss Lindsey K., * (Mrs. D.W.C.
  Mallon), M.A., (1990)

STEWART, Sheriff Nikola C. (1987)

STEWART, The Hon. Lord (1975)

STEWART, The Lord of Dirleton Q.C., M.A.
  (Hons) LL.B. (1993)

STIRLING, Miss Alison N., M.A. (Hons), LL.B.
  (1997)

STIRLING, W.M.C., LL.B. (1976)

STOBART, Alice L., M.A. (Hons), LL.B.,
  [Westwater Advocates] (2007)

STUART, M.A. Q.C., B.A., LL.B.
  [Ampersand] (2003)

STUART, Philip M., LL.B.
  [Ampersand] (1996)

STURROCK, J.G., Q.C., LL.B. (Hons), LL.M.
  (1986)

SUMMERS, The Hon. Lord (1994)

SUTHERLAND, Alexander C.M., M.A(Hons), LL.B,
  Dip LP
  [Ampersand] (2018)

SUTHERLAND, Miss Lauren, * Q.C., LL.B.,
  Dip.L.P.
  [Ampersand] (1996)

SUTHERLAND, R.D., M.A.(Hons), LL.B.
  [Terra Firma Chambers] (1992)

SUTHERLAND, The Rt. Hon. Lord (1956)

SWANNEY, D.A.D., MA(Hons), LL.B, Dip LP
  [Compass Chambers] (2017)

TAIT, Miss Arabella E.C.C., # (Mrs. Marcus Dean),
  B.A. (Hons), LL.M.
  [Arnot Manderson Advocates] (1995)

TANNER, Mrs Susanne L.M. * Q.C., LL.B. (Hons)
  [Ampersand] (2000)

TARGOWSKI, E.G.M., Q.C., LL.B. (Hons)
  [Optimum Advocates] (1975)

TARIQ, Usman, LL.M (Cantab), LL.B (Hons), Dip.
  LP
  [Ampersand] (2011)

TAYLOR, David C., LL.B. (Hons) Dip LP
  [Black Chambers] (2020)

TAYLOR, W.J., * Q.C.,(Q.C. England & Wales)
  M.A.(Hons), LL.B., F.R.S.A (1971)

TEMPLETON, Sean, B.Sc., LL.B.,
  [Virtual Stable] (2006)

THOMSON, Craig A., LL.B., (2006)

THOMSON, D.M. Q.C., LL.B. (Hons)
  [Axiom Advocates] (2004)

THOMSON, Fergus C.M., LL.B. (Hons), M.Sc
  (2009)

THOMSON, J.G., LL.B.
  [Thomson Chambers] (1990)

THOMSON, Laura J., LLB (Hons), Dip LP
  [Arnot Manderson Advocates] (2014)

THOMSON, M.G., # Q.C., LL.B.
  [Ampersand] (1974)

THOMSON, R.N., Q.C., B.Com., LL.B. (1990)

THORNLEY, Gavin J., LL.B. (Hons),
  [Compass Chambers] (2009)

THORNTON, Miss Pauline M., (Mrs. Q.J.
  McQuoney), LL.B. (1997)

TONER, Emma C., LL.B. (Hons), Dip. F.M.
  [Compass Chambers] (2009)

TONNER, A.F., M.A., LL.B. (1996)

TOSH, Neale A., LL.B. (Hons) Dip LP
  [Axiom Advocates] (2020)

TRAINER, Sarah L., LL.B (Hons)., Dip LP
  [Arnot Manderson Advocates] (2021)

TURNBULL, The Hon. Lord (1982)

TURNER, David J., B.Sc., LL.B. (Hons), Dip.L.P.
  [Arnot Manderson Advocates] (2012)

TYRE, Kirsty E., M.A.(hons), LL.B, Dip LP
  [Axiom Advocates] (2017)

TYRE, The Hon. Lord, Q.C., C.B.E. (1987)

UIST, The Hon. Lord (1975)

UPTON, M.G.J., B.A., LL.B., LL.M.,
 C.E.D.R.-Accredited Mediator
 [Themis Advocates] (1991)
VENGOECHEA, Ms. Ximena, LL.B. (Hons), M.A.,
 LL.B.,
 [Black Chambers] (2013)
WADE, Mrs. Gillian A., Q.C., LL.B. (Hons), (1998)
WALKER, G.J. Q.C., LL.B. (Hons)
 [Axiom Advocates] (2003)
WALKER, Miss Isabel C., LL.B. (1992)
WALKER, S.P. Q.C., LL.B., M.C.I. Arb.,
 [Themis Advocates] (1999)
WALLACE OF TANKERNESS, The Rt. Hon. Lord
 Q.C., M.A., LL.B. (1979)
WATSON, Craig B.,* LL.B (Hons), (2010)
WATT, G.H., B.A. (Hons), M.Phil., LL.B.,
 [Terra Firma Chambers] (2007)
WATTS, Miss Helen M., (Mrs Gavin Henderson)
 B.A. (Hons), LL.B. (Hons)
 [Axiom Advocates] (2009)
WAUGH, Yvonne E., LL.B. (Hons)
 [Compass Chambers] (2006)
WAY, Michael., LL.B.
 [Ampersand] (2019)
WEBSTER, A.G., Q.C., LL.B. (Hons), F.R.S.A.
 [Themis Advocates] (1992)
WEIR, R.B., Q.C., B.A., LL.B. (1995)
WEIR, The Hon. Lord (1959)
WELSH, Antonia L., BA (Hons)., LL.B. Dip LP
 [Westwater Advocates] (2020)
WELSH, David., M.A.(Hons), LL.B, Dip LP
 [Axiom Advocates] (2017)
WESTHUIZEN, Miss L. van der, Q.C., B.Sc.,
 B.Sc.(Hons), M.Sc., LL.B.(Hons)

[Ampersand] (2009)
WHYTE, Fergus., LL.B. (Hons) B.A. (Hons) LL.M
 [Arnot Manderson Advocates] (2020)
WILD, Miss Alison M., (Mrs R.S. Curtis)
 [Westwater Advocates] (2008)
WILLIAMSON, Miss Jacqueline LL.B. (Hons) LL.M.
 (1997)
WILSON, Calum S., M.A. (Hons), LL.B.,
 [Compass Chambers] (2002)
WILSON, Christopher C., M.A., LL.B. (Hons),
 C.A.,
 [Axiom Advocates] (2005)
WILSON, Miss Ailsa M., Q.C., LL.B. (Hons)
 [Ampersand] (1993)
WINTER, Stephen F. LL.B. (Hons) LL.M.
 [Terra Firma Chambers] (2011)
WISE, The Hon. Lady (1993)
WOLFFE, The Hon. Lady (1994)
WOLFFE, The Rt. Hon. James, Q.C., LL.B. (Hons),
 B.C.L.,
 [Axiom Advocates] (1992)
WOOLMAN, The Hon. Lord (1987)
WRAY, Mrs. Laura M.S., M.A., LL.B.,
 [Westwater Advocates] (2003)
WRIGHT, J.N., Q.C., B.A. (Hons), LL.B. (1983)
WYLIE, Miss Isobel C., LL.B., (1992)
YOUNG, A.R.W., Q.C., LL.B. (Hons),
 [Arnot Manderson Advocates] (1992)
YOUNG, D.A.C., Q.C., LL.B. (Hons), (1998)
YOUNG, James Timothy, LL.B. (Hons), Dip.L.P.,
 [Ampersand] (2013)
YOUNG, Miss Victoria J., LL.B (Hons)
 [Optimum Advocates] (1995)

Queen's Counsel

Bar		QC
1952	The Right Hon. Lord Ross, P.C., LL.D	1964
1955	The Right Hon. the Lord Mackay of Clashfern, KT	1965
1952	The Hon. Lord Cowie	1967
1956	The Rt. Hon. Lord Sutherland	1969
1957	John G. Mitchell, Q.C.	1970
1959	The Hon. Lord Weir	1971
1953	Sir Gerald H Gordon, C.B.E., Q.C.	1972
1958	The Rt.Hon. The Lord Cameron of Lochbroom	1972
1960	The Rt.Hon. The Lord Cullen of Whitekirk	1973
1962	Professor Sir David Edward, KCMG, QC, LLD, FRSE	1974
1963	The Rt. Hon. Lord Marnoch	1975
1964	The Rt. Hon. Lord Maclean	1977
1965	The Right Hon. The Lord Hope of Craighead KT, P.C., LL.D.	1978
1964	The Rt.Hon. Lord Penrose, LL.D., D.Univ.	1978
1966	The Rt. Hon. Lord Abernethy, P.C.	1979
1975	Ian R. Hamilton Q.C.	1980
1965	Sheriff J.M.S. Horsburgh, Q.C.	1980
1966	Sheriff RG Craik, Q.C.	1981
1967	The Hon. Lord McEwan	1981
1967	The Rt. Hon. Lord Gill	1981
1968	Charles P.C. Boag-Thomson Q.C.	1982
1968	Colin N. McEachran Q.C.	1982
1968	The Rt. Hon Lord Campbell of Pittenweem CH CBE QC	1982
1968	The Rt. Hon. Lord Hamilton	1982
1969	The Rt. Hon. Lord Nimmo Smith	1982
1969	Hugh H. Campbell Q.C.	1983
1969	The Hon. Lord McGhie	1983
1973	The Hon. Lord Philip, P.C.	1984
1971	Christopher Haddow, Q.C.	1985
1957	J. Fleming Wallace, Q.C.	1985
1970	The Rt Hon Sir Malcolm Rifkind, KCMG, QC MP	1985
1973	The Rt. Hon. the Lord Hardie	1985
1972	Rt. Hon. Lord Dalgetty of Sikotilani	1986
1973	Sheriff B A Kerr, Q.C.	1986
1972	The Right Honourable Lord Eassie	1986
1972	The Rt. Hon. Lord Emslie	1986
1971	William J. Taylor Q.C.	1986
1974	John L. Mitchell Q.C.	1987
1974	Malcolm G. Thomson Q.C.	1987
1972	Professor Robert Black Q.C.	1987
1974	Sheriff T.A.K. Drummond, Q.C.	1987
1974	The Right Honourable Lord Kingarth	1987
1976	The Rt. Hon. Lord Brodie	1987
1975	Donald R. Findlay Q.C.	1988
1972	Ian S. Forrester Q.C.	1988
1975	Sheriff N.M.P Morrison QC	1988
1976	The Hon. Lord Drummond Young	1988
1975	The Hon. Lord Stewart	1988
1975	The Hon. Lord Uist	1988
1977	Colin J. MacAulay Q.C.	1989
1971	DJ May, Q.C.	1989
1975	Edward G.M. Targowski Q.C.	1989
1964	Neville D. Shaffer Q.C.	1989
1976	Sheriff C.W. McFarlane, Q.C.	1989
1977	The Hon. Lady Clark of Calton	1989
1978	The Rt. Hon. Lord Clarke	1989
1976	Sheriff G.R. Fleming, Q.C.	1990
1978	Sheriff Principal R. Alastair Dunlop Q.C.	1990
1977	The Rt. Hon. Lord Carloway	1990
1977	The Hon. Lord Malcolm	1990
1977	The Rt. Hon. Lady Paton	1990
1979	Gordon Jackson Q.C.	1990
1977	The Hon. Lord Burns	1991
1978	James W. McNeill Q.C.	1991
1978	Malcolm C.N. Scott Q.C.	1991
1977	Sheriff Susan A.O. Raeburn Q.C.	1991
1978	The Hon. Lord Kinclaven	1991
1968	The Rt. Hon. Lady Cosgrove	1991
1978	The Rt. Hon. Lord Menzies	1991
1978	Alexander Bolland Q.C.	1992
1970	Herbert A. Kerrigan Q.C.	1992
1976	Iain G. Mitchell Q.C.	1992
1979	Jonathan J. Mitchell Q.C.	1992
1979	Neil D. Murray Q.C.	1992
1979	Sheriff C.J. Harris, Q.C.	1992
1970	Sheriff Principal EF Bowen,CBE,T.D., Q.C.	1992
1982	The Hon. Lady Rae	1992
1979	The Hon. Lord Matthews	1992
1966	The Hon. Lord Wheatley	1992
1980	D. Ian Mackay Q.C.	1993
1969	Edgar Prais Q.C.	1993
1959	Sheriff A.B. Wilkinson, Q.C.	1993
1979	The Hon. Lord Bannatyne	1993
1979	The Lord Davidson of Glen Clova Q.C.	1993
1980	The Rt. Hon. Lady Smith	1993
1984	The Rt. Hon. Lord Bonomy	1993
1980	The Rt. Hon. The Lord Keen of Elie QC	1993
1980	W. Stuart Gale Q.C.	1993

Bar		QC	Bar		QC
1979	James A. Peoples Q.C.	1994	2008	The Rt. Hon. Dame Elish Angiolini, DBE, QC	2001
1981	Sherif Principal Ian R. Abercrombie Q.C.	1994	1989	Alan R. Dewar Q.C.	2002
1981	The Hon. Lord Brailsford	1994	1986	Brian W. Napier Q.C.	2002
1981	The Rt. Hon. Lady Dorrian	1994	1990	Gerald F. Hanretty Q.C.	2002
1963	Sheriff Alastair L. Stewart, Q.C.	1995	1989	Laura J. Dunlop Q.C.	2002
1981	Sheriff Elizabeth Jarvie, Q.C.	1995	1991	The Hon. Lady Scott	2002
1982	Sir Crispin Agnew of Lochnaw Bt. Q.C.	1995	1987	Maria B. Maguire Q.C.	2002
1983	The Hon. Lord Reed	1995	1992	Peter L. Gray Q.C.	2002
1982	The Hon. Lord Pentland	1995	1988	Sheriff Charles N. Macnair Q.C.	2002
1983	The Rt. Hon. Lord Boyd of Duncansby, Q.C	1995	1977	Sheriff Principal Sir S.S.T. Young Q.C.	2002
1985	The Rt. Hon. Lord Bracadale	1995	1987	Simon R. Di Rollo Q.C.	2002
1981	Gordon R. Steele Q.C.	1996	1984	Andrew J. Lamb, Q.C.	2002
1983	John N. Wright Q.C.	1996	1988	Andrew Smith, Q.C.	2002
1983	Sheriff Fiona L Reith, Q.C.	1996	1986	Dennis J. Crawley, Q.C.	2002
1985	Sheriff J.C. Morris, Q.C.	1996	1990	Nicholas St. John Ellis, Q.C.	2002
1982	The Honourable Lord Turnbull	1996	1988	Robert B. Anthony, Q.C.	2002
1970	The Marquis of Lothian, PC, DL, QC, MP	1996	1990	Ronald G. Clancy, Q.C.	2002
1983	The Rt. Hon. Lord Hodge	1996	1988	Mhairi R. Richards, Q.C.	2003
1968	The Rt. Hon. Lord Selkirk of Douglas, PC, Q.C.	1996	1987	Professor Gerard Maher, Q.C.	2003
1984	G. Jack Davidson Q.C.	1997	1992	Sheriff Johanna M. Johnston, Q.C.	2003
1985	Gerry J.B. Moynihan Q.C.	1997	1994	Sheriff Martin Jones, Q.C.	2003
2017	Ian D. Truscott Q.C.	1997	1990	Sheriff Norman Ritchie, Q.C.	2003
1984	James R. Campbell QC	1997	1992	Sheriff Robert A. McCreadie, Q.C.	2003
1982	Sheriff Thomas Welsh Q.C.	1997	1992	Sheriff Sean F. Murphy, Q.C.	2003
1984	The Hon. Lord Doherty	1997	1987	Alastair J. Kinroy, Q.C.	2005
1979	The Rt. Hon. Lord Wallace of Tankerness Q.C.	1997	1994	Brian McConnachie, Q.C.	2005
1987	Derek W. Batchelor Q.C.	1998	1992	David E.L. Johnston, Q.C.	2005
1985	Frances J. McMenamin Q.C.	1998	1978	Donald R. MacLeod, Q.C.	2005
1981	John D. Campbell Q.C.	1998	1990	Lesley M. Shand, Q.C.	2005
1984	Mungo Bovey Q.C.	1998	1988	Mark L. Stewart, Q.C.	2005
1987	Susan O'Brien Q.C.	1998	1987	Peter W. Ferguson, Q.C.	2005
1992	The Hon. Lord Glennie	1998	1990	Douglas Armstrong, Q.C.	2005
1987	The Hon. Lord Tyre C.B.E.	1998	1993	Morag B. Wise, Q.C.	2005
1987	The Hon. Lord Woolman	1998	1991	The Hon. Lord Arthurson	2005
1987	Aidan O'Neill Q.C.	1999	1993	The Hon. Lord Beckett	2005
1986	Professor John G. Sturrock Q.C.	1999	2008	The Rt. Hon. Lord Mulholland	2005
1985	Ralph A. Smith Q.C.	1999	1993	Ailsa M. Wilson, Q.C.	2007
1985	R. Gilmour Ivey Q.C.	1999	1992	Andrew R.W. Young, Q.C.	2007
1988	Sheriff Michael G. O'Grady Q.C.	1999	1992	Calum H.S. MacNeill, Q.C.	2007
1991	Sheriff Ruth A. Anderson Q.C.	1999	1991	Daniel Kelly, Q.C.	2007
1987	The Hon. Lady Stacey	1999	1994	Dorothy R. Bain, Q.C.	2007
1995	David P. Sellar Q.C.	2000	1994	Gary J.G. Allan, Q.C.	2007
1987	Iain W.F. Ferguson Q.C.	2000	1994	Jamie Gilchrist, Q.C.	2007
1988	Ian M. Duguid Q.C.	2000	1992	Janys M. Scott, Q.C.	2007
1990	Laurence Murphy Q.C.	2000	1994	The Hon. Lord Clark	2007
1986	Marion Caldwell Q.C.	2000	1992	The Rt. Hon. James Wolffe, Q.C.	2007
1973	P.J. Layden, T.D., Q.C.	2000	1993	Alan W.D. McLean, Q.C.	2008
1986	Robert B.M. Howie Q.C.	2000	1993	Graham S. Primrose, Q.C.	2008
1989	Rory W.J. Anderson Q.C.	2000	1994	Jonathan C. Lake, Q.C.	2008
1987	Scott Brady, Q.C.	2000	1990	Leo Hofford, Q.C.	2008
1986	Iain G. Armstrong Q.C.	2000	1992	Marian L.B.G. Gilmore, Q.C.	2008
			1994	Murdo A. Macleod, Q.C.	2008
			1990	Roderick N. Thomson, Q.C.	2008
			1993	Ruth Crawford, Q.C.	2008

Bar		QC	Bar		QC
1994	The Hon. Lord Summers	2008	2003	Morag V. Ross, Q.C.	2016
1993	The Hon. Lady Carmichael	2008	1994	Sheriff Ross P. Macfarlane,	
1994	The Hon Lady Wolffe	2008		Q.C.	2016
1995	Angela T. Grahame, Q.C.	2009	2001	Steven A. Love, Q.C.	2016
1991	David A. Stephenson, Q.C.	2009	1999	Steven Walker, Q.C.	2016
1992	Geoffrey D. Mitchell, Q.C.	2009	2000	Susanne L.M. Tanner, Q.C.	2016
1995	James D. McF. H. Mure, Q.C.	2009	2003	Almira Delibegovic-Broome,	
1995	Joanna Cherry, Q.C.	2009		Q.C.	2017
1996	Michael P. Howlin, Q.C.	2009	2002	Anthony J. Graham, Q.C.	2017
1994	P. Jonathan Brodie, Q.C.	2009	2004	David M. Thomson, Q.C.	2017
1995	Robert G. Milligan, Q.C.	2009	1999	David R. Parratt, Q.C.	2017
1995	Simon D.R. Bowie, Q.C.	2009	2003	Gavin J. Walker, Q.C.	2017
1996	The Hon. Lord Ericht	2009	2008	James d.C. Findlay, Q.C.	2017
1996	The Hon. Lord Sandison	2009	2003	Jonathan M. Barne, Q.C.	2017
1995	Andrew L. Brown, Q.C.	2010	2005	Lynda J. Brabender, Q.C.	2017
1998	David A.C. Young, Q.C.	2010	2004	The Hon. Lord Richardson	2017
1999	I. Julian Ghosh, Q.C.	2010	2003	Michael A. Stuart, Q.C.	2017
1996	The Hon. Lady Haldane	2010	2000	Gavin L. MacColl, Q.C.	2017
1995	The Hon. Lord Weir	2010	2000	Thomas L. Ross, Q.C.	2017
1998	Roderick W. Dunlop, Q.C.	2010	1992	Andrew G. Webster, Q.C.	2018
1993	Eugene P. Creally Q.C.	2011	1998	Sheriff Bruce A. Erroch, Q.C.	2018
1998	Lorna A. Drummond Q.C.	2011	2002	Sheriff Jane C. Farquharson,	
1996	Mark S.H. Lindsay Q.C.	2011		Q.C.	2018
1998	Sheriff John R.A. Hamilton		2001	Ronaldo A. Renucci, Q.C.	2018
	Q.C.	2011	2005	Ruth M. Innes, Q.C.	2018
1996	Sheriff Kenneth Campbell		1999	Una Doherty, Q.C.	2018
	Q.C.	2011	1999	Vinit Khurana, Q.C.	2018
1985	Sheriff William Dunlop Q.C.	2011	1999	Astrid E. Smart Q.C.	2019
1963	Sir A.M.M. Grossart, Q.C.,		2006	Sheriff C. Euan Duthie, Q.C.	2019
	C.B.E.	2011	2003	Claire M. Mitchell QC	2019
1993	The Lord Stewart of Dirleton		2000	Fred Mackintosh QC	2019
	QC	2011	2000	Sheriff Matthew D. Jackson,	
1999	Alastair J. Duncan Q.C.	2012		Q.C.	2019
1997	Andrew John Bowen Q.C.	2012	2004	Isla R. Davie QC	2019
1986	Sheriff Principal Craig A.L.		2000	Matthew D. Jackson, Q.C.	2019
	Scott Q.C.	2012	2003	Michael E.A. Meehan QC	2019
1999	The Hon. Lord Fairley	2012	1999	Neil R. Mackenzie QC	2019
1998	The Honourable Lady Poole	2012	2006	Alasdair J. Burnet Q.C.	2020
1999	The Hon. Lord Harrower	2012	2005	Amber Galbraith Q.C.	2020
2000	Catherine Dowdalls, Q.C.	2013	2005	Barry T. Smith Q.C.	2020
1998	David H. Sheldon Q.C.	2013	2004	James T. Dawson Q.C.	2020
1998	Gillian A. Wade Q.C.	2013	2007	John N.M. MacGregor Q.C.	2020
2000	Kenneth McBrearty Q.C.	2013	2000	Kevin F. McCallum Q.C.	2020
1974	Sheriff J.A. Farrell, Q.C.	2013	2005	Lisa J. Gillespie Q.C.	2020
1994	The Hon. Lord Minginish	2013	2004	Paul R. O'Brien Q.C.	2020
2000	Garry Borland QC	2014	2000	Ruth B. Charteris Q.C.	2020
2002	John J. Scullion QC	2014	1992	Archie MacSporran Q.C.,	
2001	Philip J.D. Simpson QC	2014		Esq.	2021
2005	Rhoderick R. McIlvride QC	2014	1997	Robert Hayhow Q.C.	2021
2014	Sheriff Principal Stephen	2015	2000	Mark D. Moir, Q.C.	2021
2000	Joseph J. Morrow Q.C.	2015	2002	Jennifer S. Bain, Q.C.	2021
2001	Kirsty J. Hood Q.C.	2015	2003	David McNaughtan, Q.C.	2021
2000	Roisin A. Higgins Q.C.	2015	2003	Graeme I. Hawkes, Q.C.	2021
2000	Shelagh M. McCall Q.C.	2015	2003	Graeme S. Middleton, Q.C.	2021
2000	Ashley A. Edwards, Q.C.	2016	2005	Jonathan S.G. Bremner, Q.C.	2021
1998	Douglas B. Ross, Q.C.	2016	2006	Duncan G. Hamilton, Q.C.	2021
1999	Euan G. Mackenzie, Q.C.	2016	2007	Catherine Smith, Q.C.	2021
1999	Kay M. Springham, Q.C.	2016	2007	Kirsty Malcolm, Q.C.	2021
1996	Lauren Sutherland, Q.C.	2016	2009	Laura-Anne van der	
1995	Lisa M. Henderson, Q.C.	2016		Westhuizen, Q.C.	2021
2000	Marcus E. McKay, Q.C.	2016			

Advocates' Clerks

Faculty Services Limited
Parliament Square, Edinburgh EH1 1RF
Tel: 0131 226 5071
DX: 549302 Edinburgh-36
Web: www.advocates.org.uk
Email: info@advocates.org.uk

AMPERSAND ADVOCATES
Advocates' Clerk:-
Alan Moffat
Tel: 0131 260 5710
Email: alan.moffat@advocates.org.uk
Deputies:
Jennifer Dunn
Tel: 0131 260 5614
Email: jennifer.dunn@advocates.org.uk
Sheena Hume,
Tel: 0131 260 5809
Email: sheena.hume@advocates.org.uk
Shawn McArthur
Tel: 0131 260 5616
Email: shawn.mcarthur@advocates.org.uk
Kathryn Ferguson
Tel: 0131 260 5660
Email: kathryn.ferguson@advocates.org.uk
Web: www.ampersandadvocates.com
Emma Busby
Tel: 0131 260 5628
Email: emma.busby@advocates.org.uk
Web: www.ampersandadvocates.com
Tel: 0131 260 5674 Email: ampersandclerks@advocates.org.uk

ARNOT MANDERSON ADVOCATES
Advocates' Clerks:-
Elizabeth Manderson
Tel: 0131 260 5699
Email: elizabethmanderson@amadvocates.co.uk
Andrew Sutherland
Tel: 0131 260 5824
Email: andrewsutherland@amadvocates.co.uk
Deputies:
Nicola-Jane Mallace
Tel: 0131 260 5713
Email: nicolajanemallace@amadvocates.co.uk
Dawn Teitsma
Tel: 0131 260 5655
Email: dawnteitsma@amadvocates.co.uk
Anne Webster
Tel: 0131 260 5817
Email: annewebster@amadvocates.co.uk
Web: www.amadvocates.co.uk
Email: clerks@amadvocates.co.uk
Tel: 0131 260 5824 Fax: 0131 225 3642 DX: ED 549302 Edinburgh 36

AXIOM ADVOCATES
Practice Manager:-
Lesley Flynn
Tel: 0131 260 5651

Email: lesley.flynn@axiomadvocates.com
Deputies:
Catriona Still
Tel: 0131 260 5653
Email: catriona.still@axiomadvocates.com
Cheryl Wilson
Tel: 0131 260 5692
Email: cheryl.wilson@axiomadvocates.com
Colleen Adams
Tel: 0131 260 5652
Email: colleen.adams@axiomadvocates.com
Veronica Darling
Tel: 0131 260 5656
Email: veronica.darling@axiomadvocates.com
Steffi Amos
Tel: 0131 260 5686
Email: Steffi.amos@axiomadvocates.com
Web: www.axiomadvocates.com
Tel: 0131 226 2881 Facsimile: 0131 225 3642 DX: ED 549302 Edinburgh 36

BLACK CHAMBERS
Advocates' Clerk:-
Lee-Anne Black
Tel: 0131 260 5681
Email: leeanne.black@blackchambers.co.uk
Deputies:
Steven Burns
Tel: 0131 260 5829
Email: steven.burns@blackchambers.co.uk
Elaine wilson
Tel: 0131 260 5681
Email: clerks@blackchambers.co.uk
Web: www.blackchambers.co.uk
Email: clerks@blackchambers.co.uk
DX: 549302 Edinburgh 36

COMPASS CHAMBERS
Practice Manager:-
Gavin Herd
Tel: 0131 260 5648
Email: gavin.herd@compasschambers.com
Deputies:
Lesley Hogg
Tel: 0131 260 5661
Email: lesley.hogg@compasschambers.com
Lucy McConville
Tel: 0131 260 5657
Email: lucy.mcconville@compasschambers.com
Leona Crosby
Tel: 0131 260 5610
Email: leona.crosby@compasschambers.com
Erica Marmo,
Tel: 0131 260 5696
Email: erica.marmo@compasschambers.com
Web: www.compasschambers.com
Tel: 0131 260 5661 Fax: 0131 225 3642 Email: clerks@compasschambers.com DX: ED 549302
    Edinburgh 36

OPTIMUM ADVOCATES
Practice Manager:-
Angela Bath
Tel: 0141 370 8669
Email: angela.bath@advocates.org.uk
Deputy:

Laura Kenney
Tel: 0141 370 8668
Email: laura.kenney@advocates.org.uk
Web: www.optimumadvocates.com
Tel: 0141 370 8667 Fax: 0141 552 7832 DX: DX 501555, SALTMARKET

TERRA FIRMA CHAMBERS
Practice Manager:-
Emma Caskie-Potter
Tel: 0131 260 5830
Email: emma.potter@terrafirmachambers.com
Deputies:
Andrew Veitch
Tel: 0131 260 5833
Email: andrew.veitch@terrafirmachambers.com
Tracy Whitelaw
Tel: 0131 260 5606
Email: tracy.whitelaw@terrafirmachambers.com
Catriona Downie
Tel: 0131 260 5606
Email: catriona.downie@terrafirmachambers.com
Web: www.terrafirmachambers.com
Tel: 0131 260 5830 Email: clerks@terrafirmachambers.com

THEMIS ADVOCATES
Senior Clerk:
Kiera Johnston
Tel: 0131 260 5654
Email: kiera.johnston@themis-advocates.co.uk
Deputies:
Elizabeth Archibald
Tel: 0131 260 5818
Email: elizabeth.archibald@themis-advocates.co.uk
Sara Mauriello
Tel: 0131 260 5705
Email: sara.mauriello@themis-advocates.co.uk
John-Ross Morland
Tel: 0131 226 2881
Email: jr.morland@themis-advocates.co.uk
Web: www.themis-advocates.co.uk
Tel: 0131 226 2881 Email: clerks@themis-advocates.co.uk DX: 549302 Edinburgh 36

WESTWATER ADVOCATES
Clerk:-
Sheila Westwater
Tel: 0131 260 5700
Email: sheila.westwater@westwateradvocates.com
Deputies:
Christina Ballantyne
Tel: 0131 260 5641
Email: christina.ballantyne@westwateradvocates.com
Debbie Dawson
Tel: 0131 260 5619
Email: debbie.dawson@westwateradvocates.com
Jane Morrison
Tel: 0131 260 5828
Email: jane.morrison@westwateradvocates.com
Web: www.westwateradvocates.com
DX: 549302 Edinburgh 36

Stables (Outwith Faculty Services Limited)

Thomas Ross
Thomas. L. Ross, QC
Tel: 07818 080435

Email: thomasleonardross@icloud.com

Alyson Forbes
Alyson Forbes
Tel: 07805 588883
Email: alyson.forbes@advocates.org.uk

Edith Forrest
Edith F.D. Forrest
Tel: 07764 765927
Email: edithforrest@googlemail.com

Alistair Forsyth
Alistair .J.M. Forsyth
Tel:0131 226 5071Tel:
Email: alistair.forsyth@advocates.org.uk

Anne Gilbride
Simon J. Gilbride
Clerk: Anne Gilbride
Tel: 0141 560 3395 Mob: 07870 830 416
Email: simongilbride@ntlworld.com

Andrew Mason
Andrew D.K. Mason
Tel: 07789 961 719
Email: andrew.mason@advocates.org.uk
Web: www.andrewmasonadvocate.com

Margaret McFarlane
Margaret McFarlane
Tel: 0131 226 5071
Email: margaret.mcfarlane@advocates.org.uk

Andrew Murphy
Andrew J. Murphy
Tel: 07920 596 990
Email: andrew.murphy@advocates.org.uk

Stuart Nicoll
Stuart D.D. Nicoll
Tel: 0131 667 0067 Mob: 07739 639 223
Email: snicoll@advocates.org.uk

Robertson
Graham Robertson
Tel: 07751 534810
Email: jamesgrahamrobertson@yahoo.co.uk

Sean Templeton
Virtual Stable
Clerk: Carolyn Dunlop Tel: 07751 848502
Email: sean.templeton@advocates.org.uk

Thomson Chambers
John G. Thomson
Tel: 0131 343 2436

Email: johnthomson@btinternet.com

Eugene Creally
Eugene P. Creally Q.C.
Tel: 07815 903993
Email: eugene.creally@advocates.org.uk

Gerry Facenna
Gerald C. Facenna
Tel: 020 7468 6369
Email: gerry.facenna@advocates.org.uk

Fees Only FSL Subscribers

Juliette M. Casey
Juliette M. Casey
Tel: 0131 226 5071
Email: juliette.casey@advocates.org.uk

Graeme A. Dalgleish
Graeme A. Dalgleish
Email: graeme.dalgleish@advocates.org.uk
Tel: 0131 226 5071

Christopher Kelly
Christopher Kelly
Tel: 07834 190 388
Email: christopher.kelly@advocates.org.uk

Advocates Stables

AMPERSAND ADVOCATES

Advocates' Library, Parliament House,
Edinburgh EH1 1RF
Tel: (0131) 260 5674
DX: ED549302 Edinburgh 36
Web: www.ampersandadvocates.com

Ampersand provides the full range of services offered by the Scottish Bar, both in contentious and non-contentious work, including advocacy, advice and related written work. Amongst its members are some of the Scottish Bar's most highly rated and successful QCs and junior counsel. Established in 1981 the stable presently has 59 counsel, including 29 QCs. Ampersand has core strength in the fields of Commercial, Planning and Public law, Clinical and Professional Negligence and Personal Injury.

Advocates

Simon D.R. Bowie QC
Isla R. Davie QC
James T. Dawson QC
Alan R. Dewar QC
Simon R. Di Rollo QC
Una Doherty QC
Ian S. Forrester QC
Graeme I. Hawkes QC
Lisa M. Henderson QC
Robert B.M. Howie QC
Vinit Khurana QC
Euan G. Mackenzie QC
Archie MacSporran QC
Maria B. Maguire QC
Marcus E. McKay QC
Geoffrey D. Mitchell QC
Aidan O'Neill QC
Graham S. Primrose QC
Douglas B. Ross QC
David P. Sellar QC
David A. Stephenson QC
Michael A. Stuart QC
Lauren Sutherland QC
Susanne L.M. Tanner QC
Malcolm G. Thomson QC
Laura-Anne van der Westhuizen QC
Ailsa M. Wilson QC
Ross G. Anderson
Stephen A. Bell
Mark S. Boni
Russell Bradley
Roderick A.M. Campbell
Alan Cowan
Fiona C. Drysdale
Shane Dundas
Mark J. Fitzpatrick
Brian Fitzpatrick
Dana Forbes
Jamie R. Gardiner

Laurence C. Kennedy
Graham M. Maciver
Eoghainn C.M. Maclean
Christian D. Marney
Nicholas A. McAndrew
James McConnell
Louise J. Milligan
Jennifer Nicholson-White
Paul Reid
Giles Reid
Euan D.N. Scott
Mary Ellen Stewart
Philip M. Stuart
Alexander Sutherland
Usman Tariq
Michael Way
Timothy Young

ARNOT MANDERSON

Advocates Library, Parliament House,
Edinburgh EH1 1RF
Tel: (0131) 226 2881
DX: ED 549302 Edinburgh 36
E-mail: clerks@amadvocates.co.uk
Web: www.amadvocates.co.uk

Advocates

P. Jonathan Brodie QC
Joanna Cherry QC
Marian L.B.G. Gilmore QC
Duncan G. Hamilton QC
Gordon Jackson QC
Colin J. MacAulay QC
Neil R. Mackenzie QC
Iain G. Mitchell QC
Jonathan J. Mitchell QC
Andrew R.W. Young QC
Peter G.S. Barclay
Manus A. Blessing
D. Frank M. Burr
Marie H. Clark
David W. Cobb
Patricia B. Comiskey
Simon P. Crabb
Martin Crawford
Andrew J. Crosbie
Paul G. Davies
Gavin Dewar
Stephen Donnelly
Nick Gardiner
Nicola J. Gilchrist
B. J. Gill
John Halley
Paul G. Harvey
Stephen J. Hughes
Alan Inglis
Wojciech Jajdelski
Maurice Jamieson
Ceit-Anna MacLeod

John Macpherson
Catriona J. MacQueen
E. Kevin McCaffery
Stephen F. McCloy
Jonathan Murphy
Charles J.C. Oliver
Hugh J. Olson
A. Price-Marmion
Eric W. Robertson
David H. Small
Arabella E.C.C. Tait
Laura Thomson
Sarah Trainer
David J. Turner
Fergus Whyte

AXIOM ADVOCATES

Advocates Library, Parliament House,
Edinburgh EH1 1RF
Tel: (0131) 226 2881
Fax: (0131) 225 3642
DX: ED 549302 Edinburgh 36
Web: www.axiomadvocates.com

Axiom Advocates is a set specialising in
commercial and public law. In the short time
since its formation in 2007, it has already
established a reputation for high quality
advice and advocacy. Unlike the traditional
Scottish 'stables' of counsel, Axiom's
membership has been selected on merit. The
set contains many of the most highly rated
senior and junior counsel at the Scottish Bar.
Many senior and junior counsel within the set
are regarded as the foremost, or leading,
counsel in their chosen spheres. Its members
have consistently appeared in the most
significant cases in Scotland in recent years.
Work Undertaken: The set is particularly strong
in commercial law at the Scottish Bar. The
work undertaken encompasses almost all
aspects of commerce and finance. In
particular, Axiom offers specialists in
commercial contracts, construction, corporate
finance, energy, insolvency, intellectual
property, media and entertainment, planning,
property, professional negligence and sports
law. In the public law, human rights and
regulatory fields, the set has an unrivalled
concentration of talent at the Scottish Bar.
Several members have appointments as
standing junior counsel to the Scottish
Government and the Advocate General. Its
members have acted in many ground
breaking decisions in public law and human
rights, particularly arising out of devolution
and the incorporation into Scots law of the
European Convention on Human Rights.
Members are also regularly instructed for
disciplinary hearings and for planning inquiries
and appeals.
International: The work of the set includes
advice and advocacy in relation to
cross-border and international issues and
disputes.

Advocates

Jonathan M. Barne QC
Garry Borland QC
Jonathan S.G. Bremner QC
Ruth Crawford QC
The Lord Davidson of Glen Clova
Almira Delibegovic-Broome QC
The Rt. Hon. Lord Drummond Young
Alastair J. Duncan QC
Roderick W. Dunlop QC
Iain W.F. Ferguson QC
I. Julian Ghosh QC
The Rt. Hon. Lord Glennie
The Rt. Hon. Lord Hamilton
Roisin A. Higgins QC
David E.L. Johnston QC
The Rt. Hon. The Lord Keen of Elie QC
Jonathan C. Lake QC
Mark S.H. Lindsay QC
John N.M. MacGregor QC
Kenneth McBrearty QC
Gerry J.B. Moynihan QC
James D. McF. H. Mure QC
Paul R. O'Brien QC
Morag V. Ross QC
David M. Thomson QC
Gavin J. Walker QC
James Wolffe QC
Victoria M. Arnott
David R. Blair
Jonathan Broome
Jonathan A. Brown
Daniel Byrne
Ewen Campbell
Megan Dewart
Jacqueline Fordyce
Miranda I.H. Hamilton
Lesley Irvine
Scott Manson
David Massaro
Ross McClelland
Alasdair N. McKenzie
Adam J. McKinlay
Andrew J. McWhirter
Susan P. Ower
Chris Paterson
Elizabeth Roxburgh
Murray Steel
Neale A. Tosh
Kirsty E. Tyre
Helen M. Watts
David Welsh
Christopher C. Wilson

BLACK CHAMBERS

Parliament House, Edinburgh EH1 1RF
Tel: (0131) 260 5681
DX: ED549302 Edinburgh 36
E-mail: leeanne.black@blackchambers.co.uk
Web: www.blackchambers.co.uk

Advocates
Jennifer S. Bain QC
I.M. Duguid QC
Ashley A. Edwards QC
Lisa J. Gillespie QC
Herbert A. Kerrigan QC
Andrew J. Lamb QC
Shelagh M. McCall QC
Brian McConnachie QC
Frances J. McMenamin QC
Michael E.A. Meehan QC
Ronaldo A. Renucci QC
Lorenzo Alonzi
Michael D. Anderson
Margaret J. Barron
Steven C. Borthwick
John Brannigan
Kenneth W. Cloggie
Jonathan Crowe
Victoria Dow
Kelly M. Duling
Charles Ferguson
Craig Findlater
George C. Gebbie
Gail I. Gianni
Gareth Jones
Leigh Lawrie
Tony Lenehan
Katariina S. Maguire
Drew McKenzie
David J. Moggach
Frederick (Derick) J. Nelson
Lili Prais
Iain Smith
David Taylor
Ximena Vengochea

COMPASS CHAMBERS
The Faculty of Advocates, Parliament House,
Edinburgh EH1 1RF
Tel: (0131) 226 2881
Fax: (0131) 225 3642
DX: ED 549302 Edinburgh 36
E-mail: info@compasschambers.com
Web: www.compasschambers.com
Compass Chambers is a welcoming set of
leading Advocates with a long-standing
reputation for excellence.
Our ethos is simple: to demonstrate excellence
at all times while working with you to achieve
the best possible outcome. Our membership,
based exclusively on merit, embraces this
ethos and is central to our well-deserved
reputation.
Compass advocates have vast experience of
representing parties in all Scottish Courts and
in the UK Supreme Court.
Our advocates and clerks are all professional
and hard-working but at the same time noted
for their friendliness and helpfulness. We pride
ourselves in striving to deliver a high quality
service across our practice areas and look to

add value by, among other things, hosting
regular conferences and providing bespoke
training programmes.
Advocates
Amber Galbraith QC
Angela T. Grahame QC
Peter L. Gray QC
Steven A. Love QC
D. Ian Mackay QC
Murdo A. MacLeod QC
David McNaughtan QC
Graeme S. Middleton QC
Robert G. Milligan QC
Claire M. Mitchell QC
John J. Scullion QC
Lesley M. Shand QC
David H. Sheldon QC
Astrid E. Smart QC
Andrew Smith QC
Barry T. Smith QC
Catherine Smith QC
Kay M. Springham QC
Mark L. Stewart QC
David P. Adams
Gavin J. Anderson
Gordon S. Balfour
Kate Bennett
Andrew J. Bergin
Adam Black
Tom Brownlee
Kenneth M. Christine
Robin G. Cleland
Clare Connelly
Carla R. Fraser
James B. Hastie
Richard S. Henderson
Stephen A. Laing
Bruce Langlands
Preston Lloyd
Ranald Macpherson
Grant Markie
Hugh L. Masters
Jan McCall
Malcolm B. McGregor
Craig M. Murray
David Nicolson
Richard J. Pugh
Gregor Rolfe
Barney Ross
Elaine J. Russell
Dominic Scullion
Cameron N. Smith
David Swanney
Gavin J. Thornley
Emma C. Toner
Yvonne E. Waugh
Calum S. Wilson

OPTIMUM ADVOCATES
Glasgow High Court, 1 Mart Street, Glasgow
G1 5JT
Tel: (0141) 370 8667
Fax: (0141) 552 7832

DX: 501555 Saltmarket
E-mail: optimuminfo@advocates.org.uk
Web: www.optimumadvocates.com
Optimum Advocates is the only group within the Faculty of Advocates based in the City of Glasgow, whilst at the same time retaining a presence in Edinburgh.
Currently one of the largest stables of Advocates, our Counsel are increasingly instructed as the most effective source of legal representation in Scotland.
As a leading provider of Referral Legal Services in Scotland, Optimum Advocates includes some of the best known and highly regarded Advocates at all levels of seniority presently in practice. Instructing solicitors tell us that what sets Optimum Advocates apart from other stables is our approach to serving clients best. This has led Optimum Advocates to extend beyond our origins in criminal law, where we are rightly regarded as pre-eminent, to include highly regarded practitioners in other fields, including Commercial, Family, Employment, Immigration and Regulatory Law.
We provide representation for clients in all Courts throughout Scotland, Tribunals, Hearings and Enquiries at all levels, both in Scotland and elsewhere in the UK.
Our Advocates' experience and special interests are wide ranging as can be seen from their areas of practice as detailed on their individual profile pages on the website.
We accept instructions on both a legal aid and private client basis.

Advocates

Gary J.G Allan QC
Donald R. Findlay QC
Anthony J. Graham QC
Mark D. Moir QC
Neil D. Murray QC
Edward G.M. Targowski QC
Bill R. Adam
Julian Aitken
Adam Ardrey
Donna Armstrong
Louise M. Arrol
Patricia M. Baillie
Joseph A. Barr
Neil J. Beardmore
Frances C. Connor
Euan A. Dow
Gregory Farrell
Geoffrey Forbes
Lorraine M. Glancy
Janice Green
Rosemary M. Guinnane
Wendy Hay
Kevin J. Henry
Callum A. Hiller
Dale Hughes
Lewis K. Kennedy
Sarah M. Livingstone
Caroline F. MacBride

Lynsey MacDonald
Alan A. Mackay
Allan J. Macleod
David Ross MacLeod
Niall R. McCluskey
John McElroy
Shirley McKenna
Duncan H. McPhie
Rosalyn J. McTaggart
Alan N. Melvin-Farr
Valentina Mori
Owen Mullan
Paul M. Nelson
Laura Anne Radcliffe
Stewart P. Ronnie
Gillian Ross
Neil Shand
Victoria J. Young

TERRA FIRMA CHAMBERS
Parliament House, Edinburgh EH1 1RF
Tel: (0131) 260 5830
DX: ED 549302 Edinburgh 36
E-mail: clerks@terrafirmachambers.com
Web: www.terrafirmachambers.com
Terra Firma Chambers is recognised as one of the leading stables at the Scottish Bar, providing expert advice and representation in property, planning, commercial and administrative law. Established in 2008 to meet the changing demands of modern legal practice, Terra Firma combines formidable strength and depth in its core practice areas, with approachable clerks and a commercial, client-orientated service. In addition to our core areas of practice, our Members offer unrivalled expertise in taxation, employment, local government and licensing law and we are the only stable at the Scottish Bar to provide a dedicated arbitration service, TFArb. 11 members, including 7 QC's, have dual-qualification in Scotland and England & Wales which is more than any other stable at the Scottish Bar. This makes Terra Firma Chambers particularly well placed to come to as a source of advice or representation for clients with UK wide interests. Our collective and individual commitment to excellence has been recognised by leading directories, Chambers and Partners and the Legal 500. Working together with clients and instructing agents we will strive to ensure that our practice continues to develop to meet their needs and to maintain the highest standards of professional service.

Advocates

Douglas Armstrong QC
Andrew John Bowen QC
Scott Brady QC
Alasdair J. Burnet QC
Peter W. Ferguson QC
James d. C. Findlay QC
W. Stuart Gale QC

Michael P. Howlin QC (non practising in
England & Wales)
Fred Mackintosh QC
Rhoderick R. McIlvride QC
Philip J.D. Simpson QC
Gordon R. Steele QC
Faryma Bahrami
Neil Beynon
Scott Blair
Ewen D. Brown
Fergus A.M. Colquhoun
Brian Crook
Graham A. Dunlop
Denis J. Edwards
William J. Frain-Bell
Derek R.L. Francis
Denis Garrity
Peter A. Grant-Hutchison
Nicholas W. Holroyd
Jonathan Kiddie
Neil C. Kinnear
Mark Lazarowicz
M. Luise S. Locke
David J.T. Logan
Catriona MacLeod
Roderick MacLeod
Mark C. Mohammed
Maurice O'Carroll
Robert G. Skinner
Robert D. Sutherland
Gordon H. Watt
Stephen Frederic Winter

THEMIS ADVOCATES
Advocates Library, Parliament House,
Edinburgh EH1 1RF
Tel: (0131) 226 2881
Fax: (0131) 225 3642
DX: 549302 Edinburgh 36
E-mail: clerks@themis-advocates.co.uk
Web: www.themis-advocates.co.uk/
Advocates
Mungo Bovey QC
Andrew L. Brown QC
John D. Campbell QC
Laura J. Dunlop QC
Leo Hofford QC
Kirsty J. Hood QC
Gavin L. MacColl QC
Alan W.D. McLean QC
Brian W. Napier QC
Steven Walker QC
Andrew G. Webster QC
David F. Ballantyne
Michael J. Bell
Tracey Brown
Alan B. Caskie
Maria Clarke
Gerard F. Coll
Andrew Crawford
Donald Davidson
Michael Dempsey
Andrew W. Devlin

Susan Fallone
Kenneth H. Forrest
Kenneth J.S. Gibson
Tim Haddow
Alasdair F. Hardman
Ewan Hawthorn
Graeme M. Henderson
Robert S. Hovey
Christopher Jones
David N. Leighton
Catherine MacColl
Ann MacNeill
Julie McKinlay
David McLean
Fintan M. McShane
Graham Middleton
Christopher Miller
John A.P. Moir
Ross Pilkington
Christopher J. Pirie
Katerina Stein
Michael G.J. Upton

WESTWATER ADVOCATES
Faculty of Advocates, Parliament House,
Edinburgh EH1 1RF
Tel: (0131) 260 5700
DX: 549302 Edinburgh 36
E-mail:
sheila.westwater@westwateradvocates.com
Web: www.westwateradvocates.com
Advocates
Lynda J Brabender QC
Nicholas St John Ellis QC
Robert Hayhow QC
Ruth M. Innes QC
Calum H.S. MacNeill QC
Kirsty Malcom QC
James A. Peoples QC
Janys M. Scott QC
Mark Allison
David Anderson
Melanie J. Barbour
Anne Bennie
Emily J. Bradbury
Julianna F. Cartwright
Desmond Cheyne
Laurence G. Cunningham
Amy J. Donachie
Colin Edward
Isabella R. Ennis
David J.P. Hay
Bryan J. Heaney
Maggie Hughes
Gordon J.S. Lindhorst
Neil MacDougall
Andrew K. MacMillan
Scott McAlpine
Kenneth McGuire
Jane Rattray
C. Gregory Sanders
Ian Sharpe
Rachel Shewan

Adrian G Stalker
Alice L. Stobart
Antonia L. Welsh

Alison M. Wild
Laura M.S. Wray

Solicitor Advocates

Queen's Counsel

Solicitors granted extended rights of audience in Civil and Criminal cases (the Court of Session, House of Lords and Judicial Committee of the Privy Council; and the High Court of Justiciary)

CARRUTHERS, John, Director, Oraclelaw Limited, Glasgow Tel: (0141) 4041091
Email: jc@oraclelaw.com

CONNAL, Robert, Solicitor

CORMACK, James, Partner, Pinsent Masons LLP, Edinburgh Tel: (0131) 777 7000
Email: jim.cormack@pinsentmasons.com

LINDSAY, Ranald, Partner, Lindsay, Dumfries
Tel: (01387) 259236
Email: ranald@lindsaysolicitors.co.uk

RAM, Manjit, Partner, East End Law, Glasgow
Tel: (0141) 5544556
Email: manjitram@eastendlaw.co.uk

Solicitors granted extended rights of audience in Civil cases only (the Court of Session, House of Lords and Judicial Committee of the Privy Council)

ADAM, Michelle, Partner, Thorntons Law LLP, Edinburgh Tel: (0131) 2258705
Email: madam@thorntons-law.co.uk

ANDERSON, Lesley, Director, Lesley Anderson Law Ltd, Falkirk Tel: (01324) 278 565
Email: enquiries@lesleyandersonlaw.co.uk

ANDERSON, Michael, Consultant, Levy & McRae Solicitors LLP, Glasgow Tel: (0141) 3072311
Email: PAnderson@lemac.co.uk

ARMSTRONG, David, Partner, Lindsays LLP, Glasgow Tel: (0141) 2216551
Email: davidarmstrong@lindsays.co.uk

ATKINSON, Beverley, Associate, DAC Beachcroft Scotland LLP, Edinburgh Tel: (0131) 5247790
Email: batkinson@dacbeachcroft.com

AYRE, Victoria, Employee, Scottish Government, Edinburgh Tel: (0131) 244 0815
Email: Victoria.Ayre@gov.scot

BAIN, Julie, Employee, Scottish Government, Edinburgh Tel: (0131) 244 0815
Email: julie.bain@gov.scot

BARBOUR, Alistair, Employee, BTO Solicitors LLP, Glasgow Tel: (0141) 2218012
Email: awb@bto.co.uk

BARNES, Eilidh, Employee, Scottish Legal Aid Board, Edinburgh Tel: (0131) 2267061
Email: barnesei@slab.org.uk

BATCHELOR, Duncan, Partner, Clyde & Co (Scotland) LLP, Edinburgh
Tel: (0131) 5571545
Email: duncan.batchelor@clydeco.com

BAXENDALE, Laura, Employee, Keoghs Scotland LLP, Glasgow Tel: (0141) 2380100
Email: lbaxendale@keoghs.co.uk

BLANE, Laura, Partner, Thompsons, Glasgow
Tel: (0141) 2218840
Email: laura.blane@thompsons-scotland.co.uk

BLANE, Stephen, Partner, Urquharts, Edinburgh
Tel: (0131) 5562896
Email: stephenblane@urquharts.co.uk

BLYTH, Douglas, Partner, Dentons UK and Middle East LLP, Glasgow Tel: (0330) 2220050
Email: Douglas.Blyth@dentons.com

BRYCELAND, Stephen, Partner, BTO Solicitors LLP, Glasgow Tel: (0141) 2218012
Email: sbr@bto.co.uk

BUSBY, Seonaid, Partner, Weightmans (Scotland) LLP, Glasgow Tel: (0345) 073 9900
Email: Seonaid.busby@weightmans.com

CAMERON, Karen, Associate, Ledingham Chalmers LLP, Inverness Tel: (01463) 667400
Email: karen.cameron@ledinghamchalmers.com

CAMPBELL, Brian, Employee, Brodies LLP, Glasgow Tel: (0141) 2484672
Email: brian.campbell@brodies.com

CAMPBELL, Martin, Employee, Build Hollywood Ltd, London N1

CARMICHAEL, Deborah, Partner, Jones Whyte LLP, Glasgow Tel: (0141) 375 1222
Email: deborah.carmichael@joneswhyte.co.uk

CARR, Robert, Partner, Anderson Strathern LLP, Edinburgh Tel: (0131) 2707700
Email: robert.carr@andersonstrathern.co.uk

CATTO, Simon, Partner, Addleshaw Goddard LLP, Edinburgh Tel: (0131) 2282400
Email: Simon.Catto@addleshawgoddard.com

CHALMERS, John, Partner, Ledingham Chalmers LLP, Edinburgh Tel: (0131) 2001000
Email: john.chalmers@ledinghamchalmers.com

CLANCY, Kevin, Partner, Shepherd and Wedderburn LLP, Edinburgh
Tel: (0131) 2289900
Email: kevin.clancy@shepwedd.com

CLARK, Iain, Partner, Gilson Gray LLP, Glasgow
Tel: (0141) 5302021
Email: iclark@gilsongray.co.uk

CLUBB, Stuart, Partner, Shoosmiths, Edinburgh
Tel: (03700) 868000
Email: stuart.clubb@shoosmiths.co.uk

COLLINS, Michael, Associate, Pinsent Masons LLP, Glasgow Tel: (0141) 567 8400
Email: michael.collins@pinsentmasons.com

CONWAY, Ronald, Director, The Conway Accident Law Practice Ltd, Glasgow
Tel: (0141) 319 8240
Email: ronniec@accidentlawscotland.com

COOPER, Louise, Partner, Reid Cooper, Glasgow
Tel: (0141) 4294656
Email: lcc@reidcooper.co.uk

CORNWELL, Jonathan, Partner, Lindsays LLP, Glasgow Tel: (0141) 2216551
Email: jonathancornwell@linsdays.co.uk

COULL, Elaine, Employee, National Health Service Scotland, Edinburgh
Tel: (0131) 2757800
Email: elaine.coull@nhs.scot

CRAWFORD, Clare, Employee, Kennedys Scotland, Glasgow Tel: (0141) 433 7115
Email: Clare.Crawford@kennedyslaw.com

CROOKS, Peter, Partner, Lanarkshire Accident Law, Coatbridge Tel: (01236) 222888
Email: peter.crooks@lanaccidentlaw.co.uk

CULLEN, Joyce, Partner, Brodies LLP, Edinburgh
Tel: (0131) 2283777
Email: joyce.cullen@brodies.com

CURRIE, Catherine, Partner, BTO Solicitors LLP, Glasgow Tel: (0141) 2218012
Email: ccr@bto.co.uk

DAILLY, Michael, Partner, Dailly, Walker and Co., Solicitors, Glasgow Tel: (0141) 4402503
Email: m@govanlc.com

DALYELL, Gordon, Partner, Digby Brown LLP, Edinburgh Tel: (0333) 200 5925
Email: gordon.dalyell@digbybrown.co.uk

DANGERFIELD, Gordon, Consultant, Archer Coyle, Glasgow Tel: (0141) 6372434
Email: gordondangerfield@archercoyle.co.uk

DAVEY, Jane, Employee, Highland Council, Inverness Tel: (01463) 702000
Email: jane.davey@highland.gov.uk

DEAN, Alistair, Partner, Anderson Strathern LLP, Edinburgh Tel: (0131) 2707700
Email: alistair.dean@andersonstrathern.co.uk

DICKSON, Jennifer, Partner, Morton Fraser LLP, Edinburgh Tel: (0131) 2471000
Email: Jenny.dickson@morton-fraser.com

DICKSON, John, Employee, Scottish Legal Aid Board, Edinburgh Tel: (0131) 2267061
Email: dicksonia@slab.org.uk

DONALD, Laura, Partner, BTO Solicitors LLP, Edinburgh Tel: (0131) 2222939
Email: ljd@bto.co.uk

DONALDSON, Mark, Partner, Clyde & Co (Scotland) LLP, Aberdeen Tel: (01224) 624924
Email: mark.donaldson@clydeco.com

DRUMMOND, Iain, Partner, Shepherd and Wedderburn LLP, Edinburgh
Tel: (0131) 2289900
Email: iain.drummond@shepwedd.com

EDWARD, Graeme, Partner, Ledingham Chalmers LLP, Aberdeen Tel: (01224) 408408
Email: graeme.edward@ledinghamchalmers.com

EDWARD, Timothy, Partner, MBM Commercial LLP, Edinburgh Tel: (0131) 2268200
Email: Tim.Edward@mbmcommercial.co.uk

FERRY, Noel, Partner, Weightmans (Scotland) LLP, Glasgow Tel: (0345) 073 9900
Email: noel.ferry@weightmans.com

FORBES, Mary, Associate, CMS Cameron McKenna Nabarro Olswang LLP, Aberdeen
Tel: (01224) 622002
Email: mary.forbes@cms-cmno.com

FORREST, Carly, Partner, Brodies LLP, Glasgow
Tel: (0141) 2484672
Email: carly.forrest@brodies.com

FORRESTER, Emma, Employee, Ennova Limited, Dundee Tel: (01382) 938118
Email: eforrester@ennova-law.com

FOYLE, Andrew, Partner, Shoosmiths, Edinburgh
Tel: (03700) 868000
Email: andrew.foyle@shoosmiths.co.uk

FYFFE, Linda, Partner, Laurie & Co Solicitors LLP, Aberdeen Tel: (01224) 645 085
Email: Linda@laurieandco.co.uk

GARIOCH, Alexander, Partner, Gilson Gray LLP, Edinburgh Tel: (0131) 5165354
Email: agarioch@gilsongray.co.uk

GIBSON, Andrew, Associate, Morton Fraser LLP, Glasgow Tel: (0141) 2741100
Email: Andrew.Gibson@morton-fraser.com

GILDEA, John, Associate, John Jackson & Dick Limited, Hamilton Tel: (01698) 281747
Email: jgildea@jacksondicklaw.com

GILLIES, Joanne, Partner, Pinsent Masons LLP, Glasgow Tel: (0141) 567 8400
Email: joanne.gillies@pinsentmasons.com

GODDEN, Richard, Partner, Blackadders LLP, Edinburgh Tel: (0131) 2228000
Email: richard.godden@blackadders.co.uk

GORDON, Alisdair, Partner, A. J. Gordon & Co, Glasgow Tel: (07812) 000554
Email: al@algordonlawyers.co.uk

GRAHAM, Gilles, Partner, Clyde & Co (Scotland) LLP, Glasgow Tel: (0141) 2482666
Email: gilles.graham@clydeco.com

GRATWICK, Edward, Associate, Addleshaw Goddard LLP, Edinburgh Tel: (0131) 2282400
Email: Edward.Gratwick@addleshawgoddard.com

GRIBBEN, Raymond, Associate, Levy & McRae Solicitors LLP, Glasgow Tel: (0141) 3072311
Email: RGribben@lemac.co.uk

GRIEVE, Erin, Employee, Addleshaw Goddard LLP, Edinburgh Tel: (0131) 2282400
Email: Erin.Grieve@addleshawgoddard.com

GUILD, Steven, Partner, Burness Paull LLP, Aberdeen Tel: (01224) 621621
Email: Steven.Guild@burnesspaull.com

HAMILTON, Colin, Partner, Gillespie Macandrew LLP, Edinburgh Tel: (0131) 2251677
Email: colin.hamilton@gillespiemacandrew.co.uk

HAMILTON, Julie, Partner, MacRoberts LLP, Edinburgh Tel: (0131) 2295046
Email: julie.hamilton@macroberts.com

HARRIS, Emma, Employee, Diageo Scotland Limited, Edinburgh Tel: (0131) 519 2261
Email: Emma.Harris@diageo.com

HARRIS, Jacqueline, Partner, Pinsent Masons LLP, Edinburgh Tel: (0131) 777 7000
Email: jacqueline.harris@pinsentmasons.com

HARRIS, Julie, Partner, Allan McDougall McQueen LLP, Edinburgh Tel: (0131) 2252121
Email: julieharris@allanmcdougall.co.uk

HASTINGS, Mark, Associate, BTO Solicitors LLP, Glasgow Tel: (0141) 2218012
Email: mfh@bto.co.uk

HAYWOOD, Brent, Partner, Lindsays LLP, Edinburgh Tel: (0131) 2291212
Email: brenthaywood@lindsays.co.uk

HENDERSON, Andrew, Partner, Thompsons, Glasgow Tel: (0141) 2218840
Email: andrew.henderson@thompsons-scotland.co.uk

HENNESSY, David, Partner, Keoghs Scotland LLP, Glasgow Tel: (0141) 2380100
Email: DHennessy@keoghs.scot

HOGG, Nicola, Employee, West Lothian Council, Livingston Tel: (01506) 280000
Email: Nicola.Hogg@westlothian.gov.uk

HOLLAND, Robert, Partner, Balfour + Manson LLP, Edinburgh Tel: (0131) 2001200
Email: robert.holland@balfour-manson.co.uk

HOLMES, Stuart, Employee, National Health Service Scotland, Edinburgh
Tel: (0131) 2757800
Email: Stuart.Holmes@nhs.scot

HUGHES, David, Partner, Addleshaw Goddard LLP, Edinburgh Tel: (0131) 2282400

HUNTER, Nikki, Associate, Morton Fraser LLP, Glasgow Tel: (0141) 2741100
Email: nikki.hunter@morton-fraser.com

HUTCHISON, Rona, Solicitor

IRELAND, Andrew, Employee, DAC Beachcroft Scotland LLP, Glasgow Tel: (0141) 2486688
Email: aireland@dacbeachcroft.com

JAAP, Douglas, Director, Jaaplaw Limited, Falkirk Tel: (01324) 710137 Email: dwj@dwjlaw.com

JANSCH, Steven, Partner, Gilson Gray LLP, Edinburgh Tel: (0131) 5165354
Email: sjansch@gilsongray.co.uk

JONES, Alan, Partner, Russel + Aitken Edinburgh LLP, Edinburgh Tel: (0131) 2285500
Email: alan.jones@russelaitken-edinburgh.com

JONES, Antony, Partner, Brodies LLP, Edinburgh Tel: (0131) 2283777
Email: tony.jones@brodies.com

KANE, Kristopher, Employee, Kennedys Scotland, Edinburgh Tel: (0131) 2256145
Email: kristopher.kane@kennedyslaw.com

KELLY, Caroline, Partner, Thorntons Law LLP, Dundee Tel: (01382) 229 111
Email: ckelly@thorntons-law.co.uk

KING, Robert, Partner, Clyde & Co (Scotland) LLP, Glasgow Tel: (0141) 2482666
Email: robert.king@clydeco.com

KIRK, Karen, Partner, Kirk Hanlon, Glasgow Tel: (0141) 3786653
Email: karen@kirkhanlon.com

LAUDER, Kenneth, Employee, Gilson Gray LLP, Edinburgh Tel: (0131) 5165354
Email: klauder@gilsongray.co.uk

LEACH, Ian, Partner, Berrymans Lace Mawer LLP, Edinburgh Tel: (0131) 2259855
Email: Ian.Leach@blmlaw.com

LEE, John, Partner, Ledingham Chalmers LLP, Edinburgh Tel: (0131) 2001000
Email: john.lee@ledinghamchalmers.com

LITTLEJOHN, Peter, Consultant, Raeburn Christie Clark & Wallace LLP, Aberdeen
Tel: (01224) 332400
Email: Peter.Littlejohn@raeburns.co.uk

LOGAN, Anne, Employee, DAC Beachcroft Scotland LLP, Glasgow Tel: (0141) 2486688
Email: alogan@dacbeachcroft.com

LUMSDAINE, Katrina, Partner, Anderson Strathern LLP, Edinburgh Tel: (0131) 2707700
Email: katrina.lumsdaine@andersonstrathern.co.uk

MACDOUGALL, Greg, Partner, Berrymans Lace Mawer LLP, Edinburgh Tel: (0131) 2259855
Email: Greg.MacDougall@blmlaw.com

MACFARLANE, Lynne, Employee, DWF LLP, Glasgow Tel: (0141) 228 8000
Email: lynne.macfarlane@dwf.law

MACGREGOR, Fiona, Employee, Dentons UK and Middle East LLP, Glasgow Tel: (0330) 2220050
Email: Fiona.macgregor@dentons.com

MACKAY, Malcolm, Partner, Brodies LLP, Aberdeen Tel: (01224) 392242
Email: malcolm.mackay@brodies.com

MACKENZIE, Andrew, Partner, Harper Macleod LLP, Glasgow Tel: (0141) 2218888
Email: andrew.mackenzie@harpermacleod.co.uk

MACKENZIE, John, Partner, Shepherd and Wedderburn LLP, Edinburgh
Tel: (0131) 2289900
Email: John.Mackenzie@shepwedd.com

MACLEAN, Catriona, Partner, MBM Commercial LLP, Edinburgh Tel: (0131) 2268200
Email: cat.maclean@mbmcommercial.co.uk

MACNIVEN, Ruaraidh, Employee, Scottish Government, Edinburgh Tel: (0131) 244 0815
Email: ruaraidh.macniven@gov.scot

MACPHERSON, Robin, Solicitor

MALONE, Brandon, Director, Brandon Malone & Company Limited, Edinburgh
Tel: (0131) 357 8549
Email: brandon@brandonmalone.com

MATTHEW, John, Employee, Scottish Water, Dunfermline Tel: (01383) 665410
Email: steve.matthew@scottishwater.co.uk

MCCABE, Laura, Employee, Anderson Strathern LLP, Edinburgh Tel: (0131) 2707700
Email: laura.mccabe@andersonstrathern.co.uk

MCCARTNEY, Natalie, Employee, BTO Solicitors LLP, Edinburgh Tel: (0131) 2222939
Email: nem@bto.co.uk

MCCLUSKIE, Peter, Partner, Keoghs Scotland LLP, Glasgow Tel: (0141) 2380100
Email: mmccluskie@keoghs.co.uk

MCDAID, Arlene, Solicitor

MCENTEGART, Thomas, Partner, TLT LLP, Glasgow Tel: (0333) 006 0400
Email: Tom.McEntegart@tltsolicitors.com

MCGARRIGLE, Suzanne, Partner, Harper Macleod LLP, Glasgow Tel: (0141) 2218888
Email: suzanne.mcgarrigle@harpermacleod.co.uk

MCGLADRIGAN, Peter, Employee, TLT LLP, Edinburgh Tel: (0131) 2207460
Email: peter.mcgladrigan@tltsolicitors.com

MCGUIRE, Patrick, Partner, Thompsons, Glasgow Tel: (0141) 2218840
Email: patrick.mcguire@thompsons-scotland.co.uk

MCHUGH, Edward, Employee, Lord President's Private Office, Edinburgh Tel: (0131) 2406701
Email: emchugh@scotcourts.gov.uk

MCHUGH, John, Partner, Harper Macleod LLP, Edinburgh Tel: (0131) 2472500
Email: john.mchugh@harpermacleod.co.uk

MCLAREN, Stephen, Associate, Ledingham Chalmers LLP, Aberdeen Tel: (01224) 408408
Email: stephen.mclaren@ledinghamchalmers.com

MCLEAN, Niall, Partner, Brodies LLP, Edinburgh Tel: (0131) 2283777
Email: niall.mclean@brodies.com

MCLEARY, Rosemary, Employee, Scottish Courts and Tribunals Service, Glasgow
Tel: (0141) 4298888
Email: RMcleary@scotcourts.gov.uk

MCMEEKEN, Richard, Partner, Morton Fraser LLP, Edinburgh Tel: (0131) 2471000
Email: richard.mcmeeken@morton-fraser.com

MCMILLAN, Alan, Partner, Burness Paull LLP, Edinburgh Tel: (0131) 4736000
Email: Alan.McMillan@burnesspaull.com

MCMILLAN, Laura, Partner, Brodies LLP, Edinburgh Tel: (0131) 2283777
Email: laura.mcmillan@brodies.com

MCSHERRY, Euan, Partner, Aberdein Considine and Company, Aberdeen Tel: (01224) 589700
Email: emcsherry@acandco.com

MEIKLE, Claire, Employee, Scottish Government, Edinburgh Tel: (0131) 244 0815
Email: claire.meikle@gov.scot

MILLAR, Gail, Aston Gowman Limited, London TW8 Tel: (0333) 3447277

MILLAR, Glen, Partner, Thompsons, Edinburgh Tel: (0131) 2254297
Email: glen.millar@thompsons-scotland.co.uk

MILLER, Stephen, Partner, Clyde & Co (Scotland) LLP, Glasgow Tel: (0141) 2482666
Email: stephen.miller@clydeco.com

MILNE, Deborah, Partner, Jackson Boyd LLP, Glasgow Tel: (0141) 2214325
Email: dmilne@jacksonboyd.co.uk

MITCHELL, Ross, Employee, Brodies LLP, Edinburgh Tel: (0131) 2283777
Email: ross.mitchell@brodies.com

MOORE, George, Consultant, Berrymans Lace Mawer LLP, Glasgow Tel: (0141) 3532121
Email: gmooreqc@gmail.com

MORRISON, Neil, Employee, Vestas-Celtic Wind Technology Ltd, Edinburgh
Email: nejmo@vestas.com

MORTON, Mark, Partner, BTO Solicitors LLP, Glasgow Tel: (0141) 2218012
Email: macm@bto.co.uk

MOTION, Elaine, Partner, Balfour + Manson LLP, Edinburgh Tel: (0131) 2001200
Email: elaine.motion@balfour-manson.co.uk

MOTION, Paul, Partner, BTO Solicitors LLP, Edinburgh Tel: (0131) 2222939
Email: prm@bto.co.uk

MOUNTAIN, Susannah, Employee, Brodies LLP, Aberdeen Tel: (01224) 392242
Email: susie.mountain@brodies.com

MUIRS, Fiona, Partner, Balfour + Manson LLP, Edinburgh Tel: (0131) 2001200
Email: fiona.muirs@balfour-manson.co.uk

MUNDY, Fiona, Consultant, Johnson Legal, Edinburgh Tel: (0131) 6229222
Email: fiona@johnsonlegal.co.uk

MURDOCH, Alistair, Employee, Murnin McCluskey, Glasgow Tel: (0141) 2221760
Email: am@murnin.co.uk

MURDOCH, Stuart, Partner, DLA Piper Scotland LLP, Edinburgh Tel: (08700) 111111
Email: Stuart.Murdoch@dlapiper.com

NEWCOMBE, Claire, Employee, DAC Beachcroft Scotland LLP, Edinburgh Tel: (0131) 5247790
Email: cnewcombe@dacbeachcroft.com

NISBET, Jonathan, Director, Nisbets Solicitors Limited, Edinburgh Tel: (07967) 754488
Email: jn@nisbetssolicitors.com

NORMAND, Andrew, Employee, DAC Beachcroft Scotland LLP, Edinburgh Tel: (0131) 5247790
Email: cnormand@dacbeachcroft.com

O'HANLON, Mark, Partner, Mains Solicitors, East Kilbride Tel: (01355) 225111
Email: mohanlon@mainslegal.com

O'NEILL, Christine, Partner, Brodies LLP, Edinburgh Tel: (0131) 2283777
Email: christine.oneill@brodies.com

OGILVIE, Lindsey, Partner, Turcan Connell, Edinburgh Tel: (0131) 2288111
Email: lindsey.ogilvie@turcanconnell.com

PEDEN, James, Employee, Plexus Law LLP, Edinburgh Tel: (0131) 3229 250
Email: james.peden@plexuslaw.co.uk

PRYDE, Naomi, Partner, DWF LLP, Manchester Tel: (0161) 6035000
Email: naomi.pryde@dwf.law

QUAIL, Thomas, Partner, Wright, Johnston & Mackenzie LLP, Glasgow Tel: (0141) 2483434
Email: tlq@wjm.co.uk

RAE, Lauren, Partner, Thorntons Law LLP, Dundee Tel: (01382) 229 111
Email: lrae@thorntons-law.co.uk

REEKIE, Deborah, Employee, BTO Solicitors LLP, Edinburgh Tel: (0131) 2222939
Email: der@bto.co.uk

REEKIE, James, Associate, Brodies LLP, Edinburgh Tel: (0131) 2283777
Email: jamie.reekie@brodies.com

REID, Robert, Partner, McGovern Reid Court Lawyers, Wishaw Tel: (01698) 359550
Email: br@mcgovernreid.co.uk

RENTON, Andrew, Director, Castletown Law Limited, Edinburgh Tel: (0131) 2403880
Email: andrew.renton@castletownlaw.com

RICHARDSON, Lewis, Employee, BTO Solicitors LLP, Edinburgh Tel: (0131) 2222939
Email: lri@bto.co.uk

RUSHBURY, Gillian, Employee, DAC Beachcroft Scotland LLP, Glasgow Tel: (0141) 2486688
Email: GRushbury@dacbeachcroft.com

RUTHERFORD, Iain, Partner, Brodies LLP, Edinburgh Tel: (0131) 2283777
Email: iain.rutherford@brodies.com

SANDILANDS, Colin, Partner, Stronachs LLP, Inverness Tel: (01463) 713225
Email: colin.sandilands@stronachs.com

SELLAR, Michael, Employee, Carpenters Scotland Limited, Glasgow Tel: (0141) 3285452

SHARP, Jennifer, Employee, Wheatley Housing Group Limited, Glasgow Tel: (0845) 9001001
Email: jennifer.sharp@wheatley-group.com

SHERIDAN, John, Partner, TLT LLP, Glasgow Tel: (0333) 006 0400
Email: jp.Sheridan@tltsolicitors.com

SHIELDS, Bruce, Partner, Thompsons, Glasgow Tel: (0141) 2218840
Email: bruce.shields@thompsons-scotland.co.uk

SINCLAIR, Martin, Partner, Mackinnons Solicitors LLP, Aberdeen Tel: (01224) 632464
Email: martin@mackinnons.com

SINGER, Richard, Associate, Thompsons, Edinburgh Tel: (0131) 2254297 Email: richard.singer@thompsons-scotland.co.uk

SLEE, Kirsten, Employee, Scottish Government, Edinburgh Tel: (0131) 244 0815 Email: kirsty.slee@gov.scot

SOUTER, Caitlin, Employee, National Health Service Scotland, Edinburgh Tel: (0131) 2757800 Email: caitlin.souter@nhs.scot

STACHURA, Karen, Employee, Brodies LLP, Edinburgh Tel: (0131) 2283777 Email: karen.stachura@brodies.com

STEELE, Hilary, Director, Starling Lawyers Limited, Edinburgh Tel: (0131) 2857499 Email: hilarysteele@starlinglawyers.com

STEPHEN, Fiona, Partner, Anderson Strathern LLP, Edinburgh Tel: (0131) 2707700 Email: fiona.stephen@andersonstrathern.co.uk

STEVENSON, Andrew, Employee, Waddell & Mackintosh Solicitors Ltd, Troon Tel: (01292) 312222 Email: andrew@wmtroon.co.uk

STEWART, Alan, Employee, Law Society of Scotland, Edinburgh Tel: (0131) 2267411 Email: BreckStewart@lawscot.org.uk

STEWART, Christopher, Partner, Digby Brown LLP, Glasgow Tel: (0333) 200 5925 Email: chris.stewart@digbybrown.co.uk

STEWART, Neil, Partner, Stewart Legal, Edinburgh Tel: (0131) 2352426 Email: neil@stewartlegal.co.uk

STIRLING, John, Partner, Gillespie Macandrew LLP, Edinburgh Tel: (0131) 2251677 Email: john.stirling@gillespiemacandrew.co.uk

STRAIN, Alan, Consultant, Davidson Chalmers Stewart LLP, Edinburgh Tel: (0131) 6259191 Email: alan.strain@dcslegal.com

STRUCKMEIER, Anne, Partner, Addleshaw Goddard LLP, Edinburgh Tel: (0131) 2282400 Email: Anne.Struckmeier@addleshawgoddard.com

SUTHERLAND, Alasdair, Partner, Burness Paull LLP, Edinburgh Tel: (0131) 4736000

SWARBRICK, Duncan, Partner, Swarbrick Law, Aviemore Tel: (01479) 811180 Email: duncan@swarbricklaw.co.uk

TAGGART, Ross, Partner, Taggart Meil Mathers, Aberdeen Tel: (01224) 588020 Email: ross@tmmsolicitors.co.uk

TAIT, John, Partner, Tait Macleod, Falkirk Tel: (01324) 888877 Email: fraser@taitmacleod.com

TAYLOR, David, Employee, Berrymans Lace Mawer LLP, Glasgow Tel: (0141) 3532121 Email: David.Taylor@blmlaw.com

THOMSON, Fergus, Associate, Gildeas Limited, Glasgow Tel: (0141) 331 6071 Email: FThomson@gildeas.net

THOMSON, Kirsten, Employee, Addleshaw Goddard LLP, Edinburgh Tel: (0131) 2282400

THOMSON, Wendy, Partner, BTO Solicitors LLP, Edinburgh Tel: (0131) 2222939 Email: wjt@bto.co.uk

THORNBER, Claire, Partner, Weightmans (Scotland) LLP, Glasgow Tel: (0345) 073 9900 Email: claire.thornber@weightmans.com

WACLAWSKI, Stephen, Employee, National Health Service Scotland, Edinburgh Tel: (0131) 2757800 Email: stephen.waclawski@nhs.scot

WALKER, Lynsey, Partner, Addleshaw Goddard LLP, Edinburgh Tel: (0131) 2282400 Email: Lynsey.Walker@addleshawgoddard.com

WALLS, Charles, Employee, Pinsent Masons LLP, Edinburgh Tel: (0131) 777 7000 Email: alastair.walls@pinsentmasons.com

WATSON, Graeme, Partner, Clyde & Co (Scotland) LLP, Edinburgh Tel: (0131) 5571545 Email: graeme.watson@clydeco.com

WATT, Craig, Partner, Brodies LLP, Edinburgh Tel: (0131) 2283777 Email: Craig.Watt@brodies.com

WATT, Vikki, Partner, BTO Solicitors LLP, Glasgow Tel: (0141) 2218012 Email: vwa@bto.co.uk

WEATHERSTON, Graham, Associate, DWF LLP, Glasgow Tel: (0141) 228 8000 Email: Graham.Weatherston2@dwf.law

WHEATLEY, Laurel, Employee, Aberdeenshire Council, Aberdeen Tel: (0345) 608 1208 Email: laurel.wheatley@aberdeenshire.gov.uk

WILKINSON, John, Consultant, Cannons Law Practice LLP, Glasgow Tel: (0141) 2045115 Email: John@cannonslaw.com

WILSON, David, Partner, Digby Brown LLP, Glasgow Tel: (0333) 200 5925 Email: david.wilson@digbybrown.co.uk

Solicitors granted extended rights of audience in Criminal cases only (the High Court of Justiciary)

ALLAN, David, Partner, Wardlaw Stephenson Allan, Edinburgh Tel: (0131) 5578020
Email: dave@wsalawyers.com

ANDERSON, Callum, Partner, Levy & McRae Solicitors LLP, Glasgow Tel: (0141) 3072311
Email: canderson@lemac.co.uk

ANDERSON, Rhonda, Employee, Bruce McCormack Limited, Motherwell
Tel: (01698) 260033

BEATTIE, Louise, Employee, Procurator Fiscal Service, Edinburgh Tel: (0844) 561 3268
Email: louise.beattie@copfs.gov.uk

BELL, Michael, Consultant, Central Court Lawyers, Livingston Tel: (01506) 416999

BIGGAM, Stephen, Director, Marshall Wilson Law Group Limited, Falkirk Tel: (01324) 612569
Email: sbiggam@marshallwilson.com

BONE, Clare, Partner, BTO Solicitors LLP, Glasgow Tel: (0141) 2218012
Email: cbo@bto.co.uk

BRANNAGAN, Michelle, Employee, Procurator Fiscal Service, Glasgow Tel: (0300) 0203000
Email: michelle.brannagan@copfs.gov.uk

BROWN, Gerard, Consultant, Livingstone Brown Limited, Glasgow Tel: (0141) 4298166
Email: gb@livbrown.co.uk

BROWN, Graeme, Consultant, Bridge Legal Limited, Glasgow Tel: (0141) 4293100
Email: grbrown@bridgelitigationuk.com

BROWN, Ross, Partner, Dunipace Brown, Kilsyth
Tel: (01236) 826147
Email: ross@dunipacebrown.co.uk

BROWN, Simon, Partner, Matthew Brown, Irvine
Tel: (01294) 273721
Email: simon@matthewbrownsolicitors.co.uk

BRYCE, Ian, Consultant, Central Court Lawyers, Livingston Tel: (01506) 416999
Email: ianbryce@centralcourtlawyers.co.uk

BUCHANAN, Derek, Employee, Procurator Fiscal Service, Glasgow Tel: (0300) 0203000
Email: derek.buchanan@copfs.gov.uk

BURNETT, Michael, Partner, Burnett Criminal Defence, Aberdeen Tel: (07515) 964194
Email: mike@burnettcriminaldefence.co.uk

CAIRNS, David, Employee, Office of the Advocate General, Edinburgh
Tel: (0131) 2441635
Email: david.cairns@advocategeneral.gov.uk

CALLENDER, Patricia, Employee, Procurator Fiscal Service, Glasgow Tel: (0300) 0203000
Email: patricia.callender@copfs.gov.uk

CAMERON, Alan, Employee, Procurator Fiscal Service, Edinburgh Tel: (0300) 0203168
Email: alan.cameron@copfs.gov.uk

CAMPBELL, Erin, Employee, Procurator Fiscal Service, Edinburgh Tel: (0300) 0203168
Email: erin.campbell@copfs.gov.uk

CAMPBELL, Jonathan, Director, Capital Defence Lawyers Ltd, Edinburgh Tel: (07867) 637638
Email: jcampbell@capdef.co.uk

CAMPBELL, Patrick, Partner, Campbell & McCartney, Glasgow Tel: (0141) 4232222
Email: pc@patrickcampbellsolicitors.co.uk

CARSON, Stuart, Partner, Wilson McLeod, Edinburgh Tel: (0131) 5560055
Email: setcgcarson@tiscali.co.uk

CASSIDY, Kevin, Consultant, Cassidys' Advice & Solicitor Services, Glasgow
Tel: (0141) 3532195
Email: kevincassidy@cassidysolicitors.co.uk

CHAPMAN, Michael, Employee, Chapman Solicitors, Inverness Tel: (01463) 240477
Email: michael@chapmansolicitors.com

CLARK, Julie, Employee, Procurator Fiscal Service, Glasgow Tel: (0300) 0203000
Email: julie.clark@copfs.gov.uk

COLLINS, Simon, Director, Collins & Co Defence Lawyers Ltd, Edinburgh Tel: (0131) 661 3210
Email: scollins@collinsandcolawyers.com

COYLE, Paul, Director, Kavanagh Coyle Limited, Glasgow Tel: (0141) 2265500
Email: paul@solad.co.uk

CROSS, Leanne, Employee, Procurator Fiscal Service, Edinburgh Tel: (0300) 0203168
Email: leanne.cross@copfs.gov.uk

CURRIE, Alexander, Consultant, McCluskey Browne, Kilmarnock Tel: (01563) 544545
Email: SandyC@mccluskeybrowne.co.uk

DALZIEL, Lindsey, Employee, Procurator Fiscal Service, Edinburgh Tel: (0844) 561 3268
Email: lindsey.dalziel@copfs.gov.uk

DAR, Urfan, Employee, Scullion Law Limited, Hamilton Tel: (01698) 283265
Email: urfan@scullionlaw.com

DEAN, Kieran, Partner, Dean & Co, Glasgow
Tel: (0141) 6494159
Email: deanandco@btinternet.com

DICKSON, David, Employee, Procurator Fiscal Service, Edinburgh Tel: (0300) 0203168
Email: DavidJ.Dickson@copfs.gov.uk

DOUGAN, Elizabeth, Partner, Brazenall & Orr,
Dumfries Tel: (01387) 255695
Email: elizabeth@brazenallandorr.co.uk

DRYDEN, Stephen, Partner, Stephen Dryden,
Solicitor Advocate, Glasgow
Tel: (07802) 449390
Email: stephen.dryden@sky.com

FITZPATRICK, Brian, Partner, Fitzpatrick & Co.,
Glasgow Tel: (0141) 2042200
Email: bf@fitzpatrickandco.co.uk

FREEMAN, Richard, Partner, Richard Freeman &
Co., Glasgow Tel: (0141) 353 2223
Email: rte@richardfreemanlaw.com

GILFEDDER, Brian, Director, Gilfedder & McInnes
Limited, Edinburgh Tel: (0131) 5543550
Email: gilfedder@btconnect.com

GILLIES, Alasdair, Partner, BTO Solicitors LLP,
Glasgow Tel: (0141) 2218012
Email: adg@bto.co.uk

GILMARTIN, Kristofer, Director, Kris Gilmartin
Solicitor Advocate Ltd, Dundee
Tel: (07540) 400871
Email: krisgilmartin@sol-ad.co.uk

GILROY, Edward, Partner, Gilroy & Co, Glasgow
Tel: (0141) 4293344
Email: eddie.gilroy@btinternet.com

GOODFELLOW, Gail, Partner, Gail Goodfellow,
Solicitor Advocate, Aberdeen
Tel: (01224) 878417
Email: gail@gailgoodfellow.com

GRAVELLE, Alan, Employee, Beltrami & Co
Limited, Glasgow Tel: (0141) 4292262
Email: alan.gravelle@beltramiandcompany.co.
uk

GRAY, Alastair, Rradar (Scotland) Limited,
Glasgow Email: Alastair.Gray@rradar.com

GRAY, Angela, Employee, Procurator Fiscal
Service, Hamilton Tel: (0844) 5613245
Email: angela.gray@copfs.gov.uk

GRAY, Ann, Employee, Procurator Fiscal Service,
Edinburgh Tel: (0300) 0203000
Email: ann.gray@copfs.gov.uk

GUARINO, Marco, Director, Guarino & Thomson
Limited, East Kilbride Tel: (01355) 263848
Email: admin@guarinothomson.co.uk

HARAN, Paul, Employee, Public Defence
Solicitors Office, Edinburgh
Tel: (0131) 557 1222
Email: pharan@pdso.org.uk

HARPER, Kathleen, Employee, Procurator Fiscal
Service, Edinburgh Tel: (0300) 0203168
Email: kathleen.harper@copfs.gov.uk

HARROWER, Jennifer, Employee, Procurator Fiscal
Service, Edinburgh Tel: (0844) 561 3268
Email: jennifer.harrower@copfs.gov.uk

HARVIE, David, Employee, Procurator Fiscal
Service, Edinburgh Tel: (0300) 0203168
Email: david.harvie@copfs.gov.uk

HAY, Neil, Director, MTM Defence Lawyers
Limited, Edinburgh Tel: (0131) 3060115
Email: nhay@mtmdefence.co.uk

HOUSTON, Andrew, Partner, McSporrans,
Edinburgh Tel: (0131) 5579151
Email: awhouston@hotmail.co.uk

HUTCHISON, Judith, Employee, Scullion Law
Limited, Hamilton Tel: (01698) 283265
Email: jhutchison@scullionlaw.com

IRVINE, James, Employee, Public Defence
Solicitors Office, Ayr Tel: (01292) 269139
Email: jamesirvine57@gmail.com

IRVINE, Laura, Partner, Davidson Chalmers
Stewart LLP, Edinburgh Tel: (0131) 6259191
Email: laura.irvine@dcslegal.com

JESSOP, Graeme, Employee, Procurator Fiscal
Service, Edinburgh Tel: (0300) 0203168
Email: graeme.jessop@copfs.gov.uk

JOHNSTON, Krista, Director, Martin, Johnston &
Socha Limited, Alloa Tel: (01259) 725922
Email: krista.
johnston@mjscriminaldefencelawyers.co.uk

KEARNEY, Paul, Employee, Procurator Fiscal
Service, Edinburgh Tel: (0300) 0203168
Email: paul.kearney@copfs.gov.uk

KEEGAN, James, Consultant, Thorley Stephenson
Ltd, Edinburgh Tel: (0131) 5569599
Email: jdkeegan1@msn.com

KENNEDY, Alastair, Solicitor

LATIF, Shahid, Director, Craig Wood Solicitors
Limited, Inverness Tel: (01463) 225544
Email: shahid.latif@craigwood.co.uk

LAVELLE, William, Director, Bridge Legal Limited,
Glasgow Tel: (0141) 4293100
Email: billymlavelle@gmail.com

LAVERTY, James, Partner, MML Legal, Dundee
Tel: (01382) 206 000
Email: jim@muirmyleslaverty.co.uk

LOCKIE, Brent, Director, James McKay Defence
Solicitors Limited, Elgin Tel: (01343) 556500
Email: brent@jamesmckay.uk

MACARA, John, Consultant, Beltrami & Co
Limited, Glasgow Tel: (0141) 4292262
Email: murray.macara@beltramiandcompany.
co.uk

MACINTOSH, Christopher, Employee, Procurator
Fiscal Service, Dundee Tel: (01382) 342559
Email: christopher.macintosh@copfs.gov.uk

MACINTOSH, Michael, Employee, Procurator
Fiscal Service, Hamilton Tel: (0844) 5613245
Email: Michael.macintosh@copfs.gov.uk

MACKENZIE, Pauline, Employee, Public Defence
Solicitors Office, Glasgow Tel: (0141) 5530794
Email: pmckenzie@pdso.org.uk

MARTIN, Gordon, Director, Martin, Johnston &
Socha Limited, Dunfermline
Tel: (01383) 730466
Email: gordon.
martin@mjscriminaldefencelawyers.co.uk

MATHERS, George, Consultant, George Mathers
& Co, Aberdeen Tel: (01224) 588599
Email: g.mathers@georgemathers.co.uk

MCATEER, James, Director, Beltrami & Co
Limited, Glasgow Tel: (0141) 4292262
Email: gary.mcateer@beltramiandcompany.co.
uk

MCAULEY, Francis, Partner, Lynch & Co.,
Solicitors, Glasgow Tel: (0141) 4276162
Email: frankmcauley@hotmail.com

MCCAIG, David, Director, Doonan, McCaig &
Co. Ltd, Kilmarnock Tel: (0141) 5526600
Email: davidmccaig4@gmail.com

MCCLELLAND, Peter, Employee, Procurator Fiscal
Service, Kilmarnock Tel: (01563) 536211
Email: peter.mcclelland@copfs.gov.uk

MCCLURE, Gerald, Director, McClure Collins
Limited, Glasgow Tel: (0141) 4237181
Email: gerry@mcclurecollins.com

MCGEEHAN, Anthony, Employee, Procurator
Fiscal Service, Glasgow
Email: anthony.mcgeehan@copfs.gov.uk

MCGOVERN, John, Director, Corporate Defence
Ltd, Glasgow Tel: (0141) 3031274
Email: john@corporatedefence.co.uk

MCILWHAM, Raymond, Director, Glasgow
Defence Lawyers Limited, Glasgow
Tel: (0141) 4297677
Email: info@glasgowdefencelawyers.com

MCROBERT, Lauren, Employee, Procurator Fiscal
Service, Glasgow Tel: (0300) 0203000
Email: lauren.mcrobert@copfs.gov.uk

MCSPORRAN, Iain, Partner, Iain McSporran QC,
Solicitor Advocate, Edinburgh
Tel: (07891) 529849
Email: iainmcsporran@btinternet.com

MCWILLIAMS, Philip, Partner, Finnieston Franchi
& McWilliams, Glasgow Tel: (0141) 2263000
Email: philip@ffmcw.co.uk

MITCHELL, Robert, Partner, Tod & Mitchell,
Paisley Tel: (0141) 8891444
Email: enquiries@todandmitchell.co.uk

MOORE, Francis, Partner, Russells Gibson
McCaffrey, Glasgow Tel: (0141) 271 1000
Email: f.moore@russellsgm.co.uk

MORE, Robert, Partner, Robert More and
Company, Edinburgh Tel: (0131) 5571110
Email: robert@moredefence.co.uk

MORROW, Martin, Director, MTM Defence
Lawyers Limited, Falkirk Tel: (01324) 633221
Email: mmorrow@mtmdefence.co.uk

MOWBERRY, John-Paul, Consultant, Bridge Legal
Limited, Glasgow Tel: (0141) 4293100

MUIR, Alan, Employee, Scottish Legal Aid Board,
Edinburgh Tel: (0131) 2267061
Email: muirar@slab.org.uk

MULGREW, James, Partner, Russells Gibson
McCaffrey, Glasgow Tel: (0141) 271 1000
Email: jj.mulgrew@russellsgm.co.uk

MULLEN, Paul, Director, Livingstone Brown
Limited, Glasgow Tel: (0141) 7789657
Email: pm@livbrown.co.uk

MURRAY, Alistair, Partner, Alistair Murray Solicitor
Advocate, Blantyre Tel: (01698) 721999
Email: blantyrecriminallawyers@gmail.com

OGG, Ann, Partner, Ann Ogg, Edinburgh
Tel: (0131) 3370912
Email: an.og@btinternet.com

PARFERY, Alan, Employee, Procurator Fiscal
Service, Glasgow
Email: Alan.Parfery@copfs.gov.uk

PARKES, Katrina, Employee, Procurator Fiscal
Service, Glasgow Tel: (0300) 0203000
Email: katrina.parkes@copfs.gov.uk

PATERSON, Iain, Director, Paterson Bell Limited,
Edinburgh Tel: (0131) 2256111
Email: patersonsolicitoradvocate@gmail.com

PHILLIPS, Andrew, Employee, The Scottish
Football Association, Glasgow
Tel: (0141) 6166000
Email: compliance.officer@scottishfa.co.uk

PHILLIPS, Catherine, Partner, Kate Phillips,
Glasgow Tel: (0141) 4206120
Email: katephillips21@yahoo.co.uk

POLLOCK, George, Partner, Pollock, Ross & Co,
Stirling Tel: (01786) 449933
Email: george@pollockross.com

PRENTICE, Alexander, Employee, Procurator
Fiscal Service, Edinburgh Tel: (0300) 0203168
Email: Alex.Prentice@copfs.gov.uk

RITCHIE, Ann, Employee, Moir and Sweeney LLP,
Glasgow Tel: (0141) 4292724

ROBERTSON, Eilidh, Employee, Procurator Fiscal
Service, Dundee Tel: (01382) 342559
Email: Eilidh.Robertson@copfs.gov.uk

ROBERTSON, Liam, Director, L & G Robertson Limited, Glasgow Tel: (0141) 4297979
Email: liam@liamrobertsonsolicitors.co.uk

ROBERTSON, Peter, Partner, Robertson Wyse, Cowdenbeath Tel: (01383) 515020
Email: peter.e.robertson@gmail.com

ROSS, Elizabeth, Employee, Inspectorate of Prosecution in Scotland, Glasgow
Email: elizabeth.ross@copfs.gov.uk

ROSS, Stephanie, Employee, Procurator Fiscal Service, Edinburgh Tel: (0300) 0203168
Email: Stephanie.Ross@copfs.gov.uk

ROY, Ewen, Partner, Adams Whyte, Edinburgh Tel: (0131) 555 7220
Email: ewenroy@adamswhyte.com

SCHOFIELD, Kim, Employee, Procurator Fiscal Service, Edinburgh Tel: (0300) 0203000
Email: Kim.Schofield@copfs.gov.uk

SCOTT, John, Partner, John Scott QC, Edinburgh Tel: (07779) 328656
Email: johndscott@talk21.com

SMYTH, Maurice, Partner, Gordon & Smyth, Bishopbriggs Tel: (0141) 7724186
Email: mslawman@hotmail.com

SOUTER, Richard, Partner, George More & Company LLP, Edinburgh Tel: (0131) 2026552
Email: richardsouter@hotmail.com

SPEED, Blair, Employee, Procurator Fiscal Service, Edinburgh Tel: (0300) 0203168
Email: Blair.Speed@copfs.gov.uk

STEPHENSON, James, Consultant, Thorley Stephenson Ltd, Edinburgh
Tel: (0131) 5569599
Email: jps@thorleystephenson.com

SWEENEY, Gerard, Partner, G. Sweeney Solicitors Limited, Glasgow Tel: (0141) 4290677
Email: gerardsweeney@btconnect.com

TAIT, Cameron, Director, Capital Defence Lawyers Ltd, Edinburgh Tel: (07867) 637638
Email: ctait@capdef.co.uk

TEMPLETON, Philip, Partner, Wilson McLeod, Edinburgh Tel: (0131) 5560055
Email: wilsonmcleod@btconnect.com

THOMSON, Douglas, Employee, J. Myles & Co., Carnoustie Tel: (01241) 855769

VAUGHAN, Robert, Partner, R.S. Vaughan & Co, Glasgow Tel: (0141) 2215482
Email: rvaughan@rsvaughan.co.uk

WALKER, Alexandra, Partner, Hughes Walker, Edinburgh Tel: (0131) 6038676
Email: swalker.hugheswalker@gmail.com

WALLACE, James, Partner, James R. Wallace, Glasgow Tel: (07949) 133123
Email: james.robertson@wallace.ms

WATSON, Peter, Partner, PBW Law Solicitors, Glasgow Tel: (0141) 439 1990
Email: pbw@pbwlaw.co.uk

WEIR, Calum, Partner, Penmans, Glasgow Tel: (0141) 429 4489
Email: cjmweir@hotmail.co.uk

WHYTE, Simon, Employee, Beltrami & Co Limited, Glasgow Tel: (0141) 4292262
Email: simon.whyte@beltramiandcompany.co.uk

WILSON, Neil, Partner, Ferguson and Wilson, Inverness Tel: (01463) 222221
Email: enquiries@fergusonandwilson.co.uk

WOODWARD-NUTT, Ian, Partner, Woodward Lawson, Aberdeen Tel: (01224) 619330
Email: ian@woodwardlawson.com

YUILL, Ross, Director, Carr & Co (Solicitors) Limited, Glasgow Tel: (0141) 6412912/8346
Email: ry@theglasgowlawpractice.co.uk

Alphabetical List of Certificated Solicitors

ABBOTT, Fiona Katherine (Sept 2006)
(Employee)
Scottish Social Services Council,
Dundee . . . .(p.1218)
T: 0345 6030 891
E: fiona.abbott@sssc.uk.com

ABBOTT, Mitchell Robert (Oct 2018)
(Employee)
CMS Cameron McKenna Nabarro Olswang LLP,
Glasgow. . . . .(p.962)
T: 0141 2222200
E: mitchell.abbott@cms-cmno.com

ABBOTT, Pamela Maria (Jan 2006) (Employee)
Menzies Distribution Ltd,
Edinburgh . . . .(p.1225)
T: 0131 469 4553
E: pamela.abbott@menziesdistribution.com

ABERCROMBIE, Eric (Jan 1981) (Partner)
McCarron & Co., Airdrie . . . .(p.750)
T: 01236 762012
E: eric@mccarronlaw.co.uk

ABERDEIN, Robert Douglas (Mar 2005)
(Director)
Alston Law, Glasgow. . . . .(p.940)
T: 0344 5715205
E: rob.aberdein@alstonlaw.co.uk

ABERDEIN, Ruth Mary (Aug 2000) (Partner)
Aberdein Considine and Company,
Aberdeen . . . .(p.718)
T: 01224 589700
E: raberdein@acandco.com

ABERNETHY, Douglas Alexander (Oct 2010)
(Employee)
Latham & Watkins (London) LLP, London
EC2 . . . .(p.1266)
T: 020 7710 1000
E: Douglas.Abernethy@lw.com

ABERNETHY, Philippa Rose (Nov 2019)
(Employee)
Lindsays LLP, Glasgow. . . . .(p.1001)
T: 0141 2216551
E: philippa.abernethy@lindsays.co.uk

ABLETT, Calum Mark (Mar 2019) (Employee)
Morrison & Foerster, London EC3 . . . . .(p.1266)
T: 020 7920 4047
E: cablett@mofo.com

ABLETT, Rebecca Fiona (Dec 2015) (Employee)
Burness Paull LLP, Glasgow . . . .(p.954)
T: 0141 2484933
E: rebecca.ablett@burnesspaull.com

ABOUD, Daniah (Oct 2021) (Employee)
Maguire Solicitors, Glasgow . . . .(p.1017)
T: 0141 3312885

ABRAHAMSON, Judith Sharon (Oct 1999)
(Employee)
Glasgow City Council, Glasgow . . . . . .(p.1239)
T: 0141 2877054
E: sharon.abrahamson@glasgow.gov.uk

ABRAMI, Joseph George (Oct 1990) (Employee)
East Renfrewshire Council, Giffnock . . .(p.1237)
T: 0141 5773000
E: joe.abrami@eastrenfrewshire.gov.uk

ABRAMS, Helen Cecilia (Nov 2001) (Partner)
Brodies LLP, Edinburgh . . . .(p.845)
T: 0131 2283777
E: helen.abrams@brodies.com

ADAIR, Gail Cameron (Jan 2001) (Employee)
Procurator Fiscal Service, Glasgow . . . .(p.1241)
T: 0300 0203000
E: gail.adair@copfs.gov.uk

ADAIR, Jack Scott (Sept 1993) (Partner)
Adairs, Dumbarton . . . .(p.798)
T: 01389 767625
E: sadair@adairssolicitors.com

ADAIR, Shona Agnes (Oct 1997) (Employee)
Aberdeen Corporate Services Limited,
Edinburgh . . . .(p.1220)
T: 0131 245 7508
E: shona.x.adair@abrdn.com

ADAM, Alan Robert (Feb 2016) (Employee)
Aberdeenshire Council, Aberdeen . . . . .(p.1211)
T: 0345 608 1208
E: alan.adam@aberdeenshire.gov.uk

ADAM, Beverley Jane (Oct 2003) (Employee)
Procurator Fiscal Service, Kirkcaldy . . . .(p.1249)
T: 0300 0203000
E: Beverley.Adam@copfs.gov.uk

ADAM, Christine Murray (Nov 1983)
(Employee)
Renfrewshire Council, Paisley . . . .(p.1252)
T: 0141 6187176
E: christine.adam@renfrewshire.gov.uk

ADAM, Colin George (Sept 1986) (Partner)
McLennan Adam Davis, Ayr . . . .(p.764)
T: 01292 289584
E: colina@mad-law.co.uk

ADAM, Colin Grant (Feb 1982) (Partner)
McCarrys Solicitors, Glasgow . . . .(p.1006)
T: 0141 9451911
E: colinadam@mccarrys.com

ADAM, David Keith (Oct 1981) (Employee)
Shetland Islands Council, Lerwick . . . . . (p.1250)
  T: 01595 744550
  E: keith.adam@shetland.gov.uk

ADAM, Deborah Mary (Jan 2001) (Employee)
Burness Paull LLP, Edinburgh . . . . (p.850)
  T: 0131 473 6909
  E: deborah.adam@burnesspaull.com

ADAM, John Henry (Sept 1996) (Partner)
Gray & Gray LLP, Peterhead . . . . (p.1153)
  T: 01779 480 222
  E: john@graygraylaw.com

ADAM, Lyndsey (Nov 2007) (Director)
Cochran Dickie, Paisley . . . . (p.1137)
  T: 0141 8892245
  E: la@cochrandickie.co.uk

ADAM, Michelle (Oct 1996) (Partner)
Thorntons Law LLP, Edinburgh . . . . (p.906)
  T: 0131 2258705
  E: madam@thorntons-law.co.uk

ADAM, Neil James (Jan 2005) (Employee)
Baker Hughes Ltd., Aberdeen . . . . (p.1212)
  T: 01224 401357
  E: neil.adam@bakerhughes.com

ADAM, Zoe Anne (Sept 2017) (Employee)
Transocean Onshore Support Services Limited,
  Aberdeen . . . . (p.1214)
  T: 01224 944000
  E: zoe.adam@deepwater.com

ADAMS, Claire Margaret (Sept 1998)
  (Employee)
The Weir Group PLC, Glasgow . . . . (p.1245)
  E: claire.adams@mail.weir

ADAMS, David (Dec 2009) (Employee)
Thompsons, Glasgow . . . . (p.1046)
  T: 0141 2218840
  E: david.adams@thompsons-scotland.co.uk

ADAMS, David (Sept 1982) (Employee)
Wheatley Housing Group Limited,
  Glasgow . . . . (p.1246)
  T: 0845 9001001
  E: david.adams@wheatley-group.com

ADAMS, David William John (Nov 1985)
  (Partner)
Cockburns, Elgin . . . . (p.915)
  T: 01343 542684
  E: david.adams@cockburns-solicitors.com

ADAMS, Eilidh Gillian (Oct 2008) (Partner)
Gillespie Macandrew LLP, Perth . . . . . . (p.1148)
  T: 01738 231000
  E: eilidh.adams@gillespiemacandrew.co.uk

ADAMS, Farhat Kauser (Feb 2002) (Director)
Adams Legal Solutions Limited,
  Edinburgh . . . . (p.835)
  T: 0131 4434436
  E: farah@adams-law.co.uk

ADAMS, Gordon Robert (Aug 2018)
  (Employee)
Castle Water, Blairgowrie . . . . (p.1216)
  T: 01250 718700
  E: gordon.adams@castlewater.co.uk

ADAMS, Graham Reid (Oct 1986) (Employee)
Wright, Johnston & Mackenzie LLP,
  Glasgow . . . . (p.1054)
  T: 0141 2483434
  E: ga@wjm.co.uk

ADAMS, Jennifer Lynne (Jul 2013) (Employee)
The Weir Group PLC, Glasgow . . . . (p.1245)
  E: Jennifer.adams@mail.weir

ADAMS, Jennifer Margaret (Dec 1993)
  (Consultant)
Burness Paull LLP, Glasgow . . . . (p.954)
  T: 0141 2484933
  E: jennifer.adams@burnesspaull.com

ADAMS, John Paul (Nov 2010) (Employee)
Procurator Fiscal Service, Dundee . . . . . (p.1218)
  T: 01382 342559
  E: John.Adams@copfs.gov.uk

ADAMS, Julia Rosalind Richmal H (Dec 2019)
  (Solicitor)
NO FIRM

ADAMS, Lucy (Nov 2014) (Employee)
Procurator Fiscal Service, Glasgow . . . . (p.1241)
  T: 0300 0203000
  E: lucy.adams@copfs.gov.uk

ADAMS, Paul William (Jul 2005) (Partner)
Wright, Johnston & Mackenzie LLP,
  Inverness . . . . (p.1083)
  T: 01463 234445
  E: pwa@wjm.co.uk

ADAMS, Rhona Anne (Apr 1991) (Partner)
Morton Fraser LLP, Edinburgh . . . . (p.891)
  T: 0131 2471000
  E: rhona.adams@morton-fraser.com

ADAMS, Richard Oliver Frederick (Sept 2020)
  (Employee)
McEwan Fraser Legal, Edinburgh . . . . . . (p.885)
  T: 0131 5249797
  E: richard.adams@mcewanfraserlegal.co.uk

ADAMS, Sarah Elizabeth (Nov 2019)
  (Employee)
Stronachs LLP, Aberdeen . . . . (p.744)
  T: 01224 845845
  E: Sarah.Adams@stronachs.com

ADAMSON, Bruce Alan (Feb 2006) (Employee)
Children & Young People's Commissioner
  Scotland, Edinburgh . . . . (p.1221)
  T: 0131 346 5350
  E: bruce.adamson@cypcs.org.uk

ADDIS, Neil Michael (Oct 1996) (Partner)
Addleshaw Goddard LLP,
Edinburgh . . . . (p.835)
T: 0131 2282400
E: Neil.Addis@addleshawgoddard.com

ADDISON, Beverley May (Sept 2016)
(Employee)
BTO Solicitors LLP, Glasgow . . . . (p.952)
T: 0141 2218012
E: bea@bto.co.uk

ADDISON, Gayle Jane (Sept 1995) (Consultant)
Keegan Smith, SSC., Livingston . . . . . . (p.1119)
T: 01506 497500

ADDISON, Gordon (Oct 1989) (Director)
Nelsons Solicitors Falkirk Limited,
Falkirk . . . . (p.923)
T: 01324 613316
E: gordon@nelsonslawyers.co.uk

AEDY, Rachel Jennifer (Jul 2010) (Employee)
Procurator Fiscal Service,
Edinburgh . . . . (p.1227)
T: 0300 0203168
E: rachel.aedy@copfs.gov.uk

AFZAL-ALI, Sana Shahida (Dec 2019)
(Employee)
AVEVA Solutions Ltd, Cambridge . . . . . (p.1259)

AGNEW, Andrew Graham (May 2019)
(Employee)
Carpenters Scotland Limited,
Glasgow. (p.956)
T: 0141 3285452
E: AAGN@carpentersgroup.co.uk

AGNEW, Christopher Thomas (Apr 2014)
(Employee)
Harper Macleod LLP, Glasgow . . . . (p.983)
T: 0141 2218888
E: christopher.agnew@harpermacleod.co.uk

AGNEW, Stuart Charles (Oct 2013) (Employee)
Royal Air Force, High Wycombe . . . . . . (p.1260)
E: stuart.agnew101@mod.gov.uk

AGOSTI, Siobhan Rhonwen (Oct 2015)
(Employee)
BTO Solicitors LLP, Glasgow . . . . (p.952)
T: 0141 2218012
E: sra@bto.co.uk

AGRAWAL, Angela (Oct 2003) (Solicitor)
Stuart & Stuart, Edinburgh . . . . (p.905)
T: 0131 2286449
E: aagrawal@stuartandstuart.co.uk

AGYAKO, Lisa Rose Abena (Oct 2019)
(Employee)
Cartys, Blantyre . . . . (p.777)
T: 01698 820896
E: lagyako@cartylaw.co.uk

AHMAD, Fozia Samara (Nov 2012) (Employee)
Scottish Government, Edinburgh . . . . . (p.1231)
T: 0131 244 0815
E: fozia.ahmad@gov.scot

AHMAD, Zahrah Mumtaz (Oct 2012)
(Employee)
Scottish Legal Aid Board,
Edinburgh . . . . (p.1233)
T: 0131 2267061
E: ahmadza@slab.org.uk

AHMAD-ALI, Nadhia (Jul 2010) (Solicitor)
NO FIRM

AHMED, Amnah Sehar (Oct 2020) (Employee)
Pinsent Masons LLP, Glasgow . . . . (p.1031)
T: 0141 567 8400
E: amnah.ahmed@pinsentmasons.com

AHMED, Gulfraz (Jan 2015) (Partner)
Meliora, Glasgow . . . . (p.1018)
T: 0141 266 0270
E: fraz.ahmed@melioralegal.com

AHMED, Omair Maubeen (Jan 2013)
(Employee)
Austin Lafferty Limited, East
Kilbride . . . . (p.830)
T: 01355 263777
E: OAhmed@laffertylaw.com

AHMED, Raeesa (Mar 2021) (Employee)
Procurator Fiscal Service, Airdrie . . . . . . (p.1214)
T: 01236 747027
E: Raeesa.Ahmed@copfs.gov.uk

AHMED, Sabihah (Aug 2020) (Employee)
Thorntons Law LLP, Edinburgh . . . . (p.906)
T: 0131 2258705
E: sahmed@thorntons-law.co.uk

AHMED, Saira (Nov 2015) (Employee)
Digby Brown LLP, Edinburgh . . . . (p.862)
T: 0333 200 5925
E: Saira.Ghulam@digbybrown.co.uk

AHMED, Samirah Tariq (Aug 2019) (Employee)
Drummond Miller LLP, Edinburgh . . . . . (p.864)
T: 0131 2265151
E: sahmed@dm-property.com

AHMED, Sarah Margarette (Sept 2017)
(Employee)
The National Trust for Scotland,
Edinburgh . . . . (p.1235)
T: 0844 4932100
E: sahmed@nts.org.uk

AHMED, Yousif Shafin (Nov 2012) (Solicitor)
NO FIRM

AIKMAN, Peter Mackintosh (Oct 1991)
(Director)
Aikman Bell Limited, Edinburgh . . . . (p.837)
T: 0131 6610015
E: peter@aikmanbell.co.uk

AINSLIE, Sophie Katherine (Sept 2021)
(Employee)
Burness Paull LLP, Edinburgh . . . . (p.850)
   T: 7787055891
   E: Sophie.Ainslie@burnesspaull.com

AIRD, Lorna Janette (Feb 2002) (Director)
Airds & Co Limited, Edinburgh . . . . . . (p.837)
   T: 0131 3328411
   E: lja@airdsandco.co.uk

AIRTH, Sophie Elizabeth (Aug 2020)
(Employee)
Brodies LLP, Glasgow . . . . (p.948)
   T: 0141 2484672
   E: sophie.airth@brodies.com

AITCHISON, Lauren (Jun 2018) (Employee)
Bridge Legal Limited, Glasgow . . . . (p.948)
   T: 0141 4293100
   E: laitchison@bridgelegalglasgow.co.uk

AITCHISON, Nicola Jane (Sept 2011)
(Employee)
The Edrington Group Limited,
   Glasgow . . . . (p.1245)
   T: 0141 9404000
   E: nicola.aitchison@edrington.com

AITKEN, Andrew Proven (Jun 2002) (Partner)
Adams Whyte, Livingston . . . . (p.1117)
   T: 01506 401999
   E: andyaitken@adamswhyte.com

AITKEN, Archibald Henry (Sept 1986)
(Employee)
NORTH LANARKSHIREre Council,
   Motherwell . . . . (p.1251)
   T: 07939 280102
   E: aitkena@northlan.gov.uk

AITKEN, Douglas Henderson (Apr 2003)
(Employee)
Artisanal Spirits Company Plc,
   Edinburgh . . . . (p.1220)
   E: douglas.aitken@artisanal-spirits.com

AITKEN, Elizabeth Ann (Aug 2009) (Employee)
Procurator Fiscal Service, Glasgow . . . . (p.1241)
   T: 0300 0203000
   E: Elizabeth.Aitken@copfs.gov.uk

AITKEN, Emma Roberta Marjory (Aug 2020)
(Employee)
MacRoberts LLP, Edinburgh . . . . (p.887)
   T: 0131 2295046
   E: emma.aitken@macroberts.com

AITKEN, James McGill (Jun 2002) (Employee)
Freshfields Service Company, London
   EC2 . . . . (p.1264)
   T: 020 7936 4000
   E: james.aitken@freshfields.com

AITKEN, James Roy (Sept 1994) (Consultant)
ELP Arbuthnott McClanachan,
   Edinburgh . . . . (p.867)
   T: 0131 5548649

AITKEN, Karen Elizabeth (Oct 2005)
(Employee)
Procurator Fiscal Service, Inverness . . . . (p.1248)
   T: 0844 5612926
   E: Karen.Aitken@copfs.gov.uk

AITKEN, Kirsty Rosalind (Nov 2020) (Employee)
Scottish Government, Edinburgh . . . . . (p.1231)
   T: 0131 244 0815
   E: kirsty.aitken@gov.scot

AITKEN, Murray Watson (Oct 1996) (Director)
MTM Defence Lawyers Limited,
   Falkirk . . . . (p.923)
   T: 01324 633221
   E: maitken@mtmdefence.co.uk

AITKEN, Peter Madden (Oct 1972) (Consultant)
Forsyth WS Limited, Haddington . . . . . (p.1064)
   T: 01620 824045
   E: pa@forsythsolicitors.co.uk

AITKEN, Ryan James (Jun 2019) (Employee)
Hodge Solicitors LLP, Blairgowrie . . . . . . (p.775)
   T: 01250 874441
   E: rjaitken@hodgesolicitors.co.uk

AITKEN, Sian Elizabeth Margaret (Jan 2003)
(Partner)
CMS Cameron McKenna Nabarro Olswang LLP,
   Edinburgh . . . . (p.856)
   T: 0131 2288000
   E: Sian.Aitken@cms-cmno.com

AITKEN, Steven Andrew Boyd (Sept 1984)
(Consultant)
Inksters, Glasgow . . . . (p.990)
   T: 0141 2290880
   E: steven.aitken@inksters.com

AITKEN, Susannah May (Aug 2021) (Employee)
Dickson Minto, Edinburgh . . . . (p.861)
   T: 0131 2254455
   E: susannah.aitken@dmws.com

AITKEN, Thomas Wilson (Nov 1980)
(Consultant)
Dentons UK and Middle East LLP,
   Glasgow . . . . (p.968)
   T: 0330 2220050
   E: Wilson.Aitken@dentons.com

AITKENHEAD, James Alister (Nov 1975)
(Consultant)
Anderson Strathern LLP, Glasgow . . . . . . (p.940)
   T: 0141 2426060
   E: Alister.Aitkenhead@andersonstrathern.co.uk

AKHTAR, Raksana (Jul 2009) (Employee)
NORTH LANARKSHIREre Council,
Motherwell...................(p.1251)
T: 01698 302440
E: akhtarr@northlan.gov.uk

AKHTAR, Sanaa Hussain (Jul 2016) (Solicitor)
CMS Cameron McKenna Nabarro Olswang LLP,
Glasgow.....................(p.962)
T: 0141 2222200
E: sanaa.akhtar@cms-cmno.com

AKHTAR, Zain Tarim Bin Tariq (Nov 2019)
(Employee)
CMS Cameron McKenna Nabarro Olswang LLP,
Glasgow.....................(p.962)
T: 0141 2222200
E: zain.akhtar@cms-cmno.com

AKINTEWE, Andrew Abayomi (Nov 2002)
(Partner)
Brodies LLP, Edinburgh.............(p.845)
T: 0131 2283777
E: andrew.akintewe@brodies.com

AL NAEME, Noor Fakhir (Jul 2014) (Employee)
Notonthehighstreet, Surrey.........(p.1272)
T: 0203 318 5115
E: nooralnaeme@notonthehighstreet.com

AL WALI, Summer (Nov 2015) (Solicitor)
NO FIRM

AL-HASSANI, Layla Louise (Jun 2006)
(Employee)
BP International Ltd,
Sunbury-on-Thames ....(p.1271)
T: 07825 114 653
E: layla.al-hassani@uk.bp.com

AL-LAMKI, Lamia Lorraine (Oct 2018)
(Employee)
Dentons UK and Middle East LLP,
Glasgow.....................(p.968)
T: 0330 2220050
E: lamia.al-lamki@dentons.com

AL-NASSER, Zaynab (May 2014) (Employee)
Turcan Connell, Glasgow...........(p.1049)
T: 0141 441 2111
E: zaynab.alnasser@turcanconnell.com

AL-SAFFAR, Ainsley Leigh (May 2021)
(Employee)
Connelly & Yeoman Law Limited,
Arbroath ....(p.757)
T: 01241 434200
E: Ainsley@connellyyeoman.com

ALBISTON, Catherine Elizabeth (Jul 2019)
(Employee)
Balfour + Manson LLP, Aberdeen ......(p.721)
T: 01224 498080
E: Katie.Albiston@balfour-manson.co.uk

ALBISTON, Matthew James (Nov 2019)
(Employee)
Munro & Noble, Inverness ....(p.1080)
T: 01463 221727
E: matthewa@munronoble.com

ALBIZZATI, Sara Elena (Oct 2016) (Employee)
BTO Solicitors LLP, Edinburgh ....(p.849)
T: 0131 2222939
E: sal@bto.co.uk

ALCOCK, Judith Aileen (Mar 2000) (Employee)
Scottish Hospital Inquiry, Glasgow ....(p.1244)
E: judith.alcock@hospitalsinquiry.scot

ALDEN, Katie Marie (Mar 2019) (Employee)
Royal London, Edinburgh ....(p.1230)
T: 0131 4567703
E: Katie.Alden@royallondon.com

ALDER, Mark David (Nov 2002) (Partner)
Innes Johnston LLP, Leven ....(p.1115)
T: 01333 429320
E: malder@innesjohnston.co.uk

ALDERDICE, Hon, Peter James (Jul 2009)
(Associate)
Shepherd and Wedderburn LLP,
Edinburgh ....(p.900)
T: 0131 2289900
E: peter.alderdice@shepwedd.com

ALDRIDGE, Catriona Jan (May 2007) (Partner)
CMS Cameron McKenna Nabarro Olswang LLP,
Edinburgh ....(p.856)
T: 0131 2288000
E: Catriona.Aldridge@cms-cmno.com

ALEMAN, David Carr (Jul 2018) (Solicitor)
NO FIRM

ALEXANDER, Amy Meadows (Feb 2012)
(Employee)
City of Edinburgh Council,
Edinburgh ....(p.1221)
T: (0131) 5294145
E: Amy.Alexander@edinburgh.gov.uk

ALEXANDER, Andrew James Griffen
(Mar 2013) (Employee)
K&L Gates LLP, London EC4 ....(p.1265)
T: (0207) 360 8161
E: jim.alexander@klgates.com

ALEXANDER, Ann Kathryn MargaretJean
(Aug 2015) (Employee)
Dechert LLP, London EC4 ....(p.1263)
T: 020 7184 7000
E: kathryn.alexander@dechert.com

ALEXANDER, Beth Anne (Jan 2021) (Employee)
Pinsent Masons LLP, Glasgow ....(p.1031)
T: 0141 567 8400
E: beth.alexander@pinsentmasons.com

ALEXANDER, Caitlin Jessica McEwan
(Mar 2021) (Employee)
Katani & Co. Ltd, Glasgow . . . . (p.994)
T: 0141 2217788
E: caitlinalexander@kataniandco.com

ALEXANDER, David William (Oct 1998)
(Partner)
Gilson Gray LLP, Edinburgh . . . . (p.874)
T: 0131 5165354
E: dalexander@gilsongray.co.uk

ALEXANDER, Elizabeth Mary (Oct 1989)
(Partner)
Scott Alexander, Montrose . . . . (p.1125)
T: 01674 671477
E: elizabeth@scottalexandersolicitors.co.uk

ALEXANDER, Ewan Grant (Feb 1991) (Partner)
Pinsent Masons LLP, Edinburgh . . . . (p.895)
T: 0131 7777000
E: ewan.alexander@pinsentmasons.com

ALEXANDER, Fiona Caroline (Jan 1992)
(Associate)
Pinsent Masons LLP, Edinburgh . . . . (p.895)
T: 0131 777 7000
E: fiona.alexander@pinsentmasons.com

ALEXANDER, Fraser Miller (Sept 2004)
(Employee)
Procurator Fiscal Service,
Kilmarnock . . . . (p.1249)
T: 01563 536211
E: fraser.alexander@copfs.gov.uk

ALEXANDER, Gillian Ellen (Oct 2007)
(Employee)
Law Society of Scotland,
Edinburgh . . . . (p.1224)
T: 0131 2267411
E: gillianalexander@lawscot.org.uk

ALEXANDER, Graham (Sept 2016) (Employee)
Sykes Global Services Limited,
Edinburgh . . . . (p.1234)
T: 0131 458 6500
E: graham.alexander@sykes.com

ALEXANDER, Jenna Smith (Oct 2014)
(Employee)
ITV Plc, London WC1 . . . . (p.1265)
E: jenna.alexander@itv.com

ALEXANDER, Jon Stuart (Apr 1998) (Employee)
Lloyds Banking Group Plc,
Edinburgh . . . . (p.1224)
T: (0131) 442 9579
E: jon.alexander@lloydsbanking.com

ALEXANDER, Kristin Margaret (Aug 2007)
(Partner)
Scott Alexander, Montrose . . . . (p.1125)
T: 01674 671477
E: kristin@scottalexander.org.uk

ALEXANDER, Liam (Sept 2018) (Employee)
WSA BannermanBurke Defence Lawyers,
Edinburgh . . . . (p.842)
T: 0131 5578020
E: liam@wsalawyers.com

ALEXANDER, Lisa Jane (Feb 2020) (Employee)
Shepherd and Wedderburn LLP,
Edinburgh . . . . (p.900)
T: 0131 2289900
E: lisa.alexander@shepwedd.com

ALEXANDER, Louise Alma (Jan 2016)
(Employee)
Procurator Fiscal Service,
Livingston . . . . (p.1250)
T: (0300) 020 3696
E: Louise.Alexander@copfs.gov.uk

ALEXANDER, Mhairi Jessica (Dec 2013)
(Employee)
Procurator Fiscal Service, Glasgow . . . . (p.1241)
T: 0300 0203000
E: mhairi.alexander@copfs.gov.uk

ALEXANDER, Morven Elizabeth (Sept 2015)
(Associate)
Eversheds Sutherland (International) LLP,
Salford . . . . (p.1271)
T: 0161 831 8142
E:
morvenalexander@eversheds-sutherland.com

ALEXANDER, Nathaniel Duncan (Dec 2013)
(Solicitor)
The McKinstry Company LLP, Ayr . . . . . (p.765)
T: 01292 281711
E: nalexander@mckinstry.co.uk

ALEXANDER, Rachel Mary Louise (Sept 2004)
(Employee)
Scottish Social Services Council,
Dundee . . . . (p.1218)
T: 0345 6030 891
E: rachel.alexander@sssc.uk.com

ALEXANDER, Rory Drummond (Apr 2004)
(Partner)
Morton Fraser LLP, Edinburgh . . . . (p.891)
T: 0131 2471000
E: Rory.Alexander@morton-fraser.com

ALEXANDER, Rowan James (Oct 2013)
(Employee)
CMS Cameron McKenna Nabarro Olswang LLP,
Glasgow . . . . (p.962)
T: 0141 2222200
E: rowan.alexander@cms-cmno.com

ALEXANDER, Sarah Louise (Oct 2007)
(Associate)
Dentons UK and Middle East LLP,
Edinburgh . . . . (p.860)
T: 0330 2220050
E: Sarah.Alexander@dentons.com

ALEXANDER, Sarah Zoe (Mar 2016) (Employee)
Law Society of Scotland,
Edinburgh . . . .(p.1224)
T: 0131 2267411
E: sarahalexander@lawscot.org.uk

ALEXANDER, Shaun William (Oct 2016)
(Employee)
Procurator Fiscal Service,
Edinburgh . . . .(p.1229)
T: 0300 0203000
E: shaun.alexander@copfs.gov.uk

ALEXANDER, Susan Margaret (Mar 2010)
(Employee)
Morgans, Dunfermline . . . .(p.824)
T: 01383 620222
E: susiealexander@morganlaw.co.uk

ALEXANDER, Vicki (Nov 2018) (Employee)
Thorntons Law LLP, Dundee . . . .(p.819)
T: 01382 229 111
E: valexander@thorntons-law.co.uk

ALEXANDER-SMITH, Lauren Louise
(Aug 2019) (Employee)
Watermans Solicitors Limited,
Edinburgh . . . .(p.912)
T: 0131 5557055

ALI, Aisha (Jan 2015) (Employee)
Hunter & Robertson Limited,
Paisley . . . .(p.1138)
T: 0141 8893196
E: conveyancing@hunter-robertson.co.uk

ALI, Isra Jabbar (Nov 2020) (Solicitor)
Carpenters Scotland Limited,
Birkenhead . . . .(p.1258)

ALI, Munawar (Oct 2008) (Partner)
Rightway Legal, Glasgow . . . .(p.1035)
T: 0141 4238920
E: rightwaylegal@hotmail.co.uk

ALI, Omar Farooq (Nov 2001) (Partner)
Harper Macleod LLP, Glasgow . . . .(p.983)
T: 0141 2218888
E: omar.ali@harpermacleod.co.uk

ALI, Qasim Hussain (Sept 2020) (Employee)
Lindsays LLP, Glasgow. . . . .(p.1001)
T: 0141 2216551
E: qasimali@lindsays.co.uk

ALI, Saima (Dec 2016) (Employee)
Digby Brown LLP, Ayr . . . .(p.761)
T: 0333 200 59285
E: Saima.Ali@digbybrown.co.uk

ALI, Saira (Nov 2020) (Solicitor)
NO FIRM

ALI, Samera Yasmine (Feb 2015) (Employee)
Miller Hendry, Perth . . . .(p.1150)
T: 01738 637311
E: SameraAli@millerhendry.co.uk

ALI, Shah Zabe (Jan 2015) (Employee)
Ashurst LLP, Glasgow . . . .(p.1237)
T: (0141) 375 4242
E: Shaz.Ali@ashurst.com

ALI, Sidra (Aug 2015) (Partner)
Ali & Co Solicitors, Glasgow . . . .(p.939)
T: 07849 007162
E: S.ali@ali-legal.co.uk

ALI, Sophina Mehmood (Jul 2008) (Employee)
QC Law Solicitors Limited,
Liversedge . . . .(p.1260)
T: 01484 818123

ALI, Vajiha (Feb 2014) (Employee)
BBM Solicitors Limited, Wick . . . .(p.1180)
T: 01955 604188
E: vah@bbmsolicitors.co.uk

ALLALI, Jade Lara (Jan 2012) (Employee)
Red Rock Power Limited,
Edinburgh . . . .(p.1230)
T: 0131 5577101
E: jade.allali@redrockpower.co.uk

ALLAN, Aime (Jul 2018) (Employee)
Martin, Johnston & Socha Limited,
Dunfermline . . . .(p.824)
T: 01383 730466
E: aime.allan@mjscriminaldefencelawyers.co.uk

ALLAN, Alexandra Mary (Jul 2018) (Solicitor)
NO FIRM

ALLAN, Amanda Louise (May 2017) (Employee)
Procurator Fiscal Service, Glasgow . . . .(p.1241)
T: 0300 0203000
E: Amanda.Allan@copfs.gov.uk

ALLAN, Anthony John (Oct 2005) (Employee)
National Health Service Scotland,
Edinburgh . . . .(p.1225)
T: 0131 2757800
E: tony.allan@nhs.scot

ALLAN, Caitlin Janina (May 1996) (Employee)
City of Edinburgh Council,
Edinburgh . . . .(p.1221)
T: (0131) 5294145
E: caitlin.allan@edinburgh.gov.uk

ALLAN, Caroline Robertson (Jul 2000)
(Associate)
Burness Paull LLP, Glasgow . . . .(p.954)
T: 0141 2484933
E: Caroline.Elder@burnesspaull.com

ALLAN, Christie Margaret (Jan 2021)
(Employee)
Pinsent Masons LLP, Glasgow . . . .(p.1031)
T: 0141 567 8400
E: christie.allan@pinsentmasons.com

ALLAN, Christine Catherine (Feb 2021)
(Employee)
Procurator Fiscal Service,
Edinburgh ....(p.1227)
T: 0300 0203168
E: Christine.Allan@copfs.gov.uk

ALLAN, Christopher David (Feb 1999) (Partner)
Thorntons Law LLP, Dundee ....(p.819)
T: 01382 229 111
E: callan@thorntons-law.co.uk

ALLAN, Christopher Douglas (Dec 2013)
(Partner)
CDA Law, Cromarty ....(p.789)
T: 01381 625259
E: chris@cdalaw.co.uk

ALLAN, Christopher Gordon Simpson
(Nov 2007) (Employee)
AGS Airports Limited, Paisley ....(p.1252)
T: 0141 8484567
E: Chris.Allan@glasgowairport.com

ALLAN, Craig James Thomas (Sept 2011)
(Employee)
National Westminster Bank PLC,
Edinburgh ....(p.1226)
T: (0131) 626 2925
E: Craig.Allan@rbs.co.uk

ALLAN, Crawford William (Apr 2007) (Partner)
Next Law (Scotland) LLP, Perth ......(p.1151)
T: 01738 707274
E: crawford.allan@next-law.co.uk

ALLAN, David Stewart (Nov 1982) (Partner)
Davidson Chalmers Stewart LLP,
Glasgow......................(p.967)
T: 0141 4283258
E: david.allan@dcslegal.com

ALLAN, David William Tait (Aug 1988) (Partner)
Wardlaw Stephenson Allan,
Edinburgh ....(p.910)
T: 0131 5578020
E: dave@wsalawyers.com

ALLAN, Deborah Jane (Oct 2017) (Employee)
Burness Paull LLP, Glasgow ....(p.954)
T: 0141 2484933
E: deborah.allan@burnesspaull.com

ALLAN, Emily Frances (Nov 2005) (Associate)
Allan McDougall McQueen LLP,
Edinburgh ....(p.837)
T: 0131 2252121
E: EmilyAllan@allanmcdougall.co.uk

ALLAN, Emma Devaney (Nov 1997) (Employee)
Miller Hendry, Perth ....(p.1150)
T: 01738 637311
E: emmaallan@millerhendry.co.uk

ALLAN, George Keith (Oct 1975) (Employee)
Raeburn Christie Clark & Wallace LLP,
Aberdeen ....(p.741)
T: 01224 332400
E: keith.allan@raeburns.co.uk

ALLAN, Gillian Emma (Sept 2017) (Employee)
NORTH LANARKSHIRere Council,
Motherwell..................(p.1251)
T: 07790 847883
E: allang@northlan.gov.uk

ALLAN, Hugo John (Sept 1994) (Partner)
Thorntons Law LLP, Edinburgh ....(p.906)
T: 0131 2258705
E: hallan@thorntons-law.co.uk

ALLAN, Ian MacLachlan (Sept 1976) (Partner)
Stenhouse, Husband & Irvine,
Dunfermline ....(p.825)
T: 01383 724949
E: ian@shisolicitors.co.uk

ALLAN, Isobel Fortune (Mar 2007) (Employee)
The General Teaching Council for Scotland,
Edinburgh ....(p.1234)
T: 0131 314 6000
E: Isobel.Allan@gtcs.org.uk

ALLAN, Jennifer Mary (Oct 2005) (Partner)
CMS Cameron McKenna Nabarro Olswang LLP,
Edinburgh ....(p.856)
T: 0131 2288000
E: Jenny.Allan@cms-cmno.com

ALLAN, Katherine Elizabeth (Nov 2000)
(Employee)
National Westminster Bank PLC,
Edinburgh ....(p.1226)
T: 0131 5568555
E: katherine.allan@natwest.com

ALLAN, Kendall Duncan (Sept 2020)
(Employee)
Burness Paull LLP, Edinburgh ....(p.850)
T: 0131 4736000
E: kendall.allan@burnesspaull.com

ALLAN, Lesley (Sept 1994) (Partner)
Clyde & Co (Scotland) LLP,
Glasgow.....................(p.961)
T: 0141 2482666
E: lesley.allan@clydeco.com

ALLAN, Margaret Jean (Jan 1990) (Partner)
Thorntons Law LLP, Cupar...........(p.793)
T: 01334 652285
E: mallan@thorntons-law.co.uk

ALLAN, Mark Robert (Oct 1995) (Employee)
Procurator Fiscal Service, Glasgow ....(p.1241)
T: 0300 0203000
E: mark.allan@copfs.gov.uk

ALLAN, Mark William (Jun 2008) (Partner)
James & George Collie LLP,
Aberdeen . . . .(p.728)
T: 01224 581581
E: m.allan@jgcollie.co.uk

ALLAN, Melanie Jane (Apr 1999) (Employee)
Sotheby's, London W1 . . . .(p.1268)
E: Melanie.Allan@sothebys.com

ALLAN, Michael Iain (Oct 1995) (Partner)
Pinsent Masons LLP, Glasgow . . . .(p.1031)
T: 0141 567 8400
E: michael.allan@pinsentmasons.com

ALLAN, Natalie Linda Urquhart (Aug 2014)
(Employee)
McEwan Fraser Legal, Edinburgh . . . . . .(p.885)
T: 0131 5249 797
E: natalie.allan@mcewanfraserlegal.co.uk

ALLAN, Rachel Louise (Oct 2007) (Associate)
Burness Paull LLP, Edinburgh . . . .(p.850)
T: 0131 4736000
E: Rachel.Allan@burnesspaull.com

ALLAN, Richard John (Nov 2005) (Partner)
Richard John Allan Solicitor,
Glasgow. . . . .(p.940)
T: 0141 3399444
E: info@richardjohnallan.co.uk

ALLAN, Robert Hugh (Sept 1983) (Partner)
Pomphreys, Wishaw . . . .(p.1182)
T: 01698 373365
E: rha@pomphreyslaw.com

ALLAN, Rosie Emily (Nov 2018) (Employee)
Ledingham Chalmers LLP,
Aberdeen . . . .(p.734)
T: 01224 408408
E: Rosie.Allan@ledinghamchalmers.com

ALLAN, Scott (Sept 2005) (Partner)
Andersonbain LLP, Aberdeen . . . .(p.721)
T: 01224 456789
E: sallan@andersonbain.co.uk

ALLAN, Steven (Jun 2014) (Partner)
James & George Collie LLP,
Aberdeen . . . .(p.728)
T: 01224 581581
E: s.allan@jgcollie.co.uk

ALLAN, Stuart Norman (Oct 2016) (Employee)
Travers Smith LLP, London EC1 . . . . . .(p.1269)
T: (0207) 2953387
E: stuart.allan@traverssmith.com

ALLAN, Thomas Peterson (Feb 1985) (Partner)
Allans, Lerwick . . . .(p.1112)
T: 01595 690749
E: allans1@btinternet.com

ALLAN, Valerie Louise (Nov 1998) (Partner)
CMS Cameron McKenna Nabarro Olswang LLP,
Aberdeen . . . .(p.727)
T: 01224 622002
E: valerie.allan@cms-cmno.com

ALLAN, Yvonne (Nov 2004) (Associate)
Dentons UK and Middle East LLP,
Glasgow. . . . .(p.968)
T: 0330 2220050
E: Yvonne.Allan@dentons.com

ALLAN, Zoe (Mar 2009) (Employee)
AEMS Limited, Monifieth . . . .(p.1125)
T: 01382 539313

ALLARDICE, Ross John (Oct 2004) (Solicitor)
NO FIRM

ALLEN, Katie Elizabeth (Feb 2016) (Partner)
Burges Salmon LLP, Bristol. . . . .(p.1258)
T: 0117 9392000
E: katie.allen@burges-salmon.com

ALLEN, Kirsty Victoria (Nov 2010) (Employee)
Lloyds Banking Group Plc,
Edinburgh . . . .(p.1224)
T: (0131) 442 9579
E: Kirsty.Allen@lloydsbanking.com

ALLEN, Kyle Michael James (Sept 2021)
(Employee)
CMS Cameron McKenna Nabarro Olswang LLP,
Aberdeen . . . .(p.727)
T: 01224 622002
E: kyle.allen@cms-cmno.com

ALLEN, Mark Francis Paul (Oct 1985) (Partner)
Dunlop, Allen & Co., Glasgow . . . .(p.972)
T: 0141 5521726
E: jrdunlopallen@gmail.com

ALLEN, Shirley Jean (Apr 2003) (Partner)
Pinsent Masons LLP, Aberdeen . . . .(p.739)
T: 01224 377900
E: Shirley.Allen@pinsentmasons.com

ALLEN, Tessa Maxine (Nov 1998) (Employee)
Standard Life Investments Limited,
Edinburgh . . . .(p.1234)
T: 0131 245 4153
E: Tessa.Allen@abrdn.com

ALLEYNE, Jacqueline Lees (Mar 2008)
(Employee)
Aberdein Considine and Company,
Glasgow. . . . .(p.937)
T: 0141 2278200
E: jalleyne@acandco.com

ALLISON, Brian George Thomas (Sept 1988)
(Consultant)
Black & Markie, Dunfermline . . . .(p.822)
T: 01383 610 547

ALLISON, Laura Catherine (Nov 2010)
(Employee)
Jacobs U.K. Limited, Glasgow........(p.1240)
T: 0141 243 8722
E: Laura.Allison@jacobs.com

ALLISON, Maree Catherine (Sept 2002)
(Employee)
Scottish Social Services Council,
Dundee ....(p.1218)
T: 0345 6030 891
E: maree.allison@sssc.uk.com

ALLISON, Philip James (Oct 1979) (Consultant)
Kerr Stirling LLP, Stirling ....(p.1165)
T: 01786 463414
E: pja@kerrstirling.co.uk

ALLISON, Scott Malcolm (Feb 2013)
(Employee)
CMS Cameron McKenna Nabarro Olswang LLP,
Glasgow.....................(p.962)
T: 0141 2222200
E: Scott.Allison@cms-cmno.com

ALLISON, Simon David (Nov 2001) (Partner)
Blackadders LLP, Dundee............(p.805)
T: 01382 229222
E: simon.allison@blackadders.co.uk

ALLISON, Victoria (Jul 2005) (Employee)
Scottish Investments Services Limited,
Edinburgh ....(p.1233)
E: victoria.allison@thebank.scot

ALLOUBANI, Norma Mary Bell (Oct 2007)
(Employee)
Stirling & Gilmour LLP, Alexandria .....(p.752)
T: 01389 752641
E: n.bell@stirlingandgilmour.co.uk

ALMOND, Lorraine Caroline (Nov 1998)
(Employee)
Procurator Fiscal Service,
Edinburgh ....(p.1229)
T: 0300 0203000
E: lorraine.almond@copfs.gov.uk

ALMOND, Neil Charles Dempster
(Jul 2004) (Employee)
Procurator Fiscal Service,
Edinburgh ....(p.1229)
T: 0300 0203000
E: Neil.Almond@copfs.gov.uk

ALPINE, John Robert (Nov 1998) (Employee)
Gneiss Energy Limited, Edinburgh ....(p.1223)
E: john.alpine@gneissenergy.com

ALSTON, Euan (Nov 2019) (Employee)
Kirkland & Ellis International LLP, London
EC3 ....(p.1265)
T: 0207 4692000
E: euan.alston@kirkland.com

AMBLER, Jesse Clare (Jun 2018) (Employee)
Government Legal Department, London
SW1 ....(p.1264)
T: 0207 004 1293
E: jesse.ambler@dexeu.gov.uk

AMBRUS, Lisa (Aug 2018) (Employee)
Shepherd and Wedderburn LLP,
Edinburgh ....(p.900)
T: 0131 2289900
E: lisa.ambrus@shepwedd.com

AMIGUES-MACRAE, Rona Carron Ann
(Oct 2013) (Employee)
Lalive, Geneva ....(p.1276)
E: rmacrae@lalive.law

AMIN, Amina (Oct 2020) (Employee)
Kennedys Scotland, Glasgow ....(p.995)
T: 0141 433 7115
E: amina.amin@kennedyslaw.com

AMIN, Sidrah (Aug 2019) (Employee)
CMS Cameron McKenna Nabarro Olswang LLP,
Edinburgh ....(p.856)
T: 0131 2288000
E: Sidrah.Amin@cms-cmno.com

AMIR, Qurra-Tulain Mughal (Apr 2019)
(Employee)
Jackson Boyd LLP, Glasgow ....(p.991)
T: 0141 2214325
E: qamir@jacksonboyd.co.uk

AMJAD, Mohammed Sohail (Nov 2021)
(Employee)
Gildeas Limited, Edinburgh ....(p.872)
T: 0141 331 6079
E: samjad@gildeas.net

AMNER, Neil McDonald (Sept 1990)
(Consultant)
Anderson Strathern LLP, Glasgow......(p.940)
T: 0141 2426060
E: Neil.Amner@andersonstrathern.co.uk

AMOS, Dorothy Janet (Nov 1991) (Partner)
Taits, Jedburgh ....(p.1089)
T: 01835 344911
E: dorothy.amos@taits.co.uk

ANAND, Monica Rani (Dec 2017) (Employee)
Latta Law Limited, Glasgow..........(p.998)
T: 0141 222 2185
E: ma@lattalaw.co.uk

ANDERSON, Adele (Aug 2009) (Employee)
Stronachs LLP, Aberdeen ....(p.744)
T: 01224 845845
E: Adele.Anderson@stronachs.com

ANDERSON, Alasdair Forrest (Feb 2019)
(Employee)
Shepherd and Wedderburn LLP,
Edinburgh ....(p.900)
T: 0131 2289900
E: alasdair.anderson@shepwedd.com

ANDERSON, Alistair Robert, WS (Nov 1975)
(Consultant)
Morton Fraser LLP, Edinburgh . . . .(p.891)
T: 0131 2471000
E: Alistair.Anderson@morton-fraser.com

ANDERSON, Amy (Oct 2013) (Employee)
BTO Solicitors LLP, Glasgow . . . .(p.952)
T: 0141 2218012
E: aan@bto.co.uk

ANDERSON, Anthony Karl (Sept 1992)
(Partner)
Rollos Law LLP, Cupar . . . .(p.792)
T: 01334 654 081
E: tonyanderson@rollos.co.uk

ANDERSON, Arlene Mary (Nov 1986) (Solicitor)
NO FIRM

ANDERSON, Barbara Anne (Nov 2003)
(Director)
Archibald Sharp & Son Limited,
Glasgow . . . .(p.1039)
T: 0141 3393036
E: banderson@archibaldsharp.co.uk

ANDERSON, Callum George (Aug 2005)
(Partner)
Levy & McRae Solicitors LLP,
Glasgow . . . .(p.1000)
T: 0141 3072311
E: canderson@lemac.co.uk

ANDERSON, Chlo Rose (Mar 2020) (Employee)
Thorntons Law LLP, Dundee . . . .(p.819)
T: 01382 229 111
E: canderson@thorntons-law.co.uk

ANDERSON, Christopher Edward (Sept 2007)
(Employee)
WEST DUNBARTONSHIREhire Council,
Dumbarton . . . .(p.1217)
T: 01389 737000
E:
christopher.anderson@west-dunbarton.gov.uk

ANDERSON, Christopher James, WS
(Dec 1979) (Partner)
Stuart & Stuart, Edinburgh . . . .(p.905)
T: 0131 2286449
E: canderson@stuartandstuart.co.uk

ANDERSON, Claire Jayne (Sept 2000)
(Employee)
Office of the Advocate General,
Edinburgh . . . .(p.1227)
T: 0131 2441635
E: Claire.Anderson@advocategeneral.gov.uk

ANDERSON, Claire Joy (Apr 2007) (Employee)
TAQA Bratani Limited, Aberdeen . . . . .(p.1214)
T: 01224 275275
E: Claire.Anderson@taqaglobal.com

ANDERSON, Danny Sean (Aug 2017)
(Employee)
Aberdein Considine and Company,
Aberdeen . . . .(p.718)
T: 01224 589700
E: danderson@acandco.com

ANDERSON, David Jack Noble (Dec 2006)
(Partner)
Addleshaw Goddard LLP,
Edinburgh . . . .(p.835)
T: 0131 2282400
E: david.anderson@addleshawgoddard.com

ANDERSON, David James (Sept 2000)
(Employee)
Energy Law Unlimited LLP,
Glasgow . . . .(p.974)
T: 0141 2210276
E: dave.anderson@elu-llp.com

ANDERSON, David John William (Feb 1992)
(Partner)
Shepherd and Wedderburn LLP,
Edinburgh . . . .(p.900)
T: 0131 2289900
E: david.anderson@shepwedd.com

ANDERSON, Dawn Melrose (Oct 1993)
(Employee)
Lindsays LLP, Edinburgh . . . .(p.882)
T: 0131 2291212
E: dawnanderson@lindsays.co.uk

ANDERSON, Deirdre Helen (Mar 2000)
(Partner)
Energy Law Unlimited LLP,
Glasgow . . . .(p.974)
T: 0141 2210276
E: danderson@elu-llp.com

ANDERSON, Douglas Eric Alexander
(Oct 2005) (Employee)
Tughans, Belfast . . . .(p.1275)
T: 028 90553330
E: douglas.anderson@tughans.com

ANDERSON, Emma Jane (Sept 2007)
(Employee)
Procurator Fiscal Service, Glasgow . . . .(p.1241)
T: 0300 0203000
E: emma.anderson@copfs.gov.uk

ANDERSON, Euan Graham (Sept 2013)
(Employee)
Addleshaw Goddard LLP,
Edinburgh . . . .(p.835)
T: 0131 2282400
E: Euan.Anderson@addleshawgoddard.com

ANDERSON, Euan Robert Allan (Nov 2002)
(Employee)
Bank of New York Mellon, London
E14 . . . .(p.1262)
T: 0778 759 5943
E: Euan.Anderson@bnymellon.com

ANDERSON, Findlay Iain (Sept 2001)
(Employee)
Baker Hughes Ltd., Portlethen . . . .(p.1254)
T: 01224 720000
E: FINDLAY.ANDERSON@BAKERHUGHES.COM

ANDERSON, Fiona Elizabeth (Oct 1995)
(Associate)
MTM Family Law LLP, Glasgow . . . . . .(p.1025)
T: 0141 6117535
E: fea@mtmfamilylaw.co.uk

ANDERSON, Georgina Ann (May 2002)
(Employee)
The Moray Council, Elgin . . . .(p.1236)
T: 01343 543451
E: georgina.anderson@moray.gov.uk

ANDERSON, Gillian Anne (Oct 1998) (Partner)
Anderson Strathern LLP, Edinburgh . . . .(p.839)
T: 0131 2707700
E: gillian.anderson@andersonstrathern.co.uk

ANDERSON, Gillian Catherine (Oct 2005)
(Associate)
Pinsent Masons LLP, Glasgow . . . .(p.1031)
T: 0141 567 8400
E: Gillian.anderson@pinsentmasons.com

ANDERSON, Gordon James (Nov 1984)
(Employee)
East Ayrshire Council, Kilmarnock . . . . .(p.1249)
T: 01563 576161
E: gordon.anderson@east-ayrshire.gov.uk

ANDERSON, Gordon MacDonald (Dec 1981)
(Partner)
DMD Law LLP, Edinburgh . . . .(p.864)
T: 0131 3164666
E: mail@dmdpartnership.co.uk

ANDERSON, Greig Cameron Polson
(Oct 2002) (Employee)
Bilfinger Salamis UK Limited,
Aberdeen . . . .(p.1212)
T: 01224 246311
E: greig.anderson@bilfinger.com

ANDERSON, Hazel Lynne Barclay (Dec 2009)
(Employee)
Blackadders LLP, Dundee. . . . .(p.805)
T: 01382 229222
E: hazel.anderson@blackadders.co.uk

ANDERSON, Iain Craig (Mar 2011) (Employee)
Maples and Calder (Singapore) LLP,
Singapore. . . . .(p.1276)

ANDERSON, Ian (Nov 1984) (Employee)
Alliance Trust PLC, Dundee . . . .(p.1217)
T: 01382 938320
E: ian.anderson@alliancetrust.co.uk

ANDERSON, Ian Robert Edgar (Nov 1998)
(Director)
Macdonald Henderson Limited,
Glasgow. . . . .(p.1008)
T: 0141 2484957
E: ia@macdonaldhenderson.co.uk

ANDERSON, Ian Ruaridh (Feb 2021)
(Employee)
Robert More and Company,
Edinburgh . . . .(p.890)
T: 0131 5571110

ANDERSON, Jessica Maria (Nov 2004)
(Employee)
Aberdeen City Council, Aberdeen. . . . . .(p.1211)
T: 01224 522000
E: jeanderson@aberdeencity.gov.uk

ANDERSON, Katharine Jennifer (Sept 2001)
(Director)
Masson Cairns Limited,
Grantown-on-Spey . . . .(p.1059)
T: 01479 874800
E: ka@lawscot.com

ANDERSON, Katherine Jane (Oct 2014)
(Employee)
DAC Beachcroft Scotland LLP,
Glasgow. . . . .(p.964)
T: 0141 2486688
E: katanderson@dacbeachcroft.com

ANDERSON, Keith Downie (Jul 2010) (Partner)
Gilson Gray LLP, Edinburgh . . . .(p.874)
T: 0131 5165354
E: kanderson@gilsongray.co.uk

ANDERSON, Keith Thomas (Dec 1981)
(Partner)
Vialex WS, Edinburgh . . . .(p.910)
T: 03332 400 306
E: keith.anderson@vialex.co.uk

ANDERSON, Kevin Gerrard (Dec 2017)
(Employee)
Allan, Black & McCaskie, Elgin . . . .(p.915)
T: 01343 543355
E: KAnderson@abmsols.co.uk

ANDERSON, Kirsten Elizabeth McDougall
(Oct 1991) (Director)
Anderson Legal Ltd, Kirkintilloch . . . . .(p.1104)
T: 0141 775 4235
E: ka@andersonlegal.scot

ANDERSON, Kirsten Louise (Jan 2013)
(Employee)
Stronachs LLP, Aberdeen . . . .(p.744)
T: 01224 845845
E: kirsten.anderson@stronachs.com

ANDERSON, Kirsty (Mar 2011) (Employee)
Office of the Advocate General,
Edinburgh . . . .(p.1227)
T: 0131 2441635
E: Kirsty.Anderson@advocategeneral.gov.uk

ANDERSON, Laura Ellen (Jun 2006) (Employee)
Procurator Fiscal Service, Hamilton . . . .(p.1247)
  T: 0844 5613245
  E: laura.anderson@copfs.gov.uk

ANDERSON, Laura Kay (Aug 2014) (Employee)
Stephenson Harwood LLP, Dubai . . . . .(p.1278)
  E: Laura.Anderson@shlegal.com

ANDERSON, Lauren Jane (Oct 2017)
  (Employee)
Harper Macleod LLP, Glasgow . . . .(p.983)
  T: 0141 2218888
  E: Lauren.anderson@harpermacleod.co.uk

ANDERSON, Laurie Erin (Sept 2018)
  (Employee)
Addleshaw Goddard LLP, Glasgow . . . . .(p.938)
  T: 0141 2212300
  E: laurie.anderson@addleshawgoddard.com

ANDERSON, Laurie Gallacher (Sept 2007)
  (Employee)
Ellis Whittam Limited, Glasgow . . . . . .(p.1239)
  T: (0345) 226 8393
  E: laurieanderson@elliswhittam.com

ANDERSON, Leigh (Feb 2009) (Employee)
Aberdeenshire Council, Aberdeen . . . . .(p.1211)
  T: 01224 664618
  E: leigh.anderson@aberdeenshire.gov.uk

ANDERSON, Lesley Bell (Sept 2006) (Director)
Lesley Anderson Law Ltd, Falkirk . . . . . .(p.920)
  T: 01324 278 565
  E: enquiries@lesleyandersonlaw.co.uk

ANDERSON, Lesley Louise (Sept 2013) (Partner)
Paris Steele, North Berwick . . . .(p.1133)
  T: 01620 892 138
  E: landerson@parissteele.com

ANDERSON, Lindsay Ellen (Nov 2008)
  (Associate)
Stewart & Watson, Turriff . . . .(p.1177)
  T: 01888 563773
  E: landerson@stewartwatson.co.uk

ANDERSON, Lindsay Sarah (Feb 1996)
  (Employee)
Scottish Government, Edinburgh . . . . .(p.1231)
  T: 0131 2440117
  E: lindsay.anderson@gov.scot

ANDERSON, Lorna Jane (Sept 1993) (Partner)
Kelly & Co., Glasgow . . . .(p.995)
  T: 0141 5544141
  E: gerry@kellysolicitors.com

ANDERSON, Mairi-Claire (Aug 2008)
  (Employee)
Scottish Criminal Cases Review Commission,
  Glasgow. . . . .(p.1243)
  T: 0141 2707030
  E: mcanderson@sccrc.org.uk

ANDERSON, Mathew Balfour (Jan 2021)
  (Employee)
Stevenson & Marshall LLP,
  Dunfermline . . . .(p.825)
  T: 01383 721141
  E: manderson@stevenson-marshall.co.uk

ANDERSON, Megan (Feb 2021) (Employee)
Anderson Strathern LLP, Edinburgh . . . .(p.839)
  T: 0131 2707700
  E: megan.anderson@andersonstrathern.co.uk

ANDERSON, Megan Ailsa (Sept 2021)
  (Employee)
Latta Law Limited, Glasgow . . . .(p.998)
  T: 0141 222 2185
  E: megananderson@lattalaw.co.uk

ANDERSON, Michael Alexander George
  (Sept 1999) (Employee)
Gilson Gray LLP, Edinburgh . . . .(p.874)
  T: 0131 5165354

ANDERSON, Michael Peter (Jan 1976)
  (Consultant)
Levy & McRae Solicitors LLP,
  Glasgow. . . . .(p.1000)
  T: 0141 3072311
  E: PAnderson@lemac.co.uk

ANDERSON, Michael Shanley (Sept 2018)
  (Employee)
Ogier, St Helier . . . .(p.1274)
  T: 01534 514393
  E: michael.anderson@ogier.com

ANDERSON, Michael William (Sept 1986)
  (Director)
Q&A Law Practice Limited,
  Aberdeen . . . .(p.740)
  T: 7770996601
  E: mike@qalawpractice.co.uk

ANDERSON, Natasha (Apr 2014) (Employee)
Spirit Production (Services) Limited,
  Aberdeen . . . .(p.1214)
  T: 01224 411653
  E: natasha.anderson@spirit-energy.com

ANDERSON, Neal David (Feb 2012) (Employee)
Pinsent Masons LLP, Glasgow . . . .(p.1031)
  T: 0141 567 8400
  E: neal.anderson@pinsentmasons.com

ANDERSON, Neil (Dec 1998) (Employee)
ENGIE Power Limited, Leeds . . . .(p.1260)
  T: 0113 3062149
  E: neil.anderson1@engie.com

ANDERSON, Neil Robert (May 1996)
  (Consultant)
Rooney Nimmo Limited,
  Edinburgh . . . .(p.899)
  T: 0131 220 9570
  E: neil.anderson@rooneynimmo.co.uk

ANDERSON, Neil Welch Paxton (Nov 1980)
(Director)
Performance Living Limited,
Newburgh . . . .(p.1130)
T: 07714 411415
E: neil@performanceliving.co.uk

ANDERSON, Paul Anthony (Dec 2011)
(Employee)
Public Defence Solicitors Office,
Glasgow. . . . .(p.1243)
T: 0141 5530794
E: panderson@pdso.org.uk

ANDERSON, Paul Nathan (Oct 2015) (Solicitor)
NO FIRM

ANDERSON, Peter Duthie (Sept 1982)
(Consultant)
Andersonbain LLP, Aberdeen . . . .(p.721)
T: 01224 456789
E: PDA@andersonbain.co.uk

ANDERSON, Rachel (Sept 2017) (Employee)
Thorntons Law LLP, Dundee . . . .(p.819)
T: 01382 229 111
E: randerson@thorntons-law.co.uk

ANDERSON, Rhonda Margaret (Dec 1987)
(Employee)
Bruce McCormack Limited,
Motherwell. . . . .(p.1127)
T: 01698 260033

ANDERSON, Rory William (Jul 2019)
(Employee)
Berrymans Lace Mawer LLP,
Edinburgh . . . .(p.842)
T: 0131 2259855
E: Rory.Anderson@blmlaw.com

ANDERSON, Ross (Feb 2014) (Employee)
Jones Whyte LLP, Glasgow. . . . .(p.993)
T: 0141 375 1222
E: ross.anderson@joneswhyte.co.uk

ANDERSON, Ross Drummond (Dec 2013)
(Employee)
Dalling, Stirling . . . .(p.1164)
T: 01786 448111
E: ra@dalling.co.uk

ANDERSON, Ross William David (Sept 2003)
(Associate)
Latham & Watkins (London) LLP, London
EC2 . . . .(p.1266)
T: 020 7710 1199
E: ross.anderson@lw.com

ANDERSON, Rumyana Vladimirova
(Jan 2014) (Employee)
Alrum Limited, Edinburgh . . . .(p.1220)
E: rumyana.anderson@gmail.com

ANDERSON, Sally-Anne (Jan 2007) (Partner)
Aberdein Considine and Company,
Edinburgh . . . .(p.833)
T: 0131 2212424
E: sanderson@acandco.com

ANDERSON, Victoria Louise (Nov 2009)
(Associate)
Brodies LLP, Glasgow . . . .(p.948)
T: 0141 2484672
E: victoria.anderson@brodies.com

ANDERSON-SPRATT, Laurie (Mar 2013)
(Employee)
National Health Service Scotland,
Edinburgh . . . .(p.1225)
T: 0131 2757800
E: laurie.anderson-spratt@nhs.scot

ANDERSON-WARD, Freya (Aug 2020)
(Employee)
Procurator Fiscal Service,
Edinburgh . . . .(p.1227)
T: 0300 0203168
E: Freya.Anderson-Ward@copfs.gov.uk

ANDREW, Amy Elizabeth (Oct 2015)
(Employee)
Attest Technologies Limited, London
EC2 . . . .(p.1261)
E: Amy.andrew@askattest.com

ANDREW, Ellen Jane (Sept 2018) (Employee)
Brodies LLP, Edinburgh . . . .(p.845)
T: 0131 2283777
E: ellen.andrew@brodies.com

ANDREW, James Clarke (Dec 1984) (Partner)
Miller Hendry, Perth . . . .(p.1150)
T: 01738 637311
E: jamesandrew@millerhendry.co.uk

ANDREW, Jennifer (Sept 2015) (Associate)
Morton Fraser LLP, Glasgow . . . .(p.1022)
T: 0141 2741100
E: Jennifer.Andrew@morton-fraser.com

ANDREW, Jill Shaw (Sept 1996) (Director)
Alston Law, Edinburgh . . . .(p.838)
T: 0131 581 5700
E: jill.andrew@simpsonmarwick.com

ANDREW, Louise Jane (Sept 2010) (Employee)
University of Glasgow, Glasgow . . . . . .(p.1245)
T: (0141) 330 7725
E: Louise.Andrew.2@glasgow.ac.uk

ANDREW, Richard Robert (Jan 2014)
(Associate)
Dallas McMillan, Glasgow . . . .(p.966)
T: 0141 3336750
E: richard.andrew@dallasmcmillan.co.uk

ANDREWS, Nikita-Hedy Velvet Kimberly F
(Nov 2021) (Employee)
James & George Collie LLP,
Aberdeen . . . . (p.728)
T: 01224 581581
E: v.andrews@jgcollie.co.uk

ANFIELD, Jenny Margaret (Sept 2016)
(Employee)
BayWa R.e. UK Limited, Edinburgh . . . . (p.1221)
T: (0131) 4663689
E: Jenny.Anfield@baywa-re.co.uk

ANG, Jennifer Su-Ian (Aug 2011) (Associate)
JustRight Scotland LLP, Glasgow . . . . . . (p.994)
T: 0141 406 5350
E: jen@justrightscotland.org.uk

ANGELOV, Filip (May 2017) (Solicitor)
NO FIRM

ANGUS, Hugh Donald Walter (Nov 1987)
(Partner)
Balfour + Manson LLP, Edinburgh . . . . . (p.841)
T: 0131 2001200
E: hugh.angus@balfour-manson.co.uk

ANGUS, Ian Alistair (Jul 2014) (Associate)
Raeburn Christie Clark & Wallace LLP,
Inverurie . . . . (p.1085)
T: 01467 629300
E: Ian.Angus@raeburns.co.uk

ANGUS, Jennifer Grace (Dec 2014) (Employee)
Lloyds Banking Group, Edinburgh . . . . (p.1224)
T: 0131 655 7773
E: Jennifer.Angus@Lloydsbanking.com

ANGUS, Kathryn Charlotte (Sept 2012)
(Employee)
Brodies LLP, Glasgow . . . . (p.948)
T: 0141 2484672
E: Katy.angus@brodies.com

ANGUS, Keith Alistair (Nov 2005) (Employee)
Equinor Production UK Limited,
Aberdeen . . . . (p.1212)
T: 01224 653350
E: kangu@equinor.com

ANNAN, Alastair Martin (Sept 1992)
(Consultant)
Kilpatrick & Walker, Ayr . . . . (p.763)
T: 01292 618585
E: martin@kilpatrickwalker.com

ANNAN, Elspeth (Nov 1989) (Employee)
Church of Scotland, Edinburgh . . . . . . (p.1221)
T: 0131 2255722
E: eannan@churchofscotland.org.uk

ANNAND, Katherine Elizabeth (Oct 2014)
(Employee)
National Westminster Bank PLC,
Edinburgh . . . . (p.1226)
T: (0131) 626 2925
E: katherine.annand@rbs.co.uk

ANNIS, Stephen David (Sept 2020) (Employee)
Blackadders LLP, Dundee . . . . (p.805)
T: 01382 229 222
E: stephen.annis@blackadders.co.uk

ANTHONY, Sally Jane MacRae (Sept 2001)
(Employee)
Morton Fraser LLP, Edinburgh . . . . (p.891)
T: 0131 2471000
E: sally.anthony@morton-fraser.com

ANTONELLI, David (Oct 2003) (Associate)
Burness Paull LLP, Edinburgh . . . . (p.850)
T: 0131 4736000
E: david.antonelli@burnesspaull.com

ANTONELLI, Jennifer Margaret (Mar 2003)
(Associate)
CMS Cameron McKenna Nabarro Olswang LLP,
Edinburgh . . . . (p.856)
T: 0131 200 7630
E: Jennifer.Antonelli@cms-cmno.com

ANWAR, Aadil Shamoon (Jul 2021) (Employee)
Thorntons Law LLP, Dundee . . . . (p.819)
T: 01382 229 111
E: aanwar@thorntons-law.co.uk

ANWAR, Aysha (Feb 2018) (Employee)
Dundee City Council, Dundee . . . . (p.1217)
T: 01382 434209
E: aysha.anwar@dundeecity.gov.uk

ANWAR, Mohammed Aamer (Dec 2001)
(Partner)
Aamer Anwar & Co, Glasgow . . . . (p.941)
T: 0141 4297090
E: aamer@aameranwar.com

ANWAR, Mohammed Awais (Dec 2020)
(Employee)
Foot Anstey LLP, Bristol . . . . (p.1259)
T: 0117 915 4900

ANWAR, Omar (Jul 2015) (Employee)
White & Case LLP, London EC2 . . . . . . (p.1269)
T: 0207 5321000
E: omi.anwar@hotmail.co.uk

ANWAR, Zarah (Jun 2020) (Employee)
Maguire Solicitors, Glasgow . . . . (p.1017)
T: 0141 3312885

APOSTOLOVA, Lora Yulianova (Aug 2017)
(Employee)
Procurator Fiscal Service, Dundee . . . . . (p.1218)
T: 01382 342559
E: Lora.Apostolova@copfs.gov.uk

APTED, Jamie (Jan 2017) (Employee)
MBM Commercial LLP, Edinburgh . . . . . (p.889)
T: 0131 226 8215
E: jamie.apted@mbmcommercial.co.uk

ARABSHAHI, Arveen (Dec 2014) (Associate)
Davidson Chalmers Stewart LLP,
   Edinburgh . . . . (p.859)
   T: 0131 6259191
   E: arveen.arabshahi@dcslegal.com

ARCARI, Emma Geraldine (Apr 2010)
   (Associate)
Wright, Johnston & Mackenzie LLP,
   Edinburgh . . . . (p.913)
   T: 0131 5241500
   E: ega@wjm.co.uk

ARCHER, Dawn Elizabeth (Oct 2005)
   (Employee)
Scottish Government, Edinburgh . . . . . (p.1231)
   T: 0131 244 0815
   E: dawn.archer@gov.scot

ARCHIBALD, Colin John (Sept 1998) (Partner)
Shepherd and Wedderburn LLP,
   Edinburgh . . . . (p.900)
   T: 0131 2289900
   E: colin.archibald@shepwedd.com

ARCHIBALD, Heidi Louise (Sept 1995)
   (Associate)
Eversheds Sutherland (International) LLP,
   Edinburgh . . . . (p.869)
   T: 0207 9194500
   E: heidiarchibald@eversheds-Sutherland.com

ARCHIBALD, Holly (Aug 2021) (Employee)
Turcan Connell, Edinburgh . . . . (p.908)
   T: 0131 2288111
   E: holly.archibald@turcanconnell.com

ARCHIBALD, Jamila Ruby Louise (Jun 2020)
   (Employee)
SSE PLC, Glasgow . . . . (p.1244)
   T: 0141 224 7248
   E: jamila.archibald@sse.com

ARCHIBALD, Scott Michael (Jul 2020)
   (Employee)
Scottish Borders Council, Newtown St.
   Boswells . . . . (p.1251)
   T: 01835 825 225
   E: Scott.archibald@scotborders.gov.uk

ARGUE, Allan John (Sept 2015) (Partner)
Argue & Co Legal, Glasgow . . . . (p.942)
   T: 0141 3784145
   E: aar@argueandco.co.uk

ARIAS, Clare (Oct 2002) (Employee)
Procurator Fiscal Service, Glasgow . . . . (p.1241)
   T: 0300 020 3000
   E: clare.arias@copfs.gov.uk

ARKLESS, Richard Lambert Thomas
   (Oct 2008) (Employee)
Williamson & Henry LLP,
   Kirkcudbright . . . . (p.1104)
   T: 01557 330692
   E: rarkless@williamsonandhenry.co.uk

ARLOW, Christine Isabel (Oct 1996) (Partner)
Arlow Brown, Dunfermline . . . . (p.822)
   T: 01383 626626
   E: arlowbrownlegal@gmail.com

ARMOUR, Brian Oetegenn (May 1994)
   (Partner)
TLT LLP, Glasgow . . . . (p.1048)
   T: 0333 006 0400
   E: Brian.Armour@tltsolicitors.com

ARMOUR, Fiona Frances (Oct 2004) (Associate)
MacRoberts LLP, Glasgow . . . . (p.1015)
   T: 0141 3031100
   E: fiona.armour@macroberts.com

ARMOUR, Robert Malcolm, WS (Nov 1983)
   (Consultant)
Gowling WLG (UK) LLP, London
   SE1 . . . . (p.1265)
   E: Robert.Armour@gowlingwlg.com

ARMSTRONG, Abbi (Feb 2017) (Employee)
McJerrow & Stevenson, Lockerbie . . . . (p.1122)
   T: 01576 202123
   E: am.mcjerrows@btconnect.com

ARMSTRONG, Amanda Jordan (Jan 2016)
   (Employee)
Burness Paull LLP, Edinburgh . . . . (p.850)
   T: 0131 4736000
   E: Amanda.armstrong@burnesspaull.com

ARMSTRONG, Angus Stuart (Sept 2013)
   (Employee)
Scottish Power Limited, Glasgow . . . . . (p.1244)
   T: 0141 6140000
   E: aarmstrong@scottishpower.com

ARMSTRONG, Callum Charles (Oct 2014)
   (Employee)
Stronachs LLP, Aberdeen . . . . (p.744)
   T: 01224 845845
   E: Callum.Armstrong@stronachs.com

ARMSTRONG, Camille Janey (Aug 2012)
   (Partner)
Drummond Miller LLP, Glasgow . . . . . . (p.971)
   T: 0141 3320086
   E: jarmstrong@drummondmiller.co.uk

ARMSTRONG, Caroline Kathreen Macdonald
   (Nov 2001) (Partner)
Addleshaw Goddard LLP,
   Edinburgh . . . . (p.835)
   T: 0131 2282400
   E: carrie.armstrong@addleshawgoddard.com

ARMSTRONG, Claire (Nov 1999) (Partner)
Dentons UK and Middle East LLP,
   Edinburgh . . . . (p.860)
   T: 0330 2220050
   E: Claire.Armstrong@dentons.com

ARMSTRONG, Craig Marshall (Aug 2017)
   (Employee)
Optical Express Limited

ARMSTRONG, David James (Nov 1988)
(Partner)
Lindsays LLP, Glasgow . . . . (p.1001)
T: 0141 221 6551
E: davidarmstrong@lindsays.co.uk

ARMSTRONG, David John (Oct 1993) (Partner)
Neill Clerk & Murray, Greenock . . . . . . (p.1062)
T: 01475 724522
E: dja@neillclerkmurray.co.uk

ARMSTRONG, Douglas Alexander
(Oct 1998) (Partner)
Dickson Minto, Edinburgh . . . . (p.861)
T: 0131 2254455
E: douglas.armstrong@dmws.com

ARMSTRONG, Ivor Iain Mitchell (Feb 1985)
(Partner)
DMD Law LLP, Edinburgh . . . . (p.864)
T: 0131 3164666
E: iima@dmdpartnership.co.uk

ARMSTRONG, Johanna Joyce (Sept 2004)
(Employee)
Abu Dhabi National Oil Company, Abu
Dhabi . . . . (p.1277)
E: jarmstrong@adnoc.ae

ARMSTRONG, John Bryson (Aug 1971)
(Director)
Smail & Ewart Ltd, Biggar . . . . (p.774)
T: 01899 220058
E: jarmstrong@smail-ewart.co.uk

ARMSTRONG, Josephine Vance (Oct 2005)
(Employee)
Scottish Environment Protection Agency,
Holytown . . . . (p.1248)
T: (01698) 839 000
E: josephine.armstrong@sepa.org.uk

ARMSTRONG, Kyla Louise (Aug 2012)
(Employee)
Halliburton Management Ltd,
Dyce . . . . (p.1219)
T: 01224 777000
E: kyla.armstrong@halliburton.com

ARMSTRONG, Laura Kilpatrick (Oct 1993)
(Employee)
Jacobs U.K. Limited, Glasgow . . . . (p.1240)
T: 0141 2438825
E: laura.armstrong@jacobs.com

ARMSTRONG, Lesley Ann (Oct 1999)
(Employee)
Smail & Ewart Ltd, Biggar . . . . (p.774)
T: 01899 220058
E: larmstrong@smail-ewart.co.uk

ARMSTRONG, Lewis William (Apr 2021)
(Employee)
Stronachs LLP, Aberdeen . . . . (p.744)
T: 01224 845845
E: lewis.armstrong@stronachs.com

ARMSTRONG, Lindsey Maureen (Jul 2007)
(Employee)
Procurator Fiscal Service,
Edinburgh . . . . (p.1229)
T: 0844 5612000
E: Lindsey.Armstrong@copfs.gov.uk

ARMSTRONG, Mandy (Dec 2013) (Employee)
Anderson Strathern LLP, Edinburgh . . . . (p.839)
T: 0131 2707700
E: mandy.armstrong@andersonstrathern.co.uk

ARMSTRONG, Marc James (Sept 2005)
(Partner)
CMS Cameron McKenna Nabarro Olswang LLP,
Edinburgh . . . . (p.856)
T: 0131 2288000
E: Marc.Armstrong@cms-cmno.com

ARMSTRONG, Marie-Louise (Dec 2003)
(Employee)
James & George Collie LLP,
Aberdeen . . . . (p.728)
T: 01224 581581
E: l.armstrong@jgcollie.co.uk

ARMSTRONG, Miriam Eileen Rose
(Oct 2007) (Employee)
Brodies LLP, Edinburgh . . . . (p.845)
T: 0131 2283777
E: miriam.armstrong@brodies.com

ARMSTRONG, Nicola Mary (Sept 2003)
(Employee)
Aberdeen Corporate Services Limited,
Edinburgh . . . . (p.1220)
T: 0131 245 7508
E: Nicola.Armstrong@abrdn.com

ARMSTRONG-SURGENOR, Valerie Muriel
(Mar 2001) (Partner)
MacRoberts LLP, Glasgow . . . . (p.1015)
T: 0141 3031100
E: valerie.surgenor@macroberts.com

ARNOT, Helen (Dec 1992) (Employee)
STV Television Limited, Glasgow . . . . . . (p.1245)
T: 0141 3003000
E: helen.arnot@stv.tv

ARNOT, Joanne Kennedy (Jun 2017)
(Employee)
Scottish Social Services Council,
Dundee . . . . (p.1218)
T: 0345 6030 891
E: Joanne.Arnot@sssc.uk.com

ARNOTT, Andrew Peter (Mar 2009) (Employee)
Wood Group UK Limited,
Aberdeen . . . . (p.1214)
T: 01224 851000
E: andrew.arnott@woodgroup.com

ARNOTT, David Scott (Jan 1993) (Partner)
Brodies LLP, Edinburgh . . . . (p.845)
T: 0131 2283777
E: david.arnott@brodies.com

ARNOTT, Elaine (Sept 2010) (Employee)
Allingham & Co (Solicitors) Limited,
 Edinburgh . . . .(p.838)
 T: 0131 4479341
 E: elainearnott@allingham.co.uk

ARNOTT, Harriet Clara (Mar 2010) (Employee)
Chrysaor Production (U.K.) Limited,
 Aberdeen . . . .(p.1212)
 T: 01224 205333
 E: harriet.arnott@chrysaor.com

ARNOTT, Lynne Kathryn Telford (Oct 1996)
 (Associate)
MBM Commercial LLP, Edinburgh . . . . .(p.889)
 T: 0131 2268200
 E: lynne.arnott@mbmcommercial.co.uk

ARNOTT, Paula Anne (Feb 1992) (Associate)
Turcan Connell, Edinburgh . . . .(p.908)
 T: 0131 2288111
 E: paula.arnott@turcanconnell.com

ARRABAL WARD, Caterine Elisabet
 (Jul 2018) (Employee)
Procurator Fiscal Service, Paisley . . . . . .(p.1252)
 T: 0141 8497940
 E: caterina.ward@copfs.gov.uk

ARREDONDO REBOA, Camilo Jorge
 (Jul 2017) (Employee)
Scottish Government, Edinburgh . . . . .(p.1231)
 T: 0131 244 8395
 E: camilo.arredondo@gov.scot

ARROL, James Edward Harris (Jun 2010)
 (Director)
The Robert Kerr Partnership Limited,
 Paisley . . . .(p.1141)
 T: 0141 8896458
 E: ja@therobertkerrpartnership.com

ARSHAD, Mohammad Azeem (Aug 2016)
 (Employee)
Blackadders LLP, Glasgow . . . .(p.946)
 T: 0141 2481888
 E: azeem.arshad@blackadders.co.uk

ARSHAD, Nadia (Aug 2017) (Employee)
Jones Whyte LLP, Glasgow . . . .(p.993)
 T: 0141 375 1222
 E: nadia.arshad@joneswhyte.co.uk

ARSHAD, Sadia (Nov 2006) (Employee)
Scottish Child Law Centre,
 Edinburgh . . . .(p.1230)
 T: 0131 6676333
 E: sadia@sclc.org.uk

ARSHAD, Shahana Andaleeb (Oct 2018)
 (Employee)
Glasgow City Council, Glasgow . . . . . .(p.1239)
 T: 0141 287 3098
 E: shahana.arshad@ced.glasgow.gov.uk

ARSHED, Yasmin (Aug 2008) (Employee)
Jacobs U.K. Limited, Glasgow . . . .(p.1240)
 T: 0141 2042511
 E: yasmin.arshed@jacobs.com

ARTHUR, Jacqueline (Oct 2007) (Employee)
Shepherd and Wedderburn LLP,
 Glasgow . . . .(p.1039)
 T: 0141 5669900
 E: Jacqueline.Arthur@shepwedd.com

ARTHUR, Laura (Jun 2012) (Employee)
Procurator Fiscal Service, Inverness . . . .(p.1248)
 T: 0844 5612954
 E: Laura.Arthur@copfs.gov.uk

ARTHUR, Louise Anne (Oct 2008) (Employee)
Gebbie & Wilson LLP, Strathaven . . . . .(p.1172)
 T: 01357 520082
 E: louise@gebbiewilson.co.uk

ARTHUR, Lucy May (Sept 2019) (Employee)
Anderson Strathern LLP, Edinburgh . . . .(p.839)
 T: 0131 2707700
 E: lucy.arthur@andersonstrathern.co.uk

ASANTE, Catherine Ama (Nov 2007)
 (Employee)
Scottish Human Rights Commission,
 Edinburgh . . . .(p.1233)
 T: 0131 297 5759
 E: Cathy.Asante@scottishhumanrights.com

ASBURY, Craig James (Mar 2017) (Employee)
Brodies LLP, Glasgow . . . .(p.948)
 T: 0141 2484672
 E: craig.asbury@brodies.com

ASHBOLT, Katrina Larisa (Oct 2005) (Director)
Macleod & MacCallum Limited,
 Inverness . . . .(p.1080)
 T: 01463 239393
 E: katrina.ashbolt@macandmac.co.uk

ASHBY, Toni Louise (Sept 2000) (Partner)
Clyde & Co (Scotland) LLP,
 Edinburgh . . . .(p.855)
 T: 0131 5571545
 E: toni.ashby@clydeco.com

ASHKANANI, Tariq Essa Abedali (Sept 2012)
 (Employee)
National Health Service Scotland,
 Edinburgh . . . .(p.1225)
 T: 0131 275 7924
 E: tariq.ashkanani@nhs.scot

ASHRAF, Amna (Dec 2013) (Associate)
Burness Paull LLP, Glasgow . . . .(p.954)
 T: 0141 2484933
 E: amna.ashraf@burnesspaull.com

ASHRAF, Miriam (Oct 2011) (Employee)
Pinsent Masons LLP, Glasgow . . . .(p.1031)
 T: 0141 567 8400
 E: Miriam.Ashraf@pinsentmasons.com

ASHRAF, Rabia Isha (Sept 2016) (Employee)
Blair & Bryden, Clydebank...........(p.784)
T: 0141 9523322
E: rashraf@blair-bryden.co.uk

ASHRAF, Sadif (Sept 2002) (Employee)
Sheku Bayoh Public Inquiry,
Edinburgh ....(p.1233)
E: sadif.ashraf@shekubayohinquiry.scot

ASHRAF, Waqqas Abrar (Aug 2013) (Director)
WA Legal Ltd, Glasgow ....(p.1050)
T: 0330 1334563
E: waqqaslegal@gmail.com

ASHTON, Gareth Oliver (Oct 2005) (Solicitor)
NO FIRM

ASHTON STRINGER, Danielle Maria
(Oct 2018) (Employee)
Gleeson McCafferty Law,
Glenrothes ....(p.1057)
T: 01592 611660

ASKEW BLAIN, Andrew John (Jan 2014)
(Employee)
Brodies LLP, Aberdeen.............(p.723)
T: 01224 392242
E: andrew.askewblain@brodies.com

ASLAM, Hamaira Kausar (Nov 2015)
(Employee)
Burness Paull LLP, Edinburgh ....(p.850)
T: 0131 4736000
E: Hamaira.aslam@burnesspaull.com

ASLAM, Muhammad Usman (Jan 2016)
(Employee)
Rea Law Ltd, Glasgow ....(p.1034)
T: 0141 3701241
E: usman@realaw.co.uk

ASPINWALL, Rebecca Charlotte (Jan 2008)
(Associate)
Pinsent Masons LLP, London EC2 .....(p.1267)
T: 0207 490 6162
E: Becca.aspinwall@pinsentmasons.com

ASPLIN, Marion Flora Celia (Oct 2007)
(Employee)
Shepherd and Wedderburn LLP,
Edinburgh ....(p.900)
T: 0131 2289900
E: flora.asplin@shepwedd.com

ATHERTON, Colin Gordon (Jul 2013)
(Employee)
Neos Networks Limited, Perth ....(p.1253)
E: Colin.Atherton@sse.com

ATHERTON, Lewis Christopher (Jul 2016)
(Employee)
Latham & Watkins (London) LLP, London
EC2 ....(p.1266)
T: 02077101000 / 44.20.
E: lewis.atherton@lw.com

ATKINS, Alison Jane (Oct 1999) (Employee)
Procurator Fiscal Service,
Edinburgh ....(p.1227)
T: 0844 5612936
E: alison.atkins@copfs.gov.uk

ATKINS, Nicholas John (Jan 1984) (Consultant)
Morton Fraser LLP, Edinburgh ....(p.891)
T: 0131 2471000
E: nick.atkins@morton-fraser.com

ATKINSON, Beverley (Oct 2001) (Associate)
DAC Beachcroft Scotland LLP,
Edinburgh ....(p.858)
T: 0131 5247790
E: batkinson@dacbeachcroft.com

ATKINSON, Pamela May (Jul 2005) (Employee)
Lloyds Banking Group Plc,
Edinburgh ....(p.1224)
T: (0131) 442 9579
E: Pamela.Atkinson@LloydsBanking.com

AU-YEUNG, Ka Man (Feb 2013) (Employee)
Lindsays LLP, Glasgow.............(p.1001)
T: 0141 2216551
E: kamanauyeung@lindsays.co.uk

AULD, Cassandra Louise (Sept 1996) (Partner)
Weightmans (Scotland) LLP,
Glasgow....................(p.1051)
T: 0345 073 9900
E: cassandra.auld@weightmans.com

AULD, Heather Elizabeth Cameron
(Sept 2007) (Employee)
Scottish Government, Glasgow ......(p.1243)
T: (0141) 2727933
E: Heather.Auld@gov.scot

AULD, Laura Elizabeth (Nov 2015) (Employee)
Ellis Whittam Limited, Glasgow ......(p.1239)
T: 0345 226 8393
E: lauraauld@elliswhittam.com

AULD, Rebecca (Nov 2021) (Employee)
Elizabeth Welsh Family Law Practice,
Ayr ....(p.766)
T: 01292 284786
E: rebecca.auld@familylawpractice.co.uk

AUSTIN, Ian (Director)
Davidson & Robertson Ltd, Currie ....(p.1329)
T: (0131) 449 6212
E: IA@drrural.co.uk

AUSTIN, Nigel John (Jan 1990) (Employee)
Dechert LLP, London EC4 ....(p.1263)
T: 020 7184 7000
E: nigel.austin@dechert.com

AVINO, Fiona (Oct 2009) (Employee)
Procurator Fiscal Service,
Edinburgh ....(p.1227)
T: 0300 0203168
E: fiona.avino@copfs.gov.uk

AXELSSON, Emma Kristina Nathalie
(Jun 2016) (Employee)
Thompsons, Edinburgh . . . . (p.906)
   T: 0131 2254297
   E:
   nathalie.axelsson@thompsons-scotland.co.uk

AYRE, Victoria Frances (Jun 2000) (Employee)
Scottish Government, Edinburgh . . . . . (p.1231)
   T: 0131 244 0815
   E: Victoria.Ayre@gov.scot

AYRES, Graham (Oct 2004) (Employee)
University of Edinburgh, Edinburgh . . . (p.1235)
   T: (0131) 651 4330
   E: graham.ayres@ed.ac.uk

BACCHUS, Gayle Louise (Jul 2012) (Employee)
Aberdeen Corporate Services Limited,
   Edinburgh . . . . (p.1220)
   T: 0131 245 7508
   E: gayle.bacchus@abrdn.com

BADGER FINLAYSON, Morven Anne
(May 2003) (Employee)
Gunnercooke SCO LLP, Glasgow . . . . . . (p.982)
   E: morven.finlayson@gunnercooke.com

BAGHA, Baljit Kaur (Sept 2003) (Employee)
The Pharmacists' Defence Association,
   Birmingham . . . . (p.1258)
   T: 0121 6947000
   E: baljit.bagha@the-pda.org

BAGNALL, Suzanne Elizabeth (May 2019)
(Employee)
McAuley, McCarthy & Co.,
   Renfrew . . . . (p.1159)
   T: 0141 5614449
   E: suzanne@mmscotland.co.uk

BAGRI, Tanya (Dec 2015) (Employee)
Jones Whyte LLP, Glasgow . . . . (p.993)
   T: 0141 375 1222
   E: tanya.bagri@joneswhyte.co.uk

BAHRU, Joshua Levi (Jun 2021) (Solicitor)
NO FIRM

BAIG, Faisal (Nov 2016) (Employee)
Royal London, Edinburgh . . . . (p.1230)
   T: 0131 4567703
   E: faisal.baig@royallondon.com

BAIG, Sabrina (Jul 2015) (Employee)
Bready & Co., Glasgow . . . . (p.947)
   T: 0141 334 2265
   E: sbaig@breadyandco.com

BAIJAL, Eric Marcus (Jun 2005) (Director)
BBM Solicitors Limited, Wick . . . . (p.1180)
   T: 01955 604188
   E: emb@bbmsolicitors.co.uk

BAILEY, Anna Sophie (Jul 2008) (Employee)
Shepherd and Wedderburn LLP,
   Edinburgh . . . . (p.900)
   T: 0131 2289900
   E: sophie.bailey@shepwedd.com

BAILEY, Christopher Patrick (Sept 2013)
(Employee)
Scottish Social Services Council,
   Dundee . . . . (p.1218)
   T: 01382 207 101
   E: christopher.bailey@sssc.uk.com

BAILEY, Nigel (Oct 1986) (Employee)
MOV8 Real Estate Limited,
   Glasgow . . . . (p.1023)
   T: 0345 646 0208
   E: nigel.bailey@move8realestate.com

BAILEY, Rachael (Aug 2019) (Employee)
Ashurst LLP, Glasgow . . . . (p.1237)
   T: (0141) 375 4242
   E: Rachael.Bailey@ashurst.com

BAILLIE, Alan John (Oct 1980) (Employee)
Gilson Gray LLP, Dundee . . . . (p.812)
   E: abaillie@gilsongray.co.uk

BAILLIE, Andrew (Aug 1991) (Partner)
Andrew Baillie, Kinross . . . . (p.1098)
   T: 01577 861000
   E: andrewbaillie@andrewbaillie.co.uk

BAILLIE, Annette Helen (Aug 2013) (Employee)
Kirkland & Ellis International LLP, London
   EC3 . . . . (p.1265)
   T: 0207 4692000
   E: annette.baillie@kirkland.com

BAILLIE, Christelle Olivia St phanie M.
(Jan 2020) (Employee)
Vialex Limited, Edinburgh . . . . (p.1235)
   T: 0333 2400127
   E: christellebaillie@gmail.com

BAILLIE, Christina Hill (Jan 1987) (Associate)
Thorntons Law LLP, Dundee . . . . (p.819)
   T: 01382 229 111
   E: cbaillie@thorntons-law.co.uk

BAILLIE, Christine Margaret (Nov 1990)
(Employee)
Dewar Spence, Leven . . . . (p.1114)
   T: 01333 425200
   E: mail@dewarspence.co.uk

BAILLIE, Dawn Samantha (May 2021)
(Employee)
Stork Technical Services UK Limited,
   Dyce . . . . (p.1219)
   T: 01224 722888
   E: dawn.baillie@stork.com

BAILLIE, Gemma Clare (Jun 2009) (Partner)
McLean & Stewart LLP, Dunblane . . . . . (p.804)
   T: 01786 823217
   E: gemma.baillie@mcleanandstewart.co.uk

BAILLIE, Sarah (Sept 2002) (Partner)
Addleshaw Goddard LLP,
   Edinburgh . . . .(p.835)
   T: 0131 2282400
   E: Sarah.Baillie@addleshawgoddard.com

BAILLIE, Stewart Alastair James (Mar 2011)
(Partner)
Macnabs LLP, Perth . . . .(p.1150)
   T: 01738 623432
   E: stewartbaillie@macnabs-law.co.uk

BAIN, Amie Sutherland (Jun 2011) (Employee)
Shepherd and Wedderburn LLP,
   Glasgow. . . . .(p.1039)
   T: 0141 5667228
   E: amie.bain@shepwedd.com

BAIN, Coral (Nov 2000) (Employee)
Addleshaw Goddard LLP,
   Edinburgh . . . .(p.835)
   T: 0131 2282400
   E: Coral.bain@addleshawgoddard.com

BAIN, Daniel Clark (Oct 2004) (Employee)
Shepherd and Wedderburn LLP,
   Edinburgh . . . .(p.900)
   T: 0131 2289900
   E: daniel.bain@shepwedd.com

BAIN, Fiona Elizabeth (Feb 2018) (Employee)
Wilson McKendrick Solicitors Limited,
   Glasgow. . . . .(p.1053)
   T: 0141 2227950

BAIN, Gavin Murray (Jan 1984) (Partner)
Gavin Bain & Co., Aberdeen . . . .(p.721)
   T: 01224 623040
   E: g.bain@gavin-bain.co.uk

BAIN, Hayden Thomas (Mar 2021) (Employee)
Thompsons, Glasgow . . . .(p.1046)
   T: 0141 2218840
   E: Hayden.Bain@thompsons-scotland.co.uk

BAIN, Heather Laura (Nov 2012) (Employee)
Standard Life Assets and Employee Services
   Limited, Edinburgh . . . .(p.1234)
   T: 0131 2457508
   E: heather_bain@standardlife.com

BAIN, Helen Mary (Nov 2010) (Employee)
Office of the Advocate General,
   Edinburgh . . . .(p.1227)
   T: 0131 2441635
   E: helen.bain@advocategeneral.gov.uk

BAIN, Isabelle Eliza (Sept 2021) (Employee)
Morton Fraser LLP, Edinburgh . . . .(p.891)
   T: 0131 2471000
   E: isabelle.bain@morton-fraser.com

BAIN, John Randal (Apr 1978) (Consultant)
Morgans, Dunfermline . . . .(p.824)
   T: 01383 620222
   E: johnbain@morganlaw.co.uk

BAIN, Julie (Oct 2004) (Employee)
Scottish Government, Edinburgh . . . . .(p.1231)
   T: 0131 244 0815
   E: julie.bain@gov.scot

BAIN, Leanne Margaret (Sept 2014)
(Employee)
TAQA Bratani Limited, Aberdeen . . . . .(p.1214)
   T: 01224 275275
   E: leanne.bain@taqaglobal.com

BAIN, Louise Marie (Aug 2006) (Employee)
Carr & Co (Solicitors) Limited,
   Glasgow. . . . .(p.957)
   T: 0141 6412912/8346
   E: lb@theglasgowlawpractice.co.uk

BAIN, Nicola (Aug 2012) (Employee)
Highland Council, Inverness. . . . .(p.1248)
   T: 01463 702000
   E: nicola.bain@highland.gov.uk

BAIN, Rachael Catherine (Oct 2019)
(Employee)
Mackinnons Solicitors LLP,
   Aberdeen . . . .(p.736)
   T: 01224 632464
   E: rachael@mackinnons.com

BAIN, Steven James (Jan 2021) (Employee)
Jones Whyte LLP, Glasgow. . . . .(p.993)
   T: 0141 375 1222
   E: steven.bain@joneswhyte.co.uk

BAIN, Stuart McDonald (Nov 1986) (Partner)
Andersonbain LLP, Aberdeen . . . .(p.721)
   T: 01224 456789
   E: sbain@andersonbain.co.uk

BAINES, Gary Alexander (Sept 2010) (Partner)
MacRoberts LLP, Glasgow . . . .(p.1015)
   T: 0141 3031100
   E: gary.baines@macroberts.com

BAIRD, Debbie Margaret (Dec 2009)
(Employee)
Bank of New York Mellon,
   Edinburgh . . . .(p.1221)
   T: 0131 635 2612
   E: Debbie.Baird@bnymellon.com

BAIRD, Derek William (Feb 1992) (Employee)
Simpson Thacher & Bartlett LLP, London
   EC2 . . . .(p.1268)
   T: 020 7275 6500
   E: derek.baird@stblaw.com

BAIRD, Iain Alastair (Nov 2009) (Employee)
Brodies LLP, Glasgow . . . .(p.948)
   T: 0141 2484672
   E: iain.baird@brodies.com

BAIRD, Karen Louise (Dec 2005) (Director)
Hall Baird Solicitors Ltd, Castle
   Douglas . . . .(p.784)
   T: 01556 502764
   E: karen@hallbaird.co.uk

BAIRD, Kenneth (Oct 1987) (Employee)
Freshfields Service Company, London
    EC2 . . . .(p.1264)
    T: 0207 832 7168
    E: ken.baird@freshfields.com

BAIRD, Michelle (Jul 2016) (Employee)
SSE PLC, Glasgow . . . .(p.1244)
    T: 0141 224 7248
    E: Michelle.Rae@sse.com

BAIRD, Paul John (Jun 2017) (Associate)
CMS Cameron McKenna Nabarro Olswang LLP,
    Edinburgh . . . .(p.856)
    T: 0131 2288000
    E: paul.baird@cms-cmno.com

BAIRD, Rona (Dec 1987) (Employee)
Procurator Fiscal Service,
    Edinburgh . . . .(p.1227)
    T: 0300 0203168
    E: rona.baird@copfs.gov.uk

BAIRD, Samantha (Nov 2011) (Employee)
DMD Law LLP, Edinburgh . . . .(p.864)
    T: 0131 3164666
    E: samantha@dmdpartnership.co.uk

BAIRNER, Stacey (Jul 2006) (Partner)
Pinsent Masons LLP, Glasgow . . . .(p.1031)
    T: 0141 567 8400
    E: Stacey.Bairner@pinsentmasons.com

BAIRSTOW, Natasha Ann Kirk (Jan 2013)
(Employee)
Bedell Cristin Jersey Partnership, St
    Helier . . . .(p.1274)
    T: 01534 814814
    E: Natasha.Bairstow@bedellcristin.com

BAKER, Emma Louise (Sept 2020) (Employee)
Procurator Fiscal Service, Glasgow . . . .(p.1241)
    T: 0300 0203000
    E: emma.baker@copfs.gov.uk

BAKER, Georgia Emma (Jul 2010) (Employee)
Procurator Fiscal Service,
    Kilmarnock . . . .(p.1249)
    T: 01563 536211
    E: georgia.baker@copfs.gov.uk

BAKER, Gillian Catherine (Dec 1999) (Director)
Baker Gostelow Law, Blantyre . . . .(p.776)
    T: 01698 820700
    E: gillian@bgfamilylaw.co.uk

BAKER, Joanne Mary (Oct 2016) (Employee)
Legal Secretariat to the Lord Advocate,
    Edinburgh . . . .(p.1224)
    T: (0300) 020 3364
    E: joanne.baker@gov.scot

BAKER, Kirsteen (Jan 2010) (Employee)
Scottish Government, Edinburgh . . . . .(p.1231)
    T: 0131 244 0815
    E: kirsteen.baker@gov.scot

BALES, David (Apr 2015) (Employee)
Brodies LLP, Edinburgh . . . .(p.845)
    T: 0131 2283777
    E: david.bales@brodies.com

BALFOUR, Lorna Margaret Claire (Jan 2015)
(Associate)
Gillespie Macandrew LLP,
    Edinburgh . . . .(p.872)
    T: 0131 2251677
    E: Lorna.balfour@gillespiemacandrew.co.uk

BALFOUR, Martin Drew (Apr 2019) (Employee)
Burness Paull LLP, Edinburgh . . . .(p.850)
    T: 0131 4736000
    E: Martin.Balfour@burnesspaull.com

BALI, Depak (Jul 2004) (Employee)
Portknockie Whisky, Glasgow . . . .(p.1241)
    E: db@portknockie.com

BALI, Sanjeev (Feb 1989) (Director)
Gildeas Limited, Glasgow . . . .(p.979)
    T: 0141 331 6071
    E: sbali@gildeas.net

BALLANTYNE, Ailidh Catherine (May 2013)
(Employee)
Thompsons, Glasgow . . . .(p.1046)
    T: 0141 2218840
    E: Ailidh.Ballantyne@thompsons-scotland.co.uk

BALLANTYNE, Jennifer Anne (Dec 1991)
(Partner)
Pinsent Masons LLP, Glasgow . . . .(p.1031)
    T: 0141 567 8400
    E: jennifer.ballantyne@pinsentmasons.com

BALLANTYNE, Melanie Sarah (Feb 1996)
(Employee)
Blackadders LLP, Aberdeen . . . .(p.722)
    T: 01224 588913
    E: melanie.ballantyne@blackadders.co.uk

BALLANTYNE, Michael (Jan 2021) (Employee)
Thompsons, Glasgow . . . .(p.1046)
    T: 0141 2218840
    E:
michael.ballantyne@thompsons-scotland.co.uk

BALMER, Steven (Mar 2016) (Employee)
Carey Olsen, St Peter Port . . . .(p.1273)
    T: (+44) 1481 741505

BAMBER, John Frederick (Sept 1980) (Solicitor)
NO FIRM

BANAG MONGO, Ana s Gw naelle Christine
(Oct 2021) (Employee)
Gillespie Macandrew LLP,
    Edinburgh . . . .(p.872)
    T: 0131 2251677
    E: Anais.Banag@gillespiemacandrew.co.uk

BANFRO, Rhoda Nyaaba (Oct 2017)
(Employee)
Highland Council, Inverness.........(p.1248)
   T: 01463 702000
   E: rhoda.banfro@highland.gov.uk

BANKS, Aileen Catherine (Jun 2018)
(Employee)
Dentons UK and Middle East LLP,
   Edinburgh ....(p.860)
   T: 0330 2220050
   E: Aileen.Banks@dentons.com

BANKS, James Scott (Mar 1980) (Partner)
Banks Devlin & Co., Paisley.........(p.1136)
   T: 0141 8894949
   E: scott.banks@banksdevlin.com

BANN, Gerrard (Nov 1990) (Partner)
Adams Whyte, Livingston ....(p.1117)
   T: 01506 401999
   E: gerrybann@adamswhyte.com

BANNERMAN, Roderick William Alastair
(Oct 1987) (Partner)
Bannerman Burke Law, Hawick ......(p.1070)
   T: 01450 372 750
   E: rory@bannermanburke.co.uk

BANNERMAN, Sarah Louise (Jul 2017)
(Employee)
Clan Childlaw Limited, Glasgow.......(p.959)
   T: 0808 129 0522
   E: sarah.bannerman@clanchildlaw.org

BANSAL, Nina (Jul 2008) (Employee)
TSB Bank Plc, Edinburgh ....(p.1235)
   T: (0131) 260 0051
   E: nina.bansal@tsb.co.uk

BANSAL, Sharonne (Jan 2010) (Solicitor)
NO FIRM

BANSAL, Virvardhan (Mar 2021) (Employee)
Ormistons Law Practice Limited,
   Glenrothes ....(p.1057)
   T: 0800 7810413
   E: vbansal@ormistonslaw.co.uk

BARBER, Lyndsey Heather (May 2014)
(Employee)
Paisley Defence Lawyers (Scotland) Limited,
   Paisley ....(p.1141)
   T: 0141 5619999
   E: lyndsey.barber@mccuskerlaw.co.uk

BARBER, Rachael Winifred (Dec 2020)
(Employee)
Carey Olsen, St Helier ....(p.1274)
   T: 01534 888900
   E: rachael.barber@careyolsen.com

BARBER, Wendy Margaret (Feb 1995)
(Employee)
Falkirk Council, Falkirk.............(p.1236)
   T: 01324 506070
   E: wendy.barber@falkirk.gov.uk

BARBER-FLEMING, Valerie Janet, WS
(Feb 1979) (Employee)
Procurator Fiscal Service,
   Edinburgh ....(p.1227)
   T: 0844 561 3729
   E: valerie.barber-fleming@copfs.gov.uk

BARBOUR, Alistair William (Apr 2007)
(Employee)
BTO Solicitors LLP, Glasgow ....(p.952)
   T: 0141 2218012
   E: awb@bto.co.uk

BARBOUR, Brian Scott (Aug 2019) (Employee)
MacRoberts LLP, Edinburgh..........(p.887)
   T: 0131 2295046
   E: brian.barbour@macroberts.com

BARBOUR, David George (Dec 1991)
(Employee)
National Health Service Scotland,
   Edinburgh ....(p.1225)
   T: 0131 2757800
   E: david.barbour@nhs.scot

BARBOUR, Norman Cameron Smith
(Aug 1998) (Employee)
J.B. Barbour & Co. Ltd, Glasgow .....(p.1240)
   T: 0141 4293999
   E: Norrie@barbourfitout.co.uk

BARCLAY, Ailie Stuart Lamb (Oct 1991)
(Solicitor)
NO FIRM

BARCLAY, Catriona Ann (Sept 2007)
(Employee)
Peterkins, Aberdeen ....(p.739)
   T: 01224 428000
   E: cab@peterkins.com

BARCLAY, Dana (Sept 2020) (Employee)
Procurator Fiscal Service, Paisley......(p.1252)
   T: 0141 8875225
   E: dana.barclay@copfs.gov.uk

BARCLAY, David Alan (Oct 1988) (Employee)
Procurator Fiscal Service, Wick ....(p.1256)
   T: 01955 602197
   E: david.barclay@copfs.gov.uk

BARCLAY, David Alastair (Nov 2006) (Associate)
Kerr Stirling LLP Trading As Gibson & Kennedy
   WS, Falkirk ....(p.922)
   T: 01324 622741
   E: ab@kerrstirling.co.uk

BARCLAY, Emma Robertson (Oct 2013)
(Partner)
BTO Solicitors LLP, Glasgow ....(p.952)
   T: 0141 2218012
   E: eba@bto.co.uk

BARCLAY, Gordon Taylor, SSC (Jul 1996)
(Employee)
Church of Scotland, Edinburgh ......(p.1221)
T: 0131 2255722
E: Gordon.Barclay@churchofscotland.org.uk

BARCLAY, Kathryn Mackay (Aug 2013)
(Employee)
Life Technologies Limited, Paisley .....(p.1252)
T: 0141 8146100
E: katy.barclay@thermofisher.com

BARCLAY, Kim (Oct 1984) (Partner)
Kim Barclay, Dundee...............(p.805)
T: 01382 228722
E: law@kimbarclay.co.uk

BARCLAY, Matthew Alexander (Oct 2015)
(Partner)
Morton Fraser LLP, Edinburgh ....(p.891)
T: 0131 2471000
E: matthew.barclay@morton-fraser.com

BARCLAY, Nicholas (Oct 1984) (Partner)
Thorntons Law LLP, Dundee ....(p.819)
T: 01382 229 111
E: nbarclay@thorntons-law.co.uk

BARCLAY, Patricia Barbara Ann (Aug 1986)
(Director)
Bonaccord Ecosse Limited,
Edinburgh ....(p.844)
T: 0131 2026527
E: patricia@bonaccord.law

BARCLAY, Stephen Ross (Sept 2016) (Associate)
Allen & Overy LLP, London E1 ....(p.1261)
T: 020 3088 0000
E: stephen.barclay@allenovery.com

BARCLAY, Valmai Jane (Nov 2006) (Employee)
Tideway, London SE1 ....(p.1269)
T: 07966 266069
E: valmai.barclay@tideway.london

BARCLAY, William Douglas (Dec 1984)
(Partner)
Raeburn Christie Clark & Wallace LLP,
Aberdeen ....(p.741)
T: 01224 564636
E: bill.barclay@raeburns.co.uk

BARCLAY-SMITH, Linsey Jane (Nov 1987)
(Partner)
Anderson Strathern LLP, Edinburgh ....(p.839)
T: 0131 2707700
E:
Linsey.Barclay-Smith@andersonstrathern.co.uk

BAREKAT, Afson (Oct 2013) (Employee)
Scottish Government, Edinburgh .....(p.1231)
T: 0131 244 0815
E: afson.barekat@gov.uk

BARETTE, Julia Audrey (Sept 2015) (Employee)
Addleshaw Goddard LLP,
Edinburgh ....(p.835)
T: 0131 2282400
E: julia.barette@addleshawgoddard.com

BARKER, Alana Jessica Sieczkowska
(Oct 2018) (Associate)
CMS Cameron McKenna Nabarro Olswang LLP,
Glasgow....................(p.962)
T: 0141 2222200
E: Alana.Barker@cms-cmno.com

BARKER, Fiona (Sept 2009) (Employee)
Eversheds Sutherland (International) LLP,
Salford ....(p.1271)
T: 0845 497 8569
E: fionabarker@eversheds-Sutherland.com

BARKER, Fiona Margaret (Oct 1992)
(Employee)
Andersonbain LLP, Aberdeen ....(p.721)
T: 01224 456789
E: fbarker@andersonbain.co.uk

BARKER, Juliet Catriona Louise (Aug 2016)
(Employee)
Turcan Connell, Edinburgh ....(p.908)
T: 0131 2288111
E: juliet.barker@turcanconnell.com

BARLOW, Michael John (Sept 1998) (Partner)
MacRoberts LLP, Edinburgh ....(p.887)
T: 0131 2295046
E: mike.barlow@macroberts.com

BARN, Lewis Fraser (Nov 2020) (Employee)
Miller Samuel Hill Brown LLP,
Glasgow....................(p.1020)
T: 0141 2211919
E: lfb@mshblegal.com

BARNES, Christopher Stephen (Nov 2019)
(Employee)
Levy & McRae Solicitors LLP,
Glasgow....................(p.1000)
T: 0141 3072311
E: cbarnes@lemac.co.uk

BARNES, Eilidh Catherine (Nov 2012)
(Employee)
Scottish Legal Aid Board,
Edinburgh ....(p.1233)
T: 0131 2267061
E: barnesei@slab.org.uk

BARNES, Jillian (Oct 2003) (Partner)
Stevenson & Marshall LLP,
Dunfermline ....(p.825)
T: 01383 721141
E: jbarnes@stevenson-marshall.co.uk

BARNES, Julia (Sept 2019) (Employee)
John W. Gilbertson Limited,
Glenrothes ....(p.1057)
T: 01592 759557
E: julia@johnwgilbertson.co.uk

BARNES, Lianda Jane (Jun 2007) (Partner)
Digby Brown LLP, Kirkcaldy . . . .(p.1099)
T: 0333 200 5925
E: lianda.barnes@digbybrown.co.uk

BARNES-INSCH, Victoria Margaret Helen
(Aug 2012) (Employee)
Chrysaor Production (U.K.) Limited,
Aberdeen . . . .(p.1212)
T: 01224 205333
E: victoria.barnes-insch@chrysaor.com

BARNETT, Emma Victoria (Aug 2021)
(Employee)
Brodies LLP, Edinburgh . . . .(p.845)
T: 0131 2283777
E: emma.barnett@brodies.com

BARNETT, Leigh (Sept 1993) (Consultant)
Parker Bullen LLP, Salisbury . . . .(p.1271)
T: 1722412000
E: leigh.barnett@parkerbullen.com

BARNETT, Patrick Ronald (Sept 2017)
(Employee)
Addleshaw Goddard LLP,
Edinburgh . . . .(p.835)
T: 0131 2282400
E: patrick.barnett@addleshawgoddard.com

BARNETT, Paul Scott (Apr 1997) (Partner)
George Mathers & Co, Aberdeen . . . . . .(p.737)
T: 01224 588599
E: p.barnett@georgemathers.co.uk

BARNSLEY, Christine Frances (Nov 2010)
(Associate)
Eversheds Sutherland (International) LLP,
Edinburgh . . . .(p.869)
T: 0207 9194500
E:
ChristineBarnsley@eversheds-Sutherland.com

BARON, Ross (Jun 2019) (Employee)
Gillespie Macandrew LLP,
Edinburgh . . . .(p.872)
T: 0131 2251677
E: ross.baron@gillespiemacandrew.co.uk

BARR, Alan Roderic (Feb 1984) (Partner)
Brodies LLP, Edinburgh . . . .(p.845)
T: 0131 2283777
E: alan.barr@brodies.com

BARR, Caroline Sinclair (Sept 2009) (Associate)
CMS Cameron McKenna Nabarro Olswang LLP,
Edinburgh . . . .(p.856)
T: 0131 2288000
E: Caroline.Barr@cms-cmno.com

BARR, Chloe Melissa (Jul 2019) (Employee)
Jones Whyte LLP, Glasgow . . . .(p.993)
T: 0141 375 1222
E: chloe.barr@joneswhyte.co.uk

BARR, Christina Amy (Aug 2014) (Employee)
Lloyds Banking Group Plc,
Edinburgh . . . .(p.1224)
T: (0131) 442 9579
E: christina.barr@lloydsbanking.com

BARR, Eileen Elizabeth (May 2018) (Employee)
TC Young LLP, Glasgow . . . .(p.1055)
T: 0141 2215562
E: EEB@tcyoung.co.uk

BARR, Ellen Jane (Sept 2010) (Employee)
Procurator Fiscal Service, Aberdeen . . .(p.1213)
T: 0300 0202336

BARR, Fiona Anne (May 2016) (Employee)
National Westminster Bank PLC,
Edinburgh . . . .(p.1226)
T: 0131 6263433/0778830
E: fiona.barr@rbs.co.uk

BARR, Gordon Scott (Jul 2005) (Employee)
Al Tamimi & Company, Dubai . . . .(p.1277)
T: +971 4 364 1641
E: G.Barr@tamimi.com

BARR, Greg Robb (Sept 2020) (Employee)
Anderson Strathern LLP, Edinburgh . . . .(p.839)
T: 0131 2707700
E: greg.barr@andersonstrathern.co.uk

BARR, Jennifer Claire (Nov 2013) (Employee)
Dailly, Walker and Co., Solicitors,
Glasgow. . . . .(p.965)
T: 0141 4402503
E: jbarr@govanlc.com

BARR, Jennifer Margaret Elizabeth
(Jul 2008) (Associate)
CMS Cameron McKenna Nabarro Olswang LLP,
Glasgow. . . . .(p.962)
T: 0141 2222200
E: Jennifer.Barr@cms-cmno.com

BARR, Julie Anne (Jun 2000) (Employee)
A.G. Barr P.l.c, Cumbernauld . . . .(p.1216)
T: 01236 852400
E: JulieBarr@AGBarr.co.uk

BARR, Katherine Flora (Mar 2012) (Employee)
Life Technologies Limited, Paisley . . . . .(p.1252)
T: 0141 8146100
E: katie.barr@thermofisher.com

BARR, Kay (May 1988) (Director)
Raeside Chisholm Solicitors Limited,
Glasgow. . . . .(p.1034)
T: 0141 2483456
E: k.barr@raesidechisholm.co.uk

BARR, Martin Douglas (Sept 2007) (Employee)
Facebook UK Limited, London
NW1 . . . .(p.1264)

BARR, Peter Robin (Jan 2016) (Employee)
Collins & Co Defence Lawyers Ltd,
Edinburgh . . . .(p.857)
T: 0131 661 3210
E: pbarr@collinsandcolawyers.com

BARR, Robert John (Oct 2010) (Employee)
Stirling Developments Limited,
Dunfermline . . . .(p.1219)
T: 01383 720768
E: Robert@stirlingdevelopments.co.uk

BARR, Stuart John (Feb 1999) (Partner)
Pinsent Masons LLP, Glasgow . . . .(p.1031)
T: 0141 567 8400
E: stuart.barr@pinsentmasons.com

BARR, Susan Mary (Jul 2009) (Employee)
Procurator Fiscal Service, Paisley . . . . . .(p.1252)
T: 0141 8875225
E: Susan.barr@copfs.gov.uk

BARR, Wendy Ann Brown (Jan 1981)
(Employee)
Procurator Fiscal Service,
Edinburgh . . . .(p.1227)
T: 0300 0203168
E: Wendy.Barr@copfs.gov.uk

BARRAG N DE LA CRUZ, Maribel (Jul 2021)
(Associate)
CMS Cameron McKenna Nabarro Olswang LLP,
Aberdeen . . . .(p.727)
T: 01224 622002
E: Maribel.Barrag n@cms-cmno.com

BARRASS, Rebecca Mary (Mar 2016) (Associate)
MacRoberts LLP, Glasgow . . . .(p.1015)
T: 0141 3031100
E: rebecca.barrass@macroberts.com

BARRATT, Madeleine (Sept 2016) (Employee)
Pinsent Masons LLP, Edinburgh . . . .(p.895)
T: 0131 777 7000
E: madeleine.barratt@pinsentmasons.com

BARRATT, Stephanie (Jul 2017) (Employee)
Brodies LLP, Edinburgh . . . .(p.845)
T: 0131 2283777
E: stephanie.barratt@brodies.com

BARRETT, Angela O'Hara (Nov 1992) (Partner)
Russel + Aitken Denny LLP, Denny . . . . .(p.796)
T: 01324 822194
E: ab@radenny.co.uk

BARRETT, Michael John (Aug 1989) (Employee)
SOUTH LANARKSHIRERe Council,
Hamilton . . . .(p.1247)
E: michael.barrett@southlanarkshire.gov.uk

BARRIE, Douglas Jaffray (Mar 1982) (Solicitor)
NO FIRM

BARRIE, Ian Fraser (Nov 2006) (Employee)
Dentons UK and Middle East LLP,
Glasgow . . . .(p.968)
T: 0330 2220050
E: ian.barrie@dentons.com

BARRIE, Jane (Feb 2017) (Employee)
Austin Lafferty Limited, Glasgow . . . . . .(p.943)
T: 0141 6212212
E: jbarrie@laffertylaw.com

BARRIE, John (Oct 1989) (Employee)
Plexus Law LLP, Edinburgh . . . .(p.897)
T: 0344 2454802
E: John.Barrie@plexuslaw.co.uk

BARRIE, June Anne (Sept 1985) (Employee)
Fife Council, Glenrothes . . . .(p.1246)
T: 03451 550000
E: june.barrie@fife.gov.uk

BARRIE, Laura Elizabeth (Aug 2009) (Employee)
Scottish Government's Parliamentary Counsel
Office, Edinburgh . . . .(p.1233)
T: 0131 244 6483
E: laura.barrie@gov.scot

BARRIE, Lynne Louise (Feb 2003) (Employee)
Procurator Fiscal Service,
Edinburgh . . . .(p.1229)
E: lynne.barrie@copfs.gov.uk

BARRIE, Richard Alexander (Apr 1986) (Partner)
Levy & McRae Solicitors LLP,
Glasgow . . . .(p.1000)
T: 0141 3072311
E: rbarrie@lemac.co.uk

BARRIE, Rosalind Clark (Oct 2008) (Solicitor)
NO FIRM

BARRON, Jonathan Frederick Arthur
(Oct 2017) (Employee)
DWF LLP, Edinburgh . . . .(p.865)
T: 0131 2265541
E: Jonathan.Barron@dwf.law

BARRON, Michael John, SSC (Oct 1977)
(Solicitor)
NO FIRM

BARRON, Paul Thomas (Aug 2005) (Partner)
Dickson Minto, London EC2 . . . .(p.1263)
T: 020 7628 4455
E: paul.barron@dmws.com

BARROWMAN, James Gilchrist (Aug 2003)
(Employee)
Scottish Social Services Council,
Dundee . . . .(p.1218)
T: 01382 207253
E: james.barrowman@sssc.uk.com

BARRY, John Charles (Jan 1973) (Solicitor)
NO FIRM

BARSZCZ, Christine Anne (Sept 2004)
(Employee)
Tesco Personal Finance Plc,
Edinburgh . . . .(p.1234)
T: (0131) 274 3426
E: christine.barszcz@tescobank.com

BARTLETT, Christopher James (Sept 2004)
(Employee)
Burges Salmon LLP, Bristol . . . .(p.1258)
T: 0117 9392000
E: christopher.bartlett@burges-salmon.com

BARTLETT, Gordon (Feb 2010) (Employee)
Allen & Overy LLP, London E1 . . . .(p.1261)
T: 020 3088 0000

BARTLETT, Janet Elizabeth (Nov 2008)
(Employee)
Scottish Government, Edinburgh . . . . .(p.1231)
T: 0131 244 0815
E: janet.bartlett@gov.scot

BARTON, Eric James (Sept 1980) (Partner)
Barton & Hendry, Cumbernauld . . . . . .(p.790)
T: 01236 735466
E: eric@bartonandhendry.co.uk

BARTON, Heather-Anne (Sept 1990) (Solicitor)
NO FIRM

BARTON, Iain Fraser James (Oct 2003)
(Employee)
Aegon UK, Edinburgh . . . .(p.1220)
T: 1315493986
E: iain.barton@aegon.co.uk

BARTON, Natalie (Sept 2018) (Employee)
Scottish Government, Edinburgh . . . . .(p.1231)
T: 0131 244 0815
E: natalie.barton@gov.scot

BARTON, Stuart Alastair (Jul 2008) (Partner)
Digby Brown LLP, Glasgow . . . .(p.970)
T: 0333 200 5925
E: stuart.barton@digbybrown.co.uk

BASCOMBE, Charlotte Louise (Oct 2013)
(Employee)
CMS Cameron McKenna Nabarro Olswang LLP,
London EC4 . . . .(p.1263)
T: 0207 3673000
E: charlotte.bascombe@cms-cmno.com

BASHFORD, S R, MSc MRICS (Partner &
Director)
Eric Young & Co, Edinburgh . . . .(p.1338)
T: (0131) 226 2641

BASHIR, Imran Raza (Nov 2003) (Employee)
Procurator Fiscal Service, Hamilton . . . .(p.1247)
T: 0844 5613245
E: imran.bashir@copfs.gov.uk

BASHIR, Marrya Anwar (Mar 2018) (Employee)
Shepherd and Wedderburn LLP,
Glasgow . . . .(p.1039)
T: 0141 5669900
E: Marrya.Bashir@shepwedd.com

BASHIR, Zibya (Aug 2004) (Employee)
Miller Samuel Hill Brown LLP,
Glasgow . . . .(p.1020)
T: 0141 2211919
E: zba@mshblegal.com

BASRAI, Harsharan Kaur (Oct 2014) (Employee)
ISG Central Services Limited, London
EC3 . . . .(p.1265)
E: Sharan.Basrai@isgltd.com

BASTEKIN, Sara May (Aug 2021) (Employee)
DWF LLP, Edinburgh . . . .(p.865)
T: 0131 2265541
E: sara.bastekin@dwf.law

BASTEN, Graham John (Jul 1993) (Partner)
BSW Solicitors LLP, Dunfermline . . . .(p.823)
T: 01383 621144
E: graham@bastensneddon.co.uk

BASTIANELLI, Tarryn (Aug 2012) (Employee)
SSE Plc, Perth . . . .(p.1253)
T: 01738 456 000
E: tarryn.bastianelli@sse.com

BATCHELOR, Duncan James (Oct 2002)
(Partner)
Clyde & Co (Scotland) LLP,
Edinburgh . . . .(p.855)
T: 0131 5571545
E: duncan.batchelor@clydeco.com

BATCHELOR, Lynda Anne (Jan 1982)
(Employee)
Fife Council, Glenrothes . . . .(p.1246)
T: 03451 550000
E: lynda.batchelor@fife.gov.uk

BATCHELOR, Susanne Nicola (Aug 1998)
(Partner)
Brodies LLP, Edinburgh . . . .(p.845)
T: 0131 2283777
E: susanne.batchelor@brodies.com

BATCHELOR, Theresa Alison (Sept 2012)
(Employee)
Highland Council, Inverness . . . .(p.1248)
T: 01463 702148
E: theresa.batchelor@highland.gov.uk

BATEMAN, Antony George (Mar 2013)
(Employee)
DAC Beachcroft Scotland LLP,
Glasgow . . . .(p.964)
T: 0141 2486688
E: abateman@dacbeachcroft.com

BATEMAN, Jackson (Oct 2014) (Director)
Charles Ferguson Solicitor Advocate Limited,
Hamilton . . . .(p.1066)
T: 01698 285 885
E: Jackson@charlesferguson.co.uk

BATH, Bhalindra Singh (Jan 2006) (Employee)
Telehouse International Corporations of Europe
Ltd, London E14 . . . .(p.1268)
E: bhalindra.bath@uk.telehouse.net

BATHGATE, Colin John (Nov 2021) (Employee)
Gillespie Macandrew LLP,
Edinburgh . . . .(p.872)
T: 0131 2251677
E: colin.bathgate@gillespiemacandrew.co.uk

BATHGATE, Derek (Director)
Davidson & Robertson Ltd, Currie . . . .(p.1329)
T: (0131) 449 6212
E: DB@drrural.co.uk

BATHGATE, Euan George (Aug 2019)
(Employee)
City of Edinburgh Council,
Edinburgh . . . .(p.1221)
T: (0131) 5294145
E: euan.bathgate@edinburgh.gov.uk

BATHGATE, Gordon Foggo (Oct 1986)
(Partner)
Allan McDougall McQueen LLP,
Edinburgh . . . .(p.837)
T: 0131 2252121
E: gordonbathgate@allanmcdougall.co.uk

BATHGATE, Shona Kirsten Robertson
(Oct 1994) (Employee)
Office of the Advocate General,
Edinburgh . . . .(p.1227)
T: 0131 2441635
E: Shona.bathgate@advocategeneral.gov.uk

BATHO, Iain Mark Scott (Jun 2012) (Employee)
Procurator Fiscal Service,
Edinburgh . . . .(p.1229)
T: 0300 0203000
E: iain.batho@copfs.gov.uk

BATTERSBY, Bruce (Apr 2014) (Associate)
BTO Solicitors LLP, Glasgow . . . .(p.952)
T: 0141 2218012
E: bba@bto.co.uk

BAUCHOP, Alan Chambers-Hunter
(Jan 1985) (Employee)
Wright, Johnston & Mackenzie LLP,
Edinburgh . . . .(p.913)
T: 0131 5241500
E: ab@wjm.co.uk

BAUCHOP, Duncan Alan Chambers-Hunter
(Nov 2018) (Employee)
Turcan Connell, Edinburgh . . . .(p.908)
T: 0131 2288111
E: duncan.bauchop@turcanconnell.com

BAULD, James (Oct 1986) (Partner)
TC Young LLP, Glasgow . . . .(p.1055)
T: 0141 2215562
E: jdb@tcyoung.co.uk

BAXENDALE, Laura Jane Naismith
(Sept 2009) (Employee)
Keoghs Scotland LLP, Glasgow. . . . .(p.996)
T: 0141 2380100
E: lbaxendale@keoghs.co.uk

BAXTER, Alan Desmond (Jan 1983) (Associate)
Morgans, Dunfermline . . . .(p.824)
T: 01383 620222
E: desbaxter@morganlaw.co.uk

BAXTER, Bernadette Mary (Oct 1989) (Partner)
Mellicks, Incorporating Naftalin Duncan & Co.,
Glasgow. . . . .(p.1019)
T: 0141 3320902
E: bernadette.baxter@mellicks.co.uk

BAXTER, Ewart Leslie (Jan 1998) (Employee)
Lloyds Banking Group Plc,
Edinburgh . . . .(p.1224)
T: 0131 442 9579
E: Ewart.Baxter@lloydsbanking.com

BAXTER, Hannah (May 2021) (Employee)
CN Defence Ltd, Edinburgh. . . . .(p.857)
T: 0131 5571000
E: Hannah@cndefence.com

BAXTER, James (Feb 1987) (Consultant)
Macnabs LLP, Blairgowrie . . . .(p.776)
T: 01738 623432
E: jamiebaxter@macnabs-law.co.uk

BAXTER, Judith Liadhan (Sept 2018)
(Employee)
Morton Fraser LLP, Edinburgh . . . .(p.891)
T: 0131 2471000
E: Judith.Baxter@morton-fraser.com

BAXTER, Patrick Joseph (Dec 1978) (Director)
Matthews Legal Limited, Newton
Stewart . . . .(p.1131)
T: 01671 404100
E: joebaxter@abamatthews.com

BAYLEY, Alan Robert (Sept 1991) (Partner)
Stodarts LLP, Hamilton . . . .(p.1069)
T: 01698 200302
E: alanbayley@stodarts.co.uk

BAYLEY, Jan Margaret (Oct 1992) (Partner)
Gebbie & Wilson LLP, Strathaven . . . . .(p.1172)
T: 01357 520082
E: jan@gebbiewilson.co.uk

BAYLIS, Piers Alexander Sebastian
(Jan 2018) (Employee)
BTO Solicitors LLP, Edinburgh . . . .(p.849)
T: 0131 2222939
E: pba@bto.co.uk

BAYNE, John Dominic (Dec 2002) (Employee)
Jones Whyte LLP, Glasgow. . . . .(p.993)
T: 0141 375 1222
E: John.bayne@joneswhyte.co.uk

BAYNE, Juliet Miranda Lomax (May 2003)
(Partner)
Brodies LLP, Edinburgh . . . .(p.845)
T: 0131 2283777
E: juliet.bayne@brodies.com

BAYNE, Lindzi Marion (Aug 2016) (Employee)
Procurator Fiscal Service,
Kilmarnock . . . .(p.1249)
T: 01563 536211
E: Lindzi.Bayne@copfs.gov.uk

BAYNHAM, Michael James (Nov 1981)
(Employee)
Caledonian Trust PLC, Edinburgh . . . . .(p.1221)
T: 0131 2200416
E: michael.baynham@caledoniantrust.com

BEACH, Howard Jeremy (Nov 1983) (Partner)
TLT LLP, Glasgow . . . .(p.1048)
T: 0333 006 0400
E: howard.beach@tltsolicitors.com

BEACH, Nicholas Joseph (Aug 2020)
(Employee)
Skyrora Limited, Edinburgh . . . .(p.1234)
E: nicholas.beach@skyrora.com

BEADIE, Emma-Louise Mary (Sept 2015)
(Employee)
Pinsent Masons LLP, Aberdeen . . . .(p.739)
T: 01224 377900
E: emma-louise.beadie@pinsentmasons.com

BEADSWORTH, Andrew Jonathan
(Jan 1998) (Employee)
Procurator Fiscal Service,
Edinburgh . . . .(p.1229)
T: (0844) 561 3268
E: Andrew.Beadsworth@copfs.gov.uk

BEADSWORTH, Eileen Lamont (Aug 2001)
(Employee)
Procurator Fiscal Service, Glasgow . . . .(p.1241)
T: 0300 020 3690
E: eileen.beadsworth@copfs.gov.uk

BEAGRIE, Derek (Sept 2010) (Employee)
Jain, Neil & Ruddy, Glasgow . . . .(p.992)
T: 0141 2218778
E: derek@jnrsolicitors.com

BEALE, Anna Maura (Sept 2012) (Employee)
Trip Air Ticketing (UK) Limited,
Edinburgh . . . .(p.1235)
E: anna_beale@Ctrip.com

BEALE, Ronan Sean (Dec 2009) (Employee)
SSE PLC, Glasgow. . . . .(p.1244)
T: 0141 224 7721
E: ronan.beale@sse.com

BEAN, Carolyn Mary (Sept 1982) (Partner)
Baird & Company Lawyers & Estate Agents LLP,
Glenrothes . . . .(p.1056)
T: 01592 759555
E: cbean@bairdco.co.uk

BEARHOP, Alix Joan (Dec 1988) (Partner)
Brodies LLP, Glasgow . . . .(p.948)
T: 0141 2456212
E: alix.bearhop@brodies.com

BEATON, Eileen (Jan 2016) (Employee)
Dentons UK and Middle East LLP,
Glasgow. . . . .(p.968)
T: 0330 2220050
E: Eileen.Beaton@dentons.com

BEATON, Holly (Sept 2021) (Employee)
Pinsent Masons LLP, Glasgow . . . .(p.1031)
T: 0141 567 8400
E: holly.beaton@pinsentmasons.com

BEATON, Murdoch Charles (Dec 1971)
(Consultant)
Low Beaton Richmond LLP,
Glasgow. . . . .(p.1005)
T: 0141 2218931
E: Murdoch@lbr-law.co.uk

BEATON, Paul Euan (Nov 2007) (Employee)
Scottish Government Children & Families
Directorate, Edinburgh . . . .(p.1232)
T: 0131 2444521
E: Paul.Beaton@gov.scot

BEATS, Lesley Joyce (Jun 2010) (Employee)
Scottish Courts and Tribunals Service,
Dundee . . . .(p.1218)

BEATSON, Ian (Aug 1987) (Partner)
Ian Beatson, Dunfermline . . . .(p.822)
T: 7762412943
E: ibeatson@hotmail.co.uk

BEATTIE, Andrew Watt (May 1997) (Employee)
Scottish Government's Parliamentary Counsel
Office, Edinburgh . . . .(p.1233)
T: 0131 244 1760
E: ChiefParliamentaryCounsel@gov.scot

BEATTIE, Bethany Anne (May 2021) (Employee)
McVey & Murricane, Glasgow . . . .(p.1017)
T: 0141 333 9688
E: bbeattie@mcvey-murricane.com

BEATTIE, Calum Robert (Mar 2014) (Solicitor)
NO FIRM

BEATTIE, Caroline Elizabeth (Aug 1988)
(Employee)
Scottish Government, Edinburgh . . . . .(p.1231)
T: 0131 244 0815
E: Caroline.Beattie@gov.scot

BEATTIE, Carolyn Guild (Nov 1988) (Employee)
The Medical & Dental Defence Union of
 Scotland, Glasgow . . . .(p.1245)
 T: 0141 228 1228
 E: lbeattie@mddus.com

BEATTIE, Cheryl (Jun 2008) (Employee)
Public Defence Solicitors Office,
 Kirkwall . . . .(p.1250)
 T: 01856 870100
 E: cbeattie@pdso.org.uk

BEATTIE, Fiona Margaret (Nov 2002)
 (Employee)
Macfarlanes LLP, London EC4 . . . .(p.1266)
 T: 020 7791 4044
 E: Fiona.Beattie@macfarlanes.com

BEATTIE, Jennifer (Jan 2009) (Employee)
National Westminster Bank PLC,
 Edinburgh . . . .(p.1226)
 T: (0131) 626 2925
 E: Jennifer.A.Beattie@natwest.com

BEATTIE, Dr, Kevin James (Sept 2010)
(Associate)
Pinsent Masons LLP, Glasgow . . . .(p.1031)
 T: 0141 567 8400
 E: kevin.beattie@pinsentmasons.com

BEATTIE, Kirstie Jane (Jul 2017) (Employee)
Law at Work Ltd, Glasgow . . . .(p.1240)
 T: 0141 2715555
 E: kirstie.beattie@lawatwork.co.uk

BEATTIE, Kirstin (Sept 2015) (Employee)
Burness Paull LLP, Glasgow . . . .(p.954)
 T: 0141 2484933
 E: kirstin.beattie@burnesspaull.com

BEATTIE, Louise Catherine (Oct 2005)
 (Employee)
Procurator Fiscal Service,
 Edinburgh . . . .(p.1229)
 T: (0844) 561 3268
 E: louise.beattie@copfs.gov.uk

BEATTIE, Robin Douglas (Oct 2003) (Partner)
Anderson Strathern LLP, Edinburgh . . . .(p.839)
 T: 0131 2707700
 E: Robin.Beattie@andersonstrathern.co.uk

BEATTIE, Robin Malcolm Dickson (Oct 2010)
 (Partner)
Thorntons Law LLP, Arbroath . . . .(p.757)
 T: 01241 872683
 E: rbeattie@thorntons-law.co.uk

BEATTIE, Theresa Ann (May 2010) (Partner)
Barton & Hendry, Cumbernauld . . . . . .(p.790)
 T: 01236 735466
 E: theresa@bartonandhendry.co.uk

BEATTIE, Vanessa Margaret (Sept 2004)
 (Associate)
Lindsays LLP, Edinburgh . . . .(p.882)
 T: 0131 2291212
 E: vanessabeattie@lindsays.co.uk

BEAUMONT, Hannah Louise (Sept 2016)
 (Employee)
Pinsent Masons LLP, Glasgow . . . .(p.1031)
 T: 0141 567 8400

BEAUMONT, Lynn Jennifer (Jan 1994)
 (Employee)
Shepherd and Wedderburn LLP,
 Edinburgh . . . .(p.900)
 T: 0131 2289900
 E: Lynn.Beaumont@shepwedd.com

BEAUMONT, Nigel James Bruce (Nov 1978)
 (Partner)
Nigel Beaumont & Co., Edinburgh . . . . .(p.842)
 T: 0131 5573565
 E: office@nigelbeaumont.co.uk

BECHELLI, Damien Paul (Jun 2003) (Partner)
TLT LLP, Glasgow . . . .(p.1048)
 T: 0333 006 0400
 E: Damien.Bechelli@TLTsolicitors.com

BECHER, Katherine Ann (Sept 2020) (Associate)
CMS Cameron McKenna Nabarro Olswang LLP,
 Edinburgh . . . .(p.856)
 T: 0131 2288000
 E: katherine.becher@cms-cmno.com

BECHER, Miranda Justine (Apr 1997) (Partner)
Drummond Miller LLP, Edinburgh . . . . .(p.864)
 T: 0131 2265151
 E: mbecher@drummondmiller.co.uk

BECK, Frances Margaret (Nov 1987)
 (Employee)
Scottish Government, Edinburgh . . . . .(p.1231)
 T: 0131 244 0561
 E: frances.beck@gov.scot

BECK, James Andrew (Sept 2020) (Solicitor)
Renewable Energy Systems Limited,
 Glasgow . . . .(p.1243)
 T: (0141) 4045591
 E: james.beck@res-group.com

BECK, John Alastair (Apr 2019) (Employee)
Insights Learning & Development Ltd,
 Dundee . . . .(p.1218)
 E: jabeck1403@hotmail.com

BECKETT, Alistair Iain (Nov 1994) (Director)
John Roddick & Son (Solicitors) Ltd,
 Annan . . . .(p.755)
 T: 01461 202822
 E: office@roddicks.co.uk

BECKFORD, Renata (Oct 2000) (Solicitor)
NO FIRM

BEDFORD, John (Oct 2005) (Employee)
Procurator Fiscal Service, Glasgow . . . . (p.1241)
T: 0300 0203000
E: john.bedford@copfs.gov.uk

BEDRULE, Constantin (Nov 2020) (Employee)
Digby Brown LLP, Edinburgh . . . . (p.862)
T: 0333 200 5925
E: constantin.bedrule@digbybrown.co.uk

BEEDIE, Linda Agnes Jane (Sept 2006)
(Director)
First Employment Law Limited,
Aberdeen . . . . (p.731)
T: 01224 619 282
E: linda@felaw.co.uk

BEG, Shabana (Apr 2009) (Partner)
Ruthven, Keenan, Pollock & Co.,
Glasgow . . . . (p.1037)
T: 0141 4238951
E: shabana@rkpsolicitors.co.uk

BEGBIE, Peter Alexander (Dec 2016)
(Employee)
Brodies LLP, Edinburgh . . . . (p.845)
T: 0131 2283777
E: petebegbie@hotmail.com

BEGG, Katy (Aug 2012) (Employee)
Procurator Fiscal Service, Aberdeen . . . (p.1213)
T: 0844 561 3000
E: Katy.Begg@copfs.gov.uk

BEGG, Laura Candice (Jan 2007) (Employee)
Office of the Advocate General,
Edinburgh . . . . (p.1227)
T: 0131 2441635
E: Laura.Begg@advocategeneral.gov.uk

BEIRNE, Leigh Sorcha (Oct 2015) (Employee)
Harper Macleod LLP, Glasgow . . . . (p.983)
T: 0141 2218888
E: Leigh.Beirne@harpermacleod.co.uk

BELARDO, Paul Michael (Feb 1995) (Director)
Manini Belardo Limited,
Coatbridge . . . . (p.787)
T: 01236 426070
E: maninibelardo@btconnect.com

BELFORD, Joanna Margaret (Mar 2021)
(Employee)
Shetland Islands Council, Lerwick . . . . . (p.1250)
T: 01595 744550
E: joanna.belford@shetland.gov.uk

BELK, Kirsten Joanne (Jan 2018) (Employee)
Shoosmiths, Edinburgh . . . . (p.902)
T: 03700 868000
E: kirsten.belk@shoosmiths.co.uk

BELL, Adrian Edward Robert (Nov 1991)
(Partner)
Morton Fraser LLP, Edinburgh . . . . (p.891)
T: 0131 2471000
E: adrian.bell@morton-fraser.com

BELL, Alan Duncan (Sept 2019) (Solicitor)
NO FIRM

BELL, Alasdair Robert McKee (Oct 1988)
(Employee)
FIFA, Zurich . . . . (p.1277)
E: alasdair.bell@fifa.org

BELL, Caitlin Marie Ferguson (Sept 2020)
(Employee)
Gilson Gray LLP, Edinburgh . . . . (p.874)
T: 0131 5165354
E: cbell@gilsongray.co.uk

BELL, Calum Iain (Nov 1990) (Partner)
Andersonbain LLP, Aberdeen . . . . (p.721)
T: 01224 456789
E: cbell@andersonbain.co.uk

BELL, Colin (Aug 1994) (Partner)
Robert Wilson & Son, Thornhill . . . . . . (p.1174)
T: 01848 330251
E: thornhill@robertwilsonandson.co.uk

BELL, Dale Brian (Mar 2021) (Employee)
Clackmannanshire Council, Alloa . . . . . (p.1215)
T: 01259 450000
E: dalebell@clacks.gov.uk

BELL, David Alan (Nov 1994) (Director)
Paterson Bell Limited, Kirkcaldy . . . . . . (p.1102)
T: 01592 646600
E: david.patersonbell@gmail.com

BELL, David Bryce (Dec 1984) (Employee)
Irwin Mitchell Scotland LLP,
Glasgow . . . . (p.991)
T: 0141 3004300

BELL, David Graham (Nov 1987) (Partner)
Wright, Johnston & Mackenzie LLP,
Glasgow . . . . (p.1054)
T: 0141 2483434
E: gb@wjm.co.uk

BELL, David William John (Oct 1988) (Partner)
Harper Macleod LLP, Glasgow . . . . (p.983)
T: 0141 2218888
E: david.bell@harpermacleod.co.uk

BELL, Derek Wright (Oct 1990) (Director)
Clark Boyle Limited, Glasgow . . . . (p.960)
T: 0141 2272200
E: derek.bell@clarkboyle.co.uk

BELL, Emma (Oct 2008) (Employee)
Procurator Fiscal Service,
Edinburgh . . . . (p.1229)
T: 0300 020 3778
E: Emma.Bell@copfs.gov.uk

BELL, Ernest Brian (Sept 1995) (Director)
Bell Brodie Ltd, Forfar . . . . (p.925)
T: 01307 475320
E: brian@bellbrodie.com

BELL, Fergus Carson Pattison (Mar 1989)
(Director)
Bell & Craig Limited, Stirling . . . .(p.1164)
T: 01786 470444
E: fergusbell@bellandcraig.co.uk

BELL, Helen Elizabeth (Nov 1991) (Employee)
Scottish Legal Aid Board,
Edinburgh . . . .(p.1233)
T: 0131 2267061
E: bellhe@slab.org.uk

BELL, Hilary Christina (Aug 2008) (Solicitor)
NO FIRM

BELL, Jacqueline (May 2005) (Employee)
Dundee City Council, Dundee . . . . . .(p.1217)
T: 01382 434101
E: jackie.bell@dundeecity.gov.uk

BELL, James Gordon (Oct 1991) (Partner)
Dallas McMillan, Glasgow . . . .(p.966)
T: 0141 3336750
E: gb@dallasmcmillan.co.uk

BELL, Jason Stuart (Aug 1994) (Employee)
Procurator Fiscal Service, Ayr . . . .(p.1215)
T: 01292 267481
E: jason.bell@copfs.gov.uk

BELL, Jonathan Richard Miles (Jan 1997)
(Partner)
Twin Deer Law, Fort William . . . .(p.930)
T: 07740 110202
E: johnnybell@twindeerlaw.co.uk

BELL, Joy (Oct 2014) (Employee)
Digby Brown LLP, Glasgow . . . .(p.970)
T: 0333 200 5925
E: joy.bell@digbybrown.co.uk

BELL, Katie Margaret (Jun 2017) (Employee)
Procurator Fiscal Service, Glasgow . . . .(p.1241)
T: 0300 0203000
E: katie.bell@copfs.gov.uk

BELL, Kirsteen Joanne (Jun 2017) (Employee)
Skyscanner, Edinburgh . . . .(p.1234)
E: kirsteen.bell@skyscanner.net

BELL, Kirsty Margaret (Jul 2017) (Employee)
Turcan Connell, Edinburgh . . . .(p.908)
T: 0131 2288111
E: kirsty.bell@turcanconnell.com

BELL, Laura (Jun 2013) (Employee)
Scottish Courts and Tribunals Service,
Aberdeen . . . .(p.1214)
T: 01224 657248
E: LBell2@scotcourts.gov.uk

BELL, Louise Jessica (Aug 2019) (Employee)
Freshfields Bruckhaus Deringer,
Amsterdam. . . . .(p.1275)
E: louise.bell@freshfields.com

BELL, Lyndsey (Dec 2008) (Associate)
Friends Legal, Glasgow . . . .(p.978)
T: 0141 442 0602
E: Lyndsey.Bell@friends-legal.co.uk

BELL, Malcolm Fraser (Dec 2009) (Employee)
Aberdeen City Council, Aberdeen. . . . . .(p.1211)
T: 01224 522000
E: frbell@aberdeencity.gov.uk

BELL, Michael John (Dec 1980) (Consultant)
Central Court Lawyers, Livingston . . . .(p.1118)
T: 01506 416999

BELL, Mitchel Kyle (Feb 2021) (Employee)
Walker & Sharpe, Dumfries . . . .(p.803)
T: 01387 267222
E: mitchel.bell@walker-sharpe.co.uk

BELL, Natalia Eve (Aug 2020) (Employee)
Drummond Miller LLP, Edinburgh . . . . .(p.864)
T: 0131 2265151
E: nbell@drummondmiller.co.uk

BELL, Natalia Jade (Apr 2021) (Employee)
Blackadders LLP, Glasgow . . . .(p.946)
T: 0141 2481888
E: natalia.bell@blackadders.co.uk

BELL, Rachel Sarah (Oct 2017) (Employee)
Idox Software Limited, Glasgow. . . . . .(p.1240)
T: 0141 2277600

BELL, Ruthven Colin (Sept 2004) (Employee)
Digby Brown LLP, Glasgow . . . .(p.970)
T: 0333 200 5925
E: ruthven.bell@digbybrown.co.uk

BELL, Ryan William (Jun 2019) (Employee)
Brodies LLP, Glasgow . . . .(p.948)
T: 0141 2484672
E: ryan.bell@brodies.com

BELL, Stewart John (Sept 2015) (Employee)
Procurator Fiscal Service, Glasgow . . . .(p.1241)
T: 0300 0203000
E: Stewart.Bell@copfs.gov.uk

BELL, Susan Carol (Feb 1994) (Director)
Bell Legal Limited, Kilmarnock . . . .(p.1093)
T: 01563 535545
E: susanbell@bell-co.co.uk

BELL, Tabitha Kate McGregor (Sept 1991)
(Employee)
Blackadders LLP, Dundee. . . . .(p.805)
T: 01382 229222
E: Tabitha.Bell@blackadders.co.uk

BELL, Vicki Lee (Jul 2005) (Employee)
Procurator Fiscal Service, Dundee . . . . .(p.1218)
T: 0844 561 2887
E: Vicki.Bell@gov.scot

BELTRAMI, Jason Joseph (Sept 1995)
(Consultant)
MSM Solicitors Limited, Glasgow . . . . .(p.1024)
  T: 0141 5548111
  E: jjb@msmlaw.co.uk

BENES, Ruzena Martina (Jul 2020) (Employee)
Latta Law Limited, Glasgow . . . .(p.998)
  T: 0141 222 2185

BENFIELD, Amy Ann (Sept 2020) (Employee)
Turcan Connell, Edinburgh . . . .(p.908)
  T: 0131 2288111
  E: amy.benfield@turcanconnell.com

BENFIELD, Jeremy Peter (May 2001) (Partner)
MacPhee & Partners LLP, Fort
  William . . . .(p.930)
  T: 01397 701000
  E: jeremybenfield@macphee.co.uk

BENHAM, Peter Mark (Mar 2020) (Employee)
Angus McIntosh & Simon Hodge,
  Glasgow. . . . .(p.1012)
  T: 0141 6340313
  E: peter.benham@castlemilklawcentre.co.uk

BENNET, Craig (Sept 1992) (Partner)
Morgans, Dunfermline . . . .(p.824)
  T: 01383 629814
  E: craigbennet@morganlaw.co.uk

BENNETT, Adam Scott (Mar 2019) (Solicitor)
NO FIRM

BENNETT, Anna Eila (Oct 2002) (Employee)
WS Society, Edinburgh . . . .(p.1236)
  T: 0131 2203249
  E: abennett@wssociety.co.uk

BENNETT, Claire Rhian (Aug 2005) (Employee)
National Westminster Bank PLC,
  Edinburgh . . . .(p.1226)
  T: 0131 626 2925
  E: claire.1.bennett@rbs.co.uk

BENNETT, Claudia (Feb 2010) (Employee)
The Scottish Parliament, Edinburgh . . .(p.1235)
  T: (0131) 3486653
  E: Claudia.Bennett@parliament.scot

BENNETT, Ebony Jane (Mar 2021) (Employee)
DAC Beachcroft Scotland LLP,
  Glasgow. . . . .(p.964)
  T: 0141 2486688
  E: ebbennett@dacbeachcroft.com

BENNETT, Fraser Andrew (May 2007)
(Employee)
Multrees Investor Services,
  Edinburgh . . . .(p.1225)
  T: 0131 2473220
  E: Fraser.Bennett@multrees.com

BENNETT, Hannah Lucy (Apr 2007) (Partner)
Thompsons, Glasgow . . . .(p.1046)
  T: 0141 2218840
  E: hannah.bennett@thompsons-scotland.co.uk

BENNETT, Julia Elizabeth Allen (Sept 2013)
(Employee)
Procurator Fiscal Service,
  Edinburgh . . . .(p.1229)
  E: julia.bennett@civilrecoveryunit.gov.scot

BENNETT, Martin David (Nov 1994) (Associate)
Harper Macleod LLP, Edinburgh . . . .(p.877)
  T: 0131 2472500
  E: martin.bennett@harpermacleod.co.uk

BENNETT, Natalie Elizabeth Victoria
(Nov 2019) (Employee)
Burges Salmon LLP, Edinburgh . . . .(p.850)
  T: 0131 3142112
  E: natalie.bennett@burges-salmon.com

BENNETT, Ross Thomas (Oct 1984) (Partner)
Campbell Boath, Dundee . . . .(p.808)
  T: 01382 200110
  E: RBennett@campbellboath.com

BENNETT-MITCHELL, Amanda Anne
(Jul 2013) (Employee)
Procurator Fiscal Service,
  Edinburgh . . . .(p.1229)
  E: Amanda.Bennett-Mitchell@copfs.gov.uk

BENNIE, Lorna (Aug 1998) (Employee)
Clydesdale Bank Plc, Glasgow . . . .(p.1238)
  T: 0141 2232883
  E: Lorna.Bennie@cybg.com

BENNION, Samantha Jane Scott (Oct 2001)
(Partner)
Stewart & Watson, Buckie . . . .(p.781)
  T: 01542 833255
  E: sbennion@stewartwatson.co.uk

BENSON, Christopher Derek (Mar 1988)
(Partner)
MHD Law LLP, Edinburgh . . . .(p.890)
  T: 0131 5550616
  E: Chris.Benson@mhdlaw.co.uk

BENSON, Jane Ann Raeburn (Mar 1988)
(Employee)
Procurator Fiscal Service, Falkirk . . . . . .(p.1236)
  T: 0300 020 3000
  E: jane.benson@copfs.gov.uk

BENTLEY, Lynn Frances (Aug 1992) (Partner)
Aberdein Considine and Company,
  Aberdeen. . . . .(p.718)
  T: 01224 337421
  E: lbentley@acandco.com

BENTLEY, Stephen Thomas Wilson
(Jul 2009) (Partner)
Bentley Law, Glasgow . . . .(p.945)
  T: 07713 403020
  E: Stephen@bentleylaw.co.uk

BENZIE, Ainslie Ann Ginn (Oct 2005)
(Associate)
TLT LLP, Glasgow . . . .(p.1048)
T: 0333 006 0400
E: ainslie.benzie@tltsolicitors.com

BENZIES, Charles (Sept 1993) (Partner)
Northern Law, Aberdeen . . . .(p.739)
T: 01224 379440
E: charliebenzies@msn.com

BERESFORD, Belinda Hannah Mary
(Aug 2016) (Employee)
Dickson Minto, Edinburgh . . . .(p.861)
T: 0131 2254455
E: Belinda.beresford@dmws.com

BERESFORD, William Samuel (Mar 1986)
(Partner)
R. & R.S. Mearns, Glasgow . . . .(p.1018)
T: 0141 6326162
E: wsbmearns@gmail.com

BERLOW, Matthew Philip (Oct 1995)
(Consultant)
Graham Walker, Glasgow . . . .(p.1050)
T: 0141 946 0111

BERLOW-JACKSON, Barry Charles
(Jul 2010) (Associate)
Walker Laird, Paisley . . . .(p.1142)
T: 0141 8875271
E: barry.berlow-jackson@walkerlaird.co.uk

BERLOW-RAHMAN, Jelina Raheema
(Sept 2003) (Partner)
Berlow Rahman Solicitors, Glasgow . . . .(p.945)
T: 0141 890 1999
E: JR@brlaw.uk

BERMAN, Martin (Oct 1978) (Director)
Carr Berman Crichton Limited,
   Rutherglen . . . .(p.1159)
T: 0141 6479851
E: martin@cbcsolicitors.co.uk

BERNARD, David Michael (Aug 2011)
(Employee)
Procurator Fiscal Service,
   Edinburgh . . . .(p.1229)
T: 0300 0203000
E: david.bernard@copfs.gov.uk

BERRILL, Catherine Elizabeth (May 2014)
(Employee)
Hill & Robb Limited, Stirling . . . .(p.1164)
T: 01786 450985
E: catherineberrill@hillandrobb.co.uk

BERRY, Arwen Elaine (Aug 2004) (Employee)
Baker & McKenzie. Wong & Leow,
   Singapore . . . .(p.1276)
E: arwen.berry@bakermckenzie.com

BERRY, David Richard (Nov 2010) (Employee)
Jackson Boyd LLP, Glasgow . . . .(p.991)
T: 0141 2214325
E: DBerry@jacksonboyd.co.uk

BERRY, Emma Louise (Sept 2009) (Employee)
Procurator Fiscal Service, Glasgow . . . .(p.1241)
T: 0300 0203000
E: Emma.Berry@copfs.gov.uk

BERRY, Karen Meikle (Aug 1994) (Employee)
Scottish Environment Protection Agency,
   Edinburgh . . . .(p.1230)
T: 0131 4497296
E: karen.berry@sepa.org.uk

BERRY, Kimberley Anne (Feb 2014) (Associate)
RGM Solicitors Limited,
   Grangemouth . . . .(p.1059)
T: 01324 482197
E: kim@rgmsolicitors.co.uk

BERRY, Sophie Catriona Boyd (Mar 2020)
(Employee)
Dailly, Walker and Co., Solicitors,
   Glasgow . . . .(p.965)
T: 0141 4402503
E: sberry@govanlc.com

BERTRAM, Andrew David John (Sept 2000)
(Partner)
Stuart & Stuart, Penicuik . . . .(p.1145)
T: 01968 677294
E: abertram@stuartandstuart.co.uk

BESTGEN, Benjamin (Dec 2015) (Employee)
HSBC Bank Plc, St Helier . . . .(p.1274)
E: benjamin.bestgen@hsbc.com

BETT, John Alexander (Oct 2004) (Partner)
Lindsays LLP, Glasgow . . . .(p.1001)
T: 0141 2216551
E: johnbett@lindsays.co.uk

BETT, Rebecca Louise (Jan 2018) (Employee)
Andersonbain LLP, Aberdeen . . . .(p.721)
T: 01224 456789
E: rebecca@andersonbain.co.uk

BETTS, Leigh (Jul 2006) (Solicitor)
NO FIRM

BEVANS BROWN, Kay (Nov 2010) (Partner)
Munro & Noble, Inverness . . . .(p.1080)
T: 01463 221727
E: kayb@munronoble.com

BEVERIDGE, Bruce Cameron, WS (Nov 1994)
(Director)
Purdie & Co Ltd, Edinburgh . . . .(p.898)
T: 0131 3467240
E: bruce@purdiesolicitors.co.uk

BEVERIDGE, Carryl Mairi Anna (Nov 2006)
(Partner)
Morton Fraser LLP, Edinburgh . . . .(p.891)
T: 0131 2471000
E: carryl.beveridge@morton-fraser.com

BEVERIDGE, Claudia Suzanne (Jun 2003)
(Employee)
Aliter Capital LLP, Glasgow ....(p.1237)
E: cbeveridge@alitercap.com

BEVERIDGE, David Brannigan (May 1999)
(Director)
Macdonald Henderson Limited,
Glasgow....................(p.1008)
T: 0141 2484957
E: db@macdonaldhenderson.co.uk

BEVERIDGE, Eilidh Jane (Nov 2013) (Employee)
CMS Cameron McKenna Nabarro Olswang LLP,
Edinburgh ....(p.856)
T: 0131 2007408
E: eilidh.beveridge@cms-cmno.com

BEVERIDGE, Lori (Oct 2018) (Employee)
Brodies LLP, Glasgow ....(p.948)
T: 0141 2484672
E: lori.beveridge@brodies.com

BEVERIDGE, Martin Jacob (Mar 2009)
(Associate)
CMS Cameron McKenna Nabarro Olswang LLP,
Glasgow.....................(p.962)
T: 0141 2222200
E: Martin.Beveridge@cms-cmno.com

BEVERIDGE, Philippa Louise (Aug 2011)
(Employee)
TLT LLP, Glasgow ....(p.1048)
T: 0333 006 0400
E: Philippa.Beveridge@tltsolicitors.com

BEVERIDGE, Stuart Gordon Nicholas
(Jan 1993) (Director)
Grant Smith Law Practice Limited,
Aberdeen ....(p.743)
T: 01224 621620
E: stuart.beveridge@grantsmithlaw.co.uk

BEVILACQUA, Karen Frankish (Mar 2007)
(Employee)
Orkney Islands Council, Kirkwall......(p.1250)
T: 01856 873535
E: karen.bevilacqua@orkney.gov.uk

BHATTI, Ikra Kausar (Oct 2019) (Employee)
Glasgow City Council, Glasgow ......(p.1239)
T: 0141 2872000
E: ikra.bhatti@glasgow.gov.uk

BHATTI, Khurrum Waheed Tariq (Nov 2009)
(Solicitor)
NO FIRM

BHATTI, Shabnam Ellahie (Jun 2018)
(Employee)
Burness Paull LLP, Glasgow ....(p.954)
T: 0141 2484933
E: shabnam.bhatti@burnesspaull.com

BHATTI, Zahra Yasmin (Feb 2018) (Employee)
LKW Solicitors Ltd, Glasgow ....(p.1004)
T: 0141 4236999
E: Zahra@lkwsolicitors.co.uk

BHEBHE, Nganele Wordsworth (Sept 2016)
(Employee)
Blackwall Legal LLP, Perth ....(p.1257)

BICKET, Alexander David (Jul 2010) (Employee)
National Westminster Bank PLC, London
EC2......................(p.1266)
E: Alexander.Bicket@Natwest.com

BICKNELL, Rachael Louise (Jan 2007) (Solicitor)
NO FIRM

BIGGAM, Mary (Nov 1994) (Partner)
DJ Mackay and Partners LLP,
Glasgow....................(p.1012)
T: 0141 353 8700
E: mary.biggam@djmp-solicitors.co.uk

BIGGAM, Stephen James (Sept 1993) (Director)
Marshall Wilson Law Group Limited,
Falkirk ....(p.922)
T: 01324 612569
E: sbiggam@marshallwilson.com

BIGGAR, Walter Duncan (Aug 2021)
(Employee)
Turcan Connell, Edinburgh ....(p.908)
T: 0131 2288111
E: duncan.biggar@turcanconnell.com

BIGGART, Gayle Anne (Nov 2014) (Employee)
VisitScotland, Edinburgh ....(p.1236)
T: 0131 472 2382
E: Gayle.Biggart@visitscotland.com

BIGGART, Sandra Elizabeth (Dec 1996)
(Associate)
Levy & McRae Solicitors LLP,
Glasgow....................(p.1000)
T: 0141 3072311
E: sbiggart@lemac.co.uk

BILOTTI, Emma Rachel (Aug 2018) (Employee)
Dickson Minto, Edinburgh ....(p.861)
T: 0131 2254455
E: emma.bilotti@dmws.com

BINGHAM, April (Aug 2002) (Director)
Bellwether Green Limited, Glasgow ....(p.944)
T: 0141 2184900
E: april.bingham@bellwethergreen.com

BINGHAM, Joanna Gayle (Aug 2009)
(Associate)
Mackintosh & Wylie LLP,
Kilmarnock...................(p.1095)
T: 01563 525104
E: joannandolivia@gmail.com

BINGHAM, John Paul (Mar 1993) (Director)
Bellwether Green Limited, Glasgow ....(p.944)
T: 0141 2184900
E: john.bingham@bellwethergreen.com

BINGHAM, Stewart Mark (Feb 2011)
(Employee)
National Westminster Bank PLC,
Edinburgh . . . .(p.1226)
T: (0131) 626 2925
E: Stewart.Bingham@rbs.co.uk

BINNIE, Chloe Sarah (Aug 2019) (Employee)
A Fraser Solicitors Ltd, Inverness . . . . . .(p.1076)
T: 01463 229917
E: chloe@afrasersolicitors.com

BINNIE, Fiona Margaret (Nov 1997)
(Employee)
Aberdeenshire Council, Aberdeen . . . . .(p.1211)
T: 01467 530759
E: Fiona.binnie@Aberdeenshire.gov.uk

BINNIE, Pamela Elizabeth (Sept 2012)
(Employee)
Shepherd and Wedderburn LLP,
Glasgow. . . . .(p.1039)
T: 0141 5669900
E: pamela.binnie@shepwedd.com

BINNING, Robert Andrew (Oct 1986) (Solicitor)
NO FIRM

BIRCH, Margaret Shannon (Aug 2014)
(Employee)
Scottish Equity Partners LLP,
Glasgow. . . . .(p.1243)
T: 0141 2734000
E: margaret.birch@sep.co.uk

BIRD, Andrea Jane (Aug 2007) (Employee)
CNR International (U.K.) Limited,
Aberdeen . . . .(p.1212)
T: 01224 303653
E: andrea.bird@cnrl.com

BIRD, Andrew Duncan (Oct 2009) (Associate)
Slater and Gordon Scotland Limited,
Edinburgh . . . .(p.903)
T: 0131 7184150
E: Andrew.Bird@slatergordon.co.uk

BIRD, Heather Christina (Nov 2007)
(Employee)
Shepherd and Wedderburn LLP,
Edinburgh . . . .(p.900)
T: 0131 2289900
E: heather.bird@shepwedd.com

BIRD, Kay Diane (Jul 2009) (Associate)
Gillespie Gifford & Brown LLP, Castle
Douglas . . . .(p.783)
T: 01556 503744
E: kay.bird@ggblaw.co.uk

BIRD, Natalie Joan (Feb 2016) (Director)
DANDHLAW LIMITED, Thurso . . . .(p.1174)
T: 01847 894379
E: nb@dandhlaw.co.uk

BIRD, Susan Jane (Jan 2006) (Associate)
Munro & Noble, Inverness . . . .(p.1080)
T: 01463 221727
E: susanjb@munronoble.com

BIRDSALL, Roslyn (Dec 1998) (Employee)
Lloyds Banking Group Plc,
Edinburgh . . . .(p.1224)
T: 0131 442 9554
E: RoslynBirdsall@lloydsbanking.com

BIRNIE, Joanne Hunter (Oct 1998) (Employee)
Stewart & Watson, Peterhead . . . .(p.1155)
T: 01779 476351
E: jbirnie@stewartwatson.co.uk

BIRSE, Mary McLaughlin (Jan 2012) (Employee)
Kinnear & Falconer, Stonehaven . . . . .(p.1168)
T: 01569 763555
E: m.birse@jgcollie.co.uk

BIRSE, Scott David (Feb 2014) (Employee)
BlackRock, Edinburgh . . . .(p.1221)
T: (306) 978 749 900
E: scott.birse@blackrock.com

BISHOP, Lindsay (Feb 1999) (Director)
Macleod & MacCallum Limited,
Inverness . . . .(p.1080)
T: 01463 239393
E: lindsay.bishop@macandmac.co.uk

BISSET, Amy Louise (Jul 2016) (Director)
Orme Law-A Trading Name of Kirklands,
Falkirk . . . .(p.924)
T: 01324 882551
E: amyb@orme-law.co.uk

BISSET, Brent Wemyss (Oct 2010) (Employee)
Procurator Fiscal Service,
Edinburgh . . . .(p.1227)
T: 0844 5613893
E: brent.bisset@copfs.gov.uk

BISSET, Kenna Charlotte (Feb 2020)
(Employee)
Shepherd and Wedderburn LLP,
Edinburgh . . . .(p.900)
T: 0131 2289900
E: kenna.bisset@shepwedd.com

BISSET, Laura Anne (Jan 2015) (Employee)
Premier Oil UK Limited, Aberdeen . . . .(p.1213)
T: 01224 618900
E: lbisset@PREMIER-OIL.com

BISSETT, Fiona Alison (Oct 2016) (Employee)
Digby Brown LLP, Kirkcaldy . . . .(p.1099)
T: 01592 802535
E: Fiona.Bissett@digbybrown.co.uk

BISSETT, Norman Shirsinger (Feb 1997)
(Consultant)
Hadiputranto, Hadinoto & Partners,
Jakarta . . . .(p.1273)
T: +62 21 2960 8678
E: norman.bissett@bakermckenzie.com

BISSETT, Thomas (Mar 2013) (Employee)
East Dunbartonshire Council,
Kirkintilloch . . . .(p.1249)
T: 0141 5788000
E: Thomas.Bissett@eastdunbarton.gov.uk

BLACK, Allison Elizabeth (Aug 1997)
(Employee)
Renfrewshire Council, Paisley . . . .(p.1252)
T: 0141 6187175
E: Alison.Black@renfrewshire.gov.uk

BLACK, Amanda Jane (Mar 2002) (Employee)
Scottish Fire and Rescue Service,
Hamilton . . . .(p.1247)
T: 0141 646 4699
E: Amanda.Black@firescotland.gov.uk

BLACK, Amy Natasha Paula (Aug 2018)
(Employee)
Lawson Coull & Duncan, Dundee . . . . .(p.813)
T: 01382 227555
E: ABlack@lawsoncoull.co.uk

BLACK, Andrew David Paterson (Jan 2009)
(Employee)
Scottish Power Limited, Glasgow . . . . .(p.1244)
T: 0141 6140000
E: andrew.black@scottishpower.com

BLACK, Andrew Peter (May 2018) (Employee)
Burness Paull LLP, Glasgow . . . .(p.954)
T: 0141 2484933
E: andrew.black@burnesspaull.com

BLACK, Barbara-Jane (Aug 2007) (Partner)
Taylor & Henderson LLP, Saltcoats . . . .(p.1160)
T: 01294 464341
E: bblack@taylorandhenderson.co.uk

BLACK, Brian (Aug 2005) (Partner)
Black & Markie, Dunfermline . . . .(p.822)
T: 01383 610 547
E: bbblackandmarkie@hotmail.co.uk

BLACK, Catherine Lorraine (Nov 2020)
(Employee)
Gebbie & Wilson LLP, Strathaven . . . . .(p.1172)
T: 01357 520082
E: catherine@gebbiewilson.co.uk

BLACK, Catriona (Mar 2020) (Employee)
Lindsays LLP, Dundee . . . .(p.814)
T: 01382 224112

BLACK, Charles Richard, WS (Oct 1983)
(Associate)
Murray Beith Murray, Edinburgh . . . . . .(p.893)
T: 0131 2251200
E: richard.black@murraybeith.co.uk

BLACK, Dianne (Dec 1988) (Employee)
National Health Service Scotland,
Edinburgh . . . .(p.1225)
T: 0131 2757800
E: dianne.black@nhs.scot

BLACK, Elspeth Catherine (Nov 1973) (Partner)
Corrigall Black, Dunoon . . . .(p.828)
T: 01369 702941
E: elspeth.black@corrigallblack.com

BLACK, Fiona Kathleen (Jun 1998) (Partner)
Rollos Law LLP, Cupar . . . .(p.792)
T: 01334 654081
E: kateblack@rollos.co.uk

BLACK, Gillian Stewart (Dec 1995) (Partner)
Urquharts, Edinburgh . . . .(p.909)
T: 0131 5562896
E: gillianblack@urquharts.co.uk

BLACK, Hannah Emma (Jun 2018) (Employee)
Ledingham Chalmers LLP,
Aberdeen . . . .(p.734)
T: 01224 408408
E: Hannah.Black@ledinghamchalmers.com

BLACK, Ian Webster (Sept 2019) (Employee)
TC Young LLP, Edinburgh . . . .(p.914)
T: 0131 2207660
E: iwb@tcyoung.co.uk

BLACK, James (Jul 2005) (Director)
Stirling & Mair Limited, Johnstone . . . .(p.1090)
T: 01505 329373
E: jim.black@stirlingmair.com

BLACK, Kathryn Louise (Nov 1997) (Associate)
Harper Macleod LLP, Glasgow . . . .(p.983)
T: 0141 2218888
E: kathryn.black@harpermacleod.co.uk

BLACK, Louisa Gair (Dec 2008) (Employee)
Dentons Global Services (UK) Holdings Limited,
London EC4 . . . .(p.1263)
E: Louisa.Black@dentons.com

BLACK, Lysanne Jane Warren (Oct 1993)
(Employee)
Lloyds Banking Group Plc,
Edinburgh . . . .(p.1225)
T: 0131 2438625
E: Lysanne.Black@lloydsbanking.com

BLACK, Martin Campbell (Jun 2006)
(Employee)
Police Scotland, Glasgow . . . .(p.1241)
E: martin.black2@scotland.pnn.police.uk

BLACK, Patricia (Oct 1983) (Director)
P Black Solicitors Limited, Dingwall . . . .(p.797)
T: 01349 863222
E: trish@pblacksolicitors.co.uk

BLACK, Rachel Margaret (Jan 2019) (Employee)
Digby Brown LLP, Edinburgh . . . .(p.862)
T: 0333 200 5925
E: rachel.black@digbybrown.co.uk

BLACK, Rachel Mary (Mar 2015) (Employee)
Search Consultancy Limited,
Glasgow . . . .(p.1244)
T: 0141 2273490
E: rachel.black@search.co.uk

BLACK, Sophie Louise (Sept 2002) (Employee)
Burges Salmon LLP, Edinburgh ....(p.850)
T: 0131 3142112
E: sophie.black@burges-salmon.com

BLACK, Susan Alexandra (Feb 2002) (Partner)
Bradley Campbell & Co., Greenock ...(p.1060)
T: 01475 726363
E: susan.black@bradleycampbell.co.uk

BLACK, Susan Catherine (Feb 2017) (Employee)
Ledingham Chalmers LLP, Stirling ....(p.1165)
T: 01786 478100
E: susan.black@ledinghamchalmers.com

BLACKETT, Emily Catherine Sarah
(Sept 2009) (Employee)
Clyde & Co LLP, Newcastle Upon
Tyne ....(p.1270)
T: 0191 249 5400
E: Emily.Blackett2@clydeco.com

BLACKIE, Frederick George (Jan 1981)
(Director)
A.C. Miller & Mackay Limited,
Perth ....(p.1151)
T: 01738 620087
E: fb@acmm.co.uk

BLACKLOCK, Telfer George (Jan 1984) (Partner)
Blacklocks, Edinburgh ....(p.844)
T: 0131 5553888
E: tgb@blacklocks.co.uk

BLACKMAN, Hayley Maree (Sept 2020)
(Employee)
Thorntons Law LLP, Dundee ....(p.819)
T: 01382 229 111
E: hblackman@thorntons-law.co.uk

BLACKWOOD, Jane Alexandra (Feb 2010)
(Employee)
Harper Macleod LLP, Glasgow ....(p.983)
T: 0141 2218888
E: jane.blackwood@harpermacleod.co.uk

BLACKWOOD, John Grahame (Oct 1991)
(Employee)
Chancery Legal, Hamilton ....(p.1257)
T: +441 400 3884
E: jblackwood@cl.bm

BLACKWOOD, Lisa Ann (Aug 2008) (Employee)
Morton Fraser LLP, Glasgow ....(p.1022)
T: 0141 2741100
E: Lisa.Blackwood@morton-fraser.com

BLAIKIE, Daniel (Apr 2018) (Employee)
Scottish Government, Edinburgh .....(p.1231)
T: 0131 244 0815

BLAIKIE, Kathryn Mary (Dec 1977) (Partner)
Quill Legal, Edinburgh ....(p.898)
T: 0131 5641044
E: kay@quilllegal.co.uk

BLAIKIE, Samantha Claire (Aug 2019)
(Employee)
Ofgem, Glasgow ....(p.1241)
T: (0141) 354 5425
E: samantha.blaikie@ofgem.gov.uk

BLAIN, Andrew John (Dec 1990) (Partner)
Shepherd and Wedderburn LLP,
Edinburgh ....(p.900)
T: 0131 2289900
E: andrew.blain@shepwedd.com

BLAIN, Emma Jane (Sept 1987) (Employee)
Scottish Environment Protection Agency,
Dingwall ....(p.1217)
T: 01349 862021
E: emma.blain@sepa.org.uk

BLAIR, Alison (Aug 2012) (Employee)
Shepherd and Wedderburn LLP,
Edinburgh ....(p.900)
T: 0131 2289900
E: alison.blair@shepwedd.com

BLAIR, Audrey Sanderson (Apr 2003)
(Associate)
BTO Solicitors LLP, Glasgow ....(p.952)
T: 0141 2218012
E: abl@bto.co.uk

BLAIR, Deborah Marie (Oct 2004) (Employee)
Scottish Government, Glasgow ......(p.1243)
T: 0141 2727933
E: deborah.blair@gov.scot

BLAIR, Elizabeth Eunson Aitken (Oct 1995)
(Employee)
Scottish Government, Edinburgh .....(p.1231)
T: 0131 244 0633
E: elizabeth.blair@gov.scot

BLAIR, Elizabeth Reid (Mar 1990) (Partner)
Reid Blair, Isle of Arran ....(p.1088)
T: 01770 870 370
E: reidblairsolicitors@gmail.com

BLAIR, Frances Yvonne (Sept 1991) (Associate)
Archibald Sharp & Son Limited,
Glasgow....................(p.1039)
T: 0141 3393036

BLAIR, Fraser William (Sept 2019) (Associate)
CMS Cameron McKenna Nabarro Olswang LLP,
Edinburgh ....(p.856)
T: 0131 2288000
E: Fraser.Blair@cms-cmno.com

BLAIR, Hamish Noble (Dec 2013) (Employee)
EDF Energy Renewables,
Edinburgh ....(p.1222)
T: (0131) 460 3654
E: Hamish.Blair@edf-re.uk

BLAIR, James Don (Feb 1988) (Consultant)
Anderson Strathern LLP, Edinburgh ....(p.839)
T: 0131 2707700
E: james.blair@andersonstrathern.co.uk

BLAIR, John Michael Greene (Jun 1982)
(Partner)
Gillespie Macandrew LLP, Perth ......(p.1148)
T: 01738 231020
E: Mike.Blair@gillespiemacandrew.co.uk

BLAIR, Kayleigh Nicola (Nov 2019) (Employee)
Scottish Government, Edinburgh .....(p.1231)
T: 0131 244 0815
E: kayleigh.blair@gov.scot

BLAIR, Lesley Jane (Nov 1994) (Solicitor)
NO FIRM

BLAIR, Lizanne (Aug 2016) (Employee)
Linklaters LLP, London EC2 ....(p.1266)
T: 0207 4562000
E: lizanne.blair@linklaters.com

BLAIR, Marjory Elizabeth (Sept 1983)
(Associate)
BTO Solicitors LLP, Glasgow ....(p.952)
T: 0141 2218012
E: meb@bto.co.uk

BLAIR, Philip Robert (Oct 1989) (Employee)
Fife Council, Glenrothes ....(p.1246)
T: 03451 550000 Ext 442
E: Philip.Blair@fife.gov.uk

BLAIR, Rachel Elizabeth McLeod (Jun 2009)
(Employee)
NORTH LANARKSHIREre Council,
Motherwell.................(p.1251)
T: 01698 302196
E: blairr@northlan.gov.uk

BLAIR, Scott Forbes (Mar 1991) (Employee)
The MFY Partnership, Airdrie ....(p.751)
T: 01236 607180
E: scott@mfypartnership.co.uk

BLAIR, Stephanie Elizabeth (Jul 2004)
(Employee)
Procurator Fiscal Service, Glasgow ....(p.1241)
T: 0300 0203000
E: stephanie.blair@copfs.gov.uk

BLAIR, Victoria Ann (Jul 2019) (Employee)
Burness Paull LLP, Aberdeen ....(p.724)
T: 01224 621621
E: victoria.blair@burnesspaull.com

BLAKE, Alexis Elizabeth (Jul 2007) (Employee)
Procurator Fiscal Service,
Edinburgh ....(p.1229)
T: 0300 020 2133
E: alexis.blake@copfs.gov.uk

BLAKE, Walter (Apr 1996) (Partner)
Shepherd and Wedderburn LLP, London
EC2 ....(p.1268)
T: 020 74294900
E: walter.blake@shepwedd.com

BLAKELEY, Yvonne Louise (Jun 2007)
(Employee)
Neilsons, Edinburgh ....(p.894)
T: 0131 3164444
E: yvonnelblakeley@neilsons.co.uk

BLANCE, Kirsty Margaret (Nov 2015)
(Employee)
CMS Cameron McKenna Nabarro Olswang LLP,
Edinburgh ....(p.856)
T: 0131 200 7444
E: kirsty.blance@cms-cmno.com

BLAND, Stephen (Jul 2009) (Employee)
Storie, Cruden & Simpson,
Aberdeen.....................(p.743)
T: 01224 587261
E: sbland@storiecs.co.uk

BLANE, Laura Anne (Sept 2003) (Partner)
Thompsons, Glasgow ....(p.1046)
T: 0141 2218840
E: laura.blane@thompsons-scotland.co.uk

BLANE, Stephen Martin (Nov 1992) (Partner)
Urquharts, Edinburgh ....(p.909)
T: 0131 5562896
E: stephenblane@urquharts.co.uk

BLANE, Steven James (Oct 2009) (Associate)
Pinsent Masons LLP, Edinburgh ....(p.895)
T: 0131 777 7000
E: steven.blane@pinsentmasons.com

BLANEY, Hannah Louise (Nov 2019)
(Employee)
Strefford Tulips Limited, Hamilton ....(p.1070)
T: 01698 429428
E: h.blaney@strefford-tulips.co.uk

BLANEY, Jonathan Paul (Oct 2007) (Solicitor)
NO FIRM

BLOODWORTH, Hayley (Sept 1987)
(Consultant)
Mackinnons Solicitors LLP,
Aberdeen...................(p.736)
T: 01224 632464
E: hayleyb@mackinnons.com

BLUNDELL, Emma Louise (Oct 2013) (Solicitor)
Pinsent Masons LLP, Glasgow ....(p.1031)
T: 0141 567 8400
E: emma.blundell@pinsentmasons.com

BLUNDELL, Jonathan David (Oct 1987)
(Partner)
Thomas S. Veitch & Son,
Linlithgow ....(p.1117)
T: 01506 842100
E: jon@tsveitch.com

BLYTH, Alison Lorna (Feb 2011) (Employee)
National Westminster Bank PLC,
Edinburgh ....(p.1226)
T: 0131 6264084
E: Alison.Blyth@natwest.com

BLYTH, Douglas (Oct 1994) (Employee)
Falkirk Council, Falkirk . . . .(p.1236)
T: 01324 506070
E: douglas.blyth@falkirk.gov.uk

BLYTH, Douglas John (Jan 2001) (Partner)
Dentons UK and Middle East LLP,
Glasgow . . . .(p.968)
T: 0330 2220050
E: Douglas.Blyth@dentons.com

BLYTH, Graham (Sept 2014) (Partner)
Blackadder & McMonagle, Falkirk . . . . .(p.921)
T: 01324 612999
E: graham.blyth@blackandmac.com

BLYTH, Kellie Linden (Nov 2007) (Employee)
Baker McKenzie Habib Al Mulla,
Dubai . . . .(p.1277)
E: Kellie.Blyth@bakermckenzie.com

BLYTH, Laura Margaret (Sept 2001) (Employee)
Renewable Energy Systems Limited,
Glasgow. . . . .(p.1243)
T: (0141) 4045591
E: laura.blyth@res-group.com

BLYTH, Lynsey Kristen (Aug 2011) (Employee)
Michelmores LLP, Exeter . . . .(p.1259)
T: 01392 688 688

BLYTH, Nicola Ann (Oct 2009) (Employee)
The National Trust for Scotland,
Edinburgh . . . .(p.1235)
T: 0131 458 0293
E: nblyth@nts.org.uk

BLYTHE, Jonathan William (Sept 1985)
(Employee)
Eurasia Consultants Ltd, Istanbul . . . . .(p.1277)
T: +90 212 361 50 66
E: jonathan.blythe@eurasia.com.tr

BOA, Kevin William (Oct 1996) (Partner)
Pinsent Masons LLP, London EC2 . . . . .(p.1267)
T: 020 7418 7000
E: kevin.boa@pinsentmasons.com

BOAG, David Allan (Oct 2009) (Associate)
Harper Macleod LLP, Glasgow . . . .(p.983)
T: 0141 2218888
E: David.Boag@harpermacleod.co.uk

BOAG-THOMSON, Joanna Susan (Nov 1990)
(Partner)
Shepherd and Wedderburn LLP,
Glasgow. . . . .(p.1039)
T: 0141 5669900
E: joanna.bt@shepwedd.com

BOARDLEY, Nicola Claire Fiona (Apr 2016)
(Employee)
Brodies LLP, Glasgow . . . .(p.948)
T: 0141 2484672
E: nicola.boardley@brodies.com

BOATH, Ernest Sinclair (Sept 1991) (Partner)
Miller Hendry, Dundee . . . .(p.816)
T: 01382 200000
E: ernestboath@millerhendry.co.uk

BOBKOVA, Lucia (Sept 2015) (Employee)
Scottish Fire and Rescue Service,
Hamilton . . . .(p.1247)
T: 0141 646 4699
E: lucia.bobkova@firescotland.gov.uk

BOCCOLI, Andrew (Aug 2008) (Employee)
Lindsays LLP, Edinburgh . . . .(p.882)
T: 0131 2291212

BOENDERMAKER, Simon Andrew
(Oct 2020) (Employee)
Murray Beith Murray, Edinburgh . . . . . .(p.893)
T: 0131 2251200
E: simon.boendermaker@murraybeith.co.uk

BOGIE, Martin John Methven (Oct 1999)
(Employee)
Addleshaw Goddard LLP,
Edinburgh . . . .(p.835)
T: 0131 2282400
E: Martin.Bogie@addleshawgoddard.com

BOGLE, Anne-Claire (Jun 2010) (Employee)
Baillie Gifford & Co, Edinburgh . . . . . .(p.1220)
T: 0131 2752000
E: anne-claire.bogle@bailliegifford.com

BOLAND, Anthony Edward John (Mar 2018)
(Employee)
Tod & Mitchell, Paisley . . . .(p.1142)
T: 0141 8891444
E: Anthony.boland@todandmitchell.co.uk

BOLAND, Linzi (Jan 2021) (Employee)
Digby Brown LLP, Glasgow . . . .(p.970)
T: 0333 200 5925

BOLE, Colin John (Oct 1999) (Employee)
Simmons & Simmons LLP, London
EC2 . . . .(p.1268)
T: 2078253170
E: colin.bole@simmons-simmons.com

BOLGER, Anne Marie (Oct 2002) (Director)
McClure Collins Limited, Glasgow . . . .(p.1007)
T: 0141 4237181
E: anne@mcclurecollins.com

BOLLEN, Christopher Thomas (Oct 2015)
(Director)
C.T. Bollen Limited, Glasgow . . . .(p.947)
T: 07702 031976

BOLLING, Murray Mackay (Feb 1994) (Partner)
Harper, Robertson & Shannon,
Annan . . . .(p.754)
T: 01461 203418
E: murray@hrands.co.uk

BOLT, Kathleen Janet (Aug 1991) (Employee)
DJ Mackay and Partners LLP,
Glasgow.....................(p.1012)
T: 0141 353 8700

BON, Hazel (Sept 2005) (Employee)
Civil Legal Assistance Office,
Edinburgh ....(p.1222)
T: 0131 2401960
E: bonha@clao.org.uk

BON, Neil John (Jan 2005) (Director)
Bon Law Ltd, Edinburgh ....(p.845)
T: 0131 5641460
E: neil@bon-law.co.uk

BONAR, Jessica Ruth (Nov 2021) (Employee)
Brodies LLP, Edinburgh ....(p.845)
T: 0131 2283777

BONAR, Roisin Mary (Mar 2017) (Partner)
Cameron Pinkerton & Co LLP,
Paisley ....(p.1137)
T: 0141 8875211
E: roisin@cameronpinkerton.co.uk

BONAVINO, Kiril Walter (May 2019) (Solicitor)
NO FIRM

BOND, Kate Denise (Jul 2008) (Associate)
Anderson Strathern LLP, Edinburgh ....(p.839)
T: 0131 2707700
E: kate.bond@andersonstrathern.co.uk

BONE, Anthony Francis (Jan 2016) (Partner)
Anthony Bone, Kilmarnock ....(p.1094)
T: 01563 559166
E: law@tonybonelegal.com

BONE, Caroline Jane (Nov 2017) (Employee)
Burness Paull LLP, Edinburgh ....(p.850)
T: 0131 4736000
E: caroline.bone@burnesspaull.com

BONE, Clare Jane (Dec 1997) (Partner)
BTO Solicitors LLP, Glasgow ....(p.952)
T: 0141 2218012
E: cbo@bto.co.uk

BONE, David James (Oct 1985) (Partner)
Harper Macleod LLP, Glasgow ....(p.983)
T: 0141 2218888
E: david.bone@harpermacleod.co.uk

BONE, Hazel Jeanette (Jan 1989) (Partner)
Hamilton Watt & Co, Aberdeen ....(p.731)
T: 01224 586685
E: hazelz@hamiltonwatt.co.uk

BONELLIE, Susan (Jun 2010) (Employee)
Scottish Government, Edinburgh .....(p.1231)
T: 0131 244 0815
E: susan.bonellie@gov.scot

BONNAR, Anthony Joseph (Nov 2003)
(Employee)
Procurator Fiscal Service,
Edinburgh ....(p.1227)
T: 0844 5613897
E: anthony.bonnar@copfs.gov.uk

BONNAR, Damian Colin (Sept 1999) (Director)
Bonnar Law Limited, East Kilbride .....(p.830)
T: 01355 268866
E: bonnar.law@tiscali.co.uk

BONNAR, Philip Peter (Dec 2012) (Employee)
Russel + Aitken (Falkirk + Alloa) Ltd,
Alloa ....(p.753)
T: 01259 723201
E: philbonnar@randa-fa.co.uk

BONNINGTON, Kenneth Stewart (Sept 1979)
(Consultant)
Cartys, Hamilton................(p.1066)
T: 01698 285432
E: ksb@cartylaw.co.uk

BONOMY, Ann (Aug 2005) (Associate)
Clyde & Co (Scotland) LLP,
Glasgow.....................(p.961)
T: 0141 2482666
E: ann.bonomy@clydeco.com

BONTHRONE, Nicola (Aug 1989) (Partner)
McArthur Stanton, Helensburgh ......(p.1072)
T: 01436 672212
E: nb@mcarthurstanton.co.uk

BOOKER-MILBURN, Simon Donald
(Sept 1995) (Partner)
Simon D Booker-Milburn, Nairn ......(p.1129)
T: 07769 682588
E: simon@sdbmlaw.net

BOON, Felix Denzil Edward (Dec 2015)
(Employee)
Zurich Insurance Plc, London EC3 ....(p.1270)
E: felix.boon@uk.zurich.com

BOOTH, Charlotte Elizabeth (Oct 2012)
(Employee)
Pinsent Masons LLP, Aberdeen ....(p.739)
T: 01224 377900
E: Charlotte.Booth@pinsentmasons.com

BOOTH, Gary Alexander (Oct 2001)
(Employee)
The Scottish Football Association,
Glasgow.....................(p.1245)
T: 0141 6166000
E: Gary.Booth@scottishfa.co.uk

BOOTH, Gayle (Sept 2010) (Employee)
Royal London, Edinburgh ....(p.1230)
T: 0131 4567703
E: Gayle.Booth@royallondon.com

BOOTH, Lauren Nicola (Aug 2013) (Associate)
Mitchells Roberton Ltd, Glasgow . . . . . (p.1020)
T: 0141 552 3422
E: Lauren@mitchells-roberton.co.uk

BOOTH, Robert Hugh (Jan 2012) (Employee)
Al Busaidy, Mansoor Jamal & Co.,
Ruwi . . . . (p.1275)
T: 00968 2482 9269
E: robert.booth@amjoman.com

BOOTH, Sarah Francesca (Dec 2015)
(Employee)
Scottish Government, Edinburgh . . . . . (p.1231)
T: 0131 244 0815
E: sarah.booth@gov.scot

BORLA, Elisabetta (Mar 2018) (Employee)
Katani & Co. Ltd, Glasgow . . . . (p.994)
T: 0141 2217788
E: elisabetta.borla@kataniandco.com

BORLAND, Marisa (Oct 2014) (Director)
Bridge Legal Limited, Glasgow . . . . (p.948)
T: 0141 4293100
E: MBorland@bridgelitigationuk.com

BORRER, Denise Christine (Oct 2015)
(Employee)
Stirling District Citizens Advice Bureau Ltd,
Stirling . . . . (p.1255)
E: Denise.Borrer@StirlingCAB.casonline.org.uk

BORROWMAN, Alan Ronald (Jan 1982)
(Director)
Garden Stirling Burnet Solicitors Limited,
Haddington . . . . (p.1064)
T: 01620 824996
E: aborrowman@gsbsolicitors.co.uk

BORROWMAN, Suzanne (Oct 2010) (Employee)
SSE Plc, Perth . . . . (p.1253)
T: 01738 456 000
E: Suzanne.Borrowman@sse.com

BORROWS, Keith William James (Sept 2005)
(Employee)
Baillie Gifford & Co, Edinburgh . . . . . . (p.1220)
T: 0131 2752000
E: keith.borrows@bailliegifford.com

BORTHWICK, Catriona Sarah (Nov 2004)
(Employee)
PRA Group (UK) Limited,
Kilmarnock . . . . (p.1249)
T: 07912 467322
E: catriona.borthwick@pragroup.co.uk

BORTHWICK, Nicola Joy (Dec 2003) (Solicitor)
NO FIRM

BOSTON, Thomas Christopher (Oct 2013)
(Solicitor)
NO FIRM

BOSWALL, Julian Roderick Gerard
(May 2018) (Partner)
Burges Salmon LLP, Bristol . . . . (p.1258)
T: 0117 9392000
E: julian.boswall@burges-salmon.com

BOSWELL, Kaitlin Tress (Oct 2019) (Employee)
Hamilton Ross, Airdrie . . . . (p.749)
T: 01236 627627
E: kaitlin@hamiltonross.co.uk

BOSWELL, Khloe Joanne (Mar 2021)
(Employee)
Strefford Tulips Limited, Hamilton . . . . (p.1070)
T: 01698 429428
E: k.boswell@strefford-tulips.co.uk

BOSWELL, Tina (Aug 2008) (Employee)
Scottish Social Services Council,
Dundee . . . . (p.1218)
T: 0345 6030 891
E: tina.boswell@sssc.uk.com

BOTTOMLEY, Claire Elizabeth (Aug 2011)
(Employee)
Procurator Fiscal Service,
Edinburgh . . . . (p.1229)
T: 0300 0203728
E: Claire.Bottomley@copfs.gov.uk

BOULTON-JONES, Thomas Owen (Oct 1999)
(Partner)
Brodies LLP, Aberdeen. . . . . (p.723)
T: 01224 392242
E: tom.boulton-jones@brodies.com

BOUSIE, Karin Gwynneth (Mar 2004)
(Employee)
Gilson Gray LLP, Dundee. . . . . (p.811)
T: 01382 549321
E: kbousie@gilsongray.co.uk

BOUTTELL, Ruth Whiteford (Oct 2009)
(Solicitor)
NO FIRM

BOVINGDON, Harriet Daisy (Mar 2014)
(Associate)
Collas Crill, St Helier . . . . (p.1274)
T: 01534 601783
E: daisy.bovingdon@collascrill.com

BOWDEN, Neil Alexander (Apr 1997)
(Employee)
Allen & Overy LLP, London E1 . . . . (p.1261)
T: 020 3088 3431
E: neil.bowden@allenovery.com

BOWEN, Gethin (Jan 2017) (Employee)
Dentons UK and Middle East LLP,
Glasgow. . . . . (p.968)
T: 0330 2220050
E: gethin.bowen@dentons.com

BOWEN, Isla Mary (Oct 2010) (Employee)
National Health Service Scotland,
Edinburgh . . . . (p.1225)
T: 0131 2757800
E: isla.bowen@nhs.scot

BOWEN, Laura Julie (Jan 2014) (Employee)
Anderson Strathern LLP, Edinburgh . . . . (p.839)
T: 0131 2707700
E: Laura.Bowen@andersonstrathern.co.uk

BOWIE, Carolyn (Jul 2019) (Employee)
Weightmans (Scotland) LLP,
Glasgow. . . . . (p.1051)
T: 0345 073 9900
E: carolyn.bowie@weightmans.com

BOWIE, Christopher John (Aug 2016)
(Associate)
CMS Cameron McKenna Nabarro Olswang LLP,
Edinburgh . . . . (p.856)
T: 0131 2288000
E: Christopher.Bowie@cms-cmno.com

BOWIE, Connor Kenneth (Sept 2020)
(Employee)
Gilson Gray LLP, Glasgow . . . . (p.980)
T: 0141 5302021
E: cbowie@gilsongray.co.uk

BOWIE, Euan Forbes (Nov 2020) (Employee)
Harper Macleod LLP, Glasgow . . . . (p.983)
T: 0141 2218888
E: euan.bowie@harpermacleod.co.uk

BOWIE, Ian Martin (Sept 1993) (Partner)
MacRoberts LLP, Glasgow . . . . (p.1015)
T: 0141 3031147
E: ian.bowie@macroberts.com

BOWIE, John Columba (Oct 1984) (Consultant)
Miller Beckett & Jackson Limited,
Glasgow. . . . . (p.1019)
T: 0141 2042833
E: jbowie@mbjsolicitors.co.uk

BOWIE, Ryan (Dec 2008) (Employee)
Brodies LLP, Glasgow . . . . (p.948)
T: 0141 2484672
E: ryan.bowie@brodies.com

BOWMAN, Alice Evelyn (Aug 2019) (Employee)
Allan McDougall McQueen LLP,
Edinburgh . . . . (p.837)
T: 0131 2252121
E: alicebowman@allanmcdougall.co.uk

BOWMAN, Alistair MacGregor (Oct 1982)
(Partner)
MacGregor Bowman WS,
Edinburgh . . . . (p.885)
T: 0131 4454177
E: mail@macgregorbowman.co.uk

BOWMAN, David Robert (Nov 2011)
(Employee)
Renewables Unlimited LLP,
Glasgow. . . . . (p.1243)
T: 0141 221 0276
E: dbowman@ru-llp.com

BOWMAN, Gillian Louise (Sept 2013) (Partner)
Cairns Brown, Alexandria . . . . (p.751)
T: 01389 756979
E: g.bowman@cairnsbrown.co.uk

BOWMAN, Helen (Nov 1995) (Employee)
TSB Bank Plc, Edinburgh . . . . (p.1235)
T: (0131) 260 0051
E: helen.bowman@tsb.co.uk

BOWMAN, John William (Sept 2008)
(Employee)
Baker Hughes Energy FZE, Dubai . . . . . (p.1277)
T: +971 4 8211650
E: John.Bowman@bakerhughes.com

BOWMAN, Thomas Colin Francis (Nov 1994)
(Employee)
Procurator Fiscal Service, Glasgow . . . . (p.1241)
T: 0300 0203000
E: thomas.bowman@copfs.gov.uk

BOYACK, Louisa (Mar 2012) (Employee)
DP World, Dubai . . . . (p.1278)
T: +9714 8080 778
E: Louisa.Boyack@dpworld.com

BOYCE, Amy (Oct 2020) (Employee)
MacRoberts LLP, Edinburgh . . . . (p.887)
T: 0131 2295046
E: amy.boyce@macroberts.com

BOYCE, Fiona Jane (Oct 1996) (Employee)
National Westminster Bank PLC,
Edinburgh . . . . (p.1226)
E: fiona.j.boyce@rbs.co.uk

BOYCE, Samuel Alexander (Sept 2019)
(Employee)
Digby Brown LLP, Glasgow . . . . (p.970)
T: 0333 200 5925

BOYD, Alexander Vitalievich (Jun 2015)
(Partner)
Alexander Boyd Solicitors, Glasgow . . . . (p.939)
T: 0141 2373137
E: alexanderboydsolicitors@gmail.com

BOYD, Anne (Nov 1982) (Consultant)
Raeburn Christie Clark & Wallace LLP,
Aberdeen . . . . (p.741)
T: 01224 332400
E: anne.boyd@raeburns.co.uk

BOYD, Carol Jane (Feb 2000) (Employee)
Levy & McRae Solicitors LLP,
Glasgow. . . . . (p.1000)
T: 0141 3072311
E: CBoyd@lemac.co.uk

BOYD, Carolyn Mary Linden (Jan 2017)
(Employee)
Scottish Government, Edinburgh . . . . . (p.1231)
T: 0131 244 0815
E: cmlboyd@gmail.com

BOYD, Christopher Martin James (Aug 2011)
(Solicitor)
NO FIRM

BOYD, Diana Glennie (Nov 1989) (Director)
Boyd Legal Limited, Edinburgh . . . . (p.845)
T: 0131 2267464
E: diana.boyd@boydlegaluk.com

BOYD, Gregor John (Apr 2008) (Employee)
ADNOC Global Trading LTD, Abu
Dhabi . . . . (p.1277)
T: +971 270 66608
E: gboyd@adnoc.ae

BOYD, Iain Alexander (Oct 2018) (Employee)
Thorntons Law LLP, Edinburgh . . . . (p.906)
T: 0131 2258705
E: iboyd@thorntons-law.co.uk

BOYD, Johanna Catherine (Nov 2019)
(Employee)
Brodies LLP, Edinburgh . . . . (p.845)
T: 0131 2283777
E: johanna.boyd@brodies.com

BOYD, Joseph George (Aug 2010) (Director)
Joseph G Boyd & Co Court Lawyers Ltd,
Edinburgh . . . . (p.845)
T: 07746 767776
E: jboydlawyers@gmail.com

BOYD, Kerrie (Mar 2021) (Employee)
Norrie Moore Limited,
Cumbernauld . . . . (p.790)
T: 01236 729868
E: kerrie@nmlegal.co.uk

BOYD, Kevin John (Jul 1984) (Partner)
Mathie-Morton, Ayr . . . . (p.764)
T: 01292 263549
E: KevinBoyd@mathie-morton.co.uk

BOYD, Laura Frances (Feb 2021) (Employee)
Bridge Legal Limited, Glasgow . . . . (p.948)
T: 0141 4293100
E: lboyd@bridgelegalglasgow.co.uk

BOYD, Magdalene (Oct 2005) (Employee)
Scottish Government, Edinburgh . . . . . (p.1231)
T: 0131 244 0815
E: Magdalene.boyd@gov.scot

BOYD, Michael William (Feb 2003) (Partner)
Boyds Law, Forfar . . . . (p.926)
T: 01307 460499
E: mboyd@boydslaw.co.uk

BOYD, Robert Findlay (Oct 2002) (Director)
Anderson Shaw & Gilbert Limited,
Inverness . . . . (p.1075)
T: 01463 236123
E: fb@solicitorsinverness.com

BOYD, William Peter (Dec 1973) (Director)
Boyd Legal Limited, Edinburgh . . . . (p.845)
T: 0131 2267464
E: peter.boyd@boydlegaluk.com

BOYD, William Thomson, WS (Dec 1983)
(Partner)
Wilkie & Dundas, Kirriemuir. . . . . (p.1107)
T: 01575 572608
E: wtb@wdws.co.uk

BOYLAN, Carla Louise (Jun 2011) (Associate)
Russells Gibson McCaffrey,
Glasgow. (p.1037)
T: 0141 271 1000
E: carla@russellsgm.co.uk

BOYLE, Christopher Francis (Sept 1981)
(Director)
C.F. Boyle & Co Limited, Glasgow . . . . . (p.947)
T: 0141 2043897
E: c.f.boyle@btinternet.com

BOYLE, Christopher Ross (Oct 2013)
(Employee)
Macfarlanes LLP, London EC4 . . . . (p.1266)
T: (020) 7791 4044
E: Chris.Boyle@macfarlanes.com

BOYLE, Ciara (Dec 2019) (Employee)
Digby Brown LLP, Aberdeen . . . . (p.729)
T: 0333 200 5925
E: ciara.boyle@digbybrown.co.uk

BOYLE, Daniel John (Nov 2007) (Employee)
Clifford Chance LLP, Dubai . . . . (p.1278)
T: +971 4503 2729
E: daniel.boyle@cliffordchance.com

BOYLE, Eugene Francis (Dec 1983) (Partner)
The PRG Partnership, Clydebank . . . . . . (p.786)
T: 0141 9520019
E: efboyle@prg.co.uk

BOYLE, Henry Thompson Dalgety
(Sept 1991) (Partner)
Clyde & Co (Scotland) LLP,
Aberdeen . . . . (p.726)
T: 01224 624924
E: harry.boyle@clydeco.com

BOYLE, Jack Glass (Nov 2010) (Employee)
Blackadders LLP, Dundee. . . . . (p.805)
T: 01382 229 222
E: jack.boyle@blackadders.co.uk

BOYLE, Jennifer Lynn (Oct 2012) (Employee)
Connell & Connell, WS, Edinburgh . . . . (p.857)
T: 0131 5562993
E: jlb@connellws.co.uk

BOYLE, John Ross (Mar 2006) (Partner)
Boyles Solicitors, Dundee . . . .(p.806)
T: 01382 221 214
E: jboyle@wgboyle.co.uk

BOYLE, Lauren Margaret Bertram
(Apr 2019) (Employee)
Windhoist Limited, Glasgow . . . .(p.1246)

BOYLE, Mairi (Feb 2003) (Employee)
Procurator Fiscal Service,
Edinburgh . . . .(p.1227)
T: 0300 0203168
E: mairi.boyle@copfs.gov.uk

BOYLE, Margaret Mary (Nov 1967)
(Consultant)
Bilkus & Boyle, Glasgow . . . .(p.946)
T: 0141 8823221
E: law@bilkusandboyle.com

BOYLE, Mathew Desmond (Nov 2006)
(Consultant)
White & Case LLP, London EC2 . . . . . .(p.1269)
T: 020 7532 1960
E: mathew.boyle@whitecase.com

BOYLE, Scott (Nov 1995) (Employee)
CIGNA International, Glasgow . . . .(p.1238)
T: 01475 788679
E: Scott.Boyle@cigna.com

BOYLE, Terence (May 2000) (Director)
T Boyle & Co Limited, Glasgow . . . .(p.947)
T: 07752 266001
E: terryboyle703@gmail.com

BOYLE, William Gordon (May 1977)
(Consultant)
NO FIRM

BOYLEN, Lucy Anne (Mar 2021) (Employee)
McKennas Law Practice Limited,
Glenrothes . . . .(p.1057)
T: 01592 756449

BOYNTON, Daniel Stuart (Sept 2015)
(Employee)
Shepherd and Wedderburn LLP,
Edinburgh . . . .(p.900)
T: 0131 2289900
E: daniel.boynton@shepwedd.com

BOYNTON, Rozanne Choi Ling (Nov 2007)
(Employee)
Road Traffic Accident Law (Scotland) LLP,
Aberdeen . . . .(p.742)
T: 01721 728238
E: Roz.Boynton@RTALaw.scot

BRAAT, Philip Masterson (Sept 2001) (Solicitor)
NO FIRM

BRACKEN, Alastair (Jan 1992) (Partner)
Ross & Connel LLP, Dunfermline . . . . . .(p.825)
T: 01383 721156
E: abracken@ross.connel.co.uk

BRADBURY, Kate (Jul 2016) (Employee)
Brodies LLP, Aberdeen . . . .(p.723)
T: 01224 392683
E: kate.bradbury@brodies.com

BRADBURY, Marie Angela (Nov 1977)
(Employee)
Mitchells Roberton Ltd, Glasgow . . . . .(p.1020)
T: 0141 5523422
E: marie@mitchells-roberton.co.uk

BRADFORD, Stephen (Dec 1996) (Partner)
Lockharts Law LLP, Ayr . . . .(p.764)
T: 01292 265045
E: stephenbradford@lockhartslaw.com

BRADING, Peter Edward (Oct 2013)
(Employee)
Brodies LLP, Edinburgh . . . .(p.845)
T: 0131 2283777
E: peter.brading@brodies.com

BRADLEY, Alexandra Hannah (Mar 2018)
(Associate)
CMS Cameron McKenna Nabarro Olswang LLP,
Glasgow . . . .(p.962)
T: 0141 2222200
E: alexandra.bradley@cms-cmno.com

BRADLEY, Andrew John (Oct 1996) (Director)
AJ Bradley & Co Ltd, Glasgow . . . .(p.947)
T: 0141 374 0474
E: ajbradwk@gmail.com

BRADLEY, Cheryl (Jul 2018) (Employee)
Midlothian Council, Dalkeith . . . .(p.1216)
T: 0131 2707500
E: cheryl.bradley@midlothian.gov.uk

BRADLEY, Ciara Claire Pia (Sept 2020)
(Employee)
Fleming & Reid, Glasgow . . . .(p.977)
T: 0141 3311144
E: cb@flemingandreid.co.uk

BRADLEY, Edward Alan (Jan 2001) (Solicitor)
NO FIRM

BRADLEY, Jennifer Alison (Jan 2012) (Solicitor)
NO FIRM

BRADLEY, Laura (Jul 2016) (Employee)
Procurator Fiscal Service, Glasgow . . . .(p.1241)
T: 0300 0203000
E: Laura.Bradley@copfs.gov.uk

BRADLEY, Marie-Claire (Oct 2004) (Solicitor)
NO FIRM

BRADLEY, Nicola Anne (Nov 2020) (Employee)
Scottish Government, Edinburgh . . . . .(p.1231)
T: 0131 244 0815
E: nicola.bradley@gov.scot

BRADLEY, Pauline Anne (Jan 1989) (Employee)
Greyfriars Investments Limited,
Edinburgh . . . .(p.1223)
T: 0131 220 6719
E: pauline.bradley@greyfriarsinvestments.co.uk

BRADLEY, Tessa Mary (Sept 2009) (Employee)
Procurator Fiscal Service,
Edinburgh . . . .(p.1229)
T: 0300 0203000
E: tessa.bradley@copfs.gov.uk

BRADSHAW, Anne-Louise (Jul 2015) (Employee)
Drummond Miller LLP, Glasgow. . . . . . .(p.971)
T: 0141 3320086
E: abradshaw@drummondmiller.co.uk

BRADSHAW, Anne-Marie (Oct 2005)
(Employee)
The Hut Group PLC, Manchester . . . . .(p.1270)
E: Annemarie.bradshaw@thehutgroup.com

BRADSHAW, Clare-Frances (Jul 2005)
(Employee)
Celeros Flow Technology, Glasgow. . . .(p.1238)
T: 07827 878 267
E: clarefrances.bradshaw@celerosft.com

BRADSHAW, Gillian Elizabeth (Sept 2002)
(Employee)
Procurator Fiscal Service, Glasgow . . . .(p.1241)
T: 0300 0203000
E: gillian.bradshaw@copfs.gov.uk

BRADSHAW, Graeme Stuart (Aug 2001)
(Partner)
Burness Paull LLP, Glasgow . . . .(p.954)
T: 0141 2484933
E: Graeme.Bradshaw@burnesspaull.com

BRADSHAW, Pamela Katy (Feb 2013)
(Associate)
Jackson Boyd LLP, Glasgow . . . .(p.991)
T: 0141 2214325
E: PBradshaw@jacksonboyd.co.uk

BRADSHAW, Pauline Marie (Sept 1992)
(Employee)
Glasgow City Council, Glasgow . . . . . .(p.1240)
E: Pauline.Bradshaw@ced.glasgow.gov.uk

BRADSHAW, Robert Craig (Aug 1998)
(Employee)
Dentons UK and Middle East LLP,
Glasgow. . . . .(p.968)
T: 0330 2220050
E: craig.bradshaw@dentons.com

BRADSHAW-WONG, Tak Lan Teresa
(Aug 2014) (Associate)
CMS Cameron McKenna Nabarro Olswang LLP,
Edinburgh . . . .(p.856)
T: 0131 2288000
E: Teresa.Bradshaw-Wong@cms-cmno.com

BRADY, Derek Allan (Dec 1978) (Consultant)
Rollos Law LLP, Glenrothes . . . .(p.1058)
T: 01592 759414
E: derekbrady@rollos.co.uk

BRADY, Dionne Linda (Aug 2019) (Employee)
Gillespie Macandrew LLP, Perth . . . . . .(p.1148)
T: 01738 231000
E: dionne.brady@gillespiemacandrew.co.uk

BRADY, Gillian Michelle Anne (Jun 2010)
(Employee)
The Scottish Parliament, Edinburgh . . .(p.1235)
T: (0131) 3486653
E: Gillian.Brady@parliament.scot

BRADY, Hugh Anthony (Jul 2000) (Employee)
Procurator Fiscal Service, Greenock. . . .(p.1246)
T: 07752 182 465
E: hugh.brady@copfs.gov.uk

BRADY, Kevin Joseph (Jun 2005) (Employee)
Callahan McKeown & Co Ltd,
Renfrew . . . .(p.1158)
T: 0141 8851212
E: Callahanmckeownandco@gmail.com

BRADY, Mark James (Feb 2006) (Employee)
Appleby, St Helier. . . . .(p.1274)
T: 01534 888 777
E: mbrady@applebyglobal.com

BRADY, Nicholas David (Sept 2018) (Employee)
Travers Smith LLP, London EC1 . . . . . .(p.1269)
T: (0207) 2953387
E: nick.brady@traverssmith.com

BRADY, Pamela (Sept 1999) (Employee)
Procurator Fiscal Service, Greenock. . . .(p.1246)
T: 0300 020 0859
E: pamela.brady@copfs.gov.uk

BRADY, Yvonne Therese (Dec 1984)
(Employee)
Morton Fraser LLP, Edinburgh . . . .(p.891)
T: 0131 2471000
E: yvonne.brady@morton-fraser.com

BRAIDWOOD, Catherine Emily (Oct 2007)
(Partner)
Braidwoods, Dumfries . . . .(p.800)
T: 01387 257272
E: katie.braidwood@braidwoods.com

BRAIDWOOD, Matthew Campbell
(Nov 2018) (Employee)
Braidwoods, Dumfries . . . .(p.800)
T: 01387 257272
E: matthew.braidwood@braidwoods.com

BRAIDWOOD, Peter Maxwell (Sept 2006)
(Partner)
Braidwoods, Dumfries . . . .(p.800)
T: 01387 257272
E: info@braidwoods.com

BRAIDWOOD, Robert Maxwell (Dec 1976)
(Partner)
Braidwoods, Dumfries . . . .(p.800)
T: 01387 257272
E: info@braidwoods.com

BRAILSFORD, Elaine Nicola, WS (Jan 1983)
(Partner)
Shepherd and Wedderburn LLP,
Edinburgh . . . .(p.900)
T: 0131 2289900
E: Elaine.Brailsford@shepwedd.com

BRAND, Mhairi Catriona (Feb 2021) (Employee)
Procurator Fiscal Service, Glasgow . . . .(p.1241)
T: 0300 0203000
E: Mhairi.Brand@copfs.gov.uk

BRANDON, Rachael Anne (Jan 2014) (Director)
Boyd Legal Limited, Edinburgh . . . .(p.845)
T: 0131 2267464
E: rachael.brandon@boydlegaluk.com

BRANNAGAN, Michelle Margaret
(Jul 2013) (Employee)
Procurator Fiscal Service, Glasgow . . . .(p.1241)
T: 0300 0203000
E: michelle.brannagan@copfs.gov.uk

BRANNAN, Holly Margaret (Sept 2017)
(Employee)
Pinsent Masons LLP, Edinburgh . . . .(p.895)
T: 0131 777 7000
E: holly.brannan@pinsentmasons.com

BRASH, Peter Melrose (Sept 1991) (Partner)
Grigor & Young LLP, Elgin . . . .(p.916)
T: 01343 544077
E: peter@grigor-young.co.uk

BRASS, Colin John Stewart (Dec 1983)
(Partner)
Wright, Johnston & Mackenzie LLP,
Glasgow . . . .(p.1054)
T: 0141 2483434
E: cjb@wjm.co.uk

BRAZEL, Hannah Louise (Jul 2017) (Employee)
MBM Commercial LLP, Edinburgh . . . . .(p.889)
T: 0131 2268200
E: hannah.brazel@mbmcommercial.co.uk

BRAZENALL, Claire Robertson (Aug 2010)
(Solicitor)
NO FIRM

BRAZENDALE, Sara Louise (Oct 1991)
(Employee)
Pinsent Masons LLP, Aberdeen . . . .(p.739)
T: 01224 377900
E: Sara.Brazendale@pinsentmasons.com

BREADY, Eileen Maeve (Nov 1974) (Employee)
Bready & Co., Glasgow . . . .(p.947)
T: 0141 334 2265
E: ebready@breadyandco.com

BREADY, James (Aug 1979) (Partner)
Bready & Co., Glasgow . . . .(p.947)
T: 0141 334 2265
E: jbready@breadyandco.com

BREADY, Kathryn Anne (Nov 2008) (Employee)
Mitchells Roberton Ltd, Glasgow . . . . .(p.1020)
T: 0141 5523422
E: kb@mitchells-roberton.co.uk

BREAKEY, Leon (Oct 2002) (Partner)
MacRoberts LLP, Glasgow . . . .(p.1015)
T: 0141 3031100
E: leon.breakey@macroberts.com

BRECHANY, Ian (Sept 1991) (Consultant)
The Glasgow Law Practice,
Glasgow . . . .(p.1043)
T: 0141 6412912
E: ib@theglasgowlawpractice.co.uk

BREE, Robert Macdonald (Oct 1986) (Partner)
Morton Fraser LLP, Glasgow . . . .(p.1022)
T: 0141 2741100
E: Robert.Bree@morton-fraser.com

BREEN, Mandy Lees (Sept 1998) (Employee)
Curle Stewart Limited, Glasgow . . . .(p.964)
T: 0141 227 6200
E: mb@curlestewart.co.uk

BREEN, Michael Denis (Dec 2009) (Employee)
Artemis Investment Management LLP,
Edinburgh . . . .(p.1220)
T: 0131 7180517
E: mickey.breen@artemisfunds.com

BREEN, Paul Douglas (Jun 2011) (Employee)
Brodies LLP, Edinburgh . . . .(p.845)
T: 0131 2283777
E: paul.breen@brodies.com

BREGG, Quentin Murray (Sept 2011)
(Associate)
Collas Crill, St Peter Port . . . .(p.1273)
T: 01481 723191
E: Quentin.Bregg@collascrill.com

BREMNER, Claire (Feb 2014) (Employee)
Procurator Fiscal Service, Kirkcaldy . . . .(p.1249)
T: 0300 0203000
E: claire.bremner@copfs.gov.uk

BREMNER, Colin Scott (Nov 1992) (Partner)
Burnett & Reid LLP, Aberdeen . . . .(p.726)
T: 01224 644333
E: CSBremner@burnett-reid.co.uk

BREMNER, Elizabeth Anne (Mar 2005)
(Associate)
Gillespie Macandrew LLP,
Edinburgh . . . .(p.872)
T: 0131 2251677
E:
elizabeth.bremner@gillespiemacandrew.co.uk

BREMNER, Euan McIntosh (Nov 1999) (Partner)
Burges Salmon LLP, Bristol . . . .(p.1258)
T: 0117 9392000
E: euan.bremner@burges-salmon.com

BREMNER, Laura Jane (Dec 2006) (Employee)
Aberdeenshire Council, Aberdeen . . . . .(p.1211)
T: 01467 535847
E: laura.bremner@aberdeenshire.gov.uk

BREMNER, Sarah Lorraine (Oct 2011)
(Employee)
Subsea 7 France, Suresnes Cedex . . . . .(p.1273)
T: +33 1 40 976300
E: sarah.bremner@subsea7.com

BRENNAN, Donna-Marie (Sept 1996)
(Employee)
BTO Raeburn Hope, Helensburgh . . . . .(p.1072)
T: 01436 671221
E: dbr@bto.co.uk

BRENNAN, Laura Margaret (May 2019)
(Employee)
Gilson Gray LLP, Edinburgh . . . .(p.874)
T: 0131 5165354
E: lm.brennan@yahoo.com

BRENNEN, Laura Greta (Dec 2020) (Employee)
Rradar (Scotland) Limited,
Glasgow . . . .(p.1036)
E: laura.brennen@rradar.com

BREWSTER, Devon Clair (Nov 2015) (Employee)
Dickson Minto, London EC2 . . . .(p.1263)
T: 020 76284455
E: Devon.Brewster@dmws.com

BRICKNELL, Heather Michelle (Sept 2016)
(Employee)
Baker Hughes Ltd., Aberdeen . . . .(p.1212)
T: (01224) 401357
E: Heather.Bricknell@bakerhughes.com

BRIDGE, Joanne (Sept 2006) (Solicitor)
NO FIRM

BRIDGE, Olivia Frances (Jul 2016) (Employee)
MacPhee & Partners LLP, Fort
William . . . .(p.930)
T: 01397 701000
E: oliviabridge@macphee.co.uk

BRIERLEY, Kirsten Laura (Jul 2018) (Employee)
Procurator Fiscal Service, Paisley . . . . . .(p.1252)
T: 0141 8875225
E: kirsten.brierley@copfs.gov.uk

BRIGGS, Dorothy Anne Chalmers
(Sept 1984) (Employee)
Renfrewshire Council, Paisley . . . .(p.1252)
T: 0141 6187172
E: dorothy.briggs@renfrewshire.gov.uk

BRIGGS, Ian (Feb 1981) (Partner)
J. & J. McCosh, Dalry . . . .(p.795)
T: 01294 832112
E: info@jjmccosh.co.uk

BRIGGS, Karen Boyd (Nov 1989) (Employee)
South Ayrshire Council, Ayr . . . .(p.1215)
T: 01292 612420
E: karen.briggs@south-ayrshire.gov.uk

BRIGGS, Megan Alison (Mar 2014) (Employee)
Burness Paull LLP, Glasgow . . . .(p.954)
T: 0141 2484933
E: Megan.Briggs@burnesspaull.com

BRIGGS, Suzanne-Claire McGlennan
(Aug 1999) (Solicitor)
NO FIRM

BRINDLE, Jonathan (Nov 1996) (Solicitor)
NO FIRM

BRIODY-SCOTT, Sara Imelda (Apr 2011)
(Employee)
TauRx Therapeutics Ltd, Aberdeen . . . .(p.1214)
T: 01224 440911
E: s.briody-scott@taurx.com

BRITTON, Douglas Mitchell (Jul 2021)
(Employee)
Katani & Co. Ltd, Glasgow . . . .(p.994)
T: 0141 2217788
E: douglas.britton@kataniandco.com

BROADLEY, Craig Philip Alexander
(Jun 2012) (Employee)
Beltrami & Co Limited, Glasgow . . . . . .(p.944)
T: 0141 4292262
E: craig.broadley@beltramiandcompany.co.uk

BROATCH, Jennifer Susan (Nov 2003)
(Employee)
Thorntons Law LLP, Edinburgh . . . .(p.906)
T: 0131 2258705
E: jbroatch@thorntons-law.co.uk

BROCK, Struan Barr (Sept 2015) (Employee)
Wireless Infrastructure Group,
Bellshill . . . .(p.1216)
T: 01698 846545
E: sbrock@wirelessinfrastructure.co.uk

BROCKBANK, James Alan (Sept 2009)
(Employee)
British Telecommunications PLC, London
EC1 . . . .(p.1262)
T: 0207 356 6921
E: james.brockbank@bt.com

BROCKLEBANK, Andrew Edward (Dec 1990)
(Employee)
Shell U.K. Ltd., Aberdeen . . . .(p.1214)
T: 01224 883860
E: a.brocklebank@shell.com

BRODIE, Carly (Feb 2007) (Director)
Frazer Coogans Ltd, Ayr . . . .(p.763)
T: 01292 280499
E: carly.brodie@frazercoogans.co.uk

BRODIE, Caroline (Jul 2009) (Employee)
Lloyds Banking Group Plc,
Edinburgh . . . .(p.1224)
T: (0131) 442 9579
E: Caroline.Brodie@lloydsbanking.com

BRODIE, Craig Murdoch (Feb 2015) (Employee)
Shepherd and Wedderburn LLP,
Glasgow. . . . .(p.1039)
T: 0141 5669900
E: craig.brodie@shepwedd.com

BRODIE, Karen Susan (Nov 1984) (Partner)
BTO Solicitors LLP, Glasgow . . . .(p.952)
T: 0141 2218012
E: ksb@bto.co.uk

BRODIE, Lisa Jane (Feb 2014) (Employee)
Law Society of Scotland,
Edinburgh . . . .(p.1224)
T: 0131 2267411
E: lisabrodie@lawscot.org.uk

BRODIE, Nicole April (Sept 2020) (Employee)
Livingstone Brown Limited,
Glasgow. . . . .(p.1003)
T: 0141 4298166
E: nicoleb@livbrown.co.uk

BRODIE, Robbie (Oct 2016) (Employee)
Livingstone Brown Limited,
Glasgow. . . . .(p.1003)
T: 0141 4298166
E: robbie@livbrown.co.uk

BRODTKORB, Julie Anne (Aug 2016)
(Employee)
Berrymans Lace Mawer LLP,
Glasgow. . . . .(p.945)
T: 0141 3532121
E: julie.brodtkorb@blmlaw.com

BROGAN, Debbie Morag (Sept 2009)
(Employee)
Morton Fraser LLP, Glasgow . . . .(p.1022)
T: 0141 2741100
E: debbie.brogan@morton-fraser.com

BROGAN, Gavin Daniel (Mar 2007) (Partner)
Digby Brown LLP, Glasgow . . . .(p.970)
T: 0141 566 9528
E: gavin.brogan@digbybrown.co.uk

BROGAN, James Arthur (Mar 2007) (Employee)
Stuart & Stuart, Edinburgh . . . .(p.905)
T: 0131 2286449
E: jbrogan@stuartandstuart.co.uk

BROLLY, Ashley Louise (Nov 2020) (Employee)
Drummond Miller LLP, Edinburgh . . . . .(p.864)
T: 0131 2265151
E: ABrolly@drummondmiller.co.uk

BROOKS, Adam Peter (May 2014) (Employee)
Brodies LLP, Dingwall . . . .(p.796)
T: 01349 860111
E: adam.brooks@brodies.com

BROOKS, Lindsey Jane (Jun 1998) (Employee)
Procurator Fiscal Service, Falkirk . . . . . .(p.1236)
T: 0300 020 3000
E: lindsey.brooks@copfs.gov.uk

BROOKS, Natalie Lauren (Nov 2019)
(Employee)
Gillespie Macandrew LLP,
Edinburgh . . . .(p.872)
T: 0131 2251677
E: natalie.brooks@gillespiemacandrew.co.uk

BROOMHALL, Alison Claire (Mar 2016)
(Employee)
SSE Plc, Perth . . . .(p.1253)
T: 01738 456 000
E: Alison.Broomhall@sse.com

BROPHY, Andrew Edward (Aug 1983) (Partner)
Andrew Brophy, Hamilton . . . .(p.1066)
T: 07919 490999
E: ab@andrewbrophy.co.uk

BROPHY, Anne (Aug 1991) (Director)
Brophy Carey & Co Ltd, Hamilton . . . .(p.1066)
T: 01698 200111
E: ab@brophycareylaw.com

BROPHY, Seonaid Catriona (Jan 2014) (Partner)
Thompsons, Glasgow . . . .(p.1046)
T: 0141 2218840
E: Seonaid.Brophy@thompsons-scotland.co.uk

BROTHERHOOD, Kelly Marie (Jun 2010)
(Associate)
Berrymans Lace Mawer LLP,
Glasgow. . . . .(p.945)
T: 0141 3532121
E: Kelly.Brotherhood@blmlaw.com

BROUGH, Cecilia Mary (Oct 1983) (Director)
Murdoch Stewarts Limited,
Glasgow. . . . .(p.1025)
T: 0141 226 3333
E: cbrough@murdochstewarts.co.uk

BROWN, Aileen Linda (Sept 2011) (Employee)
CMS Cameron McKenna Nabarro Olswang LLP,
London EC4 . . . .(p.1263)
T: 0207 3673000
E: aileen.brown@cms-cmno.com

BROWN, Alexander David (Sept 1996) (Partner)
Drummond Miller LLP, Edinburgh . . . . .(p.864)
T: 0131 2265151
E: dbrown@drummondmiller.co.uk

BROWN, Alison Margaret Shiach (Jan 1990)
(Employee)
Scottish Courts and Tribunals Service,
Edinburgh . . . .(p.1230)
T: 0131 2252525
E: ABrown2@scotcourts.gov.uk

BROWN, Amie (Sept 2016) (Associate)
MacRoberts LLP, Glasgow . . . .(p.1015)
T: 0141 3031100
E: amie.brown@macroberts.com

BROWN, Amy Elizabeth (Dec 2019) (Employee)
CMS Cameron McKenna Nabarro Olswang LLP,
Glasgow. . . . .(p.962)
T: 0141 2222200
E: Amy.brown@cms-cmno.com

BROWN, Andrew James William (Feb 2007)
(Partner)
Anderson Strathern LLP, Edinburgh . . . .(p.839)
T: 0131 2707700
E: andrew.brown@andersonstrathern.co.uk

BROWN, Andrew Norman (Mar 2020)
(Employee)
Procurator Fiscal Service, Paisley. . . . . .(p.1252)
T: 0141 8875225

BROWN, Andrew Roy Lazenby (Nov 1988)
(Employee)
Office of the Advocate General,
Edinburgh . . . .(p.1227)
T: 07857 656216
E: andrew.brown@advocategeneral.gov.uk

BROWN, Andrew Thomas (Jan 1995) (Partner)
Stevenson & Marshall LLP,
Dunfermline . . . .(p.825)
T: 01383 721141
E: atb@stevenson-marshall.co.uk

BROWN, Anna Bridgetta (Feb 1990) (Partner)
Addleshaw Goddard LLP,
Edinburgh . . . .(p.835)
T: 0131 2282400
E: Anna.Brown@addleshawgoddard.com

BROWN, Benjamin Ian (Nov 2020) (Employee)
Law at Work Ltd, Glasgow. . . . .(p.1240)
T: 0141 2715555
E: ben.brown@lawatwork.co.uk

BROWN, Catriona Emma Robertson
(Aug 2011) (Employee)
The Cranemere Group Limited, London
W1 . . . .(p.1268)

BROWN, Charles Robertson (Dec 1997)
(Partner)
Jones Whyte LLP, Glasgow. . . . .(p.993)
T: 0141 375 1222
E: charles.brown@joneswhyte.co.uk

BROWN, Cheryl Prentice (Oct 1986) (Partner)
McWhinney Richards, Airdrie . . . .(p.750)
T: 01236 754571
E: cheryl.brown@mcwhinneyrichards.com

BROWN, Claire Elizabeth Anne (Jun 2021)
(Employee)
Brodies LLP, Edinburgh . . . .(p.845)
T: 0131 2283777
E: claire.brown@brodies.com

BROWN, Claire Marie Wills (Jan 2019)
(Employee)
Lindsays LLP, Edinburgh . . . .(p.882)
T: 0131 2291212
E: clairebrown@lindsays.co.uk

BROWN, Colin Reid (Sept 1998) (Associate)
Burness Paull LLP, Edinburgh . . . .(p.850)
T: 0131 4736000
E: colin.brown@burnesspaull.com

BROWN, Craig (Aug 2008) (Employee)
Scottish Social Services Council,
Dundee . . . .(p.1218)
T: 0345 6030 891
E: craig.brown@sssc.uk.com

BROWN, Craig (Apr 2021) (Employee)
Ellis Whittam Limited, Glasgow . . . . . .(p.1239)
T: (0345) 226 8393
E: craigbrown@elliswhittam.com

BROWN, Craig (Jul 2010) (Partner)
Patten & Prentice LLP, Greenock . . . . .(p.1062)
T: 01475 720306
E: craigb@patten.co.uk

BROWN, Daniel Peter (Jan 2019) (Employee)
Dentons UK and Middle East LLP,
Glasgow. . . . .(p.968)
T: 0330 2220050
E: daniel.brown@dentons.com

BROWN, Derek Gardiner (Aug 1988)
(Employee)
Heriot-Watt University, Edinburgh . . . .(p.1223)
T: 0131 4513405
E: d.g.brown@hw.ac.uk

BROWN, Douglas Alexander (Dec 1985)
(Partner)
Tait & Mackenzie LLP,
Grangemouth . . . .(p.1059)
T: 01324 471121
E: db@taitandmackenzie.co.uk

BROWN, Emma (Aug 2018) (Employee)
EDF Energy, Croydon . . . .(p.1259)
T: 07809 593900

BROWN, Gerard Anthony (Oct 1973)
(Consultant)
Livingstone Brown Limited,
Glasgow. . . . .(p.1003)
T: 0141 4298166
E: gb@livbrown.co.uk

BROWN, Gilbert Angus (Sept 2016) (Employee)
Harper Macleod LLP, Inverness. . . . . . .(p.1077)
T: 01463 798777
E: Angus.Brown@harpermacleod.co.uk

BROWN, Gillian Jane (Aug 1988) (Partner)
Blackadders LLP, Glasgow . . . .(p.946)
T: 0141 2481888
E: gillian.brown@blackadders.co.uk

BROWN, Graeme Robert (Oct 2005)
(Consultant)
Bridge Legal Limited, Glasgow . . . . (p.948)
T: 0141 4293100
E: grbrown@bridgelitigationuk.com

BROWN, Hannah Erin (May 2018) (Employee)
Addleshaw Goddard LLP, Glasgow . . . . . (p.938)
T: 0141 2212300
E: hannah.brown@addleshawgoddard.com

BROWN, Hansa Elizabeth (Jun 2015)
(Employee)
Procurator Fiscal Service, Hamilton . . . . (p.1247)
T: 0844 5613245
E: Hansa.Brown@copfs.gov.uk

BROWN, Helena Anne (Oct 2000) (Partner)
Addleshaw Goddard LLP,
Edinburgh . . . . (p.835)
T: 0131 2282400
E: Helena.Brown@addleshawgoddard.com

BROWN, Iain Lindsay (Nov 2009) (Employee)
Ashurst LLP, Glasgow . . . . (p.1237)
T: 0141 375 4242
E: Iain.Brown@ashurst.com

BROWN, Iain Mackenzie (Nov 2019)
(Employee)
DLA Piper Scotland LLP, Edinburgh . . . . (p.863)
T: 08700 111111
E: iain.brown@dlapiper.com

BROWN, Iona Jane (Sept 1999) (Associate)
Digby Brown LLP, Ayr . . . . (p.761)
T: 0333 200 59285
E: iona.brown@digbybrown.co.uk

BROWN, Jill Anna (Oct 1999) (Employee)
Clydesdale Bank Plc, Glasgow . . . . (p.1238)
T: 1412423253
E: jill.brown@cybg.com

BROWN, John (Aug 1990) (Consultant)
John Brown (Scotland) Ltd,
Glasgow . . . . (p.951)
T: 0141 7810000
E: browns.solicitors@hotmail.co.uk

BROWN, John Edward (Jun 2011) (Employee)
Directorate of Army Legal Services,
Andover . . . . (p.1258)
T: 01980 615013
E: john.brown@westpoint.edu

BROWN, Jonathan Gregor (Nov 2003)
(Employee)
Scottish Government's Parliamentary Counsel
Office, Edinburgh . . . . (p.1233)
T: 0131 244 1665
E: jonathan.brown3@gov.scot

BROWN, Judith Alexandra (Oct 2000)
(Employee)
Scottish Government, Edinburgh . . . . . (p.1231)
T: 0131 244 0815
E: judith.brown@gov.scot

BROWN, Julie (Oct 2005) (Employee)
PRA Group (UK) Limited,
Kilmarnock . . . . (p.1249)
T: (07912) 467322
E: julie.brown@pragroup.co.uk

BROWN, Karl Alexander (Jan 1991) (Partner)
Aberdein Considine and Company,
Aberdeen . . . . (p.718)
T: 01224 589 700
E: kbrown@acandco.com

BROWN, Katie (Sept 2018) (Employee)
Gillespie Macandrew LLP,
Edinburgh . . . . (p.872)
T: 0131 2251677
E:
Katie.McCormack@gillespiemacandrew.co.uk

BROWN, Kelly (Sept 2011) (Employee)
Addleshaw Goddard LLP,
Edinburgh . . . . (p.835)
T: 0131 2282400
E: Kelly.Brown@addleshawgoddard.com

BROWN, Leann Marie (Apr 2010) (Employee)
RSB Lindsays, Dundee . . . . (p.818)
T: 01382 224112
E: LeannBrown@lindsays.co.uk

BROWN, Leslie Armour (Dec 1987) (Employee)
Procurator Fiscal Service, Hamilton . . . . (p.1247)
T: 0844 561 2707
E: les.brown@copfs.gov.uk

BROWN, Lindsey Louise (Jul 2009) (Partner)
Rollos Law LLP, Glenrothes . . . . (p.1058)
T: 01592 759414
E: lindseybrown@rollos.co.uk

BROWN, Lindsey Pirelli (Sept 2010) (Employee)
Accenture (UK) Limited, London
EC3 . . . . (p.1260)
E: lindsey.brown@accenture.com

BROWN, Lisa (Aug 1994) (Employee)
Alliance Trust PLC, Dundee . . . . (p.1217)
T: 01382 938320
E: lisa.brown@alliancetrust.co.uk

BROWN, Lorna Harriet (Feb 2001) (Director)
Caritas Legal Limited, Dunfermline . . . . (p.823)
T: 01383 431 101
E: lornabrown@caritaslegal.co.uk

BROWN, Lucy Catherine (Feb 2012) (Employee)
Lloyds Banking Group Plc,
Edinburgh . . . . (p.1224)
T: (0131) 442 9579

BROWN, Lynsey (Oct 2015) (Employee)
Harper Macleod LLP, Glasgow . . . .(p.983)
T: 0141 2218888
E: Lynsey.Brown@harpermacleod.co.uk

BROWN, Lynsey Clare (Oct 2007) (Employee)
East Dunbartonshire Council,
Kirkintilloch . . . .(p.1249)
T: 0141 5788000
E: lynsey.brown@eastdunbarton.gov.uk

BROWN, Lynsey Meiklem (Dec 2016)
(Employee)
Livingstone Brown Limited,
Glasgow. . . . .(p.1003)
T: 0141 4298166
E: Lynsey@livbrown.co.uk

BROWN, Martin Stuart (Oct 2018) (Employee)
Scottish Government, Edinburgh . . . . .(p.1231)
T: 0131 244 0815
E: martin.brown3@gov.scot

BROWN, Mhairi Margaret (Dec 2020)
(Employee)
DAC Beachcroft Scotland LLP,
Glasgow. . . . .(p.964)
T: 0141 2486688
E: mhabrown@dacbeachcroft.com

BROWN, Michael Andrew (Nov 1975) (Partner)
Michael A Brown Solicitors,
Dundee . . . .(p.806)
T: 01382 204242
E: law@michaelabrown.co.uk

BROWN, Monica Anne (Sept 1998) (Partner)
The Kerr Brown Partnership,
Glasgow. . . . .(p.1044)
T: 0141 2214880
E: mb@kerrbrown.co.uk

BROWN, Nicola O'Donnell (Aug 1994)
(Employee)
Public Defence Solicitors Office,
Dundee . . . .(p.1218)
T: 01382 226051
E: nbrown@pdso.org.uk

BROWN, Nicola Tamara (Dec 1992) (Associate)
Blackadders LLP, Aberdeen . . . .(p.722)
T: 01224 588913
E: Nicola.brown@blackadders.co.uk

BROWN, Paul Daniel (Aug 2000) (Director)
Hay Cassels Ltd, Hamilton . . . .(p.1067)
T: 01698 284844
E: pbrown@haycassels.com

BROWN, Paul David (Jan 1982) (Partner)
Brown & Co Legal LLP, Glasgow . . . . . .(p.950)
T: 0141 3533354
E: paulbrown@lsa.org.uk

BROWN, Paul James (Oct 1990) (Employee)
Glasgow Caledonian University,
Glasgow. . . . .(p.1239)
E: paul.brown@gcu.ac.uk

BROWN, Paul Lawrence (Sept 1992)
(Employee)
W. & J.S. Gordon, Forfar . . . .(p.926)
T: 01307 462188
E: pbrown@wjsgordon.co.uk

BROWN, Paula Lorraine (Oct 2011) (Employee)
ISG Central Services Limited,
Glasgow. . . . .(p.1240)
E: paula.brown@isgltd.com

BROWN, Raymond Leslie (Aug 1987) (Director)
Hay Cassels Ltd, Hamilton . . . .(p.1067)
T: 01698 284844
E: rbrown@haycassels.com

BROWN, Richard Lauchlan (Sept 2013)
(Employee)
Procurator Fiscal Service,
Edinburgh . . . .(p.1229)
T: 0300 0203000
E: Richard.Brown@copfs.gov.uk

BROWN, Ronald Walter (Nov 1984) (Partner)
Burness Paull LLP, Glasgow . . . .(p.954)
T: 0141 2484933
E: Ronnie.Brown@burnesspaull.com

BROWN, Rory David (Mar 2021) (Employee)
Digby Brown LLP, Edinburgh . . . .(p.862)
T: 0333 200 5925
E: rory.brown@digbybrown.co.uk

BROWN, Ross Alexander (Oct 2008) (Partner)
BTO Solicitors LLP, Glasgow . . . .(p.952)
T: 0141 2218012
E: rbr@bto.co.uk

BROWN, Ross James Elrick (Oct 1983) (Partner)
Dunipace Brown, Kilsyth . . . .(p.1097)
T: 01236 826147
E: ross@dunipacebrown.co.uk

BROWN, Samantha (Jul 2013) (Employee)
Procurator Fiscal Service, Falkirk . . . . . .(p.1236)
T: 0300 020 3000
E: Samantha.Brown@copfs.gov.uk

BROWN, Sarah Margaret (Jan 2013) (Partner)
J & H Mitchell LLP, Pitlochry . . . .(p.1155)
T: 01796 472606
E: sarah.brown@hmitchell.co.uk

BROWN, Scott Alexander (Jan 1993) (Partner)
Warners Solicitors LLP, Edinburgh. . . . . .(p.911)
T: 0131 6624747
E: sbrown@warnersllp.com

BROWN, Selena Campbell (Jun 2004)
(Employee)
Procurator Fiscal Service, Glasgow . . . .(p.1241)
T: 0300 0203000
E: Selena.Brown@copfs.gov.uk

BROWN, Shona Margaret (Oct 1995) (Partner)
Balfour + Manson LLP, Edinburgh . . . . .(p.841)
T: 0131 2001203
E: Shona.Brown@balfour-manson.co.uk

BROWN, Shonagh Margaret (Feb 2011)
(Employee)
Pinsent Masons LLP, Aberdeen . . . .(p.739)
T: 01224 377900
E: shonagh.brown@pinsentmasons.com

BROWN, Simon David (Oct 1996) (Partner)
Matthew Brown, Irvine . . . .(p.1087)
T: 01294 273721
E: simon@matthewbrownsolicitors.co.uk

BROWN, Simon Thomas David, WS
(Dec 1986) (Partner)
Anderson Strathern LLP, Edinburgh . . . .(p.839)
T: 0131 2707700
E: simon.brown@andersonstrathern.co.uk

BROWN, Siobhan Catherine (Oct 2021)
(Employee)
Clarity Simplicity Ltd, Glasgow . . . .(p.960)
T: 0141 4332626
E: s.brown@claritysimplicity.co.uk

BROWN, Sophie (Jun 2020) (Associate)
CMS Cameron McKenna Nabarro Olswang LLP,
Aberdeen . . . .(p.727)
T: 01224 622002
E: sophie.brown@cms-cmno.com

BROWN, Stephanie Laura MacKenzie
(Jun 2011) (Employee)
Scottish Social Services Council,
Dundee . . . .(p.1218)
T: 0345 6030 891
E: stephanie.brown@sssc.uk.com

BROWN, Stewart David (Nov 1998) (Employee)
Artemis Investment Management LLP,
Edinburgh . . . .(p.1220)
T: 0131 7180441
E: stewart.brown@artemisfunds.com

BROWN, Susan Margaret (Aug 1989)
(Employee)
Procurator Fiscal Service, Glasgow . . . .(p.1241)
T: 0300 0203000
E: Susan.Brown@copfs.gov.uk

BROWN, Tracey Kathryn Elizabeth
(Aug 1998) (Consultant)
Matthew Brown, Irvine . . . .(p.1087)
T: 01294 273721
E: tkebrown@outlook.com

BROWN, Victoria (Oct 2010) (Employee)
Turcan Connell, Edinburgh . . . .(p.908)
T: 0131 2288111
E: victoria.brown@turcanconnell.com

BROWN, Vincent (Dec 1983) (Director)
Vincent Brown Limited, Erskine . . . .(p.920)
T: 07740 877627
E: vincent@vincentbrownlaw.com

BROWNE, Laura Margaret (Jun 2009) (Partner)
Aberdein Considine and Company,
Glasgow. . . . .(p.937)
T: 0141 2278200
E: lbrowne@acandco.com

BROWNE, Lesley Ann (Aug 2004) (Employee)
Scottish Hospital Inquiry, Glasgow . . . .(p.1244)
E: lesley.browne@hospitalsinquiry.scot

BROWNE, Wilson Forbes (Dec 2015) (Partner)
Coulters Legal LLP, Edinburgh . . . .(p.858)
T: 0131 603 7333
E: wilson.browne@coulters.io

BROWNLEE, Natasha (Mar 2013) (Associate)
Burness Paull LLP, Edinburgh . . . .(p.850)
T: 0131 4736000
E: Natasha.Brownlee@burnesspaull.com

BROWNLIE, Christine Jane (Dec 2019)
(Employee)
Procurator Fiscal Service,
Edinburgh . . . .(p.1227)
T: 0300 0203168
E: Christine.Brownlie@copfs.gov.uk

BROWNLIE, William Kirkwood Loudon
(Dec 1990) (Partner)
Stirling & Gilmour LLP,
Helensburgh. . . . .(p.1073)
T: 01436 678185
E: l.brownlie@stirlingandgilmour.co.uk

BRUBAKER, Rachel Hutchinson (Jan 2016)
(Employee)
Legal Secretariat to the Lord Advocate,
Edinburgh . . . .(p.1224)
T: (0300) 020 3364
E: rachel.brubaker@gov.scot

BRUCE, Allison Elizabeth (Dec 2014) (Associate)
TLT LLP, Glasgow . . . .(p.1048)
T: 0333 006 0400
E: allison.bruce@tltsolicitors.com

BRUCE, Amy Rosalind (Nov 2015) (Solicitor)
NO FIRM

BRUCE, Andrew Buchan (Jul 2007) (Associate)
Raeburn Christie Clark & Wallace LLP,
Ellon . . . .(p.919)
T: 01358 720777
E: Andrew.Bruce@raeburns.co.uk

BRUCE, Angela West (Jan 1987) (Partner)
Gavin Bain & Co., Aberdeen . . . .(p.721)
T: 01224 623040
E: a.bruce@gavin-bain.co.uk

BRUCE, Ashleigh (Aug 2011) (Employee)
CMS Cameron McKenna Nabarro Olswang LLP,
Dubai . . . .(p.1278)
T: +971 4374 2813
E: ashleigh.bruce@cms-cmno.com

BRUCE, Claire Patricia (Nov 2015) (Employee)
Burness Paull LLP, Aberdeen . . . .(p.724)
T: 01224 621621
E: claire.bruce@burnesspaull.com

BRUCE, David Grant (Aug 2001) (Employee)
R. Bruce & Co., Arbroath . . . .(p.757)
T: 01241 430660
E: info@bruce-co.co.uk

BRUCE, Denise Josephine (Aug 1990)
(Employee)
Procurator Fiscal Service, Hamilton . . . .(p.1247)
T: 0844 5613245
E: denise.bruce@copfs.gov.uk

BRUCE, Diarmid Noel (Sept 1993) (Director)
Bruce McCormack Limited,
Motherwell . . . .(p.1127)
T: 01698 260033
E: admin@brucethelawyers.co.uk

BRUCE, Elizabeth Janette Simpson
(Aug 1999) (Associate)
Brodies LLP, Edinburgh . . . .(p.845)
T: 0131 2283777
E: liz.bruce@brodies.com

BRUCE, Euan (Sept 2017) (Employee)
Sheku Bayoh Public Inquiry,
Edinburgh . . . .(p.1233)
E: euan.bruce@shekubayohinquiry.scot

BRUCE, Euan Alan (Nov 2011) (Employee)
DLA Piper Scotland LLP, Edinburgh . . . .(p.863)
T: 08700 111111
E: euan.bruce@dlapiper.com

BRUCE, Felicity Serena (Apr 2021) (Employee)
Innes Johnston LLP, Kirkcaldy . . . .(p.1100)
T: 01592 263455
E: fbruce@innesjohnston.co.uk

BRUCE, Graeme Murray (Jan 1983) (Partner)
CMS Cameron McKenna Nabarro Olswang LLP,
Glasgow. . . . .(p.962)
T: 0141 2222200
E: Graeme.Bruce@cms-cmno.com

BRUCE, Hannah Kate (Jul 2009) (Employee)
Clydesdale Bank Plc, Glasgow . . . .(p.1238)
T: 0141 2423733
E: hannah.bruce@cybg.com

BRUCE, Hannah May (Aug 2017) (Employee)
Shepherd and Wedderburn LLP,
Glasgow. . . . .(p.1039)
T: 0141 5669900
E: hannah.bruce@shepwedd.com

BRUCE, Heather Catherine (Aug 2007)
(Employee)
Turcan Connell, Edinburgh . . . .(p.908)
T: 0131 2288111
E: heather.bruce@turcanconnell.com

BRUCE, Jonathan David Robertson
(Sept 2015) (Employee)
Scottish Water, Dunfermline . . . .(p.1219)
T: (01383) 665410
E: jonathan.bruce@scottishwater.co.uk

BRUCE, Kenneth (Nov 1978) (Solicitor)
NO FIRM

BRUCE, Laura Margaret (Oct 2001) (Employee)
Procurator Fiscal Service,
Edinburgh . . . .(p.1229)
T: 0300 0203000
E: laura.bruce@copfs.gov.uk

BRUCE, Lindsay Jane (Nov 2008) (Associate)
Lefevres (Scotland) Limited,
Edinburgh . . . .(p.882)
T: 0845 305 2555
E: LJB@lefevres.law

BRUCE, Martin John (Nov 2007) (Employee)
FNZ, Edinburgh . . . .(p.1223)
T: 0131 5241900
E: Martin.Bruce@fnz.co.uk

BRUCE, Matthew Alexander (Oct 2016)
(Employee)
Brodies LLP, Edinburgh . . . .(p.845)
T: 0131 2283777
E: matthew.bruce@brodies.com

BRUCE, Natalie Dawn (Nov 2013) (Employee)
Harper Macleod LLP, Inverness. . . . . . .(p.1077)
T: 01463 798777
E: natalie.bruce@harpermacleod.co.uk

BRUCE, Neil Thomas (Oct 2008) (Partner)
Burness Paull LLP, Edinburgh . . . .(p.850)
T: 0131 4736000
E: Neil.Bruce@burnesspaull.com

BRUCE, Nigel (Oct 1990) (Partner)
Adams Whyte, Edinburgh . . . .(p.835)
T: 0131 555 7220
E: nigelbruce@adamswhyte.com

BRUCE, Rachel (Oct 2021) (Employee)
Brown & McRae LLP, Fraserburgh . . . . .(p.930)
T: 01346 514761
E: r.bruce@brown-mcrae.co.uk

BRUCE, Vivienne Margaret (Sept 2007)
(Employee)
James & George Collie LLP,
Aberdeen . . . .(p.728)
T: 01224 581581
E: v.bruce@jgcollie.co.uk

BRUNGER, Alison (Jul 2017) (Employee)
Burness Paull LLP, Edinburgh . . . . (p.850)
  T: 0131 4736000
  E: alison.brunger@burnesspaull.com

BRUNTON, Jennifer Margaret (Sept 2020)
(Employee)
Walkers, St Helier . . . . (p.1274)
  T: (01534) 700723
  E: jbrunton@walkersglobal.com

BRYAN, Lewis Greig (Nov 2020) (Employee)
Sneddon Morrison, Bathgate . . . . (p.772)
  T: 01506 635590
  E: lewis.bryan@sneddons-ssc.co.uk

BRYCE, Alasdair David (Feb 1995) (Partner)
Pollock & McLean, Dumfries . . . . (p.802)
  T: 01387 255414
  E: alasdairbryce@pollockmclean.co.uk

BRYCE, Alida Delmaestro (Nov 1986) (Partner)
Munro & Noble, Inverness . . . . (p.1080)
  T: 01463 221727
  E: Alidab@munronoble.com

BRYCE, Alison Helen (Sept 1999) (Partner)
Dentons UK and Middle East LLP,
  Glasgow. . . . . (p.968)
  T: 0330 2220050
  E: Alison.Bryce@dentons.com

BRYCE, Ian George (Aug 1993) (Consultant)
Central Court Lawyers, Livingston . . . . (p.1118)
  T: 01506 416999
  E: ianbryce@centralcourtlawyers.co.uk

BRYCE MACKAY, Lindsay Davina Frances
(Nov 2012) (Solicitor)
Gillespie Macandrew LLP, Perth . . . . . . (p.1148)
  T: 01738 231000
  E:
  lindsay.brycemackay@gillespiemacandrew.co.
  uk

BRYCELAND, Ryan Thomas Drury
(May 2019) (Employee)
Freelands, Motherwell . . . . (p.1126)
  T: 01698 352600
  E: rbryceland@freelands.co.uk

BRYCELAND, Stephen Charles (Nov 1996)
(Partner)
BTO Solicitors LLP, Glasgow . . . . (p.952)
  T: 0141 2218012
  E: sbr@bto.co.uk

BRYDEN, David James (Nov 2013) (Employee)
Pinsent Masons LLP, Edinburgh . . . . . . (p.895)
  T: 0131 777 7000
  E: David.Bryden@pinsentmasons.com

BRYDEN, James (Oct 2009) (Employee)
Taylor Wessing LLP, London EC4 . . . . . (p.1268)
  T: 020 7300 4995
  E: j.bryden@taylorwessing.com

BRYDEN, Julia Helen (Oct 2008) (Employee)
Medical Protection Society, Leeds. . . . . (p.1260)
  E: Julia.Bryden@medicalprotection.org

BRYDEN, Victoria (Aug 2008) (Employee)
Reed Smith LLP, London EC2 . . . . (p.1267)
  E: vbryden@reedsmith.com

BRYDON, Kenneth Dick (Nov 1976)
(Consultant)
Blair Cadell, Edinburgh . . . . (p.844)
  T: 0131 555 5800
  E: ken.brydon@blaircadell.com

BRYMER, Louise Jane (Oct 2013) (Associate)
CMS Cameron McKenna Nabarro Olswang LLP,
  Glasgow. . . . . (p.962)
  T: 0141 2222200
  E: Louise.Brymer@cms-cmno.com

BRYMER, Professor, Stewart, OBE
(Oct 1981) (Director)
Brymer Legal Limited, Edinburgh . . . . . . (p.848)
  T: 7801034530
  E: stewart@brymerlegal.co.uk

BRYNES, Alison (Mar 2006) (Partner)
TC Young LLP, Glasgow . . . . (p.1055)
  T: 0141 2215562
  E: ahb@tcyoung.co.uk

BRYSON, Andrew John (Mar 1990) (Director)
Nelsons Solicitors Falkirk Limited,
  Falkirk . . . . (p.923)
  T: 01324 613316
  E: andy@nelsonslawyers.co.uk

BRYSON, David Steele (Nov 1999) (Employee)
Baillie Gifford & Co, Edinburgh . . . . . . (p.1220)
  T: 0131 275 3122
  E: david.bryson@bailliegifford.com

BRYSON, Donna (Sept 2004) (Associate)
Morton Fraser LLP, Glasgow . . . . (p.1022)
  T: 0141 2741100
  E: donna.bryson@morton-fraser.com

BRYSON, Fiona Margaret Lindsay
(Aug 1985) (Partner)
Robert Ferguson & Sons, Hamilton. . . . (p.1066)
  T: 01698 282551
  E: fiona@robert-ferguson-solicitors.co.uk

BRYSON, Graham Robert (Nov 1982) (Partner)
Bryson's Legal Services, Glasgow . . . . . . (p.952)
  T: 07841 875853
  E: Brysonlegal@aol.com

BRYSON, Linsey (Oct 2019) (Employee)
Gallen & Company Ltd, Glasgow. . . . . . (p.978)
  T: 0141 4201441
  E: linsey.bryson@gallenandco.com

BRYSON, Lynn Jane (Feb 1990) (Associate)
Drummond Miller LLP, Edinburgh . . . . . (p.864)
  T: 0131 2265151
  E: lbryson@drummondmiller.co.uk

BUCHAN, Alexander Dalrymple Stewart
(Nov 1996) (Partner)
Brodies LLP, Edinburgh . . . .(p.845)
T: 0131 2283777
E: alex.buchan@brodies.com

BUCHAN, Andrew John (Jun 1997) (Employee)
Scottish Equity Partners LLP,
Glasgow . . . .(p.1243)
T: 0141 2734000
E: andrew.buchan@sep.co.uk

BUCHAN, Ashleigh (Jun 2020) (Employee)
Andersonbain LLP, Aberdeen . . . .(p.721)
T: 01224 456789

BUCHAN, Erica (Oct 2005) (Associate)
Ledingham Chalmers LLP,
Aberdeen . . . .(p.734)
T: 01224 408408
E: erica.buchan@ledinghamchalmers.com

BUCHAN, Gavin James Alexander
(Nov 2002) (Partner)
Lindsays LLP, Edinburgh . . . .(p.882)
T: 0131 2291212
E: gavinbuchan@lindsays.co.uk

BUCHAN, Iain James (Jul 2021) (Employee)
Thorntons Law LLP, Dundee . . . .(p.819)
T: 01382 229 111
E: ibuchan@thorntons-law.co.uk

BUCHAN, Jan (Jan 2007) (Employee)
Aberdeen Corporate Services Limited,
Edinburgh . . . .(p.1220)
T: 0131 245 7508
E: jan.buchan@abrdn.com

BUCHAN, John Scott (Dec 1991) (Partner)
BTO Solicitors LLP, Glasgow . . . .(p.952)
T: 0141 2218012
E: jsb@bto.co.uk

BUCHAN, Laura (Nov 2003) (Employee)
Procurator Fiscal Service,
Edinburgh . . . .(p.1229)
T: 0300 0203000
E: laura.buchan@copfs.gov.uk

BUCHAN, Lauren Margaret Catherine
(Oct 2015) (Employee)
Dentsu International Limited, London
NW1 . . . .(p.1263)
E: lauren.buchan@dentsu.com

BUCHAN, Lorna Gilmore (Sept 1994) (Partner)
Patience & Buchan, Aberdeen . . . .(p.739)
T: 01224 648222
E: lorna@patienceandbuchan.com

BUCHAN, Paul Andrew (Aug 2006) (Partner)
Dickson Minto, London EC2 . . . .(p.1263)
T: 020 76284455
E: paul.buchan@dmws.com

BUCHAN, Philip Stanley (May 2005)
(Employee)
Blackadders LLP, Edinburgh . . . .(p.843)
T: 0131 2228000
E: Phil.Buchan@blackadders.co.uk

BUCHAN, Robert James Nicol (Oct 2007)
(Solicitor)
NO FIRM

BUCHAN, Staci Ann (Jun 2016) (Employee)
Brown & McRae LLP, Fraserburgh . . . . .(p.930)
T: 01346 514761
E: Staci-Ann@brown-mcrae.co.uk

BUCHAN, Ulrike (Oct 2012) (Employee)
Aberdeen Corporate Services Limited,
Edinburgh . . . .(p.1220)
T: 0131 245 7508
E: ulrike.buchan@abrdn.com

BUCHANAN, Amanda Mary (Jan 1996)
(Employee)
Levy & McRae Solicitors LLP,
Glasgow . . . .(p.1000)
T: 0141 3072311
E: abuchanan@lemac.co.uk

BUCHANAN, Bethany (Dec 2020) (Employee)
Blackadders LLP, Dundee . . . .(p.805)
T: 01382 229222
E: bethany.buchanan@blackadders.co.uk

BUCHANAN, Chloe Alexis (Feb 2014) (Solicitor)
NO FIRM

BUCHANAN, Derek Henderson (Sept 1995)
(Director)
Westcourts Litigation Ltd,
Greenock . . . .(p.1063)
T: 01475 601999
E: dbuchanan@westcourts.co.uk

BUCHANAN, Derek John (Sept 1986)
(Employee)
Procurator Fiscal Service, Glasgow . . . .(p.1241)
T: 0300 0203000
E: derek.buchanan@copfs.gov.uk

BUCHANAN, Fiona Murray (Jun 1998) (Partner)
Shepherd and Wedderburn LLP,
Edinburgh . . . .(p.900)
T: 0131 2289900
E: Fiona.Buchanan@shepwedd.com

BUCHANAN, Gillian Coutts (Aug 1990)
(Partner)
Thorntons Law LLP, Dundee . . . .(p.819)
T: 01382 229 111
E: gbuchanan@thorntons-law.co.uk

BUCHANAN, Gillian May (Oct 2013)
(Employee)
Shepherd and Wedderburn LLP,
Edinburgh . . . .(p.900)
T: 0131 2289900
E: Gillian.Buchanan@shepwedd.com

BUCHANAN, Heather Anne (Sept 1997)
(Employee)
Clackmannanshire Council, Alloa . . . . . (p.1215)
T: 01259 450000
E: HBuchanan@clacks.gov.uk

BUCHANAN, Jacqueline Margaret
(Jan 1990) (Employee)
Angus Council, Forfar . . . . (p.1237)
T: 01307 476228
E: BuchananJ@angus.gov.uk

BUCHANAN, John (Nov 1979) (Director)
Buchanan Burton Limited, East
Kilbride . . . . (p.830)
T: 01355 249228
E: ianb@buchananburton.co.uk

BUCHANAN, John Murray Stevenson
(Oct 1989) (Employee)
Shell International Limited,
Aberdeen . . . . (p.1214)
T: 01224 882000
E: murray.buchanan@shell.com

BUCHANAN, Karen Elaine (Sept 1987) (Partner)
Buchanan Macleod, Glasgow . . . . (p.953)
T: 0141 2214440
E: KBuchanan@buchananmacleod.co.uk

BUCHANAN, Kristopher Ross (Apr 2013)
(Employee)
Scullion Law Limited, Hamilton . . . . . . (p.1069)
T: 01698 283265
E: krisbuchanan@scullionlaw.com

BUCHANAN, Lauren (Sept 2019) (Employee)
Garden Stirling Burnet Solicitors Limited,
Haddington . . . . (p.1064)
T: 01620 824996
E: lbuchanan@gsbsolicitors.co.uk

BUCHANAN, Murray John (Aug 1994)
(Employee)
Two Rivers Media Ltd, Glasgow . . . . . . (p.1245)
E: murray.buchanan@tworiversmedia.co.uk

BUCHANAN, Nicola Jean (Oct 1994)
(Employee)
Scullion Law Limited, Hamilton . . . . . . (p.1069)
T: 01698 283265
E: nicola@scullionlaw.com

BUCHANAN, Rebecka (Aug 2018) (Employee)
Government Legal Department, London
SW1 . . . . (p.1264)
T: (020) 7210 1476
E: rebecka.buchanan@defra.gov.uk

BUCHANAN, Sadaf (Apr 1999) (Employee)
Dentons & Co, Ruwi . . . . (p.1275)
T: +968 2457 3000
E: Sadaf.Buchanan@dentons.com

BUCHANAN, Victoria Anne (Oct 2008)
(Partner)
Jameson + Mackay LLP, Perth . . . . (p.1148)
T: 01738 631666
E: Victoria.Buchanan@jamesonmackay.co.uk

BUCKINGHAM, Nathaniel Thomas
(Sept 2014) (Employee)
Shepherd and Wedderburn LLP,
Edinburgh . . . . (p.900)
T: 0131 2289900
E: Nathaniel.Buckingham@shepwedd.com

BUICK, Gregor Robert, WS (Jul 2000)
(Employee)
Church of Scotland, Edinburgh . . . . . . (p.1221)
T: 0131 2255722
E: gbuick@churchofscotland.org.uk

BUIST, Elaine Marie (Aug 1991) (Employee)
Black & Markie, Dunfermline . . . . (p.822)
T: 01383 610 547
E: blackandmarkie@hotmail.com

BUIST, Kyrsten Leona (Jun 2012) (Employee)
Procurator Fiscal Service,
Edinburgh . . . . (p.1227)
T: 0300 020 3000.
E: Kyrsten.Buist@copfs.gov.uk

BUIST, Paul Alexander (Dec 1991) (Partner)
Smith & Grant, Leven . . . . (p.1116)
T: 01333 423441
E: paul@smithandgrant.com

BUJANDA-VALIENTE, Vladimir Ernesto
(Sept 2008) (Employee)
Dumfries & Galloway Council,
Dumfries . . . . (p.1217)
T: 01387 245 903
E: vlad.valiente@dumgal.gov.uk

BULCHENKO, Ella (Mar 2009) (Employee)
MTL Law, Glasgow . . . . (p.1024)
T: 0141 2225793
E: ella@mtllaw.co.uk

BULL-CLEARIE, Jennifer Sarah (Nov 2012)
(Employee)
AutoRek, Glasgow . . . . (p.1238)
E: jen.bull-clearie@autorek.com

BULPITT, James Edward (Sept 2012)
(Employee)
Shepherd and Wedderburn LLP,
Edinburgh . . . . (p.900)
T: 0131 2289900
E: james.bulpitt@shepwedd.com

BUONACCORSI, Marco Carlo (Jun 2005)
(Employee)
Public Defence Solicitors Office,
Glasgow . . . . (p.1243)
T: 0141 5530794
E: mbuonaccorsi@pdso.org.uk

BURBIDGE, Natasha Chalaki (Jan 2014)
(Associate)
Osborne Clarke, Bristol . . . .(p.1259)
T: 0117 917 3108
E: natasha.burbidge@osborneclarke.com

BURD, Duncan McKinnon (Aug 1985)
(Director)
Anderson, MacArthur Limited,
  Portree. . . . .(p.1156)
T: 01478 612197
E: dmburd@amac.co.uk

BURDEN, Colette Catherine Maria
(May 2004) (Employee)
Addleshaw Goddard LLP,
  Edinburgh . . . .(p.835)
T: 0131 2282400
E: colette.burden@addleshawgoddard.com

BURDEN, Fiona (Jan 1998) (Employee)
Tesco Personal Finance Plc,
  Edinburgh . . . .(p.1234)
T: (0131) 274 3426
E: Fiona.Burden@i.tescobank.com

BURGESS, Anthony John (Oct 2003) (Partner)
Just Defence Law Practice,
  Aberdeen . . . .(p.733)
T: 01224 644999
E: info@jdlp.org.uk

BURGESS, Neil Ross (Nov 1995) (Partner)
Brodies LLP, Glasgow . . . .(p.948)
T: 0141 2484672
E: neil.burgess@brodies.com

BURGOYNE, Laura Katrina (Aug 2007)
(Employee)
Law Commission, London SW1 . . . . . .(p.1266)
T: 0203 3345327
E: laura.burgoyne@lawcommission.gov.uk

BURKE, Aileen (Nov 2005) (Employee)
Ocean Winds UK Limited,
  Edinburgh . . . .(p.1227)
T: 0131 5567602
E: aileen.burke@oceanwinds.com

BURKE, Iain Thomas (Sept 1991) (Partner)
Burke Legal, Galashiels . . . .(p.932)
T: 01896 750350
E: iain@burkelegal.co.uk

BURKE, Jennifer (Dec 1998) (Employee)
National Westminster Bank PLC,
  Edinburgh . . . .(p.1226)
T: (0131) 626 2925
E: Jennifer.Burke@natwest.com

BURKE, Kieran Robert (Sept 2006) (Employee)
Scottish Legal Aid Board,
  Edinburgh . . . .(p.1233)
T: 0131 2267061

BURKE, Kirstyn Faye (Nov 2013) (Associate)
Brodies LLP, Glasgow . . . .(p.948)
T: 0141 2484672
E: kirstyn.burke@brodies.com

BURKE, Leonie Sarah Rose (Sept 2001)
(Partner)
Aberdein Considine and Company,
  Edinburgh . . . .(p.833)
T: 0333 004 4333
E: lburke@acandco.com

BURKE, Lynne (Oct 2000) (Associate)
Ledingham Chalmers LLP,
  Aberdeen . . . .(p.734)
T: 01224 408408
E: lynne.burke@ledinghamchalmers.com

BURKINSHAW, Leonard James (Aug 1988)
(Partner)
Burkinshaw Criminal Defence,
  Peterhead. . . . .(p.1153)
T: 01779 476453
E: burkinshaws@outlook.com

BURLEIGH, Alistair John, WS (Mar 1982)
(Employee)
Adams Whyte, Livingston . . . .(p.1117)
T: 01506 401999

BURLEY, Ruth Alexandra (Dec 2015)
(Employee)
South Ayrshire Council, Ayr . . . .(p.1215)
T: 01292 612420
E: ruth.burley@south-ayrshire.gov.uk

BURN, Alexander McLennan (Sept 1996)
(Partner)
Burn & McGregor, Aberdeen . . . .(p.726)
T: 01224 639660
E: alex.b-m@btconnect.com

BURN, Jenny Marion Ione (Apr 2016)
(Employee)
Eversheds Sutherland (International) LLP,
  Edinburgh . . . .(p.869)
T: 0207 9194500
E: jennyburn@eversheds-sutherland.com

BURNET, Lorna (Sept 2003) (Employee)
Sainsbury's Bank plc, Edinburgh. . . . . .(p.1230)
T: (0131) 286 0807

BURNETT, Douglas (Jan 1977) (Director)
Burnett Legal Services Limited,
  Aberdeen . . . .(p.726)
T: 01224 648797

BURNETT, Heather Elizabeth (Aug 2015)
(Employee)
Turcan Connell, Edinburgh . . . .(p.908)
T: 0131 2288111
E: heather.burnett@turcanconnell.com

BURNETT, Jennifer Ann (Aug 2002)
(Consultant)
Raeburn Christie Clark & Wallace LLP,
Ellon ....(p.919)
T: 01358 720777
E: Jennifer.Burnett@raeburns.co.uk

BURNETT, Kendall Laurie (Mar 2011)
(Employee)
Latham & Watkins (London) LLP, London
EC2........................(p.1266)
T: 020 7710 1000
E: kendall.burnett@lw.com

BURNETT, Michael Ian James (Aug 2008)
(Partner)
Burnett Criminal Defence,
Aberdeen ....(p.725)
T: 07515 964194
E: mike@burnettcriminaldefence.co.uk

BURNETT, Seona Anne (Aug 1994) (Employee)
Vialex Limited, Edinburgh ....(p.1235)
T: 0333 2400127
E: seona.burnett@vialex.co.uk

BURNETT, Victoria Elizabeth (May 2010)
(Employee)
Burnett & Reid LLP, Banchory ....(p.768)
T: 01330 828684
E: victoria.burnett@burnett-reid.co.uk

BURNHAM, Yvonne Glenison (Apr 2003)
(Associate)
Holmes Mackillop Limited,
Glasgow....................(p.986)
T: 0141 226 4942
E: yburnham@homack.co.uk

BURNS, Alan George Robert (Apr 2019)
(Associate)
MacRoberts LLP, Edinburgh ....(p.887)
T: 0131 2295046
E: alan.burns@macroberts.com

BURNS, Alison Ruth (Oct 1999) (Employee)
P3 Music Limited, Alyth ....(p.1215)
T: 01828 632133
E: alison@p3music.com

BURNS, Andrew James (Jul 2019) (Employee)
Latta Law Limited, Glasgow..........(p.998)
T: 0141 222 2185
E: ab@lattalaw.co.uk

BURNS, Austen Purdie (Feb 2015) (Employee)
Gillespie Macandrew LLP,
Edinburgh ....(p.872)
T: 0131 2251677
E: Austen.burns@gillespiemacandrew.co.uk

BURNS, Carolyn Helen (May 2003) (Associate)
Dentons UK and Middle East LLP,
Glasgow....................(p.968)
T: 0330 2220050
E: Carolyn.Burns@dentons.com

BURNS, Eileen (Dec 1986) (Employee)
Scottish Courts and Tribunals Service,
Paisley ....(p.1252)
T: 0141 8875291
E: eburns@scotcourts.gov.uk

BURNS, Emma (Aug 2021) (Employee)
Brophy Carey & Co Ltd, Hamilton ....(p.1066)
T: 01698 200111

BURNS, Isla Russell Urquhart (Sept 2018)
(Employee)
Pinsent Masons LLP, Glasgow ....(p.1031)
T: 0141 567 8400
E: isla.burns@pinsentmasons.com

BURNS, Jennifer (Aug 1983) (Employee)
Angus Council, Forfar ....(p.1237)
T: 01307 476228
E: BurnsJ1@angus.gov.uk

BURNS, Jennifer Louise (Jul 2015) (Associate)
MacRoberts LLP, Glasgow ....(p.1015)
T: 0141 3031100
E: jennifer.burns@macroberts.com

BURNS, Katie Isabella (Jun 2017) (Employee)
McEwan Fraser Legal, Edinburgh ......(p.885)
T: 0131 5249797
E: katie.burns@mcewanfraserlegal.co.uk

BURNS, Lesa (Jul 2005) (Employee)
SSE PLC, Glasgow................(p.1244)
T: 0141 224 7248
E: lesa.burns@sse.com

BURNS, Martin David Cameron (Oct 1991)
(Director)
Bathgate Family Law Practice Limited,
Bathgate ....(p.770)
T: 01506 656820
E: mdcb@bathgateflp.co.uk

BURNS, Martine Mary (Sept 1998) (Employee)
Vodafone Group Enterprise Limited,
Glasgow....................(p.1245)
T: 0141 3032141
E: martine.burns@vodafone.com

BURNS, Maureen Anne (Aug 2006) (Associate)
Brodies LLP, Glasgow ....(p.948)
T: 0141 2484672
E: maureen.burns@brodies.com

BURNS, Michelle (Nov 2008) (Employee)
Thorntons Law LLP, Dundee ....(p.819)
T: 01382 229 111
E: mburns@thorntons-law.co.uk

BURNS, Robert (Jan 1997) (Partner)
Burness Paull LLP, Edinburgh ....(p.850)
T: 0131 4736000
E: Robert.Burns@burnesspaull.com

BURNS, Rona Estelle (Aug 2018) (Employee)
Boyd Legal Limited, Edinburgh ....(p.845)
T: 0131 2267464
E: rona.burns@boydlegaluk.com

BURNS, Sarah Elizabeth (Jul 2019) (Employee)
Mourant Ozannes, St Helier . . . . (p.1274)
T: 1481731513
E: sarah.burns@mourantozannes.com

BURNS, Scott John (Oct 1999) (Employee)
Aegon UK, Edinburgh . . . . (p.1220)
T: 1315493986
E: scott.burns@aegon.co.uk

BURNS, Trudy Eva (Nov 2014) (Employee)
Morton Fraser LLP, Edinburgh . . . . (p.891)
T: 0131 2471000
E: trudy.burns@morton-fraser.com

BURNSIDE, David Melville (Oct 1966)
(Consultant)
Aberdein Considine and Company,
Aberdeen . . . . (p.718)
T: 01224 589700
E: dburnside@acandco.com

BURNSIDE, Lucy Clare (Sept 2011) (Employee)
National Westminster Bank PLC,
Edinburgh . . . . (p.1226)
T: 0131 5568555
E: lucy.burnside@natwest.com

BURNSIDE, Sarah Elizabeth Stewart
(Sept 2009) (Employee)
Eversheds Sutherland (International) LLP,
Edinburgh . . . . (p.869)
T: 0207 9194500
E: SarahBurnside@eversheds-sutherland.com

BURR, Ally Jordan (Aug 2018) (Employee)
Dentons UK and Middle East LLP,
Glasgow. (p.968)
T: 0330 2220050
E: ally.burr@dentons.com

BURR, Malcolm (Dec 1991) (Employee)
Comhairle Nan Eilean Siar,
Stornoway . . . . (p.1255)
T: 01851 822600
E: m.burr@cne-siar.gov.uk

BURROWS, Caroline Sarah (Dec 2014)
(Employee)
Drummond Miller LLP, Edinburgh . . . . . (p.864)
T: 0131 2265151
E: cburrows@drummondmiller.co.uk

BURSILL, Pamela Winifred Sharon
(Sept 1994) (Associate)
Mackinnons Solicitors LLP,
Aberdeen . . . . (p.737)
T: 01224 868687
E: pamelab@mackinnons.com

BURTON, Alexandria Catherine Thorburn
(Jan 1981) (Director)
Buchanan Burton Limited, East
Kilbride . . . . (p.830)
T: 01355 249228
E: sandraburton@buchananburton.co.uk

BURTON, Gary John (Oct 2010) (Associate)
Anderson Strathern LLP, Edinburgh . . . .(p.839)
T: 0131 2707700
E: gary.burton@andersonstrathern.co.uk

BURTON, Gavin Gerard (Sept 2019) (Employee)
Procurator Fiscal Service, Dundee . . . . .(p.1218)
T: 01382 342559
E: gavin.burton@copfs.gov.uk

BURTON, Paige Anne (Aug 2021) (Employee)
MBS Solicitors, Edinburgh . . . . (p.889)
T: 0131 3374100

BURY, Catherine Anne (Mar 2004) (Employee)
Stewart & Watson, Turriff . . . . (p.1177)
T: 01888 563773
E: cbury@stewartwatson.co.uk

BUSBY, Claire Elizabeth (Jul 2016) (Employee)
Capricorn Energy Ltd, Edinburgh . . . . .(p.1221)
T: 0131 4753000
E: Claire.Busby@cairnenergy.com

BUSBY, Hilary Clare (Jul 2018) (Employee)
Turcan Connell, Edinburgh . . . .(p.908)
T: 0131 2288111
E: hilary.sharkey@turcanconnell.com

BUSBY, Nevin Neil (Dec 2013) (Employee)
Wrights, Motherwell . . . .(p.1128)
T: 01698 267361
E: neil.busby@wrightsolicitors.com

BUSBY, Seonaid Buchanan (Mar 1992)
(Partner)
Weightmans (Scotland) LLP,
Glasgow . . . . (p.1051)
T: 0345 073 9900
E: Seonaid.busby@weightmans.com

BUSCHMAN, Niamh Boyd (Nov 2012)
(Employee)
Bell Russell & Company Limited,
Airdrie . . . . (p.748)
T: 01236 764781
E: nbuschman@bell-russell.com

BUSH, Cathryn Rachel (Sept 2019) (Employee)
Lothian Pension Fund, Edinburgh . . . . .(p.1225)
T: 07395 84879
E: Bus38k33@lpf.org.uk

BUSHNELL, Adam Nicholas Iain (Aug 2017)
(Employee)
Burness Paull LLP, Glasgow . . . .(p.954)
T: 0141 2484933
E: adam.bushnell@burnesspaull.com

BUTTERY, Alistair Kilgour (Nov 1991) (Partner)
Freelands, Motherwell . . . .(p.1126)
T: 01698 352600
E: abuttery@freelands.co.uk

BUXTON, Kieran David Alexander
(Sept 2020) (Employee)
Burness Paull LLP, Edinburgh . . . .(p.850)
T: 0131 4736000
E: kieran.buxton@burnesspaull.com

BYARS, Lisa Claire (Jul 2012) (Associate)
Pinsent Masons LLP, Aberdeen . . . .(p.739)
T: 01224 377900
E: Lisa.Byars@pinsentmasons.com

BYFORD, Ross Alan (Jun 2014) (Employee)
MBM Commercial LLP, Edinburgh . . . . .(p.889)
T: 0131 2268200
E: Ross.Byford@mbmcommercial.co.uk

BYNOTH, Jillian (Sept 2004) (Employee)
Turcan Connell, Glasgow . . . .(p.1049)
T: 0141 441 2111
E: jillian.bynoth@turcanconnell.com

BYRNE, Anthony Joseph (Nov 2000)
(Employee)
KCA Deutag Drilling Ltd,
Portlethen . . . .(p.1254)
T: 01224 987000
E: Tony.Byrne@kcadeutag.com

BYRNE, Christopher James (Dec 2002) (Partner)
Thorntons Law LLP, Dundee . . . .(p.819)
T: 01382 229 111
E: cbyrne@thorntons-law.co.uk

BYRNE, Lisa (Aug 2011) (Employee)
Digby Brown LLP, Glasgow . . . .(p.970)
T: 0333 200 5925
E: Lisa.Byrne@digbybrown.co.uk

BYRNE, Michael James (Apr 2014) (Employee)
Life Technologies Limited, Paisley . . . . .(p.1252)
T: 0141 8146100
E: michael.byrne@thermofisher.com

BYRNE, Yvonne (May 2000) (Employee)
Burness Paull LLP, Glasgow . . . .(p.954)
T: 0141 2484933
E: Yvonne.Byrne@burnesspaull.com

BYRNE-LEITCH, Jonathan Nicholas
(Oct 2016) (Associate)
Ashurst LLP, London E1 . . . .(p.1261)
T: (020) 7859 2145
E: jonny.byrne-leitch@ashurst.com

BYROM, Rory James Lambert (May 2013)
(Employee)
Harper Macleod LLP, Glasgow . . . .(p.983)
T: 0141 2218888
E: rory.byrom@harpermacleod.co.uk

BYRON, Fiona Jane (Oct 2008) (Associate)
Morton Fraser LLP, Edinburgh . . . .(p.891)
T: 0131 2471000
E: fiona.byron@morton-fraser.com

BYTH, Sheila Janet (Jun 1997) (Employee)
McKinnon Forbes, Tranent . . . .(p.1175)
T: 01875 611211
E: sheila.byth@mckinnonforbes.co.uk

CABREY, Katie (Jul 2021) (Employee)
Miller Samuel Hill Brown LLP,
Glasgow . . . .(p.1020)
T: 0141 2211919
E: kca@mshblegal.com

CACACE, Antonio Gerardo (Oct 2016)
(Employee)
Barton & Hendry, Cumbernauld . . . . . .(p.790)
T: 01236 735466
E: antonio@bartonandhendry.co.uk

CACKETTE, Paul Henry (Oct 1985) (Solicitor)
NO FIRM

CADDEN, Edward Arthur George (Jul 2017)
(Employee)
Burnett Christie Knowles McCourts,
Edinburgh . . . .(p.852)
T: 0131 2253456
E: edward.cadden@bckm.co.uk

CAGE, Mhairi Lorna (Aug 2012) (Associate)
Miller Hendry, Perth . . . .(p.1150)
T: 01738 637311
E: mhairicage@millerhendry.co.uk

CAHILL, Iain Patrick (Jun 2012) (Employee)
Levy & McRae Solicitors LLP,
Glasgow . . . .(p.1000)
T: 0141 3072311
E: ICahill@lemac.co.uk

CAHUSAC, Jonathan George Woodd
(Mar 2021) (Employee)
Lindsays LLP, Edinburgh . . . .(p.882)
T: 0131 2291212
E: jonathancahusac@lindsays.co.uk

CAIRD, James Ronald Archibald (Mar 1987)
(Partner)
Caird & Vaughan, Dundee . . . .(p.807)
T: 01382 229399
E: cairdvaughan@btconnect.com

CAIRD, Jane Elizabeth (May 2017) (Employee)
Caird & Vaughan, Dundee . . . .(p.807)
T: 01382 229399

CAIRNEY, Diane Christine (Aug 1992) (Partner)
Miller Samuel Hill Brown LLP,
Glasgow . . . .(p.1020)
T: 0141 2211919
E: dcc@mshblegal.com

CAIRNS, Allan Steven (Sept 2005) (Partner)
Brodies LLP, Edinburgh . . . .(p.845)
T: 0131 2283777
E: allan.cairns@brodies.com

CAIRNS, Angela Mary (Jan 1976) (Solicitor)
NO FIRM

CAIRNS, Anne Frances (May 1997) (Employee)
Scottish Government, Glasgow . . . . . .(p.1243)
T: 0141 2727233
E: anne.cairns@gov.scot

CAIRNS, Cheryl (Oct 2004) (Employee)
Trowers & Hamlins LLP, Dubai . . . .(p.1278)
T: +971 (0)4 3025 137
E: CCairns@trowers.com

CAIRNS, David Alexander (Jun 2011)
(Employee)
Office of the Advocate General,
Edinburgh . . . .(p.1227)
T: 0131 2441635
E: david.cairns@advocategeneral.gov.uk

CAIRNS, Ewen Ross, WS (Nov 2007) (Employee)
Osprey Charging Network, London
SE1 . . . .(p.1267)
T: 0800 0588400
E: ewen.cairns@ospreycharging.co.uk

CAIRNS, Fiona Marie (Nov 2007) (Director)
FMC Legal Limited, Clydebank. . . . . . .(p.785)
T: 01389 879791
E: fiona-fmcsolicitors@btconnect.com

CAIRNS, Gordon Douglas (Aug 1981)
(Consultant)
Connell & Connell, WS, Edinburgh . . . .(p.857)
T: 0131 5562993
E: GDC@connellws.co.uk

CAIRNS, Roddy Gordon (Nov 2016) (Employee)
Burness Paull LLP, Glasgow . . . .(p.954)
T: 0141 2484933
E: roddy.cairns@burnesspaull.com

CAIRNS, Rodger William (Oct 1996) (Partner)
Shepherd and Wedderburn LLP,
Glasgow. . . . .(p.1039)
T: 0141 5669900
E: rodger.cairns@shepwedd.com

CALDER, Joy Margaret (Jan 2016) (Employee)
CMS Cameron McKenna Nabarro Olswang LLP,
Edinburgh . . . .(p.856)
T: 0131 2288000
E: Joy.Calder@cms-cmno.com

CALDER, Lynne Anne (Mar 2002) (Associate)
Collas Crill, St Helier . . . .(p.1274)
T: 01534 601783
E: Lynne.Calder@collascrill.com

CALDER, Susan Jane (Nov 1984) (Consultant)
Thorntons Law LLP, Edinburgh . . . .(p.906)
T: 0131 2258705
E: sjcalder@thorntons-law.co.uk

CALDERWOOD, Alan (Jun 2014) (Employee)
Thompsons, Edinburgh . . . .(p.906)
T: 0131 225 4297
E:
Alan.Calderwood@thompsons-scotland.co.uk

CALDERWOOD, Heather Elizabeth
(Sept 2006) (Partner)
Harper Macleod LLP, Glasgow . . . .(p.983)
T: 0141 227 9301
E: heather.calderwood@harpermacleod.co.uk

CALDERWOOD, Zoe Carroll (Jun 2016)
(Employee)
Scottish Police Authority, Police Scotland,
Glasgow. . . . .(p.1244)
T: 01786 895727
E: zoe.calderwood@scotlalnd.pnn.police.uk

CALDOW, Bruce Alan (Jan 2003) (Partner)
Harper Macleod LLP, Glasgow . . . .(p.983)
T: 1412279339
E: bruce.caldow@harpermacleod.co.uk

CALDOW, Fiona Lindsay (Oct 2003) (Employee)
Dentons UK and Middle East LLP,
Glasgow. . . . .(p.968)
T: 0330 2220050
E: Fiona.Caldow@dentons.com

CALDWELL, Fiona Helen (Oct 2008) (Employee)
Procurator Fiscal Service,
Edinburgh . . . .(p.1229)
T: 0300 0203000
E: fiona.caldwell@copfs.gov.uk

CALDWELL, John Macrae (Apr 1997)
(Consultant)
Shepherd and Wedderburn LLP,
Edinburgh . . . .(p.900)
T: 0131 2289900
E: john.caldwell@shepwedd.com

CALDWELL, Kenneth Andrew (Jan 1988)
(Partner)
Patten & Prentice LLP, Greenock . . . . .(p.1062)
T: 01475 720306
E: KenC@patten.co.uk

CALDWELL, Ross Graham (Nov 1998) (Partner)
Morton Fraser LLP, Edinburgh . . . .(p.891)
T: 0131 2471000
E: ross.caldwell@morton-fraser.com

CALLAGHAN, Emily Rae (Aug 2017) (Employee)
Scottish Government, Edinburgh . . . . .(p.1231)
T: 0131 244 0815
E: emily.callaghan@gov.scot

CALLAGHAN, Gavin Thomas Robert
(Aug 2003) (Employee)
Procurator Fiscal Service, Dundee . . . . .(p.1218)
T: 01382 342559
E: gavin.callaghan@copfs.gov.uk

CALLAGHAN, Helen Elizabeth (Oct 2017)
(Employee)
Scottish Power Limited, Glasgow . . . . .(p.1244)
T: 0141 6140000
E: h.callaghan@scottishpower.com

CALLAGHAN, Michael Andrew (Nov 1993)
(Associate)
Irwin Mitchell Scotland LLP,
  Glasgow...................(p.991)
  T: 0141 3004300
  E: michael.callaghan@irwinmitchell.com

CALLAHAN, Edward Anthony (Aug 1991)
(Director)
Callahan McKeown & Co Ltd,
  Renfrew...................(p.1158)
  T: 0141 885 1212
  E: callahanmckeownandco@gmail.com

CALLAN, Margaret Ann (Aug 1991) (Employee)
Callan & Co (Glasgow) Limited,
  Glasgow...................(p.955)
  T: 0141 7792114
  E: mac@callanandco.net

CALLAN, Martin James (Oct 1982) (Director)
Callan & Co (Glasgow) Limited,
  Glasgow...................(p.955)
  T: 0141 7792114
  E: mjc@callanandco.net

CALLANDER, Ailidh Jean Gunn (Nov 2015)
(Employee)
The Scottish Parliament, Edinburgh ...(p.1235)
  T: (0131) 3486653
  E: ailidh.callander@parliament.scot

CALLANDER, Marie Pauline (Oct 2013)
(Employee)
Angus Council, Forfar.............(p.1237)
  T: 01307 471837
  E: callanderm@angus.gov.uk

CALLENDER, John Munro (Sept 2019)
(Employee)
Clyde & Co (Scotland) LLP,
  Edinburgh.................(p.855)
  T: 0131 5571545
  E: John.Callender2@clydeco.com

CALLENDER, Patricia Mary (Jan 1992)
(Employee)
Procurator Fiscal Service, Glasgow ....(p.1241)
  T: 0300 020 3071
  E: patricia.callender@copfs.gov.uk

CALLERY, Craig Bryan (Oct 2012) (Solicitor)
NO FIRM

CALOTHIS, Marinos Thomas Gladstone
(Nov 2015) (Employee)
Cullen Kilshaw, Hawick ....(p.1071)
  T: 01450 372336
  E: marinos.calothis@cullenkilshaw.com

CALVERT, Alan Donald (Oct 1984) (Partner)
Brodies LLP, Edinburgh............(p.845)
  T: 0131 2283777
  E: alan.calvert@brodies.com

CALVERT, Eilidh Marion Rarity (Apr 2015)
(Employee)
Brodies LLP, Aberdeen.............(p.723)
  T: 01224 392242
  E: eilidh.calvert@brodies.com

CAMERON, Alan George (Oct 2005)
(Employee)
Procurator Fiscal Service,
  Edinburgh.................(p.1227)
  T: 0300 0203168
  E: alan.cameron@copfs.gov.uk

CAMERON, Alan Ian (Jul 2006) (Partner)
Jackson Boyd LLP, Glasgow..........(p.991)
  T: 0141 2214325
  E: acameron@jacksonboyd.co.uk

CAMERON, Alastair (Jul 2008) (Employee)
Gildeas Limited, Glasgow ....(p.979)
  T: 0141 331 6071
  E: acameron@gildeas.net

CAMERON, Anna Graham (Jun 2011)
(Employee)
Ventient Energy, Edinburgh.........(p.1235)
  E: anna.cameron@ventientenergy.com

CAMERON, Anthony James William
(Dec 2001) (Partner)
Harper Macleod LLP, Glasgow........(p.983)
  T: 0141 2218888
  E: Tony.Cameron@harpermacleod.co.uk

CAMERON, Audrey Clare (Aug 1992) (Partner)
Anderson Strathern LLP, Glasgow......(p.940)
  T: 0141 2426060
  E: audrey.cameron@andersonstrathern.co.uk

CAMERON, Barry Nicholas (Sept 1994)
(Employee)
Baker Hughes Australia Pty Ltd,
  Perth.....................(p.1257)
  E: barry.cameron@bakerhughes.com

CAMERON, Carol Ann (Mar 1992) (Employee)
Procurator Fiscal Service, Paisley......(p.1252)
  T: 0141 8875225
  E: carol.cameron@copfs.gov.uk

CAMERON, Colette Anne (Oct 2018)
(Employee)
NORTH LANARKSHIREre Council,
  Motherwell.................(p.1251)
  T: 01698 302196
  E: CameronCol@northlan.gov.uk

CAMERON, Daniel Graham (Jul 2014)
(Employee)
John Pryde, SSC, Edinburgh..........(p.897)
  T: 0131 2202160
  E: dan@johnpryde.co.uk

CAMERON, Derek Robert (Sept 1980)
(Consultant)
CMS Cameron McKenna Nabarro Olswang LLP,
Aberdeen . . . . (p.727)
T: 01224 622002
E: derek.cameron@cms-cmno.com

CAMERON, Emma Grace (Aug 2005)
(Employee)
Wheatley Housing Group Limited,
Glasgow . . . . (p.1246)
T: 0845 9001001
E: emma.cameron@wheatley-group.com

CAMERON, Ewan Ross (Jul 2013) (Employee)
Franklin Templeton Global Investors Limited,
Edinburgh . . . . (p.1223)
T: 0131 2424000
E: ecameron@martincurrie.com

CAMERON, Fiona (Oct 2008) (Partner)
Shoosmiths LLP, Glasgow . . . . (p.1040)
T: 0370 086 8300
E: Fiona.Cameron@shoosmiths.co.uk

CAMERON, Fiona Jane (Feb 2012) (Partner)
Gillespie Macandrew LLP,
Edinburgh . . . . (p.872)
T: 0131 2251677
E: Fiona.Cameron@gillespiemacandrew.co.uk

CAMERON, Fiona Jane (Jul 1991) (Employee)
Pinsent Masons LLP, Glasgow . . . . (p.1031)
T: 0141 567 8400
E: fiona.cameron@pinsentmasons.com

CAMERON, Fraser Alexander (Mar 2017)
(Employee)
Gilson Gray LLP, Glasgow . . . . (p.980)
T: 0141 5302021
E: fcameron@gilsongray.co.uk

CAMERON, Gemma Frances (Oct 2014)
(Employee)
Renfrewshire Council, Paisley . . . . (p.1252)
T: 0141 8403648
E: gemma.cameron-cs@renfrewshire.gov.uk

CAMERON, Gordon Glen (Sept 1993)
(Consultant)
Fraser & Mulligan, Aberdeen . . . . (p.731)
T: 01224 646428
E: ggc@fraser-mulligan.co.uk

CAMERON, Heather (Jun 2021) (Employee)
Anderson Beaton Lamond, Perth . . . . . (p.1146)
T: 01738 639999
E: hcameron@abl-law.co.uk

CAMERON, Jann Henderson (Oct 2006)
(Employee)
Scottish Enterprise, Glasgow . . . . (p.1243)
T: 0141 2482700
E: jann.cameron@scotent.co.uk

CAMERON, Jennifer Ann (Jun 2006) (Associate)
Adams Whyte, Edinburgh . . . . (p.835)
T: 0131 555 7220
E: jennifercameron@adamswhyte.com

CAMERON, Joseph Gordon, WS (Nov 1983)
(Consultant)
Stuart & Stuart, Edinburgh . . . . (p.905)
T: 0131 2286449
E: gcameron@stuartandstuart.co.uk

CAMERON, Julia Margaret (Dec 1981) (Partner)
South Forrest, Inverness . . . . (p.1082)
T: 01463 237171
E: julia@southforrest.co.uk

CAMERON, Julie Louvain (Jan 1996) (Employee)
Procurator Fiscal Service, Hamilton . . . . (p.1247)
T: 0300 0202887
E: julie.cameron@copfs.gov.uk

CAMERON, Karen Myra Shaw (Jan 1996)
(Associate)
Ledingham Chalmers LLP,
Inverness . . . . (p.1078)
T: 01463 667400
E: karen.cameron@ledinghamchalmers.com

CAMERON, Kirsty Claire (Mar 2015)
(Employee)
Ashurst LLP, Glasgow . . . . (p.1237)
T: (0141) 375 4242
E: kirsty.cameron@ashurst.com

CAMERON, Laura Elaine (Dec 1991) (Partner)
Pinsent Masons LLP, Glasgow . . . . (p.1031)
T: 0141 567 8400
E: laura.cameron@pinsentmasons.com

CAMERON, Laura Elizabeth (Aug 2014)
(Employee)
Aberdeen Corporate Services Limited,
Edinburgh . . . . (p.1220)
T: 0131 245 7508
E: Laura.cameron@abrdn.com

CAMERON, Linda May (Sept 1989) (Employee)
Swellfix UK Limited, Westhill . . . . (p.1255)
E: linda.cameron@tendeka.com

CAMERON, Louise (Oct 2009) (Employee)
Parabis Scotland Limited, Glasgow . . . . (p.1029)
T: 0141 442 0621
E: louise.cameron@friends-legal.co.uk

CAMERON, Malcolm Keith MacAulay
(Dec 1986) (Partner)
Cameron Macaulay, Glasgow . . . . (p.956)
T: 0141 204 7844
E: malcolm@cameronmacaulay.law

CAMERON, Nicola Jane (Aug 2005) (Employee)
Scottish Legal Aid Board,
Edinburgh . . . . (p.1233)
T: 0131 2267061
E: cameronni@slab.org.uk

CAMERON, Richard Kenneth, WS (Oct 1984)
(Director)
Fraser Brooks & Company WS Limited,
Edinburgh . . . .(p.871)
T: 0131 2256226
E: kenneth.cameron@fraserbrooks.com

CAMERON, Rona Jane (Nov 1998) (Employee)
Standard Life Assets and Employee Services
Limited, Edinburgh . . . .(p.1234)
T: 0131 2457508
E: rona_j_cameron@standardlife.com

CAMERON, Ross Robert (Oct 2013) (Associate)
Anderson Strathern LLP, Glasgow . . . . . .(p.940)
T: 0141 2426060
E: ross.cameron@andersonstrathern.co.uk

CAMERON, Siobhan Marina (Nov 2017)
(Employee)
DWF LLP, Glasgow . . . .(p.973)
T: 0141 228 8000
E: siobhan.cameron@dwf.law

CAMERON, Sonia Ann (Apr 2005) (Employee)
Dril-Quip (Europe) Limited,
Aberdeen . . . .(p.1212)
T: 01224 727000
E: Sonia_Cameron@dril-quip.com

CAMILLERI-BRENNAN, Dr, Rachel
(Feb 2011) (Partner)
Caesar & Howie, Alloa . . . .(p.752)
T: 01259 723408
E: rcb@caesar-howie.co.uk

CAMPBELL, Aidan George (Mar 1998) (Partner)
CMS Cameron McKenna Nabarro Olswang LLP,
Glasgow. . . . .(p.962)
T: 0141 304 6112
E: Aidan.Campbell@cms-cmno.com

CAMPBELL, Alanah Janna Tara (Sept 2021)
(Employee)
Hills Solicitors, Lanark . . . .(p.1108)
T: 01555 664220

CAMPBELL, Alasdair Duncan Bowie
(Nov 2004) (Solicitor)
NO FIRM

CAMPBELL, Alexander James Murray
(Sept 2021) (Employee)
Davidson Chalmers Stewart LLP,
Edinburgh . . . .(p.859)
T: 0131 6259191
E: alexander.campbell@dcslegal.com

CAMPBELL, Alistair Carnegie, WS (Oct 1979)
(Consultant)
Brodies LLP, Edinburgh . . . .(p.845)
T: 0131 2283777
E: alistair.campbell@brodies.com

CAMPBELL, Allison Margaret (Sept 2013)
(Employee)
Addleshaw Goddard LLP, Glasgow . . . . .(p.938)
T: 0141 2212300
E: Allison.Campbell@addleshawgoddard.com

CAMPBELL, Amy Leigh (Jul 2012) (Associate)
CMS Cameron McKenna Nabarro Olswang LLP,
Edinburgh . . . .(p.856)
T: 0131 2288000
E: amy.campbell@cms-cmno.com

CAMPBELL, Andrew Graeme (Sept 1998)
(Employee)
Lord President's Private Office,
Edinburgh . . . .(p.1225)
T: 0131 2406701
E: acampbell3@scotcourts.gov.uk

CAMPBELL, Brian James (Sept 1996)
(Employee)
Brodies LLP, Glasgow . . . .(p.948)
T: 0141 2484672
E: brian.campbell@brodies.com

CAMPBELL, Carol Anne Stewart (May 1991)
(Solicitor)
NO FIRM

CAMPBELL, Catriona Elizabeth (Sept 2018)
(Employee)
Dickson Minto, Edinburgh . . . .(p.861)
T: 0131 2254455
E: catriona.campbell@dmws.com

CAMPBELL, Charles Berry (Dec 1984) (Partner)
W. & A.S. Bruce, Dunfermline . . . .(p.822)
T: 01383 738000
E: charles@wasbruce.co.uk

CAMPBELL, Christopher Edward (Sept 2016)
(Employee)
W. & A.S. Bruce, Dunfermline . . . .(p.822)
T: 01383 738000
E: chris@wasbruce.co.uk

CAMPBELL, Claire Louise (Apr 2021) (Associate)
Burness Paull LLP, Aberdeen . . . .(p.724)
T: 01224 621621
E: claire.campbell@burnesspaull.com

CAMPBELL, Claire Louise (Sept 2013) (Partner)
Thompsons, Glasgow . . . .(p.1046)
T: 0141 2218840
E: Claire.Campbell@thompsons-scotland.co.uk

CAMPBELL, Colin John (Oct 2011) (Employee)
Clydesdale Bank Plc, Glasgow . . . .(p.1238)
T: 0141 2423089
E: colin.j.campbell@cybg.com

CAMPBELL CORCORAN, James Patrick
(Jul 2014) (Employee)
Addleshaw Goddard LLP, Glasgow . . . . .(p.938)
T: 0141 2212300
E: Patrick.Campbell@addleshawgoddard.com

CAMPBELL, David Haddow (Nov 1989)
(Partner)
Anderson Strathern LLP, Edinburgh . . . .(p.839)
T: 0131 2707700
E: david.campbell@andersonstrathern.co.uk

CAMPBELL, Donald Malcolm (Nov 1988)
(Employee)
East Lothian Council, Haddington . . . .(p.1246)
T: 01620 827827
E: dcampbell@eastlothian.gov.uk

CAMPBELL, Douglas Colin (Sept 2013)
(Employee)
Scott+Scott UK LLP, London EC4 . . . . .(p.1268)
E: dcampbell@scott-scott.com

CAMPBELL, Douglas John (Sept 1996)
(Employee)
Renfrewshire Council, Paisley . . . .(p.1252)
T: 0141 6187172
E: douglas.campbell@renfrewshire.gov.uk

CAMPBELL, Duncan (Nov 1990) (Employee)
Scottish Police Authority, Police Scotland,
Glasgow. . . . .(p.1244)
T: 01786 895786
E: Duncan.Campbell3@scotland.pnn.police.uk

CAMPBELL, Duncan Craig (Jun 1997) (Partner)
Stronachs LLP, Aberdeen . . . .(p.744)
T: 01224 845845
E: duncan.campbell@stronachs.com

CAMPBELL, Eidann Carina (Aug 2016)
(Employee)
Mellicks, Incorporating Naftalin Duncan & Co.,
Glasgow. . . . .(p.1019)
T: 0141 3320902
E: eidann.campbell@mellicks.co.uk

CAMPBELL, Eilidh Heather (Aug 2018)
(Employee)
Burnett Christie Knowles McCourts,
Edinburgh . . . .(p.852)
T: 0131 2253456
E: eilidh.campbell@bckm.co.uk

CAMPBELL, Eilidh Morag (Aug 2021)
(Employee)
Brodies LLP, Edinburgh . . . .(p.845)
T: 0131 2283777
E: eilidh.campbell@brodies.com

CAMPBELL, Elaine Constance (Sept 1976)
(Director)
Wm. Skelton & Co. Limited, Isle of
Bute . . . .(p.1089)
T: 01700 502881/504793
E: elaine@wmskelton.co.uk

CAMPBELL, Eleanor Ann (Oct 1994)
(Employee)
West Lothian Council, Livingston . . . . .(p.1250)
T: 01506 280000
E: eleanor.campbell@westlothian.gov.uk

CAMPBELL, Emily Louise (Jun 2021) (Employee)
Anderson Strathern LLP, Glasgow . . . . . .(p.940)
T: 0141 2426060
E: emily.campbell@andersonstrathern.co.uk

CAMPBELL, Emma Frances (Dec 2003)
(Employee)
Scottish Water, Dunfermline . . . .(p.1219)
T: (01383) 665410
E: Emma.Campbell@SCOTTISHWATER.CO.UK

CAMPBELL, Erin Anderson (Oct 2008)
(Employee)
Procurator Fiscal Service,
Edinburgh . . . .(p.1227)
T: 0300 0203168
E: erin.campbell@copfs.gov.uk

CAMPBELL, Euan Colin (Oct 2021) (Employee)
Shepherd and Wedderburn LLP,
Edinburgh . . . .(p.900)
T: 0131 2289900

CAMPBELL, Eve Marion (Sept 2017) (Employee)
East Dunbartonshire Council,
Kirkintilloch . . . .(p.1249)
T: 0141 5788000
E: evie.campbell@eastdunbarton.gov.uk

CAMPBELL, Ewan Mackenzie (Dec 1991)
(Employee)
SKO Family Law Specialists LLP,
Edinburgh . . . .(p.903)
T: 0131 3226669
E: Ewan.Campbell@sko-family.co.uk

CAMPBELL, Finlay Norman (Nov 2007)
(Employee)
DLA Piper Scotland LLP, Edinburgh . . . .(p.863)
T: 08700 111111
E: finlay.campbell@dlapiper.com

CAMPBELL, Fiona (Jan 1998) (Employee)
University of Edinburgh, Edinburgh . . .(p.1235)
T: (0131) 651 4330
E: fiona.campbell@ed.ac.uk

CAMPBELL, Fiona Jane (Nov 1989) (Director)
Macleod & MacCallum Limited,
Inverness . . . .(p.1080)
T: 01463 239393
E: fiona.campbell@macandmac.co.uk

CAMPBELL, Gail (Oct 2002) (Associate)
Philpott Platt Niblett & Wight,
Clydebank . . . .(p.785)
T: 0141 9529545
E: gcampbell@ppnw.co.uk

CAMPBELL, Gary Angus (Nov 1991) (Partner)
Harper Macleod LLP, Inverness. . . . . . .(p.1077)
T: 01463 798777
E: gary.campbell@harpermacleod.co.uk

CAMPBELL, George Alexander (Nov 1999)
(Employee)
Pinsent Masons LLP, Edinburgh . . . .(p.895)
T: 0131 777 7000
E: george.campbell@pinsentmasons.com

CAMPBELL, Gillian Aida (Oct 1988) (Partner)
MacRoberts LLP, Edinburgh . . . .(p.887)
T: 0131 2295046
E: gillian.campbell@macroberts.com

CAMPBELL, Gillian Fay (Oct 2009) (Partner)
Shepherd and Wedderburn LLP,
Aberdeen . . . .(p.742)
T: 01224 621166
E: gillian.campbell@shepwedd.com

CAMPBELL, Grant Stewart (Sept 1995)
(Partner)
Brodies LLP, Edinburgh . . . .(p.845)
T: 0131 2283777
E: grant.campbell@brodies.com

CAMPBELL, Hamish William Gordon
(Jan 2015) (Employee)
Pinsent Masons LLP, Edinburgh . . . .(p.895)
T: 0131 777 7000
E: Hamish.campbell@pinsentmasons.com

CAMPBELL, Iona Margaret (Oct 2019)
(Employee)
Balfour + Manson LLP, Aberdeen . . . . . .(p.721)
T: 01224 498080
E: iona.campbell@balfour-manson.co.uk

CAMPBELL, Dr, Jacqueline Mary (Jul 2005)
(Employee)
Dales Solicitors LLP, Galston . . . .(p.934)
T: 01563 820216
E: jackie@dalesllp.co.uk

CAMPBELL, James Patrick (Apr 2014)
(Employee)
Law Society of Scotland,
Edinburgh . . . .(p.1224)
T: 0131 2267411
E: JamesCampbell@lawscot.org.uk

CAMPBELL, James Peter (Sept 2008) (Partner)
Ledingham Chalmers LLP,
Inverness . . . .(p.1078)
T: 01463 667400
E: jp.campbell@ledinghamchalmers.com

CAMPBELL, Jamie Donald Montgomery
(Dec 2012) (Employee)
Aberdeen Corporate Services Limited,
Edinburgh . . . .(p.1220)
T: 0131 245 7508
E: jamie.campbell@abrdn.com

CAMPBELL, Janet Frances (Sept 1986) (Partner)
Murray, Little & Knox, Annan . . . .(p.755)
T: 01461 202866
E: Frances.Campbell@mlandk.co.uk

CAMPBELL, Jenna Louise (Nov 2006)
(Employee)
DAC Beachcroft Scotland LLP,
Glasgow. . . . .(p.964)
T: 0141 2486688
E: jecampbell@dacbeachcroft.com

CAMPBELL, Jennifer Anne (Feb 2008)
(Employee)
Church of Scotland, Edinburgh . . . . . .(p.1221)
T: 0131 2402258
E: jcampbell@churchofscotland.org.uk

CAMPBELL, Jessica Mary (Sept 2016)
(Employee)
Amazon UK Services Ltd, London
EC2 . . . .(p.1261)
E: campjm@amazon.com

CAMPBELL, John Alexander, WS (Dec 1980)
(Partner)
Beveridge & Kellas, Edinburgh . . . .(p.843)
T: 0131 5546321
E: j.campbell@beveridgekellas.com

CAMPBELL, Jonathan James Marley
(Sept 2009) (Director)
Capital Defence Lawyers Ltd,
Edinburgh . . . .(p.853)
T: 07867 637638
E: jcampbell@capdef.co.uk

CAMPBELL, Kathryn Claire (Apr 2009)
(Employee)
TV Squared Ltd, Edinburgh . . . .(p.1235)
E: claire.campbell@tvsquared.com

CAMPBELL, Keith Fraser (Jul 2008) (Associate)
CMS Cameron McKenna Nabarro Olswang LLP,
Edinburgh . . . .(p.856)
T: 0131 2288000
E: Keith.Campbell@cms-cmno.com

CAMPBELL, Kenneth (Mar 2007) (Associate)
Harper Macleod LLP, Inverness. . . . . . .(p.1077)
T: 01463 798777
E: kenneth.campbell@harpermacleod.co.uk

CAMPBELL, Kim (Nov 2012) (Employee)
Thorntons Law LLP, Dundee . . . .(p.819)
T: 01382 229 111
E: kimcampbell@thorntons-law.co.uk

CAMPBELL, Laura Ray (Aug 2017) (Employee)
Gilson Gray LLP, Glasgow . . . .(p.980)
T: 0141 5302021
E: lcampbell@gilsongray.co.uk

CAMPBELL, Lisa Jane (May 2017) (Employee)
Duncan & McConnell Solicitors Limited,
Dundee . . . .(p.809)
T: 07761 301390
E: lcampbell@duncanandmcconnell.com

CAMPBELL, Louise Ellen Rose (Oct 2015)
(Employee)
Scottish Government, Edinburgh . . . . . (p.1231)
T: 0131 244 2789
E: Louise.Campbell2@gov.scot

CAMPBELL, Margaret April (Sept 1999)
(Partner)
Aberdein Considine and Company,
Aberdeen . . . . (p.718)
T: 01224 589 700
E: a.campbell@acandco.com

CAMPBELL, Martin (Jun 2003) (Employee)
Build Hollywood Ltd, London N1 . . . . . (p.1262)

CAMPBELL, Martin Donald (Aug 2011)
(Employee)
Law Society of Scotland,
Edinburgh . . . . (p.1224)
T: 0131 2267411
E: martincampbell@lawscot.org.uk

CAMPBELL, Martin Stuart (Jun 2003) (Partner)
Anderson Strathern LLP, Edinburgh . . . . (p.839)
T: 0131 2707700
E: martin.campbell@andersonstrathern.co.uk

CAMPBELL, Matthew Stewart (Sept 2021)
(Employee)
Addleshaw Goddard LLP, Glasgow . . . . . (p.938)
T: 0141 2212300
E: matthew.campbell@addleshawgoddard.com

CAMPBELL, Morag (Sept 1981) (Consultant)
Dentons UK and Middle East LLP,
Glasgow. . . . . (p.968)
T: 0330 2220050
E: Morag.Campbell@dentons.com

CAMPBELL, Neil (Dec 1981) (Partner)
Currie, Gilmour & Co., Edinburgh . . . . . (p.858)
T: 0131 2295304
E: neilcampbell@curriegilmour.co.uk

CAMPBELL, Neil Colin (Feb 2011) (Employee)
Shepherd and Wedderburn LLP,
Edinburgh . . . . (p.900)
T: 0131 473 5416
E: neil.campbell@shepwedd.com

CAMPBELL, Neil John (Dec 1995) (Employee)
National Westminster Bank PLC,
Edinburgh . . . . (p.1226)
T: (0131) 626 2925
E: Neil.J.Campbell@RBS.co.uk

CAMPBELL, Nicola-Jane (Jan 2008) (Employee)
Frederick & Co Solicitors Limited,
Glasgow. . . . . (p.977)
T: 0141 2215575
E: nicolajane@frederickandco.co.uk

CAMPBELL, Nikki (Aug 2013) (Employee)
National Westminster Bank PLC,
Edinburgh . . . . (p.1226)
T: (0131) 626 2925
E: nikki.campbell@rbs.co.uk

CAMPBELL, Patrick Ian (Jul 1998) (Partner)
Campbell & McCartney, Glasgow . . . . . (p.956)
T: 0141 423 2222
E: pc@patrickcampbellsolicitors.co.uk

CAMPBELL, Rachel Sarah (Nov 2020)
(Employee)
Digby Brown LLP, Glasgow . . . . (p.970)
T: 0333 200 5925
E: rachel.campbell@digbybrown.co.uk

CAMPBELL, Robert Bamford (Oct 1971)
(Partner)
R.B. Campbell & Co, Ayr. . . . . (p.761)
T: 01292 261125
E: catherine@rbcampbell.co.uk

CAMPBELL, Ross Donald (Nov 1989)
(Employee)
DLA Piper Scotland LLP, Edinburgh . . . . (p.863)
T: 08700 111111
E: ross.campbell@dlapiper.com

CAMPBELL, Ross Donald (Sept 2011)
(Employee)
Brodies LLP, Glasgow . . . . (p.948)
T: 0141 2484672
E: r.campbell@brodies.com

CAMPBELL, Ross Grant (Nov 2013) (Employee)
Aberdeen City Council, Aberdeen. . . . . (p.1211)
T: 01224 522000
E: roscampbell@aberdeencity.gov.uk

CAMPBELL, Scott (Jan 2000) (Director)
The Chamber Practice Ltd, Dundee . . . . (p.819)
T: 01382 203000
E: scott@thechamberpractice.co.uk

CAMPBELL, Scott Andrew (Sept 2014)
(Employee)
National Westminster Bank PLC,
Edinburgh . . . . (p.1226)
T: (0131) 626 2925
E: Scott.Campbell@natwest.com

CAMPBELL, Shane Paul (Sept 1991) (Employee)
Hingston's Law Limited, Aberdeen . . . . . (p.732)
T: 01224 562300
E: shane@hingstonslaw.co.uk

CAMPBELL, Simon David (Dec 2019)
(Employee)
Carpenters Scotland Limited,
Glasgow. . . . . (p.956)
T: 0141 3285452
E: SMNC@carpentersgroup.co.uk

CAMPBELL, Sinead Garster (Sept 2003)
(Employee)
Lord President's Private Office,
Edinburgh . . . .(p.1225)
T: 0131 2406701
E: scampbell3@scotcourts.gov.uk

CAMPBELL, Stacy Elise (Oct 2005) (Director)
McKee Campbell Morrison Limited,
Glasgow. . . . .(p.1013)
T: 0141 4883680
E: stacy@mcmsolicitors.co.uk

CAMPBELL, Stuart Edward (Jun 2009)
(Associate)
Burnett & Reid LLP, Aberdeen . . . .(p.726)
T: 01224 644333
E: stuart.campbell@burnett-reid.co.uk

CAMPBELL, Susan Anne (May 2017)
(Employee)
Procurator Fiscal Service, Glasgow . . . .(p.1242)
T: 0300 020 3000
E: susan.campbell@copfs.gov.uk

CAMPBELL-HYND, Tracey Margaret
(Dec 2002) (Partner)
TCH Law, Hamilton . . . .(p.1070)
T: 01698 312080
E: tch@tchlaw.co.uk

CAMPBELL-SMITH, Joanna Mary (May 2001)
(Employee)
Brodies LLP, Glasgow . . . .(p.948)
T: 0141 2484672
E: jo.campbell-smith@brodies.com

CAMPOS RIO, Dr, Carol (Jan 2021) (Solicitor)
NO FIRM

CANDA, Stephanie Martina (Oct 2014)
(Associate)
Kennedys Scotland, Edinburgh. . . . .(p.880)
T: 0131 2256145
E: stephanie.canda@kennedyslaw.com

CANHAM, Rachel Eleanor (Jul 2006)
(Employee)
British Telecommunications PLC, London
EC4 . . . .(p.1262)
E: rachel.canham@bt.com

CANNAVAN, Paul Thomas Alexander
(Aug 2010) (Employee)
Public Defence Solicitors Office,
Edinburgh . . . .(p.1230)
T: 0131 557 1222
E: pcannavan@pdso.org.uk

CANNIBAL, Miranda Gwen (Sept 2015)
(Solicitor)
NO FIRM

CANNING, Claire Patricia (Dec 1996)
(Employee)
Registers of Scotland, Edinburgh . . . . .(p.1230)
T: 131659611
E: Claire.canning@ros.gov.uk

CANNING, Daniel (Nov 2018) (Employee)
Jones Whyte LLP, Glasgow. . . . .(p.993)
T: 0141 375 1222
E: daniel.canning@joneswhyte.co.uk

CANNING, Marie Josephine (Oct 1992)
(Employee)
River Clyde Homes, Greenock . . . .(p.1246)
T: 01475 788887
E: Marie.Canning@riverclydehomes.org.uk

CANNING, Ross Bradley (Sept 2021)
(Employee)
Procurator Fiscal Service,
Edinburgh . . . .(p.1227)
T: 0300 0203168
E: ross.canning@copfs.gov.uk

CANNON, Francis (Aug 1968) (Partner)
Cannons Law Practice LLP,
Glasgow. . . . .(p.956)
T: 0141 2045115
E: frankcannon@cannonslaw.com

CANNON, Kevin Bernard (Aug 2010)
(Employee)
EDF Energy Renewables,
Edinburgh . . . .(p.1222)
T: 0131 460 3654
E: Kevin.Cannon@nngoffshorewind.com

CANNON, Monica Eleanor (Sept 2006)
(Employee)
SOUTH LANARKSHIREre Council,
Hamilton . . . .(p.1247)
E: Monica.Cannon@southlanarkshire.gov.uk

CANNON, Nicola Simone (Mar 1997) (Partner)
Cannons Law Practice LLP,
Glasgow. . . . .(p.956)
T: 0141 2045115
E: Nicola@cannonslaw.com

CANNON, Richard (Aug 2002) (Partner)
DWF LLP, Glasgow . . . .(p.973)
T: 0141 228 8000
E: ricky.cannon@dwf.law

CANT, Charles Thomas (Oct 2002) (Director)
Charles Wood & Son Limited,
Kirkcaldy . . . .(p.1103)
T: 01592 261621
E: charles@charleswoodlaw.co.uk

CANT, Colin William (Oct 2002) (Director)
Charles Wood & Son Limited,
Kirkcaldy . . . .(p.1103)
T: 01592 261621
E: colin@charleswoodlaw.co.uk

CAPALDI, Francesca Marianna (Dec 2020)
(Employee)
Gilson Gray LLP, Glasgow . . . .(p.980)
T: 0141 5302021
E: fcapaldi@gilsongray.co.uk

CAPALDI, Louis Gregory (Aug 2012) (Partner)
Stewart & Osborne Legal LLP,
Beith . . . .(p.772)
T: 01505 503345
E: louisgcapaldi@stewartandosborne.co.uk

CAPLAN, Anthony Max (Oct 1977) (Partner)
Levy & McRae Solicitors LLP,
Glasgow. . . . .(p.1000)
T: 0141 3072311
E: TCaplan@lemac.co.uk

CARDOW, Lynne Margaret Wallace
(Nov 2000) (Partner)
BTO Solicitors LLP, Glasgow . . . .(p.952)
T: 0141 2218012
E: lca@bto.co.uk

CARDWELL, David Ivor William (Oct 2007)
(Associate)
Baker Botts (Belgium) LLP, Brussels. . . .(p.1257)
T: +32 (0)2 891 7330
E: david.cardwell@bakerbotts.com

CARENA, Pauline (Sept 1986) (Employee)
Dundee City Council, Dundee . . . .(p.1217)
T: 01382 434000
E: pauline.carena@dundeecity.gov.uk

CAREY, Alice Elizabeth Anne (Jan 2021)
(Employee)
Procurator Fiscal Service,
Edinburgh . . . .(p.1227)
T: 0300 0203168
E: alice.carey@copfs.gov.uk

CAREY, Fiona Janet (Jul 1989) (Director)
Brophy Carey & Co Ltd, Hamilton . . . .(p.1066)
T: 01698 200111
E: fjc@brophycareylaw.com

CAREY, Georgia May (Oct 2020) (Employee)
Russel + Aitken Denny LLP, Denny . . . . .(p.796)
T: 01324 822194
E: gc@radenny.co.uk

CAREY, Martin John (Sept 1982) (Director)
Carey Hughes Limited, High
Blantyre . . . .(p.1073)
T: 01698 404616
E: martin@careyhughes.co.uk

CAREY, Michael Peter (Jul 1998) (Employee)
Scottish Government, Edinburgh . . . . .(p.1231)
T: 0131 244 0498
E: michael.carey@gov.scot

CARGILL, David Ian (Aug 2008) (Employee)
Schlumberger Oilfield Europe SRL,
Bucharest . . . .(p.1276)
T: 07833 465 886
E: DCargill@slb.com

CARGILL, Jennifer Anne (Jul 2009) (Employee)
Lloyds Banking Group Plc,
Edinburgh . . . .(p.1224)
T: 0131 4429540
E: Jennifer.Cargill@lloydsbanking.com

CARGILL, Kirsty Elizabeth (Nov 2003) (Partner)
KW Law, Livingston . . . .(p.1119)
T: 01506 415333
E: kirstyc@kwlaw.co.uk

CARGILL, Lynsay Katherine (Sept 2007)
(Associate)
MacRoberts LLP, Edinburgh . . . .(p.887)
T: 0131 2295046
E: lynsay.cargill@macroberts.com

CARGILL, Ross Ian (Feb 2021) (Employee)
Thorntons Law LLP, Dundee . . . .(p.819)
T: 01382 229 111
E: rcargill@thorntons-law.co.uk

CARGILL, Sophie Margaret (Nov 2012)
(Associate)
Mellicks, Incorporating Naftalin Duncan & Co.,
Glasgow. . . . .(p.1019)
T: 0141 3320902
E: sophie.cargill@mellicks.co.uk

CARLAW, Wynne Stewart (Jan 1985)
(Employee)
South Ayrshire Council, Ayr . . . .(p.1215)
T: 01292 612420
E: wynne.carlaw@south-ayrshire.gov.uk

CARLE, Emma Joy Katherine (Oct 2003)
(Partner)
Stephen & Robb LLP, Keith . . . .(p.1090)
T: 01542 886267
E: emma.carle@stephenrobb.co.uk

CARLIN, Dawn Louise (Oct 2010) (Associate)
Friends Legal, Glasgow . . . .(p.978)
T: 0844 8921250
E: dawn.carlin@friends-legal.co.uk

CARLIN, Fiona Jacqueline (Sept 2004)
(Associate)
Dickson Minto, Edinburgh . . . .(p.861)
T: 0131 2254455
E: fiona.carlin@dmws.com

CARLIN, Louise Elizabeth Anne (Nov 2010)
(Employee)
Scottish Government, Edinburgh . . . . .(p.1231)
T: 0131 244 0815
E: louise.carlin@gov.scot

CARLIN, Mairi Taylor (Aug 2005) (Employee)
Brodies LLP, Glasgow . . . .(p.948)
T: 0141 2484672
E: Mairi.Carlin@brodies.com

CARLIN, Margaret (Sept 1989) (Consultant)
Linda George Family Law Limited,
Hamilton . . . . (p.1067)
T: 01698 459200
E: mcarlin@lgfamilylaw.co.uk

CARLIN, Mark (Oct 1984) (Director)
Friels Solicitors Limited,
Uddingston . . . . (p.1177)
T: 01698 815114
E: markcarlin@frielssolicitors.co.uk

CARLIN, Michael Thomas (Aug 1971)
(Consultant)
Thomas, Carlin & Pender, Glasgow . . . (p.1046)
T: 0141 8836227
E: michaeltcarlin@btconnect.com

CARLIN, Nicholas Charles (Nov 2005) (Partner)
Pinsent Masons LLP, Glasgow . . . . (p.1031)
T: 0141 567 8400
E: nicholas.carlin@pinsentmasons.com

CARLSSON-TAIT, Vanessa Patricia
(Dec 2019) (Employee)
Ormistons Law Practice Limited,
Glenrothes . . . . (p.1057)
T: 0800 7810413
E: vtait@ormistonslaw.co.uk

CARLTON, Blair Nicholas George (Jul 2010)
(Employee)
Element Materials Technology Group,
Edinburgh . . . . (p.1222)
T: 0131 333 8053
E: blair.carlton@element.com

CARLYLE, Alison Janet (Sept 2004) (Employee)
Scottish Government's Parliamentary Counsel
Office, Edinburgh . . . . (p.1233)
T: 0131 244 1668
E: alison.carlyle@gov.scot

CARLYLE, Paul Haining (Nov 1995) (Partner)
Shepherd and Wedderburn LLP,
Edinburgh . . . . (p.900)
T: 0131 2289900
E: Paul.Carlyle@shepwedd.com

CARMICHAEL, Deborah Louise (Dec 2004)
(Partner)
Jones Whyte LLP, Glasgow . . . . (p.993)
T: 0141 375 1222
E: deborah.carmichael@joneswhyte.co.uk

CARMICHAEL, Emily Morrison (Sept 2021)
(Employee)
Latta Law Limited, Glasgow . . . . (p.998)
T: 0141 222 2185
E: EC@lattalaw.co.uk

CARMICHAEL, Emma Louise (Jul 2013)
(Associate)
Morton Fraser LLP, Edinburgh . . . . (p.891)
T: 0131 2471000
E:
Emma.Carmichael-Stewart@morton-fraser.com

CARMICHAEL, Helen Elizabeth (Oct 1990)
(Employee)
Scottish Police Authority, Police Scotland,
Glasgow . . . . (p.1244)
T: 01786 895727
E: helen.carmichael@scotland.pnn.police.uk

CARMICHAEL, Keni Campbell (Dec 2020)
(Employee)
Harper Macleod LLP, Glasgow . . . . (p.983)
T: 0141 2218888
E: keni.carmichael@harpermacleod.co.uk

CARMICHAEL LEMAIRE, Gillian Elizabeth
(Sept 1984) (Employee)
Carmichael Lemaire Ltd, London
WC2 . . . . (p.1262)
E: gillian.lemaire@carmichael-lemaire.com

CARMICHAEL, Melanie Claire (Jan 2012)
(Employee)
Scottish Police Authority, Police Scotland,
Glasgow . . . . (p.1244)
T: 0141 435 1141
E: Melanie.Carmichael@scotland.pnn.police.uk

CARNAN, Fiona Anne (Aug 1984) (Employee)
Procurator Fiscal Service, Hamilton . . . . (p.1247)
T: 0844 5613245
E: fiona.carnan@copfs.gov.uk

CARNAN, Paul Blaney (Sept 1983) (Partner)
Blaney Carnan, Glasgow . . . . (p.947)
T: 0141 2488111
E: pbc@blaneycarnan.com

CARNOCHAN, Lynda (Sept 2016) (Employee)
Procurator Fiscal Service,
Edinburgh . . . . (p.1227)
T: 0300 0203168

CAROLAN, Daniel John (Sept 2019) (Employee)
Dickson Minto, London EC2 . . . . (p.1263)
T: 020 76284455
E: daniel.carolan@dmws.com

CARR, Andrew (Oct 1995) (Solicitor)
NO FIRM

CARR, Annie Rose (Sept 2016) (Employee)
Baringa Partners LLP, London SW1 . . . . (p.1262)
E: Annie.Carr@baringa.com

CARR, Bethany Ann (Jul 2020) (Employee)
Stephenson Harwood LLP, London
EC2 . . . . (p.1268)
T: 020 7329 4422
E: bethany.carr@shlegal.com

CARR, Caroline Ann (Jan 1993) (Partner)
BTO Solicitors LLP, Glasgow . . . . (p.952)
T: 0141 2218012
E: cac@bto.co.uk

CARR, Colin Peter (Oct 1980) (Partner)
MacDonald Lynch Solicitors,
Glasgow....................(p.1009)
T: 0141 6499552
E: colincarr4@btinternet.com

CARR, Lindsay Nicol (Aug 2017) (Employee)
Lindsays LLP, Dundee ....(p.814)
T: 01382 224112
E: LindsayCarr@lindsays.co.uk

CARR, Rachel Elizabeth (Jun 2012) (Associate)
Clyde & Co (Scotland) LLP,
Edinburgh ....(p.855)
T: 0131 5571545
E: rachel.carr@clydeco.com

CARR, Robert, WS (Dec 1982) (Partner)
Anderson Strathern LLP, Edinburgh ....(p.839)
T: 0131 625 7278 Extn 2
E: robert.carr@andersonstrathern.co.uk

CARR, Robert Adam (Oct 2005) (Employee)
Gibson, Dunn & Crutcher LLP, London
EC4 ....(p.1264)
T: (0207) 0714249
E: rcarr@gibsondunn.com

CARR, Roger (Jul 2017) (Employee)
Addleshaw Goddard LLP,
Edinburgh ....(p.835)
T: 0131 2282400
E: Roger.Carr@addleshawgoddard.com

CARR, Stephanie Margaret Mary (Sept 1999)
(Partner)
Blackadders LLP, Glasgow ....(p.946)
T: 0141 2481888
E: Stephanie.Carr@blackadders.co.uk

CARR, Thomas Peter (Dec 2017) (Employee)
DLA Piper Scotland LLP, Edinburgh ....(p.863)
T: 08700 111111
E: thomas.carr@dlapiper.com

CARRICK, Jill Elizabeth (Oct 1984) (Partner)
Blair & Bryden, Greenock ....(p.1059)
T: 01475 888777
E: jcarrick@blair-bryden.co.uk

CARRIGAN, Derek (Feb 2000) (Partner)
Lawford Kidd, Edinburgh............(p.881)
T: 0131 2255214
E: derek.carrigan@lawfordkidd.co.uk

CARROLL, Deborah Ann (Nov 1993)
(Employee)
Procurator Fiscal Service, Glasgow ....(p.1241)
T: 0300 0203000
E: deborah.carroll@copfs.gov.uk

CARROLL, Lindsey Marie (Aug 1998)
(Associate)
Grigor & Young LLP, Forres ....(p.928)
T: 01309 672126
E: lindsey@grigor-young.co.uk

CARROLL, Michael Joseph (Oct 2018)
(Employee)
L J Wade Ltd, Perth...............(p.1152)
T: 07310 164305
E: michael@louisawade.co.uk

CARROLL, Nicholas Steven (Nov 2019)
(Employee)
CMS Cameron McKenna Nabarro Olswang LLP,
Glasgow....................(p.962)
T: 0141 2222200
E: nicholas.carroll@cms-cmno.com

CARROLL, Robert Adamson (May 2004)
(Director)
MOV8 Real Estate Limited,
Edinburgh ....(p.893)
T: 0345 646 0208
E: robert.carroll@mov8realestate.com

CARRUTHERS, John (Sept 1992) (Director)
Oraclelaw Limited, Glasgow.........(p.1027)
T: 0141 4041091
E: jc@oraclelaw.com

CARRUTHERS, Kenneth William (Aug 1991)
(Partner)
Morton Fraser LLP, Edinburgh ....(p.891)
T: 0131 2471000
E: kenneth.carruthers@morton-fraser.com

CARSLAW, Neil Alexander (Aug 2016)
(Associate)
Pinsent Masons LLP, Edinburgh ....(p.895)
T: 0131 777 7000
E: neil.carslaw@pinsentmasons.com

CARSON, Donna Lee (Aug 2012) (Associate)
Levy & McRae Solicitors LLP,
Glasgow....................(p.1000)
T: 0141 3072311
E: dcarson@lemac.co.uk

CARSON, Elaine Margaret (Aug 1989)
(Employee)
Wilson McLeod, Edinburgh ....(p.912)
T: 0131 5560055

CARSON, Elspeth Campbell (Dec 1991)
(Solicitor)
NO FIRM

CARSON, John Robin Wilson (Aug 1988)
(Employee)
Friels Solicitors Limited, Coatbridge ....(p.786)
T: 01236 421 136
E: john@frielssolicitors.co.uk

CARSON, Rona Catherine (Oct 1996)
(Employee)
Scottish Government, Edinburgh .....(p.1231)
T: 0300 244 4000
E: rona.carson@gov.scot

CARSON, Rory Alexander (Nov 2021)
(Employee)
Macleod & MacCallum Limited,
Inverness . . . . (p.1080)
T: 01463 239393
E: rory.carson@macandmac.co.uk

CARSON, Stuart Graham (Dec 1988) (Partner)
Wilson McLeod, Edinburgh . . . . (p.912)
T: 0131 5560055
E: setcgcarson@tiscali.co.uk

CARSS, Holly Amy (Aug 2019) (Employee)
Herbert Smith Freehills LLP, London
EC2 . . . . (p.1265)
T: (020) 7466 2422
E: holly.carss@hsf.com

CARSWELL, Christie Rose (Oct 2020)
(Employee)
MacRoberts LLP, Edinburgh . . . . (p.887)
T: 0131 2295046
E: Christie.Carswell@macroberts.com

CARTER, Ashley Jane (Jul 2020) (Employee)
Dentons UK and Middle East LLP,
Glasgow . . . . (p.968)
T: 0330 2220050
E: ashley.carter@dentons.com

CARTER, Emma (Jun 2015) (Employee)
Marshall Wilson Law Group Limited,
Falkirk . . . . (p.922)
T: 01324 612569
E: ecarter@marshallwilson.com

CARTER, Paul Barry (Nov 1990) (Partner)
CMS Cameron McKenna Nabarro Olswang LLP,
Glasgow . . . . (p.962)
T: 0141 2222200
E: Paul.Carter@cms-cmno.com

CARTHY, Jade Elizabeth (Oct 2011) (Partner)
A.C. O'Neill & Co., Dumbarton . . . . (p.799)
T: 01389 762997

CARTNEY, Marie Patricia (Jul 1998) (Employee)
Ledingham Chalmers LLP,
Edinburgh . . . . (p.881)
T: 0131 2001000
E: marie.cartney@ledinghamchalmers.com

CARTWRIGHT, Lindsey Jane (Feb 1996)
(Partner)
Morton Fraser LLP, Glasgow . . . . (p.1022)
T: 0141 2741100
E: lindsey.cartwright@morton-fraser.com

CARTY, Gillian Anne (Feb 1995) (Partner)
Shepherd and Wedderburn LLP,
Edinburgh . . . . (p.900)
T: 0131 2289900
E: Gillian.Carty@shepwedd.com

CARTY, Margaret Elizabeth (May 2001)
(Employee)
National Westminster Bank PLC,
Edinburgh . . . . (p.1226)
T: (0131) 626 2925
E: Margaret.Carty@natwest.com

CARTY, Stephen Patrick (Jul 1997) (Employee)
James McKay Defence Solicitors Limited,
Elgin . . . . (p.917)
T: 01343 556500
E: stephen@jamesmckay.uk

CARVEL, Ross Stewart (Jul 2014) (Employee)
Procurator Fiscal Service,
Edinburgh . . . . (p.1229)
T: 0300 0203000
E: Ross.Carvel@copfs.gov.uk

CARWOOD BARRON, Rebecca Mary
(Sept 2015) (Employee)
Akin Gump Strauss Hauer & Feld LLP, London
E1 . . . . (p.1261)
T: (+44) 20.7012.9842
E: Rebecca.CarwoodBarron@akingump.com

CASEBY, Derek George Alexander
(Aug 1988) (Associate)
Grant Smith Law Practice Limited,
Banff . . . . (p.769)
T: 01261 815678
E: derek.caseby@grantsmithlaw.co.uk

CASEY, Cornelius Kevin (Oct 2009) (Employee)
Shepherd and Wedderburn LLP,
Glasgow . . . . (p.1039)
T: 0141 5669900
E: neil.casey@shepwedd.com

CASEY, Mhairi (Feb 2013) (Employee)
East Dunbartonshire Council,
Kirkintilloch . . . . (p.1249)
T: 0141 5788000
E: mhairi.casey@eastdunbarton.gov.uk

CASIDAY, Augustine Michael Cortney
(Sept 2021) (Employee)
Beltrami & Co Limited, Glasgow . . . . . . (p.944)
T: 0141 4292262
E:
augustine.casiday@beltramiandcompany.co.uk

CASSELL, Gaenor Judith (Nov 1999) (Partner)
Addleshaw Goddard LLP,
Edinburgh . . . . (p.835)
T: 0131 2282400
E: Gaenor.Cassell@addleshawgoddard.com

CASSELLS, John Graham (Dec 1986) (Director)
Young & Partners Business Lawyers Limited,
Dunfermline . . . . (p.827)
T: 01383 721621
E: jgc@businesslaw.co.uk

CASSELS, Alan McLeod (Sept 1999) (Partner)
Pinsent Masons LLP, Glasgow . . . .(p.1031)
T: 0141 567 8400
E: alan.cassels@pinsentmasons.com

CASSELS, James McEwan (Nov 1980)
(Consultant)
The PRG Partnership, Glasgow . . . .(p.1045)
T: 0141 3530550
E: jamescassels@prg.co.uk

CASSELS, Sandra Isobel McDonald
(Oct 1987) (Partner)
Morton Fraser LLP, Edinburgh . . . .(p.891)
T: 0131 2471000
E: sandra.cassels@morton-fraser.com

CASSIDY, Anne Margaret (Nov 1990)
(Employee)
Laurie & Co Solicitors LLP,
Aberdeen . . . .(p.733)
T: 01224 645 085
E: anne@laurieandco.co.uk

CASSIDY, Caroline Isabel (Aug 2001) (Solicitor)
NO FIRM

CASSIDY, Kevin Francis (Nov 1990)
(Consultant)
Cassidys' Advice & Solicitor Services,
Glasgow . . . .(p.958)
T: 0141 3532195
E: kevincassidy@cassidysolicitors.co.uk

CASSIDY, Kirsty Louise (Oct 2006) (Employee)
Clyde & Co (Scotland) LLP,
Edinburgh . . . .(p.855)
T: 0131 5571545
E: kirsty.cassidy@clydeco.com

CASSIDY, Madelaine (Sept 2018) (Employee)
Clyde & Co (Scotland) LLP,
Edinburgh . . . .(p.855)
T: 0131 5571545
E: Madelaine.Cassidy@clydeco.com

CASSIDY, Stacey-Anne (Sept 2003) (Partner)
TLT LLP, Glasgow . . . .(p.1048)
T: 0333 006 0400
E: stacey.cassidy@tltsolicitors.com

CASSIDY, Stuart Joseph (Feb 1988) (Employee)
Procurator Fiscal Service, Hamilton . . . .(p.1247)
T: 0300 020 3000
E: stuart.cassidy@copfs.gov.uk

CASTER, Jack Stanley (Dec 2020) (Employee)
Procurator Fiscal Service,
Livingston . . . .(p.1250)
T: (0300) 020 3696
E: jack.caster@copfs.gov.uk

CASTLE, Brian Christopher (Sept 1995)
(Partner)
Digby Brown LLP, Dundee . . . .(p.808)
T: 3332005925
E: brian.castle@digbybrown.co.uk

CASTLE, Helen Anne (Sept 2006) (Employee)
Robert Gordon University,
Aberdeen . . . .(p.1214)
T: 01224 262021
E: h.a.castle@rgu.ac.uk

CATHCART, Moira Ann Ray (Feb 1995)
(Employee)
The Office of the Scottish Charity Regulator,
Dundee . . . .(p.1219)
T: 01382 220446
E: moira.cathcart@oscr.org.uk

CATHCART, Nicola Jane (Jul 2019) (Employee)
Jones Whyte LLP, Glasgow . . . .(p.993)
T: 0141 375 1222
E: nicola.cathcart@joneswhyte.co.uk

CATHIE, Duncan Craig (Jan 2012) (Employee)
Brodies LLP, Edinburgh . . . .(p.845)
T: 0131 2283777
E: duncan.cathie@brodies.com

CATTERALL, Kim (May 2013) (Employee)
Digby Brown LLP, Edinburgh . . . .(p.862)
T: 0333 200 5925
E: Kim.Catterall@digbybrown.co.uk

CATTO, Simon James Dawson (Feb 1997)
(Partner)
Addleshaw Goddard LLP,
Edinburgh . . . .(p.835)
T: 0131 2282400
E: Simon.Catto@addleshawgoddard.com

CAVANAGH, Hollie Kathleen Rose
(Nov 2020) (Employee)
Ledingham Chalmers LLP,
Aberdeen . . . .(p.734)
T: 01224 408408
E: hollie.cavanagh@ledinghamchalmers.com

CAVANAGH, John Gerard (Nov 1993) (Partner)
Campbell Smith LLP, Edinburgh . . . .(p.852)
T: 0131 5563737
E: john.cavanagh@camsmith.co.uk

CAVERS, Neil (Nov 1972) (Consultant)
Cavers & Co., Kirkcudbright . . . .(p.1103)
T: 01557 331217
E: ncavers@caversandco.com

CAVERS, Paul Neil (Sept 2011) (Partner)
Cavers & Co., Kirkcudbright . . . .(p.1103)
T: 01557 331217
E: pcavers@caversandco.com

CAVES, Catriona Jane (Sept 1992) (Employee)
South Ayrshire Council, Ayr . . . .(p.1215)
T: 01292 612420
E: catriona.caves@south-ayrshire.gov.uk

CAVIN, Fiona Scott (Nov 1988) (Employee)
Office of the Advocate General,
Edinburgh . . . .(p.1227)
T: 0131 2441635
E: fiona.cavin@advocategeneral.gov.uk

CENT, Louise Anne (Dec 1997) (Employee)
Pinsent Masons LLP, Glasgow . . . .(p.1031)
T: 0141 567 8400
E: louise.cent@pinsentmasons.com

CERESA, Laura Viviana Maria (Nov 1982)
(Consultant)
Peacock Johnston, Glasgow . . . .(p.1030)
T: 0141 3339505
E: lvmc@peacockjohnston.co.uk

CHADWICK, Rosalie Madeleine (Mar 2002)
(Partner)
Pinsent Masons LLP, Glasgow . . . . . .(p.1031)
T: 0141 567 8400
E: rosalie.chadwick@pinsentmasons.com

CHAFFEY, Marie-Claire Elizabeth (Sept 2010)
(Employee)
Procurator Fiscal Service,
Edinburgh . . . .(p.1227)
T: 0844 5613000
E: marie-claire.chaffey@copfs.gov.uk

CHALL, Jatinder Kaur (Nov 1999) (Partner)
MacRae and Kaur LLP, Glasgow . . . . . .(p.1015)
T: 0141 6116000
E: jc@mackaur.co.uk

CHALMERS, Andrew Simon (Nov 1988)
(Partner)
Davidson Chalmers Stewart LLP,
Edinburgh . . . .(p.859)
T: 0131 6259191
E: andrew.chalmers@dcslegal.com

CHALMERS, Ann-Marie (Jul 1993) (Employee)
Rooney Family Law Limited,
Uddingston . . . .(p.1178)
T: 01698 815 620
E: amc@rooneyfamilylaw.co.uk

CHALMERS, Apryl (Sept 1992) (Employee)
East Renfrewshire Council, Giffnock . . .(p.1237)
T: 0141 5773000
E: apryl.chalmers@eastrenfrewshire.gov.uk

CHALMERS, Catherine Elizabeth (Nov 1990)
(Partner)
Robert F MacDonald Solicitors,
Kirkcaldy . . . .(p.1101)
T: 01592 643357
E: cath@robertfmacdonald.org.uk

CHALMERS, James David (Oct 1994) (Partner)
Stronachs LLP, Aberdeen . . . .(p.744)
T: 01224 845845
E: david.chalmers@stronachs.com

CHALMERS, Jeanette Ann (May 2008)
(Associate)
CMS Cameron McKenna Nabarro Olswang LLP,
Edinburgh . . . .(p.856)
T: 0131 2288000
E: Jeanette.Chalmers@cms-cmno.com

CHALMERS, John Alexander Gunn
(Feb 1987) (Partner)
Ledingham Chalmers LLP,
Edinburgh . . . .(p.881)
T: 0131 2001000
E: john.chalmers@ledinghamchalmers.com

CHALMERS, Leigh Suzanne (Apr 2002)
(Employee)
University of Edinburgh, Edinburgh . . .(p.1235)
T: 0131 651 4330
E: leigh.chalmers@ed.ac.uk

CHALMERS, Margaret Claire (Dec 1988)
(Partner)
Murray, Hamilton & Chalmers,
Bellshill . . . .(p.773)
T: 01698 327488
E: margaret.chalmers@mhcsol.co.uk

CHALMERS, Michael John (Nov 1998)
(Employee)
Scottish Government Children & Families
Directorate, Edinburgh . . . .(p.1232)
T: 0131 2444521
E: michael.chalmers2@gov.scot

CHALMERS, Philip Hugh (Nov 2003)
(Employee)
BP Exploration Operating Company Ltd.,
Dyce . . . .(p.1219)
T: 01224 832353
E: philip.chalmers@uk.bp.com

CHAM, Jennifer (May 2005) (Associate)
Ledingham Chalmers LLP,
Aberdeen . . . .(p.734)
T: 01224 408408
E: Jennifer.Cham@ledinghamchalmers.com

CHAMBERS, Fiona Lesley (Oct 2005)
(Employee)
Balfour Beatty Group, London SW1 . . .(p.1261)
E: fiona.chambers@balfourbeatty.co.uk

CHAMBERS, Jennifer Jane (Sept 2006)
(Employee)
Lloyds Banking Group Plc, London
EC2 . . . .(p.1266)
E: Jennifer.Chambers@lloydsbanking.com

CHAMBERS, Lesley Allan (Jun 2004) (Employee)
Procurator Fiscal Service, Glasgow . . . .(p.1241)
T: 0300 0203000
E: lesley.chambers@copfs.gov.uk

CHAMBERS, Louise (Oct 2006) (Employee)
Burness Paull LLP, Glasgow . . . .(p.954)
T: (0141) 2484933
E: Louise.Chambers@burnesspaull.com

CHAMBERS, Lucy Mary (Sept 2020) (Employee)
Pinsent Masons LLP, Edinburgh . . . .(p.895)
T: 0131 777 7000
E: Lucy.chambers@pinsentmasons.com

CHAMBERS, Mark Allan (Sept 1995) (Partner)
Tod & Mitchell, Paisley . . . .(p.1142)
T: 0141 8891444
E: enquiries@todandmitchell.co.uk

CHAMBERS, Peter Martin Antony
(May 2004) (Partner)
Burness Paull LLP, Edinburgh . . . .(p.850)
T: 0131 4736000
E: peter.chambers@burnesspaull.com

CHAN, Chloe (Nov 2017) (Employee)
King & Wood Mallesons, Hong
Kong . . . .(p.1273)
T: +852 3443 1181
E: chloe.chan@hk.kwm.com

CHAN, Jessica Sen Tin (Mar 2016) (Employee)
West Lothian Council, Livingston . . . . .(p.1250)
T: 01506 280000
E: jessica.chan@westlothian.gov.uk

CHAN, Paula Shao Lan (Mar 2009) (Employee)
Brahams Dutt Badrick French LLP, London
EC2 . . . .(p.1262)
E: paulachan@bdbf.co.uk

CHAN, Shuiken Nora (Feb 2003) (Employee)
The Institute of Chartered Accountants of
Scotland, Edinburgh . . . .(p.1235)
T: 0131 3470100
E: schan@icas.com

CHAN, Stephen Ka Leung (Feb 2000) (Partner)
Harper Macleod LLP, Edinburgh . . . .(p.877)
T: 0131 2472500
E: stephen.chan@harpermacleod.co.uk

CHAN, Ying On Anthea (Mar 2020) (Employee)
Morton Fraser LLP, Edinburgh . . . .(p.891)
T: 0131 2471000

CHANDLER, Graham Richard (Dec 2016)
(Employee)
Aberdeen City Council, Aberdeen . . . . .(p.1211)
T: 01224 522000
E: GChandler@aberdeencity.gov.uk

CHANNIN, Sarah Mary Jane (Feb 2010)
(Employee)
ENGIE, Newcastle Upon Tyne . . . .(p.1270)
E: sarah.channin@engie.com

CHANZ JORD N, Ignacio (Feb 2013) (Director)
Spanish + Scottish Law Practice Limited,
Aberdeen . . . .(p.743)
T: 01224 581581
E: ignacio@sslawpractice.co.uk

CHAPMAN, Anne Margaret (Oct 2006)
(Partner)
Anderson Strathern LLP, Edinburgh . . . .(p.839)
T: 0131 2707700
E: anne.chapman@andersonstrathern.co.uk

CHAPMAN, Gary George (Nov 2002)
(Employee)
Centurion Group, Aberdeen . . . .(p.1212)
T: 01224 215 411
E: gchapman@centuriongroup.co.uk

CHAPMAN, Michael (Mar 1983) (Employee)
Chapman Solicitors, Inverness . . . .(p.1075)
T: 01463 240477
E: michael@chapmansolicitors.com

CHAPMAN, Pauline (Nov 1983) (Partner)
Chapman Solicitors, Inverness . . . .(p.1075)
T: 01463 240477
E: pauline@chapmansolicitors.com

CHAPMAN, Rosanna Louise (Mar 2013)
(Employee)
Procurator Fiscal Service,
Edinburgh . . . .(p.1229)
T: 0300 0203000
E: Rosanna.Chapman@copfs.gov.uk

CHAPMAN, Ruth Anne (Mar 2006) (Solicitor)
NO FIRM

CHARLTON, Gavin Iain (Apr 2009) (Employee)
Shepherd and Wedderburn LLP,
Glasgow . . . .(p.1039)
T: 0141 5669900
E: gavin.charlton@shepwedd.com

CHARRIER, Marianne Fiona H l ne
(Mar 2011) (Employee)
Scottish Enterprise, Glasgow . . . .(p.1243)
T: (0)141 468 6271
E: Marianne.Charrier@scotent.co.uk

CHARTERS, Michael Alec (Oct 1986) (Partner)
Fleetwood & Robb, Inverness . . . .(p.1076)
T: 01463 226232
E: mike@fleetwoodandrobb.co.uk

CHAUDRY, Henna Noor (Oct 2006) (Employee)
Procurator Fiscal Service, Glasgow . . . .(p.1241)
T: 0300 0203000
E: henna.chaudry@copfs.gov.uk

CHAUDRY, Jalal Noor (Nov 2015) (Employee)
Latta Law Limited, Glasgow . . . .(p.998)
T: 0141 222 2185
E: JCH@lattalaw.co.uk

CHEEMA, Nimarta Kaur (Nov 2015) (Employee)
Lindsays LLP, Edinburgh . . . .(p.882)
T: 0131 2291212
E: nimartacheema@lindsays.co.uk

CHEEMA, Sonia Kaur (Sept 2011) (Solicitor)
NO FIRM

CHEN, Qi Rui (Aug 2016) (Employee)
Latham & Watkins (London) LLP, London
EC2 . . . .(p.1266)
T: 020 7710 1000
E: carry.chen@lw.com

CHENG, Fiona Gai Man (Oct 2008) (Employee)
Zurich Insurance (Hong Kong), Hong
Kong . . . . (p.1273)
E: fiona.cheng@hk.zurich.com

CHERRY, Naomi Elizabeth Ross (Aug 2014)
(Employee)
Baillie Gifford & Co, Edinburgh . . . . . . (p.1220)
T: 0131 2752000
E: naomi.cherry@bailliegifford.com

CHESNEY, Steven (Oct 2004) (Associate)
Burness Paull LLP, Glasgow . . . . (p.954)
T: 0141 2484933
E: Steven.Chesney@burnesspaull.com

CHETTY, Milena Kate (Oct 2010) (Employee)
Renewable Energy Systems Limited,
Glasgow. . . . . (p.1243)
T: 0141 4045591
E: Milena.Chetty@res-group.com

CHEUNG, Man Yi (Oct 2016) (Employee)
Alexander Dennis Limited, Larbert . . . . (p.1250)
T: 01324 614 720
E: jennie.cheung@alexander-dennis.com

CHEUNG, Taut-Yang (Jan 2013) (Solicitor)
NO FIRM

CHEYNE, Lewis William (Sept 2021) (Employee)
Pinsent Masons LLP, Glasgow . . . . (p.1031)
T: 0141 567 8400
E: Lewis.Cheyne@pinsentmasons.com

CHILMAN, Amy Valerie (Sept 2020) (Employee)
Scottish Social Services Council,
Dundee . . . . (p.1218)
T: 0345 6030 891
E: amy.chilman@sssc.uk.com

CHILTON, Sarah Jane (Sept 2006) (Employee)
CM Murray LLP, London EC3 . . . . (p.1263)
T: 020 79339133
E: sarah.chilton@cm-murray.com

CHINN, Samantha Jane (Jul 2010) (Employee)
Chevron Canada Resources,
Calgary . . . . (p.1257)

CHISHOLM, Alison Mary (Nov 1983) (Director)
Raeside Chisholm Solicitors Limited,
Glasgow. . . . . (p.1034)
T: 0141 2483456
E: a.chisholm@raesidechisholm.co.uk

CHISHOLM, Anna (Aug 2018) (Employee)
Procurator Fiscal Service,
Edinburgh . . . . (p.1227)
T: 0300 0203168

CHISHOLM, Craig James McIntosh
(Jul 2019) (Employee)
Clarity Simplicity Ltd, Glasgow. . . . . . . (p.960)
T: 0141 4332626
E: c.chisholm@claritysimplicity.co.uk

CHISHTI, Ibrar Mahmood (Jul 2004)
(Employee)
Saudi Arabian General Investment Authority,
Riyadh . . . . (p.1276)
E: imc@sagia.gov.sa

CHITTY, Suzanne (Aug 2014) (Associate)
Simpson & Marwick, Edinburgh. . . . . . . (p.903)
T: 01224 606210
E: suzanne.chitty@alstonlaw.co.uk

CHIVERTON, Maxine (Jul 2018) (Employee)
Blackadders LLP, Perth . . . . (p.1146)
T: 01738 440088
E: maxine.chiverton@blackadders.co.uk

CHOPRA, Louise (Aug 2006) (Partner)
TLT LLP, Glasgow . . . . (p.1048)
T: 0333 006 0400
E: Louise.Chopra@tltsolicitors.com

CHOUDRI, Rabia (Nov 2004) (Solicitor)
NO FIRM

CHOUDRY, Mubasher Latif (Jan 2003)
(Director)
MCFLS Limited, Aberdeen . . . . (p.736)
T: 01224 467266
E: mubasher@mcfls.co.uk

CHOWDHURY, Tayeeba (Nov 2021) (Solicitor)
NO FIRM

CHRISTENSEN, Josephine Hartmann
(Apr 2021) (Solicitor)
NO FIRM

CHRISTI, Anoop (Aug 2020) (Employee)
Frazer Coogans Ltd, Ayr . . . . (p.763)
T: 01292 280499
E: anoop.christi@frazercoogans.co.uk

CHRISTIE, Ailie Elizabeth (Jun 2020) (Employee)
Connell & Connell, WS, Edinburgh . . . . (p.857)
T: 0131 5562993
E: aec@connellws.co.uk

CHRISTIE, Andrew John (Oct 2007) (Partner)
Burness Paull LLP, Edinburgh . . . . (p.850)
T: 0131 4736000
E: andrew.christie@burnesspaull.com

CHRISTIE, Carolyn (Nov 1999) (Solicitor)
NO FIRM

CHRISTIE, Catherine Mary (Oct 1999) (Partner)
Dickson Minto, Edinburgh . . . . (p.861)
T: 0131 2254455
E: catherine.christie@dmws.com

CHRISTIE, Claire (Jun 2007) (Associate)
SKO Family Law Specialists LLP,
Edinburgh . . . . (p.903)
T: 0131 3226669
E: claire.christie@sko-family.co.uk

CHRISTIE, Craig Jamieson (Nov 2016)
(Employee)
Drummond Miller LLP, Glasgow . . . . . . (p.971)
T: 0141 3320086
E: cchristie@drummondmiller.co.uk

CHRISTIE, Diane Margaret Morrison
(Nov 1990) (Associate)
Murdoch, McMath & Mitchell,
Huntly . . . . (p.1074)
T: 01466 792291
E: dmmc@murdoch-mcmath-mitchell.com

CHRISTIE, Edward Norman Christie
(Aug 1988) (Partner)
Ross & Connel LLP, Dunfermline . . . . . (p.825)
T: 01383 721156
E: echristie@ross.connel.co.uk

CHRISTIE, Fergus John Francis (Feb 1987)
(Partner)
Burnett Christie Knowles McCourts,
Edinburgh . . . . (p.852)
T: 0131 2253456
E: fc@bckm.co.uk

CHRISTIE, Gillian (May 2010) (Employee)
Barclays Bank PLC, London E14 . . . . . . (p.1262)
T: (0207) 116 1000
E: gillian.christie@barclays.com

CHRISTIE, Gordon John (Jan 1991) (Partner)
Murdoch, McMath & Mitchell,
Huntly . . . . (p.1074)
T: 01466 792291
E: christieg@btconnect.com

CHRISTIE, Graham Peter (Aug 2009)
(Employee)
Scottish Widows Limited,
Edinburgh . . . . (p.1233)
T: 0131 6557230
E: Graham.Christie@lloydsbanking.com

CHRISTIE, Hazel (Jul 1993) (Employee)
Procurator Fiscal Service,
Edinburgh . . . . (p.1229)
T: 0300 0203000
E: hazel.christie@copfs.gov.uk

CHRISTIE, Jillian Louise (Jul 2001) (Employee)
Shell U.K. Ltd., Aberdeen . . . . (p.1214)
T: 01224 882000
E: jillian.christie@shell.com

CHRISTIE, John Alexander (Feb 1960) (Partner)
Murdoch, McMath & Mitchell,
Huntly . . . . (p.1074)
T: 01466 792 291
E: christieg@btconnect.com

CHRISTIE, Lisa Jane (Sept 2009) (Employee)
Aberdeen City Council, Aberdeen . . . . . (p.1211)
T: 01224 522000
E: lisachristie@aberdeencity.gov.uk

CHRISTIE, Morag Mary (Nov 2011) (Employee)
Law Society of Scotland,
Edinburgh . . . . (p.1224)
T: 0131 2267411
E: moragchristie@lawscot.org.uk

CHRISTIE, Nicola Jane (Oct 1987) (Employee)
Scottish Canals, Glasgow . . . . (p.1243)
T: 07795 027348
E: nicola.christie@scottishcanals.co.uk

CHRISTIE, Ninian Francis (Nov 2002)
(Employee)
Scottish Government, Edinburgh . . . . . (p.1231)
T: 0131 244 0815
E: Ninian.Christie@gov.scot

CHRISTIE, Stacey Graham (Feb 2013)
(Associate)
Pinsent Masons LLP, Edinburgh . . . . . . (p.895)
T: 0131 777 7000
E: Stacey.Christie@pinsentmasons.com

CHRISTIE, Susan (Oct 1988) (Employee)
SOUTH LANARKSHIREre Council,
Hamilton . . . . (p.1247)
T: 01698 454785
E: susan.christie@southlanarkshire.gov.uk

CHRISTIE, Victoria Yvonne (Sept 2000)
(Employee)
Blackadders LLP, Dundee . . . . (p.805)
T: 01382 229222
E: Vicky.Christie@blackadders.co.uk

CHRISTIE, Yvonne Karen (Mar 1989)
(Employee)
Loch Lomond and The Trossachs National Park
Authority, Balloch . . . . (p.1215)
T: 01389 727745
E: Yvonne.Christie@lochlomond-trossachs.org

CHRISTIE-CARMICHAEL, Stephanie Louise
(Oct 2005) (Consultant)
Inksters, Glasgow . . . . (p.990)
T: 0141 2290880

CHRISTINE, Laura Mary (Nov 2012) (Employee)
Jones Whyte LLP, Glasgow . . . . (p.993)
T: 0141 375 1222
E: laura.christine@joneswhyte.co.uk

CHRISTINE, Lorna Margaret (Sept 2002)
(Partner)
Thorntons Law LLP, Dundee . . . . (p.819)
T: 01382 229 111
E: LChristine@thorntons-law.co.uk

CHRISTISON, Duncan Iain (Nov 2000)
(Employee)
Dickson Minto, Edinburgh . . . . (p.861)
T: 0131 2254455
E: duncan.christison@dmws.com

CHRISTISON, John Kyle (Dec 2006) (Director)
Christison Law Practice Ltd,
Livingston . . . .(p.1118)
T: 0800 1588455
E: christisonlaw@ymail.com

CHRISTODOULOU, Melissa Sophia
(Nov 2013) (Employee)
Scottish Children's Reporter Administration,
Hamilton . . . .(p.1247)
T: 0131 2448676
E: melissa.christodoulou@scra.gov.uk

CHRISTOFOROU, Angela-Jean (Sept 2014)
(Employee)
Simmons & Simmons LLP, London
EC2 . . . .(p.1268)
T: +44 20 7 825 4477
E:
Angela.Christoforou@simmons-simmons.com

CHUNG, Shirley Wing Yeng (Oct 2001)
(Employee)
Hong Kong Monetary Authority, Hong
Kong . . . .(p.1273)
T: +852 28788196

CHUNG, Shuk Chun Catherine (Apr 2003)
(Employee)
DAC Beachcroft Scotland LLP,
Glasgow. . . . .(p.964)
T: 0141 2486688
E: cchung@dacbeachcroft.com

CHUNG, Vincent Wai Ki (Jul 2015) (Employee)
Dixcart Legal, Addlestone . . . .(p.1258)
T: 0333 1220010
E: vincent.chung@dixcartlegal.com

CHUNG, Yumann Murray (Jun 2011) (Director)
CCMC Limited, Glasgow . . . .(p.958)
T: 0141 2482204
E: Yumann@chungrea.com

CHURCH, Rachael Marie (Jul 2019) (Employee)
Gillespie Macandrew LLP,
Edinburgh . . . .(p.872)
T: 0131 2251677
E: rachael.church@gillespiemacandrew.co.uk

CHURCH, Sophie Frances (Mar 2018)
(Employee)
McCash & Hunter LLP, Perth . . . .(p.1149)
T: 01738 620451
E: sophiechurch@mccash.co.uk

CHURCHWARD, Nicholas Stephen
(Aug 2017) (Partner)
Burges Salmon LLP, Bristol. . . . .(p.1258)
T: 0117 9392000
E: nick.churchward@burges-salmon.com

CHUTE, Fiona Mary Jervis (May 2014)
(Employee)
Brodies LLP, Edinburgh . . . .(p.845)
T: 0131 2283777
E: fiona.chute@brodies.com

CHYLINSKA, Malgorzata (Jul 2015) (Employee)
Pacitti Jones Legal Limited,
Glasgow. . . . .(p.1028)
T: 0141 3346444
E: Malgorzata@pjglasgow.co.uk

CIERANS, Sorcha Elizabeth (Aug 2021)
(Employee)
Dentons UK and Middle East LLP,
Edinburgh . . . .(p.860)
T: 0330 222 0050
E: sorcha.cierans@dentons.com

CLANCY, John Tosh (Aug 2002) (Employee)
MML Legal, Dundee . . . .(p.817)
T: 01382 206 000
E: jclancy@mmllaw.co.uk

CLANCY, Kevin John (Oct 2007) (Partner)
Shepherd and Wedderburn LLP,
Edinburgh . . . .(p.900)
T: 0131 2289900
E: kevin.clancy@shepwedd.com

CLANCY, Michael Paul, OBE (Feb 1982)
(Employee)
Law Society of Scotland,
Edinburgh . . . .(p.1224)
T: 0131 2267411
E: michaelclancy@lawscot.org.uk

CLANCY, Paul Harvey (Dec 1977) (Director)
Clancys Solicitors and Estate Agents Limited,
Edinburgh . . . .(p.854)
T: 0131 337 7771
E: paulsnr@clancys-solicitors.co.uk

CLAPHAM, David Charles, SSC (Sept 1981)
(Consultant)
Claphams, Glasgow . . . .(p.959)
T: 0141 6200800
E: davidcclapham@hotmail.com

CLAPHAM, Debra Harriet (Dec 1989) (Partner)
Claphams, Glasgow . . . .(p.959)
T: 0141 6200800
E: debralawagents@davidcclapham.co.uk

CLARK, Andrew (Nov 2009) (Associate)
Latham & Watkins LLP, California . . . . .(p.1279)
E: andrew.clark@lw.com

CLARK, Andrew Jamie (Sept 2021) (Employee)
Dickson Minto, Edinburgh . . . .(p.861)
T: 0131 2254455
E: andrew.clark@dmws.com

CLARK, Ashleigh Kay (Aug 2010) (Employee)
The Edrington Group Limited,
Glasgow. . . . .(p.1245)
T: 0141 9404000
E: ashleigh.k.clark@edrington.com

CLARK, Campbell John Scott (Mar 1997)
(Partner)
Blackadders LLP, Dundee . . . .(p.805)
T: 01382 229222
E: campbell.clark@blackadders.co.uk

CLARK, Caroline Mary (Apr 2004) (Consultant)
Bellwether Green Limited, Glasgow . . . .(p.944)
T: 0141 2184900
E: caroline.clark@bellwethergreen.com

CLARK, Cheryl Lynne (Aug 2015) (Employee)
Procurator Fiscal Service,
Edinburgh . . . .(p.1227)
T: 0844 5612113
E: Cheryl.Clark@copfs.gov.uk

CLARK, Christopher Louis (Feb 2018)
(Employee)
Shepherd and Wedderburn LLP,
Edinburgh . . . .(p.900)
T: 0131 2289900
E: christopher.clark@shepwedd.com

CLARK, Connor Scott (Sept 2015) (Employee)
Pinsent Masons LLP, Glasgow . . . .(p.1031)
T: 0141 567 8400
E: connor.clark@pinsentmasons.com

CLARK, David Andrew (Mar 2010) (Employee)
Dickson Minto, Edinburgh . . . .(p.861)
T: 0131 2254455
E: david.clark@dmws.com

CLARK, Dawn (Nov 2009) (Partner)
Fraser & Mulligan, Aberdeen . . . .(p.731)
T: 01224 646428
E: dc@fraser-mulligan.co.uk

CLARK, Deborah Jane (May 2021) (Employee)
Kennedys Scotland, Edinburgh . . . .(p.880)
T: 0131 2256145
E: deborah.clark@kennedyslaw.com

CLARK, Farah Mary (Aug 2009) (Employee)
Kier Limited, Salford . . . .(p.1271)
E: Farah.Clark@kier.co.uk

CLARK, Geoffrey Alan (Nov 1998) (Consultant)
Burness Paull LLP, Aberdeen . . . .(p.724)
T: 01224 621621
E: Geoffrey.Clark@burnesspaull.com

CLARK, Gordon William (Jul 2018) (Employee)
Gillespie Macandrew LLP,
Edinburgh . . . .(p.872)
T: 0131 2251677
E: gordon.clark@gillespiemacandrew.co.uk

CLARK, Graeme Johnson (May 2000) (Partner)
Andrew T. Gilbertson, Dalkeith . . . .(p.795)
T: 0131 6609888
E: gclarkdefence@outlook.com

CLARK, Hannah (Aug 2021) (Employee)
Brodies LLP, Edinburgh . . . .(p.845)
T: 0131 2283777
E: hannah.clark@brodies.com

CLARK, Harold Henry, WS (Jul 1994) (Associate)
DMD Law LLP, Edinburgh . . . .(p.864)
T: 0131 3164666
E: hc@dmdpartnership.co.uk

CLARK, Heather Kathleen (Jul 2015)
(Employee)
Scottish Government, Edinburgh . . . . .(p.1231)
T: 0131 244 0815
E: heather.clark@gov.scot

CLARK, Heather Rachel (Jul 2018) (Employee)
Reynolds Porter Chamberlain LLP, London
E1 . . . .(p.1267)
E: heather.clark@rpc.co.uk

CLARK, Iain Kemley (Oct 1993) (Partner)
Gilson Gray LLP, Glasgow . . . .(p.980)
T: 0141 530 2025
E: iclark@gilsongray.co.uk

CLARK, Ian (Jan 2013) (Employee)
Harneys, Hong Kong . . . .(p.1273)
T: +852 3195 7200
E: ian.clark@harneys.com

CLARK, Ian Robert, WS (Oct 1985) (Partner)
Turcan Connell, Edinburgh . . . .(p.908)
T: 0131 2288111
E: ian.clark@turcanconnell.com

CLARK, James Innes (Nov 1997) (Partner)
Morton Fraser LLP, Edinburgh . . . .(p.891)
T: 0131 2471000
E: innes.clark@morton-fraser.com

CLARK, James Mackenzie (Mar 2014)
(Employee)
Scottish Children's Reporter Administration,
Edinburgh . . . .(p.1230)
T: 0131 6679431
E: James.Clark@scra.gov.uk

CLARK, Jennifer (Nov 1997) (Employee)
Blackwood Partners LLP, Aberdeen . . . . .(p.723)
T: 01224 446230
E: Jennifer.Clark@blackwood-partners.com

CLARK, Joanna Christine (Oct 1996)
(Employee)
CMS Cameron McKenna Nabarro Olswang LLP,
Edinburgh . . . .(p.856)
T: 0131 2288000
E: Joanna.Clark@cms-cmno.com

CLARK, Johnston Peter Campbell (Oct 1985)
(Partner)
Blackadders LLP, Dundee . . . .(p.805)
T: 01382 229222
E: johnston.clark@blackadders.co.uk

CLARK, Judith Lesley (Oct 2007) (Associate)
Gillespie Macandrew LLP,
Edinburgh . . . .(p.872)
T: 0131 2251677
E: Judith.Clark@gillespiemacandrew.co.uk

CLARK, Julie (Dec 1986) (Employee)
Procurator Fiscal Service, Glasgow . . . . (p.1241)
T: 0844 5612250
E: julie.clark@copfs.gov.uk

CLARK, Katrina Eileen (Nov 1994) (Employee)
Paterson Bell Limited, Kirkcaldy . . . . . . (p.1102)
T: 01592 646600
E: katrina.patersonbell@gmail.com

CLARK, Laura Yvonne (Jul 2012) (Employee)
Educational Institute of Scotland,
Edinburgh . . . . (p.1222)
T: 0131 225 6244
E: Lclark@EIS.org.uk

CLARK, Lauren (Aug 2017) (Employee)
Pinsent Masons LLP, Aberdeen . . . . (p.739)
T: 01224 377900
E: lauren.clark@pinsentmasons.com

CLARK, Lesley Helen (Sept 1987) (Director)
Lesley Clark & Co Limited, Elgin . . . . . . (p.915)
T: 01343 553 950
E: lesleyclark@lesleyclarkandco.com

CLARK, Lewis Andrew (Dec 2015) (Employee)
Burness Paull LLP, Glasgow . . . . (p.954)
T: 0141 2484933
E: lewis.clark@burnesspaull.com

CLARK, Linda Elisabeth Ewing (Sept 1993)
(Employee)
Culley & McAlpine, Perth . . . . (p.1147)
T: 01738 626644
E: l.clark@culleymcalpine.co.uk

CLARK, Linda Jane (Aug 2006) (Director)
Mactaggart & Co Limited, Largs . . . . . (p.1110)
T: 01475 674646
E: linda.clark@mactaggarts.co.uk

CLARK, Lorna Esther (Sept 2009) (Partner)
CMC Law LLP, Glasgow . . . . (p.961)
T: 7731536911
E: lornaeclark@outlook.com

CLARK, Louise Catherine (Dec 2020)
(Employee)
Gibson Kerr Limited, Edinburgh . . . . . . (p.872)
T: 0131 2257558
E: louise.clark@gibsonkerr.co.uk

CLARK, Lucia Elaine (Sept 2004) (Partner)
Morton Fraser LLP, Edinburgh . . . . (p.891)
T: 0131 2471000
E: lucia.clark@morton-fraser.com

CLARK, Lynne Sarah (Sept 2000) (Employee)
Perth & Kinross Council, Perth . . . . (p.1253)
T: 01738 475000
E: LynneClark@pkc.gov.uk

CLARK, Margaret Anne Soderqvist
(Sept 2003) (Employee)
Scotmid Cooperative Society,
Edinburgh . . . . (p.1230)

CLARK, Martha (Jun 2004) (Partner)
McSherry Halliday LLP, Kilmarnock . . . . (p.1096)
T: 01563 533121
E: mc@mcsherryhalliday.co.uk

CLARK, Miriam Christine (Jun 2020) (Employee)
Procurator Fiscal Service,
Edinburgh . . . . (p.1229)
T: 0300 0203000
E: miriam.clark@copfs.gov.uk

CLARK, Paul John (Oct 2002) (Consultant)
Burges Salmon LLP, Bristol . . . . (p.1258)
T: 0117 9392000
E: paul.clark@burges-salmon.com

CLARK, Rebecca (Dec 2020) (Employee)
Procurator Fiscal Service,
Edinburgh . . . . (p.1227)
T: 0300 0203168
E: rebecca.clark@copfs.gov.uk

CLARK, Rebecca Susan (Aug 2015) (Employee)
Pinsent Masons LLP, Edinburgh . . . . (p.895)
T: 0131 2250003
E: Rebecca.Clark@pinsentmasons.com

CLARK, Sally Margaret (Dec 2003) (Employee)
Procurator Fiscal Service,
Edinburgh . . . . (p.1229)
T: (0844) 561 3268
E: sally.clark@copfs.gov.uk

CLARK, Stephen John (Nov 2007) (Associate)
Morton Fraser LLP, Edinburgh . . . . (p.891)
T: 0131 2471000
E: Stephen.Clark@morton-fraser.com

CLARK, Susie (Nov 1995) (Employee)
Boyles Solicitors, Dundee . . . . (p.806)
T: 01382 221214
E: sclark@wgboyle.co.uk

CLARK, Victor William George (Oct 1985)
(Partner)
Henderson & Mackay, Lockerbie . . . . . (p.1121)
T: 01576 202137
E: vwgc@lockerbielaw.co.uk

CLARK, Walter James (Feb 2002) (Partner)
Burness Paull LLP, Edinburgh . . . . (p.850)
T: 0131 4736000
E: walter.clark@burnesspaull.com

CLARK-SPENCE, Julie Ann (Jan 2004) (Partner)
Balfour + Manson LLP, Aberdeen . . . . . . (p.721)
T: 01224 498080
E: julie.clark-spence@balfour-manson.co.uk

CLARKE, Alison (Nov 2006) (Employee)
Burness Paull LLP, Glasgow . . . . (p.954)
T: 0141 2484933
E: alison.clarke@burnesspaull.com

CLARKE, Delanie Robyn (Jun 2018) (Partner)
Mathie, Lennox & Co., Kilsyth . . . . (p.1097)
T: 01236 823139
E: dclarke@mathielennox.co.uk

CLARKE, Eleanor (Sept 2020) (Solicitor)
The McKinstry Company LLP, Ayr . . . . .(p.765)
T: 01292 281711
E: eleanor@mckinstry.co.uk

CLARKE, Fiona Marie (Nov 2010) (Partner)
Burness Paull LLP, Aberdeen . . . .(p.724)
T: 01224 621621
E: Fiona.Clarke@burnesspaull.com

CLARKE, Francis Eric (Jun 1998) (Employee)
The Robert Kerr Partnership Limited,
Greenock . . . .(p.1063)
T: 07542 890000
E: rkerrpartnership@hotmail.co.uk

CLARKE, Gail Anne (Dec 1991) (Associate)
MacRoberts LLP, Edinburgh . . . .(p.887)
T: 0131 2295046
E: gail.clarke@macroberts.com

CLARKE, James Thomas (Aug 1994) (Employee)
Hunter & Robertson Limited,
Paisley . . . .(p.1138)
T: 0141 8893196
E: clarkes28@btinternet.com

CLARKE, John Bernard, WS (Nov 1979)
(Partner)
Wright, Johnston & Mackenzie LLP,
Dunfermline . . . .(p.826)
T: 01383 626666
E: jbc@wjm.co.uk

CLARKE, Leigh Anne (Sept 2001) (Employee)
Office of the Advocate General,
Edinburgh . . . .(p.1227)
T: 0131 2441635
E: leigh.clarke@advocategeneral.gov.uk

CLARKE, Lorna Anne (Aug 2015) (Associate)
Teacher Stern LLP, London WC1 . . . . .(p.1268)
T: 020 72423191
E: l.clarke@teacherstern.com

CLARKE, Matthew Robert (Oct 1993)
(Employee)
City of Edinburgh Council,
Edinburgh . . . .(p.1221)
T: (0131) 5294145
E: matthew.clarke@edinburgh.gov.uk

CLARKE, Patrick Anthony James (Oct 2015)
(Solicitor)
NO FIRM

CLARKE, Stephanie Carole (Dec 2014)
(Employee)
Brodies LLP, Glasgow . . . .(p.948)
T: 0141 2484672
E: stephanie.clarke@brodies.com

CLARKE, Stuart Andrew (Nov 1999) (Employee)
Scottish Enterprise, Glasgow . . . .(p.1243)
T: 0141 2282813
E: stuart.clarke@scotent.co.uk

CLARKSON, Christopher (Nov 2012)
(Employee)
Burness Paull LLP, Glasgow . . . .(p.954)
T: 0141 2484933
E: chris.clarkson@burnesspaull.com

CLARKSON, Hayley (Mar 2018) (Employee)
Scottish Social Services Council,
Dundee . . . .(p.1218)
T: 0345 6030 891
E: Hayley.Clarkson@sssc.uk.com

CLAYSON, Donald Bruce (Jan 1994) (Solicitor)
NO FIRM

CLAYSON, Laura (Aug 2009) (Solicitor)
NO FIRM

CLELLAND, Colin McArthur (Sept 1985)
(Associate)
Burness Paull LLP, Glasgow . . . .(p.954)
T: 0141 2484933
E: Colin.Clelland@burnesspaull.com

CLELLAND, Courtney Margaret Scott
(Nov 2014) (Associate)
Shoosmiths, Edinburgh . . . .(p.902)
T: 03700 868000
E: Courtney.Clelland@shoosmiths.co.uk

CLELLAND, James Robert (Oct 2019)
(Employee)
Scottish Government, Edinburgh . . . . .(p.1231)
T: 0131 244 0815
E: james.clelland@gov.scot

CLELLAND, Lynsey Ross (Feb 2008) (Associate)
McSparran McCormick, Glasgow . . . . .(p.1016)
T: 0141 2487962
E: lynseyclelland@hotmail.com

CLELLAND, Peter Healy Miller (Sept 2016)
(Employee)
Pinsent Masons LLP, Edinburgh . . . .(p.895)
T: 0131 777 7000
E: peter.clelland@pinsentmasons.com

CLELLAND, Sharon Louise (Oct 2003)
(Employee)
Scottish Fire and Rescue Service,
Hamilton . . . .(p.1247)
T: 0141 646 4699
E: Sharon.Clelland@firescotland.gov.uk

CLEMENCE, Nicola Jane (Nov 1998) (Partner)
Burness Paull LLP, Edinburgh . . . .(p.850)
T: 0131 4736000
E: nicky.clemence@burnesspaull.com

CLEMENTS, Eilidh (Dec 2011) (Employee)
Renfrewshire Council, Paisley . . . .(p.1252)
T: 0141 8403648
E: eilidh.clements@renfrewshire.gov.uk

CLEMENTS, Ross (Nov 2004) (Employee)
Goldman Sachs, London EC4 . . . .(p.1264)
T: +44 (0) 20 7774 1454
E: ross.clements@gs.com

CLEMENTSMITH, Pol Stanley (Jan 2017)
(Employee)
Martin, Johnston & Socha Limited,
Kirkcaldy . . . .(p.1102)
T: 01592 640680
E:
pol.clementsmith@mjscriminaldefencelawyers.
co.uk

CLETHEROE, Kelly Christina (Aug 2021)
(Solicitor)
NO FIRM

CLIFFORD, Carrie-Anne (Aug 2006) (Employee)
Lesley Govan Associates, Glasgow . . . . .(p.981)
T: 07983 811298
E: cac@lesleygovanassociates.uk

CLINCH, Jonathan Charles Alexander
(Oct 1988) (Partner)
McArthur Stanton, Helensburgh . . . . . .(p.1072)
T: 01436 672212
E: jcac@mcarthurstanton.co.uk

CLINKSCALE, Stephanie Louise (Nov 2013)
(Partner)
Robert More and Company,
Edinburgh . . . .(p.890)
T: 0131 5571110
E: stephanie@moredefence.co.uk

CLINTON, Heather Marion Margaret
(Jan 1999) (Employee)
Wheatley Housing Group Limited,
Glasgow. . . . .(p.1246)
T: 0845 9001001
E: heather.clinton@wheatley-group.com

CLOHERTY, Katherine Briege (Nov 2015)
(Employee)
Digby Brown LLP, Glasgow . . . .(p.970)
T: 0333 200 5925
E: Katecloherty@gmail.com

CLOSS, Fiona (Jan 2016) (Employee)
Burness Paull LLP, Aberdeen . . . . (p.724)
T: 01224 621621
E: fiona.closs@burnesspaull.com

CLOUGH, Mark Gerard, QC (Mar 2013)
(Employee)
Dentons Europe LLP, Brussels . . . . (p.1257)
T: +32 2 552 2935
E: mark.clough@dentons.com

CLOUGHLEY, Carol (Jan 2001) (Employee)
EDF Energy Renewables,
Edinburgh . . . . (p.1222)
T: (0131) 460 3654
E: Carol.Cloughley2@edf-re.uk

CLUBB, Stuart Alexander (Jun 2002) (Partner)
Shoosmiths, Edinburgh . . . .(p.902)
T: 03700 868000
E: stuart.clubb@shoosmiths.co.uk

CLUBLEY, Graeme Matheson (Nov 2003)
(Partner)
CMS Cameron McKenna Nabarro Olswang LLP,
Aberdeen . . . .(p.727)
T: 01224 622002
E: Graeme.Clubley@cms-cmno.com

CLUBLEY, Sarah (Dec 2003) (Employee)
Aberdeen City Council, Aberdeen. . . . .(p.1211)
T: 01224 522000
E: sclubley@aberdeencity.gov.uk

CLUNESS, Euan Alastair (Jan 2004) (Partner)
Addleshaw Goddard LLP,
Edinburgh . . . .(p.835)
T: 0131 2282400
E: Euan.Cluness@addleshawgoddard.com

CLYDE, John Mair (Dec 1979) (Employee)
McVey & Murricane, Glasgow . . . .(p.1017)
T: 0141 3339688
E: jclyde@mcvey-murricane.com

CLYDE, Karen Lucy (Nov 2020) (Employee)
Scottish Government, Edinburgh . . . . .(p.1231)
T: 0131 244 0815
E: karen.clyde@gov.scot

CLYDE, Peter Ian (Oct 2019) (Employee)
Addleshaw Goddard LLP,
Edinburgh . . . .(p.835)
T: 0131 2229532
E: peter.clyde@addleshawgoddard.com

COADY, Margaret Frances (Dec 1988)
(Employee)
Eversheds Sutherland (International) LLP,
Edinburgh . . . .(p.869)
T: 0207 9194500
E: MargaretCoady@eversheds-sutherland.com

COATES, Katie Louise (Oct 2013) (Employee)
BTO Solicitors LLP, Glasgow . . . . (p.952)
T: 0141 221 8012
E: kco@bto.co.uk

COATS, Greg (Sept 2016) (Employee)
MBM Commercial LLP, Edinburgh . . . . .(p.889)
T: 0131 2268200
E: greg.coats@mbmcommercial.co.uk

COBB, Kevin (Oct 2009) (Employee)
Acces Legal FZ LLC, Dubai. . . . .(p.1277)
E: kcobb@acceslegal.ae

COBURN, Greg (Oct 2016) (Employee)
Mourant Ozannes (Guernsey) LLP, St Peter
Port . . . .(p.1273)
E: Greg.Coburn@mourant.com

COCHRAN, Alasdair Stuart (Nov 1994)
(Director)
Slater and Gordon Scotland Limited,
Edinburgh . . . .(p.903)
T: 0131 7184150
E: SCochran@slatergordon.co.uk

COCHRAN, Jennifer May (Aug 2006) (Director)
Cochran Dickie, Paisley . . . .(p.1137)
T: 0141 8892245
E: jmc@cochrandickie.co.uk

COCHRAN, Sascha Jane (Sept 2001) (Employee)
Harper Macleod LLP, Edinburgh . . . .(p.877)
T: 0131 2472500
E: Sascha.cochran@harpermacleod.co.uk

COCHRANE, Alastair Norman (Sept 1987)
(Partner)
Barnetts, Kilmarnock . . . .(p.1093)
T: 01563 522137
E: AlastairNCochrane@barnettslaw.co.uk

COCHRANE, Claire Elizabeth (Aug 2018)
(Employee)
Dailly, Walker and Co., Solicitors,
Glasgow. . . . .(p.965)
T: 0141 4402503
E: ccochrane@govanlc.com

COCHRANE, Gail Gwendoline (Nov 2008)
(Employee)
Natixis, Paris . . . .(p.1272)

COCHRANE, Kathryn Judith (Nov 2000)
(Employee)
McCarthy Law, Glasgow . . . .(p.1006)
T: 0141 3376678

COCHRANE, Seonaid Claire (Aug 2016)
(Employee)
SKO Family Law Specialists LLP,
Edinburgh . . . .(p.903)
T: 0131 3226669
E: seonaid.cochrane@sko-family.co.uk

COCHRANE, Steven Francis (Jan 2006) (Partner)
CMS Cameron McKenna Nabarro Olswang LLP,
London EC4 . . . .(p.1263)
T: 0207 3673000
E: steven.cochrane@cms-cmno.com

COCHRANE, Susan Catriona (Oct 1994)
(Employee)
Scottish Environment Protection Agency,
Holytown . . . .(p.1248)
T: 01698 839 000
E: susan.cochrane@sepa.org.uk

COCKBAIN, Caroline McShane (Oct 2002)
(Associate)
Just Employment Law Ltd,
Glasgow. . . . .(p.1240)
T: 0141 3315150
E: carolinecockbain@justemploymentlaw.co.uk

COCKBURN, Barbara Susan (Jan 1982)
(Partner)
Cockburn McGrane, Anstruther . . . .(p.755)
T: 01333 730 803
E: barbara@cockburnmcgrane.co.uk

COCKBURN, Charlotte Anne (Jun 2019)
(Employee)
Scottish Social Services Council,
Dundee . . . .(p.1218)
T: 0345 6030 891
E: charlotte.cockburn@sssc.uk.com

COCKBURN, Elizabeth Ross (Aug 1972)
(Partner)
Cockburn & Co., Bridge of Weir . . . . . .(p.780)
T: 01505 690500
E: ercockburn@cockburnandco.com

COCKBURN, Kirsten (Sept 2010) (Employee)
Procurator Fiscal Service,
Edinburgh . . . .(p.1229)
T: 0300 0203000
E: Kirsten.Cockburn@copfs.gov.uk

COCKBURN, Linda Jean (Aug 2000) (Employee)
Procurator Fiscal Service,
Edinburgh . . . .(p.1227)
T: 0300 0203168
E: linda.cockburn@copfs.gov.uk

COCKBURN, Richard James (Oct 1995)
(Partner)
Womble Bond Dickinson (UK) LLP,
Edinburgh . . . .(p.913)
T: 0345 415 0000
E: richard.cockburn@wbd-uk.com

COCKBURN, Ruth Lindsay (Aug 2020)
(Employee)
Procurator Fiscal Service, Glasgow . . . .(p.1241)
T: 0300 0203000
E: ruth.cockburn@copfs.gov.uk

COCKSEDGE, Shona Louise (Dec 2017)
(Employee)
Thompsons, Glasgow . . . .(p.1046)
T: 0141 2218840
E:
shona.cocksedge@thompsons-scotland.co.uk

COFFEY, Sophie (Aug 2005) (Associate)
Burness Paull LLP, Edinburgh . . . .(p.850)
T: 0131 4736000
E: Sophie.Coffey@burnesspaull.com

COFFIELD, Matthew James (Jan 2001) (Partner)
MJC LAW, Paisley . . . .(p.1140)
T: 0141 849 2041
E: matthew@mjclaw.co.uk

COHEN, Dorothy Zedzani (Jun 2012)
(Employee)
Scottish Government, Glasgow . . . . . .(p.1243)
T: 0141 2727226
E: Dorothy.Cohen@gov.scot

COHEN, Philip Harris (Sept 1989) (Director)
Philip Cohen Solicitors Limited,
Glasgow. . . . .(p.963)
T: 0141 6312412
E: lawyer@philipcohen.co.uk

COLALUCA, Natalie (Jul 2009) (Associate)
Pinsent Masons LLP, Glasgow . . . .(p.1031)
T: 0141 567 8400
E: Natalie.Colaluca@pinsentmasons.com

COLE, Gillian Catherine (Jan 2019) (Employee)
Dentons UK and Middle East LLP,
Edinburgh . . . .(p.860)
T: 0330 2220050
E: gillian.cole@dentons.com

COLE, Lauren (Aug 2016) (Employee)
Procurator Fiscal Service, Airdrie . . . . . .(p.1214)
T: 01236 747027
E: Lauren.Cole@copfs.gov.uk

COLE, Robbie (Oct 2019) (Employee)
Rradar (Scotland) Limited,
Glasgow. . . . .(p.1036)
E: Robbie.cole@rradar.com

COLE, Ruaridh Mark (Oct 2009) (Partner)
Burness Paull LLP, Edinburgh . . . .(p.850)
T: 0131 4736119
E: ruaridh.cole@burnesspaull.com

COLE, Victoria Stefanie (Aug 2014) (Employee)
Burness Paull LLP, Edinburgh . . . .(p.850)
T: 0131 4736000
E: Victoria.Marsden@burnesspaull.com

COLE, William Pitkaithley (Apr 2001) (Partner)
BTO Solicitors LLP, Edinburgh . . . .(p.849)
T: 0131 2222939
E: wco@bto.co.uk

COLEMAN, Hannah Clara (Sept 2004)
(Employee)
Scottish Social Services Council,
Dundee . . . .(p.1218)
T: 0345 6030 891
E: hannah.coleman@sssc.uk.com

COLEMAN, Rachel Jane (Oct 2014) (Employee)
Pinsent Masons LLP, Edinburgh . . . .(p.895)
T: 0131 777 7000
E: rachel.coleman@pinsentmasons.com

COLES, Thomas Harry (Jul 2017) (Employee)
TotalEnergies E&P UK Limited,
Westhill . . . .(p.1255)
T: 01224 297818
E: tom.coles@total.com

COLHOUN, Jan Claire (Nov 2012) (Employee)
DLA Piper UK LLP, London EC1 . . . . . .(p.1263)
T: 020 77966017
E: jan.colhoun@dlapiper.com

COLHOUN, Louise (Jul 2019) (Employee)
MacArthur Legal, Oban . . . .(p.1134)
T: 01631 562215
E: louise@macarthurlegal.co.uk

COLL, Natalie Debra Thoars (Sept 2018)
(Employee)
Ledingham Chalmers LLP,
Inverness . . . .(p.1078)
T: 01463 667400
E: natalie.coll@ledinghamchalmers.com

COLLAR, Neil Andrew (Feb 1993) (Partner)
Brodies LLP, Edinburgh . . . .(p.845)
T: 0131 2283777
E: neil.collar@brodies.com

COLLEDGE, Jennifer Claire (Sept 1996)
(Partner)
Colledge & Shields LLP, Dumfries . . . . .(p.800)
T: 01387 240044
E: jcc@colledgeandshields.co.uk

COLLEDGE, Roger Parker (Nov 1990) (Partner)
Brazenall & Orr, Dumfries . . . .(p.800)
T: 01387 255695
E: roger@brazenallandorr.co.uk

COLLIE, Barbara Anne (Nov 1989) (Employee)
W. & A.S. Bruce, Dunfermline . . . .(p.822)
T: 01383 738000
E: barbara@wasbruce.co.uk

COLLIN, Alastair Buchan (Oct 1993) (Associate)
Turcan Connell, Edinburgh . . . .(p.908)
T: 0131 2288111
E: Alastair.collin@turcanconnell.com

COLLINGHAM, Douglas (Dec 1990) (Partner)
TC Young LLP, Glasgow . . . .(p.1055)
T: 0141 2215562
E: dxc@tcyoung.co.uk

COLLINGHAM, Lynne (Oct 1990) (Partner)
TC Young LLP, Glasgow . . . .(p.1055)
T: 0141 2215562
E: lyc@tcyoung.co.uk

COLLINS, Eilidh Jane (Jan 2021) (Employee)
Pinsent Masons LLP, Edinburgh . . . .(p.895)
T: 0131 777 7000
E: eilidh.collins@pinsentmasons.com

COLLINS, Francis (Oct 1986) (Partner)
Brunton Miller, Glasgow . . . .(p.951)
T: 0141 3371199
E: frankcollins@bruntonmiller.com

COLLINS, Martin John Forrester, WS
(Sept 1983) (Employee)
Procurator Fiscal Service,
Edinburgh . . . .(p.1227)
T: 0300 0203168
E: Martin.collins@civilrecoveryunit.gov.scot

COLLINS, Michael Alan (Oct 2008) (Associate)
Pinsent Masons LLP, Glasgow . . . .(p.1031)
T: 0141 567 8400
E: michael.collins@pinsentmasons.com

COLLINS, Michael Philip (Apr 2014) (Employee)
TLT LLP, Glasgow . . . .(p.1048)
T: 0333 006 0400
E: michael.collins@tltsolicitors.com

COLLINS, Sarah Marie (Dec 2012) (Employee)
Educational Institute of Scotland,
Edinburgh . . . .(p.1222)
T: (0131) 225 6244
E: scollins@EIS.org.uk

COLLINS, Sharon Louise (Aug 2007)
(Employee)
Harold W. Joseph, Glasgow . . . .(p.994)
T: 0141 4201896
E: sharon.collins@live.co.uk

COLLINS, Simon Gerard Corrieri (Sept 1993)
(Director)
Collins & Co Defence Lawyers Ltd,
Edinburgh . . . .(p.857)
T: 0131 661 3210
E: scollins@collinsandcolawyers.com

COLLINS-WHYTE, Patricia Jane (Jan 2014)
(Employee)
Delaney Graham Limited, Glasgow . . . . .(p.968)
T: 0141 4834450
E: j.collins-whyte@delaneygraham.co.uk

COLLINSON, Duncan John (Jan 1984) (Director)
Allingham & Co (Solicitors) Limited,
Edinburgh . . . .(p.838)
T: 0131 4479341
E: duncan@allingham.co.uk

COLLISTON, Caroline Anne Watt (Oct 1998)
(Partner)
DWF LLP, Edinburgh . . . .(p.865)
T: 0131 474 2333
E: Caroline.Colliston@dwf.law

COLLISTON, Stephen David (Nov 1995)
(Partner)
Shepherd and Wedderburn LLP,
Edinburgh . . . .(p.900)
T: 0131 2289900
E: stephen.colliston@shepwedd.com

COLQUHOUN, Annmaria (Aug 2002)
(Employee)
Procurator Fiscal Service, Glasgow . . . .(p.1241)
T: 0300 0203000
E: Annmaria.Colquhoun@copfs.gov.uk

COLQUHOUN, Mark James (Jun 2002)
(Associate)
BTO Solicitors LLP, Edinburgh . . . .(p.849)
T: 0131 2222939
E: mcl@bto.co.uk

COLQUHOUN, Scott Houston (Sept 1992)
(Employee)
Taylor Wimpey UK Limited, Paisley . . . .(p.1253)
T: 0141 849 5583
E: scott.colquhoun@taylorwimpey.com

COLTART, Rebecca Carol (Sept 2019)
(Employee)
Miller Hendry, Perth . . . .(p.1150)
T: 01738 637311
E: rebeccacoltart@millerhendry.co.uk

COLTMAN, Eilidh Margaret (May 2021)
(Employee)
Thorley Stephenson Ltd,
Edinburgh . . . .(p.906)
T: 0131 5569599

COLVIN, Jennifer Anne (Oct 2016) (Employee)
Pinsent Masons LLP, Aberdeen . . . .(p.739)
T: 01224 377900
E: Jenni.Colvin@pinsentmasons.com

COMBE, Lyndsey Helen Janet (Sept 2014)
(Associate)
Clyde & Co (Scotland) LLP,
Edinburgh . . . .(p.855)
T: 0131 5571545
E: lyndsey.combe@clydeco.com

COMBE, Sarah Anne (May 2015) (Employee)
Pinsent Masons LLP, Edinburgh . . . .(p.895)
T: 0131 777 7000
E: sarah.combe@pinsentmasons.com

COMFORT, Christopher Robert (Jul 2011)
(Partner)
Aberdein Considine and Company,
Aberdeen . . . .(p.718)
T: 01224 267067
E: ccomfort@acandco.com

COMFORT, Eleanor Clare (Sept 2014)
(Employee)
Aberdein Considine and Company,
Aberdeen . . . .(p.717)
T: 01224 723737
E: ecomfort@acandco.com

COMISKEY, Louise Marion (Feb 2002)
(Employee)
Ofgem, Glasgow . . . .(p.1241)
T: (0141) 354 5425
E: louise.comiskey@ofgem.gov.uk

COMRIE, Eva Margaret (Aug 1986) (Partner)
Comrie Law, Alva . . . .(p.754)
T: 01259 235567
E: eva@comrielaw.co.uk

COMRIE-BRYANT, Fraser Ronald (Jul 2021)
(Employee)
Tait Macleod, Falkirk . . . .(p.925)
T: 01324 888877

CONACHER, Eildh Jayne (Mar 2021) (Employee)
Brodies LLP, Dingwall . . . .(p.796)
T: 01349 860111
E: Eildh.conacher@brodies.com

CONAGHAN, Mark John (Oct 1993) (Employee)
Renfrewshire Council, Paisley . . . . (p.1252)
T: 0141 6187177
E: mark.conaghan@renfrewshire.gov.uk

CONDIE, Alexis Kasia (Aug 2005) (Associate)
Dentons UK and Middle East LLP,
Edinburgh . . . . (p.860)
T: 0330 2220050
E: Alexis.Condie@dentons.com

CONDIE, Karen Tracey (Nov 1988) (Director)
Holmes Mackillop Limited,
Glasgow . . . . (p.986)
T: 0141 226 4942
E: kcondie@homack.co.uk

CONINGTON, Sam Patrick (Sept 2020)
(Employee)
Gillespie Macandrew LLP,
Edinburgh . . . . (p.872)
T: 0131 2251677
E: sam.conington@gillespiemacandrew.co.uk

CONLIN, John Thomas (Nov 2002) (Employee)
Bryan Cave Leighton Paisner LLP, London
EC4 . . . . (p.1262)
E: John.conlin@bclplaw.com

CONLON, Gillian Frances (Aug 1994) (Partner)
Beveridge & Kellas, Edinburgh . . . . (p.843)
T: 0131 5546321
E: g.conlon@beveridgekellas.com

CONN, Joel Martin (Sept 1998) (Director)
Mitchells Roberton Ltd, Glasgow . . . . . (p.1020)
T: 0141 5523422
E: jmc@mitchells-roberton.co.uk

CONN, Lucy Ferguson (Oct 2013) (Solicitor)
NO FIRM

CONNACHAN, Claire (May 2009) (Employee)
Procurator Fiscal Service, Paisley . . . . . . (p.1252)
T: 0141 8875225
E: claire.connachan@copfs.gov.uk

CONNAL, Robert Craig, QC (Aug 1977)
(Solicitor)
NO FIRM

CONNARTY, Scott Owen (Oct 2013)
(Employee)
Ridgewall Limited, London EC1 . . . . . . (p.1267)
E: scott.connarty@ridgewall.co.uk

CONNELL, Collette Catherine (Feb 2002)
(Director)
Bell Russell & Company Limited,
Airdrie . . . . (p.748)
T: 01236 764781
E: cconnell@bell-russell.com

CONNELL, Danielle Mari (Sept 2021)
(Employee)
Thorntons Law LLP, Dundee . . . . (p.819)
T: 01382 229 111
E: dconnell@thorntons-law.co.uk

CONNELL, Elizabeth Sarah (Sept 2011)
(Employee)
Office of the Advocate General,
Edinburgh . . . . (p.1227)
T: 0131 2441635
E: lizzie.connell@advocategeneral.gov.uk

CONNELL, Lianne (Aug 2021) (Employee)
Gilson Gray LLP, Edinburgh . . . . (p.874)
T: 0131 5165354
E: lconnell@gilsongray.co.uk

CONNELLY, John James (Aug 2010) (Employee)
Irwin Mitchell Scotland LLP,
Glasgow . . . . (p.991)
T: 0141 3004300
E: john.connelly@irwinmitchellscotland.com

CONNELLY, Kate (Oct 2021) (Employee)
Scottish Government, Edinburgh . . . . . (p.1231)
T: 0131 244 0815
E: kate.connelly@gov.scot

CONNELLY, Martin John (Jul 2013) (Employee)
Burness Paull LLP, Edinburgh . . . . (p.850)
T: 0131 4736000
E: Martin.Connelly@burnesspaull.com

CONNELLY, Pamela-Jane (Oct 2016)
(Employee)
Procurator Fiscal Service, Glasgow . . . . (p.1241)
T: 0300 0203000
E: pamela-jane.connelly@copfs.gov.uk

CONNER, Rosemary (Feb 1990) (Employee)
North Ayrshire Council, Irvine . . . . (p.1249)
T: 01294 310000
E: rconner@north-ayrshire.gov.uk

CONNERTON, Dr, Janet (Mar 2009) (Employee)
Covance Clinical and Periapproval Services Ltd,
Edinburgh . . . . (p.1222)
T: 0131 5507700
E: Jan.Connerton@covance.com

CONNOLLY, Caitlin (Mar 2020) (Employee)
Lindsays LLP, Edinburgh . . . . (p.882)
T: 0131 2291212
E: caitlinconnolly@lindsays.co.uk

CONNOLLY, Fiona Agnes (Jun 2005) (Partner)
Mackintosh & Wylie LLP,
Kilmarnock . . . . (p.1095)
T: 01563 525104
E: fconnolly@mackwylie.com

CONNOLLY, Julie Marie (Aug 2012) (Employee)
Ashurst LLP, London E1 . . . . (p.1261)
T: (020) 7859 2145
E: julie.connolly@ashurst.com

CONNOLLY, Mark (Sept 1998) (Director)
JC Hughes Solicitors Limited,
Glasgow . . . . (p.988)
T: 0141 6470700
E: mc@jchughes.net

CONNOLLY, Monica Louise (Aug 2011)
(Employee)
Brodies LLP, Glasgow . . . .(p.948)
T: 0141 2484672
E: monica.connolly@brodies.com

CONNOLLY, Paul Anthony (Nov 2000)
(Partner)
Pinsent Masons LLP, Glasgow . . . .(p.1031)
T: 0141 567 8400
E: paul.connolly@pinsentmasons.com

CONNOLLY, Paul Macintyre (Sept 2007)
(Employee)
Dentons UK and Middle East LLP,
Glasgow. . . . .(p.968)
T: 0330 2220050
E: paul.connolly@dentons.com

CONNOLLY, Stephen David (Mar 2004)
(Partner)
Blackadders LLP, Glasgow . . . .(p.946)
T: 0141 2481888
E: stephen.connolly@blackadders.co.uk

CONNON, Roger Gordon (Sept 1988)
(Employee)
Pinsent Masons LLP, Aberdeen . . . .(p.739)
T: 01224 377900
E: roger.connon@pinsentmasons.com

CONNON, Sarah Catherine Guthrie
(Jan 1976) (Employee)
Campbell Smith LLP, Edinburgh . . . .(p.852)
T: 0131 473 7709
E: sarah.connon@camsmith.co.uk

CONNOR, Abby (Sept 2017) (Employee)
Thompson Family Law, Glasgow . . . . .(p.1046)
T: 0141 4046575
E: abby@tflaw.co.uk

CONNOR, Caitlin McNally (Oct 2018)
(Employee)
Carey Olsen, St Helier . . . .(p.1274)
T: 01534 888900
E: caitlin.connor@careyolsen.com

CONNOR, Deborah Anne (Oct 2001)
(Associate)
DWF LLP, Glasgow . . . .(p.973)
T: 0141 228 8000
E: debbie.connor@dwf.law

CONNOR, Kevin Paul (Sept 2015) (Employee)
Wardlaw Stephenson Allan,
Edinburgh . . . .(p.910)
T: 0131 5578020
E: kevin@wsalawyers.com

CONNOR, Laura (Feb 2008) (Partner)
Thompsons, Glasgow . . . .(p.1046)
T: 0141 2218840
E: laura.connor@thompsons-scotland.co.uk

CONNOR, Scott James Duncan (Sept 2017)
(Employee)
Aberdeen City Council, Aberdeen . . . . .(p.1211)
T: 01224 522000
E: sconnor@aberdeencity.gov.uk

CONNOR, Stephanie Josephine (Jul 2014)
(Employee)
Fullbrook Associates, Stirling . . . .(p.1254)
T: 01786 451903
E: stephanie@fullbrookassociates.com

CONROY, Alan (Dec 1984) (Director)
Conroy McInnes Limited, Glasgow . . . . .(p.963)
T: 0141 6166622
E: mail@conroymcinnes.co.uk

CONROY, Louise Kathleen (Jul 2008)
(Associate)
Burness Paull LLP, Glasgow . . . .(p.954)
T: 0141 2484933
E: louise.conroy@burnesspaull.com

CONROY, Mark John Michael (Sept 2016)
(Employee)
Ofgem, Glasgow . . . .(p.1241)
T: (0141) 354 5425
E: mark.conroy@ofgem.gov.uk

CONROY, Michael Christopher (Jan 1991)
(Partner)
Harper Macleod LLP, Glasgow . . . .(p.983)
T: 0141 2218888
E: michael.conroy@harpermacleod.co.uk

CONROY, Nicole (Jan 2015) (Director)
Thorley Stephenson Ltd,
Edinburgh . . . .(p.906)
T: 0131 5569599
E: ncc@thorleystephenson.com

CONROY, Susan (Mar 1994) (Employee)
Scottish Government, Glasgow . . . . . .(p.1243)
T: 0141 2727225
E: susan.conroy@gov.scot

CONSIDINE, Daniel John (Nov 2020)
(Employee)
Anderson Strathern LLP, Edinburgh . . . .(p.839)
T: 0131 2707700
E: daniel.considine@andersonstrathern.co.uk

CONSIDINE, Laura Jane (Jan 2005) (Partner)
Aberdein Considine and Company,
Stonehaven . . . .(p.1168)
T: 01569 766166
E: lconsidine@acandco.com

CONSTABLE, Andrew Alan (Nov 1996)
(Partner)
Clyde & Co (Scotland) LLP,
Edinburgh . . . .(p.855)
T: 0131 5571545
E: andrew.constable@clydeco.com

CONVERY, Anthony (Nov 2008) (Employee)
Pinsent Masons LLP, Glasgow . . . .(p.1031)
T: 0141 567 8400
E: anthony.convery@pinsentmasons.com

CONVERY, Anthony Peter (Aug 2018)
(Employee)
Brodies LLP, Glasgow . . . .(p.948)
T: 0141 2484672
E: tony.convery@brodies.com

CONVERY, Marc (Mar 2013) (Employee)
Russel + Aitken (Falkirk + Alloa) Ltd,
Falkirk . . . .(p.924)
T: 01324 622888
E: marcconvery@russel-aitken.co.uk

CONWAY, Emma Louise (Oct 2016) (Employee)
Lindsays LLP, Dundee . . . .(p.814)
T: 01382 224112
E: emmaconway@lindsays.co.uk

CONWAY, Keren Louise (Jun 2015) (Employee)
East Lothian Council, Haddington . . . .(p.1246)
T: 01620 827827
E: kconway@eastlothian.gov.uk

CONWAY, Nyree Mary (Feb 1999) (Director)
Thorley Stephenson Ltd,
Edinburgh . . . .(p.906)
T: 0131 5569599
E: nc@thorleystephenson.com

CONWAY, Rachel Anne (Apr 2019) (Employee)
The Conway Accident Law Practice Ltd,
Glasgow. . . . .(p.1043)
T: 0141 319 8240
E: rachelc@accidentlawscotland.com

CONWAY, Ronald Edward (Jan 1978) (Director)
The Conway Accident Law Practice Ltd,
Glasgow. . . . .(p.1043)
T: 0141 319 8240
E: ronniec@accidentlawscotland.com

COOGAN, John Patrick (Jul 2010) (Employee)
Procurator Fiscal Service, Hamilton . . . .(p.1247)
T: 0844 5613245

COOK, Alan Russell (Dec 1992) (Partner)
Pinsent Masons LLP, Glasgow . . . .(p.1031)
T: 0141 567 8400
E: alan.cook@pinsentmasons.com

COOK, Alison Jean (Oct 1991) (Employee)
Social Care and Social Work Improvement
Scotland, Aberdeen . . . .(p.1214)
T: 01224 793870
E: alison.cook@careinspectorate.gov.scot

COOK, Amy Jane Frances (Oct 2006)
(Employee)
Renfrewshire Council, Paisley . . . .(p.1252)
T: 0141 6187171
E: amy.cook@renfrewshire.gov.uk

COOK, Catherine Stacey (Nov 1994) (Solicitor)
NO FIRM

COOK, Faye Elizabeth (Oct 2005) (Employee)
Procurator Fiscal Service,
Edinburgh . . . .(p.1227)
T: 03000 203529
E: faye.cook@copfs.gov.uk

COOK, Fiona Elspeth (Aug 1994) (Partner)
Cook, Stevenson & Co., Greenock . . . .(p.1061)
T: 01475 722100
E: mcaleescook@gmail.com

COOK, Jacqueline Elizabeth (Aug 2009)
(Employee)
Davidson Chalmers Stewart LLP,
Edinburgh . . . .(p.859)
T: 0131 6259191
E: Jacqueline.Cook@dcslegal.com

COOK, Kenneth Craig (Aug 1990) (Employee)
Ferguson Whyte, Glasgow . . . .(p.975)
T: 0141 3398432

COOK, Lauren Rose (May 2011) (Associate)
DANDHLAW LIMITED, Kirkwall. . . . . . .(p.1106)
T: 01856 872216
E: lrc@dandhlaw.co.uk

COOK, Nadia Ann (Sept 2019) (Employee)
DAC Beachcroft Scotland LLP,
Glasgow. . . . .(p.964)
T: 0141 2486688
E: nadcook@dacbeachcroft.com

COOK, Nicole Louise (Jul 2010) (Associate)
MacRoberts LLP, Glasgow . . . .(p.1015)
T: 0141 3031100
E: nicole.cook@macroberts.com

COOK, Rosie (Dec 2015) (Employee)
Procurator Fiscal Service,
Edinburgh . . . .(p.1227)
T: 0844 5613000
E: Rosie.Cook@copfs.gov.uk

COOKE, Abigail Louise (Sept 2017) (Associate)
Clyde & Co (Scotland) LLP,
Edinburgh . . . .(p.855)
T: 0131 5571545
E: Abigail.Cooke@clydeco.com

COOKE, Amanda Jayne (Oct 1996) (Associate)
Eversheds Sutherland (International) LLP,
Edinburgh . . . .(p.869)
T: 0207 9194500
E: AmandaCooke@eversheds-sutherland.com

COOKE, Christina (Oct 2014) (Employee)
Pinsent Masons LLP, London EC2 . . . . .(p.1267)
T: 020 7418 7000
E: christina.cooke@pinsentmasons.com

COOKE, Gordon Wilson (Feb 1995) (Partner)
McKenzies, Kirkcaldy . . . .(p.1101)
T: 01592 206605
E: gordoncooke@mckenzies-sols.co.uk

COOKE, Nigel Charles (Oct 1985) (Partner)
McKenzies, Kirkcaldy . . . . (p.1101)
T: 01592 206605
E: nigelcooke@mckenzies-sols.co.uk

COOKE, Rachael Elizabeth (Aug 2014)
(Employee)
Hymans Robertson LLP, Glasgow . . . . . (p.1240)
T: 0141 5667777
E: rachael.cooke@hymans.co.uk

COOLEY, Sheelagh (Nov 2002) (Partner)
Shoosmiths, Edinburgh . . . . (p.902)
T: 03700 868000
E: Sheelagh.Cooley@shoosmiths.co.uk

COOMBS, Maria Francesca (Sept 1995)
(Director)
Coombs Solicitors and Notaries Limited,
Edinburgh . . . . (p.858)
T: 07764 186588
E: francesca.coombs@coombs-solicitors.com

COONEY, Ann Frances (Nov 2003) (Partner)
DWF LLP, Glasgow . . . . (p.973)
T: 0141 228 8000
E: AnnFrances.Cooney@dwf.law

COONEY, Brian (Aug 2013) (Partner)
Fleming & Reid, Glasgow . . . . (p.977)
T: 0141 3311144

COONEY, Monique (May 2018) (Employee)
Procurator Fiscal Service, Glasgow . . . . (p.1241)
T: 0300 0203000
E: Monique.Cooney@copfs.gov.uk

COONEY, Samantha (Sept 2019) (Employee)
Pinsent Masons LLP, Glasgow . . . . (p.1031)
T: 0141 567 8400
E: samantha.cooney@pinsentmasons.com

COOPER, Diane Caroline (Oct 2009) (Associate)
Digby Brown LLP, Glasgow . . . . (p.970)
T: 0333 200 5925
E: diane.cooper@digbybrown.co.uk

COOPER, Donna Marie (Nov 2006) (Associate)
Brodies LLP, Edinburgh . . . . (p.845)
T: 0131 2283777
E: donna.cooper@brodies.com

COOPER, Gavin Bruce (May 2003) (Associate)
Raeburn Christie Clark & Wallace LLP,
Aberdeen . . . . (p.741)
T: 01224 564636
E: gavin.cooper@raeburns.co.uk

COOPER, Kirstine Ann (Apr 1989) (Employee)
AVIVA Plc, London EC3 . . . . (p.1261)
T: 020 7662 6646
E: kirsty.cooper@aviva.com

COOPER, Kirsty Anne (Oct 2005) (Associate)
Lindsays LLP, Edinburgh . . . . (p.882)
T: 0131 2291212
E: kirstycooper@lindsays.co.uk

COOPER, Kirsty Emma (Mar 2013) (Employee)
Brodies LLP, Edinburgh . . . . (p.845)
T: 0131 2283777
E: kirsty.cooper@brodies.com

COOPER, Louise Catherine (Aug 1985)
(Partner)
Reid Cooper, Glasgow. . . . . (p.1034)
T: 0141 4294656
E: lcc@reidcooper.co.uk

COOPER, Michael Andrew (Sept 2010)
(Employee)
Trustpilot, Edinburgh . . . . (p.1235)
E: mcoo@trustpilot.com

COOPER, Rachel Elizabeth Ellen (Oct 2016)
(Employee)
Kingsley Napley LLP, London EC2 . . . . (p.1265)
T: 0207 8141200
E: rcooper@kingsleynapley.co.uk

COOPER, Ross Filshie (Oct 2014) (Employee)
Pinsent Masons LLP, Glasgow . . . . (p.1031)
T: 0141 567 8400
E: Ross.Cooper@pinsentmasons.com

COOPER, Sarah (Jun 2017) (Employee)
Thorntons Law LLP, Dundee . . . . (p.819)
T: 01382 229 111
E: sarahcooper@thorntons-law.co.uk

COOPER, Timothy (Aug 2019) (Partner)
Addleshaw Goddard LLP,
Edinburgh . . . . (p.835)
T: 0131 2282400
E: tim.cooper@addleshawgoddard.com

COPLAND, Eli ka (Jun 2015) (Solicitor)
NO FIRM

COPLAND, Rhea (Jul 2018) (Employee)
Procurator Fiscal Service, Aberdeen . . . (p.1213)
T: (0300) 0202336
E: rhea.copland@copfs.gov.uk

COPP, Fiona Elizabeth (May 2017) (Employee)
Mackinnons Solicitors LLP,
Aberdeen . . . . (p.736)
T: 01224 632464
E: fionacopp@mackinnons.com

CORBETT, Iain Steven (Sept 2015) (Employee)
FNZ, Edinburgh . . . . (p.1223)
T: (0131) 5241900
E: iain.corbett@fnz.co.uk

CORBETT, John Robin Bryson (Dec 1978)
(Solicitor)
NO FIRM

CORBETT, Nicola (Sept 2004) (Employee)
CNR International (U.K.) Limited,
Aberdeen . . . . (p.1212)
T: 01224 308066
E: nicola.corbett@cnrl.com

CORLEY, Victoria Mary Louise (Nov 2006)
(Solicitor)
NO FIRM

CORMACK, Emma Christine (Oct 2007)
(Employee)
National Health Service Scotland,
Edinburgh . . . .(p.1225)
T: 0131 2757197
E: emma.cormack@nhs.scot

CORMACK, Helen Jane (Feb 1990) (Employee)
MHD Law LLP, Edinburgh . . . .(p.890)
T: 0131 5550616
E: jane.cormack@mhdlaw.co.uk

CORMACK, James Shearer (Dec 1992) (Partner)
Pinsent Masons LLP, Edinburgh . . . .(p.895)
T: 0131 7777356
E: jim.cormack@pinsentmasons.com

CORMACK, Laura (Apr 2019) (Director)
Innes & Mackay Limited, Inverness . . . .(p.1078)
T: 01463 232273
E: laurac@innesmackay.com

CORMACK, Lee (Oct 1996) (Employee)
Glasgow City Council, Glasgow . . . . . .(p.1239)
T: 0141 2874145
E: lee.cormack@ced.glasgow.gov.uk

CORMACK, Myles Alexander (Aug 2017)
(Employee)
Allen & Overy LLP, London E1 . . . .(p.1261)
T: 020 3088 0000
E: myles.cormack@allenovery.com

CORMACK, Roderick Stewart (Aug 1999)
(Associate)
Wright, Johnston & Mackenzie LLP,
Inverness . . . .(p.1083)
T: 01463 234445
E: rsc@wjm.co.uk

CORNELIUS, Amy Audrey (Sept 2011)
(Employee)
Dentons UK and Middle East LLP,
Glasgow . . . .(p.968)
T: 0330 2220050
E: amy.cornelius@dentons.com

CORNELIUS, Anne Bicket (May 1996) (Solicitor)
NO FIRM

CORNWELL, Jonathan Islay (Mar 1999)
(Partner)
Lindsays LLP, Glasgow. . . . .(p.1001)
T: 0141 2216551
E: jonathancornwell@linsdays.co.uk

CORNWELL, Karen Margaret (Aug 1999)
(Employee)
Thorntons Law LLP, Dundee . . . .(p.819)
T: 01382 229 111
E: kcornwell@thorntons-law.co.uk

CORR, Catherine Mary (Sept 2004) (Employee)
Scottish Enterprise, Glasgow . . . .(p.1243)
T: 0141 2482700
E: Catherine.Corr@scotent.co.uk

CORR, Kevin James (Dec 2016) (Employee)
Graham Walker, Glasgow . . . .(p.1050)
T: 0141 9460111
E: kc@gwsolicitors.com

CORR, Lee (Jun 2016) (Employee)
Thorntons Law LLP, Dundee . . . .(p.819)
T: 01382 229 111
E: lcorr@thorntons-law.co.uk

CORR, Michael Brian (Aug 2017) (Employee)
Aberdeen Corporate Services Limited,
Edinburgh . . . .(p.1220)
T: 0131 245 7508
E: michael.corr@abrdn.com

CORRANCE, Joanna Mary (Jan 2016)
(Employee)
Digby Brown LLP, Inverness . . . .(p.1075)
T: 0333 200 5925
E: Joanna.Corrance@digbybrown.co.uk

CORRIERI, Claire McGilvary (Nov 2018)
(Employee)
Neilsons, Edinburgh . . . .(p.894)
T: 0131 3164444

CORRIGALL, David Peter (Apr 2021)
(Employee)
Katani & Co. Ltd, Glasgow . . . .(p.994)
T: 0141 2217788
E: david.corrigall@kataniandco.com

CORRIGAN, Catriona Margaret (Oct 2002)
(Employee)
Vialex Limited, Edinburgh . . . .(p.1235)
T: 0333 2400127
E: Katie.Corrigan@vialex.co.uk

CORRIGAN, James Paul Kennedy (Nov 1999)
(Employee)
NORTH LANARKSHIREre Council,
Motherwell. . . . .(p.1251)
T: 01698 302196
E: CorriganPa@northlan.gov.uk

CORRIGAN, Mairead Clare (Mar 2021)
(Employee)
Burnett Christie Knowles McCourts,
Edinburgh . . . .(p.852)
T: 0131 2253456
E: mc@bckm.co.uk

CORRIGAN, Sin ad (Sept 2010) (Partner)
Corrigan Law, Glasgow . . . .(p.964)
T: 07763 704253
E: mail@corriganlaw.co.uk

CORRINS, Henry Kevin (Jun 2012) (Employee)
Procurator Fiscal Service, Glasgow . . . .(p.1241)
T: 0300 0203000
E: kevin.corrins@copfs.gov.uk

CORRINS, Maire Sineidin (Dec 1997)
(Employee)
Procurator Fiscal Service, Falkirk . . . . . . (p.1236)
T: 0300 020 3000
E: sineidin.corrins@copfs.gov.uk

COSGROVE, Hannah Louise (Jan 2015)
(Employee)
Latta Law Limited, Glasgow . . . . (p.998)
T: 0141 222 2185
E: HannahCosgrove@lattalaw.co.uk

COSSAR, Karen Anne (Sept 2015) (Associate)
CMS Cameron McKenna Nabarro Olswang LLP,
Glasgow . . . . (p.962)
T: 0141 2222200
E: karen.cossar@cms-cmno.com

COSTA, Lindsay Christina (Sept 2009)
(Employee)
Procurator Fiscal Service, Glasgow . . . . (p.1242)
E: Lindsay.Costa@copfs.gov.uk

COSTELLO, Greg (Sept 2014) (Employee)
Brodies LLP, Edinburgh . . . . (p.845)
T: 0131 2283777
E: greg.costello@brodies.com

COSTELLO, Luke Joseph (Aug 2019) (Employee)
Pinsent Masons LLP, London EC2 . . . . . (p.1267)
T: 020 7418 7000
E: luke.costello@pinsentmasons.com

COTTON, Roger Hamish (Jan 2001) (Partner)
Brodies LLP, Edinburgh . . . . (p.845)
T: 0131 2283777
E: roger.cotton@brodies.com

COTTON, Stephen Michael (Dec 1978)
(Partner)
Wright, Johnston & Mackenzie LLP,
Edinburgh . . . . (p.913)
T: 0131 5241500
E: smc@wjm.co.uk

COTTRELL, Beverley Susan (Dec 1987)
(Employee)
Gibson Kerr (incorporating Marwicks and
Grange), Edinburgh . . . . (p.871)
T: 0131 2257558
E: beverley.cottrell@gibsonkerr.co.uk

COULL, Alison Jane (Oct 1991) (Employee)
Scottish Government, Edinburgh . . . . . (p.1231)
T: 0131 2441470
E: alison.coull@gov.scot

COULL, Elaine Rose (Oct 1989) (Employee)
National Health Service Scotland,
Edinburgh . . . . (p.1225)
T: 0131 2757800
E: elaine.coull@nhs.scot

COULTER, Caroline (Jun 2000) (Associate)
Addleshaw Goddard LLP, Glasgow . . . . . (p.938)
T: 0141 2212300
E: caroline.coulter@addleshawgoddard.com

COULTER, Fiona Elizabeth (Jun 2000)
(Employee)
Glasgow City Council, Glasgow . . . . . . (p.1239)
T: 0141 2872000
E: fiona.coulter@glasgow.gov.uk

COULTER, Lee Donald (Mar 2012) (Employee)
Perth & Kinross Council, Perth . . . . (p.1253)
T: 01738 475000
E: LCoulter@pkc.gov.uk

COULTER, Morven Kirsty (Oct 2001)
(Employee)
City of Edinburgh Council,
Edinburgh . . . . (p.1221)
T: (0131) 5294145

COULTHARD, Pamela Clare (Dec 2002)
(Associate)
Dentons UK and Middle East LLP,
Glasgow . . . . (p.968)
T: 0330 2220050
E: Pamela.Coulthard@dentons.com

COUPER, Derek Grant (Oct 2015) (Associate)
Morton Fraser LLP, Edinburgh . . . . (p.891)
T: 0131 2471000
E: Derek.Couper@morton-fraser.com

COURT, Caroline Isobel (Oct 1980) (Partner)
Davidson Chalmers Stewart LLP,
Edinburgh . . . . (p.859)
T: 0131 6259191
E: caroline.court@dcslegal.com

COURT, Jennifer Louise (Jul 2008) (Employee)
The Kellas Partnership, Inverurie . . . . . . (p.1086)
T: 01467 627300
E: jlc@kellas.biz

COURTNEY, Laura Caroline (Sept 2004)
(Employee)
National Westminster Bank PLC,
Edinburgh . . . . (p.1226)
T: 7825098816
E: laura.courtney@natwest.com

COUSTON, Robert James Gair (Dec 1982)
(Partner)
Shiells, Brechin . . . . (p.779)
T: 01356 622171
E: gair.couston@shiells-law.co.uk

COUTTS, David Michael (Oct 2012) (Director)
Simpson & Marwick, Edinburgh . . . . (p.903)
T: 01224 606210
E: David.Coutts@simpsonmarwick.com

COUTTS, Fiona Lynne (Oct 1995) (Partner)
Raeburn Christie Clark & Wallace LLP,
Aberdeen . . . . (p.741)
T: 01224 332400
E: fiona.coutts@raeburns.co.uk

COUTTS, Hazel Anne (Oct 2004) (Associate)
Brodies LLP, Edinburgh . . . . (p.845)
T: 0131 2283777
E: hazel.coutts@brodies.com

COUTTS, Morna Jane (Sept 1995) (Partner)
Thorntons Law LLP, Edinburgh . . . . . . (p.906)
T: 0131 2258705
E: mcoutts@thorntons-law.co.uk

COUTTS, Rachel Jane (Oct 2009) (Employee)
Scottish Government, Edinburgh . . . . . (p.1231)
T: 0131 244 0815

COWAN, Alastair Lindsay (Mar 2000) (Partner)
Addleshaw Goddard LLP,
Edinburgh . . . . (p.835)
T: 0131 2282400
E: Alastair.Cowan@addleshawgoddard.com

COWAN, Alyson Lyndsay (Oct 2015) (Associate)
TLT LLP, Glasgow . . . . (p.1048)
T: 0333 006 0400
E: alyson.cowan@TLTsolicitors.com

COWAN, Andrew Neil (May 2008) (Associate)
Shepherd and Wedderburn LLP,
Edinburgh . . . . (p.900)
T: 0131 2289900
E: neil.cowan@shepwedd.com

COWAN, Andrew Stuart (Jan 1988) (Partner)
TC Young LLP, Glasgow . . . . (p.1055)
T: 0141 2215562
E: asc@tcyoung.co.uk

COWAN, Carolyn Frances (Dec 1983)
(Employee)
Dumfries & Galloway Council,
Dumfries . . . . (p.1217)
T: 01387 260000
E: carolyn.cowan@dumgal.gov.uk

COWAN, Douglas John Lockhart (Oct 1998)
(Partner)
Keoghs Scotland LLP, Glasgow. . . . . . . (p.996)
T: 0141 2380100
E: dcowan@keoghs.co.uk

COWAN, Ian Murdoch (Mar 2005) (Employee)
Lloyds Banking Group Plc,
Edinburgh . . . . (p.1224)
T: (0131) 442 9579
E: ian.cowan@lloydsbanking.com

COWAN, Jennifer (Dec 2001) (Solicitor)
NO FIRM

COWAN, Jennifer Scott (Sept 2010) (Employee)
Latta Law Limited, Glasgow . . . . (p.998)
T: 0141 222 2185
E: jennifercowan@lattalaw.co.uk

COWAN, John Blyth (Jan 1982) (Partner)
Miller Samuel Hill Brown LLP,
Glasgow. (p.1020)
T: 0141 2211919
E: jbc@mshblegal.com

COWAN, Kitty Alexa (Aug 2006) (Employee)
Morton Fraser LLP, Edinburgh . . . . (p.891)
T: 0131 2471000
E: kitty.cowan@morton-fraser.com

COWAN, Lucy Margaret (Sept 2012)
(Employee)
Scottish Environment Protection Agency,
Edinburgh . . . . (p.1230)
T: 0131 4497296

COWAN, Rory Andrew Burriss (Jul 1997)
(Partner)
Bannatyne, Kirkwood, France & Co.,
Glasgow. (p.943)
T: 0141 2216020
E: rorycowan@bkf.co.uk

COWAN, Ross Duncan (Nov 2004) (Employee)
STV Group plc, Glasgow . . . . (p.1245)
T: 0141 3003300
E: ross.cowan@stv.tv

COWAN, Stephen (Nov 1978) (Director)
Yuill & Kyle Ltd, Glasgow . . . . (p.1056)
T: 0141 3327107
E: stephen.cowan@yuill-kyle.co.uk

COWAN, Susie Kathleen (Nov 1999) (Associate)
Monteith Solicitors Limited, Nairn . . . . (p.1129)
T: 0141 370 0900
E: susie@monteithsolicitors.com

COWAN, Victoria Elizabeth (Jan 2014)
(Employee)
Burness Paull LLP, Glasgow . . . . (p.954)
T: 0141 2484933
E: Vicky.Cowan@burnesspaull.com

COWDEN, Davinia-Elizabeth (Oct 2002)
(Associate)
CMS Cameron McKenna Nabarro Olswang LLP,
Glasgow. (p.962)
T: 0141 2222200
E: Davinia.Cowden@cms-cmno.com

COWDEN, Stephen John (Dec 1976) (Solicitor)
NO FIRM

COWIE, Emma Louise (Apr 2018) (Employee)
James Guthrie & Company LLP,
Kilmarnock . . . . (p.1095)
T: 01563 525155
E: emma@jamesguthrie.co.uk

COWIE, Gillian (Sept 1991) (Partner)
Wright, Johnston & Mackenzie LLP,
Glasgow. (p.1054)
T: 0141 2483434
E: gzc@wjm.co.uk

COWIE, Lauren Jacquelene (May 2007)
(Employee)
Aberdeenshire Council, Aberdeen . . . . . (p.1211)
T: 01467 534938
E: Lauren.Cowie@aberdeenshire.gov.uk

COWIE, Louise Anne (Nov 2001) (Employee)
Repsol Sinopec Resources UK Limited,
    Aberdeen . . . .(p.1213)
    T: 01224 353205
    E: Louise.Cowie@repsolsinopecuk.com

COWIE, Sam Rennie (Feb 2012) (Associate)
Digby Brown LLP, Inverness . . . .(p.1075)
    T: 0333 200 5925
    E: Sam.Cowie@digbybrown.co.uk

COWIE, Scott Russell (Nov 1993) (Partner)
Paterson Holms, Glasgow . . . .(p.1029)
    T: 0141 9428825
    E: scott@patersonholms.co.uk

COWIE, William Roger Murray (May 1989)
    (Partner)
R & R Urquhart LLP, Forres . . . .(p.929)
    T: 01309 672216
    E: willcowie@r-r-urquhart.com

COWNIE, Scott Graham (Sept 1989)
    (Employee)
Scottish Legal Aid Board,
    Edinburgh . . . .(p.1233)
    T: 0131 2267061
    E: cowniesc@slab.org.uk

COWPERTHWAITE, Alison Jane (May 2008)
    (Employee)
Raeburn Christie Clark & Wallace LLP,
    Aberdeen . . . .(p.741)
    T: 01224 332400
    E: alison.cowperthwaite@raeburns.co.uk

COX, Alan Bryce (Nov 1986) (Employee)
SOUTH LANARKSHIREre Council,
    Hamilton . . . .(p.1247)
    E: Alan.Cox@southlanarkshire.gov.uk

COX, Calum McKenzie (Jun 2013) (Employee)
Scottish Social Services Council,
    Dundee . . . .(p.1218)
    T: 0345 6030 891

COX, Darren James (Jul 2019) (Employee)
Lord President's Private Office,
    Edinburgh . . . .(p.1225)
    T: 0131 2406701

COX, Elizabeth Anne (Sept 2010) (Employee)
Vialex Limited, Edinburgh . . . .(p.1235)
    T: 0333 2400127
    E: liz.chalmers@vialex.co.uk

COX, Heather Elizabeth (Oct 2014) (Employee)
NORTH LANARKSHIREre Council,
    Motherwell . . . .(p.1251)
    T: 01698 302196
    E: coxh@northlan.gov.uk

COX, Michael Andrew (Oct 2007) (Associate)
BTO Solicitors LLP, Edinburgh . . . .(p.849)
    T: 0131 2222939
    E: mxc@bto.co.uk

COX, Rebecca Antonia (Sept 2016) (Associate)
MacRoberts LLP, Glasgow . . . .(p.1015)
    T: 0141 3031100
    E: rebecca.cox@macroberts.com

COX, Thomas Martin (Jun 2015) (Solicitor)
NO FIRM

COYLE, Caroline Louise (Nov 2001) (Employee)
DWF LLP, Glasgow . . . .(p.973)
    T: 0141 228 8000
    E: Caroline.Coyle@dwf.law

COYLE, Christopher James (Sept 2016)
    (Employee)
Scottish Government's Parliamentary Counsel
    Office, Edinburgh . . . .(p.1233)
    T: 0131 244 1668
    E: Christopher.Coyle@gov.scot

COYLE, Dominic Paul (Feb 2019) (Employee)
Austin Lafferty Limited, East
    Kilbride . . . .(p.830)
    T: 01355 263777
    E: dcoyle@laffertylaw.com

COYLE, Elizabeth June (Oct 1985) (Partner)
Archer Coyle, Glasgow . . . .(p.941)
    T: 0141 6372434
    E: elizabethcoyle@archercoyle.co.uk

COYLE, Fiona Julie (Aug 2013) (Employee)
Scottish Power Limited, Glasgow . . . . .(p.1244)
    T: 0141 6140000
    E: fiona.coyle@scottishpower.com

COYLE, Michael John Northcote (Aug 2016)
    (Employee)
Kavanagh Coyle Limited, Glasgow . . . . .(p.995)
    T: 0141 2265500
    E: Michael@kavanaghcoyle.co.uk

COYLE, Patricia Ann (Aug 1984) (Director)
Kavanagh Coyle Limited, Glasgow . . . . .(p.995)
    T: 0141 2265500
    E: pat@kavanaghcoyle.co.uk

COYLE, Paul (Mar 2011) (Employee)
Burness Paull LLP, Edinburgh . . . .(p.850)
    T: 0131 4736000
    E: paul.coyle@burnesspaull.com

COYLE, Paul Vincent (Jul 1984) (Director)
Kavanagh Coyle Limited, Glasgow . . . . .(p.995)
    T: 0141 2265500
    E: paul@solad.co.uk

COYNE, Jennifer Claire (Oct 2015) (Employee)
North Ayrshire Council, Irvine . . . .(p.1249)
    T: 01294 324390
    E: Jennifercoyne@north-ayrshire.gov.uk

COYNE, Samantha (Jul 2009) (Employee)
SSE Plc, Perth . . . .(p.1253)
    T: 01738 456 000
    E: samantha.coyne@sse.com

CRABBE, Norna Forsyth (Oct 1970) (Partner)
West Anderson & Co., Glasgow . . . . . . (p.1052)
T: 0141 3326671
E: law@westanderson.co.uk

CRADDEN, Joan Mary (Jul 1994) (Partner)
Brodies LLP, Glasgow . . . . (p.948)
T: 0141 2484672
E: joan.cradden@brodies.com

CRADOCK, Innes John (Nov 1986) (Associate)
Hendrie Legal Limited, Edinburgh . . . . . (p.878)
T: 0131 370 0470
E: Innes.cradock@ralphhendrie.legal

CRADOCK, Kathleen Harriet Brocklebank
(Jan 2016) (Employee)
Perform Group, Feltham . . . . (p.1259)
E: kathleen.cradock@dazn.com

CRADOCK, Rory (Sept 1984) (Employee)
Inksters, Aberdeen . . . . (p.732)
T: 01224 252730
E: rory@inksters.com

CRAIG, Aileen Mary (Aug 1986) (Employee)
North Ayrshire Council, Irvine . . . . (p.1249)
T: 01294 310000
E: acraig@north-ayrshire.gov.uk

CRAIG, Alasdair Calum (Feb 2017) (Employee)
Galloway & Ayrshire Partnership LLP,
Girvan . . . . (p.935)
T: 01465 712345
E: ac@smithvalentine.co.uk

CRAIG, Andrew Robin (Feb 1988) (Employee)
McVey & Murricane, Glasgow . . . . (p.1017)
T: 0141 3339688
E: rcraig@mcvey-murricane.com

CRAIG, Angela Janet (Mar 1985) (Director)
Garden Stirling Burnet Solicitors Limited,
Haddington . . . . (p.1064)
T: 01620 824996
E: acraig@gsbsolicitors.co.uk

CRAIG, Bruce (Oct 1989) (Partner)
Pinsent Masons LLP, Aberdeen . . . . (p.739)
T: 01224 377900
E: bruce.craig@pinsentmasons.com

CRAIG, Cristin Rosa Eileen (Oct 2017)
(Employee)
Baxendale Employee Ownership Limited, London
SE1 . . . . (p.1262)
T: 020 3598 9982
E: cristin.craig@baxendale.co.uk

CRAIG, Darren Alexander (Sept 2000) (Partner)
CMS Cameron McKenna Nabarro Olswang LLP,
Edinburgh . . . . (p.856)
T: 0131 2288000
E: Darren.Craig@cms-cmno.com

CRAIG, George Scott (Nov 1985) (Partner)
Warners Solicitors LLP, Edinburgh . . . . . . (p.911)
T: 0131 6624747
E: scraig@warnersllp.com

CRAIG, Gregor Alexander (Aug 1997)
(Employee)
Premier Asset Management Limited,
Guildford . . . . (p.1259)
E: gregorcraig@premierfunds.co.uk

CRAIG, Hope Margaret Jean (Oct 2015)
(Employee)
University of St Andrews
T: +44 (0)1334 46 2146
E: hmjc1@st-andrews.ac.uk

CRAIG, James William (Sept 1986) (Director)
Archibald Sharp & Son Limited,
Glasgow. . . . . (p.1039)
T: 0141 3393036
E: jcraig@archibaldsharp.co.uk

CRAIG, Jamie Charles Melville (Feb 2009)
(Partner)
Peterkins, Huntly . . . . (p.1074)
T: 01466 792101
E: jc@peterkins.com

CRAIG, Karen Yvonne (Feb 2007) (Associate)
Anderson Strathern LLP, Edinburgh . . . . (p.839)
T: 0131 2707700
E: karen.mchale@andersonstrathern.co.uk

CRAIG, Katrine Shearer (Oct 2000) (Employee)
Procurator Fiscal Service,
Edinburgh . . . . (p.1227)
T: 0300 0203168
E: katrine.craig@copfs.gov.uk

CRAIG, Kirsten Mary (Feb 2002) (Employee)
CIGNA International, Glasgow . . . . (p.1238)
T: 01475 492388
E: Kirsten.Craig@Cigna.com

CRAIG, Laura Margaret (Apr 2021) (Employee)
Burges Salmon LLP, Edinburgh . . . . (p.850)
T: 0131 3142112
E: laura.craig@burges-salmon.com

CRAIG, Lois (Apr 2016) (Employee)
Ledingham Chalmers LLP,
Aberdeen . . . . (p.734)
T: 01224 408522
E: Lois.Craig@ledinghamchalmers.com

CRAIG, Louise Allison Cairns (Jun 2017)
(Employee)
Public Defence Solicitors Office,
Ayr . . . . (p.1215)
T: 01292 269139
E: LCraig@pdso.org.uk

CRAIG, Margaret Robins (Nov 1989)
(Employee)
Renfrewshire Council, Paisley . . . .(p.1252)
T: 0141 6187170
E: margaret.craig-cs@renfrewshire.gov.uk

CRAIG, Ronan Andrew (Sept 2018) (Employee)
Dickson Minto, London EC2 . . . .(p.1263)
T: 020 76284455
E: ronan.craig@dmws.com

CRAIG, Stuart Andrew (Sept 2021) (Employee)
BTO Solicitors LLP, Glasgow . . . .(p.952)
T: 0141 2218012
E: scr@bto.co.uk

CRAIG, Stuart Andrew (Aug 2021) (Employee)
McIntosh McCann Ltd, Glasgow . . . . .(p.1012)
T: 0141 212 2222
E: stuart@mcintoshmccann.com

CRAIG, William Andrew (Sept 1984) (Partner)
Gair & Gibson LLP, Falkirk . . . .(p.922)
T: 01324 623928
E: andrewcraig@gairgibson.co.uk

CRAIG, William Campbell (Sept 1986)
(Employee)
Procurator Fiscal Service, Airdrie . . . . . .(p.1214)
T: 01236 747027
E: bill.craig@copfs.gov.uk

CRAIGEN, James Innes (Oct 1984) (Employee)
Procurator Fiscal Service, Aberdeen . . .(p.1213)
T: 03000 202200
E: jim.craigen@copfs.gov.uk

CRAIGIE, Julie (Oct 2002) (Associate)
Lynn Herbert & Co., Leven . . . .(p.1115)
T: 01333 429007
E: jcraigie@lynnherbert.co.uk

CRAIK, Graham Duncan Dunbar (Oct 2001)
(Partner)
Levy & McRae Solicitors LLP,
Glasgow . . . .(p.1000)
T: 0141 3072311
E: gcraik@lemac.co.uk

CRAIK, Hazel Frances (Dec 1991) (Employee)
National Health Service Scotland,
Edinburgh . . . .(p.1225)
T: 0131 2757800
E: hazel.craik@nhs.scot

CRAINE, April Alison (Feb 2021) (Employee)
DAC Beachcroft Scotland LLP,
Glasgow . . . .(p.964)
T: 0141 2486688
E: apcraine@dacbeachcroft.com

CRAINIE, Evan (Sept 2017) (Employee)
Ofgem, Glasgow . . . .(p.1241)
T: (0141) 354 5425
E: Evan.Crainie@ofgem.gov.uk

CRAN, James Douglas (Mar 2000) (Associate)
Pinsent Masons LLP, Edinburgh . . . .(p.895)
T: 0131 7777000
E: james.cran@pinsentmasons.com

CRAN, Lucy Ann (Dec 2004) (Employee)
Ledingham Chalmers LLP,
Aberdeen . . . .(p.734)
T: 01224 408408
E: Lucy.Cran@ledinghamchalmers.com

CRANDLES, Gillian (Nov 2000) (Partner)
Turcan Connell, Edinburgh . . . .(p.908)
T: 0131 2288111
E: gillian.crandles@turcanconnell.com

CRANSTON, Clair Margaret Helen
(Jul 2012) (Employee)
Macnabs LLP, Perth . . . .(p.1150)
T: 01738 623432
E: claircranston@macnabs-law.co.uk

CRANSTON, David Gordon (Aug 1994)
(Director)
Martin, Johnston & Socha Limited,
Kirkcaldy . . . .(p.1102)
T: 01592 640680
E:
david.cranston@mjscriminaldefencelawyers.co.
uk

CRANSTON, Emily Chrisanne (Jul 2020)
(Employee)
Dentons UK and Middle East LLP,
Edinburgh . . . .(p.860)
T: 0330 2220050
E: emily.cranston@dentons.com

CRANSTON, Pamela (Dec 1999) (Employee)
Tesco Personal Finance Plc,
Edinburgh . . . .(p.1234)
T: (0131) 274 3426
E: pamela.cranston@tescobank.com

CRANSTON, Robert Coutts (Sept 2012)
(Employee)
Thompsons, Edinburgh . . . .(p.906)
T: 0131 2254297
E: Robert.Cranston@thompsons-scotland.co.uk

CRANSTON, Stephen Robert (Sept 2009)
(Employee)
Murchison Law Limited, Inverness . . . .(p.1081)
T: 01463 709992
E: stephen@murchisonlaw.co.uk

CRASKE, John Simon (Jan 1998) (Associate)
CMS Cameron McKenna Nabarro Olswang LLP,
Edinburgh . . . .(p.856)
T: 0131 2288000
E: John.Craske@cms-cmno.com

CRATE, Evelyn Ferguson (Mar 2016) (Associate)
Macleod & MacCallum Limited,
Inverness . . . .(p.1080)
T: 01463 239393
E: evelyn.crate@macandmac.co.uk

CRAW, Jacquelynn Forsyth (Nov 1991)
(Employee)
The Offshore Pollution Liability Association
Limited, London EC2 . . . . (p.1268)
T: 01224 392242
E: Jacquelynn.craw@cms-cmno.com

CRAW, Stephanie Fiona (Nov 2016) (Employee)
Morrison & Foerster, London EC3 . . . . (p.1266)
T: 020 7920 4047
E: SCraw@mofo.com

CRAWFORD, Ailie Elizabeth (Sept 2015)
(Employee)
Ofgem, Glasgow . . . . (p.1241)
T: (0141) 354 5425
E: ailie.crawford@ofgem.gov.uk

CRAWFORD, Angus (May 2001) (Employee)
Procurator Fiscal Service, Glasgow . . . . (p.1241)
T: 0300 0203000
E: angus.crawford@copfs.gov.uk

CRAWFORD, Angus Kirkwood (Jan 2014)
(Partner)
BTO Solicitors LLP, Glasgow . . . . (p.952)
T: 0141 2218012
E: akc@bto.co.uk

CRAWFORD, Ann Barrie (Nov 1996) (Employee)
Scottish Widows Limited,
Edinburgh . . . . (p.1233)
T: 0131 655 3808
E: Ann.Crawford@scottishwidows.co.uk

CRAWFORD, Antonia McCarry (Feb 2011)
(Employee)
Beltrami & Co Limited, Glasgow . . . . . . (p.944)
T: 0141 4292262
E:
antonia.crawford@beltramiandcompany.co.uk

CRAWFORD, Clair Catherine (Feb 2006)
(Employee)
Balfour Beatty Regional Civil Engineering,
Motherwell . . . . (p.1251)
T: 01698 647 500
E: clair.crawford@balfourbeatty.com

CRAWFORD, Claire Helen (Feb 2001) (Director)
Duffy Toshner & Co Limited,
Cambuslang . . . . (p.782)
T: 0141 6418081
E: claire@duffytoshner.co.uk

CRAWFORD, Clare Louise (Jun 2007)
(Employee)
Kennedys Scotland, Glasgow . . . . (p.995)
T: 0141 433 7115
E: Clare.Crawford@kennedyslaw.com

CRAWFORD, David Andrew (Oct 2005)
(Employee)
Procurator Fiscal Service, Glasgow . . . . (p.1241)
T: 0300 0203000
E: david.crawford@copfs.gov.uk

CRAWFORD, Douglas James (Jan 1989)
(Partner)
Brodies LLP, Aberdeen . . . . (p.723)
T: 01224 392242
E: douglas.crawford@brodies.com

CRAWFORD, Eilidh Lindsay (Jun 2018)
(Employee)
Harper Macleod LLP, Glasgow . . . . (p.983)
T: 0141 2218888
E: eilidh.crawford@harpermacleod.co.uk

CRAWFORD, Elaine Valerie (Mar 1992)
(Employee)
Law Society of Scotland,
Edinburgh . . . . (p.1224)
T: 0131 2267411
E: elainecrawford@lawscot.org.uk

CRAWFORD, Jayne (Mar 2005) (Partner)
Thompsons, Edinburgh . . . . (p.906)
T: 0131 2254297
E: jayne.crawford@thompsons-scotland.co.uk

CRAWFORD, Jennifer Laura Clare (Oct 2009)
(Employee)
Brodies LLP, Glasgow . . . . (p.948)
T: 0141 2484672
E: jennifer.crawford@brodies.com

CRAWFORD, John (Apr 2006) (Employee)
ContractPod Technologies Limited,
Glasgow . . . . (p.1238)
T: 0141 280 1600

CRAWFORD, John Stewart (Nov 1983)
(Consultant)
MacRoberts LLP, Glasgow . . . . (p.1015)
T: 0141 3031100
E: john.crawford@macroberts.com

CRAWFORD, Laura Margaret (Sept 2013)
(Employee)
A.C. White, Ayr . . . . (p.766)
T: 01292 266900
E: Laura.Crawford@acwhiteayr.co.uk

CRAWFORD, Richard Alasdair (Aug 2002)
(Employee)
East Ayrshire Council, Kilmarnock . . . . . (p.1249)
T: 01563 576161
E: richard.crawford@east-ayrshire.gov.uk

CRAWFORD, Ross Andrew (Sept 2018)
(Employee)
Health Law Limited, Edinburgh . . . . (p.878)
T: 0800 920 2080
E: rc@health-law.uk

CRAWFORD, Sarah Jane (Aug 2009) (Employee)
Scottish Government, Edinburgh . . . . . (p.1231)
T: 0131 244 0815
E: Sarah.Crawford3@gov.scot

CRAWFORD, Virgil Martin (Aug 1991) (Partner)
Virgil M. Crawford, Stirling . . . . (p.1164)
T: 01786 464055
E: vmc@virgil-crawford.com

CRAWLEY, Andrew Wilson (Feb 1987)
(Employee)
Scottish Government, Edinburgh . . . . . (p.1231)
T: 0131 244 0815
E: andrew.crawley@gov.scot

CREARIE, William Bryden (Dec 1987) (Partner)
Aberdein Considine and Company,
Glasgow. (p.936)
T: 0141 342 5570
E: bcrearie@acandco.com

CREE, Lauren Hazel (Jan 2010) (Employee)
Scottish Social Services Council,
Dundee . . . . (p.1218)
T: 0345 6030 891
E: Lauren.Cree@sssc.uk.com

CREE, Murray James (Aug 2012) (Associate)
Burness Paull LLP, Edinburgh . . . . (p.850)
T: 0131 4736000
E: murray.cree@burnesspaull.com

CREEGAN, Michael Gerard (Jul 1995)
(Employee)
Scottish Legal Aid Board,
Edinburgh . . . . (p.1233)
T: 0131 2267061
E: CreeganMi@slab.org.uk

CRERAR, Ian Stuart (Nov 1983) (Employee)
National Health Service Scotland,
Edinburgh . . . . (p.1225)
T: 0131 2757800
E: ian.crerar@nhs.scot

CRERAR, Professor, Lorne Donald
(Dec 1978) (Partner)
Harper Macleod LLP, Glasgow . . . . (p.983)
T: 0141 2218888
E: lorne.crerar@harpermacleod.co.uk

CREWES, Sarah Helen (Oct 2003) (Partner)
Clyde & Co (Scotland) LLP,
Edinburgh . . . . (p.855)
T: 0131 5571545
E: Sarah.Crewes@clydeco.com

CREWES, Scott Edward (Jun 2001) (Employee)
Aberdeen Corporate Services Limited,
Edinburgh . . . . (p.1220)
T: 0131 245 7508
E: scott.crewes@abrdn.com

CRICHTON, Andrew John Young (Feb 2003)
(Employee)
Pinsent Masons LLP, Edinburgh . . . . (p.895)
T: 0131 7777000
E: andrew.crichton@pinsentmasons.com

CRICHTON, Elouisa Margaret Leonard
(Jun 2011) (Employee)
Dentons UK and Middle East LLP,
Glasgow. (p.968)
T: 0330 2220050
E: elouisa.crichton@dentons.com

CRICHTON, Karen Louise (Jun 2015) (Associate)
Addleshaw Goddard LLP, Glasgow . . . . . (p.938)
T: +44 (0)141 574 2320
E: karen.crichton@addleshawgoddard.com

CRICHTON, Louise Heather (Sept 2017)
(Employee)
Maguire Solicitors, Glasgow . . . . (p.1017)
T: 0141 3312885

CRICHTON, Lynn Heather (Sept 2016)
(Employee)
Uber London Limited, London E1 . . . . . (p.1269)
E: lynn.crichton@uber.com

CRIGGIE, William Lawson (Sept 2008)
(Employee)
Latta Law Limited, Glasgow . . . . (p.998)
T: 0141 222 2185
E: bc@lattalaw.co.uk

CRIGHTON, Calum George (Aug 2009)
(Partner)
Gilson Gray LLP, Edinburgh . . . . (p.874)
T: 0131 5165354
E: ccrighton@gilsongray.co.uk

CRIGHTON, Mary Agnes Duffy Finlay
(Sept 1974) (Partner)
Calders, Dundee. . . . . (p.807)
T: 01382 224391
E: m.crighton6469@btinternet.com

CRIGHTON, Rachel Elizabeth (Sept 2020)
(Employee)
Blackadders LLP, Dundee. . . . . (p.805)
T: 01382 229222
E: rachel.crighton@blackadders.co.uk

CRILLEY, Emma Francesca (Nov 2014)
(Employee)
DAC Beachcroft Scotland LLP,
Glasgow. (p.964)
T: 0141 739 7158
E: ecrilley@dacbeachcroft.com

CRILLEY, Noel Thomas George (Jan 2011)
(Employee)
Aggreko plc, Glasgow . . . . (p.1237)
T: 0141 2255900
E: noel.crilley@aggreko.co.uk

CRILLY, Anna (Jul 2010) (Employee)
University of Edinburgh, Edinburgh . . . (p.1235)
T: (0131) 651 4330
E: Anna.Crilly@ed.ac.uk

CRILLY, Laura Margaret (Sept 2000)
(Employee)
Pinsent Masons LLP, Edinburgh . . . .(p.895)
T: 0131 7777000
E: laura.crilly@pinsentmasons.com

CRILLY, Stephen Charles (Sept 2001)
(Employee)
Scottish Law Commission,
Edinburgh . . . .(p.1233)
T: 0131 6682131
E: Stephen.Crilly@scotlawcom.gov.uk

CRITCHLEY, Alexander Dexter James O. R.
(Sept 2015) (Employee)
Turcan Connell, Edinburgh . . . .(p.908)
T: 0131 2288111
E: alex.critchley@turcanconnell.com

CRITCHLEY, Fiona (May 2006) (Employee)
Barclays Bank PLC, Dubai . . . .(p.1277)
T: +971 04 365 0863
E: fiona.critchley@barclays.com

CROCKART, Grant Ogilvie (Oct 1994)
(Employee)
Aviva Plc, Norwich . . . .(p.1270)
T: 01603 683 614
E: Grant.crockart@aviva.com

CROCKATT, Neil (Jan 1994) (Director)
Your Conveyancer Limited,
Dunfermline . . . .(p.827)
T: 01383 667550
E: neil.crockatt@yourconveyancer.co.uk

CROCKER, Colin John (Mar 2014) (Employee)
Scottish Widows Limited,
Edinburgh . . . .(p.1233)
T: 0131 6557230
E: Colin.Crocker@lloydsbanking.com

CROCKETT, Jody Stephen (Nov 2006) (Partner)
Burness Paull LLP, Glasgow . . . .(p.954)
T: 0141 2484933
E: jody.crockett@burnesspaull.com

CROFTS, Ellen (Nov 2015) (Employee)
Morton Fraser LLP, Edinburgh . . . .(p.891)
T: 0131 2471000
E: Ellen.Crofts@morton-fraser.com

CROFTS, Lewis (Oct 2014) (Employee)
Lindsays LLP, Edinburgh . . . .(p.882)
T: 0131 2291212
E: lewiscrofts@lindsays.co.uk

CROLLA, Sofia Rosa-Maria (Jul 2009)
(Employee)
Levy & McRae Solicitors LLP,
Glasgow . . . .(p.1000)
T: 0141 3072311
E: SCrolla@lemac.co.uk

CROMAN, Ruth Catriona (Sept 1998) (Partner)
Macnabs LLP, Perth . . . .(p.1150)
T: 01738 623 432
E: ruthcroman@macnabs-law.co.uk

CROMBIE, Dale Samuel (Nov 2020) (Employee)
Cochran Dickie, Paisley . . . .(p.1137)
T: 0141 8892245
E: dc@cochrandickie.co.uk

CROMBIE, Douglas John (Oct 1988) (Partner)
Raeburn Christie Clark & Wallace LLP,
Aberdeen . . . .(p.741)
T: 01224 332400
E: douglas.crombie@raeburns.co.uk

CROMBIE, Fraser William (Nov 2019)
(Employee)
Dentons UK and Middle East LLP,
Glasgow . . . .(p.968)
T: 0330 2220050
E: Fraser.Crombie@dentons.com

CROMBIE, Graham William (Oct 2007)
(Employee)
Scottish Government, Edinburgh . . . . .(p.1232)
T: 0131 2442678
E: graham.crombie@gov.scot

CROMBIE, Ian (Feb 2019) (Employee)
Shepherd and Wedderburn LLP,
Edinburgh . . . .(p.900)
T: 0131 2289900
E: ian.crombie@shepwedd.com

CROMBIE, June (Jan 1987) (Partner)
DWF LLP, Glasgow . . . .(p.973)
T: 0141 228 8000
E: june.crombie@dwf.law

CROMPTON, Mary Claire (Jun 2016)
(Employee)
Procurator Fiscal Service,
Edinburgh . . . .(p.1227)
T: 0844 5613720
E: claire.crompton@copfs.gov.uk

CRONE, Carl Alexander (Sept 1984) (Partner)
Mathie-Morton, Ayr . . . .(p.764)
T: 01292 263549
E: carlcrone@mathie-morton.co.uk

CROOK, Jamie Alexander Rushford
(Aug 2013) (Employee)
Dickson Minto, Edinburgh . . . .(p.861)
T: 0131 2254455
E: Jamie.Crook@dmws.com

CROOKS, James William (Sept 2007)
(Employee)
Sidley Austin LLP, London EC3 . . . .(p.1268)
T: 2073602040
E: JCrooks@sidley.com

CROOKS, Peter (Feb 1996) (Partner)
Lanarkshire Accident Law,
Coatbridge . . . .(p.787)
T: 01236 222888
E: peter.crooks@lanaccidentlaw.co.uk

CROSBIE, James Lewis (Jul 2013) (Employee)
Procurator Fiscal Service,
Edinburgh . . . .(p.1229)
T: 0300 0203000
E: JamesLewis.Crosbie@copfs.gov.uk

CROSBIE, Stewart James (Sept 2014)
(Associate)
Gillespie Macandrew LLP,
Edinburgh . . . .(p.872)
T: 0131 2251677
E: Stewart.Crosbie@gillespiemacandrew.co.uk

CROSBIE, Thomas (Oct 2008) (Employee)
Procurator Fiscal Service,
Edinburgh . . . .(p.1229)
T: 0300 0203000
E: thomas.crosbie@copfs.gov.uk

CROSBY, Anna Katharine (Jan 2015)
(Employee)
Fieldfisher LLP, London EC4 . . . .(p.1264)
T: (0207) 8614339

CROSS, Kimberley Anne (Nov 2012)
(Employee)
CMS Cameron McKenna Nabarro Olswang LLP,
Glasgow . . . .(p.962)
T: 0141 2222200
E: Kimberley.Cross@cms-cmno.com

CROSS, Leanne (Nov 1997) (Employee)
Procurator Fiscal Service,
Edinburgh . . . .(p.1227)
T: 0844 561 3785
E: leanne.cross@copfs.gov.uk

CROSS, Rebecca (Jul 2012) (Director)
Jackson & Co (Fife) Limited, Leven . . . .(p.1115)
T: 01333 422330
E: rebecca@jacksonsolicitors.co.uk

CROSSAN, David James (Oct 2012) (Employee)
Pinsent Masons LLP, Glasgow . . . .(p.1031)
T: 0141 567 8400
E: david.crossan@pinsentmasons.com

CROSSAN, Finlay George (Sept 2003)
(Consultant)
Brodies LLP, Aberdeen . . . .(p.723)
T: 01224 392242
E: finlay.crossan@brodies.com

CROTHERS, Karen (Nov 2002) (Employee)
Bartys, Dunblane . . . .(p.804)
T: 01786 822296
E: kac@wjm.co.uk

CROWE, Catherine Margaret (Nov 2007)
(Employee)
West Lothian Council, Livingston . . . . .(p.1250)
T: 01506 280000
E: Catherine.Crowe@westlothian.gov.uk

CROWE, Gavin John Finlay (Mar 1982)
(Consultant)
Aberdein Considine and Company,
Glasgow . . . .(p.937)
T: 0141 227 8200
E: gcrowe@acandco.com

CROWE, Michael (Sept 2003) (Employee)
Aegon Asset Management UK Plc,
Edinburgh . . . .(p.1220)
T: 0131 549 3062
E: michael.crowe@aegonam.com

CROWE, Sarah Lesley Louise (Sept 2019)
(Employee)
DLA Piper UK LLP, London EC1 . . . . . .(p.1263)
T: 020 77966017
E: Sarah.Crowe@dlapiper.com

CROWTHER, Carol Jane (Nov 1998) (Employee)
Duncan Taylor Scotch Whiskey,
Huntly . . . .(p.1248)
E: carol.crowther@duncantaylor.com

CROWTHER, Johanna Helen Brechin
(Oct 2017) (Employee)
Scottish Police Authority, Police Scotland,
Glasgow . . . .(p.1244)
T: 01786 895727
E: Jo.Crowther@scotland.pnn.police.uk

CROZIER, Anita Ingrid (Oct 2009) (Associate)
CMS Cameron McKenna Nabarro Olswang LLP,
Glasgow . . . .(p.962)
T: 0141 304 6011
E: anita.crozier@cms-cmno.com

CRUICKSHANK, Adel (May 2009) (Employee)
Equinor Production UK Limited,
Aberdeen . . . .(p.1212)
T: 01224 653350
E: ADCR@equinor.com

CRUICKSHANK, Ann (Oct 1980) (Partner)
Grigor & Young LLP, Elgin . . . .(p.916)
T: 01343 544077
E: ann@grigor-young.co.uk

CRUICKSHANK, Colin Mark (Oct 2005)
(Employee)
National Westminster Bank PLC,
Edinburgh . . . .(p.1226)
T: (0131) 626 2925
E: mark.cruickshank@rbs.co.uk

CRUICKSHANK, Lisa Anne (Oct 2005)
(Employee)
Dentons UK and Middle East LLP,
Edinburgh . . . .(p.860)
T: 0330 2220050
E: Lisa.Cruickshank@dentons.com

CRUICKSHANK, Mhairi Fiona (Jul 2018)
(Employee)
Addleshaw Goddard LLP,
Edinburgh . . . . (p.835)
T: 0131 2282400
E:
Mhairi.Cruickshank@addleshawgoddard.com

CRUICKSHANK, Robert Magnus (Oct 1990)
(Partner)
Allan, Black & McCaskie, Elgin . . . . (p.915)
T: 01343 543 355
E: rmc@abmsols.co.uk

CRUICKSHANKS, Ross Allan (Aug 2018)
(Employee)
Dickson Minto, London EC2 . . . . (p.1263)
T: 020 76284455
E: Ross.Cruickshanks@dmws.com

CRUIKSHANK, Paul Anthony (Jan 2021)
(Employee)
Ian C. McCarthy Ltd, Glasgow . . . . . . (p.1007)
T: 0141 7631366
E: Paulc@iancmccarthy.co.uk

CUCKOW, Emma Louise (Dec 2003) (Employee)
University of the West of Scotland,
Paisley . . . . (p.1253)
T: 0141 848 3577
E: Emma.Cuckow@uws.ac.uk

CUDDIHY, Aoife Lynda (Dec 2015) (Employee)
SSE Plc, Perth . . . . (p.1253)
T: 01738 516765
E: aoife.cuddihy@sse.com

CUGINI, Amy Elise (Aug 2005) (Employee)
Brodies LLP, Edinburgh . . . . (p.845)
T: 0131 2283777
E: amy.cugini@brodies.com

CULLEN, Claire Frances (Sept 2002) (Employee)
Scottish Government, Edinburgh . . . . . (p.1231)
T: 0131 244 0501
E: claire.cullen@gov.scot

CULLEN, Felicity Rose (Aug 2000) (Employee)
Scottish Government, Edinburgh . . . . . (p.1231)
T: 0131 244 0815
E: Felicity.Cullen@gov.scot

CULLEN, Joyce, WS (Dec 1981) (Partner)
Brodies LLP, Edinburgh . . . . (p.845)
T: 0131 2283777
E: joyce.cullen@brodies.com

CULLEN, Marisa Anne (Jun 2005) (Partner)
Family Law Matters Scotland LLP,
Glasgow. (p.975)
T: 0141 4202430
E: marisa.cullen@flmscotland.co.uk

CULLEN, Richard James (Aug 2016) (Employee)
Vodafone Group Services Limited, London
W2 . . . . (p.1269)
E: richard.cullen1@vodafone.com

CULLEN, Stephen John (Nov 1991) (Employee)
Miles & Stockbridge P.C.,
Maryland . . . . (p.1279)
T: 001 4103853629
E: scullen@milesstockbridge.com

CULLENS, Albert John (Dec 1979) (Partner)
Jardine Donaldson, Alloa . . . . (p.752)
T: 01259 724411
E: bert.cullens@jardinedonaldson.co.uk

CULLENS, Andrew John (Jul 2012) (Partner)
Jardine Donaldson, Alloa . . . . (p.752)
T: 01259 724411
E: andrew.cullens@jardinedonaldson.co.uk

CULLERTON, Pauline (Jun 2006) (Partner)
Culley & McAlpine, Perth . . . . (p.1147)
T: 01738 626644
E: p.cullerton@culleymcalpine.co.uk

CULLUM, Louise Susan (Mar 2013) (Employee)
University of Edinburgh, Edinburgh . . . (p.1235)
T: (0131) 651 4330
E: louise.cullum@ed.ac.uk

CUMMING, Caroline Elspet (Sept 1999)
(Partner)
Mackinnons Solicitors LLP,
Aberdeen . . . . (p.736)
T: 01224 632464
E: Caroline@mackinnons.com

CUMMING, Claire Monique (Jun 2007)
(Employee)
Procurator Fiscal Service,
Edinburgh . . . . (p.1227)
T: 0300 0203168
E: Claire.Cumming@copfs.gov.uk

CUMMING, Donald Ian, WS (Dec 1976)
(Consultant)
CMS Cameron McKenna Nabarro Olswang LLP,
Edinburgh . . . . (p.856)
T: 0131 2288000
E: Donald.Cumming@cms-cmno.com

CUMMING, Gillian Emma (Mar 2005)
(Employee)
Just Employment Law Ltd,
Glasgow. (p.1240)
T: 0141 3315150
E: gilliancumming@justemploymentlaw.co.uk

CUMMING, Hugh Patrick Herries (Jan 1990)
(Partner)
Stewart & Watson, Buckie . . . . (p.781)
T: 01542 833255
E: hcumming@stewartwatson.co.uk

CUMMING, Jane Elizabeth (Feb 1985)
(Associate)
J. Myles & Co., Dundee . . . . (p.817)
T: 01382 204625
E: janecumming@jmylessols.co.uk

CUMMING, John Matheson Macleod
(Dec 1988) (Director)
Ennova Limited, Edinburgh . . . .(p.869)
T: 0131 6624555
E: jcumming@ennova-law.com

CUMMING, Kenneth George (Jul 2013)
(Employee)
Hexagon Positioning Intelligence,
Dyce . . . .(p.1219)
T: 01224 965897
E: ken.cumming@hexagon.com

CUMMING, Lindsay Alison (Aug 2018)
(Employee)
Drummond Miller LLP, Glasgow. . . . . . .(p.971)
T: 0141 3320086
E: lcumming@drummondmiller.co.uk

CUMMING, Sarah Helen Mary (Jul 2019)
(Employee)
Anderson Shaw & Gilbert Limited,
Inverness . . . .(p.1075)
T: 01463 236123
E: scumming@solicitorsinverness.com

CUMMING, Victoria Maud (Sept 2001)
(Employee)
Equinor Production UK Limited,
Aberdeen . . . .(p.1212)
T: 01224 653350
E: VCUM@equinor.com

CUMMINGS, Alasdair William Donald
(Dec 1987) (Partner)
Lindsays LLP, Edinburgh . . . .(p.882)
T: 0131 2291212
E: alasdaircummings@lindsays.co.uk

CUMMINGS, Jennifer Margaret (Jan 2007)
(Employee)
Lockton Companies LLP,
Edinburgh . . . .(p.1225)
T: 0131 345 5550
E: Jennifer.Cummings@uk.lockton.com

CUMMINS, John Carlisle (Oct 1978)
(Consultant)
Hill Brown Licensing, Glasgow . . . .(p.986)
T: 0141 221 1919
E: JCC@mshblicensing.com

CUNNIFF, Philippa Jayne (Sept 1998) (Partner)
Gilson Gray LLP, Edinburgh . . . .(p.874)
T: 0131 5165354
E: pcunniff@gilsongray.co.uk

CUNNING, Ronan James (Oct 1997)
(Employee)
Glasgow City Council, Glasgow . . . . . .(p.1239)
T: 0141 2873529
E: ronan.cunning@ced.glasgow.gov.uk

CUNNINGHAM, Ailsa McLaren (May 1994)
(Employee)
City of Edinburgh Council,
Edinburgh . . . .(p.1221)
T: (0131) 5294145
E: ailsa.cunningham@edinburgh.gov.uk

CUNNINGHAM, Amanda Mary (Oct 2009)
(Employee)
Glasgow City Council, Glasgow . . . . . .(p.1239)
T: 0141 2872000
E: amanda.cunningham@glasgow.gov.uk

CUNNINGHAM, Con (May 2012) (Partner)
Con Cunningham Legal Services Ltd,
Glasgow. . . . .(p.964)
T: 077447 446188
E: info@concunningham.com

CUNNINGHAM, David Lindsay (Sept 2009)
(Employee)
Scottish Power Limited, Glasgow . . . . .(p.1244)
T: 0141 6140000
E: david.cunningham@scottishpower.com

CUNNINGHAM, Emma Jane (Oct 2014)
(Employee)
Baillie Gifford & Co, Edinburgh . . . . . .(p.1220)
T: 0131 2752000
E: emma.cunningham@bailliegifford.com

CUNNINGHAM, Fiona Ellen Margaret
(Jan 1989) (Partner)
Morgan Cunningham Solicitors,
Edinburgh . . . .(p.891)
T: 0131 6239323
E: info@morgancunningham.com

CUNNINGHAM, Gordon Lindsay (Mar 1981)
(Employee)
The Erinbeg Consultancy LLP,
Largs . . . .(p.1250)

CUNNINGHAM, Graeme Miller (Sept 2003)
(Partner)
GMC Criminal Lawyers,
Kilmarnock . . . .(p.1095)
T: 01563 533338
E: graeme@kilmarnockcriminallawyers.co.uk

CUNNINGHAM, Greg James (Jul 2014)
(Employee)
Public Defence Solicitors Office,
Glasgow. . . . .(p.1243)
T: 0141 5530794
E: GCunningham@pdso.org.uk

CUNNINGHAM, Jennifer Mary (Aug 2020)
(Employee)
Procurator Fiscal Service,
Edinburgh . . . .(p.1227)
T: 0300 0203168
E: jennifer.cunningham@copfs.gov.uk

CUNNINGHAM, Joanne Rachel (Oct 1982)
(Employee)
Procurator Fiscal Service,
Kilmarnock . . . .(p.1249)
T: 0844 561 2770
E: jo.cunningham@copfs.gov.uk

CUNNINGHAM, Katie (Jul 2020) (Employee)
Procurator Fiscal Service, Falkirk . . . . . .(p.1236)
T: 0300 020 3000
E: Katie.Cunningham@copfs.gov.uk

CUNNINGHAM, Lesley Alexandra Jane
(Sept 2015) (Employee)
Public Defence Solicitors Office,
Edinburgh . . . .(p.1230)
T: 0131 5571222
E: LCunningham@pdso.org.uk

CUNNINGHAM, Lesley Susan (Dec 2002)
(Partner)
Caesar & Howie, Bathgate. . . . .(p.770)
T: 01506 815900
E: lc@caesar-howie.co.uk

CUNNINGHAM, Lynne (Jul 2009) (Employee)
Fiona McPhail Solicitors, Edinburgh . . . .(p.886)
T: 0344 5152410
E: Lynne_Cunningham@shelter.org.uk

CUNNINGHAM, Michael James (Oct 2019)
(Employee)
Procurator Fiscal Service, Paisley . . . . . .(p.1252)
T: 0141 8875225
E: Michael.Cunningham@copfs.gov.uk

CUNNINGHAM, Nancy Stevenson
(Feb 1999) (Associate)
Blair & Bryden, Greenock . . . .(p.1060)
T: 01475 558420
E: nanette@blair-bryden.co.uk

CUNNINGHAM, Nicola Faye (Mar 2016)
(Employee)
Scottish Courts and Tribunals Service,
Aberdeen . . . .(p.1214)
T: 01224 657248

CUNNINGHAM, Robert James Craig
(Jul 2018) (Employee)
Dales Solicitors LLP, Galston . . . .(p.934)
T: 01563 820216

CUNNINGHAM, Sarah Louise (Feb 2018)
(Employee)
DWF LLP, Edinburgh . . . .(p.865)
T: 0131 2265541
E: sarah.cunningham@dwf.law

CUNNINGHAM, Stewart (Oct 2010) (Employee)
Dana Petroleum Limited, Aberdeen . . .(p.1212)
T: 01224 616000
E: stewart.cunningham@dana-petroleum.com

CUNNINGHAM, Stewart Duncan (Aug 2005)
(Employee)
Scottish Government, Edinburgh . . . . .(p.1231)
T: 0131 244 0815
E: stewart.cunningham@gov.scot

CURLE, Elspeth (Aug 1999) (Director)
Curle Stewart Limited, Glasgow . . . .(p.964)
T: 0141 227 6202
E: ec@curlestewart.co.uk

CURLE, Philip (Dec 1999) (Director)
Curle Stewart Limited, Glasgow . . . .(p.964)
T: 0141 227 6201
E: pc@curlestewart.co.uk

CURRAN, Sarah Allison (Sept 2019) (Employee)
Burness Paull LLP, Glasgow . . . .(p.954)
T: 0141 2484933

CURRAN, Victoria Eve (Aug 2017) (Employee)
Glasgow City Council, Glasgow . . . . . .(p.1239)
T: 0141 2872000
E: Victoria.Curran@ced.glasgow.gov.uk

CURREN, Victoria (Sept 2010) (Associate)
Gillespie Macandrew LLP,
Edinburgh . . . .(p.872)
T: 0131 2251677
E: victoria.watson@gillespiemacandrew.co.uk

CURRIE, Adam (Oct 1976) (Partner)
Adam Currie & Co., Irvine . . . .(p.1086)
T: 01294 273735
E: mail@currieirvine.co.uk

CURRIE, Alexander Blair (Nov 1981)
(Consultant)
McCluskey Browne, Kilmarnock . . . . . .(p.1095)
T: 01563 544545
E: SandyC@mccluskeybrowne.co.uk

CURRIE, Anthony David (Mar 1999) (Director)
1st Legal Limited, Ayr . . . .(p.760)
T: 01292 290 666
E: tony@1stlegal.co.uk

CURRIE, Catherine Ann (Aug 1986) (Partner)
BTO Solicitors LLP, Glasgow . . . .(p.952)
T: 0141 2218012
E: ccr@bto.co.uk

CURRIE, Claire Elizabeth (Aug 2017) (Associate)
1st Legal Limited, Ayr . . . .(p.760)
T: 01292 290666
E: claire@1stlegal.co.uk

CURRIE, Craig Stewart William (Jun 2014)
(Partner)
Galloway & Ayrshire Partnership LLP,
Girvan . . . .(p.935)
T: 01465 712345
E: craig.currie@smithvalentine.co.uk

CURRIE, David Gerard (Sept 2014) (Employee)
Notamvis Limited, London NW6 . . . . .(p.1267)

CURRIE, David John (Aug 1991) (Employee)
Hewats, Castle Douglas . . . . (p.784)
T: 01556 502391
E: davidc@hewats.co.uk

CURRIE, David Owen (Aug 2021) (Employee)
Procurator Fiscal Service, Perth . . . . (p.1253)
T: 01738 637272
E: David.Currie@copfs.gov.uk

CURRIE, Douglas Jackson (Feb 2000) (Partner)
Alexr. McAllister & McKechnie,
Paisley . . . . (p.1136)
T: 0141 8878961
E: douglasc@ammlaw.co.uk

CURRIE, Fraser Macfarlane (Jul 1998) (Partner)
Alexr. McAllister & McKechnie,
Paisley . . . . (p.1136)
T: 0141 8878961
E: fraserc@ammlaw.co.uk

CURRIE, Hannah Frances (Sept 2009)
(Employee)
Dentons UK and Middle East LLP,
Edinburgh . . . . (p.860)
T: 0330 2220050
E: hannah.currrie@dentons.com

CURRIE, Jill Barbara (Feb 2021) (Employee)
Procurator Fiscal Service,
Edinburgh . . . . (p.1229)
T: 0300 0203000
E: jill.currie@copfs.gov.uk

CURRIE, Julie Angela (Nov 2008) (Employee)
Carey Olsen, St Helier . . . . (p.1274)
T: 01534 888900
E: julie.currie@careyolsen.com

CURRIE, Katherine (Jan 2021) (Employee)
Criminal Injuries Compensation Authority,
Glasgow . . . . (p.1239)
T: 0141 2281419
E: katherine.currie@cica.gov.uk

CURRIE, Kevin Robert (Jan 2020) (Employee)
Cullen Kilshaw, Galashiels . . . . (p.933)
T: 01896 800 800
E: kevin.currie@cullenkilshaw.com

CURRIE, Lesley Ann (Sept 2009) (Employee)
Renfrewshire Council, Paisley . . . . (p.1252)
T: 0141 6187610
E: lesleyann.currie@renfrewshire.gov.uk

CURRIE, Matthew John (Jan 1999) (Associate)
Jones Whyte LLP, Glasgow. . . . . (p.993)
T: 0141 375 1222
E: matthew.currie@joneswhyte.co.uk

CURRIE, Michael Fraser (Jul 2017) (Partner)
Aberdein Considine and Company,
Glasgow. (p.937)
T: 0141 2278200
E: mcurrie@acandco.com

CURRIE, Robin (Dec 1978) (Associate)
MacArthur Legal, Oban . . . . (p.1134)
T: 01631 562215
E: robin@macarthurlegal.co.uk

CURRIE, Siobh n Connor (May 2011)
(Employee)
Procurator Fiscal Service, Glasgow . . . . (p.1241)
T: 0300 0203000
E: Siobhan.Currie@copfs.gov.uk

CURRIE, Susan Elizabeth (May 2014)
(Employee)
EDF Energy Renewables,
Edinburgh . . . . (p.1222)
T: (0131) 460 3654
E: susan.currie@edf-re.uk

CURRIE, Susan Elizabeth (Sept 2016)
(Employee)
Blackadders LLP, Glasgow . . . . (p.946)
T: 0141 2481888
E: susan.currie@blackadders.co.uk

CURRIE, Ursula Sophie (Oct 2009) (Employee)
DWF LLP, Edinburgh. . . . . (p.865)
T: 0131 2265541
E: ursula.currie@dwf.law

CUSCHIERI, Elizabeth Emma (Aug 1994)
(Employee)
Scottish Legal Aid Board,
Edinburgh . . . . (p.1233)
T: 0131 2267061
E: cuschierili@slab.org.uk

CUSHLEY, Jonathan Edward (Aug 1999)
(Associate)
Austin Lafferty Limited, Hamilton . . . . . (p.1065)
T: 01698 477 614
E: jcushley@laffertylaw.com

CUSHLEY, Maria-Claire (Nov 2005) (Employee)
Glasgow City Council, Glasgow . . . . . . (p.1239)
T: 0141 2874720
E: maria-claire.cushley@ced.glasgow.gov.uk

CUTHBERT, April Anne (Oct 2007) (Partner)
Macfarlane & Co., Glasgow . . . . (p.1009)
T: 0141 248 3307
E: ac@macfarlane-law.co.uk

CUTHBERTSON, Kay (Sept 2021) (Employee)
Shoosmiths, Edinburgh . . . . (p.902)
T: 03700 868000
E: kay.cuthbertson@shoosmiths.co.uk

CUTHILL, David George (Aug 2019) (Employee)
Burness Paull LLP, Edinburgh . . . . (p.850)
T: 0131 4736000
E: david.cuthill@burnesspaull.com

DA PRATO, Neil John (Jun 2003) (Director)
Matthews Legal Limited, Dumfries . . . . . (p.802)
T: 01387 257300
E: neildaprato@abamatthews.com

DAGGER, Linsey Elizabeth (Nov 2005)
(Associate)
McDougall McQueen LLP,
Bonnyrigg ....(p.778)
T: 0131 666 2424
E: LinseyDagger@mcdougallmcqueen.co.uk

DAGLEISH, Gordon Paul (Jun 1989) (Employee)
Argyll & Bute Council,
Lochgilphead ....(p.1251)
T: 01546 604164
E: gordon.dagleish@argyll-bute.gov.uk

DAGLISH, Grant Stephen (Aug 2017)
(Employee)
James McKay Defence Solicitors Limited,
Elgin ....(p.917)
T: 01343 556500
E: grant@jamesmckay.uk

DAHMS, Jozanne Kathleen Kyna (Jul 2015)
(Employee)
Aberdeen Corporate Services Limited,
Edinburgh ....(p.1220)
T: 0131 245 7508
E: jozanne.dahms@aberdeen-asset.com

DAILLY, Kirk Anthony (Oct 2006) (Partner)
Blackadders LLP, Dundee...........(p.805)
T: 01382 229222
E: kirk.dailly@blackadders.co.uk

DAILLY, Michael Ronald (Oct 1995) (Partner)
Dailly, Walker and Co., Solicitors,
Glasgow.....................(p.965)
T: 0141 4402503
E: m@govanlc.com

DAILLY, Victoria Jayne (Dec 2008) (Employee)
Scottish Social Services Council,
Dundee ....(p.1218)
T: 0345 6030 891
E: Victoria.Dailly@sssc.uk.com

DALE, Alastair John (Dec 2003) (Partner)
Dales Solicitors LLP, Galston ....(p.934)
T: 01563 820216
E: alastair@dalesllp.co.uk

DALE, John Mungall (Jan 1973) (Partner)
Dales Solicitors LLP, Galston ....(p.934)
T: 01563 820216
E: liz@dalesllp.co.uk

DALE, Timothy Daniel (Oct 2000) (Solicitor)
Pinsent Masons LLP, Edinburgh ....(p.895)
T: 0131 7777000
E: tim.dale@pinsentmasons.com

DALEY, Michael Charles (Sept 1985) (Partner)
Stewart & Watson, Huntly ....(p.1074)
T: 01466 792331
E: mdaley@stewartwatson.co.uk

DALGARNO, Colin Scott (Aug 2021)
(Employee)
Burness Paull LLP, Aberdeen ....(p.724)
T: 01224 621621
E: colin.dalgarno@burnesspaull.com

DALGLEISH, Lauren (Oct 2020) (Employee)
Clarity Simplicity Ltd, Dumfries ....(p.800)
E: l.dalgleish@claritysimplicity.co.uk

DALGLEISH, Wendy Mary (Dec 1988)
(Employee)
Scottish Legal Aid Board,
Edinburgh ....(p.1233)
T: 0131 2267061
E: DalgleishWe@slab.org.uk

DALLAS, Scott (Jul 2011) (Director)
Macleod & MacCallum Limited,
Inverness ....(p.1080)
T: 01463 239393
E: scott.dallas@macandmac.co.uk

DALLING, Kenneth Alexander Robertson
(Aug 1988) (Partner)
Dalling, Stirling ....(p.1164)
T: 01786 448111
E: kd@dallings.co.uk

DALRYMPLE, Catriona (Dec 1998) (Employee)
Scottish Government, Edinburgh .....(p.1232)
T: 0131 244 3078
E: catriona.dalrymple@gov.scot

DALRYMPLE, Lynne (Sept 1993) (Employee)
TechnipFMC Subsea France,
Courbevoie..................(p.1272)
E: lynne.dalrymple@technipfmc.com

DALTON, Fiona (Sept 1999) (Employee)
Hunter & Robertson Limited,
Paisley ....(p.1138)
T: 0141 8893196
E: fdalton@hunter-robertson.co.uk

DALY, Charlotte Margaret (Aug 2009)
(Employee)
Rollos Law LLP, Cupar.............(p.792)
T: 01334 654081
E: charlottedaly@rollos.co.uk

DALY, Edward Thomas (Sept 2021) (Employee)
BK Gill Solicitors, Bearsden ....(p.772)
T: 0141 9423007

DALY, Lauren Katy Paterson (Jul 2012)
(Director)
Fords Daly Legal Limited, Kirkcaldy....(p.1100)
T: 01592 640630
E: lauren@fordsdalylegal.co.uk

DALY, Nicola Irene (Sept 2000) (Employee)
Procurator Fiscal Service,
Edinburgh ....(p.1229)
E: nicola.daly@copfs.gov.uk

DALYELL, Gordon (Sept 1990) (Partner)
Digby Brown LLP, Edinburgh . . . . (p.862)
T: 0333 200 5925
E: gordon.dalyell@digbybrown.co.uk

DALZIEL, Jennifer Anne (Nov 2007) (Solicitor)
NO FIRM

DALZIEL, Kyle Greg (Oct 2019) (Employee)
Procurator Fiscal Service, Glasgow . . . . (p.1241)
T: 0300 0203000
E: Kyle.Dalziel@copfs.gov.uk

DALZIEL, Lindsey K. (Nov 2003) (Employee)
Procurator Fiscal Service,
Edinburgh . . . . (p.1229)
T: (0844) 561 3268
E: lindsey.dalziel@copfs.gov.uk

DALZIEL, Morag (Jan 1999) (Employee)
McGrade & Co Limited, Glasgow . . . . . (p.1011)
T: 0141 2214488
E: Morag.dalziel@mcgrade.co.uk

DALZIEL, Sandra Jane (May 2004) (Employee)
Loch Lomond and The Trossachs National Park
Authority, Balloch . . . . (p.1215)
T: 01389 722600
E: sandra.dalziel@lochlomond-trossachs.org

DANCE, Karen (Jul 1990) (Partner)
Berrymans Lace Mawer LLP,
Glasgow. (p.945)
T: 0141 3532121
E: Karen.Dance@blmlaw.com

DANGERFIELD, Gordon (Oct 1985)
(Consultant)
Archer Coyle, Glasgow . . . . (p.941)
T: 0141 6372434
E: gordondangerfield@archercoyle.co.uk

DANIEL, Stephanie Anne (Oct 2005)
(Employee)
International Cricket Council,
Dubai . . . . (p.1278)
E: stephanie_daniel@hotmail.com

DANIELS, Craig David George (Sept 2009)
(Employee)
J. & J. Denholm Limited, Glasgow . . . . (p.1240)
T: 0141 353 2090
E: Craig.Daniels@denholm-group.co.uk

DANKS, Edward Andrew (Jul 1997) (Partner)
Paris Steele, North Berwick . . . . (p.1133)
T: 01620 892138
E: edanks@parissteele.com

DANKS, Gavin Richard (Oct 2013) (Employee)
BNP Paribas, Glasgow . . . . (p.1238)
E: gavin.danks@uk.bnpparibas.com

DANKS, Richard Robert (Oct 2016) (Employee)
National Westminster Bank PLC,
Edinburgh . . . . (p.1226)
T: (0131) 626 2925
E: Richard.Danks@rbs.co.uk

DAR, Urfan Hameed (Sept 2004) (Employee)
Scullion Law Limited, Hamilton . . . . . . (p.1069)
T: 01698 283265
E: urfan@scullionlaw.com

DARGIE, John Arthur (May 2014) (Partner)
Blackadders LLP, Aberdeen . . . . (p.722)
T: 01224 588913
E: john.dargie@blackadders.co.uk

DARGIE, Kiera Jane (Oct 2007) (Employee)
Scottish Government, Edinburgh . . . . . (p.1231)
T: 0131 244 0815
E: Kiera.Dargie2@gov.scot

DARLEY, Elizabeth Louise (Sept 2019)
(Associate)
Dentons UK and Middle East LLP,
Glasgow. (p.968)
T: 0330 222 0050
E: elizabeth.darley@dentons.com

DARLING, Craig Charles (Feb 1996) (Partner)
Gilson Gray LLP, Edinburgh . . . . (p.874)
T: 0131 5165354
E: cdarling@gilsongray.co.uk

DARLING, Jennifer (Jan 2011) (Associate)
CMS Cameron McKenna Nabarro Olswang LLP,
Edinburgh . . . . (p.856)
T: 0131 2288000
E: jenni.darling@cms-cmno.com

DARLING, Kay Anne (Oct 2009) (Associate)
Clyde & Co (Scotland) LLP,
Edinburgh . . . . (p.855)
T: 0131 5571545
E: kay.darling@clydeco.com

DARLING, Neil Andrew (Nov 1995) (Associate)
Thorntons Law LLP, Edinburgh . . . . . . (p.906)
T: 0131 2258705
E: ndarling@thorntons-law.co.uk

DARLING, Robert Neil (Sept 2012) (Employee)
Lloyds Banking Group Plc,
Edinburgh . . . . (p.1224)
T: (0131) 442 9579
E: robbie.darling@lloydsbanking.com

DARNELL, Hannah Louise (Aug 2018)
(Employee)
Stewart & Watson, Turriff . . . . (p.1177)
T: 01888 563773
E: hdarnell@stewartwatson.co.uk

DARROCH, Elinor Morag (Jul 1992) (Director)
JAB Legal Ltd, Dundee . . . . (p.813)
T: 01382 200411
E: EDarroch@jackbrownsolicitors.co.uk

DARROCH, Geraldine (Oct 2013) (Director)
Strefford Tulips Limited, Hamilton . . . . (p.1070)
T: 01698 429428
E: g.darroch@strefford-tulips.co.uk

DARROCH, Joan Burns (Feb 2013) (Employee)
STV Television Limited, Glasgow......(p.1245)
T: 0141 3003000
E: joan.darroch@stv.tv

DARROCH, Julie Louise (Jul 1995) (Employee)
Miller Hendry, Crieff...............(p.789)
T: 01764 655151
E: juliedarroch@millerhendry.co.uk

DARROCH, Lindsay Duncan Gunn
(Apr 1995) (Partner)
Gilson Gray LLP, Dundee...........(p.811)
T: 01382 549321
E: ldarroch@gilsongray.co.uk

DARVISHZADEH-KOOCHESFEHANI, Arezo
(Oct 2013) (Employee)
Legal Secretariat to the Lord Advocate,
Edinburgh ....(p.1224)
T: (0300) 020 3364
E: arezo.darvishzadeh@gov.scot

DAUBNEY, Neil Alexander (Nov 2002)
(Employee)
Dickson Minto, Edinburgh...........(p.861)
T: 0131 2254455
E: neil.daubney@dmws.com

DAVENPORT, Kathryn Laura (Nov 2007)
(Employee)
Wright, Johnston & Mackenzie LLP,
Glasgow....................(p.1054)
T: 0141 2483434
E: kld@wjm.co.uk

DAVENPORT, Mark (Dec 1994) (Employee)
DLA Piper Scotland LLP, Edinburgh ....(p.863)
T: 08700 111111
E: mark.davenport@dlapiper.com

DAVEY, Jane Elizabeth (Dec 1997) (Employee)
Highland Council, Inverness.........(p.1248)
T: 01463 702000
E: jane.davey@highland.gov.uk

DAVID, Anne Fearon (Oct 1983) (Employee)
Highland Council, Inverness.........(p.1248)
T: 01463 702000
E: anne.david@highland.gov.uk

DAVID, Euan Fearon (Dec 1981) (Associate)
Mitchells Roberton Ltd, Glasgow .....(p.1020)
T: 0141 5523422
E: efd@mitchells-roberton.co.uk

DAVIDSON, Adam Alexander (Oct 1999)
(Employee)
Stobart Group, Widnes ....(p.1272)
E: Adam.Davidson@stobartgroup.com

DAVIDSON, Agnes Shirley (Dec 1982)
(Employee)
Church of Scotland, Edinburgh ......(p.1221)
T: 0131 2255722
E: Shirley.Davidson@churchofscotland.org.uk

DAVIDSON, Alan James (Oct 1989) (Partner)
Sturrock, Armstrong & Thomson,
Edinburgh ....(p.905)
T: 0131 5560159
E: ad@satsolicitors.co.uk

DAVIDSON, Angus Robert (Aug 2010)
(Employee)
National Westminster Bank PLC,
Edinburgh ....(p.1226)
T: (0131) 626 2925
E: Angus.Davidson@rbs.co.uk

DAVIDSON, Anna (Sept 2020) (Associate)
Drummond Miller LLP, Edinburgh .....(p.864)
T: 0131 2265151
E: ADavidson@drummondmiller.co.uk

DAVIDSON, Chloe (Oct 2017) (Employee)
Connell & Connell, WS, Edinburgh ....(p.857)
T: 0131 5562993
E: cd@connellws.co.uk

DAVIDSON, Colin Graham (Sept 2015)
(Employee)
Edwards Duthie Shamash, London
SE1 ....(p.1264)
E: cds@edwardsduthieshamash.co.uk

DAVIDSON, David William (Feb 1992) (Partner)
Burness Paull LLP, Edinburgh ....(p.850)
T: 0131 4736000
E: David.Davidson@burnesspaull.com

DAVIDSON, Donna Grace (Mar 2001)
(Employee)
Procurator Fiscal Service, Dundee.....(p.1218)
T: 0300 020 4285
E: donna.davidson@copfs.gov.uk

DAVIDSON, Emma Christian (Feb 2021)
(Employee)
Shepherd and Wedderburn LLP,
Edinburgh ....(p.900)
T: 0131 2289900
E: Emma.Davidson@shepwedd.com

DAVIDSON, Fiona Gail (Sept 2011) (Employee)
Aberdeen Corporate Services Limited,
Edinburgh ....(p.1220)
T: 0131 245 7508
E: fiona.davidson@spedge.com

DAVIDSON, Gale McLelland (Oct 2006)
(Employee)
Austin Kelly & Co.,, Irvine ....(p.1086)
T: 01294 275215
E: court@austinkelly.net

DAVIDSON, Graeme Sinclair (Aug 1999)
(Solicitor)
NO FIRM

DAVIDSON, Helen McNab (Oct 1985)
(Employee)
Hill & Robb Limited, Stirling . . . .(p.1164)
T: 01786 450985
E: helendavidson@hillandrobb.co.uk

DAVIDSON, Iain Finlay (Mar 1990) (Employee)
Scottish Borders Council, Newtown St.
Boswells . . . .(p.1251)
T: 01835 825 225
E: idavidson@scotborders.gov.uk

DAVIDSON, Ian Graham (Dec 1987) (Partner)
Harper Macleod LLP, Elgin . . . .(p.916)
T: 01343 542623
E: ian.davidson@harpermacleod.co.uk

DAVIDSON, James Valentine (Oct 1984)
(Director)
Hill & Robb Limited, Stirling . . . .(p.1164)
T: 01786 450985
E: jimdavidson@hillandrobb.co.uk

DAVIDSON, Jennifer Isobel Douglas
(Aug 2006) (Associate)
Eden Legal Limited, Perth . . . .(p.1147)
T: 01738 310047
E: JenniferDavidson@eden-legal.co.uk

DAVIDSON, Karen Jane (Oct 1997) (Partner)
Brodies LLP, Glasgow . . . .(p.948)
T: 0141 2484672
E: karen.davidson@brodies.com

DAVIDSON, Lindsay (Jul 1997) (Director)
Lefevres (Scotland) Limited,
Edinburgh . . . .(p.882)
T: 0845 305 2555
E: ld@lefevres.law

DAVIDSON, Lorna (Nov 2012) (Employee)
Gilson Gray LLP, Glasgow . . . .(p.980)
T: 0141 433 7743
E: ldavidson@gilsongray.co.uk

DAVIDSON, Louise Manzie (Jul 2009)
(Employee)
National Westminster Bank PLC,
Edinburgh . . . .(p.1226)
E: louise.m.davidson@rbs.co.uk

DAVIDSON, Neil Christopher Cowins
(Jul 2008) (Partner)
Digby Brown LLP, Aberdeen . . . .(p.729)
T: 01224 608775
E: neil.davidson@digbybrown.co.uk

DAVIDSON, Neil Gillespie (Dec 2000) (Director)
Davidson & Company Solicitors Limited,
Glasgow . . . .(p.967)
T: 0141 6335600
E: neil@dcosolicitors.co.uk

DAVIDSON, Nicola Jane (Nov 2001) (Director)
Connelly & Yeoman Law Limited,
Arbroath . . . .(p.757)
T: 01241 434200
E: nicola@connellyyeoman.com

DAVIDSON, Richard (Aug 2018) (Employee)
Castle Water, Blairgowrie . . . .(p.1216)
T: 01250 718700
E: richard.davidson@Castlewater.co.uk

DAVIDSON, Robert Gordon William
(Aug 2003) (Partner)
Peterkins, Aberdeen . . . .(p.739)
T: 01224 428000
E: rd@peterkins.com

DAVIDSON, Robert Graham Richmond
(Nov 1982) (Partner)
Miller Samuel Hill Brown LLP,
Glasgow . . . .(p.1020)
T: 0141 2211919
E: gd@mshblegal.com

DAVIDSON, Sarah Shirley Douglas
(Jan 2021) (Employee)
Glasgow City Council, Glasgow . . . . . .(p.1240)
E: Sarah.Davidson@glasgow.gov.uk

DAVIDSON, Timothy John (Aug 2017)
(Employee)
Shepherd and Wedderburn LLP,
Edinburgh . . . .(p.900)
T: 0131 2289900
E: tim.davidson@shepwedd.com

DAVIE, Alan Robert (Dec 2001) (Employee)
Dewar Spence, Leven . . . .(p.1114)
T: 01333 425200

DAVIE, John Robert (Nov 1976) (Partner)
John Davie & Co, Alford . . . .(p.752)
T: 01224 656356
E: john.davie@johndavieandco.com

DAVIES, Adam Dennis (Jun 2017) (Employee)
Kirkland & Ellis International LLP, London
EC3 . . . .(p.1265)
T: 0207 4692000
E: adam.davies@kirkland.com

DAVIES, Alan Graham (Nov 1983) (Partner)
McCash & Hunter LLP, Perth . . . .(p.1149)
T: 01738 620451
E: alandavies@mccash.co.uk

DAVIES, Ann Dale (Aug 1992) (Employee)
Scottish Government, Edinburgh . . . . .(p.1231)
T: 0131 244 0815
E: ann.davies@gov.scot

DAVIES, Jennifer Michelle (Nov 2003)
(Employee)
Scottish Futures Trust, Edinburgh . . . . .(p.1231)
T: 0131 5100800
E: jenny.davies@scottishfuturestrust.org.uk

DAVIES, Joe Alexander (Oct 2016) (Employee)
Gilson Gray LLP, Edinburgh . . . .(p.874)
T: 0131 5165354
E: jdavies@gilsongray.co.uk

DAVIES, Michael Howard (Aug 2004)
(Employee)
Scottish Power Limited, Glasgow . . . . .(p.1244)
T: 0141 6140000
E: Michael.Davies@ScottishPower.com

DAVIES, Naomi Rhiannon Elspeth
(Oct 2020) (Employee)
Ledingham Chalmers LLP,
Aberdeen . . . .(p.734)
T: 01224 408408
E: naomi.davies@ledinghamchalmers.com

DAVIES, Rachel Emily (Nov 2006) (Employee)
Stuart & Stuart, Bonnyrigg . . . .(p.779)
T: 0131 6637135
E: RDavies@stuartandstuart.co.uk

DAVIES, Rachel Mae Christina (Sept 2014)
(Employee)
Addleshaw Goddard LLP,
Edinburgh . . . .(p.835)
T: 0131 2282400
E: Rachel.Davies@addleshawgoddard.com

DAVIES, Rhidian Andrew Spencer
(Feb 2003) (Employee)
National Health Service Scotland,
Edinburgh . . . .(p.1225)
T: 0131 2757800
E: rhidian.davies@nhs.scot

DAVIES, Ruby Megan (Aug 2021) (Employee)
Dentons UK and Middle East LLP, London
EC4 . . . .(p.1263)
T: 020 7242 1212

DAVIES, Sophie Marie (Jul 2020) (Employee)
Dentons UK and Middle East LLP,
Glasgow. . . . .(p.968)
T: 0330 2220050
E: sophie.davies@dentons.com

DAVIES, Stuart Leslie William (Feb 2014)
(Employee)
Skyscanner, Edinburgh . . . .(p.1234)
E: stuart.davies@skyscanner.net

DAVIS, Alexander Glenn (Aug 1983) (Partner)
McLennan Adam Davis, Ayr . . . .(p.764)
T: 01292 289584
E: glennd@mad-law.co.uk

DAVIS, Gavin Stewart (Dec 2002) (Employee)
Aberdeen Corporate Services Limited,
Edinburgh . . . .(p.1220)
T: 0131 372 1625
E: gavin.s.davis@abrdn.com

DAVIS, Gerard Martin (Feb 2018) (Employee)
Allan McDougall McQueen LLP,
Edinburgh . . . .(p.837)
T: 0131 2281926
E: GerardDavis@mcdougallmcqueen.co.uk

DAVIS, Jean Thomson (Jun 1998) (Employee)
Scottish Courts and Tribunals Service,
Perth . . . .(p.1253)
T: 01738 492933
E: JDavis@scotcourts.gov.uk

DAVIS, Lorna (Aug 2002) (Partner)
Harper Macleod LLP, Glasgow . . . .(p.983)
T: 0141 2218888
E: lorna.davis@harpermacleod.co.uk

DAVIS, Marion Elizabeth (Sept 1998)
(Associate)
BTO Solicitors LLP, Glasgow . . . .(p.952)
T: 0141 2218012
E: mda@bto.co.uk

DAVIS, Victoria Jacqueline (Jan 2012)
(Employee)
Burness Paull LLP, Glasgow . . . .(p.954)
T: 0141 2484933
E: Victoria.Davis@burnesspaull.com

DAVISON, Tara (Jun 2019) (Employee)
Shepherd and Wedderburn LLP,
Edinburgh . . . .(p.900)
T: 0131 2289900
E: tara.davison@shepwedd.com

DAWSON, Anthony James (Nov 1975)
(Consultant)
James & George Collie LLP,
Aberdeen . . . .(p.728)
T: 01224 581581
E: a.dawson@jgcollie.co.uk

DAWSON, Fraser Anthony (Sept 2004)
(Employee)
Gibson, Dunn & Crutcher LLP,
Dubai . . . .(p.1278)
T: +971 4 318 4619
E: fdawson@gibsondunn.com

DAWSON, Kathryn Margaret (Jun 2012)
(Solicitor)
NO FIRM

DAWSON, Lorna Keri (Nov 1997) (Employee)
BP Exploration Operating Company Ltd.,
Dyce . . . .(p.1219)
T: 01224 832353
E: lorna.dawson@bp.com

DAY, Mairi Jean (Nov 2000) (Partner)
Digby Brown LLP, Edinburgh . . . .(p.862)
T: 0131 319 8132
E: mairi.day@digbybrown.co.uk

DAY, Margaret Lancaster (Sept 1979)
(Associate)
Gillespie Macandrew LLP,
Edinburgh . . . . (p.872)
T: 0131 2251677
E: margaret.day@gillespiemacandrew.co.uk

DAY, Matthew George (Mar 2013) (Employee)
SSE Plc, Perth . . . . (p.1253)
T: 01738 456 000
E: matthew.day@sse.com

DAY, Morgan (Oct 2017) (Employee)
Anika Jethwa & Co, Dundee . . . . (p.813)
T: 01382 223399

DAY, Natasha Mary (Apr 2019) (Employee)
Aberdein Considine and Company,
Aberdeen . . . . (p.718)
T: 01224 589700
E: nday@acandco.com

DAY, Nicholas Donald (Oct 2000) (Employee)
University of Edinburgh, Edinburgh . . . (p.1235)
T: (0131) 651 4330
E: nicky.day@ed.ac.uk

DE CANDIA, Amanda Jane (Mar 1993)
(Employee)
Aberdeenshire Council, Aberdeen . . . . . (p.1211)
T: 01467 536673
E: amanda.decandia@aberdeenshire.gov.uk

DE GAETANO, Honor Fiona (Nov 2001)
(Employee)
Procurator Fiscal Service,
Edinburgh . . . . (p.1227)
T: 0300 0203168
E: Fiona.DeGaetano@copfs.gov.uk

DE GIOIA-CARABELLESE, Professor,
Pierdomenico (Oct 2010) (Solicitor)
NO FIRM

DE GROOTE, Cecilia (Oct 1988) (Employee)
Procurator Fiscal Service, Hamilton . . . . (p.1247)
T: 0844 5613245
E: cecilia.degroote@copfs.gov.uk

DE MARCO, Giulia (Sept 2001) (Employee)
Brodies LLP, Glasgow . . . . (p.948)
T: 0141 2484672
E: giulia.demarco@brodies.com

DE ROSA, Darren Michael (Aug 2008)
(Solicitor)
NO FIRM

DE SAILLY, Emma Mary (Apr 2012) (Employee)
Shepherd and Wedderburn LLP,
Edinburgh . . . . (p.900)
T: 0131 2289900
E: emma.desailly@shepwedd.com

DE STE CROIX, Adam McAinsh (Oct 2017)
(Employee)
Harper Macleod LLP, Glasgow . . . . (p.983)
T: 0141 2218888
E: adam.destecroix@harpermacleod.co.uk

DE SYLVA, Nicola (Jan 1998) (Employee)
DLA Piper Middle East LLP, Abu
Dhabi . . . . (p.1277)
T: +971 2 4941500
E: nicola.desylva@dlapiper.com

DE VILLIERS, Christopher Martin (Apr 2004)
(Employee)
Aberdeenshire Council, Aberdeen . . . . . (p.1211)
T: 01224 665142
E: chris.devilliers@aberdeenshire.gov.uk

DE VOS, Emma Ethel Bennett (Sept 1991)
(Partner)
Calders, Dundee . . . . (p.807)
T: 01382 224391
E: edv@calders.com

DE WERT, Bruce Gregor (May 1980) (Partner)
Georgesons, Wick . . . . (p.1180)
T: 01955 606060
E: bruce.de.wert@georgesons.co.uk

DE-PELLETTE, Nicole (Sept 2021) (Employee)
Jones Whyte LLP, Glasgow . . . . (p.993)
T: 0141 375 1222
E: nicole.depellette@joneswhyte.co.uk

DE-SMID, Kim Jacqueline (Nov 1996)
(Employee)
MacRoberts LLP, Dundee . . . . (p.815)
T: 01382 339340
E: Kim.DeSmid@macroberts.com

DEAKIN, Lucy Jean (May 2018) (Employee)
Ashurst LLP, Glasgow . . . . (p.1237)
T: (0141) 375 4242
E: lucy.deakin@ashurst.com

DEAN, Alistair Fraser (May 1995) (Partner)
Anderson Strathern LLP, Edinburgh . . . . (p.839)
T: 0131 2707700
E: alistair.dean@andersonstrathern.co.uk

DEAN, Claudia Catherine Anne (Jan 2021)
(Employee)
Pinsent Masons LLP, Edinburgh . . . . (p.895)
T: 0131 777 7000
E: claudia.dean@pinsentmasons.com

DEAN, Gillian Elaine (Aug 1985) (Employee)
Lloyds Banking Group, Edinburgh . . . . (p.1224)
T: 0131 446 5428
E: Gillian.Dean@lloydsbanking.com

DEAN, Kieran William (Oct 1991) (Partner)
Dean & Co, Glasgow . . . . (p.968)
T: 0141 6494159
E: deanandco@btinternet.com

DEAN, Michael John (Nov 1985) (Partner)
Dentons UK and Middle East LLP,
Glasgow......................(p.968)
T: 0330 2220050
E: Michael.Dean@dentons.com

DEANE, Campbell Strachan (Oct 1990)
(Partner)
Bannatyne, Kirkwood, France & Co.,
Glasgow......................(p.943)
T: 0141 2216020
E: campbelldeane@bkf.co.uk

DEANE, David William (Jan 1989) (Consultant)
Bannatyne, Kirkwood, France & Co.,
Glasgow......................(p.943)
T: 0141 2216020
E: daviddeane@bkf.co.uk

DEANE, Gordon Fletcher (Mar 2001) (Partner)
Balfour + Manson LLP, Edinburgh .....(p.841)
T: 0131 2001200
E: gordon.deane@balfour-manson.co.uk

DEANE, Margaret Catherine (Jan 2000)
(Employee)
City of Edinburgh Council,
Edinburgh ....(p.1221)
T: (0131) 5294145
E: maggie.deane@edinburgh.gov.uk

DEANS, Andrew Harry (Jan 2018) (Employee)
Brodies LLP, Edinburgh ....(p.845)
T: 0131 2283777
E: andrew.deans@brodies.com

DEANS, Catriona Ann (Feb 2016) (Employee)
Office of the Queen's and Lord Treasurer's
Remembrancer, Edinburgh........(p.1227)
T: (0300) 020 3512
E: catriona.deans@qltr.gov.uk

DEANS, Emily Mary (Sept 2020) (Employee)
Balfour + Manson LLP, Edinburgh .....(p.841)
T: 0131 2001200
E: Emily.Deans@balfour-manson.co.uk

DEANS, Leslie George (Aug 1975) (Consultant)
Deans Solicitors and Estate Agents LLP,
Edinburgh ....(p.860)
T: 0131 6671900
E: leslie.deans@deansproperties.co.uk

DEANS, Paul Michael (Mar 2011) (Employee)
Thompsons, Edinburgh ....(p.906)
T: 0131 2254297
E: paul.deans@thompsons-scotland.co.uk

DEANS, Ramsey Mungo Orwin (Jun 2016)
(Employee)
Baillie Gifford & Co, Edinburgh ......(p.1220)
T: 0131 2752000
E: ramsey.deans@bailliegifford.com

DEARIE, Christopher John (Sept 2005)
(Employee)
Apollo Management International LLP, London
W1 ....(p.1261)
T: 020 3320 1562
E: cdearie@apollo.com

DEAS, Christina Frances (Jan 2020) (Solicitor)
NO FIRM

DEEGAN, Jennifer (Oct 1994) (Associate)
BTO Raeburn Hope, Helensburgh.....(p.1072)
T: 01436 671221
E: jde@bto.co.uk

DEELEY, Amanda (Jan 2005) (Employee)
Citation Limited, Wilmslow ....(p.1272)
E: amandadeeley@citation.co.uk

DEELEY, Breda Martina (Nov 2003) (Employee)
Brodies LLP, Edinburgh ....(p.845)
T: 0131 2283777
E: breda.deeley@brodies.com

DEELEY, Mandy (Oct 2006) (Employee)
Cirrus Logic International Semiconductor Ltd,
Edinburgh ....(p.1221)
T: 0131 2727000
E: Mandy.Deeley@cirrus.com

DEEMING, Eleanor Marion (Oct 2012)
(Employee)
Scottish Human Rights Commission,
Edinburgh ....(p.1233)
T: 0131 297 5750

DEENEY, Jemma Ann (Jun 2021) (Employee)
Brodies LLP, Edinburgh ....(p.845)
T: 0131 2283777
E: jemma.deeney@brodies.com

DEEPROSE, Gavin Montgomery Sutherlan
(Nov 2000) (Employee)
DLA Piper Scotland LLP, Edinburgh ....(p.863)
T: 08700 111111
E: gavin.deeprose@dlapiper.com

DEERY, Darren James Crilley (Aug 2008)
(Partner)
Drummond Miller LLP, Edinburgh .....(p.864)
T: 0131 2265151
E: DDeery@drummondmiller.co.uk

DEL VALLE, Elaine Reilly (Sept 1993) (Associate)
Gillespie Macandrew LLP,
Edinburgh ....(p.872)
T: 0131 2251677
E: Elaine.Delvalle@gillespiemacandrew.co.uk

DELANEY, Alan Joseph (Aug 2002) (Employee)
Morton Fraser LLP, Edinburgh ....(p.891)
T: 0131 2471000
E: Alan.Delaney@morton-fraser.com

DELANEY, Rachael Joanne (Mar 2018)
(Employee)
Blackadders LLP, Dundee. . . . .(p.805)
T: 01382 229222
E: rachael.delaney@blackadders.co.uk

DELANEY, Rhona (Oct 2015) (Employee)
Burness Paull LLP, Edinburgh . . . .(p.850)
T: 0131 4736000
E: rhona.mcadam@burnesspaull.com

DELANEY, Sian Marie (Feb 2015) (Director)
Delaney Graham Limited, Glasgow. . . . .(p.968)
T: 0141 4834450
E: s.delaney@delaneygraham.co.uk

DEMARCO, Dario (Aug 2015) (Employee)
Blackadders LLP, Glasgow . . . .(p.946)
T: 0141 2481888
E: dario.demarco@blackadders.co.uk

DEMATAGODA, Susith Dilanka (Oct 2009)
(Employee)
Peacock Johnston, Glasgow . . . .(p.1030)
T: 0141 3339505
E: sd@peacockjohnston.co.uk

DEMELLWEEK, Dawn Alison (May 2010)
(Employee)
Aggreko plc, Glasgow . . . .(p.1237)
T: 0141 2255900
E: dawn.demellweek@aggreko.co.uk

DEMICK, Deborah Rose O'Brien (Oct 2000)
(Employee)
Procurator Fiscal Service, Glasgow . . . .(p.1241)
T: 0300 0203000
E: Deborah.Demick@copfs.gov.uk

DEMICK, Peter Adrian (Sept 2000) (Partner)
Kennedys Scotland, Edinburgh. . . . .(p.880)
T: 0131 2256145
E: Peter.Demick@kennedyslaw.com

DEMPSEY, Simon Matthew (Feb 2018)
(Employee)
Digby Brown LLP, Edinburgh . . . .(p.862)
T: 0333 200 5925
E: simon.dempsey@digbybrown.co.uk

DEMPSEY, Zita Louise (Sept 2018) (Employee)
Pinsent Masons LLP, Glasgow . . . .(p.1031)
T: 0141 567 8400
E: zita.dempsey@pinsentmasons.com

DEMPSTER, Victoria Louise (Aug 2009)
(Employee)
Walter Scott & Partners Limited,
Edinburgh . . . .(p.1236)
T: 0131 225 1357
E: vdempster@walterscott.com

DENG, Ling Shan (Jun 2017) (Employee)
Thorntons Law LLP, Dundee . . . .(p.819)
T: 01382 229 111

DENHAM, Kaitlyn Emery (Aug 2019)
(Employee)
Dentons UK and Middle East LLP,
Edinburgh . . . .(p.860)
T: 0330 2220050
E: Kaitlyn.Denham@dentons.com

DENHOLM, Hilary Doreen (Dec 1989)
(Associate)
McSparran McCormick, Glasgow . . . . .(p.1016)
T: 0141 6331557
E: clarkston@mcsparranmccormick.co.uk

DENNIS, David William Ramsay (Aug 2010)
(Associate)
CMS Cameron McKenna Nabarro Olswang LLP,
Glasgow. . . . .(p.962)
T: 0141 2222200
E: david.dennis@cms-cmno.com

DERRIN, Nina Mary (Feb 2017) (Employee)
TC Young LLP, Edinburgh . . . .(p.914)
T: 0131 2207660

DESAI, Mohammed Ebrahim (Mar 2019)
(Employee)
Anderson Strathern LLP, Glasgow. . . . . .(p.940)
T: 0141 2426060
E: mohammed.desai@andersonstrathern.co.uk

DESCHILDRE, Lorraine Allison (May 2019)
(Employee)
AXA Assistance (UK) Limited,
Surrey . . . .(p.1271)
E: lorraine.deschildre@axa-assistance.co.uk

DEUCHARS, Elaine (May 2019) (Employee)
Addleshaw Goddard LLP,
Edinburgh . . . .(p.835)
T: 0131 2282400
E: elaine.deuchars@addleshawgoddard.com

DEVANEY, Aline (Sept 1992) (Employee)
Procurator Fiscal Service, Glasgow . . . .(p.1241)
T: 0300 0203000
E: aline.devaney@copfs.gov.uk

DEVANEY, Gerard John (Nov 1989) (Employee)
Bruce McCormack Limited,
Glasgow. . . . .(p.1007)
T: 0141 429 0010
E: admin@brucethelawyers.co.uk

DEVANEY, Rebecca Danielle (Sept 2017)
(Employee)
Pinsent Masons LLP, London EC2 . . . . .(p.1267)
T: 020 7418 7000
E: rebecca.devaney@pinsentmasons.com

DEVANNEY, Brendan Joseph Gerald
(Dec 2000) (Employee)
Procurator Fiscal Service, Hamilton . . . .(p.1247)
T: 3000202884
E: brendan.devanney@copfs.gov.uk

DEVANNEY, Kathryn (Apr 1988) (Director)
Friels Solicitors Limited,
Uddingston ....(p.1177)
T: 01698 815114
E: kd@frielssolicitors.co.uk

DEVANNEY, Patrick Eamonn (Dec 1999)
(Director)
Carey Hughes Limited, High
Blantyre ....(p.1073)
T: 01698 404616
E: eamonn@careyhughes.co.uk

DEVANNY, Kevin Alexander (Apr 1998)
(Partner)
Pinsent Masons LLP, Glasgow ....(p.1031)
T: 0141 567 8400
E: kevin.devanny@pinsentmasons.com

DEVINE, Angela (Sept 2001) (Employee)
Scottish Courts and Tribunals Service,
Paisley ....(p.1252)
T: 0141 8875291
E: adevine@scotcourts.gov.uk

DEVINE, Catherine Alice (Feb 2012) (Associate)
CMS Cameron McKenna Nabarro Olswang LLP,
London EC4 ....(p.1263)
T: 0207 3673000
E: Catherine.Devine@cms-cmno.com

DEVINE, Christopher Edward (Oct 1994)
(Partner)
Devine & Co., Cambuslang ....(p.782)
T: 0141 6460911
E: devineandco@btconnect.com

DEVINE, Daniel (Jan 2004) (Partner)
Devine Legal, Tayport ....(p.1173)
T: 01382 554408
E: danieldevine05@gmail.com

DEVINE, David Martin (Oct 1986) (Partner)
David Devine & Co., Glasgow ....(p.969)
T: 0141 3527230
E: david@daviddevine.co.uk

DEVINE, Derek Michael (Feb 2001) (Employee)
T. Duncan & Co., Montrose ....(p.1125)
T: 01674 672533
E: derek@tduncan.com

DEVINE, Joan Gabrielle (Jun 1989) (Partner)
Addleshaw Goddard LLP, Glasgow .....(p.938)
T: 0141 2212300
E: Joan.Devine@addleshawgoddard.com

DEVINE, Lindsey Fiona (Sept 2004) (Director)
Norrie Moore Limited,
Cumbernauld ....(p.790)
T: 01236 729868
E: Lindsey@NMLegal.co.uk

DEVINE, Martin Gerard (Oct 2002) (Partner)
Pinsent Masons LLP, Glasgow ....(p.1031)
T: 0141 567 8400
E: martin.devine@pinsentmasons.com

DEVINE, Meghan (Jul 2019) (Employee)
Dentons & Co, Dubai ....(p.1278)
E: Meghan.Devine@dentons.com

DEVINE, Rebecca (Mar 2021) (Employee)
Jones Whyte LLP, Glasgow...........(p.993)
T: 0141 375 1222
E: rebecca.devine@joneswhyte.co.uk

DEVLIN, Alistair Thomson (Aug 2014)
(Employee)
National Westminster Bank PLC,
Edinburgh ....(p.1226)
T: (0131) 626 2925
E: alistair.devlin@rbs.co.uk

DEVLIN, Christopher (Mar 2010) (Employee)
Anderson Strathern LLP, Edinburgh ....(p.839)
T: 0131 2707700
E: chris.devlin@andersonstrathern.co.uk

DEVLIN, Clare Elizabeth (Jan 2015) (Employee)
Brodies LLP, Edinburgh ....(p.845)
T: 0131 656 0029
E: clare.devlin@brodies.com

DEVLIN, David Robert Lewis Henry
(Aug 1984) (Partner)
Connor Malcolm, Edinburgh ....(p.888)
T: 0131 5576566
E: david.devlin@connormalcolm.com

DEVLIN, Jamie (Jun 2018) (Employee)
Anderson Strathern LLP, Edinburgh ....(p.839)
T: 0131 2707700
E: jamie.devlin@andersonstrathern.co.uk

DEVLIN, Julie Maura (Aug 1992) (Associate)
CMS Cameron McKenna Nabarro Olswang LLP,
Glasgow.....................(p.962)
T: 0141 2222200

DEVLIN, Nuala Ann (Oct 2006) (Employee)
Public Defence Solicitors Office,
Falkirk ....(p.1237)
T: 01324 631475
E: ndevlin@pdso.org.uk

DEVLIN, Terence (Oct 1980) (Partner)
Banks Devlin & Co., Paisley ....(p.1136)
T: 0141 8894949
E: terry.devlin@banksdevlin.com

DEWAR, Barry George (Jun 2009) (Director)
Connelly & Yeoman Law Limited,
Arbroath ....(p.757)
T: 01241 434200
E: barry@connellyyeoman.com

DEWAR, Carolyn Louise (Oct 2007) (Employee)
Ofgem, Glasgow ....(p.1241)
T: (0141) 354 5425
E: Carolyn.Dewar@ofgem.gov.uk

DEWAR, Clare Margaret Henderson
(Aug 2005) (Associate)
Brodies LLP, Edinburgh . . . . (p.845)
T: 0131 2283777
E: clare.dewar@brodies.com

DEWAR, Craig McInnes (Oct 2004) (Partner)
Harding & Co., Glasgow . . . . (p.983)
T: 0141 5528880
E: craigdewar@btinternet.com

DEWAR, David Peter (Oct 1984) (Partner)
Dewar & Murray, Fort William . . . . (p.929)
T: 01397 702455
E: david@macarthurstewart.co.uk

DEWAR, Deborah Campbell (Jul 2009)
(Employee)
Thorntons Law LLP, Perth . . . . (p.1151)
T: 01738 621212
E: ddewar@thorntons-law.co.uk

DEWAR, Emma Morag (Sept 1995) (Associate)
Burness Paull LLP, Edinburgh . . . . (p.850)
T: 0131 4736000
E: emma.dewar@burnesspaull.com

DEWAR, Imogen Ruth (Sept 2016) (Employee)
Pinsent Masons LLP, Glasgow . . . . (p.1031)
T: 0141 567 8400
E: imogen.dewar@pinsentmasons.com

DEWAR, Michael James (Mar 1997) (Partner)
Wright, Johnston & Mackenzie LLP,
Edinburgh . . . . (p.913)
T: 0131 524 1500
E: mjd@wjm.co.uk

DEWAR, Robert Coldwell (Dec 1986)
(Employee)
Williams Mullen, Richmond . . . . (p.1271)
T: +001 804 4206935
E: rdewar@williamsmullen.com

DHAMI, Amerdeep (May 2012) (Employee)
Brodies LLP, Edinburgh . . . . (p.845)
T: 0131 2283777
E: amerdeep.dhami@brodies.com

DHESI, Amal Kaur (Jul 2006) (Partner)
Shakespeare Martineau (Glasgow) LLP,
Glasgow . . . . (p.1038)
T: 0121 214 0000
E: amal.kaur@shma.co.uk

DHESI, Anita Kaur (Dec 2020) (Employee)
Mourant Ozannes, St Helier . . . . (p.1274)
T: 1481731513
E: anita.dhesi@mourant.com

DI CIACCA, Liana (Aug 2010) (Employee)
Shoosmiths, Edinburgh . . . . (p.902)
T: 03700 868000
E: Liana.DiCiacca@shoosmiths.co.uk

DI EMIDIO, Tiziana Angela Maria
(Oct 1991) (Employee)
Procurator Fiscal Service, Glasgow . . . . (p.1241)
T: 0300 0203000
E: tiziana.diemidio@copfs.gov.uk

DI PAOLA, David John (Nov 2003) (Employee)
Church of Scotland, Edinburgh . . . . . . (p.1221)
T: 0131 2255722
E: DDiPaola@churchofscotland.org.uk

DI PAOLA, John Joseph (Oct 2009) (Employee)
Aberdein Considine and Company,
Glasgow . . . . (p.937)
T: 0141 2278200
E: jdipaola@acandco.com

DI ROLLO, Graeme Alasdair (Mar 2019)
(Employee)
Trustpilot Limted, London EC3 . . . . (p.1269)

DIAMOND, Alan Lindsay (Oct 1995) (Partner)
Pinsent Masons LLP, Edinburgh . . . . (p.895)
T: 0131 777 7000
E: alan.diamond@pinsentmasons.com

DIAMOND, Andrew Russell (Sept 1993)
(Partner)
Lindsays LLP, Edinburgh . . . . (p.882)
T: 0131 2291212
E: andrewdiamond@lindsays.co.uk

DIAMOND, Harvie Samuel (May 1979)
(Employee)
Swinburne & Co, Glasgow . . . . (p.1042)
T: 0141 2222213
E: harvie@harviediamondlaw.com

DIAZ LIMACO, Moyra Lucia (Jul 2018)
(Employee)
Turcan Connell, Edinburgh . . . . (p.908)
T: 0131 2288111
E: moyra.diazlimaco@turcanconnell.com

DIBIASIO, Lynne Violet (Sept 1992) (Partner)
Aitkens The Family Law Solicitors,
Livingston . . . . (p.1117)
T: 01506 417737
E: ldb@aitkenstfls.co.uk

DICK, Sarah Alexandra (Dec 2017) (Associate)
Addleshaw Goddard LLP,
Edinburgh . . . . (p.835)
T: 0131 2282400
E: Sarah.Dick@addleshawgoddard.com

DICK, Stephen Robert (Apr 1997) (Employee)
DLA Piper Scotland LLP, Edinburgh . . . . (p.863)
T: 08700 111111
E: stephen.dick@dlapiper.com

DICK, Steven Marshall (Jun 2010) (Partner)
Eversheds Sutherland (International) LLP,
Edinburgh . . . . (p.869)
T: 0207 9194500
E: stevendick@eversheds-Sutherland.com

DICK, Stuart David James (Sept 2013)
(Employee)
Morton Fraser LLP, Edinburgh . . . .(p.891)
T: 0131 2471000
E: stuart.dick@morton-fraser.com

DICK, William Ronald Desmond (Nov 1979)
(Associate)
McCash & Hunter LLP, Perth . . . .(p.1149)
T: 01738 620451
E: desmond@mccash.co.uk

DICKERS, Jane Pauline (Jun 2011) (Partner)
Gray & Gray LLP, Peterhead . . . .(p.1153)
T: 01779 480 222
E: jane@graygraylaw.com

DICKIE, Catriona Janet Nisbet (May 2013)
(Employee)
Procurator Fiscal Service, Perth. . . . . . .(p.1253)
T: 0844 561 3000
E: catriona.dickie@copfs.gov.uk

DICKIE, John William Keene (Jan 1981)
(Partner)
Blackadder & McMonagle, Falkirk . . . . .(p.921)
T: 01324 612999
E: john.dickie@blackandmac.com

DICKIE, Stuart Robert (Sept 2021) (Employee)
Burness Paull LLP, Edinburgh . . . .(p.850)
T: 0131 4736000
E: stuart.dickie@burnesspaull.com

DICKSON, Alastair Ronald, WS (Nov 1976)
(Employee)
Dickson Minto, London EC2 . . . .(p.1263)
T: 020 76284455
E: alastair.dickson@dmws.com

DICKSON, Amy (Jul 2008) (Director)
J.D. Clark & Allan Limited, Duns . . . . . .(p.829)
T: 01361 882501
E: amy.dickson@jdca.co.uk

DICKSON, Amy Vittoria (Jan 2009) (Employee)
Harper Macleod LLP, Glasgow . . . .(p.983)
T: 0141 2218888
E: amy.dickson@harpermacleod.co.uk

DICKSON, Barry (Sept 1979) (Employee)
Procurator Fiscal Service, Glasgow . . . .(p.1241)
T: 0300 0200485
E: barry.dickson@copfs.gov.uk

DICKSON, Christian Macdonald (Nov 1980)
(Employee)
J. & J. McCosh, Dalry . . . .(p.795)
T: 01294 832112
E: kirsty.dickson@jjmccosh.co.uk

DICKSON, Christopher John (Mar 2009)
(Associate)
CMS Cameron McKenna Nabarro Olswang LLP,
Glasgow. . . . .(p.962)
T: 0141 2222200
E: Christopher.Dickson@cms-cmno.com

DICKSON, Daryle Anne (Feb 2015) (Employee)
SOUTH LANARKSHIRE re Council,
Hamilton . . . .(p.1247)
T: (01698) 454785
E: Daryle.Dickson@southlanarkshire.gov.uk

DICKSON, David Alexander (Jul 1991)
(Solicitor)
NO FIRM

DICKSON, David James (Nov 1989) (Employee)
Procurator Fiscal Service,
Edinburgh . . . .(p.1227)
T: 1312433055
E: DavidJ.Dickson@copfs.gov.uk

DICKSON, David John Oliver (Feb 1980)
(Partner)
The PRG Partnership, Glasgow . . . .(p.1045)
T: 0141 3530550
E: djodickson@prg.co.uk

DICKSON, Dawn (Feb 2000) (Partner)
Eversheds Sutherland (International) LLP,
Edinburgh . . . .(p.869)
T: 0207 9194500
E: dawndickson@eversheds-Sutherland.com

DICKSON, Eilidh Margaret Mackenzie
(Oct 2019) (Solicitor)
NO FIRM

DICKSON, Erica Joan (Mar 2014) (Employee)
Burness Paull LLP, Glasgow . . . .(p.954)
T: 0141 2484933
E: Erica.Dickson@burnesspaull.com

DICKSON, Fiona Clare (Jan 2015) (Employee)
Heineken UK Limited, Edinburgh . . . . .(p.1223)
T: 0131 5281000
E: Fiona.Dickson@heineken.co.uk

DICKSON, Graeme Ross Campbell
(Oct 2001) (Associate)
Thorntons Law LLP, Dundee . . . .(p.819)
T: 01382 229 111
E: gdickson@thorntons-law.co.uk

DICKSON, Helen Mary (Sept 1997) (Partner)
Burness Paull LLP, Aberdeen . . . .(p.724)
T: 01224 621621
E: Helen.Dickson@burnesspaull.com

DICKSON, James Scotland (Jun 2006)
(Employee)
Mellicks, Incorporating Naftalin Duncan & Co.,
Glasgow. . . . .(p.1019)
T: 0141 3320902
E: scot.dickson@mellicks.co.uk

DICKSON, Jennifer Alison (Mar 2002) (Partner)
Morton Fraser LLP, Edinburgh . . . .(p.891)
T: 0131 2471000
E: Jenny.dickson@morton-fraser.com

DICKSON, Jessica Alexandra (Mar 2021)
(Employee)
Storie, Cruden & Simpson,
Aberdeen . . . .(p.743)
T: 01224 587261

DICKSON, John (Aug 1984) (Employee)
Scottish Legal Aid Board,
Edinburgh . . . .(p.1233)
T: 0131 2267061
E: dicksonia@slab.org.uk

DICKSON, Leslie James (Aug 2021) (Employee)
Burness Paull LLP, Glasgow . . . .(p.954)
T: 0141 2484933
E: jamie.dickson@burnesspaull.com

DICKSON, Marc Campbell (Nov 1992)
(Director)
Jack Gowans & Marc Dickson Solicitors Limited,
Inverness . . . .(p.1076)
T: 01463 710677
E: marc@gowansdickson.com

DICKSON, Mhairi Elaine (Jun 2007) (Partner)
Grieve, Grierson, Moodie & Walker,
Dumfries . . . .(p.801)
T: 01387 266250
E: Mhairi.Chalmers@ggmw.co.uk

DICKSON, Paul Ian Robert (Oct 2002)
(Employee)
Slaughter and May, London EC1 . . . . .(p.1268)
T: 020 7600 1200
E: Paul.Dickson@SlaughterandMay.com

DICKSON, Sophie Rhiannon (May 2019)
(Employee)
SSE Plc, Perth . . . .(p.1253)
T: 01738 456 000
E: sophie.dickson@sse.com

DICKSON, Stephen George (Feb 2019)
(Employee)
MOV8 Real Estate Limited,
Edinburgh . . . .(p.893)
T: 0131 297 7999
E: stephen.dickson@mov8realestate.com

DICKSON, Susan (Nov 2003) (Employee)
Procurator Fiscal Service,
Edinburgh . . . .(p.1227)
T: 8445614001
E: susan.dickson@copfs.gov.uk

DIGNAN, Amy Dawn (Feb 2012) (Employee)
Ledingham Chalmers LLP,
Edinburgh . . . .(p.881)
T: 0131 200 1000
E: amy.dignan@ledinghamchalmers.com

DIGNAN, Scot James McLeod (Sept 2013)
(Employee)
Procurator Fiscal Service, Glasgow . . . .(p.1241)
T: 0300 0203000

DILASSER, Hollie (Jan 2011) (Associate)
Digby Brown LLP, Edinburgh . . . .(p.862)
T: 0333 200 5925
E: hollie.dilasser@digbybrown.co.uk

DILLEY, Sarah Michelle (Jan 2004) (Employee)
Burness Paull LLP, Edinburgh . . . .(p.850)
T: 0131 4736000
E: sarah.dilley@burnesspaull.com

DILLON, Heather (Mar 2000) (Employee)
Scottish Enterprise, Glasgow . . . .(p.1243)
T: 0141 2482700
E: heather.dillon@scotent.co.uk

DILLON, John Paul (Jan 2013) (Employee)
Watermans Solicitors Limited,
Edinburgh . . . .(p.912)
T: 0131 5557055
E: johndillon@watermans.co.uk

DILOO, Zara Banu Margaret (Oct 2008)
(Employee)
Scottish National Investment Bank,
Edinburgh . . . .(p.1233)
E: zara.diloo@thebank.scot

DIMITROVA, Iliyana Georgieva (Apr 2019)
(Employee)
Skyscanner, Edinburgh . . . .(p.1234)
E: iliyana.dimitrova@skyscanner.net

DIN, Mohsen Saleem (Sept 2009) (Employee)
DAC Beachcroft Scotland LLP,
Glasgow. . . . .(p.964)
T: 0141 223 8597
E: mdin@dacbeachcroft.com

DINGWALL, Elizabeth Anne (Jan 1979)
(Director)
DHW Legal Limited, Kirkintilloch . . . . .(p.1104)
T: 0141 7767104
E: liz@dhwlegal.co.uk

DINGWALL, Greg Stewart (Oct 2010)
(Associate)
Pinsent Masons LLP, Glasgow . . . .(p.1031)
T: 0141 567 8400
E: greg.dingwall@pinsentmasons.com

DINGWALL, Joanna Ruth (Apr 2007)
(Employee)
Scottish Government, Edinburgh . . . . .(p.1231)
T: 0131 2440055
E: Joanna.Dingwall@gov.scot

DINGWALL, Kathryn Louise (Nov 2015)
(Employee)
Latta Law Limited, Glasgow. . . . .(p.998)
T: 0141 222 2185
E: KD@lattalaw.co.uk

DINNETT, Craig Robert (May 2019) (Employee)
Collas Crill, St Helier . . . .(p.1274)
T: 01534 601783
E: Craig.Dinnett@collascrill.com

DINSMORE, Keith Charles (Oct 1998) (Partner)
Vialex WS, Edinburgh . . . .(p.910)
T: 03332 400127
E: keith.dinsmore@vialex.co.uk

DIPPENAAR, Sarah Marie (Dec 2001)
(Employee)
Shepherd and Wedderburn LLP,
Glasgow. . . . .(p.1039)
T: 0141 5669900
E: Sarah.Dippenaar@shepwedd.com

DISSAKE, Natalie (Sept 2006) (Partner)
Harper Macleod LLP, Glasgow . . . .(p.983)
T: 0141 2218888
E: natalie.dissake@harpermacleod.co.uk

DIXON, Emma Jane (Mar 2006) (Employee)
Oil & Gas Authority, Aberdeen . . . . . .(p.1213)
T: 0300 020 1068
E: emma.dixon@ogauthority.co.uk

DIXON, Karen Christine (Sept 2021)
(Employee)
Turcan Connell, Edinburgh . . . .(p.908)
T: 0131 2288111
E: karen.dixon@turcanconnell.com

DIXON, Leanne Jane (Jun 2004) (Employee)
Associated British Foods Plc, London
WC1 . . . .(p.1261)
E: Leanne.Dixon@abfoods.com

DIXON, Robert Stuart (Nov 2000) (Employee)
Gibson, Dunn & Crutcher LLP, London
EC4 . . . .(p.1264)
T: (0207) 0714249
E: rdixon@gibsondunn.com

DOBBIE, Sarah Jane Matheson (May 2018)
(Employee)
CMS Cameron McKenna Nabarro Olswang LLP,
Aberdeen . . . .(p.727)
T: 01224 622002
E: sarah.dobbie@cms-cmno.com

DOBBIN, Amy (Jun 2016) (Employee)
Livingstone Brown Limited,
Glasgow. . . . .(p.1004)
T: 0141 7789657

DOBBS, Nicholas Paul (Aug 2018) (Employee)
Anderson Strathern LLP, Edinburgh . . . .(p.839)
T: 0131 2707700
E: nick.dobbs@andersonstrathern.co.uk

DOBIE, James Alexander (Jan 1991)
(Consultant)
Shepherd and Wedderburn LLP,
Edinburgh . . . .(p.900)
T: 0131 2289900
E: James.Dobie@shepwedd.com

DOBIE, Robert Latta, WS (Dec 1979)
(Employee)
Campbell Smith LLP, Edinburgh . . . .(p.852)
T: 0131 5563737
E: robert.dobie@camsmith.co.uk

DOBSON, Carron Marr (Oct 2010) (Employee)
Juniper Partners Limited,
Edinburgh . . . .(p.1224)
E: cdobson@junipartners.com

DOBSON, Eilidh May (Jun 2019) (Employee)
Shepherd and Wedderburn LLP,
Edinburgh . . . .(p.900)
T: 0131 2289900
E: eilidh.dobson@shepwedd.com

DOBSON, Pamela Lesley (Jul 2008) (Employee)
Scottish Children's Reporter Administration,
Glenrothes . . . .(p.1246)
T: 01592 583314
E: Pamela.Dobson@scra.gov.uk

DOCHERTY, Amy Elizabeth (Jan 2021)
(Employee)
Cochran Dickie, Paisley . . . .(p.1137)
T: 0141 8892245
E: aed@cochrandickie.co.uk

DOCHERTY, Andrew Thomas (Aug 2011)
(Employee)
Public Defence Solicitors Office,
Edinburgh . . . .(p.1230)
T: 0131 5571222
E: adocherty@pdso.org.uk

DOCHERTY, Cara Elizabeth (Oct 2009)
(Employee)
BTO Solicitors LLP, Glasgow . . . .(p.952)
T: 0141 2218012
E: cdo@bto.co.uk

DOCHERTY, Danielle Sharon (Aug 2008)
(Employee)
Moir and Sweeney LLP, Glasgow . . . . .(p.1021)
T: 0141 4292724

DOCHERTY, Gail (Aug 1998) (Associate)
Patten & Prentice LLP, Greenock . . . . .(p.1062)
T: 01475 720306
E: gaild@patten.co.uk

DOCHERTY, Grant Euan Turner (Dec 1988)
(Director)
Rooney Nimmo Limited,
Edinburgh . . . .(p.899)
T: 0131 220 9570
E: grant.docherty@rooneynimmo.co.uk

DOCHERTY, John (Director)
Graham & Sibbald, Weybridge . . . . . .(p.1358)
T: (07831) 353 572
E: john.docherty@g-s.co.uk

DOCHERTY, Katherine Maria (Sept 2015)
(Employee)
Pinsent Masons LLP, Glasgow . . . .(p.1031)
T: 0141 567 8400
E: katy.docherty@pinsentmasons.com

DOCHERTY, Kirsty (Jun 2017) (Employee)
MacFarlane Young Limited, Paisley . . . .(p.1139)
T: 0141 8893257

DOCHERTY, Patrick Daniel (Oct 1997)
(Employee)
Glasgow City Council, Glasgow . . . . . .(p.1239)
T: 0141 2874107
E: pat.docherty@glasgow.gov.uk

DOCHERTY, Roisin Marie (Jan 2014) (Partner)
Roisin Docherty Solicitors, Glasgow . . . .(p.971)
T: 0141 571 9193
E: roisin.docherty@live.co.uk

DOCHERTY, Sandra Love (Jul 1989) (Partner)
Cameron Pinkerton & Co LLP,
Paisley . . . .(p.1137)
T: 0141 8875211
E: sandra@cameronpinkerton.co.uk

DOCHERTY, Scott Charles (Sept 2001) (Partner)
McArthur Stanton, Dumbarton . . . .(p.798)
T: 01389 762266
E: sd@mcarthurstanton.co.uk

DOCHERTY, Sean Kevin (Sept 2021)
(Employee)
Procurator Fiscal Service,
Edinburgh . . . .(p.1229)
T: 0300 0203000
E: sean.docherty@copfs.gov.uk

DOCHERTY, Stefan Edward (Feb 2017)
(Employee)
Blackadders LLP, Glasgow . . . .(p.946)
T: 0141 2481888
E: Stefan.Docherty@blackadders.co.uk

DOCHERTY, Steven John (Oct 1998) (Partner)
Wright, Johnston & Mackenzie LLP,
Glasgow. . . . .(p.1054)
T: 0141 2483434
E: sd@wjm.co.uk

DOCHERTY, Terence John (Sept 1994)
(Associate)
Hunter & Robertson Limited,
Paisley . . . .(p.1138)
T: 0141 8893196
E: tdocherty@hunter-robertson.co.uk

DOCHERTY, Thomas Edward (Sept 1985)
(Partner)
Thomas Docherty Solicitors, Falkirk. . . . .(p.921)
T: 01324 875 870
E: thomas.docherty@tdlaw.co.uk

DOCHERTY, Thomas Martin (Oct 1991)
(Associate)
Anderson Strathern LLP, Glasgow . . . . . .(p.940)
T: 0141 2426060
E: Tom.Docherty@andersonstrathern.co.uk

DOCI, Ledia (Jan 2021) (Employee)
Pinsent Masons LLP, Glasgow . . . .(p.1031)
T: 0141 567 8400
E: ledia.doci@pinsentmasons.com

DODDS, Bethany Norma (Sept 2017)
(Employee)
Clyde & Co (Scotland) LLP,
Edinburgh . . . .(p.855)
T: 0131 5571545
E: bethany.dodds@clydeco.com

DODDS, Nicola (Sept 1999) (Employee)
Procurator Fiscal Service, Glasgow . . . .(p.1241)
T: 0300 0203000
E: nicola.dodds@copfs.gov.uk

DODS, Domhnall McDonald (Nov 1989)
(Employee)
Cityfibre Holdings Limited,
Edinburgh . . . .(p.1222)
E: domhnall.dods@cityfibre.com

DOHERTY, Benjamin John (Jul 2014) (Partner)
Lindsays LLP, Glasgow. . . . .(p.1001)
T: 0141 2216551
E: bendoherty@lindsays.co.uk

DOHERTY, Carol Knox (Sept 2020) (Solicitor)
Procurator Fiscal Service, Dundee . . . . .(p.1218)
T: 01382 342559
E: carol.doherty@copfs.gov.uk

DOHERTY, Gaelen Jenniffer Jamieson
(Jun 2006) (Associate)
Burness Paull LLP, Glasgow . . . .(p.954)
T: 0141 2484933
E: Gaelen.Doherty@burnesspaull.com

DOHERTY, Jacqueline Mary (Jan 1998)
(Employee)
Market Operator Services Limited,
Southampton . . . .(p.1271)
E: Jacqueline.Doherty@mosl.co.uk

DOHERTY, Kevin (Sept 2009) (Employee)
Procurator Fiscal Service, Glasgow . . . .(p.1241)
T: 0300 0203000
E: kevin.doherty@copfs.gov.uk

DOHERTY, Lauren (Nov 2019) (Employee)
Ledingham Chalmers LLP,
Edinburgh . . . .(p.881)
T: 0131 2001000
E: lauren.doherty@ledinghamchalmers.com

DOHERTY, Lene Borgmann (Sept 2011)
(Solicitor)
NO FIRM

DOHERTY, Pamela Josephine (Nov 2002)
(Employee)
Collas Crill, St Helier . . . .(p.1274)
T: 01534 601783
E: Pamela.Doherty@collascrill.com

DOHERTY, Seana (Jan 1998) (Employee)
Procurator Fiscal Service, Glasgow . . . .(p.1241)
T: 0300 0203000
E: seana.doherty@copfs.gov.uk

DOIG, Abby MacKinnon (Dec 2015)
(Employee)
Shepherd and Wedderburn LLP,
Glasgow. . . . .(p.1039)
T: 0141 5669900
E: abby.doig@shepwedd.com

DOIG, Ailsa Catherine (Nov 2017) (Employee)
Raeside Chisholm Solicitors Limited,
Glasgow. . . . .(p.1034)
T: 0141 2483456
E: a.doig@raesidechisholm.co.uk

DOIG, Elspeth Catherine (Dec 1988)
(Employee)
R. & R.S. Mearns, Glasgow . . . .(p.1018)
T: 0141 6326162

DOIG, Jade Nicola (Aug 2016) (Employee)
Procurator Fiscal Service,
Edinburgh . . . .(p.1227)
T: 0300 0203168
E: Jade.Doig@copfs.gov.uk

DOIG, William David Forrester (Sept 1987)
(Director)
Raeside Chisholm Solicitors Limited,
Glasgow. . . . .(p.1034)
T: 0141 2483456
E: d.doig@raesidechisholm.co.uk

DOLAN, Rosina Marie (Sept 1996) (Partner)
Wright, Johnston & Mackenzie LLP,
Glasgow. . . . .(p.1054)
T: 0141 2483434
E: rmd@wjm.co.uk

DONACHIE, Josey Patricia (Mar 2021)
(Employee)
Patterson & Paterson Defence Lawyers,
Inverness . . . .(p.1082)
T: 014 63 418277
E: josey@ppcd.co.uk

DONACHIE, Kathryn (Oct 2004) (Associate)
Brodies LLP, Edinburgh . . . .(p.845)
T: 0131 2283777
E: kate.donachie@brodies.com

DONALD, Brian Robert (Feb 1988) (Employee)
EDF Energy Renewables,
Edinburgh . . . .(p.1222)
T: (0131) 460 3654
E: Brian.Donald@nngoffshorewind.com

DONALD, Callum (Jul 2018) (Employee)
Burness Paull LLP, Edinburgh . . . .(p.850)
T: 0131 4736000
E: callum.donald@burnesspaull.com

DONALD, Christina (Apr 1992) (Employee)
Scottish Borders Council, Newtown St.
Boswells . . . .(p.1251)
T: 01835 825 225
E: CDonald@scotborders.gov.uk

DONALD, Craig Brian (Oct 2014) (Employee)
Aberdeen City Council, Aberdeen. . . . .(p.1211)
T: 01224 522000
E: CDonald@aberdeencity.gov.uk

DONALD, Ewan (Jan 1991) (Director)
Innes & Mackay Limited, Inverness. . . .(p.1078)
T: 01463 232273
E: ewand@innesmackay.com

DONALD, Faye Louise (Apr 2006) (Partner)
Raeburn Christie Clark & Wallace LLP,
Aberdeen . . . .(p.741)
T: 01224 332400
E: faye.donald@raeburns.co.uk

DONALD, Fraser Alexander (Aug 2012)
(Employee)
Scottish Widows Limited,
Edinburgh . . . .(p.1233)
T: 0131 6557230
E: fraser.donald1@lloydsbanking.com

DONALD, Gillian Scott (Nov 2001) (Associate)
Brodies LLP, Aberdeen. . . . .(p.723)
T: 01224 392242

DONALD, Kathleen Elizabeth (Nov 2008)
(Director)
Ergo Law Limited, Edinburgh . . . .(p.869)
T: 0131 618 7007
E: cathy.donald@ergolaw.co.uk

DONALD, Laura Jane (Dec 1989) (Partner)
BTO Solicitors LLP, Edinburgh . . . .(p.849)
T: 0131 2222939
E: ljd@bto.co.uk

DONALD, Malcolm James Robert (Dec 2001)
(Partner)
Stronachs LLP, Aberdeen . . . .(p.744)
T: 01224 845845
E: malcolm.donald@stronachs.com

DONALD, Natalie Susan (Jul 2016) (Employee)
Thompsons, Galashiels . . . .(p.933)
T: 0800 0015163
E: Natalie.Donald@thompsons-scotland.co.uk

DONALD, Neil (Apr 1999) (Employee)
Shell U.K. Ltd., Aberdeen . . . .(p.1214)
T: 01224 882000
E: neil.donald@shell.com

DONALD, Paul Robert Alexander (Jul 1996)
(Partner)
Shepherd and Wedderburn LLP,
Edinburgh . . . .(p.900)
T: 0131 473 5161
E: paul.donald@shepwedd.com

DONALD, Steven Reginald (May 1993)
(Partner)
Steven Donald & Co, Edinburgh . . . . . .(p.864)
T: 0131 664 6777
E: steve.donald@btconnect.com

DONALDSON, Alix Jacqueline (Aug 1998)
(Employee)
Scottish Environment Protection Agency,
Holytown . . . .(p.1248)
T: (01698) 839 000

DONALDSON, Campbell Victor (Sept 1995)
(Partner)
Lawson Coull & Duncan, Dundee . . . . .(p.813)
T: 01382 227555
E: cdonaldson@lawsoncoull.co.uk

DONALDSON, Clare McMillan (Jul 2010)
(Employee)
Aegon UK, Edinburgh . . . .(p.1220)
T: 1315493986
E: clare.donaldson@aegon.co.uk

DONALDSON, Daniel James (Jul 2010)
(Director)
Legal Spark Solicitors and Notaries Ltd,
Glasgow. . . . .(p.1000)
T: 0141 2800330
E: danield@legalspark.scot

DONALDSON, Elizabeth Jane (Oct 2008)
(Employee)
Conde Nast Publications Limited, London
WC2 . . . .(p.1263)
E: lizzie.donaldson@condenast.com

DONALDSON, Emma Elizabeth (Sept 2006)
(Employee)
BTO Solicitors LLP, Glasgow . . . .(p.952)
T: 0141 2218012
E: edo@bto.co.uk

DONALDSON, Euan James (Sept 1984)
(Employee)
RUCOFIKE Limited, Inverness . . . .(p.1248)

DONALDSON, Graeme John (Sept 2009)
(Employee)
Scottish Widows Limited,
Edinburgh . . . .(p.1233)
T: 0131 6557230
E: graeme.donaldson@lloydsbanking.com

DONALDSON, Ian (Oct 1985) (Consultant)
Munro & Noble, Inverness . . . .(p.1080)
T: 01463 221727
E: iand@munronoble.com

DONALDSON, Ian William (Jan 1973) (Partner)
Gorrie & Davidson, Dunfermline . . . . . .(p.823)
T: 01383 723618
E: iwd@gorriedavidson.co.uk

DONALDSON, Jennifer Ross (Dec 2020)
(Employee)
Addleshaw Goddard LLP,
Edinburgh . . . .(p.835)
T: 0131 2282400
E: jennifer.donaldson@addleshawgoddard.com

DONALDSON, Kyla Jean (Dec 2019) (Employee)
Addleshaw Goddard LLP,
Edinburgh . . . .(p.835)
T: 0131 2282400
E: Kyla.Donaldson@addleshawgoddard.com

DONALDSON, Mark Mackenzie (Oct 1993)
(Partner)
Clyde & Co (Scotland) LLP,
Aberdeen . . . .(p.726)
T: 01224 624924
E: mark.donaldson@clydeco.com

DONALDSON, Richard Mark (Jul 2011)
(Partner)
RD Law Practice, Virkie . . . .(p.1178)
T: 01950 310125
E: info@rdlawpractice.co.uk

DONALDSON, Rory James (Aug 2021)
(Employee)
Dentons UK and Middle East LLP,
Glasgow . . . .(p.968)
T: 0330 2220050
E: rory.donaldson@dentons.com

DONALDSON, Sarah Louise (Dec 2013)
(Employee)
Medical Protection Society, Leeds. . . . .(p.1260)
E: Sarah.Donaldson@medicalprotection.org

DONALDSON, Susannah Elizabeth
(Sept 2004) (Employee)
Pinsent Masons LLP, Glasgow . . . .(p.1031)
T: 0141 567 8400
E: susannah.donaldson@pinsentmasons.com

DONCASTER, Julie (Nov 2006) (Partner)
Harper Macleod LLP, Inverness. . . . . . .(p.1077)
T: 01463 798777
E: julie.doncaster@harpermacleod.co.uk

DONE, Murray Ralph (Feb 2000) (Solicitor)
NO FIRM

DONEGAN, Sabina (Nov 1994) (Director)
Frederick & Co Solicitors Limited,
Glasgow . . . .(p.977)
T: 0141 2215575
E: sabina@frederickandco.co.uk

DONNACHIE, Hope Catherine (Sept 2021)
(Employee)
DWF LLP, Glasgow . . . . (p.973)
T: 0141 228 8000
E: hope.donnachie@dwf.law

DONNACHIE, Paul Kenneth (Apr 1982)
(Partner)
Donnachie Law, Dunfermline . . . . (p.823)
T: 0800 678 5167
E: paul.donnachie@DonnachieLaw.com

DONNACHIE, Sarah (Sept 2018) (Employee)
Anderson Strathern LLP, Edinburgh . . . . (p.839)
T: 0131 2707700
E: sarah.donnachie@andersonstrathern.co.uk

DONNACHIE, Susan (Feb 2019) (Employee)
SSE PLC, Glasgow . . . . (p.1244)
T: 0141 224 7248
E: Susan.Donnachie@sse.com

DONNELLY, Candice Elizabeth Philippa
(Oct 2008) (Employee)
Skyscanner, Edinburgh . . . . (p.1234)
E: candice.donnelly@skyscanner.net

DONNELLY, Claire (Aug 2009) (Employee)
Lanarkshire Law Practice Limited,
Bellshill . . . . (p.773)
T: 01698 747171
E: clairedonnelly@lanarkshirelaw.co.uk

DONNELLY, Claire Catherine (Nov 2001)
(Employee)
Jacobs U.K. Limited, Glasgow . . . . (p.1240)
T: 0141 243 8568
E: Claire.Donnelly@jacobs.com

DONNELLY, Craig Thomas (Nov 2015)
(Employee)
Brodies LLP, Glasgow . . . . (p.948)
T: 0141 248 4672
E: craig.donnelly@brodies.com

DONNELLY, George Cullerton (Oct 1979)
(Consultant)
Lawson Coull & Duncan, Dundee . . . . . (p.813)
T: 01382 227555
E: gdonnelly@lawsoncoull.co.uk

DONNELLY, Helen Mary (Jul 2016) (Employee)
Morton Fraser LLP, Edinburgh . . . . (p.891)
T: 0131 2471000
E: helen.donnelly@morton-fraser.com

DONNELLY, Joanna Rachel (Oct 2010)
(Associate)
Pinsent Masons LLP, Glasgow . . . . (p.1031)
T: 0141 567 8400
E: Joanna.Donnelly@pinsentmasons.com

DONNELLY, John Gerard (Nov 1987)
(Employee)
Scottish Courts and Tribunals Service,
Airdrie . . . . (p.1215)
T: 01236 439174
E: jdonnelly@scotcourts.gov.uk

DONNELLY, John Gerard (Oct 2005) (Associate)
Peterkin & Kidd, Linlithgow . . . . (p.1116)
T: 01506 845191
E: maildesk@peterkinandkidd.co.uk

DONNELLY, Julia Elisabeth (Aug 2002)
(Director)
Clan Childlaw Limited, Edinburgh . . . . . (p.854)
T: 0808 129 0522
E: julia.donnelly@clanchildlaw.org

DONNELLY, Julia Rosalind (Jul 1992) (Director)
Livingstone Brown Limited,
Glasgow . . . . (p.1003)
T: 0141 4298166
E: jd@livbrown.co.uk

DONNELLY, Karen Marie (Sept 1993)
(Employee)
East Dunbartonshire Council,
Kirkintilloch . . . . (p.1249)
T: 0141 5788000
E: Karen.Donnelly@eastdunbarton.gov.uk

DONNELLY, Kenneth William (May 1990)
(Employee)
Mathie-Morton, Ayr . . . . (p.764)
T: 01292 263549
E: ken.donnelly@mathie-morton.co.uk

DONNELLY, Kenneth William (Sept 1989)
(Employee)
Procurator Fiscal Service,
Edinburgh . . . . (p.1229)
T: 0300 0203000
E: kenny.donnelly@copfs.gov.uk

DONNELLY, Kirstie (Feb 2017) (Employee)
TC Young LLP, Glasgow . . . . (p.1055)
T: 0141 2215562
E: kid@tcyoung.co.uk

DONNELLY, Laura Marie (Oct 2012) (Solicitor)
NO FIRM

DONNELLY, Louisa Rose (Oct 2011) (Associate)
Pinsent Masons (Australia), Sydney . . . . (p.1257)
T: +61 2 8024 2808
E: louisa.donnelly@pinsentmasons.com

DONNELLY, Roisin Colleen (Jul 2020)
(Employee)
Thorntons Law LLP, Edinburgh . . . . (p.906)
T: 0131 2258705
E: rdonnelly@thorntons-law.co.uk

DONNELLY, Ross David (Jun 2010) (Employee)
Lawson Coull & Duncan, Dundee . . . . . (p.813)
T: 01382 227555
E: rdonnelly@lawsoncoull.co.uk

DONNELLY, Sarah-Marie (Oct 2017)
(Employee)
Clifford Chance LLP, London E14 . . . . . (p.1262)
E: sarah.donnelly@cliffordchance.com

DONOGHUE, Claire Margaret (Jan 2001)
(Consultant)
S. Grady Solicitors, Glasgow . . . .(p.981)
T: 0141 2214000
E: clairemdonoghue@gmail.com

DONOHOE, Laura Charlotte (Aug 2021)
(Employee)
Burness Paull LLP, Edinburgh . . . .(p.850)
T: 0131 4736000
E: laura.donohoe@burnesspaull.com

DOOGAN, Patricia Ann (Feb 1985) (Employee)
Buchanan Macleod, Glasgow . . . .(p.953)
T: 0141 2214440
E: pdoogan@buchananmacleod.co.uk

DOOHAN, Iona Marie (Jan 2018) (Employee)
Groom Hill, Monaco . . . .(p.1275)
T: +377 97 70 23 00
E: id@groomhill.com

DOOL, Jennifer Helen (Apr 2019) (Employee)
Pinsent Masons LLP, Glasgow . . . .(p.1031)
T: 0141 567 8400

DOOLE, Louisa Elizabeth (Jul 2016) (Employee)
McSherry Halliday LLP, Troon . . . .(p.1175)
T: 01292 313737
E: led@mcsherryhalliday.co.uk

DORAN, Aaron Charles (Jul 2008) (Associate)
Raeburn Christie Clark & Wallace LLP,
Aberdeen . . . .(p.741)
T: 01224 332400
E: Aaron.Doran@raeburns.co.uk

DORAN, Aimee Julia (Jan 2016) (Employee)
Procurator Fiscal Service, Glasgow . . . .(p.1241)
T: 0300 0203000
E: aimee.doran@copfs.gov.uk

DORAN, Beatrice Joyce (Mar 1984) (Solicitor)
NO FIRM

DORAN, Iain Arthur (Sept 1981) (Consultant)
CMS Cameron McKenna Nabarro Olswang LLP,
Glasgow. . . . .(p.962)
T: 0141 2222200
E: Iain.Doran@cms-cmno.com

DORAN, Katherine Ellen Clarissa (Apr 2007)
(Employee)
Holman Fenwick Willan LLP, London
EC3 . . . .(p.1265)
T: 020 7264 8000
E: Katherine.Doran@hfw.com

DORGHAM-MILNE, Nicola (Sept 2009)
(Employee)
Petrofac International Limited,
Sharjah . . . .(p.1279)
T: +971 5580239
E: nicola.milne@petrofac.com

DORIAN, Sean Henry (Aug 2016) (Employee)
Ekco Group International,
Edinburgh . . . .(p.1222)
E: sean.dorian@ek.co

DORMAN, Fiona Macdonald (Sept 2016)
(Employee)
DAC Beachcroft Scotland LLP,
Glasgow. . . . .(p.964)
T: 0141 2486688
E: fdorman@dacbeachcroft.com

DORMER, Nadine Dorothy (Oct 2005)
(Consultant)
Jonathan Paul Solicitors, Alexandria . . . .(p.751)
T: 01389 756785

DOSSETT, Hannah Jean (Jul 2017) (Employee)
Thorntons Law LLP, Edinburgh . . . .(p.906)
T: 0131 2258705
E: hdossett@thorntons-law.co.uk

DOUGALL, Lindsay June (Mar 2013) (Associate)
CMS Cameron McKenna Nabarro Olswang LLP,
Glasgow. . . . .(p.962)
T: 0141 2222200
E: Lindsay.Dougall@cms-cmno.com

DOUGAN, Elizabeth (Dec 1993) (Partner)
Brazenall & Orr, Dumfries . . . .(p.800)
T: 01387 255695
E: elizabeth@brazenallandorr.co.uk

DOUGAN, Mairi-Claire (Dec 2000) (Director)
Edinburgh Corporate Solicitors Limited,
Kinglassie . . . .(p.1098)
T: 01592 882205
E: mairi-claire@edinburghcorporate.com

DOUGAN, Michaela (Dec 2016) (Employee)
Thorntons Law LLP, Edinburgh . . . .(p.906)
T: 0131 2258705
E: mdougan@thorntons-law.co.uk

DOUGAN, Valerie Anne (Sept 1999) (Employee)
CMS Cameron McKenna Nabarro Olswang LLP,
Glasgow. . . . .(p.962)
T: 0141 2222200
E: Val.Dougan@cms-cmno.com

DOUGHERTY, Ciaran Francis (Jul 2010)
(Employee)
The Kerr Brown Partnership,
Glasgow. . . . .(p.1044)
T: 0141 2214880
E: Ciaran@kerrbrown.co.uk

DOUGLAS, Alan Shaw (Sept 1989) (Employee)
WEST DUNBARTONSHIREhire Council,
Dumbarton . . . .(p.1217)
T: 01389 737000
E: alan.douglas@west-dunbarton.gov.uk

DOUGLAS, Alexander Struan (Sept 1991)
(Director)
Purdie & Co Ltd, Edinburgh . . . .(p.898)
T: 0131 3467240
E: struan@purdiesolicitors.co.uk

DOUGLAS, Caitlin Ann (Jan 2013) (Employee)
Scottish Enterprise, Glasgow . . . .(p.1243)
T: 0141 248 2514
E: Caitlin.Douglas@scotent.co.uk

DOUGLAS, Caroline Anne (Sept 2017)
(Employee)
Lloyds Banking Group Plc,
Edinburgh . . . .(p.1224)
T: (0131) 442 9579
E: caroline.douglas@lloydsbanking.com

DOUGLAS, Eilidh Sharrod (May 2016)
(Associate)
CMS Cameron McKenna Nabarro Olswang LLP,
Edinburgh . . . .(p.856)
T: 0131 2007375
E: Eilidh.Douglas@cms-cmno.com

DOUGLAS, Greg David (Jul 2014) (Associate)
Caesar & Howie, Livingston . . . .(p.1118)
T: 01506 448307
E: greg@caesar-howie.co.uk

DOUGLAS, Isabelle Alexandra (Jul 2008)
(Partner)
Aberdein Considine and Company,
Aberdeen . . . .(p.718)
T: 01224 589700
E: idouglas@acandco.com

DOUGLAS, James Anthony (Sept 2003)
(Employee)
Scottish Police Authority, Police Scotland,
Glasgow. . . . .(p.1244)
T: 01786 895727
E: James.Douglas3@scotland.pnn.police.uk

DOUGLAS, Kevin John (Aug 1984) (Solicitor)
NO FIRM

DOUGLAS, Laurence William (Nov 1999)
(Partner)
Brodies LLP, Edinburgh . . . .(p.845)
T: 0131 2283777
E: laurence.douglas@brodies.com

DOUGLAS, Lisa Gillian (Aug 2012) (Employee)
National Westminster Bank PLC,
Edinburgh . . . .(p.1227)
T: (07711) 925720
E: lisa.douglas1@natwest.com

DOUGLAS, Morag Simpson (Sept 1980)
(Employee)
South Ayrshire Council, Ayr . . . .(p.1215)
T: 01292 617687
E: Morag.Douglas@south-ayrshire.gov.uk

DOUGLAS, Morven Jean Kilpatrick
(Sept 2002) (Employee)
BTO Solicitors LLP, Glasgow . . . .(p.952)
T: 0141 2218012
E: mjd@bto.co.uk

DOUGLAS, Nyree Leanne (Jan 2016)
(Employee)
Ferguson & Company, Stranraer . . . . .(p.1171)
T: 01776 702561

DOUGLAS, Ross (Sept 2013) (Employee)
National Westminster Bank PLC,
Edinburgh . . . .(p.1226)
T: 0131 5568555
E: ross.douglas@rbs.co.uk

DOUGLAS, Rowan (Oct 2009) (Associate)
Anderson Strathern LLP, Edinburgh . . . .(p.839)
T: 0131 2707700
E: rowan.douglas@andersonstrathern.co.uk

DOUGLAS, Sarah (Nov 2003) (Associate)
Digby Brown LLP, Glasgow . . . .(p.970)
T: 0333 200 5925
E: sarah.douglas@digbybrown.co.uk

DOUGLAS, Sarah Kirsten (Aug 2001)
(Employee)
McEwan Fraser Legal, Edinburgh . . . . . .(p.885)
T: 0131 5249797
E: sarah.douglas@mcewanfraserlegal.co.uk

DOUGLAS, Scott Simpson (Oct 2020)
(Employee)
Thorntons Law LLP, Edinburgh . . . .(p.906)
T: 0131 2258705
E: sdouglas@thorntons-law.co.uk

DOUGLAS, Suzanne Claire (Sept 2011)
(Employee)
Aberdeen City Council, Aberdeen . . . . .(p.1211)
T: 01224 522000
E: sudouglas@aberdeencity.gov.uk

DOUGLAS-HOME, Richard (Jul 2021)
(Associate)
Turcan Connell, Edinburgh . . . .(p.908)
T: 0131 2288111
E: richard.douglas-home@turcanconnell.com

DOUGLAS-SMITH, Sara (Dec 2020) (Employee)
Harper Macleod LLP, Glasgow . . . .(p.983)
T: 0141 2218888
E: sara.douglas-smith@harpermacleod.co.uk

DOULL, Edward Alexander (Jan 1978) (Partner)
Brunton Miller, Glasgow . . . .(p.951)
T: 0141 3371199
E: eddiedoull@bruntonmiller.com

DOW, Andrea Mary Louise (May 2002)
(Employee)
Sainsbury's Bank plc, Edinburgh . . . . . .(p.1230)
T: (0131) 286 0807
E: andrea.dow@sainsburysbank.co.uk

DOW, Barbara Elizabeth (Jan 1982) (Employee)
MacRoberts LLP, Glasgow . . . .(p.1015)
T: 0141 3031100
E: barbara.dow@macroberts.com

DOW, Catriona Margaret (Oct 1996)
(Employee)
Procurator Fiscal Service,
Edinburgh . . . .(p.1227)
T: 0300 0200505
E: catriona.dow@copfs.gov.uk

DOW, Colin James (Nov 2005) (Employee)
Cofra Jersey Limited, St Helier . . . .(p.1274)
T: 01534 754 500
E: c.dow@cofraholding.com

DOW, Fergus James (Nov 1997) (Employee)
Murdoch, McMath & Mitchell,
Huntly . . . .(p.1074)
T: 01466 792291
E: fergus@murdoch-mcmath-mitchell.com

DOW, Gary Peter (Nov 1993) (Employee)
Procurator Fiscal Service, Hamilton . . . .(p.1247)
T: 0844 5613245
E: Gary.Dow@copfs.gov.uk

DOW, Jacqueline Jane (Sept 1992) (Partner)
Kippen Campbell LLP, Perth . . . .(p.1149)
T: 01738 635353
E: jd@kcllp.co.uk

DOW, Karen Ann (Apr 1999) (Employee)
Procurator Fiscal Service, Aberdeen . . .(p.1213)
T: 0300 0202336
E: karen.dow@copfs.gov.uk

DOW, Katharine Rose (Nov 2018) (Employee)
Thorntons Law LLP, Dundee . . . .(p.819)
T: 01382 229 111
E: kdow@thorntons-law.co.uk

DOW, Ross Michael (Feb 2000) (Partner)
Wardlaw Stephenson Allan,
Galashiels . . . .(p.934)
T: 01896 668669
E: ross@wsalawyers.com

DOWDALLS, Lesley (Aug 1988) (Partner)
Mackintosh & Wylie LLP,
Kilmarnock . . . .(p.1095)
T: 01563 525104
E: ldowdalls@mackwylie.com

DOWDLES, Margaret (Oct 1988) (Solicitor)
NO FIRM

DOWDS, Martin (Jun 1992) (Employee)
National Health Service Scotland,
Edinburgh . . . .(p.1225)
T: 0131 2757800
E: martin.dowds@nhs.scot

DOWERS, Alison Sarah (Apr 2015) (Solicitor)
NO FIRM

DOWIE, Josh Alexander (Feb 2021) (Employee)
Carpenters Scotland Limited,
Glasgow . . . .(p.956)
T: 0141 3285452

DOWLE, Claire Louise (May 2014) (Employee)
Standard Life Investments Limited,
Edinburgh . . . .(p.1234)
T: (0131) 245 4153
E: claire.dowle@abrdn.com

DOWNIE, Gordon Harry (Dec 1992) (Partner)
Shepherd and Wedderburn LLP,
Edinburgh . . . .(p.900)
T: 0131 2289900
E: Gordon.Downie@shepwedd.com

DOWNIE, James Forbes (Sept 1995) (Partner)
Stronachs LLP, Aberdeen . . . .(p.744)
T: 01224 845845
E: james.downie@stronachs.com

DOWNIE, Marcus MacKenzie (Dec 2017)
(Employee)
Gillespie Macandrew LLP, Glasgow . . . . .(p.979)
T: 0141 4735555
E: marcus.downie@gillespiemacandrew.co.uk

DOYLE, Jacqueline (Oct 1993) (Partner)
Jacqueline Doyle & Co., Glasgow . . . . . .(p.971)
T: 0141 5502333
E: jacqueline.doyle@jdsolicitors.co.uk

DOYLE, Lee Jane (Jun 2002) (Partner)
Lee Doyle, Solicitors, Glasgow . . . .(p.971)
T: 0141 3704161
E: lee@leedoylesolicitor.com

DOYLE, Lorelle (Feb 2019) (Employee)
Dentons UK and Middle East LLP,
Glasgow . . . .(p.968)
T: 0330 2220050
E: lorelle.doyle@dentons.com

DOYLE, Rosaleen Jessie (Jun 2006) (Solicitor)
NO FIRM

DRAIN, David James (Dec 1975) (Employee)
Macallans Limited, Glasgow . . . .(p.1005)
T: 0141 6131787/6474441
E: dd@macallans.co.uk

DRAKE, Sarajane (Aug 2017) (Employee)
Wright, Johnston & Mackenzie LLP,
Glasgow . . . .(p.1054)
T: 0141 2483434
E: sjd@wjm.co.uk

DRAKE, Steven (Jan 2016) (Partner)
Thorntons Law LLP, Dundee . . . .(p.819)
T: 01382 229 111
E: sdrake@thorntons-law.co.uk

DRANE, Andrew James Jonathan (Nov 1993)
(Partner)
Davidson Chalmers Stewart LLP,
Edinburgh . . . . (p.859)
T: 0131 6259191
E: andy.drane@dcslegal.com

DRENNAN, Nerissa Louise (Oct 2008)
(Employee)
Scottish Legal Aid Board,
Edinburgh . . . . (p.1233)
T: 0131 2267061

DROMGOOLE, Fiona Mhairi (Feb 2002)
(Employee)
Brodies LLP, Glasgow . . . . (p.948)
T: 0141 2484672
E: fiona.dromgoole@brodies.com

DROMGOOLE, Lisa (Dec 2003) (Employee)
Womble Bond Dickinson (UK) LLP,
Edinburgh . . . . (p.913)
T: 0345 415 0000
E: Lisa.Dromgoole@wbd-uk.com

DRON, Lindsay Diane (May 1986) (Employee)
Stronachs LLP, Aberdeen . . . . (p.744)
T: 01224 845845
E: lindsay.dron@stronachs.com

DRUGAN, Gerard Philip (Oct 2007) (Employee)
Procurator Fiscal Service,
Edinburgh . . . . (p.1229)
T: 0300 0203000
E: Gerard.Drugan@copfs.gov.uk

DRUMMOND, Abigail Laura (Sept 2005)
(Employee)
City of Edinburgh Council,
Edinburgh . . . . (p.1221)
T: (0131) 5294145
E: Abigail.Drummond@edinburgh.gov.uk

DRUMMOND, Alistair David (Jan 1995)
(Partner)
DLA Piper Scotland LLP, Edinburgh . . . . (p.863)
T: 08700 111111
E: alistair.drummond@dlapiper.com

DRUMMOND, Charles William (Nov 2012)
(Employee)
Keith J. Tuck, Glasgow. . . . . (p.1049)
T: 0141 3362020

DRUMMOND, Iain Kerr (Mar 1995) (Partner)
Shepherd and Wedderburn LLP,
Edinburgh . . . . (p.900)
T: 0131 2289900
E: iain.drummond@shepwedd.com

DRUMMOND, Jill Clare (Oct 2006) (Employee)
Procurator Fiscal Service, Forfar . . . . . . (p.1237)
T: 0300 0204048
E: jill.drummond@copfs.gov.uk

DRUMMOND, Roy Alexander (Nov 1994)
(Employee)
University of ST ANDREWS
T: 01334 464103
E: chieflegal@st-andrews.ac.uk

DRUMMOND, Sarah Jo (Feb 2020) (Employee)
BayWa R.e. UK Limited, Edinburgh . . . . (p.1221)
T: (0131) 4663689
E: sarah.drummond@baywa-re.co.uk

DRUMMOND, Sarah Louise (Sept 2010)
(Employee)
The Institute and Faculty of Actuaries,
Edinburgh . . . . (p.1234)
T: (020) 7632 1488
E: sarah.drummond@actuaries.org.uk

DRUMMOND, William Archibald (Sept 2000)
(Employee)
Aberdeen Corporate Services Limited,
Edinburgh . . . . (p.1220)
T: 0131 245 7508
E: william.drummond@abrdn.com

DRURY, Lucy Catherine (Sept 2020) (Employee)
MBM Commercial LLP, Edinburgh . . . . . (p.889)
T: 0131 2268200
E: lucy.drury@mbmcommercial.co.uk

DRYBURGH, Adam Keith (Dec 2011)
(Employee)
Credit Suisse AG, Singapore. . . . . (p.1276)
E: adam.dryburgh@credit-suisse.com

DRYBURGH, Elizabeth Ann (Nov 2021)
(Employee)
Smith & Grant, Leven . . . . (p.1116)
T: 01333 423441

DRYDEN, Stephen Thomas (Aug 1989)
(Partner)
Stephen Dryden, Solicitor Advocate,
Glasgow . . . . (p.972)
T: 07802 449390
E: stephen.dryden@sky.com

DRYSDALE, Elspeth Fiona (Oct 2020)
(Employee)
Thompsons, Glasgow . . . . (p.1046)
T: 0141 2218840
E: elspeth.drysdale@thompsons-scotland.co.uk

DRYSDALE, James Cunison, WS (Feb 1982)
(Partner)
Ledingham Chalmers LLP, Stirling . . . . (p.1165)
T: 01786 478100
E: jim.drysdale@ledinghamchalmers.com

DRYSDALE, Michael Christopher (Oct 2008)
(Employee)
Vialex Limited, Edinburgh . . . . (p.1235)
T: 0333 2400127
E: michael.drysdale@vialex.co.uk

DRYSDALE, Sharon Kristina (Dec 1992)
(Associate)
Lindsays LLP, Edinburgh . . . .(p.882)
T: 0131 2291212
E: sharondrysdale@lindsays.co.uk

DU, Heather Haiyan (Jun 2018) (Employee)
Liu's Legal Solutions Ltd, Glasgow . . . .(p.1002)
T: 0141 3320047
E: du@liuslaw.co.uk

DUCK, Colin Jamie (Oct 2008) (Employee)
The McKinstry Company LLP, Ayr . . . . .(p.765)
T: 01292 281711
E: colin@mckinstry.co.uk

DUCKETT, Carly Suzanne (Feb 2021)
(Employee)
Shepherd and Wedderburn LLP,
Edinburgh . . . .(p.900)
T: 0131 473 5139
E: carly.duckett@shepwedd.com

DUDDY, Laura-Ann (Jul 2018) (Employee)
Drummond Miller LLP, Glasgow. . . . . . .(p.971)
T: 0141 3320086
E: LDuddy@dm-property.com

DUFF, Alexandra Nichol (Oct 2013) (Employee)
National Westminster Bank PLC,
Edinburgh . . . .(p.1226)
T: 0131 5568555
E: alexandra.duff@rbs.co.uk

DUFF, Andrew James (Oct 1987) (Associate)
Lindsays LLP, Edinburgh . . . .(p.882)
T: 0131 2291212
E: andrewduff@lindsays.co.uk

DUFF, Christopher William (Oct 2009) (Partner)
Brodies LLP, Edinburgh . . . .(p.845)
T: 0131 2283777
E: chris.duff@brodies.com

DUFF, Corey Gavin (Sept 2011) (Employee)
TotalEnergies E&P UK Limited,
Westhill . . . .(p.1255)
T: 01224 297000
E: corey.duff@total.com

DUFF, Cynthia Jamieson (Feb 1979) (Director)
Robert F Duff & Co Limited, Largs . . . .(p.1109)
T: 01475 673 663

DUFF, Fiona Margaret Elizabeth (Nov 1987)
(Partner)
Cameron Stephen & Co.,
Edinburgh . . . .(p.852)
T: 0131 5551234
E: fiona@cameronstephen.co.uk

DUFF, George James (Jul 1985) (Partner)
Cameron Pinkerton & Co LLP,
Paisley . . . .(p.1137)
T: 0141 8875211
E: george@cameronpinkerton.co.uk

DUFF, James David (Jul 2013) (Associate)
MacRoberts LLP, Edinburgh . . . .(p.887)
T: 0131 2295046
E: james.duff@macroberts.com

DUFF, Leona Jane (Jul 2018) (Employee)
Anderson Strathern LLP, Edinburgh . . . .(p.839)
T: 0131 2707700
E: leona.duff@andersonstrathern.co.uk

DUFF, Lucy Georgina (Jul 2020) (Employee)
Brodies LLP, Edinburgh . . . .(p.845)
T: 0131 2283777
E: lucy.duff@brodies.com

DUFF, Peter (Nov 1981) (Partner)
Blackadders LLP, Glasgow . . . .(p.946)
T: 0141 2481888
E: peter.duff@blackadders.co.uk

DUFF, Seamus Rory McCallum (Jan 2021)
(Employee)
Scottish Government, Edinburgh . . . . .(p.1231)
T: 0131 244 0815
E: seamus.duff@gov.scot

DUFF, Stephen Henry (Oct 2013) (Employee)
Digby Brown LLP, Glasgow . . . .(p.970)
T: 0333 200 5925
E: stephen.duff@digbybrown.co.uk

DUFF, Susan Margaret (Sept 1989) (Partner)
Thorntons Law LLP, Cupar. . . . .(p.793)
T: 01334 652285
E: sduff@thorntons-law.co.uk

DUFF, Zoe Emma (Aug 2018) (Employee)
Cullen Kilshaw, Galashiels . . . .(p.933)
T: 01896 800 800
E: zoe.duff@cullenkilshaw.com

DUFFILL, Alan (Feb 1994) (Partner)
Stewart & Watson, Banff . . . .(p.769)
T: 01261 818883
E: aduffill@stewartwatson.co.uk

DUFFUS, Anna Louise (Jun 1996) (Consultant)
Bird & Bird LLP, London EC4 . . . .(p.1262)
T: 0207 415 6000
E: anna.duffus@twobirds.com

DUFFY, Blair (Dec 2019) (Employee)
Harper Macleod LLP, Glasgow . . . .(p.983)
T: 0141 2218888

DUFFY, Brian Christopher (Jun 1998)
(Employee)
Procurator Fiscal Service,
Edinburgh . . . .(p.1229)
E: brian.duffy@copfs.gov.uk

DUFFY, Christopher Michael (Oct 2009)
(Employee)
Celtic plc., Glasgow . . . .(p.1238)
T: 0871 226 1888
E: cduffy@celticfc.co.uk

DUFFY, Gr inne M ire (May 2021) (Employee)
CMS Cameron McKenna Nabarro Olswang LLP,
London EC4 . . . .(p.1263)
T: 0207 3673000
E: Grainne.Duffy@cms-cmno.com

DUFFY, Gregory (Sept 1986) (Solicitor)
NO FIRM

DUFFY, John Kevin (Feb 1978) (Partner)
Ruthven, Keenan, Pollock & Co.,
Glasgow . . . .(p.1038)
T: 0141 9542901
E: kevin.duffy@rkpsolicitors.co.uk

DUFFY, Karina Marie (Sept 1996) (Employee)
Procurator Fiscal Service, Glasgow . . . .(p.1242)
E: karina.duffy@copfs.gov.uk

DUFFY, Kevin John (Nov 2013) (Employee)
Scottish Engineering, Glasgow . . . .(p.1243)
T: 0141 2213181
E: kevinduffy@scottishengineering.org.uk

DUFFY, Lisa Jane (Jul 2012) (Employee)
Scottish Social Services Council,
Dundee . . . .(p.1218)
T: 0345 6030 891
E: lisa.duffy@sssc.uk.com

DUFFY, Louise Elizabeth (Sept 2005)
(Employee)
Brodies LLP, Glasgow . . . .(p.948)
T: 0141 2484672
E: louise.duffy@brodies.com

DUFFY, Martin Vincent (Dec 1988) (Partner)
Martin Duffy, Kilmarnock . . . .(p.1094)
T: 01563 528580
E: duffy.martin@hotmail.co.uk

DUFFY, Maureen (Oct 2021) (Employee)
Martin, Johnston & Socha Limited,
Dunfermline . . . .(p.824)
T: 01383 730466
E:
maureen.duffy@mjscriminaldefencelawyers.co.
uk

DUFFY, Michael John (Feb 2011) (Employee)
Pinsent Masons LLP, Edinburgh . . . .(p.895)
T: 0131 7777000
E: Michael.Duffy@pinsentmasons.com

DUFFY, Nicholas Jude Steven (Sept 2000)
(Employee)
Scottish Government, Edinburgh . . . . .(p.1231)
T: 0131 244 0815
E: nicholas.duffy@gov.scot

DUFFY, Rachel (Jul 2021) (Employee)
Scottish Social Services Council,
Dundee . . . .(p.1218)
T: 0345 6030 891
E: Rachel.duffy@sssc.uk.com

DUFFY, Richard Thomas (Jan 2006) (Employee)
Blackadders LLP, Glasgow . . . .(p.946)
T: 0141 2481888
E: richard.duffy@blackadders.co.uk

DUFFY, Rosemary Dornan (Oct 2002)
(Employee)
East Ayrshire Council, Kilmarnock . . . . .(p.1249)
T: 01563 576161
E: Rosemary.Duffy@east-ayrshire.gov.uk

DUFFY, William Hugh (Feb 1988) (Employee)
Procurator Fiscal Service, Glasgow . . . .(p.1241)
T: 0300 0203000
E: william.duffy@copfs.gov.uk

DUFFY-WELSH, Naomi Frances (Jul 2018)
(Employee)
Procurator Fiscal Service, Inverness . . . .(p.1248)
T: 0844 5612926
E: naomi.duffy-welsh@copfs.gov.uk

DUGAN, Kevin Anthony (Nov 1984) (Partner)
Adams Whyte, Livingston . . . .(p.1117)
T: 01506 401999
E: kevindugan@adamswhyte.com

DUGAN, Roisin Anne (Jul 2020) (Employee)
Keegan Smith, SSC., Livingston . . . . . .(p.1119)
T: 01506 497500
E: roisin@keegansmith.org

DUGUID, Hannah Katharina (Aug 2015)
(Employee)
Turcan Connell, Edinburgh . . . .(p.908)
T: 0131 2288111
E: hannah.duguid@turcanconnell.com

DUGUID, Tom (Oct 2004) (Partner)
Turcan Connell, Edinburgh . . . .(p.908)
T: 0131 2288111
E: tom.duguid@turcanconnell.com

DUHERIC, Damir (Jan 2005) (Partner)
D. Duheric & Co Solicitors,
Edinburgh . . . .(p.865)
T: 0131 2255444
E: damir.duheric@dduhericsolicitors.co.uk

DUKE, Patricia Jane (Nov 1990) (Employee)
Procurator Fiscal Service, Glasgow . . . .(p.1241)
T: 0300 0203000
E: patricia.duke@copfs.gov.uk

DUN, Christopher Peter (Feb 1988) (Partner)
Brodies LLP, Edinburgh . . . .(p.845)
T: 0131 2283777
E: chris.dun@brodies.com

DUNBAR, Craig (Oct 1983) (Employee)
Russel + Aitken (Falkirk + Alloa) Ltd,
Falkirk . . . .(p.924)
T: 01324 622888
E: craigdunbar@randa-fa.co.uk

DUNBAR, Douglas Mitchell (Jun 2015)
(Employee)
Burness Paull LLP, Edinburgh . . . .(p.850)
T: 0131 473 5557
E: douglas.dunbar@burnesspaull.com

DUNBAR, James Robertson (Jun 2014)
(Employee)
Procurator Fiscal Service, Oban . . . . . .(p.1252)
T: 01631 64088
E: James.Dunbar@copfs.gov.uk

DUNBAR, Joanna Carolyn Pyper (Jul 2004)
(Partner)
Solicitors Direct, Aberdeen. . . . .(p.743)
T: 01224 327 437
E: joanna@solicitorsdirect.info

DUNBAR, Joy Patricia (Dec 1979) (Partner)
Solicitors Direct, Aberdeen. . . . .(p.743)
T: 01224 327 437
E: joy@solicitorsdirect.info

DUNBAR, Julia Ann Katherine (Sept 1989)
(Employee)
Scottish Courts and Tribunals Service,
Edinburgh . . . .(p.1230)
T: 0131 2252525
E: jdunbar@scotcourts.gov.uk

DUNBAR, Mark Morrison (Mar 1993) (Director)
MSM Solicitors Limited, Glasgow . . . . .(p.1024)
T: 0141 5548111
E: mmd@msmlaw.co.uk

DUNBAR, Megan (Oct 2017) (Employee)
Harper Macleod LLP, Glasgow . . . .(p.983)
T: 0141 2218888
E: megan.dunbar@harpermacleod.co.uk

DUNBAR, Stewart John (Nov 2011) (Employee)
Blackadders LLP, Edinburgh . . . .(p.843)
T: 0131 2228000
E: stewart.dunbar@blackadders.co.uk

DUNCAN, Alistair David (Oct 1997) (Employee)
Procurator Fiscal Service, Hamilton . . . .(p.1247)
T: 0300 020 0456
E: Alistair.Duncan@copfs.gov.uk

DUNCAN, Alistair Ross (Nov 1997) (Partner)
Miller Hendry, Dundee . . . .(p.816)
T: 01382 200000
E: alistairduncan@millerhendry.co.uk

DUNCAN, Andrew William (Sept 2000)
(Solicitor)
NO FIRM

DUNCAN, Angela (Sept 2016) (Employee)
Angus McIntosh & Simon Hodge,
Glasgow. . . . .(p.1012)
T: 0141 6340313
E: angela.duncan@castlemilklawcentre.co.uk

DUNCAN, Anna Helen (Sept 2017) (Employee)
Cullen Kilshaw, Galashiels . . . .(p.933)
T: 01896 800 800
E: anna.duncan@cullenkilshaw.com

DUNCAN, Anya Dorothy (Oct 2004) (Partner)
Stronachs LLP, Aberdeen . . . .(p.744)
T: 01224 845845
E: Anya.Duncan@stronachs.com

DUNCAN, Blair Ian James (Dec 2018)
(Employee)
Blackadders LLP, Dundee. . . . .(p.805)
T: 01382 229222
E: Blair.Duncan@blackadders.co.uk

DUNCAN, Charlene Elizabeth Cunningham
(Aug 2017) (Employee)
Neill Clerk & Murray, Greenock . . . . . .(p.1062)
T: 01475 724522
E: charlene@neillclerkmurray.co.uk

DUNCAN, Cinzia Chiara (Jun 2016) (Employee)
Harper Macleod LLP, Glasgow . . . .(p.983)
T: 0141 2218888
E: cinzia.duncan@harpermacleod.co.uk

DUNCAN, David Walter (Dec 2003) (Employee)
Baker & McKenzie LLP, London
EC4 . . . .(p.1261)
T: 0207 9191000
E: David.Duncan@bakermckenzie.com

DUNCAN, David William (Mar 2005) (Director)
Duncan & McConnell Solicitors Limited,
Dundee . . . .(p.809)
T: 07761 301390
E: enquiries@duncanandmcconnell.com

DUNCAN, Eilean Margaret Anne (Sept 2013)
(Employee)
Falkirk Council, Falkirk . . . .(p.1236)
T: 01324 506382
E: eilean.duncan@falkirk.gov.uk

DUNCAN, Esther Mary (Oct 1996) (Employee)
University of Edinburgh, Edinburgh . . .(p.1235)
T: 0131 651 4202
E: Esther.Duncan@ed.ac.uk

DUNCAN, Euan Findlay (Jan 1991) (Partner)
MacRoberts LLP, Glasgow . . . .(p.1015)
T: 0141 3031100
E: euan.duncan@macroberts.com

DUNCAN, Fergus Alfred Sloss (Sept 1996)
(Director)
Mactaggart & Co Limited, Largs . . . . .(p.1110)
T: 01475 674646
E: fergus@mactaggarts.co.uk

DUNCAN, Graeme Lindesay, WS (Nov 1980)
(Partner)
Beveridge & Kellas, Edinburgh . . . .(p.843)
T: 0131 5546321
E: g.duncan@beveridgekellas.com

DUNCAN, Hannah Louise (Jun 2021)
(Employee)
Cullen Kilshaw, Peebles . . . .(p.1143)
T: 01721 723 999
E: hannah.duncan@cullenkilshaw.com

DUNCAN, Howat Douglas (Jun 2021)
(Employee)
Pinsent Masons LLP, Edinburgh . . . .(p.895)
T: 0131 777 7000
E: howat.duncan@pinsentmasons.com

DUNCAN, Hugh Joss (Sept 1995) (Employee)
Public Defence Solicitors Office,
Ayr . . . .(p.1215)
T: 01292 269139
E: hduncan@pdso.org.uk

DUNCAN, James Ross (Sept 2019) (Employee)
Dickson Minto, London EC2 . . . .(p.1263)
T: 020 76284455
E: Jamie.Duncan@dmws.com

DUNCAN, John Derek (Jan 1984) (Partner)
RSB Lindsays, Dundee . . . .(p.818)
T: 01382 224112
E: derekduncan@lindsays.co.uk

DUNCAN, Joseph Malcolm Leslie (Oct 1988)
(Director)
Anderson Shaw & Gilbert Limited,
Inverness . . . .(p.1075)
T: 01463 236123
E: jd@solicitorsinverness.com

DUNCAN, Kathryn May (Jan 2020) (Solicitor)
NO FIRM

DUNCAN, Louise Emily (Dec 2014) (Employee)
Axiom Global Limited, London
EC1 . . . .(p.1261)
E: louise.duncan1@lloydsbanking.com

DUNCAN, Molly Grace (Oct 2021) (Employee)
Lindsays LLP, Edinburgh . . . .(p.882)
T: 0131 2291212
E: MollyDuncan@lindsays.co.uk

DUNCAN, Pamela Dorothy (Aug 2006)
(Partner)
Somerville & Russell, Musselburgh . . . .(p.1129)
T: 0131 6659041
E: pduncan@somervilleandrussell.co.uk

DUNCAN, Sara Elisabeth (Sept 2004)
(Employee)
ASCO Group Limited, Aberdeen . . . . . .(p.1212)
T: 01224 580396
E: sara.duncan@ascoworld.com

DUNCAN, Sarah Lucia (Jan 1990) (Employee)
Highland Council, Inverness . . . .(p.1248)
T: 01463 702000
E: sarah.duncan@highland.gov.uk

DUNCAN, Scott George (Apr 2007) (Employee)
Pinsent Masons LLP, Edinburgh . . . .(p.895)
T: 0131 225 0095
E: scott.duncan@pinsentmasons.com

DUNCAN, Stewart William (Sept 2016)
(Employee)
Procurator Fiscal Service, Dundee . . . . .(p.1218)
T: 01382 342559
E: Stewart.Duncan@copfs.gov.uk

DUNCAN, Stuart, WS (Jun 1979) (Partner)
Davidson Chalmers Stewart LLP,
Edinburgh . . . .(p.859)
T: 0131 6259191
E: stuart.duncan@dcslegal.com

DUNCAN, Stuart Andrew Weir (Jun 1998)
(Employee)
Offshore Helicopter Services UK Limited,
Aberdeen . . . .(p.1213)
T: 01224 215186
E: Stuart.Duncan2@babcockinternational.com

DUNCAN, Thomas (Dec 1979) (Partner)
Thomas Duncan Solicitor,
Linlithgow . . . .(p.1116)
T: 07887 835321
E: tom@scotlandlegal.co.uk

DUNCAN, Thomas Wilson (Oct 1979)
(Consultant)
Peterkins, Aberdeen . . . .(p.739)
T: 01224 428000
E: td@peterkins.com

DUNDAS, James Andrew (Sept 2013)
(Associate)
CMS Cameron McKenna Nabarro Olswang LLP,
Edinburgh . . . .(p.856)
T: 0131 2288000
E: James.Dundas@cms-cmno.com

DUNDAS, Nicola Jane (Oct 1987) (Partner)
Gillespie Macandrew LLP,
Edinburgh . . . .(p.872)
T: 0131 2251677
E: Nikki.Dundas@gillespiemacandrew.co.uk

DUNFORD, Kirsten Annette (Jan 2013)
(Associate)
Raeburn Christie Clark & Wallace LLP,
Aberdeen . . . .(p.741)
T: 01224 332400
E: kirsten.dunford@raeburns.co.uk

DUNIPACE, Margaret Shona (Sept 1996)
(Employee)
Procurator Fiscal Service, Glasgow . . . .(p.1241)
T: 0300 0203000
E: margaret.dunipace@copfs.gov.uk

DUNLOP, Aileen-Clare (Dec 1986) (Associate)
Brodies LLP, Edinburgh . . . .(p.845)
T: 0131 6560276
E: clare.dunlop@brodies.com

DUNLOP, Andrew Alexander (Nov 1987)
(Partner)
Burges Salmon LLP, Bristol . . . .(p.1258)
T: 0117 9392000
E: andrew.dunlop@burges-salmon.com

DUNLOP, Brian Hugh (Oct 1974) (Consultant)
Black Hay, Prestwick . . . .(p.1158)
T: 01292 477235
E: brian.dunlop@blackhay.co.uk

DUNLOP, Deborah (Jul 2008) (Partner)
The McKinstry Company LLP,
Girvan . . . .(p.935)
T: 01465 713118
E: debbie@mckinstry.co.uk

DUNLOP, Diane (Oct 2010) (Employee)
Sterling & Sterling LLC, Glasgow . . . . .(p.1245)
E: ddunlop@sterlinganalytics.com

DUNLOP, Grierson Robert (Nov 2001) (Partner)
Turcan Connell, Edinburgh . . . .(p.908)
T: 0131 2288111
E: grierson.dunlop@turcanconnell.com

DUNLOP, Jennifer Amanda (Nov 2011)
(Employee)
Brodies LLP, Edinburgh . . . .(p.845)
T: 0131 2283777
E: jennifer.dunlop@brodies.com

DUNLOP, John William (Nov 2007) (Employee)
Shoosmiths, Edinburgh . . . .(p.902)
T: 03700 868000
E: john.dunlop@shoosmiths.co.uk

DUNLOP, Keith Martin (Oct 2005) (Director)
Ennova Limited, Edinburgh . . . .(p.869)
T: 0131 5104969
E: kdunlop@ennova-law.com

DUNLOP, Lucy Claire (Jun 2020) (Employee)
Irwin Mitchell Scotland LLP,
Glasgow . . . .(p.991)
T: 0141 3004300
E: lucy.dunlop@irwinmitchellscotland.com

DUNLOP, Michael Stephen (Mar 2021)
(Employee)
Procurator Fiscal Service,
Edinburgh . . . .(p.1229)
T: 0300 0203000
E: michael.dunlop@copfs.gov.uk

DUNLOP, Robin John Muir (Nov 2012)
(Employee)
Thorntons Law LLP, Edinburgh . . . .(p.906)
T: 0131 2258705
E: RDunlop@thorntons-law.co.uk

DUNN, Alasdair Ian (Sept 2004) (Employee)
Brodies LLP, Glasgow . . . .(p.948)
T: 0141 2484672
E: alasdair.dunn@brodies.com

DUNN, Alastair Kenneth (Feb 1990) (Partner)
BTO Solicitors LLP, Glasgow . . . .(p.952)
T: 0141 2218012
E: akd@bto.co.uk

DUNN, Christopher Martin (Sept 2017)
(Employee)
Clyde & Co (Scotland) LLP,
Edinburgh . . . .(p.855)
T: 0131 5571545
E: chris.dunn@clydeco.com

DUNN, Eilidh Louise (Oct 2017) (Employee)
Brodies LLP, Glasgow . . . .(p.948)
T: 0141 2484672
E: eilidh.dunn@brodies.com

DUNN, Fiona Louise (Oct 2005) (Employee)
Procurator Fiscal Service, Glasgow . . . .(p.1241)
T: 0300 0203000
E: Fiona.Dunn@copfs.gov.uk

DUNN, Iain Cameron (Apr 1981) (Partner)
Wright, Johnston & Mackenzie LLP,
Glasgow. . . . .(p.1054)
T: 0141 2483434
E: icd@wjm.co.uk

DUNN, Jo (Sept 2019) (Employee)
Procurator Fiscal Service,
Edinburgh . . . .(p.1229)
T: 0300 0204401
E: jo.dunn@civilrecoveryunit.gov.scot

DUNN, Katriona Rosemary (May 2018)
(Employee)
CMS Cameron McKenna Nabarro Olswang LLP,
Edinburgh . . . .(p.856)
T: 0131 2288000
E: katriona.dunn@cms-cmno.com

DUNN, Kyle Zander (Sept 2017) (Employee)
Allen & Overy LLP, London E1 . . . .(p.1261)
T: 020 3088 0000
E: kyle.dunn@allenovery.com

DUNN, Murray Lochtie (Sept 2015) (Employee)
Wyelands Capital, London W1 . . . .(p.1269)

DUNN, Rachel Elizabeth (Mar 2015)
(Employee)
Dentons UK and Middle East LLP,
Glasgow. . . . .(p.968)
T: 0330 2220050
E: Rachel.Dunn@dentons.com

DUNN, Robert Ferguson (Oct 1980) (Director)
Hunter & Robertson Limited,
Paisley . . . .(p.1138)
T: 0141 8893196
E: rdunn@hunter-robertson.co.uk

DUNN, Steven Dickson (Jan 1994) (Associate)
Anderson Strathern LLP, Glasgow . . . . . .(p.940)
T: 0141 2426060
E: steven.dunn@andersonstrathern.co.uk

DUNN, Susan (Aug 2003) (Associate)
Thorntons Law LLP, Anstruther . . . .(p.755)
T: 01333 314395
E: sdunn@thorntons-law.co.uk

DUNN, William Alexander (Feb 1988)
(Employee)
SOUTH LANARKSHIRERe Council,
Hamilton . . . .(p.1247)
T: (01698) 454785
E: bill.dunn@southlanarkshire.gov.uk

DUNN, Yvonne Louise (Dec 1997) (Partner)
Pinsent Masons LLP, Glasgow . . . .(p.1031)
T: 0141 567 8400
E: yvonne.dunn@pinsentmasons.com

DUNNE, Barry Malcolm (Oct 2004) (Employee)
Procurator Fiscal Service, Hamilton . . . .(p.1247)
T: 0844 5613208
E: barry.dunne@copfs.gov.uk

DUNNE, James Stephen (Jun 2014) (Employee)
Brodies LLP, Edinburgh . . . .(p.845)
T: 0131 656 0024
E: jamie.dunne@brodies.com

DUNNE, John Paul (Jan 2017) (Employee)
McArdle, Glasgow . . . .(p.1005)
T: 0141 8101001
E: jd@mcardle-solicitors.co.uk

DUNNE, Paul Joseph (Sept 2006) (Partner)
Dunne Defence Lawyers,
Edinburgh . . . .(p.865)
T: 0131 466 5630
E: paul@dunnedefence.com

DUNNING, Kirsty Marie (Jun 2014) (Employee)
Murdoch, McMath & Mitchell,
Huntly . . . .(p.1074)
T: 01466 792291
E: kirsty@murdoch-mcmath-mitchell.com

DUNPHY, Siobhan (Aug 2013) (Employee)
Shepherd and Wedderburn LLP,
Edinburgh . . . .(p.900)
T: 0131 2289900
E: Siobhan.Dunphy@shepwedd.com

DUNSIRE, David Ness, WS (Dec 1982)
(Consultant)
Lindsays LLP, Edinburgh . . . .(p.882)
T: 0131 2291212
E: DavidDunsire@lindsays.co.uk

DUNSMUIR, Hazel (Aug 2021) (Employee)
Cannons Law Practice LLP,
Glasgow . . . .(p.956)
T: 0141 2045115

DUNSMURE, William Edward Henry
(Jun 2014) (Employee)
Forsa Energy Gas Holdings Limited,
Greenock . . . .(p.1246)
T: 01475 749950

DUNZ, Jodie Emma Nicola (Sept 2013)
(Employee)
Addleshaw Goddard LLP,
Edinburgh . . . .(p.835)
T: 0131 2282400
E: Jodie.Dunz@addleshawgoddard.com

DUPONT, Jade Heloise (Jul 2004) (Director)
Dupont Legal Solutions Limited,
Glasgow. . . . .(p.972)
T: 0141 221 1403
E: jade@dupontassociates.co.uk

DURIE, Jennifer Mary Robertson (Feb 2003)
(Associate)
CMS Cameron McKenna Nabarro Olswang LLP,
Edinburgh . . . .(p.856)
T: 0131 2288000
E: jennydurie@cms-cmno.com

DURIE, Katherine Anne (May 2013) (Employee)
CALA Group Ltd, Edinburgh . . . .(p.1221)
T: 0131 5355200
E: kdurie@cala.co.uk

DURIE, Katrina Margaret (Aug 2020)
(Associate)
Addleshaw Goddard LLP,
Edinburgh . . . .(p.835)
T: 0131 2282400
E: katrina.durie@addleshawgoddard.com

DURIE, Wendy (Oct 1991) (Partner)
Thompsons, Glasgow . . . .(p.1046)
T: 0141 2218840
E: wendy.durie@thompsons-scotland.co.uk

DURKAN, Gerard (Nov 1990) (Employee)
Curle Stewart Limited, Glasgow . . . .(p.964)
T: 0141 227 6200
E: gd@curlestewart.co.uk

DURKIN, Eilidh Molly (Aug 2018) (Employee)
Shoosmiths LLP, Glasgow . . . .(p.1040)
T: 0370 086 8300

DURKIN, Natasha (Oct 1996) (Associate)
Shepherd and Wedderburn LLP,
Edinburgh . . . .(p.900)
T: 0131 2289900
E: Natasha.durkin@shepwedd.co.uk

DURLO, Szymon Andrzej (Oct 2018)
(Employee)
Walkers (Dubai) LLP, Dubai . . . .(p.1278)
E: szymon.durlo@walkersglobal.com

DUTHIE, Andrew (Dec 1981) (Director)
Grant Smith Law Practice Limited,
Aberdeen . . . .(p.743)
T: 01224 621620
E: andrew.duthie@grantsmithlaw.co.uk

DUTHIE, Gregor Ian (Aug 2005) (Associate)
Gilson Gray LLP, Glasgow . . . .(p.980)
T: 0141 433 7753
E: gduthie@gilsongray.co.uk

DUTHIE, Victoria Anne (Jul 2017) (Employee)
Burness Paull LLP, Aberdeen . . . . (p.724)
T: 01224 621621
E: Victoria.Duthie@burnesspaull.com

DUTHIE, William James (Oct 2012) (Employee)
Altera Infrastructure, Westhill . . . . (p.1255)
E: william.duthie@alterainfra.com

DYCE, Holly (Jan 2019) (Employee)
Scottish Government, Edinburgh . . . . . (p.1231)
T: 0131 244 0815
E: Holly.Dyce@gov.scot

DYER, Hilary Susan (Oct 1996) (Employee)
Procurator Fiscal Service,
  Edinburgh . . . . (p.1227)
T: 0300 0203168
E: hilary.dyer@copfs.gov.uk

DYNAN, Paul (Jul 2001) (Employee)
SSE PLC, Glasgow . . . . (p.1244)
T: 0141 224 7129
E: paul.dynan@sse.com

DYSON, Emma Caitlin (Sept 2016) (Employee)
Brodies LLP, Edinburgh . . . . (p.845)
T: 0131 2283777
E: emma.dyson@brodies.com

EADIE, Alan William (Feb 1993) (Partner)
BTO Solicitors LLP, Glasgow . . . . (p.952)
T: 0141 2218012
E: awe@bto.co.uk

EADIE, Cara Marion (Oct 2007) (Employee)
Civil Legal Assistance Office,
  Aberdeen . . . . (p.1212)
T: 01224 402330
E: EadieCa@clao.org.uk

EADIE, Charles Wesley (Apr 2021) (Employee)
BTO Solicitors LLP, Glasgow . . . . (p.952)
T: 0141 2218012
E: cxe@bto.co.uk

EADIE, Fiona Margaret (Mar 2001) (Employee)
Procurator Fiscal Service, Kirkcaldy . . . . (p.1249)
T: 0300 0203000
E: FDASecretary@copfs.gov.uk

EADIE, Jemima Elizabeth (Nov 2013)
(Employee)
Procurator Fiscal Service,
  Edinburgh . . . . (p.1227)
T: 0777 3555386
E: Jemma.Eadie@copfs.gov.uk

EADIE, Kristen Lauren (Sept 2020) (Employee)
Burness Paull LLP, Edinburgh . . . . (p.850)
T: 0131 4736000
E: kristen.eadie@burnesspaull.com

EADIE, Russell John (Nov 1995) (Associate)
Balfour + Manson LLP, Edinburgh . . . . . (p.841)
T: 0131 2001200
E: russell.eadie@balfour-manson.co.uk

EADIE-CAMPBELL, Mairi Maclean (Jan 2009)
(Employee)
Clydesdale Bank Plc, Glasgow . . . . (p.1238)
T: 7824476497
E: mairi.eadie-campbell@cybg.com

EAKIN, Amy Catherine (Aug 2016) (Employee)
Turcan Connell, Edinburgh . . . . (p.908)
T: 0131 2288111
E: amy.stevenson@turcanconnell.com

EARLY, David MacGregor (Sept 2017)
(Employee)
Allen & Overy LLP, London E1 . . . . (p.1261)
T: 020 3088 0000
E: david.early@allenovery.com

EARLY, Zara Rachel (Oct 2014) (Associate)
Pinsent Masons LLP, Glasgow . . . . (p.1031)
T: 0141 567 8400
E: zara.early@pinsentmasons.com

EARNSHAW, Caroline Rose (Oct 2003)
(Associate)
Morton Fraser LLP, Edinburgh . . . . (p.891)
T: 0131 2471000
E: caroline.earnshaw@morton-fraser.com

EASON, David (Sept 1980) (Partner)
Harper Macleod LLP, Glasgow . . . . (p.983)
T: 0141 2218888
E: david.eason@harpermacleod.co.uk

EASTON, Angus David (Jul 2012) (Employee)
Mackinnons Solicitors LLP,
  Aberdeen . . . . (p.736)
T: 01224 632464
E: angus@mackinnons.com

EASTON, Douglas Alexander (Sept 2007)
(Employee)
JPIMedia Limited, Edinburgh . . . . (p.1224)
E: Douglas.Easton@jpimedia.co.uk

EASTON, Ian William (Oct 2010) (Employee)
Enquest Britain Limited, Aberdeen . . . . (p.1212)
T: 01224 975000
E: ian.easton@enquest.com

EASTON, Mark Alexander (Nov 2007)
(Employee)
Stirling Council, Stirling . . . . (p.1255)
T: 01786 233065
E: eastonm@stirling.gov.uk

EASTON, Rebecca Helen (Jul 2017) (Employee)
Brodies LLP, Edinburgh . . . . (p.845)
T: 0131 2283777
E: Rebecca.Easton@brodies.com

EASTON, Stuart William (Aug 2005) (Director)
Eastons Solicitors Limited, Glasgow . . . . (p.974)
T: 0141 5331976
E: stuart@eastonssolicitors.co.uk

EASTWOOD, Martina Gertrud Henrietta
(Jul 2016) (Employee)
Procurator Fiscal Service, Inverness . . . . (p.1248)
T: 0844 5612926
E: martina.eastwood@copfs.gov.uk

EATON, Jessica (Mar 2021) (Employee)
CMS Cameron McKenna Nabarro Olswang LLP,
Edinburgh . . . . (p.856)
T: 0131 2288000
E: jessica.eaton@cms-cmno.com

EBDY, Alicia Sylvester (Nov 2009) (Employee)
Barclays Bank PLC, London E14 . . . . . . (p.1262)
T: (0207) 116 1000
E: alicia.ebdy@barclayscorp.com

ECCLES, Alan William (Oct 2004) (Partner)
Bannatyne, Kirkwood, France & Co.,
Glasgow. (p.943)
T: 0141 2216020
E: alaneccles@bkf.co.uk

ECCLES, Christopher Nigel (Sept 1993)
(Solicitor)
NO FIRM

ECKFORD, Alison Margaret Ross (Jun 2004)
(Partner)
Pinsent Masons LLP, London EC2 . . . . . (p.1267)
T: 020 7418 7000
E: alison.rosseckford@pinsentmasons.com

EDDIE, Wayne (Jul 2008) (Employee)
Enquest Britain Limited, Aberdeen . . . . (p.1212)
T: 01224 570573
E: wayne.eddie@enquest.com

EDE, Miles Jonathan (Apr 1997) (Partner)
Addleshaw Goddard LLP,
Edinburgh . . . . (p.835)
T: 0131 2282400
E: Miles.Ede@addleshawgoddard.com

EDGAR, Barry (Nov 2003) (Partner)
Dentons UK and Middle East LLP,
Glasgow. (p.968)
T: 0330 2220050
E: Barry.Edgar@dentons.com

EDGAR, Charlotte Mary (Aug 2016) (Associate)
CMS Cameron McKenna Nabarro Olswang LLP,
Edinburgh . . . . (p.856)
T: 0131 2288000
E: Charlotte.Edgar@cms-cmno.com

EDGAR, Cheryl Anne (Feb 1991) (Associate)
Gilson Gray LLP, North Berwick . . . . . . (p.1132)
T: 01620 893481
E: cedgar@gilsongray.co.uk

EDGAR, Claire Danielle (Sept 2013) (Associate)
Anderson Strathern LLP, Edinburgh . . . . (p.839)
T: 0131 2707700
E: Danielle.Edgar@andersonstrathern.co.uk

EDGAR, Deborah (Aug 2020) (Employee)
1st Legal Limited, Ayr . . . . (p.760)
T: 01292 290666
E: deborah@1stlegal.co.uk

EDGAR, Laura Margaret (Oct 2002) (Employee)
Dentons UK and Middle East LLP,
Glasgow. (p.968)
T: 0330 2220050
E: Laura.Edgar@dentons.com

EDGAR, Nicola Mary (Oct 2008) (Associate)
Morton Fraser LLP, Glasgow . . . . (p.1022)
T: 0141 2741100
E: nicola.edgar@morton-fraser.com

EDGAR, Robert David (Aug 2018) (Employee)
Clifford Chance LLP, London E14 . . . . . (p.1262)
E: robert.edgar@cliffordchance.com

EDGECOMBE, Steven Graeme (Nov 1988)
(Partner)
DLA Piper Scotland LLP, Edinburgh . . . . (p.863)
T: 08700 111111
E: steve.edgecombe@dlapiper.com

EDINGTON, Susan Jane (Dec 1979) (Director)
Edington Law Limited, Galashiels . . . . . . (p.933)
T: 01896 756161
E: susanedington@edingtonlaw.co.uk

EDISON, Laura Robyn (Nov 2008) (Employee)
Skyrora Limited, Edinburgh . . . . (p.1234)
E: laura.edison@skyrora.com

EDMENT, John Euan (Nov 1985) (Employee)
McJerrow & Stevenson, Lockerbie . . . . (p.1122)
T: 01576 202123

EDMONDSON, Alison Elizabeth Redpath
(Sept 2004) (Partner)
SKO Family Law Specialists LLP,
Edinburgh . . . . (p.903)
T: 0131 3226669
E: Alison.Edmondson@sko-family.co.uk

EDMONDSON, Isabelle Anne (Sept 2017)
(Employee)
Jackson's, Newcastle Upon Tyne . . . . . . (p.1270)
E: IEdmondson@jacksons-law.com

EDMONSTONE, Jennifer Jane (Aug 2010)
(Employee)
Sportscotland, Glasgow . . . . (p.1244)
T: 0141 5346500
E: jennifer.edmonstone@sportscotland.org.uk

EDMUNDS, Chris (Director)
Davidson & Robertson Ltd, Currie . . . . (p.1329)
T: (0131) 449 6212
E: CE@drrural.co.uk

EDMUNDS, Laura-Anne Campbell
(Nov 2009) (Employee)
Ledingham Chalmers LLP,
Aberdeen . . . . (p.734)
T: 01224 408408
E: laura.edmunds@ledinghamchalmers.com

EDMUNDSON, Ione Skye (Aug 2021)
(Employee)
Dickson Minto, Edinburgh . . . .(p.861)
T: 0131 2254455
E: ione.edmundson@dmws.com

EDWARD, Craig James (Jul 2016) (Associate)
MBM Commercial LLP, Edinburgh . . . . .(p.889)
T: 0131 2268200
E: Craig.Edward@mbmcommercial.co.uk

EDWARD, Graeme Mark Kynoch (Oct 1996)
(Partner)
Ledingham Chalmers LLP,
Aberdeen . . . .(p.734)
T: 01224 408408
E: graeme.edward@ledinghamchalmers.com

EDWARD, Hazel Elizabeth (Nov 1991)
(Employee)
Procurator Fiscal Service, Dundee . . . . .(p.1218)
T: 01382 342559
E: hazel.edward@copfs.gov.uk

EDWARD, Timothy James (Nov 1989) (Partner)
MBM Commercial LLP, Edinburgh . . . . .(p.889)
T: 0131 2268200
E: Tim.Edward@mbmcommercial.co.uk

EDWARDS, Jacqueline (Oct 1994) (Employee)
Scottish Enterprise, Glasgow . . . .(p.1243)
T: 1412282383
E: jackie.edwards@scotent.co.uk

EDWARDS, Jonathan Philip (Jan 1980)
(Consultant)
McVey & Murricane, Glasgow . . . .(p.1017)
T: 0141 3339688
E: jedwards@mcvey-murricane.com

EDWARDS, Laurence John (Nov 1982)
(Employee)
Pension Protection Fund, Croydon . . . .(p.1259)
T: 020 8633 4957
E: laurence.edwards@ppf.co.uk

EDWARDS, Lindsay (Mar 2020) (Employee)
Pinsent Masons LLP, Edinburgh . . . .(p.897)
T: 0131 2250000
E: Lindsay.edwardstmt@pinsentmasons.com

EGGELING, Mark Andrew (Jan 2008)
(Employee)
Scottish Government's Parliamentary Counsel
Office, Edinburgh . . . .(p.1233)
T: 0131 244 1668
E: mark.eggeling@gov.scot

EJSMONT, Kirstin (Jun 2011) (Employee)
Mackinnons Solicitors LLP,
Aberdeen . . . .(p.736)
T: 01224 632464
E: kirstin@mackinnons.com

EKINLI, Fiona Sinclair Nicolson (May 1999)
(Employee)
NORTH LANARKSHIREre Council,
Motherwell . . . .(p.1251)
T: 01698 302196
E: ekinlif@northlan.gov.uk

EL-ALAMI, Emma Louise Ann (Nov 2003)
(Employee)
National Westminster Bank PLC,
Edinburgh . . . .(p.1226)
T: (0131) 626 2925
E: emma.elalami@natwestmarkets.com

EL-SHAFEI, Latifa (Dec 2016) (Employee)
Kirkland & Ellis International LLP, London
EC3 . . . .(p.1265)
T: 0207 4692000
E: latifa.elshafei@kirkland.com

ELDER, Aimee Louise (Mar 2017) (Employee)
Watermans Solicitors Limited,
Glasgow . . . .(p.1051)
T: 0141 4307055
E: AimeeElder@watermans.co.uk

ELDER, Elaine (Sept 2012) (Employee)
Aberdein Considine and Company,
Aberdeen . . . .(p.718)
T: 01224 589700
E: eelder@acandco.com

ELDER, Gemma Margaret (Jun 2016) (Director)
The Robert Kerr Partnership Limited,
Paisley . . . .(p.1141)
T: 0141 8896458
E: ge@therobertkerrpartnership.com

ELDER, Joanna Clare (Sept 2017) (Employee)
BBC, London W1 . . . .(p.1262)
E: joanna.elder@bbc.co.uk

ELDER, John Whyte (May 1996) (Employee)
Shepherd and Wedderburn LLP,
Glasgow . . . .(p.1039)
T: 0141 5669900
E: John.Elder@shepwedd.com

ELDER, Lynsey (Oct 2010) (Employee)
Criminal Injuries Compensation Authority,
Glasgow . . . .(p.1239)
T: 0141 2281419
E: lynsey.elder@cica.gov.uk

ELFALLAH, Farida (Feb 2017) (Associate)
JustRight Scotland LLP, Glasgow . . . . . .(p.994)
T: 0141 406 5350
E: Farida@justrightscotland.org.uk

ELHAMI-KHORASANI, Darran (Mar 2010)
(Employee)
DAC Beachcroft Scotland LLP,
Glasgow . . . .(p.964)
T: 0141 2486688
E: dkhorasani@dacbeachcroft.com

ELLIOT, Catherine Mary Anne (Sept 2013)
(Partner)
Elliot & Co., WS, Perth . . . .(p.1147)
T: 01738 638246
E: celliot@elliotsperth.co.uk

ELLIOT, Donald George, WS (Aug 1975)
(Partner)
Elliot & Co., WS, Perth . . . .(p.1147)
T: 01738 638246
E: delliot@elliotsperth.co.uk

ELLIOT, Jennifer Susan Elizabeth (Feb 2014)
(Employee)
OVO (S) Electricity Ltd, Perth . . . .(p.1253)
E: Jennie.Elliot@sse.com

ELLIOTT, Colin David (Aug 1994) (Employee)
Perth & Kinross Council, Perth . . . .(p.1253)
T: 01738 475131
E: cdelliott@pkc.gov.uk

ELLIOTT, Jack (Jul 2015) (Employee)
Heineken UK Limited, Edinburgh . . . . .(p.1223)
T: 0131 5281000
E: Jack.Elliott@heineken.co.uk

ELLIOTT, Nicola Hannah (Dec 2003) (Director)
Your Conveyancer Limited,
Dunfermline . . . .(p.827)
T: 01383 667550
E: nicola.elliott@yourconveyancer.co.uk

ELLIS, David Graeme Dougall (Mar 1989)
(Consultant)
Mattac Limited, Edinburgh . . . .(p.888)
T: 0131 510 8740
E: david.ellis@mattac.legal

ELLIS, Mark Julian (Oct 2000) (Partner)
Burness Paull LLP, Edinburgh . . . .(p.850)
T: 0131 4736000
E: mark.ellis@burnesspaull.com

ELLIS, Rebecca Elizabeth (Apr 2021)
(Employee)
Weightmans (Scotland) LLP,
Glasgow. . . . .(p.1051)
T: 0345 073 9900
E: rebecca.ellis@weightmans.com

ELLISON, Rachel Katherine (Jun 2016)
(Solicitor)
National Westminster Bank PLC,
Edinburgh . . . .(p.1226)
T: (0131) 626 2925
E: Rachel.k.ellison1@natwest.com

ELLWOOD, Rebecca Erin (May 2015)
(Employee)
Thorntons Law LLP, Perth . . . .(p.1151)
T: 01738 621212
E: rellwood@thorntons-law.co.uk

ELMSLIE, Derek James (Nov 1983) (Director)
Elmslie's Ltd, Edinburgh . . . .(p.866)
T: 0131 2255484
E: dje@elmslies.co.uk

ELRICK, Donna Marie (Sept 2013) (Employee)
Aberdeenshire Council, Aberdeen . . . . .(p.1211)
T: 0345 608 1208
E: donna.elrick@aberdeenshire.gov.uk

ELRICK, Lesley Macpherson (Feb 1993)
(Partner)
Connell & Connell, WS, Edinburgh . . . .(p.857)
T: 0131 5562993
E: lme@connellws.co.uk

ELRICK, Suzanne Louise (Mar 2005) (Employee)
Banijay UK, Glasgow . . . .(p.1238)
T: 0141 3533222
E: suzanne.elrick@zodiakmedia.com

ELSBY, Donna Margaret (Oct 2011) (Director)
Galloway & Elsby Legal Limited,
Kilmarnock . . . .(p.1094)
T: 01563 527 564
E: delsby@gallowayandelsby.co.uk

ELSTON, David Aiken (Feb 1978) (Solicitor)
NO FIRM

EMBLETON, Lloyd Railton (Oct 2000)
(Employee)
Pinsent Masons LLP, Glasgow . . . .(p.1031)
T: 0141 567 8400
E: lloyd.embleton@pinsentmasons.com

EMMERSON, Hazel (Nov 2003) (Employee)
Procurator Fiscal Service, Glasgow . . . .(p.1241)
T: 0300 0203000
E: hazel.emmerson@copfs.gov.uk

EMMERSON, Keith Robert (Nov 2003)
(Associate)
Gillespie Macandrew LLP, Glasgow . . . . .(p.979)
T: 0141 4735555
E: keith.emmerson@gillespiemacandrew.co.uk

ENAYATI, Elizabeth (Nov 2005) (Employee)
Davidson Chalmers Stewart LLP,
Edinburgh . . . .(p.859)
T: 0131 6259191
E: lizzy.enayati@dcslegal.com

ENNIS, Frances Margaret (Nov 2005) (Director)
Bellwether Green Limited, Glasgow . . . .(p.944)
T: 0141 2184900
E: frances.ennis@bellwethergreen.com

ENNIS, Sarah Frances (Jul 2010) (Employee)
Digby Brown LLP, Glasgow . . . .(p.970)
T: 0333 200 5925
E: Sarah.Ennis@digbybrown.co.uk

ENTWISTLE, Aileen Margaret (Oct 2005)
(Partner)
Aberdein Considine and Company,
Glasgow......................(p.937)
T: 0141 227 8200
E: aentwistle@acandco.com

ENTWISTLE, Amy Anne (Oct 1996) (Partner)
Morton Fraser LLP, Edinburgh ....(p.891)
T: 0131 2471000
E: amy.entwistle@morton-fraser.com

ENTWISTLE, Liam Anthony (Dec 1991)
(Partner)
Wright, Johnston & Mackenzie LLP,
Glasgow....................(p.1054)
T: 0141 2483434
E: lae@wjm.co.uk

ENWEGBARA, Philips Anthony Anaemeze
(Jun 2020) (Solicitor)
NO FIRM

EODANABLE, James Joseph (Aug 1999)
(Employee)
Scottish Social Services Council,
Dundee ....(p.1218)
T: 0345 6030 891
E: James.Eodanable@sssc.uk.com

ERVINE, Gale Marion (Sept 2009) (Employee)
DLA Piper Scotland LLP, Edinburgh ....(p.863)
T: 08700 111111
E: gale.ervine@dlapiper.com

ERVINE, Paul Alan (Sept 2009) (Employee)
Capricorn Energy Ltd, Edinburgh .....(p.1221)
T: 0131 4753000
E: paul.ervine@cairnenergy.com

ESSON, Joni (Nov 2005) (Director)
Esson Aberdein, Aberdeen ....(p.731)
T: 01224 606210
E: joni.esson@alstonlaw.co.uk

ETCHELLS, Simon Paul (Feb 1988) (Partner)
Gunnercooke SCO LLP, Edinburgh .....(p.876)
E: simon.etchells@gunnercooke.com

ETHERINGTON, David Murray (May 2006)
(Partner)
Thorntons Law LLP, Dundee ....(p.819)
T: 01382 346291
E: metherington@thorntons-law.co.uk

ETTLES, Nigel William (Jan 1981) (Employee)
WEST DUNBARTONSHIREhire Council,
Dumbarton ....(p.1217)
T: 01389 737000
E: nigel.ettles@west-dunbarton.gov.uk

EUNSON, Ellen Catherine (Sept 2003) (Partner)
Blackadders LLP, Aberdeen ....(p.722)
T: 01224 588913
E: ellen.eunson@blackadders.co.uk

EVANS, Bethan Frances (Aug 2016) (Employee)
Turcan Connell, Edinburgh ....(p.908)
T: 0131 2288111
E: beth.evans@turcanconnell.com

EVANS, Ceri Victoria (Jul 2014) (Associate)
Airdrie Legal Chambers Limited,
Airdrie ....(p.748)
T: 01236 779970
E: CVEvans@ocurry.net

EVANS, Danielle Gail (May 2021) (Employee)
Livingstone Brown Limited,
Glasgow...................(p.1003)
T: 0141 4298166
E: danielle@livbrown.co.uk

EVANS, Esther May (Apr 1980) (Partner)
Ruth Anderson & Co., Kilwinning.....(p.1097)
T: 01294 551551
E: ruthanderson_co@btconnect.com

EVANS, Frances Bridget Geraldine
(Oct 2003) (Partner)
Frances Evans Commercial Law Practice,
Paisley ....(p.1138)
T: 0141 8894835
E: frances@fevans.co.uk

EVANS, Karen Lesley Stuart (Jan 1987)
(Employee)
Procurator Fiscal Service, Glasgow ....(p.1241)
T: 0300 0203000
E: kate.evans@copfs.gov.uk

EVANS, Mari Jean (Jul 2017) (Employee)
Scottish Government, Edinburgh .....(p.1231)
T: 0131 244 0815
E: Mari.Evans@gov.scot

EVANS, Nicola Jane (Nov 1995) (Employee)
Hogan Lovells International LLP, London
EC1 ....(p.1265)
T: 020 7296 2861
E: nicola.evans@hoganlovells.com

EVANS, Shirley Patricia (Jun 1986) (Associate)
Anderson Strathern LLP, Edinburgh ....(p.839)
T: 0131 2707836
E: Shirley.Evans@andersonstrathern.co.uk

EVANS, Victoria (Oct 2015) (Employee)
Gillespie Gifford & Brown LLP, Castle
Douglas ....(p.783)
T: 01556 503744
E: vicky.evans@ggblaw.co.uk

EVANS-JONES, Allegra Elizabeth (Nov 2019)
(Solicitor)
NO FIRM

EVERDEN, James Ross (Nov 2009) (Employee)
Siemens Gamesa Renewable Energy, Newcastle
Upon Tyne ....(p.1270)
T: 07917 890322
E: james.everden@siemens.com

EVES, Arlene Margaret (Dec 2003) (Employee)
Pinsent Masons LLP, Edinburgh . . . .(p.895)
T: 0131 777 7000
E: Arlene.Eves@pinsentmasons.com

EVES, Jonathan William (Oct 2016) (Partner)
Burges Salmon LLP, Bristol. . . . .(p.1258)
T: 0117 9392000
E: jonathan.eves@burges-salmon.com

EVITT, Paul Charles (Jul 2009) (Employee)
Aberdeen Corporate Services Limited,
Edinburgh . . . .(p.1220)
T: 0131 245 7508
E: paul.evitt@abrdn.com

EWAN, Martin William (Sept 2000) (Partner)
Brodies LLP, Aberdeen. . . . .(p.723)
T: 01224 392242
E: martin.ewan@brodies.com

EWART, Laura Dawn (Feb 2003) (Employee)
National Health Service Scotland,
Edinburgh . . . .(p.1225)
T: 0131 2757800
E: laura.ewart@nhs.scot

EWEN, Nicola Patricia (Aug 1994) (Employee)
Laurie & Co Solicitors LLP,
Aberdeen . . . .(p.733)
T: 01224 645 085

EWEN, Shona Catherine (Jun 2017) (Employee)
Scottish Social Services Council,
Dundee . . . .(p.1218)
T: 0345 6030 891
E: shona.maclean@sssc.uk.com

EWING, Annabelle Janet, MSP (Mar 1986)
(Solicitor)
NO FIRM

EWING, Corrie Alexandra Kelso (Nov 2016)
(Associate)
Addleshaw Goddard LLP, Glasgow . . . . .(p.938)
T: 0141 2212300
E: Corrie.Ewing@addleshawgoddard.com

EWING, Isabel Elder (Oct 1991) (Partner)
TC Young LLP, Glasgow . . . .(p.1055)
T: 0141 2215562
E: iee@tcyoung.co.uk

EWING, Mark Espie (Nov 1985) (Partner)
TC Young LLP, Glasgow . . . .(p.1055)
T: 0141 2215562
E: mee@tcyoung.co.uk

EWING, Maureen Frances (Jul 1990) (Director)
Scanlon Ewing Limited, Clydebank . . . . .(p.785)
T: 0141 9529297
E: maureen@scanlonewing.co.uk

EWING, Paul (Nov 1994) (Partner)
Addleshaw Goddard LLP,
Edinburgh . . . .(p.835)
T: 0131 2282400
E: Paul.Ewing@addleshawgoddard.com

EYNON, David Alan (Oct 2006) (Employee)
Aberdeen Corporate Services Limited,
Edinburgh . . . .(p.1220)
T: 0131 245 7508
E: david.eynon@abrdn.com

EYNON, Sarah (Oct 2005) (Employee)
Scottish Futures Trust, Edinburgh . . . . .(p.1231)
T: 0131 5100800
E: sarah.eynon@scottishfuturestrust.org.uk

FABIJANSKA, Irena Janina (Dec 1988)
(Employee)
Kingsley Wood & Co Solicitors Limited,
Kilmacolm . . . .(p.1093)
T: 01505 874114

FAGAN, Stephen Gerard (Nov 1988)
(Employee)
McWhinney Richards, Airdrie . . . .(p.750)
T: 01236 754571

FAHEEM, Saima Khatija (Jan 2019) (Employee)
Peacock Johnston, Glasgow . . . .(p.1030)
T: 0141 3339505
E: sf@peacockjohnston.co.uk

FAIR, Alasdair Ross (Nov 2007) (Partner)
Blackwood Partners LLP, Aberdeen . . . . .(p.723)
T: 01224 446230
E: Ross.Fair@blackwood-partners.com

FAIR, James Alexander (Aug 2019) (Employee)
Shepherd and Wedderburn LLP,
Edinburgh . . . .(p.900)
T: 0131 2289900
E: alec.fair@shepwedd.com

FAIRBAIRN, Struan Robertson (Aug 2005)
(Employee)
Lothian Pension Fund, Edinburgh . . . . .(p.1225)
T: 0131 529 4689
E: Fai94S99@lpf.org.uk

FAIRBRIDGE, Paul David (Nov 2008) (Director)
Pollock Fairbridge Schiavone Limited,
Glasgow. . . . .(p.1033)
T: 0141 7792577
E: pf@pfssolicitors.co.uk

FAIRFIELD, Andrea Elizabeth (Oct 1999)
(Employee)
Handelsbanken, Edinburgh . . . .(p.1223)
T: 0131 225 1250
E: anfa19@handelsbanken.co.uk

FAIRFIELD, Lesley (Sept 2011) (Partner)
Fairfield Family Law, Whitburn . . . .(p.1180)
T: 01501 643999
E: lesley@fairfieldfamilylaw.co.uk

FAIRGRIEVE, Brian Arthur (Oct 1985) (Partner)
Thorntons Law LLP, Edinburgh . . . .(p.906)
T: 0131 2258705
E: bfairgrieve@thorntons-law.co.uk

FAIRGRIEVE, Elspeth Rosemary (Feb 1995)
(Employee)
Standard Life Assets and Employee Services
Limited, Edinburgh . . . .(p.1234)
T: 0131 2457508
E: elspeth_fairgrieve@thephoenixgroup.com

FAIRGRIEVE, Laura Jane (Oct 2019) (Employee)
Gillespie Macandrew LLP,
Edinburgh . . . .(p.872)
T: 0131 2251677
E: laura.fairgrieve@gillespiemacandrew.co.uk

FAIRGRIEVE, Raymond George (Oct 2008)
(Partner)
MHD Law LLP, Edinburgh . . . .(p.890)
T: 0131 5550616
E: raymond.fairgrieve@mhdlaw.co.uk

FAIRLEY, Cherry Zivia (Apr 2006) (Associate)
Grigor & Young LLP, Elgin. . . . .(p.916)
T: 01343 544077
E: cherry@grigor-young.co.uk

FAIRLEY, Rebecca (Apr 2003) (Employee)
Scottish Power Limited, Glasgow . . . . .(p.1244)
T: 0141 614 3087
E: rebecca.fairley@scottishpower.com

FAIRLEY, Ross (Sept 2016) (Partner)
Burges Salmon LLP, Bristol. . . . .(p.1258)
T: 0117 9392000
E: ross.fairley@burges-salmon.com

FAIRLIE, Andrew Stewart (Jan 2003) (Employee)
Renewable Energy Systems Limited,
Glasgow. . . . .(p.1243)
T: (0141) 4045591
E: andrew.fairlie@res-group.com

FAIRNIE, David John Morris (Dec 1989)
(Director)
Lows Orkney Limited, Kirkwall . . . .(p.1106)
T: 01856 873151
E: David.Fairnie@lowsorkney.co.uk

FAIRWEATHER, Ross Fyfe (Oct 2016) (Associate)
Clyde & Co (Scotland) LLP,
Edinburgh . . . .(p.855)
T: 0131 5571545
E: ross.fairweather@clydeco.com

FAITH, David Louis (Oct 2014) (Employee)
University of Edinburgh, Edinburgh . . .(p.1235)
T: (0131) 651 4330
E: dfaith@exseed.ed.ac.uk

FAITH, Kathryn (Jul 2014) (Employee)
Wheatley Housing Group Limited,
Glasgow. . . . .(p.1246)
T: 0845 9001001
E: Kate.Faith@wheatley-group.com

FALCONER, Alison (Oct 1982) (Employee)
City of Edinburgh Council,
Edinburgh . . . .(p.1221)
T: (0131) 5294145
E: alison.falconer@edinburgh.gov.uk

FALCONER, Anna (Jan 2020) (Solicitor)
NO FIRM

FALCONER, Ashleigh Jayne (Feb 2018)
(Employee)
Culley & McAlpine, Perth . . . .(p.1147)
T: 01738 626644
E: a.falconer@culleymcalpine.co.uk

FALCONER, Craig Stanley (Mar 2008)
(Employee)
Addleshaw Goddard LLP,
Aberdeen. . . . .(p.719)
T: (+44) (0) 1224 96 5410
E: Craig.Falconer@addleshawgoddard.com

FALCONER, Elizabeth Ann (Sept 1985)
(Employee)
Aberdeen City Council, Aberdeen. . . . .(p.1211)
T: 01224 522000
E: efalconer@aberdeencity.gov.uk

FALCONER, Karianne (Oct 2010) (Employee)
MJC LAW, Paisley . . . .(p.1140)
T: 0141 849 2041
E: karianne@mjclaw.co.uk

FALCONER, Keith Diarmid (Sept 1988)
(Partner)
MacPhee & Partners LLP, Fort
William . . . .(p.930)
T: 01397 701000
E: keithfalconer@macphee.co.uk

FALCONER, Neil Beattie Manzie (May 2014)
(Employee)
Thorntons Law LLP, Edinburgh . . . . . .(p.906)
T: 0131 2258705
E: nfalconer@thorntons-law.co.uk

FALCONER, Robin Andrew (Nov 1986)
(Partner)
Falconers, Oldmeldrum . . . .(p.1136)
T: 01651 873962
E: robin@falconerslaw.com

FALCONER, Suzanne Gillian (Sept 2005)
(Employee)
Brunton Miller, Helensburgh . . . .(p.1071)
T: 01436 675454
E: suziefalconer@bruntonmiller.com

FALCUS, Stephanie (Jul 2010) (Employee)
ASCO Group Limited, Aberdeen. . . . . .(p.1212)
T: 01224 580396
E: Stephanie.Falcus@ascoworld.com

FALLAN, Susan (Sept 2012) (Solicitor)
NO FIRM

FALLAS, Robin Kenneth (Jan 2004) (Partner)
MacRoberts LLP, Edinburgh . . . .(p.887)
T: 0131 2295046
E: robin.fallas@macroberts.com

FALLON, Chellsey Margaret Jane (Sept 2021)
(Employee)
Neilsons, Edinburgh . . . .(p.894)
T: 0131 3164444
E: chellseyfallon@neilsons.co.uk

FALLON, Collette Louise (Sept 2011)
(Employee)
Procurator Fiscal Service, Falkirk . . . . . .(p.1236)
T: 0300 020 3000
E: Collette.fallon@copfs.goc.uk

FALLON, Kathleen Ann (Aug 2010) (Associate)
Pinsent Masons LLP, Glasgow . . . .(p.1031)
T: 0141 567 8400
E: Katie.fallon@pinsentmasons.com

FALLON, Mark (Oct 2009) (Employee)
Nelsons Solicitors Falkirk Limited,
Falkirk . . . .(p.923)
T: 01324 613 316
E: Mark@nelsonslawyers.co.uk

FALLS, Daniel Joseph (Sept 1984) (Partner)
D.J. Falls & Co., Uddingston . . . .(p.1177)
T: 01698 810102
E: enquiries@djfalls.co.uk

FALLS, Laura Sian (Mar 2007) (Associate)
Addleshaw Goddard LLP,
Edinburgh . . . .(p.835)
T: 0131 2282400
E: Laura.Falls@addleshawgoddard.com

FAQIR, Shabnam (Nov 2003) (Employee)
City of Edinburgh Council,
Edinburgh . . . .(p.1221)
T: 0131 5294145
E: shabnam.faqir@edinburgh.gov.uk

FAQIR, Tabasam (Oct 2007) (Employee)
Freshfields Bruckhaus Deringer,
Dubai . . . .(p.1278)
E: tabasam.faqir@freshfields.com

FARHAN, Nowsheen (Jan 2015) (Director)
Farhan & Co Solicitors Limited,
Glasgow. . . . .(p.975)
T: 0141 2378787
E: info@farhanlaw.co.uk

FARMER, Emma Janet Suzanne (Sept 2016)
(Employee)
Procurator Fiscal Service, Dundee . . . . .(p.1218)
T: 01382 342559
E: emma.farmer@copfs.gov.uk

FARMER, Georgina Marie (Oct 2010)
(Employee)
Barclays Bank PLC, London E14 . . . . . .(p.1262)
T: 0207 116 1000
E: georgina.farmer@barclays.com

FARMER, Steven Thomas (Aug 2012) (Director)
Road Traffic Law.com Limited,
Glasgow. . . . .(p.1035)
T: 0141 2214645
E: sf@roadtrafficlaw.com

FAROOQ, Miriam (Sept 2021) (Employee)
BTO Solicitors LLP, Glasgow . . . .(p.952)
T: 0141 2218012
E: mfa@bto.co.uk

FARQUHAR, Andrew Brian (Sept 2009)
(Employee)
Trustpilot A/S, Copenhagen . . . .(p.1257)
T: (+45) 31 676988
E: afa@trustpilot.com

FARQUHAR, Bruce (Sept 1996) (Partner)
Anderson Strathern LLP, Edinburgh . . . .(p.839)
T: 0131 2707700
E: bruce.farquhar@andersonstrathern.co.uk

FARQUHAR, Gavin Blair (Aug 1985) (Partner)
Pinsent Masons LLP, Edinburgh . . . . . .(p.895)
T: 0131 7777000
E: gavin.farquhar@pinsentmasons.com

FARQUHAR, Lauren Ruth (Apr 2018)
(Employee)
Wright, Johnston & Mackenzie LLP,
Inverness . . . .(p.1083)
T: 01463 234445
E: lrf@wjm.co.uk

FARQUHAR, Peter James (Dec 1980)
(Employee)
Falkirk Council, Falkirk . . . .(p.1236)
T: 01324 506070
E: peter.farquhar@falkirk.gov.uk

FARQUHAR, Peter James (May 1981)
(Employee)
Guild Homes (Tayside) Ltd, Forfar . . . .(p.1237)
T: 01307 460011
E: p.farquhar@guild-homes.co.uk

FARQUHAR, Richard Alexander (Jan 2006)
(Employee)
Shepherd and Wedderburn LLP,
Edinburgh . . . .(p.900)
T: 0131 2289900
E: Richard.Farquhar@shepwedd.com

FARQUHARSON-BLACK, Elaine (Dec 1990)
(Partner)
Brodies LLP, Edinburgh . . . .(p.845)
T: 0131 2283777
E: efb@brodies.com

FARR, Sarah (Aug 2005) (Partner)
Ferguson, MacSween & Stewart,
Portree. . . . .(p.1156)
T: 01478 612991
E: sarah@fmslaw.co.uk

FARRELL, Angela Jane (Dec 1999) (Employee)
Procurator Fiscal Service,
Edinburgh . . . .(p.1229)
T: (0844) 561 3268
E: angela.farrell@copfs.gov.uk

FARRELL, Ashleigh (Jun 2008) (Associate)
DWF LLP, Glasgow . . . .(p.973)
T: 0141 228 8000
E: Ashleigh.Farrell@dwf.law

FARRELL, Christopher William (May 2013)
(Employee)
Procurator Fiscal Service, Glasgow . . . .(p.1241)
T: 0300 0203000
E: christopher.farrell1@copfs.gov.uk

FARRELL, Frances Peel (Oct 1984) (Employee)
Peter G. Farrell, Glasgow . . . .(p.975)
T: 0141 5520033
E: marshall5780@yahoo.co.uk

FARRELL, Joanne Lynsey (Nov 2003) (Associate)
Weightmans (Scotland) LLP,
Glasgow. . . . .(p.1051)
T: 0345 073 9900
E: joanne.farrell@weightmans.com

FARRELL, Justin Edward (Apr 1997) (Employee)
Procurator Fiscal Service, Hamilton . . . .(p.1247)
T: 0844 5613245
E: justin.farrell@copfs.gov.uk

FARRELL, Karen (Mar 2016) (Employee)
Dentons UK and Middle East LLP,
Glasgow. . . . .(p.968)
T: 0330 2220050
E: karen.farrell@dentons.com

FARRELL, Matthew (Feb 2006) (Partner)
Brodies LLP, Glasgow . . . .(p.948)
T: 0141 2484672
E: matthew.farrell@brodies.com

FARRELL, Neil Robert (Dec 1990) (Partner)
Anderson Strathern LLP, Edinburgh . . . .(p.839)
T: 0131 2707700
E: neil.farrell@andersonstrathern.co.uk

FARRELL, Peter Gerard (Dec 1981) (Partner)
Peter G. Farrell, Glasgow . . . .(p.975)
T: 0141 5520033
E: paton.farrell@btconnect.com

FARRELL, Raymond (Oct 1995) (Employee)
Glasgow City Council, Glasgow . . . . . .(p.1239)
T: 0141 2875057
E: raymond.farrell@ced.glasgow.gov.uk

FARRELL, Stephanie Elizabeth (Nov 2009)
(Associate)
Bellwether Green Limited, Glasgow . . . .(p.944)
T: 0141 2184900
E: stephanie.farrell@bellwethergreen.com

FARRELL, Stephen James (Sept 2010)
(Employee)
Burness Paull LLP, Edinburgh . . . .(p.850)
T: 0131 4736000
E: stephen.farrell@burnesspaull.com

FARRER, Simone (Aug 2021) (Employee)
Mourant Ozannes, St Helier . . . .(p.1274)
T: 1481731513
E: simone.farrer@mourant.com

FARRIER, Rachel Helen (Nov 2020) (Employee)
Baker Gostelow Law Limited,
Hamilton . . . .(p.1065)
T: 01698 820 700
E: rachel@bgfamilylaw.co.uk

FAST, Dixcee Rae (Aug 2008) (Employee)
Eversheds Sutherland (International) LLP,
Edinburgh . . . .(p.869)
T: 0131 476 8379
E: dixceefast@eversheds-Sutherland.com

FAULDS, Catherine Lindsay (Oct 2008)
(Employee)
Arthur J Gallagher, Glasgow. . . . .(p.1237)
T: 0141 285 3056
E: kate_faulds@ajg.com

FAULDS, Euan Allan (Oct 2006) (Consultant)
Bellwether Green Limited, Glasgow . . . .(p.944)
T: 0141 2184900
E: euan.faulds@bellwethergreen.com

FAULKINER, Scott Charles (Nov 2004)
(Employee)
Scottish Power Limited, Glasgow . . . . .(p.1244)
T: 0141 6140000
E: scott.faulkiner@scottishpower.com

FAURE, Stuart John (Aug 2014) (Employee)
Procurator Fiscal Service, Glasgow . . . .(p.1241)
T: 0300 0203000
E: Stuart.Faure@copfs.gov.uk

FAY, Alasdair Graham Hood (Oct 2006)
(Employee)
Procurator Fiscal Service,
Edinburgh . . . .(p.1227)
T: 0845 606 6212
E: alasdair.fay@copfs.gov.uk

FECSKOVICS, Fanny S ra (Sept 2018)
(Employee)
CMS Cameron McKenna Nabarro Olswang LLP,
Edinburgh . . . .(p.856)
T: 0131 2288000
E: fanny.fecskovics@cms-cmno.com

FEECHAN, Catherine Mary (Oct 1993) (Partner)
Davidson Chalmers Stewart LLP,
Glasgow. . . . .(p.967)
T: 0141 4283258
E: catherine.feechan@dcslegal.com

FEENEY, Gregor (Oct 2017) (Employee)
Ferguson & Company, Stranraer . . . . .(p.1171)
T: 01776 702561
E: gregor@ferguson-company.co.uk

FEENEY, Paul (May 1993) (Partner)
Ferguson & Company, Stranraer . . . . .(p.1171)
T: 01776 702561
E: pfeeney@ferguson-company.co.uk

FEENEY, Sarah Louise Helen (Jan 2008)
(Employee)
Gilson Gray LLP, Glasgow . . . .(p.980)
T: 0141 5302021
E: sfeeney@gilsongray.co.uk

FEHILLY, Christopher Mark (Oct 2005)
(Employee)
John Pryde, SSC, Edinburgh. . . . .(p.897)
T: 0131 2202160
E: chris@johnpryde.co.uk

FEKETE, Ir n (Apr 2021) (Employee)
Jain, Neil & Ruddy, Glasgow . . . .(p.992)
T: 0141 9504672
E: iren@jnrsolicitors.com

FELL, Laura Jane (Nov 2010) (Employee)
Brodies LLP, Edinburgh . . . .(p.845)
T: 0131 228 3777
E: laura.fell@brodies.com

FELL, Steven James (Oct 1994) (Director)
Malcolm, Jack & Matheson Limited,
Dunfermline . . . .(p.824)
T: 01383 723444
E: steven@malcolmjack.co.uk

FELLOWS, Deborah (Nov 2000) (Partner)
Thorntons Law LLP, Dundee . . . .(p.819)
T: 01382 229 111
E: dfellows@thorntons-law.co.uk

FELTHAM, Stephen Graham (Dec 2001)
(Employee)
Scottish Government's Parliamentary Counsel
Office, Edinburgh . . . .(p.1233)
T: 0131 244 0598
E: stephen.feltham@gov.scot

FENDER-ALLISON, Jane Elizabeth (Feb 2008)
(Associate)
CMS Cameron McKenna Nabarro Olswang LLP,
Glasgow. . . . .(p.962)
T: 0141 2222200
E: Jane.Fender-Allison@cms-cmno.com

FENN, Daniel Colin (Nov 2006) (Employee)
Scottish Criminal Cases Review Commission,
Glasgow. . . . .(p.1243)
T: 0141 2707030
E: dfenn@sccrc.org.uk

FENTON, Trevor Earl (Jan 2015) (Director)
Plain English Law Limited, Dundee . . . . .(p.817)
T: 01382 848458
E: tfenton@plainenglish.law

FERGUSON, Aimee Alice Rebecca (Dec 2012)
(Employee)
Optical Express Limited
E: aimeewatson@opticalexpress.com

FERGUSON, Amy Louise (Sept 2011)
(Employee)
Burges Salmon LLP, Edinburgh . . . .(p.850)
T: 0131 3142112
E: amy.ferguson@burges-salmon.com

FERGUSON, Carole Anne (Jan 2009) (Director)
Ferguson Legal Limited, Banchory . . . . .(p.768)
T: 07917 848453
E: carole@fergusonlegal.co.uk

FERGUSON, Cheryl Anne (Nov 2019)
(Employee)
Scottish Courts and Tribunals Service,
Edinburgh . . . .(p.1230)
T: 0131 2252525
E: cferguson2@scotcourts.gov.uk

FERGUSON, Claire Louise (May 2016)
(Employee)
Stirling Council, Stirling. . . . .(p.1255)
T: 01786 233065
E: fergusonc@stirling.gov.uk

FERGUSON, Colin (Aug 2007) (Director)
Gildeas Limited, Glasgow . . . .(p.979)
T: 0141 331 6071
E: cferguson@gildeas.net

FERGUSON, Edward (Oct 2017) (Employee)
MacRoberts LLP, Glasgow . . . .(p.1015)
T: 0141 3031100
E: edward.ferguson@macroberts.com

FERGUSON, Garry William (Sept 1993)
(Partner)
BTO Solicitors LLP, Glasgow . . . .(p.952)
T: 0141 2218012
E: gfe@bto.co.uk

FERGUSON, Helen Gilmour (Sept 1989)
(Partner)
Campbell Smith LLP, Edinburgh . . . .(p.852)
T: 0131 5563737
E: helen.ferguson@camsmith.co.uk

FERGUSON, Ian Cameron (Dec 1978) (Director)
Mitchells Roberton Ltd, Glasgow . . . . .(p.1020)
T: 0141 5523422
E: Ian@mitchells-roberton.co.uk

FERGUSON, James Alexander (Oct 2016)
(Employee)
Pinsent Masons LLP, Edinburgh . . . .(p.895)
T: 0131 777 7000
E: James.Ferguson@pinsentmasons.com

FERGUSON, Jane Margaret Wilson
(Nov 1990) (Partner)
R & R Urquhart LLP, Forres . . . .(p.929)
T: 01309 672216
E: janeferguson@r-r-urquhart.com

FERGUSON, Jasmine (Mar 2021) (Employee)
MooreMarshall Limited, Falkirk . . . .(p.923)
  T: 01324 614020
  E: jasmine.ferguson@mooremarshall.co.uk

FERGUSON, Joanne Elizabeth (Jul 2014)
(Employee)
Derek Mackenzie & Company Limited,
  Stornoway . . . .(p.1170)
  T: 01851 702211
  E: joanne@derek-mackenzie.com

FERGUSON, Justine Ann (Sept 1997)
(Employee)
National Westminster Bank PLC,
  Edinburgh . . . .(p.1227)
  T: 0131 6264100
  E: justine.ferguson@rbs.co.uk

FERGUSON, Kenneth Francis (Aug 1985)
(Partner)
Ferguson and Wilson, Inverness . . . . . .(p.1076)
  T: 01463 222221
  E: enquiries@fergusonandwilson.co.uk

FERGUSON, Kirsten Annette (Sept 2003)
(Employee)
Scottish Children's Reporter Administration,
  Dumbarton . . . .(p.1217)
  T: 01389 764268

FERGUSON, Linsey Rachel (Sept 2007) (Partner)
Drummond Miller LLP,
  Musselburgh . . . .(p.1129)
  T: 0131 6657393
  E: lferguson@drummondmiller.co.uk

FERGUSON, Lorna Roseanne (Nov 2005)
(Associate)
Berrymans Lace Mawer LLP,
  Glasgow . . . .(p.945)
  T: 0141 3532121
  E: Lorna.Ferguson@blmlaw.com

FERGUSON, Martin (Oct 1991) (Partner)
Ferguson Whyte, Glasgow . . . .(p.975)
  T: 0141 3398432
  E: mf@fergusonwhyte.co.uk

FERGUSON, Morag (Nov 1990) (Employee)
East Lothian Council, Haddington . . . .(p.1246)
  T: 01620 827827
  E: mferguson@eastlothian.gov.uk

FERGUSON, Peter Joseph (May 1994) (Partner)
Harper Macleod LLP, Glasgow . . . .(p.983)
  T: 0141 2218888
  E: peter.ferguson@harpermacleod.co.uk

FERGUSON, Raymond (Jan 1991) (Employee)
Scottish Legal Aid Board,
  Edinburgh . . . .(p.1233)
  T: 0131 2267061
  E: fergusonra@slab.org.uk

FERGUSON, Ross Graham (Oct 2021)
(Employee)
DWF LLP, Glasgow . . . .(p.973)
  T: 0141 228 8000
  E: ross.ferguson@dwf.law

FERGUSON, Ruaraidh (Aug 2015) (Employee)
Procurator Fiscal Service, Glasgow . . . .(p.1241)
  T: 0300 0203000
  E: Ruaraidh.Ferguson@copfs.gov.uk

FERGUSON, Shirley Elizabeth (Jun 1984)
(Employee)
Scottish Government, Edinburgh . . . . .(p.1231)
  T: 0131 244 0574
  E: shirley.ferguson@gov.scot

FERGUSON, Stephen Douglas (Oct 2008)
(Employee)
Procurator Fiscal Service,
  Edinburgh . . . .(p.1229)
  T: 0300 0203000
  E: stephen.ferguson@copfs.gov.uk

FERGUSON, Struan Alexander (May 2012)
(Partner)
Blackwood & Smith LLP, Peebles . . . . .(p.1143)
  T: 01721 720131
  E: struan@blackwoodsmith.com

FERGUSON, Thomas Millar (Mar 2013)
(Employee)
Russell-Cooke LLP, London WC1 . . . . .(p.1268)
  T: 0207 4056566
  E: thomas.ferguson@russell-cooke.co.uk

FERGUSON, Victoria (Oct 2020) (Employee)
Procurator Fiscal Service, Glasgow . . . .(p.1242)
  T: (0300) 020 3000
  E: victoria.ferguson@copfs.gov.uk

FERGUSON-SNEDDEN, Susan Elizabeth
(Jun 2003) (Employee)
Historic Environment Scotland,
  Edinburgh . . . .(p.1223)
  T: 0131 6688987
  E: susan.ferguson-snedden@hes.scot

FERGUSON-WALKER, Carole Barbra
(Jun 2001) (Employee)
Registers of Scotland, Edinburgh . . . . .(p.1230)
  T: 131659611
  E: carole.ferguson-walker@ros.gov.uk

FERGUSSON, Hannah Margaret (Aug 2021)
(Employee)
Brodies LLP, Edinburgh . . . .(p.845)
  T: 0131 2283777
  E: hannah.fergusson@brodies.com

FERN, Emma Lorn (Oct 2014) (Employee)
Balfour Beatty Regional Civil Engineering,
  Motherwell . . . .(p.1251)
  T: 01698 647 500
  E: Emma.Fern@balfourbeatty.com

FERN, Isla Alexandra McIntosh (Oct 2018)
(Employee)
Brodies LLP, Glasgow . . . .(p.948)
T: 0141 2484672
E: isla.fern@brodies.com

FERRIE, Audrey Jane (Sept 1979) (Employee)
Pinsent Masons LLP, Glasgow . . . .(p.1031)
T: 0141 567 8400
E: audrey.ferrie@pinsentmasons.com

FERRIE, John James (Aug 1999) (Consultant)
Bruce, Short & Co., Dundee . . . .(p.806)
T: 01382 223400

FERRIE, Michael John (Feb 2003) (Partner)
Mike Ferrie Solicitor, Dundee . . . .(p.810)
T: 01382 523977
E: mikeferrie@outlook.com

FERRIE, Michael Joseph (Dec 1991) (Employee)
STV Television Limited, Glasgow . . . . . .(p.1245)
T: 0141 3003000
E: michael.ferrie@stv.tv

FERRIE, Paul Steven (Jan 2015) (Associate)
Fulton's, Glasgow . . . .(p.1010)
T: 0141 6322248
E: pferrie@fultonslaw.co.uk

FERRIE, William (Nov 1988) (Employee)
Scottish Government's Parliamentary Counsel
Office, Edinburgh . . . .(p.1233)
T: 0131 244 1668
E: willie.ferrie@gov.scot

FERRIER, Scott David (Oct 2003) (Associate)
DLA Piper Scotland LLP, Edinburgh . . . .(p.863)
T: 0207 3490296
E: scott.ferrier@dlapiper.com

FERRIER, Thomas Neil (Aug 1984) (Partner)
Pinsent Masons LLP, Glasgow . . . .(p.1031)
T: 0141 567 8400
E: tom.ferrier@pinsentmasons.com

FERRY, Noel Francis (Sept 1996) (Partner)
Weightmans (Scotland) LLP,
Glasgow. . . . .(p.1051)
T: 0345 073 9900
E: noel.ferry@weightmans.com

FETTES, Lauren Jane Marr (Jul 2012)
(Employee)
Thorntons Law LLP, Edinburgh . . . .(p.906)
T: 0131 2258705
E: lfettes@thorntons-law.co.uk

FETTES, Lindsey Mary (May 1982) (Partner)
Wilsone & Duffus, Aberdeen . . . .(p.746)
T: 01224 651700
E: lindsey.fettes@wilsoneduffus.co.uk

FIELDING, Douglas Harvey (Nov 1971)
(Consultant)
Fielding, McLean & Co., Glasgow . . . . .(p.975)
T: 0141 9591674
E: douglas.fielding@fieldingmclean.co.uk

FIELDING, Nicola Anne (Aug 2011) (Partner)
Fielding, McLean & Co., Glasgow . . . . .(p.975)
T: 0141 9591674
E: nicola.fielding@fieldingmclean.co.uk

FIELDING, Ross Douglas (Nov 2006) (Partner)
Fielding, McLean & Co., Glasgow . . . . .(p.975)
T: 0141 9591674
E: ross.fielding@fieldingmclean.co.uk

FIFE, Calum Andrew (Aug 2005) (Partner)
Keoghs Scotland LLP, Glasgow. . . . .(p.996)
T: 0141 2380100
E: CFife@keoghs.co.uk

FIFE, Robert Allan (Oct 1998) (Director)
Simpson & Marwick, Edinburgh . . . .(p.903)
T: 0131 581 5717
E: bobby.fife@simpsonmarwick.com

FILMER, Benjamin Philip Thomas (Oct 2016)
(Employee)
Freeths LLP, Oxford . . . .(p.1271)
E: ben.filmer@freeths.co.uk

FINCH, Emma Christina (Jan 2018) (Employee)
TLT LLP, Glasgow . . . .(p.1048)
T: 0333 006 0400
E: emma.finch@tltsolicitors.com

FINDLAY, David (May 2005) (Employee)
Crofting Commission, Inverness . . . . . .(p.1248)
T: 0143 663 430
E: David.Findlay@crofting.scotland.gov.uk

FINDLAY, Diane (Jul 2011) (Employee)
Hingston's Law Limited, Aberdeen . . . . .(p.732)
T: 01224 562300
E: diane@hingstonslaw.co.uk

FINDLAY, Donald Fraser (Nov 1995)
(Employee)
Burness Paull LLP, Edinburgh . . . .(p.850)
T: 0131 4736000
E: donald.findlay@burnesspaull.com

FINDLAY, Eilidh Grant (Mar 2012) (Employee)
Brodies LLP, Edinburgh . . . .(p.845)
T: 0131 2283777
E: eilidh.findlay@brodies.com

FINDLAY, Emma Louise (Sept 2011) (Employee)
Orkney Islands Council, Kirkwall . . . . . .(p.1250)
T: 01856 873535
E: Emma.Findlay@orkney.gov.uk

FINDLAY, Henry Douglas Wyllie (Feb 1993)
(Employee)
Procurator Fiscal Service, Glasgow . . . .(p.1241)
T: 0300 0200669
E: harry.findlay@copfs.gov.uk

FINDLAY, John (Nov 2000) (Employee)
Stork Technical Services UK Limited,
Dyce . . . .(p.1219)
T: 01224 722888
E: john.findlay@stork.com

FINDLAY, Jonathan (Aug 1997) (Associate)
John Jackson & Dick Limited,
Hamilton . . . .(p.1067)
T: 01698 281747
E: jfindlay@jacksondicklaw.com

FINDLAY, Linda Kathleen (Oct 2004) (Partner)
Penmans, Glasgow . . . .(p.1031)
T: 0141 3366646
E: lindafindlay@penmanslawyers.co.uk

FINGLAND, Fiona Iona Heather (Mar 2021)
(Employee)
Pinsent Masons LLP, Edinburgh . . . .(p.895)
T: 0131 777 7000
E: fiona.fingland@pinsentmasons.com

FINLAY, Bronagh Ann (Sept 2018) (Employee)
Clyde & Co (Scotland) LLP,
Edinburgh . . . .(p.855)
T: 0131 5571545
E: bronagh.finlay@clydeco.com

FINLAY, Frances Isabel (Sept 2003) (Employee)
Scottish Police Authority, Police Scotland,
Dundee . . . .(p.1218)
T: 0300 1112222
E: Frances.Finlay@scotland.pnn.police.uk

FINLAY, George Henry (Jan 2021) (Employee)
Sidley Austin LLP, London EC3 . . . .(p.1268)
T: 2073602040

FINLAY, Lauren (Oct 2013) (Employee)
Shepherd and Wedderburn LLP,
Edinburgh . . . .(p.900)
T: 0131 2289900
E: lauren.finlay@shepwedd.com

FINLAY, Mark Ernest (Nov 1986) (Employee)
Brodies LLP, Edinburgh . . . .(p.845)
T: 0131 2283777
E: mark.finlay@brodies.com

FINLAY, Theo William (Dec 1984) (Partner)
GFM Law, Dundee . . . .(p.811)
T: 01382 223505
E: theo@gfmlaw.co.uk

FINLAY, Yvonne (Jan 2011) (Employee)
Moir and Sweeney LLP, Glasgow . . . . .(p.1021)
T: 0141 4292724
E: yvonne@moirandsweeney.com

FINLAYSON, Bryan George (Oct 1998)
(Director)
Curle Stewart Limited, Glasgow . . . .(p.964)
T: 0141 227 6200
E: bf@curlestewart.co.uk

FINLAYSON, Joanne (Feb 2021) (Employee)
Harper Macleod LLP, Glasgow . . . .(p.983)
T: 0141 227 9395
E: Joanne.Finlayson@harpermacleod.co.uk

FINLAYSON, Lesley Michelle (Sept 2017)
(Employee)
Pinsent Masons LLP, Glasgow . . . .(p.1031)
T: 0141 567 8400
E: lesley.finlayson@pinsentmasons.com

FINLAYSON, Lorna Helen (Feb 1990) (Partner)
Addleshaw Goddard LLP,
Edinburgh . . . .(p.835)
T: 0131 2282400
E: Lorna.Finlayson@addleshawgoddard.com

FINLAYSON, Neil Kerr (Feb 1987) (Partner)
Andersonbain LLP, Edinburgh . . . .(p.839)
T: 0131 2282000
E: nfinlayson@andersonbain.co.uk

FINLAYSON, William Alexander (Jan 1981)
(Partner)
Finlaysons, Kilwinning . . . .(p.1097)
T: 01294 551151
E: William.Finlayson@finlaysonslawyers.co.uk

FINNIE, Donna Elaine (Nov 2018) (Employee)
MacRae Stephen & Co.,
Fraserburgh . . . .(p.931)
T: 01346 514545
E: donna@macraestephen.co.uk

FINNIE, Kenneth Scott (Jul 1989) (Director)
Duffy Toshner & Co Limited,
Cambuslang . . . .(p.782)
T: 0141 641 8081
E: kenny@duffytoshner.co.uk

FINNIE, Matthew Kenneth (Nov 2019)
(Employee)
Addleshaw Goddard LLP,
Edinburgh . . . .(p.835)
T: 0131 2282400
E: matthew.finnie@addleshawgoddard.com

FINNIESTON, Colette Marie (Oct 2004)
(Associate)
Clyde & Co (Scotland) LLP,
Edinburgh . . . .(p.855)
T: 0131 5571545
E: Colette.Finnieston@clydeco.com

FINNIGAN, Laura Elizabeth (Jul 2021)
(Employee)
Nellany & Company LLP, Saltcoats . . . .(p.1160)
T: 01294 464175
E: laura@nellanysols.co.uk

FISH, Sian Marie (Oct 2019) (Employee)
George Mathers & Co, Aberdeen . . . . . .(p.737)
T: 01224 588599
E: s.fish@georgemathers.co.uk

FISHER, Florence Catherine (Apr 2013)
(Employee)
BBM Solicitors Limited, Wick . . . .(p.1180)
T: 01955 604188
E: fcf@bbmsolicitors.co.uk

FISHER, Graham Robert (Dec 1999) (Employee)
Scottish Government, Edinburgh . . . . . (p.1231)
T: 0131 244 0815
E: Graham.Fisher@gov.scot

FISHER, Julie (Oct 2004) (Associate)
Plexus Law LLP, Edinburgh . . . . (p.897)
T: 0344 2454802
E: julie.fisher@plexuslaw.co.uk

FISHER, Louise (Sept 2004) (Employee)
Baxendale Employee Ownership Limited, London
SE1 . . . . (p.1262)
T: 020 3598 9982
E: louise.fisher@baxendale.co.uk

FISHER, Malcolm Hugh (Nov 2006) (Associate)
Addleshaw Goddard LLP, Glasgow . . . . . (p.938)
T: 0141 2212300
E: Calum.Fisher@addleshawgoddard.com

FISHER, Rachel Anne (Aug 2016) (Associate)
Addleshaw Goddard LLP,
Edinburgh . . . . (p.835)
T: 0131 2282400
E: Rachel.Fisher@addleshawgoddard.com

FISKEN, David McNicol (Aug 2005) (Partner)
Murphy, Robb + Sutherland,
Glasgow. . . . . (p.1025)
T: 0141 4182931
E: df@murphyrobbsutherland.co.uk

FISKEN, Graham (Aug 2016) (Employee)
Turcan Connell, Edinburgh . . . . (p.908)
T: 0131 2288111

FITZGERALD, Alison Louise (Nov 1991)
(Partner)
Miller Hendry, Dundee . . . . (p.816)
T: 01382 200000
E: alisonfitzgerald@millerhendry.co.uk

FITZGERALD, Caitlin Rebecca (Sept 2019)
(Employee)
Government Legal Department, London
SW1 . . . . (p.1264)
T: 0207 4495952
E: Caitlin.Fitzgerald@governmentlegal.gov.uk

FITZGERALD, Chloe Ellen (Sept 2012)
(Employee)
Brodies LLP, Aberdeen. . . . . (p.723)
T: 01224 392242
E: chloe.fitzgerald@brodies.com

FITZGERALD, Edward (Sept 2021) (Employee)
Gilson Gray LLP, Edinburgh . . . . (p.874)
T: 0131 5165354
E: efitzgerald@gilsongray.co.uk

FITZGERALD, Lesley Alexander (Oct 1989)
(Associate)
Anderson Strathern LLP, Edinburgh . . . . (p.839)
T: 0131 2707700
E: lesley.fitzgerald@andersonstrathern.co.uk

FITZGERALD, Michael Philip (Oct 1989)
(Solicitor)
NO FIRM

FITZGERALD, Dr, Sharon Lesley (Mar 1999)
(Partner)
DLA Piper Scotland LLP, Edinburgh . . . . (p.863)
T: 08700 111111
E: sharon.fitzgerald@dlapiper.com

FITZGIBBON, Eilidh Ann (Feb 2015) (Employee)
CMS Cameron McKenna Nabarro Olswang LLP,
Glasgow. (p.962)
T: 0141 2222200
E: eilidh.fitzgibbon@cms-cmno.com

FITZGIBBON, Hannah Louise (Oct 2014)
(Employee)
Stuart & Stuart, Edinburgh . . . . (p.905)
T: 0131 2286449
E: hfitzgibbon@stuartandstuart.co.uk

FITZGIBBON, Joseph Maurice Patrick
(Oct 2014) (Employee)
Shepherd and Wedderburn LLP,
Glasgow. . . . . (p.1039)
T: 0141 5669900
E: joseph.fitzgibbon@shepwedd.com

FITZPATRICK, Andrew (Oct 1990) (Partner)
The MFY Partnership, Airdrie . . . . (p.751)
T: 01236 607180
E: andrew@mfypartnership.co.uk

FITZPATRICK, Brian James (Dec 1978) (Partner)
Fitzpatrick & Co., Glasgow . . . . (p.976)
T: 0141 2042200
E: bf@fitzpatrickandco.co.uk

FITZPATRICK, David (May 2016) (Employee)
Peters & Peters Solicitors LLP, London
EC4 . . . . (p.1267)
T: 020 7822 7777
E: dfitzpatrick@petersandpeters.com

FITZPATRICK, David Bernard John
(Jan 1980) (Partner)
Fitzpatrick & Co., Glasgow . . . . (p.976)
T: 0141 2042200
E: df@fitzpatrickandco.co.uk

FITZPATRICK, David James (Sept 2012)
(Employee)
Scottish Criminal Cases Review Commission,
Glasgow. . . . . (p.1243)
T: 0141 2707030
E: dfitzpatrick@sccrc.org.uk

FITZPATRICK, Jonathan Scott McGlade
(Sept 1998) (Employee)
Gneiss Energy Limited, London W1 . . . (p.1264)
E: jon.fitzpatrick@gneissenergy.com

FITZPATRICK, Kathryn Margaret (Mar 2014)
(Employee)
Shepherd and Wedderburn LLP,
Edinburgh . . . . (p.900)
T: 0131 2289900
E: katy.fitzpatrick@shepwedd.com

FITZPATRICK, Kieran Gerard (Jul 1994)
(Partner)
MHD Law LLP, Edinburgh . . . . (p.890)
T: 0131 5550616
E: kieran.fitzpatrick@mhdlaw.co.uk

FITZPATRICK, Laura Jane (Jun 2018) (Employee)
Burness Paull LLP, Glasgow . . . . (p.954)
T: 0141 2484933
E: laura.fitzpatrick@burnesspaull.com

FITZPATRICK, Louisa Margaret (Dec 2004)
(Employee)
CBRE Ltd, Sydney . . . . (p.1257)

FITZPATRICK, Peter (Nov 1976) (Partner)
Ruthven, Keenan, Pollock & Co.,
Glasgow . . . . (p.1038)
T: 0141 9542901
E: peter@rkpsolicitors.co.uk

FITZPATRICK, Poppy Catherine (Nov 2020)
(Employee)
Finnieston Franchi & McWilliams,
Glasgow . . . . (p.976)
T: 0141 2263000
E: poppy@ffmcw.co.uk

FITZPATRICK, Richard (Sept 1976) (Partner)
Fitzpatrick & Co., Glasgow . . . . (p.976)
T: 0141 2042200
E: rf@fitzpatrickandco.co.uk

FITZPATRICK, Robert (Aug 1984) (Director)
Carr & Co (Solicitors) Limited,
Glasgow . . . . (p.957)
T: 0141 7794466
E: rf@theglasgowlawpractice.co.uk

FITZPATRICK, Stephen James (Jan 2019)
(Employee)
CMS Cameron McKenna Nabarro Olswang LLP,
Edinburgh . . . . (p.856)
T: 0131 2288000
E: stephen.fitzpatrick@cms-cmno.com

FITZSIMMONS, Eleanor Frances (Jun 2005)
(Employee)
Macallans Limited, Glasgow . . . . (p.1005)
T: 0141 6131787/6474441
E: EF@macallans.co.uk

FITZSIMMONS, Stuart Thomas (Dec 2004)
(Partner)
Dentons UK and Middle East LLP,
Glasgow . . . . (p.968)
T: 0330 2220050
E: Stuart.Fitzsimmons@dentons.com

FLAHERTY, Lisa (Aug 2020) (Employee)
Anderson Strathern LLP, Edinburgh . . . . (p.839)
T: 0131 2707700
E: Lisa.Flaherty@andersonstrathern.co.uk

FLANAGAN, Ashley Kim (Apr 2012) (Employee)
Burness Paull LLP, Glasgow . . . . (p.954)
T: 0141 2484933
E: ashley.flanagan@burnesspaull.com

FLANAGAN, John Gerard (Oct 2009) (Partner)
Flanagan & Co, Glasgow . . . . (p.976)
T: 0141 334 7686
E: johngflanagan1@yahoo.co.uk

FLANAGAN, Sean Paul (Jul 1990) (Partner)
S.P. Flanagan, Bishopbriggs . . . . (p.774)
T: 0141 5630553
E: seanpflanagan@hotmail.com

FLANIGAN, Deirdre Christine (Apr 2016)
(Employee)
Thompsons, Glasgow . . . . (p.1046)
T: 0141 2218840
E: Deirdre.Flanigan@thompsons-scotland.co.uk

FLANNIGAN, Scott Charles (Sept 2011)
(Associate)
Anderson Strathern LLP, Edinburgh . . . . (p.839)
T: 0131 2707700
E: scott.flannigan@andersonstrathern.co.uk

FLECHER-HERD, Paul (Jan 2020) (Employee)
Andersonbain LLP, Aberdeen . . . . (p.721)
T: 01224 456789
E: pfh@andersonbain.co.uk

FLEETWOOD, Andrew Beathan (Oct 2002)
(Partner)
Andrew Fleetwood, Dundee . . . . (p.804)
T: 07801 581765
E: andrew@fleetwoodlegal.com

FLEMING, Alasdair Robin (Dec 2002)
(Associate)
Brodies LLP, Edinburgh . . . . (p.845)
T: 0131 2283777
E: alasdair.robin.fleming@brodies.com

FLEMING, Andrew James Graham
(Feb 2011) (Associate)
Pinsent Masons LLP, Edinburgh . . . . . . (p.895)
T: 0131 7777000
E: andrew.fleming@pinsentmasons.com

FLEMING, Catherine Fiona Downie
(Oct 1980) (Employee)
Mitchells Roberton Ltd, Glasgow . . . . . (p.1020)
T: 0141 5523422
E: fionaf@mitchells-roberton.co.uk

FLEMING, Charlotte Alexandra (Jul 2020)
(Employee)
BTO Solicitors LLP, Glasgow . . . . (p.952)
T: 0141 2218012

FLEMING, Charlotte Mary Todd (Dec 1991)
(Employee)
City of Edinburgh Council,
Edinburgh . . . .(p.1221)
T: (0131) 5294145
E: charlotte.fleming@edinburgh.gov.uk

FLEMING, Christopher James (Dec 2016)
(Director)
Flemings Legal Services Limited,
Edinburgh . . . .(p.871)
T: 0131 473 2343
E: christopher.fleming@flemingslegal.co.uk

FLEMING, Darren (Jun 2016) (Employee)
Livingstone Brown Limited,
Glasgow. . . . .(p.1004)
T: 0141 7789657
E: darren.fleming@livbrown.co.uk

FLEMING, David Alan (Jul 2011) (Partner)
Carruthers, Curdie, Sturrock & Co.,
Kilmarnock . . . .(p.1094)
T: 01563 572727
E:
davidfleming@carrutherscurdiesturrock.co.uk

FLEMING, Deborah Anne (Jul 2012) (Partner)
KW Law, Livingston . . . .(p.1119)
T: 01506 415333
E: debbief@kwlaw.co.uk

FLEMING, Elizabeth Alice Stewart
(Aug 2013) (Employee)
Wright, Johnston & Mackenzie LLP,
Glasgow. . . . .(p.1054)
T: 0141 2483434
E: basf@wjm.co.uk

FLEMING, Euan Kenneth James (Nov 2006)
(Partner)
Gilson Gray LLP, Edinburgh . . . .(p.874)
T: 0131 5165354
E: efleming@gilsongray.co.uk

FLEMING, Fiona Ross (Jul 1987) (Partner)
Blackwood & Smith LLP, Peebles . . . . .(p.1143)
T: 01721 723312
E: fiona@blackwoodsmith.com

FLEMING, Gillian Margaret (Sept 2013)
(Employee)
The Children's Investment Fund Foundation
(UK), London W1 . . . .(p.1268)
E: GFleming@ciff.org

FLEMING, Kate (Aug 2004) (Employee)
Procurator Fiscal Service,
Edinburgh . . . .(p.1229)
T: 0844 561 3268
E: Kate.Fleming@copfs.gov.uk

FLEMING, Katie Louise (May 2021) (Employee)
CMS Cameron McKenna Nabarro Olswang LLP,
Aberdeen . . . .(p.727)
T: 01224 622002
E: katie.fleming@cms-cmno.com

FLEMING, Kirsten (Dec 2014) (Employee)
Addleshaw Goddard LLP,
Edinburgh . . . .(p.835)
T: 0131 2282400
E: Kirsten.Fleming@addleshawgoddard.com

FLEMING, Sandra Margaret (Oct 1988)
(Partner)
Freelands, Motherwell . . . .(p.1126)
T: 01698 352600
E: sfleming@freelands.co.uk

FLEMING, Sharon Eddington (Apr 2018)
(Partner)
Drummond Miller LLP, Bathgate . . . . . .(p.771)
T: 01506 656645
E: sfleming@drummondmiller.co.uk

FLEMING, William Alasdair (Nov 1985)
(Partner)
Brodies LLP, Glasgow . . . .(p.948)
T: 0141 2484672
E: alasdair.fleming@brodies.com

FLETCHER, Anne Constance (Sept 1992)
(Director)
MacFarlane Young Limited, Paisley . . . .(p.1139)
T: 0141 8893257
E: anne@macfarlaneyoung.com

FLETCHER, Christopher Michael (Nov 1995)
(Partner)
Berrymans Lace Mawer LLP,
Salford . . . .(p.1271)
T: 0161 2362002
E: chris.fletcher@blmlaw.com

FLETCHER, Gregory Bennett (Sept 2013)
(Employee)
National Health Service Scotland,
Edinburgh . . . .(p.1225)
T: 0131 2757800
E: greg.fletcher@nhs.scot

FLETCHER, Robin Ian Douglas (Oct 1989)
(Employee)
Dumfries & Galloway Council,
Dumfries . . . .(p.1217)
T: 01387 260681
E: robin.fletcher@dumgal.gov.uk

FLETT, Alanna Jamie (Aug 2010) (Employee)
Climate Transition Capital LLP,
Bristol . . . .(p.1259)
E: aflett@climatetransitioncapital.com

FLETT, Alexander (Dec 1993) (Director)
Martin, Johnston & Socha Limited,
Dunfermline . . . .(p.824)
T: 01383 730466
E:
zander.flett@mjscriminaldefencelawyers.co.uk

FLETT, Greg (Oct 2008) (Partner)
Davidson Chalmers Stewart LLP,
Edinburgh . . . .(p.859)
T: 0131 6259 191
E: greg.flett@dcslegal.com

FLETT, James Michael Patrick (Jul 2018)
(Employee)
Addleshaw Goddard LLP,
Edinburgh . . . .(p.835)
T: 0131 2282400
E: michael.flett@addleshawgoddard.com

FLETT, Roy John (Nov 1988) (Consultant)
Lows Orkney Limited, Kirkwall . . . .(p.1106)
T: 01856 873151
E: roy.flett@lowsorkney.co.uk

FLETT-GRANT, Emily Monica Margaret
(Jul 2019) (Employee)
Anderson Strathern LLP, Edinburgh . . . .(p.839)
T: 0131 2707700
E: Emily.Flett-Grant@andersonstrathern.co.uk

FLINT, David (Dec 1979) (Consultant)
Inksters, Glasgow . . . .(p.990)
T: 0141 2290880
E: david.flint@inksters.com

FLOOD, Charlotte Louise (Nov 2014)
(Employee)
City of Edinburgh Council,
Edinburgh . . . .(p.1221)
T: (0131) 5294145
E: lottie.flood@edinburgh.gov.uk

FLORANCE, James Andrew (Aug 2008)
(Employee)
Ledingham Chalmers LLP,
Aberdeen . . . .(p.734)
T: 01224 408408
E: james.florance@ledinghamchalmers.com

FLORENCE, Andrew Douglas (Jul 2009)
(Employee)
Lee & Thompson, London W1 . . . .(p.1266)
T: 020 3073 7653
E: andrewflorence@leeandthompson.com

FLORENCE, Lorraine Joanne (Nov 2007)
(Employee)
Procurator Fiscal Service, Glasgow . . . .(p.1241)
T: 0300 0203000
E: Lorraine.Florence@copfs.gov.uk

FLOUNDERS, Laura Jane (Nov 2017)
(Employee)
Anderson Strathern LLP, Edinburgh . . . .(p.839)
T: 0131 2707700
E: Laura.Flounders@andersonstrathern.co.uk

FLOWERDEW, Jessica Kate (Jul 2013)
(Associate)
Brodies LLP, Edinburgh . . . .(p.845)
T: 0131 2283777
E: jessica.flowerdew@brodies.com

FLOWERDEW, Sebastien Marc (Jul 2021)
(Employee)
Beltrami & Co Limited, Glasgow . . . . . .(p.944)
T: 0141 4292262
E:
sebastien.flowerdew@beltramiandcompany.co.
uk

FLOWERDEW, Stuart Alan (Oct 1990) (Partner)
Gray & Gray LLP, Peterhead . . . .(p.1153)
T: 01779 480 222
E: stuart@graygraylaw.com

FLYNN, Austin (Apr 1999) (Partner)
Morton Fraser LLP, Edinburgh . . . .(p.891)
T: 0131 2471000
E: austin.flynn@morton-fraser.com

FLYNN, Ian Taylor (Jul 2000) (Solicitor)
NO FIRM

FLYNN, Laurence (Jan 1987) (Partner)
Flynn & Co., Dundee . . . .(p.810)
T: 01382 223145
E: laurence.flynn@btconnect.com

FLYNN, Pamela Jane (Jul 2006) (Employee)
Procurator Fiscal Service, Hamilton . . . .(p.1247)
T: 0844 5613245
E: Pamela.Flynn@copfs.gov.uk

FLYNN, Paul Christopher (Jan 2011) (Employee)
Herbert Smith Freehills LLP, Tokyo . . . .(p.1274)
E: paul.flynn@hsf.com

FLYNN, Stephen Gerard (Dec 2019) (Employee)
Brodies LLP, Aberdeen. . . . .(p.723)
T: 01224 392242
E: stephen.flynn@brodies.com

FOARD, Susan Jane Campbell (Apr 1994)
(Employee)
Procurator Fiscal Service, Kirkwall . . . . .(p.1250)
T: 0300 020 2669
E: sue.foard@copfs.gov.uk

FOGG, Geoffrey David (Sept 1987) (Employee)
Perth & Kinross Council, Perth . . . .(p.1253)
T: 01738 475000
E: gfogg@pkc.gov.uk

FOGGO, Alison (Dec 1993) (Employee)
Munro & Noble, Inverness . . . .(p.1080)
T: 01463 221727
E: AlisonF@munronoble.com

FOGGO, Jill Glen Allan (Sept 1994) (Associate)
Adairs, Dumbarton . . . .(p.798)
T: 01389 767625
E: JFoggo@adairssolicitors.com

FOLAN, Sean Patrick (Oct 2018) (Employee)
BTO Solicitors LLP, Glasgow . . . .(p.952)
T: 0141 2218012
E: sfo@bto.co.uk

FOLEY, Jane Alison (Feb 2005) (Solicitor)
NO FIRM

FOLLAN, Leanne (May 2014) (Employee)
Wright, Johnston & Mackenzie LLP,
Glasgow . . . .(p.1054)
T: 0141 2483434
E: lf@wjm.co.uk

FONG, E-Ming (Dec 2003) (Partner)
Harper Macleod LLP, Glasgow . . . .(p.983)
T: 0141 2218888
E: e-ming.fong@harpermacleod.co.uk

FORBES, Claire (Jun 2016) (Partner)
Innes Johnston LLP, Leven . . . .(p.1115)
T: 01333 429320
E: cforbes@innesjohnston.co.uk

FORBES, Colin Edward (Nov 1987) (Employee)
TUV SUD Services (UK) Ltd, East
Kilbride . . . .(p.1219)
T: 01355 593700
E: Colin.Forbes@tuv-sud.co.uk

FORBES, David Gordon (Jul 1992) (Partner)
Walker Laird, Paisley . . . .(p.1142)
T: 0141 8875271
E: david.forbes@walkerlaird.co.uk

FORBES, David Ross (Oct 2009) (Employee)
FTI Consulting Media Center FZ LLC,
Dubai . . . .(p.1278)
E: david.forbes@fticonsulting.com

FORBES, Dr, Emma Elizabeth (Oct 2001)
(Employee)
Procurator Fiscal Service, Glasgow . . . .(p.1241)
T: 0300 0203000
E: emma.forbes@copfs.gov.uk

FORBES, Euan Scott (Oct 2019) (Employee)
Aberdein Considine and Company,
Edinburgh . . . .(p.833)
T: 0131 2212424
E: eforbes@acandco.com

FORBES, Gregor David Edward (Aug 1985)
(Partner)
A.C. White, Ayr . . . .(p.766)
T: 01292 266900
E: gregor.forbes@acwhiteayr.co.uk

FORBES, Hamish Douglas John (Sept 2007)
(Employee)
Anderson Strathern LLP, Edinburgh . . . .(p.839)
T: 0131 2707700
E: hamish.forbes@andersonstrathern.co.uk

FORBES, James Bennie Cook (Oct 1990)
(Partner)
Burness Paull LLP, Glasgow . . . .(p.954)
T: 0141 2484933
E: James.Forbes@burnesspaull.com

FORBES, Jemma Lyon (Aug 2009) (Partner)
Innes Johnston LLP, Glenrothes . . . . . .(p.1057)
T: 01592 757114
E: jforbes@innesjohnston.co.uk

FORBES, Jennifer (Aug 1998) (Employee)
Procurator Fiscal Service, Glasgow . . . .(p.1241)
T: 7879521828
E: jennifer.forbes@copfs.gov.uk

FORBES, Judith Katy (Feb 2009) (Employee)
Aberdeen City Council, Aberdeen. . . . .(p.1211)
T: 01224 522000
E: JuForbes@aberdeencity.gov.uk

FORBES, Mary Flora Muriel (Sept 2001)
(Associate)
CMS Cameron McKenna Nabarro Olswang LLP,
Aberdeen . . . .(p.727)
T: 01224 622002
E: mary.forbes@cms-cmno.com

FORBES, Neil David (Jun 1997) (Partner)
Stronachs LLP, Aberdeen . . . .(p.744)
T: 01224 845845
E: neil.forbes@stronachs.com

FORBES, Ronald Christopher (Aug 1983)
(Partner)
Smith Solicitors Stonehaven,
Stonehaven . . . .(p.1169)
T: 01569 767778
E: ronald.forbes@smithstonehaven.com

FORBES, Rory Alasdair Gordon (Nov 2014)
(Employee)
Brodies LLP, Edinburgh . . . .(p.845)
T: 0131 2283777
E: rory.forbes@brodies.com

FORBES, Sheila Margaret (Dec 1993)
(Employee)
Aberdeenshire Council, Aberdeen. . . . .(p.1211)
T: 01224 665337
E: sheila.forbes@aberdeenshire.gov.uk

FORBES, Sophie Margaret (Oct 2013)
(Employee)
Axiom Global Limited, London
EC1 . . . .(p.1261)
E: Sophie.Forbes@axiomlaw.net

FORBES, Susan Elizabeth (Aug 1986)
(Associate)
Frazer Coogans Ltd, Ayr . . . .(p.763)
T: 01292 280499
E: susan.forbes@frazercoogans.co.uk

FORBES, Susan Jane (Oct 1985) (Partner)
McKinnon Forbes, Tranent. . . . .(p.1175)
T: 01875 611211
E: susan.forbes@mckinnonforbes.co.uk

FORD, Blaire (Feb 2018) (Employee)
Procurator Fiscal Service,
Kilmarnock . . . . (p.1249)
T: 01563 536211
E: Blaire.Ford@copfs.gov.uk

FORD, David Allan (Jul 2017) (Employee)
Brodies LLP, Edinburgh . . . . (p.845)
T: 0131 2283777
E: david.ford@brodies.com

FORD, Fiona Agnes (Nov 1983) (Director)
Fords Daly Legal Limited, Kirkcaldy . . . . (p.1100)
T: 01592 640630
E: Fiona@fdlegal.co.uk

FORD, Michael Gregory (Aug 1986) (Partner)
Ross, Strachan & Co., Dundee . . . . (p.818)
T: 01382 201010
E: mford@ross-strachan.co.uk

FORD, Nigel William Frew (Sept 1983)
(Consultant)
Fords Daly Legal Limited, Kirkcaldy . . . . (p.1100)
T: 01592 640630
E: nigel@fordsdalylegal.co.uk

FORD, Scott William (May 2013) (Director)
Fords Daly Legal Limited, Kirkcaldy . . . . (p.1100)
T: 01592 640630
E: scott@fordsdalylegal.co.uk

FORDYCE, Amy Catherine (Nov 2018)
(Employee)
Pinsent Masons LLP, Aberdeen . . . . (p.739)
T: 01224 377900
E: Amy.Fordyce@pinsentmasons.com

FORDYCE, Graham Alexander (Jan 1985)
(Partner)
G A Fordyce & Co, Bearsden . . . . (p.772)
T: 0141 9423538
E: mail@gafordyce.com

FORDYCE, Ross Alistair MacDonald
(Dec 2016) (Employee)
Proserv UK Limited, Westhill . . . . (p.1255)
E: Ross.Fordyce@proserv.com

FORDYCE, William Andrew (Oct 2005)
(Employee)
Pinsent Masons LLP, Glasgow . . . . (p.1031)
T: 0141 567 8400
E: andrew.fordyce@pinsentmasons.com

FORGAN, Richard George (Jan 2016)
(Employee)
Eni UK Limited, London SW1 . . . . (p.1264)
T: 0207 3446330
E: richard.forgan@eni.com

FORGIE, Eilidh Kara (Aug 2015) (Employee)
Baillie Gifford & Co, Edinburgh . . . . . . (p.1220)
T: 0131 2752000
E: eilidh.gillanders@bailliegifford.com

FORGIE, Roderick Watson McDougal
(Aug 2015) (Employee)
Shepherd and Wedderburn LLP,
Edinburgh . . . . (p.900)
T: 0131 2289900
E: Roddy.Forgie@shepwedd.com

FORMAN, Adrienne MacKenzie (Oct 1997)
(Employee)
Scottish Government, Edinburgh . . . . . (p.1231)
T: 0131 2447579
E: adrienne.forman@gov.scot

FORMAN, Robert Andrew (Nov 2003) (Partner)
Burges Salmon LLP, Edinburgh . . . . (p.850)
T: 0131 3142112
E: robert.forman@burges-salmon.com

FORREST, Avril Agnes Elizabeth (Nov 1986)
(Employee)
East Ayrshire Council, Kilmarnock . . . . . (p.1249)
T: 01563 576161
E: avril.forrest@east-ayrshire.gov.uk

FORREST, Carly Louise (Oct 2002) (Partner)
Brodies LLP, Glasgow . . . . (p.948)
T: 0141 2484672
E: carly.forrest@brodies.com

FORREST, Douglas Bruce (Oct 1979) (Partner)
Forrest Campbell & Anderson,
Carluke . . . . (p.783)
T: 01555 771383
E: douglas@fcasolicitors.co.uk

FORREST, Elspeth McInnes (Sept 1980)
(Consultant)
Ness Gallagher Solicitors Limited,
Motherwell . . . . (p.1127)
T: 01698 254644
E: ef@nessgallagher.co.uk

FORREST, Ian Alexander (Jun 1991) (Employee)
East Lothian Council, Haddington . . . . (p.1246)
T: 01620 827389
E: iforrest@eastlothian.gov.uk

FORREST, Jean Young (Mar 2011) (Employee)
Dales Solicitors LLP, Galston . . . . (p.934)
T: 01563 820216
E: jean@dalesllp.co.uk

FORREST, Jemma Margaret (Jul 2017)
(Employee)
Anderson Strathern LLP, Glasgow . . . . . . (p.940)
T: 0141 2426060
E: Jemma.Forrest@andersonstrathern.co.uk

FORREST, Jonathan William (Oct 2019)
(Employee)
Clifford Chance LLP, London E14 . . . . . (p.1262)
E: jonathan.forrest@cliffordchance.com

FORREST, Lesley Scott Wilson (Mar 1985)
(Director)
Murdoch Stewarts Limited,
Glasgow . . . .(p.1025)
T: 0141 226 3333
E: lforrest@murdochstewarts.co.uk

FORREST, Margot-Joy (Nov 1998) (Employee)
Standard Life Investments Limited,
Edinburgh . . . .(p.1234)
T: (0131) 245 4153
E: Margot.Forrest@abrdn.com

FORREST, Morag Mason (Jul 1990) (Employee)
Standard Life Assets and Employee Services
Limited, Edinburgh . . . .(p.1234)
T: 0131 2457508
E: morag_forrest@standardlife.com

FORREST, Ross Anthony (Oct 2015) (Employee)
Kennedys Scotland, Edinburgh . . . .(p.880)
T: 0131 2256145
E: Ross.Forrest@kennedyslaw.com

FORRESTER, David James (Sept 2020)
(Employee)
Morton Fraser LLP, Edinburgh . . . .(p.891)
T: 0131 2471000
E: David.Forrester@morton-fraser.com

FORRESTER, Emma Louise (Oct 2008)
(Employee)
Ennova Limited, Dundee . . . .(p.810)
T: 01382 938118
E: eforrester@ennova-law.com

FORRESTER, Graeme Bruce (Nov 2010)
(Employee)
Stirling Council, Stirling . . . .(p.1255)
T: 01786 233065
E: forresterg@stirling.gov.uk

FORRESTER, Laura Anne (May 2016)
(Employee)
Scottish Widows Limited,
Edinburgh . . . .(p.1233)
T: 0131 6557230
E: laura.forrester@lloydsbanking.com

FORSTER, Chantelle Angela (Jun 2014)
(Employee)
Bank of America Merrill Lynch, London
EC1 . . . .(p.1261)
T: 0207 995 0765
E: chantelle.forster@bofa.com

FORSTER, Craig Mercer (Oct 1999) (Partner)
Allan McDougall McQueen LLP,
Edinburgh . . . .(p.837)
T: 0131 2281926
E: craigforster@mcdougallmcqueen.co.uk

FORSTER, Louise Mary (Feb 1996) (Partner)
Pinsent Masons LLP, Edinburgh . . . .(p.895)
T: 0131 777 7000
E: louise.forster@pinsentmasons.com

FORSYTH, Alex (Apr 1983) (Solicitor)
NO FIRM

FORSYTH, Alison Jane (Jun 1997) (Director)
Forsyth Legal Limited, Pitlochry . . . . . .(p.1155)
E: alison@forsythemploymentlaw.co.uk

FORSYTH, Andrew Campbell (May 2005)
(Partner)
Burness Paull LLP, Edinburgh . . . .(p.850)
T: 0131 4736000
E: andrew.forsyth@burnesspaull.com

FORSYTH, Callum Joseph Chambers
(Jun 2012) (Employee)
Procurator Fiscal Service, Hamilton . . . .(p.1247)
T: 0844 5613245
E: Callum.Forsyth@copfs.gov.uk

FORSYTH, Elizabeth Ann (Mar 1996) (Partner)
The Kellas Partnership, Inverurie . . . . . .(p.1086)
T: 01467 627300
E: eaf@kellas.biz

FORSYTH, Ellen Anne (Sept 1998) (Director)
Forsyth WS Limited, Haddington . . . . .(p.1064)
T: 01620 824045
E: af@forsythsolicitors.co.uk

FORSYTH, Jennifer Gail (Oct 2010) (Employee)
Glasgow City Council, Glasgow . . . . . .(p.1239)
T: 0141 2872000
E: jen.forsyth@glasgow.gov.uk

FORSYTH, John Francis (Oct 1989) (Employee)
Lloyds Banking Group Plc,
Edinburgh . . . .(p.1225)
T: 07824 320663
E: John.Forsyth@lloydsbanking.com

FORSYTH, John Simpson (Mar 2016)
(Employee)
Aberdeen City Council, Aberdeen . . . . .(p.1211)
T: 01224 522000
E: jforsyth@aberdeencity.gov.uk

FORSYTH, Samantha Louise (Jan 2020)
(Employee)
Nursing and Midwifery Council,
Edinburgh . . . .(p.1227)
T: 0131 624 5024
E: samantha.forsyth@nmc-uk.org

FORSYTH, Stephen James (Sept 2009) (Partner)
MML Legal, Dundee . . . .(p.817)
T: 01382 206 000
E: stephen@mmllaw.co.uk

FORSYTH, Valerie Elizabeth (Oct 1985)
(Consultant)
KW Law, Livingston . . . .(p.1119)
T: 01506 415333
E: vforsyth@kwlaw.co.uk

FORSYTHE, Eleanor Kate (Aug 2019) (Solicitor)
NO FIRM

FOSTER, Christy (Jul 2020) (Employee)
Brodies LLP, Glasgow . . . . (p.948)
T: 0141 2484672
E: christy.foster@brodies.com

FOSTER, Clare Elizabeth (Nov 1995) (Partner)
Shepherd and Wedderburn LLP,
Edinburgh . . . . (p.900)
T: 0131 2289900
E: clare.foster@shepwedd.com

FOSTER, Fiona Elizabeth (Dec 2004) (Associate)
Shepherd and Wedderburn LLP,
Edinburgh . . . . (p.900)
T: 0131 2289900
E: fiona.foster@shepwedd.com

FOSTER, Janette (May 1989) (Employee)
Energy Law Unlimited LLP,
Glasgow. . . . . (p.974)
T: 07983 827139
E: jfoster@elu-llp.com

FOSTER, Michael Anthony (Jan 1985) (Partner)
Hughes Dowdall, Glasgow. . . . . (p.987)
T: 0141 2407020
E: michael.foster@hughesdowdall.com

FOTHERINGHAM, Georgia Rossetta
(Jul 2019) (Employee)
Burness Paull LLP, Edinburgh . . . . (p.850)
T: 0131 4736000
E: georgia.fotheringham@burnesspaull.com

FOTHERINGHAM, Lydia Margaret
(Oct 1996) (Partner)
Anderson Beaton Lamond, Perth . . . . . (p.1146)
T: 01738 639999
E: lydia@abl-law.co.uk

FOTHERINGHAM, Suzanne (Jun 2009)
(Employee)
Procurator Fiscal Service, Glasgow . . . . (p.1241)
T: 0300 0203000
E: suzanne.fotheringham@copfs.gov.uk

FOULIS, Gary Souter (Jul 2008) (Partner)
Bruce, Short & Co., Dundee . . . . (p.806)
T: 01382 223400
E: gfoulis@hotmail.co.uk

FOULIS, Jamie Munro (Sept 2012) (Partner)
Balfour + Manson LLP, Edinburgh . . . . . (p.841)
T: 0131 200 1200
E: jamie.foulis@balfour-manson.co.uk

FOULIS, Ruth Lamont (Mar 2019) (Employee)
Scottish Government, Edinburgh . . . . . (p.1231)
T: 0131 244 0815
E: Ruth.Foulis@gov.scot

FOWLE, Fiona (Sept 2004) (Employee)
Burness Paull LLP, Glasgow . . . . (p.954)
T: 0141 2484933
E: fiona.fowle@burnesspaull.com

FOWLE, Fiona Margaret (Sept 2008)
(Employee)
Digby Brown LLP, Glasgow . . . . (p.970)
T: 0333 200 5925
E: fiona.fowle@digbybrown.co.uk

FOWLER, Gordon David (Sept 2012)
(Employee)
Scottish Legal Aid Board,
Edinburgh . . . . (p.1233)
T: 0131 2267061
E: FowlerGo@slab.org.uk

FOWLER, Lauren (Aug 1988) (Associate)
Frazer Coogans Ltd, Ayr . . . . (p.763)
T: 01292 280499
E: lauren.fowler@frazercoogans.co.uk

FOWLER, Lauren Margaret (Sept 2015)
(Employee)
Pinsent Masons LLP, Edinburgh . . . . (p.895)
T: 0131 225 0125
E: lauren.fowler@pinsentmasons.com

FOWLER, Linda (Nov 2008) (Employee)
The Scottish Parliament, Edinburgh . . . (p.1235)
T: (0131) 3486653
E: linda.fowler@parliament.scot

FOWLER, Victoria (Sept 2017) (Employee)
Office of the Advocate General,
Edinburgh . . . . (p.1227)
T: 0131 2441635
E: Victoria.Fowler@advocategeneral.gov.uk

FOWLER, William (Oct 1992) (Partner)
Dentons UK and Middle East LLP,
Edinburgh . . . . (p.860)
T: 0330 2220050
E: bill.fowler@dentons.com

FOWLIE, Frank Alexander (Oct 2000) (Partner)
CMS Cameron McKenna Nabarro Olswang LLP,
Aberdeen . . . . (p.727)
T: 01224 622002
E: frank.fowlie@cms-cmno.com

FOWLIE, Zoe Olivia (Oct 2016) (Employee)
Vialex Limited, Edinburgh . . . . (p.1235)
T: 0333 2400127
E: zoe.fowlie@vialex.co.uk

FOX, Amy Elspeth (Jul 2002) (Employee)
MML Legal, Dundee . . . . (p.817)
T: 01382 206 000
E: amy@muirmyleslaverty.co.uk

FOX, Helena Grace (Mar 1995) (Director)
Matthews Legal Limited, Newton
Stewart . . . . (p.1131)
T: 01671 404100
E: helenafox@abamatthews.com

FOX, Marie-Louise (May 2000) (Employee)
Scottish Legal Aid Board,
Edinburgh . . . . (p.1233)
T: 0131 2267061

FOX, Ryan Andrew (Feb 2008) (Partner)
Aberdein Considine and Company,
Stonehaven . . . .(p.1168)
T: 01569 766166
E: rfox@acandco.com

FOX, Valerie Elizabeth (May 2018) (Employee)
CMS Cameron McKenna Nabarro Olswang LLP,
London EC4 . . . .(p.1263)
T: 0207 3673000
E: valerie.fox@cms-cmno.com

FOXTON, Victoria Ann (Apr 2008) (Solicitor)
NO FIRM

FOYE, Mhairi Clare (Feb 2014) (Employee)
Morton Fraser LLP, Edinburgh . . . .(p.891)
T: 0131 2471000
E: Mhairi.Blair@morton-fraser.com

FOYLE, Andrew Joseph (Oct 2002) (Partner)
Shoosmiths, Edinburgh . . . .(p.902)
T: 03700 868000
E: andrew.foyle@shoosmiths.co.uk

FRAHM, Hannah (Aug 2019) (Solicitor)
NO FIRM

FRAME, Calum Isam Sinclair (Aug 2018)
(Employee)
Procurator Fiscal Service, Airdrie . . . . . .(p.1214)
T: 01236 747027
E: calum.frame@copfs.gov.uk

FRAME, David Andrew Love (Jan 1985)
(Partner)
Buchanan Dickson Frame, Paisley . . . . .(p.1137)
T: 0141 8480303
E: df@bdflaw.co.uk

FRAME, John Alasdair (Feb 2016) (Employee)
Menzies Aviation, Edinburgh . . . .(p.1225)
T: 0131 459 8049
E: john.frame@johnmenzies.aero

FRAME, Laura Jane (Jun 2016) (Employee)
Davidson & Shirley Limited, Lanark . . .(p.1107)
T: 01555 662576/7

FRAME, Rhea (Jul 2019) (Employee)
Civil Legal Assistance Office,
Inverness . . . .(p.1248)
T: 01463 641770
E: framerh@clao.org.uk

FRAME, Robert Fulton (Jan 1983) (Director)
Miller Beckett & Jackson Limited,
Glasgow . . . .(p.1019)
T: 0141 2042833
E: rframe@mbjsolicitors.co.uk

FRAME, Shona McNae (Sept 1993) (Partner)
CMS Cameron McKenna Nabarro Olswang LLP,
Glasgow . . . .(p.962)
T: 0141 304 6379
E: Shona.Frame@cms-cmno.com

FRANCESCHI, Marika Simona Leonora
(Oct 2003) (Partner)
MacRoberts LLP, Edinburgh . . . .(p.887)
T: 0131 2295046
E: marika.franceschi@macroberts.com

FRANCHI, Leandro Ottavio (Nov 1987)
(Partner)
Franchi Law LLP, Glasgow . . . .(p.977)
T: 0141 225 3810
E: leandro@franchilaw.co.uk

FRANCIS, Raymond Innis (Aug 2021)
(Employee)
Caesar & Howie, Bathgate . . . .(p.770)
T: 01506 815900
E: rf@caesar-howie.co.uk

FRANCIS, Robin James Douglas (Jan 2007)
(Partner)
Thorntons Law LLP, Dundee . . . .(p.819)
T: 01382 229 111
E: rfrancis@thorntons-law.co.uk

FRANCKSEN, Ellen (Oct 2019) (Employee)
Harper Macleod LLP, Glasgow . . . .(p.983)
T: 0141 2218888
E: ellen.francksen@harpermacleod.co.uk

FRANCO, Corah Joanne (Nov 2018) (Employee)
Blackadders LLP, Dundee . . . .(p.805)
T: 01382 229222
E: corah.franco@blackadders.co.uk

FRANKLIN, Iain Christopher (Sept 2014)
(Employee)
DAC Beachcroft Scotland LLP,
Glasgow . . . .(p.964)
T: 0141 2486688
E: ifranklin@dacbeachcroft.com

FRANKLIN, Lindsey Arlene (Sept 2019)
(Employee)
Pinsent Masons LLP, Glasgow . . . .(p.1031)
T: 0141 567 8400
E: Lyndsey.Franklin@pinsentmasons.com

FRASER, Alan (Aug 1994) (Partner)
MML Legal, Dundee . . . .(p.817)
T: 01382 206 000
E: alan@muirmyleslaverty.co.uk

FRASER, Alasdair (Apr 1986) (Director)
A Fraser Solicitors Ltd, Inverness . . . . . .(p.1076)
T: 01463 229917
E: alfraser@afrasersolicitors.com

FRASER, Alasdair William (Sept 2020)
(Employee)
Gilson Gray LLP, Glasgow . . . .(p.980)
T: 0141 5302021
E: afraser@gilsongray.co.uk

FRASER, Alison Jean (Sept 1995) (Employee)
Scottish Law Commission,
Edinburgh . . . .(p.1233)
T: 0131 6682131
E: alison.fraser@scotlawcom.gov.uk

FRASER, Alistair (Jul 1977) (Associate)
Jas Campbell & Co Ltd, Saltcoats . . . . .(p.1160)
T: 01294 464301
E: a.fraser@jascampbell.co.uk

FRASER, Alistair David (May 2013) (Employee)
The University of Law, London EC1 . . .(p.1269)

FRASER, Allan (Oct 1996) (Partner)
Dickson Minto, Edinburgh . . . .(p.861)
T: 0131 2254455
E: allan.fraser@dmws.com

FRASER, Andrea May (Jul 2020) (Employee)
Justice, London EC4 . . . .(p.1265)

FRASER, Andrew Douglas James (Sept 2009)
(Partner)
Albany Fraser Limited, Glasgow . . . .(p.939)
T: 0141 4637065
E: andrew@albanyfraser.com

FRASER, Andrew Neil (Feb 2003) (Employee)
Scottish Widows Limited,
Edinburgh . . . .(p.1233)
T: 0131 6557230
E: andrew-n.fraser@scottishwidows.co.uk

FRASER, Anne-Marie (Oct 1998) (Employee)
TotalEnergies E&P UK Limited,
Westhill . . . .(p.1255)
T: 01224 297000
E: anne-marie.fraser@totalenergies.com

FRASER, Calum Donald (Aug 1978) (Director)
Hannay Fraser & Co Ltd, Glasgow . . . . .(p.983)
T: 0141 2211381
E: calum@hannayfraser.co.uk

FRASER, Caroline Allison (Oct 2007) (Partner)
Lindsays LLP, Dundee . . . .(p.814)
T: 01382 224112
E: carolinefraser@lindsays.co.uk

FRASER, Caroline Lorna (Nov 2008) (Associate)
Lyons Davidson Scotland LLP,
Edinburgh . . . .(p.883)
T: 0131 344 0225
E: cfraser@lyonsdavidson.co.uk

FRASER, Catherine Margaret (Sept 2013)
(Employee)
Procurator Fiscal Service, Falkirk . . . . . .(p.1236)
T: 0300 020 3000
E: Catherine.fraser@copfs.gov.uk

FRASER, Charles William Simpson
(Apr 1986) (Partner)
Aberdein Considine and Company,
Perth . . . .(p.1145)
T: 01738 473016
E: cfraser@acandco.com

FRASER, Colin John (Oct 1994) (Partner)
Pinsent Masons LLP, Glasgow . . . .(p.1031)
T: 0141 567 8400
E: colin.fraser@pinsentmasons.com

FRASER, Craig Delargy (Mar 2011) (Employee)
K&L Gates LLP, London EC4 . . . .(p.1265)
T: 0207 360 8161
E: craig.fraser@klgates.com

FRASER, Cristina (Aug 2006) (Partner)
South Forrest, Inverness . . . .(p.1082)
T: 01463 237171
E: cristina@southforrest.co.uk

FRASER, Dean Ross (Jun 2019) (Employee)
South Forrest, Inverness . . . .(p.1082)
T: 01463 237171
E: dean@southforrest.co.uk

FRASER, Emma Victoria (Apr 2014) (Employee)
EDF Energy Renewables,
Edinburgh . . . .(p.1222)
T: (0131) 460 3654
E: Emma.fraser@edf-re.uk

FRASER, Finlay Ian (Sept 2016) (Employee)
White & Case LLP, London EC2 . . . . . .(p.1269)
T: 0207 5321000
E: finlay.fraser@whitecase.com

FRASER, Fiona Elizabeth (Nov 2011) (Associate)
Middleton Ross & Arnot Limited,
Dingwall . . . .(p.797)
T: 01349 862214
E: fef@middletonross.co.uk

FRASER, Geraldine Margaret (Feb 2003)
(Employee)
Aberdeenshire Council, Aberdeen . . . . .(p.1211)
T: 01224 664014
E: Geraldine.Fraser@Aberdeenshire.gov.uk

FRASER, Glenn James (Jul 1995) (Director)
Fraser & Co Criminal Defence Ltd,
Livingston . . . .(p.1119)
T: 01506 420532
E: glennfraser@fraserandco.net

FRASER, Gordon Andrew (Feb 1977) (Director)
PRP Legal Limited, Glasgow . . . .(p.1033)
T: 0141 3311050
E: gordon@prp-legal.co.uk

FRASER, Gordon Geddes Dominic
(Jun 1988) (Partner)
Fraser & Mulligan, Aberdeen . . . .(p.731)
T: 01224 646428
E: ggdf@fraser-mulligan.co.uk

FRASER, Heather Alexandra (Feb 2019)
(Employee)
Wilson McKendrick Solicitors Limited,
Glasgow . . . .(p.1053)
T: 0141 2227950
E: HeatherFraser@wilsonmckendrick.co.uk

FRASER, Hugh (Dec 1988) (Solicitor)
HFI Consulting International Limited,
Aberdeen . . . .(p.1212)
T: 01224 766650

FRASER, Ian Karlheinz (Dec 1998) (Partner)
Thorntons Law LLP, Edinburgh . . . .(p.906)
T: 0131 2258705
E: ifraser@thorntons-law.co.uk

FRASER, Jacqueline Christina (Jul 1993)
(Partner)
Harper Macleod LLP, Glasgow . . . .(p.983)
T: 0141 2218888
E: jacqui.fraser@harpermacleod.co.uk

FRASER, Jeremy William (Jan 1987) (Employee)
TSB Bank Plc, Edinburgh . . . .(p.1235)
T: (0131) 260 0051
E: Jeremy.fraser1@tsb.co.uk

FRASER, Kelly Moyra (Oct 2012) (Employee)
Harper Macleod LLP, Glasgow . . . .(p.983)
T: 0141 2218888
E: Kelly.Fraser@harpermacleod.co.uk

FRASER, Kellyann (Mar 2014) (Employee)
Aberdeen Citizens Advice Bureau,
Aberdeen . . . .(p.1211)
T: 01224 569757
E:
kellyann.fraser@aberdeencab.casonline.org.uk

FRASER, Kerry (Sept 2020) (Employee)
Dickson Minto, Edinburgh . . . .(p.861)
T: 0131 2254455
E: kerry.fraser@dmws.com

FRASER, Laura Anne (Sept 2011) (Employee)
Burness Paull LLP, Aberdeen . . . .(p.724)
T: 01224 618 510
E: laura.fraser@burnesspaull.com

FRASER, Lindsay Margaret (Oct 1999)
(Employee)
Dickson Minto, Edinburgh . . . .(p.861)
T: 0131 2254455
E: lindsay.fraser@dmws.com

FRASER, Louise Anne (Nov 2008) (Partner)
DM MacKinnon, Oban . . . .(p.1134)
T: 01631 563014
E: laf@dmmk.co.uk

FRASER, Lynn Morton (Apr 2010) (Associate)
Thompsons, Glasgow . . . .(p.1046)
T: 0141 2218840
E: Lynn.Fraser@thompsons-scotland.co.uk

FRASER, Martin Alan (Dec 1988) (Partner)
A.C. Morrison & Richards LLP,
Aberdeen . . . .(p.737)
T: 01224 573321
E: mfraser@acmr.co.uk

FRASER, Morag (Sept 1987) (Partner)
Fraser Shepherd, Falkirk . . . .(p.921)
T: 01324 630700
E: morag@frasershepherd.co.uk

FRASER, Natalia Paulina (Sept 2014)
(Employee)
Brodies LLP, Aberdeen . . . .(p.723)
T: 01224 392242
E: natalia.fraser@brodies.com

FRASER, Natalie Ellen (Aug 2015) (Employee)
Wood Group UK Limited,
Aberdeen . . . .(p.1214)
T: 01224 851000
E: Natalie.Fraser@woodplc.com

FRASER, Neil (Nov 2001) (Partner)
Raeburn Christie Clark & Wallace LLP,
Aberdeen . . . .(p.741)
T: 01224 332400
E: neil.fraser@raeburns.co.uk

FRASER, Neil Duncan (Feb 2001) (Associate)
Anderson Strathern LLP, Edinburgh . . . .(p.839)
T: 0131 2707700
E: neil.fraser@andersonstrathern.co.uk

FRASER, Nicholas Jonathan (Oct 1999)
(Employee)
City of Edinburgh Council,
Edinburgh . . . .(p.1221)
T: (0131) 5294145
E: nicholas.fraser@edinburgh.gov.uk

FRASER, Norman (May 1973) (Employee)
T. Duncan & Co., Montrose . . . .(p.1125)
T: 01674 672533
E: norman@tduncan.com

FRASER, Norman John (Jan 1997) (Employee)
Wallace Hodge & Company Limited,
Ayr . . . .(p.766)
T: 01292 611177
E: norman.fraser@wallace-hodge.co.uk

FRASER, Rebecca Louise (Dec 2017) (Employee)
MacPhee & Partners LLP, Fort
William . . . .(p.930)
T: 01397 701000
E: rebeccafraser@macphee.co.uk

FRASER, Rebecca Rose (Jun 2017) (Partner)
South Forrest, Inverness . . . .(p.1082)
T: 01463 237171
E: rebecca@southforrest.co.uk

FRASER, Robert Malcolm (Nov 1983) (Partner)
Aberdein Considine and Company,
Aberdeen . . . .(p.718)
T: 01224 267067
E: rfraser@acandco.com

FRASER, Sean (Feb 2021) (Employee)
Carey Hughes Limited, High
Blantyre . . . .(p.1073)
T: 01698 404616
E: sean@careyhughes.co.uk

FRASER, Sheila (Sept 1986) (Employee)
Murchison Law Limited, Inverness . . . .(p.1081)
T: 01463 709992
E: sheila@murchisonlaw.co.uk

FRASER, Stewart David (Feb 1993) (Employee)
Highland Council, Inverness . . . .(p.1248)
T: 01463 702000
E: stewart.fraser@highland.gov.uk

FRASER, Stuart Blair (Nov 2003) (Employee)
Pinsent Masons LLP, Aberdeen . . . .(p.739)
T: 01224 377900
E: stuart.fraser@pinsentmasons.com

FRASER, Stuart Mackie (Nov 1987) (Director)
Scotia Personal Injury Solicitors Limited,
Kilmarnock . . . .(p.1096)
T: 01563 522433

FRAZER, Lucy Alexandra (Jan 2016) (Employee)
Clan Childlaw Limited, Edinburgh . . . . .(p.854)
T: 0808 129 0522
E: lucy.frazer@clanchildlaw.org

FREEDMAN, Daniel (Sept 1995) (Employee)
Freedman + Hilmi LLP, London W1 . . .(p.1264)
T: +44(0)20 7871 8600
E: df@freedmanhilmi.com

FREEDMAN, Leonard (Dec 1978) (Consultant)
TC Young LLP, Glasgow . . . .(p.1055)
T: 0141 2215562
E: lef@tcyoung.co.uk

FREELAND, Jack Alexander (Aug 2019)
(Employee)
Shepherd and Wedderburn LLP,
Edinburgh . . . .(p.900)
T: 0131 2289900
E: Jack.Freeland@shepwedd.com

FREELAND, Lynne Alexander (Sept 1997)
(Consultant)
Lefevre Litigation, Aberdeen . . . .(p.736)
T: 01224 657657
E: laf@lefevre-litigation.com

FREELAND, Robert Norman Karl (Nov 2007)
(Employee)
Scottish Government, Edinburgh . . . . .(p.1231)
T: 0131 244 0815
E: Robert.Freeland@gov.scot

FREEMAN, Alasdair Charles (Feb 1997)
(Partner)
Burness Paull LLP, Aberdeen . . . .(p.724)
T: 01224 621621
E: Alasdair.Freeman@burnesspaull.com

FREEMAN, Andrew David (Oct 2006)
(Employee)
Park Plaza Hotels UK Services Limited, London
SE1 . . . .(p.1267)
E: afreeman@pphe.com

FREEMAN, Emily (Feb 2017) (Employee)
Sheku Bayoh Public Inquiry,
Edinburgh . . . .(p.1233)
E: emily.freeman@shekubayoinquiry.scot

FREEMAN, Nadine Margaret (Oct 1996)
(Employee)
Procurator Fiscal Service, Paisley . . . . . .(p.1252)
T: 0141 8875225
E: nadine.freeman@copfs.gov.uk

FREEMAN, Richard Aaron (Oct 1987) (Partner)
Richard Freeman & Co., Glasgow . . . . . .(p.978)
T: 0141 353 2223
E: rte@richardfreemanlaw.com

FREESTONE, Laura Jane (Oct 2005) (Employee)
PricewaterhouseCoopers LLP, London
WC2 . . . .(p.1267)
T: 020 7212 1616
E: laura.j.freestone@uk.pwc.com

FRENCH, Ashley Marshall (Dec 2019)
(Employee)
Urquharts, Edinburgh . . . .(p.909)
T: 0131 5562896
E: ashleyfrench@urquharts.co.uk

FRENCH, Caitlin Margaret (Sept 2020)
(Employee)
Procurator Fiscal Service,
Edinburgh . . . .(p.1227)
T: 0300 0202948
E: caitlin.french@copfs.gov.uk

FRENCH, Michael Craig (Dec 1990) (Employee)
Scottish Government, Edinburgh . . . . .(p.1231)
T: 0131 244 0815
E: craig.french@gov.scot

FRENZ, Amanda Jane (Sept 1993) (Partner)
Miller Hendry, Perth . . . .(p.1150)
T: 01738 637311
E: amandafrenz@millerhendry.co.uk

FRENZ, Richard Alan (Oct 1980) (Partner)
Miller Hendry, Perth . . . .(p.1150)
T: 01738 637311
E: richardfrenz@millerhendry.co.uk

FRESHWATER, Alison Margaret (Feb 2008)
(Employee)
Standard Life Investments Limited,
Edinburgh . . . .(p.1234)
T: (0131) 245 4153
E: Alison.Freshwater@abrdn.com

FRETWELL, Lauren (Jan 2021) (Employee)
Multrees Investor Services,
Edinburgh . . . . (p.1225)
T: 0131 2473220
E: lauren.fretwell@multrees.com

FREW, Andrew (Sept 1986) (Employee)
Pollock Fairbridge Schiavone Limited,
Glasgow . . . . (p.1033)
T: 0141 7792577
E: af@pfssolicitors.co.uk

FREW, Gillian Elizabeth (Aug 2003) (Partner)
Pinsent Masons LLP, Edinburgh . . . . (p.895)
T: 0131 777 7000
E: gillian.frew@pinsentmasons.com

FREW, Rachel Alice (Sept 2020) (Employee)
Anderson Strathern LLP, Glasgow . . . . . . (p.940)
T: 0141 2426060
E: rachel.frew@andersonstrathern.co.uk

FREW, Richard Christopher (Oct 1980)
(Consultant)
Lefevres (Scotland) Limited,
Edinburgh . . . . (p.882)
T: 0845 305 2555

FRIEL, Anne Sarah (Oct 2007) (Employee)
ClientEarth Belgium AISBL, Brussels . . . (p.1257)
E: afriel@clientearth.org

FRIEND, Clemency Alice (Apr 2009) (Employee)
Aegon UK, Edinburgh . . . . (p.1220)
T: 1315493986
E: Clem.Friend@aegon.co.uk

FRIER, George William (Jul 1987) (Partner)
Shepherd and Wedderburn LLP,
Glasgow . . . . (p.1039)
T: 0141 566 9900
E: George.Frier@shepwedd.com

FROOD, Alastair McGarva (Sept 1995) (Partner)
Eversheds Sutherland (International) LLP,
Edinburgh . . . . (p.869)
T: 0131 476 7902
E: alastairfrood@eversheds-sutherland.com

FROST, Elizabeth Margaret (Oct 1996)
(Partner)
MacRoberts LLP, Edinburgh . . . . (p.887)
T: 0131 2295046
E: Lisa.Frost@macroberts.com

FROSTWICK, Lara Lesley (Mar 2021)
(Employee)
DAC Beachcroft Scotland LLP,
Glasgow . . . . (p.964)
T: 0141 2486688
E: lfrostwick@dacbeachcroft.com

FROTAN, Emma (Jul 2020) (Employee)
Maguire Solicitors, Glasgow . . . . (p.1017)
T: 0141 3312885
E: emma@maguiresolicitors.co.uk

FRYER, Jill Elizabeth (Sept 2000) (Partner)
Harper Macleod LLP, Inverness . . . . (p.1077)
T: 01463 798777
E: Jill.Fryer@harpermacleod.co.uk

FRYER, Kirsty Robyn (Jun 2021) (Employee)
CMS Cameron McKenna Nabarro Olswang LLP,
Edinburgh . . . . (p.856)
T: 0131 2288000
E: kirsty.fryer@cms-cmno.com

FULTON, Alan David Crowther (Dec 1998)
(Partner)
CMS Cameron McKenna Nabarro Olswang LLP,
Edinburgh . . . . (p.856)
T: 0131 2288000
E: Alan.Fulton@cms-cmno.com

FULTON, Ben Robert (Sept 2021) (Employee)
Pinsent Masons LLP, Glasgow . . . . (p.1031)
T: 0141 567 8400
E: ben.fulton@pinsentmasons.com

FULTON, Gail (Nov 2015) (Employee)
Scottish Enterprise, Glasgow . . . . (p.1243)
T: 0141 2482700
E: Gail.fulton@scotent.co.uk

FULTON, Gemma (Feb 2015) (Employee)
Frazer Coogans Ltd, Ayr . . . . (p.763)
T: 01292 280499
E: gemma.fulton@frazercoogans.co.uk

FULTON, Joanna Margaret (Jan 2009) (Partner)
Burness Paull LLP, Edinburgh . . . . (p.850)
T: 0131 4736000
E: joanna.fulton@burnesspaull.com

FULTON, John Paul (May 2005) (Partner)
Gilson Gray LLP, Edinburgh . . . . (p.874)
T: 0131 5165354
E: jfulton@gilsongray.co.uk

FULTON, Karen Elizabeth (Feb 1995) (Partner)
Blackadders LLP, Glasgow . . . . (p.946)
T: 0141 2481888
E: Karen.Fulton@blackadders.co.uk

FULTON, Katie Helen (Nov 2018) (Employee)
Gibson Kerr Limited, Edinburgh . . . . (p.872)
T: 0131 2257558
E: katie.fulton@gibsonkerr.co.uk

FULTON, Patrick Struan (Sept 2013) (Employee)
DLA Piper Scotland LLP, Edinburgh . . . . (p.863)
T: 08700 111111
E: patrick.fulton@dlapiper.com

FULTON, Scott Callum (Aug 2019) (Employee)
Watermans Solicitors Limited,
Glasgow . . . . (p.1051)
T: 0141 4307055
E: scottfulton@watermans.co.uk

FUNG, Christopher Sea Loon (Nov 2012)
(Solicitor)
NO FIRM

FURNESS, Hannah Zoe (Sept 2018) (Employee)
Scottish Environment Protection Agency,
Edinburgh . . . .(p.1230)
T: 0131 4497296
E: hannah.furness@sepa.org.uk

FUSARO, Jennefer Charlotte (Apr 2016)
(Associate)
CMS Cameron McKenna Nabarro Olswang LLP,
Edinburgh . . . .(p.856)
T: 0131 2288000
E: jennefer.fusaro@cms-cmno.com

FUSI, Daniela Leda (Oct 2000) (Partner)
Clyde & Co (Scotland) LLP,
Glasgow. . . . .(p.961)
T: 0141 2482666
E: daniela.fusi@clydeco.com

FYALL, Sharon Stewart (Aug 1999) (Partner)
Pollock & McLean, Thornhill . . . .(p.1173)
T: 01848 330207
E: sharonfyall@pollockmclean.co.uk

FYFE, Angela Cameron (Sept 2006) (Partner)
Stevenson & Marshall LLP,
Dunfermline . . . .(p.825)
T: 01383 721141
E: af@stevenson-marshall.co.uk

FYFE, Graeme Douglas John (Aug 1994)
(Employee)
Pinsent Masons LLP, Glasgow . . . . . .'. .(p.1031)
T: 0141 567 8400
E: graeme.fyfe@pinsentmasons.com

FYFE, Hamish Montgomery (Jul 1980)
(Employee)
Blackadders LLP, Dundee. . . . .(p.805)
T: 01382 229222
E: hamish.fyfe@blackadders.co.uk

FYFE, Helen Elizabeth (Oct 2010) (Associate)
CMS Cameron McKenna Nabarro Olswang LLP,
London EC4 . . . .(p.1263)
T: 0207 3673000
E: Helen.Fyfe@cms-cmno.com

FYFE, Norman Alexander, WS (Dec 1980)
(Director)
Miller Beckett & Jackson Limited,
Glasgow. . . . .(p.1019)
T: 0141 2042833
E: nfyfe@mbjsolicitors.co.uk

FYFE, Scott Andrew (Oct 2017) (Associate)
Anderson Strathern LLP, Edinburgh . . . .(p.839)
T: 0131 2707700
E: Scott.Fyfe@andersonstrathern.co.uk

FYFFE, Andrew Robert Urquhart (Aug 2020)
(Employee)
McGlashan MacKay Solicitors,
Glasgow. . . . .(p.1011)
T: 0141 3757557
E: andrew@mcglashanmackay.com

FYFFE, Kirstin Charlotte Glen (Aug 2014)
(Associate)
Weil, Gotshal & Manges (London) LLP, London
EC4 . . . .(p.1269)
E: kirstin.fyffe@weil.com

FYFFE, Linda Kirstine (May 1996) (Partner)
Laurie & Co Solicitors LLP,
Aberdeen . . . .(p.733)
T: 01224 645 085
E: Linda@laurieandco.co.uk

FYFFE, Nicola Lynne (Jul 1998) (Employee)
Scottish Children's Reporter Administration,
Dundee . . . .(p.1218)

FYVIE, Ellyn Sarah (Aug 2017) (Employee)
Friends Legal, Glasgow . . . .(p.978)
T: 0844 8921250
E: ellyn.fyvie@friends-legal.co.uk

GABERT, Kirsten Iona Megan (Jul 2017)
(Employee)
Idox Software Limited, Glasgow . . . . . .(p.1240)
T: 0141 2277600
E: kirsten.gabert@idoxgroup.com

GADDIE, Hannah Janet Patricia (Sept 2021)
(Employee)
Gillespie Macandrew LLP,
Edinburgh . . . .(p.872)
T: 0131 2251677
E: hannah.gaddie@gillespiemacandrew.co.uk

GAFFAR, Pamela Ann (Oct 2010) (Associate)
Connelly & Yeoman Law Limited,
Arbroath . . . .(p.757)
T: 01241 434200
E: pamela@connellyyeoman.com

GAFFNEY, Gillian Anne (Jun 2003) (Employee)
Barton & Hendry, Cumbernauld . . . . . .(p.790)
T: 01236 735466
E: gillian@bartonandhendry.co.uk

GAILEY, Karen (Sept 1992) (Partner)
Family Law Matters Scotland LLP,
Glasgow. . . . .(p.975)
T: 0141 4202430
E: karen.gailey@flmscotland.co.uk

GAIR, Marie Clare (Nov 2006) (Employee)
Serco UK, Europe & SGS, Glasgow . . . .(p.1244)
E: marie.clare.gair@serco.com

GAIR, Pauline Ann (Feb 1987) (Employee)
Procurator Fiscal Service, Inverness . . . .(p.1248)
T: 0844 5612926
E: pauline.gair@copfs.gov.uk

GAIRNS, Megan Jane (Sept 2019) (Employee)
Willkie Farr & Gallagher (UK) LLP, London
EC2 . . . .(p.1269)
E: MGairns@willkie.com

GALASTRO, Sebastiano Lorenzo (Aug 2016)
(Employee)
DLA Piper Scotland LLP, Edinburgh . . . . (p.863)
T: 08700 111111
E: seb.galastro@dlapiper.com

GALBRAITH, Eric Roger (Sept 1985) (Partner)
Brodies LLP, Glasgow . . . . (p.948)
T: 0141 2484672
E: eric.galbraith@brodies.com

GALBRAITH, Jordan Michael (Apr 2019)
(Employee)
CMS Cameron McKenna Nabarro Olswang LLP,
Glasgow. . . . . (p.962)
T: 0141 2222200

GALBRAITH, Linzi Rachel (Sept 2021)
(Employee)
Tod & Mitchell, Paisley . . . . (p.1142)
T: 0141 8891444
E: linzi.galbraith@todandmitchell.co.uk

GALBRAITH, Nicola Ann (Oct 2001) (Employee)
Scottish Water, Dunfermline . . . . (p.1219)
T: (01383) 665410
E: Nicola.Galbraith@SCOTTISHWATER.CO.UK

GALL, Sarah Victoria Peace (Sept 2009)
(Associate)
Brodies LLP, Aberdeen. . . . . (p.723)
T: 01224 392242
E: sarah.gall@brodies.com

GALL, Tessa Iona Arbuthnot (Oct 2016)
(Employee)
Highland Council, Inverness. . . . . (p.1248)
T: 01463 702000
E: Tessa.Gall@highland.gov.uk

GALL, Victoria Patricia Elizabeth (Jan 2009)
(Employee)
Barclays Bank PLC, London E14 . . . . . . (p.1262)
T: 020 3555 1132
E: victoria.gall@barclays.com

GALLACHER, Alison Mary (Oct 1995)
(Employee)
NORTH LANARKSHIREre Council,
Motherwell. . . . . (p.1251)
T: 01698 302196
E: GallacherA@northlan.gov.uk

GALLACHER, Amanda Jane (Jan 2007)
(Employee)
Procurator Fiscal Service, Glasgow . . . . (p.1241)
T: 0300 0203000
E: Amanda.Gallacher@copfs.gov.uk

GALLACHER, Dean John (Mar 2021) (Employee)
Jonathan Paul Solicitors, Alexandria . . . . (p.751)
T: 01389 756785

GALLACHER, Eileen (Mar 1999) (Employee)
Procurator Fiscal Service, Glasgow . . . . (p.1243)
T: (0300) 020 2944
E: eileen.gallagher@copfs.gov.uk

GALLACHER, Jenna Katrina (Dec 2018)
(Employee)
Wright, Johnston & Mackenzie LLP,
Inverness . . . . (p.1083)
T: 01463 234445
E: jkg@wjm.co.uk

GALLACHER, John (Jul 1978) (Consultant)
Morton Fraser LLP, Edinburgh . . . . (p.891)
T: 0131 2471000
E: john.gallacher@morton-fraser.com

GALLACHER, John Paul (Mar 2015) (Director)
Trainor Alston Limited, Coatbridge . . . . (p.787)
T: 01236 600600

GALLACHER, Kathleen Frances (Oct 2017)
(Employee)
Addleshaw Goddard LLP,
Edinburgh . . . . (p.835)
T: 0131 2282400
E: kathleen.gallacher@addleshawgoddard.com

GALLACHER, Kirsty (Oct 2007) (Employee)
Pinsent Masons LLP, Edinburgh . . . . . . (p.895)
T: 0131 7777000
E: kirsty.gallacher@pinsentmasons.com

GALLACHER, Mhari (Jul 2018) (Employee)
Thompsons, Glasgow . . . . (p.1046)
T: 0141 2218840
E: mhari.gallacher@thompsons-scotland.co.uk

GALLACHER, Sophie Jane (Dec 2019)
(Employee)
CMS Cameron McKenna Nabarro Olswang LLP,
London EC4 . . . . (p.1263)
T: 0207 3673000
E: sophie.gallacher@cms-cmno.com

GALLACHER, Stephanie Aileen (Jul 2012)
(Employee)
Scottish Social Services Council,
Dundee . . . . (p.1218)
T: 0345 6030 891
E: Stephanie.Gallacher@sssc.uk.com

GALLACHER, Steven Mark (Jul 2010)
(Employee)
Scottish Social Services Council,
Dundee . . . . (p.1218)
T: 01382 207339
E: Steven.Gallacher@sssc.uk.com

GALLAGHER, Aidan Vincent (Oct 1993)
(Partner)
Aidan Gallagher & Company,
Greenock . . . . (p.1061)
T: 01475 726677
E: aidangallaghersolicitor@gmail.com

GALLAGHER, Ann (Dec 2016) (Employee)
Harper Macleod LLP, Glasgow . . . . (p.983)
T: 0141 2218888
E: ann.gallagher@harpermacleod.co.uk

GALLAGHER, Cheryl Marie (Sept 2016)
(Employee)
Drummond Miller LLP, Glasgow . . . .(p.971)
T: 0141 3320086
E: cgallagher@drummondmiller.co.uk

GALLAGHER, Collette (Oct 2010) (Employee)
Scottish Children's Reporter Administration,
Glasgow . . . .(p.1243)
T: 0300 2001444
E: Collette.Gallagher@scra.gov.uk

GALLAGHER, David Ewart (May 2010)
(Employee)
Brodies LLP, Glasgow . . . .(p.948)
T: 0141 2484672
E: david.gallagher@brodies.com

GALLAGHER, David Joseph (Oct 2019)
(Employee)
Procurator Fiscal Service,
Dumbarton . . . .(p.1217)
T: 0300 020 3000
E: david.gallagher@copfs.gov.uk

GALLAGHER, Gemma Helen (Oct 2011)
(Employee)
DWF LLP, Glasgow . . . .(p.973)
T: 0141 228 8000
E: gemma.gallagher@dwf.law

GALLAGHER, Jennifer (Nov 1998) (Partner)
Lindsays LLP, Dundee . . . .(p.814)
T: 01382 224112
E: JenniferGallagher@lindsays.co.uk

GALLAGHER, John Robert (Jul 2003) (Partner)
McLennan Adam Davis, Ayr . . . .(p.764)
T: 01292 289584
E: johng@mad-law.co.uk

GALLAGHER, Kara (Oct 2015) (Employee)
Shepherd and Wedderburn LLP,
Edinburgh . . . .(p.900)
T: 0131 2289900
E: Kara.Gallagher@Shepwedd.com

GALLAGHER, Kerry (Oct 2007) (Associate)
Lindsays LLP, Edinburgh . . . .(p.882)
T: 0131 2291212
E: KerryGallagher@lindsays.co.uk

GALLAGHER, Lindsay Catherine (Oct 2004)
(Employee)
National Health Service Scotland,
Edinburgh . . . .(p.1225)
T: 0131 2757800
E: Lindsay.gallagher@nhs.scot

GALLAGHER, Louise Alison (Sept 1986)
(Employee)
DAC Beachcroft Scotland LLP,
Glasgow . . . .(p.964)
T: 0141 2486688
E: Louise.Gallagher@blmlaw.com

GALLAGHER, Michael Joseph (Oct 2020)
(Employee)
MacRoberts LLP, Glasgow . . . .(p.1015)
T: 0141 3031100
E: michael.gallagher@macroberts.com

GALLAGHER, Paul John (Dec 2008) (Associate)
Carr & Co (Solicitors) Limited,
Glasgow . . . .(p.957)
T: 0141 6412912/8346
E: pg@theglasgowlawpractice.co.uk

GALLAGHER, Shona (Aug 2005) (Employee)
D.W. Shaw, Ayr . . . .(p.765)
T: 01292 265033
E: sgallagher@dwshaw.co.uk

GALLAGHER, Veronica Mary (Feb 1988)
(Solicitor)
NO FIRM

GALLAHER, Martin (Dec 1998) (Solicitor)
NO FIRM

GALLANAGH, Terence (Jul 1996) (Director)
Paisley Defence Lawyers (Scotland) Limited,
Paisley . . . .(p.1141)
T: 0141 5619999
E: Terry.Gallanagh@mccuskerlaw.co.uk

GALLEN, Michael John (Sept 2000) (Partner)
Fleming & Reid, Glasgow . . . .(p.977)
T: 0141 3311144
E: MJG@flemingandreid.co.uk

GALLEN, Richard Fenwick (Jun 2018)
(Employee)
Harper Macleod LLP, Edinburgh . . . .(p.877)
T: 0131 2472500
E: Richard.Gallen@harpermacleod.co.uk

GALLEN, Roselyn (Sept 2009) (Partner)
Murray Solicitors & Notaries,
Kilmarnock . . . .(p.1096)
T: 07719 043747
E: roselyn.gallen@gmail.com

GALLETLY, Elaine Clare (Nov 1991) (Employee)
Glasgow City Council, Glasgow . . . . . .(p.1239)
T: 0141 2872000
E: elaine.galletly@glasgow.gov.uk

GALLETLY, Peter William (Dec 1981) (Solicitor)
NO FIRM

GALLI, Maria Joanna (Oct 1990) (Employee)
Children & Young People's Commissioner
Scotland, Edinburgh . . . .(p.1221)
T: 0131 346 5350
E: maria.galli@cypcs.org.uk

GALLOWAY, Lucy May (Oct 1989) (Employee)
Scottish Government, Edinburgh . . . . .(p.1231)
T: 0131 244 0815
E: Lucy.Galloway@gov.scot

GALLOWAY, Penelope Elizabeth (Mar 2010)
(Partner)
Elizabeth Welsh Family Law Practice,
Ayr . . . .(p.766)
T: 01292 284786
E: penny.galloway@familylawpractice.co.uk

GALLOWAY, Sharon Ann (Nov 1991) (Partner)
JHS Law, Dumfries . . . .(p.801)
T: 01387 739000
E: sharon.galloway@jhslaw.co.uk

GAMBA, John Stephen (Sept 2001) (Associate)
Gillespie Macandrew LLP,
Edinburgh . . . .(p.872)
T: 0131 2251677
E: stephen.gamba@gillespiemacandrew.co.uk

GAMMIE, Carol Elizabeth (Jun 2010)
(Employee)
Procurator Fiscal Service, Aberdeen . . .(p.1213)
T: 0300 0202336
E: Carol.Gammie@copfs.gov.uk

GANNON, Amy (Oct 2013) (Employee)
Digby Brown LLP, Glasgow . . . .(p.970)
T: 0333 200 5925
E: amy.gannon@digbybrown.co.uk

GANNON, Eleanor Rachel (Nov 2018)
(Employee)
Shepherd and Wedderburn LLP,
Edinburgh . . . .(p.900)
T: 0131 2289900
E: ellie.gannon@shepwedd.com

GANNON, John (Oct 2012) (Employee)
The Royal Bank of Scotland PLC,
Edinburgh . . . .(p.1235)
T: 0131 5568555
E: john.gannon@rbs.co.uk

GANNON, Lucy Rae (Jan 2004) (Partner)
Blackadders LLP, Glasgow . . . .(p.946)
T: 0141 2481888
E: lucy.gannon@blackadders.co.uk

GAPINSKI, Leigh (Aug 2015) (Employee)
Reynolds Porter Chamberlain LLP, London
E1 . . . .(p.1267)
E: leigh.gapinski@rpc.co.uk

GARCIA, Edward Liam (Nov 2006) (Employee)
Nomura Asset Management U.K. Limited,
London EC4 . . . .(p.1266)
E: Edward.Garcia@nomura-asset.co.uk

GARCIA-ALIS, Catriona Lesley Shirreffs
(Sept 2000) (Associate)
CMS Cameron McKenna Nabarro Olswang LLP,
Edinburgh . . . .(p.856)
T: 0131 2288000
E: Catriona.Garcia-Alis@cms-cmno.com

GARDEN, Alexander Kenneth (Oct 1999)
(Partner)
Turcan Connell, Edinburgh . . . .(p.908)
T: 0131 2288111
E: alexander.garden@turcanconnell.com

GARDEN, Christopher George (Mar 2012)
(Employee)
Shepherd and Wedderburn LLP,
Aberdeen . . . .(p.742)
T: 01224 621166
E: christopher.garden@shepwedd.com

GARDEN, Phyllis (Jan 1991) (Partner)
Ledingham Chalmers LLP,
Aberdeen . . . .(p.734)
T: 01224 408408
E: phyllis.garden@ledinghamchalmers.com

GARDINER, Adam Daniel (Nov 2017)
(Employee)
Lindsays LLP, Edinburgh . . . .(p.882)
T: 0131 2291212
E: adamgardiner@lindsays.co.uk

GARDINER, Christopher Peter John
(Jul 2016) (Associate)
MacRoberts LLP, Dundee. . . . .(p.815)
T: 01382 339340
E: chris.gardiner@macroberts.com

GARDINER, Gregory Blair Calderwood
(Sept 2015) (Employee)
Anderson Strathern LLP, Edinburgh . . . .(p.839)
T: 0131 2707700
E: gregory.gardiner@andersonstrathern.co.uk

GARDINER, John (Nov 1980) (Partner)
Turcan Connell, Glasgow. . . . .(p.1049)
T: 0141 441 2111
E: jack.gardiner@turcanconnell.com

GARDINER, Ross James (Jul 2020) (Employee)
Brodies LLP, Aberdeen. . . . .(p.723)
T: 01224 392242
E: ross.gardiner@brodies.com

GARDINER, Ruth Margaret (Apr 2021)
(Employee)
CMS Cameron McKenna Nabarro Olswang LLP,
Aberdeen . . . .(p.727)
T: 01224 622002
E: ruth.gardiner@cms-cmno.com

GARDINER, Stuart George (Aug 2013)
(Associate)
Burness Paull LLP, Aberdeen . . . .(p.724)
T: 01224 621621
E: Stuart.Gardiner@burnesspaull.com

GARDNER, Hannah Claire (Mar 2020)
(Employee)
National Westminster Bank PLC,
Edinburgh . . . .(p.1226)
T: (0131) 626 2925
E: Hannah.gardner@natwest.com

GARDNER, John (Jun 2004) (Partner)
John Gardner and Company,
Paisley . . . .(p.1138)
T: 0141 8896458
E: jg@therobertkerrpartnership.com

GARDNER, Moira (Dec 1992) (Director)
Pacitti Jones Legal Limited,
Bishopbriggs . . . .(p.774)
T: 0141 7722211
E: moira@pjglasgow.co.uk

GARDNER, Ross Alan (Sept 1993) (Partner)
Adams Whyte, Edinburgh . . . .(p.835)
T: 0131 555 7220
E: rossgardner@adamswhyte.com

GARDNER, Ross Scott (Dec 2001) (Partner)
Stronachs LLP, Aberdeen . . . .(p.744)
T: 01224 845845
E: Ross.Gardner@stronachs.com

GARDNER, Sharon (Sept 2001) (Partner)
The Cumbernauld Law Practice,
Cumbernauld . . . .(p.791)
T: 01236 731911
E: sharongardner@cumbernauldlaw.co.uk

GARGAN, Leigh (May 2013) (Employee)
Warners Solicitors LLP, Edinburgh. . . . . .(p.911)
T: 0131 6624747
E: lgargan@warnersllp.com

GARIOCH, Alexander (Oct 1989) (Partner)
Gilson Gray LLP, Edinburgh . . . .(p.874)
T: 0131 5165354
E: agarioch@gilsongray.co.uk

GARLAND, Ailsa Mary (Dec 1998) (Employee)
Scottish Government, Edinburgh . . . . .(p.1231)
T: 0131 244 0815
E: ailsa.garland@gov.scot

GARLAND, Charles Edward Birks (Nov 1995)
(Employee)
Scottish Law Commission,
Edinburgh . . . .(p.1233)
T: 0131 6682131
E: charles.garland@scotlawcom.gov.uk

GARNER, Anne-Marie Mackay (Jan 2001)
(Solicitor)
NO FIRM

GARNESS, Anne Ellanor (Sept 1997)
(Employee)
Scottish Social Services Council,
Dundee . . . .(p.1218)
T: 0345 6030 891
E: Anne.Garness@sssc.uk.com

GARRATT, Frances Elizabeth (Dec 2013)
(Associate)
CMS Cameron McKenna Nabarro Olswang LLP,
Glasgow. . . . .(p.962)
T: 0141 2222200
E: Frances.Garratt@cms-cmno.com

GARRETT, Ruth Helen McLaren (Jan 1986)
(Employee)
National Health Service Scotland,
Edinburgh . . . .(p.1225)
T: 0131 275 7843
E: Ruth.Garrett@nhs.scot

GARRICK, Hannah Jane (Sept 2017) (Employee)
AXA UK Plc, London EC3. . . . .(p.1261)
E: Hannah.garrick@axa-uk.co.uk

GARRIGAN, Rosemary Margaret (Dec 1998)
(Director)
Efficax Limited, Edinburgh . . . .(p.866)
T: 07917 817584
E: rosie@efficax.co

GASKELL, Jonathan Edwin (Oct 2001)
(Employee)
DWF LLP, Edinburgh . . . .(p.865)
T: 0131 2265541
E: jonathan.gaskell@dwf.law

GASS, Graeme Rodger (Oct 2010) (Partner)
Turcan Connell, Edinburgh . . . .(p.908)
T: 0131 2288111
E: graeme.gass@turcanconnell.com

GASTON, Benjamin David (Jul 2019)
(Employee)
Scottish Government, Edinburgh . . . . .(p.1231)
T: 0131 244 0815
E: ben.gaston@gov.scot

GATES, Thomas Edward (Jun 2017) (Employee)
Reed Smith LLP, London EC2. . . . .(p.1267)
E: tgates@reedsmith.com

GATHERUM, Karen (Jan 2020) (Employee)
Aberdeen City Council, Aberdeen. . . . .(p.1211)
T: 01224 522 462
E: Kgatherum@aberdeencity.gov.uk

GATT, Alastair Morrison (Aug 1989)
(Employee)
Minter Ellison Rudd Watt,
Auckland . . . .(p.1275)
E: alastair.gatt@minterellison.co.nz

GAUGHAN, Kathleen (Mar 2017) (Employee)
Lindsays LLP, Glasgow. . . . .(p.1001)
T: 0141 2216551
E: KathleenGaughan@lindsays.co.uk

GAUGHAN, Lindsay Ann (Apr 2012) (Partner)
Cassidys' Advice & Solicitor Services,
Glasgow. . . . .(p.958)
T: 0141 3532195
E: lindsaygaughan@cassidysolicitors.co.uk

GAUGHAN, Shannon Michelle (Jan 2019)
(Employee)
Clarity Simplicity Ltd, East Kilbride . . . . .(p.831)
T: 0141 4332626
E: s.gaughan@claritysimplicity.co.uk

GAULD, Steven Ian (Jul 2009) (Partner)
Brown & McRae LLP, Fraserburgh . . . . . (p.930)
T: 01346 514761
E: Steven@brown-mcrae.co.uk

GAULD, Valerie McDonald (Dec 2004)
(Employee)
Macnabs LLP, Perth . . . . (p.1150)
T: 01738 623432
E: valgauld@macnabs-law.co.uk

GAULE, Lisa Chalmers (Oct 2012) (Employee)
Digby Brown LLP, Edinburgh . . . . (p.862)
T: 0333 200 5925
E: Lisa.Gaule@digbybrown.co.uk

GAULT, Shareen Bibi (Oct 2004) (Employee)
Johnston Carmichael LLP Accountants,
Glasgow. (p.1240)
T: 0141 2225800
E: Shareen.Gault@jcca.co.uk

GAVIN, Adrian Matthew (Sept 1999)
(Employee)
Repsol Sinopec Resources UK Limited,
Aberdeen . . . . (p.1213)
T: 01224 352500
E: adrian.gavin@repsolsinopecuk.com

GAVIN, Kathryn Jane Graham (Mar 2013)
(Associate)
DAC Beachcroft Scotland LLP,
Glasgow. (p.964)
T: 0141 2486688
E: kgavin@dacbeachcroft.com

GAVIN, Susan Norma (Nov 2000) (Employee)
BP Exploration Operating Company Ltd.,
Dyce . . . . (p.1219)
T: 01224 832353
E: Susan.Gavin@uk.bp.com

GEAR, Jennifer Morag (Sept 2009) (Employee)
Harper Macleod LLP, Lerwick . . . . (p.1113)
T: 01595 695583
E: jenni.gear@harpermacleod.co.uk

GECEVICIUTE, Gabriele Ruta (Jan 2021)
(Solicitor)
Pinsent Masons LLP, London EC2 . . . . . (p.1267)
T: 020 7418 7000
E: gabriele.geceviciute@pinsentmasons.com

GEDDES, David James Irving (Dec 1994)
(Director)
Irving Geddes, WS Limited, Crieff . . . . . . (p.788)
T: 01764 653 771
E: david@irvinggeddes.co.uk

GEDDES, Fraser Alexander John (Jan 1994)
(Partner)
Anderson Strathern LLP, Glasgow . . . . . . (p.940)
T: 0141 2426060
E: fraser.geddes@andersonstrathern.co.uk

GEDDES, John Smith (Aug 2009) (Employee)
CMS Cameron McKenna Nabarro Olswang LLP,
Dubai . . . . (p.1278)
T: +971 4374 2813
E: john.geddes@cms-cmno.com

GEDDES, Marjory Elizabeth (Sept 1995)
(Employee)
Dundee City Council, Dundee . . . . (p.1217)
T: 01382 434000
E: madge.geddes@dundeecity.gov.uk

GEDDES, Norman George (Oct 1976)
(Director)
Frazer Coogans Ltd, Ayr . . . . (p.763)
T: 01292 280499
E: norman.geddes@frazercoogans.co.uk

GEE, Calum (Jun 2011) (Associate)
Harper Macleod LLP, Edinburgh . . . . . . (p.877)
T: 0131 247 2551
E: Calum.Gee@harpermacleod.co.uk

GEEKIE, Scott Miller (Jun 2003) (Associate)
Lindsays LLP, Edinburgh . . . . (p.882)
T: 0131 2291212
E: scottgeekie@lindsays.co.uk

GEHLEN, Nadia Neelum (Jul 2015) (Associate)
DLA Piper Scotland LLP, Edinburgh . . . . (p.863)
T: 08700 111111
E: nadia.gehlen@dlapiper.com

GELL, Alexandra (Dec 2016) (Employee)
Turcan Connell, Edinburgh . . . . (p.908)
T: 0131 2288111
E: alexandra.gell@turcanconnell.com

GEMMELL, Cheree Flora (Jul 2015) (Associate)
Freshfields Bruckhaus Deringer, Abu
Dhabi . . . . (p.1277)
T: + 971 2652 1706
E: Cheree.GEMMELL@freshfields.com

GEMMELL, Kirsty Catherine Anne Hird
(Mar 2000) (Employee)
Maguire Solicitors, Glasgow . . . . (p.1017)
T: 0141 3312885
E: kirsty@maguiresolicitors.co.uk

GEMMELL, Lorna Pauline (Oct 2006)
(Employee)
Law at Work Ltd, Glasgow . . . . (p.1240)
T: 0141 2715555
E: lorna.gemmell@lawatwork.co.uk

GEMMELL, Shelby Alana (Aug 2021)
(Employee)
Burness Paull LLP, Edinburgh . . . . (p.850)
T: 0131 4736000
E: shelby.gemmell@burnesspaull.com

GEMMELL, William Ruthven, WS (Dec 1981)
(Partner)
Murray Beith Murray, Edinburgh . . . . . . (p.893)
T: 0131 2251200
E: ruthven.gemmell@murraybeith.co.uk

GEMMILL, Thomas William (Nov 1981)
(Partner)
Carruthers Gemmill, Glasgow . . . .(p.958)
T: 0141 3330 033
E: twg@carruthersgemmill.co.uk

GENTLE, Chloe Margaret (Aug 2019)
(Employee)
Morton Fraser LLP, Edinburgh . . . .(p.891)
T: 0131 2471000
E: chloe.gentle@morton-fraser.com

GENTLES, Rosa-Maria Vittoria (Dec 2011)
(Employee)
Scottish Legal Aid Board,
   Edinburgh . . . .(p.1233)
T: 0131 2267061
E: gentlesro@slab.org.uk

GEOGHEGAN, Paul James Thomas
(Oct 2007) (Partner)
Morton Fraser LLP, Edinburgh . . . .(p.891)
T: 0131 2471000
E: paul.geoghegan@morton-fraser.com

GEORGE, Heather Margaret (Nov 2007)
(Associate)
Taylor & Henderson LLP, Irvine . . . . . .(p.1087)
T: 01294 278306
E: hgeorge@taylorandhenderson.co.uk

GEORGE, Linda Elizabeth (Oct 1991) (Director)
Linda George Family Law Limited,
   Hamilton . . . .(p.1067)
T: 01698 459200
E: leg@lgfamilylaw.co.uk

GEORGE, Owen Daniel (Aug 2010) (Employee)
Brodies LLP, Glasgow . . . .(p.948)
T: 0141 2484672
E: Daniel.George@brodies.com

GEORGE, Shaun Arthur (Oct 1988) (Partner)
Brodies LLP, Aberdeen. . . . .(p.723)
T: 01224 392242
E: shaun.george@brodies.com

GEORGESON, Gary Peter (Jan 2008) (Associate)
CMS Cameron McKenna Nabarro Olswang LLP,
   Edinburgh . . . .(p.856)
T: 0131 2288000
E: Gary.Georgeson@cms-cmno.com

GEORGIEV, Yavor Miroslavov (Aug 2019)
(Associate)
Addleshaw Goddard LLP,
   Edinburgh . . . .(p.835)
T: 0131 2282400
E: Yavor.Georgiev@addleshawgoddard.com

GERAGHTY, Pauline (Sept 1995) (Associate)
Buchanan Burton Limited, East
   Kilbride . . . .(p.830)
T: 01355 249228
E: paulineg@buchananburton.co.uk

GERBER, David Roger (Oct 2001) (Employee)
Bracher Rawlins LLP, London WC2 . . . .(p.1262)
T: 0207 4001540
E: David.Gerber@bracherrawlins.co.uk

GERBER, Kenneth Steven (Dec 1980) (Director)
Mitchells Roberton Ltd, Glasgow . . . . .(p.1020)
T: 0141 5523422
E: ksg@mitchells-roberton.co.uk

GERRARD, Callum David (Nov 1983) (Solicitor)
NO FIRM

GERVAISE, Rachel Magdalene (Sept 1999)
(Employee)
Zonal Retail Data Systems Limited,
   Edinburgh . . . .(p.1236)
T: 07970 172738
E: Rachel.Gervaise@zonal.co.uk

GERVER, Alexander Nathaniel (Aug 1994)
(Solicitor)
NO FIRM

GETTINBY, Michael John (Feb 2005)
(Employee)
University of St Andrews
T: 07541 675359
E: mike.gettinby@st-andrews.ac.uk

GHAFAR, Shagufta (Mar 2010) (Director)
Ghafar & Co Ltd, Glasgow . . . .(p.979)
T: 0141 4237800
E: sghafar@ghafarandco.co.uk

GHAFAR, Shamielah (Oct 2017) (Employee)
Scottish Social Services Council,
   Dundee . . . .(p.1218)
T: 0345 6030 891
E: shamielah.ghafar@sssc.uk.com

GHEE, Gordon Arnott (Nov 1987) (Partner)
Nellany & Company LLP, Saltcoats. . . .(p.1160)
T: 01294 464175
E: gordon@nellanysols.co.uk

GIANNELLI, Paula Elaine (Sept 2005) (Director)
GWG Ltd, Glasgow. . . . .(p.982)
T: 0141 7769960
E: paula@gwg-ltd.com

GIANOLA, Danica Maria Teresa (Jul 2017)
(Employee)
Studio Legale Danica M.T. Gianola,
   Lugano . . . .(p.1277)
T: +41 91 921 24 43
E: avv.danica.gianola@icloud.com

GIBB, Alexandra Jane (Sept 2017) (Employee)
Pinsent Masons LLP, Edinburgh . . . . . .(p.895)
T: 0131 777 7000
E: alexandra.gibb@pinsentmasons.com

GIBB, Amanda Jane (Jul 2012) (Associate)
Raeburn Christie Clark & Wallace LLP,
   Aberdeen . . . .(p.741)
T: 01224 332400
E: amanda.gibb@raeburns.co.uk

GIBB, Fiona Helen, WS (Jan 1984) (Partner)
Anderson Strathern LLP, Edinburgh . . . . (p.839)
　T: 0131 2707700
　E: fiona.gibb@andersonstrathern.co.uk

GIBB, Freya Fiona (Aug 2018) (Employee)
DWF LLP, Glasgow . . . . (p.973)
　T: 0141 228 8000
　E: freya.gibb@dwf.law

GIBB, Justyna Dominika (Nov 2020) (Employee)
Digby Brown LLP, Edinburgh . . . . (p.862)
　T: 0333 200 5925
　E: justyna.gibb@digbybrown.co.uk

GIBB, Kathryn Louise (Jun 2011) (Associate)
Walker Laird, Paisley . . . . (p.1142)
　T: 0141 847 4948
　E: kathryn.gibb@walkerlaird.co.uk

GIBB, Lorna Jane (Dec 2003) (Employee)
Nokia, London W2 . . . . (p.1266)
　E: lorna.gibb@nokia.com

GIBB, Morag Agnes (Mar 1991) (Employee)
BTO Solicitors LLP, Glasgow . . . . (p.952)
　T: 0141 2218012
　E: MXG@bto.co.uk

GIBB, Natalie Leslie (Sept 2012) (Associate)
Clyde & Co (Scotland) LLP,
　Edinburgh . . . . (p.855)
　T: 0131 5571545
　E: natalie.gibb@clydeco.com

GIBB, Nigel Quentin Dewar (Jan 1989)
　(Employee)
Lewis Silkin LLP, London EC4 . . . . (p.1266)
　T: 0207 0748 137
　E: Nigel.dewargibb@lewissilkin.com

GIBB, Rachel (Jun 2019) (Employee)
Dentons UK and Middle East LLP,
　Glasgow. (p.968)
　T: 0330 2220050
　E: Rachel.Gibb@dentons.com

GIBB, Robert James Forsyth (Sept 2015)
　(Employee)
Latta Law Limited, Glasgow . . . . (p.998)
　T: 0141 222 2185

GIBB, Roderick Bruce (Nov 2003) (Employee)
D. Duheric & Co Solicitors,
　Edinburgh . . . . (p.865)
　T: 0131 2255444
　E: roddy.gibb@dduhericsolicitors.co.uk

GIBB, Stephen John (Dec 1988) (Partner)
Shepherd and Wedderburn LLP,
　Edinburgh . . . . (p.900)
　T: 0131 2289900
　E: Stephen.Gibb@shepwedd.com

GIBB, Stuart Hamilton Ferguson (Mar 1986)
　(Associate)
Turcan Connell, Glasgow . . . . (p.1049)
　T: 0141 441 2111
　E: stuart.gibb@turcanconnell.com

GIBB, Susan Mary (Jun 2004) (Employee)
Capricorn Energy Ltd, Edinburgh . . . . . (p.1221)
　T: 0131 4753000
　E: susan.gibb@cairnenergy.com

GIBBONS, Aimee Louise (Jul 2014) (Employee)
Thorntons Law LLP, Dundee . . . . (p.819)
　T: 01382 229 111
　E: agibbons@thorntons-law.co.uk

GIBBONS, Gillian Ann (May 2007) (Employee)
Blackadders LLP, Dundee. . . . . (p.805)
　T: 01382 229222
　E: Gillian.gibbons@blackadders.co.uk

GIBBONS, Jennifer (Oct 2013) (Employee)
DLA Piper UK LLP, London EC1 . . . . . . (p.1263)
　T: 020 77966017
　E: Jennifer.Gibbons@dlapiper.com

GIBBONS, Karen Louise (Sept 2004) (Partner)
Harper Macleod LLP, Edinburgh . . . . . . (p.877)
　T: 0131 2472500
　E: Karen.Gibbons@harpermacleod.co.uk

GIBBS, Arlene Louise (Feb 2013) (Employee)
Aberdeenshire Council, Aberdeen . . . . . (p.1211)
　T: 01467 538089
　E: arlene.gibbs@aberdeenshire.gov.uk

GIBLIN, Jonathan William (Oct 2019)
　(Employee)
Weightmans (Scotland) LLP,
　Glasgow. (p.1051)
　T: 0345 073 9900
　E: jonathan.giblin@weightmans.com

GIBSON, Alan David (Sept 2016) (Employee)
Burness Paull LLP, Edinburgh . . . . (p.850)
　T: 0131 4736000
　E: alan.gibson@burnesspaull.com

GIBSON, Andrew Robert (Oct 2002) (Associate)
Morton Fraser LLP, Glasgow . . . . (p.1022)
　T: 0141 2741100
　E: Andrew.Gibson@morton-fraser.com

GIBSON, Carlene Louise (Nov 2012)
　(Employee)
Stuart & Stuart, Edinburgh . . . . (p.905)
　T: 0131 2286449
　E: cgibson@stuartandstuart.co.uk

GIBSON, Christopher Duncan (Jan 2010)
　(Partner)
Gillespie Macandrew LLP,
　Edinburgh . . . . (p.872)
　T: 0131 2251677
　E: chris.gibson@gillespiemacandrew.co.uk

GIBSON, Collette (Mar 2014) (Associate)
Shoosmiths LLP, Glasgow . . . .(p.1040)
T: 0370 086 8300
E: collette.gibson@shoosmiths.co.uk

GIBSON, Dana Lesley (Sept 2012) (Employee)
IMG (UK) Ltd, London W4 . . . .(p.1265)
T: 020 8233 5300
E: dana.gibson@img.com

GIBSON, David Bisset (Oct 1986) (Partner)
BTO Solicitors LLP, Glasgow . . . .(p.952)
T: 0141 2218012
E: dbg@bto.co.uk

GIBSON, Fraser Alexander Wright
(Feb 1993) (Employee)
Procurator Fiscal Service, Hamilton . . . .(p.1247)
T: 0844 5613245
E: fraser.gibson@copfs.gov.uk

GIBSON, Garry (Oct 1986) (Associate)
Lindsays LLP, Glasgow. . . . .(p.1001)
T: 0141 2216551
E: garrygibson@lindsays.co.uk

GIBSON, Gemma Ann (Jul 2013) (Employee)
Littlewoods Limited, Liverpool . . . .(p.1260)
T: 0844 292 2630
E: gemma.gibson@theverygroup.com

GIBSON, Graham MacFarlane (Jan 1983)
(Director)
Kirklands Law Limited, Perth . . . .(p.1149)
T: 01738 500 764
E: gmg@kirklands-law.co.uk

GIBSON, Graham Martin (Feb 2015) (Solicitor)
NO FIRM

GIBSON, Hannah Elizabeth (Mar 2021)
(Employee)
CMS Cameron McKenna Nabarro Olswang LLP,
Glasgow. . . . .(p.962)
T: 0141 2222200
E: hannah.gibson@cms-cmno.com

GIBSON, Hayley Sherry (Feb 2013) (Employee)
Hymans Robertson LLP, Glasgow . . . . .(p.1240)
T: 0141 5667777
E: hayley.gibson@hymans.co.uk

GIBSON, Heather (Apr 2008) (Associate)
Brodies LLP, Glasgow . . . .(p.948)
T: 0141 2484672
E: heather.gibson@brodies.com

GIBSON, Ian James (Oct 2006) (Employee)
Brodies LLP, Aberdeen. . . . .(p.723)
T: 01224 392242
E: ian.gibson@brodies.com

GIBSON, James (Jan 1977) (Partner)
Mathie, Lennox & Co., Kilsyth . . . .(p.1097)
T: 01236 823139
E: jgibson@mathielennox.co.uk

GIBSON, James Stuart (Jan 2013) (Associate)
Pinsent Masons LLP, Edinburgh . . . . . .(p.895)
T: 0131 777 7000
E: james.gibson@pinsentmasons.com

GIBSON, Karen Judith (Aug 2015) (Solicitor)
NO FIRM

GIBSON, Kate Elizabeth (May 2016)
(Employee)
OVO (S) Electricity Ltd, Perth . . . .(p.1253)
E: kate.gibson@sseenergyservices.com

GIBSON, Kelsey Thomson (Aug 1986) (Partner)
MacRoberts LLP, Glasgow . . . .(p.1015)
T: 0141 3031100
E: kelsey.gibson@macroberts.com

GIBSON, Kevin (Dec 2006) (Employee)
Scottish Government, Edinburgh . . . . .(p.1231)
T: 0131 244 0815
E: kevin.gibson@gov.scot

GIBSON, Lauren Muriel (Mar 2015) (Employee)
Brodies LLP, Edinburgh . . . .(p.845)
T: 0131 2283777
E: lauren.gibson@brodies.com

GIBSON, Lisa Grace (Jun 2010) (Associate)
Brodies LLP, Edinburgh . . . .(p.845)
T: 0131 2283777
E: lisa.gibson@brodies.com

GIBSON, Louise (Aug 2005) (Associate)
MacRoberts LLP, Glasgow . . . .(p.1015)
T: 0141 303 1144
E: Louise.Gibson@macroberts.com

GIBSON, Mairi Anne (Nov 1991) (Employee)
Revenue Scotland, Edinburgh . . . .(p.1230)
E: mairi.gibson@revenue.scot

GIBSON, Mark Dalziel (Oct 2004) (Partner)
Digby Brown LLP, Glasgow . . . .(p.970)
T: 0333 200 5925
E: mark.gibson@digbybrown.co.uk

GIBSON, Nicola Kay (Aug 2007) (Partner)
Sturrock, Armstrong & Thomson,
Edinburgh . . . .(p.905)
T: 0131 5560159
E: ng@satsolicitors.co.uk

GIBSON, Robert Andrew (Aug 2014)
(Employee)
Procurator Fiscal Service, Hamilton . . . .(p.1247)
T: 0844 5613245
E: andrew.gibson@copfs.gov.uk

GIBSON, Ross Balfour (Feb 2021) (Employee)
Shepherd and Wedderburn LLP,
Edinburgh . . . .(p.900)
T: 0131 2289900
E: ross.gibson@shepwedd.com

GIBSON, Scott Henry (Nov 2012) (Employee)
Hogan Lovells International LLP, London
EC1 . . . .(p.1265)
T: 020 7296 2000
E: scott.gibson@hoganlovells.com

GIBSON, Shannon Kerry Joanne (Jun 2014)
(Partner)
Walker & Sharpe, Dumfries . . . .(p.803)
T: 01387 267222
E: Shannon.Gibson@walker-sharpe.co.uk

GIBSON, Stewart (Apr 2015) (Employee)
Brodies LLP, Edinburgh . . . .(p.845)
T: 0131 2283777
E: stewart.gibson@brodies.com

GIBSON, Stuart James (Jul 2008) (Associate)
Frazer Coogans Ltd, Ayr . . . .(p.763)
T: 01292 280499
E: stuart.gibson@frazercoogans.co.uk

GIBSON, Susan Elizabeth (Jul 2009) (Employee)
Penmans, Glasgow . . . .(p.1031)
T: 0141 3366646
E: sgpenmans@gmail.com

GIBSON, William George (Nov 1987) (Director)
Ennova Limited, Edinburgh . . . .(p.869)
T: 0131 6624555
E: bgibson@ennova-law.com

GILBERT, Caitlin Grace Esther (Feb 2017)
(Employee)
Freelands, Wishaw . . . .(p.1181)
T: 01698 355936
E: CGilbert@freelands.co.uk

GILBERT, Karen Anne Duncan (Jul 2010)
(Solicitor)
CIGNA Insurance Middle East S.A.L,
Dubai . . . .(p.1277)
E: Karen.Gilbert@Cigna.com

GILBERT, Laura Elizabeth (Oct 2007)
(Associate)
MacRoberts LLP, Edinburgh . . . .(p.887)
T: 0131 229 5046
E: Laura.Gilbert@macroberts.com

GILBERT, Samantha Diane (Sept 2011)
(Employee)
Aberdein Considine and Company,
Aberdeen . . . .(p.718)
T: 01224 589700
E: smorrice@acandco.com

GILBERTSON, Thomas John (Aug 2013)
(Director)
John W. Gilbertson Limited,
Glenrothes . . . .(p.1057)
T: 01592 759557
E: tom@johnwgilbertson.co.uk

GILCHRIST, Allyson (Nov 2007) (Director)
Mitchells Roberton Ltd, Glasgow . . . . .(p.1020)
T: 0141 5523422
E: ag@mitchells-roberton.co.uk

GILCHRIST, Colin Robert (Nov 1988)
(Employee)
Scottish Government, Edinburgh . . . . .(p.1231)
T: 0131 5285643
E: Colin.Gilchrist@gov.scot

GILCHRIST, David William (Nov 2001)
(Solicitor)
Castletown Law Limited,
Edinburgh . . . .(p.853)
T: 0131 2403880
E: David.Gilchrist@castletownlaw.com

GILCHRIST, Ewan Caldwell (Nov 1996)
(Partner)
Dickson Minto, Edinburgh . . . .(p.861)
T: 0131 2254455
E: ewan.gilchrist@dmws.com

GILCHRIST, Karen (Aug 1999) (Employee)
Hymans Robertson LLP, Edinburgh . . . .(p.1223)
T: 0131 656 5187
E: Karen.Gilchrist@hymans.co.uk

GILCHRIST, Lindsay Mairi (Aug 2006)
(Employee)
Wrights, Motherwell . . . .(p.1128)
T: 01698 267361
E: lindsay.gilchrist@wrightsolicitors.com

GILCHRIST, Lynsey Sheilagh (Aug 2003)
(Employee)
SSE PLC, Glasgow . . . .(p.1244)
T: (0141) 224 7248
E: lynsey.gilchrist@sse.com

GILCHRIST, Rachel Marion (Oct 2016)
(Employee)
Gillespie Macandrew LLP,
Edinburgh . . . .(p.872)
T: 0131 2251677
E: rae.gilchrist@gillespiemacandrew.co.uk

GILCHRIST, Shaunagh Mairead (Oct 2017)
(Employee)
TLT LLP, Glasgow . . . .(p.1048)
T: 0333 006 0400
E: Shaunagh.Gilchrist@TLTsolicitors.com

GILCHRIST, Susan (Dec 1997) (Associate)
Pinsent Masons LLP, Glasgow . . . .(p.1031)
T: 0141 567 8400
E: sue.gilchrist@pinsentmasons.com

GILDA, Jocelyn Louise (Feb 2009) (Employee)
Harper Macleod LLP, Glasgow . . . .(p.983)
T: 0141 2218888
E: Jocelyn.Gilda@harpermacleod.co.uk

GILDEA, John Connell (Dec 1991) (Associate)
John Jackson & Dick Limited,
Hamilton . . . . (p.1067)
T: 01698 281747
E: jgildea@jacksondicklaw.com

GILFEDDER, Brian Gerard (Oct 1976) (Director)
Gilfedder & McInnes Limited,
Edinburgh . . . . (p.872)
T: 0131 5543550
E: gilfedder@btconnect.com

GILFILLAN, Alan Robert John (Jul 2010)
(Partner)
Balfour + Manson LLP, Edinburgh . . . . . (p.841)
T: 0131 2001200
E: Alan.Gilfillan@balfour-manson.co.uk

GILFILLAN, Ruth (May 2021) (Employee)
Hughes Dowdall, Glasgow. . . . . (p.987)
T: 0141 2407020
E: ruth.gilfillan@hughesdowdall.com

GILHOOLY, Caragh Meriel (Mar 2018)
(Employee)
Aberdeen City Council, Aberdeen. . . . . (p.1211)
T: 01224 522000
E: CGilhooly@aberdeencity.gov.uk

GILHOOLY, Matthew Thomas (Sept 2016)
(Employee)
Dentons UK and Middle East LLP, London
EC4 . . . . (p.1263)
T: 020 7242 1212
E: matthew.gilhooly@dentons.com

GILIUS, Keir Diarmid (Feb 2017) (Employee)
Black Hay, Ayr . . . . (p.760)
T: 01292 268988
E: keir.gilius@blackhay.co.uk

GILKINSON, Anne Elizabeth (Nov 1994)
(Employee)
Robertson Capital Projects Limited,
Stirling. . . . . (p.1254)
T: 01786 277865
E: a.gilkinson@robertson.co.uk

GILL, Beljit Kaur (Dec 1996) (Partner)
BK Gill Solicitors, Bearsden . . . . (p.772)
T: 0141 9423007
E: bel@bkgillsolicitors.com

GILL, Eleanor Jane (Jan 2014) (Employee)
Helical Plc, London W1 . . . . (p.1265)
T: 020 7629 0113
E: eg@helical.co.uk

GILL, Muneeb Javed (Oct 2016) (Solicitor)
NO FIRM

GILL, Trudy Ann (Nov 2010) (Employee)
Fiona McPhail Solicitors, Edinburgh . . . . (p.886)
T: 0344 5152410
E: trudy_gill@shelter.org.uk

GILLAM, Neil (Oct 2002) (Employee)
Unite the Union, London WC1 . . . . (p.1269)
E: neil.gillam@unitetheunion.org

GILLAN, Claire (Sept 2007) (Employee)
Falkirk Council, Falkirk . . . . (p.1236)
T: 01324 506070
E: claire.gillan@falkirk.gov.uk

GILLAN, Fiona Sarah (Oct 2013) (Solicitor)
NO FIRM

GILLAN, Rachel (Sept 2019) (Solicitor)
CMS Cameron McKenna Nabarro Olswang LLP,
Edinburgh . . . . (p.856)
T: 0131 2288000

GILLAN, Wendy Ann (Feb 2003) (Employee)
Pinsent Masons LLP, Glasgow . . . . (p.1031)
T: 0141 567 8400
E: wendy.gillan@pinsentmasons.com

GILLARD, Nicola Margaret (Mar 1990) (Partner)
Neill Clerk & Murray, Greenock . . . . . . (p.1062)
T: 01475 724522
E: nmg@neillclerkmurray.co.uk

GILLES, June Valerie (Dec 1983) (Employee)
CMS Cameron McKenna Nabarro Olswang LLP,
Edinburgh . . . . (p.856)
T: 0131 2288000
E: june.gilles@cms-cmno.com

GILLESPIE, Caroline (Nov 1989) (Employee)
Berrymans Lace Mawer LLP,
Glasgow. . . . . (p.945)
T: 0141 3532121
E: Caroline.Gillespie@blmlaw.com

GILLESPIE, John Mark (Sept 2000) (Associate)
Pinsent Masons LLP, Edinburgh . . . . . . (p.895)
T: 0131 777 7000
E: mark.gillespie@pinsentmasons.com

GILLESPIE, Kirstin Fiona (Mar 2019) (Employee)
Brodies LLP, Glasgow . . . . (p.948)
T: 0141 2484672
E: Kirstin.Gillespie@brodies.com

GILLESPIE, Linda Jane (Jan 2015) (Employee)
DAC Beachcroft Scotland LLP,
Glasgow. . . . . (p.964)
T: 0141 2486688
E: lgillespie@dacbeachcroft.com

GILLESPIE, Lisa Ann (Aug 2011) (Director)
Morison & Smith Limited, Lanark. . . . . (p.1108)
T: 01555 662488
E: lisa@morisonandsmith.com

GILLESPIE, Michael John (Oct 1995) (Employee)
BAM PPP UK Limited, stepps . . . . (p.1254)
T: 0141 7798609
E: michael.gillespie@bam.com

GILLESPIE, Niamh Patricia (Sept 2010)
(Employee)
Lloyds Banking Group Plc,
Edinburgh . . . .(p.1224)
T: (0131) 442 9579
E: niamh.gillespie@lloydsbanking.com

GILLESPIE, Nicola (Oct 2000) (Employee)
Procurator Fiscal Service, Dundee . . . . .(p.1218)
T: 01382 342559
E: nicola.gillespie@copfs.gov.uk

GILLIATT, Karagh Elisabeth Scott (May 2000)
(Partner)
CMS Cameron McKenna Nabarro Olswang LLP,
Edinburgh . . . .(p.856)
T: 0131 2288000
E: Karagh.Gilliatt@cms-cmno.com

GILLICK, Marisa Nicole (Jul 2016) (Employee)
Scottish Government's Parliamentary Counsel
Office, Edinburgh . . . .(p.1233)
T: 0131 244 1668
E: marisa.gillick@gov.scot

GILLIES, Alana (Jan 2008) (Employee)
Mourant Ozannes, St Helier . . . .(p.1274)
T: 1481731513
E: Alana.Gillies@mourantozannes.com

GILLIES, Alasdair Duncan (Sept 2000) (Partner)
BTO Solicitors LLP, Glasgow . . . .(p.952)
T: 0141 2218012
E: adg@bto.co.uk

GILLIES, Alasdair Henry (May 1983) (Associate)
Anderson Strathern LLP, Glasgow . . . . . .(p.940)
T: 0141 2426060
E: Alasdair.Gillies@andersonstrathern.co.uk

GILLIES, Angus Macdonald (Jun 2012)
(Employee)
BTO Solicitors LLP, Glasgow . . . .(p.952)
T: 0141 2218012
E: agi@bto.co.uk

GILLIES, Colin Alexander (Jul 2016) (Employee)
Burness Paull LLP, Edinburgh . . . .(p.850)
T: 0131 4736000

GILLIES, Fraser Anthony Brian (Oct 2001)
(Partner)
Wright, Johnston & Mackenzie LLP,
Edinburgh . . . .(p.913)
T: 0131 5241500
E: fzg@wjm.co.uk

GILLIES, Joanne (Nov 2001) (Partner)
Pinsent Masons LLP, Glasgow . . . .(p.1031)
T: 0141 567 8400
E: joanne.gillies@pinsentmasons.com

GILLIES, John Ian (Aug 1985) (Partner)
Gillies Maxwell, Ayr . . . .(p.763)
T: 01292 288860
E: enquiries@gilliesmaxwell.com

GILLIES, Kate Louise (Mar 2009) (Employee)
Harper Macleod LLP, Edinburgh . . . .(p.877)
T: 0131 2472500
E: kate.gillies@harpermacleod.co.uk

GILLIES, Katherine Elizabeth (Oct 2010)
(Employee)
Turcan Connell, Edinburgh . . . .(p.908)
T: 0131 2288111
E: katy.gillies@turcanconnell.com

GILLIES, Louise Mary (Aug 2007) (Employee)
Ness Gallagher Solicitors Limited,
Motherwell . . . .(p.1127)
T: 01698 254644
E: LG@nessgallagher.co.uk

GILLIES, Stuart Michael (Mar 2015) (Associate)
Dentons UK and Middle East LLP,
Edinburgh . . . .(p.860)
T: 0330 2220050
E: Stuart.Gillies@dentons.com

GILLIGAN, Eric John (Nov 1997) (Employee)
CMS Cameron McKenna Nabarro Olswang LLP,
Aberdeen . . . .(p.727)
T: 01224 622002
E: Eric.Gilligan@cms-cmno.com

GILLILAND, Emma Lauren (Sept 2021)
(Employee)
Procurator Fiscal Service,
Edinburgh . . . .(p.1227)
T: 0300 0203168
E: emma.gilliland@copfs.gov.uk

GILLON, Caitlin Lynda (Nov 2021) (Employee)
Kingsley Wood & Co Solicitors Limited,
Kilmacolm . . . .(p.1093)
T: 01505 874114
E: cgillon@kingsleywood.co.uk

GILLON, Susan Christine (Feb 1989) (Associate)
Dentons UK and Middle East LLP,
Glasgow . . . .(p.968)
T: 0330 2220050
E: Susan.Gillon@dentons.com

GILMARTIN, Charmaine (Jul 2006) (Employee)
Procurator Fiscal Service, Dundee . . . . .(p.1218)
T: 01382 342559
E: charmaine.gilmartin@copfs.gov.uk

GILMARTIN, Kirsty Margaret Mary
(Sept 2012) (Employee)
Janus Henderson Investors, London
EC2 . . . .(p.1265)
E: kirsty.gilmartin@Janushenderson.com

GILMARTIN, Kristofer Gerald (Jul 2003)
(Director)
Kris Gilmartin Solicitor Advocate Ltd,
Dundee . . . .(p.813)
T: 07540 400871
E: krisgilmartin@sol-ad.co.uk

GILMARTIN, Michael Alexander Stuart
(Sept 2004) (Employee)
Harper Macleod LLP, Edinburgh . . . . (p.877)
T: 0131 2472500
E: Michael.Gilmartin@harpermacleod.co.uk

GILMORE, Claire Marie (Jan 2007) (Employee)
Traffic Commissioner for Scotland,
Edinburgh . . . . (p.1235)
T: 0131 2004905

GILMOUR, Andrew Kenneth (Sept 1998)
(Partner)
Berrymans Lace Mawer LLP,
Glasgow. . . . . (p.945)
T: 0141 3532121
E: Andrew.Gilmour@blmlaw.com

GILMOUR, Jennifer Helen (Aug 2016)
(Employee)
Procurator Fiscal Service, Glasgow . . . . (p.1241)
T: 0300 0203000
E: jennifer.gilmour@copfs.gov.uk

GILMOUR, Joan Ann (Sept 2014) (Employee)
Procurator Fiscal Service,
Edinburgh . . . . (p.1227)
T: 0300 0203168
E: joanne.gilmour@copfs.gov.uk

GILMOUR, Melissa Jane (Aug 1999) (Partner)
Low Beaton Richmond LLP,
Glasgow. . . . . (p.1005)
T: 0141 2218931
E: Melissa@lbr-law.co.uk

GILMOUR, Pamela Marie (Jun 2006)
(Employee)
Pinsent Masons LLP, Edinburgh . . . . . . (p.895)
T: 0131 7777000
E: pamela.gilmour@pinsentmasons.com

GILMOUR, Robert Lister (Oct 1996) (Partner)
SKO Family Law Specialists LLP,
Edinburgh . . . . (p.903)
T: 0131 3226669
E: robert.gilmour@sko-family.co.uk

GILMOUR, Simon George (Jul 2011)
(Employee)
Bruce McCormack Limited,
Motherwell. . . . . (p.1127)
T: 01698 260033
E: admin@brucethelawyers.co.uk

GILMOUR, Sophie (Nov 2005) (Employee)
Aberdeen Corporate Services Limited,
Edinburgh . . . . (p.1220)
T: 0131 245 7508
E: Sophie.Gilmour@abrdn.com

GILMOUR, William (Mar 2007) (Employee)
Health Law Limited, Edinburgh . . . . . . (p.878)
T: 0800 920 2080
E: wg@health-law.uk

GILPIN, Emma Louise (Aug 2005) (Employee)
The Institute and Faculty of Actuaries,
Edinburgh . . . . (p.1234)
T: (020) 7632 1488
E: Emma.Gilpin@actuaries.org.uk

GILROY, Edward (Sept 1991) (Partner)
Gilroy & Co, Glasgow . . . . (p.980)
T: 0141 429 3344
E: eddie.gilroy@btinternet.com

GILROY, Kevin James (Oct 2009) (Employee)
Dechert LLP, London EC4 . . . . (p.1263)
T: 020 7184 7000
E: kevin.gilroy@dechert.com

GILSON, Alison Mary (Oct 2002) (Partner)
Shoosmiths, Edinburgh . . . . (p.902)
T: 0131 2708123
E: alison.gilson@shoosmiths.co.uk

GILSON, Glen Douglas (Nov 2003) (Partner)
Gilson Gray LLP, Edinburgh . . . . (p.874)
T: 0131 5165354
E: ggilson@gilsongray.co.uk

GILZEAN, Sarah Anne (Oct 2003) (Associate)
Morton Fraser LLP, Edinburgh . . . . (p.891)
T: 0131 2471000
E: sarah.gilzean@morton-fraser.com

GINDHA, Rahul (Aug 2005) (Employee)
Impact Radius Limited, London
W1 . . . . (p.1265)
E: rahul.gindha@impact.com

GINN, Tracey Margaret (Aug 1988) (Partner)
MBM Commercial LLP, Edinburgh . . . . . (p.889)
T: 0131 2268200
E: tracey.ginn@mbmcommercial.co.uk

GINNIVER, Deborah Elizabeth Alice
(Aug 2018) (Employee)
Just Defence Law Practice,
Aberdeen . . . . (p.733)
T: 01224 644999

GIRDWOOD, Lisa Anne Irvine (Oct 1989)
(Partner)
Brodies LLP, Glasgow . . . . (p.948)
T: 0141 2484672
E: lisa.girdwood@brodies.com

GIRVAN, Karen Watson (Sept 2005) (Employee)
Cochran Dickie, Paisley . . . . (p.1137)
T: 0141 889 2245
E: kg@cochrandickie.co.uk

GIRVAN, Kirsty Helen Madeline (Jun 2016)
(Employee)
Dentons UK and Middle East LLP,
Glasgow. . . . . (p.968)
T: 0330 2220050
E: Kirsty.Girvan@dentons.com

GIUSTI, Stephen John (Oct 1977) (Consultant)
Levy & McRae Solicitors LLP,
Glasgow....................(p.1000)
T: 0141 3072311
E: sgiusti@lemac.co.uk

GIZZI, Angela (Sept 2020) (Employee)
Harper Macleod LLP, Glasgow........(p.983)
T: 0141 2218888
E: angela.gizzi@harpermacleod.co.uk

GLANCEY, Meghan Anne (Aug 2018)
(Employee)
Procurator Fiscal Service, Glasgow ....(p.1243)
T: (0300) 020 2944
E: meghan.glancey@copfs.gov.uk

GLANCY, David Christopher, OBE TD
(Mar 1986) (Employee)
Procurator Fiscal Service, Hamilton ....(p.1247)
T: 0844 5613245
E: david.glancy@copfs.gov.uk

GLASS, Kenneth Mitchell (Oct 1980)
(Employee)
Gilson Gray LLP, Dundee............(p.812)
E: kglass@gilsongray.co.uk

GLASS, Lisa Samantha (Sept 1991) (Employee)
Philip Cohen Solicitors Limited,
Glasgow....................(p.963)
T: 0141 6312412
E: lawyer@philipcohen.co.uk

GLEESON, Kirstyn Bald (Sept 2015) (Employee)
Pinsent Masons LLP, Glasgow ....(p.1031)
T: 0141 567 8400
E: kirstyn.gleeson@pinsentmasons.com

GLEESON, Steven Thomas (Nov 1983) (Partner)
Gleeson McCafferty Law,
Glenrothes ....(p.1057)
T: 01592 611660
E: gleesonmccafferty@hotmail.co.uk

GLEN, Alan Boyd (Jun 2004) (Employee)
DWF LLP, Edinburgh..............(p.865)
T: 0131 2265541
E: Alan.Glen@dwf.law

GLEN, Fiona Maclachlan (Jun 2003) (Employee)
Scottish Legal Aid Board,
Edinburgh ....(p.1233)
T: 0131 2267061
E: GlenFi@slab.org.uk

GLEN, Heather Anderson (Jun 1997)
(Employee)
Hall Norrie Warden LLP, Dundee ......(p.812)
T: 01382 472200

GLEN, Jeremy Stewart (Jan 1990) (Partner)
BTO Solicitors LLP, Glasgow ....(p.952)
T: 0141 2218012
E: jsg@bto.co.uk

GLENDINNING, Christopher William
(Feb 2020) (Employee)
Fife Council, Glenrothes ....(p.1246)
T: 03451 550000

GLENDINNING, Francesca Ellen (Nov 2018)
(Employee)
Anderson Strathern LLP, Edinburgh ....(p.839)
T: 0131 2707700
E: Francesca.Allanson@andersonstrathern.co.uk

GLENNAN, Kirsty (Dec 2014) (Employee)
Burness Paull LLP, Edinburgh.........(p.850)
T: 0131 4736000
E: kirsty.glennan@burnesspaull.com

GLENNIE, Patrick James Nicoll (Oct 2015)
(Solicitor)
NO FIRM

GLENNIE, Sarah Jane (Sept 2015) (Solicitor)
NO FIRM

GLENNIE, Stephen (Sept 1984) (Partner)
Gavin Bain & Co., Aberdeen ....(p.721)
T: 01224 623040
E: s.glennie@gavin-bain.co.uk

GLENNIE, Timothy Mark Douglas
(Nov 1985) (Employee)
States of Jersey, St Helier...........(p.1274)
E: T.Glennie@gov.je

GLIORI-CHRISTMAN, Benjamin David
(Oct 2019) (Employee)
Brown & Co Legal LLP, Glasgow ......(p.950)
T: 0141 3533354
E: benchristman@lsa.org.uk

GODDARD, Amanda Elizabeth (Jul 2004)
(Employee)
Argonon Ltd, London N1 ....(p.1261)
E: amanda.goddard@argonon.com

GODDARD, James Paul Alexander
(Sept 2020) (Employee)
Mourant Ozannes, St Helier.........(p.1274)
T: 1481731513
E: james.goddard@mourant.com

GODDARD, Malcolm James Buchanan
(Nov 2002) (Director)
Raeside Chisholm Solicitors Limited,
Glasgow....................(p.1034)
T: 0141 2483456
E: m.goddard@raesidechisholm.co.uk

GODDEN, Richard Anthony James
(Sept 1988) (Partner)
Blackadders LLP, Edinburgh ....(p.843)
T: 0131 2228000
E: richard.godden@blackadders.co.uk

GODFREY, Aimee Laura (May 2019) (Employee)
Latham & Watkins (London) LLP, London
EC2 ....(p.1266)
T: 020 7710 1000
E: aimee.godrey@lw.com

GODFREY-FAUSSETT, Matthew Charles Richard (Nov 2000) (Partner)
Pinsent Masons LLP, Edinburgh . . . .(p.895)
T: 0131 777 7000
E: matthew.godfrey-faussett@pinsentmasons.com

GODWIN, Philippa Grace Rozelle (Sept 2011) (Associate)
Pinsent Masons LLP, Glasgow . . . .(p.1031)
T: 0141 567 8400
E: philippa.godwin@pinsentmasons.com

GOH, Carmen Kahmun (Aug 2021) (Employee)
Dentons UK and Middle East LLP,
Glasgow. . . . .(p.968)
T: 0330 2220050
E: Kahmun.Goh@dentons.com

GOH, Kimberley (Jul 2008) (Associate)
Dentons UK and Middle East LLP,
Glasgow. . . . .(p.968)
T: 0330 2220050
E: Kimberley.Goh@dentons.com

GOLD, Aimi Clare Amber (Jun 2017) (Employee)
Ashurst LLP, Glasgow . . . .(p.1237)
T: (0141) 375 4242
E: aimi.gold@ashurst.com

GOLD, Elliott Jon (Jul 2014) (Solicitor)
NO FIRM

GOLDBERG, Sarah Louise (Feb 2010) (Employee)
Fife Council, Glenrothes . . . .(p.1246)
T: 03451 550000
E: sarah.goldberg@fife.gov.uk

GOLDIE, Angela Ruth (Sept 2007) (Employee)
1st Legal Limited, Ayr . . . .(p.760)
T: 01292 290666
E: angela@1stlegal.co.uk

GOLDIE, Kevin John McInnes (Jan 1983) (Employee)
SOUTH LANARKSHIREre Council,
Hamilton . . . .(p.1247)
E: kevin.goldie@southlanarkshire.gov.uk

GOLDIE, Stephen Malcolm (Sept 1999) (Partner)
Brodies LLP, Edinburgh . . . .(p.845)
T: 0131 2283777
E: stephen.goldie@brodies.com

GOLDING, Katherine Anne (Jul 2011) (Employee)
Addleshaw Goddard (Europe) LLP,
Paris . . . .(p.1272)
E: katherine.golding@aglaw.com

GOLDMAN, Natasha Louise (Oct 2019) (Employee)
BTO Solicitors LLP, Glasgow . . . .(p.952)
T: 0141 2218012

GOLDSMITH, Hannah Katherine (Oct 2012) (Employee)
Brown & Co Legal LLP, Glasgow . . . . . .(p.950)
T: 0141 3533354
E: HannahGoldsmith@lsa.org.uk

GOLDSMITH, Mary Patricia (Sept 1983) (Director)
Goldsmith & Hughes Ltd, East
Kilbride . . . .(p.831)
T: 01355 260602
E: mary@goldsmithhughes.co.uk

GOLLAN, Rosie Grace (Sept 2017) (Employee)
Womble Bond Dickinson (UK) LLP,
Edinburgh . . . .(p.913)
T: 0345 415 0000
E: Rosie.Gollan@wbd-uk.com

GON ALVES, Armando Denis (Sept 2021) (Associate)
Dentons UK and Middle East LLP,
Glasgow. . . . .(p.968)
T: 0330 2220050
E: armando.goncalves@dentons.com

GONG, Hannah (Aug 2019) (Employee)
Dickson Minto, London EC2 . . . .(p.1263)
T: 020 76284455
E: hannah.gong@dmws.com

GONNELLA, Nicola Kay (May 2010) (Partner)
Weightmans (Scotland) LLP,
Glasgow. . . . .(p.1051)
T: 0345 073 9900
E: Nicola.Gonnella@weightmans.com

GOOCH, James Robert (Jan 2016) (Partner)
Shakespeare Martineau (Glasgow) LLP,
Glasgow. . . . .(p.1038)
T: 0121 214 0000
E: james.gooch@shma.co.uk

GOOD, John Andrew (Aug 1998) (Director)
Good & Stewart Limited,
Edinburgh . . . .(p.875)
T: 0131 6629177
E: goodandstewart@btconnect.com

GOOD, Victoria Jayne (Oct 2000) (Partner)
V. Good & Co., Edinburgh . . . .(p.875)
T: 0131 6223349
E: vgoodlaw@hotmail.co.uk

GOODBRAND, Amy Lesley (Oct 2002) (Employee)
QS Quacquarelli Symonds Limited, London
NW3 . . . .(p.1267)
E: amy@qs.com

GOODBRAND, Andrew Bruce (Feb 1998) (Partner)
Clyde & Co (Scotland) LLP,
Edinburgh . . . .(p.855)
T: 0131 5571545
E: bruce.goodbrand@clydeco.com

GOODBRAND, David James (Dec 1998)
(Partner)
Burness Paull LLP, Edinburgh . . . .(p.850)
T: 0131 4736000
E: david.goodbrand@burnesspaull.com

GOODENOUGH, Caroline Rose (Jan 1991)
(Employee)
Keenan Solicitors, Greenock . . . .(p.1061)
T: 01475 732122
E: cgoodenough@keenansolicitors.com

GOODFELLOW, Gail (Sept 1985) (Partner)
Gail Goodfellow, Solicitor Advocate,
Aberdeen . . . .(p.731)
T: 01224 878417
E: gail@gailgoodfellow.com

GOODFELLOW, Richard (Sept 1989) (Partner)
Burness Paull LLP, Aberdeen . . . .(p.724)
T: 01224 621621
E: Richard.Goodfellow@burnesspaull.com

GOODFIELD, Ruaridh Andrew Allen
(Nov 2012) (Employee)
Google UK Limited, London SW1 . . . . .(p.1264)
T: 020 7346 2927
E: ruaridh@google.com

GOODMAN, Alastair Gordon (Dec 1991)
(Partner)
Lindsays LLP, Glasgow . . . .(p.1001)
T: 0141 2216551
E: alastairgoodman@lindsays.co.uk

GOODWILLIE, Jay (Apr 2015) (Employee)
Dalling, Stirling . . . .(p.1164)
T: 01786 448111
E: jg@dallings.co.uk

GOODWIN, Elaine (May 2018) (Employee)
Anderson Strathern LLP, Glasgow . . . . . .(p.940)
T: 0141 2426060
E: elaine.goodwin@andersonstrathern.co.uk

GOODWIN, Joanne (Aug 2010) (Associate)
Thompsons, Glasgow . . . .(p.1046)
T: 0141 226 5738
E: joanne.goodwin@thompsons-scotland.co.uk

GORDON, Aileen Catherine (Sept 1988)
(Employee)
Procurator Fiscal Service,
Edinburgh . . . .(p.1229)
T: 0300 0203000
E: aileen.gordon@copfs.gov.uk

GORDON, Aileen Elizabeth (Nov 2013)
(Employee)
Shepherd and Wedderburn LLP,
Edinburgh . . . .(p.900)
T: 0131 2289900
E: aileen.gordon@shepwedd.com

GORDON, Alisdair (Oct 1984) (Partner)
A. J. Gordon & Co, Glasgow . . . .(p.981)
T: 07812 000554
E: al@algordonlawyers.co.uk

GORDON, Alison Mary (Oct 1987) (Associate)
Warners Solicitors LLP, Edinburgh . . . . . .(p.911)
T: 0131 6624747
E: agordon@warnersllp.com

GORDON, Amanda (Jun 2019) (Employee)
Dentons UK and Middle East LLP,
Glasgow . . . .(p.968)
T: 0330 2220050
E: amanda.gordon@dentons.com

GORDON, Amy Catherine (Aug 2018)
(Employee)
Dentons UK and Middle East LLP,
Glasgow . . . .(p.968)
T: 0330 2220050

GORDON, Calum Taylor (Jan 2019) (Employee)
Martin, Johnston & Socha Limited,
Kirkcaldy . . . .(p.1102)
T: 01592 640 680
E:
calum.gordon@mjscriminaldefencelawyers.co.
uk

GORDON, Calvin Andrew Manson
(Sept 2010) (Employee)
Fiona McPhail Solicitors, Edinburgh . . . .(p.886)
T: 0344 5152410
E: Calvin_Gordon@shelter.org.uk

GORDON, David Cargill (Nov 1978) (Partner)
Hasties, Glasgow . . . .(p.985)
T: 0141 3321454
E: dgordon@hasties.co.uk

GORDON, Fayona Ann (Feb 2005) (Partner)
Alex Hutcheon & Co., Aberdeen . . . . . .(p.732)
T: 01224 623423
E: fayona.gordon@mortgageandproperty.co.uk

GORDON, Fiona (Jan 2006) (Associate)
Addleshaw Goddard LLP,
Edinburgh . . . .(p.835)
T: 0131 2282400
E: fiona.gordon@addleshawgoddard.com

GORDON, Fiona Mary (Oct 1990) (Partner)
Bradley Campbell & Co., Greenock . . .(p.1060)
T: 01475 726363
E: fiona.gordon@bradleycampbell.co.uk

GORDON, Gregor Ross (Jun 2017) (Employee)
Sidley Austin LLP, London EC3 . . . .(p.1268)
T: 2073602040
E: gregor.gordon@sidley.com

GORDON, Hilary McKee (Oct 1994) (Employee)
Burness Paull LLP, Edinburgh . . . .(p.850)
T: 0131 4736000
E: Hilary.Gordon@burnesspaull.com

GORDON, Ian (Dec 1981) (Partner)
Pinsent Masons LLP, Glasgow . . . .(p.1031)
T: 0141 567 8400
E: ian.gordon@pinsentmasons.com

GORDON, Jamie Peter (May 2018) (Employee)
Kirkland & Ellis International LLP, London
EC3 . . . .(p.1265)
T: 0207 4692000
E: jamie.gordon@kirkland.com

GORDON, Jodi (Nov 2012) (Employee)
Road Traffic Accident Law (Scotland) LLP,
Peebles . . . .(p.1144)
T: 01721 728238
E: Jodi.gordon@thompsons-scotland.co.uk

GORDON, Kathryn Grace (Jul 2003) (Partner)
Anderson & Goodlad, Lerwick . . . .(p.1112)
T: 01595 692297
E: kgordon@anderson-goodlad.co.uk

GORDON, Kenneth Stewart (Jan 1982)
(Solicitor)
NO FIRM

GORDON, Leanne (Jun 2012) (Employee)
Lindsays LLP, Edinburgh . . . .(p.882)
T: 0131 2291212
E: LeanneGordon@lindsays.co.uk

GORDON, Lesley Jane (Feb 1995) (Partner)
BTO Solicitors LLP, Edinburgh . . . .(p.849)
T: 0131 2222939
E: lxg@bto.co.uk

GORDON, Matthew Stewart (Sept 2012)
(Employee)
Shell U.K. Ltd., Aberdeen . . . .(p.1214)
T: 01224 882000
E: matthew.m.gordon@shell.com

GORDON, Michael John (Jul 2017) (Employee)
Lindsays LLP, Edinburgh . . . .(p.882)
T: 0131 2291212
E: michaelgordon@lindsays.co.uk

GORDON, Michelle Ann (Apr 2007) (Employee)
Lloyds Banking Group Plc,
Edinburgh . . . .(p.1224)
T: (0131) 442 9579
E: michelle.gordon@lloydsbanking.com

GORDON, Nicholas St. John (Oct 1991)
(Consultant)
JHS Law, Dumfries . . . .(p.801)
T: 01387 739000
E: nick.gordon@jhslaw.co.uk

GORDON, Richard Clifford (Nov 1998)
(Employee)
Royal London, Edinburgh . . . .(p.1230)
T: 0131 6726150
E: Richard.Gordon@royallondon.com

GORDON, Sara Clare (Feb 2010) (Employee)
Petrofac Services Limited,
Aberdeen . . . .(p.1213)
T: 01224 247000
E: Sara.Gordon@petrofac.com

GORDON, Sharon (Aug 2013) (Employee)
Urquharts, Edinburgh . . . .(p.909)
T: 0131 5562896
E: SharonGordon@urquharts.co.uk

GORDON, Sheona Anne (Dec 1980)
(Employee)
The Edinburgh Property Search Company Ltd,
Edinburgh . . . .(p.1234)
T: 797415678
E: Sheona@epsc.co.uk

GORDON, Stewart Henry (Jul 2015) (Associate)
Anderson Strathern LLP, Glasgow . . . . . .(p.940)
T: 0141 2426060
E: stewart.gordon@andersonstrathern.co.uk

GORDON, Tanya Ann (Oct 1993) (Partner)
Clyde & Co (Scotland) LLP,
Edinburgh . . . .(p.855)
T: 0131 5571545
E: tanya.gordon@clydeco.com

GORMLEY, Kathryn Rose (Oct 2011)
(Employee)
National Health Service Scotland,
Edinburgh . . . .(p.1225)
T: 0131 2757800
E: Kathryn.gormley@nhs.scot

GORMLY, Ailsa Anne (Sept 1998) (Solicitor)
Experian Limited, Nottingham . . . .(p.1271)

GORRY, Daniel Stephen (Oct 2005) (Employee)
Law at Work Ltd, Glasgow . . . .(p.1240)
T: 0141 2715555
E: daniel.gorry@lawatwork.co.uk

GORRY, Fiona Louise (Oct 2010) (Employee)
Just Employment Law Ltd,
Glasgow . . . .(p.1240)
T: 0141 3315150
E: fionagorry@justemploymentlaw.co.uk

GOSNEY, Euan (Oct 2009) (Director)
Thorley Stephenson Ltd,
Edinburgh . . . .(p.906)
T: 0131 5569599
E: eg@thorleystephenson.com

GOSNEY, Joanne Margaret (Oct 2009)
(Employee)
Digby Brown LLP, Edinburgh . . . .(p.862)
T: 0333 200 5925
E: Joanne.Gosney@digbybrown.co.uk

GOSTELOW, Paul Gerard (Mar 1995) (Director)
Baker Gostelow Law Limited,
Hamilton . . . .(p.1065)
T: 01698 820 700
E: paul@bgfamilylaw.co.uk

GOTTS, Christopher Phillip (Oct 1998)
(Partner)
Burness Paull LLP, Edinburgh . . . .(p.850)
T: 0131 4736000
E: chris.gotts@burnesspaull.com

GOUGH, Fraser Norman Moore (Oct 2007)
(Employee)
Scottish Government's Parliamentary Counsel
Office, Edinburgh . . . .(p.1233)
T: 0131 244 1671
E: fraser.gough@gov.scot

GOULD, Leigh (Aug 2002) (Partner)
Brodies LLP, Aberdeen. . . . .(p.723)
T: 01224 392 242
E: leigh.gould@brodies.com

GOURLAY, David McRae (Sept 1994) (Partner)
MacRoberts LLP, Edinburgh . . . .(p.887)
T: 0131 2295046
E: david.gourlay@macroberts.com

GOURLAY, Douglas John (Sept 1994) (Partner)
TLT LLP, Glasgow . . . .(p.1048)
T: 0333 006 0400
E: douglas.gourlay@tltsolicitors.com

GOURLEY, Alison Janet (Sept 1993) (Associate)
Raeside Chisholm Solicitors Limited,
Glasgow. . . . .(p.1034)
T: 0141 2483456
E: a.gourley@raesidechisholm.co.uk

GOURLEY, Stacey Elizabeth (Jun 2017)
(Employee)
Brodies LLP, Edinburgh . . . .(p.845)
T: 0131 2283777
E: stacey.gourley@brodies.com

GOVAN, Faye Louise (May 2011) (Employee)
Facebook UK Limited, London
NW1 . . . .(p.1264)
E: faye@fb.com

GOVAN, Lesley Anne (May 2014) (Partner)
Lesley Govan Associates, Glasgow . . . . .(p.981)
T: 07983 811298
E: lg@lesleygovanassociates.uk

GOW, Alison Margaret (Jan 1983) (Partner)
CMS Cameron McKenna Nabarro Olswang LLP,
Edinburgh . . . .(p.856)
T: 0131 2288000
E: Alison.Gow@cms-cmno.com

GOW, Annabelle Louise (Oct 2015) (Associate)
Harper Macleod LLP, Elgin. . . . .(p.916)
T: 01343 542623
E: annabelle.gow@harpermacleod.co.uk

GOW, Jonathan Scott Elliot (Jul 1998) (Partner)
James Guthrie & Company LLP,
Kilmarnock . . . .(p.1095)
T: 01563 525155
E: scott@jamesguthrie.co.uk

GOW, Laura Janet (Apr 2007) (Employee)
The Institute of Chartered Accountants of
Scotland, Edinburgh . . . .(p.1235)
T: 0131 3470100
E: lgow@icas.com

GOWANS, Rebecca Duncan (Sept 2020)
(Employee)
DWF LLP, Glasgow . . . .(p.973)
T: 0141 228 8000
E: Rebecca.Gowans@dwf.law

GOWANS, Ruaridh Howard Mackinnon
(Sept 2007) (Director)
Craig Wood Solicitors Limited,
Inverness . . . .(p.1083)
T: 01463 225544
E: rory.gowans@craigwood.co.uk

GRACE, Anna Wiktoria (Dec 2019) (Employee)
Scottish Government, Glasgow . . . . . .(p.1243)
T: (0141) 2727233
E: ania.grace@gov.scot

GRACE, Hannah Sarah (Sept 2020) (Employee)
Harper Macleod LLP, Glasgow . . . .(p.983)
T: 0141 2218888
E: hannah.grace@harpermacleod.co.uk

GRACE, Jean Beattie (Jun 1986) (Employee)
Aviva, Perth . . . .(p.1253)
T: 01738 895327
E: jean.grace@aviva.com

GRACE, Robin Joseph Jesse (Oct 2020)
(Employee)
The Morgan Law Partnership,
Dunfermline . . . .(p.826)
T: 01383 620222

GRACIE, Laura Sophia (Jun 2009) (Employee)
Burn & McGregor, Aberdeen . . . .(p.726)
T: 01224 639660
E: laura.b-m@btconnect.com

GRADY, John Andrew Dominic (Jan 1998)
(Partner)
Shepherd and Wedderburn LLP,
Glasgow. . . . .(p.1039)
T: 0141 5669900
E: john.grady@shepwedd.com

GRADY, Stephen Martin (Jul 1984) (Partner)
S. Grady Solicitors, Glasgow . . . .(p.981)
T: 0141 2214000
E: stephen_grady@hotmail.co.uk

GRAHAM, Alexis Irene (Feb 2006) (Partner)
Shepherd and Wedderburn LLP,
Glasgow. . . . .(p.1039)
T: 0141 5669900
E: Alexis.Graham@shepwedd.co.uk

GRAHAM, Angela Kathleen (Feb 2003)
(Employee)
Civil Legal Assistance Office,
Inverness . . . . (p.1248)
T: 01463 641770
E: Grahaman@clao.org.uk

GRAHAM, Anne Catherine (Aug 2021)
(Employee)
McEwan Fraser Legal, Edinburgh . . . . . . (p.885)
T: 0131 5249797
E: anne.graham@mcewanfraserlegal.co.uk

GRAHAM, Archibald Gordon (Aug 1985)
(Solicitor)
NO FIRM

GRAHAM, Caroline Barbara (Mar 1988)
(Employee)
Oil & Gas Authority, Aberdeen . . . . . . (p.1213)
T: 0300 020 1068
E: Caroline.Graham@ogauthority.co.uk

GRAHAM, Colin Thomas, WS (Oct 1983)
(Partner)
Thorntons Law LLP, Dundee . . . . (p.819)
T: 01382 229 111
E: cgraham@thorntons-law.co.uk

GRAHAM, David William Denning
(Sept 2000) (Employee)
BAE Systems, Blackburn . . . . (p.1258)
T: 01229 874236
E: david.graham8@baesystems.com

GRAHAM, Gilles Robert (Sept 1992) (Partner)
Clyde & Co (Scotland) LLP,
Glasgow . . . . (p.961)
T: 0141 2482666
E: gilles.graham@clydeco.com

GRAHAM, James Donald (May 1979)
(Consultant)
The PRG Partnership, Kirkintilloch . . . . . (p.1105)
T: 0141 7762298
E: jdgraham@prg.co.uk

GRAHAM, Jennifer Mary (Jul 2018) (Employee)
Procurator Fiscal Service,
Edinburgh . . . . (p.1230)
T: 0844 5612000
E: Jennifer.Graham@copfs.gov.uk

GRAHAM, Katherine Sarah (Oct 2008)
(Employee)
Wheatley Housing Group Limited,
Glasgow . . . . (p.1246)
T: 0845 9001001
E: Katie.Graham@wheatley-group.com

GRAHAM, Kathleen Anne (Sept 1980)
(Director)
Pieri Graham Ltd, Glasgow . . . . (p.1031)
T: 0141 3322525
E: kathleen@pierigraham.com

GRAHAM, Kenneth Andrew (Feb 1985)
(Employee)
Renfrewshire Council, Paisley . . . . (p.1252)
T: 0141 8403648
E: ken.graham@renfrewshire.gov.uk

GRAHAM, Kevin (Jan 2004) (Employee)
Revenue Scotland, Edinburgh . . . . (p.1230)
E: Kevin.Graham2@revenue.scot

GRAHAM, Kirsty Elizabeth (Oct 2013)
(Employee)
Brodies LLP, Edinburgh . . . . (p.845)
T: 0131 2283777
E: kirsty.graham@brodies.com

GRAHAM, Lara (Jan 2018) (Employee)
Digby Brown LLP, Glasgow . . . . (p.970)
T: 0333 200 5925
E: Lara.Graham@digbybrown.co.uk

GRAHAM, Laura Marie (Nov 1991) (Solicitor)
NO FIRM

GRAHAM, Lesley Anne (Feb 2021) (Employee)
Campbell & McCartney, Glasgow . . . . . (p.956)
T: 0141 4232222
E: lg@patrickcampbellsolicitors.co.uk

GRAHAM, Leslie Drysdale, WS (Jan 1983)
(Partner)
Brodies LLP, Edinburgh . . . . (p.845)
T: 0131 2283777
E: drysdale.graham@brodies.com

GRAHAM, Lisa Christine (Jul 2013) (Associate)
Davidson Chalmers Stewart LLP,
Edinburgh . . . . (p.859)
T: 0131 6259191
E: Lisa.Graham@dcslegal.com

GRAHAM, Lorne Campbell (Feb 2002)
(Associate)
Brodies LLP, Glasgow . . . . (p.948)
T: 0141 245 6725
E: lorne.graham@brodies.com

GRAHAM, Louise (Jul 2006) (Solicitor)
Procurator Fiscal Service, Kirkcaldy . . . . (p.1249)
T: 0300 0203000
E: louise.graham@copfs.gov.uk

GRAHAM, Mairi Jessica (Sept 2020) (Employee)
Procurator Fiscal Service,
Edinburgh . . . . (p.1227)
T: 0300 0203168
E: mairi.graham@copfs.gov.uk

GRAHAM, Mark Macleod (Sept 2013)
(Employee)
Modulr, Edinburgh . . . . (p.1225)
E: mark.graham@modulrfinance.com

GRAHAM, Michael Joseph (Apr 1998) (Director)
Delaney Graham Limited, Glasgow . . . . . (p.968)
T: 0141 4834450
E: m.graham@delaneygraham.co.uk

GRAHAM, Peter (Nov 1986) (Partner)
BTO Solicitors LLP, Glasgow . . . .(p.952)
 T: 0141 2218012
 E: pgr@bto.co.uk

GRAHAM, Ross Calum (Jan 2015) (Employee)
Renfrewshire Council, Paisley . . . .(p.1252)
 T: 0141 8403648
 E: ross.graham@renfrewshire.gov.uk

GRAHAM, Selena (Aug 2012) (Employee)
Educational Institute of Scotland,
 Dundee . . . .(p.1218)
 E: sgraham@eis.org.uk

GRAHAM, Sophie Patricia (Oct 2015)
(Employee)
SSE Plc, Perth . . . .(p.1253)
 T: 01738 456 000
 E: Sophie.Graham@sse.com

GRAHAM, Steven John (Nov 2018) (Employee)
Brodies LLP, Edinburgh . . . .(p.845)
 T: 0131 2283777
 E: steven.graham@brodies.com

GRAHAM-SMITH, Andrew Colin (May 2018)
(Employee)
Urquharts, Edinburgh . . . .(p.909)
 T: 0131 5562896

GRAINGER, Gwyneth (Nov 2000) (Solicitor)
NO FIRM

GRANDISON, Alison Murray (Mar 2007)
(Partner)
Urquharts, Edinburgh . . . .(p.909)
 T: 0131 5562896
 E: AlisonGrandison@urquharts.co.uk

GRANGER, Alison Catherine (Oct 1990)
(Employee)
Scottish Legal Aid Board,
 Edinburgh . . . .(p.1233)
 T: 0131 2267061
 E: grangeral@slab.org.uk

GRANT, Adam Brian (Dec 2013) (Employee)
Peterkins, Aberdeen . . . .(p.739)
 T: 01224 428000
 E: ABG@peterkins.com

GRANT, Aidan Dean (Jul 2017) (Employee)
Macleod & MacCallum Limited,
 Inverness . . . .(p.1080)
 T: 01463 239393
 E: aidan.grant@macandmac.co.uk

GRANT, Alasdair Euan (Aug 2016) (Employee)
Aegon UK, Edinburgh . . . .(p.1220)
 T: 1315493986
 E: alasdair.grant@aegon.co.uk

GRANT, Alison MacIntyre (Oct 1984) (Partner)
DWF LLP, Glasgow . . . .(p.973)
 T: 0141 228 8000
 E: Alison.Grant@dwf.law

GRANT, Edith Elizabeth (Oct 1985) (Solicitor)
Conroy McInnes Limited, Glasgow . . . . .(p.963)
 T: 0141 6166622
 E: mail@conroymcinnes.co.uk

GRANT, Eileen Cameron (Nov 1993)
(Employee)
West Lothian Council, Livingston . . . . .(p.1250)
 T: 01506 280000

GRANT, Eilidh Blake (May 2021) (Employee)
Martin, Johnston & Socha Limited,
 Kirkcaldy . . . .(p.1102)
 T: 01592 640680

GRANT, Elaine Helen (Oct 1984) (Partner)
Jack Grant & Co., Motherwell . . . .(p.1127)
 T: 01698 254 636
 E: elaine-grant@btconnect.com

GRANT, Elizabeth Sheila (Oct 2006)
(Employee)
Medical Protection Society, Leeds. . . . .(p.1260)
 E: Liz.Grant@medicalprotection.org

GRANT, Erin Louise (Jun 2009) (Employee)
Springfield Properties Plc, Elgin . . . . . .(p.1236)
 E: erin.grant@springfield.co.uk

GRANT, Eugene-Paul (Sept 1999) (Employee)
Directorate of Army Legal Services,
 Andover. . . . .(p.1258)
 T: + 44 300 162 0981
 E: eugene-paul.grant216@mod.gov.uk

GRANT, Ewan Alastair (Nov 1983) (Employee)
Stirling Council, Stirling. . . . .(p.1255)
 T: 01786 233065
 E: grante@stirling.gov.uk

GRANT, Fraser Mark (Dec 2017) (Employee)
DLA Piper UK LLP, London EC1 . . . . . .(p.1263)
 T: 020 77966017
 E: fraser.grant@dlapiper.com

GRANT, Gavin Stewart (Oct 2006) (Employee)
University of Strathclyde, Glasgow . . . .(p.1245)
 T: (0141) 5485905
 E: gavin.grant@strath.ac.uk

GRANT, Guy Maximilian George (Aug 2014)
(Associate)
Anderson Strathern LLP, Edinburgh . . . .(p.839)
 T: 0131 2707700
 E: guy.grant@andersonstrathern.co.uk

GRANT, Hugh Jamison (Jul 1980) (Employee)
Mitchells Roberton Ltd, Glasgow . . . . .(p.1020)
 T: 0141 5523422
 E: hjg@mitchells-roberton.co.uk

GRANT, Iain Harry (Feb 2015) (Employee)
Gilson Gray LLP, Edinburgh . . . .(p.874)
 T: 0131 5165354
 E: igrant@gilsongray.co.uk

GRANT, James Roy McCulloch (Aug 1968)
(Consultant)
Fraser & Mulligan, Aberdeen . . . .(p.731)
T: 01224 646428
E: mail@fraser-mulligan.co.uk

GRANT, James Russell (Mar 1987) (Partner)
Shepherd and Wedderburn LLP,
Glasgow. . . . .(p.1039)
T: 0141 5669900
E: jamie.grant@shepwedd.com

GRANT, John Drummond (Oct 2002)
(Associate)
Wright, Johnston & Mackenzie LLP,
Glasgow. . . . .(p.1054)
T: 0141 2483434
E: jzg@wjm.co.uk

GRANT, John Melrose (Apr 1980) (Partner)
Jack Grant & Co., Motherwell . . . .(p.1127)
T: 01698 254 636
E: jackgrant@btconnect.com

GRANT, Katie Jane (Apr 2012) (Employee)
Scottish Social Services Council,
Dundee . . . .(p.1218)
T: 0345 6030 891
E: katie.grant@sssc.uk.com

GRANT, Lauren (Mar 2017) (Associate)
Harper Macleod LLP, Glasgow . . . .(p.983)
T: 0141 2218888
E: lauren.grant@harpermacleod.co.uk

GRANT, Lesley Jane (Jun 2006) (Employee)
BTO Solicitors LLP, Glasgow . . . .(p.952)
T: 0141 2218012
E: ljg@bto.co.uk

GRANT, Michael John (Jun 2017) (Employee)
Weil, Gotshal & Manges (London) LLP, London
EC4 . . . .(p.1269)
E: michael.grant@weil.com

GRANT, Moira (Oct 1981) (Partner)
McCarrys Solicitors, Glasgow . . . .(p.1006)
T: 0141 9451911
E: moiragrant@mccarrys.com

GRANT, Nicholas Roy (Sept 2014) (Employee)
Dickson Minto, Edinburgh. . . . .(p.861)
T: 0131 2254455
E: Nicholas.Grant@dmws.com

GRANT, Nicola Marion (Jun 2011) (Associate)
Ledingham Chalmers LLP,
Inverness . . . .(p.1078)
T: 01463 667400
E: nicola.grant@ledinghamchalmers.com

GRANT, Rachel Mary (Aug 1985) (Employee)
Manolete Partners PLC, London
W1 . . . .(p.1266)
E: Rachel@manolete-partners.com

GRANT, Shavonne (Apr 2013) (Employee)
Scottish Water, Dunfermline . . . .(p.1219)
T: (01383) 665410
E: Shavonne.Berry@scottishwater.co.uk

GRANT, Stephen Ross (Mar 2013) (Employee)
Wright, Johnston & Mackenzie LLP,
Glasgow. . . . .(p.1054)
T: 0141 2483434
E: srg@wjm.co.uk

GRANT, William Marr Couper, WS
(Dec 1986) (Consultant)
Mitchells Roberton Ltd, Glasgow . . . . .(p.1020)
T: 0141 5523422
E: wmcg@mitchells-roberton.co.uk

GRATTAN, Jenna (Nov 2018) (Employee)
Procurator Fiscal Service, Hamilton . . . .(p.1247)
T: 0844 5613245
E: Jenna.Grattan@copfs.gov.uk

GRATWICK, Edward Stuart (Oct 2007)
(Associate)
Addleshaw Goddard LLP,
Edinburgh . . . .(p.835)
T: 0131 2282400
E: Edward.Gratwick@addleshawgoddard.com

GRAVELLE, Alan Joseph (Aug 2011) (Employee)
Beltrami & Co Limited, Glasgow . . . . . .(p.944)
T: 0141 429 2262
E: alan.gravelle@beltramiandcompany.co.uk

GRAVELLE, Maria Christine (Oct 2019)
(Employee)
Thorntons Law LLP, Dundee . . . .(p.819)
T: 01382 229 111
E: mgravelle@thorntons-law.co.uk

GRAY, Alasdair Iain (Sept 2014) (Employee)
Procurator Fiscal Service, Inverness . . . .(p.1248)
T: 0844 5612926
E: Iain.Gray@copfs.gov.uk

GRAY, Alastair Neil (Dec 2011) (Solicitor)
Rradar (Scotland) Limited,
Glasgow. . . . .(p.1036)
E: Alastair.Gray@rradar.com

GRAY, Andrew Michael (Oct 2013) (Employee)
Willkie Farr & Gallagher (UK) LLP, London
EC2 . . . .(p.1269)
E: AGray@willkie.com

GRAY, Angela Jane (Sept 2001) (Employee)
Procurator Fiscal Service, Hamilton . . . .(p.1247)
T: 0844 5613245
E: angela.gray@copfs.gov.uk

GRAY, Angela Michelle (Oct 2017) (Employee)
SSE Plc, Perth . . . .(p.1253)
T: 01738 456 000
E: Angela.Gray@sse.com

GRAY, Ann Elliot (Oct 1995) (Employee)
Procurator Fiscal Service,
   Edinburgh . . . .(p.1229)
   T: 0300 0203000
   E: ann.gray@copfs.gov.uk

GRAY, Colin Francis (Oct 1985) (Solicitor)
NO FIRM

GRAY, David Neil (Sept 2015) (Associate)
DWF LLP, Edinburgh . . . .(p.865)
   T: 0131 2265541
   E: david.gray@dwf.law

GRAY, Donna Louise (Aug 2017) (Employee)
Thorntons Law LLP, Dundee . . . .(p.819)
   T: 01382 229 111
   E: dgray@thorntons-law.co.uk

GRAY, Douglas Iain Gilfillan (Sept 1994)
   (Director)
WilliamsGrayWilliams Ltd, Cupar . . . . . .(p.793)
   T: 01334 656644
   E: dgray@williamsgraywilliams.co.uk

GRAY, Emma Louise (Aug 2002) (Partner)
Blackadders LLP, Dundee. . . . .(p.805)
   T: 01382 229222
   E: Emma.Gray@Blackadders.co.uk

GRAY, Fiona Alison (Jun 2008) (Employee)
Clydesdale Bank Plc, Glasgow . . . .(p.1238)
   T: 0748 330 7246
   E: fiona.gray@cybg.com

GRAY, Gillian (Sept 2000) (Employee)
SOUTH LANARKSHIREre Council,
   Hamilton . . . .(p.1247)
   E: gillian.gray@southlanarkshire.gov.uk

GRAY, Helen Muriel Nicoll (Jul 2009)
   (Employee)
Pinsent Masons LLP, London EC2 . . . . .(p.1267)
   T: 020 7418 7000
   E: Helen.Gray@pinsentmasons.com

GRAY, Henry Harvey (Oct 1980) (Partner)
Blair & Bryden, Greenock . . . .(p.1060)
   T: 01475 558420
   E: hgray@blair-bryden.co.uk

GRAY, Jennifer Sarah (Oct 2007) (Partner)
Kilpatrick & Walker, Ayr . . . .(p.763)
   T: 01292 618585
   E: jennifer@kilpatrickwalker.com

GRAY, Joanne Lauren (Oct 2010) (Employee)
Ingenico Group, Dalgety Bay . . . .(p.1216)
   E: Joanne.GRAY@ingenico.com

GRAY, Joanne Marlene Margaret (Dec 2015)
   (Employee)
Digby Brown LLP, Glasgow . . . .(p.970)
   T: 0333 200 5925
   E: joanne.gray@digbybrown.co.uk

GRAY, Jordan Murray (Sept 2017) (Employee)
DWF LLP, Edinburgh . . . .(p.865)
   T: 0131 2265541
   E: jordan.gray@dwf.law

GRAY, Joshua Andrew (Aug 2020) (Employee)
Your Conveyancer Limited,
   Dunfermline . . . .(p.827)
   T: 01383 667550
   E: Joshua.Gray@yourconveyancer.co.uk

GRAY, Kenneth David (Nov 1992) (Partner)
Lindsays LLP, Edinburgh . . . .(p.882)
   T: 0131 2291212
   E: kennygray@lindsays.co.uk

GRAY, Kenneth Whitton (Jan 1996) (Director)
WilliamsGrayWilliams Ltd, Cupar . . . . . .(p.793)
   T: 01334 656644
   E: kenneth.gray@williamsgraywilliams.co.uk

GRAY, Kirsty Margaret Campbell (Nov 2020)
   (Employee)
DLA Piper Scotland LLP, Edinburgh . . . .(p.863)
   T: 08700 111111
   E: kirsty.gray@dlapiper.com

GRAY, Laura Charlotte (Jul 2021) (Employee)
Stronachs LLP, Aberdeen . . . .(p.744)
   T: 01224 845845
   E: laura.gray@stronachs.com

GRAY, Lauren Margaret (Sept 2017)
   (Employee)
Carey Olsen, St Helier . . . .(p.1274)
   T: 01534 822322
   E: lauren.gray@careyolsen.com

GRAY, Lesley Anne (Dec 1975) (Partner)
Lesley A. Gray, Gullane . . . .(p.1063)
   T: 01620 843872
   E: lesley@lagray.co.uk

GRAY, Lesley Helen (Oct 2002) (Associate)
BTO Solicitors LLP, Glasgow . . . .(p.952)
   T: 0141 2218012
   E: lgr@bto.co.uk

GRAY, Lynn (Aug 2013) (Employee)
Life Technologies Limited, Paisley . . . . .(p.1252)
   T: 0141 8146100
   E: lynn.gray@thermofisher.com

GRAY, Lynne Carol (Nov 1995) (Partner)
Burness Paull LLP, Aberdeen . . . .(p.724)
   T: 01224 621621
   E: Lynne.Gray@burnesspaull.com

GRAY, Matthew Alan (May 2021) (Employee)
Morton Fraser LLP, Glasgow . . . .(p.1022)
   T: 0141 2741100
   E: matthew.gray@morton-fraser.com

GRAY, Nicola Jane (Jul 2009) (Partner)
Aberdein Considine and Company,
   Aberdeen . . . .(p.718)
   T: 01224 589700
   E: ngray@acandco.com

GRAY, Patricia Joy (Aug 1982) (Partner)
Mackinnons Solicitors LLP,
Aberdeen . . . .(p.737)
T: 01224 868687
E: patricia@mackinnons.com

GRAY, Rachel Audrey Margaret (Sept 2018)
(Employee)
OVO (S) Electricity Ltd, Perth . . . .(p.1253)
E: Rachel.Gray@sseenergyservices.com

GRAY, Rebecca Chloe Elizabeth (Aug 2021)
(Employee)
Aberdein Considine and Company,
Edinburgh . . . .(p.833)
T: 0131 2212424
E: rgray@acandco.com

GRAY, Richard William James (Dec 2010)
(Employee)
George More & Company LLP,
Edinburgh . . . .(p.891)
T: 0131 2026552
E: office@moreandcompany.com

GRAY, Robert McKenzie (Oct 2007) (Employee)
Baker & McKenzie LLP, London
EC4 . . . .(p.1261)
T: 0207 919 1667
E: robert.gray@bakermckenzie.com

GRAY, Ross (Oct 2010) (Employee)
Scottish Legal Aid Board,
Edinburgh . . . .(p.1233)
T: 0131 2267061
E: grayro@slab.org.uk

GRAY, Thomas Stephen (Oct 2014) (Employee)
Harper Macleod LLP, Glasgow . . . .(p.983)
T: 0141 227 9305
E: Thomas.Gray@harpermacleod.co.uk

GRAYDON, Kirsty Anne (Oct 2014) (Associate)
Clyde & Co (Scotland) LLP,
Glasgow. . . . .(p.961)
T: 0141 2482666
E: kirsty.graydon@clydeco.com

GREAVES, Scott Alexander (Dec 2015)
(Employee)
Dentons UK and Middle East LLP,
Glasgow. . . . .(p.968)
T: 0330 2220050
E: Scott.Greaves@dentons.com

GRECU, Diana Maria (Dec 2017) (Employee)
InterGen (UK) Limited, Edinburgh . . . .(p.1223)
T: 0131 624 7500
E: dgrecu@intergen.com

GREEN, Alexander Michael Stuart
(May 1995) (Employee)
H.M. Court of the Lord Lyon,
Edinburgh . . . .(p.1223)
T: 0131 553 4259
E: alex@the-lawagency.com

GREEN, David Stuart Austin (Dec 1982)
(Employee)
Procurator Fiscal Service, Glasgow . . . .(p.1241)
T: 0300 0203000
E: david.green@copfs.gov.uk

GREEN, Eoghann David MacLeod
(Feb 2010) (Employee)
Brodies LLP, Glasgow . . . .(p.948)
T: 0141 2484672
E: eoghann.green@brodies.com

GREEN, Jonathan (Dec 1987) (Director)
WGM Legal Limited, Glasgow . . . .(p.1052)
T: 0141 6166655
E: jonathan@wgmlegal.co.uk

GREEN, Paul (Oct 2020) (Employee)
Mourant Ozannes, St Helier . . . .(p.1274)
T: 1481731513
E: paul.green@mourant.com

GREEN, Susannah (Feb 2021) (Employee)
Wright, Johnston & Mackenzie LLP,
Edinburgh . . . .(p.913)
T: 0131 5241500
E: szg@wjm.co.uk

GREENE, Grace Kelly (Aug 2016) (Partner)
Cockburn & Co., Bridge of Weir . . . . . .(p.780)
T: 01505 690500
E: admin@cockburnandco.com

GREENE, Pauline (May 2007) (Solicitor)
NO FIRM

GREENER, Kenneth Matthew (Sept 1991)
(Director)
Kenneth M. Greener Limited,
Stonehouse . . . .(p.1169)
T: 01698 793366
E: kenneth@kmglaw.co.uk

GREENHILL, Paul Harris (Jun 2005) (Associate)
Harper Macleod LLP, Glasgow . . . .(p.983)
T: 0141 2218888
E: paul.greenhill@harpermacleod.co.uk

GREENHORN, Camilla Ann (Feb 2021)
(Employee)
Carpenters Scotland Limited,
Glasgow. . . . .(p.956)
T: 0141 3285452

GREENHORN, Jonathan James (Sept 2019)
(Employee)
R.S. Vaughan & Co, Glasgow. . . . .(p.1050)
T: 0141 2215482
E: jgreenhorn@rsvaughan.co.uk

GREENSHIELDS, Lauren (Oct 2020) (Employee)
BlackRock, Edinburgh . . . .(p.1221)
T: (306) 978 749 900
E: lauren.greenshields@blackrock.com

GREENWOOD, Stuart Henry (Aug 2010)
(Partner)
Shepherd and Wedderburn LLP,
Edinburgh . . . . (p.900)
T: 0131 2289900
E: stuart.greenwood@shepwedd.com

GREER, Andrew Roy (Dec 2014) (Employee)
SSE Plc, Perth . . . . (p.1253)
T: 01738 456 000
E: andrew.greer2@sse.com

GREER, Carolyn Joy (Oct 2011) (Employee)
Neos Networks Limited, Perth . . . . (p.1253)

GREER, Keira (Nov 2019) (Employee)
BTO Solicitors LLP, Glasgow . . . . (p.952)
T: 0141 2218012
E: kgr@bto.co.uk

GREER, Natalie (Feb 2012) (Employee)
Hymans Robertson LLP, Glasgow . . . . . (p.1240)
T: 0141 566 7942
E: Natalie.Greer@hymans.co.uk

GREGOR, Simon (Jun 2020) (Employee)
Good & Stewart Limited,
Edinburgh . . . . (p.875)
T: 0131 6629177

GREGORY, Claire Linda (Sept 2020) (Employee)
East Ayrshire Council, Kilmarnock . . . . . (p.1249)
T: 01563 576161
E: claire.gregory@east-ayrshire.gov.uk

GREGORY, Lisa Jane (Aug 1994) (Consultant)
Grant Smith Law Practice Limited,
Aberdeen . . . . (p.743)
T: 01224 621620
E: lisa.gregory@grantsmithlaw.co.uk

GREIG, Brian (Nov 1989) (Consultant)
Penmans, Glasgow . . . . (p.1031)
T: 0141 3366646
E: thejudge60@hotmail.co.uk

GREIG, Cameron James (Jul 2016) (Associate)
Morton Fraser LLP, Edinburgh . . . . (p.891)
T: 0131 2471000
E: cameron.greig@morton-fraser.com

GREIG, Catherine Jean (Oct 1991) (Director)
Greig Employment Law Limited,
Glasgow . . . . (p.981)
T: 07584 244565
E: catherine@greigemploymentlaw.com

GREIG, Christopher Euan (Oct 2009)
(Employee)
Serco Belgium SA, Bruxelles . . . . (p.1257)

GREIG, Colin Gordon (Oct 1991) (Partner)
DWF LLP, Glasgow . . . . (p.973)
T: 0141 228 8000
E: colin.greig@dwf.law

GREIG, Julie Helen (Oct 2002) (Associate)
Burness Paull LLP, Aberdeen . . . . (p.724)
T: 01224 621621
E: Julie.Greig@burnesspaull.com

GREIG, Lynne Jenny Isobelle (Mar 1991)
(Employee)
National Health Service Scotland,
Edinburgh . . . . (p.1225)
T: 0131 2757800
E: lynne.greig@nhs.scot

GREIG, Michael Kennedy (Dec 1994)
(Associate)
DLA Piper Scotland LLP, Edinburgh . . . . (p.863)
T: 0131 242 5506
E: michael.greig@dlapiper.com

GREIG, Rebecca Evelyn (Jul 2015) (Employee)
Paris Steele, North Berwick . . . . (p.1133)
T: 01620 892138
E: rgreig@parissteele.com

GREWAR, Sara Lauren Macdonald
(Oct 2004) (Employee)
Medical Protection Society, Leeds . . . . . (p.1260)
E: Sara.Grewar@medicalprotection.org

GREY, Andrew Neil (Feb 2005) (Director)
Grey & Co Solicitors Ltd, Inverness . . . . (p.1076)
T: 01463 239011
E: andrew@greyandcosolicitors.co.uk

GREYBE, Elizabeth Ann (Oct 1990) (Employee)
University of Edinburgh, Edinburgh . . . (p.1235)
E: Ann.Greybe@ed.ac.uk

GRIBBEN, Karen Anne (Sept 1995) (Employee)
Network Rail Infrastructure Ltd,
Glasgow . . . . (p.1241)
T: 0141 555 4470
E: karen.gribben@networkrail.co.uk

GRIBBEN, Raymond Scott (Sept 1992)
(Associate)
Levy & McRae Solicitors LLP,
Glasgow . . . . (p.1000)
T: 0141 3072311
E: RGribben@lemac.co.uk

GRIBBON, Clare Marie (May 2008) (Employee)
Glasgow City Council, Glasgow . . . . . . (p.1239)
T: 0141 2872000
E: Clare.Gribbon@glasgow.gov.uk

GRIBBON, Margaret (Oct 1997) (Director)
Bridge Employment Solicitors Limited,
Glasgow . . . . (p.948)
T: 0141 4292181
E: mgribbon@bridgeemplaw.com

GRIER, David Robert (Feb 2016) (Employee)
North Ayrshire Council, Irvine . . . . (p.1249)
T: 01294 310000
E: davidgrier@north-ayrshire.gov.uk

GRIERSON, Brian John (Oct 2014) (Employee)
Pinsent Masons LLP, Edinburgh . . . .(p.895)
T: 0131 777 7000

GRIERSON, Susan Leigh (Mar 2001) (Employee)
Clarity Simplicity Ltd, Glasgow. . . . .(p.960)
T: 0141 4332626
E: s.grierson@claritysimplicity.co.uk

GRIEVE, Alexander George Kerr (Sept 2009)
(Employee)
Shine Effort Inc Limited, Hong
Kong . . . .(p.1273)

GRIEVE, Andrew (Sept 1996) (Partner)
W. & A.S. Bruce, Kirkcaldy . . . .(p.1099)
T: 01592 204774
E: andy@wasbruce.co.uk

GRIEVE, Antonia Kate (Mar 2013) (Employee)
Addleshaw Goddard (Middle East) LLP,
Dubai . . . .(p.1277)
E: a.grieve@aglaw.com

GRIEVE, Erin Louise (Mar 2015) (Employee)
Addleshaw Goddard LLP,
Edinburgh . . . .(p.835)
T: 0131 2282400
E: Erin.Grieve@addleshawgoddard.com

GRIEVE, Kenneth George (Jul 1998) (Employee)
Procurator Fiscal Service,
Dumbarton . . . .(p.1217)
T: 0300 020 3000
E: kenneth.grieve@copfs.gov.uk

GRIEVE, Stephanie Kathleen Laura
(Mar 2017) (Employee)
Beltrami & Co Limited, Glasgow . . . . . .(p.944)
T: 0141 4292262
E:
stephanie.grieve@beltramiandcompany.co.uk

GRIFFIN, James Joseph (Dec 1989) (Employee)
Strathclyde Partnership for Transport,
Glasgow. . . . .(p.1245)
T: 0141 333 3789
E: jim.griffin@spt.co.uk

GRIFFIN, Marianne Robinson (Jun 1998)
(Associate)
Brodies LLP, Glasgow . . . .(p.948)
T: 0141 2484672
E: marianne.griffin@brodies.com

GRIFFITHS, Camilla Rose (Jul 2020) (Employee)
Blackadders LLP, Dundee. . . . .(p.805)
T: 01382 229222
E: Millie.Griffiths@blackadders.co.uk

GRIFFITHS, Debbie Joanna (Feb 2021)
(Employee)
Cognizant Worldwide Limited,
Glasgow. . . . .(p.1238)
T: (0141) 2221561
E: debbie.griffiths@cognizant.com

GRIFFITHS, Gareth John (Jul 2004) (Employee)
Baillie Gifford & Co, Edinburgh . . . . . .(p.1220)
T: 0131 2752000
E: Gareth.Griffiths@bailliegifford.com

GRIFFITHS, Lucy Fiona (Sept 2019) (Employee)
Pinsent Masons LLP, Aberdeen . . . .(p.739)
T: 01224 377900
E: lucy.griffiths@pinsentmasons.com

GRIFFITHS, Rhian Louise (Jan 2017) (Employee)
Energy Law Unlimited LLP,
Glasgow. . . . .(p.974)
T: 0141 2210276

GRILLI, Carlo Domenico (Jun 2006) (Employee)
East Lothian Council, Haddington . . . .(p.1246)
T: 01620 827827
E: cgrilli@eastlothian.gov.uk

GRIMASON, Declan William (Oct 2019)
(Employee)
TLT LLP, Glasgow . . . .(p.1048)
T: 0333 006 0400
E: declan.grimason@tltsolicitors.com

GRIMMOND, Joanne Elizabeth (Oct 2005)
(Partner)
Blackadders LLP, Perth . . . .(p.1146)
T: 01738 440088
E: joanne.grimmond@blackadders.co.uk

GROAT, Alison (Sept 2010) (Employee)
FES Ltd, Stirling . . . .(p.1254)
T: 01786 819600
E: agroat@fes-group.co.uk

GROOM, Andrew Charles (Jul 2014)
(Employee)
Brodies LLP, Edinburgh . . . .(p.845)
T: 0131 2283777
E: andrew.groom@brodies.com

GROSSI, Lynsey Jane (Nov 2008) (Solicitor)
NO FIRM

GROSVENOR, Jennifer (Oct 2016) (Employee)
Harper Macleod LLP, Glasgow . . . .(p.983)
T: 0141 226 8554
E: Jennifer.Grosvenor@harpermacleod.co.uk

GROV DEMPSTER, Anelda (Aug 2021)
(Employee)
MBM Commercial LLP, Edinburgh . . . . .(p.889)
T: 0131 2268200

GRUBB, Caroline Rebecca (Aug 2018)
(Employee)
Lindsays LLP, Edinburgh . . . .(p.882)
T: 0131 2291212
E: carolinegrubb@lindsays.co.uk

GRUBB, Stacey Leigh (Jun 2021) (Employee)
Stephen & Robb LLP, Keith . . . .(p.1090)
T: 01542 886267
E: stacey.grubb@stephenrobb.co.uk

GRUNDY, Edward John Philip (Sept 2017)
(Employee)
Brodies LLP, Edinburgh . . . . (p.845)
T: 0131 2283777
E: edward.grundy@brodies.com

GRUNENBERG, Emma Margaretha
(Jun 2021) (Employee)
Blackadders LLP, Aberdeen . . . . (p.722)
T: 01224 588913
E: emma.grunenberg@blackadders.co.uk

GRUNENBERG, Petra Anna Frieda Cornelia
(Jul 2000) (Partner)
Blackadders LLP, Dundee. . . . . (p.805)
T: 01382 229222
E: petra.grunenberg@blackadders.co.uk

GUARINO, Marco Filippo (Aug 1983) (Director)
Guarino & Thomson Limited, East
Kilbride . . . . (p.831)
T: 01355 263848
E: admin@guarinothomson.co.uk

GUIDI, Nicole Valerie (Sept 2009) (Director)
Frank Irvine Solicitors Ltd, Glasgow . . . . (p.990)
T: 0141 3759000
E: nvg@frankirvine.com

GUIDI, Paul Gerard (Sept 1983) (Employee)
NORTH LANARKSHIREre Council,
Motherwell. . . . . (p.1251)
T: 01698 302196
E: guidip@northlan.gov.uk

GUILD, Nicola (Jun 2012) (Employee)
Scottish Government, Edinburgh . . . . . (p.1231)
T: 0131 244 0815
E: Nicola.Guild@gov.scot

GUILD, Steven James (Sept 2004) (Partner)
Burness Paull LLP, Aberdeen . . . . (p.724)
T: 01224 621621
E: Steven.Guild@burnesspaull.com

GUILD, Victoria (Oct 2019) (Employee)
Brodies LLP, Edinburgh . . . . (p.845)
T: 0131 2283777
E: victoria.guild@brodies.com

GUINEA, Connor James (Jan 2020) (Employee)
Brodies LLP, Glasgow . . . . (p.948)
T: 0141 2484672
E: connor.guinea@brodies.com

GUNN, Alexander David (Aug 1987)
(Consultant)
Anderson Strathern LLP, Edinburgh . . . . (p.839)
T: 0131 2707700
E: alex.gunn@andersonstrathern.co.uk

GUNN, Daniel John (Sept 2006) (Partner)
Arthur & Carmichael LLP, Dornoch . . . . (p.797)
T: 01862 810202
E: djg@arthur-carmichael.co.uk

GUNN, Laura (Aug 2021) (Employee)
McVey & Murricane, Glasgow . . . . (p.1017)
T: 0141 3339688
E: lgunn@mcvey-murricane.com

GUNN, Paul George (Feb 2009) (Employee)
CNOOC Petroleum Europe Limited,
Uxbridge . . . . (p.1272)
T: 01895 555 165
E: Paul.Gunn@intl.cnoocltd.com

GUNN, Roisin Eleanor (May 2021) (Employee)
Jones Whyte LLP, Glasgow. . . . . (p.993)
T: 0141 375 1222
E: roisin.gunn@joneswhyte.co.uk

GUNNYEON, Malcolm John (Dec 2001)
(Partner)
Dentons UK and Middle East LLP,
Edinburgh . . . . (p.860)
T: 0330 2220050
E: Malcolm.Gunnyeon@dentons.com

GUPTA, Jaya Rajoriya (Oct 1993) (Partner)
Addleshaw Goddard LLP, London
EC1 . . . . (p.1261)
T: 0207 6068855
E: jaya.gupta@addleshawgoddard.com

GURPEGUI GARCIA, Maite (Jul 2013)
(Employee)
Digby Brown LLP, Edinburgh . . . . (p.862)
T: 0131 3198168
E: Maite.Gurpegui@digbybrown.co.uk

GUTHRIE, Catherine Joan (Aug 2015)
(Employee)
Turcan Connell, Edinburgh . . . . (p.908)
T: 0131 228 8111
E: catherine.guthrie@turcanconnell.com

GUTHRIE, Emma Fiona Helen (Sept 2014)
(Employee)
Shepherd and Wedderburn LLP,
Edinburgh . . . . (p.900)
T: 0131 2289900
E: Emma.Guthrie@shepwedd.com

GUTHRIE, Michaela Jill (Sept 2015) (Associate)
Balfour + Manson LLP, Edinburgh . . . . . (p.841)
T: 0131 200 1246
E: Michaela.Guthrie@balfour-manson.co.uk

GUTHRIE-CADGE, Calum Christopher
(Sept 2016) (Solicitor)
NO FIRM

GUTTRIDGE, Mark Eric (Oct 2016) (Employee)
Addleshaw Goddard LLP, London
EC1 . . . . (p.1261)
T: 0207 6068855
E: mark.guttridge@addleshawgoddard.com

GUY, Jennifer (Jun 2018) (Employee)
Procurator Fiscal Service, Hamilton . . . . (p.1247)
T: 0300 020 3477
E: jennifer.guy@copfs.gov.uk

GUY, Jennifer Elizabeth (Sept 2012) (Employee)
Brodies LLP, Glasgow . . . . (p.948)
T: 0141 2484672
E: jennifer.guy@brodies.com

GY RI, Dr, Csilla Zsuzsanna (Jan 2018)
(Associate)
Eversheds Sutherland (International) LLP,
Edinburgh . . . . (p.869)
T: 0207 9194500
E: csillagyori@eversheds-sutherland.com

HAAS, David Milton (Nov 1992) (Employee)
Highland Council, Inverness . . . . (p.1248)
T: 01463 785018
E: David.Haas@highland.gov.uk

HABIB, Aliya (Dec 2018) (Employee)
Edinburgh Airport Limited,
Edinburgh . . . . (p.1222)
T: (07901) 811 652
E: aliya_habib@edinburghairport.com

HABIB, Nadia (Oct 2004) (Solicitor)
NO FIRM

HADDEN, Anthony Archibald (Feb 1999)
(Partner)
Brodies LLP, Edinburgh . . . . (p.845)
T: 0131 2283777
E: tony.hadden@brodies.com

HADDEN, Nicola Margaret Dorina
(May 2021) (Employee)
Thorley Stephenson Ltd,
Edinburgh . . . . (p.906)
T: 0131 5569599

HADI, Faris Radhwan (Jan 2009) (Employee)
Investment Corporation of Dubai,
Dubai . . . . (p.1278)
T: +971 04 7071539
E: F.Hadi@icd.gov.ae

HAEFNER, Natalie Jayde (Dec 2019) (Employee)
CMS Cameron McKenna Nabarro Olswang LLP,
Aberdeen . . . . (p.727)
T: 01224 622002
E: natalie.haefner@cms-cmno.com

HAGAN, Christine (Jul 2009) (Associate)
McKenzies, Kirkcaldy . . . . (p.1101)
T: 01592 206605
E: christine.hagan@mckenzies-sols.co.uk

HAGART, Caitlin Rose Anne (Sept 2020)
(Employee)
Carey Olsen, St Helier . . . . (p.1274)
T: 01534 888900
E: caitlin.hagart@careyolsen.com

HAGGART, Liam Thomas, SSC (Jul 1992)
(Employee)
Procurator Fiscal Service, Airdrie . . . . . . (p.1214)
T: 0844561 3955
E: liam.haggart@copfs.gov.uk

HAGGERTY, Charles John (Aug 1999)
(Employee)
Stirling Council, Stirling . . . . (p.1255)
T: 01786 233065
E: haggertyc@stirling.gov.uk

HAGGERTY, Gwen Patricia (Dec 1999)
(Employee)
BSW Solicitors LLP, Dunfermline . . . . (p.823)
T: 01383 621144
E: gwen@bastensneddon.co.uk

HAIGH, Iain Davidson, WS (Jan 1983) (Partner)
Davidsons, Edinburgh . . . . (p.860)
T: 0131 5589999
E: iainhaigh@davidsons-solicitors.co.uk

HAINEY, Kimberley Christina Helen
(Jul 2015) (Employee)
Frazer Coogans Ltd, Ayr . . . . (p.763)
T: 01292 280499
E: kimberley.hainey@frazercoogans.co.uk

HAINEY, Lisa May (Jul 2008) (Employee)
Thorntons Law LLP, Cupar . . . . (p.793)
T: 01334 652285
E: lhainey@thorntons-law.co.uk

HAINEY, Megan Torano (Jul 2016) (Employee)
Blackadders LLP, Dundee . . . . (p.805)
T: 01382 229222
E: megan.hainey@blackadders.co.uk

HAIR, Carolyne Jane (Aug 2005) (Partner)
DLA Piper Scotland LLP, Edinburgh . . . . (p.863)
T: 08700 111111
E: carolyne.hair@dlapiper.com

HALDANE, Juliet Lorna (Dec 1991) (Employee)
Brodies LLP, Glasgow . . . . (p.948)
T: 0141 2484672
E: juliet.haldane@brodies.com

HALE, Gareth Jonathan (Apr 2005) (Partner)
Brodies LLP, Glasgow . . . . (p.948)
T: 0141 2484672
E: gareth.hale@brodies.com

HALE, Joshua James (Oct 2019) (Employee)
NO FIRM

HALE, Lorna Alison (Aug 2015) (Employee)
Drummond Miller LLP, Edinburgh . . . . . (p.864)
T: 0131 2265151
E: LHale@drummondmiller.co.uk

HALEY, Clare Campbell (Oct 1997) (Employee)
BP International Ltd,
Sunbury-on-Thames . . . . (p.1271)
T: (07825) 114 653
E: clare.haley@uk.bp.com

HALL, Andrew William Macdonald
(May 1995) (Partner)
Shepherd and Wedderburn LLP,
Glasgow . . . . (p.1039)
T: 0141 5669900
E: Andrew.Hall@shepwedd.com

HALL, Christine Keegan (Dec 2013) (Employee)
Ashurst LLP, Glasgow . . . .(p.1237)
T: (0141) 375 4242
E: Christine.Hall@ashurst.com

HALL, David Robert Fredrick (Dec 2000)
(Director)
Hall Baird Solicitors Ltd, Castle
Douglas . . . .(p.784)
T: 01556 502764
E: david@hallbaird.co.uk

HALL, David Warrack (Dec 1981) (Partner)
Hall & Haughey, Glasgow . . . .(p.982)
T: 0141 4180505
E: David@Hall-Haughey.co.uk

HALL, Ewan Stuart (Oct 2002) (Employee)
Baxendale Employee Ownership Limited, London
SE1 . . . .(p.1262)
T: 020 3598 9982
E: ewan.hall@baxendale.co.uk

HALL, Gareth David (Aug 2018) (Employee)
The Scottish Football Association,
Glasgow. . . . .(p.1245)
T: 0141 6166000
E: Gareth.Hall@scottishfa.co.uk

HALL, Heather Catherine (Aug 2021)
(Employee)
Aberdeen Corporate Services Limited,
Edinburgh . . . .(p.1220)
T: 0131 245 7508
E: heather.hall@abrdn.com

HALL, Jenna (Jan 2018) (Employee)
Clan Childlaw Limited, Edinburgh . . . . .(p.854)
T: 0808 129 0522
E: jenna.hall@clanchildlaw.org

HALL, John (Aug 1983) (Partner)
McAuley, McCarthy & Co.,
Renfrew . . . .(p.1159)
T: 0141 5614449
E: john@mmscotland.co.uk

HALL, Keith Ramsay (Aug 2011) (Employee)
Brodies LLP, Edinburgh . . . .(p.845)
T: 0131 2283777
E: ramsay.hall@brodies.com

HALL, Maureen Frances (Oct 1985) (Solicitor)
NO FIRM

HALL, Melissa (Sept 2016) (Associate)
MacRoberts LLP, Glasgow . . . .(p.1015)
T: 0141 3031100
E: melissa.hall@macroberts.com

HALL, Miriam Roncalli (Feb 2008) (Employee)
Santander, London NW1 . . . .(p.1268)
E: miriam.hall@santander.co.uk

HALL, Philip Duncan (Oct 2008) (Employee)
National Westminster Bank PLC,
Edinburgh . . . .(p.1226)
T: (0131) 626 2925
E: Philip.Hall@rbs.co.uk

HALL, Samuel Fergus (Aug 2015) (Employee)
Norwich City Football Club Plc,
Norwich. . . . .(p.1270)
T: 01603 721902
E: sam.hall@canaries.co.uk

HALL, Sara Lisa (Sept 2020) (Employee)
J.D. Clark & Allan Limited, Duns . . . . . .(p.829)
T: 01361 882501
E: sara.hall@jdca.co.uk

HALL, Tracy Margaret (Jul 2016) (Employee)
Brodies LLP, Edinburgh . . . .(p.845)
T: 0131 6560084
E: tracy.hall@brodies.com

HALLEY, James (Jul 2020) (Employee)
Jackson Boyd LLP, Glasgow . . . .(p.991)
T: 0141 2214325
E: jhalley@jacksonboyd.co.uk

HALLIDAY, David James Finlay, WS
(Nov 1988) (Partner)
Halliday Campbell W.S., Edinburgh . . . .(p.876)
T: 0131 6683000
E: david.halliday@hallidaycampbell.com

HALLIDAY, Jordan Thomas (Oct 2008)
(Employee)
Brodies LLP, Glasgow . . . .(p.948)
T: 0141 2484672
E: jordan.halliday@brodies.com

HALLIDAY, Karen Isobel (Oct 2006) (Employee)
Shell International B.V., The Hague . . . .(p.1275)
E: Karen.halliday@shell.com

HALLIDAY, Lesley Mhairi (Oct 2005)
(Employee)
SSE Plc, Perth . . . .(p.1253)
T: 01738 456 000
E: lesley.halliday@sse.com

HALLIDAY, Nicola Louise (Dec 2019)
(Employee)
CMS Cameron McKenna Nabarro Olswang LLP,
Glasgow. . . . .(p.962)
T: 0141 2222200
E: nicola.halliday@cms-cmno.com

HALLIDAY, Paul Anand (Dec 2017) (Employee)
ELP Arbuthnott McClanachan,
Edinburgh . . . .(p.867)
T: 0131 3127276
E: pah@elpamsolicitors.co.uk

HALLIGAN, David Timothy Paul Doherty
(Feb 2017) (Employee)
Gillespie Macandrew LLP,
Edinburgh . . . .(p.872)
T: 0131 2251677
E: David.Halligan@gillespiemacandrew.co.uk

HALPIN, Irene Margaret (Feb 1996) (Employee)
Renfrewshire Council, Paisley . . . . (p.1252)
T: 0141 8403648
E: irene.halpin@renfrewshire.gov.uk

HAMEED, Abrar (Jun 2009) (Employee)
R. & R.S. Mearns, Glasgow . . . . (p.1018)
T: 0141 6326162
E: ahmearns@gmail.com

HAMID, Abdullah Faisal (Jul 2008) (Partner)
Philip Rooney & Co., Glasgow . . . . (p.1036)
T: 0141 423 0000
E: a.hamid@philiprooney.com

HAMILL, Derek (May 1999) (Partner)
Gilson Gray LLP, Glasgow . . . . (p.980)
T: 0141 5302021
E: dhamill@gilsongray.co.uk

HAMILL, Julie Ann (Mar 2012) (Employee)
Esson Aberdein, Aberdeen . . . . (p.731)
T: 01224 606210
E: Julie.hamill@essonaberdein.com

HAMILL, Lindsey Emma (Oct 2019) (Associate)
Dentons UK and Middle East LLP,
Glasgow . . . . (p.968)
T: 0330 2220050
E: lindsey.hamill@dentons.com

HAMILTON, Bethia Mary (Oct 1984) (Partner)
Bartys, Dunblane . . . . (p.804)
T: 01786 822296
E: bmh@wjm.co.uk

HAMILTON, Calum Alexander McKillop
(Oct 2015) (Employee)
D C Thomson & Co Ltd, Dundee . . . . . (p.1217)
E: calum.hamilton@dcthomson.co.uk

HAMILTON, Colin Stuart (Oct 2007) (Partner)
Gillespie Macandrew LLP,
Edinburgh . . . . (p.872)
T: 0131 2251677
E: colin.hamilton@gillespiemacandrew.co.uk

HAMILTON, Douglas Kennedy (Jul 1985)
(Employee)
Procurator Fiscal Service, Paisley . . . . . . (p.1252)
T: 0141 8875225
E: douglas.hamilton@copfs.gov.uk

HAMILTON, Duncan Martin Reid (Nov 2017)
(Employee)
ELP Arbuthnott McClanachan,
Edinburgh . . . . (p.867)
T: 0131 5548649
E: dmrh@elpamsolicitors.co.uk

HAMILTON, Eleanor (Mar 1994) (Employee)
Ascent Legal Scotland, Glasgow . . . . . . (p.942)
T: 0141 3004300
E: eleanor.hamilton@ascent.co.uk

HAMILTON, Elizabeth Anne (Aug 2013)
(Employee)
MDS Estates Limited, Edinburgh . . . . . (p.1225)
E: lhamilton@buccleuch.com

HAMILTON, Fiona Elspeth (Sept 2013)
(Employee)
Procurator Fiscal Service, Selkirk . . . . . . (p.1254)
T: 01750 20345
E: Fiona.Hamilton@copfs.gov.uk

HAMILTON, Grant (Nov 1991) (Solicitor)
NO FIRM

HAMILTON, Gregor Steven (Jan 1994)
(Employee)
Strategic Investment Board, Belfast . . . . (p.1275)
T: 028 9090 9441
E: gregor.hamilton@sibni.org

HAMILTON, Hazel Alexandra Mountain
(Nov 1988) (Employee)
Cochran Dickie, Paisley . . . . (p.1137)
T: 0141 8892245
E: hh@cochrandickie.co.uk

HAMILTON, Jack Andrew (Jan 2021)
(Employee)
Pinsent Masons LLP, Glasgow . . . . (p.1031)
T: 0141 567 8400
E: jack.hamilton@pinsentmasons.com

HAMILTON, James Robert (Oct 2001)
(Employee)
Scottish Government, Edinburgh . . . . . (p.1231)
T: 0131 244 0603
E: james.hamilton@gov.scot

HAMILTON, Jennifer Ann (Jan 2014)
(Employee)
Procurator Fiscal Service,
Edinburgh . . . . (p.1227)
T: 0300 0203168
E: jennifer.hamilton@copfs.gov.uk

HAMILTON, Joanna (Oct 2005) (Employee)
TLT LLP, Glasgow . . . . (p.1048)
T: 0333 006 0400
E: Joanna.Hamilton@TLTsolicitors.com

HAMILTON, Jonathan Philip (Jan 1999)
(Employee)
Inverclyde Council, Greenock . . . . (p.1246)
T: 01475 717171
E: jonathan.hamilton@inverclyde.gov.uk

HAMILTON, Julie Dawn (Feb 2003) (Employee)
Procurator Fiscal Service, Glasgow . . . (p.1241)
T: 0300 020 3388
E: julie.hamilton@copfs.gov.uk

HAMILTON, Julie Patricia (Sept 1994) (Partner)
MacRoberts LLP, Edinburgh . . . . (p.887)
T: 0131 2295046
E: julie.hamilton@macroberts.com

HAMILTON, Karen Lesley (Oct 1996) (Partner)
Brodies LLP, Glasgow . . . . (p.948)
T: 0141 2484672
E: karen.hamilton@brodies.com

HAMILTON, Linda Alexandra (Sept 2005)
(Employee)
HMRC, Belfast . . . . (p.1275)
E: linda.hamilton@hmrc.gov.uk

HAMILTON, Lindsay Alice (Aug 2021)
(Employee)
Drummond Miller LLP, Bathgate . . . . . . (p.771)
T: 01506 656645
E: LHamilton@drummondmiller.co.uk

HAMILTON, Louise Anne (Oct 1999)
(Employee)
Vialex Limited, Edinburgh . . . . (p.1235)
T: 0333 2400127
E: louise.hamilton@vialex.co.uk

HAMILTON, Louise Josephine (Jul 2009)
(Associate)
Walkers, St Helier . . . . (p.1274)
T: 01534 700723
E: louise.hamilton@walkersglobal.com

HAMILTON, Mark Russell (Sept 1987) (Partner)
Dentons UK and Middle East LLP,
Edinburgh . . . . (p.860)
T: 0330 2220050
E: Mark.Hamilton@dentons.com

HAMILTON, Mirren (Aug 2021) (Employee)
Bell & Craig Limited, Stirling . . . . (p.1164)
T: 01786 470444
E: mirrenhamilton@bellandcraig.co.uk

HAMILTON, Nichola Irene (Apr 2017) (Solicitor)
NO FIRM

HAMILTON, Paula Margaret (Aug 2012)
(Employee)
Procurator Fiscal Service, Stranraer . . . . (p.1255)
T: 01776 704321
E: paula.hamilton@copfs.gov.uk

HAMILTON, Rachel Louise (Nov 2013)
(Employee)
Scottish Social Services Council,
Dundee . . . . (p.1218)
T: 0345 6030 891
E: rachel.hamilton@sssc.uk.com

HAMILTON, Ronald Grant (Sept 1991)
(Partner)
Thorntons Law LLP, Kirkcaldy . . . . (p.1102)
T: 01592 268608
E: ghamilton@thorntons-law.co.uk

HAMILTON, Stuart James Watson
(Aug 2016) (Employee)
Public Defence Solicitors Office,
Dundee . . . . (p.1218)
T: 01382 22 6051
E: shamiltondundee@pdso.org.uk

HAMILTON, Stuart John (Oct 1978) (Employee)
Police Scotland, Glasgow . . . . (p.1241)

HAMILTON, Zoe Charlotte (Oct 2007)
(Employee)
Lloyds Banking Group Plc,
Edinburgh . . . . (p.1224)
T: (0131) 442 9579
E: Zoe.Hamilton@lloydsbanking.com

HAMMELL, Leanne Marion (May 2015)
(Employee)
CMS Cameron McKenna Nabarro Olswang LLP,
Edinburgh . . . . (p.856)
T: 0131 2288000
E: leanne.hammell@cms-cmno.com

HAMMOND, Catherine Frances (Oct 2006)
(Employee)
Digby Brown LLP, Edinburgh . . . . (p.862)
T: 0333 200 5925
E: catherine.hammond@digbybrown.co.uk

HAMMOND, Charles Graham (Jan 1986)
(Employee)
Forth Ports Limited, Edinburgh . . . . . . (p.1223)
T: 0131 5558700
E: charles.hammond@forthports.co.uk

HAMMOND, Michael James (Jul 2015)
(Employee)
Chrysaor Production (U.K.) Limited,
Aberdeen . . . . (p.1212)
T: 01224 205333
E: michael.hammond@chrysaor.com

HAMMOND, Simon John (Jul 2006) (Partner)
Digby Brown LLP, Edinburgh . . . . (p.862)
T: 0333 200 5925
E: simon.hammond@digbybrown.co.uk

HAMPSEY, Ross Hugh (Mar 2021) (Employee)
Harper Macleod LLP, Glasgow . . . . (p.983)
T: 0141 2218888
E: ross.hampsey@harpermacleod.co.uk

HAMPTON, Donna (Nov 1995) (Employee)
Bowmans, Dundee . . . . (p.806)
T: 01382 322267
E: dh@bowmansolicitors.co.uk

HAMPTON, Kevin (Sept 1995) (Partner)
MML Legal, Dundee . . . . (p.817)
T: 01382 206 000
E: kevin@muirmyleslaverty.co.uk

HAMPTON, Lindsay (Apr 1988) (Employee)
University of Edinburgh, Edinburgh . . . (p.1235)
T: (0131) 651 4330
E: Lindsay.Hampton@ed.ac.uk

HAND, Fergus George Curnow (Dec 2017)
(Employee)
Coutts & Co, London WC2 . . . . (p.1263)
E: fergus.hand@coutts.com

HANDS, Stephanie Lindsay (Jun 2018)
(Employee)
TLT LLP, Glasgow . . . .(p.1048)
T: 0333 006 0400
E: Stephanie.Hands@TLTsolicitors.com

HANIF, Fehmida (Oct 2011) (Associate)
Brodies LLP, Edinburgh . . . .(p.845)
T: 0131 2283777
E: fehmida.hanif@brodies.com

HANIF, Jwad (Nov 2012) (Director)
Miller Beckett & Jackson Limited,
    Glasgow. . . . .(p.1019)
T: 0141 2042833
E: jwad@mbjsolicitors.co.uk

HANIF, Shabnam (Sept 2007) (Partner)
EMW Law (Scotland) LLP, Glasgow . . . .(p.974)
E: Shabnam.Hanif@emwllp.com

HANIF-KIDD, Sobia (Mar 2021) (Employee)
Procurator Fiscal Service, Glasgow . . . .(p.1242)
T: (0300) 020 3000
E: sobia.hanif-kidd@copfs.gov.uk

HANIFORD, Paul Sydney, WS (Nov 1980)
(Partner)
Dentons UK and Middle East LLP,
    Glasgow. . . . .(p.968)
T: 0330 2220050
E: Paul.Haniford@dentons.com

HANKIN, Robert Iain Christopher
(Sept 1980) (Employee)
Portfolio Legal Ltd, Sutton
    Coldfield . . . .(p.1272)
E: rhankin@portfoliolegal.co.uk

HANKINSON, Michael Richard (Sept 2009)
(Director)
Macdonald Henderson Limited,
    Glasgow. . . . .(p.1008)
T: 0141 2484957
E: michael@macdonaldhenderson.co.uk

HANLON, Deirdre Elizabeth (Sept 2000)
(Partner)
Kirk Hanlon, Glasgow . . . .(p.997)
T: 0141 3786653
E: deirdre@kirkhanlon.com

HANLON, Sophie (Oct 2016) (Employee)
Procurator Fiscal Service,
    Edinburgh . . . .(p.1229)
T: 0300 0204134
E: Sophie.Hanlon@copfs.gov.uk

HANN, Benjamin Nephi (Aug 2011) (Director)
Hann & Co Solicitors Ltd,
    Edinburgh . . . .(p.876)
T: 0131 2352100
E: ben@hannandco.com

HANN, Joseph Timothy (Sept 2001) (Director)
Hann & Co Solicitors Ltd, Annan . . . . . .(p.754)
T: 01461 203836
E: joe@hannandco.com

HANNAH, Daniel Jamie (Oct 2017) (Employee)
Burness Paull LLP, Edinburgh . . . .(p.850)
T: 0131 4736000
E: daniel.hannah@burnesspaull.com

HANNAH, Jennifer Linda Graham
(Sept 2006) (Employee)
Scottish Social Services Council,
    Dundee . . . .(p.1218)
T: 0345 6030 891
E: Jennifer.Hannah@sssc.uk.com

HANNAH, Megan Jayne (Jul 2017) (Employee)
Aberdein Considine and Company,
    Glasgow. . . . .(p.937)
T: 0141 2278200
E: mhannah@acandco.com

HANNAH, Nicole Michelle (Sept 2021)
(Employee)
DWF LLP, Edinburgh . . . .(p.865)
T: 0131 2265541
E: nicole.hannah@dwf.law

HANNAH, Paul Martin Jennings (Mar 1987)
(Partner)
Paul Hannah Solicitors, Glasgow . . . . . .(p.982)
T: 0141 5587433
E: ph@paulhannah.org

HANNAH, Timothy John (Sept 1998) (Solicitor)
NO FIRM

HANNAN, Lee-Anne Moira Margaret
(Sept 2020) (Employee)
Procurator Fiscal Service, Kirkcaldy . . . .(p.1249)
T: 0300 0203000
E: lee-anne.hannan@copfs.gov.uk

HANNAWAY, Kenneth Joseph (Oct 1996)
(Employee)
Scottish Government, Edinburgh . . . . .(p.1231)
T: 0131 244 0815
E: kenneth.hannaway@gov.scot

HANNAY, Emma (Jul 2008) (Employee)
Criminal Injuries Compensation Authority,
    Glasgow. . . . .(p.1239)
T: 0141 2281419
E: emma.hannay@cica.gov.uk

HANNAY, Fiona Jean (Dec 1999) (Consultant)
Thomas Duncan Solicitor, East
    Kilbride . . . .(p.831)
T: 07939 340170
E: fiona@scotlandlegal.co.uk

HANNAY, James Samuel (Mar 1977) (Director)
Hannay Fraser & Co Ltd, Glasgow . . . . .(p.983)
T: 0141 2211381
E: jim@hannayfraser.co.uk

HANNAY, Laura Anne Scanlan (Nov 2021)
(Employee)
Cloch Solicitors Limited, Glasgow . . . . . .(p.960)
T: 0141 221 8029
E: laura@cloch.co.uk

HANNAY, Philip Adamson (Jun 2003) (Director)
Cloch Solicitors Limited, Glasgow . . . . . .(p.960)
T: 0141 221 8029
E: philip@cloch.co.uk

HANNAY, Richard (Jun 2001) (Employee)
Procurator Fiscal Service,
Dumbarton . . . .(p.1217)
T: 0300 020 3000
E: Richard.Hannay@copfs.gov.uk

HANNIGAN, Kirsty Anne (Dec 2016)
(Employee)
Pinsent Masons LLP, Glasgow . . . .(p.1031)
T: 0141 567 8400
E: Kirsty.Hannigan@pinsentmasons.com

HANRAHAN, Julian Paul (Nov 2001) (Associate)
Bonnar Accident Law Ltd,
Dunfermline . . . .(p.822)
T: 01383 604110
E: julian.hanrahan@bonnarandco.com

HANTON, Andrew David (Jun 2003)
(Employee)
Procurator Fiscal Service, Aberdeen . . .(p.1213)
T: 0300 020 4036
E: Andrew.Hanton@copfs.gov.uk

HANVIDGE, Ian Rannochan (Jan 1985)
(Associate)
Middleton Ross & Arnot Limited,
Dingwall . . . .(p.797)
T: 01349 862214
E: irh@middletonross.co.uk

HAQ, Abrarr (Aug 2021) (Employee)
Stodarts LLP, Hamilton . . . .(p.1069)
T: 01698 200302
E: barryhaq@stodarts.co.uk

HAQ, Rana Abid (Jul 2018) (Employee)
Maguire Solicitors, Glasgow . . . .(p.1017)
T: 0141 3312885
E: Abid@maguiresolicitors.co.uk

HAQUE, Fariha (Sept 2017) (Employee)
East Lothian Council, Haddington . . . .(p.1246)
T: 01620 827827
E: fhaque@eastlothian.gov.uk

HARAN, Paul Anthony (Mar 2002) (Employee)
Public Defence Solicitors Office,
Edinburgh . . . .(p.1230)
T: 0131 5571222
E: pharan@pdso.org.uk

HARBISON, Grace Christina (May 2018)
(Employee)
Drummond Miller LLP, Glasgow . . . .(p.971)
T: 0141 3320086
E: gharbison@drummondmiller.co.uk

HARBISON, Nicholas John (Jun 1999)
(Employee)
Scullion Law Limited, Hamilton . . . . . .(p.1069)
T: 01698 283265
E: nick@scullionlaw.com

HARCUS, Colin Angus (Sept 2008) (Director)
Orkney Law Ltd, Kirkwall . . . .(p.1107)
T: 01856 878550
E: colin@orkneylaw.co.uk

HARDIE, Gemma Louise (May 2011) (Solicitor)
Thorntons Law LLP, Dundee . . . .(p.819)
T: 01382 229 111
E: ghardie@thorntons-law.co.uk

HARDIE, James Fraser McBride (Jan 1985)
(Partner)
Blackadders LLP, Edinburgh . . . .(p.843)
T: 0131 2228000
E: fraser.hardie@blackadders.co.uk

HARDIE, John Michael Ewart (Sept 1997)
(Consultant)
W. & J.S. Gordon, Forfar . . . .(p.926)
T: 01307 462188
E: jhardie@wjsgordon.co.uk

HARDIE, John Robert Simpson (Jan 1995)
(Partner)
Gavin Bain & Co., Aberdeen . . . .(p.721)
T: 01224 623040
E: j.hardie@gavin-bain.co.uk

HARDIE, Julie Joanne (Nov 2009) (Employee)
Spirit Production (Services) Limited,
Aberdeen . . . .(p.1214)
T: 01224 415000
E: Julie.hardie@spirit-energy.com

HARDIE, Katharine Helen (Jan 1992) (Partner)
Pinsent Masons LLP, Glasgow . . . .(p.1031)
T: 0141 567 8400
E: katharine.hardie@pinsentmasons.com

HARDIE, Randolph Wemyss Lawrence
(Oct 2015) (Employee)
Ennova Limited, Edinburgh . . . .(p.869)
T: 0131 6624555
E: rhardie@ennova-law.com

HARDIE, Suzanne Claire (Dec 2004) (Partner)
Morton Fraser LLP, Edinburgh . . . .(p.891)
T: 0131 2471000
E: suzanne.hardie@morton-fraser.com

HARDIE, William John Adam (Sept 1973)
(Partner)
W. & J.S. Gordon, Forfar . . . .(p.926)
T: 01307 462188
E: whardie@wjsgordon.co.uk

HARDING, Andrew Paul (Jun 2020) (Employee)
Procurator Fiscal Service, Perth . . . .(p.1253)
T: 01738 637272
E: andrew.harding@copfs.gov.uk

HARDING, Debbie Mary (Mar 2004)
(Employee)
Dobbies Garden Centres, Lasswade . . .(p.1250)
E: debbie.harding@dobbies.com

HARDING, Graham Stewart (Nov 1989)
(Solicitor)
NO FIRM

HARDING, Jennifer (Nov 2007) (Employee)
National Health Service Scotland,
Edinburgh . . . .(p.1225)
T: 0131 2757800
E: jennifer.harding@nhs.scot

HARDING, Dr, Matthew Ian (Nov 1988)
(Consultant)
Harding & Co., Glasgow . . . .(p.983)
T: 0141 5528880
E: matthewharding@btinternet.com

HARDY, Alice Elizabeth (Sept 2020) (Associate)
CMS Cameron McKenna Nabarro Olswang LLP,
Edinburgh . . . .(p.856)
T: 0131 2288000
E: Alice.Hardy@cms-cmno.com

HARE, Lindsay (Jul 2005) (Director)
Gildeas Limited, Glasgow . . . .(p.979)
T: 0141 331 6071
E: lhare@gildeas.net

HARINGTON, Lucy Aline (Aug 2008) (Associate)
TLT LLP, Glasgow . . . .(p.1048)
T: 0333 006 0400
E: Lucy.Harington@tltsolicitors.com

HARKIN, Aoibheann (Aug 2021) (Employee)
Dickson Minto, London EC2 . . . .(p.1263)
T: +44 (0) 20 7649 6961

HARKIN, Jennifer Anne (Jun 2015) (Employee)
Neil Kilcoyne & Co., Glasgow . . . .(p.996)
T: 0141 4332700
E: JHarkin@kilcoyne-solicitors.co.uk

HARKIN, Paul Matthew (Nov 1980) (Partner)
Pinsent Masons LLP, Birmingham . . . . .(p.1258)
T: 0121 2001050
E: paul.harkin@pinsentmasons.com

HARKINS, Jacqueline Anne (Nov 1991)
(Employee)
Carr & Co (Solicitors) Limited,
Glasgow . . . .(p.957)
T: 0141 7794466
E: jh@theglasgowlawpractice.co.uk

HARKINS, Jennifer Mary (Sept 2017)
(Employee)
Procurator Fiscal Service, Glasgow . . . .(p.1241)
T: 0300 0203000
E: Jennifer.Harkins@copfs.gov.uk

HARKINS, Juliet Claire (Nov 2003) (Employee)
Procurator Fiscal Service,
Edinburgh . . . .(p.1227)
T: 0300 0203168
E: Juliet.Harkins@copfs.gov.uk

HARKINS, Kelly-Anne (Jan 2015) (Employee)
Ali & Co Solicitors, Glasgow . . . .(p.939)
T: 07849 007162
E: k.harkins@ali-legal.co.uk

HARKINS, Mhairi Patricia (Apr 2015)
(Employee)
Fitzpatrick & Co., Glasgow . . . .(p.976)
T: 0141 2042200
E: mh@fitzpatrickandco.co.uk

HARKINS, Owen Stephen (Jul 2014) (Employee)
John Menzies Plc, Edinburgh . . . .(p.1224)
E: owen.harkins@johnmenziesplc.com

HARKNESS, Andrew Michael (Dec 2010)
(Employee)
Financial Conduct Authority,
Edinburgh . . . .(p.1223)
T: 7725552025
E: Andrew.Harkness@fca.org.uk

HARKNESS, Elisabeth Louise (Feb 1996)
(Employee)
DWF LLP, Edinburgh . . . .(p.865)
T: 0131 474 2466
E: louise.Harkness@dwf.law

HARKNESS-MCKINLAY, Gillian Anne
(Feb 2006) (Employee)
Anderson Strathern LLP, Glasgow . . . . . .(p.940)
T: 0141 2426060
E:
gillian.harkness-mckinlay@andersonstrathern.
co.uk

HARLEY, Abbie (Jul 2013) (Associate)
CMS Cameron McKenna Nabarro Olswang LLP,
Edinburgh . . . .(p.856)
T: 0131 2288000
E: Abbie.Harley@cms-cmno.com

HARLEY, David James Bryce (Aug 1985)
(Partner)
Rollos Law LLP, Cupar . . . .(p.792)
T: 01334 654081
E: davidharley@rollos.co.uk

HARMAN, Gillian Allison (Sept 2010)
(Employee)
BTO Solicitors LLP, Glasgow . . . .(p.952)
T: 0141 2218012
E: gah@bto.co.uk

HARPER, Alastair Paul Ludovic (Mar 1990)
(Partner)
Lindsays LLP, Edinburgh . . . .(p.882)
T: 0131 2291212
E: paulharper@lindsays.co.uk

HARPER, Alexis Rachel (Jun 2008) (Partner)
Harper Macleod LLP, Glasgow . . . .(p.983)
T: 0141 2218888
E: Alexis.Harper@harpermacleod.co.uk

HARPER, Andrew (Sept 2017) (Employee)
Sacker & Partners LLP, London
EC2 . . . .(p.1268)
E: Andrew.Harper@sackers.com

HARPER, John (Aug 2011) (Employee)
Scottish Legal Aid Board,
Edinburgh . . . .(p.1233)
T: 0131 2267061

HARPER, John David (Jul 2019) (Solicitor)
NO FIRM

HARPER, Kathleen Marie (Oct 1984)
(Employee)
Procurator Fiscal Service,
Edinburgh . . . .(p.1227)
T: 0300 0203168
E: kathleen.harper@copfs.gov.uk

HARPER, Linzi Jane (Jun 2017) (Employee)
Frazer Coogans Ltd, Ayr . . . .(p.763)
T: 01292 280499
E: linzi.harper@frazercoogans.co.uk

HARPER, Marina (Mar 2009) (Partner)
Harper Macleod LLP, Glasgow . . . .(p.983)
T: 0141 2218888
E: marina.harper@harpermacleod.co.uk

HARPER, Oliver James Hughes (Jul 2010)
(Employee)
Carpenters Scotland Limited,
Glasgow. . . . .(p.956)
T: 0141 3285452
E: OH@carpenters-law.co.uk

HARPER, Rhona Alison (Mar 1993) (Employee)
Water Industry Commission For Scotland,
Stirling. . . . .(p.1255)
T: 01786 430 200
E: rhona.harper@watercommission.co.uk

HARRAGHY, Noele Ellen, WS (Nov 1990)
(Employee)
Allan McDougall McQueen LLP,
Edinburgh . . . .(p.837)
T: 0131 6221771
E: noeleharraghy@mcdougallmcqueen.co.uk

HARRATS, Michael (Jul 2009) (Employee)
Legal & General Investment Management Ltd,
London EC2 . . . .(p.1266)
T: 020 3124 3983
E: Michael.Harrats@lgim.com

HARRINGTON, Gillian (Oct 2009) (Employee)
Burness Paull LLP, Aberdeen . . . .(p.724)
T: 01224 621621
E: Gillian.Harrington@burnesspaull.com

HARRIS, Andrew John Forsyth (Oct 1993)
(Partner)
MBM Commercial LLP, Edinburgh . . . . .(p.889)
T: 0131 2268200
E: andy.harris@mbmcommercial.co.uk

HARRIS, Calum (Oct 2021) (Employee)
Martin, Johnston & Socha Limited,
Dunfermline . . . .(p.824)
T: 01383 730 466
E:
calum.harris@mjscriminaldefencelawyers.co.uk

HARRIS, David John Campbell (Dec 1983)
(Consultant)
Allan McDougall McQueen LLP,
Edinburgh . . . .(p.837)
T: 0131 2252121
E: davidharris@allanmcdougall.co.uk

HARRIS, David Malcolm (Mar 2003) (Employee)
Lloyds Banking Group Plc,
Edinburgh . . . .(p.1224)
T: (0131) 442 9579
E: david.harris@lloydsbanking.com

HARRIS, David Ross Ward (Sept 2012)
(Employee)
Stephenson Harwood LLP, London
EC2 . . . .(p.1268)
T: 020 7329 4422
E: david.harris@shlegal.com

HARRIS, Emma Jane (Oct 2006) (Employee)
Diageo Scotland Limited,
Edinburgh . . . .(p.1222)
T: (0131) 519 2261
E: Emma.Harris@diageo.com

HARRIS, Jacqueline Marie (Dec 1988) (Partner)
Pinsent Masons LLP, Edinburgh . . . .(p.895)
T: 0131 7777000
E: jacqueline.harris@pinsentmasons.com

HARRIS, Jill Louise (Sept 2010) (Associate)
Brodies LLP, Edinburgh . . . .(p.845)
T: 0131 2283777
E: jill.harris@brodies.com

HARRIS, Julia Adrienne (May 2014) (Associate)
Rooney Family Law Limited,
Uddingston . . . .(p.1178)
T: 01698 815620
E: julia@rooneyfamilylaw.co.uk

HARRIS, Julie Elizabeth (Sept 1995) (Partner)
Allan McDougall McQueen LLP,
Edinburgh . . . .(p.837)
T: 0131 2252121
E: julieharris@allanmcdougall.co.uk

HARRIS, Leigh Sarah (Nov 2012) (Consultant)
Thomas Docherty Solicitors, Falkirk. . . . .(p.921)
T: 01324 875870

HARRIS, Lorna Sarah Bridget (Jun 2012)
(Employee)
Procurator Fiscal Service, Glasgow . . . . (p.1241)
T: 0300 0203000
E: lorna.harris@copfs.gov.uk

HARRIS, Redmond Porch (Oct 2019)
(Employee)
Scottish Government, Edinburgh . . . . . (p.1231)
T: 0131 244 0815

HARRIS, Thomas Philip (Oct 1995) (Associate)
Shepherd and Wedderburn LLP,
Edinburgh . . . . (p.900)
T: 0131 2289900
E: phil.harris@shepwedd.com

HARRIS-EVANS, Anna Ietskina (Jun 2017)
(Solicitor)
NO FIRM

HARRISON, Caroline Nicola (Jun 2008)
(Director)
Harrison Legal Limited, Kilmarnock . . . . (p.1095)
T: 01563 508114
E: caroline@harrisonlaw.legal

HARRISON, Carolyn (Oct 2007) (Employee)
Aberdeen City Council, Aberdeen . . . . . (p.1211)
T: 01224 522000
E: CaHarrison@aberdeencity.gov.uk

HARRISON, Diane Parker (Oct 2013)
(Employee)
Arthur J Gallagher, Glasgow . . . . (p.1237)
T: 0141 285 3056
E: diane.wilson@ajg.com

HARRISON, Dominic Charles (Nov 1991)
(Employee)
Channel 4 Television Corporation, London
SW1 . . . . (p.1262)
T: 0207 306 8119
E: DHarrison@channel4.co.uk

HARRISON, Graeme Stephen James
(Sept 2016) (Associate)
MacRoberts LLP, Glasgow . . . . (p.1015)
T: 0141 3031100
E: graeme.harrison@macroberts.com

HARRISON, Joanne Louise Isobel (Sept 2021)
(Employee)
Pinsent Masons LLP, Edinburgh . . . . . . (p.895)
T: 0131 777 7000
E: jo.harrison@pinsentmasons.com

HARRISON, John David (Nov 1998) (Employee)
National Westminster Bank PLC,
Edinburgh . . . . (p.1226)
E: john.harrison@natwesttds.com

HARRISON, Louise Margaret (Oct 2002)
(Employee)
Aggreko plc, Glasgow . . . . (p.1237)
T: 0141 2255900
E: Louise.Harrison@aggreko.co.uk

HARRISON, Lynn Louisa (Oct 1987) (Partner)
Beveridge & Kellas, Edinburgh . . . . (p.843)
T: 0131 5546321
E: l.harrison@beveridgekellas.com

HARRISON, Mark Nicholas (Nov 1991)
(Director)
Flexlaw Ltd, Edinburgh . . . . (p.871)
T: 0131 2026363
E: mark.harrison@flexlaw.co.uk

HARRISON, Roderick Alexander Louden
(Dec 1990) (Partner)
Wright, Johnston & Mackenzie LLP,
Edinburgh . . . . (p.913)
T: 0131 5241500
E: rah@wjm.co.uk

HARRISON, Sophia Victoria (Jul 2016)
(Associate)
Burness Paull LLP, Edinburgh . . . . (p.850)
T: 0131 4736000
E: Sophia.Harrison@burnesspaull.com

HARROW, Audrey Georgina Kennedy
(Nov 1998) (Associate)
Burness Paull LLP, Edinburgh . . . . (p.850)
T: 0131 4736000
E: audrey.harrow@burnesspaull.com

HARROWER, Jennifer (Dec 1987) (Employee)
Procurator Fiscal Service,
Edinburgh . . . . (p.1229)
T: (0844) 561 3268
E: jennifer.harrower@copfs.gov.uk

HARROWER, Mark Alexander (Sept 1993)
(Partner)
Wardlaw Stephenson Allan,
Edinburgh . . . . (p.910)
T: 0131 557 8020
E: mark@wsalawyers.com

HART, Alastair Ralph (Sept 1985) (Partner)
Alastair Hart & Co., Aberdeen . . . . (p.731)
T: 01224 310600
E: alastair.hart@alastairhart.co.uk

HART, Bryony Elizabeth (Aug 2018) (Employee)
Addleshaw Goddard LLP,
Edinburgh . . . . (p.835)
T: 0131 2282400
E: bryony.hart@addleshawgoddard.com

HART, Catherine Ballingall (Apr 1991) (Partner)
Digby Brown LLP, Glasgow . . . . (p.970)
T: 0141 566 9578
E: Catherine.Hart@digbybrown.co.uk

HART, David Millar (Aug 2013) (Director)
Miller Gerrard Limited, Blairgowrie . . . . . (p.776)
T: 01250 873468
E: David@millergerrard.co.uk

HART, Deirdre Elizabeth Mary (Jan 1996)
(Partner)
Munro & Noble, Inverness . . . .(p.1080)
T: 01463 221727
E: deirdreh@munronoble.com

HART, Lauren Elizabeth (Jan 2011) (Associate)
Morton Fraser LLP, Edinburgh . . . .(p.891)
T: 0131 2471000
E: Lauren.Hart@morton-fraser.com

HART, Richard Gordon (Oct 1991) (Associate)
Shepherd and Wedderburn LLP,
Glasgow. . . . .(p.1039)
T: 0141 5669900
E: richard.hart@shepwedd.com

HART, Sonja Hannele (Mar 2015) (Employee)
Burness Paull LLP, Edinburgh . . . .(p.850)
T: 0131 4736000
E: sonja.hart@burnesspaull.com

HART, Victoria Margaret (Aug 2005)
(Employee)
Procurator Fiscal Service, Glasgow . . . .(p.1241)
T: 0300 0203000
E: victoria.hart@copfs.gov.uk

HARTE, Christopher Joseph (Mar 1996)
(Partner)
Morton Fraser LLP, Edinburgh . . . .(p.891)
T: 0131 2471000
E: chris.harte@morton-fraser.com

HARTE, Stephen John (Sept 1994) (Employee)
KCA Deutag Drilling Ltd,
Portlethen . . . .(p.1254)
T: 01224 987000
E: stephen.harte@kcadeutag.com

HARTE, Steven Gerard (Oct 2009) (Associate)
Weightmans (Scotland) LLP,
Glasgow. . . . .(p.1051)
T: 0345 073 9900
E: steven.harte@weightmans.com

HARTER, Sally Gwen (Oct 1986) (Partner)
Harter & Co., Glasgow . . . .(p.985)
T: 0141 4270901
E: hartersolicitors@tiscali.co.uk

HARTLEY, Sandra Elizabeth (Oct 2002)
(Employee)
Balfour Beatty Investments Limited, London
NW1 . . . .(p.1261)
E: sandra.hartley@balfourbeatty.com

HARTLEY-ZELS, Richard Gordon (Apr 2016)
(Director)
Miller Gerrard Limited, Blairgowrie . . . . .(p.776)
T: 01250 873468
E: richard@millergerrard.co.uk

HARTY, Darren (Sept 2021) (Employee)
Procurator Fiscal Service,
Edinburgh . . . .(p.1227)
T: 0300 0203168
E: darren.harty@copfs.gov.uk

HARVEY, David James (Mar 2019) (Employee)
Addleshaw Goddard LLP,
Edinburgh . . . .(p.835)
T: 0131 2282400

HARVEY, Douglas James (Jun 2020) (Employee)
Morton Fraser LLP, Edinburgh . . . .(p.891)
T: 0131 2471000
E: douglas.harvey@morton-fraser.com

HARVEY, Joshua Alexander (Aug 2019)
(Employee)
Burness Paull LLP, Edinburgh . . . .(p.850)
T: 0131 4736000
E: joshua.harvey@burnesspaull.com

HARVEY, Michele (Oct 2008) (Employee)
Procurator Fiscal Service, Glasgow . . . .(p.1241)
T: 0300 0203000
E: michele.harvey@copfs.gov.uk

HARVEY, Nicola (Dec 2017) (Employee)
Dentons UK and Middle East LLP,
Edinburgh . . . .(p.860)
T: 0330 2220050
E: Nicola.Harvey@dentons.com

HARVEY, Nicola (Jan 1993) (Partner)
Stewart & Watson, Peterhead . . . .(p.1155)
T: 01779 476351
E: nharvey@stewartwatson.co.uk

HARVEY, Peter James (Jan 1982) (Partner)
Blair & Bryden, Greenock . . . .(p.1059)
T: 01475 888777
E: peterharvey@blair-bryden.co.uk

HARVIE, Alison Jane (Dec 1991) (Director)
J. Watson Scott & Co Ltd,
Hamilton . . . .(p.1070)
T: 01698 282370
E: ajh@watsonscott.co.uk

HARVIE, Bruce Douglas (Feb 2012) (Associate)
CMS Cameron McKenna Nabarro Olswang LLP,
Edinburgh . . . .(p.856)
T: 0131 2288000
E: Bruce.Harvie@cms-cmno.com

HARVIE, Craig Robert (Oct 1995) (Director)
Eden Legal Limited, Perth . . . .(p.1147)
T: 01738 310047
E: craigharvie@eden-legal.co.uk

HARVIE, David Bryce (Sept 1993) (Employee)
Procurator Fiscal Service,
Edinburgh . . . .(p.1227)
T: 0300 0203168
E: david.harvie@copfs.gov.uk

HARVIE, Jennifer Elaine Proudfoot
(Feb 2012) (Employee)
Clyde & Co (Scotland) LLP,
Edinburgh . . . .(p.855)
T: 0131 5571545
E: jennifer.harvie@clydeco.com

HARVIE, Karen Joan (Nov 1988) (Associate)
Aberdein Considine and Company,
Edinburgh . . . .(p.833)
T: 0131 2212424
E: kharvie@acandco.com

HARWOOD, Caroline (Oct 2009) (Employee)
Addleshaw Goddard LLP,
Aberdeen . . . .(p.719)
T: (+44) (0) 1224 96 5410
E: Caroline.Harwood@addleshawgoddard.com

HASHMI, Danielle Frances Lobo (Jun 2006)
(Employee)
Afridi & Angell, Dubai . . . .(p.1277)
T: 00971 4330 3900
E: dlobo@afridi-angell.com

HASLER, Dorothy Catherine (Nov 1994)
(Employee)
Shell U.K. Ltd., Aberdeen . . . .(p.1214)
T: 01224 882000
E: dorothy.hasler@shell.com

HASLETT, Andrew (Sept 2017) (Employee)
Mourant Ozannes, St Helier . . . .(p.1274)
T: 1481731513
E: Andrew.Haslett@mourant.com

HASSAN, Grant Simon (Mar 2013) (Employee)
Harper Macleod LLP, Inverness . . . .(p.1077)
T: 01463 798777
E: Grant.Hassan@harpermacleod.co.uk

HASSAN, Haseeb Ul (Jan 2013) (Associate)
Berlow Rahman Solicitors, Glasgow . . . .(p.945)
T: 0141 890 1999
E: HH@brlaw.uk

HASSARD, Niall John Norman (Oct 2009)
(Employee)
TLT LLP, Edinburgh . . . .(p.908)
T: 0333 006 0500
E: Niall.Hassard@TLTsolicitors.com

HASSELL, Lucie Charlotte (Sept 2018)
(Employee)
Brodies LLP, Aberdeen . . . .(p.723)
T: 01224 392242
E: lucie.hassell@brodies.com

HASTIE, Alexander Young (Aug 2002) (Partner)
Harper Macleod LLP, Edinburgh . . . .(p.877)
T: 0131 2472500
E: sandy.hastie@harpermacleod.co.uk

HASTIE, Samantha (Nov 2015) (Employee)
Acturis Ltd, London EC1 . . . .(p.1261)
E: Samantha.Hastie@acturis.com

HASTINGS, Mark Francis (Oct 2009) (Associate)
BTO Solicitors LLP, Glasgow . . . .(p.952)
T: 0141 2218012
E: mfh@bto.co.uk

HASTINGS, Maureen Teresa (Dec 1984)
(Employee)
WEST DUNBARTONSHIREhire Council,
Dumbarton . . . .(p.1217)
T: 01389 737000
E: maureen.hastings@west-dunbarton.gov.uk

HASTINGS, Ronald Andrew (Oct 1981)
(Director)
Borders Legal Limited, Kelso . . . .(p.1091)
T: 01573 226999
E: rh@hastingslegal.co.uk

HASTINGS, Sinead Eveleen (Oct 2005)
(Employee)
Pinsent Masons LLP, Glasgow . . . .(p.1031)
T: 0141 567 8400
E: sinead.hastings@pinsentmasons.com

HASTON, Nicola (Jul 2020) (Employee)
Stewart and O'Neill Defence Limited,
Edinburgh . . . .(p.904)
T: 0131 225 2900

HASWELL, Calum Samuel (Sept 2020)
(Employee)
James Guthrie & Company LLP,
Kilmarnock . . . .(p.1095)
T: 01563 525155
E: calum@jamesguthrie.co.uk

HATCH, Nicole Elaine (Feb 2006) (Solicitor)
NO FIRM

HAUGHNEY, Kenneth Mark Paul (Jan 1989)
(Partner)
Haughney Solicitors, Dalkeith . . . .(p.795)
T: 0131 6632132
E: khaughney@hotmail.co.uk

HAUGHNEY, Philippa Clare (Oct 2018)
(Solicitor)
Shepherd and Wedderburn LLP,
Glasgow . . . .(p.1039)
T: 0141 5669900
E: philippa.haughney@shepwedd.com

HAUGHTON, Amy Elizabeth (Jul 2016)
(Employee)
Thompsons, Glasgow . . . .(p.1046)
T: 0141 2218840
E: amy.haughton@thompsons-scotland.co.uk

HAWTHORN, Lilian Patricia (Jan 1986)
(Consultant)
Shepherd and Wedderburn LLP,
Glasgow . . . .(p.1039)
T: 0141 5669900
E: patricia.hawthorn@shepwedd.com

HAWTHORNE, Claire Margaret (Sept 2021)
(Employee)
Burness Paull LLP, Glasgow . . . .(p.954)
T: 0141 2484933
E: claire.hawthorne@burnesspaull.com

HAWTHORNE, Simon (Dec 1996) (Employee)
UnitedHealthcare Global Solutions,
Minnesota . . . .(p.1279)
E: simon.hawthorne@uhcglobal.com

HAXBY, Kirsty (Apr 2013) (Employee)
SSE PLC, Glasgow . . . .(p.1244)
T: 0141 224 7752
E: Kirsty.Haxby@sse.com

HAY, Ailidh Margaret (Sept 2004) (Employee)
Brodies LLP, Aberdeen . . . .(p.723)
T: 01224 392242
E: ailidh.hay@brodies.com

HAY, Angela (Feb 2006) (Employee)
Wilsone & Duffus, Aberdeen . . . .(p.746)
T: 01224 651700
E: Angela.Hay@wilsoneduffus.co.uk

HAY, Charles Wilson (Sept 1988) (Associate)
Brodies LLP, Glasgow . . . .(p.948)
T: 0141 2484672
E: charles.hay@brodies.com

HAY, George Alexander (Feb 1974) (Partner)
D. & J. Dunlop, Ayr . . . .(p.762)
T: 01292 264091
E: gah@djdunlop.co.uk

HAY, Gordon Douglas (Oct 2001) (Partner)
CMS Cameron McKenna Nabarro Olswang LLP,
Edinburgh . . . .(p.856)
T: 0131 2288000
E: gordon.hay@cms-cmno.com

HAY, Jacob David (Sept 2019) (Employee)
Pinsent Masons LLP, Glasgow . . . .(p.1031)
T: 0141 567 8400
E: jacob.hay@pinsentmasons.com

HAY, John Andrew (Dec 1981) (Partner)
D. & J. Dunlop, Ayr . . . .(p.762)
T: 01292 264091
E: jahay@djdunlop.co.uk

HAY, Jordan William (Jul 2018) (Employee)
Morgans, Dunfermline . . . .(p.824)
T: 01383 620222
E: jordanhay@morganlaw.co.uk

HAY, Kenneth John Clunie (May 2000)
(Associate)
Holmes Mackillop Limited,
Giffnock . . . .(p.934)
T: 0141 638 7405
E: khay@homack.co.uk

HAY, Laura Ann (Oct 2006) (Associate)
Burness Paull LLP, Aberdeen . . . .(p.724)
T: 01224 621621
E: Laura.Hay@burnesspaull.com

HAY, Laura Margaret (Nov 2014) (Employee)
National Westminster Bank PLC,
Edinburgh . . . .(p.1226)
T: (0131) 626 2925
E: Laura.hay@rbs.co.uk

HAY, Neil David (Jul 1996) (Director)
MTM Defence Lawyers Limited,
Edinburgh . . . .(p.893)
T: 0131 3060115
E: nhay@mtmdefence.co.uk

HAY, Nicholas William (May 2017) (Employee)
Jones Whyte LLP, Glasgow . . . .(p.993)
T: 0141 375 1222
E: nick.hay@joneswhyte.co.uk

HAY, Robert Andrew (Sept 2014) (Employee)
Dickson Minto, London EC2 . . . .(p.1263)
T: 020 76284455
E: robbie.hay@dmws.com

HAY, Ronald Andrew (Sept 2010) (Employee)
Procurator Fiscal Service, Kirkcaldy . . . .(p.1249)
T: 0300 0203000
E: ronald.hay@copfs.gov.uk

HAY, Sarah Isabel (Jan 2015) (Employee)
Watermans Legal Limited,
Edinburgh . . . .(p.911)
T: 0131 4675566
E: sarahhay@watermanslegal.co.uk

HAY, Stephen James (Aug 1998) (Director)
Gildeas Limited, Glasgow . . . .(p.979)
T: 0141 331 6071
E: shay@gildeas.net

HAYNES, Amanda Claire (Oct 2016) (Employee)
MacRoberts LLP, Edinburgh . . . .(p.887)
T: 0131 2295046
E: amanda.hodge@macroberts.com

HAYWARD, David Anthony (Sept 2016)
(Employee)
Linklaters LLP, Dubai . . . .(p.1278)
E: david.hayward@linklaters.com

HAYWOOD, Brent William (Dec 1993) (Partner)
Lindsays LLP, Edinburgh . . . .(p.882)
T: 0131 2291212
E: brenthaywood@lindsays.co.uk

HAYWOOD, Iain David Cairns (Jan 1981)
(Associate)
Rollos Law LLP, Glenrothes . . . .(p.1058)
T: 01592 759414
E: iainhaywood@rollos.co.uk

HAYWORTH, Gregor Robert (Oct 2012)
(Associate)
Shepherd and Wedderburn LLP,
Edinburgh . . . .(p.900)
T: 0131 2289900
E: Gregor.Hayworth@shepwedd.com

HAYWORTH, Rona Jean (Nov 2012) (Associate)
Digby Brown LLP, Edinburgh . . . .(p.862)
T: 0333 200 5925
E: rona.hayworth@digbybrown.co.uk

HAZELTON, Ewan Alistair (Dec 2017)
(Employee)
BBM Solicitors Limited, Edinburgh . . . . .(p.842)
T: 0131 526 3280
E: eah@bbmsolicitors.co.uk

HAZLIE, Lauren Elizabeth (Aug 2020)
(Employee)
Jones Whyte LLP, Glasgow. . . . .(p.993)
T: 0141 375 1222
E: lauren.hazlie@joneswhyte.co.uk

HEADDEN, Kirsty Sinclair (Nov 2007)
(Employee)
Shepherd and Wedderburn LLP,
Edinburgh . . . .(p.900)
T: 0131 2289900
E: kirsty.headden@shepwedd.com

HEADLEY, Catriona Alexandra Montgomery
(Sept 2008) (Employee)
Digby Brown LLP, Edinburgh . . . .(p.862)
T: 0333 200 5925
E: catriona.headley@digbybrown.co.uk

HEALEY, Stewart McNeill (Oct 2013)
(Employee)
Clyde & Co LLP, London EC3 . . . .(p.1263)
T: 020 7876 5000
E: stewart.healey@clydeco.com

HEALING, Sarah Louise (Nov 2003) (Employee)
Procurator Fiscal Service, Airdrie . . . . . .(p.1214)
T: 01236 747027
E: Sarah.Healing@copfs.gov.uk

HEALY, Carina Pearl (Nov 1996) (Partner)
CMS Cameron McKenna Nabarro Olswang LLP,
Glasgow. . . . .(p.962)
T: 0141 2222200
E: Carina.Healy@cms-cmno.com

HEALY, Laura Elizabeth (Mar 2010) (Employee)
Carey Olsen, St Helier . . . .(p.1274)
T: 01534 888900
E: laura.healy@careyolsen.com

HEALY, Rebecca (Sept 2020) (Employee)
Lindsays LLP, Edinburgh . . . .(p.882)
T: 0131 2291212
E: rebeccahealy@lindsays.co.uk

HEANEY, Colette Rose (Oct 2018) (Employee)
Ofgem, Glasgow . . . .(p.1241)
T: (0141) 354 5425
E: colette.heaney@ofgem.gov.uk

HEANEY, Elizabeth Metcalfe (Sept 2018)
(Employee)
Brodies LLP, Glasgow . . . .(p.948)
T: 0141 2484672
E: elizabeth.heaney@brodies.com

HEANEY, Jonathan (Sept 1998) (Partner)
Burness Paull LLP, Edinburgh . . . .(p.850)
T: 0131 4736000
E: jonathan.heaney@burnesspaull.com

HEANEY, Lauren Anne (Feb 2015) (Director)
Clark Boyle Limited, Glasgow. . . . .(p.960)
T: 1412272217
E: Lauren.Heaney@clarkboyle.co.uk

HEANEY, Zara Amber (Sept 2011) (Employee)
Glasgow City Council, Glasgow . . . . . .(p.1239)
T: 0141 276 2233
E: Amber.Heaney@glasgow.gov.uk

HEARD, Christina Balmain (Sept 2017)
(Employee)
Anderson Strathern LLP, Edinburgh . . . .(p.839)
T: 0131 2707700
E: christina.heard@andersonstrathern.co.uk

HEATH, Adam James (Jul 2014) (Employee)
Perth & Kinross Council, Perth . . . .(p.1253)
T: 01738 475165
E: aheath@pkc.gov.uk

HEATHCOTE, Rachel Claire (Sept 2012)
(Associate)
DWF LLP, Edinburgh . . . .(p.865)
T: 0131 2265541
E: Rachel.Heathcote@dwf.law

HECHT, Laura Jane (Aug 2006) (Solicitor)
NO FIRM

HECHT, Philip Michael (Sept 2006) (Solicitor)
NO FIRM

HEDALEN, Linzi Grace (Jul 2012) (Employee)
Dentons UK and Middle East LLP,
Glasgow. . . . .(p.968)
T: 0330 2220050
E: Linzi.hedalen@dentons.com

HEDGES, Sean (Oct 2017) (Employee)
Mourant Ozannes, St Helier . . . .(p.1274)
T: 1481731513
E: sean.hedges@mourant.com

HEDLEY, Calum Iain (Feb 2021) (Employee)
Carey Olsen, St Helier . . . .(p.1274)
T: 01534 888900
E: calum.hedley@careyolsen.com

HEENEY, Caroline (Nov 2006) (Employee)
Apleona HSG Ltd, Motherwell . . . .(p.1251)
E: caroline.heeney@apleona.com

HEEPS, Alexander John (Feb 2020) (Employee)
McGlashan MacKay Solicitors,
Glasgow. . . . .(p.1011)
T: 0141 3757557
E: alexander@mcglashanmackay.com

HEEPS, Gayle Joan (Nov 2008) (Employee)
Austin Lafferty Limited, East
Kilbride . . . .(p.830)
T: 01355 263777
E: gheeps@laffertylaw.com

HEGARTY, Alice Catherine (Sept 2021)
(Employee)
Rollos Law LLP, Cupar . . . .(p.792)
T: 01334 654081
E: alicehegarty@rollos.co.uk

HEGGIE, Catriona May Coom (Jun 2014)
(Employee)
Brodies LLP, Glasgow . . . .(p.948)
T: 0141 428 3367
E: catriona.heggie@brodies.com

HEGGIE, Clare Mary (Oct 2018) (Employee)
CMS Cameron McKenna Nabarro Olswang LLP,
Edinburgh . . . .(p.856)
T: 0131 2288000
E: clare.heggie@cms-cmno.com

HEHIR, Neil Graeme Douglas (Sept 2004)
(Employee)
Pinsent Masons LLP, Aberdeen . . . .(p.739)
T: 01224 377900
E: neil.hehir@pinsentmasons.com

HEINE, Ailsa Elizabeth Christine (Dec 1991)
(Employee)
Scottish Government, Edinburgh . . . . .(p.1231)
T: 0131 244 0815
E: ailsa.heine@gov.scot

HEMFREY, Irene Kyle (Nov 1997) (Employee)
Glasgow City Council, Glasgow . . . . . .(p.1239)
T: 0141 2874726
E: irene.hemfrey@ced.glasgow.gov.uk

HEMPLEMAN, Thomas (Sept 2014) (Employee)
Ross & Connel LLP, Dunfermline . . . . . .(p.825)
T: 01383 721156
E: thempleman@ross.connel.co.uk

HEMPSEY, Alison Morag (Feb 2008) (Partner)
TC Young LLP, Glasgow . . . .(p.1055)
T: 0141 2215562
E: amh@tcyoung.co.uk

HEMSI, Musab (Oct 2011) (Employee)
Anderson Strathern LLP, Glasgow . . . . . .(p.940)
T: 0141 242 7988
E: Musab.hemsi@andersonstrathern.co.uk

HEMSI, Nur (May 2016) (Employee)
Abrdn Financial Planning and Advice Limited,
Edinburgh . . . .(p.1220)
E: nur.hemsi@abrdn.com

HENDERSON, Andrew David (Dec 1990)
(Partner)
Thompsons, Glasgow . . . .(p.1046)
T: 0141 2218840
E:
andrew.henderson@thompsons-scotland.co.uk

HENDERSON, Andrew Paterson (Mar 1990)
(Employee)
Innes & Mackay Limited, Inverness . . . .(p.1078)
T: 01463 232273
E: andrewh@innesmackay.com

HENDERSON, Anne Pamela (Jan 1988)
(Associate)
Anderson Strathern LLP, Edinburgh . . . .(p.839)
T: 0131 625 7280
E: anne.henderson@andersonstrathern.co.uk

HENDERSON, Claire Mary (Aug 2021)
(Employee)
Dickson Minto, Edinburgh . . . .(p.861)
T: 0131 2254455
E: claire.henderson@dmws.com

HENDERSON, Claire Patricia (Oct 2004)
(Employee)
Ergo Law Limited, Edinburgh . . . .(p.869)
T: 0131 618 7007
E: claire.henderson@ergolaw.co.uk

HENDERSON, Colin Bruce (Mar 1990)
(Consultant)
Anderson Strathern LLP, Edinburgh . . . .(p.839)
T: 0131 2707700
E: colin.henderson@andersonstrathern.co.uk

HENDERSON, David William (Sept 2011)
(Employee)
Digby Brown LLP, Glasgow . . . .(p.970)
T: 0333 200 5925
E: david.henderson@digbybrown.co.uk

HENDERSON, Deborah Elise (Aug 1998)
(Employee)
Glasgow City Council, Glasgow . . . . . .(p.1239)
T: 0141 2872000
E: deborah.henderson@glasgow.gov.uk

HENDERSON, Donald Alexander David
(May 1979) (Partner)
R. & R.S. Mearns, Glasgow . . . .(p.1018)
T: 0141 6326162
E: dhmearns@gmail.com

HENDERSON, Fiona Elizabeth (Dec 2014)
(Associate)
CMS Cameron McKenna Nabarro Olswang LLP,
Aberdeen . . . .(p.727)
T: 01224 267 170
E: Fiona.Henderson@cms-cmno.com

HENDERSON, Gavin Paul (Jun 2004) (Partner)
Clyde & Co (Scotland) LLP,
Edinburgh . . . .(p.855)
T: 0131 5571545
E: gavin.henderson@clydeco.com

HENDERSON, Grant William (Apr 1993)
(Employee)
DLA Piper UK LLP, London EC1 . . . . . .(p.1263)
T: 020 77966017
E: grant.henderson@dlapiper.com

HENDERSON, Iain Wallace (Aug 1994)
(Employee)
Falkirk Council, Falkirk . . . .(p.1236)
T: 01324 506070
E: iain.henderson@falkirk.gov.uk

HENDERSON, Jacqueline (Dec 1989) (Partner)
Thorntons Law LLP, Dundee . . . .(p.819)
T: 01382 229 111
E: jacquelinehenderson@thorntons-law.co.uk

HENDERSON, James Bryce Duncan
(Nov 1987) (Partner)
Inverness Legal Services, Inverness . . . .(p.1078)
T: 01463 229 981
E: duncan@inverness-legal.co.uk

HENDERSON, Karen Mary (Jul 2013) (Associate)
Fried, Frank, Harris, Shriver & Jacobson (London)
LLP, London EC2 . . . .(p.1264)
T: 0207 9729600
E: Karen.Henderson@friedfrank.com

HENDERSON, Kirsteen Cameron (Oct 2005)
(Employee)
National Health Service Scotland,
Edinburgh . . . .(p.1225)
T: 0131 2757800
E: Kirsteen.henderson2@nhs.scot

HENDERSON, Laura Anne (Dec 2013)
(Employee)
Lyon & Turnbull, Edinburgh . . . .(p.1225)
E: laura.henderson@lyonandturnbull.com

HENDERSON, Lorna (Nov 1999) (Associate)
Dentons UK and Middle East LLP,
Glasgow. . . . .(p.968)
T: 0330 2220050
E: lorna.henderson@dentons.com

HENDERSON, Lorna Melanie (Sept 2003)
(Employee)
Social Care and Social Work Improvement
Scotland, Dunfermline . . . .(p.1219)
E: lorna.henderson@careinspectorate.gov.scot

HENDERSON, Lynsay Anne (Aug 2002)
(Solicitor)
NO FIRM

HENDERSON, Mark Thomas (Sept 2003)
(Employee)
NORTH LANARKSHIRERe Council,
Motherwell. . . . .(p.1251)
T: 01698 302214
E: hendersonm@northlan.gov.uk

HENDERSON, Michael Gordon (Nov 1993)
(Partner)
Shepherd and Wedderburn LLP,
Glasgow. . . . .(p.1039)
T: 0141 5669900
E: Michael.Henderson@shepwedd.com

HENDERSON, Natalie (Aug 1997) (Employee)
Procurator Fiscal Service, Glasgow . . . .(p.1241)
T: 0300 0203000
E: natalie.henderson@copfs.gov.uk

HENDERSON, Niall Peter (Apr 1986)
(Consultant)
Allan McDougall McQueen LLP,
Edinburgh . . . .(p.837)
T: 0131 2252121
E: niallhenderson@allanmcdougall.co.uk

HENDERSON, Nicola (Mar 2002) (Employee)
Aberdeenshire Council, Aberdeen . . . . .(p.1211)
T: 0345 608 1208
E: nicola.henderson3@aberdeenshire.gov.uk

HENDERSON, Patricia O'Neill (Oct 1977)
(Partner)
John Y. Robertson, Hamilton . . . .(p.1068)
T: 01698 282900
E: patricia@jyrlaw.co.uk

HENDERSON, Rebecca Marie (Jul 2018)
(Associate)
MacRoberts LLP, Glasgow . . . .(p.1015)
T: 0141 3031100
E: rebecca.henderson@macroberts.com

HENDERSON, Simon Stuart (Oct 2000)
(Solicitor)
NO FIRM

HENDERSON, Sorley Thorburn (Apr 1987)
(Director)
Shaw's Law Ltd, Oban . . . .(p.1135)
T: 01631 705007
E: sorley@shawslaw.co.uk

HENDERSON, Vikki Sara (Aug 2010) (Employee)
Shepherd and Wedderburn LLP,
Edinburgh . . . .(p.900)
T: 0131 2289900
E: vikki.henderson@shepwedd.com

HENDERSON, Wendy Mari (Oct 1994)
(Employee)
Law Society of Scotland,
Edinburgh . . . .(p.1224)
T: 0131 2267411
E: wendyhenderson@lawscot.org.uk

HENDERSON, William Alexander (Mar 2009)
(Employee)
National Health Service Scotland,
Edinburgh . . . .(p.1225)
T: 0131 2757800
E: will.henderson2@nhs.scot

HENDRIE, Mark Eric (Aug 2006) (Director)
Hendrie Legal Limited, Edinburgh . . . . .(p.878)
T: 0131 370 0470
E: mark.hendrie@ralphhendrie.legal

HENDRY, Alasdair William (Dec 1982) (Partner)
Blair & Bryden, Port Glasgow . . . .(p.1156)
T: 01475 745117
E: awhendry@hotmail.co.uk

HENDRY, Alexander Gordon (Nov 2011)
(Employee)
Latham & Watkins LLP, Dubai . . . .(p.1278)
T: +971.4.704.6385
E: Alexander.Hendry@lw.com

HENDRY, Bruce Alexander (Oct 1994)
(Employee)
Varde Partners Europe Limited, London
W1 . . . .(p.1269)
T: 020 7078 0091
E: bhendry@varde.com

HENDRY, Careen Margaret (Oct 2005)
(Employee)
NORTH LANARKSHIRERe Council,
Motherwell. . . . .(p.1251)
T: 01698 302 239
E: hendryc@northlan.gov.uk

HENDRY, Christopher Charles (Oct 2014)
(Solicitor)
NO FIRM

HENDRY, Douglas MacNicol (Sept 1984)
(Employee)
Argyll & Bute Council,
Lochgilphead . . . .(p.1251)
T: (01546) 604194
E: douglas.hendry@argyll-bute.gov.uk

HENDRY, Jenna Erin (May 2018) (Employee)
Ledingham Chalmers LLP,
Aberdeen . . . .(p.734)
T: 01224 408408
E: jenna.hendry@ledinghamchalmers.com

HENDRY, John Fraser (Dec 1970) (Partner)
Campbell Connon, Aberdeen. . . . .(p.726)
T: 01224 585585
E: john.hendry@campbellconnon.co.uk

HENDRY, Katie (Apr 2021) (Employee)
BTO Solicitors LLP, Glasgow . . . .(p.952)
T: 0141 2218012
E: khe@bto.co.uk

HENDRY, Lewis Andrew (Feb 2014) (Associate)
Harper Macleod LLP, Glasgow . . . .(p.983)
T: 0141 2218888
E: lewis.hendry@harpermacleod.co.uk

HENDRY, Rachel Louise (Jul 2018) (Employee)
Dallas McMillan, Glasgow . . . .(p.966)
T: 0141 3336750
E: rachel.hendry@dallasmcmillan.co.uk

HENDRY, Sharif (Feb 2012) (Solicitor)
NO FIRM

HENDRY, Stefanie Rollan (Jun 2021)
(Employee)
Stronachs LLP, Aberdeen . . . .(p.744)
T: 01224 845845
E: stefanie.hendry@stronachs.com

HENDRY, Stephanie (May 2016) (Employee)
Law Society of Scotland,
Edinburgh . . . .(p.1224)
T: 0131 2267411
E: StephanieHendry@lawscot.org.uk

HENDRY, Stuart James Falconer (Oct 1999)
(Partner)
MBM Commercial LLP, Edinburgh . . . . .(p.889)
T: 0131 2268200
E: stuart.hendry@mbmcommercial.co.uk

HENDRY, William (Jun 2010) (Partner)
Hendry Law, Falkirk . . . .(p.922)
T: 01324 227273
E: hendrylaw@outlook.com

HENERY, Irene Ann (May 1989) (Employee)
Equality and Human Rights Commission,
Glasgow. . . . .(p.1239)
T: 0141 2285966
E: irene.henery@equalityhumanrights.com

HENNECKE, Claudia Katharina Maria
(Jul 2004) (Employee)
Swiss Re, London EC3 . . . .(p.1268)
T: 020 7933 4235
E: Claudia_Hennecke@swissre.com

HENNESSY, David John (Jan 2006) (Partner)
Keoghs Scotland LLP, Glasgow. . . . .(p.996)
T: 0141 2380100
E: DHennessy@keoghs.scot

HENNESSY, Joanne Elizabeth (Aug 2005)
(Employee)
Pinsent Masons LLP, Glasgow . . . .(p.1031)
T: 0141 567 8400
E: Joanne.Hennessy@pinsentmasons.com

HENRETTY, Rory Andrew (Jun 2019)
(Employee)
Burness Paull LLP, Edinburgh . . . .(p.850)
T: 0131 4736000
E: Rory.Henretty@burnesspaull.com

HENRETTY, Susan Elizabeth (Dec 2017)
(Solicitor)
Gillespie Macandrew LLP,
Edinburgh . . . .(p.872)
T: 0131 2251677
E: susan.henretty@gillespiemacandrew.co.uk

HENRY, Catherine Dawn (Aug 2013) (Associate)
TC Young LLP, Glasgow . . . .(p.1055)
T: 0141 2215562
E: cdm@tcyoung.co.uk

HENRY, Craig Andrew (May 2018) (Employee)
Brodies LLP, Edinburgh . . . .(p.845)
   T: 0131 2283777
   E: craig.henry@brodies.com

HENRY, David Andrew (Oct 2003) (Employee)
Spirit Production (Services) Limited,
   Aberdeen . . . .(p.1214)
   T: 01224 415000
   E: david.henry@spirit-energy.com

HENRY, George Bruce (Dec 1987) (Partner)
Sinclairs, Edinburgh . . . .(p.903)
   T: 0131 662 4205
   E: georgehenry@sinclairscdl.co.uk

HENRY, Liza-Ann (May 2018) (Employee)
Ruthven, Keenan, Pollock & Co.,
   Glasgow . . . .(p.1038)
   T: 0141 9542901
   E: liza@rkpsolicitors.co.uk

HENRY, Rachel Anne (Aug 2007) (Employee)
Berrymans Lace Mawer LLP,
   Glasgow . . . .(p.945)
   T: 0141 3532121
   E: rachel.henry@blmlaw.com

HENRY, Taylor (Sept 2020) (Employee)
Balfour + Manson LLP, Edinburgh . . . . .(p.841)
   T: 0131 2001200
   E: taylor.henry@balfour-manson.co.uk

HENSON, Matthew James (Nov 2019)
(Employee)
Burges Salmon LLP, Edinburgh . . . .(p.850)
   T: 0131 3142112
   E: Matthew.Henson@burges-salmon.com

HENSTOCK, Gerrit Johannes (Aug 2004)
(Employee)
Tesco Personal Finance Plc,
   Edinburgh . . . .(p.1234)
   T: (0131) 274 3426
   E: gerrit.henstock@tescobank.com

HEPBURN, Alice Margaret (May 2015)
(Employee)
Pinsent Masons LLP, Glasgow . . . .(p.1031)
   T: 0141 567 8400
   E: Alice.Hepburn@pinsentmasons.com

HEPBURN, Catriona Grace (Jul 2017)
(Employee)
Government Legal Department, London
   SW1 . . . .(p.1264)
   T: 0207 4495952
   E: catghepburn@gmail.com

HEPBURN, Holly Anne (Feb 2021) (Employee)
Harrison Legal Limited, Kilmarnock . . . .(p.1095)
   T: 01563 508114
   E: holly@harrisonlaw.legal

HEPBURN, Stephanie Frances (Mar 2011)
(Employee)
Shepherd and Wedderburn LLP,
   Edinburgh . . . .(p.900)
   T: 0131 2289900
   E: stephanie.hepburn@shepwedd.co.uk

HEPBURN, Thomas Clark (Sept 2010)
(Employee)
Roofoods Ltd, London EC4 . . . .(p.1267)
   E: tom.hepburn@deliveroo.co.uk

HEPWORTH, Alan Neil (Mar 1986) (Partner)
Hepworth & Co., Cambuslang . . . .(p.782)
   T: 0141 6410089
   E: alan@hepworthsolicitors.co.uk

HERALD, Alison Margaret (Feb 2006)
(Employee)
Procurator Fiscal Service, Dumfries . . . .(p.1217)
   T: 0300 020 3273
   E: alison.herald@copfs.gov.uk

HERBERT, Lynn Kathryn Wightman
(Oct 1981) (Partner)
Lynn Herbert & Co., Leven . . . .(p.1115)
   T: 01333 429007
   E: lherbert@lynnherbert.co.uk

HERBERTSON, Barry Graeme (Nov 2010)
(Employee)
Burness Paull LLP, Edinburgh . . . .(p.850)
   T: 0131 4736000
   E: Barry.Herbertson@burnesspaull.com

HERBERTSON, Gemma Catherine
(Nov 2003) (Employee)
Pinsent Masons LLP, Glasgow . . . .(p.1031)
   T: 0141 567 8400
   E: gemma.herbertson@pinsentmasons.com

HERBERTSON, James (Nov 2006) (Partner)
Burnett & Reid LLP, Aberdeen . . . .(p.726)
   T: 01224 644333
   E: jherbertson@burnett-reid.co.uk

HERD, Georgette (Oct 1990) (Employee)
Orkney Islands Council, Kirkwall . . . . . .(p.1250)
   T: 01856 873535
   E: georgette.herd@orkney.gov.uk

HERD, Gordon William (May 2016) (Employee)
Dentons UK and Middle East LLP,
   Glasgow . . . .(p.968)
   T: 0330 2220050
   E: gordon.herd@dentons.com

HERD, James George (Oct 1986) (Employee)
Scottish Fire and Rescue Service,
   Hamilton . . . .(p.1247)
   T: 0141 646 4699
   E: James.herd@firescotland.gov.uk

HERD, Leigh Anne (Sept 2013) (Employee)
Shepherd and Wedderburn LLP,
Edinburgh . . . .(p.900)
T: 0131 473 5182
E: Leigh.Herd@shepwedd.com

HERD, Louise Mary (Feb 2021) (Employee)
Clan Childlaw Limited, Edinburgh . . . . .(p.854)
T: 0808 129 0522
E: louise.herd@clanchildlaw.org

HERD, Megan Alice (Oct 2013) (Employee)
Neptune E&P UK Ltd, Aberdeen . . . . .(p.1213)
T: +44 (0) 1224 281223
E: Megan.Herd@neptuneenergy.com

HERD, Shona Jane (Apr 1995) (Employee)
Scottish Legal Aid Board,
Edinburgh . . . .(p.1233)
T: 0131 2267061
E: herdsh@slab.org.uk

HERD, Thomas James (Aug 2008) (Employee)
Norton Rose Fulbright (Middle East) LLP,
Dubai . . . .(p.1278)
E: thomas.herd@nortonrosefulbright.com

HERON, Alison Margaret (Aug 2010) (Director)
John Brown (Scotland) Ltd,
Glasgow. . . . .(p.951)
T: 0141 7810000
E: ah@browns-solicitors.co.uk

HERRELL, Fiona Jane (Sept 2007) (Partner)
Brodies LLP, Aberdeen. . . . .(p.723)
T: 01224 392242
E: fiona.herrell@brodies.com

HERRON, Tony Alexander (Aug 2018)
(Employee)
Weil, Gotshal & Manges (London) LLP, London
EC4 . . . .(p.1269)
E: tony.herron@weil.com

HESSETT, Peter David (Jul 1994) (Employee)
WEST DUNBARTONSHIREhire Council,
Dumbarton . . . .(p.1217)
T: 01389 737000
E: peter.hessett@west-dunbarton.gov.uk

HETHERINGTON, Judith (Nov 1991) (Employee)
National Health Service Scotland,
Edinburgh . . . .(p.1225)
T: 0131 2757800
E: judith.hetherington@nhs.scot

HETHERINGTON, Nicola (May 2004)
(Employee)
Macquarie Corporate Holdings Pty Limited (UK
Branch), London EC2 . . . .(p.1266)
E: nicola.hetherington@macquarie.com

HEVAMANAGE, Veyoma Thushari
(Sept 2009) (Employee)
Macquarie Corporate Holdings Pty Limited (UK
Branch), London EC2 . . . .(p.1266)

HEVOR, Mawulorm Jesse Kormi (Oct 2019)
(Employee)
Scottish Hospital Inquiry, Glasgow . . . .(p.1244)
E: Jesse.Hevor@hospitalsinquiry.scot

HEWITT, Frances Mary (Oct 1989) (Partner)
McKinnon Hewitt, Irvine . . . .(p.1086)
T: 01294 312801
E: frances@mckinnonhewitt.co.uk

HEWITT, Lorna Charlotte (Nov 2019)
(Employee)
Shepherd and Wedderburn LLP,
Glasgow. . . . .(p.1039)
T: 0141 5669900
E: lorna.hewitt@shepwedd.com

HEWITT, Shona Nicole Swan (Dec 1984)
(Employee)
National Health Service Scotland,
Edinburgh . . . .(p.1225)
T: 0131 2757800
E: shona.hewitt@nhs.scot

HICKS, Anne Marie (Oct 1994) (Employee)
Procurator Fiscal Service, Glasgow . . . .(p.1242)
E: annemarie.hicks@copfs.gov.uk

HICKS, Toni (Jan 2013) (Employee)
Procurator Fiscal Service, Hamilton . . . .(p.1247)
T: 0844 5613245
E: toni.hicks@copfs.gov.uk

HIGGINS, Aidan John (Oct 2008) (Employee)
Procurator Fiscal Service,
Edinburgh . . . .(p.1229)
T: 0300 0203000
E: aidan.higgins@copfs.gov.uk

HIGGINS, Alison Elizabeth (Aug 2007)
(Employee)
Fife Council, Glenrothes . . . .(p.1246)
T: 03451 550000
E: alison.higgins@fife.gov.uk

HIGGINS, Gillian Kathryn (May 2009)
(Employee)
Scottish Environment Protection Agency,
Holytown . . . .(p.1248)
T: (01698) 839 000
E: gillian.higgins@sepa.org.uk

HIGGINS, James William (Jan 1998) (Solicitor)
NO FIRM

HIGGINS, Jenny Ann (Mar 2009) (Employee)
The Institute and Faculty of Actuaries,
Edinburgh . . . .(p.1234)
T: (020) 7632 1488
E: jenny.higgins@actuaries.org.uk

HIGGINS, Karima Elizabeth (Jul 2001)
(Employee)
Ad Astra Legal Limited, Carnbroe . . . . .(p.1216)
E: Karima@adastralegal.co.uk

HIGGINS, Katie (Jul 2020) (Employee)
Brodies LLP, Edinburgh . . . . (p.845)
T: 0131 2283777
E: katie.higgins@brodies.com

HIGGINS, Mark Andrew (Oct 1993) (Partner)
Irwin Mitchell Scotland LLP,
Glasgow. (p.991)
T: 0141 3004300
E: mark.higgins@irwinmitchell.com

HIGGINS, Michael (Oct 2013) (Employee)
BTO Solicitors LLP, Glasgow . . . . (p.952)
T: 0141 2218012
E: mhi@bto.co.uk

HIGGINS, Stephen (Oct 2009) (Associate)
NO FIRM

HIGH, Rachel Joy (Sept 2015) (Employee)
Thorntons Law LLP, Dundee . . . . (p.819)
T: 01382 229 111
E: rhigh@thorntons-law.co.uk

HIGH, Sarah Ruth (Feb 2021) (Employee)
Thorntons Law LLP, Dundee . . . . (p.819)
T: 01382 229 111
E: shigh@thorntons-law.co.uk

HIGSON, Judith May (Nov 2001) (Associate)
Scullion Law Limited, Hamilton . . . . . . (p.1069)
T: 0141 374 2121
E: judith@scullionlaw.com

HIGTON, Hannah Ruth (Oct 2021) (Employee)
Scanlon Ewing Limited, Clydebank . . . . . (p.785)
T: 0141 9529297
E: hannah@scanlonewing.co.uk

HILDITCH, Jane Anderson Russell (Sept 2000)
(Employee)
Procurator Fiscal Service, Glasgow . . . . (p.1241)
T: 0300 0203000
E: jane.hilditch@copfs.gov.uk

HILL, Alan David (Oct 1993) (Director)
Robert F Duff & Co Limited, Largs . . . . (p.1109)
T: 01475 673663
E: adh@rfduff.co.uk

HILL, Alistair Ramsay (Aug 1990) (Partner)
CMS Cameron McKenna Nabarro Olswang LLP,
Glasgow. (p.962)
T: 0141 2222200
E: Alistair.Hill@cms-cmno.com

HILL, Archibald James (Oct 2001) (Partner)
Hills Solicitors, Lanark . . . . (p.1108)
T: 01555 664220
E: hillsolicitors@outlook.com

HILL, Claire Elizabeth (Jan 2014) (Employee)
Hymans Robertson LLP, Edinburgh . . . . (p.1223)
T: (0131) 656 5187
E: Claire.Hill@hymans.co.uk

HILL, Duncan Mervin Norman (Oct 1984)
(Director)
Lows Orkney Limited, Kirkwall . . . . (p.1106)
T: 01856 873151
E: duncan.hill@lowsorkney.co.uk

HILL, Kenneth (Jul 1990) (Partner)
Campbell Sievewright & Co.,
Glasgow. (p.956)
T: 0141 4222642
E: KHill@campbellsievewright.co.uk

HILL, Kenneth Macqueen (Oct 1994) (Partner)
Stevenson & Johnstone, Langholm . . . . (p.1109)
T: 01387 380428
E: kenneth@sandjlangholm.co.uk

HILL, Kenneth Thomas (Jan 2008) (Employee)
Pinsent Masons LLP, Edinburgh . . . . . . (p.895)
T: 0131 7777000
E: kenneth.hill@pinsentmasons.com

HILL, Lauren (Dec 2019) (Employee)
Addleshaw Goddard LLP,
Edinburgh . . . . (p.835)
T: 0131 2282400
E: lauren.hill@addleshawgoddard.com

HILL, Leanne (Oct 2005) (Employee)
Pinsent Masons LLP, Aberdeen . . . . (p.739)
T: 01224 377900
E: Leanne.Hill@pinsentmasons.com

HILL, Nina (Sept 2014) (Employee)
Renfrewshire Council, Paisley . . . . (p.1252)
T: 0141 8403471
E: nina.hill@renfrewshire.gov.uk

HILL, Rachel Thomson (Nov 2019) (Employee)
Procurator Fiscal Service, Dundee . . . . . (p.1218)
T: 01382 342559
E: rachel.hill@copfs.gov.uk

HILL, Richard Alexander (Jan 2014) (Employee)
Procurator Fiscal Service, Glasgow . . . . (p.1241)
T: 0300 0203000

HILL, Robin John (Nov 1983) (Director)
VMH Solicitors Limited, Edinburgh . . . . . (p.910)
T: 0131 6222626
E: robin.hill@vmh.co.uk

HILL, Stephen MacCallum (Feb 2014)
(Employee)
Kennedys Scotland, Edinburgh. . . . . (p.880)
T: 0131 285 2960
E: Stephen.Hill@kennedyslaw.com

HILL, Susan Ann Berry (Oct 2008) (Employee)
Ross & Connel LLP, Dunfermline . . . . . . (p.825)
T: 01383 721156
E: shill@ross.connel.co.uk

HILL, Susan Margaret (Apr 2007) (Employee)
Scottish Water, Dunfermline . . . . (p.1219)
T: (01383) 665410
E: susan.hill@scottishwater.co.uk

HILLAN, James John (Oct 1989) (Employee)
Gateley Plc, London EC4 . . . .(p.1264)
  E: jim.hillan@gateleylegal.com

HILLAND, Jamie Vincent (Sept 2016)
(Employee)
Procurator Fiscal Service, Kirkcaldy . . . .(p.1249)
  T: 0300 0203000
  E: jamie.hilland@copfs.gov.uk

HILLAND, Vincent Francis (Nov 1982)
(Director)
Hilland McNulty Limited, Lanark . . . . .(p.1107)
  T: 01555 663020
  E: vincent@hilland-mcnulty.co.uk

HILLEY, Anne Frances (Dec 2003) (Employee)
Procurator Fiscal Service,
  Edinburgh . . . .(p.1229)
  E: AnneFrances.Hilley@copfs.gov.uk

HILLS, Anna Alice (Sept 2020) (Employee)
Anderson Strathern LLP, Edinburgh . . . .(p.839)
  T: 0131 2707700
  E: anna.hills@andersonstrathern.co.uk

HILLS, Gemma Kirsten (Oct 2008) (Employee)
Brodies LLP, Aberdeen. . . . .(p.723)
  T: 01224 392242
  E: gemma.hills@brodies.com

HILSMITH, Craig MacRae (Nov 2007)
(Employee)
Aegon UK, Edinburgh . . . .(p.1220)
  T: 1315493986
  E: Craig.hilsmith@aegon.co.uk

HILTON, Lisa Ramsay (Oct 2008) (Employee)
Procurator Fiscal Service, Hamilton . . . .(p.1247)
  T: 0844 5613245
  E: lisa.hilton@copfs.gov.uk

HINCHIN, Michaela Louise (Nov 1987)
(Associate)
MTM Family Law LLP, Glasgow . . . . . .(p.1025)
  T: 0141 6117535
  E: mh@mtmfamilylaw.co.uk

HIND, Gemma (Sept 2009) (Employee)
Procurator Fiscal Service, Dumfries . . . .(p.1217)
  T: 01387 274585
  E: gemma.hind@copfs.gov.uk

HINGSTON, Iain David (Oct 1997) (Director)
Hingston's Law Limited, Aberdeen . . . . .(p.732)
  T: 01224 562300
  E: iain@hingstonslaw.co.uk

HINKSMAN, Aimee Francine (Nov 2009)
(Employee)
Seyfarth Shaw, Hong Kong . . . .(p.1273)
  E: AHinksman@seyfarth.com

HINSTRIDGE, Andrew Roy Wilson
(Aug 2003) (Employee)
Clydesdale Bank Plc, Glasgow . . . .(p.1238)
  T: 0141 2423733
  E: Andrew.Hinstridge@cybg.com

HIPWELL, George (Director)
Davidson & Robertson Ltd, Currie . . . .(p.1329)
  T: (0131) 449 6212
  E: GH@drrural.co.uk

HIRAM, Heather Sian (Aug 2006) (Employee)
Obaseki Solicitors, London N1 . . . .(p.1267)

HIRD, Graeme James (Nov 2012) (Employee)
Shell International Limited,
  Aberdeen . . . .(p.1214)
  T: 01224 882000
  E: graemehird01@gmail.com

HIRST, Christine Anne (May 1995) (Associate)
Macnairs & Wilson Limited, Paisley. . . .(p.1140)
  T: 0141 887 5181
  E: christine.hirst@macnairswilson.co.uk

HIRST DAWSON, Alex May Patricia
(Oct 2020) (Employee)
Thorntons Law LLP, Dundee . . . .(p.819)
  T: 01382 229 111
  E: adawson@thorntons-law.co.uk

HISCOCK, Karli Marie (Nov 2019) (Employee)
Bates Wells Braithwaite LLP, London
  EC4 . . . .(p.1262)

HISLOP, Caitlin Flora Kennedy (Nov 2020)
(Employee)
Revenue Scotland, Edinburgh . . . .(p.1230)
  E: caitlin.hislop@gov.scot

HISLOP, Gareth David (Sept 2003) (Employee)
SP Transmission Plc, Glasgow. . . . .(p.1244)
  T: 07753 622106
  E: ghislop@scottishpower.com

HO, Vivien (Aug 2021) (Employee)
Cameron Macaulay, Glasgow . . . .(p.956)
  T: 0141 204 7844

HOATH, Sean Andrew (Jun 2007) (Employee)
The Moray Council, Elgin . . . .(p.1236)
  T: 01343 563077
  E: sean.hoath@moray.gov.uk

HOBBS, Joyce Emma (Jun 2007) (Partner)
Liddle & Anderson LLP, Boness . . . .(p.777)
  T: 01506 822727
  E: jh@liddleandanderson.co.uk

HOBKIRK, Colin Gordon (Sept 1987) (Solicitor)
NO FIRM

HOBKIRK, Sarah (Sept 2017) (Employee)
Digby Brown LLP, Glasgow . . . .(p.970)
  T: 0333 200 5925

HODGE, Alison Margaret (Aug 1991) (Partner)
Watson & Lyall Bowie, Blairgowrie . . . . .(p.776)
  T: 01828 628395
  E: alison.hodge@wandlb.co.uk

HODGE, Andrew Davidson (Sept 1983)
(Partner)
Hodge Solicitors LLP, Blairgowrie . . . . . . (p.775)
T: 01250 874441
E: adhodge@hodgesolicitors.co.uk

HODGE, John Simon (May 1989) (Partner)
Angus McIntosh & Simon Hodge,
Glasgow . . . . (p.1012)
T: 0141 6340313
E: simon.hodge@castlemilklawcentre.co.uk

HODGSON, Elizabeth Ann (Jul 2020)
(Employee)
Bruce, Short & Co., Dundee . . . . (p.806)
T: 01382 223400

HODGSON, Michael James (Jul 2016)
(Employee)
Shetland Islands Council, Lerwick . . . . . (p.1250)
T: 01595 744550
E: michael.hodgson@shetland.gov.uk

HOEY, Claudia Maria Ayre (Nov 2020)
(Employee)
Jones Whyte LLP, Glasgow . . . . (p.993)
T: 0141 375 1222

HOEY, Rose Mary (Sept 1986) (Employee)
Falkirk Council, Falkirk . . . . (p.1236)
T: 01324 506070
E: rosemary.hoey@falkirk.gov.uk

HOFFORD, Sophie Emma Paterson
(Sept 2021) (Employee)
Dickson Minto, London EC2 . . . . (p.1263)
T: 020 76284455
E: Sophie.Hofford@dmws.com

HOGARTH, Amy Jane (Aug 2016) (Employee)
Scottish Government, Edinburgh . . . . . (p.1231)
T: 0131 244 0815
E: Amy.Hogarth@gov.scot

HOGARTY, Paul (Aug 2009) (Solicitor)
NO FIRM

HOGG, Cheryl Susan (Jan 2015) (Employee)
Gillespie Macandrew LLP,
Edinburgh . . . . (p.872)
T: 0131 2251677
E: Cheryl.Hogg@gillespiemacandrew.co.uk

HOGG, Derek William (Oct 1987) (Partner)
Harper Macleod LLP, Glasgow . . . . (p.983)
T: 0141 2218888
E: derek.hogg@harpermacleod.co.uk

HOGG, Fiona Margaret (Nov 1986) (Associate)
Morton Fraser LLP, Edinburgh . . . . (p.891)
T: 0131 2471000
E: fiona.hogg@morton-fraser.com

HOGG, Joanne Louise (Aug 2008) (Associate)
Stodarts LLP, Hamilton . . . . (p.1069)
T: 01698 200302
E: joanne@stodarts.co.uk

HOGG, John Russell (Jan 1984) (Employee)
CDC Group Plc, London SW1 . . . . (p.1262)
E: rhogg@cdcgroup.com

HOGG, Laura (Aug 2017) (Employee)
Procurator Fiscal Service, Dundee . . . . . (p.1218)
T: 01382 342559
E: Laura.hogg@copfs.gov.uk

HOGG, Laura Lynsey (Mar 2001) (Employee)
Baillie Gifford & Co, Edinburgh . . . . . . (p.1220)
T: 0131 2752000
E: Laura.Hogg@bailliegifford.com

HOGG, Louise (Feb 2020) (Solicitor)
NO FIRM

HOGG, Neil (Nov 1994) (Consultant)
Addleshaw Goddard LLP, Glasgow . . . . . (p.938)
T: 0141 2212300
E: neil.hogg@addleshawgoddard.com

HOGG, Nicola Marianne (Apr 2001) (Employee)
West Lothian Council, Livingston . . . . . (p.1250)
T: 01506 280000
E: Nicola.Hogg@westlothian.gov.uk

HOGG, Philip Ian (Oct 1996) (Employee)
Ofcom, London SE1 . . . . (p.1267)
T: 0207 7834297
E: Philip.hogg@ofcom.org.uk

HOGGAN, Adam Stewart (Dec 2019)
(Employee)
Miller Hendry, Dundee . . . . (p.816)
T: (01382) 200000
E: AdamHoggan@millerhendry.co.uk

HOGGAN, Suzanne Margaret (Jan 2016)
(Employee)
Offshore Renewable Energy Catapult,
Glasgow . . . . (p.1241)
E: suzanne.hoggan@ore.catapult.org.uk

HOGGAN-RADU, Damian (Nov 2021)
(Employee)
Legal Spark Solicitors and Notaries Ltd,
Glasgow . . . . (p.1000)
T: 0141 2800330
E: DamianHR@legalspark.scot

HOGWOOD, Gayle Tegen (Sept 2018)
(Employee)
Harper Macleod LLP, Edinburgh . . . . (p.877)
T: 0131 2472500
E: Gayle.Hogwood@harpermacleod.co.uk

HOLBREY, Simon Christopher (Feb 2021)
(Employee)
Thorntons Law LLP, Edinburgh . . . . (p.906)
T: 0131 2258705
E: sholbrey@thorntons-law.co.uk

HOLDEN, Brian (Jan 1988) (Employee)
Aberdeenshire Council, Aberdeen . . . . . (p.1211)
T: 01467 537387
E: Brian.Holden@aberdeenshire.gov.uk

HOLEHOUSE, Andrew Neville (Dec 1989)
(Consultant)
Shepherd and Wedderburn LLP,
Edinburgh . . . .(p.900)
T: 0131 2289900
E: andrew.holehouse@shepwedd.com

HOLEHOUSE, Elizabeth Rebecca (Aug 2021)
(Employee)
Morton Fraser LLP, Edinburgh . . . .(p.891)
T: 0131 2471000
E: elizabeth.holehouse@morton-fraser.com

HOLLAND, Adam Farquhar (Oct 2010)
(Employee)
Tullow Oil Plc, London W4 . . . .(p.1269)
T: 0203 249 9046
E: adam.holland@tullowoil.com

HOLLAND, Duncan Wesley Charles
(Oct 2001) (Employee)
Capricorn Energy Ltd, Edinburgh . . . . .(p.1221)
T: 0131 4753000
E: duncan.holland@cairnenergy.com

HOLLAND, Jacqueline (Dec 2003) (Employee)
East Lothian Council, Haddington . . . .(p.1246)
T: 01620 827827
E: jholland@eastlothian.gov.uk

HOLLAND, Robert Andrew James
(Nov 1999) (Partner)
Balfour + Manson LLP, Edinburgh . . . . .(p.841)
T: 0131 2001200
E: robert.holland@balfour-manson.co.uk

HOLLERIN, Gordon Craig (Nov 1980) (Partner)
Harper Macleod LLP, Glasgow . . . .(p.983)
T: 0141 2218888
E: gordon.hollerin@harpermacleod.co.uk

HOLLIGAN, Fiona Mairi (Jan 1998) (Employee)
Procurator Fiscal Service, Glasgow . . . .(p.1241)
T: 0300 020 3432
E: fiona.holligan@copfs.gov.uk

HOLLIGAN, Jennifer (Aug 2009) (Solicitor)
NO FIRM

HOLLIGAN, Thomas Daniel (Jul 2021)
(Employee)
BBM Solicitors Limited, Edinburgh . . . . .(p.842)
T: 0131 526 3280
E: tdh@bbmsolicitors.co.uk

HOLLIMAN, Brian David (Nov 1996) (Partner)
Douglas Wright, Kilmarnock . . . .(p.1096)
T: 01563 532177
E: brian@douglas-wright.co.uk

HOLLINS, Fergus William Sinclair (Aug 2019)
(Employee)
Wright, Johnston & Mackenzie LLP,
Edinburgh . . . .(p.913)
T: 0131 5241500

HOLLIS, Ashley (Nov 2019) (Employee)
Brodies LLP, Glasgow . . . .(p.948)
T: 0141 2484672
E: ashley.hollis@brodies.com

HOLLORAN, Anthony Dean (Nov 2015)
(Associate)
DLA Piper Scotland LLP, Edinburgh . . . .(p.863)
T: 08700 111111
E: Tony.Holloran@dlapiper.com

HOLLOWAY, Alan (Oct 1983) (Director)
Diakoneo Legal Services Limited,
Glasgow. . . . .(p.970)
T: 07534 143293
E: alan@diakoneolegal.co.uk

HOLLOWAY, Lesley Anne (Jan 2003) (Associate)
Morton Fraser LLP, Glasgow . . . .(p.1022)
T: 0141 2741100
E: lesley.holloway@morton-fraser.com

HOLLYWOOD, Samantha Mary (Feb 1993)
(Employee)
Law Society of Scotland,
Edinburgh . . . .(p.1224)
T: 0131 2267411
E: samanthahollywood@lawscot.org.uk

HOLMAN, Rhona Mary (Oct 1990) (Employee)
Jacobs U.K. Limited, Glasgow. . . . .(p.1240)
T: 0141 2042511
E: rhona.holman@ch2m.com

HOLMES, David James (Dec 1990) (Solicitor)
NO FIRM

HOLMES, David Rennie (Aug 1984) (Associate)
Ward & Co (Perth) Ltd, Perth . . . .(p.1152)
T: 01738 638461
E: dholmes_wardco@yahoo.co.uk

HOLMES, Fiona Caroline (Sept 2004)
(Employee)
Dentons UK and Middle East LLP,
Glasgow. . . . .(p.968)
T: 0330 2220050
E: fiona.holmes@dentons.com

HOLMES, Kirsten Margaret (Sept 2020)
(Employee)
Gillespie Macandrew LLP,
Edinburgh . . . .(p.872)
T: 0131 2251677
E: kirsten.holmes@gillespiemacandrew.co.uk

HOLMES, Malcolm Brian (Nov 1994)
(Employee)
Brodies LLP, Edinburgh . . . .(p.845)
T: 0131 2283777
E: malcolm_holmes@aol.com

HOLMES, Sarah Charlotte (Feb 2021)
(Employee)
Shepherd and Wedderburn LLP,
Edinburgh . . . .(p.900)
T: 0131 2289900
E: sarah.holmes@shepwedd.com

HOLMES, Stuart Dale (Oct 1998) (Employee)
National Health Service Scotland,
Edinburgh . . . .(p.1225)
T: 0131 275 7354
E: Stuart.Holmes@nhs.scot

HOLT, Rachel Louise (Oct 2015) (Employee)
Lindsays LLP, Edinburgh . . . .(p.882)
T: 0131 2291212
E: Rachelholt@lindsays.co.uk

HOLWILL, Sarah Victoria (Jul 2017) (Employee)
Eversheds Sutherland (International) LLP,
Edinburgh . . . .(p.869)
T: 0207 9194500
E: SarahHolwill@eversheds-sutherland.com

HONAN, James Alexander (Aug 2009)
(Employee)
BlackRock Investment Management (UK) Ltd,
London EC2 . . . .(p.1262)
E: james.honan@blackrock.com

HONEYMAN, Greig, WS (Oct 1979)
(Consultant)
Shepherd and Wedderburn LLP,
Edinburgh . . . .(p.900)
T: 0131 2289900
E: greig.honeyman@shepwedd.com

HONEYMAN, Katherine Spence (Sept 1997)
(Associate)
Taylor & Henderson LLP, Saltcoats . . . .(p.1160)
T: 01294 464341
E: khoneyman@taylorandhenderson.co.uk

HONEYMAN, Robert Neville (Nov 1998)
(Partner)
The McKinstry Company LLP, Ayr . . . . .(p.765)
T: 01292 281711
E: rhoneyman@mckinstry.co.uk

HOOD, Amy Mairead Hitchin (Nov 2016)
(Employee)
City of Edinburgh Council,
Edinburgh . . . .(p.1221)
T: 0131 5293237
E: Amy.Hood@edinburgh.gov.uk

HOOD, Emily Mary (Oct 2021) (Employee)
Procurator Fiscal Service,
Edinburgh . . . .(p.1229)
T: 0300 0203000
E: emily.hood@copfs.gov.uk

HOOD, Graeme James William (Nov 1994)
(Employee)
Total S.A., La Defence Cedex . . . .(p.1272)
E: graeme.hood@total.com

HOOD, Janet Hebe (Jan 1984) (Employee)
Janet Hood Training and Consulting Limited,
Brechin . . . .(p.1216)
T: 01356 648 966
E: janethood@me.com

HOOD, Katherine Olivia (Nov 2018)
(Employee)
Fergusson Law, Edinburgh . . . .(p.870)
T: 0131 556 4044
E: katy@fergussonlaw.com

HOOD, Ross Farr (Oct 1984) (Partner)
Hood Corporate, Edinburgh . . . .(p.878)
T: 0131 2125888
E: ross.hood@hoodcorporate.com

HOOK, Christian Robert MacNachtan
(Jan 1989) (Consultant)
Gunnercooke LLP, Manchester . . . .(p.1270)
T: 07775 824295
E: christian.hook@gunnercooke.com

HOOKE, Nicholas Thornton (Apr 1989)
(Associate)
Thorntons Law LLP, Edinburgh . . . . . .(p.906)
T: 0131 2258705
E: nhooke@thorntons-law.co.uk

HOOKER, Sally Georgina (Dec 2018)
(Employee)
Carey Hughes Limited, High
Blantyre . . . .(p.1073)
T: 01698 404616
E: sally@careyhughes.co.uk

HOOMAN, Laura Anne (Nov 2020) (Employee)
Energy Law Unlimited LLP,
Glasgow. . . . .(p.974)
T: 0141 2210276
E: lhooman@elu-llp.com

HOOPER, Claire Victoria Fernie (Jul 2008)
(Employee)
Morgans, Dunfermline . . . .(p.824)
T: 01383 620222
E: clairehooper@morganlaw.co.uk

HOOPER, Denise (Feb 1995) (Director)
Wright & Crawford (1906) Limited,
Paisley . . . .(p.1142)
T: 0141 8876211
E: D.Hooper@wright-crawford.co.uk

HOPE, Alastair John Douglas (Jan 1981)
(Partner)
BTO Raeburn Hope, Helensburgh . . . . .(p.1072)
T: 01436 671221
E: ajdh@bto.co.uk

HOPE, Carole, WS (Oct 1981) (Consultant)
Murray Beith Murray, Edinburgh . . . . . .(p.893)
T: 0131 2251200
E: carole.hope@murraybeith.co.uk

HOPE, Ricky Thomas (Sept 2011) (Director)
Borders Legal Limited, Duns . . . .(p.828)
T: 01361 883222
E: ricky@hastingslegal.co.uk

HOPKIN, Louise Anne (Oct 2006) (Employee)
Expedia.com Limited, London EC1 . . . . (p.1264)
T: 0203 1945179
E: lhopkin@expedia.com

HOPKIN, Susan Anne (Dec 1991) (Employee)
National Health Service Scotland,
Edinburgh . . . . (p.1225)
T: 0131 2757603
E: susan.hopkin@nhs.scot

HOPKINS, Fraser (Nov 1997) (Partner)
BTO Solicitors LLP, Glasgow . . . . (p.952)
T: 0141 2218012
E: fho@bto.co.uk

HOPPER, Morven Grace Helen (Nov 2017)
(Employee)
Burness Paull LLP, Glasgow . . . . (p.954)
T: 0141 2484933
E: Morven.Hopper@burnesspaull.com

HOPTON, Margo (Oct 1990) (Associate)
W. & A.S. Bruce, Kirkcaldy . . . . (p.1099)
T: 01592 204774
E: margo@wasbruce.co.uk

HORAN, Anthony Thomas (Sept 2003)
(Solicitor)
NO FIRM

HORN, Emily Barbara (Jul 2017) (Employee)
Mills & Reeve LLP, Cambridge . . . . (p.1259)
E: emily.horn@mills-reeve.com

HORN, Graham Charles (Mar 2014) (Associate)
MacRoberts LLP, Glasgow . . . . (p.1015)
T: 0141 3031100
E: graham.horn@macroberts.com

HORNE, Andrew George (Aug 2008) (Solicitor)
NO FIRM

HORNE, David William Murray (Dec 1987)
(Partner)
Addleshaw Goddard LLP,
Edinburgh . . . . (p.835)
T: 0131 2282400
E: David.Horne@addleshawgoddard.com

HORNE, Emma Ashley (Nov 2009) (Partner)
Stuart & Stuart, Edinburgh . . . . (p.905)
T: 0131 2286449
E: ehorne@stuartandstuart.co.uk

HORNEMAN, Camilla Heidi Karin (Sept 2019)
(Employee)
Clyde & Co (Scotland) LLP,
Edinburgh . . . . (p.855)
T: 0131 5571545
E: Camilla.Horneman@clydeco.com

HORNER, Alison Edna (Dec 1991) (Employee)
Shepherd and Wedderburn LLP,
Glasgow . . . . (p.1039)
T: 0141 5669900
E: Alison.horner@shepwedd.com

HORSBURGH, Harry David (Dec 1990)
(Employee)
SOUTH LANARKSHIREre Council,
Hamilton . . . . (p.1247)
E: david.horsburgh@southlanarkshire.gov.uk

HORSBURGH, Tristan James (Oct 2003)
(Employee)
Aberdeenshire Council, Aberdeen . . . . . (p.1211)
T: 0345 608 1208
E: tristan.horsburgh@aberdeenshire.gov.uk

HORSLEY, Margaret Anne (Jan 1986)
(Employee)
South Ayrshire Council, Ayr . . . . (p.1215)
T: 01292 612 816

HORSMAN, Graham William (Oct 2015)
(Employee)
Harper Macleod LLP, Glasgow . . . . (p.983)
T: 0141 2218888

HORSMAN, Joyce Anne (Sept 2002) (Partner)
DNLC LLP, Dundee . . . . (p.809)
T: 01382 918230
E: joyce.horsman@dundeelaw.org

HORSMAN, Michael Kenneth (Nov 1981)
(Partner)
Michael Horsman & Co., Aberdeen . . . . (p.732)
T: 01224 633333
E: horsmanm@outlook.com

HORTON, Thomas William (Apr 2016)
(Employee)
Brodies LLP, Edinburgh . . . . (p.845)
T: 0131 2283777
E: thomas.horton@brodies.com

HORVATH, Marcell (Jun 2019) (Employee)
Bruce McCormack Limited,
Glasgow . . . . (p.1007)
T: 0141 429 0010

HOSKINS, Sarah Gaylor (Oct 2005) (Solicitor)
NO FIRM

HOSSACK, David (Nov 1987) (Partner)
Morton Fraser LLP, Edinburgh . . . . (p.891)
T: 0131 2471000
E: david.hossack@morton-fraser.com

HOSSAIN, Mumotaz (Mar 2021) (Employee)
Lindsays LLP, Edinburgh . . . . (p.882)
T: 0131 2291212
E: mumotazhossain@lindsays.co.uk

HOTCHKIS, James Dunmore (Oct 1982)
(Partner)
R & R Urquhart LLP, Nairn . . . . (p.1129)
T: 01667 453278
E: jameshotchkis@r-r-urquhart.com

HOTCHKISS, Stephen Scott (May 1995)
(Associate)
JC Hughes Solicitors Limited,
Glasgow......................(p.988)
T: 0141 7782468
E: stephenhotchkiss@jchughes.net

HOTHERSALL, Richard William (Sept 2000)
(Associate)
Dickson Minto, Edinburgh...........(p.861)
T: 0131 2254455
E: richard.hothersall@dmws.com

HOUGHTON, Natasha Louise (Jul 2018)
(Employee)
Shepherd and Wedderburn LLP,
Edinburgh...................(p.900)
T: 0131 2289900

HOULISTON, Louise Claire (May 2008)
(Employee)
Kennedys Scotland, Edinburgh........(p.880)
T: 0131 285 2962
E: louise.houliston@kennedyslaw.com

HOUSE, Anne-Louise (Sept 1998) (Employee)
Procurator Fiscal Service,
Edinburgh..................(p.1227)
T: 0300 0204401
E: anne-louise.house@civilrecoveryunit.gov.scot

HOUSEGO, Abigail Morven (Nov 2018)
(Employee)
Addleshaw Goddard LLP,
Edinburgh...................(p.835)
T: 0131 2282400
E: abby.housego@addleshawgoddard.com

HOUSTON, Alastair David (Aug 2010) (Partner)
Brown & Co Legal LLP, Glasgow......(p.950)
T: 0141 3533354
E: AlastairHouston@lsa.org.uk

HOUSTON, Andrew William (Nov 1992)
(Partner)
McSporrans, Edinburgh............(p.888)
T: 0131 5579151
E: awhouston@hotmail.co.uk

HOUSTON, Cathryn Jane Marjorie
(Oct 2018) (Employee)
Carey Olsen, St Helier.............(p.1274)
T: 01534 888900
E: cathryn.houston@careyolsen.com

HOUSTON, Dawn Elizabeth (Sept 2010)
(Associate)
Pinsent Masons LLP, Edinburgh.......(p.895)
T: 0131 777 7000
E: dawn.houston@pinsentmasons.com

HOUSTON, Ian James (Feb 1975) (Employee)
Bruce, Short & Co., Dundee.........(p.806)
T: 01382 223400
E: contactus@bruceshort.co.uk

HOUSTON, Laurie Elizabeth (Apr 2012)
(Employee)
Burness Paull LLP, Glasgow..........(p.954)
T: 0141 2484933
E: laurie.houston@burnesspaull.com

HOUSTON, Rebecca Jane (Mar 2011) (Partner)
Houston Law, Glasgow.............(p.987)
T: 07834 626890
E: info@houstonlaw.co.uk

HOUSTON, Suzanne Lesley (Nov 2020)
(Employee)
Scottish Government, Edinburgh.....(p.1231)
T: 0131 244 0815
E: suzanne.houston@gov.scot

HOUSTON, Thomas Colvin (Aug 1988)
(Director)
Wallace Hodge & Company Limited,
Ayr........................(p.766)
T: 01292 611177

HOWARTH, Corrie Ann (Nov 2016) (Employee)
Mourant Ozannes, St Helier.........(p.1274)
T: 1481731513

HOWARTH, Laura Louise (Nov 2009)
(Employee)
The Weir Group PLC, Glasgow.......(p.1245)
E: laura.howarth@mail.weir

HOWAT, Jonathan Hay (Nov 2015) (Employee)
Thompsons, Glasgow.............(p.1046)
T: 0141 2218840
E: jonathan.howat@thompsons-scotland.co.uk

HOWAT, Robert Morton (Dec 1992)
(Employee)
Scottish Rugby, Edinburgh.........(p.1233)
T: 0131 3465000
E: robert.howat@sru.org.uk

HOWATSON, Victoria Anne (Sept 2016)
(Employee)
Plexus Law LLP, Edinburgh..........(p.897)
T: 0344 2454802
E: victoria.howatson@plexuslaw.co.uk

HOWE, Kelly-Anne (Nov 2001) (Director)
Martin, Johnston & Socha Limited,
Alloa......................(p.753)
T: 01259 725922
E: kelly.howe@mjscriminaldefencelawyers.co.uk

HOWE, Lauren Louise (Aug 2019) (Employee)
Terumo Aortic, Glasgow...........(p.1245)

HOWELL, Michelle (Nov 2003) (Employee)
Scottish Enterprise, Glasgow........(p.1243)
T: 0141 2282080
E: Michelle.Howell@scotent.co.uk

HOWELL, Morven Fiona (Oct 1993) (Partner)
D.W. Shaw, Ayr.................(p.765)
T: 01292 265033
E: mhowell@dwshaw.co.uk

HOWELLS, Katherine (Jul 2015) (Partner)
Lyons Davidson Scotland LLP,
  Edinburgh . . . .(p.883)
  T: 0131 344 0251
  E: khowells-price@lyonsdavidson.co.uk

HOWIE, Adam Matthew (Oct 2012) (Employee)
Dickson Minto, Edinburgh . . . .(p.861)
  T: 0131 2254455
  E: adam.howie@dmws.com

HOWIE, Catherine (Jul 2018) (Associate)
CMS Cameron McKenna Nabarro Olswang LLP,
  Edinburgh . . . .(p.856)
  T: +44 131 200 7501
  E: catherine.howie@cms-cmno.com

HOWIE, Colin Neville (Sept 1995) (Director)
Howie (Scotland) Limited,
  Aberdeen . . . .(p.732)
  E: ch@howieandco.com

HOWIE, Nicholas Alexander (Aug 2006)
  (Partner)
Anderson Strathern LLP, Edinburgh . . . .(p.839)
  T: 0131 2707700
  E: Nicholas.Howie@andersonstrathern.co.uk

HOWIE, Shona Jane (Sept 2019) (Employee)
Procurator Fiscal Service,
  Edinburgh . . . .(p.1227)
  T: 0300 0203168
  E: shona.howie@copfs.gov.uk

HOWITT, Catherine (Aug 1991) (Employee)
W. & A.S. Bruce, Dunfermline . . . .(p.822)
  T: 01383 738000
  E: katehowitt@wasbruce.co.uk

HOY, David (May 2004) (Employee)
Standard Life Assets and Employee Services
  Limited, Edinburgh . . . .(p.1234)
  T: 0131 2457508
  E: David_Hoy@standardlife.com

HOYLE, Susan Jane (Sept 1986) (Partner)
Wright, Johnston & Mackenzie LLP,
  Glasgow. . . . .(p.1054)
  T: 0141 2483434
  E: sjh@wjm.co.uk

HTET-KHIN, Kenneth (Oct 1999) (Employee)
The Scottish Parliament, Edinburgh . . .(p.1235)
  T: (0131) 3486653
  E: Kenny.Htet-Khin@parliament.scot

HUDSON, Jenna (Oct 2010) (Employee)
Hymans Robertson LLP, Edinburgh . . . .(p.1223)
  T: (0131) 656 5187
  E: jenna.hudson@hymans.co.uk

HUDSON, Kirstin Elizabeth (Jul 2017)
  (Employee)
Scottish Children's Reporter Administration,
  Livingston . . . .(p.1250)
  E: kirstin.hudson@scra.gsi.gov.uk

HUGHES, Alan David (Jul 1998) (Associate)
CMS Cameron McKenna Nabarro Olswang LLP,
  Glasgow. . . . .(p.962)
  T: 0141 2222200
  E: Alan.Hughes@cms-cmno.com

HUGHES, Angela Mary (Feb 1985) (Solicitor)
NO FIRM

HUGHES, Benjamin Francis (Jun 2011)
  (Employee)
Scottish Legal Aid Board,
  Edinburgh . . . .(p.1233)
  T: 0131 2267061
  E: HughesBE@slab.org.uk

HUGHES, David William (Nov 1991) (Partner)
Addleshaw Goddard LLP,
  Edinburgh . . . .(p.835)
  T: 0131 2282400

HUGHES, Eileen Mary (Sept 1986) (Director)
Goldsmith & Hughes Ltd, East
  Kilbride . . . .(p.831)
  T: 01355 260602
  E: eileen@goldsmithhughes.co.uk

HUGHES, Emma (Jun 2017) (Employee)
EYGS, London SE1 . . . .(p.1264)
  E: Emma.Hughes1@uk.ey.com

HUGHES, Emma Allyson (Dec 2015) (Director)
Carey Hughes Limited, High
  Blantyre . . . .(p.1073)
  T: 01698 404 616
  E: emma@careyhughes.co.uk

HUGHES, Francis (Sept 1988) (Partner)
Berrymans Lace Mawer LLP,
  Glasgow. . . . .(p.945)
  T: 0141 3532121
  E: frank.hughes@blmlaw.com

HUGHES, Geraint James Gordon (Jul 2015)
  (Associate)
Shoosmiths LLP, Glasgow . . . .(p.1040)
  T: 0370 086 8300
  E: geraint.hughes@shoosmiths.co.uk

HUGHES, Helen (Aug 1988) (Partner)
McAuley, McCarthy & Co., Paisley . . . .(p.1139)
  T: 0141 5617779
  E: helen@mmscotland.co.uk

HUGHES, Ian Alexander (Oct 1999) (Employee)
Galliford Try, Edinburgh . . . .(p.1223)
  T: 0131 3386002
  E: ian.hughes@gallifordtry.co.uk

HUGHES, John Gillies (Dec 1984) (Partner)
Connor Malcolm, Edinburgh . . . .(p.888)
  T: 0131 5576566
  E: john.hughes@connormalcolm.com

HUGHES, Kevin John (Aug 1982) (Employee)
Goldsmith & Hughes Ltd, East
Kilbride ....(p.831)
T: 01355 260602
E: kevin@goldsmithhughes.co.uk

HUGHES, Martin Francis (Nov 2018)
(Employee)
Inverclyde Council, Greenock........(p.1246)
T: 01475 717171
E: martin.hughes@inverclyde.gov.uk

HUGHES, Martin Gerard (Nov 1991) (Director)
Gallacher & Co Ltd, Kirkintilloch .....(p.1104)
T: 0141 7761111
E: martin@gallachers.co.uk

HUGHES, Michael Joseph (Oct 1987)
(Employee)
National Health Service Scotland,
Edinburgh ....(p.1225)
T: 0131 2757800
E: michael.hughes4@nhs.scot

HUGHES, Michael Patrick George
(Feb 2010) (Director)
Serenity Family Law Ltd, Glasgow ....(p.1038)
T: 07557 885013
E: michael@serenityfamilylaw.co.uk

HUGHES, Miranda Faye (Sept 2019) (Associate)
Clyde & Co (Scotland) LLP,
Glasgow....................(p.961)
T: 0141 2482666
E: miranda.hughes@clydeco.com

HUGHES, Moira (Aug 1990) (Associate)
Hill & Robb Limited, Stirling ....(p.1164)
T: 01786 450985
E: moirahughes@hillandrobb.co.uk

HUGHES, Paul Denis (Nov 1979) (Director)
Hughes Shaughnessy McFarlane Limited,
Glasgow....................(p.987)
T: 0141 6365115
E: paulhughes@hsmsolicitors.co.uk

HUGHES, Pauline Anne (Jan 2020) (Employee)
Just Employment Law Ltd,
Glasgow....................(p.1240)
T: 0141 3315150
E: paulinehughes@justemploymentlaw.co.uk

HUGHES, Richard Graham (Aug 2007)
(Associate)
DLA Piper Middle East LLP, Dubai ....(p.1278)
T: +971 (0)4 438 6315
E: richard.hughes@dlapiper.com

HUGHIESON, Niall George (Sept 2020)
(Employee)
Davidson Chalmers Stewart LLP,
Edinburgh ....(p.859)
T: 0131 6259191
E: niall.hughieson@dcslegal.com

HUGHSON, Craig James Allenby (Oct 2007)
(Associate)
Dentons & Co, Abu Dhabi ....(p.1277)
T: +971 2 613 1513
E: craig.hughson@dentons.com

HULME, Colin James Kennedy (Sept 1996)
(Partner)
Burness Paull LLP, Glasgow ....(p.954)
T: 0141 2484933
E: Colin.Hulme@burnesspaull.com

HULME, Edward Thomson (Aug 2009) (Partner)
Wardlaw Stephenson Allan,
Galashiels...................(p.934)
T: 01896 668669
E: ed@wsalawyers.com

HUME, Catriona Elizabeth (Mar 2016)
(Employee)
Baillie Gifford & Co, Edinburgh ......(p.1220)
T: 0131 2752000
E: katie.hume@bailliegifford.com

HUME, Mark Williamson (Nov 2018)
(Employee)
Proskauer Rose LLP, London EC2 .....(p.1267)
E: mhume@proskauer.com

HUME, Sarah Lucy (Nov 2005) (Employee)
Scottish Enterprise, Glasgow ....(p.1243)
T: 0141 2482700
E: sarah.hume@scotent.co.uk

HUMPHREY, Calum William Melville
(Oct 2018) (Employee)
Dickson Minto, Edinburgh...........(p.861)
T: 0131 2254455
E: calum.humphrey@dmws.com

HUMPHREY, Steven (Jan 2004) (Solicitor)
NO FIRM

HUMPHREYS, Stephen George (Jan 1985)
(Solicitor)
NO FIRM

HUMPHRIS, Kirsten Edith (May 2001)
(Director)
Murchison Law Limited, Inverness ....(p.1081)
T: 01463 709992
E: kirsten@murchisonlaw.co.uk

HUNT, Erin Macaulay (Jul 2018) (Employee)
Brodies LLP, Aberdeen..............(p.723)
T: 01224 392242
E: erin.hunt@brodies.com

HUNT, Karen Davidson (Nov 1994) (Solicitor)
NO FIRM

HUNTER, Abbie Kate (Jul 2021) (Employee)
Neil Kilcoyne & Co., Glasgow ....(p.996)
T: 0141 4332700
E: abbie@kilcoyne-solicitors.co.uk

HUNTER, Alexis Margaret (Aug 1977) (Partner)
Alexis Hunter Family Law, Glasgow ....(p.989)
   T: 0141 4040124
   E: amh@ahfamilylaw.co.uk

HUNTER, Amy Anne (Jul 2013) (Employee)
Procurator Fiscal Service, Glasgow ....(p.1241)
   T: 0300 0203000
   E: Amy.Hunter@copfs.gov.uk

HUNTER, Andrea Victoria (Nov 2015)
   (Employee)
Addleshaw Goddard LLP, Glasgow .....(p.938)
   T: 0141 2212300
   E: andrea.hunter@addleshawgoddard.com

HUNTER, Andrew John (Aug 2002) (Partner)
Harper Macleod LLP, Glasgow ....(p.983)
   T: 0141 2218888
   E: andrew.hunter@harpermacleod.co.uk

HUNTER, Anne (Nov 1985) (Solicitor)
Law Society of Scotland,
   Edinburgh ....(p.1224)
   T: 0131 2267411
   E: annehunter@lawscot.org.uk

HUNTER, Cameron Elliot Ross (Oct 1984)
   (Director)
G J Hunter & Co Limited,
   Edinburgh ....(p.879)
   T: 0131 6613414
   E: ross@gjhunter.co.uk

HUNTER, Catriona MacKay (Oct 2008)
   (Employee)
Mourant Ozannes, Hong Kong ......(p.1273)
   E: catriona.hunter@mourant.com

HUNTER, Craig Alexander (Nov 2018)
   (Employee)
DLA Piper Scotland LLP, Edinburgh ....(p.863)
   T: 08700 111111
   E: craig.hunter@dlapiper.com

HUNTER, Dionne Maria (Jul 2017) (Employee)
Clarity Simplicity Ltd, Glasgow........(p.960)
   T: 0141 4332626
   E: d.hunter@claritysimplicity.co.uk

HUNTER, Edward Mark (Jun 2012) (Employee)
Burness Paull LLP, Edinburgh ....(p.850)
   T: 0131 4736000
   E: edward.hunter@burnesspaull.com

HUNTER, Elaine Ann (Feb 1997) (Partner)
Shepherd and Wedderburn LLP,
   Glasgow....................(p.1039)
   T: 0141 5669900
   E: Elaine.Hunter@shepwedd.com

HUNTER, George Gilfillan (Oct 1982)
   (Consultant)
The PRG Partnership, Glasgow ....(p.1045)
   T: 0141 3530550
   E: gghunter@prg.co.uk

HUNTER, George Ian Tolson, WS (Feb 1979)
   (Director)
Jas Campbell & Co Ltd, Saltcoats .....(p.1160)
   T: 01294 464301
   E: i.hunter@jascampbell.co.uk

HUNTER, Grant Martin (Nov 1991) (Partner)
BTO Solicitors LLP, Glasgow ....(p.952)
   T: 0141 2218012
   E: ghu@bto.co.uk

HUNTER, Ian Bruce (Sept 2016) (Director)
Jas Campbell & Co Ltd, Saltcoats .....(p.1160)
   T: 01294 464301

HUNTER, Iona Louise Arrol (Apr 2012)
   (Associate)
CMS Cameron McKenna Nabarro Olswang LLP,
   Glasgow....................(p.962)
   T: 0141 2222200
   E: Iona.Hunter@cms-cmno.com

HUNTER, Jaimie Jean (Jan 2021) (Employee)
Pinsent Masons LLP, Aberdeen........(p.739)
   T: 01224 377900
   E: jaimie-jean.hunter@pinsentmasons.com

HUNTER, James Euan (Dec 2006) (Solicitor)
NO FIRM

HUNTER, Jamie David (Oct 2012) (Associate)
Stronachs LLP, Aberdeen ....(p.744)
   T: 01224 845845
   E: jamie.hunter@stronachs.com

HUNTER, Jennifer (Sept 2011) (Employee)
Royal London, Edinburgh ....(p.1230)
   T: 0131 456 7703
   E: jenni.hunter@royallondon.com

HUNTER, Jennifer (Oct 2011) (Employee)
Cartys, Hamilton................(p.1066)
   T: 01698 285432
   E: jhunter@cartylaw.co.uk

HUNTER, John Paterson (Jul 2017) (Employee)
Scottish Social Services Council,
   Dundee ....(p.1218)
   T: 0345 6030 891
   E: john.hunter@sssc.uk.com

HUNTER, Kay Leigh (Jul 2017) (Employee)
Debevoise & Plimpton LLP, London
   EC2 ....(p.1263)
   E: khunter@debevoise.com

HUNTER, Lucinda Jane (Dec 1992) (Consultant)
Rennie McInnes LLP, Milngavie ......(p.1124)
   T: 0141 5629540
   E: lucinda@renniemcinnes.co.uk

HUNTER, Lucy Taylor (Sept 2011) (Employee)
Neuron Mobility Pte Ltd,
   Singapore...................(p.1276)
   T: +65 82345308
   E: lucy@neuron.sg

HUNTER, Lyndsay Ann (Jul 1992) (Employee)
Procurator Fiscal Service, Dumfries . . . . (p.1217)
T: 0844 5613000
E: lyndsay.hunter@copfs.gov.uk

HUNTER, Marianne Elizabeth (Aug 1998)
(Associate)
Hannay Fraser & Co Ltd, Isle of
Bute . . . . (p.1088)
T: 01700 503112
E: marianne@hannayfraser.co.uk

HUNTER, Marielle Elizabeth (Jan 2020)
(Employee)
East Lothian Council, Haddington . . . . (p.1246)
T: 01620 827827
E: mhunter1@eastlothian.gov.uk

HUNTER, Nikki (Mar 2013) (Associate)
Morton Fraser LLP, Glasgow . . . . (p.1022)
T: 0141 2741100
E: nikki.hunter@morton-fraser.com

HUNTER, Philip John (Sept 2001) (Partner)
Brodies LLP, Edinburgh . . . . (p.845)
T: 0131 2283777
E: philip.hunter@brodies.com

HUNTER, Ruth Carol (Oct 2010) (Employee)
Heineken UK Limited, Edinburgh . . . . . (p.1223)
T: 0131 5281000
E: ruth.hunter@heineken.co.uk

HUNTER, Sandra (Dec 1996) (Associate)
Morton Fraser LLP, Glasgow . . . . (p.1022)
T: 0141 2741100
E: sandra.hunter@morton-fraser.com

HUNTER, Scott William (Oct 2008) (Employee)
Turcan Connell, Edinburgh . . . . (p.908)
T: 0131 2288111
E: scott.hunter@turcanconnell.com

HUNTER, Stuart David (Oct 1988) (Partner)
Macnabs LLP, Perth . . . . (p.1150)
T: 01738 623432
E: stuarthunter@macnabs-law.co.uk

HUNTER, Sue Elizabeth (Jan 1999) (Partner)
Morton Fraser LLP, Edinburgh . . . . (p.891)
T: 0131 2471000
E: sue.hunter@morton-fraser.com

HUNTER, Yasmin (Aug 2012) (Associate)
Pinsent Masons LLP, Edinburgh . . . . . . (p.895)
T: 0131 777 7000
E: yasmin.hunter@pinsentmasons.com

HURCOMBE, Lauren (Nov 2013) (Employee)
DLA Piper Hong Kong, Hong Kong . . . (p.1273)
T: +852 2103 0 578
E: lauren.hurcombe@dlapiper.com

HURST, Caitlin (Jan 2018) (Employee)
PricewaterhouseCoopers LLP, London
WC2 . . . . (p.1267)
T: 020 72121616
E: caitlin.hurst@pwc.com

HURST, Lesley Anne (Oct 1990) (Director)
Macallans Limited, Glasgow . . . . (p.1005)
T: 0141 613 1787/647444
E: lah@macallans.co.uk

HUSSAIN, Adeel Raza (May 2013) (Director)
Maguire Solicitors, Glasgow . . . . (p.1017)
T: 0141 3312885
E: adeel@maguiresolicitors.co.uk

HUSSAIN, Asif Jilani (Jul 2001) (Partner)
Legal and Legal Solicitors & Notaries,
Glasgow . . . . (p.999)
T: 0141 4240500
E: info@legalandlegalsolicitors.com

HUSSAIN, Irim (Nov 1996) (Employee)
Pacitti Jones Legal Limited,
Glasgow . . . . (p.1028)
T: 0141 5714444
E: irim@pjglasgow.co.uk

HUSSAIN, Mohammed Imran (Apr 2011)
(Partner)
West Regent Law, Glasgow . . . . (p.1052)
T: 07463-660-578
E: ihussain@lawyer.com

HUSSAIN, Mohammed Kashif (Apr 2019)
(Employee)
Legal and Legal Solicitors & Notaries,
Glasgow . . . . (p.999)
T: 0141 4240500

HUSSAIN, Samina Kausar (Jun 2008) (Director)
RH & Co Ltd, Glasgow . . . . (p.1035)
T: 0141 419 0897
E: samina@rhcosolicitors.com

HUSSAIN, Umar Farooq (Mar 2015) (Employee)
McGreevy & Co Limited, Glasgow . . . . (p.1011)
T: 0141 4222220/0787212

HUSSEIN, Riaz (Nov 2002) (Employee)
Scottish Social Services Council,
Dundee . . . . (p.1218)
T: 0345 6030 891
E: riaz.hussein@sssc.uk.com

HUTCHEON, Alexander Buchan (Aug 1978)
(Partner)
Alex Hutcheon & Co., Aberdeen . . . . . . (p.732)
T: 01224 623423
E: abh@mortgageandproperty.co.uk

HUTCHEON, Campbell William (Oct 2008)
(Employee)
EDF Energy Renewables,
Edinburgh . . . . (p.1222)
T: (0131) 460 3654
E: Campbell.hutcheon@edf-re.uk

HUTCHEON, Euan Fraser (Nov 2012)
(Employee)
LC Interactive Ltd, St Helier . . . . (p.1274)
E: euan.hutcheon@lcinteractive.com

HUTCHEON, Heather Anne (Jan 2013)
(Associate)
Pinsent Masons LLP, Glasgow . . . .(p.1031)
T: 0141 567 8400
E: heather.hutcheon@pinsentmasons.com

HUTCHESON, Alan James (Feb 1985) (Partner)
Hutchesons, East Kilbride. . . . .(p.832)
T: 01355 224545
E: alan@hutchesonlaw.co.uk

HUTCHESON, Brian Alexander (Oct 1996)
(Partner)
Dentons UK and Middle East LLP,
Glasgow. . . . .(p.968)
T: 0330 2220050
E: brian.hutcheson@dentons.com

HUTCHESON, Paul Richard (Nov 1988)
(Associate)
Aberdein Considine and Company,
Aberdeen . . . .(p.718)
T: 01224 589700
E: phutcheson@acandco.com

HUTCHINSON, Katie Louise (Mar 2017)
(Employee)
Aberdein Considine and Company,
Aberdeen . . . .(p.718)
T: 01224 589700
E: khutchinson@acandco.com

HUTCHISON, Alexander Burnett (Apr 2005)
(Employee)
TAQA Bratani Limited, Aberdeen . . . . .(p.1214)
T: 01224 275275
E: sandy.hutchison@taqaglobal.com

HUTCHISON, Clara (Jul 2019) (Employee)
Osborne Clarke, London EC2 . . . .(p.1267)
E: clara.hutchison@osborneclarke.com

HUTCHISON, David Martin (Dec 2012)
(Partner)
Dallas McMillan, Glasgow . . . .(p.966)
T: 0141 3336750
E: Davidhutchison@dallasmcmillan.co.uk

HUTCHISON, David Simpson (Dec 2011)
(Employee)
Clyde & Co (Scotland) LLP,
Glasgow. . . . .(p.961)
T: 0141 2482666
E: David.Hutchison@clydeco.com

HUTCHISON, Frances Patricia (Nov 2010)
(Employee)
INEOS FPS Limited, Aberdeen . . . .(p.1213)
T: 01224 084429

HUTCHISON, Gillian Louise (Jan 2001)
(Employee)
Addleshaw Goddard LLP,
Edinburgh . . . .(p.835)
T: 0131 2282400
E: Gillian.Hutchison@addleshawgoddard.com

HUTCHISON, Hannah Aileen (Nov 2015)
(Employee)
Scottish Government, Edinburgh . . . . .(p.1231)
T: 0131 244 0815
E: hannah.hutchison@gov.scot

HUTCHISON, Hollie Shona (Jan 2017)
(Employee)
Mackinnons Solicitors LLP,
Aberdeen . . . .(p.737)
T: 01224 868687
E: hollie@mackinnons.com

HUTCHISON, Hugh Forbes Aaron
(Jul 2012) (Employee)
Travers Smith LLP, London EC1 . . . . . .(p.1269)
T: (0207) 2953387
E: hugh.hutchison@traverssmith.com

HUTCHISON, Judith (Oct 2001) (Employee)
Scullion Law Limited, Hamilton . . . . . .(p.1069)
T: 01698 283265
E: jhutchison@scullionlaw.com

HUTCHISON, Mark Stephen (Sept 1984)
(Employee)
John Pryde, SSC, Edinburgh. . . . .(p.897)
T: 0131 2202160
E: markhutchisonandco@live.co.uk

HUTCHISON, Michael (Nov 2013) (Employee)
Drummond Miller LLP, Edinburgh . . . . .(p.864)
T: 0131 2265151

HUTCHISON, Morag (Oct 1999) (Partner)
Burness Paull LLP, Edinburgh . . . .(p.850)
T: 0131 4736000
E: Morag.Hutchison@burnesspaull.com

HUTCHISON, Richard (Nov 1990) (Partner)
Malcolm & Hutchison, Airdrie . . . .(p.750)
T: 01236 755050
E: richard@malcolmandhutchison.co.uk

HUTCHISON, Robin William (Aug 2007)
(Partner)
CMS Cameron McKenna Nabarro Olswang LLP,
Edinburgh . . . .(p.856)
T: 0131 2288000
E: robin.hutchison@cms-cmno.com

HUTCHISON, Rodney Alphonsious Magill
(Jan 2003) (Solicitor)
NO FIRM

HUTCHISON, Rona Nicolson (Jan 2004)
(Solicitor)
NO FIRM

HUTCHISON, Sally (Sept 1995) (Employee)
BP Exploration Operating Company Ltd.,
Dyce . . . .(p.1219)
T: 01224 832353
E: sally.hutchison@uk.bp.com

HUTCHISON, Simon John Black (Jul 1983)
(Consultant)
MTM Defence Lawyers Limited,
Falkirk . . . .(p.923)
T: 01324 633221
E: shutchison@mtmdefence.co.uk

HUTCHISON, Susannah Jane Roberta
(Nov 2007) (Employee)
Procurator Fiscal Service, Alloa . . . .(p.1215)
T: 01259 214561
E: susannah.hutchison@copfs.gov.uk

HUTCHISON, Thomas James (Nov 2008)
(Associate)
Freshfields Service Company, London
EC2 . . . .(p.1264)
T: 020 7936 4000
E: tom.hutchison@freshfields.com

HUTCHISON, Vanessa (Feb 2017) (Employee)
Abrdn Financial Planning and Advice Limited,
Glasgow. . . . .(p.1237)

HUTTON, Allan John Swan (Jan 2013) (Partner)
Buchanan Dickson Frame, Paisley . . . . .(p.1137)
T: 0141 8480303

HUTTON, Colin John George (Nov 1996)
(Partner)
CMS Cameron McKenna Nabarro Olswang LLP,
Edinburgh . . . .(p.856)
T: 0131 2288000
E: Colin.Hutton@cms-cmno.com

HUTTON, Robert (Jul 2012) (Employee)
Morgan, Lewis & Bockius UK LLP, London
EC4 . . . .(p.1266)
T: 020 3201 5000
E: robert.hutton@morganlewis.com

HUTTON, Stephanie Claire Grace
(Oct 2009) (Partner)
Jones Whyte LLP, Glasgow. . . . .(p.993)
T: 0141 375 1222
E: stephanie.hutton@joneswhyte.co.uk

HWANG, Wan-Ting (Aug 2019) (Employee)
Berrymans Lace Mawer LLP,
Glasgow. . . . .(p.945)
T: 0141 3532121
E: Annie.Hwang@blmlaw.com

HYAMS, James Robert (Nov 2016) (Associate)
Balfour + Manson LLP, Edinburgh . . . . .(p.841)
T: 0131 2001200
E: James.Hyams@balfour-manson.co.uk

HYND, Janet McLean (Dec 1981) (Employee)
Mitchells Roberton Ltd, Glasgow . . . . .(p.1020)
T: 0141 5523422
E: jmh@mitchells-roberton.co.uk

HYNDMAN, Victoria Mary (Sept 2012)
(Employee)
Glasgow City Council, Glasgow . . . . . .(p.1240)
E: victoria.hyndman@glasgow.gov.uk

HYTIRIS, Sophia Catherine (Sept 2016)
(Employee)
Aon UK Ltd, London EC3 . . . .(p.1261)
E: sophia.hytiris@aon.co.uk

IANNARELLI, Lesley Ann (Jul 2020) (Employee)
Blackadders LLP, Edinburgh . . . .(p.843)
T: 0131 2228000
E: Lesley.Iannarelli@blackadders.co.uk

IANNETTA, Paul Andrew (Nov 2015)
(Employee)
Burness Paull LLP, Edinburgh . . . .(p.850)
T: 0131 4736000
E: Paul.Iannetta@burnesspaull.com

IBRAHEEM, Muhammad (Jun 2020) (Solicitor)
NO FIRM

IDREES, Sanah Anwar (Mar 2021) (Employee)
Procurator Fiscal Service,
Edinburgh . . . .(p.1229)
T: 0300 0203000
E: sanah.indrees@copfs.gov.uk

IEROPOULOS, Amy (Nov 2005) (Director)
Wallace Quinn & Co Limited,
Livingston . . . .(p.1120)
T: 01506 353400
E: amy@wallacequinn.co.uk

ILES, Andrew Fraser (Sept 1992) (Partner)
Cartys, Blantyre . . . .(p.777)
T: 01698 820896
E: ai@cartylaw.co.uk

ILES, Sean Hugh (Nov 2020) (Employee)
Cartys, Hamilton. . . . .(p.1066)
T: 01698 285432
E: siles@cartylaw.co.uk

ILIESCU, Alexandru Damaris (Apr 2019)
(Employee)
Anderson Strathern LLP, Edinburgh . . . .(p.839)
T: 0131 2707700
E: alex.iliescu@andersonstrathern.co.uk

ILLAND, Erin Esther (Apr 2021) (Employee)
Procurator Fiscal Service,
Edinburgh . . . .(p.1227)
T: 0300 0203168
E: Erin.Illand@copfs.gov.uk

IMLACH, Elaine Isobel (Jan 1986) (Employee)
Coulters Legal LLP, Edinburgh . . . .(p.858)
T: 0131 603 7333
E: elaine.imlach@coulters.io

IMRIE, Alexandra Rachelle (Jan 2018)
(Employee)
Stevenson & Marshall LLP,
Dunfermline . . . .(p.825)
T: 01383 721141
E: aimrie@stevenson-marshall.co.uk

IMRIE, Donna (Jun 2018) (Employee)
Rollos Law LLP, Cupar . . . . (p.792)
T: 01334 654081
E: donnaimrie@rollos.co.uk

IMRIE, Eilis Marion (May 2016) (Employee)
Fife Community Law Limited,
Lochgelly . . . . (p.1120)
T: 01592 786710

IMRIE, Graeme Mitchell (Sept 2010)
(Employee)
Brodies LLP, Aberdeen . . . . (p.723)
T: 01224 392242
E: graeme.imrie@brodies.com

IMRIE, Hazel (Feb 2020) (Employee)
Rea Law Ltd, Glasgow . . . . (p.1034)
T: 0141 3701241
E: hazel@realaw.co.uk

INAM, Saroash (Aug 2011) (Employee)
Muirhall Energy Limited, Lanark . . . . . . (p.1250)
T: (01501) 785604
E: si@muirhallenergy.co.uk

INCH, Fraser Hunter (Oct 2013) (Employee)
Scottish Environment Protection Agency,
Stirling . . . . (p.1255)
T: 01786 457700
E: fraser.inch@sepa.org.uk

INCH, Graham Ian (Oct 2003) (Director)
McKennas Law Practice Limited,
Glenrothes . . . . (p.1057)
T: 01592 756449
E: grahaminch@yahoo.co.uk

INGLIS, Alison Anne MacKenzie (Sept 1993)
(Employee)
Pinsent Masons LLP, Stanley . . . . (p.1272)
T: 00500 22690
E: ainglis@pinsentmasons.co.fk

INGLIS, Amanda Elizabeth (Nov 1992)
(Employee)
Scottish Courts and Tribunals Service,
Falkirk . . . . (p.1237)
T: 01324 678212
E: ainglis@scotcourts.gov.uk

INGLIS, James (Sept 1996) (Partner)
MacRoberts LLP, Glasgow . . . . (p.1015)
T: 0141 3031100
E: james.inglis@macroberts.com

INGLIS, Jennifer Frances Mackenzie
(Aug 1999) (Employee)
National Health Service Scotland,
Edinburgh . . . . (p.1225)
T: 0131 2757800
E: jennifer.inglis@nhs.scot

INGLIS, Kirsty Sarah (Jul 2011) (Employee)
SSE PLC, Glasgow . . . . (p.1244)
T: 0141 224 7248
E: Kirsty.S.Inglis@sse.com

INGLIS, Mary Morag (Oct 1987) (Director)
Mitchells Roberton Ltd, Glasgow . . . . . (p.1020)
T: 0141 5523422
E: mmi@mitchells-roberton.co.uk

INGLIS, Ronald James (Jul 1997) (Director)
Mitchells Roberton Ltd, Glasgow . . . . . (p.1020)
T: 0141 5523422
E: rji@mitchells-roberton.co.uk

INGLIS, Stephen David (Nov 1988) (Partner)
Jameson + Mackay LLP, Perth . . . . (p.1148)
T: 01738 631666

INGLIS, Steven Stewart (Sept 1999) (Employee)
Aberdeen City Council, Aberdeen . . . . . (p.1211)
T: 01224 522000
E: singlis@aberdeencity.gov.uk

INGRAM, Gillian (Sept 1996) (Employee)
Glasgow City Council, Glasgow . . . . . . (p.1239)
T: 0141 287 5439
E: Gillian.Ingram@citybuildingglasgow.co.uk

INGRAM, Lauren Marie (Jun 2017) (Employee)
North Ayrshire Council, Irvine . . . . (p.1249)
T: 01294 310000
E: laureningram@north-ayrshire.gov.uk

INGRAM, Martin (Sept 2004) (Employee)
Aberdeenshire Council, Aberdeen . . . . . (p.1211)
T: 01467 533261
E: martin.ingram@aberdeenshire.gov.uk

INGRAM, Vanessa Clare (Sept 1998) (Director)
VI Pensions Law Limited,
Strathaven . . . . (p.1173)
E: vanessa@vipensionslaw.co.uk

INGRAM-SMITH, Rhea McNulty (Nov 2020)
(Employee)
DLA Piper Scotland LLP, Edinburgh . . . . (p.863)
T: 08700 111111
E: rhea.ingramsmith@dlapiper.com

INKSON, Gordon Mackay (Aug 1997)
(Employee)
ADNOC Logistics and Services, Abu
Dhabi . . . . (p.1277)
T: +971 2 602 8314
E: GInkson@adnoc.ae

INKSON, Susan Rose (Oct 2007) (Employee)
Capricorn Energy Ltd, Edinburgh . . . . . (p.1221)
T: 0131 4753000
E: Susie.Inkson@cairnenergy.com

INKSTER, Brian Hunter (Aug 1992) (Partner)
Inksters, Glasgow . . . . (p.990)
T: 0141 2290880
E: brian@inksters.com

INKSTER, Michael Alastair (Sept 1991) (Partner)
Michael Inkster & Co., Lerwick . . . . . . (p.1114)
T: 01595 696901
E: michaelinksterandco@lineone.net

INKSTER, Zoe (Dec 2017) (Employee)
Gillespie Macandrew LLP,
Edinburgh . . . .(p.872)
T: 0131 2251677
E: zoe.inkster@gillespiemacandrew.co.uk

INMAN, Melissa Elizabeth Gordon
(Jun 2016) (Employee)
Drummond Miller LLP, Bathgate . . . . . .(p.771)
T: 01506 656645
E: MInman@drummondmiller.co.uk

INNES, Alan Alexander, WS (Nov 1991)
(Partner)
J & H Mitchell LLP, Pitlochry . . . .(p.1155)
T: 01796 472606
E: alan.innes@hmitchell.co.uk

INNES, Alan David James (Jan 2015)
(Employee)
Burness Paull LLP, Edinburgh . . . .(p.850)
T: 0131 370 8961
E: Alan.Innes@burnesspaull.com

INNES, Alison Margaret (Nov 1983) (Employee)
Procurator Fiscal Service,
Edinburgh . . . .(p.1229)
T: 0300 0203000

INNES, Alison Susan (Nov 1978) (Solicitor)
NO FIRM

INNES, Bess Macleod (Aug 2015) (Associate)
Morton Fraser LLP, Edinburgh . . . .(p.891)
T: 0131 2471000
E: bess.innes@morton-fraser.com

INNES, Claire Louise (Nov 2020) (Employee)
Digby Brown LLP, Edinburgh . . . .(p.862)
T: 0333 200 5925
E: claire.innes@digbybrown.co.uk

INNES, Colin William (Oct 1993) (Partner)
Shepherd and Wedderburn LLP,
Edinburgh . . . .(p.900)
T: 0131 2289900
E: colin.innes@shepwedd.com

INNES, Craig Scott (Nov 1982) (Consultant)
Warners Solicitors LLP, Edinburgh . . . . . .(p.911)
T: 0131 6624747

INNES, Elisabeth Louise (May 2018) (Employee)
Campbell Smith LLP, Edinburgh . . . .(p.852)
T: 0131 5563737
E: elisabeth.innes@camsmith.co.uk

INNES, Mairi Rebecca (Jan 2019) (Employee)
Aberdein Considine and Company,
Aberdeen . . . .(p.718)
T: 01224 589700
E: minnes@acandco.com

INNES, Nicola Ann (Dec 1991) (Employee)
Medical Protection Society, Leeds. . . . .(p.1260)
E: Nicola.innes@medicalprotection.org

INNES, Sarah Charlotte (Aug 2020) (Employee)
Raeburn Christie Clark & Wallace LLP,
Aberdeen . . . .(p.741)
T: 01224 332400
E: sarah.innes@raeburns.co.uk

INNES, Stephanie Claire (May 2010)
(Employee)
Aggreko plc, Glasgow . . . .(p.1237)
T: 0141 2255900
E: steph.innes@aggreko.co.uk

ION, Andrew James (Oct 1979) (Employee)
Kerr Stirling LLP, Stirling . . . .(p.1165)
T: 01786 463414
E: ajion@kerrstirling.co.uk

IQBAL, Sumaira Zanib (Sept 2016) (Employee)
MacRoberts LLP, Glasgow . . . .(p.1015)
T: 0141 3031100
E: sumaira.iqbal@macroberts.com

IQBAL, Zahrah (Mar 2016) (Employee)
Procurator Fiscal Service, Glasgow . . . .(p.1241)
T: 0300 0203000
E: zahrah1990@hotmail.com

IRELAND, Andrew Roberts (Oct 1986)
(Employee)
DAC Beachcroft Scotland LLP,
Glasgow. . . . .(p.964)
T: 0141 2486688
E: aireland@dacbeachcroft.com

IRELAND, Cameron John (Sept 2018)
(Employee)
Pinsent Masons LLP, Glasgow . . . .(p.1031)
T: 0141 567 8400
E: cameron.ireland@pinsentmasons.com

IRONS, Gillian Grace (Sept 1988) (Associate)
Burness Paull LLP, Aberdeen . . . .(p.724)
T: 01224 621621
E: Gillian.Irons@burnesspaull.com

IRONS, Kenneth Wyness (Feb 1994) (Partner)
Gillespie Macandrew LLP,
Edinburgh . . . .(p.872)
T: 0131 2251677
E: kenneth.irons@gillespiemacandrew.co.uk

IRONS-YOUNG, Lucy Wenda (Nov 2012)
(Employee)
Dumfries & Galloway Council,
Dumfries . . . .(p.1217)
T: 01387 261234
E: lucy.irons-young@dumgal.gov.uk

IRONSIDE, Caroline Jane (Sept 2010)
(Employee)
Baillie Gifford & Co, Edinburgh . . . . . .(p.1220)
T: 0131 2752000
E: caroline.ironside@bailliegifford.com

IRVINE, Aileen Jane (Jul 2015) (Employee)
Scottish Police Authority, Police Scotland,
　　Glasgow . . . .(p.1244)
　　T: 01786 895727
　　E: Aileen.Irvine@scotland.pnn.police.uk

IRVINE, Alasdair James MF (Jun 2015)
　(Employee)
DAC Beachcroft Scotland LLP,
　　Glasgow . . . .(p.964)
　　T: 0141 2486688
　　E: airvine@dacbeachcroft.com

IRVINE, David John (Oct 2007) (Employee)
National Westminster Bank PLC, London
　　EC2 . . . .(p.1266)
　　E: David.irvine@natwest.com

IRVINE, Francis Joseph (Oct 1995) (Director)
Frank Irvine Solicitors Ltd, Glasgow . . . .(p.990)
　　T: 0141 3759000
　　E: fji@frankirvine.com

IRVINE, Graham Pattison (Sept 1983) (Partner)
Caesar & Howie, Bathgate. . . . .(p.770)
　　T: 01506 815900
　　E: gi@caesar-howie.co.uk

IRVINE, James (Oct 1988) (Employee)
Public Defence Solicitors Office,
　　Ayr . . . .(p.1215)
　　T: 01292 269139
　　E: jamesirvine57@gmail.com

IRVINE, Jill Jackson (Oct 1983) (Partner)
Brazenall & Orr, Dumfries . . . .(p.800)
　　T: 01387 255695
　　E: jill@brazenallandorr.co.uk

IRVINE, Joanne Marie (Feb 2012) (Employee)
Petrofac Services Limited,
　　Aberdeen . . . .(p.1213)
　　T: 01224 247000
　　E: joanne.irvine@petrofac.com

IRVINE, Johanna Vaughan (Mar 1998)
　(Employee)
Scottish Government, Edinburgh . . . . .(p.1231)
　　T: 0131 244 0815
　　E: johanna.irvine@gov.scot

IRVINE, Katherine Elizabeth (Oct 2001)
　(Employee)
Lindsays LLP, Edinburgh . . . .(p.882)
　　T: 0131 656 5542
　　E: KatherineIrvine@lindsays.co.uk

IRVINE, Kirsty May (Jun 2021) (Employee)
Raeburn Christie Clark & Wallace LLP,
　　Aberdeen . . . .(p.741)
　　T: 01224 332400
　　E: kirsty.irvine@raeburns.co.uk

IRVINE, Laura Jane (Aug 1999) (Partner)
Davidson Chalmers Stewart LLP,
　　Edinburgh . . . .(p.859)
　　T: 0131 6259191
　　E: laura.irvine@dcslegal.com

IRVINE, Nicola Alison (Sept 2000) (Partner)
Russells Gibson McCaffrey,
　　Glasgow . . . .(p.1037)
　　T: 0141 271 1000
　　E: nicola@russellsgm.co.uk

IRVINE OF DRUM, Alexander Hugh Richard
　(May 2001) (Employee)
City of Edinburgh Council,
　　Edinburgh . . . .(p.1221)
　　T: (0131) 5294145
　　E: Alexander.irvine@edinburgh.gov.uk

IRVINE, Rachel Helen (Feb 2017) (Employee)
Clydesdale Bank Plc, Glasgow . . . .(p.1238)
　　T: 0141 242 3933
　　E: rachel.irvine@cybg.com

IRVINE, Robert (Aug 2012) (Employee)
DDOG SINGAPORE PTE LTD,
　　Singapore. . . . .(p.1276)
　　E: robert.irvine@datadoghq.com

IRVINE, Sheila Anne (Jan 1989) (Consultant)
DLA Piper Scotland LLP, Edinburgh . . . .(p.863)
　　T: 08700 111111
　　E: sheila.irvine@dlapiper.com

IRVINE, Stephen (Sept 1997) (Partner)
Allan McDougall McQueen LLP,
　　Edinburgh . . . .(p.837)
　　T: 0131 2252121
　　E: StephenIrvine@allanmcdougall.co.uk

IRVING, Guy Anthony (Feb 1997) (Associate)
DLA Piper Scotland LLP, Edinburgh . . . .(p.863)
　　T: 08700 111111
　　E: guy.irving@dlapiper.com

IRVING, Laura Jane (Jun 2011) (Employee)
Chrysaor Limited, Aberdeen. . . . .(p.1212)
　　T: (01224) 086203
　　E: laura.irving@chrysaor.com

IRVING, Zoe Margaret (Jun 2018) (Employee)
Thorntons Law LLP, Perth . . . .(p.1151)
　　T: 01738 621212
　　E: zoeirving@thorntons-law.co.uk

IRWIN, Alexandra Emma (May 2018)
　(Employee)
Davidson Chalmers Stewart LLP,
　　Edinburgh . . . .(p.859)
　　T: 0131 6259191
　　E: alexandra.irwin@dcslegal.com

IRWIN, Corra Lisa (Sept 1997) (Director)
Macleod & MacCallum Limited,
　　Inverness . . . .(p.1080)
　　T: 01463 239393
　　E: corra.irwin@macandmac.co.uk

IRWIN, Katherine Louise (Oct 2018)
(Employee)
Procurator Fiscal Service,
Livingston . . . . (p.1250)
T: (0300) 020 3696
E: katherine.irwin@copfs.gov.uk

IRWIN, Keith Brian (Nov 2003) (Employee)
City of Edinburgh Council,
Edinburgh . . . . (p.1221)
T: 0131 5293663
E: Keith.Irwin@edinburgh.gov.uk

IRWIN, Louise (Mar 2004) (Employee)
Law At Work Incorporating Empire,
Aberdeen . . . . (p.1213)
T: (01224) 701383
E: louiseirwin@worknest.com

ISAACS, Edward (Nov 1976) (Solicitor)
NO FIRM

ISAJ, Visar (Oct 2013) (Employee)
ISG Central Services Limited, London
EC3 . . . . (p.1265)
E: visar.isaj@isgltd.com

ISDALE, Ailie Laura (Sept 2016) (Employee)
Pinsent Masons LLP, Glasgow . . . . (p.1031)
T: 0141 567 8400
E: ailie.isdale@pinsentmasons.com

ISLAM, Rabia (Dec 2018) (Employee)
Weaver & Waddell Solicitors,
Glasgow . . . . (p.1051)
T: 0141 7396100
E: rabia.islam@weaverwaddellsolicitors.com

ISMAIL, Amir Mohamed (Aug 2008) (Director)
Holmes Mackillop Limited,
Glasgow . . . . (p.986)
T: 0141 226 4942
E: aismail@homack.co.uk

JAAP, Douglas William (Aug 1990) (Director)
Jaaplaw Limited, Falkirk . . . . (p.922)
T: 01324 710137
E: dwj@dwjlaw.com

JAARSON, Rebeccah Rachael Hamilton
(Nov 2008) (Employee)
DAC Beachcroft Claims Limited,
Birmingham . . . . (p.1258)
T: 0121 6985200
E: rjaarson@dacbeachcroft.com

JACK, Amanda Rose (Oct 2019) (Employee)
Burness Paull LLP, Edinburgh . . . . (p.850)
T: 0131 473 6074
E: amanda.jack@burnesspaull.com

JACK, Andrew Richard (Sept 2004) (Employee)
Natural Power Consultants Limited,
Stirling . . . . (p.1254)
T: 01786 542 300
E: andrewj@naturalpower.com

JACK, Atlanta Tazmin (Nov 2021) (Employee)
Bridge Legal Limited, Glasgow . . . . (p.948)
T: 0141 4293100
E: ajack@bridgelegalglasgow.co.uk

JACK, David Ashley (Feb 1992) (Associate)
Brodies LLP, Edinburgh . . . . (p.845)
T: 0131 2283777
E: david.jack@brodies.com

JACK, Esther-Nina (Sept 1996) (Employee)
Lloyds Banking Group Plc,
Edinburgh . . . . (p.1224)
T: (0131) 442 9579
E: esther.jack@lloydsbanking.com

JACK, James William Lyall (Jan 1997) (Associate)
Burness Paull LLP, Aberdeen . . . . (p.724)
T: 01224 621621
E: James.Jack@burnesspaull.com

JACK, Jennifer Lorna (Nov 1999) (Partner)
Harper Macleod LLP, Edinburgh . . . . (p.877)
T: 0131 2472500
E: jennifer.jack@harpermacleod.co.uk

JACK, Karen Margaret (Nov 1991) (Solicitor)
NO FIRM

JACK, Lesley-Anne (Nov 1995) (Employee)
NewLaw Scotland LLP, Glasgow . . . . . . (p.1027)
T: 0845 4819500
E: lesley-anne.jack@newlaw-scotland.co.uk

JACK, Murray Alistair (Oct 2000) (Partner)
Addleshaw Goddard LLP, Glasgow . . . . . (p.938)
T: 0141 2212300
E: Murray.Jack@addleshawgoddard.com

JACK, Peter Reidie (Nov 1987) (Partner)
Franchi Law LLP, Glasgow . . . . (p.977)
T: 0141 225 3810
E: peter@franchilaw.co.uk

JACK, Robert Thomson Barr (Feb 1988)
(Employee)
National Health Service Scotland,
Edinburgh . . . . (p.1225)
T: 0131 2757800
E: robin.jack@nhs.scot

JACK, Sarah Anne (Oct 2009) (Partner)
Drummond Miller LLP, Edinburgh . . . . . (p.864)
T: 0131 2265151
E: sjack@drummondmiller.co.uk

JACK, Sarah Christine Elizabeth (Mar 2014)
(Employee)
Aberdein Considine and Company,
Glasgow . . . . (p.937)
T: 0141 2278200
E: sarah.jack@acandco.com

JACKMAN, Sarah Sinclair (Nov 1998)
(Employee)
Dentons UK and Middle East LLP,
Glasgow.....................(p.968)
T: 0330 2220050
E: sarah.jackman@dentons.com

JACKSON, Alan (Aug 1984) (Associate)
Adams Whyte, Livingston ....(p.1117)
T: 01506 401999
E: alanjackson@adamswhyte.com

JACKSON, Alison Julie (Oct 2008) (Partner)
Andersonbain LLP, Aberdeen ....(p.721)
T: 01224 456789
E: AJackson@andersonbain.co.uk

JACKSON, Brian James Alexander
(Aug 2013) (Associate)
Thomas S. Veitch & Son,
Linlithgow ....(p.1117)
T: 01506 842100
E: brian@tsveitch.com

JACKSON, Carolyn Sophie (Aug 2012)
(Employee)
Balfour + Manson LLP, Edinburgh .....(p.841)
T: 0131 2001200
E: carolyn.jackson@balfour-manson.co.uk

JACKSON, Charles David (Aug 1974) (Director)
Miller Beckett & Jackson Limited,
Glasgow....................(p.1019)
T: 0141 2042833
E: cjackson@mbjsolicitors.co.uk

JACKSON, Charles John Benjamin
(Dec 1981) (Employee)
Jackson & Co (Fife) Limited, Leven ....(p.1115)
T: 01333 422330
E: info@jacksonsolicitors.co.uk

JACKSON, Claire Margaret (Oct 2010)
(Employee)
Heineken UK Limited, Edinburgh .....(p.1223)
T: 0131 5281000
E: claire.jackson@heineken.co.uk

JACKSON, Craig (Jun 2012) (Employee)
Davidson Chalmers Stewart LLP,
Glasgow....................(p.967)
T: 0141 4283258
E: craig.jackson@dcslegal.com

JACKSON, Elaine Love (Oct 1995) (Employee)
Procurator Fiscal Service, Glasgow ....(p.1241)
T: 0300 0203000
E: elaine.jackson@copfs.gov.uk

JACKSON, Elise Nicole (Jan 2021) (Employee)
National Westminster Bank PLC,
Edinburgh ....(p.1226)
T: (0131) 626 2925
E: elise.jackson@natwest.com

JACKSON, Fraser Paul (Oct 2019) (Employee)
Dickson Minto, London EC2 ....(p.1263)
T: 020 76284455
E: Fraser.Jackson@dmws.com

JACKSON, Iain Alexander (Aug 2002)
(Employee)
Argyll & Bute Council,
Lochgilphead ....(p.1251)
T: 01546 602127
E: iain.jackson@argyll-bute.gov.uk

JACKSON, James Richard Graham
(Nov 1998) (Associate)
Thorntons Law LLP, Dundee ....(p.819)
T: 01382 229 111
E: gjackson@thorntons-law.co.uk

JACKSON, Julie Mansfield (Oct 1989)
(Employee)
Miller Homes Limited, Edinburgh .....(p.1225)
T: 0870 3365000
E: julie.jackson@miller.co.uk

JACKSON, Laura Anne O'Kane (Nov 1996)
(Employee)
Public Defence Solicitors Office,
Falkirk ....(p.1237)
T: 01324 631475
E: ljackson@pdso.org.uk

JACKSON, Maureen (Nov 2006) (Employee)
Wallace Quinn & Co Limited,
Glasgow....................(p.1051)
T: 0141 7713911
E: maureen@wallacequinn.co.uk

JACKSON, Michael (Apr 1985) (Director)
Frederick & Co Solicitors Limited,
Glasgow....................(p.977)
T: 0141 2215575
E: michael@frederickandco.co.uk

JACKSON, Roderick Andrew Stuart
(Feb 2001) (Partner)
Kennedys Scotland, Edinburgh........(p.880)
T: 0131 6599716
E: Rory.Jackson@kennedyslaw.com

JACKSON, Sarah Victoria (Aug 2009)
(Employee)
Turcan Connell, Edinburgh ....(p.908)
T: 0131 2288111
E: sarah.jackson@turcanconnell.com

JACKSON, Stacey Grace (Feb 2019) (Employee)
Thorntons Law LLP, Arbroath.........(p.757)
T: 01241 872683
E: SJackson@thorntons-law.co.uk

JACKSON, Stephen John (Sept 2009)
(Employee)
Scottish Government, Edinburgh .....(p.1231)
T: 0131 244 0815
E: stephen.jackson@gov.scot

JACKSON, Thea Jo-Ann Doran (Oct 2005)
(Employee)
Urquharts, Edinburgh . . . .(p.909)
T: 0131 5562896
E: theajackson@urquharts.co.uk

JACKSON, Yvonne (Oct 1995) (Employee)
Glasgow City Council, Glasgow . . . . . .(p.1239)
T: 0141 2874159
E: Yvonne.Jackson@glasgow.gov.uk

JACKSON-PLATT, Ronan James (May 2017)
(Employee)
Jones Whyte LLP, Glasgow . . . .(p.993)
T: 0141 375 1222
E: ronan.platt@joneswhyte.co.uk

JAFFRI, Syeda Masooma Zainab (Sept 2017)
(Employee)
Procurator Fiscal Service, Glasgow . . . .(p.1241)
T: 0300 0203000
E: masooma.jaffri@copfs.gov.uk

JAGLA, Catriona Esther (Jul 2020) (Employee)
Procurator Fiscal Service, Glasgow . . . .(p.1241)
T: 0300 0203000
E: catriona.jagla@copfs.gov.uk

JAHDAUT NERJOVAJ, Teuta (Sept 2019)
(Employee)
Pinsent Masons LLP, Glasgow . . . .(p.1031)
T: 0141 567 8400
E: Teuta.Jahdaut-Nerjovaj@pinsentmasons.com

JAIN, Pravin (Sept 1998) (Partner)
Jain, Neil & Ruddy, Glasgow . . . .(p.992)
T: 0141 9504672
E: pravin@jnrsolicitors.com

JAKUBOVSKIS, Arturas (Aug 2017) (Associate)
Allen & Overy LLP, London E1 . . . .(p.1261)
T: 020 3088 0000
E: Arturas.Jakubovskis@allenovery.com

JAKUCZUN, Sylwia (Jul 2020) (Employee)
Dickson Minto, Edinburgh . . . .(p.861)
T: 0131 2254455
E: sylwia.jakuczun@dmws.com

JALICY, Sara Marziyeh (Mar 2009) (Partner)
Anderson Strathern LLP, Edinburgh . . . .(p.839)
T: 0131 2707700
E: sara.jalicy@andersonstrathern.co.uk

JAMES, Caroline Sanderson (Feb 1992)
(Employee)
Vintage Malt Whisky Company Limited,
Glasgow. . . . .(p.1245)
T: 0141 955 1700
E: caroline@vintagemaltwhisky.com

JAMES, Fiona Allan (May 2019) (Employee)
Blackadders LLP, Aberdeen . . . .(p.722)
T: 01224 588913
E: fiona.james@blackadders.co.uk

JAMES, Jacquiline Angela (Oct 2005)
(Employee)
Highland Spring, Auchterarder. . . . . . .(p.1215)
T: 01764 660500
E: JacquilineJ@highlandspringgroup.com

JAMES, Lloyd David (Sept 2016) (Partner)
Burges Salmon LLP, Bristol. . . . .(p.1258)
T: 0117 9392000
E: lloyd.james@burges-salmon.com

JAMES, Louise Margaret (Sept 2020)
(Employee)
Central Court Lawyers, Livingston . . . .(p.1118)
T: 01506 416999
E: LouiseJames@centralcourtlawyers.co.uk

JAMES, Roslyn Mitchell (Mar 2007) (Employee)
Brodies LLP, Edinburgh . . . .(p.845)
T: 0131 2283777
E: ros.james@brodies.com

JAMIESON, Alisdair Tannahill (Mar 2013)
(Employee)
Eversheds Sutherland (International) LLP,
Edinburgh . . . .(p.869)
T: 0207 9194500
E: AlisdairJamieson@eversheds-Sutherland.com

JAMIESON, Barbara Jane (May 2014) (Director)
Jamieson Law Ltd, Giffnock . . . .(p.934)
T: 07703 569279
E: babs@jamiesonlaw.legal

JAMIESON, Brian Alexander (Nov 1984)
(Partner)
Gray & Gray LLP, Ellon . . . .(p.918)
T: 01358 724455
E: brian@graygraylaw.com

JAMIESON, Christie Janet (Aug 2021)
(Employee)
Dentons UK and Middle East LLP,
Edinburgh . . . .(p.860)
T: 0330 2220050
E: christie.jamieson@dentons.com

JAMIESON, Dominique Alison (Mar 2016)
(Employee)
Burness Paull LLP, Edinburgh . . . .(p.850)
T: 0131 4736000
E: dominique.jamieson@burnesspaull.com

JAMIESON, Gillian Margaret Sharp
(Nov 1996) (Partner)
Anderson Strathern LLP, Glasgow. . . . . .(p.940)
T: 0141 2426060
E: gillian.jamieson@andersonstrathern.co.uk

JAMIESON, Kirsty Moira (Sept 2014)
(Employee)
Scottish Government, Edinburgh . . . . .(p.1231)
T: 0131 244 0815
E: Kirsty.Jamieson@gov.scot

JAMIESON, Laura Ann (Sept 2010) (Partner)
Miller Samuel Hill Brown LLP,
Glasgow . . . . (p.1020)
T: 0141 2211919
E: lj@mshblegal.com

JAMIESON, Lynne Margaret (Dec 1998)
(Employee)
Procurator Fiscal Service, Hamilton . . . .(p.1247)
T: 0844 5613245
E: lynne.jamieson@copfs.gov.uk

JAMIESON, Marianne (Nov 2010) (Employee)
CNR International (U.K.) Limited,
Aberdeen . . . .(p.1212)
T: (01224) 303653
E: marianne.jamieson@cnrl.com

JAMIESON, Mark Douglas (Oct 1999)
(Employee)
Berrymans Lace Mawer LLP,
Glasgow . . . .(p.945)
T: 0141 3532121
E: mark.jamieson@blmlaw.com

JAMIESON, Matthew David (Jun 2015)
(Employee)
McArthur Glen Group, London W1 . . .(p.1266)
E: Matthew.Jamieson@mcarthurglen.com

JAMIESON, Nicola Maureen (Sept 2011)
(Employee)
Burnett & Reid LLP, Aberdeen . . . .(p.726)
T: 01224 644333
E: NMJamieson@burnett-reid.co.uk

JAMIESON, Paul Alexander (Sept 2020)
(Employee)
Procurator Fiscal Service, Glasgow . . . .(p.1241)
T: 0300 0203000
E: paul.jamieson@copfs.gov.uk

JAMIESON, Ross Crawford (Jul 2019)
(Employee)
Burness Paull LLP, Edinburgh . . . .(p.850)
T: 0131 4736000
E: ross.jamieson@burnesspaull.com

JAMIESON, Tara Sheila (Nov 2014) (Employee)
Simmons & Simmons Middle East LLP,
Dubai . . . .(p.1278)
T: 00971 4709 6600
E: tara.jamieson@simmons-simmons.com

JAMIESON, Thomas Anthony (Sept 2021)
(Employee)
Skyscanner, Edinburgh . . . .(p.1234)
E: tom.jamieson@skyscanner.net

JAMIESON, William Lewis (Sept 2020)
(Employee)
Anderson Strathern LLP, Edinburgh . . . .(p.839)
T: 0131 2707700
E: william.jamieson@andersonstrathern.co.uk

JAMIESON, William Miller (Dec 1984) (Director)
Jamiesons Solicitors Limited,
Aberdeen . . . .(p.732)
T: 01224 443204
E: wmj@jamsolaw.com

JAMISON, Dr, William Charles Lipscomb
(Jan 2020) (Solicitor)
NO FIRM

JANE, Iain Andrew (Nov 2001) (Partner)
Iain Jane & Co, Peterhead . . . .(p.1154)
T: 01779 477620
E: iain@iainjane.co.uk

JANOWSKA, Beata Katarzyna (Jul 2017)
(Employee)
Element Materials Technology Group,
Edinburgh . . . .(p.1222)
T: 0131 333 8053
E: beata.janowska@element.com

JANSCH, Steven William (Oct 2002) (Partner)
Gilson Gray LLP, Edinburgh . . . .(p.874)
T: 0131 516 5354
E: sjansch@gilsongray.co.uk

JANSSEN, Helena Margaret (Nov 2000)
(Employee)
Scottish Government, Edinburgh . . . . .(p.1231)
T: 0131 244 7410
E: helena.janssen@gov.scot

JANUS, Sebastian Ireneusz (Dec 2015)
(Employee)
Cullen Kilshaw, Galashiels . . . .(p.932)
T: 01896 752231
E: sebastian.janus@cullenkilshaw.com

JARDINE, Catriona Louise (Sept 2016)
(Employee)
Slaughter and May, London EC1 . . . . .(p.1268)
T: 020 76001200
E: catriona.jardine@slaughterandmay.com

JARDINE, Donald (Aug 1999) (Partner)
Blair Cadell, Edinburgh . . . .(p.844)
T: 0131 555 5800
E: donald.jardine@blaircadell.com

JARDINE, Louise Elizabeth (Sept 2016)
(Employee)
National Health Service Scotland,
Edinburgh . . . .(p.1225)
T: 0131 2757800
E: Louise.Jardine@nhs.scot

JARMAN-WILLIAMS, Paul (Sept 2004)
(Employee)
Full Circle Partners Limited,
Edinburgh . . . .(p.1223)
E: pjw@fcpartners.co.uk

JARROTT, Gregor Peter William (Oct 2021)
(Employee)
Charles Ferguson Solicitor Advocate Limited,
Hamilton . . . .(p.1066)
T: 01698 285885

JARVIS, Francis Theodore Caleb (Nov 2011)
(Employee)
Scottish Human Rights Commission,
Edinburgh . . . .(p.1233)
T: 0131 297 5750
E: Frank.Jarvis@scottishhumanrights.com

JARVIS, Kevin Paul (May 2017) (Employee)
Procurator Fiscal Service, Airdrie . . . . . .(p.1214)
T: 01236 747027
E: Kevin.Jarvis@copfs.gov.uk

JARVIS, Zoe Elizabeth (Aug 2019) (Associate)
Addleshaw Goddard LLP,
Edinburgh . . . .(p.835)
T: 0131 2282400
E: Zoe.Jarvis@addleshawgoddard.com

JASIN, Anton (Aug 2020) (Employee)
Burness Paull LLP, Edinburgh . . . .(p.850)
T: 0131 4736000
E: Anton.Jasin@burnesspaull.com

JAVED, Mariam Zohra (Oct 2019) (Employee)
DJ Mackay and Partners LLP,
Glasgow . . . .(p.1012)
T: 0141 353 8700
E: mariam.javed@djmp-solicitors.co.uk

JAVED, Shumail (Nov 2020) (Employee)
Brodies LLP, Edinburgh . . . .(p.845)
T: 0131 2283777
E: shumail.javed@brodies.com

JEFFERIES, Douglas Graham Buchanan
(Nov 2003) (Associate)
DWF LLP, Edinburgh . . . .(p.865)
T: 0131 2265541
E: Douglas.Jefferies@dwf.law

JEFFERIES, Michael Allan (Sept 2016)
(Employee)
DAC Beachcroft Scotland LLP,
Glasgow . . . .(p.964)
T: 0141 2486688
E: mjefferies@dacbeachcroft.com

JEFFERIES, Sian (Sept 2004) (Employee)
Ofgem, Glasgow . . . .(p.1241)
T: 0141 354 5425
E: sian.jefferies@ofgem.gov.uk

JEFFERY, Lynne (Nov 1992) (Partner)
D.W. Shaw, Cumnock . . . .(p.791)
T: 01290 421185
E: ljeffery@dwshaw.co.uk

JEFFREY, Emily Kathryn (Nov 2005) (Partner)
Keoghs Scotland LLP, Glasgow . . . .(p.996)
T: 0141 2380100
E: EJeffrey@keoghs.scot

JEFFREY, Emma Sarah (Oct 2014) (Employee)
Procurator Fiscal Service, Paisley . . . . . .(p.1252)
T: 0141 8875225
E: Emma.Jeffrey@copfs.gov.uk

JEFFRIES, David Andrew (Jan 2021) (Employee)
Pinsent Masons LLP, Edinburgh . . . .(p.895)
T: 0131 777 7000
E: david.jeffries@pinsentmasons.com

JENKINS, Caragh Rowanne (Jul 2019)
(Employee)
Travers Smith LLP, London EC1 . . . . . .(p.1269)
T: (0207) 2953387
E: caragh.jenkins@traverssmith.com

JENKINS, Hannah Dilys (Jul 2018) (Employee)
Burness Paull LLP, Glasgow . . . .(p.954)
T: 0141 2484933
E: hannah.jenkins@burnesspaull.com

JENKINS, Kris Robert (Sept 2021) (Employee)
TLT LLP, Glasgow . . . .(p.1048)
T: 0333 006 0400
E: kris.jenkins@tltsolicitors.com

JENKINS, Meghan Rachael (Oct 2017)
(Employee)
MacRoberts LLP, Glasgow . . . .(p.1015)
T: 0141 3031100
E: Meghan.Jenkins@macroberts.com

JENKINS, Ross David (Oct 2018) (Employee)
David Kinloch & Co., Glasgow . . . .(p.997)
T: 0141 3363000
E: info@kinlochlawyers.co.uk

JENNINGS, David John (Jan 1983) (Partner)
Thorntons Law LLP, Edinburgh . . . .(p.906)
T: 0131 2258705
E: djennings@thorntons-law.co.uk

JENNINGS, Joanna Louise (Oct 1997)
(Employee)
Clydesdale Bank Plc, Glasgow . . . .(p.1238)
T: 0141 2423733
E: Joanna.jennings@cybg.com

JENNINGS, Paul Knight (Apr 1989) (Partner)
Aberdein Considine and Company,
Glasgow . . . .(p.937)
T: 0141 2278200
E: pjennings@acandco.com

JENQUIN, Sabrina Rene Odile (Sept 2009)
(Employee)
William Grant & Sons Ltd., Bellshill . . .(p.1215)
T: 01698 843843
E: sabrina.jenquin@wgrant.com

JERICEVICH, Patricia (Dec 1981) (Employee)
Aberdeenshire Council, Aberdeen . . . . .(p.1211)
T: 01467 536173
E: patricia.jericevich@aberdeenshire.gov.uk

JERMAN, James Samuel John (Jan 2017)
(Employee)
Brodies LLP, Edinburgh . . . .(p.845)
T: 0131 2283777
E: james.jerman@brodies.com

JERVIS, Joanna Frances (Oct 2006) (Employee)
The Medical & Dental Defence Union of
Scotland, Glasgow . . . .(p.1245)
T: 0845 2702034
E: jjervis@mddus.com

JESPERSEN, Ross Indergaard (Sept 2020)
(Employee)
DLA Piper Scotland LLP, Edinburgh . . . .(p.863)
T: 08700 111111
E: ross.jespersen@dlapiper.com

JESSIMAN, Robert Iain (Sept 2020) (Employee)
Morton Fraser LLP, Edinburgh . . . .(p.891)
T: 0131 2471000
E: robert.jessiman@morton-fraser.com

JESSOP, Andrew David (Oct 2002) (Employee)
Hg Capital LLP, London SE1 . . . .(p.1265)
T: 020 70897992
E: andrew.jessop@hgcapital.com

JESSOP, Graeme Smethurst (Oct 1992)
(Employee)
Procurator Fiscal Service,
Edinburgh . . . .(p.1227)
T: 0300 0203168
E: graeme.jessop@copfs.gov.uk

JETHWA, Anika (Aug 1992) (Partner)
Anika Jethwa & Co, Dundee . . . .(p.813)
T: 01382 223399
E: anikajethwa@btconnect.com

JEYNES, Rebecca Louise (Dec 2020) (Employee)
Fife Council, Glenrothes . . . .(p.1246)
T: 03451 550000
E: rebecca.jeynes@fife.gov.uk

JHAKRA, Priya (Jul 2017) (Employee)
Pinsent Masons LLP, London EC2 . . . . .(p.1267)
T: 020 7418 7000
E: Priya.Jhakra@pinsentmasons.com

JOBSON, Jacqueline Elizabeth (Jan 2015)
(Consultant)
Inksters, Glasgow . . . .(p.990)
T: 0141 2290880

JOHAL, Gurpreet Singh (Nov 2014) (Director)
SJK Legal Ltd, Glasgow . . . .(p.1042)
T: 0141 6482500
E: gurpreet@sjksols.co.uk

JOHNSON, Beverley Anne (Apr 1985) (Director)
Johnson Family and Property Law Ltd,
Edinburgh . . . .(p.879)
T: 0131 6229222
E: beverley@johnsonlegal.co.uk

JOHNSON, Charlotte Emma Scott
(Oct 2013) (Employee)
CALA Group Ltd, Edinburgh . . . .(p.1221)
T: 0131 5355200
E: EJohnson@cala.co.uk

JOHNSON, Cynthia Louise (Oct 1999)
(Consultant)
CMS Cameron McKenna Nabarro Olswang LLP,
Edinburgh . . . .(p.856)
T: 0131 2288000
E: Cynthia.Johnson@cms-cmno.com

JOHNSON, David Ingram (Jan 1983) (Director)
Johnson Family and Property Law Ltd,
Edinburgh . . . .(p.879)
T: 0131 6229222
E: david@johnsonlegal.co.uk

JOHNSON, Dean Mark (Sept 2016) (Employee)
Eversheds Sutherland (International) LLP,
Edinburgh . . . .(p.869)
T: 0207 9194500
E: DeanJohnson@eversheds-sutherland.com

JOHNSON, Hazel Anderson (Oct 1989)
(Director)
Cooper Johnson Law Ltd,
Edinburgh . . . .(p.858)
T: 01577 840213
E: hazel@cooperjohnsonlaw.co.uk

JOHNSON, Ian Grant (Aug 2004) (Partner)
Lindsays LLP, Dundee . . . .(p.814)
T: 01382 224112
E: grantjohnson@lindsays.co.uk

JOHNSON, James Arthur (Oct 2016)
(Employee)
TLT LLP, Bristol . . . .(p.1259)
T: 0333 006 0000
E: James.Johnson@TLTsolicitors.com

JOHNSON, Jasmine (Oct 2014) (Employee)
Pinsent Masons LLP, Edinburgh . . . .(p.895)
T: 0131 777 7000
E: jasmine.johnson@pinsentmasons.com

JOHNSON, Jennifer Anna (Aug 2017)
(Employee)
Procurator Fiscal Service,
Edinburgh . . . .(p.1227)
T: 0300 0203168
E: jennifer.johnson@copfs.gov.uk

JOHNSON, Shereen (Sept 2009) (Employee)
Roslin Institute, Easter Bush . . . .(p.1219)
T: 0131 6519100
E: Shereen.johnson@roslin.ed.ac.uk

JOHNSTON, Adam Peter Robert (Oct 2016)
(Employee)
Scottish Government, Edinburgh . . . . .(p.1231)
T: 0131 244 0815
E: adam.johnston@gov.scot

JOHNSTON, Alastair Iain Samuel (Aug 2013)
(Employee)
Harper Macleod LLP, Edinburgh . . . .(p.877)
T: 0131 2472500
E: alastair.johnston@harpermacleod.co.uk

JOHNSTON, Carol Grant (Nov 1995)
(Employee)
West Lothian Council, Livingston . . . . . (p.1250)
T: 01506 280000
E: carol.johnston@westlothian.gov.uk

JOHNSTON, Carole Margaret (Aug 1991)
(Director)
Holmes Mackillop Limited,
Johnstone . . . . (p.1089)
T: 01505 328 271
E: cmj@homack.co.uk

JOHNSTON, Chloe Stephanie (Oct 2013)
(Solicitor)
NO FIRM

JOHNSTON, Christina Emmeline (Nov 2013)
(Employee)
Sky UK Ltd, Isleworth . . . . (p.1260)
T: 020 7032 7085
E: christina.johnston@sky.uk

JOHNSTON, Claire Anne (Apr 2001) (Employee)
Procurator Fiscal Service, Glasgow . . . . (p.1241)
T: 0300 0203000
E: claire.johnston@copfs.gov.uk

JOHNSTON, Daniele (Sept 2017) (Employee)
Burness Paull LLP, Edinburgh . . . . (p.850)
T: 0131 4736000
E: daniele.johnston@burnesspaull.com

JOHNSTON, David James Graham
(Sept 2009) (Employee)
Norton Rose Fulbright US LLP,
Riyadh . . . . (p.1276)
E: david.johnston@nortonrosefulbright.com

JOHNSTON, Elaine Isobel (Jul 2013) (Employee)
Law Society of Scotland,
Edinburgh . . . . (p.1224)
T: 0131 2267411
E: elainejohnston@lawscot.org.uk

JOHNSTON, Emma Mary (Dec 2013)
(Employee)
Pinsent Masons LLP, Edinburgh . . . . . . (p.895)
T: 0131 777 7000
E: emma.johnston@pinsentmasons.com

JOHNSTON, Erica Margaret Hatton
(Aug 2011) (Associate)
Brodies LLP, Edinburgh . . . . (p.845)
T: 0131 2283777
E: erica.johnston@brodies.com

JOHNSTON, Fergus Henry Morris
(Oct 2007) (Employee)
MHD Law LLP, Edinburgh . . . . (p.890)
T: 0131 5550616
E: Fergus.Johnston@mhdlaw.co.uk

JOHNSTON, Fraser (Oct 2017) (Employee)
Sheku Bayoh Public Inquiry,
Edinburgh . . . . (p.1233)
E: fraser.johnston@shekubayohinquiry.scot

JOHNSTON, Gemma Mairi (Mar 2021)
(Employee)
Macleod & MacCallum Limited,
Inverness . . . . (p.1080)
T: 01463 239393
E: gemma.johnston@macandmac.co.uk

JOHNSTON, Georgina Mary (Oct 2010)
(Employee)
Shepherd and Wedderburn LLP,
Edinburgh . . . . (p.900)
T: 0131 2289900
E: gina.johnston@shepwedd.com

JOHNSTON, Jacqueline Marie (Sept 1980)
(Partner)
Currie Johnston & Co, Livingston . . . . . (p.1118)
T: 01506 412377
E: curriejohnston@gmail.com

JOHNSTON, Kathryn Anne (Aug 2012)
(Employee)
Brodies LLP, Edinburgh . . . . (p.845)
T: 0131 2283777
E: kathryn.johnston@brodies.com

JOHNSTON, Kim Louise (Dec 2003) (Associate)
Burness Paull LLP, Aberdeen . . . . (p.724)
T: 01224 621621
E: kim.johnston@burnesspaull.com

JOHNSTON, Krista Isabel (Oct 1990) (Director)
Martin, Johnston & Socha Limited,
Alloa . . . . (p.753)
T: 01259 725922
E:
krista.johnston@mjscriminaldefencelawyers.co.
uk

JOHNSTON, Kristen Jane (May 2001)
(Employee)
Shetland Islands Council, Lerwick . . . . . (p.1250)
T: 01595 744 097
E: kristen.johnston@shetland.gov.uk

JOHNSTON, Laura Kathryn Alice (Nov 2010)
(Employee)
Criminal Injuries Compensation Authority,
Glasgow . . . . (p.1239)
T: 0141 2281419
E: laura.johnston@cica.gov.uk

JOHNSTON, Lesley (Dec 1986) (Partner)
Allan, Black & McCaskie, Elgin . . . . (p.915)
T: 01343 543355
E: lj@abmsols.co.uk

JOHNSTON, Louise Margaret (Dec 2006)
(Partner)
Turcan Connell, Edinburgh . . . . (p.908)
T: 0131 228 8111
E: louise.johnston@turcanconnell.com

JOHNSTON, Michael (Sept 2017) (Employee)
Miller Hendry, Perth . . . . (p.1150)
T: 01738 637311
E: michaeljohnston@millerhendry.co.uk

JOHNSTON, Michael James (Aug 2014)
(Employee)
Burness Paull LLP, Edinburgh . . . . (p.850)
T: 0131 4736000
E: michael.johnston@burnesspaull.com

JOHNSTON, Michael Robert (Sept 2003)
(Employee)
National Health Service Scotland,
Edinburgh . . . . (p.1225)
T: 0131 2757800
E: Michael.Johnston4@nhs.scot

JOHNSTON, Moira Alexandra Lauder
(Sept 2016) (Employee)
Simpson & Marwick, Edinburgh . . . . . . (p.903)
T: 01224 606210
E: moira.johnston@simpsonmarwick.com

JOHNSTON, Neil Robert James (Aug 1994)
(Partner)
Gavin Bain & Co., Aberdeen . . . . (p.721)
T: 01224 623040
E: n.johnston@gavin-bain.co.uk

JOHNSTON, Norman Scott (Oct 1983) (Partner)
Murray, Little & Knox, Annan . . . . (p.755)
T: 01461 202866
E: mlandk@mlandk.co.uk

JOHNSTON, Rachael Catherine (Apr 2016)
(Employee)
Google UK Limited, London SW1 . . . . . (p.1264)
T: 020 7346 2927
E: rcjohnston@google.com

JOHNSTON, Robin (Jan 1996) (Employee)
Scottish Police Authority, Glasgow . . . . (p.1244)
T: 0141 585 8300
E: Robin.Johnston@spa.pnn.police.uk

JOHNSTON, Samuel Christopher Barr
(Dec 2012) (Director)
Fife Community Law Limited,
Lochgelly . . . . (p.1120)
T: 01592 786710
E: sam.johnston@fifelawcentre.co.uk

JOHNSTON, Scott Alexander (Oct 2019)
(Employee)
Keoghs Scotland LLP, Glasgow. . . . . . . (p.996)
T: 0141 2380100
E: sajohnston@keoghs.co.uk

JOHNSTON, Scott Forsyth (Sept 1994) (Partner)
Pinsent Masons LLP, Aberdeen . . . . (p.739)
T: 01224 377900
E: scott.johnston@pinsentmasons.com

JOHNSTON, Stefanie (Jul 2012) (Partner)
Ince Gordon Dadds (Scotland) LLP,
Glasgow. (p.989)
E: StefanieJohnston@incegd.com

JOHNSTON, Tristan Donald (Oct 2020)
(Employee)
Addleshaw Goddard LLP, London
EC1 . . . . (p.1261)
T: 0207 6068855
E: tristan.johnston@addleshawgoddard.com

JOHNSTON, William Grant (Sept 1985)
(Partner)
Wright, Johnston & Mackenzie LLP,
Glasgow. . . . . (p.1054)
T: 0141 2483434
E: wgj@wjm.co.uk

JOHNSTONE, Alasdair Scott (Sept 2012)
(Partner)
Anderson Strathern LLP, Edinburgh . . . . (p.839)
T: 0131 2707700
E: alasdair.johnstone@andersonstrathern.co.uk

JOHNSTONE, Calum Stuart Daniel
(Jun 2016) (Employee)
William Grant & Sons Ltd., Bellshill . . . (p.1215)
T: 01698 843843
E: calum.johnstone@wgrant.com

JOHNSTONE, Cameron Alexander
(Sept 2020) (Employee)
Addleshaw Goddard LLP,
Aberdeen . . . . (p.719)
T: (+44) (0) 1224 96 5410
E:
cameron.johnstone@addleshawgoddard.com

JOHNSTONE, Catherine Holly (May 2021)
(Employee)
MacFarlane Young Limited, Paisley . . . . (p.1139)
T: 0141 8893257

JOHNSTONE, Daniel (Jan 2018) (Employee)
Carey Olsen, St Helier . . . . (p.1274)
T: 01534 888900
E: daniel.johnstone@careyolsen.com

JOHNSTONE, David Andrew (Oct 1989)
(Partner)
Aitkens The Family Law Solicitors,
Livingston . . . . (p.1117)
T: 01506 417737
E: dj@aitkenstfls.co.uk

JOHNSTONE, Eric (Sept 2011) (Employee)
Brodies LLP, Edinburgh . . . . (p.845)
T: 0131 2283777
E: eric.johnstone@brodies.com

JOHNSTONE, Frank Raine (Mar 1983)
(Consultant)
Brodies LLP, Glasgow . . . . (p.948)
T: 0141 2484672
E: frank.johnstone@brodies.com

JOHNSTONE, Gemma-Grace (Sept 2021)
(Employee)
Next Law (Scotland) LLP, Perth . . . . . . (p.1151)
T: 01738 707274
E: gemma-grace.johnstone@next-law.co.uk

JOHNSTONE, Helen Mary Anne (Jan 1991)
(Employee)
Perth & Kinross Council, Perth . . . .(p.1253)
T: 01738 475000
E: hjohnstone@pkc.gov.uk

JOHNSTONE, Jade Louise (Oct 2020)
(Employee)
R & R Urquhart LLP, Nairn . . . .(p.1129)
T: 01667 453278
E: jadejohnstone@r-r-urquhart.com

JOHNSTONE, Laurelle (Aug 2017) (Employee)
Procurator Fiscal Service, Kirkcaldy . . . .(p.1249)
T: 0300 0203000
E: laurelle.johnstone@copfs.gov.uk

JOHNSTONE, Leslie Margaret Scott
(Mar 1978) (Solicitor)
NO FIRM

JOHNSTONE, Lora (Sept 2008) (Employee)
Millen Solicitors, Glasgow . . . .(p.1019)
T: 0141 9590055
E: lj@millensolicitors.co.uk

JOHNSTONE, Louise (Oct 1985) (Consultant)
Strefford Tulips Limited, Hamilton . . . .(p.1070)
T: 01698 429428
E: l.johnstone@strefford-tulips.co.uk

JOHNSTONE, Marcia Alexandra (Jun 2009)
(Associate)
Peterkins, Aberdeen . . . .(p.739)
T: 01224 428000
E: mj@peterkins.com

JOHNSTONE, Mark Peter (Jun 2020)
(Employee)
Rutherford Sheridan Ltd, Glasgow . . . .(p.1037)
T: 0141 248 3320
E: mark@rutherfordsheridan.com

JOHNSTONE, Nicola Margaret (Aug 2010)
(Employee)
Law Society of Scotland,
Edinburgh . . . .(p.1224)
T: 0131 2267411
E: nicolajohnstone@lawscot.org.uk

JOHNSTONE, Shelby Rose (Feb 2020)
(Employee)
Marshall Wilson Law Group Limited,
Falkirk . . . .(p.922)
T: 01324 612569
E: sjohnstone@marshallwilson.com

JOHNSTONE, Siobhan Isabella (Aug 2016)
(Employee)
Kyowa Kirin International Plc,
Galashiels . . . .(p.1237)
E: Siobhan.Johnstone@kyowakirin.com

JOHNSTONE, Sylvia Marion (Sept 1986)
(Associate)
Thorntons Law LLP, Dundee . . . .(p.819)
T: 01382 229 111
E: sjohnstone@thorntons-law.co.uk

JOHNSTONE, Thomas Alexander (Jul 2014)
(Partner)
Alexander Johnstone Solicitors and Notaries,
Airdrie . . . .(p.748)
T: 01236 897171
E: alexanderjohnstonesolicitors@hotmail.com

JOHNSTONE, Vicki (Feb 2019) (Employee)
Aberdeen City Council, Aberdeen . . . . .(p.1211)
T: 01224 522000
E: vjohnstone@aberdeencity.gov.uk

JOINER, Isobel Sheila (Oct 2002) (Employee)
Scottish Government, Edinburgh . . . . .(p.1231)
T: 0131 244 0815
E: Isobel.Joiner@gov.scot

JOINER, Jane Louise (Nov 2011) (Employee)
Scottish Legal Aid Board,
Edinburgh . . . .(p.1233)
T: 0131 2267061

JOINER, Megan Catherine (Jun 2016)
(Employee)
Scottish Social Services Council,
Dundee . . . .(p.1218)
T: 0345 6030 891
E: megan.joiner@sssc.uk.com

JONES, Alan Hugh (Nov 1981) (Partner)
Russel + Aitken Edinburgh LLP,
Edinburgh . . . .(p.899)
T: 0131 2285500
E: alan.jones@russelaitken-edinburgh.com

JONES, Amelia Caitlin Catherine G.
(Aug 2017) (Employee)
Berrymans Lace Mawer LLP, London
EC3 . . . .(p.1262)
E: amelia.jones@blmlaw.com

JONES, Amy Carole (Feb 2010) (Employee)
Thorntons Law LLP, Dundee . . . .(p.819)
T: 01382 229 111
E: ajones@thorntons-law.co.uk

JONES, Andrew Daniel (Nov 2010) (Employee)
Ofgem, Glasgow . . . .(p.1241)
T: (0141) 354 5425
E: Andrew.Jones@ofgem.gov.uk

JONES, Antonia Elizabeth McPike
(Mar 2021) (Employee)
R. & R.S. Mearns, Glasgow . . . .(p.1018)
T: 0141 6326162
E: aemjmearns@gmail.com

JONES, Antony Gerald Morrell, QC
(Oct 1991) (Partner)
Brodies LLP, Edinburgh . . . .(p.845)
T: 0131 2283777
E: tony.jones@brodies.com

JONES, Bethan (Jan 2021) (Employee)
Pinsent Masons LLP, Glasgow . . . .(p.1031)
T: 0141 567 8400
E: bethan.jones@pinsentmasons.com

JONES, Blair Grant (Sept 2015) (Employee)
CMS Cameron McKenna Nabarro Olswang LLP,
Dubai . . . .(p.1278)
T: +971 4374 2813
E: blair.jones@cms-cmno.com

JONES, Calum Symon (Sept 1988) (Director)
Kepstorn Solicitors Limited,
Kilmacolm . . . .(p.1092)
T: 07935 228791
E: calum.jones@kepstorn.co.uk

JONES, Cameron Gordon (Aug 2020)
(Associate)
CMS Cameron McKenna Nabarro Olswang LLP,
London EC4 . . . .(p.1263)
T: 0207 3673000
E: Cameron.Jones@cms-cmno.com

JONES, Charlotte Stephen McAuley
(Sept 2017) (Employee)
Shetland Islands Council, Lerwick . . . . .(p.1250)
T: 01595 744550

JONES, Erica Margaret (Oct 2006) (Employee)
Plexus Law LLP, Edinburgh . . . .(p.897)
T: 0131 202 1652
E: Erica.Jones@plexuslaw.co.uk

JONES, Fiona Margaret (Nov 2012) (Employee)
SSE Plc, Perth . . . .(p.1253)
T: 01738 456 000
E: fiona.jones@sse.com

JONES, Graham Edward (Jul 1991) (Partner)
Mackinnons Solicitors LLP,
Aberdeen . . . .(p.736)
T: 01224 632464
E: graham@mackinnons.com

JONES, Hannah Claire (Jan 2009) (Employee)
Philpott Platt Niblett & Wight,
Clydebank . . . .(p.785)
T: 0141 9529545
E: hjones@ppnw.co.uk

JONES, Iain Angus (Dec 2002) (Employee)
Wood Group UK Limited,
Aberdeen . . . .(p.1214)
T: 01224 851000
E: Iain.jones@woodplc.com

JONES, Janice (Jul 1989) (Partner)
Anderson Strathern LLP, Glasgow . . . . . .(p.940)
T: 0141 2426060
E: janice.jones@andersonstrathern.co.uk

JONES, Julie Anne Meredith (Nov 2010)
(Employee)
TAQA Bratani Limited, Aberdeen . . . . .(p.1214)
T: 01224 286 910
E: julie.jones@taqaglobal.com

JONES, Keith Eyton Gwyn (Mar 2002)
(Employee)
Procurator Fiscal Service, Glasgow . . . .(p.1241)
T: 0300 0203000
E: keith.jones@copfs.gov.uk

JONES, Kristina Orianne (Sept 2021)
(Employee)
Shepherd and Wedderburn LLP,
Edinburgh . . . .(p.900)
T: 0131 2289900
E: kristina.jones@shepwedd.co.uk

JONES, Lauren Cheryl (Apr 2009) (Associate)
Pinsent Masons LLP, Glasgow . . . .(p.1031)
T: 0141 567 8400
E: lauren.jones@pinsentmasons.com

JONES, Louise Marie (Sept 2010) (Employee)
Davidson Chalmers Stewart LLP,
Edinburgh . . . .(p.859)
T: 0131 6259191
E: Louise.Jones@dcslegal.com

JONES, Louise Morgan (Sept 2007) (Employee)
Macnairs & Wilson Limited,
Glasgow . . . .(p.1014)
T: 0141 5518185
E: louise.jones@macnairswilson.co.uk

JONES, Nicholas William (Mar 1984) (Partner)
MacRoberts LLP, Edinburgh . . . .(p.887)
T: 0131 2295046
E: nick.jones@macroberts.com

JONES, Nigel David (Sept 1995) (Partner)
Mackenzie & Cormack, Tain . . . .(p.1173)
T: 01862 892046
E: nigeltain@gmail.com

JONES, Rhian-Elin (Jan 2019) (Employee)
Grigor & Young LLP, Elgin . . . .(p.916)
T: 01343 544077
E: elinjones@grigor-young.co.uk

JONES, Richard Lloyd (Nov 1998) (Associate)
Shepherd and Wedderburn LLP,
Edinburgh . . . .(p.900)
T: 0131 2289900
E: richard.jones@shepwedd.com

JONES, Robert Marshall (Jan 2018) (Employee)
Sky UK Ltd, Isleworth . . . .(p.1260)
T: (020) 7032 7085
E: robbie.jones@sky.uk

JONES, Ross Alexander (Nov 2006) (Partner)
Jones Whyte LLP, Glasgow . . . .(p.993)
T: 0141 375 1222
E: ross.jones@joneswhyte.co.uk

JONES, Samuel John (Jun 2014) (Employee)
Burness Paull LLP, Aberdeen . . . .(p.724)
  T: 01224 621621
  E: Sam.Jones@burnesspaull.com

JONES, Zara Mary (Jan 2019) (Employee)
Road Traffic Accident Law (Scotland) LLP,
  Peebles . . . .(p.1144)
  T: 01721 728238
  E: zara.jones@cyclelawscotland.co.uk

JORDAN, Andrew Richard (May 2011)
  (Employee)
Lloyds Banking Group, Edinburgh . . . .(p.1224)
  T: 0131 655 7773
  E: andrew.jordan@lloydsbanking.com

JORDAN, Emma Louise (Oct 2020) (Employee)
Turcan Connell, Edinburgh . . . .(p.908)
  T: 0131 2288111
  E: emma.jordan@turcanconnell.com

JORDAN, Gillian Ralston (Aug 1987)
  (Employee)
JTC Group, St Peter Port . . . .(p.1273)
  T: 01481 702 415
  E: gillian.jordan@jtcgroup.com

JORDAN, Neil Christopher (Jan 2007)
  (Employee)
David Brown Group Ltd, East
  Kilbride . . . .(p.1219)
  T: 01355 212010
  E: neil.jordan@dbsantasalo.com

JORDAN, Sarah Josephine (Nov 2006) (Partner)
W. & A.S. Bruce, Dunfermline . . . .(p.822)
  T: 01383 738000
  E: sarah@wasbruce.co.uk

JORDAN, Thomas Charles (Jul 2020)
  (Employee)
Dales Solicitors LLP, Galston . . . .(p.934)
  T: 01563 820216
  E: thomas@dalesllp.co.uk

JOSEPH, Harold William (Dec 1975) (Partner)
Harold W. Joseph, Glasgow . . . .(p.994)
  T: 0141 4201896
  E: harold@hwjoseph.com

JOSHI, Anoop Subhash (Jul 2012) (Employee)
Trustpilot A/S, Copenhagen . . . .(p.1257)
  T: (+45) 31 676988
  E: ajo@trustpilot.com

JOSHI, Kathryn Ailna (Jan 2010) (Employee)
Scottish Government, Edinburgh . . . . .(p.1231)
  T: 0131 2441518
  E: Katie.Joshi@gov.scot

JOSHI, Roshni Nilesh (Jul 2013) (Employee)
Procurator Fiscal Service,
  Livingston . . . .(p.1250)
  T: (0300) 020 3696
  E: roshni-joshi@hotmail.co.uk

JOSS, Jill Maria (Jul 2001) (Employee)
Aberdeenshire Council, Inverurie . . . . .(p.1248)
  T: 01467 539903
  E: jill.joss@aberdeenshire.gov.uk

JOSS, Leanne Claire (Nov 2015) (Employee)
NORTH LANARKSHIREre Council,
  Motherwell. . . . .(p.1251)
  T: 01698 302196
  E: JossL@northlan.gov.uk

JOY, Judith Laura (Nov 2012) (Employee)
BlackRock, Edinburgh . . . .(p.1221)
  T: (306) 978 749 900
  E: judith.joy@blackrock.com

JUDGE, Ben (Nov 2014) (Employee)
Ashurst LLP, Sydney . . . .(p.1257)
  T: +61 2 9258 6000
  E: ben.judge@ashurst.com

JUNNER, Audrey Anne (Aug 2009) (Director)
Hill Brown Licensing, Glasgow . . . .(p.986)
  T: 0141 3323265
  E: AJunner@hillbrown.co.uk

JURAK, Sandra Natalia (Oct 2019) (Employee)
BTO Solicitors LLP, Edinburgh . . . .(p.849)
  T: 0131 2222939
  E: sju@bto.co.uk

JURAS, Alexander (Dec 2009) (Employee)
British-American Tobacco (Holdings) Limited,
  London WC2 . . . .(p.1262)
  T: 0207 8452678
  E: alex_juras@bat.com

KAARLEHTO, Kati Johanna (Sept 2007)
  (Employee)
University College London, London
  WC1 . . . .(p.1269)
  T: 2031088729
  E: kati.kaarlehto@ucl.ac.uk

KADIRGOLAM, Brzoom Hassan (Nov 2013)
  (Partner)
Brzoom Kadirgolam, Glasgow . . . .(p.952)
  T: 0141 2042888
  E: b.kadirgolam@emlc.org.uk

KADIYSKI, Dimitar Ivanov (Mar 2021)
  (Employee)
CMS Cameron McKenna Nabarro Olswang LLP,
  Edinburgh . . . .(p.856)
  T: 0131 2288000
  E: dimitar.kadiyski@cms-cmno.com

KAHMANN, Siobhan Louise McCarville
  (May 2005) (Employee)
CMS Cameron McKenna Nabarro Olswang LLP,
  Brussels . . . .(p.1257)
  E: Siobhan.Kahmann@cms-cmno.com

KAMINSKA, Kamila Julia (Oct 2019) (Employee)
MacRoberts LLP, Edinburgh . . . .(p.887)
  T: 0131 2295046
  E: Kamila.Kaminska@macroberts.com

KANDRIS, Anna Maria (Jul 2017) (Associate)
Burness Paull LLP, Edinburgh . . . . (p.850)
T: 0131 297 2832
E: anna.kandris@burnesspaull.com

KANDYBA-CALLIS, Heidi Marta (Jan 2016)
(Partner)
Bannerman Burke Law, Hawick . . . . . .(p.1070)
T: 01450 372750
E: heidi@bannermanburke.co.uk

KANE, Aaron Alexander Hanson (Jun 2018)
(Employee)
BTO Solicitors LLP, Glasgow . . . .(p.952)
T: 0141 2218012

KANE, Ashley (Oct 2008) (Employee)
Public Defence Solicitors Office,
Ayr . . . .(p.1215)
T: 01292 269139
E: akane@pdso.org.uk

KANE, Bryan (Apr 1987) (Employee)
Trans Adriatic Pipeline AG, Baar . . . . . .(p.1276)

KANE, Cameron Macleod (Jul 2020) (Employee)
Holmes Mackillop Limited,
Glasgow. . . . .(p.986)
T: 0141 226 4942
E: ckane@homack.co.uk

KANE, Christian Edmiston (Sept 1995) (Partner)
C. & D. Mactaggart,
Campbeltown. . . . .(p.782)
T: 01586 552317
E: christian@cdm-law.co.uk

KANE, Dianne (Mar 1997) (Employee)
National Health Service Scotland,
Edinburgh . . . .(p.1225)
T: 0131 2757800
E: dianne.kane@nhs.scot

KANE, Fraser Lamont (Jun 2016) (Employee)
Bank of New York Mellon,
Edinburgh . . . .(p.1221)
T: +44 (0)131 635 2012
E: fraser.kane@bnymelllon.com

KANE, Kimberly Alison (Feb 2018) (Employee)
Lyons Davidson Scotland LLP,
Edinburgh . . . .(p.883)
T: 0344 251 0070
E: kkane@lyonsdavidson.co.uk

KANE, Kristopher Thomas (Oct 2008)
(Employee)
Kennedys Scotland, Edinburgh. . . . .(p.880)
T: 0131 2256145
E: kristopher.kane@kennedyslaw.com

KANE, Michael Anthony (Nov 1995) (Partner)
Turcan Connell, Edinburgh . . . .(p.908)
T: 0131 2288111
E: mike.kane@turcanconnell.com

KANE, Steven (Feb 1991) (Partner)
Mellicks, Incorporating Naftalin Duncan & Co.,
Glasgow. . . . .(p.1019)
T: 0141 3320902
E: steven.kane@mellicks.co.uk

KANEY, Ashleigh Anne (Jul 2019) (Employee)
Scottish Social Services Council,
Dundee . . . .(p.1218)
T: 0345 6030 891
E: ashleigh.kaney@sssc.uk.com

KANEY, Helen Mary (Nov 2003) (Employee)
Dental Protection, Edinburgh. . . . .(p.1222)
T: 0800 5611010

KANEY, Mariel Louise (Dec 2018) (Employee)
Lord President's Private Office,
Edinburgh . . . .(p.1225)
T: 0131 2406701
E: mkaney@scotcourts.gov.uk

KANTHARIA, Jennifer Anne (Sept 2014)
(Employee)
M&G Plc, Edinburgh. . . . .(p.1225)

KAPADIA, Dev (Oct 1991) (Employee)
Procurator Fiscal Service,
Dunfermline . . . .(p.1219)
T: 03000 203577
E: Dev.Kapadia@copfs.gov.uk

KAPAON, Jan Maria (Jul 2020) (Employee)
Kirkland & Ellis International LLP, London
EC3 . . . .(p.1265)
T: 0207 4692000
E: jan.kapaon@kirkland.com

KAPARAKI, Anna (Jul 2019) (Employee)
Mackinnons Solicitors LLP,
Aberdeen . . . .(p.736)
T: 01224 632464

KAPLANSKI, Lisa (Aug 2012) (Employee)
The University of Reading, Reading . . .(p.1271)
T: 0118 378 5852
E: l.kaplanski@reading.ac.uk

KARLIN, Catherine Margaret (Dec 1992)
(Director)
Horchheim Ltd, Edinburgh . . . .(p.878)
T: 0131 2401213
E: cath@cathkarlinfamilylaw.co.uk

KASEM, Rouzana (Aug 2021) (Employee)
Brodies LLP, Edinburgh . . . .(p.845)
T: 0131 2283777
E: rouzana.kasem@brodies.com

KASUSULA, Jean-Paul Alafu-Bania
(Oct 2016) (Solicitor)
NO FIRM

KATANI, Darius Behreg (Aug 2014) (Associate)
Katani & Co. Ltd, Glasgow . . . .(p.994)
T: 0141 2217788
E: darius.katani@kataniandco.com

KATANI, Kamyar (Dec 2001) (Director)
Katani & Co. Ltd, Glasgow . . . .(p.994)
T: 0141 2217788
E: kamyar.katani@kataniandco.com

KATHURIA, Vishnu Govinda (Oct 2013)
(Employee)
Procurator Fiscal Service, Hamilton . . . .(p.1247)
T: 0844 5613245
E: vish.kathuria@copfs.gov.uk

KAUR, Kirinjit Binning (Jun 2008) (Employee)
Faraday Underwriting Limited, London
EC3 . . . .(p.1264)
E: kirin.binning@faraday.com

KAUR SINGH, Harbir (Nov 2018) (Employee)
DJ Mackay and Partners LLP,
Glasgow . . . .(p.1012)
T: 0141 353 8700
E: harbir.dingh@djmp-solicitors.co.uk

KAURA, Anisha (Nov 2017) (Employee)
Harper Macleod LLP, Glasgow . . . .(p.983)
T: 0141 2218888
E: anisha.kaura@harpermacleod.co.uk

KAUSAR, Sitara Batul (Jun 2014) (Employee)
Mitchells Roberton Ltd, Glasgow . . . . .(p.1020)
T: 0141 5523422
E: sk@mitchells-roberton.co.uk

KAUSAR, Zhaira (Sept 2019) (Employee)
Scottish Social Services Council,
Dundee . . . .(p.1218)
T: 01382 721 906
E: zhaira.kausar@sssc.uk.com

KAVANAGH, Sheriff, George Collins
(Dec 1975) (Employee)
KM Law, Glasgow. . . . .(p.997)
T: 07702 735440

KAVANAGH, Paul George (Dec 1999) (Partner)
KM Law, Glasgow. . . . .(p.997)
T: (07702) 735440

KAVANAGH, Sarah Diana (Nov 2021)
(Employee)
Mill and Millard LLP, Edinburgh . . . .(p.890)
T: 0131 3227222
E: sk@millardlaw.co.uk

KAY, Dianne Rachel (Apr 2010) (Associate)
Lockharts Law LLP, Ayr . . . .(p.764)
T: 01292 265045
E: diannekay@lockhartslaw.com

KAY, Moira Alison (Nov 2003) (Partner)
Digby Brown LLP, Glasgow . . . .(p.970)
T: 0333 200 5925
E: moira.kay@digbybrown.co.uk

KAY, William Gordon James (Jul 2008)
(Employee)
Burness Paull LLP, Edinburgh . . . .(p.850)
T: 0131 473 6000
E: Billy.Kay@burnesspaull.com

KAYANI, Hussain Binn Abdul Rehman
(Aug 2013) (Employee)
Ellis Whittam Limited, Glasgow . . . . . .(p.1239)
T: (0345) 226 8393

KAYE, Darrell Elizabeth (Nov 2003) (Partner)
Digby Brown LLP, Glasgow . . . .(p.970)
T: 0141 5669522
E: darrell.kaye@digbybrown.co.uk

KAYE, David Stanley (Dec 1981) (Partner)
Harper Macleod LLP, Glasgow . . . .(p.983)
T: 0141 2218888
E: david.kaye@harpermacleod.co.uk

KEANE, Eamon Patrick (Jul 2014) (Solicitor)
NO FIRM

KEANE, Jennifer (Jan 2020) (Employee)
Sneddons SSC, Armadale . . . .(p.758)
T: 01501 733200

KEARNEY, Dominic Matthew (Jul 2013)
(Partner)
Walker & Sharpe, Dumfries . . . .(p.803)
T: 01387 267222
E: dominic.kearney@walker-sharpe.co.uk

KEARNEY, Katie Anne (Oct 2015) (Employee)
The General Teaching Council for Scotland,
Edinburgh . . . .(p.1234)
T: 0131 314 6000
E: katie.kearney@gtcs.org.uk

KEARNEY, Paul Stephen (Oct 1996) (Employee)
Procurator Fiscal Service,
Edinburgh . . . .(p.1227)
T: 0844 5613868
E: paul.kearney@copfs.gov.uk

KEARY, Olivia Margaret (Jan 2021) (Associate)
Addleshaw Goddard LLP, Glasgow . . . . .(p.938)
T: 0141 2212300
E: olivia.keary@addleshawgoddard.com

KEATINGE, Alastair John, WS (Dec 1982)
(Partner)
Lindsays LLP, Edinburgh . . . .(p.882)
T: 0131 656 5746
E: alastairkeatinge@lindsays.co.uk

KEAY, Robyn Alexandra (Aug 2017) (Employee)
Morton Fraser LLP, Edinburgh . . . .(p.891)
T: 0131 2471000
E: robyn.keay@morton-fraser.com

KEE, Jonathan Joseph (Jun 2014) (Director)
Kee Solicitors Ltd, Glasgow . . . .(p.995)
T: 0141 478 9090
E: jonathan@keesolicitors.co.uk

KEEGAN, Caitlin Mary (Sept 2016) (Employee)
Gillespie Macandrew LLP,
Edinburgh . . . .(p.872)
T: 0131 2251677
E: caitlin.keegan@gillespiemacandrew.co.uk

KEEGAN, James Douglas, SSC, QC
(Aug 1975) (Consultant)
Thorley Stephenson Ltd,
Edinburgh . . . .(p.906)
T: 0131 5569599
E: jdkeegan1@msn.com

KEEN, Stacy (Oct 2007) (Employee)
Pinsent Masons LLP, Glasgow . . . .(p.1031)
T: 0141 567 8400
E: stacy.keen@pinsentmasons.com

KEENAN, Colin Christopher (Sept 1986)
(Partner)
Brodies LLP, Glasgow . . . .(p.948)
T: 0141 2484672
E: colin.keenan@brodies.com

KEENAN, David Douglas (Oct 2013) (Employee)
Inverclyde Council, Greenock. . . . .(p.1246)
T: 01475 717171
E: david.keenan@inverclyde.gov.uk

KEENAN, Gemma Leigh (Sept 2005)
(Employee)
National Westminster Bank PLC,
Edinburgh . . . .(p.1226)
T: 07540 457 827
E: gemma.keenan@natwest.com

KEENAN, Gerard (Sept 1989) (Partner)
Keenan Solicitors, Greenock. . . . .(p.1061)
T: 01475 732122
E: gkeenan@keenansolicitors.com

KEENAN, Joseph (Feb 2015) (Employee)
JC Hughes Solicitors Limited,
Glasgow. . . . .(p.988)
T: 0141 7782468
E: jk@jchughes.net

KEENAN, Paul Gerard (Oct 2020) (Employee)
Keenan Solicitors, Greenock. . . . .(p.1061)
T: 01475 732122

KEENE, Peter Francis (Aug 1991) (Consultant)
Grant Smith Law Practice Limited,
Aberdeen . . . .(p.743)
T: 01224 621620
E: peter.keene@grantsmithlaw.co.uk

KEENEY, Alison Fiona (May 2010) (Employee)
Arnold Clark Automobiles Ltd,
Glasgow. . . . .(p.1237)
T: 0141 6481200
E: Fiona.Keeney@arnoldclark.com

KEIL, Emma Marian (Nov 2006) (Employee)
Morton Fraser LLP, Glasgow . . . .(p.1022)
T: 0141 2741100
E: Emma.Keil@morton-fraser.com

KEIR, Andrew Findlay (Nov 1998) (Employee)
Cirrus Logic International Semiconductor Ltd,
Edinburgh . . . .(p.1221)
T: 0131 2727000
E: andy.keir@cirrus.com

KEIR, Julie Elizabeth (Jan 1998) (Employee)
Brodies LLP, Edinburgh . . . .(p.845)
T: 0131 2283777
E: julie.keir@brodies.com

KEIR, Margaret Louise (Dec 2015) (Employee)
Brodies LLP, Aberdeen. . . . .(p.723)
T: 01224 392242
E: maggie.keir@brodies.com

KEIR, Murray Ronald (Apr 2008) (Employee)
Fieldfisher LLP, London EC4 . . . .(p.1264)
T: (0207) 8614339
E: Murray.Keir@fieldfisher.com

KEITH, Alexander Arthur Duncan (Jan 1991)
(Consultant)
Murchison Law Limited, Inverness . . . .(p.1081)
T: 01463 709992
E: alec@murchisonlaw.co.uk

KEITH, Alison (Sept 1996) (Director)
Kerslands Solicitors Limited,
Milngavie . . . .(p.1123)
T: 0333 6008000
E: alison.keith@kerslandsolicitors.com

KEITH, Graham David (Apr 2001) (Associate)
Coulters Legal LLP, Edinburgh . . . .(p.858)
T: 0131 603 7333
E: graham.keith@coulters.io

KEITH, James Kilpatrick (Oct 2005) (Partner)
MacRoberts LLP, Glasgow . . . .(p.1015)
T: 0141 3031100
E: james.keith@macroberts.com

KEITH, Paul Irwin (Jan 2006) (Partner)
J & H Mitchell LLP, Pitlochry . . . .(p.1155)
T: 01796 472606
E: paul.keith@hmitchell.co.uk

KEITH, Rhona Heather (Nov 2008) (Employee)
Medical Protection Society, Leeds. . . . .(p.1260)
E: rhona.keith@medicalprotection.org

KEITH, Tracey (Aug 2009) (Employee)
OGUK, Aberdeen . . . .(p.1213)
T: 01224 577250

KELBRICK, Joanne Louise (Aug 2013)
(Employee)
Brodies LLP, Glasgow . . . .(p.948)
T: 0141 2484672
E: jo.kelbrick@brodies.com

KELLAS, Dorothy Anne (Jan 1985) (Partner)
Gilson Gray LLP, North Berwick . . . . . .(p.1132)
T: 01620 893481
E: dkellas@gilsongray.co.uk

KELLIHER, Ruth Sarah Anne (Apr 2002)
(Partner)
Digby Brown LLP, Glasgow . . . .(p.970)
T: 0131 319 8148
E: ruth.kelliher@digbybrown.co.uk

KELLOCK, Nora Alison (Dec 1981) (Employee)
University of Edinburgh, Edinburgh . . .(p.1235)
T: (0131) 651 4330
E: Nora.Kellock@ed.ac.uk

KELLY, Alan Andrew (Feb 1996) (Partner)
MacRoberts LLP, Edinburgh . . . .(p.887)
T: 0131 2295046
E: alan.kelly@macroberts.com

KELLY, Alison Jean (Aug 1993) (Partner)
James Guthrie & Company LLP,
Kilmarnock . . . .(p.1095)
T: 01563 525155
E: alison@jamesguthrie.co.uk

KELLY, Amanda (Dec 2012) (Employee)
Cairns Brown, Alexandria . . . .(p.751)
T: 01389 756979
E: A.Kelly@cairnsbrown.co.uk

KELLY, Amy Margaret (Dec 2016) (Employee)
Jones Whyte LLP, Glasgow. . . . .(p.993)
T: 0141 375 1222
E: amy.kelly@joneswhyte.co.uk

KELLY, Beth Anne (Jun 2021) (Employee)
Frazer Coogans Ltd, Ayr . . . .(p.763)
T: 01292 280499
E: beth.kelly@frazercoogans.co.uk

KELLY, Caroline Patricia (Oct 2002) (Partner)
Thorntons Law LLP, Dundee . . . .(p.819)
T: 01382 229 111
E: ckelly@thorntons-law.co.uk

KELLY, Catriona Margaret Campbell
(Apr 1991) (Employee)
Aberdeen City Council, Aberdeen. . . . .(p.1211)
T: 01224 522000
E: ckelly@aberdeencity.gov.uk

KELLY, Clare (May 2016) (Employee)
Brodies LLP, Edinburgh . . . .(p.845)
T: 0131 2283777
E: clare.kelly@brodies.com

KELLY, Edward Francis (Feb 1991) (Director)
E.F. Kelly Limited, Coatbridge . . . .(p.786)
T: 01236 434347
E: kelly.e@btconnect.com

KELLY, Fiona Alexandra (Jul 2019) (Employee)
Miller Hendry, Dundee . . . .(p.816)
T: 01382 200000
E: fionakelly@millerhendry.co.uk

KELLY, Gemma (Dec 2008) (Employee)
D C Thomson & Co Ltd, Dundee. . . . .(p.1217)
E: gemma.kelly@dcthomson.co.uk

KELLY, Gerard Anthony (Nov 1983) (Partner)
Kelly & Co., Glasgow . . . .(p.995)
T: 0141 5544141
E: kellylawyers@yahoo.co.uk

KELLY, Graeme Alistair (Jan 1987) (Partner)
BTO Solicitors LLP, Edinburgh . . . .(p.849)
T: 0131 2222939
E: gak@bto.co.uk

KELLY, Gregor James (Nov 1991) (Partner)
Lefevre Litigation, Aberdeen . . . .(p.736)
T: 01224 657657
E: gjk@lefevre-litigation.com

KELLY, Helen Louise (Oct 1987) (Associate)
Gillespie Macandrew LLP,
Edinburgh . . . .(p.872)
T: 0131 2251677
E: Helen.Kelly@gillespiemacandrew.co.uk

KELLY, James Peter (Oct 1993) (Solicitor)
Office of the Advocate General,
Edinburgh . . . .(p.1227)
T: 0131 2441635
E: James.Kelly@advocategeneral.gov.uk

KELLY, Kristina (Jul 2016) (Employee)
Procurator Fiscal Service, Falkirk . . . . . .(p.1236)
T: 0300 020 3000
E: kristina.kelly@copfs.gov.uk

KELLY, Laura Jane (Oct 2019) (Employee)
McCartney Stewart Limited,
Renfrew . . . .(p.1159)
T: 0141 8851858
E: Laura@mccartneystewart.co.uk

KELLY, Lisa Margaret (Oct 2006) (Employee)
Freshfields Service Company, London
EC2 . . . .(p.1264)
T: 020 7785 2852
E: lisa.kelly@freshfields.com

KELLY, Loren Jay (Oct 2014) (Employee)
International SOS (Medical Services) UK Limited,
Aberdeen . . . .(p.1213)
T: 01224 669000
E: loren.kelly@internationalsos.com

KELLY, Lorna (Sept 1995) (Employee)
Standard Life Assets and Employee Services
Limited, Edinburgh . . . .(p.1234)
T: 1312458643
E: lorna_kelly@standardlife.com

KELLY, Lorraine Ann (Sept 2009) (Director)
Moss and Kelly Solicitors Limited,
Glasgow. . . . .(p.1023)
T: 0141 2311605
E: lkelly@mossandkelly.co.uk

KELLY, Mary-Claire (May 2000) (Director)
Clan Childlaw Limited, Edinburgh . . . . .(p.854)
T: 0808 129 0522
E: Mary-Claire.kelly@clanchildlaw.org

KELLY, Michael John (Oct 2005) (Partner)
MacRoberts LLP, Glasgow . . . .(p.1015)
T: 0141 3031100
E: michael.kelly@macroberts.com

KELLY, Miranda Anne (Oct 1994) (Employee)
Maven Capital Partners UK LLP,
Glasgow . . . . (p.1241)
T: 0141 206 0124
E: Mandy.Kelly@mavencp.com

KELLY, Neil Joseph (Nov 1984) (Partner)
MacRoberts LLP, Edinburgh . . . . (p.887)
T: 0131 2295046
E: neil.kelly@macroberts.com

KELLY, Neil Raymond (Jan 1996) (Partner)
Neil R. Kelly, Glasgow . . . . (p.995)
T: 0141 378 1111
E: neil@neilrkelly.com

KELLY, Nicholas James (Mar 2015) (Associate)
Addleshaw Goddard LLP,
Edinburgh . . . . (p.835)
T: 0131 2282400
E: nick.kelly@addleshawgoddard.com

KELLY, Nicola Jane (Mar 2021) (Employee)
MacRoberts LLP, Glasgow . . . . (p.1015)
T: 0141 3031100
E: nicola.kelly@macroberts.com

KELLY, Olga (Sept 2003) (Solicitor)
NO FIRM

KELLY, Peter Robert (Nov 1997) (Partner)
Brodies LLP, Glasgow . . . . (p.948)
T: 0141 2484672
E: peter.kelly@brodies.com

KELLY, Rosalind Sarah (Dec 1999) (Associate)
MacRoberts LLP, Edinburgh . . . . (p.887)
T: 0131 2295046
E: Rosalind.Kelly@macroberts.com

KELLY, Siobhan Catriona Therese
(Aug 1988) (Consultant)
Miller Samuel Hill Brown LLP,
Glasgow . . . . (p.1020)
T: 0141 2211919
E: ske@mshblegal.com

KELLY, Susan Mary (Mar 1994) (Partner)
Dentons UK and Middle East LLP,
Edinburgh . . . . (p.860)
T: 0330 2220050
E: Susan.Kelly@dentons.com

KELLY-GILMOUR, Donna Marie (Feb 1997)
(Partner)
Gilson Gray LLP, Glasgow . . . . (p.980)
T: 0141 5302021
E: dkellygilmour@gilsongray.co.uk

KELM, Geraldine Patricia (Oct 1993)
(Employee)
Pinsent Masons LLP, Glasgow . . . . (p.1031)
T: 0141 567 8400
E: geraldine.kelm@pinsentmasons.com

KELMAN, Jamie William (Sept 2019)
(Employee)
CMS Cameron McKenna Nabarro Olswang LLP,
Edinburgh . . . . (p.856)
T: 0131 2288000
E: jamie.kelman@cms-cmno.com

KELMAN, Katy Jane (Nov 2000) (Employee)
Lord President's Private Office,
Edinburgh . . . . (p.1225)
T: 0131 2406701
E: kkelman@scotcourts.gov.uk

KELMAN, Stevie Margaret (Sept 2017)
(Employee)
Aberdein Considine and Company,
Banchory . . . . (p.767)
T: 01330 824646
E: skelman@acandco.com

KELSEY, Rachael Joy Christina (Oct 1996)
(Partner)
SKO Family Law Specialists LLP,
Edinburgh . . . . (p.903)
T: 0131 3226669
E: Rachael.Kelsey@sko-family.co.uk

KELSO, Louise Margaret (Aug 2002) (Partner)
Brodies LLP, Edinburgh . . . . (p.845)
T: 0131 2283777
E: louise.kelso@brodies.com

KEMERLIS, Anargyros (Nov 2021) (Employee)
STV Television Limited, Glasgow . . . . . . (p.1245)
T: 0141 3003000
E: anargyros.kemerlis@stv.tv

KEMP, Abby Leigh (Sept 2018) (Employee)
Bell & Craig Limited, Stirling . . . . (p.1164)
T: 01786 470444
E: abbykemp@bellandcraig.co.uk

KEMP, Benjamin John Tizzard (Oct 2001)
(Employee)
The Institute and Faculty of Actuaries,
Edinburgh . . . . (p.1234)
T: 020 7632 1488
E: Ben.Kemp@actuaries.org.uk

KEMP, Cameron Lewis MacDonald
(Sept 2011) (Associate)
Harper Macleod LLP, Edinburgh . . . . (p.877)
T: 0131 2472500
E: lewis.kemp@harpermacleod.co.uk

KEMP, Catriona Leask (Sept 2010) (Employee)
Harper Macleod LLP, Edinburgh . . . . (p.877)
T: 0131 2472500
E: Catriona.Kemp@harpermacleod.co.uk

KEMP, Jonathan James Thomas (Sept 1993)
(Employee)
Procurator Fiscal Service,
Edinburgh . . . . (p.1227)
T: 0300 0203168
E: Jonathan.Kemp@copfs.gov.uk

KEMP, Michael William (Sept 2004) (Employee)
Thorntons Law LLP, Dundee . . . . (p.819)
T: 01382 723 171
E: mkemp@thorntons-law.co.uk

KEMPSELL, Fiona Anne (Oct 2011) (Employee)
Wright, Johnston & Mackenzie LLP,
Glasgow. . . . . (p.1054)
T: 0141 2483434
E: fak@wjm.co.uk

KEMPTON, Alan William (Jul 1986) (Employee)
Procurator Fiscal Service, Dundee . . . . . (p.1218)
T: 01382 342559
E: alan.kempton@copfs.gov.uk

KENDALL, Joan Margaret (Feb 1989)
(Employee)
Scottish Social Services Council,
Dundee . . . . (p.1218)
T: 0345 6030 891
E: joan.kendall@sssc.uk.com

KENNEDY, Alastair Stuart (Jul 1982) (Solicitor)
NO FIRM

KENNEDY, Alistair James (Sept 2005)
(Employee)
Shepherd and Wedderburn LLP,
Edinburgh . . . . (p.900)
T: 0131 2289900
E: alistair.kennedy@shepwedd.com

KENNEDY, Callum Stuart, WS (May 1986)
(Partner)
Lindsays LLP, Edinburgh . . . . (p.882)
T: 0131 2291212
E: callumkennedy@lindsays.co.uk

KENNEDY, Caroline Joanna Dunn
(Sept 2004) (Associate)
Brodies LLP, Glasgow . . . . (p.948)
T: 0141 2484672
E: caroline.kennedy@brodies.com

KENNEDY, Claire Louise (Nov 1999)
(Employee)
CIGNA International, Glasgow . . . . (p.1238)
T: 01475 492388
E: Claire.Kennedy@Cigna.com

KENNEDY, Clare Elizabeth (Jul 2018)
(Employee)
Procurator Fiscal Service,
Edinburgh . . . . (p.1229)
T: 0300 0203521
E: Clare.Kennedy@copfs.gov.uk

KENNEDY, Craig David (Oct 2005) (Partner)
Dentons UK and Middle East LLP,
Glasgow. (p.968)
T: 0330 2220050
E: craig.d.kennedy@dentons.com

KENNEDY, Elizabeth Anita (Jan 1980)
(Employee)
Davidson Chalmers Stewart LLP,
Glasgow. (p.967)
T: 0141 4283258
E: elizabeth.kennedy@dcslegal.com

KENNEDY, Fiona Margaret Mary (Feb 2021)
(Employee)
Shepherd and Wedderburn LLP,
Edinburgh . . . . (p.900)
T: 0131 473 5148
E: fiona.kennedy@shepwedd.com

KENNEDY, Hannah Martha (Jul 1997)
(Associate)
Elliot & Co., WS, Perth . . . . (p.1147)
T: 01738 638246
E: hkennedy@elliotsperth.co.uk

KENNEDY, Jade (Aug 2020) (Employee)
LumiraDx UK Ltd, Stirling . . . . (p.1254)
E: Jade.Kennedy@lumiradx.com

KENNEDY, John (Dec 1996) (Partner)
Burness Paull LLP, Aberdeen . . . . (p.724)
T: 01224 621621
E: John.Kennedy@burnesspaull.com

KENNEDY, Katie Ann (Oct 2000) (Associate)
Grigor & Young LLP, Elgin. . . . . (p.916)
T: 01343 544077
E: katie@grigor-young.co.uk

KENNEDY, Laura (Aug 2012) (Employee)
Clydesdale Bank Plc, Glasgow . . . . (p.1238)
T: 07826 873823
E: laura.kennedy@cybg.com

KENNEDY, Laura Anne (Nov 2007) (Employee)
Scottish Government, Edinburgh . . . . . (p.1231)
T: 0131 244 0815
E: Laura.Kennedy@gov.scot

KENNEDY, Laura Russell (Oct 2005) (Employee)
BAE Systems Surface Ships Limited,
Glasgow. (p.1238)
T: 07525 391 489
E: laura.kennedy@baesystems.com

KENNEDY, Mairi Louise (Oct 2010) (Employee)
MOV8 Real Estate Limited,
Edinburgh . . . . (p.893)
T: 0345 646 0208
E: louise.alexander@mov8realestate.com

KENNEDY, Neil Andrew Findlay (Nov 1999)
(Partner)
MacRoberts LLP, Glasgow . . . . (p.1015)
T: 0141 3031100
E: neil.kennedy@macroberts.com

KENNEDY, Norman (May 1999) (Partner)
Brodies LLP, Glasgow . . . . (p.948)
T: 0141 2484672
E: norman.kennedy@brodies.com

KENNEDY, Paula Elaine (Oct 1999) (Partner)
Burness Paull LLP, Edinburgh . . . . (p.850)
   T: 0131 4736000
   E: Paula.Kennedy@burnesspaull.com

KENNEDY, Pauline Eleanor (Oct 1993) (Partner)
Stevenson & Marshall LLP,
   Dunfermline . . . . (p.825)
   T: 01383 721141
   E: pkennedy@stevenson-marshall.co.uk

KENNEDY, Robin Alastair (Aug 2005)
   (Employee)
London and Cambridge Properties,
   Glasgow. (p.1241)
   T: 0141 4653391
   E: RKennedy@lcpproperties.co.uk

KENNEDY, Samantha Lillian Joan (Aug 2021)
   (Employee)
Jardine Phillips LLP, Edinburgh . . . . (p.879)
   T: 0131 4466850
   E: Sam.Kennedy@jardinephillips.com

KENNEDY, Stephen Douglas (Mar 1984)
   (Partner)
McIntyre & Co., Fort William . . . . (p.930)
   T: 01397 703231
   E: law@solicitors-scotland.com

KENNEDY, Steven James Alexander
   (Feb 2003) (Employee)
Student Loans Company Limited,
   Glasgow. (p.1245)
   T: 0141 306 2000
   E: steven_kennedy@slc.co.uk

KENNEDY-WALTON, Elaine (Jun 2015)
   (Employee)
Gillespie Macandrew LLP,
   Edinburgh . . . . (p.872)
   T: 0131 2251677
   E:
Elaine.kennedy-walton@gillespiemacandrew.
co.uk

KENNETH, Paul James (Oct 1996) (Associate)
Womble Bond Dickinson (UK) LLP,
   Edinburgh . . . . (p.913)
   T: 0345 415 0000
   E: paul.kenneth@wbd-uk.com

KENNOUCHE, Lyes (Sept 2012) (Employee)
Archer (UK)Ltd, Aberdeen . . . . (p.1211)

KENNY, Conor (Aug 2019) (Employee)
Thompsons, Glasgow . . . . (p.1046)
   T: 0141 2218840
   E: conor.kenny@thompsons-scotland.co.uk

KENNY, Janette Margaret (Feb 1988) (Director)
Hendrie Legal Limited, Edinburgh . . . . . (p.878)
   T: 0131 370 0470
   E: janette.kenny@ralphhendrie.legal

KENNY, Joanna Helen (Feb 1999) (Partner)
Beckley Kenny & Co, Laurencekirk . . . . (p.1111)
   T: 01561 377188
   E: joanna.kenny@beckleykenny.com

KENNY, Maureen (Aug 2001) (Employee)
Aberdeen Corporate Services Limited,
   Edinburgh . . . . (p.1220)
   T: 0131 245 7508
   E: maureen.kenny@abrdn.com

KENT, Claire Elizabeth (Jan 2005) (Employee)
Aberdeenshire Council, Aberdeen . . . . . (p.1211)
   T: 0345 608 1208
   E: claire.kent@aberdeenshire.gov.uk

KENTISH, Anne (Oct 1993) (Partner)
Clyde & Co (Scotland) LLP,
   Edinburgh . . . . (p.855)
   T: 0131 5571545
   E: anne.kentish@clydeco.com

KEOGH, Colette Judith (Oct 2021) (Employee)
Katani & Co. Ltd, Glasgow . . . . (p.994)
   T: 0141 2217788
   E: colette.keogh@kataniandco.com

KEOGH, Matthew Ian (Nov 2018) (Employee)
Scottish Social Services Council,
   Dundee . . . . (p.1218)
   T: 0345 6030 891

KERMODE, William (Sept 1998) (Employee)
Procurator Fiscal Service, Perth. . . . . . . (p.1253)
   T: 01738 637272
   E: Bill.Kermode@copfs.gov.uk

KERNAGHAN, Robert Alexander (Sept 2000)
   (Partner)
Digby Brown LLP, Dundee . . . . (p.808)
   T: 01382 205917
   E: robert.kernaghan@digbybrown.co.uk

KERR, Aisha Lubna (Sept 2016) (Employee)
Scottish Government, Edinburgh . . . . . (p.1232)
   E: aisha.kerr@gov.scot

KERR, Amy Elizabeth (Aug 2020) (Employee)
Kerr Law Group Limited,
   Edinburgh . . . . (p.880)
   T: 07990 734814
   E: amy.kerr@kerrandpartners.com

KERR, Andrew John (Jul 2007) (Associate)
Harper Macleod LLP, Inverness. . . . . . . (p.1077)
   T: 01463 798777
   E: andrew.kerr@harpermacleod.co.uk

KERR, Christopher James (Sept 2000) (Partner)
Harper Macleod LLP, Glasgow . . . . (p.983)
   T: 0141 2218888
   E: christopher.kerr@harpermacleod.co.uk

KERR, Colette Marie (Sept 1992) (Director)
Oraclelaw Limited, Glasgow. . . . . (p.1027)
   T: 0141 4041091
   E: cmk@oraclelaw.com

KERR, Colm (Jul 2019) (Employee)
Dentons UK and Middle East LLP,
Glasgow . . . .(p.968)
T: 0330 2220050
E: colm.kerr@dentons.com

KERR, Darina Catherine (Oct 1994) (Partner)
CMS Cameron McKenna Nabarro Olswang LLP,
Glasgow . . . .(p.962)
T: 0141 2222200
E: Darina.Kerr@cms-cmno.com

KERR, David John (Nov 2009) (Partner)
Harper Macleod LLP, Glasgow . . . .(p.983)
T: 0141 2218888
E: david.kerr@harpermacleod.co.uk

KERR, Douglas Stewart (Oct 2015) (Employee)
Scottish Government, Edinburgh . . . . .(p.1231)
T: 0131 244 0501
E: douglas.kerr@gov.scot

KERR, Eleanor Mary (Dec 1988) (Partner)
Shepherd and Wedderburn LLP,
Glasgow . . . .(p.1039)
T: 0141 5669900
E: Eleanor.Kerr@shepwedd.co.uk

KERR, Gerard William (May 1987) (Director)
Kerr Law Group Limited,
Edinburgh . . . .(p.880)
T: 07990 734814
E: kerrg@btinternet.com

KERR, Gordon John, WS (Nov 1978) (Solicitor)
NO FIRM

KERR, Hazel Rebecca (Feb 2018) (Employee)
Paul Hannah Solicitors, Glasgow . . . . . .(p.982)
T: 0141 5587433
E: hazelk@paulhannah.org

KERR, Jack McLauchlan (Jul 2015) (Partner)
Morton Fraser LLP, Edinburgh . . . .(p.891)
T: 0131 2471000
E: Jack.Kerr@morton-fraser.com

KERR, James (Nov 1982) (Employee)
Inverclyde Council, Greenock . . . .(p.1246)
T: 01475 717171
E: jim.kerr@inverclyde.gov.uk

KERR, Jamie (Jun 2006) (Partner)
Burness Paull LLP, Glasgow . . . .(p.954)
T: 0141 2484933
E: jamie.kerr@burnesspaull.com

KERR, Jan Mitchell (Mar 1980) (Associate)
Macfarlane & Co., Bishopbriggs . . . .(p.774)
T: 0141 7726063
E: jmk@macfarlane-law.co.uk

KERR, Jordan Fraser (Nov 2018) (Employee)
CMS Cameron McKenna Nabarro Olswang LLP,
Glasgow . . . .(p.962)
T: 0141 2222200
E: jordan.kerr@cms-cmno.com

KERR, Katie Elizabeth (Sept 1996) (Employee)
Fulton's, Glasgow . . . .(p.1010)
T: 0141 6322248
E: kkerr@fultonslaw.co.uk

KERR, Laura (Nov 2018) (Employee)
Harper Macleod LLP, Glasgow . . . .(p.983)
T: 0141 2218888
E: laura.kerr@harpermacleod.co.uk

KERR, Lauren Margaret (Jun 2016) (Employee)
Brodies LLP, Glasgow . . . .(p.948)
T: 0141 2484672
E: lauren.kerr@brodies.com

KERR, Lauren Maria (Aug 2008) (Partner)
L Kerr Solicitors, Dumbarton . . . .(p.798)
T: 07393 746024
E: lk@lkerrsolicitors.com

KERR, Lewis Neil (May 2017) (Employee)
Scottish Government, Edinburgh . . . . .(p.1231)
T: 0131 244 0815
E: lewis.kerr@gov.scot

KERR, Lisa (Sept 1994) (Associate)
DLA Piper Scotland LLP, Edinburgh . . . .(p.863)
T: 0131 2425531
E: Lisa.Kerr@dlapiper.com

KERR, Lorraine (Aug 2011) (Employee)
Queen Margaret University,
Musselburgh . . . .(p.1251)
T: 0131 4740000
E: lkerr2@qmu.ac.uk

KERR, Lorraine (Jun 2016) (Director)
Mair Matheson Solicitors Ltd,
Newmilns . . . .(p.1130)
T: 01560 321225
E: Lorraine.Kerr@MairMatheson.co.uk

KERR, Lynsey Christine (Feb 2012) (Partner)
Lindsays LLP, Edinburgh . . . .(p.882)
T: 0131 2291212
E: lynseykerr@lindsays.co.uk

KERR, Marina Beatrice (Jan 1980) (Consultant)
Hastings Legal Incorporating Doughtys,
Eyemouth . . . .(p.920)
T: 018907 51100
E: mk@hastingslegal.co.uk

KERR, Martin Francis (Oct 2007) (Solicitor)
NO FIRM

KERR, Matthew Liam Philip (Jan 2005)
(Employee)
Trinity Kerr Limited, Aberdeen . . . .(p.1214)
T: 01224 312767
E: liam@trinitykerr.co.uk

KERR, Matthew Peter (Jun 2017) (Employee)
Procurator Fiscal Service, Perth . . . .(p.1253)
T: 01738 637272
E: matthew.kerr@copfs.gov.uk

KERR, Orla Elizabeth (Nov 2014) (Employee)
DWF LLP, Edinburgh . . . . (p.865)
   T: 0131 2265541
   E: Orla.Kerr@dwf.law

KERR, Robert Jude Peter (Aug 1981) (Director)
The Robert Kerr Partnership Limited,
   Paisley . . . . (p.1141)
   T: 0141 8896458
   E: rjk@therobertkerrpartnership.com

KERR, Robert Peter (Mar 1980) (Partner)
The Kerr Brown Partnership,
   Glasgow . . . . (p.1044)
   T: 0141 2214880
   E: rpk@kerrbrown.co.uk

KERR, Roisin Elizabeth (Feb 2019) (Employee)
SKO Family Law Specialists LLP,
   Edinburgh . . . . (p.903)
   T: 0131 3226669
   E: roisin.kerr@sko-family.co.uk

KERR, Sarah (Oct 2018) (Employee)
Mourant Ozannes, St Helier . . . . (p.1274)
   T: 1481731513
   E: sarah.kerr@mourant.com

KERR, Scott Thomas Reid (Nov 1988) (Partner)
Harper Macleod LLP, Edinburgh . . . . . . (p.877)
   T: 0131 2472500
   E: scott.kerr@harpermacleod.co.uk

KERR, Sonia Helen Campbell (Sept 2013)
   (Employee)
Educational Institute of Scotland,
   Edinburgh . . . . (p.1222)
   T: (0131) 225 6244
   E: skerr@eis.org.uk

KERR, Victoria Anne (Oct 2016) (Employee)
Frazer Coogans Ltd, Ayr . . . . (p.763)
   T: 01292 280499
   E: victoria.kerr@frazercoogans.co.uk

KERR, Victoria Emma (Oct 2014) (Employee)
Procurator Fiscal Service, Aberdeen . . . (p.1213)
   T: 0300 0202336
   E: victoria.kerr@copfs.gov.uk

KERR, Victoria May (Nov 2019) (Solicitor)
NO FIRM

KERRIGAN, John (Mar 1980) (Consultant)
Blackadders LLP, Glasgow . . . . (p.946)
   T: 0141 2481888
   E: john.kerrigan@blackadders.co.uk

KERSHAW, Stuart John (Dec 2015) (Partner)
Masson Glennie LLP, Peterhead . . . . . . (p.1154)
   T: 01779 474271
   E: stuart.kershaw@massonglennie.co.uk

KERSHAW, Victoria Louise (Jul 2020) (Partner)
Masson Glennie LLP, Peterhead . . . . . . (p.1154)
   T: 01779 474271
   E: Louise.Kershaw@massonglennie.co.uk

KETTLEWELL, Claire Rosemary (Oct 2013)
   (Employee)
Civil Legal Assistance Office,
   Aberdeen . . . . (p.1212)
   T: 01224 402330
   E: kettlewellcl@clao.org.uk

KEYDEN, Gordon Stuart (Sept 1978)
   (Consultant)
Clyde & Co (Scotland) LLP,
   Edinburgh . . . . (p.855)
   T: 0131 5571545
   E: gordon.keyden@clydeco.com

KEYS, Graham David (Sept 1995) (Director)
Ness Gallagher Solicitors Limited,
   Wishaw . . . . (p.1182)
   T: 01698 355 525
   E: gk@nessgallagher.co.uk

KEYSE, Margaret Isobel (Jan 1994) (Employee)
Office of the Scottish Info. Commissioner
   T: 01334 464610
   E: mkeyse@itspublicknowledge.info

KHALDI, Fiona Elizabeth Margaret
   (Nov 1998) (Solicitor)
NO FIRM

KHALID, Abdullah (Mar 2021) (Employee)
Angus McIntosh & Simon Hodge,
   Glasgow . . . . (p.1012)
   T: 0141 6340313
   E: abdullah.khalid@castlemilklawcentre.co.uk

KHALID, Mohammed Hamaad (May 2016)
   (Employee)
Lindsays LLP, Edinburgh . . . . (p.882)
   T: 0131 2291212
   E: HamaadKhalid@lindsays.co.uk

KHALID, Saaima (May 2012) (Director)
JKR Law Ltd, Glasgow . . . . (p.992)
   T: 0141 473 3999
   E: SK@jklaws.co.uk

KHALID, Shehzad (Aug 2004) (Employee)
SSE PLC, Glasgow . . . . (p.1244)
   T: 0141 224 7248
   E: Shaz.Khalid@sse.com

KHALID, Zoheb Mohammed (Oct 2020)
   (Employee)
Thompsons, Glasgow . . . . (p.1046)
   T: 0141 2218840

KHALIL AHMED, Rizwan (Mar 2019) (Director)
QC Law Solicitors Limited,
   Liversedge . . . . (p.1260)
   T: 01484 818123
   E: Riz@qc-law.co.uk

KHAN, Afshan Sarwar (Oct 2003) (Employee)
Dentons UK and Middle East LLP,
   Glasgow . . . . (p.968)
   T: 0330 2220050
   E: Afshan.Khan@dentons.com

KHAN, Asim Anwar (Jun 1998) (Partner)
D and F Lawyers, Paisley . . . .(p.1138)
T: 07736 441 238
E: asim.khan@dandflawyers.com

KHAN, Bimah (Nov 2013) (Employee)
De Lage Landen Leasing Limited,
Watford . . . .(p.1272)
E: bimah.khan@dllgroup.com

KHAN, Nafeesa (Feb 2006) (Solicitor)
NO FIRM

KHAN, Nisar (Jul 2020) (Employee)
Khan Associates Immigration Limited,
Glasgow. . . . .(p.1240)
T: 0141 4292390

KHAN, Osman Saeed (Sept 2014) (Employee)
Carpenters Scotland Limited,
Glasgow. . . . .(p.956)
T: 0141 3285452
E: OK@carpentersgroup.co.uk

KHAN, Ra'ees-Mehran Kaif Sagar (May 2017)
(Director)
Khan Law Limited, Glasgow. . . . .(p.996)
T: 0141 3780514
E: raees.khan@khanlaw.co.uk

KHAN, Rai Ahmad (Apr 2009) (Director)
RH & Co Ltd, Glasgow . . . .(p.1035)
T: 0141 4190897
E: raikhan@rhcosolicitors.com

KHAN, Said Jamil (Jun 2020) (Employee)
SJK Legal Ltd, Glasgow . . . .(p.1042)
T: 0141 6482500

KHAN, Steven Martin (Jun 2018) (Employee)
Carey Olsen, St Helier . . . .(p.1274)
T: 01534 888900

KHOGALI, Ahmed Shihab Eldin Osman
(Oct 2021) (Employee)
Maguire Solicitors, Glasgow. . . . .(p.1017)
T: 0141 3312885
E: ahmed@maguiresolicitors.co.uk

KHUSHI, Lina (Apr 2015) (Employee)
Jacobs & Turner, T/a Trespass,
Glasgow. . . . .(p.1240)
T: 0141 5688000
E: linak@trespass.co.uk

KICINSKI, Maria Bronislava (Nov 2007)
(Employee)
Procurator Fiscal Service,
Edinburgh . . . .(p.1229)
T: 0300 0203000
E: maria.kicinski@copfs.gov.uk

KIDD, Danielle (Sept 2009) (Employee)
National Westminster Bank PLC,
Edinburgh . . . .(p.1226)
T: 0131 5568555
E: danielle.kidd@rbs.co.uk

KIDD, Helen Claire (Jul 2012) (Employee)
Brodies LLP, Edinburgh . . . .(p.845)
T: 0131 2283777
E: helen.kidd@brodies.com

KIDD, Julia Louise (Nov 2003) (Employee)
Anderson Strathern LLP, Edinburgh . . . .(p.839)
T: 0131 2707700
E: julia.kidd@andersonstrathern.co.uk

KIDD, Mary Ainslie, WS (Dec 1980) (Partner)
Stuart Kidd WS, Edinburgh . . . .(p.881)
T: 07764 884103
E: mkidd@stuartkiddws.co.uk

KIDD, Paula Suzanne Leslie (May 2010)
(Partner)
CMS Cameron McKenna Nabarro Olswang LLP,
Aberdeen . . . .(p.727)
T: 01224 622002
E: paula.kidd@cms-cmno.com

KIDD, Sonja Yvonne (Jul 2019) (Employee)
Bowmans, Dundee . . . .(p.806)
T: 01382 322267
E: sk@bowmansolicitors.co.uk

KIELSKI, John Andrew (Jan 2017) (Employee)
Stewart, Aulinger & Co, Vancouver . . .(p.1257)
E: jkielski@stewart-aulinger.ca

KIERAN, Roisin Anne (Oct 2008) (Partner)
Gray & Co., Glasgow . . . .(p.981)
T: 0141 9467777
E: rk@grayandcoglasgow.co.uk

KIERNAN, Laura Ann (Mar 2009) (Director)
Kiernan Law Ltd, Uddingston. . . . .(p.1177)
T: 01698 844343
E: kiernanlaw2012@gmail.com

KIERNEY, Claire Bernadette (May 2019)
(Employee)
North Ayrshire Council, Irvine . . . .(p.1249)
T: 01294 310000
E: clairekierney@north-ayrshire.gov.uk

KIERSGAARD, Sarah Irene (Mar 2014)
(Associate)
Ledingham Chalmers LLP, Stirling . . . .(p.1165)
T: 01786 478100
E: sarah.kiersgaard@ledinghamchalmers.com

KILBURN, Keith (Aug 2006) (Associate)
Brodies LLP, Glasgow . . . .(p.948)
T: 0141 2484672
E: keith.kilburn@brodies.com

KILCOYNE, John Anthony (Feb 2001) (Partner)
John Kilcoyne & Co. Solicitors,
Glasgow. . . . .(p.997)
T: 0141 4231400
E: jk@johnkilcoynesolicitors.co.uk

KILCOYNE, Neil Martin (Oct 1998) (Partner)
Neil Kilcoyne & Co., Glasgow . . . .(p.996)
T: 0141 4332700
E: nkilcoyne@kilcoyne-solicitors.co.uk

KILDARE, Fergus Patrick (Jan 2015) (Employee)
National Westminster Bank PLC,
Edinburgh . . . .(p.1226)
T: (0131) 626 2925
E: Fergus.Kildare@natwest.com

KILDARE, Liam John (Jul 2015) (Employee)
Burnett Christie Knowles McCourts,
Edinburgh . . . .(p.852)
T: 0131 2253456
E: lk@bckm.co.uk

KILGOUR, Stuart William (Apr 1989)
(Employee)
National Health Service Scotland,
Edinburgh . . . .(p.1225)
T: 0131 2757800
E: stuart.kilgour@nhs.scot

KILKERR, Michael Gerard (Jan 1980) (Partner)
Michael G. Kilkerr, Stranraer . . . .(p.1171)
T: 01776 702415
E: mgkilkerr@live.co.uk

KILLEAN, Susan Elizabeth Helen (Oct 1988)
(Employee)
Church of Scotland, Edinburgh . . . . . .(p.1221)
T: 0131 240 2233
E: skillean@cofscotland.org.uk

KILLEN, Fiona (Sept 2003) (Partner)
Burness Paull LLP, Edinburgh . . . .(p.850)
T: 0131 4736000
E: Fiona.Killen@burnesspaull.com

KILLMAN, Nicole (Sept 2019) (Employee)
Harper Macleod LLP, Inverness. . . . . . .(p.1077)
T: 01463 798777
E: nicole.killman@harpermacleod.co.uk

KILNER, Brittany Louise (Apr 2019) (Employee)
Burnett & Reid LLP, Aberdeen . . . .(p.726)
T: 01224 644333
E: brittany.robson@burnett-reid.co.uk

KILPATRICK, Douglas (Sept 1980) (Consultant)
PRP Legal Limited, Glasgow . . . .(p.1033)
T: 0141 3311050
E: douglas@prp-legal.co.uk

KILPATRICK, Jenny Louise (Feb 2003)
(Employee)
Procurator Fiscal Service,
Edinburgh . . . .(p.1227)
T: 0300 0203168
E: jenny.kilpatrick@copfs.gov.uk

KILPATRICK, Lynne (Aug 2007) (Employee)
Law Society of Scotland,
Edinburgh . . . .(p.1224)
T: 0131 2267411
E: lynnekilpatrick@lawscot.org.uk

KILSHAW, David Andrew George, OBE
(May 1979) (Partner)
Cullen Kilshaw, Galashiels . . . .(p.933)
T: 01896 800 800
E: david.kilshaw@cullenkilshaw.com

KILSHAW, Ross David (Aug 2013) (Partner)
Cullen Kilshaw, Galashiels . . . .(p.933)
T: 01896 800 800
E: ross.kilshaw@cullenkilshaw.com

KIMMITT, Lynsey Jane Martin (Jun 2014)
(Employee)
Aberdeenshire Council, Aberdeen . . . . .(p.1211)
T: 0345 608 1208
E: lynsey.kimmitt@aberdeenshire.gov.uk

KINDNESS, Fiona Claire (Apr 2007) (Employee)
Pinsent Masons LLP, Aberdeen . . . .(p.739)
T: 01224 377900
E: fiona.kindness@pinsentmasons.com

KINDNESS, John Lawrie (Oct 1989) (Partner)
Blair & Bryden, Clydebank. . . . .(p.784)
T: 0141 9523322
E: jkindness@blair-bryden.co.uk

KING, Emma (Dec 2019) (Solicitor)
NO FIRM

KING, Emma Mary Christina (Jul 2005)
(Director)
Clarity Simplicity Ltd, East Kilbride . . . . .(p.831)
T: 0141 4332626
E: emma@claritysimplicity.co.uk

KING, Frances Alexa (Nov 2001) (Partner)
Franchi Law LLP, Glasgow . . . .(p.977)
T: 0141 225 3810
E: Alexa@franchilaw.co.uk

KING, Gwyneth (Aug 2019) (Employee)
JustRight Scotland LLP, Glasgow . . . . . .(p.994)
T: 0141 406 5350
E: gwyneth@justrightscotland.org.uk

KING, Jennifer Joyce (Oct 2009) (Employee)
BTO Solicitors LLP, Glasgow . . . .(p.952)
T: 0141 2218012
E: jki@bto.co.uk

KING, Laura (Aug 2008) (Consultant)
Inksters, Glasgow . . . .(p.990)
T: 0141 2290880

KING, Laura Amie (Jul 2011) (Associate)
CMS Cameron McKenna Nabarro Olswang LLP,
Edinburgh . . . .(p.856)
T: 0131 2288000
E: Laura.King@cms-cmno.com

KING, Patricia Hunter (Sept 1980) (Employee)
J.D. Clark & Allan Limited, Duns . . . . . .(p.829)
T: 01361 882501
E: pat.king@jdca.co.uk

KING, Robert (Nov 1997) (Employee)
Insights Learning & Development Ltd,
  Dundee . . . .(p.1218)
  E: rking@insights.com

KING, Robert (Oct 1988) (Partner)
Clyde & Co (Scotland) LLP,
  Glasgow. . . . .(p.961)
  T: 0141 2482666
  E: robert.king@clydeco.com

KING, Ross Kevin (May 2013) (Associate)
Hogan Lovells International LLP, London
  EC1 . . . .(p.1265)
  T: 020 7296 2000
  E: Ross.king@hoganlovells.com

KING, Scott Alexander (Dec 2020) (Employee)
Harper Macleod LLP, Glasgow . . . .(p.983)
  T: 0141 2218888

KING, Scott Francis (Mar 2018) (Employee)
Procurator Fiscal Service, Hamilton . . . .(p.1247)
  T: 0300 0204380
  E: Scott.King@copfs.gov.uk

KING, Steven Mark (Apr 2012) (Employee)
Dentons UK and Middle East LLP,
  Edinburgh . . . .(p.860)
  T: 0330 2220050
  E: Steven.King@dentons.com

KING, Stewart Alexander (Sept 1985) (Partner)
Wright, Johnston & Mackenzie LLP,
  Glasgow. . . . .(p.1054)
  T: 0141 2483434
  E: sak@wjm.co.uk

KING, Stuart David McCallum (Sept 1994)
(Partner)
Blackadders LLP, Dundee. . . . .(p.805)
  T: 01382 229222
  E: stuart.king@blackadders.co.uk

KINGSTON, Cecily Clare (Nov 2020)
(Employee)
Jack Gowans & Marc Dickson Solicitors Limited,
  Inverness . . . .(p.1076)
  T: 01463 710677
  E: cecily@gowansdickson.com

KINLOCH, Caitlin Alexandra (Sept 2019)
(Employee)
Scottish Social Services Council,
  Dundee . . . .(p.1218)
  T: 0345 6030 891
  E: caitlin.kinloch@sssc.uk.com

KINLOCH, Daniel Alexander (Jul 2017)
(Employee)
Uber, Amsterdam . . . .(p.1275)
  E: daniel.kinloch@uber.com

KINLOCH, Dara Ann (Oct 2009) (Employee)
Ledingham Chalmers LLP,
  Aberdeen . . . .(p.734)
  T: 01224 408408
  E: dara.kinloch@ledinghamchalmers.com

KINLOCH, David Arthur (Nov 1983) (Partner)
David Kinloch & Co., Glasgow. . . . .(p.997)
  T: 0141 3363000
  E: info@kinlochlawyers.co.uk

KINLOCH, Lisa Ann (Feb 2008) (Associate)
CMS Cameron McKenna Nabarro Olswang LLP,
  Glasgow. . . . .(p.962)
  T: 0141 2222200
  E: Lisa.Kinloch@cms-cmno.com

KINMOND, Erica Joanne (Aug 2007)
(Employee)
Blackwood Partners LLP, Aberdeen . . . . .(p.723)
  T: 01224 446230
  E: erica.kinmond@blackwood-partners.com

KINNES, Andrew Mackenzie (Oct 1994)
(Partner)
Shepherd and Wedderburn LLP,
  Edinburgh . . . .(p.900)
  T: 0131 2289900
  E: Andrew.Kinnes@shepwedd.com

KINNES, Margaret White (Oct 1993)
(Associate)
MacRoberts LLP, Edinburgh . . . .(p.887)
  T: 0131 2295046
  E: margaret.kinnes@macroberts.com

KINNIBURGH, Moira Jane (Nov 1996)
(Employee)
Miller Homes Limited, Edinburgh . . . . .(p.1225)
  T: 0870 3365000
  E: moira.kinniburgh@miller.co.uk

KINROY, Lisa Paterson (Jan 2012) (Employee)
Brodies LLP, Edinburgh . . . .(p.845)
  T: 0131 656 3773
  E: lisa.kinroy@brodies.com

KINSELLA, Anne (Jan 1984) (Employee)
Scottish Courts and Tribunals Service,
  Airdrie . . . .(p.1215)
  T: 01236 439184
  E: akinsella@scotcourts.gov.uk

KINSELLA, Julie Theresa (Jan 2021) (Employee)
Macleod & MacCallum Limited,
  Inverness . . . .(p.1080)
  T: 01463 239393
  E: julie.kinsella@macandmac.co.uk

KIRCHIN, David Michael (Nov 1997) (Partner)
Addleshaw Goddard LLP,
  Edinburgh . . . .(p.835)
  T: 0131 2282400
  E: David.Kirchin@addleshawgoddard.com

KIRK, Alexandria Heather (Nov 2015)
(Employee)
Procurator Fiscal Service,
Dunfermline . . . .(p.1219)
T: 01383 723688
E: Alexandria.kirk@copfs.gov.uk

KIRK, Elaine Joanne (Oct 2015) (Employee)
Shepherd and Wedderburn LLP,
Glasgow . . . .(p.1039)
T: 0141 5669900
E: elaine.kirk@shepwedd.com

KIRK, Karen (Sept 2003) (Partner)
Kirk Hanlon, Glasgow . . . .(p.997)
T: 0141 3786653
E: karen@kirkhanlon.com

KIRK, Ronald Adam (Dec 1996) (Employee)
Scottish Borders Council, Newtown St.
Boswells . . . .(p.1251)
T: 01835 825 225
E: rkirk@scotborders.gov.uk

KIRKBY, Fiona Anne (Oct 2006) (Employee)
Procurator Fiscal Service, Hamilton . . . .(p.1247)
T: 0300 020 2822
E: fiona.kirkby@copfs.gov.uk

KIRKE, Mark Jonathan (Oct 1996) (Partner)
CMS Cameron McKenna Nabarro Olswang LLP,
Edinburgh . . . .(p.856)
T: 0131 2288000
E: Mark.Kirke@cms-cmno.com

KIRKE, Tracy Anne (Jul 1995) (Employee)
Scottish Legal Aid Board,
Edinburgh . . . .(p.1233)
T: 0131 2267061
E: KirkeTr@slab.org.uk

KIRKHOPE, Andrew (Aug 1985) (Partner)
Thorntons Law LLP, Edinburgh . . . .(p.906)
T: 0131 2258705
E: akirkhope@thorntons-law.co.uk

KIRKHOPE, Jane Baxter (Jun 1998) (Employee)
NORTH LANARKSHIREre Council,
Motherwell . . . .(p.1251)
T: 01698 302355
E: kirkhopej@northlan.gov.uk

KIRKMAN, Laura Annetta (Sept 2021)
(Employee)
Gillespie Macandrew LLP,
Edinburgh . . . .(p.872)
T: 0131 2251677
E: laura.kirkman@gillespiemacandrew.co.uk

KIRKPATRICK, Leigh (Jun 2011) (Employee)
National Westminster Bank PLC,
Edinburgh . . . .(p.1226)
T: 0131 6264054
E: leigh.kirkpatrick@rbs.co.uk

KIRKWOOD, Eileen (Oct 2006) (Employee)
Procurator Fiscal Service,
Edinburgh . . . .(p.1227)
T: 0300 0203168
E: Eileen.Kirkwood@copfs.gov.uk

KIRKWOOD, Jennifer Anne (Aug 2006)
(Partner)
Jameson + Mackay LLP, Perth . . . .(p.1148)
T: 01738 631666
E: jennifer.kirkwood@jamesonmackay.co.uk

KIRKWOOD, Jonathan Candlish (Dec 1999)
(Employee)
Pinsent Masons LLP, Edinburgh . . . .(p.895)
T: 0131 777 7000
E: jonathan.kirkwood@pinsentmasons.com

KIRKWOOD, Lesley Varennes (Oct 1981)
(Employee)
Lochalsh and Skye Housing Association,
Portree . . . .(p.1254)
T: 01478 612035
E: Lesley.Kirkwood@lsha.co.uk

KIRKWOOD, Lindsay (Apr 2017) (Employee)
Miller Hendry, Dundee . . . .(p.816)
T: 01382 200000
E: lindsaykirkwood@millerhendry.co.uk

KIRKWOOD, Paul (Sept 1993) (Solicitor)
NO FIRM

KISSEL, Jana (Apr 2008) (Employee)
Mitchell International, Inc, San
Diego . . . .(p.1279)
T: (+1) 858 368 7711
E: Jana.Kissel@mitchell.com

KISSOCK, Sarah-Jane (Sept 2009) (Employee)
West Lothian Council, Livingston . . . . .(p.1250)
T: 01506 280000
E: Sarah-Jane.Kissock@westlothian.gov.uk

KITSON, Lisa (Nov 2007) (Associate)
Davidson Chalmers Stewart LLP,
Edinburgh . . . .(p.859)
T: 0131 6259191
E: Lisa.Kitson@dcslegal.com

KITSON, Michael James (Jul 2009) (Employee)
Wheatley Housing Group Limited,
Glasgow . . . .(p.1246)
T: 0845 9001001
E: Michael.Kitson@wheatley-group.com

KLASKALA, Piotr Jozef (Jun 2018) (Associate)
CMS Cameron McKenna Nabarro Olswang LLP,
Edinburgh . . . .(p.856)
T: 0131 2288000
E: piotr.klaskala@cms-cmno.com

KLEINGLASS, Saul (Aug 1986) (Consultant)
Frederick & Co Solicitors Limited,
Glasgow . . . .(p.977)
T: 0141 2215575
E: saul@frederickandco.co.uk

KNAPTON, Aisling Marie (Sept 2018)
(Employee)
Allen & Overy LLP, London E1 . . . .(p.1261)
T: 020 3088 0000

KNIGHT, Andrew Moray (Sept 2013) (Partner)
Burness Paull LLP, Aberdeen . . . .(p.724)
T: 01224 621621
E: andrew.knight@burnesspaull.com

KNIGHT, Grant Alexander (Aug 1985) (Partner)
TC Young LLP, Edinburgh . . . .(p.914)
T: 0131 2207660
E: gak@tcyoung.co.uk

KNIGHT, Jessica Alice (Sept 2018) (Employee)
Falkirk Council, Falkirk . . . .(p.1236)
T: 01324 506070
E: jessica.knight@falkirk.gov.uk

KNIGHT, Kirsten Isobell (Sept 2008) (Partner)
Balfour + Manson LLP, Aberdeen . . . . . .(p.721)
T: 01224 498080
E: Kirsten.knight@balfour-manson.co.uk

KNIGHT, Philip Charles Andrew (Oct 2008)
(Partner)
Womble Bond Dickinson (UK) LLP,
Edinburgh . . . .(p.913)
T: 0345 415 0000
E: Philip.Knight@wbd-uk.com

KNOWLES, Adam John (Feb 2009) (Associate)
Dentons UK and Middle East LLP,
Edinburgh . . . .(p.860)
T: 0330 2220050
E: Adam.Knowles@dentons.com

KNOWLES, Alan Keith (Sept 1998) (Partner)
Brodies LLP, Edinburgh . . . .(p.845)
T: 0131 2283777
E: alan.knowles@brodies.com

KNOWLES, Catherine (Sept 1992) (Employee)
Procurator Fiscal Service, Falkirk . . . . . .(p.1236)
T: 3000203855
E: catherine.knowles@copfs.gov.uk

KNOWLES, Connor (Sept 2019) (Associate)
Addleshaw Goddard LLP,
Aberdeen . . . .(p.719)
T: (+44) (0) 1224 96 5410
E: connor.knowles@addleshawgoddard.com

KNOWLES, Kirsty Martie Grace (Jun 2006)
(Employee)
Inoapps, Aberdeen . . . .(p.1213)
E: kirsty.knowles@inoapps.com

KNOWLES, Philip Craig (Sept 1997) (Partner)
Shepherd and Wedderburn LLP, London
EC2 . . . .(p.1268)
T: 020 74294900
E: Philip.Knowles@shepwedd.com

KNOWLES, Stephen Vincent (Oct 1993)
(Partner)
Burnett Christie Knowles McCourts,
Edinburgh . . . .(p.852)
T: 0131 2253456
E: Stephen.Knowles@bckm.co.uk

KNOWLES, Suzanne Lee (Aug 2010)
(Employee)
Shepherd and Wedderburn LLP,
Edinburgh . . . .(p.900)
T: 0131 2289900
E: suzanne.knowles@shepwedd.com

KNOX, Alasdair George (Dec 2013) (Employee)
Procurator Fiscal Service,
Edinburgh . . . .(p.1227)
T: 0300 0203168

KNOX, Andrew Munro (Jul 2009) (Employee)
Fiona McPhail Solicitors, Edinburgh . . . .(p.886)
T: 0344 5152410
E: Andy_Knox@shelter.org.uk

KNOX, Eilidh Patricia (Feb 1990) (Employee)
Anderson Strathern LLP, Glasgow . . . . . .(p.940)
T: (0141) 2426060
E: eilidh.knox@andersonstrathern.co.uk

KNOX, Elizabeth Margaret Helen
(Dec 2010) (Employee)
Save the Children, London EC1 . . . . . .(p.1268)
E: e.knox@savethechildren.org.uk

KNOX, Fiona Patricia (Jul 2021) (Employee)
Blackadders LLP, Dundee . . . .(p.805)
T: 01382 229222
E: fiona.knox@blackadders.co.uk

KNOX, Gillian May (Nov 1996) (Consultant)
KW Law, Livingston . . . .(p.1119)
T: 01506 415333
E: gilliank@kwlaw.co.uk

KNOX, Laura Mary Mathieson (Jul 2016)
(Employee)
Procurator Fiscal Service, Glasgow . . . .(p.1241)
T: 0300 0203000
E: laura.knox@copfs.gov.uk

KNOX, Louisa Stewart (Nov 1992) (Partner)
Shepherd and Wedderburn LLP,
Edinburgh . . . .(p.900)
T: 0131 2289900
E: Louisa.Knox@shepwedd.com

KNOX, Lucy Rachel (May 2019) (Employee)
Shepherd and Wedderburn LLP,
Glasgow . . . .(p.1039)
T: 0141 5669900
E: lucy.knox@shepwedd.com

KNOX, Rory (Nov 2018) (Employee)
Anderson Strathern LLP, Glasgow . . . . . .(p.940)
T: 0141 2426060
E: Rory.Knox@andersonstrathern.co.uk

KNUDSEN, Christopher Peter (Jun 2017)
(Employee)
Trustpilot A/S, Copenhagen . . . .(p.1257)
T: (+45) 31 676988
E: ckn@trustpilot.com

KOBIELA, Frances Mary (Sept 1988) (Employee)
Falkirk Council, Falkirk . . . .(p.1236)
T: 01324 506070
E: frances.kobiela@falkirk.gov.uk

KOCZWARA, Monika Barbara (Aug 2021)
(Employee)
Brodies LLP, Edinburgh . . . .(p.845)
T: 0131 2283777
E: monika.koczwara@brodies.com

KOKOVWORHO, Joan Onyebuchi (Mar 2013)
(Employee)
Allingham & Co (Solicitors) Limited,
Edinburgh . . . .(p.838)
T: 0131 4479341
E: joan@allingham.co.uk

KONDOL, Leon (Jul 2004) (Partner)
McBride Kondol & Co., Glasgow . . . . .(p.1006)
T: 0141 6476400
E: mail@mcbridekondol.co.uk

KONDOL, Rebecca Hannah (Aug 2019)
(Employee)
Burness Paull LLP, Aberdeen . . . .(p.724)
T: 01224 621621
E: rebecca.kondol@burnesspaull.com

KONOPKA, Frances (Oct 1991) (Employee)
Lanarkshire Law Practice Limited,
Bellshill . . . .(p.773)
T: 01698 747171
E: franceskonopka@lanarkshirelaw.co.uk

KOPKA, Moritz (Nov 2019) (Employee)
CMS Cameron McKenna Nabarro Olswang LLP,
Glasgow. . . . .(p.962)
T: 0141 2222200
E: moritz.kopka@cms-cmno.com

KORDULA, Keith Robert William (Mar 1980)
(Partner)
W. & A.S. Bruce, Dunfermline . . . .(p.822)
T: 01383 738000
E: keith@wasbruce.co.uk

KOREN, Gillian (Sept 2009) (Employee)
Public Defence Solicitors Office,
Edinburgh . . . .(p.1230)
T: 0131 5571222
E: GKoren@pdso.org.uk

KOTSEV, Martin Krasimirov (Sept 2019)
(Employee)
MacRoberts LLP, Edinburgh . . . .(p.887)
T: 0131 2295046
E: martin.kotsev@macroberts.com

KOWALCZYK, Maria McDonald (Jul 2014)
(Employee)
Procurator Fiscal Service, Airdrie . . . . . .(p.1214)
T: 01236 747027
E: Maria.Kowalczyk@copfs.gov.uk

KRUSHAVE, Helen Elizabeth (Nov 2005)
(Employee)
Tesco Personal Finance Plc,
Edinburgh . . . .(p.1234)
T: 0131 274 3426
E: helen.x.krushave@tescobank.com

KUBALA, Caroline Mary (Sept 2010)
(Employee)
Scottish Government, Edinburgh . . . . .(p.1231)
T: 0131 244 0815
E: caroline.kubala@gov.scot

KUCERA, Vladim r (Mar 2020) (Associate)
Pinsent Masons LLP, London EC2 . . . . .(p.1267)
T: 020 7418 7000
E: vladimir.kucera@pinsentmasons.com

KULUPANA, Anushya Thejamali (Mar 2018)
(Associate)
JustRight Scotland LLP, Glasgow . . . . . .(p.994)
T: 0141 406 5350

KUREK, Ewelina Joanna (Feb 2012) (Associate)
Womble Bond Dickinson (UK) LLP,
Edinburgh . . . .(p.913)
T: 0345 415 0000
E: ewelina.kurek@wbd-uk.com

KUSZNIR, Michael James Douglas
(Jun 2016) (Associate)
Burnett & Reid LLP, Aberdeen . . . .(p.726)
T: 01224 644333
E: michael.kusznir@burnett-reid.co.uk

KWOK, Eva Yee Wah (Dec 2020) (Employee)
Gebbie & Wilson LLP, Strathaven . . . . .(p.1172)
T: 01357 520082
E: eva@gebbiewilson.co.uk

KWOK, Meela (Sept 2007) (Associate)
Ashurst LLP, London E1 . . . .(p.1261)
T: 020 7859 2145
E: meela.kwok@ashurst.com

KYDD, John William Crighton (Aug 2002)
(Partner)
Thorntons Law LLP, Dundee . . . .(p.819)
T: 01382 229 111
E: jkydd@thorntons-law.co.uk

KYLE, Leanne Irene Margaret (Oct 2007)
(Employee)
Banijay UK, Glasgow . . . .(p.1238)
T: 0141 3533222
E: leanne.kyle@IWCMedia.co.uk

KYLE, Stephanie Louise (Aug 2006) (Employee)
Burness Paull LLP, Glasgow . . . .(p.954)
T: 0141 2484933
E: Stephanie.Kyle@burnesspaull.com

KYNASTON, Rebecca Margaret Fairfax
(Oct 2005) (Employee)
Procurator Fiscal Service, Perth . . . . (p.1253)
T: 0844 561 3000
E: rebecca.kynaston2@copfs.gov.uk

LABURN, Derek George (Sept 1985) (Partner)
Rankin & Aitken, Stranraer . . . . (p.1172)
T: 01776 702336
E: dgl@rankinaitken.co.uk

LAFFERTY, Austin Joseph (Dec 1981) (Director)
Austin Lafferty Limited, Glasgow . . . . . . (p.943)
T: 0141 6212212
E: alafferty@laffertylaw.com

LAFFERTY, Megan Claire (Sept 2015)
(Employee)
JustRight Scotland LLP, Glasgow . . . . . . (p.994)
T: 0141 406 5350
E: megan@justrightscotland.org.uk

LAFFERTY, Philip Andrew (Sept 1987)
(Director)
Clyde Defence Lawyers Limited,
Clydebank . . . . (p.785)
T: 0141 9512211
E: plafferty@clydedefencelawyers.com

LAFFERTY, Stephen James (Jan 1992) (Partner)
Hodge Solicitors LLP, Blairgowrie . . . . . . (p.775)
T: 01250 874441
E: sjlafferty@hodgesolicitors.co.uk

LAHATSKAYA, Maryia Alexandrovna
(Sept 2020) (Employee)
Dickson Minto, Edinburgh . . . . (p.861)
T: 0131 2254455
E: Maria.Lahatskaya@dmws.com

LAIDLAW, Catriona Ann (Jan 2020) (Employee)
SKO Family Law Specialists LLP,
Edinburgh . . . . (p.903)
T: 0131 3226669
E: catriona.laidlaw@sko-family.co.uk

LAIDLAW, Jack Robert (Dec 2019) (Employee)
CMS Cameron McKenna Nabarro Olswang LLP,
Edinburgh . . . . (p.856)
T: 0131 2288000
E: jack.laidlaw@cms-cmno.com

LAING, Alison Mary (Oct 2007) (Employee)
Ormistons Law Practice Limited,
Glenrothes . . . . (p.1057)
T: 0800 7810413
E: Alaing@ormistonslaw.co.uk

LAING, Andrew Simon Douglas (Dec 1993)
(Employee)
Procurator Fiscal Service,
Edinburgh . . . . (p.1229)
T: (0844) 561 3268
E: andrew.laing@copfs.gov.uk

LAING, Caroline Margaret (Jul 2020)
(Employee)
Shetland Islands Council, Lerwick . . . . . (p.1250)
T: 01595 744087
E: caroline.laing@shetland.gov.uk

LAING, Emma Alexandra (Sept 2017)
(Employee)
Procurator Fiscal Service,
Edinburgh . . . . (p.1229)
T: 0300 0203000
E: emma.laing@copfs.gov.uk

LAING, Ian Forbes (Jul 1993) (Employee)
Pinsent Masons MPillay LLP,
Singapore . . . . (p.1276)
T: +65 6305 8494
E: ian.laing@pinsentmasons.com

LAING, Innes (Dec 1991) (Partner)
Digby Brown LLP, Kirkcaldy . . . . (p.1099)
T: 0333 200 5925
E: innes.laing@digbybrown.co.uk

LAING, Louise Anne (Sept 2003) (Employee)
Brodies LLP, Glasgow . . . . (p.948)
T: 0141 2484672
E: louise.laing@brodies.com

LAING, Louise Ruth Niven (Aug 2008)
(Employee)
Fife Community Law Limited,
Lochgelly . . . . (p.1120)
T: 01592 786710
E: Louise.laing@fifelawcentre.co.uk

LAING, Therese Isabel Eilidh (Aug 2018)
(Employee)
Idox Software Limited, Glasgow . . . . . . (p.1240)
T: 0333 011 1518
E: therese.laing@idoxgroup.com

LAIRD, Cheryl Davina (Apr 2016) (Employee)
Reynolds Porter Chamberlain LLP, London
E1 . . . . (p.1267)
E: Cheryl.Laird@rpc.co.uk

LAIRD, Graeme Alexander (Sept 1995)
(Partner)
Deans Solicitors and Estate Agents LLP,
Edinburgh . . . . (p.860)
T: 0131 667 1900
E: graeme.laird@deansproperties.co.uk

LAIRD, James (Mar 2021) (Employee)
Pinsent Masons LLP, Glasgow . . . . (p.1031)
T: 0141 567 8400
E: james.laird@pinsentmasons.com

LAIRD, Pamela (Oct 1995) (Associate)
Pinsent Masons LLP, Edinburgh . . . . (p.895)
T: 0131 777 7000
E: Pamela.Laird@pinsentmasons.com

LAMB, Alexander McDougal (Jun 2008)
(Partner)
Lindsays LLP, Glasgow . . . .(p.1001)
T: 0141 2216551
E: sandylamb@lindsays.co.uk

LAMB, Douglas Cameron (Dec 1983) (Partner)
MacRoberts LLP, Glasgow . . . .(p.1015)
T: 0141 3031100
E: douglas.lamb@macroberts.com

LAMB, James MacArthur (Dec 1975) (Partner)
Maitlands, Greenock . . . .(p.1062)
T: 01475 892131
E: minfo@maitlands.org.uk

LAMB, Katie Alice Jean (Jul 2008) (Employee)
Lloyds Banking Group Plc,
Edinburgh . . . .(p.1224)
T: (0131) 442 9579
E: Katie.Lamb@LloydsBanking.com

LAMB, Linda Sutherland (Oct 1993) (Solicitor)
LSL Family Law, Eastbourne . . . .(p.1259)
T: 01273 041011
E: linda@lslfamilylaw.co.uk

LAMB, Pamela Jean Booth (Feb 2021)
(Employee)
Drummond Miller LLP, Glasgow . . . . . .(p.971)
T: 0141 3320086
E: plamb@drummondmiller.co.uk

LAMB, Simon Colum (Sept 2010) (Employee)
Tesco Personal Finance Plc,
Edinburgh . . . .(p.1234)
T: (0131) 274 3426
E: Simon.Lamb@tescobank.com

LAMBERT, Alistair Scott (Dec 1983) (Partner)
Lambert & Co.,, Ayr . . . .(p.764)
T: 01292 282811
E: lambert.asl@btconnect.com

LAMBERT, Graham Ian (Jan 2006) (Employee)
Thorntons Law LLP, Perth . . . .(p.1151)
T: 01738 621212
E: glambert@thorntons-law.co.uk

LAMBERT, Roderick Stewart (Dec 2002)
(Consultant)
Gunnercooke SCO LLP, Edinburgh . . . . .(p.876)
E: Rod.Lambert@gunnercooke.com

LAMBERTON, Matthew Robert Leslie
(Oct 2016) (Employee)
Shepherd and Wedderburn LLP, London
EC2 . . . .(p.1268)
T: 020 74294900
E: matthew.lamberton@shepwedd.com

LAMBIE, Andrew (Mar 1977) (Partner)
Lambie Law Partnership, Glasgow . . . . .(p.998)
T: 0141 9597000
E: enquiries@lambielaw.co.uk

LAMBIE, Anne Rose (Feb 2011) (Employee)
Lambie Law Partnership, Glasgow . . . . .(p.998)
T: 0141 959 7000

LAMBIE, Emma Morna (Aug 2015) (Employee)
Procurator Fiscal Service,
Edinburgh . . . .(p.1227)
T: 0300 0203168
E: Emma.Lambie@copfs.gov.uk

LAMBIE, Kiera Rae (Sept 2021) (Employee)
Jones Whyte LLP, Glasgow . . . .(p.993)
T: 0141 375 1222
E: kiera.lambie@joneswhyte.co.uk

LAMLEY, Alexander James (Sept 2012)
(Associate)
MBM Commercial LLP, Edinburgh . . . . .(p.889)
T: 0131 2268200
E: Alexander.Lamley@mbmcommercial.co.uk

LAMOND, Clare Elizabeth (Oct 1993)
(Associate)
Womble Bond Dickinson (UK) LLP,
Edinburgh . . . .(p.913)
T: 0345 415 0000
E: clare.lamond@wbd-uk.com

LAMONT, Hannah Louise (Oct 2016)
(Employee)
Brodies LLP, Edinburgh . . . .(p.845)
T: 0131 2283777
E: hannah.lamont@brodies.com

LAMONT, Steven (May 1995) (Director)
Lamonts Law Limited, Dundee . . . .(p.813)
T: 01382 220202
E: stevelamont@lamontsols.com

LANCASTER, Bruce Donald Tyrie (Sept 1997)
(Partner)
Davidson Chalmers Stewart LLP,
Edinburgh . . . .(p.859)
T: 0131 6259191
E: bruce.lancaster@dcslegal.com

LANCASTER, Kevin Edward (Jul 1990) (Partner)
Watson & Lyall Bowie, Blairgowrie . . . . .(p.776)
T: 01828 628395

LAND, Douglas Richard (Nov 1999) (Partner)
CMS Cameron McKenna Nabarro Olswang LLP,
London EC4 . . . .(p.1263)
T: 0207 3673000
E: Doug.Land@cms-cmno.com

LANDA, Gary Simon (Oct 1987) (Consultant)
Austin Lafferty Limited, Glasgow . . . . . .(p.942)
T: 0141 6115221
E: gary@landalegal.com

LANDELS, Morgan Scott (May 2021)
(Employee)
MBM Commercial LLP, Edinburgh . . . . .(p.889)
T: 0131 2268200
E: morgan.landels@mbmcommercial.co.uk

LANE, Alexandra Mae (Jan 2013) (Employee)
Shepherd and Wedderburn LLP,
Aberdeen . . . .(p.742)
T: 01224 621166
E: Alexandra.Lane@shepwedd.com

LANE, Eleanor Rosamond Anne (Nov 2000)
(Partner)
CMS Cameron McKenna Nabarro Olswang LLP,
Glasgow. . . . .(p.962)
T: 0141 2222200
E: Eleanor.Lane@cms-cmno.com

LANE, Victoria Miller (Aug 2013) (Employee)
Brodies LLP, Edinburgh . . . .(p.845)
T: 0131 2283777
E: victoria.lane@brodies.com

LANE, William John McAllister (Jan 2012)
(Employee)
Peninsula Business Services Limited,
Glasgow. . . . .(p.1241)
E: william.lane@peninsula-uk.com

LANG, Carolyn Jane (Oct 2015) (Employee)
Pinsent Masons LLP, Edinburgh . . . .(p.895)
T: 0131 777 7000
E: carolyn.lang@pinsentmasons.com

LANG, Joanna Linda (Mar 2012) (Employee)
Pinsent Masons LLP, Aberdeen . . . .(p.739)
T: 01224 377900
E: joanna.lang@pinsentmasons.com

LANG, Joanna Marion (Jan 2003) (Solicitor)
NO FIRM

LANG, Karen (Aug 1999) (Partner)
Harper Macleod LLP, Glasgow . . . .(p.983)
T: 0141 2218888
E: karen.lang@harpermacleod.co.uk

LANG, Kathleen Heather (Jan 1983) (Employee)
Irwin Mitchell Scotland LLP,
Glasgow. . . . .(p.991)
T: 0141 3004300
E: kathleen.lang@irwinmitchell.com

LANG, Kenneth Balfour (May 1989) (Partner)
Mellicks, Incorporating Naftalin Duncan & Co.,
Glasgow. . . . .(p.1019)
T: 0141 3320902
E: kenneth.lang@mellicks.co.uk

LANG, Margaret Jane (Oct 1984) (Consultant)
Russel + Aitken (Falkirk + Alloa) Ltd,
Falkirk . . . .(p.924)
T: 01324 622888
E: MargaretLang@randa-fa.co.uk

LANGAN, Hazel Joyce Selena (Aug 2008)
(Partner)
McLean & Stewart LLP, Dunblane . . . . .(p.804)
T: 01786 823217
E: Hazel.Langan@mcleanandstewart.co.uk

LANGAN, Paul Damien (Aug 1981) (Partner)
Quinn, Martin & Langan, Glasgow . . . .(p.1033)
T: 0141 332 3702
E: pauldlangan@googlemail.com

LANGEROED, Jacqueline (Aug 1994)
(Employee)
Siemens Energy AS, Oslo . . . .(p.1275)
T: +47 482 67547
E: jacqueline.langeroed@siemens-energy.com

LANGLANDS, Laura-anne (Nov 2008)
(Employee)
National Health Service Scotland,
Edinburgh . . . .(p.1225)
T: 0131 2757800
E: laura-anne.langlands@nhs.scot

LANGLEY, Kimberley Patricia (Oct 2005)
(Employee)
Fife Council, Glenrothes . . . .(p.1246)
T: 03451 550000
E: kimberley.langley@fife.gov.uk

LANGLEY, Timothy Isaac (Nov 2010)
(Employee)
Comhairle Nan Eilean Siar,
Stornoway . . . .(p.1255)
T: 01851 822604
E: tim.langley@cne-siar.gov.uk

LANGRIDGE, Michael Richard (Sept 2018)
(Employee)
Baillie Gifford & Co, Edinburgh . . . . . .(p.1220)
T: 0131 2752000
E: mike.langridge@bailliegifford.com

LANGRIDGE, Robert Matthew (Sept 2013)
(Employee)
Brodies LLP, Edinburgh . . . .(p.845)
T: 0131 2283777
E: bob.langridge@brodies.com

LANGSKOG, Patrick Magnus Shepherd
(Jun 2010) (Employee)
Ashtead Technology, Westhill . . . .(p.1255)
E: Patrick.Langskog@ashtead-technology.com

LANIGAN, Brian Joseph (Nov 1975) (Partner)
B.J. Lanigan & Co, Glasgow . . . .(p.998)
T: 0141 9440671
E: brian.lanigan@btinternet.com

LANN, Liza Claire (Aug 2001) (Employee)
Procurator Fiscal Service, Hamilton . . . .(p.1247)
T: 0844 5613245
E: Liza.Lann@copfs.gov.uk

LANNIGAN, Sara Isabel (Feb 2008) (Employee)
Brodies LLP, Edinburgh . . . .(p.845)
T: 0131 2283777
E: sara.lannigan@brodies.com

LARG, Lesley Ann (Oct 2000) (Partner)
Thorntons Law LLP, Dundee . . . .(p.819)
T: 01382 229 111
E: llarg@thorntons-law.co.uk

LARGE, Christopher James (Nov 2021)
(Employee)
Robertson Wyse, Cowdenbeath . . . .(p.788)
T: 01383 515020

LARKIN, Charlotte Mary (Oct 2016) (Employee)
BTO Solicitors LLP, Glasgow . . . .(p.952)
T: 0141 2218012
E: cla@bto.co.uk

LARKIN, Jamie Paul (Jul 2012) (Employee)
Liquidity Services, London EC3 . . . . . .(p.1266)
T: 020 70983706
E: Jamie.Larkin@liquidityservices.com

LASISZ, Artur (Jun 2018) (Partner)
McEwan Fraser Legal, Edinburgh . . . . . .(p.885)
T: 0131 5249797
E: artur.lasisz@mcewanfraserlegal.co.uk

LATHAM, Jacqueline Shirley (Aug 1987)
(Partner)
Latham & Co., Dumfries . . . .(p.801)
T: 01387 252888
E: office1@lathamandco.com

LATHAM, Viktoria Katy (Aug 2015) (Employee)
Burness Paull LLP, Aberdeen . . . .(p.724)
T: 01224 621621
E: viktoria.latham@burnesspaull.com

LATIF, Shahid (Sept 1995) (Director)
Craig Wood Solicitors Limited,
Inverness . . . .(p.1083)
T: 01463 225544
E: shahid.latif@craigwood.co.uk

LATIF, Zahra Marie (Aug 2011) (Employee)
Procurator Fiscal Service, Glasgow . . . .(p.1241)
T: 0300 0203000
E: Zahra.Latif@copfs.gov.uk

LATTA, Fraser Paterson (Nov 2003) (Director)
Latta Law Limited, Glasgow . . . .(p.998)
T: 0141 222 2185
E: fl@lattalaw.co.uk

LATTA, Paul (Jun 2007) (Employee)
Glasgow City Council, Glasgow . . . . . .(p.1239)
T: 0141 2875793
E: paul.latta@glasgow.gov.uk

LATTA, Sarah Elizabeth (Nov 2019) (Employee)
Procurator Fiscal Service,
Edinburgh . . . .(p.1229)
T: 0300 0203000
E: sarah.latta@copfs.gov.uk

LAU, Ka Pui Cathy (Oct 2007) (Employee)
Burness Paull LLP, Glasgow . . . .(p.954)
T: 0141 2484933
E: Cathy.Lau@burnesspaull.com

LAU, Kylie (Mar 2021) (Employee)
AJ Bradley & Co Ltd, Glasgow . . . .(p.947)
T: 0141 374 0474

LAUCHLAN, Nicola (Apr 2003) (Employee)
NORTH LANARKSHIRERe Council,
Motherwell. . . . .(p.1251)
T: 01698 302261
E: lauchlann@northlan.gov.uk

LAUDER, Kenneth Corson, WS (Apr 1984)
(Partner)
Stuart & Stuart, Edinburgh . . . .(p.905)
T: 0131 2286449
E: klauder@stuartandstuart.co.uk

LAUDER, Kenneth William (Dec 1988)
(Employee)
Gilson Gray LLP, Edinburgh . . . .(p.874)
T: 0131 5165354
E: klauder@gilsongray.co.uk

LAUDER, Kirsty Moira (Jan 2019) (Employee)
The Scottish Parliament, Edinburgh . . .(p.1235)
T: (0131) 3486653
E: kirsty.lauder@parliament.scot

LAUGHLAND, Jennifer (Nov 1996) (Employee)
Civil Legal Assistance Office,
Edinburgh . . . .(p.1222)
T: 0131 2401960
E: laughlandje@clao.org.uk

LAUGHLAND, Russell Stuart (Nov 2013)
(Associate)
Anderson Strathern LLP, Edinburgh . . . .(p.839)
T: 0131 2707700
E: russell.laughland@andersonstrathern.co.uk

LAUGHTON, Graham Ritch (Sept 2002)
(Director)
Macleod & MacCallum Limited,
Inverness . . . .(p.1080)
T: 01463 239393
E: graham.laughton@macandmac.co.uk

LAURIE, Amanda-Jane (Sept 1993) (Partner)
Burness Paull LLP, Edinburgh . . . .(p.850)
T: 0131 4736000
E: Mandy.Laurie@burnesspaull.com

LAURIE, Jennifer Macdonald (Nov 2002)
(Associate)
Brodies LLP, Glasgow . . . .(p.948)
T: 0141 2484672
E: jennifer.laurie@brodies.com

LAURIE, Melissa Lugton (Mar 2021) (Employee)
CMS Cameron McKenna Nabarro Olswang LLP,
Edinburgh . . . .(p.856)
T: 0131 2288000
E: melissa.laurie@cms-cmno.com

LAURIE, Sian Elizabeth (May 2018) (Employee)
Starling Bank Limited, London EC2 . . .(p.1268)
E: sian.laurie@starlingbank.com

LAVELLE, Brian James (Oct 1996) (Employee)
Scottish Government, Edinburgh . . . . .(p.1231)
T: 0131 244 0815
E: Brian.Lavelle@gov.scot

LAVELLE, Jill Naysmith (Sept 2004) (Employee)
NO FIRM

LAVELLE, Nicole Lee Ann (Jan 2012) (Employee)
Procurator Fiscal Service,
Edinburgh . . . .(p.1227)
T: 0300 0203168
E: nicole.lavelle@copfs.gov.uk

LAVELLE, Paula (Jul 2003) (Partner)
Paula Lavelle Solicitor, Glasgow . . . .(p.998)
T: 07710 251587
E: paulalavelle@yahoo.co.uk

LAVELLE, William Moore (Aug 1992) (Director)
Bridge Legal Limited, Glasgow . . . .(p.948)
T: 0141 4293100
E: billymlavelle@gmail.com

LAVERTY, Denise Karen (Jan 2005) (Partner)
Gilson Gray LLP, Glasgow . . . .(p.980)
T: 0141 5302021
E: dlaverty@gilsongray.co.uk

LAVERTY, Edward Lawrence (Oct 1985)
(Partner)
Miller Samuel Hill Brown LLP,
Glasgow . . . .(p.1020)
T: 0141 2211919
E: ell@mshblegal.com

LAVERTY, James (Oct 1988) (Partner)
MML Legal, Dundee . . . .(p.817)
T: 01382 206 000
E: jim@muirmyleslaverty.co.uk

LAVERY, Alexandra Lyn (Nov 2007) (Employee)
Transport For London, London E20 . . .(p.1269)
T: 020 30543964
E: alexandralavery@tfl.gov.uk

LAVERY, Calum Euan (Apr 2021) (Employee)
MacRoberts LLP, Edinburgh . . . .(p.887)
T: 0131 2295046
E: calum.lavery@macroberts.com

LAVERY, Martin (Sept 2020) (Employee)
Balfour + Manson LLP, Edinburgh . . . . .(p.841)
T: 0131 2001200
E: Martin.Lavery@balfour-manson.co.uk

LAW, Chloe Ashton (Sept 2017) (Employee)
James Fisher and Sons Plc,
Glasgow. . . . .(p.1240)
E: C.Law@jfdglobal.com

LAW, Deborah Caroline (Sept 2011)
(Employee)
Stronachs LLP, Aberdeen . . . .(p.744)
T: 01224 845845
E: deborah.law@stronachs.com

LAW, Elizabeth Jean Marie (Feb 2007) (Partner)
Brodies LLP, Dingwall . . . .(p.796)
T: 01349 860111
E: lisa.law@brodies.com

LAW, Gavin John (Oct 2012) (Employee)
Directorate of Army Legal Services,
Andover . . . .(p.1258)
T: 07792 713 309
E: gavin.law102@mod.gov.uk

LAW, Gillian (Aug 1997) (Employee)
Nigel Beaumont & Co., Edinburgh . . . . .(p.842)
T: 0131 5573565
E: gillian.law@nigelbeaumont.co.uk

LAW, Graham Fleming (Sept 1983)
(Consultant)
Walker & Sharpe, Dumfries . . . .(p.803)
T: 01387 267222
E: graham.law@walker-sharpe.co.uk

LAW, Jacqueline (Jan 1995) (Partner)
Aberdein Considine and Company,
Aberdeen . . . .(p.718)
T: 01224 589700
E: jlaw@acandco.com

LAW, Janie Kerr (Nov 1987) (Partner)
Family Law Matters Scotland LLP,
Glasgow. . . . .(p.975)
T: 0141 4202430
E: janie.law@flmscotland.co.uk

LAW, Jean Hamilton (Nov 1988) (Employee)
North Ayrshire Council, Irvine . . . .(p.1249)
T: 01294 310000
E: jhlaw@north-ayrshire.gov.uk

LAW, Lesley (Feb 2020) (Employee)
Angus Council, Forfar . . . .(p.1237)
T: 01307 476228
E: LawL@angus.gov.uk

LAW, Naiomi India (May 2018) (Employee)
Brodies LLP, Edinburgh . . . .(p.845)
T: 0131 2283777
E: naiomi.law@brodies.com

LAW, Patricia Alexandra (Nov 1992)
(Employee)
Baillie Gifford & Co, Edinburgh . . . . . .(p.1220)
T: 0131 2752000
E: patricia.law@bailliegifford.com

LAW, Raiya (Oct 2008) (Employee)
Stronachs LLP, Aberdeen . . . .(p.744)
T: 01224 845845
E: raiya.law@stronachs.com

LAW, Stephanie Mary (Oct 2018) (Employee)
Kennedys Scotland, Edinburgh. . . . .(p.880)
T: 0131 2256145
E: stephanie.law@kennedyslaw.com

LAW, Susan Jane (Nov 2001) (Partner)
Lindsays LLP, Edinburgh . . . .(p.882)
T: 0131 656 5681
E: susanlaw@lindsays.co.uk

LAW, Teresa Anne (Dec 1999) (Associate)
Raeburn Christie Clark & Wallace LLP,
    Aberdeen . . . . (p.741)
    T: 01224 332400
    E: teresa.law@raeburns.co.uk

LAW-REED, April (Oct 2008) (Employee)
Sportscotland, Glasgow . . . . (p.1244)
    T: 0141 5346513
    E: april.law-reed@sportscotland.org.uk

LAWLESS, Robert Andrew (Nov 2019)
    (Associate)
Anderson Strathern LLP, Edinburgh . . . . (p.839)
    T: 0131 2707700
    E: robert.lawless@andersonstrathern.co.uk

LAWRENCE, Dorothy (Oct 1990) (Associate)
MacRoberts LLP, Edinburgh . . . . (p.887)
    T: 0131 2295046
    E: dorothy.lawrence@macroberts.com

LAWRENCE, Hannah Shyamali (Sept 2014)
    (Employee)
Morton Fraser LLP, Edinburgh . . . . (p.891)
    T: 0131 2471000
    E: hannah.lawrence@morton-fraser.com

LAWRENCE, Helen Anne (Sept 2004)
    (Associate)
Digby Brown LLP, Edinburgh . . . . (p.862)
    T: 0333 200 5925
    E: Helen.Lawrence@digbybrown.co.uk

LAWRENCE, Wayne (Feb 1992) (Partner)
DWF LLP, Edinburgh . . . . (p.865)
    T: 0131 2265541
    E: Wayne.Lawrence@dwf.law

LAWRIE, Andrew Livingstone (Feb 1981)
    (Partner)
Lawrie Jackson, Glasgow . . . . (p.998)
    T: 0141 2481111
    E: andrewlawrie@lawriejackson.co.uk

LAWRIE, Anne Scott (Jul 2014) (Employee)
Anderson Strathern LLP, Edinburgh . . . . (p.839)
    T: 0131 2707700
    E: anne.lawrie@andersonstrathern.co.uk

LAWRIE, Colin Thomas (Sept 1995) (Partner)
CMS Cameron McKenna Nabarro Olswang LLP,
    Edinburgh . . . . (p.856)
    T: 0131 2288000
    E: Colin.Lawrie@cms-cmno.com

LAWRIE, Emma (Jun 2011) (Employee)
Morison & Smith Limited, Lanark . . . . . (p.1108)
    T: 01555 662488
    E: emma@morisonandsmith.com

LAWRIE, Fergus Gordon (Sept 2020)
    (Employee)
Dentons UK and Middle East LLP,
    Glasgow . . . . (p.968)
    T: 0330 2220050
    E: fergus.lawrie@dentons.com

LAWRIE, Fraser Livingstone (Jul 2014)
    (Employee)
Lawrie Jackson, Glasgow . . . . (p.998)
    T: 0141 2481111
    E: fraser@lawriejackson.co.uk

LAWRIE, Lucy Emma (Apr 2002) (Employee)
Pinsent Masons LLP, Edinburgh . . . . (p.895)
    T: 0131 777 7000
    E: lucy.lawrie@pinsentmasons.com

LAWRIE MORRISON, Donald Angus
    (Jul 2019) (Employee)
Squire Patton Boggs (UK) LLP, London
    EC2 . . . . (p.1268)
    T: 020 7655 1000
    E: donald.lawriemorrison@squirepb.com

LAWSON, Angela (Jan 1998) (Employee)
Scottish Government, Edinburgh . . . . . (p.1231)
    T: 0131 244 0815
    E: Angela.Lawson@gov.scot

LAWSON, Brian Daniel (Nov 2014) (Partner)
Sneddons SSC, Boness . . . . (p.778)
    T: 01506 826232
    E: brian@sneddons.com

LAWSON, Cara Jacqueline (Mar 2016)
    (Employee)
Fergusson Law, Edinburgh . . . . (p.870)
    T: 0131 556 4044
    E: property@fergussonlaw.com

LAWSON, Christopher David Ernest
    (Aug 2019) (Employee)
Peterkins, Aberdeen . . . . (p.739)
    T: 01224 428000
    E: cel@peterkins.com

LAWSON, Gavin Ferguson (Oct 1996)
    (Employee)
Murray, Hamilton & Chalmers,
    Bellshill . . . . (p.773)
    T: 01698 327488
    E: mhc@mhcsol.co.uk

LAWSON, Greg Scott (Dec 2015) (Associate)
Peterkins, Aberdeen . . . . (p.739)
    T: 01224 428000
    E: GL@peterkins.com

LAWSON, Jay (Jan 2020) (Employee)
MML Legal, Dundee . . . . (p.817)
    T: 01382 206 000
    E: jay@mmllaw.co.uk

LAWSON, Jennifer Louise (Mar 2011)
    (Employee)
Aberdeen City Council, Aberdeen . . . . . (p.1211)
    T: 01224 522000
    E: jelawson@aberdeencity.gov.uk

LAWSON, John Francis (Oct 1984) (Partner)
Primrose & Gordon, Dumfries . . . . (p.802)
    T: 01387 267316
    E: johnfl@primroseandgordon.co.uk

LAWSON, Kathleen-Erin (Jan 2008) (Associate)
Thorntons Law LLP, Edinburgh . . . .(p.906)
T: 1312258705
E: klawson@thorntons-law.co.uk

LAWSON, Mark Crawford (Dec 1979)
(Consultant)
A D Stuart & Co. Limited,
Edinburgh . . . .(p.905)
T: 0845 056 3958
E: mark.lawson@stuart-co.com

LAWSON, Peter Alexander (Nov 1996)
(Partner)
Burness Paull LLP, Edinburgh . . . .(p.850)
T: 0131 4736000
E: Peter.Lawson@burnesspaull.com

LAWSON, Peter John (Dec 1981) (Director)
Hill Brown Licensing, Glasgow . . . .(p.986)
T: 0141 3323265
E: pjl@mshblegal.com

LAWSON, Philip Andrew (Oct 1990)
(Consultant)
Woodward Lawson, Aberdeen . . . .(p.747)
T: 01224 619330
E: philip@woodwardlawson.com

LAWSON, Rachel Linda (Jun 2018) (Employee)
Brodies LLP, Edinburgh . . . .(p.845)
T: 0131 2283777
E: rachel.lawson@brodies.com

LAWSON, Rosanna Skye (May 2013)
(Employee)
Janus Henderson Investors, London
EC2 . . . .(p.1265)
E: rosanna.lawson@janushenderson.com

LAWSON, Ruaraidh McVicar (Nov 2005)
(Partner)
Allan McDougall McQueen LLP,
Edinburgh . . . .(p.837)
T: 0131 2252121
E: rlawson@allanmcdougall.co.uk

LAWSON, Samuel Robert (Jun 2015)
(Employee)
Addleshaw Goddard LLP,
Edinburgh . . . .(p.835)
T: 0131 2282400
E: Sam.Lawson@addleshawgoddard.com

LAWTON, Isabel Graham (Jan 1995)
(Employee)
NORTH LANARKSHIRERe Council,
Motherwell. . . . .(p.1251)
T: 01698 302420
E: lawtoni@northlan.gov.uk

LAZZARIN, Andrew (Mar 2002) (Employee)
Procurator Fiscal Service,
Kilmarnock . . . .(p.1249)
T: 01563 536211
E: andrew.lazzarin@copfs.gov.uk

LE MAIN, Amber Suzanna Boyle (Sept 2013)
(Employee)
Procurator Fiscal Service,
Edinburgh . . . .(p.1227)
T: 0300 0203168
E: Amber.LeMain@copfs.gov.uk

LE SUEUR, Deborah Jane (Dec 2009)
(Employee)
Capita Business Services Limited,
Glasgow. . . . .(p.1238)
T: 07710 378547
E: debbie.lesueur@capita.co.uk

LEACH, Ian Paul (Oct 1982) (Partner)
Berrymans Lace Mawer LLP,
Edinburgh . . . .(p.842)
T: 0131 2259855
E: Ian.Leach@blmlaw.com

LEAHY, Darren John (Jul 2013) (Partner)
RSB Lindsays, Dundee . . . .(p.818)
T: 01382 224112
E: darrenleahy@lindsays.co.uk

LEAL, Allan David (Oct 2001) (Partner)
DLA Piper Scotland LLP, Edinburgh . . . .(p.863)
T: 08700 111111
E: allan.leal@dlapiper.com

LEAN, Hamish (Oct 1985) (Partner)
Shepherd and Wedderburn LLP,
Aberdeen . . . .(p.742)
T: 01224 621166
E: hamish.lean@shepwedd.com

LEATHAM, Ross James (Nov 2006) (Director)
Mitchells Roberton Ltd, Glasgow . . . . .(p.1020)
T: 0141 5523422
E: rjl@mitchells-roberton.co.uk

LECK, Morag Anne (Sept 1984) (Employee)
City of Edinburgh Council,
Edinburgh . . . .(p.1221)
T: (0131) 5294145
E: morag.leck@edinburgh.gov.uk

LECKIE, Carolyn (Nov 2016) (Employee)
GFM Law, Dundee . . . .(p.811)
T: 01382 223505

LECKIE, Emma (Nov 2012) (Solicitor)
NO FIRM

LECKIE, Kirsten Alana (Oct 2010) (Employee)
Burness Paull LLP, Glasgow . . . .(p.954)
T: 0141 2484933
E: Kirsten.Leckie@burnesspaull.com

LECKIE, Matthew William (Oct 2008) (Partner)
Digby Brown LLP, Glasgow . . . .(p.970)
T: 0141 566 9494
E: matt.leckie@digbybrown.co.uk

LECKIE, Robert Gilmour (Oct 2003) (Partner)
CMS Cameron McKenna Nabarro Olswang LLP,
London EC4 . . . .(p.1263)
   T: 0207 3673000
   E: robbie.leckie@cms-cmno.com

LEDGER, Connor Peter Philip (Jun 2021)
   (Employee)
Maguire Solicitors, Glasgow . . . .(p.1017)
   T: 0141 3312885
   E: connor@maguiresolicitors.co.uk

LEDSOM, Emma Christina (Oct 2004)
   (Employee)
Argyll & Bute Council,
   Lochgilphead . . . .(p.1251)
   T: 01546 602127
   E: emma.ledsom@argyll-bute.gov.uk

LEE ALLEN, Maya Elizabeth (Aug 2021)
   (Employee)
MacRoberts LLP, Edinburgh . . . .(p.887)
   T: 0131 2295046
   E: Maya.Allen@macroberts.com

LEE, Carol Margaret (Aug 2005) (Employee)
Spirit Production (Services) Limited,
   Aberdeen . . . .(p.1214)
   T: 01224 415000
   E: carol.lee@spirit-energy.com

LEE, Daniel Thomas (Nov 1999) (Partner)
Burges Salmon LLP, Edinburgh . . . .(p.850)
   T: 0131 3142112
   E: danny.lee@burges-salmon.com

LEE, Evalyn (Jul 2010) (Employee)
Brodies LLP, Edinburgh . . . .(p.845)
   T: 0131 2283777
   E: evalyn.lee@brodies.com

LEE, John James Armstrong (Oct 2000)
   (Partner)
Ledingham Chalmers LLP,
   Edinburgh . . . .(p.881)
   T: 0131 2001000
   E: john.lee@ledinghamchalmers.com

LEE, Katy Oi Kei (Sept 2016) (Solicitor)
NO FIRM

LEE, Laura (Nov 2019) (Employee)
Scotch Whisky Association,
   Edinburgh . . . .(p.1230)
   T: 0131 222 9200
   E: llee@swa.org.uk

LEE, Lindsay Isobel (Jan 1999) (Employee)
Brodies LLP, Edinburgh . . . .(p.845)
   T: 0131 2283777
   E: lindsay.lee@brodies.com

LEE, Minglye Lorna (Jun 1989) (Solicitor)
NO FIRM

LEE, Niamh Orla (Oct 2019) (Employee)
MML Legal, Dundee . . . .(p.817)
   T: 01382 206 000
   E: niamh@mmllaw.co.uk

LEE, Robyn Freda (Apr 2019) (Employee)
Blackadders LLP, Dundee . . . .(p.805)
   T: 01382 229222
   E: Robyn.Lee@blackadders.co.uk

LEECE, Sandra (Jul 2004) (Employee)
Vattenfall Wind Power Ltd.,
   Edinburgh . . . .(p.1235)
   T: 0131 5263131
   E: sandra.leece@vattenfall.com

LEEMING, Richard John (Feb 2016) (Partner)
Burges Salmon LLP, Bristol . . . .(p.1258)
   T: 0117 9392000
   E: richard.leeming@burges-salmon.com

LEES, Bruce David (Aug 1990) (Partner)
Taits, Kelso . . . .(p.1092)
   T: 01573 224311
   E: bruce.lees@taits.co.uk

LEES, Kerry (Jun 2021) (Employee)
Caesar & Howie, Bathgate . . . .(p.770)
   T: 01506 815900
   E: kle@caesar-howie.co.uk

LEFEVRE, Frank Hartley (May 1959) (Director)
Lefevres (Scotland) Limited,
   Edinburgh . . . .(p.882)
   T: 0845 305 2555
   E: fhl@lefevres.law

LEGGAT, Alice Margaret (Jul 2006) (Employee)
SSE Plc, Perth . . . .(p.1253)
   T: 01738 456 000
   E: alice.leggat@sse.com

LEGGAT, Eric (Sept 1993) (Employee)
Scottish Police Authority, Glasgow . . . .(p.1244)
   T: 01786 896892
   E: eric.leggat@spa.pnn.police.uk

LEGGAT, Finlay Crawford (Jul 2018) (Employee)
Morton Fraser LLP, Edinburgh . . . .(p.891)
   T: 0131 2471000
   E: finlay.leggat@morton-fraser.com

LEGGETT, Rachel Anne (Sept 2015) (Employee)
Pinsent Masons LLP, Edinburgh . . . .(p.895)
   T: +44 131 225 0090.
   E: rachel.leggett@pinsentmasons.com

LEGGETT, Richard (Sept 1982) (Director)
Holmes Mackillop Limited,
   Glasgow . . . .(p.986)
   T: 0141 956 5454
   E: rleggett@homack.co.uk

LEIGH, Simon Christopher (Jun 2017)
(Employee)
Civil Legal Assistance Office,
Inverness . . . .(p.1248)
T: 01463 641770
E: LeighSi@clao.org.uk

LEIPER, Iain James (Apr 2012) (Employee)
Mill and Millard LLP, Edinburgh . . . .(p.890)
T: 0131 3227222
E: il@millardlaw.co.uk

LEISHMAN, David James (Aug 1991) (Partner)
Black Hay, Ayr . . . .(p.760)
T: 01292 268988
E: david.leishman@blackhay.co.uk

LEISHMAN, David Michael (Jul 2015)
(Employee)
Archibald Sharp & Son Limited,
Glasgow . . . .(p.1039)
T: 0141 3393036
E: dleishman@archibaldsharp.co.uk

LEISHMAN, Keith Robert Buchanan
(Oct 2007) (Partner)
Keith Leishman & Co Defence,
Edinburgh . . . .(p.882)
T: 07590 315434
E: leishmandefence@outlook.com

LEISHMAN, Ruairidh James McIlroy
(Jul 2018) (Employee)
Shepherd and Wedderburn LLP,
Edinburgh . . . .(p.900)
T: 0131 2289900
E: ruairidh.leishman@shepwedd.com

LEITCH, Andrew David (Oct 2014) (Employee)
Bryan Cave Leighton Paisner LLP, London
EC4 . . . .(p.1262)
E: Andrew.Leitch@blplaw.com

LEITCH, Kirsty Sarah Jane (Nov 2013)
(Employee)
The McKinstry Company LLP, Ayr . . . . .(p.765)
T: 01292 281711

LEITH, Graeme William (Nov 1999) (Partner)
Brodies LLP, Edinburgh . . . .(p.845)
T: 0131 2283777
E: graeme.leith@brodies.com

LEITH, Michael (Jul 2020) (Employee)
Raeburn Christie Clark & Wallace LLP,
Aberdeen . . . .(p.741)
T: 01224 332400
E: Michael.Leith@raeburns.co.uk

LEITH, Robin James (Aug 1985) (Partner)
Andersonbain LLP, Aberdeen . . . .(p.721)
T: 01224 456789
E: rleith@andersonbain.co.uk

LEITH-PARSONS, Rachael Samantha
(Jan 2012) (Employee)
Axle Group Holdings Limited,
Glasgow . . . .(p.1238)
T: 0141 6323222
E: axle.rlp@gmail.com

LENNIE, Alasdair Hugh (Aug 2020) (Employee)
Ventient Energy, Edinburgh . . . .(p.1235)
E: Alasdair.Lennie@ventientenergy.com

LENNIE, Gemma Hope (Sept 2015) (Employee)
Pinsent Masons LLP, Edinburgh . . . .(p.895)
T: 0131 777 7000
E: gemma.lennie@pinsentmasons.com

LENNON, Claire Violet (Oct 2002) (Employee)
SSE Plc, Perth . . . .(p.1253)
T: 01738 456 000
E: claire.lennon@sse.com

LENNOX, Grace (Sept 2016) (Employee)
Scottish Children's Reporter Administration,
Glasgow . . . .(p.1243)
T: 0300 2001444
E: grace.lennox@scra.gov.uk

LENNOX, Lisa Woods (Mar 2021) (Employee)
Shepherd and Wedderburn LLP,
Glasgow . . . .(p.1039)
T: 0141 5669900
E: Lisa.Lennox@shepwedd.com

LENNOX, Sophie (Nov 2019) (Employee)
BTO Solicitors LLP, Edinburgh . . . .(p.849)
T: 0131 2222939
E: sle@bto.co.uk

LENNOX, Timothy John William (Dec 2012)
(Employee)
Kennedys Scotland, Glasgow . . . .(p.995)
T: 0141 4370 2954
E: tim.lennox@kennedyslaw.com

LENNOX, William Gordon (Nov 2010)
(Employee)
Macdonald Henderson Limited,
Glasgow . . . .(p.1008)
T: 0141 2484957
E: gordon@macdonaldhenderson.co.uk

LEON, Matthew Pablo Andrew (Oct 2013)
(Employee)
CMS Cameron McKenna Nabarro Olswang LLP,
Edinburgh . . . .(p.856)
T: 0131 2288000
E: matt.leon@cms-cmno.com

LESLIE, Andrew Stuart (Sept 2014) (Employee)
Gillespie Macandrew LLP,
Edinburgh . . . .(p.872)
T: 0131 2251677
E: Andrew.Leslie@gillespiemacandrew.co.uk

LESLIE, Douglas Grant (Oct 1983) (Partner)
Leslie Law Practice, Cupar . . . .(p.792)
T: 01334 650166
E: douglas@leslielaw.co.uk

LESLIE, Douglas Stuart (Jul 2021) (Employee)
MacRoberts LLP, Glasgow . . . .(p.1015)
T: 0141 3031100
E: Douglas.Leslie@macroberts.com

LESLIE, Forbes Gillies (Dec 1978) (Partner)
Dallas McMillan, Glasgow . . . .(p.966)
T: 0141 3336750
E: fgl@dallasmcmillan.co.uk

LESLIE, Fraser Gordon (Jan 1983) (Partner)
Gillespie Macandrew LLP,
Edinburgh . . . .(p.872)
T: 0131 2251677
E: fraser.leslie@gillespiemacandrew.co.uk

LESLIE, Hannah Christine (Sept 2018)
(Employee)
JPIMedia Limited, Edinburgh . . . .(p.1224)
E: hannah.leslie@jpimedia.co.uk

LESLIE, Iain Alexander (Oct 1986) (Partner)
Leslie & Co. SSC, Edinburgh . . . .(p.882)
T: 0131 4478182
E: iain@leslieandco.co.uk

LESLIE, Jacqueline (Oct 1993) (Partner)
Harper Macleod LLP, Glasgow . . . .(p.983)
T: 0141 2218888
E: jacqueline.leslie@harpermacleod.co.uk

LESLIE, Kim Louise (Oct 1999) (Partner)
Digby Brown LLP, Edinburgh . . . .(p.862)
T: 0131 319 8123
E: kim.leslie@digbybrown.co.uk

LESLIE, Richard Dunbar (Nov 1996) (Partner)
Shepherd and Wedderburn LLP,
Edinburgh . . . .(p.900)
T: 0131 2289900
E: richard.leslie@shepwedd.com

LESLIE, Sarah Victoria (Oct 2015) (Employee)
Shepherd and Wedderburn LLP,
Edinburgh . . . .(p.900)
T: 0131 2289900
E: sarah.leslie@shepwedd.com

LESLIE, Stuart (Apr 2014) (Employee)
NEO Energy, Aberdeen . . . .(p.1213)
T: (01224) 659120
E: stuart.leslie@neweuropeanoffshore.com

LESLIE, Susan Jane (Sept 1996) (Associate)
Morton Fraser LLP, Edinburgh . . . .(p.891)
T: 0131 2471000
E: susan.leslie@morton-fraser.com

LESLIE, Victoria Jane (Oct 2003) (Partner)
Ledingham Chalmers LLP,
Inverness . . . .(p.1078)
T: 01463 667400
E: victoria.leslie@ledinghamchalmers.com

LETFORD, Gavin (Sept 2010) (Employee)
Procurator Fiscal Service, Dundee . . . . .(p.1218)
T: 01382 342559
E: Gavin.Letford@copfs.gov.uk

LETFORD, Kirsten Watson (Sept 2014)
(Employee)
Procurator Fiscal Service, Dundee . . . . .(p.1218)
T: 01382 342559
E: Kirsten.Letford@copfs.gov.uk

LETHAM, Emma Louise (Sept 2013) (Employee)
Wright, Johnston & Mackenzie LLP,
Glasgow. . . . .(p.1054)
T: 0141 2483434
E: ell@wjm.co.uk

LETHAM, Fiona (Oct 1994) (Employee)
CMS Cameron McKenna Nabarro Olswang LLP,
Glasgow. . . . .(p.962)
T: 0141 2222200
E: Fiona.Letham@cms-cmno.com

LETSON, Jack Stewart (Aug 2007) (Partner)
CMS Cameron McKenna Nabarro Olswang LLP,
Glasgow. . . . .(p.962)
T: 0141 2222200
E: Jack.Letson@cms-cmno.com

LETSON, Sarah Grace (Jul 2009) (Employee)
DLA Piper UK LLP, London EC1 . . . . . .(p.1263)
T: 2077966639
E: sarah.letson@dlapiper.com

LEUCHARS, Catriona Ann (May 2021)
(Employee)
Miller Hendry, Dundee . . . .(p.816)
T: 01382 200000
E: catrionaleuchars@millerhendry.co.uk

LEWIN, Johanne Sinclair (Sept 2007)
(Employee)
SSE Plc, Perth . . . .(p.1253)
T: 01738 456 000
E: johanne.lewin@sse.com

LEWIN, Peter Edward James (Oct 2014)
(Solicitor)
NO FIRM

LEWIS, David William (Nov 1995) (Associate)
Shepherd and Wedderburn LLP,
Edinburgh . . . .(p.900)
T: 0131 2289900
E: david.lewis@shepwedd.com

LEWIS, Gillian Sarah (Oct 2003) (Employee)
Davitt Jones Bould Limited, London
SE1 . . . .(p.1263)

LEWIS, Holly (Oct 2021) (Employee)
Midlothian Council, Dalkeith . . . .(p.1216)
T: 0131 2707500
E: holly.lewis@midlothian.gov.uk

LEWIS, Jamie McMillan (Jul 2009) (Employee)
Leonardo UK Ltd, Edinburgh . . . .(p.1224)
T: 0131 3435957
E: jamie.lewis@leonardocompany.com

LEWIS, Vicky Lee (Oct 2001) (Partner)
TC Young LLP, Edinburgh . . . .(p.914)
T: 0131 2207660
E: vll@tcyoung.co.uk

LEWIS-LAVERTY, Christopher Lindsay
(Aug 2018) (Employee)
Sodexo Limited, London WC1 . . . .(p.1268)
T: 7824550841

LEY, Andrew Charles (Nov 1999) (Partner)
Addleshaw Goddard LLP,
Edinburgh . . . .(p.835)
T: 0131 2282400
E: Andrew.Ley@addleshawgoddard.com

LEYDEN, Erin Christina (Jun 2016) (Employee)
Renfrewshire Council, Paisley . . . .(p.1252)
T: 0141 8403471
E: erin.leyden@renfrewshire.gov.uk

LEYSHON, Donald John (Jul 1998) (Partner)
Leyshon WS, Innerleithen . . . .(p.1074)
T: 07740-589479
E: john.leyshon@leyshonws.co.uk

LI, Georgina Kit Yin (Oct 2019) (Associate)
Simpson & Marwick, Edinburgh . . . . . .(p.903)
T: 01224 606210
E: Georgina.li@simpsonmarwick.com

LI, Ningzhou Lemon (Mar 2021) (Employee)
Maguire Solicitors, Glasgow . . . .(p.1017)
T: 0141 3312885
E: lemon@maguiresolicitors.co.uk

LI, Sophia Yukyee (Feb 2008) (Associate)
Anderson Strathern LLP, Edinburgh . . . .(p.839)
T: 0131 2707700
E: sophia.li@andersonstrathern.co.uk

LI, Tsz Ching (Sept 2020) (Employee)
Paul Hastings (Europe) LLP, London
EC2 . . . .(p.1267)
T: 020 3023 5100
E: michelleli@paulhastings.com

LI-TING, Shirley (Nov 1999) (Associate)
Brodies LLP, Glasgow . . . .(p.948)
T: 0141 2484672
E: shirley.liting@brodies.com

LIAQUAT, Rizwan (Nov 2005) (Solicitor)
NO FIRM

LIAQUAT, Sofia (Jul 2018) (Employee)
LKW Solicitors Ltd, Glasgow . . . .(p.1004)
T: 0141 4236999
E: sofia@lkwsolicitors.co.uk

LIDDELL, Amy Margaret (Sept 2013)
(Employee)
Gallen & Company Ltd, Glasgow . . . . . .(p.978)
T: 0141 4201441

LIDDELL, Cheryl (Jul 2021) (Employee)
Berrymans Lace Mawer LLP,
Glasgow . . . .(p.945)
T: 0141 3532121
E: cheryl.liddell@blmlaw.com

LIDDELL, Jennifer Enid (Sept 2016) (Employee)
Gallen & Company Ltd, Glasgow . . . . . .(p.978)
T: 0141 8807148
E: jennifer.liddell@gallenandco.com

LIDDIARD, Simon James Carnegie
(Jul 1996) (Partner)
Stewart & Watson, Peterhead . . . .(p.1155)
T: 01779 476351
E: sliddiard@stewartwatson.co.uk

LIDDLE, Annie Jane MacLean (Sept 2019)
(Employee)
Scottish Courts and Tribunals Service,
Edinburgh . . . .(p.1230)
T: 0131 2252525
E: aliddle@scotcourts.gov.uk

LIDDLE, Francesca Maria (Jun 2015) (Employee)
Scottish Courts and Tribunals Service,
Edinburgh . . . .(p.1230)
T: 0131 2252525
E: fliddle@scotcourts.gov.uk

LIGERTWOOD, Neil John (May 2011)
(Employee)
Neos Networks Limited, Perth . . . .(p.1253)
E: neil.ligertwood@sse.com

LIGHT, Lucy Louise (Jul 2020) (Employee)
Laurie & Co Solicitors LLP,
Aberdeen . . . .(p.733)
T: 01224 645 085
E: lucy@laurieandco.co.uk

LIGHTBODY, David James (Jun 2008) (Partner)
Brodies LLP, Edinburgh . . . .(p.845)
T: 0131 2283777
E: david.lightbody@brodies.com

LIGHTBODY, Laura Catherine (Oct 2012)
(Employee)
National Westminster Bank PLC,
Edinburgh . . . .(p.1226)
T: 7812786132
E: laura.lightbody@rbs.co.uk

LIGHTFOOT, Darren Andrew (Sept 2014)
(Employee)
Lindsays LLP, Edinburgh . . . .(p.882)
T: 0131 2291212
E: darrenlightfoot@lindsays.co.uk

LILBURN, Laura-Ann Claire Michelle
(Jul 2015) (Employee)
Renfrewshire Council, Paisley . . . .(p.1252)
  T: 0141 8403648
  E: laura.lilburn@renfrewshire.gov.uk

LILLEY, Sarah Ann (Sept 2007) (Associate)
Brodies LLP, Dingwall . . . .(p.796)
  T: 01349 860111
  E: sarah.lilley@brodies.com

LILLIS, Heather (Oct 2019) (Employee)
Jones Whyte LLP, Glasgow. . . . .(p.993)
  T: 0141 375 1222
  E: heather.lillis@joneswhyte.co.uk

LILLY, Jennifer Hannah (Aug 2019) (Employee)
Thompsons, Glasgow . . . .(p.1046)
  T: 0141 2218840
  E: jennifer.lilly@thompsons-scotland.co.uk

LIM, Won (Aug 2020) (Employee)
Burness Paull LLP, Edinburgh . . . .(p.850)
  T: 0131 4736000
  E: won.lim@burnesspaull.com

LIMA SEVERO NUNES, Guilherme
(Jan 2021) (Solicitor)
NO FIRM

LIND, Lynne Theresa (Jul 2016) (Employee)
TC Young LLP, Glasgow . . . .(p.1055)
  T: 0141 2215562
  E: LTL@tcyoung.co.uk

LIND, Susan Elizabeth (Sept 2007) (Employee)
EDF Energy, Gloucester . . . .(p.1259)
  T: 020 3126 2208
  E: Susie.lind@edf-energy.com

LINDEN, Anthony John (Feb 1985) (Director)
Linden Law Practice Ltd,
  Coatbridge. . . . .(p.787)
  T: 01236 449921
  E: lindenlawpractice@gmail.com

LINDLEY, Christopher Gerald (Oct 1990)
(Partner)
Thorntons Law LLP, Forfar . . . .(p.927)
  T: 01307 466886
  E: clindley@thorntons-law.co.uk

LINDSAY, Andrew (Oct 2016) (Employee)
Mitchells Roberton Ltd, Glasgow . . . . .(p.1020)
  T: 0141 5523422
  E: Andrew@mitchells-roberton.co.uk

LINDSAY, Eilish Elizabeth (Jun 2016) (Associate)
Thompsons, Glasgow . . . .(p.1046)
  T: 0141 2218840
  E: eilish.lindsay@thompsons-scotland.co.uk

LINDSAY, Gillian (Jul 1985) (Solicitor)
NO FIRM

LINDSAY, Iain Charles Grant (Apr 1991)
(Partner)
CMS Cameron McKenna Nabarro Olswang LLP,
  London EC4 . . . .(p.1263)
  T: 0207 3673000
  E: Iain.Lindsay@cms-cmno.com

LINDSAY, Ian Kerr (Sept 1984) (Partner)
Wyllie & Henderson Solicitors,
  Perth . . . .(p.1153)
  T: 01738 638465
  E: ilindsay@wyllie-henderson.co.uk

LINDSAY, Ranald Bruce (Jan 1986) (Partner)
Lindsay, Dumfries . . . .(p.801)
  T: 01387 259236
  E: ranald@lindsaysolicitors.co.uk

LINDSAY, Rebecca (Oct 2020) (Employee)
BlackRock, Edinburgh . . . .(p.1221)
  T: (306) 978 749 900
  E: rebecca.lindsay@blackrock.com

LINDSAY, Rosemary Agnes MacLellan
(May 1994) (Employee)
Scottish Government, Edinburgh . . . . .(p.1231)
  T: 0131 244 0815
  E: Rosemary.Lindsay@gov.scot

LINDSAY, Vivian Gay (Nov 1985) (Employee)
Scottish Courts and Tribunals Service,
  Paisley . . . .(p.1252)
  T: 0141 8875291
  E: vlindsay@scotcourts.gov.uk

LINE, Sylvia Noami (Oct 1995) (Employee)
Thompson Family Law, Glasgow . . . . .(p.1046)
  T: 0141 4046575
  E: sylvia@tflaw.co.uk

LINEHAN, Andrew Dermot (Oct 2002) (Partner)
Murray Beith Murray, Edinburgh . . . . . .(p.893)
  T: 0131 2251200
  E: andrew.linehan@murraybeith.co.uk

LINGARD, Andrew Gerald (Sept 2009)
(Employee)
Stonegate Pub Company, Luton . . . . .(p.1270)
  E: andrew.lingard@stonegatepubs.com

LINGARD, David Robert (Aug 1977) (Director)
Leonards Solicitors Limited,
  Hamilton . . . .(p.1067)
  T: 01698 457313
  E: dlingard@leonardslaw.com

LINKLATER, Fiona Margaret (Jan 1998)
(Associate)
Lindsays LLP, Edinburgh . . . .(p.882)
  T: 0131 2291212
  E: fionalinklater@lindsays.co.uk

LINLEY-ADAMS, Guy Edward (Jan 2009)
(Employee)
Guy Linley-Adams Solicitors,
  Leominster . . . .(p.1260)
  T: 07837 881219
  E: guy@linley-adams.co.uk

LINN, Emma Anne (Dec 2002) (Employee)
Highland Council, Inverness.........(p.1248)
T: 01463 702000
E: emma.linn@highland.gov.uk

LINN, Ross Anthony (Oct 2008) (Partner)
Stronachs LLP, Inverness...........(p.1082)
T: 01463 713225
E: ross.linn@stronachs.com

LINNING, Alan Hugh (Sept 1985) (Employee)
Mayer Brown, Hong Kong..........(p.1273)
T: +852 28432231
E: alan.linning@mayerbrown.com

LINTON, Kenneth Gillespie (Jan 1994)
(Employee)
Dodge & Cox
T: +415 2489868
E: ken.linton@dodgeandcox.com

LINTON, Richard Kerr (Jan 1983) (Partner)
Pinsent Masons LLP, Edinburgh.......(p.895)
T: 0131 7777000
E: richard.linton@pinsentmasons.com

LIPTON, Faye Elizabeth (Apr 2021) (Employee)
Blackadders LLP, Dundee............(p.805)
T: 01382 229222
E: faye.lipton@blackadders.co.uk

LIPTON, Jamie Paul (Sept 2009) (Employee)
Procurator Fiscal Service, Glasgow....(p.1242)
E: jamie.lipton@copfs.gov.uk

LISS, Jennifer (Nov 2018) (Employee)
Carey Olsen, St Helier.............(p.1274)
T: 01534 888900
E: Jennifer.liss@hotmail.com

LITHGOW, Maud Cecilia (Oct 2009) (Employee)
NORTH LANARKSHIREre Council,
Motherwell..................(p.1251)
T: 01698 302196
E: lithgowm@northlan.gov.uk

LITHGOW, Sarah Elizabeth Landale
(Nov 2000) (Employee)
RTRP Limited, Glasgow............(p.1243)
T: 0141 4275880
E: Sarah.Lithgow@raisetheroofproductions.com

LITSTER, Caroline Janet (Oct 1996) (Partner)
Kerr Stirling LLP, Stirling..........(p.1165)
T: 01786 463414
E: cl@kerrstirling.co.uk

LITTLE, Andrew John (Apr 2013) (Employee)
Burness Paull LLP, Edinburgh.........(p.850)
T: 0131 4736126
E: Andrew.Little@burnesspaull.com

LITTLE, Jonathan Murray (Aug 2010)
(Employee)
EthosEnergy (GBR) Limited,
Aberdeen...................(p.1212)
T: 01224 291 764
E: joe.little@ethosenergygroup.com

LITTLE, Lauren Frances Marie (Nov 2006)
(Partner)
TC Young LLP, Glasgow............(p.1055)
T: 0141 2215562
E: lfd@tcyoung.co.uk

LITTLE, Neil Alexander (Oct 1975) (Consultant)
Neil F. McPherson, Kilmarnock.......(p.1096)
T: 01563 535363
E: nalittle@btinternet.com

LITTLEFAIR, Peter James (Apr 2014) (Employee)
Balfour + Manson LLP, Edinburgh.....(p.841)
T: 0131 2001200
E: peter.littlefair@balfour-manson.co.uk

LITTLEFIELD, Peter Southern (Jun 2001)
(Partner)
Turcan Connell, Edinburgh..........(p.908)
T: 0131 2288111
E: peter.littlefield@turcanconnell.com

LITTLEFIELD, Yvonne Elizabeth (Nov 1999)
(Associate)
Turcan Connell, Edinburgh..........(p.908)
T: 0131 2288111
E: yl@turcanconnell.com

LITTLEJOHN, Anne Sandra (Jul 2008)
(Associate)
Raeburn Christie Clark & Wallace LLP,
Aberdeen...................(p.741)
T: 01224 332400
E: Anne.Littlejohn@raeburns.co.uk

LITTLEJOHN, Peter William (Sept 1983)
(Consultant)
Raeburn Christie Clark & Wallace LLP,
Aberdeen...................(p.741)
T: 01224 332400
E: Peter.Littlejohn@raeburns.co.uk

LITTLEJOHN, Robert Edward Stuart
(Nov 1988) (Solicitor)
NO FIRM

LIU, Dr, Lihe (Nov 2014) (Director)
Liu's Legal Solutions Ltd, Glasgow....(p.1002)
T: 0141 3320047
E: liu@liuslaw.co.uk

LIVESEY, Lynn Martin (Aug 2010) (Employee)
Brodies LLP, Glasgow.............(p.948)
T: 0141 2484672
E: lynn.livesey@brodies.com

LIVINGSTON, Jonathan Macalpine
(Jul 2013) (Solicitor)
NO FIRM

LIVINGSTON, Julian Mark Campbell
(Oct 1990) (Solicitor)
NO FIRM

LIVINGSTON, Michael (Feb 2021) (Employee)
Pinsent Masons LLP, Glasgow.......(p.1031)
T: 0141 567 8400
E: michael.livingston@pinsentmasons.com

LIVINGSTONE, Alan (Sept 1982) (Director)
Borders Legal Limited, Kelso . . . .(p.1091)
T: 01573 226999
E: al@hastingslegaL.co.uk

LIVINGSTONE, Angus (Dec 1976) (Employee)
Scottish Courts and Tribunals Service,
Kilmarnock . . . .(p.1249)
E: alivingstone@scotcourts.gov.uk

LIVINGSTONE, Charles David (Oct 2003)
(Partner)
Brodies LLP, Glasgow . . . .(p.948)
T: 0141 2484672
E: charles.livingstone@brodies.com

LIVINGSTONE, Cristine Ann (Jun 2002)
(Employee)
The Scottish Parliament, Edinburgh . . .(p.1235)
T: (0131) 3486653
E: cristine.livingstone@parliament.scot

LIVINGSTONE, Peter (Apr 2009) (Employee)
Scottish Government, Edinburgh . . . . .(p.1231)
T: 0131 244 0815
E: peter.livingstone@gov.scot

LIVINGSTONE, Sarah Elizabeth (Sept 2004)
(Employee)
Ofgem, Glasgow . . . .(p.1241)
T: (0141) 354 5425
E: sarah.livingstone@ofgem.gov.uk

LLOYD, Abigail Elizabeth (Sept 2020)
(Employee)
EDF Energy, Croydon . . . .(p.1259)
T: 07809 593900
E: abigail.lloyd@edfenergy.com

LLOYD, James Semple (Oct 1989) (Partner)
Harper Macleod LLP, Glasgow . . . .(p.983)
T: 0141 2218888
E: james.lloyd@harpermacleod.co.uk

LLOYD, Suzanne Mackay (Jul 2021) (Employee)
Friends Legal, Glasgow . . . .(p.978)
T: 0844 8921250
E: suzanne.lloyd@friends-legal.co.uk

LOCH, Pamela Ann (Jul 2000) (Employee)
Loch Employment Law, Tunbridge
Wells . . . .(p.1272)
E: pam.loch@lochassociates.co.uk

LOCHRIE, Stephen Richard (Oct 1993)
(Director)
Young & Partners Business Lawyers Limited,
Dunfermline . . . .(p.827)
T: 01383 721621
E: sl@businesslaw.co.uk

LOCK, Gillian Sandra (Nov 1993) (Employee)
Scottish Environment Protection Agency,
Edinburgh . . . .(p.1230)
T: 0131 4497296
E: gillian.lock@sepa.org.uk

LOCK, Stephen Mark (Oct 1996) (Employee)
First Scottish Group, Dalgety Bay . . . . .(p.1216)
T: 01383 826777
E: stephen.lock@firstscottish.com

LOCKE, Alison Ann (Apr 2004) (Employee)
Life Technologies Limited, Paisley . . . . .(p.1252)
T: 0141 8146100
E: alison.locke@thermofisher.com

LOCKHART, Katharine Tinsley (Apr 2006)
(Employee)
Lloyds Banking Group Plc,
Edinburgh . . . .(p.1224)
T: (0131) 442 9579
E: tinsley.lockhart@scottishwidows.co.uk

LOCKHART, Peter McIlwraith Stevenson
(Jan 1979) (Partner)
Lockharts Law LLP, Ayr . . . .(p.764)
T: 01292 265045
E: peter@peterlockhart.com

LOCKHART, Richard Scott (Dec 2002)
(Employee)
Scottish Futures Trust, Edinburgh . . . . .(p.1231)
T: 0131 5100800
E: richard.lockhart@scottishfuturestrust.org.uk

LOCKHART, Susan Catherine (Oct 2007)
(Employee)
Law At Work Incorporating Empire,
Aberdeen . . . .(p.1213)
T: (01224) 701383
E: susan.lockhart@worknest.com

LOCKIE, Brent Robert Wilson (May 1991)
(Director)
James McKay Defence Solicitors Limited,
Elgin . . . .(p.917)
T: 01343 556500
E: brent@jamesmckay.uk

LODGE, Lianne Margaret (Apr 2007) (Partner)
Gillespie Macandrew LLP,
Edinburgh . . . .(p.872)
T: 0131 2251677
E: Lianne.Lodge@gillespiemacandrew.co.uk

LOFTUS, Patrick Joseph (Feb 2000) (Partner)
Anderson Strathern LLP, Edinburgh . . . .(p.839)
T: 0131 2707700
E: pat.loftus@andersonstrathern.co.uk

LOGAN, Alison Ann (Aug 2013) (Employee)
Burges Salmon LLP, Bristol . . . .(p.1258)
T: 0117 9392000
E: alison.logan@burges-salmon.com

LOGAN, Alistair James Gilchrist (Nov 1986)
(Employee)
Procurator Fiscal Service,
Edinburgh . . . .(p.1227)
T: 0300 0203168
E: alistair.logan@copfs.gov.uk

LOGAN, Ann Agnes (Feb 1989) (Partner)
Balfour + Manson LLP, Edinburgh . . . . .(p.841)
T: 0131 2001200
E: ann.logan@balfour-manson.co.uk

LOGAN, Anne (Mar 1990) (Employee)
DAC Beachcroft Scotland LLP,
Glasgow. . . . .(p.964)
T: 0141 2486688
E: alogan@dacbeachcroft.com

LOGAN, David McDiarmid (Mar 1997)
(Employee)
Argyll & Bute Council,
Lochgilphead . . . .(p.1251)
T: 01546 602127
E: david.logan@argyll-bute.gov.uk

LOGAN, Helen Claire Rafferty (Aug 1994)
(Employee)
Law Society of Scotland,
Edinburgh . . . .(p.1224)
T: 0131 2267411
E: helenlogan@lawscot.org.uk

LOGAN, Iain Stuart (Oct 2008) (Employee)
Procurator Fiscal Service,
Edinburgh . . . .(p.1227)
T: 0300 0203168
E: Iain.Logan@copfs.gov.uk

LOGAN, John Francis (Sept 1984) (Employee)
Stewart Title Ltd, London SW1 . . . .(p.1268)
T: 01698 833308
E: jologan@stewart.com

LOGAN, Karen Jean (Nov 2004) (Employee)
Sainsbury's Bank plc, Edinburgh . . . . . .(p.1230)
T: (0131) 286 0807
E: karen.logan@sainsburysbank.co.uk

LOGAN, Kirstyn (May 2017) (Employee)
Drummond Miller LLP, Edinburgh . . . . .(p.864)
T: 0131 2265151
E: klogan@dm-property.com

LOGAN, Mhairi Elizabeth (Oct 2016)
(Employee)
Logans, Cumnock. . . . .(p.791)
T: 01290 424566
E: mlogan@loganssolicitors.co.uk

LOGAN, Moira Catherine (Nov 1995)
(Employee)
Argyll & Bute Council,
Lochgilphead . . . .(p.1251)
T: 01631 567948
E: moira.logan@argyll-bute.gov.uk

LOGAN, Robert Andrew (Aug 1979) (Partner)
Logans, Cumnock. . . . .(p.791)
T: 01290 424566
E: rlogan@logansolicitors.co.uk

LOGAN, Scott Alexander (Nov 2002)
(Employee)
Brodies LLP, Edinburgh . . . .(p.845)
T: 0131 2283777
E: scott.logan@brodies.com

LOGAN, Stuart William (May 2019) (Employee)
Brodies LLP, Glasgow . . . .(p.948)
T: 0141 2484672
E: stuart.logan@brodies.com

LOGIE, James George (Oct 1991) (Employee)
Scottish Hospital Inquiry, Glasgow . . . .(p.1244)
E: jim.logie@gov.scot

LOGIE, Jamieson John (Nov 1984) (Employee)
Sullivan & Cromwell (Hong Kong), Hong
Kong . . . .(p.1273)
T: +852 2826 8616
E: logiej@sullcrom.com

LOGIE, Joanna Catherine Neill (Sept 2018)
(Associate)
Addleshaw Goddard LLP, Leeds . . . . . .(p.1260)
E: Joanna.Logie@addleshawgoddard.com

LOGIE, Shona Kerrie (Oct 2003) (Employee)
Cognizant Worldwide Limited,
Glasgow. . . . .(p.1238)
T: 0141 2221561
E: Shona.Logie@cognizant.com

LOGUE, Andrew (Sept 2017) (Employee)
Clyde & Co (Scotland) LLP,
Aberdeen . . . .(p.726)
T: 01224 624924
E: andrew.logue@clydeco.com

LOGUE, Claire Elizabeth (Jul 2006) (Associate)
BTO Solicitors LLP, Edinburgh . . . .(p.849)
T: 0131 2222939
E: clo@bto.co.uk

LOGUE, John Thomas (Dec 1995) (Employee)
Procurator Fiscal Service,
Edinburgh . . . .(p.1227)
T: 0300 020 2702
E: john.logue@copfs.gov.uk

LOGUE, Lauren Elizabeth (Jun 2017)
(Employee)
Scottish Social Services Council,
Dundee . . . .(p.1218)
T: 0345 6030 891
E: Lauren.Logue@sssc.uk.com

LOLIC, Gillian Christina (Aug 2018) (Employee)
Drummond Miller LLP, Glasgow. . . . . . .(p.971)
T: 0141 3320086
E: GLolic@drummondmiller.co.uk

LOMBARDI, Paul Cyril (Feb 1987) (Partner)
Anderson Strathern LLP, Glasgow . . . . . .(p.940)
T: 0141 2426060
E: paul.lombardi@andersonstrathern.co.uk

LONDRAGAN, Sarah Louise (Nov 2006)
(Associate)
Ledingham Chalmers LLP,
Aberdeen . . . .(p.734)
T: 01224 408408
E: sarah.londragan@ledinghamchalmers.com

LONEY, Denise Patricia (Oct 1986) (Director)
Yuill & Kyle Ltd, Glasgow . . . .(p.1056)
T: 0141 3327107
E: Denise.Loney@yuill-kyle.co.uk

LONG, Andrew Victor (Aug 2017) (Employee)
Procurator Fiscal Service,
Edinburgh . . . .(p.1227)
T: 0300 0203168
E: drew.long@copfs.gov.uk

LONG, Kenneth Burnie (Nov 1988) (Partner)
Wright, Johnston & Mackenzie LLP,
Edinburgh . . . .(p.913)
T: 0131 5241500
E: kbl@wjm.co.uk

LONGINO, Kevin Denis (Oct 1991) (Partner)
Deeside Defence, Aboyne . . . .(p.747)
T: 0771 2005551
E: deesidedefence@gmail.com

LONGMUIR, Kate Elizabeth (Mar 2015)
(Employee)
Trainline.com Limited, Edinburgh . . . . .(p.1235)
E: kate.longmuir@thetrainline.com

LONGWILL, Elaine (Dec 2012) (Employee)
Angus Council, Forfar . . . .(p.1237)
T: 01307 492175
E: LongwillE@angus.gov.uk

LONGWORTH CAMPBELL, Letitia Scarlette
(Dec 2016) (Employee)
The Scottish Parliament, Edinburgh . . .(p.1235)
T: (0131) 3486653
E: letitia.longworthcampbell@parliament.scot

LONIE, Sarah Frances (Jun 2012) (Employee)
Anderson Strathern LLP, Edinburgh . . . .(p.839)
T: 0131 2707828
E: sarah.lonie@andersonstrathern.co.uk

LOTHIAN, Ailie Joanna (Sept 2004) (Employee)
Smail & Ewart Ltd, Lanark . . . .(p.1108)
T: 01555 666111
E: alothian@smail-ewart.co.uk

LOTHIAN, Andrew William (Nov 1997)
(Partner)
DWF LLP, Edinburgh . . . .(p.865)
T: 0131 2265541
E: andrew.lothian@dwf.law

LOTHIAN, Jennifer Mitchell (Oct 2016)
(Employee)
Aberdeen Corporate Services Limited,
Edinburgh . . . .(p.1220)
T: 0131 245 7508
E: jennifer.lothian@abrdn.com

LOTHIAN, Lee Anne (Sept 2016) (Employee)
CMS Cameron McKenna Nabarro Olswang LLP,
Edinburgh . . . .(p.856)
T: 0131 2288000
E: Lee.Lothian@cms-cmno.com

LOTHIAN, Lynda (Nov 1990) (Employee)
Scottish Legal Aid Board,
Edinburgh . . . .(p.1233)
T: 0131 2267061
E: lothianly@slab.org.uk

LOTT, Andrew Michael Ernest (Jan 1981)
(Partner)
Michael Lott, Motherwell . . . .(p.1127)
T: 01698 252331
E: michaellott@btconnect.com

LOUDEN, Abigail Sue (Jun 2017) (Solicitor)
NO FIRM

LOUDON, Alasdair John, WS (Sept 1980)
(Consultant)
Gilson Gray LLP, Edinburgh . . . .(p.874)
T: 0131 5165354
E: aloudon@gilsongray.co.uk

LOUDON, Caroline Kate Powlett (Aug 2002)
(Partner)
TLT LLP, Bristol . . . .(p.1259)
T: 0333 006 0000
E: Caroline.Loudon@TLTsolicitors.com

LOUDON, Christopher James Alexander
(Sept 2009) (Employee)
Gibson, Dunn & Crutcher LLP, London
EC4 . . . .(p.1264)
T: 0207 0714249
E: cloudon@gibsondunn.com

LOUDON, Robert Duncan, WS (Dec 2001)
(Employee)
National Health Service Scotland,
Edinburgh . . . .(p.1225)
T: 0131 2757800
E: jake.loudon@nhs.scot

LOUGHERY, Gerrard (Jun 2002) (Partner)
Angus McIntosh & Simon Hodge,
Glasgow . . . .(p.1012)
T: 0141 6340313
E: gerry.loughery@castlemilklawcentre.co.uk

LOUGHRAN, Nicola (Jan 2003) (Director)
Loughran & Co Limited, Glasgow . . . .(p.1004)
T: 0141 3310374
E: nicola@loughransolicitors.com

LOVATT, Adam Michael (Sept 2009) (Associate)
CMS Cameron McKenna Nabarro Olswang LLP,
London EC4 . . . .(p.1263)
T: 0207 3673000
E: adam.lovatt@cms-cmno.com

LOVE, Barry (Sept 1993) (Director)
Environmental Law Chambers Ltd,
Glasgow......................(p.975)
T: 0141 354 7620
E: barry.love@elchambers.com

LOVE, Duncan Mackinnon (Nov 1983) (Partner)
James & George Collie LLP,
Aberdeen....................(p.728)
T: 01224 581581
E: d.love@jgcollie.co.uk

LOVE, Euan David Robert (Oct 2005) (Partner)
Digby Brown LLP, Glasgow..........(p.970)
T: 0333 200 5925
E: euan.love@digbybrown.co.uk

LOVE, Jennifer (Oct 2013) (Employee)
CMS Cameron McKenna Nabarro Olswang LLP,
Edinburgh....................(p.856)
T: 0131 2288000
E: jennifer.love@cms-cmno.com

LOVE, Katharine Isabel (Sept 2018) (Employee)
Brodies LLP, Aberdeen.............(p.723)
T: 01224 392242
E: katie.love@brodies.com

LOVE, Katrina (Oct 1993) (Employee)
Standard Life Assets and Employee Services
Limited, Edinburgh.............(p.1234)
T: 0131 2457508
E: Katrina_love@standardlife.com

LOVE, Kenneth William (Sept 1998) (Employee)
Scottish Widows Limited,
Edinburgh..................(p.1233)
T: 07500 890008
E: Ken.Love2@scottishwidows.co.uk

LOVE, Martin (Feb 2012) (Employee)
Eversheds Sutherland (International) LLP,
Edinburgh....................(p.869)
T: 0207 9194500
E: martinlove@eversheds-Sutherland.com

LOVE, Sonia (Sept 1994) (Partner)
Brodies LLP, Aberdeen.............(p.723)
T: 01224 392287
E: sonia.love@brodies.com

LOVE, Susan Thomson (Sept 2020) (Employee)
Procurator Fiscal Service, Inverness....(p.1248)
T: 0844 5612926
E: susan.love@copfs.gov.uk

LOVE, Valerie (Oct 1989) (Employee)
WEST DUNBARTONSHIREhire Council,
Dumbarton.................(p.1217)
T: 01389 737000
E: valerie.love@west-dunbarton.gov.uk

LOVE, Yolande Claire (Nov 1999) (Employee)
Procurator Fiscal Service, Glasgow....(p.1241)
T: 0300 0203000
E: yolande.love@copfs.gov.uk

LOVELL, Deborah Anne (Oct 1996) (Partner)
Anderson Strathern LLP, Edinburgh....(p.839)
T: 0131 2707700
E: deborah.lovell@andersonstrathern.co.uk

LOVELL, Fraser Keith (Jan 1999) (Employee)
Postcode Lottery Limited,
Edinburgh..................(p.1227)
T: 0131 555 (ext) 9558
E: fraser.lovell@postcodelottery.co.uk

LOVIE, Connor Alexander (Jul 2016)
(Employee)
Baker & McKenzie LLP, London
EC4......................(p.1261)
T: 0207 9191000
E: connor.lovie@bakermckenzie.com

LOVIE, Darryl (Aug 1994) (Partner)
Keegan Smith, SSC., Livingston......(p.1119)
T: 01506 497500
E: darryl@keegansmith.org

LOW, Cara Louise (Aug 2021) (Employee)
Burness Paull LLP, Aberdeen.........(p.724)
T: 01224 621621
E: cara.low@burnesspaull.com

LOW, Katy Margaret (Mar 2010) (Solicitor)
NO FIRM

LOW, Kirsten Helen (Oct 2019) (Employee)
Scottish Social Services Council,
Dundee....................(p.1218)
T: 0345 6030 891
E: kirsten.low@sssc.uk.com

LOW, Lindesay Matheson (Dec 1991)
(Employee)
Scotch Whisky Association,
Edinburgh..................(p.1230)
T: 0131 2229258
E: llow@swa.org.uk

LOW, Robert Arnott (Nov 1993) (Partner)
R A Low & Company,
Musselburgh.................(p.1129)
T: 0131 6658885
E: bob@ra-low.com

LOW, Suzi (Jan 2007) (Employee)
Blackadders LLP, Dundee............(p.805)
T: 01382 229222
E: suzi.low@blackdders.co.uk

LOWE, Deborah Alexander (Oct 1992)
(Solicitor)
NO FIRM

LOWRIE, Ewen Alexander (Aug 2017)
(Employee)
Freeths LLP, London W1..........(p.1264)
E: ewen.lowrie@freeths.co.uk

LOWRIE, Michael John (Feb 1999) (Employee)
Russel + Aitken (Falkirk + Alloa) Ltd,
Falkirk . . . .(p.924)
T: 01324 622888
E: michaellowrie@russel-aitken.co.uk

LUCAS, Jennifer Mackay (May 2016)
(Employee)
Immediate Media Company London Limited,
London W6 . . . .(p.1265)
E: Jennifer.Lucas@immediate.co.uk

LUCAS-BROADLEY, Simone Mairi (Sept 2013)
(Employee)
South Ayrshire Council, Ayr . . . .(p.1215)
T: 01292 612420
E:
simone.lucas-broadley@south-ayrshire.gov.uk

LUCHERINI, Nadia (Oct 2008) (Employee)
CMS Cameron McKenna Nabarro Olswang LLP,
Aberdeen . . . .(p.727)
T: 01224 622002
E: Nadia.Lucherini@cms-cmno.com

LUKE, Duncan William (Mar 1990) (Partner)
Blair & Bryden, Greenock . . . .(p.1060)
T: 01475 558420
E: dluke@blair-bryden.co.uk

LUKINS, Megan Sarah (Sept 2018) (Employee)
Taylor Wessing LLP, London EC4 . . . . .(p.1268)
T: (020) 7300 4995
E: M.Lukins@taylorwessing.com

LUKINS, Pauline Amanda (Sept 2010)
(Associate)
Stronachs LLP, Aberdeen . . . .(p.744)
T: 01224 845845
E: paula.lukins@stronachs.com

LUMSDAINE, Katrina Louise (Mar 1998)
(Partner)
Anderson Strathern LLP, Edinburgh . . . .(p.839)
T: 0131 2707700
E: katrina.lumsdaine@andersonstrathern.co.uk

LUMSDEN, Eric Robert (Sept 1991) (Partner)
Sneddon Morrison, Whitburn . . . .(p.1180)
T: 01501 740345
E: erl@sneddons-ssc.co.uk

LUMSDEN, Hartley Wilson (Feb 1982) (Partner)
Peterkins, Aberdeen . . . .(p.739)
T: 01224 428000
E: hwl@peterkins.com

LUMSDEN, Kirsty Catherine (Jun 2015)
(Employee)
Adams Whyte, Livingston . . . .(p.1117)
T: 01506 401999
E: kirstylumsden@adamswhyte.com

LUMSDEN, Roy Donald, SSC (Aug 1981)
(Director)
Lumsden Consultancy Limited,
Falkirk . . . .(p.922)
T: 07831 707525
E: roy@rdllaw.co.uk

LUMSDEN, Sarah (Aug 2012) (Solicitor)
NO FIRM

LUNN, Bryony Elizabeth (Oct 2012) (Employee)
DLA Piper UK LLP, Leeds . . . .(p.1260)
T: 08700 111111

LUNN, John Alexander (Sept 1987) (Partner)
Morton Fraser LLP, Edinburgh . . . .(p.891)
T: 0131 2471000
E: john.lunn@morton-fraser.com

LUNNY, Marie Clare (Feb 1993) (Employee)
SOUTH LANARKSHIREre Council,
Hamilton . . . .(p.1247)
E: marie.c.lunny@southlanarkshire.gov.uk

LUNNY, Mark Gerald (Sept 2001) (Partner)
Lunny & Co, Bellshill . . . .(p.773)
T: 01698 269387
E: mark@lunny.co.uk

LUNNY, Ruth Elaine (Oct 2005) (Solicitor)
Scottish Government, Edinburgh . . . . .(p.1231)
T: 0131 244 0815
E: Ruth.Lunny@gov.scot

LUSBY, Odhr n Mathghamhain (Nov 2019)
(Solicitor)
NO FIRM

LUSSIER, Ruth (Oct 2014) (Employee)
Raeburn Christie Clark & Wallace LLP,
Aberdeen . . . .(p.741)
T: 01224 332400
E: ruth.lussier@raeburns.co.uk

LUTON, Emma Beatrice (Oct 2008) (Employee)
Scottish Government, Edinburgh . . . . .(p.1231)
T: 0131 244 0815
E: emma.luton@gov.scot

LUTTON, Mark (Sept 2004) (Employee)
McAfee, Coatbridge . . . .(p.787)
T: 01236 423437

LUTTON, Paula Joanne (Oct 2001) (Partner)
Cartys, Airdrie . . . .(p.749)
T: 01236 761127
E: paula@cartylaw.co.uk

LYALL, Andrew Finlayson Dunnet (Sept 1971)
(Partner)
Hall Norrie Warden LLP, Dundee . . . . . .(p.812)
T: 07752 457043

LYALL, George (Aug 1983) (Employee)
Womble Bond Dickinson (UK) LLP, Newcastle
Upon Tyne . . . .(p.1270)
T: 0345 4150000
E: george.lyall@wbd-uk.com

LYALL, Ruth (Oct 2014) (Employee)
Riverstone, Brighton . . . .(p.1258)
   T: 01273 792411
   E: Ruth.Lyall@rsml.co.uk

LYALL, Valerie Jane (Mar 1996) (Partner)
Ross, Strachan & Co., Dundee . . . .(p.818)
   T: 01382 201010
   E: vjlyall@ross-strachan.co.uk

LYLE, Catriona Louise (Sept 2016) (Employee)
The Scottish Parliament, Edinburgh . . .(p.1235)
   T: (0131) 3486653
   E: Catriona.Lyle@parliament.scot

LYLE, Dalene Joyce (Oct 2011) (Associate)
Aberdein Considine and Company,
   Glasgow . . . .(p.937)
   T: 0141 2278200
   E: dlyle@acandco.com

LYLE, Helen-Anne Sarah (Oct 2016) (Employee)
Scottish Government, Edinburgh . . . . .(p.1231)
   T: 0131 244 0815
   E: helen-anne.lyle@gov.scot

LYNCH, Claire (Aug 1992) (Employee)
Rradar (Scotland) Limited,
   Glasgow. . . . .(p.1036)
   E: Claire.Lynch@rradar.com

LYNCH, Dylan Page (Sept 2016) (Employee)
Raytheon Systems Limited,
   Glenrothes . . . .(p.1246)
   T: 01592 754311
   E: dylan.lynch@raytheon.co.uk

LYNCH, Gerard Paul (Feb 1981) (Consultant)
MacDonald Lynch Solicitors,
   Glasgow. . . . .(p.1009)
   T: 0141 6499552
   E: gerard.lynch@macdonaldlynch.co.uk

LYNCH, Jennifer Jane (Aug 2021) (Employee)
Dickson Minto, London EC2 . . . .(p.1263)
   T: 020 76284455
   E: jennifer.lynch@dmws.com

LYNCH, Katherine Alison (Oct 2021)
(Employee)
DWF LLP, Glasgow . . . .(p.973)
   T: 0141 228 8000
   E: Katherine.Lynch@dwf.law

LYNCH, Kieran Patrick (Jun 2009) (Employee)
Rakuten Europe S. .r.l.,
   Luxembourg. . . . .(p.1275)
   E: kieran.lynch@rakuten.com

LYNCH, Kirsty Alison (Nov 2015) (Employee)
Thorntons Law LLP, Edinburgh . . . .(p.906)
   T: 0131 2258705
   E: KLynch@thorntons-law.co.uk

LYNCH, Lauren Helen (Oct 2021) (Employee)
Eversheds Sutherland (International) LLP,
   Edinburgh . . . .(p.869)
   T: 0207 9194500
   E: laurenlynch@eversheds-sutherland.com

LYNCH, Matthew (Nov 2002) (Employee)
Scottish Government's Parliamentary Counsel
   Office, Edinburgh . . . .(p.1233)
   T: 0131 244 0685
   E: matthew.lynch@gov.scot

LYNCH, Matthew Gerard (Oct 1982) (Partner)
Mackinlay & Suttie, Barrhead. . . . .(p.770)
   T: 0141 8811572
   E: m.lynch@mackinlay-suttie.co.uk

LYNCH, Maura Anne (Aug 1985) (Employee)
Procurator Fiscal Service, Glasgow . . . .(p.1241)
   T: 0300 0203000
   E: maura.lynch@copfs.gov.uk

LYNCH, Paul Tierney (Oct 1989) (Partner)
Tod & Mitchell, Paisley . . . .(p.1142)
   T: 0141 8891444
   E: enquiries@todandmitchell.co.uk

LYNCH, Raymond James (Nov 2001)
(Employee)
WEST DUNBARTONSHIREhire Council,
   Dumbarton . . . .(p.1217)
   T: 01389 737000
   E: raymond.lynch@west-dunbarton.gov.uk

LYNCH, Rhona Marie (Jul 1994) (Partner)
Tod & Mitchell, Paisley . . . .(p.1142)
   T: 0141 8891444
   E: enquiries@todandmitchell.co.uk

LYNCH, Sarah Elizabeth (Mar 2009) (Partner)
Pomphreys, Wishaw . . . .(p.1182)
   T: 01698 373365
   E: sl@pomphreyslaw.com

LYNCH, Sarah Mary (Feb 2016) (Employee)
National Westminster Bank PLC,
   Edinburgh . . . .(p.1226)
   T: (0131) 626 2925
   E: sarah.lynch@natwest.com

LYNCH, Sean Thomas (Sept 1984) (Partner)
McCluskey Browne, Kilmarnock . . . . . .(p.1095)
   T: 01563 544545
   E: seanl@mccluskeybrowne.co.uk

LYNCH, Stephanie Jane (Oct 2006) (Employee)
Baillie Gifford & Co, Edinburgh . . . . . .(p.1220)
   T: 0131 2752000
   E: stephanie.lynch@bailliegifford.com

LYNCH, Stephanie Jessica Anne (May 2018)
(Employee)
Burges Salmon LLP, Edinburgh . . . .(p.850)
   T: 0131 3142112
   E: stephanie.lynch@burges-salmon.com

LYNDON, Andrew Stuart (Apr 2015) (Associate)
Burness Paull LLP, Aberdeen . . . . (p.724)
T: 01224 621621
E: Andrew.Lyndon@burnesspaull.com

LYNER, Alison Patricia (Feb 1993) (Employee)
Highlands & Islands Enterprise,
Inverness . . . .(p.1248)
T: 01463 383010
E: alison.lyner@hient.co.uk

LYNER, Michael Jonathan (Sept 2016)
(Associate)
CMS Cameron McKenna Nabarro Olswang LLP,
London EC4 . . . .(p.1263)
T: 0207 3673000
E: michael.lyner@cms-cmno.com

LYNN, Hannah Anya Robertson (Aug 2019)
(Employee)
Brahams Dutt Badrick French LLP, London
EC2 . . . .(p.1262)
E: hannahlynn@bdbf.co.uk

LYNN, Keir-Ewin (Sept 2009) (Employee)
Aspris, London W14 . . . .(p.1261)
T: 0207 605 0922
E: KeiraLynn@aspris.com

LYNN, Stephen Christopher (Jun 2018)
(Employee)
Scottish Criminal Cases Review Commission,
Glasgow. . . . .(p.1243)
T: 0141 2707030
E: slynn@sccrc.org.uk

LYON, Kaye Amanda (Jun 2021) (Employee)
Digby Brown LLP, Glasgow . . . .(p.970)
T: 0333 200 5925
E: kaye.lyon@digbybrown.co.uk

LYON, Louisa Helen (May 2018) (Employee)
Scottish Police Authority, Police Scotland,
Glasgow. . . . .(p.1244)
T: 01786 895727
E: louisa.lyon@scotland.pnn.police.uk

LYON, Matthew James (Aug 2016) (Employee)
Brodies LLP, Aberdeen. . . . .(p.723)
T: 01224 392242
E: matthew.lyon@brodies.com

LYON, Michael Caithness Malcolm
(Feb 2001) (Director)
Michael Lyon Solicitors Limited,
Glasgow. . . . .(p.1005)
T: 0141 550 1074
E: ml@theroadtrafficlawyer.com

LYONS, Aaron Nigel (Oct 2008) (Employee)
DLA Piper UK LLP, Sheffield . . . .(p.1271)
T: 08700 111111
E: aaron.lyons@dlapiper.com

LYONS, Andrew David (Oct 2010) (Associate)
Davidson & Co, Dubai . . . .(p.1278)
T: (+971) 4 3438897
E: alyons@davidsoncolaw.com

LYONS, Cheryl (Aug 2013) (Employee)
Procurator Fiscal Service, Glasgow . . . .(p.1241)
T: 0300 0203000
E: Cheryl.lyons@copfs.gov.uk

LYONS, Jamie Kenneth (Jun 2017) (Employee)
Thorntons Law LLP, Dundee . . . .(p.819)
T: 01382 229 111
E: jlyons@thorntons-law.co.uk

LYONS, Jessica (Sept 2017) (Employee)
ISG Central Services Limited,
Glasgow. . . . .(p.1240)
E: jessica.lyons@isgltd.com

LYONS, Karen (Aug 1994) (Employee)
Highland Council, Inverness. . . . .(p.1248)
T: 01463 702000
E: karen.lyons@highland.gov.uk

LYONS, Kirsty Louise (Sept 2016) (Employee)
Procurator Fiscal Service,
Edinburgh . . . .(p.1229)
T: 0300 0203000
E: Kirsty.Lyons@copfs.gov.uk

LYONS, Marie (Jun 2017) (Employee)
Procurator Fiscal Service, Dundee . . . . .(p.1218)
T: 01382 342559
E: Marie.Lyons@copfs.gov.uk

LYONS, Natasha Erin (Sept 2016) (Solicitor)
NO FIRM

LYONS, Suzanne Marie (Oct 2000) (Employee)
The Institute and Faculty of Actuaries,
Edinburgh . . . .(p.1234)
T: (020) 7632 1488
E: suzie.lyons@actuaries.org.uk

MAAS, Alexia Jena (Sept 1997) (Employee)
Volvo Financial Services LLC,
Greensboro . . . .(p.1279)
T: +1 336 931 3741
E: alexia.maas@vfsco.com

MACADAM, John Hector Robert (Feb 1987)
(Associate)
Caesar & Howie, Bathgate. . . . .(p.770)
T: 01506 815900
E: jmca@caesar-howie.co.uk

MCADAM, Michael Anthony (Jan 2021)
(Employee)
Scottish Futures Trust, Edinburgh . . . . .(p.1231)
T: 0131 5100800
E: michael.mcadam@scottishfuturestrust.org.uk

MCADAM, Wendy Elizabeth (Aug 2006)
(Employee)
Procurator Fiscal Service, Airdrie . . . . . .(p.1214)
T: 01236 747027
E: wendy.mcadam@copfs.gov.uk

MCAFEE, Charlotte May (May 2018)
(Employee)
Herbert Smith Freehills LLP, Belfast . . . . (p.1275)
E: Charlotte.McAfee@hsf.com

MCAFEE, Julia Anne (Jul 1995) (Employee)
Stirling Council, Stirling . . . . (p.1255)
T: 01786 233065
E: mcafeej@stirling.gov.uk

MCALEENAN, Sin ad (Aug 2019) (Employee)
Cartys, Hamilton . . . . (p.1066)
T: 01698 285432
E: sinead@cartylaw.co.uk

MCALEER, Laura Anne (Oct 2011) (Employee)
Hutchison 3G UK Limited,
Glasgow . . . . (p.1240)
E: Laura.McAleer@three.co.uk

MCALEESE, Tracey Ann (Dec 2008) (Employee)
Glasgow City Council, Glasgow . . . . . . (p.1239)
T: 0141 2874511
E: TraceyAnn.McAleese@glasgow.gov.uk

MCALINDEN, Christopher (Nov 2012)
(Employee)
PricewaterhouseCoopers, Perth . . . . . . (p.1257)
E: chris.mcalinden@pwc.com

MCALINDEN, Katherine (Jun 2018) (Employee)
Shearman & Sterling (London) LLP, London
EC2 . . . . (p.1268)
E: katherine.mcalinden@shearman.com

MCALISTER, Maria Laura (Aug 2014)
(Employee)
Ashurst LLP, London E1 . . . . (p.1261)
T: (020) 7859 2145

MCALISTER, Ross James Fraser (Sept 2020)
(Employee)
Pinsent Masons LLP, Glasgow . . . . (p.1031)
T: 0141 567 8400
E: ross.mcalister@pinsentmasons.com

MCALISTER, Ruairidh Niall (Sept 2014)
(Employee)
Procurator Fiscal Service,
Peterhead . . . . (p.1254)
T: 01779 476628
E: ruairidh.mcalister@copfs.gov.uk

MACALLAN, Amanda Victoria (Mar 2005)
(Employee)
Scottish Government's Parliamentary Counsel
Office, Edinburgh . . . . (p.1233)
T: 0131 2440414
E: amanda.macallan@gov.scot

MACALLAN, Paul Wilson (Oct 1986) (Partner)
Peterkins, Inverurie . . . . (p.1085)
T: 01467 672800
E: pwm@peterkins.com

MCALLISTER, Douglas James (Aug 1997)
(Employee)
Moir and Sweeney LLP, Glasgow . . . . . (p.1021)
T: 0141 4292724
E: douglas@moirandsweeney.com

MACALLISTER, Gemma Mary (Sept 2011)
(Employee)
Office of the Advocate General,
Edinburgh . . . . (p.1227)
T: 0131 2441635
E: gemma.macallister@advocategeneral.gov.uk

MACALLISTER, Karen Louise (Sept 2000)
(Consultant)
DM MacKinnon, Oban . . . . (p.1134)
T: 01631 563014
E: klma@dmmk.co.uk

MCALLISTER, Liam Ross (Oct 2012) (Partner)
Lefevre Litigation, Aberdeen . . . . (p.736)
T: 01224 657657
E: lrm@lefevre-litigation.com

MCALLISTER, Megan (Nov 2021) (Employee)
Fleming & Reid, Glasgow . . . . (p.977)
T: 0141 3311144

MCALLISTER, Mhairi Theresa (Sept 1987)
(Consultant)
Eastons Solicitors Limited, Glasgow . . . . (p.974)
T: 0141 5331976
E: mhairi@mcallister-legal.co.uk

MCALLISTER, Paul (Oct 1991) (Employee)
Mazars LLP, Glasgow . . . . (p.1241)
T: 0141 2264924
E: Paul.McAllister@mazars.co.uk

MCALLISTER, Steven Ryan (Dec 2012)
(Associate)
Davidson Chalmers Stewart LLP,
Edinburgh . . . . (p.859)
T: 0131 6259191
E: steven.mcallister@dcslegal.com

MCALLISTER, Yvonne Margaret (Dec 1997)
(Employee)
BP International Ltd,
Sunbury-on-Thames . . . . (p.1271)
T: +44 203 683 1117
E: yvonne.mcallister@uk.bp.com

MACALPIN, Claire Frances (Apr 2014) (Partner)
MacPhee & Partners LLP, Fort
William . . . . (p.930)
T: 01397 701000
E: ClaireMacAlpin@macphee.co.uk

MCALPINE, Andrew James (Aug 2017)
(Employee)
Kirkland & Ellis International LLP, London
EC3 . . . . (p.1265)
T: 0207 4692000
E: andrew.mcalpine@kirkland.com

MCALPINE, Darina Anne (Oct 2007)
(Employee)
Scottish Police Authority, Police Scotland,
  Glasgow....................(p.1244)
  T: 01786 895727
  E: darina.mcalpine@scotland.pnn.police.uk

MCALPINE, David Edwin (Jan 2014) (Employee)
Pinsent Masons LLP, Glasgow ....(p.1031)
  T: 0141 567 8400
  E: david.mcalpine@pinsentmasons.com

MCALPINE, Elaine Millar (Apr 2009) (Solicitor)
NO FIRM

MCALPINE, Jean (Oct 2009) (Associate)
Coulters Legal LLP, Edinburgh ....(p.858)
  T: 0131 603 7333
  E: jean.mcalpine@coulters.io

MCALPINE, Katherine Jennifer (Oct 2015)
(Employee)
Lindsays LLP, Dundee ....(p.814)
  T: 01382 224112
  E: KatherineMcAlpine@lindsays.co.uk

MCALPINE-SCOTT, Carole Matheson Gemmell
(Oct 1985) (Partner)
MacRoberts LLP, Glasgow ....(p.1015)
  T: 0141 3031100
  E: carole.mcalpine-scott@macroberts.com

MCALPINE-SCOTT, Timothy David
(Sept 2020) (Employee)
Carey Olsen, St Helier ....(p.1274)
  T: 01534 888900
  E: Tim.McAlpineScott@careyolsen.com

MACANDREW, Donald Forbes (Nov 1984)
(Consultant)
Grant Smith Law Practice Limited,
  Aberdeen ....(p.743)
  T: 01224 621620
  E: donald.macandrew@grantsmithlaw.co.uk

MACANDREW, Hilary Anne Barrowman
(Oct 1985) (Director)
Grant Smith Law Practice Limited,
  Turriff......................(p.1176)
  T: 01888 562245
  E: hilary.macandrew@grantsmithlaw.co.uk

MCANDREW, John Paton (Oct 1986) (Partner)
Baird & Company Lawyers & Estate Agents LLP,
  Glenrothes ....(p.1056)
  T: 01592 759555

MACANDREW, Nicholas James (Sept 2021)
(Employee)
Grant Smith Law Practice Limited,
  Aberdeen ....(p.743)
  T: 01224 621620
  E: nick.macandrew@grantsmithlaw.co.uk

MCANEA, Kathleen (Sept 2001) (Associate)
Burness Paull LLP, Glasgow ....(p.954)
  T: 0141 2484933
  E: Kathleen.McAnea@burnesspaull.com

MACARA, John David Murray, QC
(Feb 1973) (Consultant)
Beltrami & Co Limited, Glasgow ......(p.944)
  T: 0141 4292262
  E: murray.macara@beltramiandcompany.co.uk

MCARA, Julie Elizabeth (Aug 2008) (Employee)
Nursing and Midwifery Council,
  Edinburgh ....(p.1227)
  T: (0131) 624 5024
  E: julie.mcara@nmc-uk.org

MCARA, Kyle Lawson (Sept 2011) (Employee)
Office of the Queen's and Lord Treasurer's
  Remembrancer, Edinburgh........(p.1227)
  T: (0300) 020 3512
  E: kyle.mcara@copfs.gov.uk

MACARA, Nicola Julie (Nov 2014) (Associate)
Clyde & Co (Scotland) LLP,
  Glasgow....................(p.961)
  T: 0141 2482666
  E: Nicola.Macara@clydeco.com

MCARDLE, Edward Garvey (Jul 1997) (Partner)
McArdle, Glasgow ....(p.1005)
  T: 0141 8101001
  E: mcardlesolicitors@yahoo.co.uk

MCARDLE, Laura Amber (Apr 2021) (Employee)
CMS Cameron McKenna Nabarro Olswang LLP,
  Edinburgh ....(p.856)
  T: 0131 2288000
  E: Laura.McArdle@cms-cmno.com

MCARTHUR, Aim e Louise (Aug 2018)
(Employee)
Dickson Minto, Edinburgh...........(p.861)
  T: 0131 2254455
  E: aimee.mcarthur@dmws.com

MCARTHUR, Alan Campbell Watt
(May 1989) (Employee)
Procurator Fiscal Service, Glasgow ....(p.1241)
  T: 0300 0203000
  E: alan.mcarthur@copfs.gov.uk

MCARTHUR, Gary (Sept 2020) (Solicitor)
NO FIRM

MACARTHUR, Heather Elaine (Nov 2002)
(Employee)
MacPhee & Partners LLP, Fort
  William ....(p.930)
  T: 01397 701000
  E: HeatherMacArthur@macphee.co.uk

MCARTHUR, James (Jan 2018) (Employee)
Arnold Clark Automobiles Ltd,
  Glasgow....................(p.1237)
  T: 0141 6481200
  E: Jamie.McArthur@arnoldclark.com

MCARTHUR, John (Jan 1987) (Partner)
Gillespie Macandrew LLP,
Edinburgh . . . .(p.872)
T: 0131 2251677
E: john.mcarthur@gillespiemacandrew.co.uk

MCARTHUR, Kathleen (Oct 1997) (Partner)
Wright, Johnston & Mackenzie LLP,
Glasgow. . . . .(p.1054)
T: 0141 2483434
E: KMcA@wjm.co.uk

MCARTHUR, Kirstin Hilary (Oct 2009)
(Employee)
FNZ, Edinburgh . . . .(p.1223)
T: 0131 4731888
E: kirstin.mcarthur@fnz.co.uk

MACARTHUR, Kirsty Isla (Nov 2003)
(Employee)
MacArthur Green Ltd, Glasgow . . . . . .(p.1241)
T: 0141 3425404
E: kirsty@macarthurgreen.com

MCARTHUR, Laura Mary (Aug 2005) (Director)
Curle Stewart Limited, Glasgow . . . .(p.964)
T: 0141 227 6200
E: lm@curlestewart.co.uk

MACARTHUR, Morna Jane (Feb 2007)
(Employee)
STV Television Limited, Glasgow. . . . . .(p.1245)
T: 0141 3003000
E: Morna.MacArthur@stv.tv

MACARTHUR, Sarah Elizabeth (Jul 2019)
(Employee)
Optical Express Limited
E: SarahMacArthur@OpticalExpress.com

MCARTHUR, Sarah-Jane (May 2004) (Partner)
Brodies LLP, Glasgow . . . .(p.948)
T: 0141 2484672
E: sarah-jane.mcarthur@brodies.com

MCARTHUR, Veronica Rachel (Sept 2008)
(Employee)
Clydesdale Bank Plc, Glasgow . . . .(p.1238)
T: 0141 2423733
E: veronica.mcarthur@cybg.com

MACASKILL, Declan (Dec 2017) (Employee)
Renfrewshire Council, Paisley . . . .(p.1252)
T: 0141 8403648
E: declan.macaskill@renfrewshire.gov.uk

MACASKILL, Katy Elizabeth (Oct 2017)
(Employee)
Dentons UK and Middle East LLP,
Glasgow. . . . .(p.968)
T: 0330 2220050
E: Katy.MacAskill@dentons.com

MCASLAN, Emma Louise (Sept 2010)
(Employee)
Forth Ports Limited, Edinburgh . . . . . .(p.1223)
T: 0131 5558770
E: emma.mcaslan@forthports.co.uk

MCATEER, Abby Claire (Sept 1999) (Partner)
Gillespie Gifford & Brown LLP,
Dalbeattie . . . .(p.794)
T: 01556 611247
E: abby.mcateer@ggblaw.co.uk

MCATEER, Alison Colette (Jul 2014) (Employee)
Brodies LLP, Glasgow . . . .(p.948)
T: 0141 2484672
E: alison.mcateer@brodies.com

MCATEER, James Gary (Oct 1984) (Director)
Beltrami & Co Limited, Glasgow . . . . . .(p.944)
T: 0141 4292262
E: gary.mcateer@beltramiandcompany.co.uk

MCATEER, Julie Elizabeth (Aug 1994)
(Employee)
Ithaca Energy (Uk) Limited,
Aberdeen . . . .(p.1213)
T: 01224 638582
E: jmcateer@ithacaenergy.com

MCATIER, Nichola (Nov 2015) (Associate)
DWF LLP, Glasgow . . . .(p.973)
T: +44 333 320 2220
E: Nikki.McAtier@dwf.law

MACAULAY, Clare Frances (Apr 2002)
(Employee)
Procurator Fiscal Service, Glasgow . . . .(p.1241)
T: 0844 561 4323
E: clare.macaulay@copfs.gov.uk

MACAULAY, Iain Angus (Sept 1985) (Partner)
Pinsent Masons LLP, Edinburgh . . . .(p.895)
T: 0131 7777000
E: iain.macaulay@pinsentmasons.com

MACAULAY, Kirsty Ramsay (May 2016)
(Employee)
Brodies LLP, Edinburgh . . . .(p.845)
T: 0131 2283777
E: kirsty.macaulay@brodies.com

MACAULAY, Mark Loudon (Jul 1994) (Partner)
Dentons UK and Middle East LLP,
Glasgow. . . . .(p.968)
T: 0330 2220050
E: Mark.Macaulay@dentons.com

MACAULAY, Pamela Jayne (Sept 2004)
(Employee)
National Westminster Bank PLC,
Edinburgh . . . .(p.1226)
T: (0131) 626 2925
E: pamela.macaulay@rbs.co.uk

MACAULAY, Paul (Jul 2004) (Partner)
Turcan Connell, Edinburgh . . . .(p.908)
T: 0131 2288111
E: paul.macaulay@turcanconnell.com

MACAULAY, Susan Anne (Jul 2015) (Associate)
MacRoberts LLP, Edinburgh . . . .(p.887)
T: 0131 2295046
E: SueAnne.MacAulay@macroberts.com

MACAULAY, Victoria (Oct 2018) (Employee)
Burges Salmon LLP, Edinburgh . . . .(p.850)
T: 0131 3142112
E: victoria.macaulay@burges-salmon.com

MCAULEY, Francis Anthony (Jan 1989)
(Partner)
Lynch & Co., Solicitors, Glasgow . . . . .(p.1005)
T: 0141 4276162
E: frankmcauley@hotmail.com

MCAULEY, Megan Rose (Jul 2018) (Associate)
Walkers, St Helier . . . .(p.1274)
T: 01534 700889
E: meg.mcauley@walkersglobal.com

MCAULEY, Michael Gerard (Dec 1988)
(Partner)
CMS Cameron McKenna Nabarro Olswang LLP,
Glasgow. . . . .(p.962)
T: 0141 2222200
E: Michael.McAuley@cms-cmno.com

MCBAIN, Malcolm David (Oct 1998)
(Employee)
Procurator Fiscal Service,
Edinburgh . . . .(p.1229)
T: 0300 0203000
E: malcolm.mcbain@copfs.gov.uk

MCBEAN, Gordon Graham (Oct 1996)
(Partner)
Thorntons Law LLP, Dundee . . . .(p.819)
T: 01382 229 111
E: gmcbean@thorntons-law.co.uk

MACBEATH, Caroline Jane (Nov 2012)
(Employee)
Gibson Kerr Limited, Edinburgh . . . .(p.872)
T: 0131 2257558
E: caroline.macbeath@gibsonkerr.co.uk

MACBEATH, Niall Alisdair (Oct 1991)
(Employee)
McIntyre & Co., Fort William . . . .(p.930)
T: 01397 703231
E: n.macbeath@solicitors-scotland.com

MCBIRNIE, Kirsty Robertson (Oct 2001)
(Associate)
Dentons UK and Middle East LLP,
Edinburgh . . . .(p.860)
T: 0330 2220050
E: kirsty.mcbirnie@dentons.com

MCBLANE, Gillian Irvine Carruthers
(Feb 1995) (Partner)
Black Hay, Ayr . . . .(p.760)
T: 01292 268988
E: gillian.mcblane@blackhay.co.uk

MCBRIDE, Blayre Rose (Sept 2020) (Employee)
DLA Piper Ireland LLP, Dublin . . . .(p.1274)
E: blayre.mcbride@dlapiper.com

MACBRIDE, Carolyn Margaret (Dec 1979)
(Partner)
MTM Family Law LLP, Glasgow . . . . . .(p.1025)
T: 0141 6117535
E: cmm@mtmfamilylaw.co.uk

MCBRIDE, Emma Margaret Mary (Mar 2015)
(Employee)
Renfrewshire Council, Paisley . . . .(p.1252)
T: 0141 8403648
E: emma.mcbride@renfrewshire.gov.uk

MCBRIDE, Georgina Margaret Kathleen
(Nov 2014) (Employee)
Abrdn Financial Planning and Advice Limited,
Edinburgh . . . .(p.1220)
E: georgina.mcbride@1825.com

MCBRIDE, John Gerard (Jul 1995) (Partner)
Newford Law, Glasgow . . . .(p.1026)
T: 0141 6441792
E: mcbride4law@gmail.com

MCBRIDE, Kathryn (Sept 2017) (Employee)
Pinsent Masons LLP, Manchester . . . . .(p.1270)
T: 0161 2348234
E: katy.mcbride@pinsentmasons.com

MCBRIDE, Mark Francis (Jun 2008) (Director)
Wallace Quinn & Co Limited,
Glasgow. . . . .(p.1051)
T: 0141 7713911
E: mark@wallacequinn.co.uk

MCBRIDE, Natalie Jean Emma (Jan 2021)
(Employee)
Pinsent Masons LLP, Aberdeen . . . .(p.739)
T: 01224 377900
E: natalie.mcbride@pinsentmasons.com

MCBRIDE, Nicolas Richard (Sept 1998)
(Partner)
BTO Solicitors LLP, Glasgow . . . .(p.952)
T: 0141 2218012
E: nmb@bto.co.uk

MCBRIDE, Pauline (Oct 1988) (Solicitor)
NO FIRM

MACBRIDE, Stephen James (Dec 1983)
(Partner)
Stephen J. MacBride & Co,
Wishaw . . . .(p.1181)
T: 01698 350310
E: sandra@sjmacbride.co.uk

MCBURNEY, Alexander John (Mar 1996)
(Partner)
Alexander McBurney Solicitors,
Glasgow....................(p.1006)
T: 0141 5764808
E: lawatwork7@hotmail.com

MCBURNIE, David Andrew George
(Jul 2017) (Employee)
Turcan Connell, Edinburgh ....(p.908)
T: 0131 2288111
E: david.mcburnie@turcanconnell.com

MCCAA, Lorna Margaret (Oct 2002) (Partner)
Dentons UK and Middle East LLP,
Glasgow....................(p.968)
T: 0141 271 5773
E: Lorna.McCaa@dentons.com

MCCABE, Adam Matthew (Apr 2014)
(Employee)
Ofgem, Glasgow ....(p.1241)
T: (0141) 354 5425
E: adam.mccabe@ofgem.gov.uk

MACCABE, Caitlyn (Dec 2010) (Employee)
Digby Brown LLP, Glasgow ....(p.970)
T: 0333 200 5925
E: Caitlyn.Maccabe@digbybrown.co.uk

MCCABE, Jennifer Ann (Jul 2017) (Employee)
Procurator Fiscal Service, Hamilton ....(p.1247)
T: 0844 5613245
E: jennifer.mccabe@copfs.gov.uk

MCCABE, Joanne Hunter (Mar 2006)
(Employee)
National Health Service Scotland,
Edinburgh ....(p.1225)
T: 0131 2757800
E: joanne.mccabe2@nhs.scot

MCCABE, Katrina (Nov 1992) (Director)
Black Woods Legal Limited,
Hamilton ....(p.1065)
T: 01698 312006
E: katrina@blackwoodslegal.com

MCCABE, Laura Anne (Jun 2011) (Employee)
Anderson Strathern LLP, Edinburgh ....(p.839)
T: 0131 2707700
E: laura.mccabe@andersonstrathern.co.uk

MCCABE, Liam Alexander (Aug 2015)
(Employee)
Shepherd and Wedderburn LLP,
Edinburgh ....(p.900)
T: 0131 2289900
E: Liam.McCabe@shepwedd.com

MCCABE, Matthew Ogilvie (Oct 2017)
(Employee)
Jones Whyte LLP, Glasgow...........(p.993)
T: 0141 375 1222
E: matthew.mccabe@joneswhyte.co.uk

MCCABE, Michelle Rose (Jul 2006) (Employee)
Dickson Minto, Edinburgh ....(p.861)
T: 0131 2254455
E: michelle.mccabe@dmws.com

MCCAFFER, Linda (Jul 2002) (Employee)
Procurator Fiscal Service, Hamilton ....(p.1247)
T: 0844 5613245
E: linda.mccaffer@copfs.gov.uk

MCCAFFERTY, Dawn (Jun 2002) (Partner)
Digby Brown LLP, Glasgow ....(p.970)
T: 0333 200 5925
E: dawn.mccafferty@digbybrown.co.uk

MCCAFFERTY, Iain David (Sept 1995) (Partner)
Gleeson McCafferty Law,
Glenrothes ....(p.1057)
T: 01592 611660
E: gleesonmccafferty@hotmail.co.uk

MCCAFFERTY, John Gerard (Feb 1984)
(Employee)
Scottish Legal Aid Board,
Edinburgh ....(p.1233)
T: 0131 2267061

MCCAFFERTY, Nicola Louise (Oct 2008)
(Associate)
Thorntons Law LLP, Dundee ....(p.819)
T: 01382 229 111
E: nmccafferty@thorntons-law.co.uk

MCCAFFERY, Sarah (Feb 2013) (Employee)
Ledingham Chalmers LLP,
Inverness ....(p.1078)
T: 01463 667400
E: Sarah.McCaffery@ledinghamchalmers.com

MCCAFFREY, Anna Patricia (Oct 2007)
(Associate)
Taylor Wessing LLP, London EC4 .....(p.1268)
T: 020 7300 4166
E: A.McCaffrey@taylorwessing.com

MCCAFFREY, Barry Dean (Sept 1995)
(Employee)
Scottish Government, Edinburgh .....(p.1231)
T: 0131 2441444
E: barry.mccaffrey@gov.scot

MCCAFFREY, John (Aug 2002) (Partner)
Austin Kelly & Co.,, Irvine ....(p.1086)
T: 01294 275215
E: court@austinkelly.net

MACCAIG, Adam John (Jan 2012) (Employee)
Matthews Legal Limited, Newton
Stewart ....(p.1131)
T: 01671 404100
E: AdamMacCaig@abamatthews.com

MCCAIG, Barry John (Nov 1998) (Partner)
Pinsent Masons LLP, Glasgow ....(p.1031)
T: 0141 567 8400
E: barry.mccaig@pinsentmasons.com

MCCAIG, Colleen Mary (Nov 2006) (Employee)
Doonan, McCaig & Co. Ltd,
   Kilmarnock . . . . (p.1094)
   T: 0141 5526600
   E: colleenmccaig@msn.com

MCCAIG, David (Aug 1984) (Director)
Doonan, McCaig & Co. Ltd,
   Kilmarnock . . . . (p.1094)
   T: 0141 5526600
   E: davidmccaig4@gmail.com

MCCAIG, Ewan (Mar 2016) (Employee)
Office of the Advocate General,
   Edinburgh . . . . (p.1227)
   T: 0131 2441635
   E: ewan.mccaig@advocategeneral.gov.uk

MCCAIG, Stephen Michael (Sept 1996)
(Employee)
City of Edinburgh Council,
   Edinburgh . . . . (p.1221)
   T: 0131 529 3689 (x3368
   E: stephen.mccaig@edinburgh.gov.uk

MCCALL, Lauren Victoria (Nov 2011) (Partner)
Carruthers, Curdie, Sturrock & Co.,
   Kilmarnock . . . . (p.1094)
   T: 01563 572727
   E: laurenmccall@carrutherscurdiesturrock.co.uk

MCCALL, Lisa Craig (Jun 2017) (Employee)
Austin Lafferty Limited, Glasgow . . . . . . (p.942)
   T: 0141 6115221
   E: lmccall@laffertylaw.com

MCCALL, Lorna Jane (Nov 1995) (Employee)
National Health Service Scotland,
   Edinburgh . . . . (p.1225)
   T: 0131 2757800
   E: lorna.mccall@nhs.scot

MCCALL, Mark (Aug 1997) (Solicitor)
NO FIRM

MCCALL, Murray (Oct 1996) (Partner)
Anderson Strathern LLP, Glasgow . . . . . . (p.940)
   T: 0141 2426060
   E: murray.mccall@andersonstrathern.co.uk

MCCALL, Peter Michael (Nov 1996) (Solicitor)
NO FIRM

MCCALL, Ruth Margaret (Jul 2005) (Partner)
Stodarts LLP, Hamilton . . . . (p.1069)
   T: 01698 200302
   E: RuthMcCall@Stodarts.co.uk

MCCALL, Sarah Campbell (Nov 2007)
(Employee)
Procurator Fiscal Service,
   Edinburgh . . . . (p.1229)
   T: (0844) 561 3268
   E: sarah.mccall@copfs.gov.uk

MCCALL, Stuart (Aug 1987) (Employee)
East Ayrshire Council, Kilmarnock . . . . . (p.1249)
   T: 01563 576161
   E: Stuart.mccall@east-ayrshire.gov.uk

MCCALLION, Jenny Suzanne (Jan 2015)
(Employee)
Scottish Children's Reporter Administration,
   Stirling . . . . (p.1254)
   T: 01786 459500
   E: Jenny.McCallion@scra.gov.uk

MCCALLISTER, Ruth (Nov 1996) (Employee)
Morton Fraser LLP, Edinburgh . . . . (p.891)
   T: 0131 2471210
   E: Ruth.McCallister@morton-fraser.com

MCCALLUM, Angela Jane (Jan 1996)
(Employee)
Legal Key Consulting Limited,
   Glasgow . . . . (p.1240)
   E: angela.mccallum@legalkc.co.uk

MCCALLUM, Catriona Malcolm (Sept 2004)
(Employee)
The Scottish Parliament, Edinburgh . . . (p.1235)
   T: 0131 3486653
   E: Catriona.McCallum@parliament.scot

MCCALLUM, David Lorne (Oct 2012)
(Associate)
CMS Cameron McKenna Nabarro Olswang LLP,
   London EC4 . . . . (p.1263)
   T: 0207 3673000
   E: david.mccallum@cms-cmno.com

MCCALLUM, Joyce Elizabeth (Jul 2014)
(Employee)
Scottish Children's Reporter Administration,
   Kilmarnock . . . . (p.1249)
   T: 01563 534176

MCCALLUM, Kimberley (Feb 2017) (Employee)
WEST DUNBARTONSHIREhire Council,
   Dumbarton . . . . (p.1217)
   T: 01389 737000
   E: kim.mccallum@west-dunbarton.gov.uk

MCCALLUM, Laura (Dec 2012) (Employee)
Aberdeen Football Club, Aberdeen . . . . (p.1211)
   E: laura.mccallum@afc.co.uk

MCCALLUM, Margaret (Mar 1996) (Employee)
Procurator Fiscal Service, Glasgow . . . . (p.1241)
   T: 0300 0203000
   E: margaret.mccallum@copfs.gov.uk

MCCALLUM, Mhairi (Sept 2012) (Associate)
Jardine Donaldson, Alloa . . . . (p.752)
   T: 01259 724411
   E: mhairi.mccallum@jardinedonaldson.co.uk

MCCALLUM, Neva Alexandra (Aug 2017)
(Employee)
Procurator Fiscal Service, Paisley . . . . . . (p.1252)
   T: 0141 8875225
   E: Neva.mccallum@copfs.gov.uk

MCCALLUM, Rachael Ann (Jul 2018)
(Employee)
Shoosmiths, Edinburgh . . . .(p.902)
T: 03700 868000
E: rachael.mccallum@shoosmiths.co.uk

MCCALLUM, Scott (Aug 2005) (Partner)
Shepherd and Wedderburn LLP,
Glasgow. . . . .(p.1039)
T: 0141 5669900

MCCALMONT, Amy Alexandra (Sept 2018)
(Employee)
Ashurst LLP, Glasgow . . . .(p.1237)
T: (0141) 375 4242
E: Amy.McCalmont@ashurst.com

MCCAMLEY, Brenda (Feb 2005) (Partner)
Paterson Holms, Glasgow . . . .(p.1029)
T: 0141 9428825
E: brenda@patersonholms.co.uk

MCCAMLEY, Flora Margaret (Aug 2021)
(Employee)
Procurator Fiscal Service,
Edinburgh . . . .(p.1227)
T: 0300 0203168
E: flora.mccamley@copfs.gov.uk

MCCANDLISH, Paul (Nov 2017) (Employee)
Stirling Council, Stirling. . . . .(p.1255)
T: 01786 233065
E: mccandlishp@stirling.gov.uk

MCCANN, Ashley Marie (May 2015)
(Employee)
Gillespie Macandrew LLP,
Edinburgh . . . .(p.872)
T: 0131 2251677
E: ashley.mccann@gillespiemacandrew.co.uk

MCCANN, Joanne Louise (Nov 1996)
(Employee)
Wilson Ward LLP, Edinburgh . . . .(p.913)
T: 0131 4677550
E: jo@wilsonward.co.uk

MCCANN, Lorna (Aug 2010) (Director)
McIntosh McCann Ltd, Glasgow . . . . .(p.1012)
T: 0141 212 2222
E: lorna@mcintoshmccann.com

MCCANN, Lucy Jane (Sept 2007) (Partner)
Brodies LLP, Edinburgh . . . .(p.845)
T: 0131 2283777
E: lucy.mccann@brodies.com

MCCANN, Mary Geraldine (Sept 1984)
(Employee)
SOUTH LANARKSHIREre Council,
Hamilton . . . .(p.1247)
T: 01698 454658
E: geraldine.mccann@southlanarkshire.gov.uk

MCCANN, Michael Ian (Jan 1997) (Partner)
CMS Cameron McKenna Nabarro Olswang LLP,
Edinburgh . . . .(p.856)
T: 0131 2288000
E: Ian.McCann@cms-cmno.com

MCCANN, Monica Mary (Jan 1990) (Employee)
Archibald Sharp & Son Limited,
Glasgow. . . . .(p.1039)
T: 0141 3393036
E: mmccann@archibaldsharp.co.uk

MCCANNELL, Helen Sharp (Nov 1990)
(Employee)
Procurator Fiscal Service, Hamilton . . . .(p.1247)
T: 7786114038
E: helen.mccannell@copfs.gov.uk

MCCARLIE, Ian Bryson (Mar 1999) (Partner)
Pinsent Masons LLP, Edinburgh . . . .(p.895)
T: 0131 7777000
E: ian.mccarlie@pinsentmasons.com

MCCARROLL, Clare Margaret (Sept 1996)
(Partner)
Lindsays LLP, Edinburgh . . . .(p.882)
T: 0131 2291212
E: claremccarroll@lindsays.co.uk

MCCARRON, Claire Annie (Aug 2011)
(Employee)
Public Defence Solicitors Office,
Glasgow. . . . .(p.1243)
T: 0141 5530794
E: CMcCarron@pdso.org.uk

MCCARRON, Edward John (Aug 1994)
(Director)
Ness Gallagher Solicitors Limited,
Wishaw . . . .(p.1182)
T: 01698 355 525
E: emcc@nessgallagher.co.uk

MCCARRON, Kevin Joseph (Aug 1987)
(Director)
Ness Gallagher Solicitors Limited,
Wishaw . . . .(p.1182)
T: 01698 355 525
E: kmcc@nessgallagher.co.uk

MCCARRON, Lucy Mary (Sept 2019)
(Employee)
Whyte & Mackay Ltd, Glasgow . . . . . .(p.1246)
E: Lucy.McCarron@whyteandmackay.com

MCCARRON, Susie Jeanne (Jul 2010) (Partner)
Jardine Donaldson, Stirling . . . .(p.1165)
T: 01786 450366
E: susie.mccarron@jardinedonaldson.co.uk

MCCARTE, Claire (Jul 2008) (Employee)
Shepherd and Wedderburn LLP,
Glasgow. . . . .(p.1039)
T: 0141 5669900
E: Claire.McCarte@shepwedd.com

MCCARTER, Jordan Stuart (Feb 2014)
(Employee)
Digby Brown LLP, Glasgow . . . .(p.970)
　T: 0333 200 5925
　E: jordan.mccarter@digbybrown.co.uk

MCCARTHY, Ian Christopher (Aug 1985)
(Director)
Ian C. McCarthy Ltd, Glasgow . . . .(p.1007)
　T: 0141 7631366
　E: ian@iancmccarthy.co.uk

MCCARTHY, Kathleen (Jun 1999) (Partner)
McCarthy Law, Glasgow . . . .(p.1006)
　T: 0141 3376678
　E: k@mccarthylaw.co.uk

MCCARTHY, Laura Elizabeth (Feb 2015)
(Partner)
Munro & Noble, Inverness . . . .(p.1080)
　T: 01463 221727
　E: lauram@munronoble.com

MCCARTNEY, Cameron Ross Smillie
(Dec 2013) (Employee)
Brazenall & Orr, Dumfries . . . .(p.800)
　T: 01387 255695
　E: cameron@brazenallandorr.co.uk

MCCARTNEY, Ciara (Sept 2020) (Employee)
MacPhee & Partners LLP, Fort
　William . . . .(p.930)
　T: 01397 701000
　E: ciaramccartney@macphee.co.uk

MCCARTNEY, Natalie Elizabeth (May 2008)
(Employee)
BTO Solicitors LLP, Edinburgh . . . .(p.849)
　T: 0131 2222939
　E: nem@bto.co.uk

MCCARTNEY, Nicola (Mar 2012) (Employee)
Irwin Mitchell Scotland LLP,
　Glasgow. . . . .(p.991)
　T: 0141 3004300
　E:
nicola.mccartney@irwinmitchellscotland.com

MCCARTNEY, Sally Ann (Sept 1997) (Partner)
Kippen Campbell LLP, Perth . . . .(p.1149)
　T: 01738 635353
　E: sal@kcllp.co.uk

MCCASKILL, Lorna (Mar 2017) (Partner)
Cameron Pinkerton & Co LLP,
　Paisley . . . .(p.1137)
　T: 0141 8875211
　E: lorna@cameronpinkerton.co.uk

MCCATHIE, Deborah Ann (Oct 1999) (Partner)
Gilson Gray LLP, Edinburgh . . . .(p.874)
　T: 0131 5165354
　E: dmccathie@gilsongray.co.uk

MCCAUL, David James (Nov 1985) (Employee)
Dickson Minto, Edinburgh . . . .(p.861)
　T: 0131 2254455
　E: david.mccaul@dmws.com

MCCAWLEY, John (Aug 2014) (Employee)
McCawley & Co, Glasgow. . . . .(p.1241)

MCCHEYNE, Robert Murray (Sept 1996)
(Director)
Murchison Law Limited, Inverness . . . .(p.1081)
　T: 01463 709992
　E: murray@murchisonlaw.co.uk

MCCHRISTIE, Laura Anne (Feb 2008)
(Employee)
South Ayrshire Council, Ayr . . . .(p.1215)
　T: 01292 612475
　E: Laura.McChristie@south-ayrshire.gov.uk

MCCLANACHAN, Catherine (Oct 1986)
(Director)
ELP Arbuthnott McClanachan,
　Edinburgh . . . .(p.867)
　T: 0131 3127276
　E: cmc@elpamsolicitors.co.uk

MCCLAY, Iain Stuart (Oct 1994) (Employee)
Aegon UK, Edinburgh . . . .(p.1220)
　T: 1315493986
　E: iain.mcclay@aegon.co.uk

MCCLEAN, Andrew David (Aug 2007)
(Employee)
Addleshaw Goddard LLP,
　Edinburgh . . . .(p.835)
　T: 0131 2282400
　E: David.McClean@addleshawgoddard.com

MCCLEAN, Fiona Davidson (Apr 1995)
(Employee)
Scottish Government, Edinburgh . . . . .(p.1231)
　T: 0131 244 0815
　E: Fiona.McClean@gov.scot

MCCLEARN, Gillian Suzanne (Oct 2005)
(Employee)
BTO Raeburn Hope, Helensburgh . . . . .(p.1072)
　T: 01436 671221
　E: gmc@bto.co.uk

MCCLEARY, Emilia Patrycja (Mar 2021)
(Employee)
Caesar & Howie, Alloa . . . .(p.752)
　T: 01259 723408
　E: emc@caesar-howie.co.uk

MCCLELLAND, Gemma Ruth (Jan 2012)
(Associate)
Macleod & MacCallum Limited,
　Inverness . . . .(p.1080)
　T: 01463 239393
　E: gemma.mcclelland@macandmac.co.uk

MCCLELLAND, Ian Mark (Sept 1991) (Director)
JC Hughes Solicitors Limited,
Glasgow . . . . (p.988)
T: 0141 7782468
E: imcc@jchughes.net

MCCLELLAND, Morag (Sept 2010) (Employee)
National Health Service Scotland,
Edinburgh . . . . (p.1225)
T: 0131 2757800
E: Morag.McClelland@nhs.scot

MCCLELLAND, Noele Gillian (Jun 1998)
(Partner)
Thorntons Law LLP, Dundee . . . . (p.819)
T: 01382 229 111
E: nmcclelland@thorntons-law.co.uk

MCCLELLAND, Peter Duncan (Aug 1989)
(Employee)
Procurator Fiscal Service,
Kilmarnock . . . . (p.1249)
T: 01563 536211
E: peter.mcclelland@copfs.gov.uk

MCCLEMENTS, David Elliott (Nov 1991)
(Partner)
Russel + Aitken Denny LLP, Denny . . . . . (p.796)
T: 01324 822194
E: dem@radenny.co.uk

MCCLEMENTS, Sean (Jul 2015) (Employee)
Aggreko plc, Glasgow . . . . (p.1237)
T: 0141 2255900
E: Sean.McClements@aggreko.co.uk

MCCLINTON, Laura Ellen Victoria
(Aug 2021) (Employee)
Burness Paull LLP, Glasgow . . . . (p.954)
T: 0141 2484933
E: laura.mcclinton@burnesspaull.com

MCCLOY, Lisa Maisie (Aug 2008) (Employee)
Scottish Government Children & Families
Directorate, Edinburgh . . . . (p.1232)
T: 0131 2444521
E: Lisa.Mccloy@gov.scot

MCCLOY-STEVENS, Carla (Sept 2001)
(Employee)
Scottish Government's Parliamentary Counsel
Office, Edinburgh . . . . (p.1233)
T: 0131 244 1405
E: carla.mccloy-stevens@gov.scot

MCCLURE, Gerald (Dec 1981) (Director)
McClure Collins Limited, Glasgow . . . . (p.1007)
T: 0141 4237181
E: gerry@mcclurecollins.com

MCCLURE, Iain Jackson (Apr 2012) (Employee)
Heriot-Watt University, Edinburgh . . . . (p.1223)
T: (0131) 4513405
E: i.mcclure@hw.ac.uk

MCCLURE, Kenneth William (Dec 1990)
(Employee)
Social Care and Social Work Improvement
Scotland, Paisley . . . . (p.1253)
T: 0141 843 6847
E: kenneth.mcclure@careinspectorate.gov.scot

MCCLUSKEY, Carol (Aug 2006) (Associate)
Matthew Brown, Irvine . . . . (p.1087)
T: 01294 273721
E: carol@matthewbrownsolicitors.co.uk

MCCLUSKEY, Christie Elizabeth (Sept 2012)
(Employee)
William Grant & Sons Ltd., Bellshill . . . (p.1215)
T: 01698 843843
E: christie.mccluskey@wgrant.com

MCCLUSKEY, Gillian Bell (Aug 2002)
(Employee)
Alston Law, Glasgow . . . . (p.940)
T: 0344 5715205
E: gillian.mccluskey@alstonlaw.co.uk

MCCLUSKEY, Jacqueline Davidson
(Oct 1993) (Partner)
BTO Solicitors LLP, Edinburgh . . . . (p.849)
T: 0131 2222939
E: jmcc@bto.co.uk

MCCLUSKEY, John Anthony (Sept 2008)
(Employee)
NORTH LANARKSHIREre Council,
Motherwell . . . . (p.1251)
T: 01698 302196
E: mccluskeyjo@northlan.gov.uk

MCCLUSKEY, Justine Hannah (Feb 2021)
(Employee)
Shepherd and Wedderburn LLP,
Edinburgh . . . . (p.900)
T: 0131 2289900
E: justine.mccluskey@shepwedd.com

MCCLUSKEY, William (Aug 1994) (Director)
William McCluskey Solicitors Limited,
Glasgow . . . . (p.1007)
T: 0141 4180418
E: wmccluskey@hotmail.co.uk

MCCLUSKIE, Nicola (Aug 2008) (Employee)
Addleshaw Goddard LLP, Glasgow . . . . . (p.938)
T: 0141 2212300
E: nicola.mccluskie@addleshawgoddard.com

MCCLUSKIE, Peter Mark (Nov 2003) (Partner)
Keoghs Scotland LLP, Glasgow . . . . (p.996)
T: 0141 2380100
E: mmccluskie@keoghs.co.uk

MCCLYMONT, Daniel Mark (Aug 2016)
(Associate)
DWF LLP, Glasgow . . . . (p.973)
T: 0141 228 8000
E: danny.mcclymont@dwf.law

MCCLYMONT, Linda (Nov 2014) (Employee)
NewLaw Scotland LLP, Glasgow . . . . . . (p.1027)
   T: 0845 4819500
   E: linda.mcclymont@newlaw-scotland.co.uk

MCCOLGAN, Donna Louise (Nov 2008)
   (Employee)
Lloyds Banking Group Plc,
   Edinburgh . . . . (p.1224)
   T: (0131) 442 9579
   E: donna.mccolgan@lloydsbanking.com

MCCOLGAN, James Patrick (Oct 2021)
   (Employee)
Cognizant Worldwide Limited,
   Glasgow . . . . (p.1238)
   T: (0141) 2221561
   E: james.mccolgan@cognizant.com

MCCOLGAN, Martin Fitzgerald (Nov 2005)
   (Employee)
Glasgow City Council, Glasgow . . . . . . (p.1239)
   T: 0141 2874665
   E: Martin.McColgan@glasgow.gov.uk

MCCOLL, Jacqueline Grace (Dec 2001)
   (Partner)
John Pryde, SSC, Edinburgh . . . . (p.897)
   T: 0131 2202160
   E: jacqueline@johnpryde.co.uk

MACCOLL, John Malcolm (Feb 1995) (Director)
Craig Wood Solicitors Limited,
   Inverness . . . . (p.1083)
   T: 01463 225544
   E: JMMacColl@craigwood.co.uk

MCCOLL, Katherine Jean (Mar 2003)
   (Employee)
Procurator Fiscal Service, Glasgow . . . . (p.1243)
   T: (0300) 020 2944
   E: katherine.mccoll@copfs.gov.uk

MCCOLL, Michael Kenneth Edward
   (Jul 2008) (Partner)
CMS Cameron McKenna Nabarro Olswang LLP,
   Glasgow . . . . (p.962)
   T: 0141 2222200
   E: Mike.McColl@cms-cmno.com

MACCOLL, Ruth Denise (Dec 1988) (Employee)
Glasgow City Council, Glasgow . . . . . . (p.1239)
   T: 0141 2874049
   E: Ruth.MacColl@glasgow.gov.uk

MACCOLL-SMITH, Anne Elizabeth
   (Oct 2001) (Employee)
Argyll & Bute Council,
   Lochgilphead . . . . (p.1251)
   T: 01546 604194
   E: Anne.MacColl-Smith@argyll-bute.gov.uk

MCCOLM, Fergus Samuel Torrance
   (Dec 2018) (Employee)
BTO Solicitors LLP, Glasgow . . . . (p.952)
   T: 0141 2218012

MCCOMBE, Derek Thomas (Oct 2005)
   (Partner)
Dentons UK and Middle East LLP,
   Glasgow . . . . (p.968)
   T: 0330 2220050
   E: Derek.McCombe@dentons.com

MCCOMBE, Helen Elizabeth (Feb 2005)
   (Employee)
SSE Plc, Perth . . . . (p.1253)
   T: 01738 456 000
   E: helen.mccombe@sse.com

MCCOMBIE, Brian William (Feb 1977) (Partner)
Masson Glennie LLP, Peterhead . . . . . . (p.1154)
   T: 01779 873 535
   E: brian.mccombie@massonglennie.co.uk

MCCOMBIE, Bruce John Daniel (Oct 2011)
   (Employee)
National Westminster Bank PLC,
   Edinburgh . . . . (p.1227)
   E: bruce.mccombie@natwest.com

MCCONDICHIE, Nicole Frances (Nov 2021)
   (Employee)
GMC Criminal Lawyers,
   Kilmarnock . . . . (p.1095)
   T: 01563 533338

MACCONNACHIE, Julia Maria (Nov 1995)
   (Partner)
Campbell Smith LLP, Edinburgh . . . . . . (p.852)
   T: 0131 5563737
   E: jm@camsmith.co.uk

MCCONNELL, Andrew David (Oct 2011)
   (Employee)
DWF LLP, Glasgow . . . . (p.973)
   T: 0141 228 8000
   E: Andrew.McConnell@dwf.law

MCCONNELL, Andrew John Gordon
   (Oct 2003) (Employee)
National Westminster Bank PLC,
   Edinburgh . . . . (p.1226)
   T: 0131 5568555
   E: andrew.mcconnell@rbs.co.uk

MCCONNELL, Ashleigh (Feb 2008) (Partner)
Mackinnons Solicitors LLP,
   Aberdeen . . . . (p.737)
   T: 01224 868687

MCCONNELL, Conner (Sept 2018) (Employee)
Gillespie Macandrew LLP,
   Edinburgh . . . . (p.872)
   T: 0131 2251677
   E:
   Conner.McConnell@gillespiemacandrew.co.uk

MCCONNELL, Douglas Iain Graham
   (Jul 2004) (Director)
Duncan & McConnell Solicitors Limited,
   Dundee . . . . (p.809)
   T: 07811 386 485
   E: enquiries@duncanandmcconnell.com

MACCONNELL, Joanne Christina (Dec 2006)
(Employee)
University of Edinburgh, Edinburgh . . . (p.1235)
T: (0131) 651 4330
E: Joanne.MacConnell@ed.ac.uk

MCCONNELL, Martin (Oct 2017) (Employee)
Pacitti Jones Legal Limited, Lenzie . . . . (p.1112)
T: 0141 7750005
E: Martin.mcconnell@pacittijones.co.uk

MCCONNELL, Rachel Elizabeth (Sept 2018)
(Employee)
Pinsent Masons LLP, London EC2 . . . . . (p.1267)
T: 020 7418 7003
E: rachel.mcconnell@pinsentmasons.com

MCCONNELL, Robert Scott (Oct 2019)
(Employee)
Harper Macleod LLP, Glasgow . . . . (p.983)
T: 0141 2218888
E: robert.mcconnell@harpermacleod.co.uk

MCCONNELL, Sarah Marie (Oct 2014)
(Employee)
Brodies LLP, Glasgow . . . . (p.948)
T: 0141 2484672
E: sarah.mcconnell@brodies.com

MCCONNELL, Sarah Rebecca (Sept 2013)
(Employee)
NHS 24, Glasgow . . . . (p.1241)
E: sarah.mcconnell@nhs24.scot.nhs.uk

MCCOO, Allison Elizabeth (Oct 1992)
(Associate)
Thorntons Law LLP, Perth . . . . (p.1151)
T: 01738 621212
E: amccoo@thorntons-law.co.uk

MCCORKELL, Peter George Alexander
(Jan 2012) (Employee)
Sidley Austin LLP, London EC3 . . . . (p.1268)
T: 2073602040
E: pmccorkell@sidley.com

MCCORMACK, Deborah (Nov 1998)
(Employee)
Pinsent Masons LLP, Glasgow . . . . (p.1031)
T: 0141 567 8400
E: deborah.mccormack@pinsentmasons.com

MCCORMACK, Joanna (Sept 1999) (Employee)
National Health Service Scotland,
Edinburgh . . . . (p.1225)
T: 0131 2757800
E: Joanna.McCormack@nhs.scot

MCCORMACK, Julie Elizabeth (Aug 1998)
(Employee)
Lloyds Banking Group Plc,
Edinburgh . . . . (p.1224)
T: 0131 4429556
E: julie.mccormack@lloydsbanking.com

MCCORMACK, Mark (Jun 2016) (Employee)
McCormacks Solicitors Limited,
Glasgow . . . . (p.1007)
T: 0141 404 0438
E: mccormacks@live.co.uk

MCCORMACK, Robert Edward (Nov 1995)
(Director)
McCormacks Solicitors Limited,
Glasgow . . . . (p.1007)
T: 0141 404 0438
E: McCormacks@live.co.uk

MCCORMACK, Samuel Alan (Apr 1986)
(Associate)
Jackson Boyd LLP, Glasgow . . . . (p.991)
T: 0141 2214325
E: AMcCormack@jacksonboyd.co.uk

MCCORMICK, Francis Paul (Aug 2012)
(Partner)
McSparran McCormick, Glasgow . . . . . (p.1016)
T: 0141 2487962
E: mail@mcsparranmccormick.co.uk

MCCORMICK, Frank Paul (Aug 1976) (Partner)
McSparran McCormick, Glasgow . . . . . (p.1016)
T: 0141 2487962
E: mail@mcsparranmccormick.co.uk

MCCORMICK, Jennifer Catherine Helen
(Jul 2009) (Associate)
Pinsent Masons LLP, Glasgow . . . . (p.1031)
T: 0141 567 8400
E: Jennifer.mccormick@pinsentmasons.com

MCCORMICK, Lindsay Margaret Grace
(Nov 2017) (Employee)
Smart Metering Systems Plc,
Glasgow . . . . (p.1244)
T: (0141) 2493909
E: Lindsay.McCormick@sms-plc.com

MCCORMICK, Matthew Donald (Nov 2020)
(Employee)
McSparran McCormick, Glasgow . . . . . (p.1016)
T: 0141 2487962

MCCORMICK, Paul Charles (Nov 1981)
(Partner)
McCarrys Solicitors, Glasgow . . . . (p.1006)
T: 0141 9451911
E: paulmccormick@mccarrys.com

MCCORMICK, Ruth Mary (Feb 2002)
(Employee)
NORTH LANARKSHIRERe Council,
Motherwell . . . . (p.1251)
T: 01698 302729
E: McCormickru@northlan.gov.uk

MCCORMICK, Sarah Louise (Sept 2012)
(Associate)
Brodies LLP, Edinburgh . . . . (p.845)
T: 0131 2283777
E: sarah.mccormick@brodies.com

MCCORMICK, Yvette Fiona (Jun 2021)
(Employee)
CMC Law LLP, Glasgow . . . .(p.961)
T: 7731536911
E: yvette.mccormick@cmclaw.co.uk

MCCORQUODALE, Kay Roslyn (Nov 1987)
(Employee)
Judicial Office For Scotland,
Edinburgh . . . .(p.1224)
T: 0131 2406701
E: KMcCorquodale@scotcourts.gov.uk

MACCORQUODALE, Kirsty Jane (Jan 2019)
(Employee)
DWF LLP, Glasgow . . . .(p.973)
T: 0141 228 8000
E: kirsty.maccorquodale@dwf.law

MCCORQUODALE, Laura Anne (Jun 2011)
(Partner)
Harper Macleod LLP, Edinburgh . . . .(p.877)
T: 0131 2472500
E: laura.mccorquodale@harpermacleod.co.uk

MCCORRY, Maeve (Oct 2015) (Employee)
Lindsays LLP, Glasgow . . . .(p.1001)
T: 0141 2216551
E: maevemccorry@lindsays.co.uk

MCCOSH, Jenna Eliza (Feb 2012) (Employee)
Brodies LLP, Aberdeen . . . .(p.723)
T: 01224 392242
E: jenna.mccosh@brodies.com

MCCOURT, Rachel (Oct 2021) (Employee)
Pinsent Masons LLP, Glasgow . . . .(p.1031)
T: 0141 567 8400
E: rachel.mccourt@pinsentmasons.com

MCCOWAN, Andrew Christopher
(Oct 1990) (Partner)
TLT LLP, Glasgow . . . .(p.1048)
T: 0333 006 0400
E: andrew.mccowan@tltsolicitors.com

MCCRACKEN, Angela (Mar 1997) (Consultant)
Bannatyne, Kirkwood, France & Co.,
Glasgow . . . .(p.943)
T: 0141 2216020
E: angelamccracken@bkf.co.uk

MCCRACKEN, Angela Lucinda Irene
(Aug 2013) (Employee)
Scottish Rugby, Edinburgh . . . .(p.1233)
T: 0131 3465000
E: angela.mccracken@sru.org.uk

MCCRACKEN, Claire Louise (Jan 2003) (Partner)
Weightmans (Scotland) LLP,
Glasgow . . . .(p.1051)
T: 0345 073 9900
E: claire.mccracken@weightmans.com

MCCRACKEN, Eric Barclay (Sept 1997)
(Employee)
Pulsant Limited, Edinburgh . . . .(p.1230)
T: 0131 514 4030
E: ricky.mccracken@pulsant.com

MCCRACKEN, Kirstin (Oct 2007) (Employee)
Eversheds Sutherland (International) LLP, London
EC2 . . . .(p.1264)
T: 0845 4979797
E: kirstinmccracken@eversheds-sutherland.com

MCCRACKEN, Lucy Charlotte (Jul 2020)
(Employee)
Brodies LLP, Edinburgh . . . .(p.845)
T: 0131 2283777
E: lucy.mccracken@brodies.com

MCCRAE, Lorna Elizabeth (Oct 1991)
(Employee)
National Health Service Scotland,
Edinburgh . . . .(p.1225)
T: 0131 2757800
E: Lorna.McCrae@nhs.scot

MCCRAN, Lyndsey Sophia (Dec 1993)
(Employee)
Malcolm, Jack & Matheson Limited,
Dunfermline . . . .(p.824)
T: 01383 723444
E: lyndsey@malcolmjack.co.uk

MCCRAN, Ralph Douglas (Nov 1988) (Director)
Malcolm, Jack & Matheson Limited,
Dunfermline . . . .(p.824)
T: 01383 723444
E: ralph@malcolmjack.co.uk

MCCREADIE, Alan John (Dec 1989) (Employee)
Law Society of Scotland,
Edinburgh . . . .(p.1224)
T: 0131 2267411
E: alanmccreadie@lawscot.org.uk

MCCREADY, Frazer Gordon Ewan
(Nov 1988) (Director)
McCready & Co Solicitors Limited,
Stirling . . . .(p.1166)
T: 01786 479628
E: frazer@fmccready.co.uk

MCCREADY, Rachael Margaret (Dec 2015)
(Employee)
Scottish Power Limited, Glasgow . . . . .(p.1244)
T: 0141 6140000
E: r.mccready@scottishpower.com

MCCREATH, Alexander Hugh (Nov 1987)
(Partner)
Thorntons Law LLP, Edinburgh . . . .(p.906)
T: 0131 2258705
E: smccreath@thorntons-law.co.uk

MCCREATH, Gordon Speirs (Jan 1997) (Partner)
Pinsent Masons LLP, Glasgow . . . .(p.1031)
T: 0141 567 8400
E: gordon.mccreath@pinsentmasons.com

MCCREATH, Lisa Jane (Sept 2017) (Employee)
Dentons UK and Middle East LLP,
Edinburgh . . . .(p.860)
T: 0330 2220050
E: Lisa.McCreath@dentons.com

MCCRONE, Alasdair Iain (Sept 2019)
(Employee)
Pinsent Masons LLP, Glasgow . . . .(p.1031)
T: 0141 567 8400
E: alasdair.mccrone@pinsentmasons.com

MCCRORIE, Lauryn Stephanie (Oct 2016)
(Employee)
Drummond Miller LLP, Glasgow. . . . . . .(p.971)
T: 0141 3320086
E: lmccrorie@drummondmiller.co.uk

MCCROSSAN, Mairead Frances (May 2019)
(Employee)
Livingstone Brown Limited,
Glasgow. . . . .(p.1003)
T: 0141 4298166
E: Mairead@livbrown.co.uk

MCCRUDDEN, Sharon Elizabeth Mary
(Sept 1988) (Employee)
Procurator Fiscal Service,
Edinburgh . . . .(p.1229)
T: (0844) 561 3268
E: sharon.mccrudden@copfs.gov.uk

MCCRUM, Paula Agnes (Nov 2016) (Employee)
John Jackson & Dick Limited,
Hamilton . . . .(p.1067)
T: 01698 281747
E: pmccrum@jacksondicklaw.com

MCCUAIG, Ryan James (Oct 2020) (Employee)
Thorntons Law LLP, Glasgow . . . .(p.1047)
T: 03330 430350
E: rmccuaig@thorntons-law.co.uk

MCCUBBIN, James Kenneth (Feb 2000)
(Employee)
Roslin Institute, Easter Bush . . . .(p.1219)
T: 0131 6519100
E: Jamie.McCubbin@ed.ac.uk

MCCUE, Callum Peter (Mar 2018) (Solicitor)
NO FIRM

MCCUE, Marie Elizabeth (Mar 2014)
(Employee)
Procurator Fiscal Service, Glasgow . . . .(p.1241)
T: 0300 0203000
E: marie.mccue@copfs.gov.uk

MCCUE, Paul Michael (Jul 2008) (Director)
Paul McCue & Co Limited,
Glasgow. . . . .(p.1008)
T: 07872 835546
E: paul.mccue@gmail.com

MACCUISH, Helen Anne (Apr 1998) (Employee)
Murdoch Stewarts Limited,
Glasgow. . . . .(p.1025)
T: 0141 226 3333
E: hmaccuish@murdochstewarts.co.uk

MCCULLAGH, Sylvia Claire (Sept 2004)
(Employee)
Balfour + Manson LLP, Edinburgh . . . . .(p.841)
T: 0131 2001200
E: Sylvia.McCullagh@balfour-manson.co.uk

MCCULLOCH, Alan (Jul 1971) (Partner)
Wrights, Motherwell . . . .(p.1128)
T: 01698 267361
E: amcculloch@wrightsolicitors.com

MCCULLOCH, Angela Dale (Sept 2007)
(Partner)
Brodies LLP, Glasgow . . . .(p.948)
T: 0141 2484672
E: angela.mcculloch@brodies.com

MCCULLOCH, Cameron Lars (Oct 2009)
(Employee)
Pinsent Masons LLP, Glasgow . . . .(p.1031)
T: 0141 567 8400
E: cameron.mcculloch@pinsentmasons.com

MCCULLOCH, Claire Margaret (Nov 2009)
(Employee)
Miller Samuel Hill Brown LLP,
Glasgow. . . . .(p.1020)
T: 0141 2211919

MCCULLOCH, Derek Ashley James
(Nov 1981) (Partner)
Gillespie Macandrew LLP,
Edinburgh . . . .(p.872)
T: 0131 2251677
E: derek.mcculloch@gillespiemacandrew.co.uk

MCCULLOCH, Elaine (Jul 2009) (Associate)
Slater and Gordon Scotland Limited,
Edinburgh . . . .(p.903)
T: 0131 7184150
E: Elaine.McCulloch@slatergordon.uk

MCCULLOCH, Euan Russell (Nov 1987)
(Employee)
Office of the Scottish Info. Commissioner
T: 01334 464610
E: emcculloch@itspublicknowledge.info

MCCULLOCH, Gillian Lorna (Feb 2015)
(Employee)
CMS Cameron McKenna Nabarro Olswang LLP,
Glasgow. . . . .(p.962)
T: 0141 2222200
E: Gillian.McCulloch@cms-cmno.com

MCCULLOCH, Hannah Elspeth (Feb 2018)
(Solicitor)
NO FIRM

MCCULLOCH, Ian David (Jan 1976) (Partner)
Mailers, Stirling . . . .(p.1166)
　　T: 01786 450555
　　E: Ian.mcculloch@mailers.co.uk

MCCULLOCH, Lindsay May Elizabeth
(Jul 2008) (Employee)
Turcan Connell, Edinburgh . . . .(p.908)
　　T: 0131 2288111
　　E: lindsay.mcculloch@turcanconnell.com

MCCULLOCH, Louise (Sept 2016) (Employee)
Digby Brown LLP, Glasgow . . . .(p.970)
　　T: 0333 200 5925
　　E: louise.mcculloch@digbybrown.co.uk

MCCULLOCH, Lynn Gibson (Oct 2016)
(Employee)
Chivas Brothers Limited, Glasgow . . . .(p.1238)
　　E: Lynn.McCulloch@pernod-ricard.com

MCCULLOCH, Megan Rae (Nov 2019)
(Employee)
CMS Cameron McKenna Nabarro Olswang LLP,
　Glasgow. . . . .(p.962)
　　T: 0141 2222200
　　E: Megan.McCulloch@cms-cmno.com

MCCULLOCH, Pauline (Oct 2011) (Employee)
Burness Paull LLP, Edinburgh . . . .(p.850)
　　T: 0131 4736000
　　E: Pauline.McCulloch@burnesspaull.com

MCCULLOCH, Shelley (Oct 2003) (Solicitor)
NO FIRM

MCCULLOUGH, Cecilia Ann (Oct 2007)
(Employee)
Scottish Government, Edinburgh . . . . .(p.1231)
　　T: 0131 2440644
　　E: cecilia.mccullough@gov.scot

MCCUNE, Carey Ann (Feb 2003) (Employee)
Procurator Fiscal Service,
　Edinburgh . . . .(p.1227)
　　T: 0300 0203168
　　E: Carey.McCune@copfs.gov.uk

MCCUSKER, Andrew Charles Robert
(Jan 2018) (Solicitor)
NO FIRM

MCCUSKER, Charles Patrick (Jan 1985)
(Employee)
Paisley Defence Lawyers (Scotland) Limited,
　Paisley . . . .(p.1141)
　　T: 0141 5619999
　　E: susan.moffat@mccuskerlaw.co.uk

MCCUSKER, Jacqueline (Nov 1993) (Employee)
East Renfrewshire Council, Giffnock . . .(p.1237)
　　T: 0141 5773000
　　E: jacqui.mccusker@eastrenfrewshire.gov.uk

MCCUSKER, James Anthony (Dec 1980)
(Director)
McCusker, Cochrane & Gunn,
　Glasgow. . . . .(p.1008)
　　T: 0141 7782222
　　E: jmccusker@prp-legal.co.uk

MCCUSKER, Susan (May 1986) (Employee)
Paisley Defence Lawyers (Scotland) Limited,
　Paisley . . . .(p.1141)
　　T: 0141 5619999
　　E: susan.mccusker@mccuskerlaw.co.uk

MCCUTCHEON, Finlay Alexander (Jan 2003)
(Employee)
SSE Plc, Perth . . . .(p.1253)
　　T: 01738 456 000
　　E: finlay.mccutcheon@sse.com

MCDADE, Kevin (Jun 2017) (Employee)
Burness Paull LLP, Glasgow . . . .(p.954)
　　T: 0141 2484933
　　E: Kevin.McDade@burnesspaull.com

MCDADE, Lynne (Mar 2011) (Director)
Strefford Tulips Limited, Hamilton . . . .(p.1070)
　　T: 01698 429428
　　E: l.mcdade@strefford-tulips.co.uk

MCDAID, Arlene Michelle (Sept 2001)
(Solicitor)
NO FIRM

MCDAID, Christopher (Oct 2002) (Partner)
Brodies LLP, Glasgow . . . .(p.948)
　　T: 0141 2484672
　　E: chris.mcdaid@brodies.com

MCDAID, Christopher (Apr 1981) (Partner)
McDaid Farrell, Glasgow . . . .(p.1008)
　　T: 0141 6340437
　　E: chris@mcdaidfarrell.com

MCDAID, Louise (Jun 2016) (Employee)
Dentons UK and Middle East LLP,
　Edinburgh . . . .(p.860)
　　T: 0330 2220050
　　E: Louise.McDaid@dentons.com

MCDAIRMANT, Clare Marie (Feb 1996)
(Employee)
Thompsons, Edinburgh . . . .(p.906)
　　T: 0131 2254297
　　E:
　　clare.mcdairmant@thompsons-scotland.co.uk

MCDERMID, Alistair Coates (Aug 2020)
(Employee)
Procurator Fiscal Service,
　Edinburgh . . . .(p.1227)
　　T: 0300 0203168
　　E: alistair.mcdermid@copfs.gov.uk

MCDERMID, Lesley (Apr 2014) (Director)
Kerslands Solicitors Limited,
Milngavie . . . .(p.1123)
T: 0333 6008000
E: Lesley.McDermid@Kerslands.com

MCDERMID, Liam John Anthony (Jun 2009)
(Associate)
DM MacKinnon, Oban . . . .(p.1134)
T: 01631 563014
E: liammcdermid@dmmk.co.uk

MCDERMOTT, Christian Francis (Oct 2008)
(Employee)
Latham & Watkins (London) LLP, London
EC2 . . . .(p.1266)
T: 020 7710 1000
E: christian.mcdermott@lw.com

MCDERMOTT, Paul Martin (May 1995)
(Associate)
Friels Solicitors Limited, Coatbridge . . . .(p.786)
T: 01236 421 136
E: paulmcdermott@frielssolicitors.co.uk

MCDEVITT, Clare Louise (Oct 2021) (Employee)
Addleshaw Goddard LLP, Glasgow . . . . .(p.938)
T: 0141 2212300
E: Clare.McDevitt@addleshawgoddard.com

MCDEVITT, Peter Denis (Jan 1995) (Partner)
W. & A.S. Bruce, Dundee . . . .(p.807)
T: 01382 568188
E: pmcd@wasbruce.co.uk

MACDIARMID, Christine Heather (Dec 1985)
(Consultant)
Miller Samuel Hill Brown LLP,
Glasgow. . . . .(p.1020)
T: 0141 2211919
E: chm@mshblegal.com

MCDIARMID, Fergus Archibald (Dec 1989)
(Partner)
Morton Fraser LLP, Glasgow . . . .(p.1022)
T: 0141 2741100
E: fergus.mcdiarmid@morton-fraser.com

MCDIARMID, Lindsey Olivia (Mar 2021)
(Employee)
Aberdein Considine and Company,
Aberdeen . . . .(p.718)
T: 01224 589700
E: lmcdiarmid@acandco.com

MCDIARMID, Robert Duncan (Oct 2008)
(Partner)
Stronachs LLP, Aberdeen . . . .(p.744)
T: 01224 845845
E: robert.mcdiarmid@stronachs.com

MCDIARMID, Stacey Louise (Oct 2018)
(Employee)
Watermans Solicitors Limited,
Edinburgh . . . .(p.912)
T: 0131 5557055
E: staceymoore@watermans.co.uk

MCDICKEN, Hollie Catherine (Mar 2019)
(Employee)
Taylor & Henderson LLP, Irvine . . . . . .(p.1087)
T: 01294 278306
E: hmcdicken@taylorandhenderson.co.uk

MCDONACH, Lauren Louise (Apr 2018)
(Employee)
Turcan Connell, Edinburgh . . . .(p.908)
T: 0131 2288111
E: lauren.mcdonach@turcanconnell.com

MCDONAGH, Laura Ann (Sept 2010) (Partner)
Drummond Miller LLP, Edinburgh . . . . .(p.864)
T: 0131 2265151
E: lmcdonagh@DrummondMiller.co.uk

MCDONAGH, Stephen James (Nov 2000)
(Partner)
Anderson Strathern LLP, Edinburgh . . . .(p.839)
T: 0131 2707700
E:
stephen.mcdonagh@andersonstrathern.co.uk

MCDONAGH, Steven Henry (Apr 2010)
(Employee)
Berrymans Lace Mawer LLP,
Glasgow. . . . .(p.945)
T: 0141 3532121
E: Steven.McDonagh@blmlaw.com

MACDONALD, Adele Phyllis (Sept 2000)
(Employee)
Procurator Fiscal Service, Glasgow . . . .(p.1241)
T: 0300 0203000
E: Adele.McDonald@copfs.gov.uk

MACDONALD, Alan (Jan 2002) (Partner)
Jackson Boyd LLP, Glasgow . . . .(p.991)
T: 0141 2214325
E: amacdonald@jacksonboyd.co.uk

MACDONALD, Alan John Robert (Apr 1993)
(Employee)
Procurator Fiscal Service, Glasgow . . . .(p.1243)
T: 0300 020 2944
E: alan.macdonald@copfs.gov.uk

MCDONALD, Alan Andrew (Mar 2012)
(Associate)
CMS Cameron McKenna Nabarro Olswang LLP,
Glasgow. . . . .(p.962)
T: 0141 2222200
E: Alan.McDonald@cms-cmno.com

MACDONALD, Alasdair (Oct 2019) (Employee)
Pinsent Masons LLP, Glasgow . . . .(p.1031)
T: 0141 567 8400
E: alasdair.macdonald@pinsentmasons.com

MACDONALD, Alastair Currie (May 2010)
(Partner)
Peterkins, Aberdeen . . . .(p.739)
T: 01224 428000
E: acm@peterkins.com

MACDONALD, Alastair MacBeath
(Feb 2018) (Employee)
Low Beaton Richmond LLP,
Glasgow . . . .(p.1005)
T: 0141 2218931
E: alastair@lbr-law.co.uk

MCDONALD, Alastair (Sept 1984) (Partner)
Mackintosh & Wylie LLP,
Stewarton . . . .(p.1163)
T: 01560 482 666
E: amcdonald@mackwylie.com

MACDONALD, Dr, Alison Jean (Jun 2008)
(Employee)
Stewart & Watson, Fraserburgh . . . .(p.931)
T: 01346 514443
E: amacdonald@stewartwatson.co.uk

MACDONALD, Alistair Iain (Oct 1982)
(Solicitor)
NO FIRM

MACDONALD, Allan Joseph (Oct 2006)
(Employee)
Comhairle Nan Eilean Siar,
Stornoway . . . .(p.1255)
T: 01851 822604
E: allan.macdonald@cne-siar.gov.uk

MACDONALD, Andrew (Sept 2019) (Employee)
Digby Brown LLP, Glasgow . . . .(p.970)
T: 0333 200 5925
E: Andy.MacDonald@digbybrown.co.uk

MACDONALD, Andrew Norman Grainger, WS
(Dec 1980) (Partner)
Blair Cadell, Edinburgh . . . .(p.844)
T: 0131 555 5800
E: andrew.macdonald@blaircadell.com

MCDONALD, Andrew (Sept 2015) (Employee)
Davidson Chalmers Stewart LLP,
Edinburgh . . . .(p.859)
T: 0131 6259191
E: Andrew.McDonald@dcslegal.com

MACDONALD, Angus William (Aug 1979)
(Director)
MacDonald, Maciver & Company Limited,
Stornoway . . . .(p.1170)
T: 01851 704343
E: amacdmac@aol.com

MACDONALD, Anne (Sept 1984) (Employee)
Procurator Fiscal Service, Aberdeen . . .(p.1213)
T: 8445612614
E: anne.macdonald@copfs.gov.uk

MACDONALD, Anne Louise (Aug 2007)
(Partner)
Harper Macleod LLP, Glasgow . . . .(p.983)
T: 0141 2218888
E: anne.macdonald@harpermacleod.co.uk

MACDONALD, Blair Forbes (Jun 2014)
(Employee)
Scottish Police Authority, Police Scotland,
Glasgow . . . .(p.1244)
T: 01786 895727
E: Blair.MacDonald@scotland.pnn.police.uk

MACDONALD, Blair Ian (Nov 2018) (Employee)
Macnabs LLP, Perth . . . .(p.1150)
T: 01738 623432
E: blairmacdonald@macnabs-law.co.uk

MACDONALD, Bruce Dey (Mar 1980) (Partner)
Bruce MacDonald & Co.,
Aberdeen . . . .(p.724)
T: 01224 643332
E: bruce@brucemacdonald.co.uk

MCDONALD, Callum Anderson (Jan 1983)
(Partner)
Raeburn Christie Clark & Wallace LLP,
Aberdeen . . . .(p.741)
T: 01224 332400
E: callum.mcdonald@raeburns.co.uk

MACDONALD, Catharine Ann Beaton
(Oct 2005) (Employee)
TLT LLP, Glasgow . . . .(p.1048)
T: 0333 006 0400
E: catharine.macdonald@tltsolicitors.com

MACDONALD, Catherine (Nov 1986)
(Employee)
Anderson Strathern LLP, Edinburgh . . . .(p.839)
T: 0131 2707700
E:
catherine.macdonald@andersonstrathern.co.uk

MACDONALD, Catriona Jane (Sept 2015)
(Employee)
Office of the Advocate General,
Edinburgh . . . .(p.1227)
T: 7842618913
E:
catriona.macdonald@advocategeneral.gov.uk

MACDONALD, Catriona Ruth (Apr 2003)
(Partner)
Blackadder & McMonagle, Falkirk . . . . .(p.921)
T: 01324 612 999
E: catriona.macdonald@blackandmac.com

MCDONALD, David John (Sept 2014)
(Employee)
Procurator Fiscal Service,
Edinburgh . . . .(p.1227)
T: 0300 0203168
E: David.McDonald@copfs.gov.uk

MACDONALD, Diana (Oct 2009) (Employee)
Procurator Fiscal Service,
Edinburgh . . . .(p.1229)
T: 0300 0203000
E: diana.macdonald@copfs.gov.uk

MACDONALD, Donald Ross (Jan 1992)
(Employee)
National Westminster Bank PLC,
  Edinburgh . . . .(p.1226)
  T: (0131) 626 2925
  E: Donald.R.Macdonald@rbs.co.uk

MACDONALD, Drew Stewart (Sept 2015)
(Employee)
Dickson Minto, London EC2 . . . .(p.1263)
  T: 020 76284455
  E: Drew.MacDonald@dmws.com

MCDONALD, Eilis Hetty (Mar 2019) (Employee)
DLA Piper Scotland LLP, Edinburgh . . . .(p.863)
  T: 08700 111 111
  E: Eilis.McDonald@dlapiper.com

MACDONALD, Elaine (Nov 2012) (Partner)
MacDonald Lynch Solicitors,
  Glasgow . . . .(p.1009)
  T: 0141 6499552
  E: elaine.macdonald@macdonaldlynch.co.uk

MACDONALD, Elizabeth Fiona Scotland
(Aug 2016) (Partner)
Boyles Solicitors, Dundee. . . . .(p.806)
  T: 01382 221214
  E: emclellan@wgboyle.co.uk

MACDONALD, Ellen (Oct 2003) (Director)
The Robert Kerr Partnership Limited,
  Paisley . . . .(p.1141)
  T: 0141 8896458
  E: rkerrpartnership@hotmail.com

MACDONALD, Euan Angus (Sept 2012)
(Employee)
Westfield Europe Limited, London
  WC1 . . . .(p.1269)
  T: 07827 256415
  E: euan.macdonald@westfield.com

MACDONALD, Euan Joseph (Nov 1986)
(Partner)
Stewart & Bennett, Dunoon . . . .(p.828)
  T: 01369 702885
  E: EMacDonald@stewartbennett.com

MACDONALD, Ewen Joseph (Sept 1989)
(Director)
Anderson Shaw & Gilbert Limited,
  Inverness . . . .(p.1075)
  T: 01463 236123
  E: ejm@solicitorsinverness.com

MACDONALD, Fiona (Nov 1993) (Employee)
National Health Service Scotland,
  Edinburgh . . . .(p.1225)
  T: 0131 2757800
  E: fiona.macdonald3@nhs.scot

MACDONALD, Fiona (Sept 1991) (Partner)
MacDonald Law, Thurso . . . .(p.1174)
  T: 01847 894515
  E: fiona@macdonaldlaw.co.uk

MACDONALD, Fiona Calder (Dec 1992)
(Partner)
Liddle & Anderson LLP, Boness . . . .(p.777)
  T: 01506 822727
  E: fm@liddleandanderson.co.uk

MACDONALD, Fiona Jane (Aug 2009) (Partner)
A.C. White, Ayr . . . .(p.766)
  T: 01292 266900
  E: fiona.macdonald@acwhiteayr.co.uk

MACDONALD, Fiona Theresa Campbell
(Sept 2016) (Employee)
Argyll & Bute Council,
  Lochgilphead . . . .(p.1251)
  E: fiona.macdonald2@argyll-bute.gov.uk

MCDONALD, Fraser Lewis (Oct 2019)
(Employee)
Turcan Connell, Edinburgh . . . .(p.908)
  T: 0131 228 8111
  E: fraser.mcdonald@turcanconnell.com

MACDONALD, Gary John (Dec 1997) (Partner)
DWF LLP, Edinburgh . . . .(p.865)
  T: 0131 2265541

MCDONALD, Gemma Louise (Jan 2014)
(Employee)
Smart Metering Systems Plc,
  Glasgow. . . . .(p.1244)
  T: (0141) 2493909
  E: gmcdonald@sms-plc.com

MACDONALD, Gillian Mathias de Proanca
(Nov 1989) (Solicitor)
NO FIRM

MACDONALD, Graeme John (Jan 2014)
(Partner)
MacDonald & Co, Glasgow . . . .(p.1008)
  T: 0141 9591999
  E: graeme@macdonald-solicitors.co.uk

MACDONALD, Graham Robert (Oct 2015)
(Employee)
Procurator Fiscal Service, Glasgow . . . .(p.1241)
  T: 0300 0203000
  E: graham.macdonald@copfs.gov.uk

MCDONALD, Iain (Jan 2001) (Director)
Anderson Shaw & Gilbert Limited,
  Inverness . . . .(p.1075)
  T: 01463 236123
  E: im@solicitorsinverness.com

MCDONALD, Iain William (Oct 1985)
(Consultant)
Gillespie Gifford & Brown LLP, Castle
  Douglas . . . .(p.783)
  T: 01556 503744
  E: iain.mcdonald@ggblaw.co.uk

MACDONALD, Ian (Dec 1980) (Partner)
Wright, Johnston & Mackenzie LLP,
Glasgow . . . .(p.1054)
T: 0141 2483434
E: im@wjm.co.uk

MACDONALD, James Anderson Cowan
(Aug 1983) (Partner)
Freelands, Motherwell . . . .(p.1126)
T: 01698 352608
E: jmacdonald@freelands.co.uk

MCDONALD, James Charles Fullarton
(Nov 2014) (Employee)
Pinsent Masons LLP, Glasgow . . . .(p.1031)
T: 0141 567 8400
E: james.mcdonald@pinsentmasons.com

MCDONALD, Jamie Thomas (Dec 2006)
(Employee)
McD Sports & Legal AB,
Stockholm . . . .(p.1276)
T: 46736895848
E: jamie@sportsandlegal.com

MACDONALD, Jennifer (Aug 2009) (Employee)
Schroders Personal Wealth, London
EC2 . . . .(p.1268)
E: Jennifer.MacDonald@spw.com

MACDONALD, Jennifer Mairi (Nov 2005)
(Employee)
The General Teaching Council for Scotland,
Edinburgh . . . .(p.1234)
T: 0131 314 6000
E: Jennifer.Macdonald@gtcs.org.uk

MACDONALD, Jennifer Margaret (Jul 2014)
(Employee)
Turcan Connell, Edinburgh . . . .(p.908)
T: 0131 2288111
E: jennifer.macdonald@turcanconnell.com

MACDONALD, John Clarke (Jan 2019) (Partner)
John MacDonald Law, Portree . . . .(p.1157)
E: john@johnmacdonaldlaw.co.uk

MACDONALD, John Sinclair Macleod
(May 1978) (Partner)
John Y. Robertson, Hamilton . . . .(p.1068)
T: 01698 282900
E: john@jyrlaw.co.uk

MCDONALD, Julia (Jan 2007) (Associate)
DWF LLP, Edinburgh . . . .(p.865)
T: 0333 320 2220
E: julia.McDonald@dwf.law

MACDONALD, Katharine Anna (Nov 2006)
(Partner)
Ferguson, MacSween & Stewart,
Portree . . . .(p.1156)
T: 01478 612991
E: admin@fmslaw.co.uk

MACDONALD, Katherine Ann Jean
(Mar 2013) (Employee)
Simpson & Marwick, Edinburgh . . . .(p.903)
T: 01224 606210
E: Katherine.macdonald@simpsonmarwick.com

MACDONALD, Kenneth John (Feb 1995)
(Partner)
Brodies LLP, Aberdeen . . . .(p.723)
T: 01224 392242
E: ken.macdonald@brodies.com

MACDONALD, Kenneth Norman (Feb 1971)
(Director)
Ken MacDonald & Co Limited,
Stornoway . . . .(p.1170)
T: 01851 704040
E: enquiries@kenmacdonaldlawyers.co.uk

MACDONALD, Kenneth (Oct 1998) (Employee)
Glasgow City Council, Glasgow . . . . . .(p.1239)
T: 0141 28725720
E: kenneth.mcdonald@ced.glasgow.gov.uk

MACDONALD, Kirsteen Anne (Oct 1997)
(Associate)
Burness Paull LLP, Glasgow . . . .(p.954)
T: 0141 2484933
E: Kirsteen.MacDonald@burnesspaull.com

MCDONALD, Kirstie Laura (Jun 2004)
(Employee)
James Walker Group Limited,
Woking . . . .(p.1272)
T: 01483 746354
E: kirstie.mcdonald@jameswalker.biz

MACDONALD, Kirstin Helen (Nov 2012)
(Employee)
Wright, Johnston & Mackenzie LLP,
Inverness . . . .(p.1083)
T: 01463 234445
E: khm@wjm.co.uk

MACDONALD, Laura Margaret (Oct 2010)
(Partner)
Jackson Boyd LLP, Glasgow . . . .(p.991)
T: 0141 2214325
E: LMacdonald@jacksonboyd.co.uk

MCDONALD, Laura Catherine (Sept 1992)
(Partner)
Lawson Coull & Duncan, Dundee . . . . .(p.813)
T: 01382 227555
E: lmcdonald@lawsoncoull.co.uk

MACDONALD, Lauren Anne (May 2012)
(Employee)
Procurator Fiscal Service, Glasgow . . . .(p.1241)
T: 0300 0203000
E: Lauren.MacDonald@copfs.gov.uk

MCDONALD, Leigh Kathryn (Feb 2016)
(Employee)
Burness Paull LLP, Edinburgh . . . .(p.850)
T: 0131 4736000
E: leigh.mcdonald@burnesspaull.com

MACDONALD, Lesley Madeline (Sept 1984)
(Partner)
Lesley Macdonald Family Law, Broughty
Ferry . . . .(p.780)
T: 01382 698600
E: lesley@lesleymacdonaldfamilylaw.co.uk

MACDONALD, Lindsay (Oct 2016) (Employee)
Drummond Miller LLP, Edinburgh . . . . .(p.864)
T: 0131 2265151
E: LMacdonald@drummondmiller.co.uk

MACDONALD, Lorna Helen (Feb 2017)
(Employee)
Scottish Environment Protection Agency,
Stirling . . . .(p.1255)
T: 01786 457700
E: Lorna.MacDonald@sepa.org.uk

MACDONALD, Lynn (Nov 2020) (Employee)
Clyde & Co (Scotland) LLP,
Glasgow. . . . .(p.961)
T: 0141 2482666
E: lynn.macdonald@clydeco.com

MACDONALD, Marie Elizabeth (Dec 1985)
(Partner)
Miller Samuel Hill Brown LLP,
Glasgow . . . .(p.1020)
T: 0141 2211919
E: mem@mshblegal.com

MACDONALD, Marie-Luise Christa
(Oct 2007) (Employee)
McIntyre & Co., Fort William . . . .(p.930)
T: 01397 703231
E: m.macdonald@solicitors-scotland.com

MACDONALD, Marion Joyce (Aug 2021)
(Employee)
Shepherd and Wedderburn LLP,
Edinburgh . . . .(p.900)
T: 0131 2289900
E: marion.macdonald@shepwedd.com

MCDONALD, Megan Rea (Nov 2013)
(Associate)
CMS Cameron McKenna Nabarro Olswang LLP,
Glasgow . . . .(p.962)
T: 0141 304 6068
E: Megan.McDonald@cms-cmno.com

MACDONALD, Moray (Dec 1980) (Partner)
Inverness Law, Inverness . . . .(p.1078)
T: 01463 832818
E: moray@invernesslaw.co.uk

MACDONALD, Moray John (Aug 2014)
(Employee)
Freshfields Service Company, London
EC2 . . . .(p.1264)
T: 020 7936 4000
E: Moray.MACDONALD@freshfields.com

MACDONALD, Natasha Mary (May 2015)
(Employee)
Burness Paull LLP, Aberdeen . . . .(p.724)
T: 01224 621621
E: Natasha.MacDonald@burnesspaull.com

MCDONALD, Neale Blair (Apr 2014) (Solicitor)
NO FIRM

MACDONALD, Neil David (Sept 2017)
(Employee)
BTO Solicitors LLP, Glasgow . . . .(p.952)
T: 0141 2218012
E: nmd@bto.co.uk

MACDONALD, Neil Iain (Apr 1982) (Employee)
Fife Council, Glenrothes . . . .(p.1246)
T: 03451 550000
E: Neil-I.macdonald@fife.gov.uk

MACDONALD, Niall (Dec 1979) (Employee)
Scottish Water, Dunfermline . . . .(p.1219)
T: (01383) 665410
E: niall.macdonald@scottishwater.co.uk

MACDONALD, Niall William (Jan 2004)
(Employee)
Procurator Fiscal Service, Inverness . . . .(p.1248)
T: 0844 5612926
E: niall.macdonald@copfs.gov.uk

MACDONALD, Oonagh Kathleen (Sept 2016)
(Employee)
Shepherd and Wedderburn LLP,
Glasgow . . . .(p.1039)
T: 0141 5669900
E: Oonagh.MacDonald@shepwedd.com

MACDONALD, Paul Michael (Sept 2010)
(Partner)
Harper Macleod LLP, Glasgow . . . .(p.983)
T: 0141 2218888
E: Paul.Macdonald@harpermacleod.co.uk

MACDONALD, Peter John (Oct 1996)
(Employee)
Inverclyde Council, Greenock. . . . .(p.1246)
T: 01475 712618
E: peter.macdonald2@inverclyde.gov.uk

MACDONALD, Rachael Hannah (Sept 2009)
(Partner)
Macnabs LLP, Perth . . . .(p.1150)
T: 01738 623432
E: rachaelmacdonald@macnabs-law.co.uk

MCDONALD, Rebecca Helen (Aug 2017)
(Employee)
Scottish Borders Council, Newtown St.
Boswells . . . .(p.1251)
T: 01835 825 225
E: becca.mcdonald@scotborders.gov.uk

MACDONALD, Richard David (Jul 2011)
(Associate)
MacRoberts LLP, Glasgow . . . .(p.1015)
T: 0141 3031185
E: richard.macdonald@macroberts.com

MACDONALD, Robert Donald (May 2000)
(Solicitor)
NO FIRM

MACDONALD, Robert Fraser (Jan 1990)
(Partner)
Robert F MacDonald Solicitors,
Kirkcaldy . . . .(p.1101)
T: 01592 643357
E: robert@robertfmacdonald.org.uk

MACDONALD, Rona Margaret (Sept 2000)
(Associate)
Turcan Connell, Edinburgh . . . .(p.908)
T: 0131 2288111
E: rona.macdonald@turcanconnell.com

MACDONALD, Roslyn (Mar 2016) (Employee)
East Dunbartonshire Council,
Kirkintilloch . . . .(p.1249)
T: 0141 5788000
E: roslyn.macdonald@eastdunbarton.gov.uk

MACDONALD, Sarah Gabrielle (Jan 2000)
(Employee)
Scottish Environment Protection Agency,
Stirling . . . .(p.1255)
T: 01786 457700
E: Gabrielle.MacDonald@sepa.org.uk

MACDONALD, Sarah-Jane (Aug 2014)
(Associate)
Gillespie Macandrew LLP,
Edinburgh . . . .(p.872)
T: 0131 2251677
E:
sarah-jane.macdonald@gillespiemacandrew.co.
uk

MACDONALD, Stephanie Alison (Jun 2012)
(Employee)
Procurator Fiscal Service, Glasgow . . . .(p.1241)
T: 0300 0203000
E: Stephanie.MacDonald@copfs.gov.uk

MCDONALD, Steven Boyd (Sept 1997)
(Employee)
Inksters, Edinburgh . . . .(p.879)
T: 0131 357 5620
E: steven@inksters.com

MCDONALD, Stuart Kevin Donald
(Jul 2019) (Employee)
Wright, Johnston & Mackenzie LLP,
Edinburgh . . . .(p.913)
T: 0131 5241500
E: skm@wjm.co.uk

MCDONALD, Suzanne (Oct 2005) (Employee)
Dales Solicitors LLP, Galston . . . .(p.934)
T: 01563 820216
E: suzanne@dalesllp.co.uk

MACDONALD, Timothy James Roxburgh
(Jul 2014) (Employee)
Lindsays LLP, Edinburgh . . . .(p.882)
T: 0131 2291212
E: TimMacdonald@lindsays.co.uk

MACDONALD, Victoria (Oct 2017) (Employee)
Burness Paull LLP, Edinburgh . . . .(p.850)
T: 0131 4736000
E: victoria.macdonald@burnesspaull.com

MACDONALD, Victoria Claire (Feb 2007)
(Employee)
Office of the Advocate General,
Edinburgh . . . .(p.1227)
T: 0131 2441635
E:
Victoria.MacDonald@advocategeneral.gov.uk

MCDONALD, William (Dec 2008) (Employee)
Fife Council, Glenrothes . . . .(p.1246)
T: 03451 550000
E: Billy.McDonald@fife.gov.uk

MCDONELL, Greig Thomas (Jan 1997)
(Associate)
Cullen Kilshaw, Galashiels . . . .(p.932)
T: 01896 752231
E: greig.mcdonell@cullenkilshaw.com

MCDONNELL, Zoe (Nov 2003) (Associate)
Berrymans Lace Mawer LLP,
Glasgow . . . .(p.945)
T: 0141 3532121
E: zoe.mcdonnell@blmlaw.com

MACDONOUGH, Carly Alana (Jun 2020)
(Employee)
Fulton's, Glasgow . . . .(p.1010)
T: 0141 6322248
E: cmacdonough@fultonslaw.co.uk

MCDOUGALL, Amy Jane (Jan 2019) (Employee)
Wright, Johnston & Mackenzie LLP,
Glasgow . . . .(p.1054)
T: 0141 2483434
E: axm@wjm.co.uk

MCDOUGALL, Euan Fraser (Apr 2014)
(Employee)
National Westminster Bank PLC,
Edinburgh . . . .(p.1226)
T: (0131) 626 2925

MACDOUGALL, Finlay Euan Cameron
(Jan 2021) (Employee)
Addleshaw Goddard LLP,
Edinburgh . . . .(p.835)
T: 0131 2282400
E: finlay.macdougall@addleshawgoddard.com

MACDOUGALL, Greg Stuart (Oct 2003)
(Partner)
Berrymans Lace Mawer LLP,
Edinburgh . . . . (p.842)
T: 0131 2259855
E: Greg.MacDougall@blmlaw.com

MCDOUGALL, Iain David (Sept 2009)
(Employee)
MBM Commercial LLP, Edinburgh . . . . . (p.889)
T: 0131 2268200
E: iain.mcdougall@mbmcommercial.co.uk

MCDOUGALL, Katherine (Jan 2015) (Employee)
CMS Cameron McKenna Nabarro Olswang LLP,
Glasgow. (p.962)
T: 0141 2222200
E: Katie.McDougall@cms-cmno.com

MCDOUGALL, Leila (Jun 2015) (Employee)
Aberdeen Corporate Services Limited,
Edinburgh . . . . (p.1220)
T: 0131 245 7508
E: leila.mcdougall@abrdn.com

MCDOUGALL, Michael (Dec 2013) (Employee)
TLT LLP, Glasgow . . . . (p.1048)
T: 0333 006 0945
E: michael.mcdougall@tltsolicitors.com

MACDOUGALL, Roderick John (Dec 2009)
(Employee)
Network Rail Infrastructure Ltd,
Glasgow. . . . . (p.1241)
T: 07809 376033
E: Roddy.Macdougall@networkrail.co.uk

MCDOWALL, Christopher Leslie (Dec 2000)
(Partner)
Anderson Strathern LLP, Glasgow. . . . . . (p.940)
T: 1412426063
E: chris.mcdowall@andersonstrathern.co.uk

MCDOWALL, David (Feb 2006) (Employee)
North Ayrshire Council, Irvine . . . . (p.1249)
T: 01294 310000
E: dmcdowall@north-ayrshire.gov.uk

MCDOWALL, Joanne (Oct 1999) (Employee)
Ofgem, Glasgow . . . . (p.1241)
T: (0141) 354 5425
E: Joanne.McDowall@ofgem.gov.uk

MCDOWALL, Kris Reid (Oct 2008) (Employee)
North Ayrshire Council, Irvine . . . . (p.1249)
T: 01294 310000
E: krismcdowall@north-ayrshire.gov.uk

MCDOWALL, Laura (Sept 2007) (Partner)
Blackadders LLP, Dundee. . . . . (p.805)
T: 01382 229222
E: laura.mcdowall@blackadders.co.uk

MCDOWALL, Robert (Oct 1982) (Partner)
Bob McDowall, Glasgow . . . . (p.1009)
T: 0141 7749996
E: law@bobmcdowall.com

MCDOWALL, Ross Hamilton (Mar 2002)
(Employee)
Pinsent Masons LLP, Glasgow . . . . . . (p.1031)
T: 0141 567 8400
E: ross.mcdowall@pinsentmasons.com

MCDOWELL, Amy Joy (Sept 2010) (Partner)
Gillespie Macandrew LLP,
Edinburgh . . . . (p.872)
T: 0131 2251677
E: amy.mcdowell@gillespiemacandrew.co.uk

MACDUFF-DUNCAN, Robert Simon, WS
(Aug 2004) (Partner)
Kippen Campbell LLP, Perth . . . . (p.1149)
T: 01738 635353
E: rmd@kcllp.co.uk

MCEACHAN, Alasdair John Stewart
(Oct 1991) (Employee)
The Moray Council, Elgin . . . . (p.1236)
T: 01343 543451
E: alasdair.mceachan@moray.gov.uk

MCEACHEN, Claudia Jane (Oct 2013)
(Employee)
Digby Brown LLP, Dundee . . . . (p.808)
T: 3332005925
E: Claudia.McEachen@digbybrown.co.uk

MACEACHEN, Gillian Elizabeth (Nov 2010)
(Employee)
Glasgow City Council, Glasgow . . . . . . (p.1239)
T: 0141 2872000
E: gillian.maceachen@glasgow.gov.uk

MCEACHEN, Philip Alexander (Nov 2011)
(Employee)
Kirkland & Ellis International LLP, London
EC3 . . . . (p.1265)
T: 0207 4692000
E: philip.mceachen@kirkland.com

MACEACHERN, John Angus (Nov 1979)
(Employee)
Dumfries & Galloway Council,
Dumfries . . . . (p.1217)
T: 01387 260061
E: John.MacEachern@dumgal.gov.uk

MCELENY, Nicola Maria (Jun 2015) (Employee)
MSM Solicitors Limited, Paisley . . . . . . (p.1140)
T: 0141 8896244
E: nmm@msmlaw.co.uk

MCELROY, David James (Nov 1998) (Partner)
Dallas McMillan, Glasgow . . . . (p.966)
T: 0141 3336750
E: davidj.mcelroy@dallasmcmillan.co.uk

MCELROY, Kathryn Therese (Sept 2009)
(Employee)
National Health Service Scotland,
Edinburgh . . . . (p.1225)
T: 0131 2757800
E: kathryn.mcelroy@nhs.scot

MCELROY, Lynne McLaren (Jun 2010)
(Employee)
Turcan Connell, Edinburgh . . . .(p.908)
T: 0131 2288111
E: lynne.mcelroy@turcanconnell.com

MCELROY, Robbie David (May 2019)
(Employee)
Macgregor Thomson Limited,
Stirling . . . .(p.1166)
T: 01786 406423
E: rmcelroy@macgregorthomson.co.uk

MCELROY, Valerie Anne (Dec 1985) (Partner)
Gillespie Gifford & Brown LLP,
Dumfries . . . .(p.800)
T: 01387 255351
E: valerie.mcelroy@ggblaw.co.uk

MCENTEE, Se n Michael (Oct 2021) (Employee)
Lindsays LLP, Edinburgh . . . .(p.882)
T: 0131 2291212
E: seanmcentee@lindsays.co.uk

MCENTEGART, Thomas Peter (Aug 1992)
(Partner)
TLT LLP, Glasgow . . . .(p.1048)
T: 0333 006 0400
E: Tom.McEntegart@tltsolicitors.com

MCERLANE, Dominique Joy (Oct 2014)
(Solicitor)
NO FIRM

MCERLEAN, Louise Veronica (Jan 2018)
(Employee)
Burness Paull LLP, Edinburgh . . . .(p.850)
T: 0131 4736000
E: louise.mcerlean@burnesspaull.com

MCEVINNEY, Claire Ceri (Aug 2011)
(Employee)
Procurator Fiscal Service, Glasgow . . . .(p.1241)
T: 0300 0203000
E: claire.gallagher1@copfs.gov.uk

MCEVINNEY, Mark Thomas (Aug 2015)
(Employee)
BTO Solicitors LLP, Glasgow . . . .(p.952)
T: 0141 2218012
E: mme@bto.co.uk

MCEWAN, Anthony Vincent (Feb 1984)
(Partner)
Shepherd and Wedderburn LLP,
Edinburgh . . . .(p.900)
T: 0131 2289900
E: anthony.mcewan@shepwedd.com

MACEWAN, Eilidh Alison Jane (Sept 2010)
(Associate)
Gilson Gray LLP, Edinburgh . . . .(p.874)
T: 0131 5165354
E: emacewan@gilsongray.co.uk

MACEWAN, Emma Rachel (Jul 2019)
(Employee)
Public Defence Solicitors Office,
Inverness . . . .(p.1248)
T: 01463 709680

MCEWAN, Fiona (Jul 2013) (Employee)
Berrymans Lace Mawer LLP,
Glasgow . . . .(p.945)
T: 0141 3532121
E: fiona.mcewan@blmlaw.com

MCEWAN, Gavin Graham Robert (Nov 1997)
(Partner)
Turcan Connell, Edinburgh . . . .(p.908)
T: 0131 2288111
E: gavin.mcewan@turcanconnell.com

MACEWAN, Gregor John (Aug 2010)
(Associate)
Lindsays LLP, Edinburgh . . . .(p.882)
T: 0131 2291212
E: gregormacewan@lindsays.co.uk

MCEWAN, Peter William (Oct 2018)
(Employee)
Macdonald Henderson Limited,
Glasgow . . . .(p.1008)
T: 0141 2484957
E: peter@macdonaldhenderson.co.uk

MCEWEN, Bruce Hamilton (Sept 2012)
(Employee)
Brodies LLP, Edinburgh . . . .(p.845)
T: 0131 2283777
E: bruce.mcewen@brodies.com

MCEWEN, Greg (Nov 2010) (Employee)
Law Society of Scotland,
Edinburgh . . . .(p.1224)
T: 0131 2267411
E: gregmcewen@lawscot.org.uk

MCEWEN, Gwen (Sept 1993) (Employee)
Aberdeen City Council, Aberdeen . . . . .(p.1211)
T: 01224 522000
E: gwenm@aberdeencity.gov.uk

MACEWEN, Lindsay Anne (Apr 2009)
(Associate)
Harper Macleod LLP, Glasgow . . . .(p.983)
T: 0141 2218888
E: Lindsay.MacEwen@harpermacleod.co.uk

MCEWING, Alan James (Jan 1990) (Employee)
Walker Laird, Paisley . . . .(p.1142)
T: 0141 8875271
E: alan.mcewing@walkerlaird.co.uk

MCEWING, David (Jan 1992) (Partner)
Addleshaw Goddard LLP,
Aberdeen . . . .(p.719)
T: (+44) (0) 1224 96 5410
E: david.mcewing@addleshawgoddard.com

MCFADDEN, Claire Anne (Mar 1998) (Partner)
J K Cameron, Glasgow . . . .(p.955)
T: 0141 221 4787
E: cam@jkcameron.co.uk

MCFADDEN, Hannah Rebecca (Feb 2020)
(Employee)
Shepherd and Wedderburn LLP,
Edinburgh . . . .(p.900)
T: 0131 2289900
E: hannah.mcfadden@shepwedd.com

MCFADDEN, Margaret Josephine Bannon
(Aug 1999) (Employee)
Fife Council, Glenrothes . . . .(p.1246)
T: 03451 550000
E: margaret.mcfadden@fife.gov.uk

MCFADDEN, Patricia Mary (Oct 2000) (Partner)
Digby Brown LLP, Edinburgh . . . .(p.862)
T: 0333 200 5925
E: trish.mcfadden@digbybrown.co.uk

MCFADYEN, Alison Anne (Aug 2021)
(Employee)
Procurator Fiscal Service,
Edinburgh . . . .(p.1227)
T: 0300 0203168
E: Alison.McFadyen@copfs.gov.uk

MCFADYEN, Antony Michael (Aug 2009)
(Employee)
Law Society of Scotland,
Edinburgh . . . .(p.1224)
T: 0131 476 8365
E: antonymcfadyen@lawscot.org.uk

MCFADYEN, Christine Teresa (Oct 2012)
(Employee)
Dickson Minto, London EC2 . . . .(p.1263)
T: 020 76284455
E: christine.mcfadyen@dmws.com

MCFADYEN, Gemma Leanne (Sept 2012)
(Employee)
Aberdeen Corporate Services Limited,
Edinburgh . . . .(p.1220)
T: 0131 245 7508
E: gemma.young@aberdeenstandard.com

MACFADYEN, Julie-Anne (Oct 2009)
(Employee)
Scottish Government, Edinburgh . . . . .(p.1232)
T: 0131 2442418
E: Julie.MacFadyen@gov.scot

MCFADYEN, Liam Doherty (Mar 2018)
(Employee)
Dentons UK and Middle East LLP,
Glasgow . . . .(p.968)
T: 0330 2220050
E: liam.mcfadyen@dentons.com

MACFADYEN, Sheila Margaret (Sept 1983)
(Employee)
Argyll & Bute Council,
Lochgilphead . . . .(p.1251)
T: 01546 604265
E: sheila.macfadyen@argyll-bute.gov.uk

MCFADYEN, Susan Lea (Jan 1999) (Partner)
Blackadders LLP, Dundee . . . .(p.805)
T: 01382 229222
E: Susan.McFadyen@blackadders.co.uk

MCFADZEAN, Duncan Ruaridh (Sept 1999)
(Director)
ELP Arbuthnott McClanachan,
Edinburgh . . . .(p.867)
T: 0131 5548649
E: drm@elpamsolicitors.co.uk

MCFADZEAN, Elizabeth Marion (Nov 2001)
(Partner)
Anderson Beaton Lamond, Perth . . . . .(p.1146)
T: 01738 639999
E: lmcfadzean@abl-law.co.uk

MCFADZEAN, Hazel Patricia Mary
(Aug 2018) (Employee)
Scottish Children's Reporter Administration,
Glasgow . . . .(p.1243)
T: 0300 2001444
E: hazel.mcfadzean@scra.gov.uk

MCFADZEAN, Jennifer Elizabeth (Jan 2001)
(Partner)
Dales Solicitors LLP, Galston . . . .(p.934)
T: 01563 820216
E: jennifer@dalesllp.co.uk

MCFADZEAN, Laura Melanie (Feb 2003)
(Director)
ELP Arbuthnott McClanachan,
Edinburgh . . . .(p.867)
T: 0131 5548649
E: lmm@elpamsolicitors.co.uk

MCFALL, Lesley Susan (Aug 1997) (Associate)
Ferguson, MacSween & Stewart,
Balivanich. . . . .(p.767)
T: 01870 602 113
E: lesley@fmslaw.co.uk

MCFARLAN, Antonia (Mar 1983) (Partner)
Peterkin & Kidd, Linlithgow . . . .(p.1116)
T: 01506 845191
E: AMcFarlan@peterkinandkidd.co.uk

MACFARLAND, Emma Rose (Aug 2017)
(Employee)
Burness Paull LLP, Aberdeen . . . .(p.724)
T: 01224 621621
E: emma.macfarland@burnesspaull.com

MACFARLANE, Alison Mary (Jan 1968) (Partner)
Macfarlane & Co., Glasgow . . . .(p.1009)
T: 0141 2483307
E: amm@macfarlane-law.co.uk

MCFARLANE, Andrew Mark (Mar 1996)
(Partner)
Wright, Johnston & Mackenzie LLP,
Glasgow . . . . (p.1054)
T: 0141 2483434
E: amm@wjm.co.uk

MCFARLANE, Angela (Oct 1992) (Associate)
Stevenson & Marshall LLP,
Dunfermline . . . . (p.825)
T: 01383 721141
E: Aamcfarlane@stevenson-marshall.co.uk

MCFARLANE, Anne Janet (Oct 1996)
(Employee)
Glasgow City Council, Glasgow . . . . . . (p.1239)
T: 0141 2874101
E: anne.mcfarlane@ced.glasgow.gov.uk

MACFARLANE, Bernard (Sept 1997) (Employee)
Perth & Kinross Council, Perth . . . . (p.1253)
T: 01738 475000
E: bmcfarlane@pkc.gov.uk

MACFARLANE, Brian Stuart (Nov 2002)
(Partner)
Morton Fraser LLP, Glasgow . . . . (p.1022)
T: 0141 2741100
E: brian.macfarlane@morton-fraser.com

MACFARLANE, Carol Ann (Aug 1989) (Employee)
FirstGroup Plc, London W2 . . . . (p.1264)
E: carol.mcfarlane@firstrail.com

MACFARLANE, Carrie (Nov 2007) (Employee)
Procurator Fiscal Service, Glasgow . . . . (p.1241)
T: 0300 0203000
E: carrie.macfarlane@copfs.gov.uk

MACFARLANE, Christopher Andrew
(Aug 2016) (Employee)
Collins & Co Defence Lawyers Ltd,
Edinburgh . . . . (p.857)
T: 0131 661 3210
E: cmacfarlane@collinsandcolawyers.com

MACFARLANE, Christopher George
(Oct 2017) (Employee)
Bristow Helicopters Limited,
Aberdeen . . . . (p.1212)
E: christopher.macfarlane@bristowgroup.com

MCFARLANE, Collette Frances (Nov 2021)
(Employee)
MOV8 Real Estate Limited,
Edinburgh . . . . (p.893)
T: 0345 646 0208
E: collette.mcfarlane@mov8realestate.com

MCFARLANE, Daniel Jamie Fergusson
(Jul 2018) (Employee)
The Kellas Partnership, Inverurie . . . . . . (p.1086)
T: 01467 627300
E: djm@kellas.biz

MCFARLANE, Donna Louise (Aug 2003)
(Employee)
Renewable Energy Systems Limited,
Glasgow . . . . (p.1243)
T: 0141 404 5509
E: Donna.McFarlane@res-group.com

MACFARLANE, Esme Ruth Eilidh (Sept 2009)
(Employee)
Wright, Johnston & Mackenzie LLP,
Glasgow . . . . (p.1054)
T: 0141 2483434
E: erem@wjm.co.uk

MACFARLANE, Gina Cameron (Apr 2019)
(Employee)
MacDonald & Co, Glasgow . . . . (p.1008)
T: 0141 9591999
E: gina@macdonald-solicitors.co.uk

MCFARLANE, Ian Alexander Nicholas
(Dec 1986) (Director)
Hughes Shaughnessy McFarlane Limited,
Glasgow . . . . (p.987)
T: 0141 6499772
E: Ian@hsmsolicitors.co.uk

MCFARLANE, Jacqueline Ann (Jul 2010)
(Employee)
Brodies LLP, Edinburgh . . . . (p.845)
T: 0131 2283777
E: jacqueline.mcfarlane@brodies.com

MCFARLANE, James Stephen Hugh
(Apr 2021) (Employee)
Burness Paull LLP, Glasgow . . . . (p.954)
T: 0141 2484933
E: james.mcfarlane@burnesspaull.com

MCFARLANE, Janey Elizabeth (Jun 2017)
(Employee)
Aberdeen City Council, Aberdeen . . . . . (p.1211)
T: 01224 522000
E: JaMcFarlane@aberdeencity.gov.uk

MACFARLANE, Jayne Agnes (Sept 2011)
(Associate)
Dentons UK and Middle East LLP,
Glasgow . . . . (p.968)
T: 0330 2220050
E: jayne.macfarlane@dentons.com

MACFARLANE, Joseph James (Oct 2021)
(Employee)
MacRoberts LLP, Glasgow . . . . (p.1015)
T: 0141 3031100
E: Joe.Macfarlane@macroberts.com

MCFARLANE, Karen (Nov 2015) (Employee)
Frederick & Co Solicitors Limited,
Glasgow . . . . (p.977)
T: 0141 2215575
E: karen@frederickandco.co.uk

MCFARLANE, Laura-Jane (Jan 2013) (Employee)
Public Defence Solicitors Office,
Inverness . . . .(p.1248)
T: 01463 709680
E: LMcFarlane@pdso.org.uk

MCFARLANE, Lauren Allison (Nov 2012)
(Employee)
BTO Solicitors LLP, Edinburgh . . . .(p.849)
T: 0131 2222939
E: lmf@bto.co.uk

MACFARLANE, Lila Nicole (Mar 2020)
(Employee)
Harper Macleod LLP, Glasgow . . . .(p.983)
T: 0141 2218888
E: Lila.Macfarlane@harpermacleod.co.uk

MCFARLANE, Linda (Dec 2004) (Employee)
McArthur Stanton, Helensburgh . . . . . .(p.1072)
T: 01436 672212
E: lmf@mcarthurstanton.co.uk

MACFARLANE, Dr, Lorna Jane (Dec 2020)
(Employee)
Dentons UK and Middle East LLP,
Edinburgh . . . .(p.860)
T: 0330 2220050
E: lorna.macfarlane@dentons.com

MACFARLANE, Lynne Mhairi (Oct 2000)
(Employee)
DWF LLP, Glasgow . . . .(p.973)
T: 0141 228 8000
E: lynne.macfarlane@dwf.law

MCFARLANE, Lynsay Margaret (Jul 2014)
(Associate)
Thorntons Law LLP, Dundee . . . .(p.819)
T: 01382 229 111
E: lmcfarlane@thorntons-law.co.uk

MCFARLANE, Mary Patricia (Jan 2002)
(Director)
VMH Solicitors Limited, Edinburgh . . . . .(p.910)
T: 0131 622 2626
E: mpm@vmh.co.uk

MACFARLANE, Matthew Alexander
(Jul 2013) (Employee)
Ogier, St Peter Port. . . . .(p.1273)
T: +44 1481 752242
E: matthew.macfarlane@ogier.com

MCFARLANE, Rhona Margaret (Sept 2005)
(Partner)
Brodies LLP, Aberdeen. . . . .(p.723)
T: 01224 392242
E: rhona.mcfarlane@brodies.com

MACFARLANE, Richard Somerville
(Feb 2017) (Employee)
Carey Olsen, London EC2 . . . .(p.1262)
T: (020) 7614 5610
E: richard.macfarlane@careyolsen.com

MACFARLANE, Stephanie Rose (Apr 2016)
(Employee)
Macdonald Hotels Limited,
Bathgate . . . .(p.1215)
T: 01506 815115
E:
stephanie.macfarlane@macdonald-hotels.co.uk

MACFARLANE, Stuart Gordon (Sept 1987)
(Director)
Macfarlane Law Limited, Glasgow . . . .(p.1010)
T: 07808 331224
E: stuart.macfarlane@macfarlanelaw.co.uk

MCFARLANE, Thomas (Mar 1978) (Partner)
International & Domestic Law Practice,
Milngavie . . . .(p.1123)
T: 0141 9424455
E: law@idlp.co.uk

MCFARLANE, Thomas Kerr (Oct 2013)
(Employee)
Shepherd and Wedderburn LLP,
Edinburgh . . . .(p.900)
T: 0131 2289900
E: thomas.mcfarlane@shepwedd.com

MCFARQUHAR, Hannah (Oct 2016) (Employee)
Creditfix Limited, Glasgow . . . .(p.1239)
T: 0141 565 1300
E: Hannah.mcfarquhar@creditfix.co.uk

MCFAULD, Helen Margaret (Oct 2008)
(Employee)
Procurator Fiscal Service, Hamilton . . . .(p.1247)
T: 0300 0203000
E: lynn.mcfauld@copfs.gov.uk

MCGACHIE, James Christopher (Oct 2005)
(Associate)
DLA Piper Scotland LLP, Edinburgh . . . .(p.863)
T: 08700 111111
E: james.mcgachie@dlapiper.com

MCGARRELL, Catherine Frances (Oct 2018)
(Employee)
Thompsons, Edinburgh . . . .(p.906)
T: 0131 2254297
E:
catherine.mcgarrell@thompsons-scotland.co.uk

MCGARRIGLE, Suzanne Margaret
(Oct 2001) (Partner)
Harper Macleod LLP, Glasgow . . . .(p.983)
T: 0141 2218888
E: suzanne.mcgarrigle@harpermacleod.co.uk

MCGARTY, Nicole Anne (May 2019)
(Employee)
Shepherd and Wedderburn LLP,
Edinburgh . . . .(p.900)
T: 0131 2289900
E: nicole.mcgarty@shepwedd.com

MCGARVEY, Alistair Campbell (Aug 2010)
(Assistant)
Beltrami & Co Limited, Glasgow . . . . . .(p.944)
   T: 0141 429 2262
   E:
   alistair.mcgarvey@beltramiandcompany.co.uk

MCGARVEY, Christopher Francis (Oct 2004)
(Partner)
CMS Cameron McKenna Nabarro Olswang LLP,
   Glasgow. . . . .(p.962)
   T: 0141 2222200
   E: chris.mcgarvey@cms-cmno.com

MCGARVEY, Katherine Stuart (Nov 2009)
(Employee)
Scottish Government, Edinburgh . . . . .(p.1231)
   T: 0131 244 0815
   E: Katherine.Mcgarvey@gov.scot

MCGEACHY, Scott John (Oct 2015) (Employee)
Burness Paull LLP, Glasgow . . . .(p.954)
   T: 0141 2484933
   E: Scott.McGeachy@burnesspaull.com

MCGEADY, Paula (Nov 2007) (Employee)
Burges Salmon LLP, Bristol. . . . .(p.1258)
   T: 0117 9392000
   E: Paula.McGeady@burges-salmon.com

MCGEE, Jon Joseph (Oct 2004) (Associate)
Anderson Strathern LLP, Glasgow . . . . . .(p.940)
   T: 0141 2427983
   E: jon.mcgee@andersonstrathern.co.uk

MCGEE, Laura Jane (Oct 2008) (Employee)
NewLaw Scotland LLP, Glasgow . . . . . .(p.1027)
   T: 0845 225 4794
   E: laura.mcgee@newlaw-scotland.co.uk

MCGEECHAN, John Bunny (Aug 2002)
(Director)
JBM Law Ltd, Larkhall . . . .(p.1111)
   T: 01698 516999
   E: admin@jbmlaw.org

MCGEEHAN, Adrian Edward (Nov 1996)
(Partner)
Bradley Campbell & Co., Greenock . . .(p.1060)
   T: 01475 726363
   E: adrian.mcgeehan@bradleycampbell.co.uk

MCGEEHAN, Anthony Martin (Nov 1997)
(Employee)
Procurator Fiscal Service, Glasgow . . . .(p.1242)
   E: anthony.mcgeehan@copfs.gov.uk

MCGEEHAN, Eamonn (Dec 1991) (Director)
McGeehan & Co Ltd, Paisley . . . .(p.1140)
   T: 0141 889 9099
   E: mcgeehan.eamonn@gmail.com

MCGEEHAN, Kirsty Jane (Nov 1996) (Director)
McGeehan & Co Ltd, Paisley . . . .(p.1140)
   T: 0141 8899099
   E: mcgeehan.kirsty@gmail.com

MCGEOCH, Roderick James (Jul 1984)
(Consultant)
Cullen Kilshaw, Galashiels . . . .(p.933)
   T: 01896 800 800
   E: roddy.mcgeoch@cullenkilshaw.com

MCGEOUGH, Clare Louise (Jan 2019)
(Employee)
Harper Macleod LLP, Glasgow . . . .(p.983)
   T: 0141 2218888
   E: clare.mcgeough@harpermacleod.co.uk

MCGEOUGH, Kirsty Elizabeth (Nov 2015)
(Employee)
Carey Olsen, St Peter Port . . . .(p.1273)
   T: (+44) 1481 741505
   E: kirsty.mcgeough@careyolsen.com

MCGHEE, Audrey Bannatyne (Feb 1988)
(Director)
Hill & Robb Limited, Stirling . . . .(p.1164)
   T: 01786 450985
   E: audreymcghee@hillandrobb.co.uk

MCGHEE, Ingrid De Quiroz (Dec 2006)
(Partner)
Weightmans (Scotland) LLP,
   Glasgow. . . . .(p.1051)
   T: 0345 073 9900
   E: ingrid.mcghee@weightmans.com

MCGHIE, Dorothy (Oct 1978) (Consultant)
Stewart & Bennett, Dunoon . . . .(p.828)
   T: 01369 702885
   E: dmcghie@stewartbennett.com

MCGHIE, Lauren Anne (Oct 2020) (Employee)
Fulton's, Glasgow . . . .(p.1010)
   T: 0141 6322248
   E: lmcghie@fultonslaw.co.uk

MCGILL, Christopher Paul (Oct 2001) (Partner)
Shepherd and Wedderburn LLP,
   Edinburgh . . . .(p.900)
   T: 0131 2289900
   E: christopher.mcgill@shepwedd.com

MCGILL, Claire Lunney (Sept 2000) (Employee)
Scottish Government, Edinburgh . . . . .(p.1231)
   T: 0131 244 0815
   E: Claire.McGill@gov.scot

MCGILL, Grace Margaret (Sept 2002) (Partner)
Burness Paull LLP, Edinburgh . . . .(p.850)
   T: 0131 4736000
   E: grace.mcgill@burnesspaull.com

MCGILL, James Alexander (Oct 2020)
(Employee)
Lindsays LLP, Edinburgh . . . .(p.882)
   T: 0131 2291212
   E: jamiemcgill@lindsays.co.uk

MCGILL, Jennifer May Templeton
(Oct 1982) (Employee)
Procurator Fiscal Service, Dumfries . . . .(p.1217)
T: 01387 274585
E: jennifer.mcgill@copfs.gov.uk

MCGILL, Karen Grace (Oct 1994) (Consultant)
Morton Fraser LLP, Edinburgh . . . .(p.891)
T: 0131 2471000
E: karen.mcgill@morton-fraser.com

MCGILL, Katherine Muriel (Jun 2011) (Partner)
Thorntons Law LLP, Perth . . . .(p.1151)
T: 01738 621212
E: kmcgill@thorntons-law.co.uk

MCGILL, Margo Kyle (Sept 1999) (Partner)
Lockharts Law LLP, Ayr . . . .(p.764)
T: 01292 265045
E: MargoMcgill@lockhartslaw.com

MCGILL, Max Conrad (Mar 1999) (Employee)
Scottish Government's Parliamentary Counsel
Office, Edinburgh . . . .(p.1233)
T: 0131 244 5404
E: max.mcgill@gov.scot

MCGILLIVRAY, Donald Norman (Dec 1976)
(Consultant)
R. & R.S. Mearns, Glasgow . . . .(p.1018)
T: 0141 6326162
E: dnmmearns@gmail.com

MCGILLIVRAY, Elizabeth Norma (Apr 1984)
(Partner)
Bowmans, Dundee . . . .(p.806)
T: 01382 322267
E: enm@bowmansolicitors.co.uk

MCGILLIVRAY, Ewan Boyd (Feb 2000)
(Associate)
Morton Fraser LLP, Edinburgh . . . .(p.891)
T: 0131 2471000
E: ewan.mcgillivray@morton-fraser.com

MCGILLIVRAY, Iain Charles (Apr 2005)
(Solicitor)
NO FIRM

MCGILLIVRAY, Rachel (May 2021) (Employee)
Anderson Shaw & Gilbert Limited,
Inverness . . . .(p.1075)
T: 01463 236123
E: rm@solicitorsinverness.com

MCGILLIVRAY, Shiona (Oct 1987) (Solicitor)
NO FIRM

MCGILLVERY, Laura (Dec 2015) (Employee)
Procurator Fiscal Service, Airdrie . . . . . .(p.1214)
T: 01236 747027
E: laura.mcgillvery@copfs.gov.uk

MCGILP, David Grant (Mar 2016) (Employee)
NewLaw Scotland LLP, Glasgow . . . . . .(p.1027)
T: 0845 4819500
E: david.mcgilp@newlaw-scotland.co.uk

MCGINLAY, Andrew Michael (Sept 2020)
(Employee)
Last Mile Infrastructure Limited,
Glasgow . . . .(p.1240)
E: andrew.mcginlay@lastmile-group.com

MCGINLAY, Ronald (Nov 1979) (Partner)
Walker Laird, Paisley . . . .(p.1142)
T: 0141 8875271
E: Ronnie.McGinlay@walkerlaird.co.uk

MCGINLAY, Ross Maxwell (Aug 2011) (Partner)
Walker Laird, Renfrew . . . .(p.1159)
T: 0141 886 5678
E: ross.mcginlay@walkerlaird.co.uk

MCGINLEY, Alannah Theresa (Mar 2016)
(Employee)
Lord President's Private Office,
Edinburgh . . . .(p.1225)
T: 0131 2406701
E: amcginley@scotcourts.gov.uk

MCGINLEY, Charles (Dec 1980) (Partner)
Gray & Co., Glasgow . . . .(p.981)
T: 0141 9467777
E: cm@grayandcoglasgow.co.uk

MCGINLEY, Colette (Sept 1995) (Employee)
Balfour Beatty Regional Civil Engineering,
Motherwell . . . .(p.1251)
T: 01698 647 500
E: Colette.mcginley@balfourbeatty.com

MCGINLEY, Declan Francis (Mar 2017)
(Partner)
Georgesons, Wick . . . .(p.1180)
T: 01955 606060
E: declan.mcginley@georgesons.co.uk

MCGINLEY, Emma (Sept 2019) (Employee)
Procurator Fiscal Service, Paisley . . . . . .(p.1252)
T: 0141 8875225
E: emma.mcginley@copfs.gov.uk

MCGINN, Craig Alan (Oct 2000) (Employee)
Smart Metering Systems Plc,
Glasgow . . . .(p.1244)
T: 0141 2493909
E: cmcginn@sms-plc.com

MCGINN, Daniel Patrick (Jun 2017) (Employee)
Thorntons Law LLP, Dundee . . . .(p.819)
T: 01382 229 111

MCGINN, James Waugh (Sept 1986) (Director)
McGinn Solicitors Limited,
Glasgow . . . .(p.1011)
T: 0141 3535355
E: jwm@mcginnsolicitors.co.uk

MCGINN, Leo John (Jul 2019) (Employee)
Adairs, Dumbarton . . . .(p.798)
T: 01389 767625

MCGINNES, Kevin (Sept 2000) (Employee)
Glasgow City Council, Glasgow . . . . . .(p.1239)
  T: 0141 2873843
  E: kevin.mcginnes@glasgow.gov.uk

MCGINNESS, Clare Patricia (Aug 2002)
(Employee)
WEST DUNBARTONSHIREhire Council,
  Dumbarton . . . .(p.1217)
  E: Clare.McGinness@west-dunbarton.gov.uk

MCGINNESS, Kevin John (Nov 1991)
(Employee)
Curach Limited, Oban. . . . .(p.1134)
  T: 01631 562317
  E: kevin@stevensonkennedy.co.uk

MCGINNESS, Rachel Catherine Alice
(Sept 2016) (Employee)
BlackRock Investment Management (UK) Ltd,
  London EC2 . . . .(p.1262)
  E: rachel.mcginness@blackrock.com

MCGINNESS, Ross Kenneth (Nov 2006)
(Employee)
Renfrewshire Council, Paisley . . . .(p.1252)
  T: 0141 8403648
  E: ross.mcginness@renfrewshire.gov.uk

MCGINNIS, Claire (Apr 2013) (Employee)
University of Dundee, Dundee . . . .(p.1219)
  T: (44) (0)1382 385340
  E: c.mcginnis@dundee.ac.uk

MCGINTY, Edel Margaret (Feb 2012)
(Associate)
Westcourts Litigation Ltd,
  Greenock . . . .(p.1063)
  T: 01475 601999
  E: emcginty@westcourts.co.uk

MCGINTY, Helen Frances (Nov 1993) (Partner)
Helen McGinty & Company,
  Edinburgh . . . .(p.885)
  T: 0131 2208380
  E: info@helenmcginty.com

MCGLADRIGAN, Peter Andrew (Oct 2007)
(Employee)
TLT LLP, Edinburgh. . . . .(p.908)
  T: 0131 2207460
  E: peter.mcgladrigan@tltsolicitors.com

MCGLADRIGAN, Rebecca Anne-Marie
(Feb 2008) (Employee)
CMS Cameron McKenna Nabarro Olswang LLP,
  Edinburgh . . . .(p.856)
  T: 0131 2288000
  E: Rebecca.mcgladrigan@cms-cmno.com

MCGLASHAN, Graham (Dec 2001) (Employee)
Scottish Law Commission,
  Edinburgh . . . .(p.1233)
  T: 0131 6682131
  E: graham.mcglashan@scotlawcom.gov.uk

MCGLEISH, Eloise Alexandra Natalie
(Jul 2004) (Employee)
Aegon UK, Edinburgh . . . .(p.1220)
  T: 0131 549 2094
  E: eloise.mcgleish@aegon.co.uk

MCGLINCHEY, Benjamin Scott (Sept 2021)
(Employee)
Burness Paull LLP, Edinburgh . . . .(p.850)
  T: 0131 4736000
  E: benjamin.mcglinchey@burnesspaull.com

MCGLINCHEY, Neil Lachlan (May 2013)
(Employee)
The Moray Council, Elgin . . . .(p.1236)
  T: 01343 543451
  E: Neil.McGlinchey@moray.gov.uk

MCGLONE, Andrew Joseph (Apr 2004)
(Employee)
Scottish Police Authority, Police Scotland,
  Glasgow. . . . .(p.1244)
  T: 01786 895727
  E: andrew.mcglone@scotland.pnn.police.uk

MACGLONE, Elaine Margaret (Sept 1993)
(Employee)
Law Society of Scotland,
  Edinburgh . . . .(p.1224)
  T: 0131 2267411
  E: elainemacglone@lawscot.org.uk

MCGLONE, Kevin Douglas (Jan 1989) (Partner)
DWF LLP, Edinburgh. . . . .(p.865)
  T: 0131 474 2303
  E: kevin.mcglone@dwf.law

MCGLYNN, Cara Elizabeth (Jul 2016)
(Associate)
CMS Cameron McKenna Nabarro Olswang LLP,
  Edinburgh . . . .(p.856)
  T: 0131 2288000
  E: cara.mcglynn@cms-cmno.com

MCGONAGLE, John Denis (Nov 2006)
(Employee)
Dentons UK and Middle East LLP,
  Glasgow. . . . .(p.968)
  T: 0330 2220050
  E: John.McGonagle@dentons.com

MCGOUGAN, Fiona Margaret (Feb 2021)
(Employee)
TC Young LLP, Edinburgh . . . .(p.914)
  T: 0131 2207660
  E: fmm@tcyoung.co.uk

MCGOVERN, Gary Peter (Sept 2004) (Partner)
Pinsent Masons LLP, Edinburgh . . . .(p.895)
  T: 0131 777 7000
  E: gary.mcgovern@pinsentmasons.com

MCGOVERN, Jennifer Clare (Sept 2017)
(Employee)
Waddell & Mackintosh Solicitors Ltd,
Troon......................(p.1176)
T: 01292 314922
E: jennifer@wmtroon.co.uk

MCGOVERN, John Martin (Apr 1990) (Director)
Corporate Defence Ltd, Glasgow ......(p.963)
T: 0141 3031274
E: john@corporatedefence.co.uk

MCGOVERN, Marie (Sept 2004) (Employee)
Mary's Meals International,
Glasgow....................(p.1241)
E: marie.mcgovern@marysmeals.org

MCGOVERN, Matthew (Oct 2017) (Employee)
McGovern Reid Court Lawyers,
Wishaw ....(p.1182)
T: 01698 359550
E: mmcg@mcgovernreid.co.uk

MCGOVERN, Maureen (Dec 1997) (Employee)
Procurator Fiscal Service,
Edinburgh ....(p.1229)
T: 0300 0203000
E: maureen.mcgovern@copfs.gov.uk

MCGOVERN, Michael James (Aug 1986)
(Partner)
Adairs, Dumbarton ....(p.798)
T: 01389 767625
E: mmcgovern@adairssolicitors.com

MCGOVERN, Vincent Gerard (Aug 1983)
(Consultant)
McGovern Reid Court Lawyers,
Wishaw ....(p.1182)
T: 01698 359550
E: vmcg@mcgovernreid.co.uk

MCGOWAN, Ailie Larissa (Nov 2015)
(Employee)
UK Anti-Doping, Croydon ....(p.1259)

MCGOWAN, Amanda (Oct 1988) (Employee)
Procurator Fiscal Service,
Edinburgh ....(p.1227)
T: 0300 0203168
E: amanda.mcgowan@copfs.gov.uk

MCGOWAN, David James (Nov 1987) (Partner)
CMS Cameron McKenna Nabarro Olswang LLP,
Glasgow....................(p.962)
T: 0141 2222200
E: David.McGowan@cms-cmno.com

MCGOWAN, David Riddick (Oct 2012)
(Associate)
Digby Brown LLP, Glasgow ....(p.970)
T: 0333 200 5925
E: david.mcgowan@digbybrown.co.uk

MCGOWAN, David Thomas (Mar 2000)
(Associate)
Dentons UK and Middle East LLP,
Glasgow....................(p.968)
T: 0330 2220050
E: David.McGowan@dentons.com

MCGOWAN, Fiona Jean (Sept 1990) (Employee)
Aberdeen Corporate Services Limited,
Edinburgh ....(p.1220)
T: 0131 245 7508
E: Fiona.McGowan@abrdn.com

MCGOWAN, Graeme William (Oct 1996)
(Director)
MSM Solicitors Limited, Paisley ......(p.1140)
T: 0141 8896244
E: gwm@msmlaw.co.uk

MCGOWAN, Gregory Patrick (Mar 1985)
(Partner)
Quinn, Martin & Langan, Glasgow....(p.1033)
T: 0141 332 3702
E: gmcgowan@qml.uk.com

MCGOWAN, Ilona Whitton (Mar 2013)
(Employee)
National Westminster Bank PLC,
Edinburgh ....(p.1226)
T: (0131) 626 2925

MCGOWAN, Jenna Elaine (Aug 2012)
(Employee)
NVent, Houston ....(p.1279)

MCGOWAN, Jessica Catherine (Aug 2017)
(Employee)
Procurator Fiscal Service, Glasgow ....(p.1241)
T: 0300 0203000
E: jessica.mcgowan@copfs.gov.uk

MCGOWAN, Kenneth Owen (Jul 2006)
(Partner)
Cairns Brown, Alexandria ....(p.751)
T: 01389 756979
E: KMcGowan@cairnsbrown.co.uk

MCGOWAN, Kirsty (Oct 2005) (Employee)
Procurator Fiscal Service, Stranraer ....(p.1255)
T: 01776 704321
E: kirsty.mcgowan@copfs.gov.uk

MCGOWAN, Michelle Antoinette Graham
(Nov 2010) (Employee)
Ofgem, Glasgow ....(p.1241)
T: (0141) 354 5425
E: michelle.mcgowan@ofgem.gov.uk

MCGOWAN, Pamela Jane (May 2016)
(Associate)
Johnson Legal, Edinburgh ....(p.880)
T: 0131 6229222
E: pamela@johnsonlegal.co.uk

MCGOWAN, Paul Gerard (Jan 1989) (Partner)
EMC Solicitors, Glasgow . . . .(p.974)
T: 0141 644 2865
E: paul@emcsolicitors.co.uk

MCGOWAN, Ross John (Jan 2021) (Employee)
MTM Defence Lawyers Limited,
Falkirk . . . .(p.923)
T: 01324 633221
E: rmcgowan@mtmdefence.co.uk

MCGOWAN, Stephen Anthony (Oct 1997)
(Employee)
Procurator Fiscal Service,
Edinburgh . . . .(p.1227)
T: 0300 0203168
E: Stephen.McGowan@copfs.gov.uk

MCGOWAN, Stephen John (Aug 2010)
(Partner)
TLT LLP, Glasgow . . . .(p.1048)
T: 0333 006 0400
E: Stephen.McGowan@TLTsolicitors.com

MCGOWAN, Vicki (Feb 2013) (Employee)
DECA Media Consultancy, London
E1 . . . .(p.1263)

MCGRADE, Anthony Michael (Dec 1986)
(Director)
McGrade & Co Limited, Glasgow . . . . .(p.1011)
T: 0141 2214488
E: tmcg@mcgrade.co.uk

MCGRADY, Molly (Oct 2019) (Employee)
Anderson Strathern LLP, Edinburgh . . . .(p.839)
T: 0131 2707700
E: molly.mcgrady@andersonstrathern.co.uk

MCGRANAGHAN, Mary Anne (Sept 2009)
(Employee)
McQuillan Glasser & Waughman,
Hamilton . . . .(p.1068)
T: 01698 200006
E: Mary_a_uk@yahoo.com

MCGRATH, Helen (Sept 2006) (Employee)
MBM Commercial LLP, Edinburgh . . . . .(p.889)
T: 0131 2268200
E: helen.mcgrath@mbmcommercial.co.uk

MCGRATH, Jennifer (Nov 2015) (Employee)
East Dunbartonshire Council,
Kirkintilloch . . . .(p.1249)
T: 0141 578 8518
E: Jennifer.Livingston@eastdunbarton.gov.uk

MCGRATH, Karen Margaret (Sept 2010)
(Employee)
PGNiG Upstream Norway AS

MCGRATH, Kathleen (Jan 2005) (Director)
Construction Legal Services Limited,
Skene . . . .(p.1162)
T: 07517 994897
E: kathleen@cls.scot

MCGRATH, Michael Paul (Mar 2007)
(Employee)
Lloyds Banking Group Plc,
Edinburgh . . . .(p.1224)
T: (0131) 442 9579
E: michael.mcgrath@lloydsbanking.com

MCGRAW, Irene Margaret (Dec 1981)
(Employee)
Wallace Quinn & Co Limited,
Glasgow . . . .(p.1051)
T: 0141 771 3911
E: irene@wallacequinn.co.uk

MCGRAW, Mark James (Mar 1999) (Partner)
Hamilton Ross, Airdrie . . . .(p.749)
T: 01236 627627
E: mark@hamiltonross.co.uk

MCGRAW, Susanne Marie (Nov 1999)
(Employee)
Watermans Solicitors Limited,
Glasgow . . . .(p.1051)
T: 0141 4307055
E: susannemcgraw@watermans.co.uk

MCGREADY, Jaimie Margaret (Dec 2019)
(Employee)
BTO Solicitors LLP, Glasgow . . . .(p.952)
T: 0141 2218012
E: jmg@bto.co.uk

MCGREEVY, Robina Tina (Jul 2000) (Director)
McGreevy & Co Limited, Glasgow . . . .(p.1011)
T: 0141 4222220/0795179
E: mcgreevyandco@btinternet.com

MCGREGOR, Alan John Alexander
(Oct 1999) (Employee)
Weatherford Drilling International,
Dubai . . . .(p.1279)
T: +971 565389910

MCGREGOR, Anne Campbell (May 1987)
(Partner)
Anderson Strathern LLP, Glasgow . . . . . .(p.940)
T: 0141 2426060
E: anne.mcgregor@andersonstrathern.co.uk

MACGREGOR, Ashleigh (Sept 2020) (Employee)
Cockburns, Elgin . . . .(p.915)
T: 01343 542684
E:
ashleigh.macgregor@cockburns-solicitors.com

MACGREGOR, Calum Stewart (Nov 1994)
(Director)
Carpenters Scotland Limited,
Glasgow . . . .(p.956)
T: 0141 3285452
E: cam@carpentersgroup.co.uk

MCGREGOR, Caroline Alys (Aug 2018)
(Employee)
Shepherd and Wedderburn LLP,
Edinburgh . . . .(p.900)
T: 0131 2289900
E: caroline.mcgregor@shepwedd.com

MCGREGOR, Catriona Seonaigh (Oct 2011)
(Employee)
Vialex Limited, Edinburgh . . . .(p.1235)
T: 0333 2400127
E: catriona.mcgregor@vialex.co.uk

MCGREGOR, Christine Alice (Nov 2010)
(Employee)
BayWa R.e. UK Limited, Edinburgh . . . .(p.1221)
T: 0131 4663689
E: christine.mcgregor@baywa-re.co.uk

MCGREGOR, Douglas Peter (Oct 1991)
(Associate)
Brodies LLP, Edinburgh . . . .(p.845)
T: 0131 228 3777
E: douglas.mcgregor@brodies.com

MACGREGOR, Elaine Elizabeth (Oct 1999)
(Associate)
Pinsent Masons LLP, Glasgow . . . .(p.1031)
T: 0141 567 8400
E: elaine.macgregor@pinsentmasons.com

MACGREGOR, Elizabeth Chalmers
(Jan 2004) (Employee)
Anderson Strathern LLP, Glasgow . . . . . .(p.940)
T: 0141 2426060
E:
Elizabeth.MacGregor@andersonstrathern.co.uk

MACGREGOR, Euan (Feb 1981) (Partner)
Macgregor & Co., Milngavie . . . .(p.1124)
T: 0141 9564263
E: enquiries@macgregorandco.co.uk

MACGREGOR, Fiona Sophia (Oct 2003)
(Employee)
Dentons UK and Middle East LLP,
Glasgow . . . .(p.968)
T: 0330 2220050
E: Fiona.macgregor@dentons.com

MACGREGOR, Gavin Niall (Nov 2012)
(Associate)
CMS Cameron McKenna Nabarro Olswang LLP,
Edinburgh . . . .(p.856)
T: 0131 2288000
E: gavin.macgregor@cms-cmno.com

MCGREGOR, Grant (Aug 2021) (Employee)
Dickson Minto, London EC2 . . . .(p.1263)
T: 020 76284455
E: grant.mcgregor@dmws.com

MCGREGOR, Grant Douglas (Mar 2016)
(Employee)
Burness Paull LLP, Aberdeen . . . .(p.724)
T: 01224 621621
E: grant.mcgregor@burnesspaull.com

MACGREGOR, Hazel Mary (Aug 2019)
(Employee)
Stronachs LLP, Inverness . . . .(p.1082)
T: 01463 713225
E: Hazel.MacGregor@stronachs.com

MCGREGOR, Iain Robert (Oct 1996) (Partner)
Burn & McGregor, Aberdeen . . . .(p.726)
T: 01224 639660
E: iain.b-m@btconnect.com

MACGREGOR, James George Nisbet
(Oct 2003) (Partner)
Harper Macleod LLP, Glasgow . . . .(p.983)
T: 0141 2218888
E: james.macgregor@harpermacleod.co.uk

MACGREGOR, Karen Fiona (Sept 1996)
(Partner)
Macmillan & Co., Alness . . . .(p.753)
T: 01349 883338
E: karenfmacgregor@btconnect.com

MCGREGOR, Katharine Laura (Jan 2016)
(Employee)
Trainline.com Limited, Edinburgh . . . . .(p.1235)
E: kate.mcgregor@thetrainline.com

MACGREGOR, Katherine Janet (Nov 2013)
(Employee)
BlackRock, Edinburgh . . . .(p.1221)
T: (306) 978 749 900
E: kate.macgregor@blackrock.com

MACGREGOR, Kathryn Elizabeth (Dec 2005)
(Employee)
Scottish Government, Edinburgh . . . . .(p.1231)
T: 0131 244 0815
E: kathryn.macgregor@gov.scot

MCGREGOR, Kimberley Anne (Jun 2012)
(Employee)
Procurator Fiscal Service, Paisley . . . . . .(p.1252)
T: 0141 8875225
E: kimberley.mcgregor@copfs.gov.uk

MACGREGOR, Kirsty Fraser (Mar 1997)
(Employee)
Parabola Group, Edinburgh . . . .(p.1227)
E: kirsty.macgregor@parabola.com

MCGREGOR, Lindsey Murray (Oct 1993)
(Employee)
The Medical & Dental Defence Union of
Scotland, Glasgow . . . .(p.1245)
T: 0845 2702034
E: lmcgregor@mddus.com

MCGREGOR, Lyndsay Mhairi (Nov 2012)
(Employee)
MDS Estates Limited, Edinburgh . . . . .(p.1225)

MCGREGOR, Neil Gordon (Oct 1986)
(Employee)
McGregor & Partners S.C.A.,
Bucharest . . . .(p.1276)
T: +40 21 312 24 25
E: neil.mcgregor@mcgregorlegal.eu

MCGREGOR, Paul Richard (Dec 1982) (Partner)
McCash & Hunter LLP, Perth . . . .(p.1149)
T: 01738 620451
E: paulrmcgregor@mccash.co.uk

MCGREGOR, Rhona Ann (Sept 1997)
(Associate)
Shepherd and Wedderburn LLP,
Edinburgh . . . .(p.900)
T: 0131 2289900
E: rhona.mcgregor@shepwedd.com

MACGREGOR, Sheelagh Helen (Feb 2013)
(Associate)
Pinsent Masons LLP, London EC2 . . . . .(p.1267)
T: 020 7418 7000
E: sheelagh.macgregor@pinsentmasons.com

MACGREGOR, Stewart (Jul 2007) (Partner)
Innes Johnston LLP, Kirkcaldy . . . .(p.1100)
T: 01592 263455
E: smacgregor@innesjohnston.co.uk

MACGREGOR, William (Oct 1989) (Director)
MacGregor Limited, Kirkcaldy . . . .(p.1101)
T: 01592 644477
E: willie@macgregorsol.com

MACGREGOR-DUKE, Kara Louise (Aug 2016)
(Employee)
McJerrow & Stevenson, Lockerbie . . . .(p.1122)
T: 01576 202123
E: kd@mcjerrowstevenson.co.uk

MCGRORY, David Alexander (Jul 2000)
(Partner)
Dentons UK and Middle East LLP,
Edinburgh . . . .(p.860)
T: 0330 2220050
E: David.McGrory@dentons.com

MCGRORY, Jordan (Jan 2017) (Employee)
Scottish Government, Edinburgh . . . . .(p.1231)
T: 0131 244 0815
E: jordan.mcgrory@gov.scot

MCGRORY, Kevin Francis (Aug 1983)
(Employee)
Energy Law Solutions Limited, Gerrards
Cross . . . .(p.1259)
E: kevinmcgrory@enlaw.co.uk

MCGUFFIE, Craig Whyte (Aug 2002)
(Employee)
Scottish Government, Edinburgh . . . . .(p.1231)
T: 0131 244 0815
E: craig.mcguffie@gov.scot

MCGUIGAN, Chloe Anne (Oct 2018)
(Employee)
Life Technologies Limited, Paisley . . . . .(p.1252)
T: 0141 8146100
E: chloe.mcguigan@thermofisher.com

MCGUIGAN, Liam Gerald (Sept 2020)
(Employee)
Procurator Fiscal Service, Glasgow . . . .(p.1241)
T: 0300 0203000
E: liam.mcguigan@copfs.gov.uk

MCGUIGAN, Lisa Jane (Aug 2016) (Employee)
McGlashan MacKay Solicitors,
Glasgow . . . .(p.1011)
T: 0141 3757557
E: lisa@mcglashanmackay.com

MCGUIGAN, Martina Louise (Oct 2012)
(Employee)
Procurator Fiscal Service,
Dumbarton . . . .(p.1217)
T: 0300 020 3000
E: Martina.McGuigan@copfs.gov.uk

MCGUIGAN, Siobhan Clare (Jul 2009) (Partner)
Anderson Strathern LLP, Glasgow . . . . . .(p.940)
T: 0141 2426060
E: Siobhan.mcguigan@andersonstrathern.co.uk

MCGUINNESS, Hazel (Aug 2008) (Employee)
Nursing and Midwifery Council,
Edinburgh . . . .(p.1227)
T: 0131 624 5024
E: Hazel.McGuinness@nmc-uk.org

MCGUINNESS, Kirsty Elizabeth (Sept 2007)
(Associate)
BTO Solicitors LLP, Glasgow . . . .(p.952)
T: 0141 2218012
E: kmg@bto.co.uk

MCGUINNESS, Martin (Aug 2016) (Employee)
Ofgem, Glasgow . . . .(p.1241)
T: (0141) 354 5425
E: martin.mcguinness@ofgem.gov.uk

MCGUINNESS, Sherylanne (Dec 2017)
(Employee)
Ormistons Law Practice Limited,
Glenrothes . . . .(p.1057)
T: 0800 7810413
E: Sherylanne93@live.co.uk

MCGUIRE, Brian John Colm (Sept 1979)
(Director)
Clyde Defence Lawyers Limited,
Dumbarton . . . .(p.798)
T: 01389 730666
E: Dumbarton@clydedefencelawyers.com

MCGUIRE, David Andrew (Mar 1996) (Partner)
MacRoberts LLP, Glasgow . . . .(p.1015)
T: 0141 3031100
E: david.mcguire@macroberts.com

MCGUIRE, Deborah Louise (Oct 2003)
(Employee)
Gerard McGuire & Co., East
Kilbride . . . .(p.832)
T: 01355 225322
E: debbie@dmcgconsultancy.com

MCGUIRE, Eilidh Marion (Aug 2014)
(Employee)
Miller Samuel Hill Brown LLP,
Glasgow . . . . (p.1020)
T: 0141 2211919
E: emcg@mshblicensing.com

MCGUIRE, Gerard (Mar 1986) (Partner)
Gerard McGuire & Co., East
Kilbride . . . . (p.832)
T: 01355 225322
E: deborahmcguire@msn.com

MCGUIRE, Jacqueline Margaret (Mar 1983)
(Partner)
Brodies LLP, Edinburgh . . . . (p.845)
T: 0131 2283777
E: jackie.mcguire@brodies.com

MCGUIRE, John Desmond (Sept 1980)
(Director)
Gallen & Company Ltd, Glasgow . . . . . . (p.978)
T: 0141 4201441
E: john.mcguire@gallenandco.com

MCGUIRE, Martin (Sept 2000) (Director)
Paterson Bell Limited, Kirkcaldy . . . . . . (p.1102)
T: 01592 646600
E: martin.patersonbell@gmail.com

MCGUIRE, Megan Claire (Nov 2012)
(Employee)
Digby Brown LLP, Glasgow . . . . (p.970)
T: 0333 200 5925
E: Megan.McGuire@digbybrown.co.uk

MCGUIRE, Patrick Gregory (Aug 1998)
(Partner)
Thompsons, Glasgow . . . . (p.1046)
T: 0141 2218840
E: patrick.mcguire@thompsons-scotland.co.uk

MCGUIRE, Stephen (Sept 1989) (Partner)
Hennessy, Bowie & Co.,
Bishopbriggs . . . . (p.774)
T: 0141 7624040
E: smg@hennessybowie.co.uk

MCGURK, Hannah (Aug 2021) (Employee)
Brodies LLP, Glasgow . . . . (p.948)
T: 0141 2484672
E: hannah.mcgurk@brodies.com

MCGURNAGHAN, Raymond (Oct 2019)
(Employee)
Baird & Company Lawyers & Estate Agents LLP,
Glenrothes . . . . (p.1056)
T: 01592 759555
E: rmcgurnaghan@bairdco.co.uk

MCHALE, Colin James (Nov 1989) (Partner)
Dickson Minto, Edinburgh . . . . (p.861)
T: 0131 2254455
E: colin.mchale@dmws.com

MCHARDY, Eluned Lucy Elizabeth
(Aug 2014) (Employee)
Drummond Miller LLP, Edinburgh . . . . . (p.864)
T: 0131 2265151
E: emchardy@drummondmiller.co.uk

MCHARDY, Gemma Marie (Aug 2009)
(Employee)
Walter Gerrard & Co., Macduff . . . . . . (p.1122)
T: 01261 832491
E: gemma@waltergerrard.co.uk

MCHARDY, Iain Reid Innes, WS (Apr 1987)
(Partner)
DWF LLP, Edinburgh . . . . (p.865)
T: 0131 2265541
E: Iain.McHardy@dwf.law

MCHARDY, Nathan Shmuel Ripley
(Oct 2019) (Employee)
Digby Brown LLP, Glasgow . . . . (p.970)
T: 0333 200 5925
E: nathan.mchardy@digbybrown.co.uk

MCHARG, Pamela (Jul 2008) (Associate)
Hogan Lovells International LLP, London
EC1 . . . . (p.1265)
T: 020 7296 2000
E: pamela.mcharg@hoganlovells.com

MCHATTIE, Jennifer Maureen (May 2018)
(Employee)
Trainline.com Limited, Edinburgh . . . . . (p.1235)
E: jenny.mchattie@thetrainline.com

MACHIN, Helen (Jun 2004) (Partner)
CMS Cameron McKenna Nabarro Olswang LLP,
Aberdeen . . . . (p.727)
T: 01224 622002
E: Helen.Machin@cms-cmno.com

MACHIN, Sinead Anne (Jun 2018) (Employee)
Clarity Simplicity Ltd, Glasgow . . . . (p.960)
T: 0141 4332626
E: s.machin@claritysimplicity.co.uk

MCHOLLAND, Paul John (Aug 1999) (Partner)
Douglas Wright, Kilmarnock . . . . (p.1096)
T: 01563 532177
E: paul@douglas-wright.co.uk

MCHUGH, Barry (Jul 2005) (Associate)
Addleshaw Goddard LLP,
Edinburgh . . . . (p.835)
T: 0131 2282400
E: barry.mchugh@addleshawgoddard.com

MCHUGH, Edward Andrew (Oct 1987)
(Employee)
Lord President's Private Office,
Edinburgh . . . . (p.1225)
T: 0131 2406701
E: emchugh@scotcourts.gov.uk

MCHUGH, Helen (Oct 2012) (Employee)
Brown & Co Legal LLP, Glasgow . . . . . .(p.950)
T: 0141 3533354
E: HelenMcHugh@lsa.org.uk

MCHUGH, John Miller (Sept 1997) (Partner)
Harper Macleod LLP, Edinburgh . . . .(p.877)
T: 0131 2472500
E: john.mchugh@harpermacleod.co.uk

MCHUGH, Louise Elizabeth (Mar 1996)
(Employee)
Glasgow City Council, Glasgow . . . . . .(p.1239)
T: 0141 2875203
E: louise.mchugh@ced.glasgow.gov.uk

MCHUTCHISON, Joan Catherine (Oct 2017)
(Employee)
Scottish Government, Glasgow . . . . . .(p.1243)
T: 0141 2727226
E: Joan.McHutchison@gov.scot

MCILMOYLE, Elizabeth Annie (Oct 2008)
(Employee)
Scottish Social Services Council,
   Dundee . . . .(p.1218)
T: 01382 207203
E: anne.mcilmoyle@sssc.uk.com

MCILRAVEY, Gary (Nov 1992) (Partner)
Lawson Coull & Duncan, Dundee . . . . .(p.813)
T: 01382 227555
E: gmcilravey@lawsoncoull.co.uk

MCILROY, Elaine Christina (Aug 2000) (Partner)
Brodies LLP, Glasgow . . . .(p.948)
T: 0141 2484672
E: elaine.mcilroy@brodies.com

MCILWAINE, Matthew Robert (Oct 2011)
(Employee)
National Westminster Bank PLC,
   Edinburgh . . . .(p.1226)
T: (0131) 626 2925
E: Matthew.Mcilwaine@natwest.com

MCILWAINE, Rebecca (Jul 2010) (Employee)
National Westminster Bank PLC,
   Edinburgh . . . .(p.1226)
T: 0131 5568555
E: rebecca.mcilwaine@natwest.com

MCILWHAM, Raymond Cahal (Sept 1997)
(Director)
Glasgow Defence Lawyers Limited,
   Glasgow. . . . .(p.981)
T: 0141 4297677
E: info@glasgowdefencelawyers.com

MCILWHAM, Sarah Frances (May 2021)
(Employee)
Bentley Law, Glasgow . . . .(p.945)
T: (07713) 403020
E: sarah@bentleylaw.co.uk

MCILWRAITH CAMERON, Debbie Anne
(Jul 2013) (Employee)
Turcan Connell, Edinburgh . . . .(p.908)
T: 0131 2288111
E:
debbie.mcilwraithcameron@turcanconnell.com

MCINDOE, David (Oct 1994) (Partner)
Harper Macleod LLP, Glasgow . . . .(p.983)
T: 0141 2218888
E: david.mcindoe@harpermacleod.co.uk

MCINNES, Aileen Jane (Apr 1988) (Partner)
Rennie McInnes LLP, Milngavie . . . . . .(p.1124)
T: 0141 5629540
E: aileen@renniemcinnes.co.uk

MACINNES, Alexandra (Jan 1994) (Partner)
The Law Cottage, Dunoon . . . .(p.828)
T: 01369 830007
E: law@lawcottage.co.uk

MCINNES, Callum Farquhar (Jun 2016)
(Associate)
Macdonald Henderson Limited,
   Glasgow. . . . .(p.1008)
T: 0141 2484957
E:
callum.mcinnes@macdonaldhenderson.co.uk

MCINNES, Christine Helen (Oct 1993)
(Employee)
Glasgow City Council, Glasgow . . . . . .(p.1239)
T: 0141 2875823
E: christine.mcinnes@ced.glasgow.gov.uk

MACINNES, Eilidh Morrison (Jul 2021)
(Employee)
MacDonald, Maciver & Company Limited,
   Stornoway . . . .(p.1170)
T: 01851 704343
E: eilidh.macinnes@macdmac.co.uk

MCINNES, Katherine Sarah (May 2018)
(Employee)
CMS Cameron McKenna Nabarro Olswang LLP,
   Glasgow. . . . .(p.962)
T: 0141 2222200
E: katherine.mcinnes@cms-cmno.com

MACINNES, Malcolm Norman (Sept 1984)
(Partner)
Black Hay, Prestwick . . . .(p.1158)
T: 01292 477235
E: malcolm.macinnes@blackhay.co.uk

MACINNES, Margaret Mary (Jan 1988)
(Employee)
Black Hay, Ayr . . . .(p.760)
T: 01292 268988
E: maggie.macinnes@blackhay.co.uk

MACINNES, Marion Ann (Aug 2005) (Partner)
Brodies LLP, Edinburgh . . . .(p.845)
T: 0131 2283777
E: marion.macinnes@brodies.com

MCINNES, Oliver James Cormack (Nov 2018)
(Employee)
Howard Kennedy LLP, London SE1 . . . .(p.1265)
E: oliver.mcinnes@howardkennedy.com

MCINNES, Rosalind Margaret Mary
(Apr 1993) (Employee)
BBC Scotland, Glasgow . . . .(p.1238)
T: 0141 4226373
E: rosalind.mcinnes@bbc.co.uk

MCINNES, Thembelihle Blessing (Oct 2008)
(Employee)
Dentons UK and Middle East LLP,
Glasgow. . . . .(p.968)
T: 0330 2220050
E: thembe.mcinnes@dentons.com

MCINTOSH, Andrew Graham (Oct 1997)
(Employee)
NEO Energy, Aberdeen . . . .(p.1213)
T: 01224 659120
E:
Andrew.mcintosh@neweuropeanoffshore.com

MCINTOSH, Angus (Dec 1985) (Partner)
Angus McIntosh & Simon Hodge,
Glasgow. . . . .(p.1012)
T: 0141 6340313
E: mail@castlemilklawcentre.co.uk

MCINTOSH, Anna Fleur (Feb 1994) (Director)
Hill & Robb Limited, Stirling . . . .(p.1164)
T: 01786 450985
E: fleurmcintosh@hillandrobb.co.uk

MCINTOSH, Caroline Elizabeth (Dec 1985)
(Associate)
Munro & Noble, Inverness . . . .(p.1080)
T: 01463 221727
E: carolinem@munronoble.com

MACINTOSH, Christopher (Sept 1986)
(Employee)
Procurator Fiscal Service, Dundee . . . . .(p.1218)
T: 01382 342559
E: christopher.macintosh@copfs.gov.uk

MCINTOSH, Colin William (Oct 1991)
(Employee)
Pinsent Masons Espana SLP,
Madrid. . . . .(p.1276)

MCINTOSH, David Stewart (Sept 1984)
(Partner)
Balfour + Manson LLP, Edinburgh . . . . .(p.841)
T: 0131 2001200
E: david.mcintosh@balfour-manson.co.uk

MCINTOSH, Euan Alexander Hamilton
(Dec 2002) (Solicitor)
NO FIRM

MCINTOSH, Hannah Rosemary (Nov 2019)
(Employee)
McAndrew & Richardson,
Stranraer . . . .(p.1171)
T: 01776 704324

MCINTOSH, Iain (Sept 2008) (Partner)
Mackenzie & Cormack, Tain . . . .(p.1173)
T: 01862 892046
E: mail@tainlaw.co.uk

MCINTOSH, Jamie Laurence (Feb 2000)
(Partner)
Addleshaw Goddard LLP,
Edinburgh . . . .(p.835)
T: 0131 2282400
E: Jamie.McIntosh@addleshawgoddard.com

MCINTOSH, Joanne Kelly (Jan 2003)
(Employee)
Pinsent Masons LLP, Edinburgh . . . .(p.895)
T: 0131 777 7000
E: joanne.mcintosh@pinsentmasons.com

MCINTOSH, Laura Margaret (Jul 2006)
(Partner)
CMS Cameron McKenna Nabarro Olswang LLP,
Edinburgh . . . .(p.856)
T: 0131 2288000
E: laura.mcintosh@cms-cmno.com

MACINTOSH, Michael Ross (Jul 2013)
(Employee)
Procurator Fiscal Service, Hamilton . . . .(p.1247)
T: 0844 5613245
E: Michael.macintosh@copfs.gov.uk

MCINTOSH, Michelle (Mar 2006) (Director)
McIntosh McCann Ltd, Glasgow . . . . .(p.1012)
T: 0141 212 2222
E: michelle@mcintoshmccann.com

MACINTOSH, Morag Sarah (Aug 1989)
(Director)
Macleod & MacCallum Limited,
Inverness . . . .(p.1080)
T: 01463 239393
E: morag.macintosh@macandmac.co.uk

MCINTOSH, Niall (Oct 2019) (Employee)
Anderson Strathern LLP, Edinburgh . . . .(p.839)
T: 0131 2707700
E: niall.mcintosh@andersonstrathern.co.uk

MCINTOSH, Paul (Sept 2005) (Partner)
Aberdein Considine and Company,
Edinburgh . . . .(p.833)
T: 0131 2212424
E: PMcIntosh@acandco.com

MCINTOSH, Paul (Oct 2002) (Director)
Mattac Limited, Edinburgh . . . .(p.888)
T: 0131 510 8740
E: paul.mcintosh@mattac.legal

MCINTOSH, Ralph Leslie (Nov 2010)
(Employee)
Kellas Midstream Limited,
   Aberdeen . . . .(p.1213)
   E: ralph.mcintosh@kellasmidstream.com

MCINTOSH, Robert (Jan 1996) (Employee)
Aberdeenshire Council, Aberdeen . . . . .(p.1211)
   T: 0146 7532970
   E: Rob.McIntosh@aberdeenshire.gov.uk

MCINTOSH, Rowena Marie (Sept 1985)
(Partner)
McIntosh Family Law, Aberdeen . . . .(p.736)
   T: 01224 593100
   E: rowena@mcintoshfamilylaw.com

MCINTOSH, Ruth (Mar 2008) (Associate)
Jones Whyte LLP, Glasgow . . . .(p.993)
   T: 0141 375 1222
   E: ruth.mcintosh@joneswhyte.co.uk

MCINTOSH, Sarah Louise (Jul 2008) (Employee)
Muirhall Energy Limited, Lanark . . . . . .(p.1250)
   T: 01501 785604
   E: smc@muirhallenergy.co.uk

MCINTOSH, Stephanie (Jan 2000) (Employee)
MCI Electronics Limited, Falkirk . . . . . .(p.1236)

MCINTOSH, William Alexander (Nov 1994)
(Partner)
Brodies LLP, Edinburgh . . . .(p.845)
   T: 0131 2283777

MCINTOSH-FARRELLY, Ella Lois (Mar 2021)
(Employee)
Shepherd and Wedderburn LLP,
   Edinburgh . . . .(p.900)
   T: 0131 2289900
   E: Ella.McIntosh-Farrelly@shepwedd.com

MCINTYRE, Alastair Hamilton (Nov 1986)
(Employee)
D.W. Shaw, Mauchline . . . .(p.1122)
   T: 01290 550249
   E: amcintyre@dwshaw.co.uk

MACINTYRE, Allan Keith (Feb 1995) (Partner)
Ami Law, Bridge of Allan . . . .(p.779)
   T: 07910 858077
   E: Allan.macintyre@amilaw.co.uk

MCINTYRE, Ashleigh (Jun 2020) (Employee)
Watermans Solicitors Limited,
   Glasgow . . . .(p.1051)
   T: 0141 4307055
   E: ashleighmcintyre@watermans.co.uk

MCINTYRE, Caroline Win (Jul 2005) (Associate)
Burness Paull LLP, Aberdeen . . . .(p.724)
   T: 01224 621621
   E: Caroline.Strathdee@burnesspaull.com

MCINTYRE, Colin Roger (Jan 2012) (Solicitor)
NO FIRM

MCINTYRE, Craig Archibald (Aug 2016)
(Employee)
M-Squared Lasers Limited
   T: 0141 9450500
   E: craig.mcintyre@m2lasers.com

MCINTYRE, Elise Margaret (May 2005)
(Employee)
Scottish Government, Edinburgh . . . . .(p.1231)
   T: 0131 244 0815
   E: Elise.McIntyre@gov.scot

MCINTYRE, Ewan Colin (Oct 1992)
(Consultant)
Burges Salmon LLP, Edinburgh . . . .(p.850)
   T: 0131 3142112

MCINTYRE, Fraser Nicol (Oct 2000) (Employee)
ASCO Group Limited, Aberdeen . . . . . .(p.1212)
   T: 01224 580396
   E: fraser.mcintyre@ascoworld.com

MCINTYRE, Gordon (Aug 1986) (Consultant)
Mailers, Alloa . . . .(p.753)
   T: 01259 217009
   E: gordon.mcintyre@mailers.co.uk

MCINTYRE, Janet Helen (Jan 1999) (Partner)
Thorntons Law LLP, Dundee . . . .(p.819)
   T: 01382 229 111
   E: jmcintyre@thorntons-law.co.uk

MACINTYRE, Johnson (Oct 2001) (Partner)
Allan McDougall McQueen LLP,
   Edinburgh . . . .(p.837)
   T: 0131 2252121
   E: JohnMacIntyre@mcdougallmcqueen.co.uk

MACINTYRE, Kirsteen Yvonne (Nov 1998)
(Employee)
Dumfries & Galloway Council,
   Dumfries . . . .(p.1217)
   T: 01387 245938
   E: kirsteen.macintyre@dumgal.gov.uk

MACINTYRE, Lynne (Oct 2011) (Associate)
Thorntons Law LLP, Forfar . . . .(p.927)
   T: 01307 466886
   E: lmacintyre@thorntons-law.co.uk

MCINTYRE, Martin James (Dec 1988)
(Employee)
Wood Group UK Limited,
   Aberdeen . . . .(p.1214)
   T: 01224 851000
   E: martin.mcintyre@woodplc.com

MCINTYRE, Melissa June (Jul 2014) (Employee)
Gilson Gray LLP, Glasgow . . . .(p.980)
   T: 0141 5302021
   E: mmcintyre@gilsongray.co.uk

MACINTYRE, Peter Eugene (Sept 1999)
(Employee)
TikTok Information Technologies UK Limited,
   London EC2 . . . .(p.1269)
   E: pete.macintyre@bytedance.com

MCINTYRE, Ross William (Jan 2017) (Employee)
Weightmans (Scotland) LLP,
  Glasgow . . . . (p.1051)
  T: 0345 073 9900
  E: Ross.McIntyre@weightmans.com

MCINTYRE, Stacey (Sept 2000) (Associate)
Claphams, Glasgow . . . . (p.959)
  T: 0141 6200800
  E: Staceylawagents@davidcclapham.co.uk

MACINTYRE, Stacie Dawn (Jan 2009)
(Employee)
Sartorius Stedim UK Limited,
  Epsom . . . . (p.1259)
  E: stacie.macintyre@sartorius.com

MCINTYRE, William Houston Simpson
(Oct 1984) (Partner)
Russel + Aitken Denny LLP, Denny . . . . . (p.796)
  T: 01324 822194
  E: wm@radenny.co.uk

MACIVER, Amanda Jane (Oct 1985) (Employee)
Ken MacDonald & Co Limited,
  Stornoway . . . . (p.1170)
  T: 01851 704040
  E: janemaciver@kenmacdonaldlawyers.co.uk

MACIVER, Archibald Duncan (Oct 1982)
(Partner)
Brunton Miller, Glasgow . . . . (p.951)
  T: 0141 3371199
  E: archiemaciver@bruntonmiller.com

MACIVER, Carmen Elizabeth (May 1987)
(Partner)
Caesar & Howie, Alloa . . . . (p.752)
  T: 01259 723408
  E: cem@caesar-howie.co.uk

MACIVER, Caroline Louise Margaret
(Nov 2003) (Partner)
Burness Paull LLP, Edinburgh . . . . (p.850)
  T: 0131 4736000
  E: Caroline.Maciver@burnesspaull.com

MACIVER, Colin John (Mar 2015) (Employee)
Addleshaw Goddard LLP,
  Edinburgh . . . . (p.835)
  T: 0131 2282400
  E: Colin.Maciver@addleshawgoddard.com

MCIVER, Colin Robert (Dec 1980) (Solicitor)
NO FIRM

MACIVER, Gillian Margaret (Jul 2021)
(Employee)
Murchison Law Limited, Inverness . . . . (p.1081)
  T: 01463 709992

MACIVER, Ian (Sept 1979) (Director)
MacDonald, Maciver & Company Limited,
  Stornoway . . . . (p.1170)
  T: 01851 704343
  E: enquiries@macdmac.co.uk

MACIVER, Ian Stewart (Oct 1999) (Partner)
Dentons UK and Middle East LLP,
  Edinburgh . . . . (p.860)
  T: 0330 2220050
  E: Stewart.Maciver@dentons.com

MACIVER, John Angus (Oct 1996) (Partner)
Pinsent Masons LLP, Edinburgh . . . . (p.895)
  T: 0131 7777000
  E: john.maciver@pinsentmasons.com

MACIVER, Jonathan Grant (Nov 2018)
(Employee)
MacDonald, Maciver & Company Limited,
  Stornoway . . . . (p.1170)
  T: 01851 704343
  E: jonathan.maciver@macdmac.co.uk

MACIVER, Kathleen Anne (Aug 1994) (Director)
The MacIver Teale Law Practice Ltd,
  Stornoway . . . . (p.1170)
  T: 01851 706070
  E: kathleen@maciverteale.co.uk

MCIVER, Kerri Anne (Oct 2020) (Employee)
Thorntons Law LLP, Dundee . . . . (p.819)
  T: 01382 229 111
  E: kmciver@thorntons-law.co.uk

MACIVER, Kirsty Anne (Jan 2003) (Employee)
Dickson Minto, Edinburgh . . . . (p.861)
  T: 0131 2254455
  E: kirsty.maciver@dmws.com

MACIVER, Roderick William (Oct 1993)
(Employee)
Glasgow City Council, Glasgow . . . . . . (p.1239)
  T: 0141 2873931
  E: roddy.maciver@glasgow.gov.uk

MCIVOR, Joanne (Apr 2007) (Employee)
Edwin Coe LLP, London WC2 . . . . (p.1264)
  T: 020 76914171
  E: joanne.mcIvor@edwincoe.com

MCIVOR, Sarah Louise (Dec 2014) (Employee)
Lloyds Banking Group Plc,
  Edinburgh . . . . (p.1224)
  T: (0131) 442 9579
  E: Sarah.SL.McIvor@lloydsbanking.com

MCJANNETT, Marianne Sarah (Oct 2011)
(Associate)
TC Young LLP, Glasgow . . . . (p.1055)
  T: 1312207660
  E: msg@tcyoung.co.uk

MCJANNETT, Shona Christina (Oct 2008)
(Employee)
Procurator Fiscal Service,
  Edinburgh . . . . (p.1229)
  T: 0300 0203000
  E: shona.mcjannett@copfs.gov.uk

MACK, Andrew Kenneth (Dec 2019)
(Employee)
Anderson Legal Ltd, Kirkintilloch . . . . .(p.1104)
T: 0141 775 4235
E: am@andersonlegal.scot

MACK, Ian Andrew (Jul 2012) (Employee)
Herbert Smith Freehills LLP, London
EC2 . . . .(p.1265)
T: (020) 7466 2422
E: ian.mack@hsf.com

MCKAIG, Eve Louise (Mar 2020) (Employee)
Anika Jethwa & Co, Dundee . . . .(p.813)
T: 01382 223399
E: eve@anikajethwasolicitors.co.uk

MCKAIG, Kenneth James (Jan 1990) (Employee)
Dundee City Council, Dundee . . . .(p.1217)
T: 01382 434000
E: kenny.mckaig@dundeecity.gov.uk

MACKAY, Alasdair Iain (Oct 2002) (Employee)
BNP Paribas, Paris . . . .(p.1272)
T: +33 1 55 77 62 24
E: alasdair.mackay@bnpparibas.com

MACKAY, Alison Anne (Sept 1993) (Employee)
Lindsays LLP, Edinburgh . . . .(p.882)
T: 0131 2291212
E: alisonmackay@lindsays.co.uk

MCKAY, Alison Doreen (Oct 2008) (Employee)
Lindsays LLP, Glasgow. . . . .(p.1001)
T: 0141 2216551
E: alisonmckay@lindsays.co.uk

MCKAY, Amy Louise (Apr 2004) (Associate)
Balfour + Manson LLP, Aberdeen . . . . . .(p.721)
T: 01224 498080
E: amy.mckay@balfour-manson.co.uk

MACKAY, Angus Reay Milne (Oct 2001)
(Associate)
Energy Law Unlimited LLP,
Glasgow. . . . .(p.974)
T: 0141 2210276
E: amackay@elu-llp.com

MACKAY, Anna Ruth (Jul 2012) (Associate)
Scullion Law Limited, Hamilton . . . . . .(p.1069)
T: 01698 283265
E: anna@scullionlaw.com

MACKAY, Anna Rose (Sept 2016) (Employee)
City of Edinburgh Council,
Edinburgh . . . .(p.1221)
T: (0131) 5294145
E: anna.mckay@edinburgh.gov.uk

MACKAY, Annis (Dec 2004) (Associate)
DAC Beachcroft Scotland LLP,
Glasgow. . . . .(p.964)
T: 0141 223 8560
E: amackay@dacbeachcroft.com

MACKAY, Calum Robert (Mar 2017) (Employee)
Holmes Mackillop Limited,
Johnstone . . . .(p.1089)
T: 01505 328 271
E: cmackay@homack.co.uk

MCKAY, Cameron James (Feb 2014) (Employee)
Brodies LLP, Glasgow . . . .(p.948)
T: 0141 2484672
E: cameron.mckay@brodies.com

MCKAY, Catherine Margaret (Feb 2017)
(Employee)
The Kellas Partnership, Inverurie . . . . . .(p.1086)
T: 01467 627300
E: cmm@kellas.biz

MACKAY, Christine Jane (Nov 1995) (Partner)
MacPhee & Partners LLP, Fort
William . . . .(p.930)
T: 01397 701000
E: ChristineMacKay@macphee.co.uk

MACKAY, Christopher Neil (Aug 1985)
(Partner)
Burness Paull LLP, Edinburgh . . . .(p.850)
T: 0131 4736000
E: Chris.Mackay@burnesspaull.com

MCKAY, Claire Christine (Apr 2011) (Associate)
Burness Paull LLP, Aberdeen . . . .(p.724)
T: 01224 621621
E: claire.mckay@burnesspaull.com

MACKAY, Colin Donald (Feb 1986) (Associate)
McIntyre & Co., Fort William . . . .(p.930)
T: 01397 703231
E: c.mackay@solicitors-scotland.com

MCKAY, Denise Sarah (Dec 1991) (Employee)
Scottish Government, Edinburgh . . . . .(p.1231)
T: 0131 244 0815
E: denise.mckay@gov.scot

MACKAY, Donald Andrew Somhairle
(Jan 2018) (Employee)
Digby Brown LLP, Edinburgh . . . .(p.862)
T: 0333 200 5925
E: Donald.Mackay@digbybrown.co.uk

MCKAY, Donna (Feb 2002) (Employee)
Brodies LLP, Aberdeen. . . . .(p.723)
T: 01224 392242
E: donna.mckay@brodies.com

MACKAY, Elizabeth Jane (Sept 1984)
(Associate)
MacPhee & Partners LLP, Oban . . . . . .(p.1135)
T: 01631 562308
E: lizmackay@macphee.co.uk

MACKAY, Euan Stewart (Aug 2006) (Partner)
McGlashan MacKay Solicitors,
Glasgow. . . . .(p.1011)
T: 0141 3757557
E: euan@mcglashanmackay.com

MACKAY, Ewan James (Oct 1999) (Solicitor)
NO FIRM

MCKAY, Ferga Claire (Nov 2002) (Employee)
DWF LLP, Glasgow . . . .(p.973)
T: 0141 228 8000
E: Ferga.McKay@dwf.law

MCKAY, Finlay Alexander (Oct 2002) (Partner)
CMS Cameron McKenna Nabarro Olswang LLP,
Edinburgh . . . .(p.856)
T: 0131 200 7362
E: Finlay.McKay@cms-cmno.com

MACKAY, Frances Mary (Jan 1984) (Partner)
Walter Gerrard & Co., Macduff . . . . . .(p.1122)
T: 01261 832491
E: frances@waltergerrard.co.uk

MACKAY, Fraser Hugh (Sept 2015) (Employee)
Brodies LLP, Aberdeen. . . . .(p.723)
T: 01224 392242
E: fraser.mackay@brodies.com

MCKAY, Fraser David (Aug 2017) (Employee)
Dickson Minto, Edinburgh . . . .(p.861)
T: 0131 2254455
E: fraser.mckay@dmws.com

MACKAY, Hannah (Dec 2015) (Employee)
Peterkins, Inverurie . . . .(p.1085)
T: 01467 672800
E: HM@peterkins.com

MACKAY, Hugh Derek (Oct 1983) (Partner)
Lawson Coull & Duncan, Dundee . . . . .(p.813)
T: 01382 227555
E: hmckay@lawsoncoull.co.uk

MACKAY, Iain Finlay Magnus (Jul 2010)
(Partner)
Wright, Johnston & Mackenzie LLP,
Inverness . . . .(p.1083)
T: 01463 234445
E: mmac@wjm.co.uk

MACKAY, Iain Lewis (Feb 2021) (Employee)
Shepherd and Wedderburn LLP,
Edinburgh . . . .(p.900)
T: 0131 2289900
E: lewis.mackay@shepwedd.com

MCKAY, Ingrid Elizabeth (Oct 2000)
(Employee)
Premier Oil UK Limited, Aberdeen . . . .(p.1213)
T: 01224 618900
E: imckay@PREMIER-OIL.com

MCKAY, James (Apr 1981) (Employee)
Aberdeenshire Council, Banff . . . .(p.1215)
T: 01261 813200
E: James.McKay@aberdeenshire.gov.uk

MCKAY, James Robert (Jul 2021) (Employee)
Anthony Bone, Kilmarnock . . . .(p.1094)
T: 01563 559166
E: james@tonybonelegal.com

MACKAY, Janice (Nov 1983) (Employee)
East Renfrewshire Council, Giffnock . . .(p.1237)
T: 0141 5773000
E: janice.mackay@eastrenfrewshire.gov.uk

MCKAY, Jennifer Alison (Aug 2001) (Employee)
Dalmore Executive Services Limited,
Edinburgh . . . .(p.1222)
E: jennifer.mckay@dalmorecapital.com

MCKAY, Jennifer Reid (Nov 2003) (Partner)
MacRoberts LLP, Edinburgh . . . .(p.887)
T: 0131 2295046
E: jennifer.mckay@macroberts.com

MACKAY, Kate (Dec 2013) (Employee)
Nude Finance, London EC4 . . . .(p.1267)

MACKAY, Kenneth Richard (Dec 1991)
(Partner)
Thorntons Law LLP, Edinburgh . . . .(p.906)
T: 0131 240 8871
E: kmackay@thorntons-law.co.uk

MCKAY, Kenneth Harris (Mar 2021) (Employee)
McCash & Hunter LLP, Perth . . . .(p.1149)
T: 01738 620451
E: kennethmckay@mccash.co.uk

MACKAY, Kimberley (Dec 2013) (Associate)
Johnson Family and Property Law Ltd,
Edinburgh . . . .(p.879)
T: 0131 622 9222
E: kimberley@johnsonlegal.co.uk

MACKAY, Kirsty (Aug 2013) (Solicitor)
NO FIRM

MACKAY, Lena Elizabeth (Dec 1999)
(Employee)
Scottish Widows Limited,
Edinburgh . . . .(p.1233)
T: 0131 6557230
E: lena.mackay@scottishwidows.co.uk

MCKAY, Liam James Nicholas (Oct 2021)
(Employee)
Dallas McMillan, Glasgow . . . .(p.966)
T: 0141 3336750
E: liam.mckay@dallasmcmillan.co.uk

MCKAY, Lorna Agnes (Aug 2006) (Associate)
Ledingham Chalmers LLP, Stirling . . . .(p.1165)
T: 01786 478100
E: lorna.mckay@ledinghamchalmers.com

MACKAY, Lyndsey Christine (Jan 2021)
(Employee)
Wright, Johnston & Mackenzie LLP,
Edinburgh . . . .(p.913)
T: 0131 5241500
E: lcm@wjm.co.uk

MACKAY, Malcolm Peter Miller (Jan 2001)
(Partner)
Brodies LLP, Aberdeen. . . . .(p.723)
T: 01224 392242
E: malcolm.mackay@brodies.com

MACKAY, Margaret Ann (Aug 2008) (Director)
Anderson MacArthur Limited,
   Stornoway . . . .(p.1170)
   T: 01851 703356
   E: Margaret.Mackay@anderson-macarthur.com

MCKAY, Nichola Jane (Sept 2012) (Employee)
Thales UK Limited, Reading . . . .(p.1271)
   T: 01932 824 825
   E: nichola.mckay@uk.thalesgroup.com

MACKAY, Nicolas Kenneth John (Oct 1991)
   (Employee)
Force 9 Energy Partners LLP,
   Glasgow. . . . .(p.1239)
   T: 0141 354 1410
   E: nickmackay@force9energy.com

MACKAY, Norman Roderick (Sept 1998)
   (Employee)
Scottish Legal Aid Board,
   Edinburgh . . . .(p.1233)
   T: 0131 2267061
   E: mackayno@slab.org.uk

MACKAY, Philip, WS (Aug 1982) (Consultant)
Burness Paull LLP, Edinburgh . . . .(p.850)
   T: 0131 4736000
   E: Philip.Mackay@burnesspaull.com

MACKAY, Rachael Margaret (Jan 2011)
   (Associate)
Burnett & Reid LLP, Aberdeen . . . .(p.726)
   T: 01224 644333
   E: rachael.mackay@burnett-reid.co.uk

MCKAY, Rachel Louise (Mar 2014) (Employee)
Burness Paull LLP, Glasgow . . . .(p.954)
   T: 0141 2736810
   E: rachel.mckay@burnesspaull.com

MCKAY, Richard Iain (Dec 1996) (Associate)
McCarrys Solicitors, Glasgow . . . .(p.1006)
   T: 0141 9451911
   E: richardmckay@mccarrys.com

MACKAY, Ronald (Feb 1996) (Partner)
Burness Paull LLP, Glasgow . . . .(p.954)
   T: 0141 2736769
   E: Ronald.Mackay@burnesspaull.com

MCKAY, Rosa Mhairi (Mar 2018) (Employee)
Mackintosh & Wylie LLP,
   Kilmarnock . . . .(p.1095)
   T: 01563 525104
   E: rmckay@mackwylie.com

MACKAY, Ross Alexander (Sept 1982) (Partner)
Coulters Legal LLP, Edinburgh . . . .(p.858)
   T: 0131 603 7333
   E: ross.mackay@coulters.io

MCKAY, Ryan Daniel (Aug 2007) (Partner)
Blackadders LLP, Aberdeen . . . .(p.722)
   T: 01224 588913
   E: ryan.mckay@blackadders.co.uk

MACKAY, Selina (Aug 2006) (Partner)
W. & A.S. Bruce, Dunfermline . . . .(p.822)
   T: 01383 738000
   E: selina@wasbruce.co.uk

MACKAY, Shona Morag (Dec 2018) (Employee)
Student Loans Company Limited,
   Glasgow . . . .(p.1245)
   T: 0141 306 2000
   E: Shona_Mackay@slc.co.uk

MACKAY, Sine MacConnell (Sept 2009)
   (Employee)
Ledingham Chalmers LLP,
   Inverness . . . .(p.1078)
   T: 01463 667400
   E: sine.mackay@ledinghamchalmers.com

MACKAY, Susan (Aug 2013) (Employee)
Macnabs LLP, Perth . . . .(p.1150)
   T: 01738 623432
   E: susanmackay@macnabs-law.co.uk

MACKAY, Susan Louise Hay (Jul 2010)
   (Associate)
Pinsent Masons LLP, Aberdeen . . . .(p.739)
   T: 01224 377900
   E: susan.mackay@pinsentmasons.com

MACKAY, William James (Oct 1984) (Employee)
Richard Freeman & Co., Glasgow . . . . . .(p.978)
   T: 0141 353 2223
   E: williemackay5@hotmail.co.uk

MCKEAN, Roderick Hugh Ross (Dec 1980)
   (Employee)
Anjarwalla & Khanna LLP, Nairobi . . . .(p.1275)
   T: +254 70 303 2000
   E: rm@africalegalnetwork.com

MCKEAND, Pamela Louise (Nov 1998) (Partner)
Allan McDougall McQueen LLP,
   Edinburgh . . . .(p.837)
   T: 0131 2252121
   E: pammckeand@mcdougallmcqueen.co.uk

MCKEARNEY, Jennifer Isobel Cruickshank
   (Aug 2007) (Employee)
Aberdeenshire Council, Aberdeen . . . . .(p.1211)
   T: 01467 538 417
   E: Jennifer.mckearney@aberdeenshire.gov.uk

MCKECHNIE, Alistair John (Jul 2012)
   (Employee)
Latham & Watkins (London) LLP, London
   EC2 . . . .(p.1266)
   T: 020 7710 1000
   E: Alistair.McKechnie@lw.com

MCKECHNIE, Gemma Garrity (Nov 2019)
   (Employee)
Procurator Fiscal Service, Paisley . . . . . .(p.1252)
   T: 0141 8875225
   E: gemma.mckechnie@copfs.gov.uk

MCKECHNIE, Peter Grant (Feb 1986)
(Employee)
Glasgow City Council, Glasgow . . . . . . (p.1239)
T: 0141 2874533
E: grant.mckechnie@ced.glasgow.gov.uk

MCKEE, Alan James (Jul 2005) (Director)
McKee Campbell Morrison Limited,
Glasgow . . . . (p.1013)
T: 0141 4883680
E: alan@mcmsolicitors.co.uk

MCKEE, Alison Jayne (Feb 1999) (Partner)
Lindsays LLP, Glasgow . . . . (p.1001)
T: 0141 2216551
E: alisonmckee@lindsays.co.uk

MCKEE, David (Oct 2005) (Associate)
Gildeas Limited, Edinburgh . . . . (p.872)
T: 0141 331 6079
E: dmcKee@gildeas.net

MCKEE, Heather Michele (Dec 2015) (Director)
Mitchells Roberton Ltd, Glasgow . . . . . (p.1020)
T: 0141 5523422
E: heather@mitchells-roberton.co.uk

MCKEE, Jennifer Claire (Aug 2018) (Employee)
Procurator Fiscal Service, Glasgow . . . . (p.1241)
T: 0300 0203000
E: jennifer.mckee@copfs.gov.uk

MCKEE, Jessica Lindsay Hay (Jul 2015)
(Associate)
Taylor & Henderson LLP, Saltcoats . . . . (p.1160)
T: 01294 464341
E: jmckee@taylorandhenderson.co.uk

MCKEE, Kevin Joseph (Oct 2005) (Employee)
City of Edinburgh Council,
Edinburgh . . . . (p.1221)
T: 0131 529 3906
E: Kevin.McKee@edinburgh.gov.uk

MCKEE, Louise (Mar 2009) (Employee)
Pinsent Masons LLP, Glasgow . . . . (p.1031)
T: 0141 567 8400
E: Louise.McKee@pinsentmasons.com

MCKEEVE, Sarah Holt (Feb 2015) (Employee)
Katani & Co. Ltd, Glasgow . . . . (p.994)
T: 0141 2217788
E: sarah.mckeeve@kataniandco.com

MCKELLAR, Christine Long (Dec 2011)
(Employee)
Dailly, Walker and Co., Solicitors,
Glasgow . . . . (p.965)
T: 0141 4402503
E: christinemckellar@govanlc.com

MCKELLAR, Craig Christopher (Jul 2018)
(Employee)
Harper Macleod LLP, Glasgow . . . . (p.983)
T: 0141 2218888
E: craig.mckellar@harpermacleod.co.uk

MCKELLAR, Vannan Fraser (Nov 1988)
(Partner)
Jackson Boyd LLP, Glasgow . . . . (p.991)
T: 0141 2214325
E: VMcKellar@jacksonboyd.co.uk

MCKELVEY, Grant Alexander Morris
(Oct 2005) (Employee)
Nasdaq Nordic, Stockholm . . . . (p.1276)

MCKELVIE, Gordon Campbell (Nov 1987)
(Employee)
Baxters Food Group, Edinburgh . . . . . . (p.1221)
T: 0131 7180612
E: Gordon.McKelvie@baxters.co.uk

MCKELVIE, Mary Josephine (Apr 1982)
(Employee)
Glasgow City Council, Glasgow . . . . . . (p.1239)
T: 0141 2875170
E: mary.mckelvie@ced.glasgow.gov.uk

MCKENDRICK, Alastair Wood (Oct 2008)
(Partner)
TC Young LLP, Edinburgh . . . . (p.914)
T: 0131 2207660
E: awm@tcyoung.co.uk

MCKENDRICK, Allan Timothy (Mar 1992)
(Director)
Wilson McKendrick Solicitors Limited,
Glasgow . . . . (p.1053)
T: 0141 2227950
E: allanmckendrick@wilsonmckendrick.co.uk

MCKENDRICK, Craig Scott (May 2012)
(Employee)
Park's of Hamilton (Holdings) Limited,
Hamilton . . . . (p.1247)
E: craig.mckendrick@parks.uk.com

MCKENNA, Alison Louisa (Dec 2006)
(Employee)
Procurator Fiscal Service, Glasgow . . . . (p.1241)
T: 0300 0203000
E: alison.mckenna@copfs.gov.uk

MCKENNA, Alison Wendy (Nov 1997) (Partner)
Bannatyne, Kirkwood, France & Co.,
Glasgow . . . . (p.943)
T: 0141 2216020
E: alisonmckenna@bkf.co.uk

MCKENNA, Chala Siskin (Dec 2008) (Employee)
Davidson Chalmers Stewart LLP,
Glasgow . . . . (p.967)
T: 0141 4283258
E: chala.mckenna@dcslegal.com

MCKENNA, Joseph Francis (Jun 1999)
(Employee)
Procurator Fiscal Service,
Edinburgh . . . . (p.1227)
T: 0300 0203168
E: joseph.mckenna@copfs.gov.uk

MCKENNA, Katie (May 2018) (Employee)
SSE PLC, Glasgow . . . . (p.1244)
T: 0141 224 7248
E: katie.mckenna@sse.com

MCKENNA, Laura Ann (Oct 2006) (Associate)
Morton Fraser LLP, Glasgow . . . . (p.1022)
T: 0141 2741100
E: laura.mckenna@morton-fraser.com

MCKENNA, Lucy (Aug 2019) (Employee)
Scullion Law Limited, Hamilton . . . . . . (p.1069)
T: 01698 283265

MCKENNA, Maria-Alaina (Oct 1997) (Solicitor)
NO FIRM

MCKENNA, Mary Josephine (Jul 1996)
(Employee)
Irwin Mitchell Scotland LLP,
Glasgow. . . . . (p.991)
T: 0141 3004300
E:
Mary-Jo.McKenna@IrwinMitchellScotland.com

MACKENNA, Ronald James (Sept 2005)
(Director)
Ron Mackenna Defence Lawyers Ltd,
Glasgow. . . . . (p.1013)
T: 07990 910 295
E: ronmackenna@me.com

MCKENNA, Yvonne (Nov 1989) (Director)
McKennas Law Practice Limited,
Glenrothes . . . . (p.1057)
T: 01592 756449
E: yvonnemckenna@aol.com

MCKENZIE, Alison Joan (Jun 2005) (Employee)
Procurator Fiscal Service, Aberdeen . . . (p.1213)
T: 0300 0202336
E: alison.mckenzie@copfs.gov.uk

MACKENZIE, Allan William (Sept 2009)
(Employee)
Raeburn Christie Clark & Wallace LLP,
Aberdeen . . . . (p.741)
T: 01224 332400
E: allan.mackenzie@raeburns.co.uk

MACKENZIE, Amy Elizabeth (Oct 2014)
(Employee)
Harper Macleod LLP, Glasgow . . . . (p.983)
T: 0141 2218888
E: Amy.Mackenzie@harpermacleod.co.uk

MACKENZIE, Andrew Paul (Jul 2004)
(Employee)
Scottish Arbitration Centre,
Edinburgh . . . . (p.1230)
T: 0131 2264686
E: chiefexec@scottisharbitrationcentre.org

MACKENZIE, Andrew William (Nov 2006)
(Employee)
University of Strathclyde, Glasgow . . . . (p.1245)
T: 0141 5485905
E: andrew.mackenzie@strath.ac.uk

MACKENZIE, Andrew William (Jun 2012)
(Partner)
Harper Macleod LLP, Glasgow . . . . (p.983)
T: 0141 2218888
E: andrew.mackenzie@harpermacleod.co.uk

MACKENZIE, Anna Lucy (Oct 2005) (Employee)
National Westminster Bank PLC,
Edinburgh . . . . (p.1226)
T: 07810 813362
E: anna.mackenzie@natwest.com

MACKENZIE, Anne (Nov 1993) (Employee)
Wheatley Housing Group Limited,
Glasgow. . . . . (p.1246)
T: 0141 274 6314
E: anne.mackenzie@wheatley-group.com

MCKENZIE, Anne Morag (Mar 1983) (Partner)
Connell & Connell, WS, Edinburgh . . . . (p.857)
T: 0131 5562993
E: ammck@connellws.co.uk

MACKENZIE, Arran Lee (Oct 2007) (Associate)
Burness Paull LLP, Aberdeen . . . . (p.724)
T: 01224 621621
E: Arran.Mackenzie@burnesspaull.com

MCKENZIE, Calum Ross (Sept 2016) (Associate)
Brodies LLP, Edinburgh . . . . (p.845)
T: 0131 2283777
E: calum.mckenzie@brodies.com

MACKENZIE, Cameron Hunter (May 1995)
(Partner)
Smith & Grant, Leven . . . . (p.1116)
T: 01333 423441
E: cameron@smithandgrant.com

MACKENZIE, Carrie-Anne Louise (Feb 2013)
(Employee)
Procurator Fiscal Service, Dundee . . . . . (p.1218)
T: 01382 342559
E: Carrie-Anne.Mackenzie@copfs.gov.uk

MACKENZIE, Colin James (Oct 1989) (Partner)
Kerr Stirling LLP, Stirling . . . . (p.1165)
T: 01786 463414
E: cjm@kerrstirling.co.uk

MCKENZIE, Colin Neil (Nov 2000) (Partner)
Burness Paull LLP, Aberdeen . . . . (p.724)
T: 01224 621621
E: Colin.McKenzie@burnesspaull.com

MACKENZIE, Derek (Oct 2002) (Director)
Derek Mackenzie & Company Limited,
Stornoway . . . . (p.1170)
T: 01851 702211
E: derek@derek-mackenzie.com

MACKENZIE, Diana (Jun 2017) (Employee)
Balfour + Manson LLP, Aberdeen . . . . . .(p.721)
    T: 01224 498080
    E: diana.mackenzie@balfour-manson.co.uk

MACKENZIE, Donald Mackay (Jan 1984)
    (Director)
MacKenzie Law Ltd, Inverness . . . .(p.1080)
    T: 01463 713718
    E: donald@mackenzie-law.co.uk

MACKENZIE, Duncan Randell (Jan 1981)
    (Partner)
Mackenzie & Mackenzie, Dundee . . . . .(p.815)
    T: 01382 458775
    E: duncan_mackenzie@hotmail.com

MACKENZIE, Duncan Stewart (Oct 1998)
    (Employee)
Procurator Fiscal Service, Lerwick . . . . .(p.1250)
    T: 01595 692808
    E: duncan.mackenzie@copfs.gov.uk

MCKENZIE, Emma Jane (Nov 2009) (Employee)
Digby Brown LLP, Glasgow . . . .(p.970)
    T: 0333 200 5925
    E: emma.mckenzie@digbybrown.co.uk

MACKENZIE, Finlay Eric Alasdair (Nov 2017)
    (Employee)
Brodies LLP, Edinburgh . . . .(p.845)
    T: 0131 2283777
    E: finlay.mackenzie@brodies.com

MACKENZIE, James Kenneth (Oct 2002)
    (Employee)
Aegon UK, Edinburgh . . . .(p.1220)
    T: 0131 5496704
    E: james.k.mackenzie@aegon.co.uk

MACKENZIE, Jennifer Margaret (Sept 2010)
    (Employee)
BTO Solicitors LLP, Glasgow . . . .(p.952)
    T: 0141 2218012
    E: jmk@bto.co.uk

MACKENZIE, Jillian Cheshire (Nov 2005)
    (Associate)
Thompsons, Glasgow . . . .(p.1046)
    T: 0141 2218840
    E: jillian.mackenzie@thompsons-scotland.co.uk

MACKENZIE, John Alexander, WS
    (Mar 1983) (Partner)
Stuart & Stuart, Edinburgh . . . .(p.905)
    T: 0131 2286449
    E: jmackenzie@stuartandstuart.co.uk

MACKENZIE, John Allan Scott (Sept 1984)
    (Employee)
Aberdeenshire Council, Aberdeen . . . . .(p.1211)
    T: 0345 608 1208
    E: allan.mackenzie@aberdeenshire.gov.uk

MACKENZIE, John Swanson (Dec 1992)
    (Partner)
Shepherd and Wedderburn LLP,
    Edinburgh . . . .(p.900)
    T: 0131 2289900
    E: John.Mackenzie@shepwedd.com

MACKENZIE, Kathryn Anne (Oct 2019)
    (Employee)
National Health Service Scotland,
    Edinburgh . . . .(p.1225)
    T: 0131 2757800
    E: kathryn.mackenzie4@nhs.scot

MACKENZIE, Keith Hamilton (Nov 1984)
    (Employee)
Moir and Sweeney LLP, Glasgow . . . . .(p.1021)
    T: 0141 4292724

MCKENZIE, Kirsten (Nov 2021) (Employee)
Ormistons Law Practice Limited,
    Glenrothes . . . .(p.1057)
    T: 0800 7810413
    E: kmckenzie@ormistonslaw.co.uk

MCKENZIE, Kirsti Jean (Sept 2017) (Employee)
CMS Cameron McKenna Nabarro Olswang LLP,
    Brussels . . . .(p.1257)
    E: kirsti.mckenzie@cms-cmno.com

MACKENZIE, Lesley Margaret (Apr 2004)
    (Employee)
Brodies LLP, Edinburgh . . . .(p.845)
    T: 0131 2283777
    E: lesley.mackenzie@brodies.com

MACKENZIE, Lillian Karen (Mar 2001) (Partner)
DLA Piper Scotland LLP, Edinburgh . . . .(p.863)
    T: 08700 111111
    E: Lillian.Mackenzie@dlapiper.com

MACKENZIE, Murdo (Nov 1969) (Employee)
Murdoch MacKenzie Ltd.,
    Motherwell . . . .(p.1251)
    T: 01698 265171
    E: lorraine@mmconstruction.co.uk

MACKENZIE, Neil Campbell (Aug 2005)
    (Employee)
Emerson Process Management,
    Aberdeen . . . .(p.1212)
    T: 01224 776242
    E: neil.mackenzie@emerson.com

MACKENZIE, Neil James (Dec 1980)
    (Consultant)
Mitchells Roberton Ltd, Glasgow . . . . .(p.1020)
    T: 0141 5523422
    E: Neil@mitchells-roberton.co.uk

MACKENZIE, Pauline Ann (Oct 1989)
    (Employee)
Public Defence Solicitors Office,
    Glasgow . . . .(p.1243)
    T: 0141 5530794
    E: pmckenzie@pdso.org.uk

MCKENZIE, Roderick Cheyne (Jul 1982)
(Employee)
The Scottish Professional Football League
   Limited, Glasgow . . . .(p.1245)
   T: 07831 859580
   E: rodmckenzie@spfl.co.uk

MACKENZIE, Roger Lorne (Nov 2004) (Partner)
Wright, Johnston & Mackenzie LLP,
   Glasgow. . . . .(p.1054)
   T: 0141 2483434
   E: rlm@wjm.co.uk

MACKENZIE, Ross Charles (Jun 2007) (Partner)
J K Cameron, Glasgow . . . .(p.955)
   T: 0141 2214787
   E: ross@jkcameron.co.uk

MCKENZIE, Ross (Feb 2009) (Partner)
Addleshaw Goddard LLP,
   Aberdeen . . . .(p.719)
   T: (+44) (0) 1224 96 5410
   E: Ross.McKenzie@addleshawgoddard.com

MCKENZIE, Sally Lewis Davidson (Nov 2002)
(Partner)
McKenzies, Kirkcaldy . . . .(p.1101)
   T: 01592 206605
   E: sally.mckenzie@mckenzies-sols.co.uk

MCKENZIE, Shelagh Anne (Jan 2006)
(Consultant)
Cavendish Employment Law, London
   EC3 . . . .(p.1262)

MACKENZIE, Stephanie Jane (Nov 1998)
(Employee)
Davidson Chalmers Stewart LLP,
   Edinburgh . . . .(p.859)
   T: 0131 6259191
   E: Stephanie.mackenzie@dcslegal.com

MACKENZIE, Stuart Johnston (Oct 2012)
(Employee)
Travers Smith LLP, London EC1 . . . . . .(p.1269)
   T: (0207) 2953387
   E: stuart.mackenzie@traverssmith.com

MACKENZIE, Suzanne Margaret (Feb 1982)
(Partner)
Mackenzie & Mackenzie, Dundee . . . . .(p.815)
   T: 01382 455263
   E: suzie_mackenzie@hotmail.com

MCKENZIE, Tracy Catherine (Jul 2011)
(Employee)
DJ Mackay and Partners LLP,
   Glasgow. . . . .(p.1012)
   T: 0141 353 8700

MCKENZIE-JUETTEN, Nico (Sept 2016)
(Employee)
Scottish Government, Edinburgh . . . . .(p.1231)
   T: 0131 244 6636
   E: nico.mckenzie-juetten@gov.scot

MCKEOWN, Anne Janette (Sept 1995) (Partner)
Thorntons Law LLP, Forfar . . . .(p.927)
   T: 01307 466886
   E: amckeown@thorntons-law.co.uk

MCKEOWN, Barry Alexander (Jan 1996)
(Partner)
Shoosmiths LLP, Glasgow . . . .(p.1040)
   T: 0370 086 8300
   E: barry.mckeown@shoosmiths.co.uk

MCKEOWN, Jane Patricia Mary (May 2013)
(Employee)
Lothian Pension Fund, Edinburgh . . . . .(p.1225)
   T: 7712239336
   E: McK39j77@lpf.org.uk

MCKEOWN, Jennifer Eilise (Sept 2021)
(Associate)
Clyde & Co (Scotland) LLP,
   Edinburgh . . . .(p.855)
   T: 0131 5571545
   E: jennifer.mckeown@clydeco.com

MCKEOWN, Mark Philip (Oct 2010) (Employee)
Turcan Connell, Edinburgh . . . .(p.908)
   T: 0131 2288111
   E: mark.mckeown@turcanconnell.com

MCKEOWN, Matthew John (Dec 2016)
(Employee)
Kerr Stirling LLP, Stirling . . . .(p.1165)
   T: 01786 463414
   E: mm@kerrstirling.co.uk

MCKEOWN, Michael (May 2005) (Director)
Callahan McKeown & Co Ltd,
   Renfrew . . . .(p.1158)
   T: 0141 8851212
   E: callahanmckeownandco@gmail.com

MCKERLIE, Abbie Carruthers (Jan 2020)
(Employee)
Procurator Fiscal Service,
   Edinburgh . . . .(p.1229)
   T: 0300 0203000
   E: Abbie.McKerlie@copfs.gov.uk

MCKERNAN, Katie Tolmie (Sept 2020)
(Employee)
DWF Law LLP, London EC3 . . . .(p.1264)
   T: 0333 3202220
   E: katie.mckernan@dwf.law

MCKERRACHER, Craig Nicholas (Mar 2007)
(Partner)
Harper Macleod LLP, Glasgow . . . .(p.983)
   T: 0141 2218888
   E: craig.mckerracher@harpermacleod.co.uk

MCKERRACHER, Rhona Mary (Nov 2012)
(Employee)
BTO Solicitors LLP, Glasgow . . . .(p.952)
   T: 0141 2218012
   E: rmk@bto.co.uk

MCKERRELL, Fiona (Oct 2001) (Partner)
Shepherd and Wedderburn LLP,
Glasgow . . . . (p.1039)
T: 0141 5669900
E: fiona.mckerrell@shepwedd.com

MCKERRELL, Katharine Elizabeth Seymour
(Nov 2010) (Employee)
Orkney Islands Council, Kirkwall . . . . . . (p.1250)
T: 01856 873535
E: katharine.mckerrell@orkney.gov.uk

MCKERRON, Kirstie (Feb 2020) (Employee)
Scottish Government, Edinburgh . . . . . (p.1231)
T: 0131 244 0815
E: kirstie.mckerron@gov.scot

MCKERROW, Christina Isobel (Dec 2010)
(Employee)
Genesis Oil & Gas Consultants Limited,
Aberdeen . . . . (p.1212)
T: 01224 623703

MCKERROW, Isabella (Oct 1993) (Partner)
Affinity Family Law, Kilmacolm . . . . (p.1092)
T: 01505873751/07739 63
E: isabella@affinityfamilylaw.co.uk

MACKEY, Andrew Liam (Jan 2012) (Employee)
Masson Glennie LLP, Peterhead . . . . . . (p.1154)
T: 01779 474271
E: Andrew.Mackey@massonglennie.co.uk

MCKIBBEN, Louise Anne (Nov 2010)
(Employee)
Burness Paull LLP, Aberdeen . . . . (p.724)
T: 01224 621621
E: louise.mckibben@burnesspaull.com

MCKIDDIE, Lister Myles (Jul 1991) (Partner)
Walker & Sharpe, Dumfries . . . . (p.803)
T: 01387 267222
E: lister.mckiddie@walker-sharpe.co.uk

MACKIE, Alasdair David (Oct 1981) (Partner)
Mailers, Bridge of Allan . . . . (p.780)
T: 01786 832314
E: alasdair.mackie@mailers.co.uk

MCKIE, Alastair John (Feb 1986) (Partner)
Anderson Strathern LLP, Edinburgh . . . . (p.839)
T: 0131 2707700
E: alastair.mckie@andersonstrathern.co.uk

MCKIE, Claire Elaine (Aug 2013) (Employee)
Backhouse Jones, Clitheroe . . . . (p.1259)
T: 0845 0575111
E: claire.mckie@backhouses.co.uk

MACKIE, Craig Peter David (Sept 2008)
(Partner)
Freelands, Wishaw . . . . (p.1181)
T: 01698 355936
E: CMackie@freelands.co.uk

MCKIE, David Robert (Sept 1997) (Partner)
Levy & McRae Solicitors LLP,
Glasgow . . . . (p.1000)
T: 0141 3072311
E: dmckie@lemac.co.uk

MCKIE, Holly Angela Jane (Oct 2019)
(Employee)
Scottish Social Services Council,
Dundee . . . . (p.1218)
T: 0345 6030 891
E: Holly.Mckie@sssc.uk.com

MACKIE, John Gordon Alexander (Aug 1986)
(Partner)
The PRG Partnership, Glasgow . . . . (p.1045)
T: 0141 3530550
E: jgamackie@prg.co.uk

MCKIE, John (Sept 2001) (Associate)
Shepherd and Wedderburn LLP,
Glasgow . . . . (p.1039)
T: 0141 5669900
E: john.mckie@shepwedd.com

MACKIE, Lesley Joyce (Nov 1981) (Associate)
Mailers, Stirling . . . . (p.1166)
T: 01786 450555
E: Lesley.mackie@mailers.co.uk

MACKIE, Samantha Jane Hamilton
(Dec 2018) (Employee)
Shoosmiths, Edinburgh . . . . (p.902)
T: 03700 868000
E: Samantha.Mackie@shoosmiths.co.uk

MACKIE, Scott Alexander (Sept 2021)
(Employee)
Gillespie Macandrew LLP,
Edinburgh . . . . (p.872)
T: 0131 2251677
E: scott.mackie@gillespiemacandrew.co.uk

MACKIE, Sharon Mary Jocelyn (Nov 1997)
(Employee)
TWMA Ltd, Bridge of Don . . . . (p.1216)
E: smackie@twma.co.uk

MACKIE, Stuart Irvine (Jul 2009) (Partner)
Thorntons Law LLP, Montrose . . . . (p.1125)
T: 01674 673 444

MACKIE, Stuart John (Jan 2003) (Associate)
Plexus Law LLP, Edinburgh . . . . (p.897)
T: 0131 322 9255
E: stuart.mackie@plexuslaw.co.uk

MCKIERNAN, Susan Beverly (Nov 2000)
(Solicitor)
NO FIRM

MCKILLIGIN, Sharon Jane (Sept 1991)
(Associate)
Mackie & Dewar, Aberdeen . . . . (p.736)
T: 01224 596341
E: sjm@mackieanddewar.co.uk

MCKILLOP, Ian (Nov 1981) (Consultant)
Austin Lafferty Limited, East
　Kilbride ....(p.830)
　T: 01355 263777
　E: IMckillop@laffertylaw.com

MCKINLAY, Ainsley Paula (Jan 2021)
　(Employee)
TC Young LLP, Glasgow ....(p.1055)
　T: 0141 2215562

MCKINLAY, Clare Christina (Feb 2013)
　(Employee)
Scottish Government, Edinburgh .....(p.1231)
　T: 0131 244 0815
　E: clare.mckinlay@gov.scot

MCKINLAY, George Lauchlan (Oct 1996)
　(Associate)
Shepherd and Wedderburn LLP,
　Glasgow....................(p.1039)
　T: 0141 5669900
　E: George.McKinlay@shepwedd.com

MCKINLAY, John Christopher (Oct 1995)
　(Partner)
DLA Piper Scotland LLP, Edinburgh ....(p.863)
　T: 08700 111111
　E: john.mckinlay@dlapiper.com

MCKINLAY, Lesley Anne (Jan 1987) (Employee)
Lindsays LLP, Edinburgh ....(p.882)
　T: 0131 2291212
　E: lesleymckinlay@lindsays.co.uk

MCKINLAY, Neil Charles (Aug 2007)
　(Employee)
Low Beaton Richmond LLP,
　Glasgow....................(p.1005)
　T: 0141 2218931
　E: neil@lbr-law.co.uk

MCKINLAY, Nuala Bernadette (Aug 1991)
　(Employee)
Scottish Borders Council, Newtown St.
　Boswells....................(p.1251)
　T: 01835 825 225
　E: NMcKinlay@scotborders.gov.uk

MCKINLAY, Sarah (Oct 1997) (Consultant)
Anderson Strathern LLP, Edinburgh ....(p.839)
　T: 0131 2707700
　E: sarah.mckinlay@andersonstrathern.co.uk

MCKINLAY, Steven (Oct 1999) (Partner)
Burness Paull LLP, Glasgow ....(p.954)
　T: 0141 2484933
　E: Steven.McKinlay@burnesspaull.com

MCKINLEY, Ann Marie (Oct 1979) (Partner)
McKinley & Co., Glasgow ....(p.1013)
　T: 0141 5761984
　E: ann.mckinley@ntlworld.com

MCKINLEY, Jenna (May 2021) (Employee)
Livingstone Brown Limited,
　Glasgow....................(p.1003)
　T: 0141 4298166
　E: jenna@livbrown.co.uk

MCKINLEY, Steven (Sept 2015) (Employee)
Pinsent Masons LLP, Glasgow ....(p.1031)
　T: 0141 567 8400
　E: steven.mckinley@pinsentmasons.com

MCKINNEY, Daniel Matthew (Oct 2019)
　(Associate)
Addleshaw Goddard LLP,
　Edinburgh ....(p.835)
　T: 0131 2282400
　E: daniel.mckinney@addleshawgoddard.com

MCKINNEY, David Jonathan (Mar 1993)
　(Partner)
Jackson Boyd LLP, Glasgow ....(p.991)
　T: 0141 221 4325
　E: DMcKinney@jacksonboyd.co.uk

MCKINNEY, Robert Craig (Jul 2009) (Employee)
Hymans Robertson LLP, Edinburgh ....(p.1223)
　T: 0131 656 5149
　E: Bobby.McKinney@hymans.co.uk

MACKINNON, Callum David (Aug 2014)
　(Employee)
Brodies LLP, Glasgow ....(p.948)
　T: 0141 2484672
　E: Callum.Mackinnon@brodies.com

MACKINNON, Daniel (Aug 2015) (Employee)
Shepherd and Wedderburn LLP,
　Glasgow....................(p.1039)
　T: 0141 5669900
　E: Daniel.MacKinnon@shepwedd.com

MACKINNON, Donald John (Sept 1995)
　(Employee)
Law at Work Ltd, Glasgow..........(p.1240)
　T: 0141 2715555
　E: donaldmackinnon@worknest.com

MCKINNON, Donald Reid (Sept 1972)
　(Consultant)
Boyd Legal Limited, Edinburgh ....(p.845)
　T: 0131 2267464
　E: donald.mckinnon@boydlegaluk.com

MACKINNON, Duncan William Neil
　(Jan 1993) (Partner)
Lindsays (Property), Dundee ....(p.814)
　T: 01382 802050

MACKINNON, Elizabeth Jane Wilson
　(Sept 1975) (Consultant)
James & George Collie LLP,
　Aberdeen ....(p.728)
　T: 01224 581581
　E: e.mackinnon@jgcollie.co.uk

MCKINNON, Fiona (Sept 1994) (Partner)
McKinnon & Co, Glasgow . . . . (p.1013)
T: 0141 770 8777/4111
E: fiona@mckinnonlaw.co.uk

MCKINNON, Fiona Catherine (May 2004)
(Associate)
Nellany & Company LLP, Saltcoats . . . . (p.1160)
T: 01294 464175
E: fionam@nellanysols.co.uk

MCKINNON, Fiona Mary (Oct 2001) (Partner)
Anderson Strathern LLP, Glasgow . . . . . . (p.940)
T: 0141 2426060
E: fiona.mckinnon@andersonstrathern.co.uk

MCKINNON, Fraser Gordon (Mar 2012)
(Employee)
Cartys, Airdrie . . . . (p.749)
T: 01236 761127
E: fmckinnon@cartylaw.co.uk

MACKINNON, James David (Nov 2006)
(Partner)
Aberdein Considine and Company,
Edinburgh . . . . (p.833)
T: 0333 004 4333
E: jmackinnon@acandco.com

MCKINNON, Kirsten (Jun 2015) (Employee)
Shepherd and Wedderburn LLP,
Edinburgh . . . . (p.900)
T: 0131 2289900
E: kirsten.mckinnon@shepwedd.com

MCKINNON, Laura (Feb 1989) (Employee)
Lindsays LLP, Edinburgh . . . . (p.882)
T: 0131 2291212
E: lauramckinnon@lindsays.co.uk

MACKINNON, Louise Anne (Nov 2019)
(Employee)
Clyde & Co (Scotland) LLP,
Edinburgh . . . . (p.855)
T: 0131 5571545
E: louise.mackinnon@clydeco.com

MCKINNON, Sarah Elizabeth (Nov 2002)
(Associate)
Lefevres (Scotland) Limited,
Edinburgh . . . . (p.882)
T: 0845 305 2555
E: smck@lefevres.law

MCKINNON, Yvonne Karon (Nov 1980)
(Partner)
McKinnon Forbes, Tranent . . . . (p.1175)
T: 01875 611211
E: yvonne.mckinnon@mckinnonforbes.co.uk

MCKINSTRAY, Gary (Apr 2012) (Employee)
Perpetual, Singapore . . . . (p.1276)
E: Gary.McKinstray@Perpetual.Com.Sg

MCKINSTRAY, Susan (May 2013) (Employee)
Carey Olsen Singapore LLP,
Singapore . . . . (p.1276)
T: 01534 888900
E: susan.mckinstray@careyolsen.com

MACKINTOSH, Caroline Ann (Jul 2011)
(Employee)
Scottish Government, Edinburgh . . . . . (p.1231)
T: 0131 244 0815
E: caroline.mackintosh@gov.scot

MACKINTOSH, Deirdre Victoria Una
(Sept 1999) (Employee)
South Ayrshire Council, Ayr . . . . (p.1215)
T: 01292 612418
E: deirdre.mackintosh@south-ayrshire.gov.uk

MACKINTOSH, Jennifer Catherine
(Mar 2016) (Employee)
Allingham & Co (Solicitors) Limited,
Edinburgh . . . . (p.838)
T: 0131 4479341
E: jenniferm@allingham.co.uk

MACKINTOSH, Lynne Frances (Sept 1997)
(Employee)
National Westminster Bank PLC,
Edinburgh . . . . (p.1227)
E: lynne.mackintosh@natwest.com

MACKINTOSH, Robin Alexander Simon
(Nov 2019) (Employee)
Brodies LLP, Edinburgh . . . . (p.845)
T: 0131 2283777
E: robin.mackintosh@brodies.com

MACKINTOSH, Sheena (Oct 2005) (Associate)
Dentons UK and Middle East LLP,
Glasgow . . . . (p.968)
T: 0330 2220050
E: Sheena.Mackintosh@dentons.com

MACKINTOSH, Sheila Jane (Oct 2019)
(Employee)
City of Edinburgh Council,
Edinburgh . . . . (p.1221)
T: (0131) 5294145
E: sheila.mackintosh@edinburgh.gov.uk

MACKINVEN, Fraser Donald (Sept 2009)
(Employee)
Flash Entertainment FZ-LLC, Abu
Dhabi . . . . (p.1277)
E: fraser@flashentertainment.com

MCKIRDY, Erin Mary (Jul 2020) (Employee)
Latham & Watkins (London) LLP, London
EC2 . . . . (p.1266)
T: 020 7710 1000
E: erin.mckirdy@lw.com

MCKISSOCK, John Napier (Apr 1998) (Partner)
Macpherson Maguire Cook,
Glasgow . . . . (p.1015)
T: 0141 221 6913
E: john@macphersonmaguirecook.com

MACKLE, Niall (Sept 2017) (Employee)
Burges Salmon LLP, Edinburgh . . . .(p.850)
　T: 0131 3142112
　E: niall.mackle@burges-salmon.com

MCKNIGHT, Cheryl Vaughan Clark
(Jun 2005) (Employee)
Culley & McAlpine, Perth . . . .(p.1147)
　T: 01738 626644
　E: c.mcknight@culleymcalpine.co.uk

MCKNIGHT, Francis (Jul 2016) (Employee)
Levy & McRae Solicitors LLP,
　Glasgow. . . . .(p.1000)
　T: 0141 3072311
　E: fmcknight@lmac.co.uk

MCKNIGHT, Isla-Dawn (Oct 2009) (Employee)
Digby Brown LLP, Glasgow . . . .(p.970)
　T: 0333 200 5925
　E: isla.mcknight@digbybrown.co.uk

MCKNIGHT, Jean Louise (May 2005) (Associate)
Gillespie Gifford & Brown LLP,
　Kirkcudbright . . . .(p.1104)
　T: 01557 330539
　E: jean.mcknight@ggblaw.co.uk

MCKNIGHT, Laura Maureen (Aug 2014)
(Director)
Macdonald Henderson Limited,
　Glasgow. . . . .(p.1008)
　T: 0141 2484957
　E: laura@macdonaldhenderson.co.uk

MCKNIGHT, Lesley (Sept 2007) (Partner)
The Law Practice, Aberdeen. . . . .(p.745)
　T: 01224 562870
　E: lmcknight@thelawpractice.org

MCKNIGHT, Nicola Alison (Jun 2018) (Solicitor)
NO FIRM

MACLACHLAN, Ashley Jane (Jan 2021)
(Employee)
Miller Beckett & Jackson Limited,
　Glasgow. . . . .(p.1019)
　T: 0141 2042833
　E: amaclachlan@mbjsolicitors.co.uk

MCLACHLAN, Clair Janet (Jun 1994) (Partner)
Russells Gibson McCaffrey,
　Glasgow. . . . .(p.1037)
　T: 0141 271 1000
　E: cm@russellsgm.co.uk

MCLACHLAN, Douglas Walter (Mar 2000)
(Partner)
Anderson Strathern LLP, Glasgow. . . . . .(p.940)
　T: 0141 2426060
　E: douglas.mclachlan@andersonstrathern.co.uk

MCLACHLAN, Elena (Oct 2011) (Employee)
The Institute and Faculty of Actuaries,
　Edinburgh . . . .(p.1234)
　T: 0131 2401828
　E: elena.mclachlan@actuaries.org.uk

MCLACHLAN, Graham Alexander
(Apr 1987) (Employee)
Procurator Fiscal Service, Glasgow . . . .(p.1241)
　T: 0300 0203000
　E: graham.mclachlan@copfs.gov.uk

MACLACHLAN, James Martin (Nov 2007)
(Partner)
Warners Solicitors LLP, Edinburgh. . . . . .(p.911)
　T: 0131 6624747
　E: jmaclachlan@warnersllp.com

MCLACHLAN, Karen Elizabeth (Oct 1991)
(Director)
Russel + Aitken (Falkirk + Alloa) Ltd,
　Falkirk . . . .(p.924)
　T: 01324 622888
　E: karenmclachlan@russel-aitken.co.uk

MCLACHLAN, Lindsey Ann (Feb 1994) (Partner)
LAM Family Law, Paisley . . . .(p.1138)
　T: 0141 8890101
　E: enquiry@lamfamilylaw.co.uk

MCLACHLAN, Lydia Ishbel (Oct 2006)
(Associate)
Brodies LLP, Aberdeen. . . . .(p.723)
　T: 01224 392242
　E: lydia.mclachlan@brodies.com

MCLACHLAN, Melanie Alicia (Jun 2016)
(Employee)
Shepherd and Wedderburn LLP,
　Edinburgh . . . .(p.900)
　T: 0131 2289900
　E: melanie.mclachlan@shepwedd.com

MCLACHLAN, Pauline (Jun 2014) (Associate)
MacRoberts LLP, Edinburgh . . . .(p.887)
　T: 0131 2482135
　E: Pauline.McLachlan@macroberts.com

MACLACHLAN, Stewart Bryce (Sept 2009)
(Employee)
Coram Children's Legal Centre, London
　WC1 . . . .(p.1263)
　T: 020 7713 2021
　E: Stewart.MacLachlan@coramclc.org.uk

MCLAFFERTY, Erin Anne (Jan 2018) (Employee)
Brodies LLP, Glasgow . . . .(p.948)
　T: 0141 2484672
　E: erin.mclafferty@brodies.com

MCLAGAN, C S, BSc(Hons) MRICS (Partner &
Director)
J & E Shepherd, Perth . . . .(p.1356)
　T: (01738) 638188

MCLAGGAN, Anna Mary (Sept 1996)
(Associate)
Lindsays LLP, Edinburgh . . . .(p.882)
　T: 0131 2291212
　E: annamclaggan@lindsays.co.uk

MCLANDERS, Vicki Louise (Jul 2014)
(Employee)
Fiona McPhail Solicitors, Edinburgh . . . .(p.886)
T: 0344 5152410
E: Vicki_Mclanders@shelter.org.uk

MCLARDY, Angela (Jul 2006) (Employee)
Whelan & Co, Arbroath . . . .(p.758)
T: 01241 431155
E: amclardy@whelanandco.co.uk

MCLARDY, Donald Patrick (Nov 2006)
(Employee)
SOUTH LANARKSHIREre Council,
Hamilton . . . .(p.1247)
E: Donald.McLardy@southlanarkshire.gov.uk

MACLAREN, Ainsley Grace (Sept 2000)
(Partner)
MacRoberts LLP, Edinburgh . . . .(p.887)
T: 0131 2295046
E: ainsley.maclaren@macroberts.com

MCLAREN, Alan Cunningham (Aug 1986)
(Partner)
Lindsays LLP, Glasgow. . . . .(p.1001)
T: 0141 2216551
E: alanmclaren@lindsays.co.uk

MACLAREN, Blair Robert John (Feb 2000)
(Employee)
ACTIVE Venture Partners SGEIC SAU,
Barcelona . . . .(p.1276)
T: +34 93 178 6868
E: maclaren@active-vp.com

MCLAREN, Bridget Mary (Jul 1992) (Partner)
Pattison & Co., Paisley . . . .(p.1141)
T: 0141 8893296
E: bridget.mclaren@pattisonandcompany.com

MCLAREN, Jamie (Sept 2010) (Employee)
Herbert Smith Freehills LLP, London
EC2 . . . .(p.1265)
T: 020 7466 2422
E: Jamie.McLaren@hsf.com

MCLAREN, Jane Alice (Aug 2012) (Employee)
E. Thornton & Co., Oban . . . .(p.1135)
T: 01631 566771
E: jane@ethornton.co.uk

MCLAREN, Jennifer Louise (Oct 2016)
(Employee)
Procurator Fiscal Service, Hamilton . . . .(p.1247)
T: 0844 5613245

MCLAREN, Kara Irena Marya (Nov 1997)
(Employee)
Pinsent Masons LLP, Glasgow . . . .(p.1031)
T: 0141 567 8400
E: kara.mclaren@pinsentmasons.com

MCLAREN, Keith Anthony (Jun 2010)
(Employee)
Shepherd and Wedderburn LLP,
Edinburgh . . . .(p.900)
T: 0131 2289900
E: keith.mclaren@shepwedd.com

MCLAREN, Kenneth Smith (Sept 1992)
(Employee)
Dentons UK and Middle East LLP,
Glasgow. . . . .(p.968)
T: 0330 2220050
E: Kenneth.McLaren@dentons.com

MCLAREN, Kerry (Aug 1999) (Employee)
Fife Council, Glenrothes . . . .(p.1246)
T: 03451 550000
E: kerry.mclaren@fife.gov.uk

MCLAREN, Kirsty Emma (Oct 2005) (Employee)
Financial Conduct Authority, London
E20 . . . .(p.1264)

MCLAREN, Louise (Apr 2016) (Director)
Hendrie Legal Limited, Edinburgh . . . . .(p.878)
T: 0131 370 0470
E: Louise@ralphhendrie.legal

MCLAREN, Marcus Robbie (Oct 2020)
(Employee)
Burness Paull LLP, Edinburgh . . . .(p.850)
T: 0131 4736000
E: Marcus.McLaren@burnesspaull.com

MCLAREN, Margaret Jean Elizabeth
(Jan 1989) (Employee)
City of Edinburgh Council,
Edinburgh . . . .(p.1221)
T: 0131 529 4299
E: Jean.McLaren@edinburgh.gov.uk

MCLAREN, Moina Kassandra (Oct 1993)
(Employee)
Perth & Kinross Council, Perth . . . .(p.1253)
T: 01738 475000
E: mkmclaren@pkc.gov.uk

MCLAREN, Nicola Dee (Sept 2008) (Employee)
City of Edinburgh Council,
Edinburgh . . . .(p.1221)
T: 0131 529 3107
E: Nicola.McLaren@edinburgh.gov.uk

MCLAREN, Richard Conor (Jun 2017)
(Employee)
Burness Paull LLP, Edinburgh . . . .(p.850)
T: 0131 4736000
E: conor.mclaren@burnesspaull.com

MCLAREN, Robert William Douglas
(Oct 2005) (Employee)
Latham & Watkins (London) LLP, London
EC2 . . . .(p.1266)
T: 020 7710 1000
E: robbie.mclaren@lw.com

MCLAREN, Stephen Charles (Jan 2003)
(Associate)
Ledingham Chalmers LLP,
Aberdeen . . . .(p.734)
T: 01224 408408
E: stephen.mclaren@ledinghamchalmers.com

MCLAREN, Steven George (Nov 1983)
(Partner)
Kippen Campbell LLP, Perth . . . .(p.1149)
T: 01738 635353
E: sm@kcllp.co.uk

MCLAREN, Victoria Lindsay Margaret
(Jul 2017) (Employee)
Thorntons Law LLP, Edinburgh . . . .(p.906)
T: 0131 2258705
E: VMcLaren@thorntons-law.co.uk

MCLARTY, Grant Campbell (Sept 2009)
(Employee)
Scottish Government, Edinburgh . . . . .(p.1231)
T: 0131 244 0815
E: grant.mclarty@gov.scot

MCLARTY, Jack David (Nov 2019) (Employee)
Levy & McRae Solicitors LLP,
Glasgow. . . . .(p.1000)
T: 0141 3072311
E: jmclarty@lemac.co.uk

MCLATCHIE, Scott Kenneth (Apr 2015)
(Employee)
McCluskey Browne, Kilmarnock . . . . . .(p.1095)
T: 01563 544545
E: scottm@mccluskeybrowne.co.uk

MCLAUCHLAN, Christopher Alan (Dec 2002)
(Employee)
Womble Bond Dickinson (UK) LLP,
Edinburgh . . . .(p.913)
T: 0345 415 0000

MCLAUCHLAN, Claire (Oct 2019) (Employee)
McVey & Murricane, Glasgow . . . .(p.1017)
T: 0141 3339688
E: cmclauchlan@mcvey-murricane.com

MCLAUGHLAN, Bernadette Anne
(Sept 2001) (Employee)
Procurator Fiscal Service, Glasgow . . . .(p.1241)
T: 03000202 855
E: bernadette.mclaughlan@copfs.gov.uk

MCLAUGHLAN, Charlene (Oct 2008)
(Associate)
DLA Piper Scotland LLP, Edinburgh . . . .(p.863)
T: 08700 111111
E: charlene.mclaughlan@dlapiper.com

MCLAUGHLAN, Jenna Louise (Jul 2018)
(Employee)
Oraclelaw Limited, Glasgow. . . . .(p.1027)
T: 0141 4041091
E: jm@oraclelaw.com

MCLAUGHLAN, Jillian Vaughan (Oct 2019)
(Employee)
Thorntons Law LLP, Dundee . . . .(p.819)
T: 01382 229 111
E: jmclaughlan@thorntons-law.co.uk

MCLAUGHLAN, Lisa Marie (Aug 2004)
(Director)
Stirling & Mair Limited, Johnstone . . . .(p.1090)
T: 01505 329373
E: lisa.mclaughlan@stirlingmair.com

MCLAUGHLAN, Stephanie Elizabeth Gillespie
(Apr 2004) (Associate)
BTO Solicitors LLP, Glasgow . . . .(p.952)
T: 0141 2218012
E: sml@bto.co.uk

MCLAUGHLIN, Andrew (Aug 2009) (Partner)
McLaughlin & Co, Kirkcaldy . . . .(p.1101)
T: 01592 645772
E: andrew@mclco.co.uk

MCLAUGHLIN, Andrew Kenneth (Oct 2012)
(Employee)
East Dunbartonshire Council,
Kirkintilloch . . . .(p.1249)
T: 0141 5788000
E: Andrew_McLaughlin@eastdunbarton.gov.uk

MCLAUGHLIN, Brian (Jul 2003) (Employee)
DJ Mackay and Partners LLP,
Glasgow. . . . .(p.1012)
T: 0141 353 8700
E: brian.mclaughlin@djmp-solicitors.co.uk

MCLAUGHLIN, Colin James (Dec 2001)
(Associate)
Matthew Brown, Irvine . . . .(p.1087)
T: 01294 273721
E: colin@matthewbrownsolicitors.co.uk

MCLAUGHLIN, Danielle Louise (Feb 2011)
(Employee)
Scottish Courts and Tribunal Service,
Edinburgh . . . .(p.1230)
T: 0131 2406886
E: DMcLaughlin2@scotcourts.gov.uk

MCLAUGHLIN, David (Aug 2014) (Employee)
Paterson Bell Limited, Kirkcaldy . . . . . .(p.1102)
T: 01592 646600

MCLAUGHLIN, Eileen (Jul 1998) (Employee)
Glasgow City Council, Glasgow . . . . . .(p.1239)
T: 0141 2875690
E: eileen.mclaughlin@glasgow.gov.uk

MCLAUGHLIN, Elizabeth Christine
(Oct 1994) (Employee)
Scottish Water, Dunfermline . . . .(p.1219)
T: (01383) 665410
E: elizabeth.mclaughlin@scottishwater.co.uk

MCLAUGHLIN, Elizabeth Margaret
(May 2018) (Employee)
Scottish Police Authority, Police Scotland,
Glasgow . . . . (p.1244)
T: 01786 895727
E:
elizabeth.mclaughlin@scotland.pnn.police.uk

MCLAUGHLIN, George (Oct 2019) (Employee)
East Dunbartonshire Council,
Kirkintilloch . . . . (p.1249)
T: 0141 5788000
E: george.mclaughlin@eastdunbarton.gov.uk

MCLAUGHLIN, John (Oct 1978) (Consultant)
Culley & McAlpine, Perth . . . . (p.1147)
T: 01738 626644
E: john@culleymcalpine.co.uk

MCLAUGHLIN, John Anthony (Nov 1989)
(Director)
JC Hughes Solicitors Limited,
Glasgow . . . . (p.988)
T: 0141 5508080
E: japmclaughlin@hotmail.com

MCLAUGHLIN, Kieran Stephen (Jul 2018)
(Employee)
Mayer Brown LLP, Singapore . . . . (p.1276)

MCLAUGHLIN, Laura Catherine (Oct 2008)
(Consultant)
McLaughlin & Co, Kirkcaldy . . . . (p.1101)
T: 01592 645772
E: laura@mclco.co.uk

MCLAUGHLIN, Lauren Helen (Sept 2020)
(Employee)
Clyde & Co (Scotland) LLP,
Edinburgh . . . . (p.855)
T: 0131 5571545
E: lauren.mclaughlin@clydeco.com

MCLAUGHLIN, Mark (Jul 2005) (Employee)
SSE Plc, Perth . . . . (p.1253)
T: 01738 456 000
E: mark.mclaughlin@sse.com

MCLAUGHLIN, Michael Joseph (Nov 1997)
(Partner)
Shoosmiths LLP, Glasgow . . . . (p.1040)
T: 0370 086 8300
E: michael.mclaughlin@shoosmiths.co.uk

MCLAUGHLIN, Paul William (Nov 2004)
(Partner)
Brodies LLP, Edinburgh . . . . (p.845)
T: 0131 2283777
E: paul.mclaughlin@brodies.com

MCLAUGHLIN, Ryan James (Sept 2018)
(Employee)
MacRoberts LLP, Glasgow . . . . (p.1015)
T: 0141 3031100
E: ryan.mclaughlin@macroberts.com

MCLAUGHLIN, Tammy Alexandra
(Aug 2017) (Employee)
Scottish Police Authority, Police Scotland,
Glasgow . . . . (p.1244)
T: 01786 895727
E: Tammy.McLaughlin@scotland.pnn.police.uk

MCLAUGHLIN-ROBERTS, Dominic Francis
(Oct 2015) (Employee)
Chivas Brothers Limited,
Dumbarton . . . . (p.1217)
T: (01389) 723 425
E: dominic.roberts@pernod-ricard.com

MCLAY, Adam Gregor (Sept 2016) (Employee)
Scottish Power Limited, Glasgow . . . . . (p.1244)
T: 0141 6140000
E: a.mclay@scottishpower.com

MCLAY, Stewart James Gordon (Jul 2019)
(Employee)
Aberdeen Corporate Services Limited,
Edinburgh . . . . (p.1220)
T: 0131 245 7508
E: Stewart.McLay@aberdeen-asset.com

MACLEAN, Alastair David (Nov 1996)
(Employee)
Baillie Gifford & Co, Edinburgh . . . . . . (p.1220)
T: 0131 2752000
E: Alastair.Maclean@bailliegifford.com

MACLEAN, Alexander Duncan (Nov 1988)
(Partner)
Brodies LLP, Edinburgh . . . . (p.845)
T: 0131 2283777
E: duncan.maclean@brodies.com

MACLEAN, Alexandra Mary (Aug 1999)
(Employee)
Murchison Law Limited, Inverness . . . . (p.1081)
T: 01463 709992
E: alix@murchisonlaw.co.uk

MCLEAN, Alistair Gordon (Dec 1984) (Partner)
Brodies LLP, Edinburgh . . . . (p.845)
T: 0131 2283777
E: alistair.mclean@brodies.com

MCLEAN, Andrew Stuart (Nov 2001)
(Consultant)
HSBC Holdings Plc, Birmingham . . . . . (p.1258)
T: 020 79925575
E: andrew.mclean@hsbc.com

MCLEAN, Ashley Elizabeth (Jul 2010)
(Employee)
Shepherd and Wedderburn LLP,
Edinburgh . . . . (p.900)
T: 0131 2289900
E: ashley.mclean@shepwedd.com

MCLEAN, Caitlin (Dec 2017) (Employee)
The Competition & Markets Authority,
Edinburgh . . . . (p.1234)
E: Caitlin.mclean@cma.gov.uk

MACLEAN, Calum Ruairidh John (Feb 2020)
(Employee)
Miller Samuel Hill Brown LLP,
Glasgow.....................(p.1020)
T: 0141 2211919
E: cma@mshblegal.com

MACLEAN, Catriona Joan (Nov 1994) (Partner)
MBM Commercial LLP, Edinburgh .....(p.889)
T: 0131 2268200
E: cat.maclean@mbmcommercial.co.uk

MACLEAN, Catriona Margaret (Jan 2006)
(Associate)
Berrymans Lace Mawer LLP,
Edinburgh ....(p.842)
T: 0131 2259855
E: Catriona.MacLean@blmlaw.com

MCLEAN, Charles Stewart (Oct 2019)
(Employee)
Procurator Fiscal Service, Glasgow ....(p.1241)
T: 0300 0203000

MACLEAN, Claire Linsey (Aug 2005)
(Employee)
Burges Salmon LLP, Edinburgh ....(p.850)
T: 0131 3142112
E: Claire.MacLean@burges-salmon.com

MACLEAN, Claire Victoria (Nov 2003)
(Employee)
Dentons UK and Middle East LLP,
Edinburgh ....(p.860)
T: 0330 2220050
E: Claire.MacLean@dentons.com

MCLEAN, Derek Robert (Sept 2004) (Partner)
Thompsons, Edinburgh ....(p.906)
T: 0131 2254297
E: derek.mclean@thompsons-scotland.co.uk

MACLEAN, Derick John (Aug 2009) (Employee)
Ellis Whittam Limited, Glasgow ......(p.1239)
T: (0345) 226 8393
E: derickmaclean@elliswhittam.com

MCLEAN, Duncan (Nov 1980) (Consultant)
Carruthers, Curdie, Sturrock & Co.,
Kilmarnock..................(p.1094)
T: 01563 572727
E:
duncanmclean@carrutherscurdiesturrock.co.uk

MACLEAN, Elaine Johan (Oct 2009) (Employee)
Pinsent Masons LLP, Glasgow ....(p.1031)
T: 0141 567 8400
E: Elaine.McLean@pinsentmasons.com

MACLEAN, Fiona Margaret (Oct 2008)
(Employee)
Latham & Watkins (London) LLP, London
EC2 ....(p.1266)
T: 020 7710 1000
E: fiona.maclean@lw.com

MACLEAN, Gavin Iain Campbell (May 1990)
(Partner)
Davidson Chalmers Stewart LLP,
Edinburgh ....(p.859)
T: 0131 6259191
E: gavin.maclean@dcslegal.com

MACLEAN, Gillian Frances, WS (Dec 1986)
(Consultant)
Gilson Gray LLP, Edinburgh ....(p.874)
T: 0131 5165354

MACLEAN, Grant Ross (Oct 1987) (Employee)
Berrymans Lace Mawer LLP,
Glasgow.....................(p.945)
T: 0141 3532121
E: Grant.Maclean@blmlaw.com

MCLEAN, Heather Elizabeth Kemmett
(Aug 2013) (Employee)
Jacobs U.K. Limited, Glasgow........(p.1240)
T: 0141 2042511
E: heather.maclean@jacobs.com

MCLEAN, Holly (Mar 2021) (Employee)
Ellis Whittam Limited, Glasgow ......(p.1239)
T: (0345) 226 8393
E: hollymclean@elliswhittam.com

MACLEAN, Iain Ronald (Nov 2012) (Employee)
Comhairle Nan Eilean Siar,
Stornoway ....(p.1255)
T: 01851 822604
E: iain.maclean@cne-siar.gov.uk

MCLEAN, Iain Robert, WS (Oct 1986) (Partner)
DWF LLP, Edinburgh ....(p.865)
T: 0131 2265541
E: Iain.McLean@dwf.law

MCLEAN, James (Nov 2004) (Employee)
Scottish Legal Aid Board,
Edinburgh ....(p.1233)
T: 0131 2267061

MCLEAN, Jamie McGiffen (Feb 2017)
(Associate)
DWF LLP, Edinburgh ....(p.865)
T: 0131 2265541
E: jamie.mclean@dwf.law

MACLEAN, Jeanette (Dec 1996) (Employee)
Procurator Fiscal Service, Paisley......(p.1252)
T: 0300 0203110
E: jeanette.maclean@copfs.gov.uk

MCLEAN, Jenna Louise Graham (Sept 2009)
(Associate)
MacRoberts LLP, Glasgow ....(p.1015)
T: 0141 3031100
E: jenna.mclean@macroberts.com

MCLEAN, Joanne Elizabeth (May 2014)
(Associate)
Addleshaw Goddard LLP,
Edinburgh ....(p.835)
T: 0131 2282400
E: Jo.McLean@addleshawgoddard.com

MACLEAN, Joy (Jun 2019) (Director)
Purdie Maclean Limited, Livingston . . . (p.1119)
T: 01506 420333
E: joy@purdiemaclean.co.uk

MACLEAN, Karen (Sept 1987) (Director)
Gallacher & Co Ltd, Kirkintilloch . . . . . (p.1104)
T: 0141 7761111
E: karen@gallachers.co.uk

MACLEAN, Kenneth (Dec 1973) (Partner)
Pollock & McLean, Sanquhar . . . . (p.1161)
T: 01659 50241
E: kennethmclean@pollockmclean.co.uk

MACLEAN, Kirsteen Margaret (Sept 1997)
(Associate)
BTO Solicitors LLP, Glasgow . . . . (p.952)
T: 0141 2218012
E: kim@bto.co.uk

MACLEAN, Kirsty Erin (Oct 2012) (Employee)
SSE Plc, Perth . . . . (p.1253)
T: 01738 456 000
E: Kirsty.Mclean2@sse.com

MACLEAN, Laura (Jan 2007) (Associate)
Harper Macleod LLP, Inverness . . . . (p.1077)
T: 01463 798 777
E: Laura.mclean@harpermacleod.co.uk

MACLEAN, Liam (Jan 2016) (Employee)
The Competition & Markets Authority,
Edinburgh . . . . (p.1234)
E: liam.maclean@cma.gov.uk

MACLEAN, Lindsay Margaret (Sept 2009)
(Director)
Gibson Kerr Limited, Edinburgh . . . . . . (p.872)
T: 0131 2257558
E: lindsay.maclean@gibsonkerr.co.uk

MACLEAN, Lyndsey Anne (Jul 2009) (Employee)
Horwich Farrelly Scotland,
Glasgow . . . . (p.987)
T: 0141 473 5755.
E: Lyndsey.McLean@h-f.co.uk

MACLEAN, Lynne (Oct 1989) (Associate)
Lindsays LLP, Glasgow . . . . (p.1001)
T: 0141 2216551
E: lynnemclean@lindsays.co.uk

MACLEAN, Magdalena (Oct 2013) (Employee)
Shepherd and Wedderburn LLP,
Edinburgh . . . . (p.900)
T: 0131 2289900
E: magdalena.maclean@shepwedd.com

MACLEAN, Margaret (Sept 1990) (Partner)
CMS Cameron McKenna Nabarro Olswang LLP,
Edinburgh . . . . (p.856)
T: 0131 2288000
E: Margaret.McLean@cms-cmno.com

MACLEAN, Mary Elizabeth Ritchie (Apr 1991)
(Employee)
Fife Council, Glenrothes . . . . (p.1246)
T: 03451 555555 442207
E: mary.mclean@fife.gov.uk

MACLEAN, Megan (Jul 2015) (Employee)
Thorntons Law LLP, Edinburgh . . . . (p.906)
T: 0131 2258705
E: mmaclean@thorntons-law.co.uk

MACLEAN, Michael John (Sept 2008) (Partner)
Jones Whyte LLP, Glasgow . . . . (p.993)
T: 0141 375 1222
E: michael.mclean@joneswhyte.co.uk

MACLEAN, Murdo (Apr 1982) (Partner)
Pinsent Masons LLP, London EC2 . . . . . (p.1267)
T: 020 7418 7000
E: murdo.maclean@pinsentmasons.com

MACLEAN, Neil John (Oct 1996) (Partner)
Shepherd and Wedderburn LLP,
Edinburgh . . . . (p.900)
T: 0131 473 5181
E: neil.maclean@shepwedd.com

MACLEAN, Niall (Aug 2009) (Partner)
Brodies LLP, Edinburgh . . . . (p.845)
T: 0131 228 3777
E: niall.mclean@brodies.com

MACLEAN, Pauline Marie (Apr 1988)
(Consultant)
Mellicks, Incorporating Naftalin Duncan & Co.,
Glasgow . . . . (p.1019)
T: 0141 3320902

MACLEAN, Philip Gordon (Oct 2009)
(Employee)
Rak Gas L.L.C., Ras Al Khaimah . . . . . (p.1279)
T: +971 562 567 900
E: philipmaclean@rakgas.ae

MACLEAN, Rachael Frances (Oct 2005)
(Employee)
Scottish Government, Edinburgh . . . . . (p.1231)
T: 0131 244 0815
E: Rachael.McLean@gov.scot

MACLEAN, Rhona Mary (Sept 2011) (Employee)
Revenue Scotland, Edinburgh . . . . (p.1230)
E: rhona.mclean@revenue.scot

MACLEAN, Dr, Robert Macdonald
(Feb 1994) (Consultant)
Squire Patton Boggs (UK) LLP,
Brussels . . . . (p.1257)
T: +32(0)2 627 7619
E: robert.maclean@squirepb.com

MACLEAN, Robert William (Sept 1999)
(Employee)
Scott Group, Dunfermline . . . . (p.1219)
T: 01383 627105
E: Robert.Maclean@scottgroupltd.com

MACLEAN, Roderick Kenneth (Jan 1994)
(Partner)
Wright, Johnston & Mackenzie LLP,
Inverness ....(p.1083)
T: 01463 234445
E: rkm@wjm.co.uk

MACLEAN, Ruth Petricia Anne (Nov 1992)
(Partner)
Anderson Strathern LLP, Edinburgh ....(p.839)
T: 0131 2707700
E: ruth.maclean@andersonstrathern.co.uk

MACLEAN, Sally Louise (May 2017) (Employee)
Lindsays LLP, Edinburgh ....(p.882)
T: 0131 2291212
E: sallymaclean@lindsays.co.uk

MCLEAN, Stephen Sutherland (Oct 1990)
(Employee)
Goldsmith & Hughes Ltd, East
Kilbride ....(p.831)
T: 01355 260602

MCLEAN, Tamsyn Nancy Cull (Nov 2003)
(Employee)
Assured Guaranty, London EC3 ......(p.1261)
T: 020 75628938
E: tmclean@agltd.com

MCLEARY, Rosemary Jane (Mar 1996)
(Employee)
Scottish Courts and Tribunals Service,
Glasgow ....(p.1243)
T: 0141 4298888
E: RMcleary@scotcourts.gov.uk

MCLEAY, Kathleen Moir (Mar 1999) (Employee)
NCM Fund Services Limited,
Edinburgh ....(p.1227)
T: 0131 6037020
E: Kathleen.mcleay@ncmfundservices.com

MCLEISH, Christopher James (Sept 2001)
(Partner)
Morton Fraser LLP, Glasgow ....(p.1022)
T: 0141 2741100
E: chris.mcleish@morton-fraser.com

MCLEISH, Jane Scott (Dec 1983) (Employee)
Midlothian Council, Dalkeith ....(p.1216)
T: 0131 2713137
E: jane.mcleish@midlothian.gov.uk

MCLEISH, Kathryn Ann (Nov 2012) (Partner)
Brodies LLP, Edinburgh ....(p.845)
T: 0131 228 3777
E: kate.mcleish@brodies.com

MCLEISH, Kirsty Hastings (Sept 2020)
(Employee)
Brodies LLP, Glasgow ....(p.948)
T: 0141 2484672
E: kirsty.mcleish@brodies.com

MCLELLAN, Andrea Jane (Oct 2002)
(Employee)
Pinsent Masons LLP, Glasgow ....(p.1031)
T: 0141 567 8400
E: andrea.mclellan@pinsentmasons.com

MACLELLAN, Fiona Mairi (Feb 2013)
(Employee)
Burness Paull LLP, Glasgow ....(p.954)
T: 0141 2484933
E: Fiona.maclellan@burnesspaull.com

MACLELLAN, Gillian Claire (Apr 2002) (Partner)
CMS Cameron McKenna Nabarro Olswang LLP,
Glasgow.....................(p.962)
T: 0141 2222200
E: Gillian.MacLellan@cms-cmno.com

MCLELLAN, Jennifer Barbara (Nov 2002)
(Employee)
Dickson Minto, London EC2 ....(p.1263)
T: 020 76284455
E: jennifer.mclellan@dmws.com

MCLELLAN, Martin David (Jan 1984) (Director)
Mitchells Roberton Ltd, Glasgow .....(p.1020)
T: 0141 5523422
E: mdm@mitchells-roberton.co.uk

MCLELLAND, Ross William (Jul 2020)
(Employee)
Dentons UK and Middle East LLP,
Glasgow.....................(p.968)
T: 0330 2220050
E: ross.mclelland@dentons.com

MACLENNAN, Claire Catherine (May 2003)
(Employee)
Baillie Gifford & Co, Edinburgh ......(p.1220)
T: (0131) 2752000
E: claire.maclennan@bailliegifford.com

MACLENNAN, David James (Oct 2015)
(Employee)
Scottish Government, Edinburgh .....(p.1231)
T: 0131 244 0815
E: david.maclennan@gov.scot

MCLENNAN, Forbes Fleming (Oct 1981)
(Partner)
James & George Collie LLP,
Aberdeen ....(p.728)
T: 01224 581581
E: f.mclennan@jgcollie.co.uk

MCLENNAN, Grant Peter (Jul 2015) (Employee)
Wyllie & Henderson Solicitors,
Perth ....(p.1153)
T: 01738 638465
E: gmclennan@wyllie-henderson.co.uk

MACLENNAN, Jacquelyn Freda (Dec 1985)
(Employee)
White & Case, Brussels ....(p.1257)
T: +32 2239 2563
E: jmaclennan@whitecase.com

MACLENNAN, Kimberley Jane (Oct 2018)
(Employee)
Digby Brown LLP, Aberdeen . . . .(p.729)
T: 0333 200 5925
E: kimberley.maclennan@digbybrown.co.uk

MACLENNAN, Laura Anne (Jan 2018)
(Employee)
DLA Piper Scotland LLP, Edinburgh . . . .(p.863)
T: 08700 111111
E: laura.maclennan@dlapiper.com

MACLENNAN, Neil Conway (Mar 2000)
(Employee)
Element Materials Technology Group,
Edinburgh . . . .(p.1222)
T: 0131 333 8053
E: neil.maclennan@element.com

MACLENNAN, Nicola Mhairi (Sept 2014)
(Employee)
Vattenfall Wind Power Ltd.,
Edinburgh . . . .(p.1235)
T: 0131 5263131
E: nicola.maclennan@vattenfall.com

MCLENNAN, Owen Daniel (Jan 2010)
(Associate)
Dentons UK and Middle East LLP,
Edinburgh . . . .(p.860)
T: 0330 2220050
E: Owen.McLennan@dentons.com

MACLENNAN, Rhoda Annabel (Sept 2019)
(Employee)
Dickson Minto, Edinburgh . . . .(p.861)
T: 0131 2254455
E: Rhoda.MacLennan@dmws.com

MACLENNAN, Sylvia Catherine (Aug 1999)
(Employee)
Inksters, Wick . . . .(p.1181)
T: 01955 950 505
E: sylvia@inksters.com

MACLEOD, Alasdair Donald (Nov 1986)
(Partner)
Miller Hendry, Perth . . . .(p.1150)
T: 01738 637311
E: donniemacleod@millerhendry.co.uk

MACLEOD, Alasdair Norman (Feb 2003)
(Employee)
Procurator Fiscal Service,
Edinburgh . . . .(p.1229)
T: 0300 0203000
E: alasdair.macleod@copfs.gov.uk

MACLEOD, Alastair David (Oct 2000)
(Associate)
Dentons UK and Middle East LLP, London
EC4 . . . .(p.1263)
T: 020 7242 1212
E: Alastair.MacLeod@dentons.com

MACLEOD, Alisdair Neil (Sept 2000)
(Employee)
Procurator Fiscal Service,
Edinburgh . . . .(p.1229)
T: (0844) 561 3268
E: alisdair.macleod@copfs.gov.uk

MCLEOD, Alison May (Jan 2015) (Employee)
Scottish Government, Edinburgh . . . . .(p.1231)
T: 0131 244 0815
E: Alison.Mcleod@gov.scot

MACLEOD, Angus George (Sept 1999)
(Partner)
Wright, Johnston & Mackenzie LLP,
Inverness . . . .(p.1083)
T: 01463 234445
E: agm@wjm.co.uk

MACLEOD, Anna Lindsay (Jul 2014) (Employee)
Murray Beith Murray, Edinburgh . . . . . .(p.893)
T: 0131 2251200
E: Anna.MacLeod@murraybeith.co.uk

MCLEOD, Bruce Martin Ronald (Aug 1990)
(Partner)
Pinsent Masons LLP, Aberdeen . . . .(p.739)
T: 01224 377900
E: Bruce.McLeod@pinsentmasons.com

MACLEOD, Callum Samuel (Sept 2020)
(Employee)
Garden Stirling Burnet Solicitors Limited,
Haddington . . . .(p.1064)
T: 01620 824996
E: cmacleod@gsbsolicitors.co.uk

MACLEOD, Calum Martin (Nov 2006) (Partner)
Harper Macleod LLP, Inverness . . . .(p.1077)
T: 01463 798777
E: calum.macleod@harpermacleod.co.uk

MACLEOD, Carly (Oct 2019) (Employee)
McAfee, Coatbridge . . . .(p.787)
T: 01236 423437
E: carlymacleod@hotmail.co.uk

MACLEOD, Caroline Quin (Nov 1984)
(Employee)
Procurator Fiscal Service,
Edinburgh . . . .(p.1229)
T: (0844) 561 3268
E: carolineq.macleod@copfs.gov.uk

MACLEOD, Catriona Mairi (Oct 1991)
(Associate)
Taggart Meil Mathers, Aberdeen . . . . . .(p.745)
T: 01224 588020
E: catriona@tmmsolicitors.co.uk

MACLEOD, Craig (Oct 2018) (Employee)
Walkers, St Helier . . . .(p.1274)
T: (01534) 700723
E: craig.macleod@walkersglobal.com

MCLEOD, David James (Sept 2015) (Employee)
Keoghs Scotland LLP, Glasgow. . . . .(p.996)
T: 0141 2380100
E: DMcLeod@keoghs.co.uk

MACLEOD, Debbie Marie (Aug 2015)
(Employee)
Jameson + Mackay LLP, Perth . . . . . .(p.1148)
T: 01738 631666
E: debbie.macleod@jamesonmackay.co.uk

MACLEOD, Donald Frank Glendinning
(Oct 2008) (Partner)
Turcan Connell, Edinburgh . . . .(p.908)
T: 0131 2288111
E: don.macleod@turcanconnell.com

MACLEOD, Eilidh Anne (Sept 2020) (Employee)
Burness Paull LLP, Glasgow . . . .(p.954)
T: 7776598234
E: eilidh.macleod@burnesspaull.com

MCLEOD, Euan Alasdair (Nov 1998) (Partner)
Shepherd and Wedderburn LLP,
Edinburgh . . . .(p.900)
T: 0131 2289900
E: euan.mcleod@shepwedd.com

MACLEOD, Ewan (Apr 1998) (Partner)
Shepherd and Wedderburn LLP,
Edinburgh . . . .(p.900)
T: 0131 2289900
E: Ewan.MacLeod@shepwedd.com

MCLEOD, Fiona (Oct 2008) (Employee)
Brodies LLP, Glasgow . . . .(p.948)
T: 0141 2484672
E: fiona.mcleod@brodies.com

MCLEOD, Fiona Anne (Nov 1988) (Associate)
Stewart Balfour & Sutherland,
Lochgilphead . . . .(p.1121)
T: 01546 602903
E: fionam@sbslaw.co.uk

MCLEOD, Fraser James Harald (Sept 2016)
(Employee)
Providence Strategic Growth LLP, London
SW1 . . . .(p.1267)
E: Fraser.McLeod@psgequity.co.uk

MACLEOD, Genoffir Maud (Sept 1993)
(Employee)
Life Technologies Limited, Carlsbad . . .(p.1279)
E: Genoffir.macleod@thermofisher.com

MACLEOD, Graeme Bruce (Oct 2003) (Partner)
CMS Cameron McKenna Nabarro Olswang LLP,
Edinburgh . . . .(p.856)
T: 0131 200 7686
E: Graeme.MacLeod@cms-cmno.com

MACLEOD, Hannah Elizabeth (Oct 2003)
(Employee)
Scottish Borders Council, Newtown St.
Boswells. . . . .(p.1251)
T: 01835 825 225

MACLEOD, Isabel Jayne (Dec 2013) (Director)
Anderson MacArthur Limited,
Stornoway . . . .(p.1170)
T: 01851 703356
E: isabelmacleod@anderson-macarthur.com

MCLEOD, Isla Isabella Gerrard (Sept 1995)
(Employee)
The Scottish Parliament, Edinburgh . . .(p.1235)
T: 0131 3486657
E: isla.mcleod@parliament.scot

MACLEOD, Jane Margaret (Dec 1975) (Partner)
Jane MacLeod, Lochgilphead . . . .(p.1120)
T: 01546 606666
E: jane@janemacleod.co.uk

MACLEOD, Jodie Elaine Chandler
(Mar 2015) (Employee)
Aberdeen Corporate Services Limited,
Aberdeen . . . .(p.1211)
T: 01224 631999
E: jodie.macleod@aberdeenstandard.com

MACLEOD, John Robert Neil, WS (Jan 1984)
(Consultant)
MacRoberts LLP, Edinburgh . . . .(p.887)
T: 0131 2295046
E: john.macleod@macrobertsl.com

MACLEOD, John Alexander (Jun 1982) (Partner)
George Mathers & Co, Aberdeen . . . . . .(p.737)
T: 01224 588599
E: j.mcLeod@georgemathers.co.uk

MACLEOD, Kenneth Gordon (Nov 1990)
(Partner)
T.F. Reid & Donaldson, Paisley . . . .(p.1141)
T: 0141 8897531
E: gordon.macleod@reidlaw.co.uk

MACLEOD, Kerry Margaret (Mar 2003)
(Employee)
Procurator Fiscal Service,
Edinburgh . . . .(p.1229)
T: 0300 020 3885
E: kerry.macleod@copfs.gov.uk

MCLEOD, Kim (Oct 2013) (Associate)
Clyde & Co (Scotland) LLP,
Aberdeen . . . .(p.726)
T: 01224 624924
E: kim.mcleod@clydeco.com

MCLEOD, Lauren Isobel (Nov 2018) (Employee)
Curle Stewart Limited, Glasgow . . . .(p.964)
T: 0141 227 6200

MCLEOD, Lauren Jayne (Oct 2015) (Employee)
Smart Metering Systems Plc,
Glasgow. . . . .(p.1244)
T: (0141) 2493909
E: lmcleod@sms-plc.com

MACLEOD, Lisa Marie (Jul 2009) (Employee)
Vattenfall Wind Power Ltd., London
  EC4 . . . .(p.1269)
  T: +44 (0) 203 301 9143
  E: lisa.macleod@vattenfall.com

MACLEOD, Lorna Janet (Aug 1987) (Partner)
Lorna MacLeod Family Law, East
  Kilbride . . . .(p.832)
  T: 01355 261361
  E: ljm@lornamacleod.co.uk

MACLEOD, Louise Rae (Sept 1991) (Associate)
CMS Cameron McKenna Nabarro Olswang LLP,
  Edinburgh . . . .(p.856)
  T: 0131 2288000
  E: Louise.Macleod@cms-cmno.com

MCLEOD, Lynsey Isabel (Jul 2009) (Employee)
Angus Council, Forfar . . . .(p.1237)
  T: 01307 476228
  E: mcleodl@angus.gov.uk

MACLEOD, Maria (Jul 2020) (Employee)
JustRight Scotland LLP, Glasgow . . . . . .(p.994)
  T: 0141 406 5350
  E: maria@justrightscotland.org.uk

MACLEOD, Mary Elizabeth (Oct 1987)
(Employee)
Church of Scotland, Edinburgh . . . . . .(p.1221)
  T: 0131 2255722
  E: mmacleod@churchofscotland.org.uk

MACLEOD, Michelle Robertson (Dec 1993)
(Employee)
Police Investigations and Review Commissioner,
  Hamilton . . . .(p.1247)
  T: (01698) 542900
  E: Michelle.MacLeod@pirc.gov.scot

MACLEOD, Muriel Ann (Oct 1986) (Employee)
Free Church of Scotland,
  Edinburgh . . . .(p.1223)
  T: 0131 226 5286
  E: muriel@freechurch.org

MACLEOD, Neil Donald MacLean
(Oct 2001) (Employee)
National Health Service Scotland,
  Edinburgh . . . .(p.1225)
  T: 0131 2757800
  E: Neil.MacLeod@nhs.scot

MACLEOD, Neil Stuart (Nov 2002) (Employee)
Scottish Government, Edinburgh . . . . .(p.1231)
  T: 0131 2442022
  E: Neil.MacLeod@gov.scot

MACLEOD, Nicola Jane (Dec 2003) (Employee)
Spirit Production (Services) Limited,
  Aberdeen . . . .(p.1214)
  T: 01224 415000
  E: nicola.macleod@spirit-energy.com

MACLEOD, Norman (Sept 1980) (Partner)
Fyfe & Murray, Greenock . . . .(p.1061)
  T: 01475 721251
  E: nmacleod@fyfemurray.co.uk

MACLEOD, Norman Torquil (Dec 1989)
(Employee)
Scottish Government, Edinburgh . . . . .(p.1231)
  T: 0131 244 0815
  E: norman.macleod@gov.scot

MACLEOD, Robyn Mairi (Oct 2020) (Employee)
Ken MacDonald & Co Limited,
  Stornoway . . . .(p.1170)
  T: 01851 704040
  E: rmacleod@kenmacdonaldlawyers.co.uk

MACLEOD, Roderick Mungall (Nov 2002)
(Partner)
Shepherd and Wedderburn LLP,
  Glasgow. . . . .(p.1039)
  T: 0141 5669900
  E: Rod.MacLeod@shepwedd.com

MACLEOD, Rona (Feb 2018) (Employee)
Brown & Co Legal LLP, Glasgow . . . . . .(p.950)
  T: 0141 3533354
  E: ronamacleod@lsa.org.uk

MACLEOD, Ross William (Mar 2012) (Solicitor)
NO FIRM

MACLEOD, Sarah Jane (Nov 1987) (Associate)
Turcan Connell, Edinburgh . . . .(p.908)
  T: 0131 2288111
  E: sarah.macleod@turcanconnell.com

MACLEOD, Sheena May (Jun 2009) (Associate)
Middleton Ross & Arnot Limited,
  Dingwall . . . .(p.797)
  T: 01349 862214
  E: smm@middletonross.co.uk

MACLEOD, Tanya Jane (Feb 1997) (Partner)
Brodies LLP, Edinburgh . . . .(p.845)
  T: 0131 2283777
  E: tanya.macleod@brodies.com

MCLINTOCK, Christine Ann (Feb 1988)
(Solicitor)
NO FIRM

MCLINTOCK, Morag Miller (Oct 2001)
(Employee)
Procurator Fiscal Service, Hamilton . . . .(p.1247)
  T: 0844 5613245
  E: morag.mclintock@copfs.gov.uk

MCLUCKIE, Peter Alexander (Oct 1993)
(Associate)
Harper Macleod LLP, Elgin. . . . .(p.916)
  T: 01343 542623
  E: peter.mcluckie@harpermacleod.co.uk

MACLURE, Alasdair Eoin (Dec 1981) (Partner)
Ledingham Chalmers LLP,
   Aberdeen . . . .(p.734)
   T: 01224 408408
   E: alasdair.maclure@ledinghamchalmers.com

MCLUSKEY, Kevin (Sept 1995) (Director)
VMH Solicitors Limited, Edinburgh . . . . .(p.910)
   T: 0131 6615911
   E: kmc@vmh.co.uk

MCLUSKEY, Nicholas Edward (Jul 2013)
   (Employee)
Clydesdale Bank Plc, Glasgow . . . .(p.1238)
   T: 0141 2423733
   E: nick.mcluskey@cybg.com

MCMACKIN, James Malcolm (Feb 2017)
   (Employee)
Paterson Bell Limited, Kirkcaldy . . . . . .(p.1102)
   T: 01592 646600
   E: james@patersonbell.co.uk

MCMAHON, Angela Mary (Sept 2006)
   (Employee)
Jones Whyte LLP, Glasgow. . . . .(p.993)
   T: 0141 375 1222
   E: angela.mcmahon@joneswhyte.co.uk

MCMAHON, Beverley Tara (Sept 2006)
   (Director)
Greentree Legal Limited, Glasgow . . . . .(p.981)
   E: beverley@greentree.org.uk

MACMAHON, Eileen Mary (Jul 2009)
   (Associate)
CMS Cameron McKenna Nabarro Olswang LLP,
   Glasgow. . . . .(p.962)
   T: 0141 2222200
   E: Eileen.MacMahon@cms-cmno.com

MCMAHON, James Michael (Oct 2018)
   (Employee)
Burness Paull LLP, Edinburgh . . . .(p.850)
   T: 0131 4736000
   E: james.mcmahon@burnesspaull.com

MCMAHON, Julie Ann (Jan 2003) (Associate)
Drummond Miller LLP, Glasgow. . . . . . .(p.971)
   T: 0141 352 8389
   E: JMcMahon@drummondmiller.co.uk

MCMAHON, Lyndsay Anne (Oct 2015)
   (Employee)
Harper Macleod LLP, Glasgow . . . .(p.983)
   T: 0141 2218888
   E: lyndsay.mcmahon@harpermacleod.co.uk

MCMAHON, Lynn Littlejohn (Nov 2005)
   (Employee)
Halliday Campbell W.S., Edinburgh . . . .(p.876)
   T: 0131 6683000
   E: lynn.mcmahon@hallidaycampbell.com

MCMAHON, Paul Dominic (Mar 2001)
   (Director)
McMahon Employment Law,
   Bearsden . . . .(p.772)
   T: 0141 447 0438
   E: paul.mcmahon@mcmahonlaw.co.uk

MCMANUS, Kelly Annmarie (Jul 2015)
   (Employee)
Navigator Employment Law Ltd,
   Edinburgh . . . .(p.1227)
   T: 0333 2400308
   E: Kelly.McManus@navigatorlaw.co.uk

MCMANUS, Kirsten Anne (Mar 2015)
   (Associate)
Morton Fraser LLP, Edinburgh . . . .(p.891)
   T: 0131 2471000
   E: kirsten.mcmanus@morton-fraser.com

MCMANUS, Laura Ann Fleming (Apr 1999)
   (Associate)
DJ Mackay and Partners LLP,
   Glasgow. . . . .(p.1012)
   T: 0141 353 8700

MCMANUS, Laura Rose (Jun 2005) (Employee)
Procurator Fiscal Service, Kirkcaldy . . . .(p.1249)
   T: 0300 0203000
   E: laura.mcmanus@copfs.gov.uk

MCMANUS, Michelle Marie (Nov 1981)
   (Employee)
Russel + Aitken Edinburgh LLP,
   Edinburgh . . . .(p.899)
   T: 0131 2285500
   E:
   michelle.mcmanus@russelaitken-edinburgh.
   com

MCMANUS, Nicholas John (Sept 2011)
   (Employee)
The Edrington Group Limited,
   Glasgow. . . . .(p.1245)
   T: 0141 9404000
   E: nicholas.mcmanus@edrington.com

MCMANUS, Veronica Mary (Oct 1993)
   (Director)
Bonnar Accident Law Ltd, Airdrie . . . . . .(p.748)
   T: 01236 756188
   E: veronica@bonnarandco.com

MCMARTIN, Jennifer Ann (Jul 1998)
   (Employee)
Glasgow City Council, Glasgow . . . . . .(p.1239)
   T: 0141 2874699
   E: jennifer.mcmartin@glasgow.gov.uk

MCMASTER, Melanie (Jan 2017) (Employee)
Criminal Injuries Compensation Authority,
   Glasgow. . . . .(p.1239)
   T: 0141 2281419
   E: Melanie.McMaster@cica.gov.uk

MCMASTER, Scott Barton (Aug 2012)
(Employee)
Collins Aerospace, Prestwick . . . .(p.1254)
T: 01292 670293
E: scott.mcmaster@utas.utc.com

MACMASTER, Siobhan (Nov 2017) (Employee)
Inverclyde Council, Greenock . . . .(p.1246)
T: 01475 717171
E: siobhan.macmaster@inverclyde.gov.uk

MCMEEKEN, Richard George (Oct 2002)
(Partner)
Morton Fraser LLP, Edinburgh . . . .(p.891)
T: 0131 2471000
E: richard.mcmeeken@morton-fraser.com

MCMEEKIN, Lucy (Jan 2012) (Employee)
DWF LLP, Glasgow . . . .(p.973)
T: 0141 228 8000
E: Lucy.McMeekin@dwf.law

MCMENAMIN, Christine (Nov 1989)
(Employee)
South Ayrshire Council, Ayr . . . .(p.1215)
T: 01292 612420
E:
Christine.McMenamin@south-ayrshire.gov.uk

MCMICHAEL, Lucy Jane (Oct 2001) (Employee)
Scottish Government, Edinburgh . . . . .(p.1231)
T: 0131 244 0815
E: lucy.mcmichael@gov.scot

MCMICHAEL-PHILLIPS, Katherine Jane
(Jan 2021) (Employee)
Clark Boyle Limited, Glasgow . . . .(p.960)
T: 0141 2272200

MCMILLAN, Alan Charles (Oct 1995) (Partner)
Burness Paull LLP, Edinburgh . . . .(p.850)
T: 0131 4736000
E: Alan.McMillan@burnesspaull.com

MACMILLAN, Caitlin Janet (Jun 2021)
(Employee)
Addleshaw Goddard LLP,
   Edinburgh . . . .(p.835)
T: 0131 2282400
E: Caitlin.MacMillan@addleshawgoddard.com

MCMILLAN, Caroline Ilse (Aug 2013)
(Employee)
Turcan Connell, Edinburgh . . . .(p.908)
T: 0131 2288111
E: caroline.mcmillan@turcanconnell.com

MCMILLAN, Eilidh (Aug 2017) (Employee)
Brodies LLP, Edinburgh . . . .(p.845)
T: 0131 2283777
E: eilidh.mcmillan@brodies.com

MACMILLAN, Fergus Stewart (Jan 1988)
(Partner)
Stuart & Stuart, Edinburgh . . . .(p.905)
T: 0131 2286449
E: fmacmillan@stuartandstuart.co.uk

MCMILLAN, Fraser James John (Aug 1990)
(Partner)
Pinsent Masons (Australia), Sydney . . . .(p.1257)
T: (+61) 2 8024 2808
E: fraser.mcmillan@pinsentmasons.com

MACMILLAN, Gemma (Sept 2009) (Employee)
SSE Plc, Perth . . . .(p.1253)
T: 01738 456 000
E: gemma.macmillan@legal.sse.com

MCMILLAN, Gillian (Oct 2010) (Employee)
Addleshaw Goddard LLP,
   Edinburgh . . . .(p.835)
T: 0131 2282400
E: Gillian.McMillan@addleshawgoddard.com

MCMILLAN, Graeme James (Dec 2017)
(Employee)
Argyll & Bute Council,
   Lochgilphead . . . .(p.1251)
T: 01546 602127
E: graeme.mcmillan2@argyll-bute.gov.uk

MCMILLAN, James Harris (Jul 2010) (Employee)
Anderson Strathern LLP, Glasgow . . . . . .(p.940)
T: 0141 2426060

MCMILLAN, James Millar (Sept 2015)
(Employee)
Clifford Chance LLP, London E14 . . . . .(p.1262)
E: james.mcmillan@cliffordchance.com

MCMILLAN, Joanne Louise (Jun 2011) (Partner)
CMC Law LLP, Glasgow . . . .(p.961)
T: 07790 074643
E: joannelmcmillan@outlook.com

MACMILLAN, John Ernest Newall
(Oct 1980) (Consultant)
MacRoberts LLP, Dundee . . . .(p.815)
T: 01382 339340
E: john.macmillan@macroberts.com

MCMILLAN, Laura (Apr 2013) (Employee)
Shepherd and Wedderburn LLP,
   Edinburgh . . . .(p.900)
T: 0131 2289900
E: laura.mcmillan@shepwedd.com

MCMILLAN, Laura Jean (Feb 2020) (Employee)
Raeburn Christie Clark & Wallace LLP,
   Stonehaven . . . .(p.1169)
T: 01569 762947
E: Laura.McMillan@raeburns.co.uk

MCMILLAN, Laura Ruth (Feb 2003) (Partner)
Brodies LLP, Edinburgh . . . .(p.845)
T: 0131 2283777
E: laura.mcmillan@brodies.com

MACMILLAN, Leon Fraser (Feb 2018)
(Employee)
Kirkland & Ellis International LLP, London
   EC3 . . . .(p.1265)
T: 0207 4692000
E: leon.macmillan@kirkland.com

MCMILLAN, Mairi-Clare (Jul 2018) (Employee)
Procurator Fiscal Service, Hamilton . . . . (p.1247)
   T: 0844 5613245
   E: Mairi-Clare.McMillan@copfs.gov.uk

MACMILLAN, Mark John (Sept 1991)
(Associate)
The Kerr Brown Partnership,
   Glasgow. (p.1044)
   T: 0141 2214880
   E: mjm@kerrbrown.co.uk

MCMILLAN, Mark Peter (May 2014) (Partner)
Barnetts, Kilmarnock . . . . (p.1093)
   T: 01563 522137
   E: markmcmillan@barnettslaw.co.uk

MCMILLAN, Pamela Sally (Jun 2014)
(Employee)
Shepherd and Wedderburn LLP,
   Glasgow. (p.1039)
   T: 0141 5669900
   E: Pamela.McMillan@shepwedd.com

MCMILLAN, Paula Christina (Feb 1998)
(Partner)
NewLaw Scotland LLP, Glasgow . . . . . . (p.1027)
   T: 0845 4819500
   E: paula.mcmillan@newlaw-scotland.co.uk

MACMILLAN, Sean Alexander (Dec 2010)
(Partner)
Aberdein Considine and Company,
   Edinburgh . . . . (p.833)
   T: 0131 2229000
   E: smacmillan@acandco.com

MCMILLAN, Stuart (Jan 2001) (Partner)
Burges Salmon LLP, Edinburgh . . . . (p.850)
   T: 0131 3142112
   E: stuart.mcmillan@burges-salmon.com

MCMILLAN, Stuart (Nov 2000) (Employee)
Procurator Fiscal Service, Glasgow . . . . (p.1241)
   T: 0300 0203000
   E: stuart.mcmillan@copfs.gov.uk

MCMILLAN, Victoria (Sept 2014) (Employee)
Procurator Fiscal Service,
   Kilmarnock . . . . (p.1249)
   T: 01563 536211
   E: vicky.mcmillan@copfs.gov.uk

MCMONAGLE, Jane Claire (Apr 2004) (Partner)
Brodies LLP, Glasgow . . . . (p.948)
   T: 0141 2484672
   E: jane.mcmonagle@brodies.com

MCMONAGLE, Liam James (Nov 2000)
(Partner)
Thorntons Law LLP, Dundee . . . . (p.819)
   T: 01382 229 111
   E: lmcmonagle@thorntons-law.co.uk

MCMONAGLE, Manus Joseph (Nov 1965)
(Consultant)
Blackadder & McMonagle, Falkirk . . . . . (p.921)
   T: 01324 612999
   E: tracey@blackandmac.com

MCMORLAND, Laura-May (Sept 2007)
(Employee)
Fairhome Group, Manchester . . . . (p.1270)
   E: laura.mcmorland@fairhomegroup.co.uk

MCMORRAN, Lynsey (Jan 2000) (Employee)
Procurator Fiscal Service, Paisley . . . . . . (p.1252)
   T: 03000 200813
   E: lynsey.mcmorran@copfs.gov.uk

MCMORROW, James Scott William
(Apr 2003) (Partner)
Harper Macleod LLP, Glasgow . . . . (p.983)
   T: 0141 2218888
   E: james.mcmorrow@harpermacleod.co.uk

MCMULDROCH, John James (May 1996)
(Consultant)
Gunnercooke SCO LLP, Edinburgh . . . . . (p.876)
   E: john.mcmuldroch@gunnercooke.com

MCMULLAN, Gary James (Oct 2015)
(Employee)
West Lothian Council, Livingston . . . . . (p.1250)
   T: 01506 280000
   E: gary.mcmullan@westlothian.gov.uk

MCMULLEN, Anji Frances (May 2010)
(Director)
McMullen Law Limited, Hamilton . . . . . (p.1067)
   T: 01698 686110
   E: am@mcmullenlaw.co.uk

MCMURCHIE, Lynn Lillian (Oct 2010) (Partner)
Pollock & McLean, Dumfries . . . . (p.802)
   T: 01387 255414
   E: lynnmcmurchie@pollockmclean.co.uk

MCMURRAY, Hannah Alison (Aug 2021)
(Employee)
Brodies LLP, Glasgow . . . . (p.948)
   T: 0141 2484672
   E: hannah.mcmurray@brodies.com

MCMURRAY, Mark (Mar 2011) (Partner)
CMS Cameron McKenna Nabarro Olswang LLP,
   Edinburgh . . . . (p.856)
   T: 0131 2288000
   E: Mark.McMurray@cms-cmno.com

MCMURRAY, Robert Dow (Aug 2005)
(Employee)
Red Rock Power Limited,
   Edinburgh . . . . (p.1230)
   T: 0131 5577101
   E: robert.mcmurray@redrockpower.co.uk

MCMURRAY, Victoria Christina (Feb 2013)
(Associate)
MacRoberts LLP, Glasgow . . . .(p.1015)
T: 0141 3031100
E: victoria.mcmurray@macroberts.com

MCMURTRIE, Thomas Stewart (Sept 2020)
(Employee)
PBW Law Solicitors, Glasgow . . . .(p.1030)
T: 0141 439 1990
E: thomas.mcmurtrie@pbwlaw.co.uk

MCNAB, Alison Elizabeth (Jun 2015)
(Employee)
Law Society of Scotland,
Edinburgh . . . .(p.1224)
T: 0131 2267411
E: alisonmcnab@lawscot.org.uk

MCNAB, Gordon Goldie (Nov 1981) (Director)
Curach Limited, Oban . . . .(p.1134)
T: 01631 562317
E: gordon@stevensonkennedy.co.uk

MCNAB, Katherine Louise (Oct 2016)
(Employee)
Shepherd and Wedderburn LLP,
Edinburgh . . . .(p.900)
T: 0131 2289900
E: Katie.McNab@shepwedd.com

MCNAB, Robert Duncan (Apr 2014) (Employee)
Burness Paull LLP, Edinburgh . . . .(p.850)
T: 0131 4736000
E: rob.mcnab@burnesspaull.com

MCNAB, Tonicha Louise (Jul 2021) (Employee)
Scottish Social Services Council,
Dundee . . . .(p.1218)
T: 0345 6030 891
E: tonicha.mcnab@sssc.uk.com

MCNAIR, James McLaughlin (Jul 2002)
(Partner)
James McNair Solicitors, Glasgow . . . . .(p.1014)
T: 07847 466951
E: jmcnairsol@gmail.com

MCNAIR, Katie Thomas (Oct 2004) (Employee)
Scottish Government, Edinburgh . . . . .(p.1231)
T: 0131 244 0815
E: katie.mcnair@gov.scot

MACNAIR, Terence Crawford (Nov 1967)
(Consultant)
MacArthur Legal, Oban . . . .(p.1134)
T: 01631 562215
E: yvonne@macarthurlegal.co.uk

MCNAMARA, Peter David (Sept 2004)
(Director)
Frazer Coogans Ltd, Ayr . . . .(p.763)
T: 01292 280499
E: peter.mcnamara@frazercoogans.co.uk

MCNAMEE, Anthony Thomas (Apr 2012)
(Employee)
Farrer & Co LLP, London WC2 . . . .(p.1264)
E: Anthony.McNamee@farrer.co.uk

MCNAUGHT, Cameron John (May 1991)
(Partner)
Plexus Law LLP, Edinburgh . . . .(p.897)
T: 0131 322 9250
E: cameron.mcnaught@plexuslaw.co.uk

MCNAUGHT, Claire Frances (Feb 2010)
(Employee)
Fulton's, Glasgow . . . .(p.1010)
T: 0141 6211816
E: cmcnaught@fultonslaw.co.uk

MCNAUGHT, Colin Henry (Dec 1981)
(Director)
Wright & Crawford (1906) Limited,
Paisley . . . .(p.1142)
T: 0141 8876211
E: C.McNaught@wright-crawford.co.uk

MCNAUGHT, Gillian (Jan 2010) (Employee)
Glasgow City Council, Glasgow . . . . . .(p.1239)
T: 0141 2874546
E: gillian.mcnaught@glasgow.gov.uk

MCNAUGHT, Ruth Mary (Sept 2009)
(Employee)
Burness Paull LLP, Glasgow . . . .(p.954)
T: 0141 2484933
E: Ruth.Mcnaught@burnesspaull.com

MCNAUGHTON, Alastair Daniel (Apr 2018)
(Associate)
CMS Cameron McKenna Nabarro Olswang LLP,
Glasgow . . . .(p.962)
T: 0141 2222200
E: alastair.mcnaughton@cms-cmno.com

MACNAUGHTON, Alexandra (Nov 2018)
(Employee)
Baillie Gifford & Co, Edinburgh . . . . . .(p.1220)
T: 0131 2752000
E: Alex.Macnaughton@bailliegifford.com

MCNAUGHTON, Fiona Barbara (Jan 1998)
(Employee)
McCash & Hunter LLP, Perth . . . .(p.1149)
T: 01738 620451
E: fionamcnaughton@mccash.co.uk

MCNAUGHTON, Ross Iain (Dec 2015)
(Employee)
Anderson Beaton Lamond, Perth . . . . .(p.1146)
T: 01738 639999
E: rmcnaughton@abl-law.co.uk

MCNAY, Emma Margaret (Aug 2014)
(Employee)
Ledingham Chalmers LLP,
Aberdeen . . . .(p.734)
T: 01224 408408
E: emma.mcnay@ledinghamchalmers.com

MACNEIL, Alexander Ian (Feb 2021)
(Employee)
Criminal Injuries Compensation Authority,
Glasgow....................(p.1239)
T: 0141 2281419
E: alexander.macneil@cica.gov.uk

MCNEIL, Alexander Ross (Sept 1986)
(Employee)
Scottish Government, Glasgow......(p.1243)
T: 0141 2727226
E: Sandy.McNeil@gov.scot

MCNEIL, Alison (Oct 1992) (Solicitor)
NO FIRM

MCNEIL, Caren (Sept 2007) (Partner)
Peterkins, Aberdeen...............(p.739)
T: 01224 428000
E: CM@peterkins.com

MACNEIL, Gordon David (Aug 1979) (Partner)
Gordon MacNeil, Cowdenbeath.......(p.788)
T: 01383 515717
E: gordon@gmacneil.co.uk

MACNEIL, Kimberley Jane (Aug 2018)
(Employee)
Anderson Strathern LLP, Glasgow......(p.940)
T: 0141 2426060
E: kimberley.macneil@andersonstrathern.co.uk

MACNEIL, Louise Anne (Aug 2014) (Employee)
Procurator Fiscal Service, Aberdeen...(p.1213)
T: 0300 0202336
E: Louise.MacNeil@copfs.gov.uk

MACNEIL, Mairi Claire (Jul 2009) (Employee)
Scottish Hospital Inquiry, Glasgow....(p.1244)
E: mairi.macneil@hospitalsinquiry.scot

MCNEIL, Maria Bridget (Nov 2005) (Employee)
Scottish Water, Dunfermline........(p.1219)
T: 07875 879175
E: maria.mcneil@scottishwater.co.uk

MACNEIL, Robyn Sarah (Oct 2020) (Employee)
Lawson Coull & Duncan, Dundee.....(p.813)
T: 01382 227555
E: rmacneil@lawsoncoull.co.uk

MCNEIL, Sarah Margaret (Feb 1987)
(Associate)
Pinsent Masons LLP, Glasgow.......(p.1031)
T: 0141 567 8400
E: margaret.mcneil@pinsentmasons.com

MCNEILL, Alexandria Emily (Aug 2019)
(Employee)
Lindsays LLP, Edinburgh............(p.882)
T: 0131 2291212
E: alexmcneill@lindsays.co.uk

MACNEILL, Colin James (Nov 1993) (Partner)
Dickson Minto, Edinburgh..........(p.861)
T: 0131 2254455
E: colin.macneill@dmws.com

MCNEILL, Ian Kerr (Feb 1988) (Employee)
Lealt Energy Limited, London W6.....(p.1266)
T: 020 8563 8080
E: ianmcneill@lealtenergy.com

MACNEILL, Lindsay MacLeod (Jun 2012)
(Employee)
BTO Solicitors LLP, Glasgow.........(p.952)
T: 0141 2218012
E: lmn@bto.co.uk

MCNEILL, Lisa Jan (Oct 2014) (Employee)
Addleshaw Goddard LLP,
Edinburgh...................(p.835)
T: 0131 2282400
E: Lisa.McNeill@addleshawgoddard.com

MCNEILL, Michelle Bruce Vater (Sept 2010)
(Employee)
Aegon UK, Edinburgh.............(p.1220)
T: 1315493986
E: michelle.mcneill@aegon.co.uk

MCNEILL, Rachel Jane (Jun 2010) (Employee)
Dentons UK and Middle East LLP,
Glasgow....................(p.968)
T: 0330 2220050
E: Rachel.McNeill@dentons.com

MCNEILL, Shirley Corrinne (Nov 2006)
(Partner)
Galloway & Ayrshire Partnership LLP,
Girvan.....................(p.935)
T: 01465 712345
E: sm@smithvalentine.co.uk

MCNEISH, Caitlin Ann (Aug 2009) (Employee)
Whyte & Mackay Ltd, Glasgow......(p.1246)
E: caitlin.mcneish@whyteandmackay.com

MCNEISH, David Ewan (Oct 1997) (Employee)
DWF LLP, Edinburgh..............(p.865)
T: 0131 2265541
E: david.mcneish@dwf.law

MCNELIS, Amy (Nov 2021) (Employee)
Patten & Prentice LLP, Greenock.....(p.1062)
T: 01475 720306
E: amym@patten.co.uk

MCNICHOL, Jennifer Margaret (Jul 2019)
(Employee)
MBM Commercial LLP, Edinburgh.....(p.889)
T: 0131 2268200
E: jennifer.mcnichol@mbmcommercial.co.uk

MACNICOL, Calum Alexander Ruaridh
(Oct 2014) (Employee)
Tesco Personal Finance Plc,
Edinburgh...................(p.1234)
T: (0131) 274 3426

MCNICOL, Jane Elizabeth (Oct 2002)
(Associate)
Macnabs LLP, Perth..............(p.1150)
T: 01738 623432
E: janemcnicol@macnabs-law.co.uk

MCNICOL, Sarah Blythe (Apr 2019) (Employee)
Jackson Boyd LLP, Glasgow . . . .(p.991)
T: 0141 2214325
E: smcnicol@jacksonboyd.co.uk

MCNICOLL, Gordon Leonard (Nov 1984)
(Employee)
Edinburgh Tram Inquiry,
Edinburgh . . . .(p.1222)
T: 0131 523 0080
E: gordon.mcnicoll@edinburghtraminquiry.org

MCNIFF, Sian Phillipa (Nov 2014) (Associate)
Pinsent Masons LLP, Glasgow . . . .(p.1031)
T: 0141 567 8400
E: Sian.Mcniff@pinsentmasons.com

MCNISH, Jamie Fraser (Aug 2019) (Employee)
Turcan Connell, Edinburgh . . . .(p.908)
T: 0131 2288111
E: jamie.mcnish@turcanconnell.com

MACNIVEN, Angela Jane (Jul 2000) (Employee)
CNR International (U.K.) Limited,
Aberdeen . . . .(p.1212)
T: (01224) 303653
E: angela.macniven@cnrl.com

MCNIVEN, Caitlin (Jun 2018) (Employee)
DAC Beachcroft Scotland LLP,
Glasgow . . . .(p.964)
T: 0141 2486688
E: cmcniven@dacbeachcroft.com

MCNIVEN, Calum Ross (Oct 2012) (Employee)
Aberdeen Corporate Services Limited,
Edinburgh . . . .(p.1220)
T: 0131 245 6092
E: calum.mcniven@abrdn.com

MACNIVEN, Ruaraidh Graeme Brander
(Oct 1997) (Employee)
Scottish Government, Edinburgh . . . . .(p.1231)
T: 0131 244 0815
E: ruaraidh.macniven@gov.scot

MCNULTY, Emma (Oct 2021) (Employee)
Reid Cooper, Glasgow . . . .(p.1034)
T: 0141 4294656
E: em@reidcooper.co.uk

MACNULTY, Gillian Margaret (Nov 1990)
(Associate)
Stevenson & Marshall LLP,
Dunfermline . . . .(p.825)
T: 01383 721141
E: gMacNulty@stevenson-marshall.co.uk

MCNULTY, Kathleen (Sept 1997) (Director)
Hilland McNulty Limited, Lanark . . . . .(p.1107)
T: 01555 663020
E: kathleen@hilland-mcnulty.co.uk

MCNULTY, Margaret Mary (Jun 2015)
(Employee)
Hilland McNulty Limited, Lanark . . . . .(p.1107)
T: 01555 663020
E: margaret@hilland-mcnulty.co.uk

MCPARLAND, James (Aug 1985) (Partner)
James McParland, Glasgow . . . .(p.1014)
T: 07811 633581
E: mcparland1710@aol.com

MCPARLAND, William Donald (Oct 2015)
(Employee)
Thompsons, Glasgow . . . .(p.1046)
T: 0141 2218840
E:
william.mcparland@thompsons-scotland.co.uk

MCPARTLIN, Donald Andrew (Jan 2008)
(Employee)
Glasgow City Council, Glasgow . . . . . .(p.1239)
T: 0141 287 3895
E: donald.mcpartlin@ced.glasgow.gov.uk

MCPARTLIN, John Patrick (Oct 1989) (Partner)
Mathie-Morton, Ayr . . . .(p.764)
T: 01292 263549
E: JMcPartlin@mathie-morton.co.uk

MCPARTLIN, Julia Lucy (Jul 2007) (Employee)
Hughes Walker, Edinburgh . . . .(p.878)
T: 0131 6038676
E: julia.mcpartlin@hugheswalkerlaw.com

MCPARTLIN, Lorraine (Aug 1991) (Employee)
South Ayrshire Council, Ayr . . . .(p.1215)
T: 01292 616664
E: Lorraine.McPartlin@south-ayrshire.gov.uk

MACPHAIL, Catriona Mhairi Robertson
(Aug 2008) (Partner)
Morton Fraser LLP, Edinburgh . . . .(p.891)
T: 0131 2471000
E: catriona.macphail@morton-fraser.com

MACPHAIL, Duncan Iain Thomas (Dec 1998)
(Partner)
Pinsent Masons LLP, Edinburgh . . . .(p.895)
T: 0131 7777000
E: iain.macphail@pinsentmasons.com

MCPHAIL, Fiona Marie (Sept 2010) (Partner)
Fiona McPhail Solicitors, Edinburgh . . . .(p.886)
T: 0344 5152410
E: fiona_mcphail@shelter.org.uk

MCPHAIL, Gregor Alexander (Jul 2014)
(Employee)
Medical Protection Society, Leeds . . . . .(p.1260)
E: Gregor.McPhail@medicalprotection.org

MCPHAIL, Iain Arnott (Aug 1984) (Partner)
Iain A. McPhail, Glasgow . . . .(p.1014)
T: 0141 331 2166
E: iain.mcphail@btinternet.com

MCPHAIL, Ian Greig (Jan 1980) (Partner)
Macfarlane & Co., Glasgow . . . .(p.1009)
  T: 0141 2483307
  E: igm@macfarlane-law.co.uk

MCPHAIL, John David (Dec 2018) (Employee)
Scottish Hospital Inquiry, Glasgow . . . .(p.1244)
  E: John.Mcphail@hospitalsinquiry.scot

MACPHAIL, Julie Grace (Nov 1988) (Employee)
Anderson Strathern LLP, Glasgow . . . . . .(p.940)
  T: 0141 2426060
  E: julie.macphail@andersonstrathern.co.uk

MACPHAIL, Madeleine Clare (Mar 2019)
(Employee)
MBM Commercial LLP, Edinburgh . . . . .(p.889)
  T: 0131 2268200
  E: madeleine.macphail@mbmcommercial.co.uk

MACPHAIL, Sophie Rose (Feb 2014) (Employee)
Law at Work Ltd, Glasgow . . . .(p.1240)
  T: 0141 2715555
  E: sophie.macphail@lawatwork.co.uk

MCPHATE, Russel (Nov 1988) (Partner)
Morgans, Dunfermline . . . .(p.824)
  T: 01383 620222
  E: russelmcphate@morganlaw.co.uk

MACPHEE, Alison Crane (Mar 2007) (Partner)
Caesar & Howie, Boness . . . .(p.777)
  T: 01506 826166
  E: acb@caesar-howie.co.uk

MACPHEE, Craig David (Jun 2002) (Associate)
Pinsent Masons LLP, Glasgow . . . .(p.1031)
  T: 0141 567 8400
  E: craig.macphee@pinsentmasons.com

MCPHEE, Shaun Lee (Jun 2021) (Employee)
Brown & Co Legal LLP, Glasgow . . . . . .(p.950)
  T: 0141 3533354
  E: shaunmcphee@lsa.org.uk

MCPHERSON, Amy (Sept 2019) (Employee)
Burges Salmon LLP, Edinburgh . . . .(p.850)
  T: 0131 314 2145
  E: Amy.McPherson@burges-salmon.com

MCPHERSON, Callum Euan (Mar 2005)
(Associate)
Ashurst LLP, London E1 . . . .(p.1261)
  T: 0207 859 3982
  E: callum.mcpherson@ashurst.com

MACPHERSON, Calum Michael (Jul 2015)
(Employee)
Brodies LLP, Glasgow . . . .(p.948)
  T: 0141 2484672
  E: calum.macpherson@brodies.com

MACPHERSON, Catherine Mary (Oct 2015)
(Associate)
Morton Fraser LLP, Edinburgh . . . .(p.891)
  T: 0131 2471000
  E: catherine.macpherson@morton-fraser.com

MACPHERSON, Claire Eileen (Nov 2003)
(Partner)
Burness Paull LLP, Glasgow . . . .(p.954)
  T: 0141 2484933
  E: claire.e.macpherson@burnesspaull.com

MACPHERSON, Claire Elizabeth (Jun 2017)
(Employee)
Hogan Lovells International LLP, London
  EC1 . . . .(p.1265)
  T: 020 7296 2000
  E: claire.macpherson@hoganlovells.com

MACPHERSON, Clare Susan (Nov 1994)
(Partner)
Thorntons Law LLP, Edinburgh . . . .(p.906)
  T: 0131 225 8705
  E: cmacpherson@thorntons-law.co.uk

MACPHERSON, Dawn Crystal (Jul 2015)
(Associate)
MacRoberts LLP, Edinburgh . . . .(p.887)
  T: 0131 2295046
  E: dawn.macpherson@macroberts.com

MACPHERSON, Henrietta Edith Matheson
(Jan 2012) (Employee)
Cockburns, Elgin . . . .(p.915)
  T: 01343 542684
  E:
  henrietta.macpherson@cockburns-solicitors.
  com

MACPHERSON, Ishbel Anne (Nov 1998)
(Solicitor)
NO FIRM

MACPHERSON, Jack McCrae (Aug 2020)
(Employee)
Rollos Law LLP, Cupar . . . .(p.792)
  T: 01334 654081
  E: jackmacpherson@rollos.co.uk

MCPHERSON, James Scott (Feb 1990)
(Employee)
Scottish Courts and Tribunals Service,
  Aberdeen . . . .(p.1214)
  T: 01224 657248
  E: jmcpherson@scotcourts.gov.uk

MACPHERSON, Jazmin Hazel (Oct 2018)
(Employee)
Warners Solicitors LLP, Edinburgh . . . . . .(p.911)
  T: 0131 6624747
  E: jmacpherson@warnersllp.com

MACPHERSON, Joanna (Sept 2017) (Employee)
J K Cameron, Glasgow . . . .(p.955)
  T: 0141 2214787
  E: joanna@jkcameron.co.uk

MACPHERSON, Joseph Oliver Champion
(Dec 2002) (Partner)
Champion MacPherson Solicitors,
  Dumfries . . . .(p.800)
  T: 07775 072 765
  E: joseph@scottishdrivinglaw.co.uk

MACPHERSON, Kathryn Lisma Violet
(Sept 1993) (Employee)
The Moray Council, Elgin . . . . (p.1236)
T: 01343 543451
E: kathryn.macpherson@moray.gov.uk

MCPHERSON, Katie Adam (Sept 2014)
(Employee)
Vistra Fund Services (Guernsey) Limited, St Peter
Port . . . . (p.1273)

MACPHERSON, Kirsty Louise (Nov 2000)
(Partner)
Brodies LLP, Edinburgh . . . . (p.845)
T: 0131 2283777
E: kirsty.macpherson@brodies.com

MCPHERSON, Lianne (Nov 2007) (Employee)
Dentons UK and Middle East LLP,
Glasgow . . . . (p.968)
T: 0330 2220050
E: lianne.mcpherson@dentons.com

MCPHERSON, Malcolm Henry, WS
(Nov 1977) (Consultant)
Addleshaw Goddard LLP,
Edinburgh . . . . (p.835)
T: 0131 2282400
E:
Malcolm.McPherson@addleshawgoddard.com

MCPHERSON, Neil Forsythe (Sept 1995)
(Partner)
Neil F. McPherson, Kilmarnock . . . . . . (p.1096)
T: 01563 535363
E: neil@neilmcphersonsolicitors.co.uk

MACPHERSON, Robin Ian (Jul 1983) (Solicitor)
NO FIRM

MCPHERSON, Sarah (Nov 2015) (Associate)
Murray Ormiston LLP, Aberdeen . . . . . . (p.738)
T: 01224 478822
E: sarah@murrayormiston.com

MACPHILLIMY, Ewan Spence (Mar 2016)
(Employee)
Cochran Dickie, Paisley . . . . (p.1137)
T: 0141 8892245
E: em@cochrandickie.co.uk

MCPHILLIMY, Louise Catherine (May 2014)
(Employee)
Cochran Dickie, Paisley . . . . (p.1137)
T: 0141 8892245
E: lm@cochrandickie.co.uk

MCQUADE, Andrea Margaret (Nov 1993)
(Employee)
J. W. Morrison Haulage Contractor,
Strathaven . . . . (p.1255)
T: 01357 300414
E: andrea@morrisonhaulage.co.uk

MCQUADE, Linzi (Aug 2018) (Employee)
Maguire Solicitors, Glasgow . . . . (p.1017)
T: 0141 3312885

MCQUADE, Michael Andrew (May 2016)
(Associate)
Brodies LLP, Glasgow . . . . (p.948)
T: 0141 2484672
E: michael.mcquade@brodies.com

MCQUADE, Tamara Elizabeth Mae
(Aug 1999) (Employee)
East Ayrshire Council, Kilmarnock . . . . . (p.1249)
T: 01563 576161
E: tamara.mcquade@east-ayrshire.gov.uk

MCQUAID, Ruth Elizabeth (Dec 1991)
(Employee)
Procurator Fiscal Service, Hamilton . . . . (p.1247)
T: 0844 5613245
E: ruth.mcquaid@copfs.gov.uk

MACQUARRIE, Eilidh (Nov 2019) (Employee)
East Dunbartonshire Council,
Kirkintilloch . . . . (p.1249)
T: 0141 5788000
E: Eilidh.MacQuarrie@eastdunbarton.gov.uk

MCQUARRIE, Elliot Kinnear (Nov 1986)
(Director)
J.D. Clark & Allan Limited, Duns . . . . . . (p.829)
T: 01361 882501
E: elliot.mcquarrie@jdca.co.uk

MCQUEEN, Alanna Davidson (Feb 2021)
(Employee)
Clyde & Co (Scotland) LLP,
Glasgow . . . . (p.961)
T: 0141 2482666
E: alanna.mcqueen@clydeco.com

MACQUEEN, Bernadette Ann (Oct 2013)
(Employee)
Walker Laird, Renfrew . . . . (p.1159)
T: 0141 886 5678
E: bernadette.macqueen@walkerlaird.co.uk

MCQUEEN, Emily Jane (Aug 2016) (Employee)
Immediate Media Company London Limited,
London W6 . . . . (p.1265)
E: emily.mcqueen@immediate.co.uk

MCQUEEN, Gavin (Oct 2019) (Employee)
Burness Paull LLP, Glasgow . . . . (p.954)
T: 0141 2484933
E: gavin.mcqueen@burnesspaull.com

MACQUEEN, Jamie (Dec 2013) (Employee)
Scottish Government, Edinburgh . . . . . (p.1231)
T: 0131 244 0815
E: Jamie.Macqueen@gov.scot

MCQUEEN, Kerrie Allison (Nov 2015)
(Employee)
Wood Group UK Limited,
Aberdeen . . . . (p.1214)
T: 01224 851000
E: kerrie.mcqueen@woodplc.com

MCQUEEN, Martin Ross (Sept 1999)
(Employee)
Harrison Clark Rickerbys Limited,
Birmingham . . . .(p.1258)
T: 0121 3124783
E: mmcqueen@hcrlaw.com

MCQUEEN, Mary Robinson (Oct 1977)
(Partner)
Allan McDougall McQueen LLP,
Edinburgh . . . .(p.837)
T: 0131 2281926
E: MaryMcQueen@mcdougallmcqueen.co.uk

MACQUEEN, Rosemary Jane Sakeena
(Aug 2014) (Employee)
Scottish Government, Edinburgh . . . . .(p.1231)
T: 0131 244 0256
E: Rosie.MacQueen@gov.scot

MCQUEEN, Stuart Alan (May 2008) (Employee)
Perth & Kinross Council, Perth . . . .(p.1253)
T: 01738 475000
E: SAMcQueen@pkc.gov.uk

MCQUILKEN, Nicole (Jul 2016) (Employee)
DWF LLP, Glasgow . . . .(p.973)
T: 0141 228 8000
E: nicole.mcquilken@dwf.law

MCQUILLAN, John Olav (Oct 1990) (Partner)
MacRoberts LLP, Glasgow . . . .(p.1015)
T: 0141 3031100
E: john.mcquillan@macroberts.com

MCQUILLAN, Stephen Gerard (Mar 1996)
(Partner)
McQuillan Glasser & Waughman,
Hamilton . . . .(p.1068)
T: 01698 200006
E: office_mcquillan@yahoo.co.uk

MCQUIRE, John Scott (Jan 1991) (Partner)
Jim Friel Solicitors, Glasgow . . . .(p.978)
T: 0141 4201234
E: scottm@jimfriel.co.uk

MCQUISTON, Courtney Elizabeth
(Jul 2017) (Employee)
Thompsons, Glasgow . . . .(p.1046)
T: 0141 2218840
E:
courtney.mcquiston@thompsons-scotland.co.
uk

MCQUISTON, Thiona Anne (Aug 2001)
(Partner)
The McKinstry Company LLP, Ayr . . . . .(p.765)
T: 01292 281711
E: thiona@mckinstry.co.uk

MACRAE, Catherine Aileen (Sept 2017)
(Employee)
Shepherd and Wedderburn LLP,
Edinburgh . . . .(p.900)
T: 0131 2289900
E: catherine.macrae@shepwedd.com

MACRAE, Christopher James (Nov 1994)
(Director)
Gordon MacRae & Co Ltd,
Edinburgh . . . .(p.887)
T: 0131 6296355
E: chris.macrae@gordonmacraeip.com

MCRAE, David Malcolm (Jan 2004) (Employee)
Just Employment Law Ltd,
Glasgow . . . .(p.1240)
T: 0141 3315150
E: davidmcrae@justemploymentlaw.co.uk

MCRAE, Harriet Ann (Sept 2016) (Employee)
Shepherd and Wedderburn LLP,
Edinburgh . . . .(p.900)
T: 0131 2289900
E: Harriet.McRae@shepwedd.com

MACRAE, Iain Michael (Aug 1992) (Partner)
GFM Law, Dundee . . . .(p.811)
T: 01382 223505
E: iain@gfmlaw.co.uk

MCRAE, Jacqueline (Nov 2007) (Employee)
The Scottish Parliament, Edinburgh . . .(p.1235)
T: (0131) 3486653
E: jackie.mcrae@parliament.scot

MACRAE, Keith Gordon (Dec 1982)
(Consultant)
Mackinnons Solicitors LLP,
Aberdeen . . . .(p.736)
T: 01224 632464
E: keith@mackinnons.com

MACRAE, Kenneth Brown (Oct 1985)
(Consultant)
Ferguson Whyte, Glasgow . . . .(p.975)
T: 0141 3398432
E: km@fergusonwhyte.co.uk

MACRAE, Kenneth Douglas (Oct 1986)
(Partner)
Macintosh Humble, Dumbarton . . . .(p.799)
T: 01389 763491
E: kennymacrae@macintosh-humble.co.uk

MACRAE, Kirsten Lindsay (Sept 2008)
(Employee)
Brodies LLP, Aberdeen . . . .(p.723)
T: 01224 392242
E: kirsten.macrae@brodies.com

MACRAE, Kirstine Rose (Oct 1993) (Partner)
BTO Raeburn Hope, Helensburgh . . . . .(p.1072)
T: 01436 671221
E: krm@bto.co.uk

MACRAE, Lisa (Jan 2012) (Employee)
Neos Networks Limited, Perth . . . .(p.1253)
E: Lisa.MacRae@neosnetworks.com

MACRAE, Murray Ross (Sept 2015) (Associate)
Gillespie Macandrew LLP,
Edinburgh . . . . (p.872)
T: 0131 2251677
E: Ross.MacRae@gillespiemacandrew.co.uk

MACRAE, Rachel Ann (Nov 2019) (Employee)
CMS Cameron McKenna Nabarro Olswang LLP,
Aberdeen . . . . (p.727)
T: 01224 622002
E: rachel.macrae@cms-cmno.com

MACRAE, William James (Nov 1992) (Partner)
Liddle & Anderson LLP, Boness . . . . (p.777)
T: 01506 822727
E: wjm@liddleandanderson.co.uk

MACREADY, Ryan James (Nov 2018)
(Employee)
Macdonald Henderson Limited,
Glasgow. . . . . (p.1008)
T: 0141 2484957
E: ryan@macdonaldhenderson.co.uk

MACREATH, Emily Gail Couperthwaite
(Jul 2008) (Employee)
Procurator Fiscal Service, Glasgow . . . . (p.1243)
T: (0300) 020 2944
E: Emily.Macreath@copfs.gov.uk

MACREATH, William Couperthwaite
(Oct 1976) (Consultant)
Levy & McRae Solicitors LLP,
Glasgow. . . . . (p.1000)
T: 0141 3072311
E: billmacreath@lemac.co.uk

MACRITCHIE, Catriona Ann (Sept 1991)
(Employee)
William Grant & Sons Ltd., Bellshill . . . (p.1215)
T: 01698 843843
E: Catriona.Macritchie@wgrant.com

MACRITCHIE, Ruth (Sept 2010) (Employee)
PricewaterhouseCoopers LLP, New
York . . . . (p.1279)
E: ruth.m.macritchie@pwc.com

MCROBB, Elizabeth Margaret Miller
(Aug 1991) (Partner)
Shepherd and Wedderburn LLP,
Glasgow. . . . . (p.1039)
T: 0141 5669900
E: liz.mcrobb@shepwedd.com

MCROBBIE, Stuart William (Feb 2018)
(Employee)
Carey Olsen, St Helier . . . . (p.1274)
T: 01534 888900
E: stuart.mcrobbie@careyolsen.com

MCROBERT, Lauren (Aug 2010) (Employee)
Procurator Fiscal Service, Glasgow . . . . (p.1241)
T: 0300 0203000
E: lauren.mcrobert@copfs.gov.uk

MCROBERT, Neil Ross (Sept 2000) (Partner)
George Mathers & Co, Aberdeen . . . . . . (p.737)
T: 01224 588599
E: n.mcrobert@georgemathers.co.uk

MCROBERTS, James (Jul 1995) (Employee)
Scottish Enterprise, Glasgow . . . . (p.1243)
T: 0141 4685579
E: jim.mcroberts@scotent.co.uk

MCRORIE, James Alexander (Dec 2005)
(Employee)
Ofgem, Glasgow . . . . (p.1241)
T: (0141) 354 5425
E: Jamie.McRorie@ofgem.gov.uk

MACROSSON, Bruce Crighton (Dec 2000)
(Employee)
Procurator Fiscal Service,
Edinburgh . . . . (p.1229)
T: 03000 203596
E: Bruce.Macrosson@copfs.gov.uk

MACRURY, Sarah Marion (Feb 1991)
(Employee)
Wood Group UK Limited,
Aberdeen . . . . (p.1214)
T: 01224 851000
E: sarah.macrury@woodgroup.com

MCSHANE, ine Louise (Aug 2017) (Employee)
Drummond Miller LLP, Edinburgh . . . . . (p.864)
T: 0131 2265151
E: amcshane@drummondmiller.co.uk

MCSHANE, Neal (Nov 1998) (Partner)
KM Law, Glasgow. . . . . (p.997)
T: 07702 735440
E: nealmcshane@yahoo.com

MCSHERRY, Anne Margaret (Nov 2006)
(Employee)
Capricorn Energy Ltd, Edinburgh . . . . . (p.1221)
T: 0131 4753000
E: anne.mcsherry@cairnenergy.com

MCSHERRY, Euan Ross Cunningham
(Oct 2005) (Partner)
Aberdein Considine and Company,
Aberdeen . . . . (p.718)
T: 01224 589 700
E: emcsherry@acandco.com

MCSPORRAN, Calum John (Jul 2017)
(Employee)
CMS Cameron McKenna Nabarro Olswang LLP,
Glasgow. . . . . (p.962)
T: 0141 2222200
E: calum.mcsporran@cms-cmno.com

MCSPORRAN, Iain, QC (Jan 1989) (Partner)
Iain McSporran QC, Solicitor Advocate,
Edinburgh . . . . (p.888)
T: 07891 529849
E: iainmcsporran@btinternet.com

MACSPORRAN, Laura Jeffrey (May 2016)
(Employee)
Miller Samuel Hill Brown LLP,
Glasgow . . . .(p.1020)
T: 0141 2211919
E: lms@mshblegal.com

MACSPORRAN, Stephen (Jul 2015) (Partner)
C. & D. Mactaggart,
Campbeltown . . . .(p.782)
T: 01586 552317
E: stephen@cdm-law.co.uk

MACSWAN, Isabel Marie Momoko
(Sept 2019) (Employee)
Morton Fraser LLP, Edinburgh . . . .(p.891)
T: 0131 2471000
E: isabel.macswan@morton-fraser.com

MACTAGGART, Karen Margaret (Aug 1991)
(Solicitor)
NO FIRM

MACTAGGART, Robert Alasdair, SSC
(Feb 1959) (Consultant)
Mactaggart & Co Limited, Largs . . . . .(p.1110)
T: 01475 674646
E: caroll@mactaggarts.co.uk

MCTAGGART, Steven Neil (Mar 2019)
(Employee)
DAC Beachcroft Scotland LLP,
Glasgow . . . .(p.964)
T: 0141 2486688
E: smctaggart@dacbeachcroft.com

MCTAVISH, Charlotte Naomi (Dec 2019)
(Employee)
Slater and Gordon Scotland Limited,
Edinburgh . . . .(p.903)
T: 0131 7184150

MACTAVISH, Gordon Ross (Aug 2015)
(Employee)
Life Technologies Limited, Paisley . . . . .(p.1252)
T: 0141 8146100
E: gordon.mactavish@thermofisher.com

MCVEAN, Andrew George (Sept 1987)
(Partner)
D.W. Shaw, Mauchline . . . .(p.1122)
T: 01290 550249
E: amcvean@dwshaw.co.uk

MCVEAN, Laura Elizabeth (Apr 2006)
(Employee)
OVO (S) Electricity Ltd, Perth . . . .(p.1253)
E: laura.mcvean@sse.com

MCVEY, Amy Elizabeth (Mar 2009) (Associate)
Burges Salmon LLP, Edinburgh . . . .(p.850)
T: 0131 3142112
E: Amy.McVey@burges-salmon.com

MCVICAR, Alexis Boylan (Jul 2008) (Partner)
Caird & Vaughan, Dundee . . . .(p.807)
T: 01382 229399
E: alexismcvicar.cairdvaughan@btconnect.com

MCVICAR, Euan Forbes (Nov 1997)
(Consultant)
Pinsent Masons LLP, Edinburgh . . . .(p.895)
T: 0131 777 7000
E: Euan.McVicar@pinsentmasons.com

MACVICAR, Lynne (Aug 2011) (Employee)
Procurator Fiscal Service, Aberdeen . . .(p.1213)
T: 0300 0202336
E: Lynne.macvicar@copfs.gov.uk

MACVICAR, Robert Livingstone (Oct 2014)
(Employee)
Fried, Frank, Harris, Shriver & Jacobson (London)
LLP, London EC2 . . . .(p.1264)
T: 0207 9729600
E: Robert.MacVicar@friedfrank.com

MACVICAR, Shonagh Katherine (Oct 2000)
(Employee)
Dubai Multi Commodities Centre,
Dubai . . . .(p.1278)
T: +971 4368 0741
E: Shonagh.MacVicar@dmcc.ae

MCWATT, Gemma Daniella (Oct 2017)
(Employee)
STV Television Limited, Glasgow . . . . . .(p.1245)
T: 0141 3003000
E: Gemma.McWatt@stv.tv

MCWHIRTER, Ellen Frances (Oct 2017)
(Employee)
Warners Solicitors LLP, Edinburgh . . . . . .(p.911)
T: 0131 6624747
E: emcwhirter@warnersllp.com

MCWHIRTER, Emma Morrison (Sept 2018)
(Employee)
Turcan Connell, Edinburgh . . . .(p.908)
T: 0131 2288111
E: emma.mcwhirter@turcanconnell.com

MCWHIRTER, Jennifer (Oct 2011) (Employee)
Scottish Environment Protection Agency,
Stirling . . . .(p.1255)
T: 01786 457700
E: jennifer.mcwhirter@sepa.org.uk

MCWHIRTER, Sarah Ann (May 2014)
(Associate)
Slater and Gordon Scotland Limited,
Edinburgh . . . .(p.903)
T: 0131 7184172
E: sarah.mcwhirter@slatergordon.co.uk

MCWILLIAM, Faye Annette (Jul 2016)
(Employee)
Scottish Social Services Council,
Dundee . . . .(p.1218)
T: 0345 6030 891
E: faye.mcwilliam@sssc.uk.com

MCWILLIAM, Neil Alistair (May 2016)
(Employee)
Thorntons Law LLP, Dundee . . . . (p.819)
T: 01382 229 111
E: nmcwilliam@thorntons-law.co.uk

MCWILLIAMS, Gerald Thomas (Oct 1990)
(Partner)
Cowan & Co., Glasgow . . . . (p.964)
T: 0141 2211803
E: gmcw@cowanandco.co.uk

MCWILLIAMS, Helen Marie (Dec 1992)
(Partner)
Cowan & Co., Glasgow . . . . (p.964)
T: 0141 2211803
E: hmcw@cowanandco.co.uk

MCWILLIAMS, Lorna Forbes (Oct 2008)
(Employee)
TLT LLP, Glasgow . . . . (p.1048)
T: 0333 006 0400
E: Lorna.McWilliams@TLTsolicitors.com

MCWILLIAMS, Philip Martin (May 2000)
(Partner)
Finnieston Franchi & McWilliams,
   Glasgow. . . . . (p.976)
T: 0141 2263000
E: philip@ffmcw.co.uk

MCWILLIAMS, Stuart Alistair (Oct 2008)
(Partner)
Morton Fraser LLP, Glasgow . . . . (p.1022)
T: 0141 2741100
E: Stuart.McWilliams@morton-fraser.com

MCWILLIAMS, Theresa Mary (Oct 1981)
(Director)
Trainor Alston Limited, Coatbridge . . . . . (p.787)
T: 01236 600600
E: megan@trainoralston.co.uk

MADDEN, Alasdair William (Sept 2021)
(Employee)
Brodies LLP, Edinburgh . . . . (p.845)
T: 0131 2283777
E: alasdair.madden@brodies.com

MADDEN, Lindsay Jean Catherine G
(Oct 2011) (Employee)
Procurator Fiscal Service, Glasgow . . . . (p.1241)
T: 0300 020 0733
E: Lindsay.madden@copfs.gov.uk

MADDEN, Lois Coulter (Jul 2016) (Employee)
Carey Olsen, St Peter Port . . . . (p.1273)
T: +44 1481 741505
E: lois.madden@careyolsen.com

MAGEE, Carys Elin (Jul 2020) (Employee)
Your Conveyancer Limited,
   Dunfermline . . . . (p.827)
T: 01383 667550
E: carys.magee@yourconveyancer.co.uk

MAGEE, David James Moy (May 2011)
(Employee)
DAC Beachcroft Scotland LLP,
   Glasgow. . . . . (p.964)
T: 0141 223 8592
E: dmagee@dacbeachcroft.com

MAGEE, Fiona Christine (Jan 2012) (Employee)
Mourant Ozannes, St Helier . . . . (p.1274)
T: 01534 676 000
E: Fiona.Magee@mourantozannes.com

MAGILL, Jennifer Carolyn (Oct 2003)
(Employee)
Scottish Government, Edinburgh . . . . . (p.1231)
T: 0131 244 0815
E: carolyn.magill@gov.scot

MAGLARA, Amalia (May 2008) (Solicitor)
NO FIRM

MAGOWAN, Caroline (Oct 2000) (Employee)
East Dunbartonshire Council,
   Kirkintilloch . . . . (p.1249)
T: 0141 5788000
E: caroline.magowan@eastdunbarton.gov.uk

MAGRO, Lynsay Mary (Oct 2013) (Employee)
Procurator Fiscal Service,
   Edinburgh . . . . (p.1227)
T: 0300 0203168
E: lynsay.magro@copfs.gov.uk

MAGSON, Tina (Oct 2005) (Employee)
MacHardy, Alexander & Whyte, WS,
   Forfar. . . . . (p.927)
T: 01307 463593
E: tmagson@machardy.co.uk

MAGUIRE, Claire Marion (Oct 1997)
(Consultant)
Flexlaw Ltd, Edinburgh . . . . (p.871)
T: 0131 2026363
E: claire.maguire@flexlaw.co.uk

MAGUIRE, Desmond James (Nov 1999)
(Director)
Allcourt Solicitors Limited,
   Livingston . . . . (p.1117)
T: 01506 443999
E: des.maguire@allcourtsolicitors.co.uk

MAGUIRE, James Patrick (Nov 1977)
(Consultant)
Jardine Phillips LLP, Edinburgh . . . . (p.879)
T: 0131 4466850
E: jim.maguire@jardinephillips.com

MAGUIRE, Julia Mary (May 1999) (Partner)
Pinsent Masons LLP, Edinburgh . . . . (p.895)
T: 0131 225 0004
E: julia.maguire@pinsentmasons.com

MAGUIRE, Lisa (Sept 2012) (Partner)
MacRoberts LLP, Edinburgh . . . . (p.887)
T: 0131 2295046
E: Lisa.Maguire@macroberts.com

MAGUIRE, Mhairi Frances (Aug 2009)
(Employee)
Enable Group, Holytown . . . .(p.1248)
T: 01698 737027
E: mhairi.maguire@enablegroup.org.uk

MAGUIRE, Michael James (Sept 2010)
(Employee)
Procurator Fiscal Service, Falkirk . . . . . .(p.1236)
T: 0300 020 3000
E: Michael.Maguire@copfs.gov.uk

MAGUIRE, Peter Andrew (Sept 2007) (Director)
Andrews Immigration Solicitors Limited,
   Glasgow. . . . .(p.941)
T: 0141 3535026
E: enquiries@andrewsimmigrationlaw.co.uk

MAGUIRE, Stephen Christopher (Sept 1995)
(Employee)
Cairns Brown, Alexandria . . . .(p.751)
T: 01389 756979
E: S.Maguire@cairnsbrown.co.uk

MAHER, Caroline (Jun 2009) (Employee)
Morton Fraser LLP, Edinburgh . . . .(p.891)
T: 0131 2471000
E: caroline.maher@morton-fraser.com

MAHER, Sean Daniel (Aug 2017) (Employee)
Procurator Fiscal Service, Falkirk . . . . . .(p.1236)
T: 0300 020 3000
E: Sean.Maher@copfs.gov.uk

MAHMOOD, Amina Arshad (Sept 2017)
(Employee)
CMS Cameron McKenna Nabarro Olswang LLP,
   Edinburgh . . . .(p.856)
T: 0131 2007432
E: amina.mahmood@cms-cmno.com

MAHMOOD, Farrah (Dec 2017) (Employee)
Scullion Law Limited, Hamilton . . . . . .(p.1069)
T: 01698 283265
E: farrah@scullionlaw.com

MAHMOOD, Irzum (Nov 2016) (Employee)
Scottish Children's Reporter Administration,
   Hamilton . . . .(p.1247)
T: 0131 244 8701
E: irzum.mahmood@scra.gov.uk

MAHON, Gerard James (Sept 1994) (Employee)
East Renfrewshire Council, Giffnock . . .(p.1237)
T: 0141 5773000
E: gerry.mahon@eastrenfrewshire.gov.uk

MAHON, Louise Antonia (Nov 2003) (Partner)
MacRoberts LLP, Glasgow . . . .(p.1015)
T: 0141 3031100
E: louise.mahon@macroberts.com

MAHON, Owen Anthony (Nov 1974) (Director)
Anthony Mahon Limited, Glasgow . . . .(p.1018)
T: 0141 3321587
E: tonymahon@btinternet.com

MAHONY, Katrina Emily (Oct 2015) (Employee)
Morton Fraser LLP, Edinburgh . . . .(p.891)
T: 0131 2471000
E: Katie.Mahony@morton-fraser.com

MAILER, Peter McIntyre Perry (Oct 2007)
(Employee)
Allen & Overy LLP, London E1 . . . .(p.1261)
T: 020 3088 0000
E: Peter.Mailer@AllenOvery.com

MAILLIE, John Parker (Oct 1987) (Partner)
DAC Beachcroft Scotland LLP,
   Glasgow. . . . .(p.964)
T: 0141 2486688
E: jmaillie@dacbeachcroft.com

MAIN, Colin Alexander (Apr 2003) (Solicitor)
NO FIRM

MAIN, Geoffrey (Dec 1997) (Employee)
Procurator Fiscal Service, Inverness . . . .(p.1248)
T: 0844 561 4426
E: Geoffrey.Main@copfs.gov.uk

MAIN, Margaret (Nov 1997) (Employee)
Scottish Government, Edinburgh . . . . .(p.1231)
T: 0131 244 0815
E: margaret.main@gov.scot

MAIN, Rachel (Aug 2012) (Employee)
National Westminster Bank PLC,
   Edinburgh . . . .(p.1226)
T: 0131 6263501
E: Rachel.Main@rbs.co.uk

MAIN, Thomas Iain (Jul 2017) (Employee)
Aberdein Considine and Company,
   Aberdeen . . . .(p.718)
T: 01224 589700
E: tmain@acandco.com

MAINLAND, Anne Elizabeth (Sept 1995)
(Employee)
Scottish Courts and Tribunals Service,
   Edinburgh . . . .(p.1230)
T: 0131 2252525
E: amainland@scotcourts.gov.uk

MAINS, Lindsay Jillian (Aug 1999) (Employee)
Procurator Fiscal Service, Airdrie . . . . . .(p.1214)
T: 01236 747027
E: lindsay.mains@copfs.gov.uk

MAIR, David John (Jul 1987) (Employee)
Glasgow City Council, Glasgow . . . . . .(p.1239)
T: 0141 2877881
E: david.mair@ced.glasgow.gov.uk

MAIR, Gillian Anne (Sept 2007) (Employee)
Brodies LLP, Glasgow . . . .(p.948)
T: 0141 2456250
E: gillian.mair@brodies.com

MAIR, Gregor Kerr Robertson, WS
(Jan 1982) (Employee)
Gibson Kerr (incorporating Marwicks and
Grange), Edinburgh . . . .(p.871)
T: 0131 2257558

MAIR, Jennifer (Feb 1999) (Partner)
Stewart Watt & Co., Edinburgh . . . .(p.912)
T: 0131 3379692
E: jennifer@stewartwatt.co.uk

MAIR, Mhairi (Aug 2012) (Employee)
Procurator Fiscal Service,
Kilmarnock . . . .(p.1249)
T: 01563 536211
E: mhairi.mair@copfs.gov.uk

MAIR, Patrick Guermont (May 1994)
(Employee)
Perth & Kinross Council, Perth . . . .(p.1253)
T: 01738 475000
E: Pmair@pkc.gov.uk

MAIR, Sally Hilary Jane (May 2019) (Employee)
Civil Legal Assistance Office,
Aberdeen . . . .(p.1212)
T: 01224 402330

MAIR, Susan Catherine (Jul 1987) (Employee)
Argyll & Bute Council,
Lochgilphead . . . .(p.1251)
T: 01546 602127
E: susan.mair@argyll-bute.gov.uk

MAIR, Zara (Aug 2008) (Partner)
Stewart Watt & Co., Edinburgh . . . .(p.912)
T: 0131 3379692
E: zara@stewartwatt.co.uk

MAITLAND, Ava Margaret Macgregor
(Feb 2016) (Employee)
Adaptavist, London SW1 . . . .(p.1261)

MAITLAND, Christopher (Jul 2006) (Partner)
George Mathers & Co, Aberdeen . . . . . .(p.737)
T: 01224 588599
E: c.maitland@georgemathers.co.uk

MAITLAND, Donna (Dec 2008) (Partner)
Maitland & Co, Glasgow . . . .(p.1018)
T: 07714 615845
E: donnamaitland@hotmail.co.uk

MAITLAND, Leanne (Aug 2016) (Employee)
Harper Macleod LLP, Inverness . . . .(p.1077)
T: 01463 798777
E: leanne.maitland@harpermacleod.co.uk

MAITLES, Anna Claire (Dec 2013) (Employee)
Morton Fraser LLP, Glasgow . . . .(p.1022)
T: 0141 2741100

MAJEED, Zaema (Mar 2021) (Employee)
Addleshaw Goddard LLP,
Edinburgh . . . .(p.835)
T: 0131 2282400
E: zaema.majeed@addleshawgoddard.com

MAJID, Aafia Suman (Sept 2018) (Employee)
Procurator Fiscal Service,
Edinburgh . . . .(p.1227)
T: 0300 0203168
E: aafia.majid@copfs.gov.uk

MAJID, Thara (Jul 2021) (Solicitor)
NO FIRM

MALCOLM, Fiona Janine (Jul 1998) (Employee)
Highland Council, Inverness . . . .(p.1248)
T: 01463 702000
E: fiona.malcolm@highland.gov.uk

MALCOLM, Irene Margaret Lynn (Nov 1980)
(Partner)
Malcolm & Hutchison, Airdrie . . . .(p.750)
T: 01236 755050
E: irene@malcolmandhutchison.co.uk

MALCOLM, Jennifer Carole (Dec 1999)
(Solicitor)
NO FIRM

MALCOLM, Jennifer Helen (Oct 2005)
(Employee)
BayWa R.e. UK Limited, Edinburgh . . . .(p.1221)
T: (0131) 4663689
E: jennifer.malcolm@baywa-re.co.uk

MALCOLM, Stuart Richard Fraser (Nov 1998)
(Employee)
M-Squared Lasers Limited
T: 0141 9450500
E: stuart.malcolm@m2lasers.com

MALCOLM, William (Sept 1999) (Employee)
Google UK Limited, London SW1 . . . . .(p.1264)
T: 020 7346 2927
E: williammalcolm@google.com

MALCOLMSON, Eileen June (Aug 1999)
(Solicitor)
NO FIRM

MALEQUE, Mohamed Tanjeel (Jun 2010)
(Employee)
Procurator Fiscal Service,
Edinburgh . . . .(p.1227)
T: 0300 0203168
E: Tanjeel.Maleque@copfs.gov.uk

MALEY, Peter Charles (Mar 1987) (Director)
Carr & Co (Solicitors) Limited,
Glasgow . . . .(p.957)
T: 0141 7732145
E: pm@theglasgowlawpractice.co.uk

MALIK, Alisha (Oct 2016) (Employee)
Allan McDougall McQueen LLP,
Gorebridge . . . .(p.1058)
T: 01875 821960
E: alishamalik@allanmcdougall.co.uk

MALIK, Haroun Tunweer (Jan 2014) (Partner)
MCO Defence Solicitors, Glasgow . . . .(p.1014)
T: 07908 167227
E: mail@mcosolicitors.co.uk

MALIK, Soraya Anne (Jul 2005) (Employee)
Procurator Fiscal Service, Glasgow . . . .(p.1241)
　　T: 0300 0203000
　　E: soraya.malik@copfs.gov.uk

MALIN, Susan Janet Clementine (Nov 1986)
(Employee)
Boyd Legal Limited, Edinburgh . . . .(p.845)
　　T: 0131 2267464

MALLON, Agnes (Apr 1999) (Partner)
Gillespie Macandrew LLP,
　　Edinburgh . . . .(p.872)
　　T: 0131 2251677
　　E: Agnes.Mallon@gillespiemacandrew.co.uk

MALLOY, Aislinn (Jul 2019) (Solicitor)
NO FIRM

MALLOY, Ann Jane Reid Watt (Jul 2008)
(Employee)
Lanarkshire Community Law Centre Ltd,
　　Airdrie . . . .(p.749)
　　T: 01236 757 337

MALOCO, Michael Joseph (Nov 1986)
(Director)
Maloco + Associates Limited,
　　Dunfermline . . . .(p.824)
　　T: 01383 629720
　　E: michael@maloco.co.uk

MALONE, Andrew James (Sept 1985) (Partner)
Hewats, Castle Douglas . . . .(p.784)
　　T: 01556 502391
　　E: ajmalone@hewats.co.uk

MALONE, Brandon James (Aug 1993) (Director)
Brandon Malone & Company Limited,
　　Edinburgh . . . .(p.888)
　　T: 0131 357 8549
　　E: brandon@brandonmalone.com

MALONE, Gina Mugnaioni (Oct 2016)
(Employee)
Shearman & Sterling (London) LLP, London
　　EC2 . . . .(p.1268)
　　E: gina.malone@shearman.com

MALONE, Hilary Jane (Aug 2016) (Employee)
Macdonald Henderson Limited,
　　Glasgow . . . .(p.1008)
　　T: 0141 2484957
　　E: hilary@macdonaldhenderson.co.uk

MALONE, Julie (Aug 2015) (Employee)
RSB Lindsays, Dundee . . . .(p.818)
　　T: 01382 224112
　　E: juliemalone@lindsays.co.uk

MALONE, Louise (Nov 2020) (Employee)
Austin Lafferty Limited, Glasgow . . . . . .(p.943)
　　T: 0141 6212212
　　E: lmalone@laffertylaw.com

MALONE, Peter Thomas (Nov 2008)
(Consultant)
Bridge Legal Limited, Glasgow . . . .(p.948)
　　T: 0141 4293100
　　E: pmalone@bridgelegalglasgow.co.uk

MALTMAN, Iain Ross (Aug 2009) (Partner)
Allan, Black & McCaskie, Elgin . . . .(p.915)
　　T: 01343 543355
　　E: im@abmsols.co.uk

MANCHESTER, Gail Louise (Nov 2009)
(Employee)
Royal London, Edinburgh . . . .(p.1230)
　　T: 0131 672 6151
　　E: gail.manchester@royallondon.com

MANDERSON, Andrew George (Sept 1985)
(Partner)
Andrew G. Manderson & Co.,
　　Dundee . . . .(p.816)
　　T: 01382 200840
　　E: andrewgmanderson@btconnect.com

MANGAN, Daryl Thomas (Nov 2008)
(Employee)
National Westminster Bank PLC,
　　Edinburgh . . . .(p.1227)
　　T: 0131 5235185
　　E: daryl.mangan@natwest.com

MANIATI, Konstantina (Oct 2019) (Employee)
BlackRock, Edinburgh . . . .(p.1221)
　　T: 306 978 749 900

MANINI, Roberto (Aug 1993) (Director)
Manini Belardo Limited,
　　Coatbridge . . . .(p.787)
　　T: 01236 426070
　　E: maninibelardo@btconnect.com

MANN, Graham Andrew (Aug 1993) (Director)
Blackwater Law Limited, Glasgow . . . . . .(p.947)
　　T: 0141 404 7778
　　E: graham.mann@blackwaterlawlimited.co.uk

MANN, Stephanie (Aug 2015) (Partner)
Laurie & Co Solicitors LLP,
　　Aberdeen . . . .(p.733)
　　T: 01224 645 085
　　E: Stephanie@laurieandco.co.uk

MANNIFIELD, Stephen Royston (Feb 2006)
(Partner)
Mannifield Templeton Defence,
　　Edinburgh . . . .(p.888)
　　T: 0131 3228777
　　E: smannifield@mtdefence.com

MANNING, Karen Margaret (Aug 2010)
(Employee)
Burness Paull LLP, Glasgow . . . .(p.954)
　　T: 0141 248 4933
　　E: Karen.manning@burnesspaull.com

MANNION, Eleanor Margaret (Jul 2011)
(Associate)
MacRoberts LLP, Glasgow . . . . (p.1015)
T: 0141 3031100
E: Eleanor.Mannion@macroberts.com

MANNION, Gary Ian (Aug 2007) (Partner)
Thorntons Law LLP, Dundee . . . . (p.819)
T: 01382 229 111
E: GMannion@thorntons-law.co.uk

MANNION, Lisa Ann (Jul 2015) (Solicitor)
Thorntons Law LLP, Dundee . . . . (p.819)
T: 01382 229 111

MANNION, Lynne Theresa (Aug 2001)
(Employee)
Procurator Fiscal Service, Dundee . . . . . (p.1218)
T: 01382 342559
E: lynne.mannion@copfs.gov.uk

MANOLACHE, Paul-Silviu (Oct 2017)
(Employee)
Harper Macleod LLP, Edinburgh . . . . (p.877)
T: 0131 2472500
E: paul.manolache@harpermacleod.co.uk

MANSLEY, Jennifer Elizabeth (May 1982)
(Partner)
Macintosh Humble, Dumbarton . . . . (p.799)
T: 01389 763491
E: jem@macintosh-humble.co.uk

MANSON, Alan Andrew (Nov 1994) (Partner)
DM MacKinnon, Oban . . . . (p.1134)
T: 01631 563014
E: aam@dmmk.co.uk

MANSON, Alexander James (Sept 2019)
(Employee)
Kirkland & Ellis International LLP, London
EC3 . . . . (p.1265)
T: 0207 4692000

MANSON, Andrew John (Aug 2021)
(Employee)
Dickson Minto, London EC2 . . . . (p.1263)
T: 020 76284455
E: andrew.manson@dmws.com

MANSON, Inez Helen (Jun 2008) (Employee)
Scottish Government, Edinburgh . . . . . (p.1231)
T: 0131 244 0815
E: inez.manson@gov.scot

MANSON, Karina (Nov 2003) (Partner)
BTO Solicitors LLP, Glasgow . . . . (p.952)
T: 0141 2218012
E: kms@bto.co.uk

MANSON, Natalie Durie (Oct 2009) (Associate)
Pinsent Masons LLP, Edinburgh . . . . . . (p.895)
T: 0131 7777000
E: Natalie.Manson@pinsentmasons.com

MAPP, Fern (Sept 2011) (Employee)
Digby Brown LLP, Edinburgh . . . . (p.862)
T: 0333 200 5925
E: fern.mapp@digbybrown.co.uk

MAPPLEBECK, Ailsa Mary Robertson
(Mar 1996) (Employee)
Irish Distillers Limted, Dublin . . . . (p.1274)
E: Ailsa.Mapplebeck@pernod-ricard.com

MARCANTONIO, Laura Francesca
(Dec 1991) (Employee)
National Health Service Scotland,
Edinburgh . . . . (p.1225)
T: 0131 2757800
E: laura.marcantonio@nhs.scot

MARCHESI-DENHAM, Clare Th r se
(Nov 2016) (Employee)
The Competition & Markets Authority,
Edinburgh . . . . (p.1234)
E: Clare.Marchesi-Denham@cma.gov.uk

MARCHINI, Mirella (Nov 2006) (Employee)
Hendrie Legal Limited, Edinburgh . . . . . (p.878)
T: 0131 370 0470
E: mirella.marchini@ralphhendrie.legal

MARINI, Giulio (Dec 2011) (Solicitor)
NO FIRM

MARKOWSKI, Nicholas (Sept 1991) (Partner)
T. Duncan & Co., Montrose . . . . (p.1125)
T: 01674 672533
E: nick@tduncan.com

MARKS, Alison Goodwin (Aug 2005)
(Employee)
Thorntons Law LLP, Dundee . . . . (p.819)
T: 01382 229 111
E: amarks@thorntons-law.co.uk

MARNOCH, Brian (Sept 1980) (Consultant)
Jameson + Mackay LLP, Perth . . . . (p.1148)
T: 01738 631666
E: brian.marnoch@jamesonmackay.co.uk

MARNOCH, Eilidh (Aug 2017) (Employee)
Dickson Minto, Edinburgh . . . . (p.861)
T: 0131 2254455
E: eilidh.marnoch@dmws.com

MARR, Alison Clare (May 2001) (Employee)
Fife Council, Glenrothes . . . . (p.1246)
T: 03451 550000
E: alison.marr@fife.gov.uk

MARR, Fiona Isabel (Aug 2005) (Associate)
Clarion Solicitors Limited, Leeds . . . . . . (p.1260)
T: 0113 2460622
E: fiona.marr@clarionsolicitors.com

MARR, Lynne Anne (Feb 2000) (Partner)
Brodies LLP, Edinburgh . . . . (p.845)
T: 0131 2283777
E: lynne.marr@brodies.com

MARR, Rae-Anne Megan (Jun 2018) (Employee)
Brodies LLP, Aberdeen . . . .(p.723)
　T: 01224 392242
　E: raeanne.marr@brodies.com

MARR, Victoria Elizabeth (Oct 2011)
(Employee)
National Westminster Bank PLC,
　Edinburgh . . . .(p.1226)
　T: 0131 626 3908
　E: victoria.marr@rbs.co.uk

MARRINER, Annie Rose (Sept 2016) (Employee)
Ashurst LLP, London E1 . . . .(p.1261)
　T: (020) 7859 2145
　E: annie.marriner@ashurst.com

MARRIOTT, Helen Joanne (Feb 2014)
(Associate)
Eversheds Sutherland (International) LLP,
　Cardiff . . . .(p.1279)
　T: 0845 4987356
　E: helenmarriott@eversheds-Sutherland.com

MARRIOTT, Kara Marie (Feb 2018) (Employee)
Neilsons, Edinburgh . . . .(p.894)
　T: 0131 5565522

MARSH, Kenneth David (Sept 1983)
(Employee)
Virgil M. Crawford, Stirling . . . .(p.1164)
　T: 01786 464055
　E: kdm@virgil-crawford.com

MARSHALL, Alastair Hannah (Nov 1997)
(Employee)
Murray Beith Murray, Edinburgh . . . . . .(p.893)
　T: 0131 2251200
　E: alastair.marshall@murraybeith.co.uk

MARSHALL, Alexander MacIntyre
(Feb 1992) (Employee)
Generation Investment Management LLP,
　London W1 . . . .(p.1264)
　E: alexander.marshall@generationim.com

MARSHALL, Alison (Jun 2007) (Partner)
Wright, Johnston & Mackenzie LLP,
　Dunfermline . . . .(p.826)
　T: 01383 626666
　E: am@wjm.co.uk

MARSHALL, Alistair William (Nov 1981)
(Partner)
Mackie & Dewar, Aberdeen . . . .(p.736)
　T: 01224 596341
　E: awm@mackieanddewar.co.uk

MARSHALL, Caroline Eve (Sept 2018)
(Employee)
Schillings, London EC4 . . . .(p.1268)
　E: Carolineevemarshall@gmail.com

MARSHALL, Catriona Elizabeth Ferguson
(Oct 2000) (Employee)
Lord President's Private Office,
　Edinburgh . . . .(p.1225)
　T: 0131 240 6849
　E: cmarshall@scotcourts.gov.uk

MARSHALL, Catriona Sarah (Jan 2018)
(Employee)
Gibson Kerr Limited, Edinburgh . . . .(p.872)
　T: 0131 2257558
　E: katie.marshall@gibsonkerr.co.uk

MARSHALL, Craig Alexander (Oct 1990)
(Partner)
Irwin Mitchell Scotland LLP,
　Glasgow . . . .(p.991)
　T: 0141 3004300
　E: craig.marshall@irwinmitchell.com

MARSHALL, David John Douglas (Jul 1993)
(Partner)
Neilsons, Edinburgh . . . .(p.894)
　T: 0131 3164444
　E: davemarshall@neilsons.co.uk

MARSHALL, David Keith (Feb 2006) (Partner)
Stronachs LLP, Aberdeen . . . .(p.744)
　T: 01224 845845
　E: David.Marshall@Stronachs.com

MARSHALL, Elaine (Jan 2007) (Associate)
Lyons Davidson Scotland LLP,
　Edinburgh . . . .(p.883)
　T: 0344 251 0070
　E: enmarshall@lyonsdavidson.co.uk

MARSHALL, Gavin (Feb 2020) (Employee)
Procurator Fiscal Service,
　Edinburgh . . . .(p.1227)
　T: 0300 0203168
　E: gavin.marshall@copfs.gov.uk

MARSHALL, Hannah Felicity Kate (Sept 2021)
(Employee)
Morton Fraser LLP, Edinburgh . . . .(p.891)
　T: 0131 2471000
　E: Hannah.Marshall@morton-fraser.com

MARSHALL, James Thomas (Apr 2012)
(Employee)
CMS Cameron McKenna Nabarro Olswang LLP,
　Edinburgh . . . .(p.856)
　T: 0131 2288000
　E: James.Marshall@cms-cmno.com

MARSHALL, Jennifer Anne (Oct 2008)
(Employee)
Highlands and Islands Airports Limited,
　Inverness . . . .(p.1248)
　T: 07967 468025
　E: jmarshall@hial.co.uk

MARSHALL, John Paul (Dec 2002) (Partner)
Brodies LLP, Edinburgh . . . .(p.845)
　T: 0131 656 0062
　E: paul.marshall@brodies.com

MARSHALL, Joyce Amanda (Dec 1986)
(Consultant)
Dallas McMillan, Glasgow . . . .(p.966)
T: 0141 3336750
E: jm@dallasmcmillan.co.uk

MARSHALL, Judith Shaw (Aug 2014)
(Employee)
MooreMarshall Limited, Falkirk. . . . .(p.923)
T: 01324 614020
E: judith.marshall@mooremarshall.co.uk

MARSHALL, Katherine Morag (Nov 1988)
(Employee)
Scottish Government, Edinburgh . . . . .(p.1231)
T: 0131 244 0815
E: Katherine.Marshall@gov.scot

MARSHALL, Keir William (Sept 2005)
(Employee)
Highlands & Islands Enterprise,
Inverness . . . .(p.1248)
T: 03000 134 833
E: keir.marshall@hient.co.uk

MARSHALL, Kenneth Archibald (Feb 1990)
(Employee)
Scottish Social Services Council,
Dundee . . . .(p.1218)
T: 0345 6030 891
E: kenneth.marshall@sssc.uk.com

MARSHALL, Kenneth Robert James
(Aug 1986) (Director)
MooreMarshall Limited, Falkirk. . . . .(p.923)
T: 01324 614020
E: Kenny.Marshall@MooreMarshall.co.uk

MARSHALL, Keri Maureen (Oct 2005)
(Employee)
Procurator Fiscal Service,
Edinburgh . . . .(p.1227)
T: 0300 0203168
E: keri.marshall@copfs.gov.uk

MARSHALL, Lisa Jayne (Nov 2003) (Employee)
Procurator Fiscal Service, Perth. . . . . . .(p.1253)
T: 0844 561 3000
E: Lisa.Marshall@copfs.gov.uk

MARSHALL, Mark Kevin (Sept 2006) (Partner)
JHS Law, Dumfries . . . .(p.801)
T: 01387 739000
E: mark.marshall@jhslaw.co.uk

MARSHALL, Nicholas Jonathan (Oct 2009)
(Partner)
Brodies LLP, Aberdeen. . . . .(p.723)
T: 01224 392242
E: nick.marshall@brodies.com

MARSHALL, Rebeca Claire (Oct 2011)
(Employee)
Clancys Solicitors and Estate Agents Limited,
Edinburgh . . . .(p.854)
T: 0131 337 7771
E: Rebeca@clancys-solicitors.co.uk

MARSHALL, Robert McAlpine (Nov 1991)
(Employee)
Scottish Government, Edinburgh . . . . .(p.1232)
T: 0131 244 3775
E: robert.marshall@gov.scot

MARSHALL, Tracy Elizabeth (Sept 2007)
(Solicitor)
Aegon UK, Edinburgh . . . .(p.1220)
T: 1315493986
E: tracy.marshall@aegon.co.uk

MARSHALL-KILCOYNE, Lisa (Aug 2011)
(Associate)
John Kilcoyne & Co. Solicitors,
Glasgow. . . . .(p.997)
T: 0141 4231400
E: lm@johnkilcoynesolicitors.co.uk

MARTEN, Genevieve Denise (Oct 2009)
(Employee)
Travers Smith LLP, London EC1 . . . . . .(p.1269)
T: 0207 2953387
E: genevieve.marten@traverssmith.com

MARTIN, Alison Kelly (Nov 2008) (Employee)
Scottish Government, Glasgow . . . . . .(p.1243)
T: 0141 2727493
E: alison.martin@gov.scot

MARTIN, Alison Margaret (Nov 1990)
(Director)
Macleod & MacCallum Limited,
Inverness . . . .(p.1080)
T: 01463 239393
E: alison.martin@macandmac.co.uk

MARTIN, Andrew John (Mar 2006) (Employee)
Burness Paull LLP, Glasgow . . . .(p.954)
T: 0141 2484933
E: Andrew.Martin@burnesspaull.com

MARTIN, Angela Helen (Sept 1994) (Employee)
SSE Plc, Perth . . . .(p.1253)
T: 01738 456 000
E: Helen.Martin@sse.com

MARTIN, Anna Grace (Jan 2015) (Associate)
Brodies LLP, Edinburgh . . . .(p.845)
T: 0131 2283777
E: Anna.bell@brodies.com

MARTIN, Ashley (May 2015) (Employee)
Civil Legal Assistance Office,
Inverness . . . .(p.1248)
T: 01463 641770
E: martinas@clao.org.uk

MARTIN, Chelsea Catherine (Jun 2018)
(Employee)
Procurator Fiscal Service,
Edinburgh . . . .(p.1229)
T: 0300 0203000
E: chelsea.martin@copfs.gov.uk

MARTIN, Christopher (May 2006) (Employee)
EDF Energy Renewables,
  Edinburgh . . . .(p.1222)
  T: (0131) 460 3654
  E: Chris.Martin@edf-re.uk

MARTIN, Christopher Derek (Jun 2001)
  (Partner)
Pinsent Masons LLP, Edinburgh . . . .(p.895)
  T: 0131 777 7000
  E: chris.martin@pinsentmasons.com

MARTIN, Claire (Oct 1997) (Employee)
National Galleries of Scotland,
  Edinburgh . . . .(p.1225)
  E: cmartin@nationalgalleries.org

MARTIN, Claire Louise Rintoul (Nov 2005)
  (Employee)
Procurator Fiscal Service, Paisley . . . . . .(p.1252)
  T: 0141 8875225
  E: claire.martin@copfs.gov.uk

MARTIN, Emma Margaret (Jun 2020)
  (Employee)
Thorley Stephenson Ltd,
  Edinburgh . . . .(p.906)
  T: 0131 5569599
  E: emm@thorleystephenson.com

MARTIN, Fiona Helen Elizabeth (Jul 2010)
  (Associate)
Pinsent Masons LLP, Aberdeen . . . .(p.739)
  T: 01224 377900
  E: Fiona.Martin@pinsentmasons.com

MARTIN, Gordon (Aug 1983) (Director)
Martin, Johnston & Socha Limited,
  Dunfermline . . . .(p.824)
  T: 01383 730466
  E:
gordon.martin@mjscriminaldefencelawyers.co.
uk

MARTIN, Harry John (Feb 2020) (Solicitor)
NO FIRM

MARTIN, Helen Marie (Sept 1988) (Employee)
Scottish Police Authority, Police Scotland,
  Glasgow . . . .(p.1244)
  T: 01786 895731
  E: helen.martin@scotland.pnn.police.uk

MARTIN, Iain David Norris (Feb 2010)
  (Employee)
Scottish Social Services Council,
  Dundee . . . .(p.1218)
  T: 0345 6030 891
  E: iain.martin@sssc.uk.com

MARTIN, Isobel (Jan 1991) (Employee)
Procurator Fiscal Service, Glasgow . . . .(p.1241)
  T: 0300 0203000
  E: isobel.martin@copfs.gov.uk

MARTIN, James Douglas (Apr 2019) (Employee)
Blackadders LLP, Dundee . . . .(p.805)
  T: 01382 229222
  E: James.Martin@blackadders.co.uk

MARTIN, Jennifer (Oct 1987) (Employee)
Scottish Police Authority, Police Scotland,
  Glasgow . . . .(p.1244)
  T: 01786 895727
  E: Jennifer.Martin2@scotland.pnn.police.uk

MARTIN, Kathleen Mary (Jul 2010) (Partner)
Harper Macleod LLP, Glasgow . . . .(p.983)
  T: 0141 2218888
  E: Kathleen.Martin@harpermacleod.co.uk

MARTIN, Kirsty Caitlin Macleod (Jan 2020)
  (Employee)
Lindsays LLP, Glasgow . . . .(p.1001)
  T: 0141 2216551
  E: kirstymartin@lindsays.co.uk

MARTIN, Leo (Jul 1985) (Consultant)
Levy & McRae Solicitors LLP,
  Glasgow . . . .(p.1000)
  T: 0141 3072311
  E: lmartin@lemac.co.uk

MARTIN, Lisa (Aug 2009) (Associate)
Gilson Gray LLP, Dundee . . . .(p.811)
  T: 01382 549321
  E: lmartin@gilsongray.co.uk

MARTIN, Lowri Clare (Mar 2016) (Employee)
Scottish Power Limited, Glasgow . . . . .(p.1244)
  T: 0141 6140000
  E: l.martin@scottishpower.com

MARTIN, Melanie Ann (Mar 2005) (Associate)
Dentons UK and Middle East LLP,
  Glasgow . . . .(p.968)
  T: 0330 2220050
  E: Melanie.Martin@dentons.com

MARTIN, Nadine (Jul 2006) (Associate)
Gibson Kerr Limited, Edinburgh . . . .(p.872)
  T: 0131 2257558
  E: nadine.martin@gibsonkerr.co.uk

MARTIN, Neil George David (Oct 2012)
  (Employee)
Nigel Beaumont & Co., Edinburgh . . . . .(p.842)
  T: 0131 5573565
  E: neil.martin@nigelbeaumont.co.uk

MARTIN, Nicola Jane (Feb 2016) (Partner)
Wright, Johnston & Mackenzie LLP,
  Edinburgh . . . .(p.913)
  T: 0131 5241500
  E: njm@wjm.co.uk

MARTIN, Norman Maclean (Feb 1988)
  (Partner)
MacRoberts LLP, Edinburgh . . . .(p.887)
  T: 0131 2295046
  E: norman.martin@macroberts.com

MARTIN, Robert Nigel (Oct 1979) (Partner)
Lockharts Law LLP, Ayr . . . .(p.764)
T: 01292 265045
E: nigelmartin@lockhartslaw.com

MARTIN, Scott (Aug 1999) (Employee)
Scottish National Party, Edinburgh . . . .(p.1233)
T: 0131 5258920
E: scott.martin@snp.org

MARTIN, Scott (Nov 2007) (Partner)
Jain, Neil & Ruddy, Glasgow . . . .(p.992)
T: 0141 2218778
E: scott@jnrsolicitors.com

MARTIN, Stacey (Jan 2019) (Employee)
Digby Brown LLP, Glasgow . . . .(p.970)
T: 0333 200 5925
E: stacey.martin@digbybrown.co.uk

MARTIN, Stacey Leith (Nov 2011) (Employee)
Watson Advisors Inc., Vancouver . . . . .(p.1257)
E: stacey@watsoninc.ca

MARTINEZ SILLARS, Jennifer (Oct 2018)
(Employee)
Procurator Fiscal Service, Glasgow . . . .(p.1241)
T: 0300 0203000
E: Jennifer.Sillars@copfs.gov.uk

MARTONE, Lucy Cathryn (Sept 2011)
(Employee)
Tesco Personal Finance Plc,
Edinburgh . . . .(p.1234)
T: 0131 479 1663
E: lucy.x.martone@tescobank.com

MARTONE, Paolo (Aug 2006) (Employee)
Scullion Law Limited, Hamilton . . . . . .(p.1069)
T: 01698 283265
E: paolo@scullionlaw.com

MARTYN, David Andrew (Jun 2011) (Partner)
Thompsons, Glasgow . . . .(p.1046)
T: 0141 2218840
E: David.Martyn@thompsons-scotland.co.uk

MARWICK, Isla Elaine (Oct 2008) (Employee)
Lloyds Banking Group Plc,
Edinburgh . . . .(p.1224)
T: (0131) 442 9579
E: isla.marwick@lloydsbanking.com

MARWICK, Jamie Graeme (Aug 2009)
(Associate)
Anderson Strathern LLP, Edinburgh . . . .(p.839)
T: 0131 2707700
E: Jamie.Marwick@andersonstrathern.co.uk

MASIA, Kal (Jul 2018) (Employee)
Burness Paull LLP, Aberdeen . . . .(p.724)
T: 01224 621621
E: kal.masia@burnesspaull.com

MASKREY, Jessica Amy (Dec 2019) (Employee)
Shepherd and Wedderburn LLP,
Edinburgh . . . .(p.900)
T: 0131 2289900
E: jessica.maskrey@shepwedd.com

MASON, Carly Nicola (Jan 2001) (Solicitor)
Brodies LLP, Glasgow . . . .(p.948)
T: 0141 2484672
E: carly.mason@brodies.com

MASON, Fenella Mary (Jul 1988) (Partner)
Burness Paull LLP, Edinburgh . . . .(p.850)
T: 0131 4736000
E: Fenella.Mason@burnesspaull.com

MASON, Fiona Robertson (May 1982)
(Associate)
Thomas H.G. Stewart, Edinburgh . . . . . .(p.904)
T: 0131 2294939
E: fiona@thomashgstewart.co.uk

MASON, Patrick Hugh (Nov 2003) (Employee)
Tesco Personal Finance Plc,
Edinburgh . . . .(p.1234)
T: (0131) 274 3426
E: patrick.mason@tescobank.com

MASON, Paul (Oct 2004) (Partner)
Womble Bond Dickinson (UK) LLP,
Edinburgh . . . .(p.913)
T: 0345 415 0000
E: paul.mason@wbd-uk.com

MASON, Peter Fraser (Feb 1995) (Director)
Macleod & MacCallum Limited,
Inverness . . . .(p.1080)
T: 01463 239393
E: peter.mason@macandmac.co.uk

MASON, Rognvald Inkster (Sept 1994)
(Director)
Waddell & Mackintosh Solicitors Ltd,
Troon. . . . .(p.1176)
T: 01292 312222
E: rm@wmtroon.co.uk

MASON, Sophie Jane (Oct 2021) (Employee)
Mitchells Roberton Ltd, Glasgow . . . . .(p.1020)
T: 0141 5523422
E: sophie@mitchells-roberton.co.uk

MASSEY, Jacob Samuel (Nov 2018) (Employee)
Rothchilds, London EC4 . . . .(p.1267)

MASSIE, Claire Catherine Lindsay
(Oct 1997) (Partner)
Pinsent Masons LLP, Glasgow . . . .(p.1031)
T: 0141 567 8400
E: claire.massie@pinsentmasons.com

MASSIE, Colin Craig (Nov 1994) (Solicitor)
NO FIRM

MASSIE, Paul Euan (Apr 2007) (Employee)
Enquest Britain Limited, Aberdeen . . . .(p.1212)
T: 01224 287842
E: paul.massie@enquest.com

MASSON, Amanda Elizabeth (Dec 2002)
(Partner)
Harper Macleod LLP, Glasgow . . . .(p.983)
T: 0141 2218888
E: Amanda.Masson@harpermacleod.co.uk

MASSON, Gareth Antony (Oct 1993) (Partner)
Blackadders LLP, Aberdeen . . . .(p.722)
T: 01224 588913
E: gareth.masson@blackadders.co.uk

MASTERS, Ellen Ruth (Oct 2018) (Employee)
Aberdein Considine and Company,
Glasgow. . . . .(p.937)
T: 0141 2278200
E: emasters@acandco.com

MASTERTON, Alan Ellis (Jan 2004) (Director)
Alan E. Masterton, Monifieth . . . .(p.1125)
T: 01382 539313
E: info@legaleagles.tv

MASTERTON, Colin George (Oct 2004)
(Employee)
Carey Olsen, London EC2 . . . .(p.1262)
T: 020 7614 5610
E: colin.masterton@careyolsen.com

MASTERTON, Susan Margaret, WS
(Aug 1986) (Partner)
Blair Cadell, Edinburgh . . . .(p.844)
T: 0131 555 5800
E: susan.masterton@blaircadell.com

MATH, Susheela (May 2005) (Employee)
Open Society Foundation London, London
EC1 . . . .(p.1267)
E: susheela.math@opensocietyfoundations.org

MATHERS, Frank George (Dec 1978) (Partner)
Taggart Meil Mathers, Aberdeen . . . . . .(p.745)
T: 01224 588020
E: frank@tmmsolicitors.co.uk

MATHERS, George Frank MacGregor
(Dec 1973) (Consultant)
George Mathers & Co, Aberdeen . . . . . .(p.737)
T: 01224 588599
E: g.mathers@georgemathers.co.uk

MATHERS, Lucy Jacqueline (Oct 2009)
(Associate)
Burness Paull LLP, Aberdeen . . . .(p.724)
T: 01224 621621
E: Lucy.Mathers@burnesspaull.com

MATHESON, Alisdair Stuart (Oct 1996)
(Partner)
Brodies LLP, Glasgow . . . .(p.948)
T: 0141 2484672
E: alisdair.matheson@brodies.com

MATHESON, Alistair Martin (Nov 2010)
(Employee)
Scottish Legal Aid Board,
Edinburgh . . . .(p.1233)
T: 0131 2267061
E: mathesonal@slab.org.uk

MATHESON, Andrew Ferrier Lister
(Oct 1972) (Director)
Mair Matheson Solicitors Ltd,
Newmilns. . . . .(p.1130)
T: 01560 321225
E: enquiries@mairmatheson.co.uk

MATHESON, David Malcolm (Feb 2013)
(Employee)
University of Edinburgh, Edinburgh . . .(p.1235)
T: (0131) 651 4330

MATHESON, Euphemia (Jul 2019) (Employee)
Bannatyne, Kirkwood, France & Co.,
Glasgow. . . . .(p.943)
T: 0141 2216020
E: euphemiamatheson@bkf.co.uk

MATHESON, Fraser Murdo (Apr 2015)
(Employee)
Procurator Fiscal Service,
Livingston . . . .(p.1250)
T: (0300) 020 3696
E: fraser.matheson@copfs.gov.uk

MATHESON, Julie Margaret (Nov 2003)
(Employee)
Kingsley Napley LLP, London EC2 . . . .(p.1265)
T: 020 73693844
E: jmatheson@kingsleynapley.co.uk

MATHESON, Maureen McKee (Jul 2010)
(Director)
McKee Campbell Morrison Limited,
Glasgow. . . . .(p.1013)
T: 0141 4883680
E: maureen@mcmsolicitors.co.uk

MATHESON, Neil Rennie (Jun 2016) (Employee)
TC Young LLP, Edinburgh . . . .(p.914)
T: 0131 2207660
E: nrm@tcyoung.co.uk

MATHESON, Scott Dean (Oct 2000) (Employee)
Scottish Government, Edinburgh . . . . .(p.1231)
T: 0131 244 0815
E: Scott.Matheson@gov.scot

MATHESON, Sylvia Joyce (Sept 2020)
(Employee)
Miller Samuel Hill Brown LLP,
Glasgow. . . . .(p.1020)
T: 0141 2211919
E: sma@mshblegal.com

MATHEWSON, Amy Mary Corcoran
(Sept 2021) (Employee)
CMS Cameron McKenna Nabarro Olswang LLP,
Edinburgh . . . .(p.856)
T: 0131 2288000
E: amy.mathewson@cms-cmno.com

MATHIE, Alexander Douglas (Nov 1995)
(Consultant)
CMS Cameron McKenna Nabarro Olswang LLP,
Glasgow . . . . (p.962)
T: 0141 2222200
E: Douglas.Mathie@cms-cmno.com

MATHIE, Anne Louise (Sept 2001) (Employee)
Scottish Government, Edinburgh . . . . . (p.1231)
T: 0131 244 0815
E: anne.mathie@gov.scot

MATHIESON, Agnieszka Anna (Sept 2017)
(Employee)
Procurator Fiscal Service,
Edinburgh . . . . (p.1227)
T: 0300 0203168
E: Agnieszka.Mathieson@copfs.gov.uk

MATHIESON, Calum Andrew (Jun 1993)
(Partner)
Plexus Law LLP, Edinburgh . . . . (p.897)
T: 0344 2454802
E: calum.mathieson@plexuslaw.co.uk

MATHIESON, Cameron Robert (Mar 2021)
(Employee)
Thorntons Law LLP, Edinburgh . . . . (p.906)
T: 0131 2258705
E: cameronmathieson@thorntons-law.co.uk

MATHIESON, David Ian (Sept 1988) (Partner)
Thorntons Law LLP, Arbroath . . . . (p.757)
T: 01241 872683
E: dmathieson@thorntons-law.co.uk

MATHIESON, Elspeth Catherine (Dec 1986)
(Employee)
Development Trusts Association Scotland,
Edinburgh . . . . (p.1222)
T: 0131 225 2080
E: elspeth@dtascot.org.uk

MATHIESON, Grant James (Jan 2020)
(Employee)
Barr Ellison LLP, Cambridge . . . . (p.1259)
E: G.Mathieson@barrellison.co.uk

MATHIESON, Lesley Catherine (Dec 1985)
(Director)
Macnairs & Wilson Limited,
Glasgow . . . . (p.1014)
T: 0141 5518185
E: lesley.mathieson@macnairswilson.co.uk

MATONTI, Suzanne (Mar 2009) (Employee)
Subsea 7 (UK Service Company) Ltd,
Westhill . . . . (p.1255)
T: 01224 344308
E: Suzanne.Matonti@Subsea7.com

MATTEO, Nicandro (Jan 1985) (Director)
Manini Belardo Limited,
Coatbridge . . . . (p.787)
T: 01236 426 070
E: mbmairdrie@btconnect.com

MATTEO, Ricardo Angelo (Oct 2015)
(Employee)
Harper Macleod LLP, Glasgow . . . . (p.983)
T: 0141 2218888
E: Ricardo.Matteo@harpermacleod.co.uk

MATTHEW, Gordon Findlay, WS (Nov 1976)
(Solicitor)
G Matthew Consultants LLP,
Geneva . . . . (p.1276)
T: +41 22 346 12 97
E: gordonfmatthew@gmail.com

MATTHEW, Hannah (Jan 2021) (Employee)
Pinsent Masons LLP, Glasgow . . . . (p.1031)
T: 0141 567 8400
E: hannah.matthew@pinsentmasons.com

MATTHEW, Heather Jane (Jun 2011)
(Employee)
Scottish Widows Limited,
Edinburgh . . . . (p.1233)
T: (0131) 6557230
E: heather.matthew@lloydsbanking.com

MATTHEW, Jennifer (Oct 2014) (Associate)
Brodies LLP, Edinburgh . . . . (p.845)
T: 0131 2283777
E: jennifer.matthew@brodies.com

MATTHEW, Joan Frances (Jun 1972) (Partner)
M.J. Brown, Son & Co., Edinburgh . . . . . (p.848)
T: 0131 332 1200
E: jmat985725@aol.com

MATTHEW, John Stephen (Dec 2001)
(Employee)
Scottish Water, Dunfermline . . . . (p.1219)
T: 01383 665410
E: steve.matthew@scottishwater.co.uk

MATTHEW, Ross Lawrie (Dec 2017) (Employee)
Gillespie Macandrew LLP,
Edinburgh . . . . (p.872)
T: 0131 2251677
E: ross.matthew@gillespiemacandrew.co.uk

MATTHEWS, Caroline Mary (Apr 2021)
(Employee)
Davidson Chalmers Stewart LLP,
Edinburgh . . . . (p.859)
T: 0131 6259191
E: caroline.matthews@dcslegal.com

MATTHEWS, Christina Fiona (Jun 2008)
(Associate)
Grant Smith Law Practice Limited,
Buckie . . . . (p.781)
T: 01542 831307
E: christina.matthews@grantsmithlaw.co.uk

MATTHEWS, Joanna Mary (Aug 2006)
(Employee)
Baker McKenzie Habib Al Mulla,
Dubai . . . . (p.1277)
E:
Joanna.Matthews-Taylor@bakermckenzie.com

MATTHEWS, Kelly Ann (Feb 2011) (Employee)
Boyd Legal Limited, Kirkcaldy . . . .(p.1099)
T: 01592 264782
E: kelly.matthews@boydlegaluk.com

MATTHEWS, Peter Alexander Hope, WS
(Nov 1977) (Director)
Matthews Legal Limited, Newton
Stewart . . . .(p.1131)
T: 01671 404100
E: petermatthews@abamatthews.com

MATTHEWS, Robert Christopher Alan
(Nov 2021) (Employee)
Ormistons Law Practice Limited,
Glenrothes . . . .(p.1057)
T: 0800 7810413
E: rmatthews@ormistonslaw.co.uk

MAUGHAN, Stephen Anthony (Mar 2012)
(Employee)
SSE PLC, Glasgow . . . .(p.1244)
T: 0141 224 7248
E: stephen.maughan@sse.com

MAVOR, Melissa Claire (Mar 2015) (Employee)
Brodies LLP, Edinburgh . . . .(p.845)
T: 0131 2283777
E: melissa.mavor@brodies.com

MAWBY, Ashley Helen (Oct 2002) (Partner)
Burness Paull LLP, Edinburgh . . . .(p.850)
T: 0131 4736000
E: ashley.mawby@burnesspaull.com

MAWBY, Duncan (Apr 1997) (Partner)
Brodies LLP, Edinburgh . . . .(p.845)
T: 0131 2283777
E: duncan.mawby@brodies.com

MAWDSLEY, Gillian Mary (Jan 1984) (Solicitor)
NO FIRM

MAXFIELD, Loretta Angela (Aug 2007)
(Partner)
Thorntons Law LLP, Dundee . . . .(p.819)
T: 01382 229 111
E: lmaxfield@thorntons-law.co.uk

MAXTON, Paul Dominic (Apr 1985) (Employee)
Orkney Islands Council, Kirkwall . . . . . .(p.1250)
T: 01856 873535
E: paul.maxton@orkney.gov.uk

MAXWELL, Andrew Bernard (Aug 1992)
(Partner)
Brazenall & Orr, Dumfries . . . .(p.800)
T: 01387 255695
E: andrew.maxwell@brazenallandorr.co.uk

MAXWELL, Andrew James Peter Spencer
(Jun 2018) (Solicitor)
Travers Smith LLP, London EC1 . . . . . .(p.1269)
T: (0207) 2953387
E: andrew.maxwell@traverssmith.com

MAXWELL, Andrew Stuart (Nov 2018)
(Employee)
Harper Macleod LLP, Glasgow . . . .(p.983)
T: 0141 2218888
E: andrew.maxwell@harpermacleod.co.uk

MAXWELL, Colette (Aug 2005) (Employee)
T.F. Reid & Donaldson, Paisley . . . .(p.1141)
T: 0141 8897531
E: Colette.Maxwell@reidlaw.co.uk

MAXWELL, Emma (Sept 2012) (Employee)
Burness Paull LLP, Glasgow . . . .(p.954)
T: 0141 2484933
E: Emma.Jardine@burnesspaull.com

MAXWELL, John Alexander (Apr 2009)
(Director)
Middleton Ross & Arnot Limited,
Dingwall . . . .(p.797)
T: 01349 862214
E: jam@middletonross.co.uk

MAXWELL, Julie (Oct 2016) (Employee)
Skyscanner, Edinburgh . . . .(p.1234)
E: julie.maxwell@skyscanner.net

MAXWELL, Steven Bowman (Feb 1988)
(Partner)
Gillies Maxwell, Ayr . . . .(p.763)
T: 01292 288860
E: enquiries@gilliesmaxwell.com

MAXWELL, Thomas (Sept 2004) (Associate)
Shoosmiths LLP, Glasgow . . . .(p.1040)
T: 0370 086 8300
E: tom.maxwell@shoosmiths.co.uk

MAY, Suzanne Ruth (Sept 2014) (Employee)
SSE PLC, Glasgow . . . .(p.1244)
T: 0141 224 7248
E: suzanne.may@sse.com

MAYBERRY, Amy (Jan 2019) (Employee)
Lindsays LLP, Edinburgh . . . .(p.882)
T: 0131 2291212
E: amymayberry@lindsays.co.uk

MAYBERRY, Hayley Jane (Jul 2013) (Employee)
National Health Service Scotland,
Edinburgh . . . .(p.1225)
T: 0131 2757800
E: hayley.mayberry@nhs.scot

MAYBERRY, Simon Jonathan Ross
(Dec 2012) (Employee)
Leyton UK Partners LLP, London
EC4 . . . .(p.1266)
E: smayberry@lexleyton.co.uk

MAYNE, Barbara Louise (Sept 2000) (Associate)
Burness Paull LLP, Glasgow . . . .(p.954)
T: 0141 2484933
E: barbara.mayne@burnesspaull.com

MAYS, Elaine Doris (Nov 1991) (Solicitor)
NO FIRM

MAYS, Gerard Charles (Feb 1996) (Employee)
SOUTH LANARKSHIRERe Council,
Hamilton . . . .(p.1247)
T: 01698 454689
E: gerry.mays@southlanarkshire.gov.uk

MAYS, Richard Paul (Sept 1993) (Solicitor)
NO FIRM

MEACOCK, Ian David (Jul 2018) (Employee)
Procurator Fiscal Service, Glasgow . . . .(p.1241)
T: 0300 0203000
E: Ian.Meacock@copfs.gov.uk

MEAKIN, Andrew Scott (Dec 1991) (Partner)
Morton Fraser LLP, Edinburgh . . . .(p.891)
T: 0131 2471000
E: andrew.meakin@morton-fraser.com

MEARNS, Anne Lesley (Nov 1988) (Partner)
Thorntons Law LLP, Perth . . . .(p.1151)
T: 01738 621212
E: lmearns@thorntons-law.co.uk

MEARNS, Naomi Elizabeth (Jul 2008) (Partner)
Raeburn Christie Clark & Wallace LLP,
Stonehaven . . . .(p.1169)
T: 01569 762947
E: naomi.mearns@raeburns.co.uk

MECHAN, Sheila Agnes (Oct 2010)
(Consultant)
Hunter & Robertson Limited,
Paisley . . . .(p.1138)
T: 0141 8893196
E: Sheila@scottishemploymentlawyer.com

MEDLOCK, Ruth Ying Hei (Mar 2021)
(Employee)
Ellis Whittam Limited, Glasgow . . . . . .(p.1239)
T: (0345) 226 8393
E: ruthmedlock@elliswhittam.com

MEECHAN, Alan Reuben (Dec 2004) (Partner)
Alan Meechan Solicitors, Blackburn . . . .(p.775)
T: 07878 159264
E: alan-m1967@live.co.uk

MEECHAN, April Agnes Cowan (Oct 1990)
(Consultant)
Aamer Anwar & Co, Glasgow . . . .(p.941)
T: 0141 4297090
E: april@aameranwar.com

MEECHAN, Emma Margaret Jean (Nov 2018)
(Employee)
Allan McDougall McQueen LLP,
Penicuik . . . .(p.1144)
T: 01968 675694
E: emmameechan@mcdougallmcqueen.co.uk

MEECHAN, Jamie (Oct 2016) (Employee)
Burness Paull LLP, Glasgow . . . .(p.954)
T: 0141 2484933
E: jamie.meechan@burnesspaull.com

MEECHAN, Dr, Kenneth Alastair (Jan 1998)
(Employee)
Glasgow City Council, Glasgow . . . . . .(p.1239)
T: 0141 2874517
E: Kenny.Meechan@glasgow.gov.uk

MEECHAN, Rachael (Feb 2020) (Employee)
Procurator Fiscal Service, Hamilton . . . .(p.1247)
T: 0844 5613245
E: Rachael.Meechan@copfs.gov.uk

MEEHAN, John Gerard (Mar 1996) (Partner)
Harper Macleod LLP, Glasgow . . . .(p.983)
T: 0141 2274622
E: john.meehan@harpermacleod.co.uk

MEEHAN, Margaret (May 1990) (Partner)
Burness Paull LLP, Glasgow . . . .(p.954)
T: 0141 2484933
E: Margaret.Meehan@burnesspaull.com

MEEK, Agnes (Nov 1990) (Employee)
Procurator Fiscal Service, Airdrie . . . . . .(p.1214)
T: 01236 747027
E: agnes.meek@copfs.gov.uk

MEEK, Alan Crawford (Jan 1992) (Partner)
Morton Fraser LLP, Glasgow . . . .(p.1022)
T: 0141 2741100
E: alan.meek@morton-fraser.com

MEEK, Fiona Anne (Jul 2017) (Employee)
Morton Fraser LLP, Edinburgh . . . .(p.891)
T: 0131 2471000
E: fiona.meek@morton-fraser.com

MEEK, Hazel Francene Stuart (Dec 2006)
(Employee)
Transocean Onshore Support Services Limited,
Aberdeen . . . .(p.1214)
T: 01224 944000
E: Hazel.Meek@deepwater.com

MEGAW, Nicola Clare (Mar 2007) (Employee)
Embark Corporate Services Limited,
Edinburgh . . . .(p.1223)
T: 0131 603 5899
E: nicola.megaw@embarkgroup.co.uk

MEIGHAN, Avril Gillian Spence (Jan 1991)
(Employee)
Anderson Shaw & Gilbert Limited,
Inverness . . . .(p.1075)
T: 01463 236123
E: gm@solicitorsinverness.com

MEIKLE, Claire Louise (Mar 2004) (Employee)
Scottish Government, Edinburgh . . . . .(p.1231)
T: 0131 244 0815
E: claire.meikle@gov.scot

MEIKLE, Eilidh Barbara (Nov 2013) (Employee)
Civil Legal Assistance Office,
Edinburgh . . . .(p.1222)
T: 0131 2401960
E: meikleei@clao.org.uk

MEIKLE, Grant Gordon (Nov 2012) (Employee)
Baillie Gifford & Co, Edinburgh . . . . . . (p.1220)
    T: 0131 2753134
    E: grant.meikle@bailliegifford.com

MEIKLE, Jacqueline Elizabeth (Oct 1996)
    (Associate)
Harper Macleod LLP, Glasgow . . . . (p.983)
    T: 0141 2218888
    E: Kirsty.Selfridge@harpermacleod.co.uk

MEIKLE, Natasha Alison (Aug 2017) (Employee)
National Health Service Scotland,
    Edinburgh . . . . (p.1225)
    T: 0131 2757800
    E: Natasha.Meikle@nhs.scot

MEIKLEJOHN, Ailsa Louise Preston
    (Oct 2009) (Partner)
Drummond Miller LLP, Edinburgh . . . . . (p.864)
    T: 0131 2265151
    E: ameiklejohn@dm-property.com

MEIKLEJOHN, Iain Maury Campbell, WS
    (Nov 1978) (Consultant)
Morton Fraser LLP, Edinburgh . . . . (p.891)
    T: 0131 2471000
    E: Iain.Meiklejohn@morton-fraser.com

MEIKLEJOHN, Mark James (Sept 2010) (Partner)
Brodies LLP, Edinburgh . . . . (p.845)
    T: 0131 2283777
    E: mark.meiklejohn@brodies.com

MEIL, Judith Anne (Sept 1983) (Partner)
Taggart Meil Mathers, Aberdeen . . . . . . (p.745)
    T: 01224 588020
    E: judith@tmmsolicitors.co.uk

MELANEY, Sarah Louise (Oct 2007) (Employee)
Brown Rudnick LLP, London W1 . . . . . (p.1262)
    E: smelaney@brownrudnick.com

MELDRUM, Brian Charles (Nov 1980) (Partner)
Bannatyne, Kirkwood, France & Co.,
    Glasgow. . . . . (p.943)
    T: 0141 2216020
    E: brianmeldrum@bkf.co.uk

MELDRUM, Gillian Ruth (Sept 1998)
    (Employee)
BAE Systems Surface Ships Limited,
    Glasgow. (p.1238)
    T: (07525) 391 489
    E: gillian.meldrum3@baesystems.com

MELDRUM, Kenneth Turnbull (Aug 1987)
    (Partner)
TLT LLP, Glasgow . . . . (p.1048)
    T: 0333 006 0400
    E: Kenneth.Meldrum@tltsolicitors.com

MELDRUM, Laura Marie (Mar 2015) (Associate)
Harper Macleod LLP, Glasgow . . . . (p.983)
    T: 0141 2218888
    E: laura.meldrum@harpermacleod.co.uk

MELDRUM, Lora Grace (Sept 2008) (Director)
Allcourt Solicitors Limited,
    Livingston . . . . (p.1117)
    T: 01506 443999
    E: lora.meldrum@allcourtsolicitors.co.uk

MELDRUM, William (Mar 2006) (Partner)
Murray Beith Murray, Edinburgh . . . . . . (p.893)
    T: 0131 2251200
    E: bill.meldrum@murraybeith.co.uk

MELLOR, Andrew Patrick Dougal (Jan 1989)
    (Partner)
Somerville & Russell, Musselburgh . . . . (p.1129)
    T: 0131 6659041
    E: amellor@somervilleandrussell.co.uk

MELLOR, Euan Andrew (Sept 2000) (Partner)
Anderson Strathern LLP, Edinburgh . . . . (p.839)
    T: 0131 2707700
    E: euan.mellor@andersonstrathern.co.uk

MELLOR, Jennifer Anne Mhairi Darcy
    (Sept 2006) (Employee)
Brodies LLP, Edinburgh . . . . (p.845)
    T: 0131 2283777
    E: jennifer.mellor@brodies.com

MELLOR, Kirsty Ann (Aug 2021) (Employee)
Taits, Kelso. (p.1092)
    T: 01573 224311
    E: kirsty.mellor@taits.co.uk

MELROSE, Jilly-Ann (Apr 2007) (Director)
Hunter & Robertson Limited,
    Paisley . . . . (p.1138)
    T: 0141 8893196
    E: jmelrose@hunter-robertson.co.uk

MELTON, Catriona Lesley (Oct 2008)
    (Associate)
DLA Piper Scotland LLP, Edinburgh . . . . (p.863)
    T: 08700 111111
    E: catriona.melton@dlapiper.com

MELVILLE, Blair (Apr 2014) (Partner)
Teneu Legal, Glasgow . . . . (p.1043)
    T: 07877 347695
    E: blair.melville@teneulegal.com

MELVILLE, Carla (Sept 2009) (Employee)
Office of the Advocate General,
    Edinburgh . . . . (p.1227)
    T: 0131 2441635
    E: Carla.Melville@advocategeneral.gov.uk

MELVILLE, Christian Kenneth Bowring
    (Nov 1994) (Employee)
Ennova Limited, Edinburgh . . . . (p.869)
    T: 0131 662 4555
    E: cmelville@ennova-law.com

MELVILLE, Gillian Carol (Aug 2011) (Employee)
University of Strathclyde Law Clinic,
    Glasgow. (p.1245)
    E: gillian.melville@strath.ac.uk

MELVILLE, Katie (Aug 2018) (Employee)
Wright, Johnston & Mackenzie LLP,
  Inverness . . . .(p.1083)
  T: 01463 234445
  E: kzm@wjm.co.uk

MELVILLE, Lynn (Sept 1996) (Partner)
Blackadders LLP, Dundee. . . . .(p.805)
  T: 01382 229222
  E: lynn.melville@Blackadders.co.uk

MELVILLE, Victoria Marchbank (Sept 2000)
  (Partner)
Clyde & Co (Scotland) LLP,
  Edinburgh . . . .(p.855)
  T: 0131 5571545
  E: vikki.melville@clydeco.com

MENEELY, James Alexander (Oct 2001)
  (Employee)
Glasgow City Council, Glasgow . . . . . .(p.1239)
  T: 0141 287 6179
  E: james.meneely@glasgow.gov.uk

MENNIE, Diana Leslie (Oct 2012) (Associate)
Dentons UK and Middle East LLP,
  Edinburgh . . . .(p.860)
  T: 0330 2220050
  E: diana.mennie@dentons.com

MENNIE, Roger William Hunter (Nov 1988)
  (Employee)
Dundee City Council, Dundee . . . .(p.1217)
  T: 01382 434000
  E: roger.mennie@dundeecity.gov.uk

MENNIE, Sarah Mary-Ann Hardie
  (Oct 2015) (Employee)
Legal Secretariat to the Advocate General,
  London SW1 . . . .(p.1266)
  T: 020 72706810
  E: sarah.mennie@advocategeneral.gov.uk

MENZIES, Rebecca Ann (Jan 2018) (Partner)
DNLC LLP, Dundee. . . . .(p.809)
  T: 01382 918230
  E:
  rebecca.menzies@dundeenorthlawcentre.co.uk

MENZIES, Samantha Ruth (Aug 2020)
  (Employee)
Callahan McKeown & Co Ltd,
  Renfrew . . . .(p.1158)
  T: 0141 885 1212

MENZIES, Dr, Tracey Jayne Houston
(Aug 1993) (Partner)
Brodies LLP, Aberdeen. . . . .(p.723)
  T: 01224 392242
  E: tracey.menzies@brodies.com

MERCER, Bonar James Lamond (Jun 2016)
  (Associate)
MacRoberts LLP, Edinburgh . . . .(p.887)
  T: 0131 2295046
  E: bonar.mercer@macroberts.com

MERCHANT, Jillian Louise (Jan 2013) (Partner)
Thompsons, Glasgow . . . .(p.1046)
  T: 0141 2218840
  E: Jillian.Merchant@thompsons-scotland.co.uk

MERCHANT, Kathryn Grace Ann (Dec 2020)
  (Employee)
Brodies LLP, Edinburgh . . . .(p.845)
  T: 0131 2283777
  E: kathryn.merchant@brodies.com

MEREDITH, Iain Paul (Feb 2011) (Employee)
Highland Council, Dingwall . . . .(p.1216)
  T: 01349 863381
  E: Iain.Meredith@highland.gov.uk

MERRY, Jenna Catherine (Jan 2010) (Director)
Jas Campbell & Co Ltd, Saltcoats . . . . .(p.1160)
  T: 01294 464301
  E: j.merry@jascampbell.co.uk

MERSON, Felicity Margaret (Dec 2002)
  (Employee)
Procurator Fiscal Service, Aberdeen . . .(p.1213)
  T: 0844 561 2594
  E: Felicity.Merson@copfs.gov.uk

MERSON, Jane Florence (Aug 2014) (Associate)
Mackinnons Solicitors LLP,
  Aberdeen . . . .(p.737)
  T: 01224 868687
  E: jane@mackinnons.com

MESBAH, Navid (Mar 2021) (Employee)
TLT LLP, Manchester . . . .(p.1270)

METCALF, Ann Lucy (May 1994) (Partner)
Thorntons Law LLP, Edinburgh . . . .(p.906)
  T: 0131 2258705
  E: lmetcalf@thorntons-law.co.uk

METCALFE, Corin Benedict Monaghan
  (May 2019) (Employee)
Shepherd and Wedderburn LLP,
  Edinburgh . . . .(p.900)
  T: 0131 2289900
  E: corin.metcalfe@shepwedd.com

METCALFE, Katherine (Oct 2005) (Employee)
Pinsent Masons LLP, Glasgow . . . .(p.1031)
  T: 0141 567 8400
  E: Katherine.metcalfe@pinsentmasons.com

METHVEN, Amanda Russell (Jan 1992) (Partner)
CMS Cameron McKenna Nabarro Olswang LLP,
  Edinburgh . . . .(p.856)
  T: 0131 2288000
  E: Amanda.Methven@cms-cmno.com

MEYER, Marichen (Oct 1999) (Consultant)
Burnett & Reid LLP, Aberdeen . . . .(p.726)
  T: 01224 644333
  E: mmeyer@burnett-reid.co.uk

MICHAEL, Sally Jane (Jan 1990) (Employee)
WEST DUNBARTONSHIREhire Council,
Dumbarton . . . .(p.1217)
T: 01389 737808
E: sally.michael@west-dunbarton.gov.uk

MICHIE, Alan Johnston (Nov 1983) (Partner)
Ledingham Chalmers LLP,
Aberdeen . . . .(p.734)
T: 01224 408408
E: alan.michie@ledinghamchalmers.com

MICHIE, Mhari Kirsten (Apr 2016) (Employee)
Ledingham Chalmers LLP,
Aberdeen . . . .(p.734)
T: 01224 408546
E: mhari.michie@ledinghamchalmers.com

MICHIE, Ross Guthrie Euan (Feb 2018)
(Employee)
Dickson Minto, Edinburgh . . . .(p.861)
T: 0131 2254455
E: ross.michie@dmws.com

MICHOPOULOU, Hilary Kay (Feb 2009)
(Solicitor)
NO FIRM

MIDDLECOTE, Andrew James (Mar 2005)
(Employee)
Life Technologies Limited, Paisley . . . . .(p.1252)
T: 0141 8146028
E: andrew.middlecote@lifetech.com

MIDDLETON, Alexander David Iain
(Dec 2017) (Assistant)
Turcan Connell, Edinburgh . . . .(p.908)
T: 0131 2288111
E: alexander.middleton@turcanconnell.com

MIDDLETON, Dylan Rees (Feb 2019)
(Employee)
Procurator Fiscal Service, Aberdeen . . .(p.1213)
T: 0300 0202336
E: dylan.middleton@copfs.gov.uk

MIDDLETON, Gayle Elizabeth (May 2008)
(Employee)
David Kinloch & Co., Glasgow . . . .(p.997)
T: 0141 552 6382
E: info@childlaw.me

MIDDLETON, Gillian (Jun 2018) (Employee)
Burness Paull LLP, Glasgow . . . .(p.954)
T: 0141 2484933
E: gill.middleton@burnesspaull.com

MIDDLETON, Robert Andrew (Feb 2021)
(Employee)
Loughran & Co Limited, Glasgow . . . .(p.1004)
T: 0141 3310374

MIDDLETON, Samantha (Apr 2017) (Employee)
R & R Urquhart LLP, Forres . . . .(p.929)
T: 01309 672216
E: samanthamiddleton@r-r-urquhart.co.uk

MIDDLETON, Stephen Renny (Jan 1987)
(Partner)
Shiells, Brechin . . . .(p.779)
T: 01356 622171
E: steve.middleton@shiells-law.co.uk

MIDDLETON, Ysabeau Hester (Sept 2018)
(Employee)
Lord President's Private Office,
Edinburgh . . . .(p.1225)
T: 0131 2406701
E: ymiddleton@scotcourts.gov.uk

MIELE, Paul Joseph (Sept 2009) (Employee)
Procurator Fiscal Service,
Edinburgh . . . .(p.1227)
T: 0300 0203168
E: paul.miele@copfs.gov.uk

MIELE, Rachel Jane (Jun 2021) (Employee)
Harper Macleod LLP, Glasgow . . . .(p.983)
T: 0141 2218888
E: rachel.miele@harpermacleod.co.uk

MIEZITIS, Janis John (Nov 1995) (Employee)
Natural Power Consultants Limited,
Stirling . . . .(p.1254)
T: 01786 542 300
E: johnmi@naturalpower.com

MIHALIC, Sophie Katherine (Aug 2016)
(Solicitor)
NO FIRM

MILES, Charlotte Victoria (Jun 2019)
(Employee)
Dentons UK and Middle East LLP, London
EC4 . . . .(p.1263)
T: 020 7242 1212
E: Charlotte.Miles@dentons.com

MILITE, Laura Elizabeth (Sept 2003) (Partner)
Taylor & Kelly, Falkirk . . . .(p.925)
T: 01324 614015
E: laura@taylorkelly.co.uk

MILL, Jane (Dec 1997) (Employee)
Shepherd and Wedderburn LLP,
Edinburgh . . . .(p.900)
T: 0131 2289900
E: jane.mill@shepwedd.com

MILL, Richard George (Feb 1995) (Partner)
Mill and Millard LLP, Edinburgh . . . .(p.890)
T: 0131 3227222
E: rgm@millardlaw.co.uk

MILL, Stephanie Rose (Jul 2012) (Employee)
Shepherd and Wedderburn LLP, London
EC2 . . . .(p.1268)
T: 020 74294900
E: Stephanie.Mill@shepwedd.com

MILLAR, Alasdair Preston (Aug 2020)
(Employee)
Procurator Fiscal Service,
Dumbarton . . . .(p.1217)
T: 0300 020 3000
E: Alasdair.Millar@copfs.gov.uk

MILLAR, Amanda (Nov 1998) (Solicitor)
NO FIRM

MILLAR, Antony Gerard (Sept 2018)
(Employee)
Davidson Chalmers Stewart LLP,
Edinburgh . . . .(p.859)
T: 0131 6259191
E: antony.millar@dcslegal.co.uk

MILLAR, Archibald James (Aug 1986) (Partner)
MacRae Stephen & Co.,
Fraserburgh . . . .(p.931)
T: 01346 514545
E: archie@macraestephen.co.uk

MILLAR, Caroline (Oct 2009) (Employee)
SKO Family Law Specialists LLP,
Edinburgh . . . .(p.903)
T: 0131 3226669
E: caroline.millar@sko-family.co.uk

MILLAR, Chloe Rebecca Georgia Chirwiro
(Sept 2009) (Employee)
Procurator Fiscal Service,
Edinburgh . . . .(p.1227)
T: 0844 5614368
E: Chloe.Millar@copfs.gov.uk

MILLAR, Claire Elise (Mar 1996) (Employee)
Procurator Fiscal Service, Kirkcaldy . . . . (p.1249)
T: 0300 0203000
E: claire.millar@copfs.gov.uk

MILLAR, Colin John (Jan 1992) (Partner)
Wright, Johnston & Mackenzie LLP,
Glasgow . . . .(p.1054)
T: 0141 2483434
E: cjm@wjm.co.uk

MILLAR, David Mitchell (Jul 2003) (Partner)
Brodies LLP, Aberdeen . . . .(p.723)
T: 01224 392242
E: david.millar@brodies.com

MILLAR, Donald James (Sept 2006) (Employee)
Collas Crill, St Peter Port . . . .(p.1273)
T: 01481 723191
E: donald.millar@collascrill.com

MILLAR, Elizabeth (Feb 1986) (Employee)
Scottish Police Authority, Police Scotland,
Glasgow . . . .(p.1244)
T: 01786 895729
E: Elizabeth.Millar2@scotland.pnn.police.uk

MILLAR, Faith Roslyn (Oct 2009) (Employee)
Procurator Fiscal Service,
Edinburgh . . . .(p.1229)
T: 0300 0203000
E: Faith.Millar@copfs.gov.uk

MILLAR, Fiona Jane (Jan 1984) (Employee)
Procurator Fiscal Service, Glasgow . . . . (p.1241)
T: 0300 0203000
E: fiona.millar@copfs.gov.uk

MILLAR, Gail Margaret (Aug 2007) (Solicitor)
Aston Gowman Limited, London
TW8 . . . .(p.1261)
T: 0333 3447277

MILLAR, Glen Archibald (Oct 1990) (Partner)
Thompsons, Edinburgh . . . .(p.906)
T: 0131 2254297
E: glen.millar@thompsons-scotland.co.uk

MILLAR, Glenn Paul, WS (Dec 1980)
(Employee)
Campion Homes Ltd, Dunfermline . . . . (p.1219)
E: glenn@campionhomes.com

MILLAR, Graham Ramsay (Jan 1998) (Partner)
Gilson Gray LLP, Glasgow . . . .(p.980)
T: 0141 5302021
E: gmillar@gilsongray.co.uk

MILLAR, Greig John (Feb 2016) (Employee)
Lloyds Banking Group Plc,
Edinburgh . . . .(p.1224)
T: (0131) 442 9579
E: greig.millar@lloydsbanking.com

MILLAR, Jacqueline Sarah (Nov 1997)
(Associate)
Bowmans, Forfar . . . .(p.926)
T: 01307 464088
E: jsm@bowmansolicitors.co.uk

MILLAR, James David (Oct 1986) (Employee)
West Lothian Council, Livingston . . . . . (p.1250)
T: 01506 281613
E: James.Millar@westlothian.gov.uk

MILLAR, Joanna Wendy Elizabeth
(Nov 1997) (Employee)
Gilson Gray LLP, Glasgow . . . .(p.980)
T: 0141 5302021
E: jmillar@gilsongray.co.uk

MILLAR, Johanna Louise (Oct 2008) (Employee)
Aberdeen Corporate Services Limited,
Edinburgh . . . .(p.1220)
T: 0131 245 7508
E: johanna.millar@abrdn.com

MILLAR, Kerry Margaret (Jan 2012) (Employee)
Baillie Gifford & Co, Edinburgh . . . . . .(p.1220)
T: 0131 2752000
E: Kerry.Millar@bailliegifford.com

MILLAR, Laura Ann (Oct 2003) (Associate)
Burness Paull LLP, Glasgow . . . .(p.954)
T: 0141 273 6800
E: Laura.Millar@burnesspaull.com

MILLAR, Laura Anne (Mar 1982) (Employee)
Procurator Fiscal Service, Paisley . . . . . .(p.1252)
T: 0141 8875225
E: laura.millar@copfs.gov.uk

MILLAR, Lewis Scott (Feb 2020) (Employee)
Blackwood Partners LLP, Aberdeen . . . . .(p.723)
T: 01224 446230
E: lewis.millar@blackwood-partners.com

MILLAR, Lynsey Jane (Jun 2004) (Director)
Lanarkshire Law Practice Limited,
Bellshill . . . .(p.773)
T: 01698 747171
E: lynseymillar@lanarkshirelaw.co.uk

MILLAR, Mairi Davidson (Oct 2001) (Employee)
Glasgow City Council, Glasgow . . . . . .(p.1239)
T: 0141 2872000
E: Mairi.Millar@glasgow.gov.uk

MILLAR, Samantha Louise (May 2018)
(Employee)
Brodies LLP, Edinburgh . . . .(p.845)
T: 0131 2283777
E: samantha.millar@brodies.com

MILLAR, Stephen Samuel Alexander
(Oct 1996) (Partner)
CMS Cameron McKenna Nabarro Olswang LLP,
London EC4 . . . .(p.1263)
T: 0207 367 3000
E: stephen.millar@cms-cmno.com

MILLAR, Stuart Graham (Sept 2009)
(Employee)
Gibson Kerr Limited, Edinburgh . . . . . .(p.872)
T: 0131 2257558
E: stuart.millar@gibsonkerr.co.uk

MILLAR, Susan Alice Mairi (Aug 2015)
(Employee)
Ashurst LLP, Glasgow . . . .(p.1237)
T: (0141) 375 4242
E: susan.millar@ashurst.com

MILLAR, William Cameron McKenzie
(Sept 2004) (Employee)
SSE Plc, Perth . . . .(p.1253)
T: 01738 456 000
E: william.millar@sse.com

MILLARD, Lucy (Nov 2010) (Partner)
Mill and Millard LLP, Edinburgh . . . .(p.890)
T: 0131 3227222
E: lm@millardlaw.co.uk

MILLEN, Dr, Catherine Dianne (Oct 2010)
(Employee)
Watermans Legal Limited,
Edinburgh . . . .(p.911)
T: 0131 4675566
E: DianneMillen@watermanslegal.co.uk

MILLEN, Julie (Sept 1995) (Partner)
Millen Solicitors, Glasgow . . . .(p.1019)
T: 0141 9590055
E: jm@millensolicitors.co.uk

MILLER, Aileen Frances (Dec 2009) (Employee)
Brown & Co Legal LLP, Glasgow . . . . . .(p.950)
T: 0141 3533354
E: aileenmiller@lsa.org.uk

MILLER, Alison (Jun 2020) (Employee)
Livingstone Brown Limited,
Glasgow . . . .(p.1004)
T: 0141 7789657
E: alisonm@livbrown.co.uk

MILLER, Allyson Michelle (Mar 2006)
(Employee)
Hunting PLC (London), Aberdeen . . . .(p.1213)
E: Allyson.Miller@hunting-intl.com

MILLER, Anne Margaret (Oct 2007) (Employee)
Thorntons Law LLP, Dundee . . . .(p.819)
T: 01382 229 111
E: amiller@thorntons-law.co.uk

MILLER, Cara Anne (Jul 2021) (Employee)
Stork Technical Services UK Limited,
Dyce . . . .(p.1219)
T: 01224 722888
E: cara.miller@stork.com

MILLER, Carolyn Ann (Oct 1999) (Solicitor)
NO FIRM

MILLER, Caryn Lynn (Dec 1992) (Partner)
CMS Cameron McKenna Nabarro Olswang LLP,
Edinburgh . . . .(p.856)
T: 0131 200 7338
E: caryn.miller@cms-cmno.com

MILLER, Catriona Margaret Binnie
(Sept 1993) (Partner)
Thorntons Law LLP, Edinburgh . . . .(p.906)
T: 0131 2258705
E: cmiller@thorntons-law.co.uk

MILLER, Cecilia (May 1990) (Employee)
East Dunbartonshire Council,
Kirkintilloch . . . .(p.1249)
T: 0141 5788000
E: cecilia.miller@eastdunbarton.gov.uk

MILLER, Christina Marie (Aug 2015)
(Employee)
Vialex Limited, Edinburgh . . . .(p.1235)
T: 0333 2400127
E: christina.miller@vialex.co.uk

MILLER, Christopher David (Jun 2021)
(Employee)
Brodies LLP, Edinburgh . . . .(p.845)
T: 0131 2283777
E: christopher.miller@brodies.com

MILLER, Claire Ann (Nov 2016) (Employee)
CMS Cameron McKenna Nabarro Olswang LLP,
Edinburgh . . . .(p.856)
T: 0131 2288000
E: claire.miller@cms-cmno.com

MILLER, Colin Barrie (Oct 1986) (Partner)
Burness Paull LLP, Edinburgh . . . .(p.850)
T: 0131 4736000
E: colin.miller@burnesspaull.com

MILLER, Collette Tracey (Nov 2010) (Partner)
Harper Macleod LLP, Glasgow . . . .(p.983)
T: 0141 2218888
E: Collette.Miller@harpermacleod.co.uk

MILLER, Deborah (Aug 2002) (Consultant)
Shepherd and Wedderburn LLP,
Edinburgh . . . .(p.900)
T: 0131 2289900
E: Deborah.Miller@shepwedd.com

MILLER, Elisa Margaret (Sept 2006) (Associate)
Wright, Johnston & Mackenzie LLP,
Inverness . . . .(p.1083)
T: 01463 234445
E: emm@wjm.co.uk

MILLER, Emma Louise (Nov 1999) (Associate)
Burness Paull LLP, Aberdeen . . . .(p.724)
T: 01224 621621
E: Emma.Miller@burnesspaull.com

MILLER, Eric Dodson (Aug 2004) (Director)
GWG Ltd, Glasgow . . . .(p.982)
T: 0141 7769960
E: eric@gwg-ltd.com

MILLER, Euan James (Aug 1999) (Employee)
BAM Properties Limited, stepps . . . . . .(p.1254)
T: 0141 2221020
E: emiller@bam.co.uk

MILLER, Ewan Kenneth (Mar 1996) (Partner)
Thorntons Law LLP, Dundee . . . .(p.819)
T: 01382 229 111
E: emiller@thorntons-law.co.uk

MILLER, Gary William Victor (Oct 2007)
(Consultant)
Jim Friel Solicitors, Glasgow . . . .(p.978)
T: 0141 4201234
E: garym@jimfriel.co.uk

MILLER, Gemma Elizabeth (Oct 2008)
(Employee)
Dundee City Council, Dundee . . . .(p.1217)
T: 01382 434000
E: gemma.miller@dundeecity.gov.uk

MILLER, Graeme Crombie (Oct 1996) (Director)
McGregor MacLeod Ltd,
Kirkintilloch . . . .(p.1105)
T: 0141 7789292
E: graememiller@mcgregormacleod.co.uk

MILLER, Helen Elizabeth (Aug 2011)
(Employee)
National Westminster Bank PLC,
Edinburgh . . . .(p.1226)
T: 07786 693433
E: helen.a.miller@natwest.com

MILLER, Iain James (Oct 2010) (Employee)
Battersea Power Station Development Company,
London SW8 . . . .(p.1262)
T: 020 7062 1912
E: IMiller@bpsdc.co.uk

MILLER, Iain Lindsay (Dec 1990) (Employee)
Glasgow City Council, Glasgow . . . . . .(p.1239)
T: 0141 2874781
E: iain.miller@glasgow.gov.uk

MILLER, Karen (Aug 1983) (Partner)
NGL (Scotland) Limited, Hamilton . . . .(p.1068)
T: 01698 207050
E: Karen.Miller@ngllawyers.com

MILLER, Keith (Dec 1980) (Partner)
Jas. S. Grosset, Leven . . . .(p.1115)
T: 01333 426023
E: keith.miller@grossets.co.uk

MILLER, Lauren (Oct 2007) (Employee)
Shoosmiths LLP, Glasgow . . . .(p.1040)
T: 0370 086 8300
E: lauren.miller@shoosmiths.co.uk

MILLER, Lindsey Mary (Nov 1991) (Employee)
Scottish Engineering, Glasgow . . . .(p.1243)
T: 0141 2213181
E: lindseymiller@scottishengineering.org.uk

MILLER, Lindsey Rae (Dec 1995) (Employee)
Procurator Fiscal Service,
Edinburgh . . . .(p.1227)
T: 0300 0203168
E: lindsey.miller@copfs.gov.uk

MILLER, Lorna Elizabeth (Sept 1993) (Partner)
Andersons LLP, Kinross . . . .(p.1098)
T: 01577 862405
E: l_miller@andersons-kinross.co.uk

MILLER, Louise Judith (Oct 1996) (Employee)
Scottish Government, Edinburgh . . . . .(p.1231)
T: 0131 244 0815
E: Louise.Miller@gov.scot

MILLER, Madeleine Louise (Mar 2021)
(Employee)
Dentons UK and Middle East LLP,
Glasgow . . . .(p.968)
T: 0330 2220050
E: maddie.miller@denton.com

MILLER, Magnus James William (Jan 2011)
(Associate)
Davidson Chalmers Stewart LLP,
Edinburgh . . . .(p.859)
T: 0131 6259191
E: Magnus.Miller@dcslegal.com

MILLER, Margot Jardine (Aug 1984) (Employee)
Jas. S. Grosset, Leven . . . .(p.1115)
T: 01333 426023
E: margot.miller@grossets.co.uk

MILLER, Matthew Sean (Jul 2016) (Employee)
Procurator Fiscal Service,
Edinburgh . . . .(p.1227)
T: 0300 0203168
E: matthew.miller@copfs.gov.uk

MILLER, Meriel Jane (Jan 2021) (Employee)
Burness Paull LLP, Edinburgh . . . .(p.850)
T: 0131 4736000
E: meriel.miller@burnesspaull.com

MILLER, Mhairi Elizabeth Anne (May 2019)
(Employee)
Brown & Co Legal LLP, Glasgow . . . . . .(p.950)
T: 0141 3533354
E: MhairiMiller@lsa.org.uk

MILLER, Nadene (May 2018) (Employee)
Buchanan Burton Limited, East
Kilbride . . . .(p.830)
T: 01355 249228
E: nadenem@buchananburton.co.uk

MILLER, Rachael Elizabeth (Sept 2021)
(Employee)
Clyde & Co (Scotland) LLP,
Edinburgh . . . .(p.855)
T: 0131 5571545
E: rachael.miller@clydeco.com

MILLER, Richard Alexander (Oct 1985)
(Partner)
Grigor & Young LLP, Elgin. . . . .(p.916)
T: 01343 544077
E: richard@grigor-young.co.uk

MILLER, Samantha Alexandra (Sept 2020)
(Employee)
Lindsays LLP, Glasgow. . . . .(p.1001)
T: 0141 2216551
E: SamanthaMiller@lindsays.co.uk

MILLER, Sarah Louise (May 1999) (Associate)
Brodies LLP, Glasgow . . . .(p.948)
T: 0141 2484672
E: sarah.miller@brodies.com

MILLER, Stephanie Lee (Jul 2004) (Employee)
Civil Legal Assistance Office,
Aberdeen . . . .(p.1212)
T: 01224 402330
E: stephaniemiller1977@gmail.com

MILLER, Stephen Charles (Oct 1989) (Partner)
Clyde & Co (Scotland) LLP,
Glasgow. . . . .(p.961)
T: 0141 2482666
E: stephen.miller@clydeco.com

MILLER, Stephen James (Nov 1995) (Partner)
Shepherd and Wedderburn LLP,
Edinburgh . . . .(p.900)
T: 0131 473 5227
E: stephen.miller@shepwedd.com

MILLER, Thomas Anthony (Jan 2013)
(Employee)
Scottish Social Services Council,
Dundee . . . .(p.1218)
T: 01382 317944
E: tom.miller@sssc.uk.com

MILLER, Thomas Mackintosh (Aug 2016)
(Employee)
Carruthers Gemmill, Glasgow . . . .(p.958)
T: 0141 3330 033
E: tmm@carruthersgemmill.co.uk

MILLER, Victoria Anne Speirs (Sept 1995)
(Partner)
Pinsent Masons LLP, Edinburgh . . . .(p.895)
T: 0131 7777000
E: victoria.miller@pinsentmasons.com

MILLER-BROWN, Anna Louise (Jul 2018)
(Employee)
Walker Laird, Paisley . . . .(p.1142)
T: 0141 8875271
E: anna.brown@walkerlaird.co.uk

MILLIGAN, Colin James (May 2010) (Partner)
Arthur & Carmichael LLP, Dornoch . . . .(p.797)
T: 01862 810202
E: cjm@arthur-carmichael.co.uk

MILLIGAN, Duncan Alexander (Jan 1979)
(Partner)
D.A. Milligan & Co., Hamilton . . . .(p.1068)
T: 01698 457733
E: damilliganandco@gmail.com

MILLIGAN, Elizabeth Deborah Carole
(Dec 1993) (Employee)
Dingwall Solicitors Ltd,
Dunfermline . . . .(p.823)
T: 01383 808198
E: emilligan@ds-solicitors.co.uk

MILLIGAN, Gordon Robert (Oct 2005)
(Employee)
Allan McDougall McQueen LLP,
Edinburgh . . . .(p.837)
T: 0131 2252121
E: gordonmilligan@allanmcdougall.co.uk

MILLIGAN, Kim Tamar (Oct 2006) (Employee)
Scottish Hospital Inquiry, Glasgow . . . .(p.1244)
E: Kim.Milligan@hospitalsinquiry.scot

MILLIGAN, Larissa Jane (Sept 2016) (Employee)
Procurator Fiscal Service, Dundee . . . . .(p.1218)
T: 01382 342559
E: Larissa.milligan@copfs.gov.uk

MILLIGAN, Laura Naysmith (Jan 1993)
(Employee)
Dobbies Garden Centres, Lasswade . . .(p.1250)
E: Laura.Milligan@dobbies.com

MILLIGAN, Marianne (Jul 2012) (Employee)
Sam Milligan & Co., Fraserburgh . . . . . .(p.931)
T: 01346 511966
E: m.milligan@sammilligan.com

MILLIGAN, Pauline Claire (Dec 1993) (Director)
John Jackson & Dick Limited,
Hamilton . . . .(p.1067)
T: 01698 281747
E: pmilligan@jacksondicklaw.com

MILLIGAN, Rosslyn Iona Margaret
(Oct 2008) (Associate)
Dallas McMillan, Glasgow . . . .(p.966)
T: 0141 3336750
E: rosslyn.milligan@dallasmcmillan.co.uk

MILLIGAN, Samuel Douglas (Aug 1987)
(Partner)
Sam Milligan & Co., Fraserburgh . . . . . .(p.931)
T: 01346 511966
E: s.milligan@sammilligan.com

MILLIGAN, Scott Stewart (Dec 2006) (Partner)
Harper Macleod LLP, Glasgow . . . .(p.983)
T: 0141 2218888
E: scott.milligan@harpermacleod.co.uk

MILLIGAN, Stephanie-Lynn (Sept 2020)
(Employee)
Sam Milligan & Co., Fraserburgh . . . . . .(p.931)
T: 01346 511966
E: sl.milligan@sammilligan.com

MILLIGAN, Tracy Jane (Nov 2000) (Associate)
PRP Legal Limited, Glasgow . . . .(p.1033)
T: 0141 3311050
E: tracy.milligan@mcgpaisley.co.uk

MILLOY, Graeme (Mar 2018) (Associate)
Clyde & Co (Scotland) LLP,
Edinburgh . . . .(p.855)
T: 0131 5571545
E: Graeme.Milloy@clydeco.com

MILLS, Alanah Beth (Mar 2019) (Employee)
Ledingham Chalmers LLP,
Aberdeen . . . .(p.734)
T: 01224 408408
E: alanah.mills@ledinghamchalmers.com

MILLS, Angela Eileen (Jun 2017) (Employee)
BBC Scotland, Glasgow . . . .(p.1238)
T: 0141 4226373
E: angela.mills@bbc.co.uk

MILLS, Claire Ruth (Oct 2005) (Employee)
Brodies LLP, Glasgow . . . .(p.948)
T: 0141 2484672
E: claire.mills@brodies.com

MILLS, Grant George (Apr 2021) (Employee)
Raeburn Christie Clark & Wallace LLP,
Aberdeen . . . .(p.741)
T: 01224 332400
E: grant.mills@raeburns.co.uk

MILLS, Sophie Rebecca (Sept 2021) (Employee)
BTO Solicitors LLP, Glasgow . . . .(p.952)
T: 0141 2218012
E: SMI@bto.co.uk

MILNE, Cameron John (Jul 2016) (Associate)
CMS Cameron McKenna Nabarro Olswang LLP,
Aberdeen . . . .(p.727)
T: 01224 622002
E: Cameron.Milne@cms-cmno.com

MILNE, Claire Catherine (Dec 1992)
(Employee)
Appleby, Douglas . . . .(p.1274)
T: 01624 647 647
E: cmilne@applebyglobal.com

MILNE, David John (Nov 1996) (Partner)
MacRoberts LLP, Dundee. . . . .(p.815)
T: 01382 339340
E: David.Milne@macroberts.com

MILNE, David Michael (Jun 2007) (Associate)
Addleshaw Goddard LLP,
Manchester . . . .(p.1270)
E: david.milne@addleshawgoddard.com

MILNE, Deborah Weir (Oct 1995) (Partner)
Jackson Boyd LLP, Glasgow . . . .(p.991)
T: 0141 221 4325
E: dmilne@jacksonboyd.co.uk

MILNE, Douglas Neil (Sept 1995) (Partner)
Morton Fraser LLP, Edinburgh . . . .(p.891)
T: 0131 2471000
E: douglas.milne@morton-fraser.com

MILNE, Eva Rebecca (Nov 2019) (Employee)
Office of the Advocate General,
Edinburgh . . . .(p.1227)
T: 0131 2441635
E: Eva.Milne@advocategeneral.gov.uk

MILNE, Fiona (Sept 2006) (Partner)
A.C. Morrison & Richards LLP,
Aberdeen . . . .(p.737)
T: 01224 573321
E: fmilne@acmr.co.uk

MILNE, Grant John (Sept 2014) (Employee)
Aberdeen City Council, Aberdeen. . . . . .(p.1211)
T: 01224 522000
E: granmilne@aberdeencity.gov.uk

MILNE, Grigor Lewis (Nov 1994) (Employee)
First Sentier Investors (UK) Services Limited,
Edinburgh . . . .(p.1223)
T: 0131 4732200
E: Grigor.Milne@stewartinvestors.com

MILNE, Heather Lorna Campbell (Oct 2016)
(Employee)
WEST DUNBARTONSHIREhire Council,
Dumbarton . . . .(p.1217)
T: 01389 737000
E: Heather.Milne@west-dunbarton.gov.uk

MILNE, Joanna Clare (Jul 2019) (Employee)
Ledingham Chalmers LLP,
Aberdeen . . . .(p.734)
T: 01224 408408

MILNE, Kirsteen Elizabeth (Dec 2004)
(Employee)
Brodies LLP, Edinburgh . . . .(p.845)
T: 0131 2283777
E: Kirsteen.Milne@brodies.com

MILNE, Laura (Oct 2012) (Employee)
Burness Paull LLP, Aberdeen . . . .(p.724)
T: 01224 621621
E: Laura.Milne@burnesspaull.com

MILNE, Mark (Feb 2020) (Employee)
MBM Commercial LLP, Edinburgh . . . . .(p.889)
T: 0131 2268200
E: mark.milne@mbmcommercial.co.uk

MILNE, Natalia Anne (Oct 2020) (Employee)
Navigator Employment Law Ltd,
Edinburgh . . . .(p.1227)
T: 0333 2400308
E: natalia.milne@navigatorlaw.co.uk

MILNE, Odell Campbell (Sept 1984)
(Consultant)
Brodies LLP, Edinburgh . . . .(p.845)
T: 0131 2283777
E: odell.milne@brodies.com

MILNE, Ramsay George Robert (Oct 1982)
(Employee)
Scottish Water, Dunfermline . . . .(p.1219)
T: 01383 668052
E: ramsay.milne@scottishwater.co.uk

MILNE, Rhoderick Michael Stuart, WS
(Nov 1989) (Partner)
Milne & Co. WS, Edinburgh . . . .(p.890)
T: 0131 5581441
E: rorymilne@irishosted.co.uk

MILNE, Richard George (Sept 1997) (Employee)
Sainsbury's Bank plc, Edinburgh . . . . . .(p.1230)
T: 0131 286 0807
E: Richard.Milne@sainsburysbank.co.uk

MILNE, Sarah Lucy (Oct 2021) (Employee)
MacRoberts LLP, Glasgow . . . .(p.1015)
T: 0141 3031100
E: sarah.milne@macroberts.com

MILNE, Sarah Mohammed (Sept 2009)
(Employee)
Dentons UK and Middle East LLP,
Edinburgh . . . .(p.860)
T: 0330 2220050
E: sara.milne@dentons.com

MILNE, Saul Morgan (Apr 2016) (Employee)
Clackmannanshire Council, Alloa . . . . .(p.1215)
T: 01259 450000
E: smilne@clacks.gov.uk

MILNE, Scott Charles (Aug 1986) (Partner)
Thorntons Law LLP, Dundee . . . .(p.819)
T: 01382 229 111
E: smilne@thorntons-law.co.uk

MILNE, Simon William (Feb 1980) (Employee)
JHS Law, Dumfries . . . .(p.801)
T: 01387 739000
E: simon.milne@jhslaw.co.uk

MILNER, Katie Jayne (May 2021) (Employee)
Clancys Solicitors and Estate Agents Limited,
Edinburgh . . . .(p.854)
T: 0131 337 7771
E: katie@clancys-solicitors.co.uk

MILSOM, Robert (Mar 2021) (Employee)
Macleod & MacCallum Limited,
Inverness . . . .(p.1080)
T: 01463 239393
E: robert.milsom@macandmac.co.uk

MILTON, Bruce (Sept 1980) (Partner)
Masson Glennie LLP, Peterhead . . . . . .(p.1154)
T: 01779 474271
E: bruce.milton@massonglennie.co.uk

MILTON, Sarah (Oct 2017) (Employee)
Masson Glennie LLP, Peterhead . . . . . .(p.1154)
T: 01779 474271
E: sarah.milton@massonglennie.co.uk

MILVENAN, Ross John (Sept 2007) (Employee)
Digby Brown LLP, Glasgow . . . .(p.970)
T: 0141 5669530
E: ross.milvenan@digbybrown.co.uk

MINCHER, Victoria Barbara (Sept 2011)
(Employee)
Aberdeen Corporate Services Limited,
Edinburgh . . . .(p.1220)
T: 0131 245 7508
E: victoria.dow@aberdeen-asset.com

MINICK, Alice Mitchell (Apr 2019) (Employee)
Dentons UK and Middle East LLP,
Edinburgh . . . .(p.860)
T: 0330 2220050
E: Alice.Minick@dentons.com

MINTO, Bruce Watson (Dec 1981) (Employee)
Dickson Minto, Edinburgh . . . .(p.861)
T: 0131 2254455
E: bruce.minto@dmws.com

MINTO, Chloe (Jul 2018) (Employee)
Dailly, Walker and Co., Solicitors,
Glasgow . . . .(p.965)
T: 0141 4402503
E: cminto@govanlc.com

MINTON, Martin MacDonald (Jan 2016)
(Employee)
Morton Fraser LLP, Glasgow . . . .(p.1022)
T: 0141 2741100
E: martin.minton@morton-fraser.com

MINTY, Alan John (Sept 1991) (Employee)
Merchant Homes Partnerships Limited,
Glasgow. . . . .(p.1241)
T: 0141 420 2026
E: Alan.Minty@merchanthomes.co.uk

MINTY, Ann Marie (Oct 1991) (Employee)
East Dunbartonshire Council,
Kirkintilloch . . . .(p.1249)
T: 0141 5788000
E: AnnMarie.Minty@eastdunbarton.gov.uk

MISSELBROOK, Peter (Jun 1978) (Consultant)
Shepherd and Wedderburn LLP,
Edinburgh . . . .(p.900)
T: 0131 2289900
E: Peter.Misselbrook@shepwedd.com

MITCHELHILL, Steven George (Nov 2000)
(Solicitor)
NO FIRM

MITCHELL, Aaron Steven (Jan 2001)
(Employee)
Asurion Singapore Pte Ltd,
Singapore. . . . .(p.1276)
E: Aaron.Mitchell@asurion.com

MITCHELL, Alastair John (Sept 2015)
(Employee)
Procurator Fiscal Service,
Edinburgh . . . .(p.1229)
T: (0844) 561 3268
E: Alastair.Mitchell@copfs.gov.uk

MITCHELL, Alison Ann (Apr 1985) (Employee)
Gilson Gray LLP, Dundee. . . . .(p.812)
E: amitchell@gilsongray.co.uk

MITCHELL, Andrew John (Dec 1988)
(Consultant)
Milne & Co. WS, Edinburgh . . . .(p.890)
T: 0131 5581441
E: andrew@milne.law

MITCHELL, Brenda Patricia (Nov 1987)
(Partner)
Road Traffic Accident Law (Scotland) LLP,
Peebles . . . .(p.1144)
T: 01721 728238
E:
brenda.mitchell@motorcyclelawscotland.co.uk

MITCHELL, Carolyn Mary (Nov 1997)
(Consultant)
Morton Fraser LLP, Edinburgh . . . .(p.891)
T: 0131 2471000
E: Carrie.Mitchell@morton-fraser.com

MITCHELL, Chelsey Paige (Mar 2020)
(Employee)
Directorate of Army Legal Services,
Andover . . . .(p.1258)
T: 01980 615013
E: Chelsey.mitchell7@hotmail.com

MITCHELL, David George (Dec 1997) (Partner)
Shepherd and Wedderburn LLP,
Edinburgh . . . .(p.900)
T: 0131 2289900
E: David.Mitchell@shepwedd.com

MITCHELL, David John (Dec 1990) (Employee)
East Ayrshire Council, Kilmarnock . . . . .(p.1249)
T: 01563 576061
E: david.mitchell@east-ayrshire.gov.uk

MITCHELL, David Paul (Nov 1986) (Partner)
A.C. White, Ayr . . . .(p.766)
T: 01292 266900
E: david.mitchell@acwhiteayr.co.uk

MITCHELL, Doran Douglas (Aug 2014)
(Associate)
Gillespie Macandrew LLP,
Edinburgh . . . .(p.872)
T: 0131 2251677
E: doran.mitchell@gillespiemacandrew.co.uk

MITCHELL, Douglas (Aug 1988) (Director)
Macnairs & Wilson Limited, Paisley. . . .(p.1140)
T: 0141 847 6404
E: douglas.mitchell@macnairswilson.co.uk

MITCHELL, Elizabeth Anne (Jul 1996) (Partner)
Harper Macleod LLP, Glasgow . . . .(p.983)
T: 0141 2218888
E: elizabeth.mitchell@harpermacleod.co.uk

MITCHELL, Euan William (Oct 1999)
(Employee)
Castle Water, Blairgowrie. . . . .(p.1216)
T: 01250 710577
E: Euan.Mitchell@Castlewater.co.uk

MITCHELL, Fiona Janet (Sept 1987)
(Consultant)
Wilsone & Duffus, Aberdeen . . . .(p.746)
T: 01224 651700
E: Fiona.Mitchell@wilsoneduffus.co.uk

MITCHELL, Fraser Jon (Sept 2004) (Partner)
Shoosmiths, Edinburgh . . . .(p.902)
T: 03700 868000
E: fraser.mitchell@shoosmiths.co.uk

MITCHELL, Gavin Hamilton (Oct 1973)
(Partner)
Wrights, Motherwell . . . .(p.1128)
T: 01698 267361
E: gmitchell@wrightsolicitors.com

MITCHELL, Gavin Rattray (Dec 1998)
(Employee)
Orkney Islands Council, Kirkwall . . . . . .(p.1250)
  T: 01856 873535
  E: gavin.mitchell@orkney.gov.uk

MITCHELL, Gillian Elizabeth Smith
(Sept 2012) (Employee)
Patience & Buchan, Aberdeen . . . .(p.739)
  T: 01224 648222
  E: gillian@patienceandbuchan.com

MITCHELL, Graham Stuart (Sept 1997)
(Partner)
Clyde & Co (Scotland) LLP,
  Glasgow. . . . .(p.961)
  T: 0141 2482666
  E: graham.mitchell@clydeco.com

MITCHELL, Gregor John (Sept 1992) (Partner)
BTO Solicitors LLP, Edinburgh . . . .(p.849)
  T: 0131 2222939
  E: gmi@bto.co.uk

MITCHELL, Hayley Jane (Aug 2010) (Associate)
Johnson Legal, Edinburgh . . . .(p.880)
  T: 0131 6229222
  E: hayley@johnsonlegal.co.uk

MITCHELL, Ian Robert (Sept 1999) (Partner)
Lindsays LLP, Glasgow. . . . .(p.1001)
  T: 0141 2216551
  E: IanMitchell@lindsays.co.uk

MITCHELL, Iona Kathleen (Jul 2013)
(Employee)
Mourant Ozannes (Guernsey) LLP, St Peter
  Port . . . .(p.1273)
  E: Iona.Mitchell@mourant.com

MITCHELL, Jacqueline (Jul 2015) (Employee)
Mair Matheson Solicitors Ltd,
  Newmilns. . . . .(p.1130)
  T: 01560 321225

MITCHELL, Jacqueline Ann (Oct 1987) (Partner)
Innes Johnston LLP, Leven . . . .(p.1115)
  T: 01333 429320
  E: jmitchell@innesjohnston.co.uk

MITCHELL, Jane Elizabeth (Feb 1994)
(Employee)
Scottish Widows Limited,
  Edinburgh . . . .(p.1233)
  T: 0131 6557560
  E: jane.mitchell@scottishwidows.co.uk

MITCHELL, Jody Bruce (Sept 2001) (Partner)
Ledingham Chalmers LLP,
  Aberdeen . . . .(p.734)
  T: 01224 408408
  E: jody.mitchell@ledinghamchalmers.com

MITCHELL, John Angus (Oct 1995) (Partner)
Anderson Strathern LLP, Edinburgh . . . .(p.839)
  T: 0131 2707700
  E: john.mitchell@andersonstrathern.co.uk

MITCHELL, John Gillan (Dec 2002) (Partner)
Ledingham Chalmers LLP,
  Aberdeen . . . .(p.734)
  T: 01224 408408
  E: john.mitchell@ledinghamchalmers.com

MITCHELL, John Paul (Sept 1994) (Employee)
WEST DUNBARTONSHIREhire Council,
  Dumbarton . . . .(p.1217)
  T: 01389 737000
  E: john.mitchell@west-dunbarton.gov.uk

MITCHELL, Kate Elisabeth Martell
(Jun 2002) (Employee)
Lloyds Banking Group Plc,
  Edinburgh . . . .(p.1224)
  T: (0131) 442 9579
  E: katie.mitchell@lloydsbanking.com

MITCHELL, Katherine Laura (Sept 2006)
(Employee)
Devro plc., Glasgow . . . .(p.1239)
  T: 01236 872 261
  E: kate.mitchell@devro.com

MITCHELL, Kelly Louise (Oct 2012) (Employee)
Premier Oil Plc, London SW1 . . . .(p.1267)
  T: 020 7730 1111
  E: kmitchell@premier-oil.com

MITCHELL, Kelly Marie (Aug 2011) (Employee)
Procurator Fiscal Service, Aberdeen . . .(p.1213)
  T: 0844 561 4571
  E: Kelly.Mitchell@copfs.gov.uk

MITCHELL, Keren Vaughan (Aug 2005)
(Associate)
C. & D. Mactaggart,
  Campbeltown. . . . .(p.782)
  T: 01586 552317
  E: keren.mitchell@cdm-law.co.uk

MITCHELL, Kimberley Jane (Sept 2011)
(Associate)
Clyde & Co (Scotland) LLP,
  Edinburgh . . . .(p.855)
  T: 0131 5571545
  E: kimberley.mitchell@clydeco.com

MITCHELL, Kirsty Beth (Mar 2021) (Associate)
CMS Cameron McKenna Nabarro Olswang LLP,
  Glasgow. . . . .(p.962)
  T: 0141 2222200
  E: kirsty.mitchell@cms-cmno.com

MITCHELL, Laura C. H. (May 2012) (Employee)
Aldermore Bank Plc, Manchester . . . . .(p.1270)
  E: laura.mitchell@aldermore.co.uk

MITCHELL, Lauren Grace (Aug 2010)
(Employee)
Pacitti Jones Legal Limited,
  Glasgow. . . . .(p.1028)
  T: 0141 6473322
  E: Lauren@pjglasgow.co.uk

MITCHELL, Lauren Margaret (Nov 2020)
(Employee)
Scottish Borders Council, Newtown St.
Boswells . . . .(p.1251)
T: 01835 825 225
E: lauren.mitchell@scotborders.gov.uk

MITCHELL, Lauri MacGregor (Sept 2014)
(Employee)
Legal Secretariat to the Advocate General,
London SW1 . . . .(p.1266)
T: 020 72706810
E: lauri.mitchell@advocategeneral.gov.uk

MITCHELL, Lyndsey Christina Elizabeth
(Oct 2014) (Employee)
Pinsent Masons LLP, Edinburgh . . . .(p.895)
T: 0131 777 7000
E: Lyndsey.Mitchell@pinsentmasons.com

MITCHELL, Lynn Catherine (Aug 1988)
(Employee)
Renfrewshire Council, Paisley . . . .(p.1252)
T: 0141 6187163
E: lynn.mitchell@renfrewshire.gov.uk

MITCHELL, Nicola Ann (Jan 2004) (Partner)
Dickson Minto, Edinburgh . . . .(p.861)
T: 0131 2254455
E: nicola.mitchell@dmws.com

MITCHELL, Robert (Aug 1987) (Partner)
Tod & Mitchell, Paisley . . . .(p.1142)
T: 0141 8891444
E: enquiries@todandmitchell.co.uk

MITCHELL, Robin Hamish George
(Oct 1993) (Partner)
Shoosmiths, Edinburgh . . . .(p.902)
T: 03700 868000
E: robin.mitchell@shoosmiths.co.uk

MITCHELL, Ross Andrew James (May 2015)
(Employee)
Brodies LLP, Edinburgh . . . .(p.845)
T: 0131 2283777
E: ross.mitchell@brodies.com

MITCHELL, Sarah (Sept 2010) (Employee)
Office of the Advocate General,
Edinburgh . . . .(p.1227)
T: 7393761461
E: sarah.mitchell@advocategeneral.gov.uk

MITCHELL, Sarah Anne (Apr 2015) (Partner)
Macnabs LLP, Perth . . . .(p.1150)
T: 01738 623432
E: sarahmitchell@macnabs-law.co.uk

MITCHELL, Thomas Finlay (Oct 2018)
(Employee)
Road Traffic Accident Law (Scotland) LLP,
Peebles . . . .(p.1144)
T: 01721 728238
E: Thomas.Mitchell@RTALaw.scot

MITCHELL, Victoria Elizabeth (Oct 2013)
(Director)
Miller Beckett & Jackson Limited,
Glasgow . . . .(p.1019)
T: 0141 2042833
E: vmitchell@mbjsolicitors.co.uk

MITCHELL, William George (Jan 1983)
(Consultant)
Patten & Prentice LLP, Greenock . . . . .(p.1062)
T: 01475 720306
E: billm@patten.co.uk

MITCHELSON, Margaret Louise (Dec 1991)
(Employee)
Gillespie Macandrew LLP,
Edinburgh . . . .(p.872)
T: 0131 2251677
E: louise.mitchelson@gillespiemacandrew.co.uk

MITREA, Alexandra-Magda (Sept 2020)
(Employee)
Cooley (UK) LLP, London EC2 . . . .(p.1263)
E: amitrea@cooley.com

MIVAL, Mhairi Daniella (Jun 2004) (Associate)
Pinsent Masons LLP, Edinburgh . . . .(p.895)
T: 0131 777 7000
E: mhairi.mival@pinsentmasons.com

MIZEN, Lauren Jane Clarke (Mar 2021)
(Employee)
Drummond Miller LLP, Edinburgh . . . . .(p.864)
T: 0131 2265151
E: LMizen@drummondmiller.co.uk

MOBSBY, Sarah Kathryn (Aug 2005)
(Employee)
Procurator Fiscal Service, Glasgow . . . .(p.1241)
T: 0300 0203000
E: sarah.mobsby@copfs.gov.uk

MODLIN, Brooke Kelly (Sept 2019) (Employee)
Link Market Services Limited, London
EC2 . . . .(p.1266)

MODLIN, Wanda Gioia (Nov 1976) (Solicitor)
NO FIRM

MOFFAT, Clare Elizabeth (Oct 2002)
(Employee)
Royal London Group, Edinburgh . . . . .(p.1230)
E: clare.moffat1@royallondon.com

MOFFAT, Colin Michael (Jan 2010) (Associate)
Digby Brown LLP, Glasgow . . . .(p.970)
T: 0333 200 5925
E: colin.moffat@digbybrown.co.uk

MOFFAT, David James (Nov 2018) (Employee)
Scottish Government, Edinburgh . . . . .(p.1231)
T: 0131 244 0815
E: david.moffat@gov.scot

MOFFAT, Ewan George (Feb 1992) (Partner)
Campbell Boath, Dundee . . . .(p.808)
T: 01382 200110
E: emoffat@campbellboath.com

MOFFAT, Gary John (Sept 1991) (Partner)
Burness Paull LLP, Glasgow . . . .(p.954)
T: 0141 2484933
E: Gary.Moffat@burnesspaull.com

MOFFAT, Hazel Elaine (Oct 1997) (Partner)
Burness Paull LLP, Edinburgh . . . .(p.850)
T: 0131 4736000
E: hazel.moffat@burnesspaull.com

MOFFAT, Julia Anne White (Sept 2011)
(Employee)
Mubadala Investment Company PJSC, Abu
Dhabi . . . .(p.1277)
E: julia.moffat@mubadalapetroleum.com

MOFFAT, Louise Anne (Jan 2017) (Employee)
Digby Brown LLP, Edinburgh . . . .(p.862)
T: 0333 200 5925
E: louise.moffat@digbybrown.co.uk

MOFFAT, Stephen William (Oct 2011)
(Employee)
Morton Fraser LLP, Edinburgh . . . .(p.891)
T: 0131 2471000
E: stephen.moffat@morton-fraser.com

MOFFETT, Graeme Robert (Oct 1998)
(Employee)
BAE Systems Surface Ships Limited,
Glasgow. . . . .(p.1238)
T: 0141 9574658
E: graeme.moffett@baesystems.com

MOFFETT, Kathryn Margaret (Mar 2015)
(Employee)
CMS Cameron McKenna Nabarro Olswang LLP,
Glasgow. . . . .(p.962)
T: 0141 2222200
E: kathryn.moffett@cms-cmno.com

MOFFETT, Morag Woodburn (Oct 2002)
(Partner)
Burness Paull LLP, Glasgow . . . .(p.954)
T: 0141 2484933
E: Morag.Moffett@burnesspaull.com

MOFFETT, Peter Gale (May 2011) (Director)
Hill & Robb Limited, Stirling . . . .(p.1164)
T: 01786 450985
E: petermoffett@hillandrobb.co.uk

MOFFETT, Ruth Marion (Oct 2016) (Employee)
Taylor Wessing LLP, London EC4 . . . . .(p.1268)
T: (020) 7300 4995
E: R.Moffett@taylorwessing.com

MOHAMED, Zara Nisa (Dec 2020) (Employee)
Oraclelaw Limited, Glasgow. . . . .(p.1027)
T: 0141 4041091
E: zm@oraclelaw.com

MOHAMMED, Omar Hassan (Jul 2020)
(Employee)
MOV8 Real Estate Limited,
Edinburgh . . . .(p.893)
T: 0345 646 0208
E: omar.mohammed@mov8realestate.com

MOHAMMED, Ramiza (Mar 2006) (Director)
MM Legal, Glasgow . . . .(p.1021)
T: 0141 2642272
E: ramiza@mmlegal.co.uk

MOIR, Anna Jane (Aug 2016) (Associate)
Raeburn Christie Clark & Wallace LLP,
Aberdeen . . . .(p.741)
T: 01224 332400
E: anna.moir@raeburns.co.uk

MOIR, Barry James (Jan 2019) (Employee)
Rutherford Sheridan Ltd, Glasgow . . . .(p.1037)
T: 0141 248 3320

MOIR, Emma Louise (Jun 2016) (Employee)
SSE PLC, Glasgow . . . .(p.1244)
T: 0141 224 7248
E: emma.moir@sse.com

MOIR, Gordon Ivor (Nov 1995) (Employee)
Wiggin LLP, London W1 . . . .(p.1269)
E: gordon.moir@wiggin.co.uk

MOIR, Hazel Marion (Oct 1986) (Partner)
Ledingham Chalmers LLP,
Aberdeen . . . .(p.734)
T: 01224 408408
E: hazel.moir@ledinghamchalmers.com

MOIR, Ian Richard (Feb 1993) (Partner)
Moir and Sweeney LLP, Glasgow . . . . .(p.1021)
T: 0141 4292724
E: ian@moirandsweeney.com

MOIR, Jack (Aug 2010) (Partner)
Brodies LLP, Glasgow . . . .(p.948)
T: 0141 248 4672
E: jack.moir@brodies.com

MOIR, Jennifer Anne (Nov 2008) (Employee)
City of Edinburgh Council,
Edinburgh . . . .(p.1221)
T: (0131) 5294145
E: Jennifer.moir@edinburgh.gov.uk

MOIR, Kyle Frank Strachan (Aug 2006)
(Partner)
MacRoberts LLP, Dundee. . . . .(p.815)
T: 01382 339340
E: kyle.moir@macroberts.com

MOIR, Malcolm MacMillan (Nov 2015)
(Employee)
Bryan Cave Leighton Paisner LLP, London
EC4 . . . .(p.1262)
E: malcolm.moir@bclplaw.com

MOIR, Richard (Jan 2016) (Employee)
Ascent Underwriting LLP, London
EC3 . . . .(p.1261)
T: 0203 8592193
E: richard.moir@ascentunderwriting.com

MOIR, Scott Andrew (Sept 2019) (Employee)
Pinsent Masons LLP, Edinburgh . . . .(p.895)
T: 0131 777 7000
E: Scott.Moir@pinsentmasons.com

MOIR, Sheryl (Jun 2014) (Employee)
Scottish Social Services Council,
Dundee . . . .(p.1218)
T: 0345 6030 891
E: Sheryl.Moir@sssc.uk.com

MOIR, Stephanie Patricia (Oct 2015)
(Employee)
Wilsone & Duffus, Aberdeen . . . .(p.746)
T: 01224 651700
E: Stephanie.Moir@wilsoneduffus.co.uk

MOIR, Suzanne Dorothy (Nov 1997) (Partner)
Addleshaw Goddard LLP,
Edinburgh . . . .(p.835)
T: 0131 2282400
E: Suzanne.Moir@addleshawgoddard.com

MOJEE, Neel Kumar (Nov 2001) (Employee)
Scottish Government, Edinburgh . . . . .(p.1231)
T: 0131 244 0815
E: neel.mojee@gov.scot

MOLLEY, Michelle Margaret (Jan 2007)
(Employee)
Procurator Fiscal Service, Inverness . . . .(p.1248)
T: 3000204197
E: Michelle.Molley@copfs.gov.uk

MOLLOY, Catherine Mary (Nov 2002)
(Employee)
East Lothian Council, Haddington . . . .(p.1246)
T: 01620 827448
E: cmolloy1@eastlothian.gov.uk

MONAGHAN, Catherine Mary (Sept 1992)
(Partner)
Moore & Partners LLP,
Cumbernauld . . . .(p.790)
T: 01236 727715
E: cmonaghan@moorepartners.com

MONAGHAN, Erin (Jan 2017) (Employee)
Aamer Anwar & Co, Glasgow . . . .(p.941)
T: 0141 4297090
E: erin@aameranwar.com

MONAGHAN, Joanna Louise (Nov 2006)
(Employee)
Burges Salmon LLP, Edinburgh . . . .(p.850)
T: 0131 3142112
E: joanna.monaghan@burges-salmon.com

MONAGHAN, Lyndsay (Aug 2017) (Employee)
JustRight Scotland LLP, Glasgow . . . . . .(p.994)
T: 0141 406 5350
E: lyndsay@justrightscotland.org.uk

MONAGHAN, Martin Francis (Sept 1991)
(Partner)
Caesar & Howie, Livingston . . . .(p.1118)
T: 01506 435271
E: mfm@caesar-howie.co.uk

MONAN, Sarah Frances (Jun 2021) (Employee)
Anderson Strathern LLP, Edinburgh . . . .(p.839)
T: 0131 2707700
E: sarah.monan@andersonstrathern.co.uk

MONCRIEFF, Eilidh Rae (Oct 2019) (Employee)
DLA Piper Scotland LLP, Edinburgh . . . .(p.863)
T: 08700 111111
E: eilidh.moncrieff@dlapiper.com

MONCRIEFF, James William (Aug 2011)
(Employee)
BSW Solicitors LLP, Dunfermline . . . .(p.823)
T: 01383 621144
E: james@bastensneddon.co.uk

MONCUR, Scott James (Oct 1990) (Employee)
Medici Legal Advisers, Edinburgh . . . . .(p.1225)
E: scott@medici-legal.com

MONKS, Siobhan Elaine (Sept 1999)
(Employee)
Procurator Fiscal Service,
Edinburgh . . . .(p.1229)
T: (0844) 561 3268
E: siobhan.monks@copfs.gov.uk

MONRO, Michael Eric (Dec 1976) (Partner)
Mackie & Dewar, Aberdeen . . . .(p.736)
T: 01224 596341
E: mem@mackieanddewar.co.uk

MONSON, Linda Jane (Jun 2008) (Partner)
McAuley, McCarthy & Co.,
Renfrew . . . .(p.1159)
T: 0141 5614449
E: linda@mmscotland.co.uk

MONTAGUE, Lesley Mary (Sept 2005)
(Employee)
West Lothian Council, Livingston . . . . .(p.1250)
T: 01506 280000
E: Lesley.Montague@westlothian.gov.uk

MONTEFORTE, James (Oct 2006) (Employee)
Heineken UK Limited, Edinburgh . . . . .(p.1223)
T: 0131 5281000
E: james.monteforte@heineken.co.uk

MONTEFORTE, Leigh Allan (Oct 2005)
(Employee)
Lexis Nexis, London EC4 . . . .(p.1266)
E: leigh.monteforte@lexisnexis.co.uk

MONTEITH, Emma (Sept 2010) (Employee)
William Grant & Sons Ltd., Bellshill . . .(p.1215)
T: 01698 573 659
E: emma.monteith@wgrant.com

MONTEITH, Jenna Alison (Nov 2010)
(Associate)
Brodies LLP, Glasgow . . . .(p.948)
T: 0141 2484672
E: Jenna.Monteith@brodies.com

MONTEITH, Thomas William (Sept 1994)
(Director)
Monteith Solicitors Limited, Nairn . . . . (p.1129)
T: (0141) 370 0900
E: tom@monteithsolicitors.com

MONTGOMERY, Alison Maria (Sept 2010)
(Employee)
Procurator Fiscal Service, Glasgow . . . . (p.1241)
T: 0300 0203000
E: Alison.Montgomery@copfs.gov.uk

MONTGOMERY, Catherine Anna (Jan 2010)
(Employee)
Superdrug Stores PLC, Croydon . . . . . . (p.1259)

MONTGOMERY, Christopher Robert
(Sept 1995) (Employee)
BP International Ltd,
Sunbury-on-Thames . . . . (p.1271)
T: 0203 401 5198
E: Chris.Montgomery1@se1.bp.com

MONTGOMERY, Claire (Mar 2018) (Employee)
Scottish Government, Edinburgh . . . . . (p.1231)
T: 0131 244 0108
E: Claire.Montgomery@gov.scot

MONTGOMERY, Hayley Gillian (Sept 2020)
(Employee)
Burness Paull LLP, Edinburgh . . . . (p.850)
T: 0131 4736000
E: Hayley.Montgomery@burnesspaull.com

MONTGOMERY, Kerri (Aug 2021) (Employee)
D C Thomson & Co Ltd, Dundee . . . . . (p.1217)
E: KMontgomery@dcthomson.co.uk

MONTGOMERY, Martin John (Oct 2008)
(Employee)
Gateley Plc, London EC4 . . . . (p.1264)
E: martin.montgomery@gateleylegal.com

MONTGOMERY, Ross Lauchlan (Sept 2007)
(Employee)
Dechert LLP, London EC4 . . . . (p.1263)
T: 020 7184 7000
E: Ross.Montgomery@dechert.com

MONTGOMERY, Ruth Catherine (Feb 2010)
(Employee)
Cullen Kilshaw, Galashiels . . . . (p.933)
T: 01896 800 800
E: ruth.montgomery@cullenkilshaw.com

MONTGOMERY, Susan Catherine
(Aug 1994) (Employee)
Scottish Police Authority, Glasgow . . . . (p.1244)
T: 01786 896981
E: Susan.Montgomery@spa.pnn.police.uk

MONTGOMERY, Tay Carmichael (Sept 2020)
(Employee)
McVey & Murricane, Glasgow . . . . (p.1017)
T: 0141 3339688
E: tmontgomery@mcvey-murricane.com

MOODIE, Colin Douglas (Mar 1993)
(Employee)
Falkirk Council, Falkirk . . . . (p.1236)
T: 01324 506070
E: colin.moodie@falkirk.gov.uk

MOODIE, Magnus Knowles, WS (Sept 1984)
(Partner)
McEwan Fraser Legal, Edinburgh . . . . . . (p.885)
T: 0131 5249797
E: magnus.moodie@mcewanfraserlegal.co.uk

MOOKER, Rupneet Kaur (Nov 2003)
(Employee)
MacRoberts LLP, Glasgow . . . . (p.1015)
T: 0141 3031100
E: rupa.mooker@macroberts.com

MOON, Rachel Macmillan (Mar 2012)
(Employee)
Dailly, Walker and Co., Solicitors,
Glasgow . . . . (p.966)
T: 0141 433 2665
E: rmoon@govanlc.com

MOONEY, Claire Danielle (Oct 2007)
(Employee)
Barclays Execution Services Limited,
Glasgow . . . . (p.1238)
E: Claire.Mooney@barclays.com

MOONEY, Joseph (Jan 1986) (Partner)
Mooneys, Edinburgh . . . . (p.890)
T: 07711 510816
E: mooneys.solicitors@hotmail.co.uk

MOONEY, Michelle Audrey (Dec 2019)
(Employee)
East Ayrshire Council, Kilmarnock . . . . . (p.1249)
T: 01563 576161
E: Michelle.Mooney@east-ayrshire.gov.uk

MOONEY, Robert John Home (Jul 2012)
(Employee)
Home Office, London SW1 . . . . (p.1265)
T: 07778 100 471
E: Robert.mooney@homeoffice.gov.uk

MOORE, Brian Hugh (Feb 1999) (Partner)
Dentons UK and Middle East LLP,
Edinburgh . . . . (p.860)
T: 0330 2220050
E: Brian.Moore@dentons.com

MOORE, Fiona Isabel (Oct 1984) (Consultant)
Drummond Miller LLP, Edinburgh . . . . . (p.864)
T: 0131 2265151
E: fmoore@drummondmiller.co.uk

MOORE, Francis Gerald (Oct 1990) (Partner)
Russells Gibson McCaffrey,
Glasgow . . . . (p.1037)
T: 0141 271 1000
E: f.moore@russellsgm.co.uk

MOORE, Gary (Dec 2002) (Employee)
National Westminster Bank PLC,
Edinburgh ....(p.1226)
T: (0131) 626 2925
E: gary.moore@rbs.co.uk

MOORE, George Kuthy, QC (Jul 1971)
(Consultant)
Berrymans Lace Mawer LLP,
Glasgow.....................(p.945)
T: 0141 3532121
E: gmooreqc@gmail.com

MOORE, Gillian Ward (Sept 2012) (Employee)
Shepherd and Wedderburn LLP,
Glasgow....................(p.1039)
T: 0141 5669900
E: Gillian.Moore@shepwedd.com

MOORE, Hannah Christie (Aug 2019)
(Employee)
Addleshaw Goddard LLP, Glasgow .....(p.938)
T: 0141 221 2300
E: hannah.moore@addleshawgoddard.com

MOORE, Iain James (Jul 2021) (Employee)
Drummond Miller LLP, Edinburgh .....(p.864)
T: 0131 2265151
E: IMoore@drummondmiller.co.uk

MOORE, Jacqueline Hazel (Sept 1999)
(Employee)
Shepherd and Wedderburn LLP,
Edinburgh ....(p.900)
T: 0131 2289900
E: Jacqueline.Moore@shepwedd.com

MOORE, James Gerad (Oct 1991) (Partner)
Moore Macdonald, Motherwell ......(p.1127)
T: 01698 262111
E: james@mooremacdonald.co.uk

MOORE, James Philip Martin (Apr 1985)
(Partner)
Sinclairs, Edinburgh ....(p.903)
T: 0131 662 4205
E: admin@sinclairscdl.co.uk

MOORE, Jillian Mary (Nov 2005) (Employee)
Burness Paull LLP, Edinburgh ....(p.850)
T: 0131 4736000
E: Jillian.Moore@burnesspaull.com

MOORE, Laura Elizabeth (Nov 2006) (Partner)
Tait & Mackenzie LLP,
Grangemouth.................(p.1059)
T: 01324 471121
E: laura@taitandmackenzie.co.uk

MOORE, Norman William (Sept 1980)
(Director)
Norrie Moore Limited,
Cumbernauld ....(p.790)
T: 01236 729868
E: norrie@nmlegal.co.uk

MOORE, Ryan (Oct 2012) (Employee)
Macfarlanes LLP, London EC4 ....(p.1266)
T: (020) 7791 4044
E: Ryan.Moore@macfarlanes.com

MOORE, Victoria (Apr 2004) (Employee)
John Menzies Plc, Edinburgh ....(p.1224)
E: victoria.moore@menziesaviation.com

MORAN, Ann (Dec 1965) (Partner)
Moran & Co., Glasgow ....(p.1022)
T: 0141 221 7479
E: annmoran@mac.com

MORAN, Kirsty Elizabeth (Dec 2018)
(Employee)
Thompsons, Glasgow ....(p.1046)
T: 0141 2218840
E: kirsty.moran@thompsons-scotland.co.uk

MORAN, Maureen (Sept 1987) (Employee)
Dundee City Council, Dundee ....(p.1217)
T: 01382 434000
E: maureen.moran@dundeecity.gov.uk

MORAN, Michelle Mary (Jul 2015) (Employee)
Stevenson & Marshall LLP,
Dunfermline ....(p.825)
T: 01383 721141
E: mmoran@stevenson-marshall.co.uk

MORAN, Rachel Louise (Oct 2005) (Employee)
Lloyds Banking Group Plc,
Edinburgh ....(p.1224)
T: (0131) 442 9579
E: Rachel.Moran@lloydsbanking.com

MORE, James Philip (Nov 2003) (Employee)
The Saudi Arabian Mining Company (Ma'aden),
Riyadh ....(p.1276)
E: MoreJP@maaden.com.sa

MORE, Janice Kathleen Mary (Nov 1984)
(Employee)
IQVIA Limited, London N1 ....(p.1265)

MORE, Jonathan James Christian (Jun 1998)
(Director)
Spencer West SCO Limited,
Edinburgh ....(p.904)
E: Jonathan.more@spencer-west.com

MORE, Robert Edwards (Aug 2007) (Partner)
Robert More and Company,
Edinburgh ....(p.890)
T: 0131 5571110
E: robert@moredefence.co.uk

MORETTI, Ilaria (Sept 2018) (Employee)
Burness Paull LLP, Glasgow ....(p.954)
T: 0141 2484933
E: Ilaria.Moretti@burnesspaull.com

MORGAN, Carolyn Nicola (Sept 2000) (Partner)
Harper Macleod LLP, Glasgow ....(p.983)
T: 0141 2218888
E: carolyn.morgan@harpermacleod.co.uk

MORGAN, Christopher Findlay (Oct 1996)
(Solicitor)
NO FIRM

MORGAN, Claire Louise (Jul 1998) (Partner)
Morgans, Dunfermline . . . . (p.824)
T: 01383 620222
E: clairemorgan@morganlaw.co.uk

MORGAN, David (Sept 1997) (Partner)
Burness Paull LLP, Glasgow . . . . (p.954)
T: 0141 2484933
E: David.Morgan@burnesspaull.com

MORGAN, Frankie (Oct 2016) (Employee)
Procurator Fiscal Service, Paisley . . . . . . (p.1252)
T: 0141 8875225
E: Frankie.morgan@copfs.gov.uk

MORGAN, John Henry (Dec 2015) (Employee)
Eversheds Sutherland (International) LLP, London
EC2 . . . . (p.1264)
T: 0845 4979797

MORGAN, Katie (Sept 2017) (Employee)
Jones Whyte LLP, Glasgow . . . . (p.993)
T: 0141 375 1222
E: katie.morgan@joneswhyte.co.uk

MORGAN, Mairi Victoria (Jun 2017) (Employee)
Heineken UK Limited, Edinburgh . . . . . (p.1223)
T: 0131 5281000
E: mairi.morgan@heineken.co.uk

MORGAN, Rosalind Carole (Sept 2007)
(Associate)
CMS Cameron McKenna Nabarro Olswang LLP,
Aberdeen . . . . (p.727)
T: 01224 622002
E: rosalind.morgan@cms-cmno.com

MORGAN, Yvonne Elizabeth (Jul 1986)
(Director)
Morgan Legal Solutions Limited,
Glasgow . . . . (p.1022)
T: 0141 2584117
E: yvonnemorgan@morganlegal.uk.com

MORISON, Jadiene Valerie Rosemary
(May 2019) (Director)
Hendrie Legal Limited, Edinburgh . . . . . (p.878)
T: 0131 370 0470
E: jadiene.morison@ralphhendrie.legal

MORRICE, Alexander Michael Freeland
(Sept 1985) (Partner)
Burness Paull LLP, Aberdeen . . . . (p.724)
T: 01224 621621
E: Mike.Morrice@burnesspaull.com

MORRICE, Stephen James (Sept 1981) (Partner)
Ledingham Chalmers LLP,
Aberdeen . . . . (p.734)
T: 01224 408408
E: stephen.morrice@ledinghamchalmers.com

MORRIS, Adelle (Sept 2011) (Employee)
AM Employment Law Ltd, Elgin . . . . . . (p.1236)
T: 01343 569293
E: adelle@am-employment-law.co.uk

MORRIS, Alessia (Sept 2010) (Solicitor)
NO FIRM

MORRIS, Alison (Jun 2009) (Employee)
Lawson Coull & Duncan, Dundee . . . . . (p.813)
T: 01382 227555
E: amorris@lawsoncoull.co.uk

MORRIS, Alistair Lindsay (Jan 1984)
(Consultant)
Andrew K. Price Limited, Kirkcaldy . . . . (p.1102)
T: 01592 205151

MORRIS, Andrew John (Nov 1984) (Consultant)
Anderson Strathern LLP, Edinburgh . . . . (p.839)
T: 0131 2707700
E: andrew.morris@andersonstrathern.co.uk

MORRIS, David (Oct 1982) (Director)
MTL Law, Glasgow . . . . (p.1024)
T: 0141 2225793
E: david@mtllaw.co.uk

MORRIS, Deborah Louise (Feb 2006)
(Employee)
The Kerr Brown Partnership,
Glasgow . . . . (p.1044)
T: 0141 2214880
E: dm@kerrbrown.co.uk

MORRIS, Jennifer Louise (Sept 2009)
(Employee)
Procurator Fiscal Service, Glasgow . . . . (p.1241)
T: 0300 0203000
E: jennifer.morris@copfs.gov.uk

MORRIS, Joanna Wilson Hunter (Sept 2009)
(Employee)
BBM Solicitors Limited, Edinburgh . . . . . (p.842)
T: 0131 526 3280
E: jwhm@bbmsolicitors.co.uk

MORRIS, John Mitchell (Feb 1997) (Partner)
Morgans, Dunfermline . . . . (p.824)
T: 01383 620222
E: johnmorris@morganlaw.co.uk

MORRIS, Louise Clare (Jan 2000) (Partner)
Cartys, Larkhall . . . . (p.1110)
T: 01698 885888
E: Louise_Morris@cartylaw.co.uk

MORRIS, Rona (Oct 1983) (Solicitor)
NO FIRM

MORRIS, Sarah Elizabeth (Nov 2003) (Partner)
Ledingham Chalmers LLP,
Edinburgh . . . . (p.881)
T: 0131 2001000
E: sarah.morris@ledinghamchalmers.com

MORRIS, Sean Patrick (Feb 2019) (Employee)
Addleshaw Goddard LLP,
Edinburgh . . . .(p.835)
T: 0131 2282400
E: Sean.Morris@addleshawgoddard.com

MORRISON, Ainslie Jayne (Aug 2019)
(Employee)
Kee Solicitors Ltd, Glasgow . . . .(p.995)
T: 0141 478 9090
E: ainslie@keesolicitors.co.uk

MORRISON, Alan (Jul 2018) (Employee)
Procurator Fiscal Service,
Edinburgh . . . .(p.1229)
T: 0300 0203000
E: Alan.Morrison@copfs.gov.uk

MORRISON, Alastair John MacKinnon
(Nov 1987) (Partner)
Pinsent Masons LLP, Glasgow . . . .(p.1031)
T: 0141 567 8400
E: alastair.morrison@pinsentmasons.com

MORRISON, Alexander Jack (Jul 1987)
(Employee)
Cartys, Hamilton. . . . .(p.1066)
T: 01698 285432
E: hamilton@cartylaw.co.uk

MORRISON, Angela Jane (Nov 2000) (Partner)
Lindsays (Property), Dundee . . . .(p.814)
T: 01382 802050

MORRISON, Ashley Michelle (Mar 2012)
(Employee)
Carey Olsen, St Helier . . . .(p.1274)
T: 01534 888900

MORRISON, Brian Thomas (Jun 1997)
(Associate)
Shoosmiths LLP, London EC4 . . . .(p.1268)
T: 03700 863000
E: Thomas.Morrison@shoosmiths.co.uk

MORRISON, Colin James (Feb 1996) (Partner)
Brodies LLP, Edinburgh . . . .(p.845)
T: 0131 2283777
E: colin.morrison@brodies.com

MORRISON, Craig Edward (Oct 2002) (Partner)
Pinsent Masons LLP, Glasgow . . . .(p.1031)
T: 0141 567 8400
E: craig.morrison@pinsentmasons.com

MORRISON, David (Mar 1972) (Partner)
Campbell Connon, Aberdeen. . . . .(p.726)
T: 01224 585585
E: dmorrison@campbellconnon.co.uk

MORRISON, David John (Sept 2006)
(Employee)
Scottish Social Services Council,
Dundee . . . .(p.1218)
T: 0345 6030 891
E: davidjohnmorrison@gmail.com

MORRISON, Deirdre Christine (Jun 1987)
(Employee)
Scottish Courts and Tribunals Service,
Edinburgh . . . .(p.1230)
T: 0131 2252525
E: dmorrison2@scotcourts.gov.uk

MORRISON, Eilidh Katherine (Jun 2018)
(Employee)
Travers Smith LLP, London EC1 . . . . . .(p.1269)
T: (0207) 2953387
E: eilidh.morrison@traverssmith.com

MORRISON, Elizabeth Anne (Oct 2015)
(Employee)
Digby Brown LLP, Glasgow . . . .(p.970)
T: 0141 5669516
E: elizabeth.morrison@digbybrown.co.uk

MORRISON, Feeza Khatoon (Aug 2008)
(Employee)
NO FIRM

MORRISON, Fraser (Jun 2013) (Director)
Ennova Limited, Dundee . . . .(p.810)
T: 01382 938118
E: fmorrison@ennova-law.com

MORRISON, Fraser Lewis (Oct 2009) (Director)
McKee Campbell Morrison Limited,
Glasgow. . . . .(p.1013)
T: 0141 4883680
E: fraser@mcmsolicitors.co.uk

MORRISON, Graeme Edward (Sept 2009)
(Employee)
ASDA Stores Ltd, Leeds . . . .(p.1260)
T: 0113 8262272
E: graeme.morrison@asda.co.uk

MORRISON, Graham (Sept 1984) (Partner)
Gavin Bain & Co., Aberdeen . . . .(p.721)
T: 01224 623040
E: g.morrison@gavin-bain.co.uk

MORRISON, Heather (Sept 2020) (Employee)
Paterson Bell Limited, Edinburgh . . . . . .(p.895)
T: 0131 2256111
E: heather@patersonbell.co.uk

MORRISON, Holly Rachel (Jul 2020) (Employee)
Duncan & McConnell Solicitors Limited,
Dundee . . . .(p.809)
T: 07761 301390
E: hmorrison@duncanandmcconnell.com

MORRISON, James (Oct 1978) (Partner)
Sneddon Morrison, Whitburn . . . .(p.1180)
T: 01501 740345
E: jm@sneddons-ssc.co.uk

MORRISON, James Bone (Feb 1982) (Partner)
McSherry Halliday LLP, Troon . . . .(p.1175)
T: 01292 313737
E: jbm@mcsherryhalliday.co.uk

MORRISON, Janet Ann (Oct 2007) (Solicitor)
NO FIRM

MORRISON, Janice Katrina (Mar 2015)
(Employee)
Scottish Social Services Council,
Dundee . . . . (p.1218)
T: 0345 6030 891
E: janice.morrison@sssc.uk.com

MORRISON, Joan Macdonald (Mar 1995)
(Solicitor)
NO FIRM

MORRISON, John (Mar 2011) (Partner)
Shepherd and Wedderburn LLP,
Edinburgh . . . . (p.900)
T: 0131 2289900
E: john.morrison@shepwedd.com

MORRISON, John Christopher Robert
(Sept 2014) (Employee)
Aegon UK, Edinburgh . . . . (p.1220)
T: 1315493986
E: john.morrison@aegon.co.uk

MORRISON, John Robert (Nov 2009) (Solicitor)
NO FIRM

MORRISON, Judith Ann (Oct 1990) (Employee)
The Scottish Parliament, Edinburgh . . . (p.1235)
T: 0131 348 6649
E: judith.morrison@parliament.scot

MORRISON, Kate Young (Aug 2012)
(Employee)
Minter Ellison, Sydney . . . . (p.1257)
E: kate.morrison@minterellison.com

MORRISON, Kathleen Anne (Dec 2003)
(Employee)
Brodies LLP, Glasgow . . . . (p.948)
T: 0141 2484672
E: kathleen.morrison@brodies.com

MORRISON, Katrina Ann (Nov 2014)
(Employee)
Dechert LLP, Dubai . . . . (p.1278)
T: +971 4 425 6346
E: katrina.morrison@dechert.com

MORRISON, Keri Lyn (Nov 2011) (Employee)
Aberdeen City Council, Aberdeen . . . . . (p.1211)
T: 01224 522000
E: KeMorrison@aberdeencity.gov.uk

MORRISON, Kirsten Elizabeth (Feb 2009)
(Director)
Belmont Legal Ltd, Glasgow . . . . (p.944)
T: 0141 7298848
E: kmorrison@kudoslegal.co.uk

MORRISON, Laura Louise (Mar 2005)
(Associate)
Dentons UK and Middle East LLP,
Edinburgh . . . . (p.860)
T: 0330 2220050
E: Laura.Morrison@dentons.com

MORRISON, Lauren Sinclair (Oct 2014)
(Solicitor)
Ashurst LLP, London E1 . . . . (p.1261)
T: (020) 7859 2145
E: lauren.morrison@ashurst.com

MORRISON, Marianne (Jan 2001) (Employee)
BAM Construct UK Ltd, stepps . . . . (p.1254)
T: 0141 7798888
E: mmorrison@bam.co.uk

MORRISON, Marie Helen (Dec 1992)
(Associate)
Grigor & Young LLP, Elgin . . . . (p.916)
T: 01343 544077
E: marie@grigor-young.co.uk

MORRISON, Mhairi Alison (Nov 2003)
(Employee)
Procurator Fiscal Service,
Edinburgh . . . . (p.1229)
T: 0300 0203000
E: mhairi.morrison@copfs.gov.uk

MORRISON, Mhairi Catriona (May 2014)
(Employee)
Pinsent Masons LLP, London EC2 . . . . . (p.1267)
T: 020 7418 7000
E: Mhairi.Morrison@pinsentmasons.com

MORRISON, Neil John (Nov 2007) (Employee)
Vestas-Celtic Wind Technology Ltd,
Edinburgh . . . . (p.1235)
E: nejmo@vestas.com

MORRISON, Niamh Catherine (Dec 2019)
(Employee)
CMS Cameron McKenna Nabarro Olswang LLP,
Aberdeen . . . . (p.727)
T: 01224 622002
E: niamh.morrison@cms-cmno.com

MORRISON, Philip (Sept 1991) (Employee)
Clarion Solicitors Limited, Leeds . . . . . . (p.1260)
T: (0113) 2460622
E: phil.morrison@clarionsolicitors.com

MORRISON, Philip David (Jan 2020) (Employee)
Travelex Central Services Limited,
Peterborough . . . . (p.1271)
E: philip.morrison@travelex.com

MORRISON, Rachael Nicole (Sept 2019)
(Employee)
Raeburn Christie Clark & Wallace LLP,
Inverurie . . . . (p.1085)
T: 01467 629300
E: rachael.morrison@raeburns.co.uk

MORRISON, Rachel Anne (Oct 2014)
(Employee)
CMS Cameron McKenna Nabarro Olswang LLP,
Glasgow . . . . (p.962)
T: 0141 2222200
E: Rachel.Morrison@cms-cmno.com

MORRISON, Robert Angus (Nov 2016)
(Employee)
Pinsent Masons LLP, Edinburgh . . . .(p.895)
T: 0131 777 7000
E: rob.morrison@pinsentmasons.com

MORRISON, Ruairidh Duncan (Nov 2020)
(Employee)
MBM Commercial LLP, Edinburgh . . . . .(p.889)
T: 0131 2268200
E: ruairidh.morrison@mbmcommercial.co.uk

MORRISON, Sean Charles (Sept 1996)
(Employee)
Public Defence Solicitors Office,
Edinburgh . . . .(p.1230)
T: 0131 5571222
E: scmorrison@pdso.org.uk

MORRISON, Shona Ann (Oct 1990) (Associate)
Raeburn Christie Clark & Wallace LLP,
Banchory . . . .(p.769)
T: 01330 822931
E: Shona.Morrison@raeburns.co.uk

MORRISON, Stephen Gordon (Apr 1988)
(Employee)
BSW Solicitors LLP, Dunfermline . . . .(p.823)
T: 01383 621144
E: stephen@bastensneddon.co.uk

MORRISON, Susan (Sept 1983) (Solicitor)
NO FIRM

MORRISON, Tricia Marianne (Oct 1993)
(Employee)
Hill Dickinson LLP, Liverpool . . . .(p.1260)
E: tricia.morrison@hilldickinson.com

MORRISSEY, Mary Elizabeth (Jan 1990)
(Employee)
Dundee City Council, Dundee . . . .(p.1217)
T: 01382 434000
E: mary.morrissey@dundeecity.gov.uk

MORROW, Catherine Dolan (Jun 2012)
(Partner)
McSherry Halliday LLP, Kilmarnock . . . .(p.1096)
T: 01563 533121
E: cmorrow@mcsherryhalliday.co.uk

MORROW, Derek (Feb 2015) (Employee)
Muirhall Energy Limited, Lanark . . . . . .(p.1250)
T: (01501) 785604
E: dm@muirhallenergy.co.uk

MORROW, Kevin Martin (Nov 2018)
(Employee)
Procurator Fiscal Service, Airdrie . . . . . .(p.1214)
T: 01236 747027
E: kevin.morrow@copfs.gov.uk

MORROW, Martin Thomas (Sept 1987)
(Director)
MTM Defence Lawyers Limited,
Falkirk . . . .(p.923)
T: 01324 633221
E: mmorrow@mtmdefence.co.uk

MORTIMER, Joanna Ruth (May 2002)
(Employee)
Scottish Courts and Tribunals Service,
Airdrie . . . .(p.1215)
T: 01236 439184
E: jmortimer@scotcourts.gov.uk

MORTIMER, Siobhan Mary (Oct 2016)
(Employee)
Digby Brown LLP, Glasgow . . . .(p.970)
T: 0333 200 5925
E: siobhan.mortimer@digbybrown.co.uk

MORTON, Alison Louise (Aug 1998) (Employee)
Walker Laird, Paisley . . . .(p.1142)
T: 0141 8875271
E: alison.morton@walkerlaird.co.uk

MORTON, Ashleigh Margaret (Apr 2014)
(Partner)
Morton Brody Law, Falkirk . . . .(p.923)
T: 07368 136435
E: am@mortonbrodylaw.co.uk

MORTON, David Ewan (Oct 1985) (Employee)
Spencer West SCO Limited,
Edinburgh . . . .(p.904)
E: david.morton@spencer-west.com

MORTON, David Michael (Jul 2012) (Employee)
Procurator Fiscal Service, Inverness . . . .(p.1248)
T: 0844 5612926
E: david.morton@copfs.gov.uk

MORTON, Douglas Lawrie McGregor
(Jun 2021) (Employee)
Burness Paull LLP, Edinburgh . . . .(p.850)
T: 0131 4736000
E: douglas.morton@burnesspaull.com

MORTON, Francesca Louise (Oct 2008)
(Employee)
Scottish Government, Edinburgh . . . . .(p.1231)
T: 0131 244 0581
E: francesca.morton@gov.scot

MORTON, Gary David (Feb 2014) (Employee)
Hamilton Ross, Airdrie . . . .(p.749)
T: 01236 627627
E: gary@hamiltonross.co.uk

MORTON, Hannah Mary (Aug 2014)
(Employee)
Burness Paull LLP, Edinburgh . . . .(p.850)
T: 0131 4736000
E: hannah.morton@burnesspaull.com

MORTON, Joanna Emily (Dec 1991) (Solicitor)
NO FIRM

MORTON, Judith Emma (Mar 1999) (Employee)
Network Rail Infrastructure Ltd,
Glasgow . . . .(p.1241)
T: 0141 5554470
E: Judith.Morton@networkrail.co.uk

MORTON, Julie Elaine (May 1997) (Employee)
The Building Societies Association, London
WC2 . . . .(p.1268)
T: 0207 520 5915
E: elaine.morton@bsa.org.uk

MORTON, Mark Alistair Craig (Oct 1992)
(Partner)
BTO Solicitors LLP, Glasgow . . . .(p.952)
T: 0141 2218012
E: macm@bto.co.uk

MORTON, Mary-Jay Clark (Jun 2004)
(Associate)
Laurie & Co Solicitors LLP, Ballater . . . . .(p.767)
T: 013397 55535
E: Mary-Jay@laurieandco.co.uk

MORTON, Paul Anthony (Aug 2010) (Associate)
Herbert Smith Freehills Paris LLP,
Paris . . . .(p.1272)
E: paul.morton@hsf.com

MORTON, Richard John (Oct 2008) (Employee)
Avensure Ltd, Manchester . . . .(p.1270)
T: 0330 100 8704
E: richardmorton@avensure.com

MORTON, Robin James Scott (Dec 1979)
(Consultant)
Morton Fraser LLP, Edinburgh . . . .(p.891)
T: 0131 2471000
E: robin.morton@morton-fraser.com

MORTON, Ryan (Jan 2018) (Employee)
Jones Whyte LLP, Glasgow. . . . .(p.993)
T: 0141 375 1222
E: ryan.morton@joneswhyte.co.uk

MORTON, Victoria Jane Sabine (Jan 2015)
(Employee)
Scottish Government, Edinburgh . . . . .(p.1231)
T: 0131 244 0815
E: Victoria.Morton@gov.scot

MOSCARDINI, Nicole Maria (Sept 2016)
(Employee)
Morton Fraser LLP, Glasgow . . . .(p.1022)
T: 0141 2741100
E: Nicole.Moscardini@morton-fraser.com

MOSEDALE, Lucy Rachel (Jan 2010) (Associate)
Harper Macleod LLP, Edinburgh . . . .(p.877)
T: 0131 2472500
E: Lucy.Mosedale@harpermacleod.co.uk

MOSEDALE, Ronald Arthur (Sept 2007)
(Employee)
Dickson Minto, Edinburgh . . . .(p.861)
T: 0131 2254455
E: ronald.mosedale@dmws.com

MOSELEY, Dr, Paul Graham (Sept 2006)
(Employee)
Scottish Futures Trust, Edinburgh . . . . .(p.1231)
T: 0131 5100800
E: paul.moseley@scottishfuturestrust.org.uk

MOSS, Garry Christopher (Oct 1993) (Director)
Moss and Kelly Solicitors Limited,
Glasgow. . . . .(p.1023)
T: 07595 350874
E: gmoss@mossandkelly.co.uk

MOSS, Joyce Mary (Oct 2003) (Director)
Mitchells Roberton Ltd, Glasgow . . . . .(p.1020)
T: 0141 5523422
E: jmm@mitchells-roberton.co.uk

MOSS, Lynne (Sept 2005) (Associate)
Burness Paull LLP, Aberdeen . . . .(p.724)
T: 01224 621621
E: Lynne.Moss@burnesspaull.com

MOST, Clifford (Apr 1989) (Employee)
Procurator Fiscal Service, Paisley. . . . . .(p.1252)
T: 0141 8875225
E: clifford.most@copfs.gov.uk

MOSTAFA, Adeeb Al (Feb 2021) (Employee)
McEwan Fraser Legal, Edinburgh . . . . . .(p.885)
T: 0131 5249797
E: adeeb.mostafa@mcewanfraserlegal.co.uk

MOTION, Elaine Joyce (Aug 1986) (Partner)
Balfour + Manson LLP, Edinburgh . . . . .(p.841)
T: 0131 2001200
E: elaine.motion@balfour-manson.co.uk

MOTION, Paul Robert (May 1984) (Partner)
BTO Solicitors LLP, Edinburgh . . . .(p.849)
T: 0131 2222932
E: prm@bto.co.uk

MOTION, Peter Thomas William (Sept 2016)
(Employee)
Procurator Fiscal Service,
Edinburgh . . . .(p.1227)
T: 0300 0203168
E: peter.motion@copfs.gov.uk

MOTYCKOVA, Adela (Dec 2019) (Employee)
Clyde & Co LLP, Dubai . . . .(p.1278)
T: +971 4331 1102
E: Adela.Motyckova@clydeco.ae

MOULTRIE, Mary Beryl Andronika
(Oct 1993) (Director)
Alex Lafferty Ltd, Tranent . . . .(p.1175)
T: 01875 614059
E: marymoultrie@gmail.com

MOUNTAIN, Susannah Elizabeth (Oct 2010)
(Employee)
Brodies LLP, Aberdeen. . . . .(p.723)
T: 01224 392242
E: susie.mountain@brodies.com

MOUNTFORD, Graham Harold (Oct 1980)
(Partner)
Wilsone & Duffus, Aberdeen . . . .(p.746)
T: 01224 251100
E: Graham.Mountford@key-moves.co.uk

MOUNTFORD, Julia Rose (Aug 2008)
(Employee)
Stirling Council, Stirling. . . . .(p.1255)
T: 01786 233065
E: mountfordj@stirling.gov.uk

MOWAT, Eilidh Louise (Jun 2009) (Employee)
Wheatley Housing Group Limited,
Glasgow . . . .(p.1246)
T: 0845 9001001
E: eilidh.mowat@wheatley-group.com

MOWAT, Ewan James Hay (Aug 1999) (Partner)
A.C. White, Ayr . . . .(p.766)
T: 01292 266900
E: ewan.mowat@acwhiteayr.co.uk

MOWAT, Ian Alastair McIvor (Aug 1992)
(Employee)
Office of the Advocate General,
Edinburgh . . . .(p.1227)
T: 07594 646051
E: ian.mowat@advocategeneral.gov.uk

MOWAT, Laura (Jun 2013) (Director)
Maloco + Associates Limited,
Dunfermline . . . .(p.824)
T: 01383 629720
E: Laura@maloco.co.uk

MOWATT, Sean Bryce (Sept 2018) (Employee)
PricewaterhouseCoopers LLP, London
SE1 . . . .(p.1267)
E: sean.b.mowatt@pwc.com

MOWBERRY, John-Paul (Aug 1999)
(Consultant)
Bridge Legal Limited, Glasgow . . . .(p.948)
T: 0141 4293100

MOWLEM, David Lonsdale (Dec 2008)
(Associate)
Turcan Connell, Edinburgh . . . .(p.908)
T: 0131 2288111
E: david.mowlem@turcanconnell.com

MOXHAM, Elizabeth Ann (Sept 1996)
(Employee)
Aegon Asset Management UK Plc,
Edinburgh . . . .(p.1220)
T: (0131) 549 3062
E: elizabeth.moxham@aegonam.com

MOY, Stewart David (Aug 2011) (Associate)
Morton Fraser LLP, Glasgow . . . .(p.1022)
T: 0141 2741100
E: stewart.moy@morton-fraser.com

MOYES, Peter Stewart William (Oct 2010)
(Employee)
Procurator Fiscal Service,
Kilmarnock . . . .(p.1249)
T: 01563 536211
E: peter.moyes@copfs.gov.uk

MOYNAN, Joanne Helen (Oct 1984) (Associate)
Addleshaw Goddard LLP,
Edinburgh . . . .(p.835)
T: 0131 2282400
E: Joanne.Moynan@addleshawgoddard.com

MUDGE, Robert Huw (Jun 2006) (Employee)
The Institute of Chartered Accountants of
Scotland, Edinburgh . . . .(p.1235)
T: 0131 347 0285
E: rmudge@icas.com

MUDIE, Alexander Bruce (Aug 2018)
(Employee)
Wright, Johnston & Mackenzie LLP,
Glasgow . . . .(p.1054)
T: 0141 2483434
E: abm@wjm.co.uk

MUDIE, James Kinnaird (Jan 2005) (Employee)
Scottish Legal Aid Board,
Edinburgh . . . .(p.1233)
T: 0131 2267061
E: mudieja@slab.org.uk

MUDIE, Rebecca Elizabeth (Jul 2016)
(Employee)
Scottish Social Services Council,
Dundee . . . .(p.1218)
T: 0345 6030 891
E: rebecca.mudie@sssc.uk.com

MUEGO, Fraser John (Sept 2014) (Employee)
John Menzies Plc, Edinburgh . . . .(p.1224)
E: fraser.muego@menziesaviation.com

MUIR, Alan Robert (Nov 1988) (Employee)
Scottish Legal Aid Board,
Edinburgh . . . .(p.1233)
T: 0131 2267061
E: muirar@slab.org.uk

MUIR, Alexander (Nov 1987) (Consultant)
Mackintosh & Wylie LLP, Irvine . . . . . .(p.1087)
T: 01294 311422
E: amuir@mackwylie.com

MUIR, Alexander Joseph (Dec 2000)
(Employee)
Falkirk Council, Falkirk . . . .(p.1236)
T: 01324 506070
E: alex.muir@falkirk.gov.uk

MUIR, Andrew Gray, WS (Mar 1961) (Director)
A. Gray Muir, WS Limited,
Edinburgh . . . .(p.875)
T: 0131 6643320
E: andrew@graymuir.co.uk

MUIR, Christopher William (Dec 1992)
(Employee)
Scottish Widows Limited,
Edinburgh . . . .(p.1233)
T: 0131 6556403
E: Chris.Muir@scottishwidows.co.uk

MUIR, Connor Ben Ronald (Mar 2021)
(Employee)
Procurator Fiscal Service,
Livingston . . . .(p.1250)
T: (0300) 020 3696
E: connor.muir@copfs.gov.uk

MUIR, Craig David (Dec 2016) (Employee)
Morton Fraser LLP, Edinburgh . . . .(p.891)
T: 0131 2471000
E: craig.muir@morton-fraser.com

MUIR, Donald Vladimir (Oct 1995) (Employee)
Brodies LLP, Glasgow . . . .(p.948)
T: 0141 2484672
E: donald.muir@brodies.com

MUIR, Elizabeth (Dec 2018) (Employee)
BNP Paribas, Glasgow . . . .(p.1238)

MUIR, James Robertson (Dec 2006) (Partner)
Stronachs LLP, Aberdeen . . . .(p.744)
T: 01224 845845
E: james.muir@stronachs.com

MUIR, John Clarke (Oct 1986) (Partner)
MML Legal, Dundee . . . .(p.817)
T: 01382 206 000
E: john@mmllaw.co.uk

MUIR, Lilia (May 2018) (Employee)
Hunter & Robertson Limited,
Paisley . . . .(p.1138)
T: 0141 8893196
E: lmuir@hunter-robertson.co.uk

MUIR, Lucy Elizabeth (Dec 2019) (Employee)
DWF LLP, Glasgow . . . .(p.973)
T: 0141 228 8000
E: lucy.muir@dwf.law

MUIR, Neil Marshall, WS (Feb 1976) (Partner)
Muirs, Edinburgh . . . .(p.893)
T: 0131 2263058
E: muirsws@btconnect.com

MUIR, Pamela Elizabeth (Jan 1997) (Partner)
Thorntons Law LLP, Glasgow . . . .(p.1047)
T: 03330 430350
E: pmuir@thorntons-law.co.uk

MUIR, Quinton (Dec 1991) (Partner)
D. & J. Dunlop, Ayr . . . .(p.762)
T: 01292 264091
E: quintonmuir@djdunlop.co.uk

MUIR, Stephen Martyn (Nov 1991) (Partner)
Ross, Strachan & Co., Dundee . . . .(p.818)
T: 01382 201010
E: smuir@ross-strachan.co.uk

MUIR, Taylor (Jul 2019) (Employee)
Russells Gibson McCaffrey,
Glasgow . . . .(p.1037)
T: 0141 271 1000
E: taylor.muir@russellsgm.co.uk

MUIRHEAD, Craig David (Nov 2015)
(Employee)
Dallas McMillan, Glasgow . . . .(p.966)
T: 0141 3336750
E: craigmuirhead@dallasmcmillan.co.uk

MUIRS, Fiona Kirsty (Nov 1998) (Partner)
Balfour + Manson LLP, Edinburgh . . . . .(p.841)
T: 0131 200 1200
E: fiona.muirs@balfour-manson.co.uk

MUKHERJEE, Elora (Sept 2007) (Employee)
Fieldfisher LLP, London EC4 . . . .(p.1264)
T: 0207 8614339
E: Elora.Mukherjee@fieldfisher.com

MUKHTAR, Isma Tahira Choudhry
(Nov 2006) (Employee)
Procurator Fiscal Service, Kirkcaldy . . . .(p.1249)
T: 0300 0203000
E: isma.mukhtar@copfs.gov.uk

MUKHTAR, Tuyub (Nov 2013) (Employee)
Latta Law Limited, Glasgow . . . .(p.998)
T: 0141 222 2185
E: TM@lattalaw.co.uk

MULCAHY, Lynne (Dec 1995) (Partner)
Balfour + Manson LLP, Aberdeen . . . . . .(p.721)
T: 01224 498080
E: lynne.mulcahy@balfour-manson.co.uk

MULES, Sindi (Dec 2002) (Partner)
Balfour + Manson LLP, Edinburgh . . . . .(p.841)
T: 0131 2001200
E: sindi.mules@balfour-manson.co.uk

MULGREW, James John (Jul 1997) (Partner)
Russells Gibson McCaffrey,
Glasgow . . . .(p.1037)
T: 0141 271 1000
E: jj.mulgrew@russellsgm.co.uk

MULHERON, William Ruairidh (Aug 2019)
(Employee)
Gilfedder & McInnes Limited,
Edinburgh . . . .(p.872)
T: 0131 5543550

MULHOLLAND, Anita Maria (Sept 2015)
(Associate)
Addleshaw Goddard LLP, Glasgow . . . . .(p.938)
T: 0141 2212300
E: Anita.Mulholland@addleshawgoddard.com

MULHOLLAND, John Mark (Aug 1988)
(Consultant)
Marshall Wilson Law Group Limited,
Falkirk . . . .(p.922)
T: 01324 612569
E: jmulholland@marshallwilson.com

MULHOLLAND, Lesley-Anne (Oct 1999)
(Employee)
Callahan McKeown & Co Ltd,
Renfrew . . . .(p.1158)
T: 0141 8851212

MULHOLLAND, Saira (Jan 2009) (Solicitor)
NO FIRM

MULHOLLAND, Tracey Louise (Oct 2010)
(Employee)
Paul Hannah Solicitors, Glasgow . . . . . .(p.982)
T: 0141 558 7433
E: tracey@paulhannah.org

MULLALLY, Dorothy Elizabeth (Dec 1984)
(Partner)
Allan McDougall McQueen LLP,
Edinburgh . . . .(p.837)
T: 0131 6221771
E: DotMullally@mcdougallmcqueen.co.uk

MULLAN, Maureen Anne (Sept 2009)
(Employee)
Procurator Fiscal Service, Paisley. . . . . .(p.1252)
T: 0141 8875225
E: maureen.mullan@copfs.gov.uk

MULLAN, Stephen (Dec 1981) (Employee)
Oraclelaw Limited, Glasgow. . . . .(p.1027)
T: 0141 4041091
E: scm@oraclelaw.com

MULLEN, Catherine Rose (Sept 1994)
(Employee)
Aberdeenshire Council, Aberdeen. . . . .(p.1211)
T: 0345 6081208
E: catherine.mullen@aberdeenshire.gov.uk

MULLEN, Claire Anne (Jun 2010) (Associate)
TC Young LLP, Glasgow . . . .(p.1055)
T: 0141 2215562
E: cag@tcyoung.co.uk

MULLEN, Hayley Louise (Nov 2003) (Partner)
Mullen and Co, Aberdeen . . . .(p.738)
T: 01224 433938
E: hm@mullenandco.com

MULLEN, Jack (Aug 2021) (Employee)
Dentons UK and Middle East LLP,
Edinburgh . . . .(p.860)
T: 0330 2220050
E: jack.mullen@dentons.com

MULLEN, Lauren (Mar 2018) (Employee)
Watermans Solicitors Limited,
Glasgow. . . . .(p.1051)
T: 0141 4307055
E: laurenmullen@watermans.co.uk

MULLEN, Michelle Rose (May 2000) (Employee)
The Institute of Chartered Accountants of
Scotland, Edinburgh . . . .(p.1235)
T: 0131 3470100
E: mmullen@icas.com

MULLEN, Paul Joseph (Oct 2009) (Director)
Livingstone Brown Limited,
Glasgow. . . . .(p.1004)
T: 0141 7789657
E: pm@livbrown.co.uk

MULLEN, Thomas Anthony (Sept 1992)
(Partner)
Mullen and Co, Aberdeen . . . .(p.738)
T: 01224 433938
E: tm@mullenandco.com

MULLEN, Victoria Elizabeth (Nov 2007)
(Employee)
TSB Bank Plc, Edinburgh . . . .(p.1235)
T: 0131 260 0051
E: Victoria.mullen@tsb.co.uk

MULLIGAN, Kevin Michael (Sept 2016)
(Employee)
Pinsent Masons LLP, Glasgow . . . .(p.1031)
T: 0141 567 8400
E: kevin.mulligan@pinsentmasons.com

MULLIGAN, Poppy Elisabeth (Apr 2021)
(Employee)
Pinsent Masons LLP, Edinburgh . . . .(p.895)
T: 0131 777 7000
E: poppy.mulligan@pinsentmasons.com

MULLIN, Joy Helen (Sept 1984) (Associate)
Stronachs LLP, Aberdeen . . . .(p.744)
T: 01224 845845
E: joy.mullin@stronachs.com

MULLIN, Rachel Kirstie (Feb 2011) (Employee)
Royal London, Edinburgh . . . .(p.1230)
T: 0131 4567703
E: rachel.mullin@royallondon.com

MULREANY, Lucy Karen (Oct 2015) (Employee)
Shepherd and Wedderburn LLP,
Glasgow. . . . .(p.1039)
T: 0141 5669900
E: Lucy.Mulreany@shepwedd.com

MUMFORD, Kenneth (Oct 1999) (Partner)
MBM Commercial LLP, Edinburgh . . . . .(p.889)
T: 0131 2268200
E: kenny.mumford@mbmcommercial.co.uk

MUNCER, Sarah Lucy (Feb 2015) (Employee)
Pinsent Masons LLP, Edinburgh . . . .(p.895)
T: 0131 777 7000
E: Sarah.Muncer@pinsentmasons.com

MUNDELL, Eve Margaret (Feb 2016)
(Employee)
Bellwether Green Limited, Glasgow . . . .(p.944)
T: 0141 2184900
E: eve.mundell@bellwethergreen.com

MUNDY, Fiona Margaret (Sept 1984)
(Consultant)
Johnson Legal, Edinburgh . . . .(p.880)
T: 0131 6228477
E: fiona@johnsonlegal.co.uk

MUNIR, Asma (Sept 2017) (Director)
Friels Solicitors Limited, Coatbridge . . . .(p.786)
T: 01236 421 136
E: asma@frielssolicitors.co.uk

MUNN, Fiona MacKay MacDonald
(Nov 1992) (Director)
Marshall Wilson Law Group Limited,
Falkirk . . . .(p.922)
T: 01324 612569
E: fmunn@marshallwilson.com

MUNRO, Alan Turner (Sept 1999) (Partner)
TLT LLP, Glasgow . . . .(p.1048)
T: 0333 006 0400
E: Alan.Munro@tltsolicitors.com

MUNRO, Alexander (Feb 1999) (Employee)
Aberdeen City Council, Aberdeen. . . . .(p.1211)
T: 01224 522000
E: AleMunro@aberdeencity.gov.uk

MUNRO, Andrew John Ross (Oct 1982)
(Employee)
Scottish Engineering, Glasgow . . . .(p.1243)
T: 0141 2213181
E: andrewmunro@scottishengineering.org.uk

MUNRO, Anna Mary (Mar 2019) (Employee)
Scottish Government, Edinburgh . . . . .(p.1231)
T: 0131 244 0815
E: anna.munro@gov.scot

MUNRO, Blair Ian James (Nov 2019)
(Employee)
Brodies LLP, Edinburgh . . . .(p.845)
T: 0131 2283777
E: blair.munro@brodies.com

MUNRO, Catriona Mary (Apr 1999)
(Consultant)
Dentons UK and Middle East LLP,
Edinburgh . . . .(p.860)
T: 0330 2220050
E: Catriona.Munro@dentons.com

MUNRO, Christopher John (Sept 2014)
(Solicitor)
NO FIRM

MUNRO, Claire (Aug 2008) (Employee)
University of Glasgow, Glasgow . . . . . .(p.1245)
T: 0141 330 7725
E: claire.munro@glasgow.ac.uk

MUNRO, Claire Louise (Mar 2021) (Employee)
Aberdein Considine and Company,
Aberdeen . . . .(p.718)
T: 01224 589700
E: cmunro@acandco.com

MUNRO, Donald John (Nov 1994) (Partner)
Harper Macleod LLP, Glasgow . . . .(p.983)
T: 0141 2218888
E: donald.munro@harpermacleod.co.uk

MUNRO, Fraser Alexander (Aug 1990)
(Solicitor)
NO FIRM

MUNRO, Gary (Aug 2017) (Associate)
Anderson Shaw & Gilbert Limited,
Inverness . . . .(p.1075)
T: 01463 236123
E: gmunro@solicitorsinverness.com

MUNRO, Gregor Callum (Dec 2013)
(Employee)
DLA Piper UK LLP, London EC1 . . . . . .(p.1263)
T: 020 77966017
E: gregor.munro@dlapiper.com

MUNRO, Harriet Anne (Mar 1998) (Partner)
CMS Cameron McKenna Nabarro Olswang LLP,
Edinburgh . . . .(p.856)
T: 0131 2288000
E: harriet.munro@cms-cmno.com

MUNRO, Jennifer Mary (Sept 2009) (Employee)
Gillespie Macandrew LLP, Perth . . . . . .(p.1148)
T: 01738 231000
E: Jennifer.Munro@gillespiemacandrew.co.uk

MUNRO, John Gary (Jul 2012) (Employee)
Angus Council, Forfar . . . .(p.1237)
T: 01307 476228
E: MunroG1@angus.gov.uk

MUNRO, Norman (Feb 2016) (Employee)
Scottish Government, Edinburgh . . . . .(p.1231)
T: 0131 244 4768
E: norman.munro@gov.scot

MUNRO, Patrick Alan (Sept 2016) (Employee)
Burges Salmon LLP, Edinburgh . . . .(p.850)
T: 0131 3142112
E: patrick.munro@burges-salmon.com

MUNRO, Rachel Erin (Jun 2019) (Employee)
Shepherd and Wedderburn LLP,
Glasgow. . . . .(p.1039)
T: 0141 5669900
E: rachel.munro@shepwedd.com

MUNRO, Roderick Neil (Aug 1997) (Partner)
MacRoberts LLP, Glasgow . . . .(p.1015)
T: 0141 3031100
E: rod.munro@macroberts.com

MUNRO, Russell William (Oct 1997) (Partner)
Pinsent Masons LLP, Edinburgh . . . .(p.895)
T: 0131 7777000
E: russell.munro@pinsentmasons.com

MUNRO, Dr, Sarah Anne (Aug 2018)
(Employee)
Livingstone Brown Limited,
Glasgow. . . . .(p.1003)
T: 0141 4298166
E: scm@livbrown.co.uk

MUNRO, Sarah Helen (Oct 2006) (Employee)
Pinsent Masons LLP, Edinburgh . . . .(p.895)
T: 0131 7777000
E: Sarah.Munro@pinsentmasons.com

MUNRO, Stuart Kenneth (Jul 1994) (Director)
Livingstone Brown Limited,
  Glasgow....................(p.1003)
  T: 0141 4298166
  E: skm@livbrown.co.uk

MUNRO, Tamsin Clare (Sept 1994) (Partner)
Brodies LLP, Aberdeen.............(p.723)
  T: 01224 392242
  E: clare.munro@brodies.com

MUNTON, Ronald Charles Gordon
(Dec 1973) (Partner)
Low Beaton Richmond LLP,
  Glasgow....................(p.1005)
  T: 0141 2218931
  E: Gabrielle@lbr-law.co.uk

MURCHISON, Andrew Alexander (Jan 1993)
(Director)
Murchison Law Limited, Inverness ....(p.1081)
  T: 01463 709992
  E: andrew@murchisonlaw.co.uk

MURCHISON, Andrew Ross (May 2014)
(Solicitor)
NO FIRM
  E: Ross.Murchison@uhi.ac.uk

MURCHISON, Jennifer Grace Denheen
(May 2013) (Employee)
National Westminster Bank PLC,
  Edinburgh ....(p.1226)
  T: (0131) 626 2925
  E: Jennifer.murchison@natwest.com

MURDANAIGUM, Ruben Valaydon
(Dec 1980) (Partner)
Rubens, Lochgilphead.............(p.1121)
  T: 01546 602084
  E: ruben.murdanaigum@btopenworld.com

MURDIE, David Gordon Amcotts (May 2019)
(Employee)
Morton Fraser LLP, Edinburgh ....(p.891)
  T: 0131 2471000
  E: david.murdie@morton-fraser.com

MURDOCH, Alan (Nov 2009) (Employee)
Jonathan Paul Solicitors, Alexandria ....(p.751)
  T: 01389 756785
  E: alan.murdoch613@gmail.com

MURDOCH, Alistair John (Sept 1989)
(Employee)
Murnin McCluskey, Glasgow ....(p.1010)
  T: 0141 2221760
  E: am@murnin.co.uk

MURDOCH, Charmaine Anne (Oct 2014)
(Employee)
Dentons UK and Middle East LLP,
  Glasgow....................(p.968)
  T: 0330 2220050
  E: Charmaine.Murdoch@dentons.com

MURDOCH, Darren Gemmell (Apr 2016)
(Director)
Waddell & Mackintosh Solicitors Ltd,
  Troon......................(p.1176)
  T: 01292 312222
  E: darren@wmtroon.co.uk

MURDOCH, David Bannerman (Sept 2014)
(Employee)
Scottish Government, Edinburgh .....(p.1231)
  T: 0131 244 0815
  E: david.murdoch@gov.scot

MURDOCH, Edward Munroe (Aug 2011)
(Employee)
BBC Scotland, Glasgow ....(p.1238)
  T: 0141 4226373
  E: edward.murdoch@bbc.co.uk

MURDOCH, Emma Jane Elizabeth
(Feb 2021) (Employee)
Thorley Stephenson Ltd,
  Edinburgh ....(p.906)
  T: 0131 5569599
  E: em@thorleystephenson.com

MURDOCH, Emma Louise (Nov 2021)
(Employee)
Schlumberger Oilfield Europe SRL,
  Bucharest...................(p.1276)
  T: (07833) 465 886
  E: EMurdoch@slb.com

MURDOCH, Kathryn Mari Victoria
(May 2018) (Employee)
Burnett & Reid LLP, Aberdeen ....(p.726)
  T: 01224 644333
  E: kathryn.murdoch@burnett-reid.co.uk

MURDOCH, Lynn (Nov 2018) (Employee)
Davidson & Shirley Limited, Lanark ...(p.1107)
  T: 01555 662576/7
  E: lynn.murdoch@davidsonandshirley.co.uk

MURDOCH, Maria Candida Angela
(Sept 2019) (Employee)
Procurator Fiscal Service, Paisley......(p.1252)
  T: 0141 8875225
  E: Maria.Murdoch@copfs.gov.uk

MURDOCH, Michelle Louise (Oct 2015)
(Associate)
VMH Solicitors Limited, Edinburgh .....(p.910)
  T: 0131 6615911
  E: michelle.murdoch@vmh.co.uk

MURDOCH, Pamela (May 2021) (Employee)
Wallace Quinn & Co Limited,
  Livingston ....(p.1120)
  T: 01506 353405
  E: pamela@wallacequinn.co.uk

MURDOCH, Richard David Cameron
(Dec 2016) (Employee)
Dechert LLP, London EC4 ....(p.1263)
  T: 020 7184 7000
  E: richard.murdoch@dechert.com

MURDOCH, Ross Matthew (May 2010)
(Employee)
Financial Conduct Authority, London
  E20 . . . .(p.1264)
  E: Ross.Murdoch@fca.org.uk

MURDOCH, Stuart Alan Wilson (Aug 2008)
(Partner)
DLA Piper Scotland LLP, Edinburgh . . . .(p.863)
  T: 08700 111111
  E: Stuart.Murdoch@dlapiper.com

MURDOCK, Thomas Oliver, WS (Nov 2011)
(Employee)
Jamf, London EC1 . . . .(p.1265)
  E: thomas.murdock@jamf.com

MURFITT, Simon John (Nov 1997) (Employee)
Keystone Law Limited, London
  WC2 . . . .(p.1265)
  T: 020 33193700
  E: simon.murfitt@keystonelaw.co.uk

MURISON, Mary (Jan 2012) (Employee)
Clydesdale Bank Plc, Glasgow . . . .(p.1238)
  T: 0141 2423733
  E: mary.murison@cybg.com

MURNIN, Marianne Joy Miranda (Sept 2020)
(Employee)
Morton Fraser LLP, Edinburgh . . . .(p.891)
  T: 0131 2471000
  E: marianne.murnin@morton-fraser.com

MURNIN, Philip Brendan (Apr 1978) (Partner)
Murnin McCluskey, Glasgow . . . .(p.1010)
  T: 0141 2221760
  E: pm@murnin.co.uk

MURPHY, Alison Mary (Aug 1992) (Associate)
Drummond Miller LLP, Glasgow . . . .(p.971)
  T: 0141 3320086
  E: amurphy@dm-property.com

MURPHY, Alistair Ian (Jan 2021) (Employee)
Burnett Christie Knowles McCourts,
  Edinburgh . . . .(p.852)
  T: 0131 2253456
  E: am@bckm.co.uk

MURPHY, Annalee Jane (Oct 2001) (Employee)
Scottish Government's Parliamentary Counsel
  Office, Edinburgh . . . .(p.1233)
  T: 0131 244 1669
  E: annalee.murphy@gov.scot

MURPHY, Barry Anthony (Jul 2002) (Employee)
Katani & Co. Ltd, Glasgow . . . .(p.994)
  T: 0141 2217788
  E: barry.murphy@kataniandco.com

MURPHY, Barry Charles (Mar 2011) (Director)
Trainor Alston Limited, Coatbridge . . . . .(p.787)
  T: 01236 600 600
  E: barry@trainoralston.co.uk

MURPHY, Charlene Alison (Sept 2018)
(Employee)
Procurator Fiscal Service,
  Edinburgh . . . .(p.1229)
  T: 0300 0203000
  E: Charlene.wilson@copfs.gov.uk

MURPHY, Christopher David (Sept 2019)
(Employee)
MacRoberts LLP, Glasgow . . . .(p.1015)
  T: 0141 3031100
  E: christopher.murphy@macroberts.com

MURPHY, David Philip (Mar 2019) (Employee)
University of Edinburgh, Edinburgh . . .(p.1235)
  E: d.murphy@ed.ac.uk

MURPHY, Donna-Marie (Aug 2009) (Employee)
Scottish Legal Aid Board,
  Edinburgh . . . .(p.1233)
  T: 0131 2267061
  E: murphydo@slab.org.uk

MURPHY, Gregor Neil (Jun 2021) (Employee)
Brodies LLP, Edinburgh . . . .(p.845)
  T: 0131 2283777
  E: gregor.murphy@brodies.com

MURPHY, Gwendoline (Sept 1996) (Associate)
MacRoberts LLP, Glasgow . . . .(p.1015)
  T: 0141 3031100
  E: Gwen.Murphy@macroberts.com

MURPHY, Jennifer Louise (Sept 2011)
(Associate)
Brodies LLP, Edinburgh . . . .(p.845)
  T: 0131 2283777
  E: jennifer.murphy@brodies.com

MURPHY, Joseph Brendan (Apr 1969) (Partner)
Murphy & Co., Glasgow . . . .(p.1025)
  T: 0141 3322804
  E: murphyandco@hotmail.com

MURPHY, Judith Anne Heidi (Dec 2020)
(Employee)
Baillie Gifford & Co, Edinburgh . . . . . .(p.1220)
  T: 0131 2752000
  E: judith.murphy@bailliegifford.com

MURPHY, Kerri Ann (Feb 2001) (Employee)
West Lothian Council, Livingston . . . . .(p.1250)
  T: 01506 280000
  E: kerri.murphy@westlothian.gov.uk

MURPHY, Kevin (Jul 2004) (Partner)
Murphy, Robb + Sutherland,
  Glasgow . . . .(p.1025)
  T: 0141 4182931
  E: murphyrobbsutherland@gmail.com

MURPHY, Laura Jane (Sept 2009) (Employee)
Clydesdale Bank Plc, Glasgow . . . .(p.1238)
  T: 0141 242 4680
  E: laura.murphy@cybg.com

MURPHY, Leanne (Jul 2007) (Employee)
Scottish Legal Aid Board,
Edinburgh . . . .(p.1233)
T: 0131 2267061
E: lmurphy@pdso.org.uk

MURPHY, Leona (Aug 2002) (Director)
Morison & Smith Limited, Lanark . . . . .(p.1108)
T: 01555 662488
E: leona@morisonandsmith.com

MURPHY, Lesley (Jun 2001) (Solicitor)
NO FIRM

MURPHY, Lyndsey (Oct 2007) (Employee)
Stodarts LLP, Hamilton . . . .(p.1069)
T: 01698 200302
E: lyndsey@stodarts.co.uk

MURPHY, Michael Gerard (Feb 1985) (Solicitor)
NO FIRM

MURPHY, Michelle (Apr 1999) (Employee)
Glasgow City Council, Glasgow . . . . . .(p.1239)
T: 0141 2870494
E: Michelle.Murphy@glasgow.gov.uk

MURPHY, Nadine Maria (Aug 2006)
(Employee)
Scottish Government, Edinburgh . . . . .(p.1231)
T: 0131 244 0815
E: nadine.murphy@gov.scot

MURPHY, Paul Joseph (Sept 2003) (Employee)
SSE PLC, Glasgow . . . .(p.1244)
T: 0141 224 7248
E: paul.murphy@sse.com

MURPHY, Siobh n Marie Ther se (Jan 2016)
(Employee)
Civil Legal Assistance Office,
Edinburgh . . . .(p.1222)
T: 0131 2401960
E: MurphySi@clao.org.uk

MURPHY, Stephen John (Oct 2014) (Employee)
Linklaters LLP, London EC2 . . . .(p.1266)
T: 0207 4562000
E: stephen.murphy@linklaters.com

MURPHY, Stewart William (Nov 2010)
(Employee)
Pinsent Masons LLP, London EC2 . . . . .(p.1267)
T: 0207 418 7022
E: stewart.murphy@pinsentmasons.com

MURPHY, Suzanne (May 2010) (Employee)
SSE PLC, Glasgow . . . .(p.1244)
T: 0141 224 7248
E: suzanne.murphy@sse.com

MURRAY, Ailie Anne (Aug 2006) (Employee)
Travers Smith LLP, London EC1 . . . . . .(p.1269)
T: 020 7295 3000
E: Ailie.Murray@traverssmith.com

MURRAY, Alan Blair (Mar 1983) (Partner)
Murray, Hamilton & Chalmers,
Bellshill . . . .(p.773)
T: 01698 327488
E: alan.murray@mhcsol.co.uk

MURRAY, Alan John (Sept 1993) (Partner)
McCluskey Browne, Kilmarnock . . . . . .(p.1095)
T: 01563 544545
E: amurray@mccluskeybrowne.co.uk

MURRAY, Alexander Moncrieff (Oct 1986)
(Partner)
MacArthur Legal, Oban . . . .(p.1134)
T: 01631 562215
E: sandy@macarthurlegal.co.uk

MURRAY, Alistair Gerard (Aug 1999) (Partner)
Alistair Murray Solicitor Advocate,
Blantyre . . . .(p.777)
T: 01698 721999
E: blantyrecriminallawyers@gmail.com

MURRAY, Andrew Peter (Sept 1975) (Partner)
My Lawyers, Alexandria . . . .(p.751)
T: 01389 755235
E: amurray@mylawyers.co.uk

MURRAY, Anthony James (Jan 1993)
(Employee)
Berrymans Lace Mawer LLP,
Glasgow . . . .(p.945)
T: 0141 3532121
E: Anthony.Murray@blmlaw.com

MURRAY, Anthony Robert (Jun 1999)
(Employee)
Murray LLP, New York . . . .(p.1279)
T: +1 212 729 3045
E: anthony@murrayllp.com

MURRAY, Callum Donald (Aug 2006)
(Associate)
Brodies LLP, Edinburgh . . . .(p.845)
T: 0131 2283777
E: callum.murray@brodies.com

MURRAY, Calum Graeme (Sept 2015)
(Employee)
Berrymans Lace Mawer LLP,
Edinburgh . . . .(p.842)
T: 0131 2259855
E: calum.murray@blmlaw.com

MURRAY, Calum Grant (Oct 1997) (Employee)
Deloitte LLP, London EC4 . . . .(p.1263)
T: (0207) 0072147
E: cgmurray@deloitte.co.uk

MURRAY, Catriona Alison (Apr 2012)
(Employee)
Renew Legal Limited, Bath . . . .(p.1258)
T: 01225 321634
E: Murray@renewlegal.com

MURRAY, Catriona Jane (Sept 2008)
(Employee)
Emerson FZE, Dubai . . . .(p.1278)
   E: Catriona.Murray@Emerson.com

MURRAY, Christopher Andrew Thomas
(Sept 2011) (Employee)
Eversheds Sutherland (International) LLP,
   Edinburgh . . . .(p.869)
   T: 0207 9194500
   E:
   christophermurray@eversheds-sutherland.com

MURRAY, Craig Gordon (Mar 1993) (Partner)
Dewar & Murray, Fort William . . . .(p.929)
   T: 01397 702455
   E: craig@macarthurstewart.co.uk

MURRAY, David Carson (Oct 1981) (Partner)
Gebbie & Wilson LLP, Strathaven . . . . .(p.1172)
   T: 01357 520082
   E: david@gebbiewilson.co.uk

MURRAY, Donald Roderick (Oct 2007)
(Director)
PRP Legal Limited, Glasgow . . . .(p.1033)
   T: 0141 3311050
   E: derek@prp-legal.co.uk

MURRAY, Euan (Sept 2004) (Partner)
Shepherd and Wedderburn LLP,
   Edinburgh . . . .(p.900)
   T: 0131 2289900
   E: euan.murray@shepwedd.com

MURRAY, Euan Campbell (Oct 2002)
(Employee)
Artemis Investment Management LLP,
   Edinburgh . . . .(p.1220)
   T: 0131 7180429
   E: euan.murray@artemisfunds.com

MURRAY, Fiona Elizabeth (Oct 1986)
(Employee)
Procurator Fiscal Service, Inverness . . . .(p.1248)
   T: 0844 5612926
   E: fiona.murray@copfs.gov.uk

MURRAY, Gavin James (Aug 2005) (Employee)
The Edrington Group Limited,
   Glasgow. . . . .(p.1245)
   T: 0141 9404000
   E: gavin.murray@edrington.com

MURRAY, Gillian Marion (Sept 2008)
(Associate)
Anderson Strathern LLP, Glasgow . . . . . .(p.940)
   T: 0141 285 3806
   E: gillian.murray@andersonstrathern.co.uk

MURRAY, Gordon Lindsay Kevan, WS
(Jan 1979) (Consultant)
MacRoberts LLP, Edinburgh . . . .(p.887)
   T: 0131 2295046
   E: gordon.murray@macroberts.com

MURRAY, Graeme Bruce (Feb 1982) (Employee)
Hingston's Law Limited, Aberdeen . . . . .(p.732)
   T: 01224 562300
   E: graeme@hingstonslaw.co.uk

MURRAY, Graeme Scott (May 1991)
(Employee)
Well-Safe Solutions Limited,
   Aberdeen . . . .(p.1214)
   T: 01224 548400
   E: graeme.murray@wellsafesolutions.com

MURRAY, Graham Neil (Nov 2003) (Partner)
Wright, Johnston & Mackenzie LLP,
   Glasgow. . . . .(p.1054)
   T: 0141 2483434
   E: gnm@wjm.co.uk

MURRAY, Graham Stewart (Oct 1986)
(Employee)
SOUTH LANARKSHIRERe Council,
   Hamilton . . . .(p.1247)
   E: graham.murray@southlanarkshire.gov.uk

MURRAY, Iain Sinclair (Dec 1982) (Partner)
JHS Law, Dumfries . . . .(p.801)
   T: 01387 739000
   E: iain.murray@jhslaw.co.uk

MURRAY, Jacqueline (Jul 2005) (Employee)
Burness Paull LLP, Edinburgh . . . .(p.850)
   T: 0131 4736000
   E: Jacqueline.Murray@burnesspaull.com

MURRAY, James Alexander (Dec 1991)
(Employee)
Dundee City Council, Dundee . . . .(p.1217)
   T: 01382 434162
   E: jim.murray@dundeecity.gov.uk

MURRAY, Jamie Alexander Caddis
(Oct 2017) (Employee)
BTO Solicitors LLP, Glasgow . . . .(p.952)
   T: 0141 2218012
   E: jmu@bto.co.uk

MURRAY, Jemma Ann (Jul 2013) (Employee)
Induction Healthcare UK Limited, London
   EC3 . . . .(p.1265)

MURRAY, Joanne Ronna (Feb 2008) (Associate)
Blackadders LLP, Aberdeen . . . .(p.722)
   T: 01224 588913
   E: joanne.murray@blackadders.co.uk

MURRAY, Johane Macmillan (Aug 1994)
(Partner)
Brodies LLP, Glasgow . . . .(p.948)
   T: 0141 2456230
   E: johane.murray@brodies.com

MURRAY, John Stephen Cunningham
(Aug 2005) (Employee)
Tesco Personal Finance Plc,
   Edinburgh . . . .(p.1234)
   T: (0131) 274 3426
   E: john.s.murray@tescobank.com

MURRAY, Julie Ellen (Aug 1994) (Employee)
Dundee City Council, Dundee . . . .(p.1217)
  T: 01382 434000
  E: julie.murray@dundeecity.gov.uk

MURRAY, Karen Ann (Aug 2010) (Employee)
Eastons Solicitors Limited, Glasgow . . . .(p.974)
  T: 0141 5331976

MURRAY, Kathleen Anne (Sept 1992) (Partner)
McKinnon Hewitt, Irvine . . . .(p.1086)
  T: 01294 312801
  E: kathleen@mckinnonhewitt.co.uk

MURRAY, Kathleen Elizabeth Joyce
(Sept 2019) (Employee)
Procurator Fiscal Service,
  Edinburgh . . . .(p.1227)
  T: 0300 020 3422
  E: katie.murray@copfs.gov.uk

MURRAY, Keith Robert (Oct 2008) (Partner)
Andrew Haddon & Crowe, Hawick. . . .(p.1070)
  T: 01450 372738
  E: keithmurray@ahcsolicitors.co.uk

MURRAY, Laura Elizabeth (Nov 2015)
(Employee)
Anderson Strathern LLP, Edinburgh . . . .(p.839)
  T: 0131 2707700
  E: laura.murray@andersonstrathern.co.uk

MURRAY, Lee Alexander (Oct 2013) (Employee)
Digby Brown LLP, Ayr . . . .(p.761)
  T: 0333 200 59285
  E: Lee.Murray@digbybrown.co.uk

MURRAY, Lindsay Claire (Aug 2016) (Employee)
Willkie Farr & Gallagher (UK) LLP, London
  EC2 . . . .(p.1269)
  E: lcmurray@willkie.com

MURRAY, Lynne (Nov 2003) (Associate)
Brodies LLP, Aberdeen. . . . .(p.723)
  T: 01224 392242
  E: lynne.murray@brodies.com

MURRAY, Lynsey Carol (Jun 2009) (Partner)
Mackintosh & Wylie LLP,
  Kilmarnock. . . . .(p.1095)
  T: 01563 525104
  E: lmurray@mackwylie.com

MURRAY, Mark Victor (Oct 2000) (Employee)
MG Management LTD., Grand
  Cayman . . . .(p.1257)
  T: +1 345 749 8181
  E: victor.murray@mgcayman.com

MURRAY, Marsali Claire (Nov 1986) (Partner)
Marsali Murray, Edinburgh . . . .(p.888)
  T: 0131 2281109
  E: marsali.murray@btinternet.com

MURRAY, Nicola Shona Elizabeth (Sept 2004)
(Associate)
Gillespie Macandrew LLP,
  Edinburgh . . . .(p.872)
  T: 0131 2251677
  E: Nicola.Murray@gillespiemacandrew.co.uk

MURRAY, Peter (Sept 1995) (Partner)
Ledingham Chalmers LLP,
  Aberdeen . . . .(p.734)
  T: 01224 408445
  E: peter.murray@ledinghamchalmers.com

MURRAY, Peter (Oct 1995) (Partner)
James Irvine, Irvine . . . .(p.1086)
  T: 01294 276116
  E: peter27murray@hotmail.com

MURRAY, Peter Frank (Nov 2017) (Partner)
James Thomson & Son, Kirkcaldy . . . . .(p.1102)
  T: 01592 268575
  E: peter@jamesthomsonandson.com

MURRAY, Rhona Anne (Sept 2004) (Associate)
Buchanan Burton Limited, East
  Kilbride . . . .(p.830)
  T: 01355 249228
  E: rhonam@buchananburton.co.uk

MURRAY, Richard David (Aug 2020)
(Employee)
Wallace Quinn & Co Limited,
  Glasgow. . . . .(p.1051)
  T: 0141 7713911
  E: richard@wallacequinn.co.uk

MURRAY, Richard James (Nov 1996) (Partner)
Connell & Connell, WS, Edinburgh . . . .(p.857)
  T: 0131 5562993

MURRAY, Robert Faulkner (Oct 2013)
(Associate)
Clyde & Co (Scotland) LLP,
  Edinburgh . . . .(p.855)
  T: 0131 5571545
  E: Bobby.Murray@clydeco.com

MURRAY, Rodger Grant (Sept 1983)
(Employee)
The Law Firm of Salah Al-Hejailan, South Doha
  District . . . .(p.1276)
  T: +966 3868 7266
  E: rodgermurray@hejailanlaw.com

MURRAY, Sarah Jayne (Oct 2011) (Associate)
Aamer Anwar & Co, Glasgow . . . .(p.941)
  T: 0141 4297090
  E: sarah@aameranwar.com

MURRAY, Sharon (Apr 1987) (Solicitor)
NO FIRM

MURRAY, Steven Archibald (Oct 1990)
(Partner)
The MMFW Partnership, Glasgow . . . .(p.1044)
  T: 0141 7631337/0141 77
  E: mcinandmacl@msn.com

MURRAY, Stewart (Jan 1983) (Director)
Murray Law Ltd, Glasgow . . . .(p.1025)
T: 0141 3575151
E: stewart.murray@murraylaw.co.uk

MURRAY, Struan Douglas Grant (Oct 2017)
(Employee)
Clifford Chance LLP, London E14 . . . . .(p.1262)
E: struan.murray@cliffordchance.com

MURRAY, Stuart (Dec 2004) (Partner)
Murray Ormiston LLP, Aberdeen . . . . . .(p.738)
T: 01224 478822
E: stuart@murrayormiston.com

MURRAY, Stuart John (Sept 2011) (Associate)
Brodies LLP, Glasgow . . . .(p.948)
T: 0141 2484672
E: stuart.murray@brodies.com

MURRAY, Stuart Ritchie (Dec 1991) (Employee)
Shoosmiths, Edinburgh . . . .(p.902)
T: 03700 868000
E: stuart.murray@shoosmiths.co.uk

MURRAY, Susan Alexandra (Sept 1984)
(Employee)
National Health Service Scotland,
Edinburgh . . . .(p.1225)
T: 0131 2757800
E: susan.murray11@nhs.scot

MURRAY, Susan Elizabeth (Sept 2011)
(Solicitor)
NO FIRM

MURRAY, Tanya Jane (May 2016) (Associate)
Lyons Davidson Scotland LLP,
Edinburgh . . . .(p.883)
T: 0344 251 0070
E: tmurray@lyonsdavidson.co.uk

MURRAY-SHERIDAN, Niamh (Sept 2018)
(Employee)
Brodies LLP, Glasgow . . . .(p.948)
T: 0141 2484672
E: niamh.murraysheridan@brodies.com

MURRIN, Peter James (Jun 2010) (Partner)
Turcan Connell, Glasgow . . . .(p.1049)
T: 0141 441 2111
E: pete.murrin@turcanconnell.com

MUSTAFA, Ahsan (May 2016) (Employee)
Nolans Law Limited, Kirkintilloch . . . . .(p.1105)
T: 0141 7776366
E: amustafa@nolanslaw.com

MUSTARD, Edwin Andrew (Nov 1994) (Partner)
Shepherd and Wedderburn LLP,
Edinburgh . . . .(p.900)
T: 0131 2289900
E: Edwin.Mustard@shepwedd.com

MUSTARD, Michael William (Jul 2005)
(Employee)
Tesco Personal Finance Plc,
Edinburgh . . . .(p.1234)
T: 0131 479 1415
E: michael.mustard@i.tescobank.com

MUTAPI, Theresa Mandisiya (Sept 2014)
(Employee)
Digby Brown LLP, Edinburgh . . . .(p.862)
T: 0333 200 5925
E: theresa.mutapi@digbybrown.co.uk

MUTCH, Kristina Elizabeth (Sept 2016)
(Employee)
University of Edinburgh, Edinburgh . . .(p.1235)

MYLES, Angela (Jul 2014) (Associate)
Morton Fraser LLP, Edinburgh . . . .(p.891)
T: 0131 247 1346
E: angela.myles@morton-fraser.com

MYLES, Deborah Jane (Nov 1996) (Employee)
Big Lottery Fund, Birmingham . . . .(p.1258)
T: 0207 211 3738
E: Deborah.Myles@tnlcommunityfund.org.uk

MYLES, Graeme John (Feb 2013) (Associate)
Ledingham Chalmers LLP,
Inverness . . . .(p.1078)
T: 01463 667400

MYLES, John Rowan (Nov 2003) (Employee)
Scottish Legal Aid Board,
Edinburgh . . . .(p.1233)
T: 0131 2267061
E: mylesia@slab.org.uk

MYLES, Joseph (Dec 1983) (Partner)
J. Myles & Co., Dundee . . . .(p.817)
T: 01382 204625
E: joemyles@jmylessols.co.uk

MYLES, Rowan Gerard (Nov 2002) (Partner)
McAfee, Coatbridge . . . .(p.787)
T: 01236 423437
E: rgmyles10@hotmail.com

MYLES, Sarah Megan (Aug 2015) (Employee)
Turcan Connell, Edinburgh . . . .(p.908)
T: 0131 2288111
E: sarah.myles@turcanconnell.com

MYLES, Yasmin Vanessa (Oct 2013) (Employee)
Macleod & MacCallum Limited,
Inverness . . . .(p.1080)
T: 01463 239393
E: yasmin.myles@macandmac.co.uk

MYRON, Debbie Maria (Jun 2016) (Employee)
Peterkins, Keith. . . . .(p.1090)
T: 01542 882537
E: dmm@peterkins.com

NADDELL, Christopher James (Oct 2020)
(Employee)
Mellicks, Incorporating Naftalin Duncan & Co.,
Glasgow.......................(p.1019)
T: 0141 3320902
E: Chris.Naddell@mellicks.co.uk

NADDELL, Nicholas Paul (Aug 1986) (Partner)
Burness Paull LLP, Glasgow ....(p.954)
T: 0141 2484933
E: nick.naddell@burnesspaull.com

NAIRN, Fiona Elizabeth (Jun 2016) (Employee)
Procurator Fiscal Service,
Edinburgh ....(p.1227)
T: 0300 0203168
E: Fiona.Nairn@copfs.gov.uk

NAISMITH, Heather Catrina Margaret
(Feb 2021) (Employee)
Procurator Fiscal Service,
Edinburgh ....(p.1229)
T: 0300 0203000
E: heather.naismith@copfs.gov.uk

NAISMITH, Kim Jane (Jan 2015) (Employee)
Mitchells Roberton Ltd, Glasgow .....(p.1020)
T: 0141 5523422
E: kjn@mitchells-roberton.co.uk

NANDWANI, Beth Maya Wallace (Sept 2020)
(Employee)
Burness Paull LLP, Edinburgh ....(p.850)
T: 0131 4736000
E: Beth.Nandwani@andersonstrathern.co.uk

NANKIVELL, Tamsin Christel (Dec 2016)
(Employee)
Law Society of Scotland,
Edinburgh ....(p.1224)
T: 0131 2267411
E: tamsinnankivell@lawscot.org.uk

NAPIER, Elizabeth Ann (Jan 1992) (Employee)
Office of the Advocate General,
Edinburgh ....(p.1227)
T: 0131 244 0359
E: elizabeth.napier@advocategeneral.gov.uk

NAPIER, Flora Elizabeth (Aug 2020) (Employee)
Procurator Fiscal Service, Glasgow ....(p.1241)
T: 0300 0203000
E: flora.napier@copfs.gov.uk

NAPIER, Fraser Robert Thomson Scott
(Jul 2019) (Employee)
Jackson Boyd LLP, Glasgow ....(p.991)
T: 0141 2214325
E: FNapier@jacksonboyd.co.uk

NAPIER, Gwen Rachel (Oct 2006) (Employee)
Shepherd and Wedderburn LLP,
Edinburgh ....(p.900)
T: 0131 2289900
E: gwen.napier@shepwedd.com

NAPIER, Janice Mary Alison (Jun 1997)
(Associate)
Thorntons Law LLP, Perth ....(p.1151)
T: 01738 621212
E: jnapier@thorntons-law.co.uk

NAPIER, Kay Isabella (May 1984) (Solicitor)
NO FIRM

NAPIER, Sophie Elizabeth (Jul 2009) (Associate)
Murray Beith Murray, Edinburgh ......(p.893)
T: 0131 2251200
E: Sophie.Napier@murraybeith.co.uk

NAPIERAJ, Lukasz (Apr 2014) (Solicitor)
NO FIRM

NARSAPUR, Asha Surendra (Sept 2008)
(Employee)
Scottish Fire and Rescue Service,
Hamilton ....(p.1247)
T: 0141 646 4699
E: Asha.Narsapur@firescotland.gov.uk

NASH, Derek Andrew (Apr 1989) (Partner)
Lindsays LLP, Edinburgh ....(p.882)
T: 0131 2291212
E: dereknash@lindsays.co.uk

NASH, Margaret Janet Mair (Jun 2002)
(Director)
Grant Smith Law Practice Limited,
Banff ....(p.769)
T: 01261 815678
E: Margaret.nash@grantsmithlaw.co.uk

NASH, Paul Francis (May 2021) (Employee)
Blackadders LLP, Glasgow ....(p.946)
T: 0141 2481888
E: paul.nash@blackadders.co.uk

NASH, Sally Elizabeth (Sept 2004) (Partner)
Gilson Gray LLP, Edinburgh ....(p.874)
T: 0131 5165354
E: snash@gilsongray.co.uk

NATARAJAN, Radhika Sekar (Sept 2008)
(Employee)
Standard Life Assets and Employee Services
Limited, Edinburgh ....(p.1234)
T: 0131 2453854
E: radhika_natarajan@standardlife.com

NAYLOR, Lisa (Dec 2002) (Solicitor)
NO FIRM

NAZAR, Ashia (Feb 2017) (Employee)
Berrymans Lace Mawer LLP,
Salford ....(p.1271)
T: 0161 2362002
E: ashia.nazar@blmlaw.com

NDUBUISI, Chigbo Humphrey (Jan 2010)
(Partner)
Drummond Miller LLP, Edinburgh .....(p.864)
T: 0131 2265151
E: hndubuisi@drummondmiller.co.uk

NEAL, Kate Boyer (Oct 1997) (Employee)
Scottish Government, Edinburgh . . . . .(p.1231)
T: 0131 244 0815
E: kate.neal@gov.scot

NEAL, Nicola Jane (May 2011) (Employee)
Brodies LLP, Edinburgh . . . .(p.845)
T: 0131 2283777
E: nicola.neal@brodies.com

NEALLY, Catriona Mairi (Sept 1999) (Employee)
MG ALBA, Stornoway . . . .(p.1255)
T: 01851 705550
E: catriona.neally@mgalba.com

NEEP, Joelle Nicole (Oct 2015) (Associate)
Aberdein Considine and Company,
Glasgow. . . . .(p.937)
T: 0141 2278200
E: jneep@acandco.com

NEIL, Camilla Nancy Martin (Mar 2016)
(Employee)
Aegon UK, Edinburgh . . . .(p.1220)
T: 1315493986
E: camilla.neil@aegon.co.uk

NEIL, Chloe Elizabeth (Nov 2020) (Employee)
Thompsons, Glasgow . . . .(p.1046)
T: 0141 2218840
E: chloe.neil@thompsons-scotland.co.uk

NEIL, Douglas Peter (Mar 1998) (Partner)
Neil Solicitors & Estate Agents,
Peebles . . . .(p.1143)
T: 01721 724199
E: douglas@neilsolicitors.com

NEIL, Lucy Bishop (Dec 2013) (Employee)
Thompsons, Glasgow . . . .(p.1046)
T: 0141 2218840
E: lucy.neil@thompsons-scotland.co.uk

NEILL, Hilary Sheila (Sept 2011) (Employee)
Standard Life Investments Limited,
Edinburgh . . . .(p.1234)
T: (0131) 245 4153
E: Hilary.Neill@aberdeenstandard.com

NEILL, Katy Elizabeth (Oct 2014) (Employee)
KCA Deutag Drilling Ltd,
Portlethen . . . .(p.1254)
T: 01224 987000
E: katy.neill@kcadeutag.com

NEILLIE, Claire Helen (Jul 1997) (Employee)
South Ayrshire Council, Ayr . . . .(p.1215)
T: 01292 612420
E: claire.neillie@south-ayrshire.gov.uk

NEILLIE, Stephen James (Oct 1995) (Employee)
Black Hay, Ayr . . . .(p.760)
T: 01292 268988
E: Stephen.Neillie@blackhay.co.uk

NEILLY, Leah Sarah (Aug 2018) (Employee)
Aberdeen Corporate Services Limited,
Edinburgh . . . .(p.1220)
T: 0131 245 7508
E: leah.neilly@abrdn.com

NEILLY, Paul David (Oct 2007) (Director)
Mitchells Roberton Ltd, Glasgow . . . . .(p.1020)
T: 0141 552 3422
E: pdn@mitchells-roberton.co.uk

NEILSON, Alison Elizabeth (Mar 1987)
(Associate)
Kerr Stirling LLP, Stirling . . . .(p.1165)
T: 01786 463414
E: alison.neilson@kerrstirling.co.uk

NEILSON, Andrew Kerr (Nov 2019) (Employee)
Procurator Fiscal Service, Hamilton . . . .(p.1247)
T: 0844 5613245
E: andrew.neilson@copfs.gov.uk

NEILSON, Clare Agnes (Feb 1997) (Employee)
Roslin Institute, Easter Bush . . . .(p.1219)
T: 0131 6519369
E: clare.neilson@roslin.ed.ac.uk

NEILSON, Craig John (Jul 2005) (Partner)
Dentons UK and Middle East LLP, London
EC4 . . . .(p.1263)
T: 020 7242 1212
E: Craig.Neilson@dentons.com

NEILSON, Ewan Craig (Apr 1996) (Partner)
Stronachs LLP, Aberdeen . . . .(p.744)
T: 01224 845845
E: ewan.neilson@stronachs.com

NEILSON, Fiona (Nov 2020) (Employee)
Ledingham Chalmers LLP,
Aberdeen . . . .(p.734)
T: 01224 405628
E: F.Neilson@ledinghamchalmers.com

NEILSON, Fiona Elizabeth (Nov 1988) (Partner)
Harper Macleod LLP, Inverness. . . . . . .(p.1077)
T: 01463 798777
E: fiona.neilson@harpermacleod.co.uk

NEILSON, Joseph Andrew (Oct 2012)
(Employee)
Dubai Properties LLC, Dubai . . . .(p.1278)
E: joseph.neilson@dp.ae

NEILSON, Kirsty (Sept 2004) (Employee)
Chivas Brothers Limited, Glasgow . . . .(p.1238)
E: kirsty.neilson@pernod-ricard.com

NEILSON, Rebecca Anne (Jan 2017) (Employee)
Office of the Advocate General,
Edinburgh . . . .(p.1227)
T: 0131 2441635
E: rebecca.neilson@advocategeneral.gov.uk

NEILSON, Stuart William (Dec 1988) (Partner)
Pinsent Masons LLP, Glasgow . . . .(p.1031)
T: 0141 567 8400
E: stuart.neilson@pinsentmasons.com

NELLANEY, David (Nov 2005) (Partner)
Digby Brown LLP, Glasgow . . . .(p.970)
T: 0141 566 2353
E: david.nellaney@digbybrown.co.uk

NELLANY, Jamie Stewart (Oct 2008) (Associate)
Brodies LLP, Glasgow . . . .(p.948)
T: 0141 2484672
E: jamie.nellany@brodies.com

NELLANY, Kirsty Jane (Nov 2010) (Solicitor)
NO FIRM

NELLANY, Michael John (Dec 1976) (Partner)
Nellany & Company LLP, Saltcoats . . . .(p.1160)
T: 01294 464175
E: michael@nellanysols.co.uk

NELLANY, Rhona Anne (Nov 2009) (Partner)
Nellany & Company LLP, Saltcoats . . . .(p.1160)
T: 01294 464175
E: rhona@nellanysols.co.uk

NELSON, Alan Fraser (Nov 1999) (Partner)
CMS Cameron McKenna Nabarro Olswang LLP,
Glasgow . . . .(p.962)
T: 0141 2222200
E: Alan.Nelson@cms-cmno.com

NELSON, David Alexander (Oct 2015)
(Employee)
Brodies LLP, Edinburgh . . . .(p.845)
T: 0131 2283777
E: david.nelson@brodies.com

NELSON, Elaine Ann (Sept 2001) (Employee)
JustRight Scotland LLP, Glasgow . . . . . .(p.994)
T: 0141 406 5350

NELSON, Ewan Panos (Nov 2003) (Associate)
Eversheds Sutherland (International) LLP, London
EC2 . . . .(p.1264)
T: 0845 4970714
E: ewannelson@eversheds-Sutherland.com

NELSON, Graham Douglas (Sept 2006)
(Employee)
City of Edinburgh Council,
Edinburgh . . . .(p.1221)
T: dd: 0131 529 2642
E: graham.nelson@edinburgh.gov.uk

NELSON, Kirsti Laura (Jul 2013) (Employee)
Scottish Police Authority, Police Scotland,
Glasgow . . . .(p.1244)
T: 01786 895 972
E: kirsti.nelson@scotland.pnn.police.uk

NELSON, Kirsty Laura (Nov 2020) (Employee)
Turcan Connell, Edinburgh . . . .(p.908)
T: 0131 2288111

NELSON, Maegan Frances (Jun 2016)
(Employee)
Strathclyde Partnership for Transport,
Glasgow . . . .(p.1245)
T: 0141 3326811
E: maegan.nelson@spt.co.uk

NELSON, William Watters (Jan 1983) (Solicitor)
Scottish Social Services Council,
Dundee . . . .(p.1218)
T: 0345 6030 891
E: William.Nelson@sssc.uk.com

NESS, Ashley Miriam (Sept 2012) (Employee)
TotalEnergies E&P UK Limited,
Westhill . . . .(p.1255)
T: 01224 297000
E: ashley.ness@external.totalenergies.com

NESS, James Iain (Feb 1981) (Employee)
Law Society of Scotland,
Edinburgh . . . .(p.1224)
T: 0131 2267411
E: jamesness@lawscot.org.uk

NESS, Owen James (Nov 1974) (Consultant)
Ness Gallagher Solicitors Limited,
Wishaw . . . .(p.1182)
T: 01698 355 525
E: ojn@nessgallagher.co.uk

NEUKIRCH, Annika (Sept 2016) (Employee)
Stronachs LLP, Aberdeen . . . .(p.744)
T: 01224 845845
E: Annika.Neukirch@stronachs.com

NEVILLE, Meghan Kathryn Grace (Jul 2012)
(Employee)
Scottish Courts and Tribunals Service,
Airdrie . . . .(p.1215)
T: 01236 439184
E: mneville@scotcourts.gov.uk

NEVIN, Jonathan Paul Harper (Jun 2010)
(Employee)
Highland Council, Inverness . . . .(p.1248)
T: 01463 702000
E: paul.nevin@highland.gov.uk

NEWCOMBE, Claire Elizabeth (Nov 1999)
(Employee)
DAC Beachcroft Scotland LLP,
Edinburgh . . . .(p.858)
T: 0131 5247790
E: cnewcombe@dacbeachcroft.com

NEWELL, Murray Angus McClements
(Aug 2021) (Employee)
Dentons UK and Middle East LLP,
Edinburgh . . . .(p.860)
T: 0330 2220050
E: murray.newell@dentons.com

NEWLANDS, Annice Robertson Cameron
(Nov 2002) (Employee)
Scottish Police Authority, Police Scotland,
Dundee . . . .(p.1218)
T: 01382 596330
E: Annice.Newlands@scotland.pnn.police.uk

NEWLANDS, Lewis (Sept 2014) (Employee)
Scottish Government, Edinburgh . . . . .(p.1231)
T: 0131 244 0815
E: Lewis.Newlands@gov.scot

NEWLANDS, Stuart Andrew (Oct 2014)
(Employee)
Pinsent Masons LLP, Glasgow . . . .(p.1031)
T: 0141 567 8400
E: stuart.newlands@pinsentmasons.com

NEWMAN, Keanu (Nov 2020) (Employee)
Appleby, St Helier . . . .(p.1274)
T: 01534 888 777
E: knewman@applebyglobal.com

NEWMAN, Sarah Ellen (Aug 2015) (Employee)
Digby Brown LLP, Inverness . . . .(p.1075)
T: 0333 200 5925
E: sarah.newman@digbybrown.co.uk

NEWNHAM, Sarah Anne (Jul 2015) (Employee)
The Law Practice, Aberdeen . . . .(p.745)
T: 01224 562870
E: snewnham@thelawpractice.org

NEWTON, Alison Sarah (Jun 1986) (Partner)
Addleshaw Goddard LLP, Glasgow . . . . .(p.938)
T: 0141 2212300
E: Alison.Newton@addleshawgoddard.com

NEWTON, Catherine Jane (Aug 1984) (Partner)
McCash & Hunter LLP, Perth . . . .(p.1149)
T: 01738 620451
E: catherinenewton@mccash.co.uk

NEWTON, Claire (Mar 2004) (Associate)
Blackadders LLP, Dundee . . . .(p.805)
T: 01382 229222
E: claire.newton@blackadders.co.uk

NEWTON, James Kenneth (Nov 2010)
(Employee)
Schroders Personal Wealth,
Edinburgh . . . .(p.1230)
E: Jamie.Newton@spw.com

NEWTON, Lois Elizabeth Anne (Feb 2012)
(Associate)
Gillespie Macandrew LLP,
Edinburgh . . . .(p.872)
T: 0131 2251677
E: Lois.Newton@gillespiemacandrew.co.uk

NGEREBARA, Ataikor Sampson (Sept 2016)
(Employee)
DLA Piper UK LLP, Leeds . . . .(p.1260)
T: 08700 111111
E: Ataikor.Ngerebara@dlapiper.com

NIBLETT, Alan Bryce (Oct 1984) (Partner)
Philpott Platt Niblett & Wight,
Dumbarton . . . .(p.799)
T: 01389 733777
E: aniblett@ppnw.co.uk

NICHOL, Barry Christopher (Mar 2000)
(Partner)
Anderson Strathern LLP, Edinburgh . . . .(p.839)
T: 0131 625 7238
E: barry.nichol@andersonstrathern.co.uk

NICHOL, David Gerrard (Oct 2005) (Employee)
CPFC Limited, London SE25 . . . .(p.1263)
T: 020 8768 6000
E: David.Nichol@cpfc.co.uk

NICHOL, Stephanie (Nov 2000) (Associate)
Balfour + Manson LLP, Edinburgh . . . . .(p.841)
T: 0131 2001200
E: stephanie.nichol@balfour-manson.co.uk

NICHOLAS, Beatrice Ecaterina (Oct 2017)
(Solicitor)
NO FIRM

NICHOLL, Emily (Oct 2020) (Employee)
Pinsent Masons LLP, Glasgow . . . .(p.1031)
T: 0141 567 8400
E: emily.nicholl@pinsentmasons.com

NICHOLLS, Claire Frances (Jul 2015)
(Employee)
Procurator Fiscal Service,
Edinburgh . . . .(p.1229)
T: 0300 0203000
E: claire.nicholls@copfs.gov.uk

NICHOLLS, Gary Christopher (Jul 2017)
(Associate)
Clyde & Co (Scotland) LLP,
Edinburgh . . . .(p.855)
T: 0131 5571545
E: gary.nicholls@clydeco.com

NICHOLSON, Alan George (Dec 2002)
(Employee)
National Westminster Bank PLC,
Edinburgh . . . .(p.1227)
T: 0131 5568555
E: alan.g.nicholson@rbs.co.uk

NICHOLSON, Andrew Gordon Tynam
(Aug 2018) (Employee)
Turcan Connell, Edinburgh . . . .(p.908)
T: 0131 2288111
E: andrew.nicholson@turcanconnell.com

NICHOLSON, Christopher William
(Nov 2006) (Employee)
Scottish Government, Edinburgh . . . . .(p.1231)
T: 0131 244 0116
E: Chris.Nicholson@gov.scot

NICHOLSON, David Joseph (Jun 2010)
(Director)
Paisley Child Law Limited, Paisley . . . . .(p.1141)
T: 07896 992 200
E: david.nicholson@mccuskerlaw.co.uk

NICHOLSON, Gemma (Mar 2011) (Employee)
Brodies LLP, Edinburgh . . . .(p.845)
T: 0131 2283777
E: gemma.nicholson@brodies.com

NICHOLSON, Jill Elizabeth (Oct 2002) (Partner)
South Forrest, Inverness . . . .(p.1082)
T: 01463 237171
E: jill@southforrest.co.uk

NICHOLSON, Julie Anne (Sept 2004)
(Employee)
East Ayrshire Council, Kilmarnock . . . . . (p.1249)
T: 01563 576161
E: Julie.Nicholson@east-ayrshire.gov.uk

NICHOLSON, Kirsty Jane (Oct 1999) (Partner)
Addleshaw Goddard LLP,
Edinburgh . . . . (p.835)
T: 0131 2282400
E: Kirsty.Nicholson@addleshawgoddard.com

NICHOLSON, Matthew (Sept 1995) (Director)
CN Defence Ltd, Edinburgh . . . . (p.857)
T: 0131 5571000
E: matthew@cndefence.com

NICHOLSON, Michael Gordon Kenneth
(Nov 1999) (Employee)
Celtic plc., Glasgow . . . . (p.1238)
T: 0871 226 1888
E: mnicholson@celticfc.co.uk

NICHOLSON, Rachel Sarah (Sept 2010)
(Employee)
Scottish Government, Edinburgh . . . . . (p.1231)
T: 0131 244 0815
E: Rachel.nicholson@gov.scot

NICHOLSON, Rebecca Kirstine (Sept 2017)
(Employee)
Shepherd and Wedderburn LLP,
Edinburgh . . . . (p.900)
T: 0131 2289900
E: rebecca.nicholson@shepwedd.com

NICHOLSON, Shona (Nov 2007) (Employee)
Procurator Fiscal Service, Aberdeen . . . (p.1213)
T: 0300 020 3000
E: shona.nicholson@copfs.gov.uk

NICHOLSON, Victoria Jane (Jun 2018)
(Employee)
Burness Paull LLP, Edinburgh . . . . (p.850)
T: 0131 4736000
E: victoria.nicholson@burnesspaull.com

NICOL, Adele Jeanne (Feb 1983) (Partner)
Anderson Strathern LLP, Edinburgh . . . . (p.839)
T: 0131 2707700
E: adele.nicol@andersonstrathern.co.uk

NICOL, Alison Morag (Nov 2011) (Employee)
Berrymans Lace Mawer LLP,
Glasgow . . . . (p.945)
T: 0141 3532121
E: alison.nicol@blmlaw.com

NICOL, Craig Orr (Nov 1994) (Partner)
Thorntons Law LLP, Dundee . . . . (p.819)
T: 01382 229 111
E: cnicol@thorntons-law.co.uk

NICOL, David John Caldwell (Dec 1980)
(Consultant)
Allan McDougall McQueen LLP,
Edinburgh . . . . (p.837)
T: 0131 2252121
E: davidnicol@allanmcdougall.co.uk

NICOL, Diane Elizabeth (Sept 1988) (Partner)
Pinsent Masons LLP, Glasgow . . . . (p.1031)
T: 0141 567 8400
E: diane.nicol@pinsentmasons.com

NICOL, Frank Samuel (Aug 1975) (Solicitor)
Airdrie Legal Chambers Limited,
Airdrie . . . . (p.748)
T: 01236 779970

NICOL, Iain William (Jul 1991) (Employee)
Lefevres (Scotland) Limited,
Glasgow . . . . (p.999)
T: 0845 3052555
E: IWN@lefevres.law

NICOL, Jennifer Helen (Dec 2009) (Employee)
Teekay Shipping (Glasgow) Limited,
Glasgow . . . . (p.1245)
T: 0141 222 9019
E: jennifer.nicol@teekay.com

NICOL, Karen Elizabeth (Sept 2009) (Employee)
Procurator Fiscal Service,
Edinburgh . . . . (p.1227)
T: 0300 0203168
E: karen.nicol@copfs.gov.uk

NICOL, Karen Lynsey (Jan 2010) (Employee)
Scottish Social Services Council,
Dundee . . . . (p.1218)
T: 01382 721658
E: Karen.Nicol@sssc.uk.com

NICOL, Kirsteen Margaret (Oct 2010)
(Employee)
Kirkland & Ellis International LLP, London
EC3 . . . . (p.1265)
T: 0207 469 2408
E: kirsteen.nicol@kirkland.com

NICOL, Lorraine (Jun 2011) (Employee)
JHS Law, Dumfries . . . . (p.801)
T: 01387 739000
E: lorraine.nicol@jhslaw.co.uk

NICOL, Margot McLeod (Sept 1991) (Partner)
Nicol, Harvey & Pierce, Stranraer . . . . . (p.1171)
T: 01776 707111
E: mn@nhpsolicitors.co.uk

NICOL, Mark James (Oct 2019) (Employee)
Procurator Fiscal Service,
Edinburgh . . . . (p.1227)
T: 0300 0203168
E: Mark.Nicol@copfs.gov.uk

NICOL, Michael John (Mar 2016) (Employee)
Argyll & Bute Council,
　Lochgilphead . . . . (p.1251)
　T: 01546 604 468
　E: Michael.Nicol@argyll-bute.gov.uk

NICOL, Ross James (Nov 2000) (Partner)
Dentons UK and Middle East LLP,
　Glasgow. . . . .(p.968)
　T: 0330 2220050
　E: Ross.Nicol@dentons.com

NICOL, Thomas William (Aug 2017) (Employee)
Scottish Government, Edinburgh . . . . .(p.1231)
　T: 0131 244 0815
　E: thomas.nicol@gov.scot

NICOLETTI, Kirsty Angela (Oct 2017)
　(Employee)
Carpenters Scotland Limited,
　Glasgow. . . . .(p.956)
　T: 0141 3285452
　E: KIB@carpenters-law.co.uk

NICOLL, Andrew James (Sept 2016) (Employee)
Nucleus Financial Group,
　Edinburgh . . . .(p.1227)
　T: 0131 2269739
　E: andy.nicoll@nucleusfinancial.com

NICOLL, Greg Bruce (Nov 2003) (Employee)
Serco UK, Europe & SGS, Hook . . . . . .(p.1260)
　T: 01256 386153
　E: greg.nicoll@serco.com

NICOLL, Katharine Anne (Jan 1987) (Employee)
Financial Conduct Authority,
　Edinburgh . . . .(p.1223)
　T: 7725552025
　E: Katie.Nicoll@fca.org.uk

NICOLL, Kerri Paula (Dec 2017) (Employee)
Harper Macleod LLP, Glasgow . . . .(p.983)
　T: 0141 2218888
　E: Kerri.Nicoll@harpermacleod.co.uk

NICOLL, Kirsty May (Nov 2019) (Employee)
Anderson Strathern LLP, Edinburgh . . . .(p.839)
　T: 0131 2707700
　E: kirsty.nicoll@andersonstrathern.co.uk

NICOLL, Lynsey Jane (Oct 2005) (Employee)
Heineken UK Limited, Edinburgh . . . . .(p.1223)
　T: 0131 5281000
　E: Lynsey.NICOLL@heineken.co.uk

NICOLSON, Andrew Alexander (Nov 2001)
　(Partner)
Dickson Minto, Edinburgh . . . .(p.861)
　T: 0131 2254455
　E: andrew.nicolson@dmws.com

NICOLSON, Charlotte Hamilton (Dec 2012)
　(Solicitor)
NO FIRM

NICOLSON, Craig Kerr (Aug 2011) (Employee)
Lloyds Banking Group Plc,
　Edinburgh . . . .(p.1224)
　T: (0131) 442 9579
　E: craig.nicolson@lloydsbanking.com

NICOLSON, Deirdre Anne (Jan 1989)
　(Employee)
Aberdeen City Council, Aberdeen. . . . .(p.1211)
　T: 01224 522000

NICOLSON, Edward Thomson Cooper
　(Jan 1991) (Director)
Lows Orkney Limited, Kirkwall . . . .(p.1106)
　T: 01856 873151
　E: eddie.nicolson@lowsorkney.co.uk

NICOLSON, Fiona Margaret McLean
　(Oct 1986) (Employee)
Keystone Law Limited, London
　WC2 . . . .(p.1265)
　T: 020 33193700
　E: fiona.nicolson@keystonelaw.co.uk

NICOLSON, Maureen Angela (Jul 1984)
　(Employee)
Paterson Holms, Glasgow . . . .(p.1029)
　T: 0141 772 0074
　E: maureen@patersonholms.co.uk

NICOLSON, Nicola Jo (Jan 2006) (Employee)
Ledingham Chalmers LLP,
　Aberdeen . . . .(p.734)
　T: 01224 408408
　E: Nicola.Nicolson@ledinghamchalmers.com

NICOLSON, Paul (Oct 1984) (Partner)
Nicolson O'Brien, Airdrie . . . .(p.751)
　T: 01236 751224
　E: paul.nicolson@nicolsonobrien.co.uk

NICOLSON, Stephen Paul (Oct 2019)
　(Employee)
Harper Macleod LLP, Glasgow . . . .(p.983)
　T: 0141 2218888
　E: Stephen.Nicolson@harpermacleod.co.uk

NICOLSON, Wendy Suzanne (Nov 1998)
　(Associate)
Pinsent Masons LLP, Glasgow . . . .(p.1031)
　T: 0141 567 8400
　E: Wendy.Nicolson@pinsentmasons.com

NIELSEN, Jennifer Elizabeth (Dec 1992)
　(Solicitor)
NO FIRM

NILSSON, Salome Maria Jessica (Feb 2019)
　(Employee)
MacRoberts LLP, Glasgow . . . .(p.1015)
　T: 0141 3031100
　E: Salome.Nilsson@macroberts.com

NIMMO, Aileen Agnes (Oct 1986) (Employee)
Scottish Government, Edinburgh . . . . .(p.1231)
　T: 0131 244 0815
　E: Aileen.Nimmo@gov.scot

NIMMO, Ashley (Sept 2005) (Associate)
Pinsent Masons LLP, Glasgow . . . .(p.1031)
T: 0141 567 8400
E: ashley.nimmo@pinsentmasons.com

NIMMO, Mary (Feb 2007) (Partner)
Munro & Noble, Inverness . . . .(p.1080)
T: 01463 221727
E: maryn@munronoble.com

NIMMO, Nicholas Michael Melville
(Jan 2005) (Employee)
Beltrami & Co Limited, Glasgow . . . . . .(p.944)
T: 0141 4292262
E:
nicholas.nimmo@beltramiandcompany.co.uk

NIMMO, Thomas William John (Dec 2002)
(Director)
Rooney Nimmo Limited,
Edinburgh . . . .(p.899)
T: 0131 220 9571
E: john.nimmo@rooneynimmo.co.uk

NISA, Hajira Noreen (Dec 2020) (Employee)
MOV8 Real Estate Limited,
Glasgow. . . . .(p.1023)
T: 0345 646 0208
E: hajira.nisa@mov8realestate.com

NISBET, Carol Margaret (Jan 2004) (Partner)
CMS Cameron McKenna Nabarro Olswang LLP,
Aberdeen . . . .(p.727)
T: 01224 622002
E: carol.nisbet@cms-cmno.com

NISBET, Caroline Margaret (Aug 1986)
(Partner)
McSherry Halliday LLP, Troon . . . .(p.1175)
T: 01292 313737
E: cmn@mcsherryhalliday.co.uk

NISBET, Claire (May 2014) (Employee)
Dentons UK and Middle East LLP,
Glasgow. . . . .(p.968)
T: 0330 2220050
E: claire.nisbet@dentons.com

NISBET, David Andrew Charles (Jul 2009)
(Employee)
Osborne Clarke, London EC2 . . . .(p.1267)
E: david.nisbet@osborneclarke.com

NISBET, Gillian Murphy (Oct 2008) (Employee)
Procurator Fiscal Service, Glasgow . . . .(p.1241)
T: 0300 0203000
E: gillian.nisbet@copfs.gov.uk

NISBET, Graeme Barry (Oct 1992) (Partner)
Harper Macleod LLP, Glasgow . . . .(p.983)
T: 0141 2218888
E: graeme.nisbet@harpermacleod.co.uk

NISBET, Iain Alister (Jun 1999) (Consultant)
Cairn Legal Ltd, Glasgow . . . .(p.955)
T: 0141 221 7948
E: iain@cairnlegal.co.uk

NISBET, Janice Fergusson (Apr 2006) (Partner)
Fergusson Law, Edinburgh . . . .(p.870)
T: 0131 556 4044
E: janice@fergussonlaw.com

NISBET, Jo-Anne Margaret (May 2011)
(Partner)
Harper Macleod LLP, Glasgow . . . .(p.983)
T: 0141 2218888
E: Jo.Nisbet@harpermacleod.co.uk

NISBET, Jonathan Alexander Foster
(Sept 2006) (Director)
Nisbets Solicitors Limited,
Edinburgh . . . .(p.894)
T: 07967 754488
E: jn@nisbetssolicitors.com

NISBET, Sharon (Jan 2007) (Employee)
Harper Macleod LLP, Glasgow . . . .(p.983)
T: 0141 2218888
E: sharon.nisbet@harpermacleod.co.uk

NIVEN, Alison Jane (Nov 1998) (Employee)
University of the West of Scotland,
Paisley . . . .(p.1253)
T: 0141 848 3577

NIVEN, Angus William Irvine (Feb 2016)
(Employee)
Box Media Agency Limited,
Edinburgh . . . .(p.1221)
E: angus@boxmedia.io

NIVEN, Jennifer Linda (Sept 2013) (Employee)
North Ayrshire Council, Irvine . . . .(p.1249)
T: 01294 310000
E: jenniferniven@north-ayrshire.gov.uk

NIVEN, Pamela Jane (Mar 1996) (Partner)
Harper Macleod LLP, Glasgow . . . .(p.983)
T: 0141 2218888
E: pamela.niven@harpermacleod.co.uk

NIXON, James Henry Joseph (Nov 2002)
(Partner)
Raeburn Christie Clark & Wallace LLP,
Ellon . . . .(p.919)
T: 01358 720777
E: Jamie.Nixon@raeburns.co.uk

NIXON, Dr, Julie Elizabeth Jane (Aug 2014)
(Associate)
Morton Fraser LLP, Edinburgh . . . .(p.891)
T: 0131 2471000
E: julie.nixon@morton-fraser.com

NIZAM, Saamir Kaiser (Jan 2017) (Employee)
Dukic & Novakovic LLP, Edinburgh . . .(p.1222)
E: Saamir.Nizam@dn-lawfirm.com

NOBLE, Amy Rebecca (Jan 2015) (Employee)
Highland Council, Inverness. . . . .(p.1248)
T: 01463 702000
E: amy.noble@highland.gov.uk

NOBLE, Christopher Alexander (Oct 2001)
(Partner)
Harper Macleod LLP, Edinburgh . . . . (p.877)
　　T: 0131 2472500
　　E: chris.noble@harpermacleod.co.uk

NOBLE, Hazel Janet (Sept 2021) (Employee)
Morton Fraser LLP, Edinburgh . . . . (p.891)
　　T: 0131 2471000
　　E: hazel.noble@morton-fraser.com

NOBLE, Joanna (May 2016) (Employee)
Score Group Limited, Peterhead . . . . . . (p.1254)
　　T: 01779 482 300
　　E: Joanna.Noble@score-group.com

NOBLE, Jonathan Taylor (Jan 1995) (Employee)
National Westminster Bank PLC,
　　Edinburgh . . . . (p.1227)
　　T: 0131 5235185
　　E: Jonathan.Noble@coutts.com

NOBLE, Kirsty Elizabeth (Jun 2009) (Employee)
Westcor International Limited, London
　　EC4 . . . . (p.1269)
　　E: Kirsty.Noble@westcorintl.com

NOBLE, Nicole Laura (Mar 2000) (Employee)
Lindsays LLP, Edinburgh . . . . (p.882)
　　T: 0131 2291212
　　E: nicolenoble@lindsays.co.uk

NOBLE, Rachael Evalyn (May 2014) (Employee)
Brodies LLP, Aberdeen . . . . (p.723)
　　T: 01224 392242
　　E: rachael.noble@brodies.com

NOBLE, Sarah Catherine (Jan 2000) (Associate)
Brodies LLP, Edinburgh . . . . (p.845)
　　T: 0131 2283777
　　E: sarah.noble@brodies.com

NOBLE, Sophie Lucinda (Oct 2010) (Associate)
Anderson Strathern LLP, Edinburgh . . . . (p.839)
　　T: 0131 2707700
　　E: sophie.noble@andersonstrathern.co.uk

NOLAN, Andrew William (Oct 2005) (Partner)
Brodies LLP, Edinburgh . . . . (p.845)
　　T: 0131 228 3777
　　E: andy.nolan@brodies.com

NOLAN, Benjamin Edward (Jun 2018)
(Employee)
Fox Williams LLP, London EC2 . . . . (p.1264)
　　E: bnolan@foxwilliams.com

NOLAN, Brandon Edward (Dec 1980) (Solicitor)
NO FIRM

NOLAN, James Gerard (Nov 1969) (Director)
Nolans Law Limited, Kirkintilloch . . . . . (p.1105)
　　T: 0141 7776366
　　E: jnolan@nolanslaw.com

NOLAN, Mairi (Aug 2018) (Employee)
Addleshaw Goddard LLP, Glasgow . . . . . (p.938)
　　T: 0141 2212300
　　E: mairi.nolan@addleshawgoddard.com

NOLAN, Martin Gerard (Sept 2007) (Employee)
Skyscanner, Edinburgh . . . . (p.1234)
　　E: Martin.Nolan@skyscanner.net

NOLAN, Simon Denis (Nov 2000) (Director)
Nolans Law Limited, Kirkintilloch . . . . . (p.1105)
　　T: 0141 7776366
　　E: snolan@nolanslaw.com

NOLIN, Kathryn Bea (Sept 2018) (Employee)
CMS Cameron McKenna Nabarro Olswang LLP,
　　Edinburgh . . . . (p.856)
　　T: 0131 2288000
　　E: kathryn.nolin@cms-cmno.com

NOON, Sarah Maureen (Dec 2011) (Employee)
Procurator Fiscal Service,
　　Edinburgh . . . . (p.1227)
　　T: 0300 0203168
　　E: sarah.noon@copfs.gov.uk

NOONE, James (Nov 2012) (Associate)
Munro & Noble, Inverness . . . . (p.1080)
　　T: 01463 221727
　　E: jamesn@munronoble.com

NOOR, Rushal Ahmed (Mar 2015) (Employee)
Allen & Overy LLP, Dubai . . . . (p.1277)
　　T: +971 442 67100
　　E: rushal.noor@allenovery.com

NOOR, Shaju Ahmed (Aug 2015) (Employee)
Aberdein Considine and Company,
　　Aberdeen . . . . (p.718)
　　T: 01224 589700
　　E: snoor@acandco.com

NORDMANN, Bernadine Mary (Mar 2002)
(Employee)
Pinsent Masons LLP, Glasgow . . . . (p.1031)
　　T: 0141 567 8400
　　E: bernadine.nordmann@pinsentmasons.com

NORFOLK, Guy Austen (May 2001) (Partner)
Dentons UK and Middle East LLP, London
　　EC4 . . . . (p.1263)
　　T: 020 7242 1212
　　E: Guy.Norfolk@dentons.com

NORMAN, Robert Adam (Oct 2012)
(Employee)
Dickson Minto, Edinburgh . . . . (p.861)
　　T: 0131 2254455
　　E: robert.norman@dmws.com

NORMAN-THORPE, Karen (Jun 2009) (Partner)
Henderson & Mackay, Lockerbie . . . . . (p.1121)
　　T: 01576 202137
　　E: info@lockerbielaw.co.uk

NORMAND, Alice Elizabeth (Jan 2005)
(Employee)
Office of the Advocate General,
Edinburgh . . . .(p.1227)
T: 0131 2441635
E: alice.normand@advocategeneral.gov.uk

NORMAND, Andrew Campbell (Oct 1986)
(Employee)
DAC Beachcroft Scotland LLP,
Edinburgh . . . .(p.858)
T: 0131 5247790
E: cnormand@dacbeachcroft.com

NORMAND, Julia Margaret (Sept 2009)
(Employee)
National Health Service Scotland,
Edinburgh . . . .(p.1225)
T: 0131 2757800
E: julia.normand@nhs.scot

NORRIE, John (Sept 2005) (Employee)
TC Young LLP, Glasgow . . . .(p.1055)
T: 0141 2215562
E: jon@tcyoung.co.uk

NORRIE, Scott Keith Sreenan (Aug 1999)
(Partner)
Hall Norrie Warden LLP, Dundee . . . . . .(p.812)
T: 07752 457043
E: scottnorrie101@hotmail.com

NORRIS, Angela Clare (Oct 2001) (Employee)
Pinsent Masons LLP, London EC2 . . . . .(p.1267)
T: 020 7418 7000
E: Angela.norris@pinsentmasons.com

NORRIS, Fiona Marie (Nov 1994) (Employee)
Murray, Hamilton & Chalmers,
Bellshill . . . .(p.773)
T: 01698 327488

NORRIS, Ljiljana Vukadinovic (Sept 2000)
(Director)
Norris Employment Limited,
Aberdeen . . . .(p.739)
T: 01224 228100
E: lili@lilihunter.com

NORRIS, Louise Dorothy (Apr 2011) (Partner)
Lindsays LLP, Edinburgh . . . .(p.882)
T: 0131 2291212
E: louisenorris@lindsays.co.uk

NORRIS, Patrick Jamie (Sept 2019) (Employee)
Stronachs LLP, Aberdeen . . . .(p.744)
T: 01224 845845
E: patrick.norris@stronachs.com

NORTON, Amy Rebecca Wright (Nov 2006)
(Associate)
CMS Cameron McKenna Nabarro Olswang LLP,
Edinburgh . . . .(p.856)
T: 0131 2288000
E: Amy.Norton@cms-cmno.com

NORVAL, Kerry Jane (Aug 2012) (Associate)
Burness Paull LLP, Edinburgh . . . .(p.850)
T: 0131 4736000

NOTARANGELO, Gabriella Anna (Sept 2012)
(Employee)
Scottish Social Services Council,
Dundee . . . .(p.1218)
T: 0345 6030 891
E: gabriella.notarangelo@sssc.uk.com

NOWLAN, Ingrid Kirsten (Jun 2014) (Solicitor)
NO FIRM

NUGENT, William (Aug 1981) (Consultant)
Pacitti Jones Legal Limited,
Glasgow. . . . .(p.1029)
T: 0141 611 8881
E: bill.nugent@pacittijones.co.uk

NUNES, Jessica (Jun 2021) (Employee)
Womble Bond Dickinson (UK) LLP,
Edinburgh . . . .(p.913)
T: 0345 415 0000
E: jess-nunes@wbd-uk.com

NUNN, Ishbel (Nov 1990) (Associate)
Raeburn Christie Clark & Wallace LLP,
Aberdeen . . . .(p.741)
T: 01224 332400
E: ishbel.nunn@raeburns.co.uk

NURSE, Kirsty Shona (Sept 2009) (Employee)
CMS Cameron McKenna Nabarro Olswang LLP,
Edinburgh . . . .(p.856)
T: 0131 2288000
E: Kirsty.nurse@cms-cmno.com

NUTTALL, Elspeth Mary Grace (Jul 2020)
(Associate)
Dentons UK and Middle East LLP,
Edinburgh . . . .(p.860)
T: 0330 2220050
E: elspeth.nuttall@dentons.com

NUTTON, Joshua William (Aug 2021)
(Employee)
Turcan Connell, Edinburgh . . . .(p.908)
T: 0131 2288111
E: joshua.nutton@turcanconnell.com

O'BRIEN, Ailidh Kate (Dec 2019) (Employee)
McAuley, McCarthy & Co., Paisley . . . .(p.1139)
T: 0141 5617779
E: ailidh@mmscotland.co.uk

O'BRIEN, Callum James (Jul 2018) (Employee)
Travers Smith LLP, London EC1 . . . . . .(p.1269)
T: (0207) 2953387
E: callum.obrien@traverssmith.com

O'BRIEN, Daniel Richard (Nov 2006)
(Employee)
Kuehne + Nagel Limited, Uxbridge. . . .(p.1272)
E: Daniel.O'Brien@kuehne-nagel.com

O'BRIEN, Jennifer (Aug 2019) (Employee)
Malcolm & Hutchison, Airdrie . . . .(p.750)
　T: 01236 755050
　E: jennifer@malcolmandhutchison.co.uk

O'BRIEN, Kathryn Melissa (Sept 2019)
(Employee)
Pinsent Masons LLP, Edinburgh . . . .(p.895)
　T: 0131 777 7000
　E: kathryn.o'brien@pinsentmasons.com

O'BRIEN, Laura-Kate (Aug 2020) (Employee)
TLT LLP, Glasgow . . . .(p.1048)
　T: 0333 006 0400
　E: Laura-Kate.O'Brien@TLTsolicitors.com

O'BRIEN, Megan Frances (Aug 2017)
(Employee)
Scottish Government, Edinburgh . . . . .(p.1231)
　T: 0131 244 0815
　E: megan.o'brien@gov.scot

O'BRIEN, Sonya Leigh (Nov 2003) (Employee)
Score Group Limited, Peterhead. . . . . .(p.1254)
　T: 01779 482 300
　E: sonya.obrien@score-group.com

O'BRIEN, William Henry (Dec 1985) (Employee)
North Ayrshire Council, Irvine . . . .(p.1249)
　T: 01294 310000
　E: wobrien@north-ayrshire.gov.uk

O'CARROLL, Michael James (Oct 2012)
(Employee)
Aegon Asset Management UK Plc,
　Edinburgh . . . .(p.1220)
　T: (0131) 549 3062
　E: michael.ocarroll@aegonam.com

O'CONNELL, Elaine Mary (Sept 1987)
(Employee)
Anthony Mahon Limited, Glasgow . . . .(p.1017)
　T: 0141 9441001
　E: eoc@amlawyer.co.uk

O'CONNELL, Jane Mai (Oct 2007) (Employee)
East Dunbartonshire Council,
　Kirkintilloch . . . .(p.1249)
　T: 0141 5788000
　E: Jane.O'Connell@eastdunbarton.gov.uk

O'CONNOR, Lyndsey Anne (Oct 2008)
(Partner)
Dentons UK and Middle East LLP,
　Edinburgh . . . .(p.860)
　T: 0330 2220050
　E: Lyndsey.O'Connor@dentons.com

O'CONNOR, Sarah Jane (Oct 2010) (Employee)
Dundee City Council, Dundee . . . .(p.1217)
　T: 01382 434208
　E: sarah.oconnor@dundeecity.gov.uk

O'CONNOR, Scott David (Sept 2020)
(Employee)
Procurator Fiscal Service, Hamilton . . . .(p.1247)
　T: 0844 5613245
　E: Scott.O Connor@copfs.gov.uk

O'CONNOR, Vanessa Charlotte (Nov 2015)
(Employee)
DJ Mackay and Partners LLP,
　Glasgow. . . . .(p.1012)
　T: 0141 254 0721
　E: vanessa.oconnor@unionlinescotland.co.uk

O'CURRY, Luke Eugene (Jun 2005) (Director)
Airdrie Legal Chambers Limited,
　Airdrie . . . .(p.748)
　T: 01236 779970
　E: admin@ocurry.net

O'DEA, Patrick William (Oct 2003) (Employee)
Public Defence Solicitors Office,
　Inverness . . . .(p.1248)
　T: 01463 709680
　E: PO'Dea@pdso.org.uk

O'DONNELL, Aislinn (Jan 2019) (Employee)
Procurator Fiscal Service, Dumfries . . . .(p.1217)
　T: 01387 274585
　E: Aislinn.O'Donnell@copfs.gov.uk

O'DONNELL, Annemarie (Mar 1989)
(Employee)
Glasgow City Council, Glasgow . . . . . .(p.1239)
　T: 0141 2874522
　E: annemarie.odonnell@ced.glasgow.gov.uk

O'DONNELL, Bryan Michael (Sept 2020)
(Employee)
Jones Whyte LLP, Glasgow. . . . .(p.993)
　T: 0141 375 1222
　E: bryan.odonnell@joneswhyte.co.uk

O'DONNELL, Caitlin (Jan 2013) (Employee)
Scotch Whisky Association,
　Edinburgh . . . .(p.1230)
　T: 0131 222 9200
　E: codonnell@swa.org.uk

O'DONNELL, Christopher Kesson (Oct 2016)
(Employee)
William Grant & Sons Ltd., Bellshill . . .(p.1215)
　T: 01698 843843
　E: Chris.ODonnell@wgrant.com

O'DONNELL, Denese (Jun 2002) (Employee)
Inverclyde Council, Greenock. . . . .(p.1246)
　T: 01475 717171
　E: Denese.O'Donnell@inverclyde.gov.uk

O'DONNELL, Fiona Clare (Oct 2005)
(Employee)
R. & R.S. Mearns, Glasgow . . . .(p.1018)
　T: 0141 6326162
　E: fomearns@gmail.com

O'DONNELL, Gerald Anthony (Nov 1985)
(Partner)
O'Donnell & Co., Glasgow . . . .(p.1027)
 T: 0141 9441441
 E: odonnelllaw@btconnect.com

O'DONNELL, Kathleen Anne (Aug 2015)
(Employee)
Procurator Fiscal Service, Glasgow . . . .(p.1241)
 T: 0300 0203000
 E: Kathleen.O'Donnell@copfs.gov.uk

O'DONNELL, Kirsty Ann (Nov 2009) (Associate)
Digby Brown LLP, Glasgow . . . .(p.970)
 T: 0141 5660896
 E: kirsty.odonnell@digbybrown.co.uk

O'DONNELL, Rose Marie (May 2003)
(Employee)
Schneider Electric Limited, Telford . . . .(p.1272)
 E: rose.odonnell@schneider-electric.com

O'DONNELL, Ross John (Oct 2020) (Employee)
TC Young LLP, Glasgow . . . .(p.1055)
 T: 0141 2215562
 E: rjo@tcyoung.co.uk

O'DOWD, Alan James (Mar 2005) (Solicitor)
NO FIRM

O'DOWD, Caitlin Andrew (Aug 2017)
(Employee)
Equator (Scotland) Ltd, Glasgow . . . . .(p.1239)
 E: caitlin.o'dowd@eqtr.com

O'DOWD, James Michael (Nov 1995) (Director)
Bell Solicitors Limited, Bellshill . . . .(p.773)
 T: 01698 749977
 E: admin@bellsolicitors.co.uk

O'DOWD, Mark Anthony McFarlane
(Oct 2002) (Partner)
Energy Law Unlimited LLP,
 Glasgow. . . . .(p.974)
 T: 0141 2210276
 E: modowd@elu-llp.com

O'FARRELL, Susan Carol (Mar 2013) (Associate)
MacRoberts LLP, Glasgow . . . .(p.1015)
 T: 0141 3031100
 E: susan.ofarrell@macroberts.com

O'HAGAN, Claire Ann Lavery (Jan 2020)
(Employee)
Procurator Fiscal Service,
 Dumbarton . . . .(p.1217)
 T: 0300 020 3000
 E: Claire.O'Hagan@copfs.gov.uk

O'HAGAN, David Andrew (Sept 1997) (Partner)
Jim Friel Solicitors, Glasgow . . . .(p.978)
 T: 0141 4201234
 E: davido@jimfriel.co.uk

O'HAGAN, Lisa Mary (Jul 2004) (Solicitor)
NO FIRM

O'HANLON, Mark (Feb 1990) (Partner)
Mains Solicitors, East Kilbride . . . .(p.832)
 T: 01355 225111
 E: mohanlon@mainslegal.com

O'HARA, Chloe Jessica (Jul 2017) (Employee)
Procurator Fiscal Service, Hamilton . . . .(p.1247)
 T: 0844 5613245
 E: Chloe.O'Hara@copfs.gov.uk

O'HARA, Holly Claire (Sept 2020) (Employee)
Turcan Connell, Edinburgh . . . .(p.908)
 T: 0131 2288111
 E: holly.o'hara@turcanconnell.com

O'HARA, Jonathan (Jan 1992) (Employee)
Scottish Widows Limited,
 Edinburgh . . . .(p.1233)
 T: 0131 6556643
 E: jonathan.o'hara@scottishwidows.co.uk

O'HARA, Julie (Oct 2013) (Employee)
Procurator Fiscal Service, Hamilton . . . .(p.1247)
 T: 0300 203928
 E: julie.o'hara@copfs.gov.uk

O'HARA, Katie (Oct 2015) (Employee)
Scottish Enterprise, Glasgow . . . .(p.1243)
 T: 0141 2482700
 E: Katie.O'Hara@scotent.co.uk

O'HARA, Marie-Louise (Sept 2004) (Employee)
Subsea 7 (UK Service Company) Ltd,
 Westhill . . . .(p.1255)
 T: 01224 526736
 E: marielouise.ohara@subsea7.com

O'HARE, Caitlin Anne (Sept 2020) (Employee)
Levy & McRae Solicitors LLP,
 Glasgow. . . . .(p.1000)
 T: 0141 3072311
 E: cohare@lemac.co.uk

O'HARE, Gerard James (Dec 2008) (Employee)
Law at Work Ltd, Glasgow . . . .(p.1240)
 T: 0141 2715555
 E: gerard.ohare@lawatwork.co.uk

O'HARE, Gerard John (Feb 1978) (Partner)
O'Hares, Dumbarton. . . . .(p.799)
 T: 01389 742346
 E: gerry@oharessolicitors.co.uk

O'HARE, Ruth Elizabeth (Oct 2005) (Employee)
Aberdeenshire Council, Aberdeen. . . . .(p.1211)
 T: 0345 608 1208
 E: ruth.o'hare@aberdeenshire.gov.uk

O'HARE, Stephen Patrick (Nov 2018)
(Employee)
Thorntons Law LLP, Dundee . . . .(p.819)
 T: 01382 229 111
 E: sohare@thorntons-law.co.uk

O'HEAR, Rebecca (Jun 2019) (Employee)
BTO Solicitors LLP, Glasgow . . . .(p.952)
 T: 0141 2218012
 E: roh@bto.co.uk

O'KANE, Charlotte Louise (Sept 2009)
(Associate)
Pinsent Masons LLP, Glasgow . . . .(p.1031)
   T: 0141 567 8400
   E: charlotte.okane@pinsentmasons.com

O'KEEFE, Declan (Jan 2021) (Employee)
Iain Jane & Co, Peterhead . . . .(p.1154)
   T: 01779 477620
   E: declan@iainjane.co.uk

O'MALLEY, Anthony John (Jul 1996) (Director)
Parabis Scotland Limited, Glasgow . . . .(p.1029)
   T: 0844 8921250
   E: tony.omalley@friends-legal.co.uk

O'MALLEY, Carolyn Mary (Oct 2002)
(Employee)
Scottish Government, Edinburgh . . . . .(p.1231)
   T: 0131 244 0815
   E: carolyn.o'malley@gov.scot

O'MARA, Alexandra Janey (Sept 2018)
(Employee)
Pinsent Masons LLP, Edinburgh . . . .(p.895)
   T: 0131 777 7000
   E: alexandra.o'mara@pinsentmasons.com

O'MAY, Alyson (Sept 2007) (Partner)
Neill Clerk & Murray, Greenock . . . . . .(p.1062)
   T: 01475 724522
   E: aom@neillclerkmurray.co.uk

O'NEIL, Anna (Dec 2020) (Employee)
Anderson Strathern LLP, Glasgow . . . . . .(p.940)
   T: 0141 2426060
   E: anna.o'neil@andersonstrathern.co.uk

O'NEIL, Elizabeth Valerie (Feb 1987) (Director)
MacFarlane Young Limited, Paisley . . . .(p.1139)
   T: 0141 8893257
   E: valerie@macfarlaneyoung.com

O'NEIL, Gillian (Nov 2019) (Employee)
Glasgow City Council, Glasgow . . . . . .(p.1239)
   T: 0141 2872000
   E: Gillian.ONeil@glasgow.gov.uk

O'NEIL, Lisa Marie (Feb 2012) (Partner)
The Cumbernauld Law Practice,
   Cumbernauld . . . .(p.791)
   T: 01236 731911
   E: lisaoneil@cumbernauldlaw.co.uk

O'NEIL, Siobhan (Jun 2011) (Employee)
Edrington UK Distribution Limited,
   Glasgow . . . .(p.1239)
   T: 0333 0161910
   E: siobhan.oneil@edrington.com

O'NEILL, Alison Christina (Aug 1992) (Partner)
A.C. O'Neill & Co., Dumbarton . . . .(p.799)
   T: 01389 762997
   E: aconeillandco@btconnect.com

O'NEILL, Bernadette (Jul 1986) (Employee)
Renfrewshire Council, Paisley . . . .(p.1252)
   T: 0141 8403648
   E: bernadette.oneill@renfrewshire.gov.uk

O'NEILL, Christine Mary, QC (Mar 1999)
(Partner)
Brodies LLP, Edinburgh . . . .(p.845)
   T: 0131 2283777
   E: christine.oneill@brodies.com

O'NEILL, Euan Peter (Jul 2019) (Employee)
Scottish Government, Edinburgh . . . . .(p.1232)
   E: Euan.O'neill@gov.scot

O'NEILL, Finn (May 2021) (Employee)
CMS Cameron McKenna Nabarro Olswang LLP,
   Aberdeen . . . .(p.727)
   T: 01224 622002
   E: finn.oneill@cms-cmno.com

O'NEILL, Grant Stephen (Oct 2019) (Employee)
Harper Macleod LLP, Glasgow . . . .(p.983)
   T: 0141 2218888
   E: grant.o'neill@harpermacleod.co.uk

O'NEILL, Jamie Tazare (Oct 2015) (Employee)
DLA Piper Scotland LLP, Edinburgh . . . .(p.863)
   T: 0131 242 5557
   E: jamie.oneill@dlapiper.com

O'NEILL, Jeremy George (Aug 2019)
(Employee)
Procurator Fiscal Service, Glasgow . . . .(p.1241)
   T: 0300 0203000
   E: jeremy.oneill@copfs.gov.uk

O'NEILL, Mark Gerard (Mar 2012) (Employee)
Alexr. McAllister & McKechnie,
   Paisley . . . .(p.1136)
   T: 0141 8878961
   E: moneill@ammlaw.co.uk

O'NEILL, Martin Thomas Burnett (Aug 2006)
(Partner)
Wright, Johnston & Mackenzie LLP,
   Glasgow . . . .(p.1054)
   T: 0141 2483434
   E: mon@wjm.co.uk

O'NEILL, Matthew Derek (Sept 2009) (Director)
Grant Smith Law Practice Limited,
   Elgin . . . .(p.917)
   T: 01343 544466
   E: matthew.oneill@grantsmithlaw.co.uk

O'NEILL, Michael (Jul 1994) (Consultant)
Moir and Sweeney LLP, Glasgow . . . . .(p.1021)
   T: 0141 4292724
   E: michael@moirandsweeney.com

O'NEILL, Peter Alexander (Sept 2008)
(Director)
Stewart and O'Neill Defence Limited,
   Edinburgh . . . .(p.904)
   T: 0131 225 2900
   E: stewartandoneill@gmail.com

O'NEILL, Rosemary Jean (Dec 2003) (Employee)
Scottish Government, Edinburgh . . . . .(p.1231)
T: 0131 244 0815
E: rosemary.o'neill@civilrecoveryunit.gov.scot

O'NEILL, Sean Adam (Sept 2004) (Employee)
SOUTH LANARKSHIRERe Council,
Hamilton . . . .(p.1247)
E: sean.o'neill@southlanarkshire.gov.uk

O'NEILL, Stacey Elizabeth (Mar 2019)
(Employee)
Scottish Children's Reporter Administration,
Paisley . . . .(p.1252)
E: stacey.o'neill@scra.gov.uk

O'RAW, Megan (Sept 2021) (Employee)
Aberdeen Corporate Services Limited,
Edinburgh . . . .(p.1220)
T: 0131 245 7508
E: megan.oraw@abrdn.com

O'REILLY, James Patrick (Oct 2005) (Employee)
Procurator Fiscal Service,
Edinburgh . . . .(p.1229)
T: 0300 0203000
E: james.oreilly@copfs.gov.uk

O'REILLY, Mairi Elizabeth (Oct 2006)
(Employee)
Scottish Children's Reporter Administration,
Paisley . . . .(p.1252)
E: Mairi.O'reilly@scra.gov.uk

O'REILLY, Mark Nicholas (Aug 2011)
(Employee)
The Medical & Dental Defence Union of
Scotland, Glasgow . . . .(p.1245)
T: 0845 2702034
E: moreilly@mddus.com

O'REILLY, Rachel E.N.R. (Aug 2014) (Employee)
Brodies LLP, Glasgow . . . .(p.948)
T: 0141 2484672
E: rachel.oreilly@brodies.com

O'ROURKE, Emma Louise (Sept 2020)
(Employee)
Dickson Minto, Edinburgh . . . .(p.861)
T: 0131 2254455
E: emma.orourke@dmws.com

O'SULLIVAN, Emily Rose (Jul 2020) (Employee)
Brodies LLP, Edinburgh . . . .(p.845)
T: 0131 2283777
E: emily.osullivan@brodies.com

O'SULLIVAN, Kate (Nov 2007) (Employee)
Procurator Fiscal Service,
Edinburgh . . . .(p.1227)
T: 0300 0203168
E: kate.o'sullivan@copfs.gov.uk

OAKSHETT, Chloe Alexandra De Falaise
(Sept 2016) (Associate)
Addleshaw Goddard LLP,
Edinburgh . . . .(p.835)
T: 0131 2282400
E: Chloe.Oakshett@addleshawgoddard.com

OATES, Robert Donald (Sept 2016) (Employee)
Macfarlanes LLP, London EC4 . . . .(p.1266)
T: (020) 7791 4044
E: robert.oates@macfarlanes.com

OATES, Susan Jane (Mar 2005) (Associate)
McDougall McQueen, Edinburgh . . . . . .(p.884)
T: 0131 6221771
E: susanoates@mcdougallmcqueen.co.uk

OCKRIM, Joanne (May 2002) (Partner)
Wright, Johnston & Mackenzie LLP,
Glasgow. . . . .(p.1054)
T: 0141 2483434
E: jo@wjm.co.uk

OCKRIM, Paul (Sept 2001) (Partner)
Addleshaw Goddard LLP, Glasgow . . . . .(p.938)
T: 0141 2212300
E: Paul.Ockrim@addleshawgoddard.com

OGDEN, Rosanne Dorothy (Oct 2006)
(Associate)
Pinsent Masons LLP, Edinburgh . . . .(p.895)
T: 0131 777 7000
E: Rosanne.Ogden@pinsentmasons.com

OGG, Ann (Nov 1986) (Partner)
Ann Ogg, Edinburgh . . . .(p.894)
T: 0131 3370912
E: an.og@btinternet.com

OGG, Kirsten Elaine (Sept 2019) (Employee)
Brodies LLP, Edinburgh . . . .(p.845)
T: 0131 2283777
E: kirsten.ogg@brodies.com

OGG, Sandra Mary (Jun 2000) (Employee)
National Health Service Scotland,
Edinburgh . . . .(p.1225)
T: 0131 2757800
E: Sandra.Ogg@nhs.scot

OGILVIE, Andrew James (Nov 1991) (Partner)
Connell & Connell, WS, Edinburgh . . . .(p.857)
T: 0131 5562993
E: ajo@connellws.co.uk

OGILVIE, Charles Stephen (Oct 2004) (Partner)
Drummond Miller LLP, Edinburgh . . . . .(p.864)
T: 0131 2265151
E: cogilvie@drummondmiller.co.uk

OGILVIE, David Stewart (May 1991) (Employee)
CNR International (U.K.) Limited,
Aberdeen . . . .(p.1212)
T: 01224 303659
E: david.ogilvie@cnrl.com

OGILVIE, Kieran Patrick (Oct 2013) (Employee)
Carey Olsen, St Peter Port . . . .(p.1273)
T: (+44) 1481 741505
E: kieran.ogilvie@careyolsen.com

OGILVIE, Lindsey (Aug 2004) (Partner)
Turcan Connell, Edinburgh . . . .(p.908)
T: 0131 2288111
E: lindsey.ogilvie@turcanconnell.com

OGILVY, David Cameron (Jan 1989) (Partner)
Turcan Connell, Edinburgh . . . .(p.908)
T: 0131 2288111
E: david.ogilvy@turcanconnell.com

OGSTON, Claire (Mar 2008) (Associate)
Ledingham Chalmers LLP,
Aberdeen . . . .(p.733)
T: 01224 622622
E: claire.ogston@ledinghamchalmers.com

OGUNYEMI, Lindsay Marie (Nov 2004)
(Associate)
DWF LLP, Glasgow . . . .(p.973)
T: 0141 228 8000
E: Lindsay.Ogunyemi@dwf.law

OKAN, Denize Ann (Dec 2019) (Employee)
McGlashan MacKay Solicitors,
Glasgow . . . .(p.1011)
T: 0141 3757557
E: denize@mcglashanmackay.com

OLABAMIJI, Olawale (Jan 2012) (Director)
Olabamiji & Co Limited, Glasgow . . . .(p.1027)
T: 0141 2311650
E: mail@dmoolabamiji-solicitors.co.uk

OLEJNIK, Elzbieta Justyna (Sept 2017)
(Employee)
Irwin Mitchell, London EC1 . . . .(p.1265)
T: 0370 1500100
E: Elzbieta.Olejnik@irwinmitchell.com

OLIFF, Harry Douglas (Feb 2021) (Employee)
Shepherd and Wedderburn LLP,
Edinburgh . . . .(p.900)
T: 0131 2289900
E: harry.oliff@shepwedd.com

OLIPHANT, Rachel Jane (Jun 1997) (Associate)
Pinsent Masons LLP, Edinburgh . . . . . .(p.895)
T: 0131 7777000
E: rachel.oliphant@pinsentmasons.com

OLIPHANT, Sara Jane (Oct 2012) (Employee)
Scottish Widows Limited,
Edinburgh . . . .(p.1233)
T: 0131 6557230
E: sara.oliphant@lloydsbanking.com

OLIVER, Ann Margaret (Jul 1997) (Partner)
Innes Johnston LLP, Kirkcaldy . . . .(p.1100)
T: 01592 263455
E: AOLIVER@INNESJOHNSTON.CO.UK

OLIVER, Fraser Charles (Nov 1992) (Partner)
Digby Brown LLP, Glasgow . . . .(p.970)
T: 0333 200 5925
E: fraser.oliver@digbybrown.co.uk

OLIVER, Henry John (Oct 2015) (Director)
Geo & Jas Oliver WS Limited,
Hawick. . . . .(p.1071)
T: 01450 372791
E: holiver@gandjoliver.co.uk

OLIVER, Jennifer Margaret (Sept 2010)
(Associate)
Pinsent Masons LLP, Glasgow . . . .(p.1031)
T: 0141 567 8400
E: Jennifer.oliver@pinsentmasons.com

OLIVER, John Anthony Lindsay, WS
(Sept 1976) (Director)
Geo & Jas Oliver WS Limited,
Hawick. . . . .(p.1071)
T: 01450 372791
E: JOliver@gandjoliver.co.uk

OLIVER, Karen Jayne (Nov 2010) (Associate)
Stronachs LLP, Aberdeen . . . .(p.744)
T: 01224 845 841
E: karen.oliver@stronachs.com

OLIVER, Louise Margaret (Sept 2011)
(Employee)
Osborne Clarke, London EC2 . . . .(p.1267)
E: louise.oliver@osborneclarke.com

OLOFSSON, Elizabeth (Oct 2020) (Employee)
Gildeas Limited, Edinburgh . . . .(p.872)
T: 0141 331 6079
E: eolofsson@gildeas.net

OLSON, Kirsti Mary (Jul 1994) (Partner)
Dentons UK and Middle East LLP,
Edinburgh . . . .(p.860)
T: 0330 2220050
E: Kirsti.Olson@dentons.com

OLTEAN, Ioan (Jan 2018) (Director)
OJ Solicitors Ltd, Glasgow . . . .(p.1027)
T: 07842 507897
E: ioan.oltean@oj-solicitors.co.uk

ONORATI, Marc Anthony (Sept 2016)
(Employee)
Jones Whyte LLP, Glasgow. . . . .(p.993)
T: 0141 375 1222
E: marc.onorati@joneswhyte.co.uk

ONUONGA, Barbara Kemunto (May 2013)
(Employee)
Norton Rose Fulbright LLP, London
SE1 . . . .(p.1267)
E: barbara.onuonga@nortonrosefulbright.com

OPENSHAW, Ryan Mackenzie (Jul 2009)
(Employee)
Brodies LLP, Aberdeen. . . . .(p.723)
T: 01224 392178
E: ryan.openshaw@brodies.com

ORCHARD, Michelle Ann (Jul 2010) (Employee)
Austin Lafferty Limited, Glasgow . . . . . . (p.943)
T: 0141 6212212
E: morchard@laffertylaw.com

ORLANDO, Nadia (Aug 2020) (Employee)
Frank Irvine Solicitors Ltd, Glasgow . . . . (p.990)
T: 0141 3759000
E: nao@frankirvine.com

ORLOVA-FARRELLY, Oksana (Oct 2014)
(Employee)
BAE Systems Surface Ships Limited,
Glasgow. (p.1238)
T: (07525) 391 489
E: Oksana.Farrelly@baesystems.com

ORME, Alan Stewart McLaren (Mar 1991)
(Director)
Orme Law-A Trading Name of Kirklands,
Falkirk . . . . (p.924)
T: 01324 882551
E: alano@orme-law.co.uk

ORMISTON, Andrew (Sept 2010) (Partner)
Murray Ormiston LLP, Aberdeen . . . . . . (p.738)
T: 01224 478822
E: andrew@murrayormiston.com

ORMISTON, Rachael Catherine Yuille
(Apr 2011) (Employee)
Sitecore USA Inc, San Francisco . . . . . . (p.1279)

ORMISTON, Trevor Andrew (May 1999)
(Director)
Ormistons Law Practice Limited,
Glenrothes . . . . (p.1057)
T: 0800 7810413
E: ormistonslaw@btconnect.com

ORR, Alexandra Jane (Sept 2019) (Employee)
Pinsent Masons LLP, Glasgow . . . . (p.1031)
T: 0141 567 8400
E: Alexandra.Orr@pinsentmasons.com

ORR, Alistair Charles (Nov 1991) (Employee)
Scottish Power Limited, Glasgow . . . . . (p.1244)
T: 0141 6140000
E: alistair.orr@scottishpower.com

ORR, Amy Francis Rosemary (Jul 2016)
(Employee)
Brazenall & Orr, Dumfries . . . . (p.800)
T: 01387 255695
E: amy@brazenallandorr.co.uk

ORR, Andrew Alexander (Apr 1992) (Partner)
Dentons UK and Middle East LLP,
Edinburgh . . . . (p.860)
T: 0330 2220050
E: Andrew.Orr@dentons.com

ORR, Ann Elizabeth (Aug 1988) (Employee)
Procurator Fiscal Service, Falkirk . . . . . . (p.1236)
T: 0300 020 3000
E: Ann.Orr@copfs.gov.uk

ORR, Caroline Mary (Oct 2007) (Employee)
Clydesdale Bank Plc, Glasgow . . . . (p.1238)
T: 0141 2423733
E: caroline.orr@cybg.com

ORR, David Patrick (Aug 2006) (Partner)
Aberdein Considine and Company,
Glasgow. (p.937)
T: 0141 227 8200
E: dorr@acandco.com

ORR, David Thomas Hunter (Apr 2014)
(Employee)
Brazenall & Orr, Dumfries . . . . (p.800)
T: 01387 255695
E: david@brazenallandorr.co.uk

ORR, Gavin John Stewart (Aug 1987) (Partner)
Brazenall & Orr, Dumfries . . . . (p.800)
T: 01387 255695
E: gavin.orr@brazenallandorr.co.uk

ORR, Karen Jean (Mar 2009) (Employee)
Associated British Foods Plc, London
WC1 . . . . (p.1261)
E: karen.orr@abfoods.com

ORR, Matthew Iain (Nov 2010) (Employee)
Nucleus Financial Group,
Edinburgh . . . . (p.1227)
T: 0131 2269739
E: Matthew.Orr@nucleusfinancial.com

ORR, Moira (Oct 1985) (Employee)
Procurator Fiscal Service, Glasgow . . . . (p.1241)
T: 0300 0203000
E: Moira.Orr@copfs.gov.uk

ORR, SallyAnn (Aug 2012) (Partner)
DM MacKinnon, Oban . . . . (p.1134)
T: 01631 563014
E: sallyorr@dmmk.co.uk

ORR, Stuart Gordon (Aug 2018) (Employee)
Anderson Strathern LLP, Edinburgh . . . . (p.839)
T: 0131 2707700
E: stuart.orr@andersonstrathern.co.uk

ORREN, Lucy Avril (Oct 2016) (Employee)
Scottish Government, Edinburgh . . . . . (p.1231)
T: 0131 244 2031
E: Lucy.Orren@gov.scot

ORZEG-WYDRA, Michal Krzysztof
(Feb 2019) (Employee)
DLA Piper UK LLP, London EC1 . . . . . . (p.1263)
T: 020 77966017
E: michal.orzeg-wydra@dlapiper.com

OSBORNE, Claire Louise (Oct 2018) (Employee)
Clan Childlaw Limited, Edinburgh . . . . . (p.854)
T: 0808 129 0522
E: claire.osborne@clanchildlaw.org

OSBORNE, Karen Louise (Dec 2014)
(Employee)
Unison Scotland, Glasgow . . . . (p.1245)
E: k.osborne2@unison.co.uk

OSBORNE, Rebecca Fay (Aug 2010) (Employee)
Scottish Courts and Tribunals Service,
   Airdrie . . . .(p.1215)
   T: 01236 439184
   E: rosborne@scotcourts.gov.uk

OSHODI, Eniola Oluwadamilola (Aug 2019)
   (Employee)
Office of the Advocate General,
   Edinburgh . . . .(p.1227)
   T: 0131 2441635
   E: eniola.oshodi@advocategeneral.gov.uk

OSLER, Duncan Farnworth (Jan 1994) (Partner)
MacRoberts LLP, Edinburgh . . . .(p.887)
   T: 0131 2295046
   E: duncan.osler@macroberts.com

OSMAN, Nesreen Isameldin (Nov 2006)
   (Employee)
Pinsent Masons LLP, Dubai . . . .(p.1278)
   E: nesreen.osman@pinsentmasons.com

OSWALD, Susan Margaret (Oct 1995) (Partner)
SKO Family Law Specialists LLP,
   Edinburgh . . . .(p.903)
   T: 0131 3226669
   E: Susan.Oswald@sko-family.co.uk

OVENDEN, Katrina Jan (Mar 2004) (Employee)
HFD Management, Bellshill . . . .(p.1215)
   E: kovenden@hfdgroup.com

OVENSTONE, Ashleigh Moira (Oct 2008)
   (Employee)
BlackRock, Edinburgh . . . .(p.1221)
   T: 0131 2221352
   E: ashleigh.ovenstone@blackrock.com

OWENS, Anna Rose (Aug 2019) (Employee)
Dentons UK and Middle East LLP,
   Glasgow. . . . .(p.968)
   T: 0330 2220050
   E: anna.owens@dentons.com

OWENS, Christopher (Oct 2006) (Associate)
Pinsent Masons LLP, Edinburgh . . . .(p.895)
   T: 0131 777 7000
   E: christopher.owens@pinsentmasons.com

OWSIANKA, Klaudia Eliza (Sept 2014)
   (Employee)
Linklaters Sp.k. Wisniewski I Wsp Inicy,
   Warsaw . . . .(p.1275)
   T: +48 22 526 5086
   E: klaudia.owsianka@linklaters.com

PACEVITCH, Laura (Dec 2002) (Employee)
Scottish Power Limited, Glasgow . . . . .(p.1244)
   T: 0141 6140000
   E: laura.pacevitch@scottishpower.com

PACITTI, Antonia Paula (Aug 2016) (Employee)
Ocean Winds UK Limited,
   Edinburgh . . . .(p.1227)
   T: 0131 5567602
   E: antonia.pacitti@oceanwinds.com

PACITTI, Frances (Oct 2005) (Employee)
Transport Scotland, Glasgow . . . .(p.1245)
   T: 0141 2727538
   E: Frances.Pacitti@transport.gov.scot

PACITTI, Linda Anne (Dec 1988) (Partner)
Morton Pacitti LLP, Falkirk . . . .(p.923)
   T: 01324 679030
   E: linda@mortonpacitti.com

PACITTI, Lynn (Jul 2010) (Director)
Strefford Tulips Limited, Hamilton . . . .(p.1070)
   T: 01698 429428
   E: l.pacitti@strefford-tulips.co.uk

PACKHAM, Jennifer Louise (Feb 2010)
   (Employee)
Weatherford, Aberdeen . . . .(p.1214)
   T: 01224 380200
   E: jennifer.packham@weatherford.com

PADDEN, Emma Marguerite (Mar 2015)
   (Employee)
Midlothian Council, Dalkeith . . . .(p.1216)
   T: 0131 2707500
   E: emma.padden@midlothian.gov.uk

PAGE, Rebekah Anne (Nov 2019) (Employee)
Law At Work Incorporating Empire,
   Aberdeen . . . .(p.1213)
   T: (01224) 701383
   E: rebekahpage@worknest.com

PAINE, Marion (Sept 1983) (Employee)
London Borough of Bromley,
   Bromley . . . .(p.1259)
   T: 07876 452009
   E: marion.paine@bromley.gov.uk

PAIRMAN, Amy Louise (Dec 2016) (Employee)
Brodies LLP, Edinburgh . . . .(p.845)
   T: 0131 2283777
   E: amy.pairman@brodies.com

PAISLEY, Roderick Ruthven Mackenzie
   (Dec 1988) (Consultant)
Mitchells Roberton Ltd, Glasgow . . . . .(p.1020)
   T: 0141 5523422

PALL, Gurjit Singh (Dec 2013) (Associate)
Thorntons Law LLP, Edinburgh . . . .(p.906)
   T: 0131 2258705
   E: gpall@thorntons-law.co.uk

PALL, Phulah Singh Mouchull (Feb 2015)
   (Employee)
Jones Whyte LLP, Glasgow. . . . .(p.993)
   T: 0141 375 1222
   E: phulah.pall@joneswhyte.co.uk

PALLOCH, Olivia Marie (Dec 2014) (Employee)
Walkers, St Helier . . . .(p.1274)
   T: (01534) 700723
   E: opalloch@walkersglobal.com

PALLUCCI, Daniela Cristina (Sept 2015)
(Employee)
Burness Paull LLP, Edinburgh . . . . (p.850)
T: 0131 4736000
E: daniela.pallucci@burnesspaull.com

PALMER, Graeme Thomas (Apr 1997) (Partner)
Burness Paull LLP, Glasgow . . . . (p.954)
T: 0141 248 4933
E: Graeme.Palmer@burnesspaull.com

PALMER, Kayleigh (Jul 2021) (Employee)
MBM Commercial LLP, Edinburgh . . . . . (p.889)
T: 0131 2268200
E: kayleigh.palmer@mbmcommercial.co.uk

PALMER, Pauline Barbara (Nov 1995)
(Employee)
Procurator Fiscal Service, Glasgow . . . . (p.1241)
T: 0300 0203000
E: pauline.palmer@copfs.gov.uk

PALMER, Robert Kenneth Alexander
(Apr 1992) (Employee)
The Pensions Ombudsman, London
E14 . . . . (p.1268)
E:
Robert.Palmer@pensions-ombudsman.org.uk

PANESAR, Ameeta (Oct 2005) (Associate)
Clyde & Co (Scotland) LLP,
Glasgow. (p.961)
T: 0141 2482666
E: ameeta.panesar@clydeco.com

PANESAR, Simran Kaur (Oct 2008) (Employee)
Turcan Connell, Glasgow . . . . (p.1049)
T: 0141 441 2111
E: Simran.Panesar-Saggu@turcanconnell.com

PANG, Ciara Maria (Apr 2007) (Employee)
Sheku Bayoh Public Inquiry,
Edinburgh . . . . (p.1233)
E: ciara.pang@shekubayohinquiry.scot

PANICO, Paolo (Jul 2015) (Solicitor)
NO FIRM

PANTON, Christine Anne (May 2011)
(Employee)
Renfrewshire Council, Paisley . . . . (p.1252)
T: 0141 8403648
E: christine.panton@renfrewshire.gov.uk

PANTONY, Jacqueline (Jan 1992) (Employee)
Scottish Government, Edinburgh . . . . . (p.1231)
T: 0131 244 1504
E: jacqueline.pantony@gov.scot

PAPANDRIANOU, Lydia (Apr 2019) (Employee)
Thorntons Law LLP, Edinburgh . . . . . . (p.906)
T: 0131 2258705
E: lpapandrianou@thorntons-law.co.uk

PARCELL, Daniel Stephen (Feb 2021)
(Employee)
Shepherd and Wedderburn LLP,
Edinburgh . . . . (p.900)
T: 0131 2289900
E: daniel.parcell@shepwedd.com

PARFERY, Alan James (Jun 2012) (Employee)
Procurator Fiscal Service, Glasgow . . . . (p.1242)
E: Alan.Parfery@copfs.gov.uk

PARHAM, Marcus Robert (Jan 1989) (Employee)
Dumfries & Galloway Council,
Dumfries . . . . (p.1217)
T: 01387 260000
E: marcus.parham@dumgal.gov.uk

PARIS-HUNTER, Emily Jean (Oct 2012)
(Employee)
Viberts Jersey Lawyers, St Helier . . . . . . (p.1274)
T: +44 (0) 1534 888666
E: Emily.Paris-Hunter@viberts.com

PARK, Andrew Graeme (Apr 2017) (Employee)
Levy & McRae Solicitors LLP,
Glasgow. (p.1000)
T: 0141 3072311
E: APark@lemac.co.uk

PARK, James Alan Pearson (Sept 1993)
(Employee)
Scotch Whisky Association,
Edinburgh . . . . (p.1230)
T: 0131 222 9200
E: apark@swa.org.uk

PARK, Kyung Jae (Aug 2021) (Employee)
Pinsent Masons LLP, Edinburgh . . . . . . (p.895)
T: 0131 777 7000
E: kyungjae.park@pinsentmasons.com

PARK, Stephen William (Jul 1989) (Partner)
The Kellas Partnership, Inverurie. . . . . . (p.1086)
T: 01467 627300
E: swp@kellas.biz

PARK, Suzanne Jane (Oct 2008) (Employee)
Centurion Group, Aberdeen . . . . (p.1212)
T: 01224 215451
E: spark@centuriongroup.co.uk

PARK, William Michael (Oct 1999) (Associate)
Pinsent Masons LLP, Aberdeen . . . . (p.739)
T: 01224 377900
E: william.park@pinsentmasons.com

PARKER, Fiona Jane (Sept 2004) (Employee)
Ofgem, Glasgow . . . . (p.1241)
T: +44 20 7901 7306
E: fiona.parker@ofgem.gov.uk

PARKER, Stacey (Jan 2010) (Director)
Maloco + Associates Limited,
Dunfermline . . . . (p.824)
T: 01383 629720
E: stacey@maloco.co.uk

PARKER-SMITH, Charlotte May (Mar 2021)
(Employee)
Thorntons Law LLP, Edinburgh . . . .(p.906)
T: 0131 2258705
E: cparker-smith@thorntons-law.co.uk

PARKER-SMITH, Gordon Paul (Jan 1982)
(Partner)
Bruce, Short & Co., Dundee . . . .(p.806)
T: 01382 223400
E: gpaulparker-smith@bruceshort.co.uk

PARKES, Katrina Anne (Sept 2001) (Employee)
Procurator Fiscal Service, Glasgow . . . .(p.1241)
T: 0300 0203000
E: katrina.parkes@copfs.gov.uk

PARKINSON, Audrey (Jul 2012) (Solicitor)
NO FIRM

PARRATT, Carol Ann (Jul 1984) (Partner)
Richmond & Co., Dundee . . . .(p.818)
T: 01382 201964
E: richmondco@btconnect.com

PARRIS, Emma Louise (Dec 1998) (Associate)
Russel + Aitken Edinburgh LLP,
Edinburgh . . . .(p.899)
T: 0131 2285500
E: emma.parris@russelaitken-edinburgh.com

PARRISH, Lisa Kathryn (Oct 1997) (Employee)
National Westminster Bank PLC,
Edinburgh . . . .(p.1226)
T: 0131 6260611
E: lisa.parrish@natwest.com

PARRY, Gareth Robert (Jan 1996) (Partner)
Shepherd and Wedderburn LLP,
Edinburgh . . . .(p.900)
T: 0131 2289900
E: gareth.parry@shepwedd.com

PARRY, Rebecca Jane (Sept 2011) (Employee)
Scottish Government, Edinburgh . . . . .(p.1231)
T: 0131 244 0815
E: rebecca.parry2@gov.scot

PARRY, Samuel Alexander (Dec 2015)
(Employee)
Clifford Chance LLP, London E14 . . . . .(p.1262)
E: Sam.Parry@CliffordChance.com

PARTRIDGE, Kirsten Marion (Feb 2008)
(Partner)
CMS Cameron McKenna Nabarro Olswang LLP,
Glasgow. . . . .(p.962)
T: 0141 304 6169
E: Kirsten.Partridge@cms-cmno.com

PASCOE, Nicola Frances (Nov 1997) (Employee)
Burness Paull LLP, Edinburgh . . . .(p.850)
T: 0131 4736000
E: Nicky.Pascoe@burnesspaull.com

PASI, Lauren Ann (Jan 2012) (Partner)
Lindsays LLP, Glasgow. . . . .(p.1001)
T: 0141 2216551
E: laurenpasi@lindsays.co.uk

PASK, Fiona Jane (Sept 2007) (Partner)
Harper Macleod LLP, Edinburgh . . . .(p.877)
T: 0131 247 2517
E: Fiona.Pask@harpermacleod.co.uk

PASSANT, Mark Iain (Mar 2011) (Associate)
Pinsent Masons LLP, Edinburgh . . . .(p.895)
T: 0131 7777000
E: mark.passant@pinsentmasons.com

PASSMORE, Margaret Jane (Oct 1994)
(Employee)
National Health Service Scotland,
Edinburgh . . . .(p.1225)
T: 0131 2757800
E: Margaret.passmore@nhs.scot

PATE, George Alexander Douglas
(Dec 1989) (Solicitor)
NO FIRM

PATERSON, Alan Stuart (Jul 2004) (Partner)
McLennan Adam Davis, Ayr . . . .(p.764)
T: 01292 289584
E: stuartp@mad-law.co.uk

PATERSON, Andrew John Neill (Oct 2003)
(Partner)
Murray Beith Murray, Edinburgh . . . . . .(p.893)
T: 0131 2251200
E: Andrew.Paterson@murraybeith.co.uk

PATERSON, Catherine Johan (Sept 1993)
(Employee)
Standard Life Assets and Employee Services
Limited, Edinburgh . . . .(p.1234)
T: 0131 245 5504
E: katie_paterson@standardlife.com

PATERSON, Christine Mary (Mar 1991)
(Employee)
Church of Scotland, Edinburgh . . . . . .(p.1221)
T: 0131 2255722
E: christine.paterson@churchofscotland.org.uk

PATERSON, Claire Elizabeth (Jul 2018)
(Employee)
Slater and Gordon Scotland Limited,
Edinburgh . . . .(p.903)
T: 0131 7184150
E: cpaterson@slatergordon.co.uk

PATERSON, David James (Aug 2010)
(Employee)
Wood Group UK Limited,
Aberdeen . . . .(p.1214)
T: 01224 777988
E: David.paterson@woodplc.com

PATERSON, Dianne Elizabeth (Jan 1982)
(Partner)
Russel + Aitken Edinburgh LLP,
Edinburgh ....(p.899)
T: 0131 2285500
E:
dianne.paterson@russelaitken-edinburgh.com

PATERSON, Eilidh Sarah Jean (Jun 2016)
(Employee)
Brodies LLP, Glasgow ....(p.948)
T: 0141 2484672
E: eilidh.paterson@brodies.com

PATERSON, Erin Maria (Aug 2011) (Employee)
Home Office, London SW1 ....(p.1265)
T: (07778) 100 471
E: erin.paterson@homeoffice.gov.uk

PATERSON, Fiona Lesley (May 2002) (Solicitor)
NO FIRM

PATERSON, George Joseph (Oct 1990)
(Employee)
Norton Rose Fulbright LLP, Paris .....(p.1273)
T: 00331 53895672
E: george.paterson@nortonrosefulbright.com

PATERSON, Gerard (Aug 2010) (Employee)
State Street Trustees Limited,
Edinburgh ....(p.1234)
T: 0131 3155833
E: gpaterson@statestreet.com

PATERSON, Iain Michael (Oct 1990) (Director)
Paterson Bell Limited, Edinburgh ......(p.895)
T: 0131 2256111
E: patersonsolicitoradvocate@gmail.com

PATERSON, Jade (Jul 2017) (Solicitor)
NO FIRM

PATERSON, Jayne Macdonald (Sept 2016)
(Employee)
Brodies LLP, Glasgow ....(p.948)
T: 0141 2484672
E: jayne.paterson@brodies.com

PATERSON, John Stephen (Mar 1988)
(Employee)
Scottish Government, Edinburgh .....(p.1231)
T: 0131 244 0815
E: John.Paterson@gov.scot

PATERSON, Joseph (Nov 2015) (Employee)
Checkout.com, London N1 ....(p.1262)
E: joseph.paterson@checkout.com

PATERSON, June Elizabeth (Nov 2011)
(Employee)
Stevenson & Marshall LLP,
Dunfermline ....(p.825)
T: 01383 721141
E: jpaterson@stevenson-marshall.co.uk

PATERSON, Karen Stedward (Dec 1978)
(Director)
Brown & McRae LLP, Fraserburgh .....(p.930)
T: 01346 514761
E: K.Paterson@brown-mcrae.co.uk

PATERSON, Kenneth George (Nov 1973)
(Partner)
Rankin & Aitken, Stranraer..........(p.1172)
T: 01776 702336
E: kgp@rankinaitken.co.uk

PATERSON, Kenneth William (Aug 1994)
(Partner)
Kenneth Paterson, Paisley ....(p.1141)
T: 0141 5612215
E: kenneth@kennethpatersonsolicitors.co.uk

PATERSON, Kevin Scott (Nov 1991) (Employee)
City of Edinburgh Council,
Edinburgh ....(p.1221)
T: 0131 529 3608
E: kevin.paterson@edinburgh.gov.uk

PATERSON, Kirsten Elizabeth (Sept 2021)
(Employee)
Innes Johnston LLP, Leven ....(p.1115)
T: 01333 429320
E: kpaterson@innesjohnston.co.uk

PATERSON, Lindsay (Sept 2006) (Employee)
Civil Legal Assistance Office,
Edinburgh ....(p.1222)
T: 0131 2401960
E: Patersonli@clao.org.uk

PATERSON, Marie Julie (Feb 1988) (Employee)
East Renfrewshire Council, Giffnock ...(p.1237)
T: 0141 5773000
E: marie.paterson@eastrenfrewshire.gov.uk

PATERSON, Melanie Caitlin (Apr 2018)
(Employee)
Pattison & Co., Glasgow ....(p.1030)
T: 0141 3347706
E:
melanie.paterson@pattisonandcompany.com

PATERSON, Natalie Elizabeth (Jan 2013)
(Partner)
Patterson & Paterson Defence Lawyers,
Inverness ....(p.1082)
T: 07738 245072
E: natalie@pattersonandpaterson.com

PATERSON, Neil (Jul 2009) (Employee)
Digby Brown LLP, Glasgow ....(p.970)
T: 0333 200 5925
E: neil.paterson@digbybrown.co.uk

PATERSON, Neil (Feb 2011) (Employee)
MLaw LLP, London W1 ....(p.1266)
E: neilpaterson@mlaw.co.uk

PATERSON, Owen Gordon (Mar 2008)
(Employee)
Chrysaor Limited, Aberdeen.........(p.1212)
 T: 01224 086203
 E: owen.paterson@chrysaor.com

PATERSON, Robert George (Feb 1981)
(Partner)
Storie, Cruden & Simpson,
 Westhill.....................(p.1179)
 T: 01224 740718
 E: rgp@storiecs.co.uk

PATERSON, Rory Edward Liston (Nov 2015)
(Employee)
Harper Macleod LLP, Edinburgh.......(p.877)
 T: 0131 2472500
 E: Rory.Paterson@harpermacleod.co.uk

PATERSON, Ruth (Jul 2013) (Employee)
Idox Software Limited, Glasgow......(p.1240)
 T: (0141) 2277600
 E: ruth.paterson@idoxgroup.com

PATERSON, Scott Callum (Jan 2021) (Employee)
Vialex Limited, Edinburgh ....(p.1235)
 T: 0333 2400127
 E: scott.paterson@vialex.co.uk

PATERSON, Steven John (Oct 1986) (Employee)
Fife Council, Glenrothes ....(p.1246)
 T: 03451 550000
 E: steven.paterson@fife.gov.uk

PATERSON, Tracy Elizabeth (Apr 2003)
(Partner)
Tracy E Paterson Solicitors,
 Glasgow....................(p.1030)
 T: 07804 149 942

PATERSON, Valerie Josephine Cecaelia
(May 1987) (Solicitor)
NO FIRM

PATERSON-HUNTER, Kirsty April Margaret
(Aug 2020) (Employee)
CMS Cameron McKenna Nabarro Olswang LLP,
 Edinburgh ....(p.856)
 T: 0131 2288000
 E: kirsty.paterson-hunter@cms-cmno.com

PATERSON-MARKE, Olus la Melville
(Nov 2011) (Employee)
Kirkland & Ellis LLP, New York ....(p.1279)
 T: +1 212 446 3157
 E: sola.patersonmarke@kirkland.com

PATIENCE, Katy Louise (Apr 2012) (Employee)
Hexagon Positioning Intelligence,
 Aberdeen...................(p.1212)
 E: Katy.patience@hexagon.com

PATON, Carol Anne Esther (Feb 1997)
(Employee)
National Westminster Bank PLC,
 Edinburgh ....(p.1226)
 T: 0790 993 6060
 E: carol.paton@natwest.com

PATON, Carolyn Jayne (Sept 1985) (Partner)
Elizabeth Welsh Family Law Practice,
 Ayr ....(p.766)
 T: 01292 284786
 E: carolyn.paton@familylawpractice.co.uk

PATON, Christopher Barnaby Ivory
(Sept 2016) (Employee)
Toyota Connected Europe Limited, London
 N1 ....(p.1269)
 E: barney.paton@toyotaconnected.eu

PATON, Elaine Alexandria (Oct 2008)
(Employee)
SOUTH LANARKSHIRERe Council,
 Hamilton ....(p.1247)
 T: 01698 454671
 E: elaine.paton@southlanarkshire.gov.uk

PATON, Eleanor Mary (Sept 2014) (Employee)
National Health Service Scotland,
 Edinburgh ....(p.1225)
 T: 0131 2757800
 E: Eleanor.Paton2@nhs.scot

PATON, Elizabeth Anne (Oct 1989) (Employee)
Procurator Fiscal Service,
 Edinburgh ....(p.1229)
 T: 0300 0203000
 E: Liz.Paton@copfs.gov.uk

PATON, Emma Barbara (Jul 2012) (Employee)
Shepherd and Wedderburn LLP,
 Edinburgh ....(p.900)
 T: 0131 2289900
 E: emma.paton@shepwedd.com

PATON, Gavin Hugh (Nov 1995) (Partner)
Burness Paull LLP, Glasgow ....(p.954)
 T: 0141 2484933
 E: Gavin.Paton@burnesspaull.com

PATON, Jennifer (Jan 2011) (Employee)
Shepherd and Wedderburn LLP,
 Edinburgh ....(p.900)
 T: 0131 2289900
 E: jennifer.paton@shepwedd.com

PATON, Jennifer Catherine (Sept 2014)
(Employee)
Law Society of Scotland,
 Edinburgh ....(p.1224)
 T: 0131 2267411
 E: jenniferpaton@lawscot.org.uk

PATON, Jennifer Yvonne (Dec 2013)
(Employee)
Aegon UK, Edinburgh ....(p.1220)
 T: 1315493986
 E: jennifer.paton@aegon.co.uk

PATON, Myrto (Jan 2021) (Employee)
Procurator Fiscal Service, Hamilton ....(p.1247)
 T: 0844 5613245
 E: myrto.paton@copfs.gov.uk

PATON, Richard Gordon (Jun 2011) (Employee)
Amber Infrastructure Limited,
   Edinburgh . . . .(p.1220)
   E: Richard.Paton@amberinfrastructure.com

PATON, Robert Graeme Bruce (Nov 1969)
   (Solicitor)
NO FIRM

PATON, Rudi Alexandra (Nov 2018) (Employee)
Scottish Government, Edinburgh . . . . .(p.1231)
   T: 0131 244 0815
   E: Rudi.Paton@gov.scot

PATON, Stephanie Jane (Sept 2018) (Employee)
Pinsent Masons LLP, Glasgow . . . .(p.1031)
   T: 0141 567 8400
   E: Stephanie.Paton@pinsentmasons.com

PATRICK, Arlene (Jul 2010) (Employee)
Aegon Asset Management UK Plc,
   Edinburgh . . . .(p.1220)
   T: 0131 549 5525
   E: arlene.patrick@aegonam.com

PATRICK, Dr, Hamish Andrew (May 1989)
   (Partner)
Shepherd and Wedderburn LLP,
   Edinburgh . . . .(p.900)
   T: 0131 2289900
   E: Hamish.Patrick@shepwedd.com

PATRICK, Mathew James (Feb 2003) (Partner)
Wardlaw Stephenson Allan,
   Edinburgh . . . .(p.910)
   T: 0131 5578020
   E: mat@wsalawyers.com

PATRICK, Nicola Kristina (Jul 1998) (Employee)
Procurator Fiscal Service, Glasgow . . . .(p.1241)
   T: 0300 0203000
   E: nicola.patrick@copfs.gov.uk

PATRICK, Sarah (Nov 2020) (Solicitor)
NO FIRM

PATRICK, Sarah Helen Swan (Oct 1996)
   (Partner)
Caesar & Howie, Falkirk . . . .(p.921)
   T: 01324 628332
   E: shp@caesar-howie.co.uk

PATTERSON, David William (Nov 2011)
   (Partner)
Patterson & Paterson Defence Lawyers,
   Inverness . . . .(p.1082)
   T: 07714 313578
   E: david@pattersonandpaterson.com

PATTERSON, Jacqueline Ann (Sept 2013)
   (Employee)
National Westminster Bank PLC,
   Edinburgh . . . .(p.1226)
   T: 0131 5568555
   E: Jackie.A.Patterson@natwest.com

PATTERSON, Keith Leslie (Jan 1992) (Partner)
Brodies LLP, Edinburgh . . . .(p.845)
   T: 0131 2283777
   E: keith.patterson@brodies.com

PATTERSON, Louise Emma (Sept 2005)
   (Employee)
Blackadders LLP, Edinburgh . . . .(p.843)
   T: 0131 2228000
   E: Louise.Patterson@blackadders.co.uk

PATTERSON, Mark Ian (Nov 1995) (Associate)
Burness Paull LLP, Glasgow . . . .(p.954)
   T: 0141 2484933
   E: Mark.Patterson@burnesspaull.com

PATTIE, Andrew Adam (Jan 2015) (Employee)
Student Loans Company Limited,
   Glasgow. . . . .(p.1245)
   T: 0141 306 2000
   E: Andrew_Pattie@slc.co.uk

PATTIE, Robert Murray (Aug 2012) (Employee)
Balfour Beatty Regional Civil Engineering,
   Motherwell. . . . .(p.1251)
   T: 01698 647 500
   E: robbie.pattie@balfourbeatty.com

PATTON, Layla Nina (Oct 2008) (Employee)
The Office of the Scottish Charity Regulator,
   Dundee . . . .(p.1219)
   T: 01382 220446
   E: layla.patton@oscr.org.uk

PATTULLO, Kim Suzanne (Jan 1992) (Partner)
Shoosmiths, Edinburgh . . . .(p.902)
   T: 03700 868000
   E: Kim.Pattullo@shoosmiths.co.uk

PAUL, Caitlin Alexandra (Sept 2019)
   (Employee)
Civil Legal Assistance Office,
   Edinburgh . . . .(p.1222)
   T: 0131 2401960
   E: PaulCa@clao.org.uk

PAUL, Emma Jayne (Jul 2021) (Employee)
Brodies LLP, Glasgow . . . .(p.948)
   T: 0141 2484672
   E: emma.paul@brodies.com

PAUL, Jonathan William (Oct 2001) (Partner)
Jonathan Paul Solicitors, Alexandria . . . .(p.751)
   T: 01389 756785
   E: jwpaul@hotmail.co.uk

PAUL, Marina (Sept 1993) (Employee)
National Westminster Bank PLC,
   Edinburgh . . . .(p.1226)
   T: (0131) 626 2925
   E: marina.paul@rbs.co.uk

PAUL, Nicola Jane (Oct 1991) (Employee)
Medical Protection Society, Leeds. . . . . .(p.1260)
   E: Nicola.Paul@medicalprotection.org

PAUL, Tobias Shaw (Jan 2020) (Associate)
DLA Piper UK LLP, Birmingham . . . . . .(p.1258)
   T: 0121 262 5947
   E: tobias.paul@dlapiper.com

PAWAR, Amrit Singh (Nov 2019) (Employee)
The Cumbernauld Law Practice,
   Cumbernauld . . . .(p.791)
   T: 01236 731911
   E: amrit@cumbernauldlaw.co.uk

PAY, Lisbeth-Ann (Oct 2004) (Director)
ELP Arbuthnott McClanachan,
   Edinburgh . . . .(p.867)
   T: 0131 5548649
   E: lap@elpamsolicitors.co.uk

PAYNE, William John (Sept 2004) (Employee)
William Grant & Sons Ltd., New
   York. . . . .(p.1279)
   T: +1 212 299 9404
   E: will.payne@wgrant.com

PEACHEY, Laura Elizabeth (Jul 2010)
   (Employee)
MBM Commercial LLP, Edinburgh . . . . .(p.889)
   T: 0131 2268200
   E: Laura.Peachey@mbmcommercial.co.uk

PEACOCK, Alasdair Graham (May 1986)
   (Partner)
DWF LLP, Edinburgh. . . . .(p.865)
   T: 0131 2265541
   E: alasdair.peacock@dwf.law

PEACOCK, Emma (Oct 2020) (Employee)
Inverclyde Council, Greenock. . . . .(p.1246)
   T: 01475 717171
   E: emma.peacock@inverclyde.gov.uk

PEACOCK, Judith Jane (Aug 1994) (Employee)
City of Edinburgh Council,
   Edinburgh . . . .(p.1221)
   T: 0131 529 4215
   E: Judith.Peacock@edinburgh.gov.uk

PEARSON, Annie Elizabeth (Nov 2006)
   (Employee)
Wright, Johnston & Mackenzie LLP,
   Glasgow. . . . .(p.1054)
   T: 0141 248 3434
   E: aep@wjm.co.uk

PEARSON, Gavin James (Dec 1997) (Director)
MOV8 Real Estate Limited,
   Edinburgh . . . .(p.893)
   T: 0345 646 0208
   E: gavin.pearson@mov8realestate.com

PEARSON, Hannah Nicola (Jan 2018)
   (Employee)
The PRG Partnership, Clydebank . . . . . .(p.786)
   T: 0141 9520019
   E: hannahpearson@prg.co.uk

PEARSON, Heather Brodie (Sept 1986)
   (Partner)
Addleshaw Goddard LLP,
   Edinburgh . . . .(p.835)
   T: 0131 2282400
   E: Heather.Pearson@addleshawgoddard.com

PEARSON, John Joseph (Oct 2010) (Employee)
Scottish Legal Aid Board,
   Edinburgh . . . .(p.1233)
   T: 0131 2267061
   E: pearsonjo@slab.org.uk

PEARSON, Victoria Jane (Oct 2006) (Solicitor)
NO FIRM

PEARSON, Zoe Jane (Oct 2004) (Employee)
Ithaca Energy (Uk) Limited,
   Aberdeen . . . .(p.1213)
   T: 01224 650 276
   E: zpearson@ithacaenergy.com

PEART, Susan Helen (Oct 1992) (Solicitor)
Scottish Social Services Council,
   Dundee . . . .(p.1218)
   T: 0345 6030 891
   E: susan.peart@sssc.uk.com

PEAT, Alison Mary (Feb 2010) (Employee)
McGrade & Co Limited, Glasgow. . . . .(p.1011)
   T: 0141 2214488
   E: apeat@mcgrade.co.uk

PEAT, Duncan Gillies (Jun 2011) (Solicitor)
Sheku Bayoh Public Inquiry,
   Edinburgh . . . .(p.1233)
   E: duncan.peat@shekubayohinquiry.scot

PEDEN, James (Aug 2005) (Employee)
Plexus Law LLP, Edinburgh . . . .(p.897)
   T: 0344 2454802
   E: james.peden@plexuslaw.co.uk

PEDRESCHI, Lara Claudia (Oct 2021)
   (Employee)
Anderson Strathern LLP, Edinburgh . . . .(p.839)
   T: 0131 2707700
   E: Lara.Pedreschi@andersonstrathern.co.uk

PEDRESCHI, Luigi Francesco (Sept 2014)
   (Employee)
Scottish Government, Edinburgh . . . . .(p.1231)
   T: 0131 244 0815
   E: luigi.pedreschi@gov.scot

PEEBLES, Alan (Dec 2003) (Employee)
Falkirk Council, Falkirk. . . . .(p.1236)
   T: 01324 506070
   E: alan.peebles@falkirk.gov.uk

PEEBLES, Gregor Kenneth John (Oct 1995)
   (Partner)
Gillespie Macandrew LLP, Glasgow. . . . .(p.979)
   T: 0141 4735555
   E: greg.peebles@gillespiemacandrew.co.uk

PEEBLES, Marc (Jun 2015) (Employee)
Scottish Power Limited, Glasgow . . . . . (p.1244)
  T: 0141 6140000
  E: m.peebles@scottishpower.com

PEEBLES, Walter Stuart Bell (Nov 1975)
  (Consultant)
Allcourt Solicitors Limited,
  Livingston . . . . (p.1117)
  T: 01506 443999
  E: stuart.peebles@allcourtsolicitors.co.uk

PEGLER-GAULT, Wendyanne Louise Slavan
  (Aug 2015) (Employee)
Sparrows Offshore Services Limited, Bridge of
  Don . . . . (p.1216)
  T: 01224 704868
  E:
  Wendyanne.Pegler-Gault@sparrowsgroup.com

PEHLIVANOV, Kiril Georgiev (Aug 2020)
  (Employee)
Morton Fraser LLP, Edinburgh . . . . (p.891)
  T: 0131 2471000
  E: kiril.pehlivanov@morton-fraser.com

PELOSI, Mark John (Sept 2021) (Employee)
Morton Fraser LLP, Edinburgh . . . . (p.891)
  T: 0131 2471000
  E: mark.pelosi@morton-fraser.com

PENCOVICH, Susannah Caroline (Mar 2016)
  (Employee)
Scottish Enterprise, Glasgow . . . . (p.1243)
  T: 0141 2482700
  E: Susannah.Pencovich@scotent.co.uk

PENDER, Anne Mary (Oct 1976) (Partner)
Thomas, Carlin & Pender, Glasgow . . . (p.1046)
  T: 0141 8836227
  E: annepender@btconnect.com

PENDER, Claire (Oct 2002) (Employee)
Scottish Police Authority, Police Scotland,
  Glasgow . . . . (p.1244)
  T: 01786 895733
  E: Claire.Pender@scotland.pnn.police.uk

PENDER, Lynsey (Oct 2008) (Employee)
Malcolm, Jack & Matheson Limited,
  Dunfermline . . . . (p.824)
  T: 01383 723444
  E: Lynsey@malcolmjack.co.uk

PENDER, Madeleine Jane (Sept 2005)
  (Employee)
North Ayrshire Council, Irvine . . . . (p.1249)
  T: 01294 310000
  E: mpender@north-ayrshire.gcsx.gov.uk

PENGELLY, Sarah Mary Katherine
  (May 2003) (Associate)
MacRoberts LLP, Edinburgh . . . . (p.887)
  T: 0131 2295046
  E: sarah.pengelly@macroberts.com

PENMAN, Iain McKie (Oct 2000) (Employee)
Brodies LLP, Edinburgh . . . . (p.845)
  T: 0131 2283777
  E: iain.penman@brodies.com

PENMAN, John Houston (Aug 2000)
  (Employee)
Procurator Fiscal Service, Greenock . . . . (p.1246)
  T: 0844 5613404
  E: john.penman2@copfs.gov.uk

PENMAN, Linzi (Oct 2014) (Employee)
DLA Piper Scotland LLP, Edinburgh . . . . (p.863)
  T: 08700 111111
  E: linzi.penman@dlapiper.com

PENMAN, Marc Robert (Oct 2019) (Employee)
Harper Macleod LLP, Inverness . . . . (p.1077)
  T: 01463 798777
  E: marc.penman@harpermacleod.co.uk

PENMAN, Marie Lorraine (Oct 2013)
  (Employee)
Scottish Government, Edinburgh . . . . . (p.1231)
  T: 0131 244 0815
  E: marie.penman@gov.scot

PENNEL, George (Mar 1996) (Employee)
Blackwood Partners LLP, Aberdeen . . . . . (p.723)
  T: 01224 446230
  E: George.Pennel@blackwood-partners.com

PENNEL, Janine Catherine Margaret
  (Nov 1987) (Employee)
Lloyds Banking Group Plc,
  Edinburgh . . . . (p.1224)
  T: 07741 232206
  E: Janine.Pennel@lloydsbanking.com

PENNY, Euain James (Nov 1988) (Director)
Lows Orkney Limited, Kirkwall . . . . (p.1106)
  T: 01856 873151
  E: euain.penny@lowsorkney.co.uk

PENNY, Lisa Florence (Aug 2016) (Employee)
Burness Paull LLP, Aberdeen . . . . (p.724)
  T: 01224 621621
  E: lisa.penny@burnesspaull.com

PENTLAND, John Barry (Oct 2001) (Partner)
Dickson Minto, Edinburgh . . . . (p.861)
  T: 0131 2254455
  E: john.pentland@dmws.com

PENTLAND, Lynn Anne (Oct 2001) (Associate)
MacRoberts LLP, Edinburgh . . . . (p.887)
  T: 0131 2295046
  E: lynn.pentland@macroberts.com

PEOCK, Sarah Lynn (Apr 2003) (Associate)
Dentons UK and Middle East LLP,
  Edinburgh . . . . (p.860)
  T: 0330 2220050
  E: Sarah.Peock@dentons.com

PEOPLES, Erin Louise (Jul 2020) (Employee)
Lindsays LLP, Dundee . . . .(p.814)
    T: 01382 224112
    E: ErinPeoples@lindsays.co.uk

PEOPLES, Kathryn Louise (Sept 2019)
(Employee)
Pinsent Masons LLP, Glasgow . . . .(p.1031)
    T: 0141 567 8400
    E: katie.peoples@pinsentmasons.com

PEPIN, Emily Anna Rebecca Eliza (Mar 2019)
(Employee)
Thorntons Law LLP, Edinburgh . . . .(p.906)
    T: 0131 2258705
    E: epepin@thorntons-law.co.uk

PEPPIETTE, Hilary Louise (Oct 1987)
(Employee)
Allingham & Co (Solicitors) Limited,
    Edinburgh . . . .(p.838)
    T: 0131 4479341
    E: hilary@allingham.co.uk

PERDIKOU, David (Nov 2017) (Employee)
Thorntons Law LLP, Edinburgh . . . .(p.906)
    T: 0131 2258705
    E: DPerdikou@thorntons-law.co.uk

PERETI, Rosemary Anne Noble (Apr 2016)
(Employee)
Civil Legal Assistance Office,
    Edinburgh . . . .(p.1222)
    T: 0131 2401960
    E: PeretiRo@clao.org.uk

PERFECT, Gemma Aitken (Jan 2009) (Partner)
Aberdein Considine and Company,
    Aberdeen . . . .(p.718)
    T: 01224 589 700
    E: gperfect@acandco.com

PERKINS, Nicole (Jan 2017) (Employee)
Optical Express Limited
    E: nicoleperkins@opticalexpress.com

PERKS, Marliese Sally (Aug 2018) (Employee)
National Westminster Bank PLC,
    Edinburgh . . . .(p.1226)
    T: 0131 5568555
    E: marliese.perks@natwest.com

PERRETT, Emily (Jan 2018) (Employee)
Dentons UK and Middle East LLP,
    Glasgow. . . . .(p.968)
    T: 0330 2220050
    E: emily.perrett@dentons.com

PERVAIZ, Mohammed Balal (Mar 2019)
(Employee)
Keoghs Scotland LLP, Glasgow. . . . .(p.996)
    T: 0141 2380100
    E: bpervaiz@keoghs.co.uk

PETER, Jacqueline Janet Ann (Aug 2002)
(Solicitor)
NO FIRM

PETERKIN, Scott Campbell Neilson
(Nov 1999) (Partner)
Burness Paull LLP, Edinburgh . . . .(p.850)
    T: 0131 4736000
    E: Scott.Peterkin@burnesspaull.com

PETERSON, Dr, Alasdair Stewart Sholto
(Jul 2018) (Solicitor)
NO FIRM

PETERSON, Eric Spence (Aug 1983) (Partner)
Tait & Peterson, Lerwick . . . .(p.1114)
    T: 01595 693010
    E: eric.peterson@tait-peterson.co.uk

PETKOVA, Anelia Stoyanova (Mar 2020)
(Employee)
Abrdn Financial Planning and Advice Limited,
    Edinburgh . . . .(p.1220)
    E: anelia.petkova@abrdn.com

PETO, George Francis John (Nov 2012)
(Employee)
Accelerant Services UK Limited, London
    EC4 . . . .(p.1260)
    E: George.Peto@accelins.com

PETRE, Oana-Iuliana (Oct 2010) (Director)
OJ Solicitors Ltd, Glasgow . . . .(p.1027)
    T: 07842 507897
    E: oana.petre@oj-solicitors.co.uk

PETRESCU, Elena-Lucia (Aug 2019) (Employee)
Barnetts, Kilmarnock . . . .(p.1093)
    T: 01563 522137
    E: l.petrescu@barnettslaw.co.uk

PETRIDES, Tessa Jayne (Nov 2009) (Associate)
Gillespie Macandrew LLP,
    Edinburgh . . . .(p.872)
    T: 0131 2251677
    E: Tessa.petrides@gillespiemacandrew.co.uk

PETRIE, Blythe Helen (Jun 2021) (Employee)
Blackadders LLP, Dundee. . . . .(p.805)
    T: 01382 229222
    E: blythe.petrie@blackadders.co.uk

PETRIE, Derek Allan (Oct 1993) (Employee)
MacRoberts LLP, Dundee. . . . .(p.815)
    T: 01382 339340
    E: Derek.Petrie@macroberts.com

PETRIE, Jillian Joanne (Oct 2002) (Partner)
BTO Solicitors LLP, Glasgow . . . .(p.952)
    T: 0141 2218012
    E: jpe@bto.co.uk

PETRIE, Laura Marie (Oct 2005) (Employee)
Brodies LLP, Aberdeen. . . . .(p.723)
    T: 01224 392242
    E: laura.petrie@brodies.com

PETROPOULOS, Stephanie (Oct 2017)
(Employee)
The Kerr Brown Partnership,
Glasgow.....................(p.1044)
T: 0141 2214880
E: stephaniep@kerrbrown.co.uk

PETROV, Tsvetan Kirilov (Dec 2019) (Employee)
Pinsent Masons LLP, London EC2.....(p.1267)
T: 020 7418 7000
E: tsvetan.petrov@pinsentmasons.com

PETTERSON, Elaine Claire (Apr 2007) (Partner)
Brodies LLP, Glasgow ....(p.948)
T: 0141 2484672
E: elaine.petterson@brodies.com

PETTERSON, Emma (Aug 2020) (Employee)
Procurator Fiscal Service,
Edinburgh ....(p.1227)
T: 0300 0203168
E: emma.petterson@copfs.gov.uk

PETTICREW, James Leonard (Nov 1987)
(Associate)
McLennan Adam Davis, Ayr..........(p.764)
T: 01292 289584
E: jimp@mad-law.co.uk

PETTIGREW, Derek William (Oct 1987)
(Partner)
Derek W. Pettigrew, Prestwick ....(p.1158)
T: 01292 475941
E: derekpettigrew@hotmail.com

PETTIGREW, Stewart William (Oct 2012)
(Employee)
Frank Irvine Solicitors Ltd, Glasgow ....(p.990)
T: 0141 3759000
E: swp@frankirvine.com

PEUTHERER, John Douglas Willison
(Sept 2006) (Partner)
Anderson Strathern LLP, Edinburgh ....(p.839)
T: 0131 2707700
E: john.peutherer@andersonstrathern.co.uk

PEVERIL, Emma Louise (Apr 2012) (Employee)
DLA Piper Scotland LLP, Edinburgh ....(p.863)
T: 08700 111111
E: Emma.Peveril@dlapiper.com

PHELPS, Donna Ann (Jan 2015) (Employee)
East Ayrshire Council, Kilmarnock.....(p.1249)
T: 01563 576161
E: donna.phelps@east-ayrshire.gov.uk

PHILIP, Andrew David Pyka (Oct 2002)
(Employee)
Scottish Power Limited, Glasgow .....(p.1244)
T: 0141 6140000
E: aphilip@ScottishPower.com

PHILIPS, Graham MacLellan (Dec 1974)
(Consultant)
Stirling & Gilmour LLP,
Helensburgh.................(p.1073)
T: 01436 678185
E: g.philips@stirlingandgilmour.co.uk

PHILLIP, Matthew (Sept 2010) (Partner)
Shepherd and Wedderburn LLP,
Edinburgh ....(p.900)
T: 0131 2289900
E: matt.phillip@shepwedd.com

PHILLIPS, Andrew David (Dec 2006)
(Employee)
The Scottish Football Association,
Glasgow....................(p.1245)
T: 0141 6166000
E: compliance.officer@scottishfa.co.uk

PHILLIPS, Catherine Mary (Sept 1993) (Partner)
Kate Phillips, Glasgow ....(p.1031)
T: 0141 4206120
E: katephillips21@yahoo.co.uk

PHILLIPS, Clive (Nov 1992) (Partner)
Brodies LLP, Aberdeen..............(p.723)
T: 01224 392 242
E: clive.phillips@brodies.com

PHILLIPS, Emma Jean (Aug 2019) (Employee)
Scottish Government, Edinburgh .....(p.1231)
T: 0131 244 0815
E: emma.phillips@gov.scot

PHILLIPS, Gordon Alexander (Sept 1997)
(Partner)
Jardine Phillips LLP, Edinburgh ....(p.879)
T: 0131 4466850
E: gordon.phillips@jardinephillips.com

PHILLIPS, Hannah (Jun 2009) (Employee)
SR Group (UK) Limited

PHILLIPS, James Edward (Feb 2016) (Partner)
Burges Salmon LLP, Bristol..........(p.1258)
T: 0117 9392000
E: james.phillips@burges-salmon.com

PHILLIPS, Jennifer Eileen (Oct 2018)
(Employee)
KPMG LLP, London E14 ....(p.1265)
E: jennifer.phillips@kpmg.co.uk

PHILLIPS, John Christian (Sept 1997) (Partner)
Thorntons Law LLP, Edinburgh ....(p.906)
T: 0131 2258705
E: cphillips@thorntons-law.co.uk

PHILLIPS, Karen Elizabeth (Oct 2004) (Partner)
Balfour + Manson LLP, Edinburgh .....(p.841)
T: 0131 2001200
E: Karen.Phillips@balfour-manson.co.uk

PHILLIPS, Melissa Anna (Oct 2021) (Employee)
Thompson Family Law, Glasgow .....(p.1046)
T: 0141 4046575
E: melissa@tflaw.co.uk

PHILLIPS, Robert Gerald (Aug 2007)
(Employee)
Addleshaw Goddard LLP,
Aberdeen . . . .(p.719)
 T: +44 (0) 1224 96 5410
 E: Robert.Phillips@addleshawgoddard.com

PHILLIPS, Sarah Ann (Oct 1997) (Associate)
Anderson Strathern LLP, Edinburgh . . . .(p.839)
 T: 0131 2707700
 E: sarah.phillips@andersonstrathern.co.uk

PHILLIPS, Sarah Jane Robertson (Feb 2013)
(Partner)
Burness Paull LLP, Edinburgh . . . .(p.850)
 T: 0131 4736906
 E: Sarah.Phillips@burnesspaull.com

PHILLIPS, Shirley Margaret (Nov 1998)
(Associate)
Thorntons Law LLP, Dundee . . . .(p.819)
 T: 01382 229 111
 E: sphillips@thorntons-law.co.uk

PHILLIPS, Stephen James (Jan 1989) (Partner)
CMS Cameron McKenna Nabarro Olswang LLP,
 Edinburgh . . . .(p.856)
 T: 0131 2288000
 E: Stephen.Phillips@cms-cmno.com

PHILP, Alan Douglas (Nov 1994) (Employee)
RBS and NatWest Mentor,
 Glasgow. . . . .(p.1243)
 T: 0141 227 4590
 E: alan.philp@mentor.uk.com

PHILP, Catriona Susan (Aug 2010) (Employee)
Abrdn Financial Planning and Advice Limited,
 Edinburgh . . . .(p.1220)
 E: Katie.Philp@1825.com

PHILP, Ian William (Nov 1984) (Director)
Garden Stirling Burnet Solicitors Limited,
 Haddington . . . .(p.1064)
 T: 01875 611616
 E: iphilp@gsbsolicitors.co.uk

PHINN, David Phillip (Sept 2020) (Employee)
Miller Samuel Hill Brown LLP,
 Glasgow. . . . .(p.1020)
 T: 0141 2211919
 E: dpp@mshblegal.com

PIA, Carlo (Oct 2015) (Employee)
Simpson Thacher & Bartlett LLP, London
 EC2 . . . .(p.1268)
 T: (020) 7275 6500
 E: Carlo.Pia@stblaw.com

PIA, Giuseppe (Aug 2020) (Employee)
Dentons UK and Middle East LLP,
 Glasgow. . . . .(p.968)
 T: 0330 2220050
 E: giuseppe.pia@dentons.com

PICKEN, Eleanor Boyd (Oct 2020) (Employee)
Turcan Connell, Edinburgh . . . .(p.908)
 T: 0131 2288111
 E: eleanor.picken@turcanconnell.com

PICKEN, James Ferber (May 1980) (Partner)
Black Hay, Prestwick . . . .(p.1158)
 T: 01292 477235
 E: james.picken@blackhay.co.uk

PICKEN, Kirsteen (Oct 2014) (Employee)
Berrymans Lace Mawer LLP,
 Glasgow. . . . .(p.945)
 T: 0141 3532121
 E: Kirsteen.Picken@blmlaw.com

PICKERING, Rebecca Joyce Ada (Sept 2004)
(Partner)
JHS Law, Dumfries . . . .(p.801)
 T: 01387 739000
 E: rebecca.pickering@jhslaw.co.uk

PIDGEON, Lori Emma (Sept 2016) (Employee)
Scottish Government, Edinburgh . . . . .(p.1231)
 T: 0131 244 0815
 E: Lori.Pidgeon@gov.scot

PIERI, Chiara (Oct 2017) (Employee)
Shepherd and Wedderburn LLP,
 Edinburgh . . . .(p.900)
 T: 0131 2289900
 E: chiara.pieri@shepwedd.com

PIERI, Dorothy (Nov 1976) (Director)
Pieri Graham Ltd, Glasgow . . . .(p.1031)
 T: 0141 3322525
 E: dorothy@pierigraham.com

PIGGOT, Elaine Fiona (Oct 2002) (Employee)
CMS Cameron McKenna Nabarro Olswang LLP,
 Edinburgh . . . .(p.856)
 T: 0131 2288000
 E: Elaine.Piggot@cms-cmno.com

PIGGOT, Michael (Feb 2020) (Employee)
Lindsays LLP, Dundee . . . .(p.814)
 T: 01382 224112
 E: mikepiggot@lindsays.co.uk

PIGNATELLI, Paul Francis (Sept 1993) (Partner)
DWF LLP, Glasgow . . . .(p.973)
 T: 0141 228 8000
 E: paul.pignatelli@dwf.law

PIGOTT, Caroline Patricia (Nov 2012)
(Employee)
HGF Ltd, Edinburgh . . . .(p.1223)
 E: cpigott@hgf.com

PIKE, Craig Andrew (Apr 2007) (Partner)
Ledingham Chalmers LLP,
 Aberdeen . . . .(p.734)
 T: 01224 408408
 E: craig.pike@ledinghamchalmers.com

PIKE, Jennifer Sylvia (Oct 2007) (Employee)
SSE PLC, Glasgow . . . . (p.1244)
T: 0141 224 7248
E: jennifer.dallimore@sse.com

PIKE, Kevin John (Jan 2014) (Director)
Livingstone Brown Limited,
Glasgow. (p.1003)
T: 0141 4298166
E: kevinp@livbrown.co.uk

PIKE, Sophie Elizabeth Hamilton (Apr 2016)
(Associate)
Balfour + Manson LLP, Aberdeen . . . . . . (p.721)
T: 01224 498080
E: Sophie.pike@balfour-manson.co.uk

PINKERTON, Evelyn Margaret (Dec 1998)
(Employee)
Renfrewshire Council, Paisley . . . . (p.1252)
T: 0141 618 7160
E: evelyn.pinkerton@renfrewshire.gov.uk

PINKERTON, Kenneth James (Oct 1993)
(Associate)
Brodies LLP, Edinburgh . . . . (p.845)
T: 0131 2283777
E: kenneth.pinkerton@brodies.com

PINNONS, Matthew Conor (Aug 2012)
(Employee)
Aberdeen Corporate Services Limited,
Edinburgh . . . . (p.1220)
T: 0131 245 7508
E: matt.pinnons@abrdn.com

PIPER, Fiona Margaret (Jan 1998) (Partner)
Davidson Chalmers Stewart LLP,
Glasgow. (p.967)
T: 0141 4283258
E: fiona.piper@dcslegal.com

PIRIE, Caitlin Mairi (Aug 2020) (Employee)
Gail Goodfellow, Solicitor Advocate,
Aberdeen . . . . (p.731)
T: 01224 878417
E: caitlin@gailgoodfellow.com

PIRIE, Christine Jane (Oct 2014) (Employee)
Pinsent Masons LLP, Glasgow . . . . (p.1031)
T: 0141 567 8400
E: christine.pirie@pinsentmasons.com

PIRIE, Claire Marie (Dec 2018) (Employee)
Irving Geddes, WS Limited, Crieff. . . . . . (p.788)
T: 01764 653771
E: claire@irvinggeddes.co.uk

PIRIE, Euan David Thomas (Nov 1995) (Partner)
Harper Macleod LLP, Edinburgh . . . . . . (p.877)
T: 0131 2472500
E: euan.pirie@harpermacleod.co.uk

PIRIE, Vicki Heather (Nov 2018) (Employee)
Fiona McPhail Solicitors, Edinburgh . . . . (p.886)
T: 0344 5152410
E: Vicki_Pirie@Shelter.org.uk

PIRRET, Martin Robert (Aug 2009) (Employee)
Addleshaw Goddard LLP,
Edinburgh . . . . (p.835)
T: 0131 2282400
E: martin.pirret@addleshawgoddard.com

PIRRIE, Robert, WS (Feb 1981) (Employee)
WS Society, Edinburgh . . . . (p.1236)
T: 0131 2250654
E: rpirrie@wssociety.co.uk

PISKORZ, Mateusz (Sept 2018) (Employee)
Procurator Fiscal Service,
Dunfermline . . . . (p.1219)
T: 01383 723688
E: mateusz.piskorz@copfs.gov.uk

PITCAIRN, Ashleigh Lesley (Nov 2007)
(Employee)
Lord President's Private Office,
Edinburgh . . . . (p.1225)
T: 0131 2406701
E: APitcairn@scotcourts.gov.uk

PITT, Natasha Racheal (Aug 2019) (Employee)
Barton & Hendry, Cumbernauld . . . . . . (p.790)
T: 01236 735466
E: natasha@bartonandhendry.co.uk

PITT, Timothy Michael (Oct 1993) (Partner)
CMS Cameron McKenna Nabarro Olswang LLP,
Edinburgh . . . . (p.856)
T: 0131 2288000
E: timothy.pitt@cms-cmno.com

PITT, Valerie Elizabeth (Oct 2007) (Employee)
Horwich Farrelly Scotland,
Glasgow. (p.987)
T: 03300 240711
E: Val.Pitt@h-f.co.uk

PITTAM, Laura Jane (Oct 2008) (Employee)
SSE Plc, Perth . . . . (p.1253)
T: 01738 453697
E: laura.pittam@sse.com

PITTENDREIGH, Dawn Michele (Nov 2003)
(Employee)
Aberdeen City Council, Aberdeen. . . . . (p.1211)
T: 01224 522000
E: MPittendreigh@aberdeencity.gov.uk

PITTS, Richard Dorian (Jan 2014) (Associate)
Digby Brown LLP, Edinburgh . . . . (p.862)
T: 0333 200 5925
E: richard.pitts@digbybrown.co.uk

PLANT, Tracy Ann (Jan 2008) (Employee)
Procurator Fiscal Service, Falkirk . . . . . . (p.1236)
T: 0300 020 3000
E: tracy.plant@copfs.gov.uk

PLATT, Charlotte Joy (Jul 2013) (Consultant)
Inksters, Thurso . . . . (p.1174)
T: 01847 630 400
E: Charlotte@inksters.com

PLENDERLEATH, John Charles (Sept 1982)
(Partner)
Blackadders LLP, Aberdeen . . . .(p.722)
T: 01224 588913
E: john.plenderleath@blackadders.co.uk

PLEWS, Elena (Oct 2008) (Solicitor)
NO FIRM

PLLU, Kirsty Nona (May 2001) (Employee)
RGM Solicitors Limited,
Grangemouth . . . .(p.1059)
T: 01324 482197
E: kirsty@rgmsolicitors.co.uk

PLOWMAN, Rona Dewar (Jun 2018)
(Employee)
BBM Solicitors Limited, Wick . . . .(p.1180)
T: 01955 604188
E: rdp@bbmsolicitors.co.uk

POCK, Thea Elizabeth (Oct 2020) (Employee)
Thorntons Law LLP, Edinburgh . . . .(p.906)
T: 0131 2258705
E: tpock@thorntons-law.co.uk

POCKLINGTON, Rachael Emma (Jan 2001)
(Employee)
National Westminster Bank PLC,
Edinburgh . . . .(p.1227)
T: 07711 925720
E: rachael.pocklington@rbsint.com

POGGI, Michael Joseph (Sept 1999) (Partner)
Berry, Poggi & Co, Glasgow . . . .(p.946)
T: 1414297211
E: michaelpoggi@gmail.com

POINTER, Jan Helen (May 2016) (Employee)
Birketts LLP, Norwich . . . .(p.1270)
T: 01603 756 477
E: Jan-Pointer@Birketts.co.uk

POKE, Karen Margaret (Nov 2018) (Employee)
Procurator Fiscal Service, Inverness . . . .(p.1248)
T: 0844 5612926
E: karen.poke@copfs.gov.uk

POLLOCK, Amy-Louise Martha (Jun 2019)
(Employee)
Macnairs & Wilson Limited,
Glasgow. . . . .(p.1014)
T: 0141 5518185
E: amy.pollock@macnairswilson.co.uk

POLLOCK, Andrew Simon (Dec 1986) (Partner)
Peacock Johnston, Glasgow . . . .(p.1030)
T: 0141 3339505
E: asp@peacockjohnston.co.uk

POLLOCK, Ashley (Sept 2016) (Employee)
Doonan, McCaig & Co. Ltd,
Kilmarnock . . . .(p.1094)
T: 0141 5526600
E: ashleypollock@hotmail.co.uk

POLLOCK, Brian (Nov 2013) (Employee)
Lindsays LLP, Glasgow . . . .(p.1001)
T: 0141 2216551
E: brianpollock@lindsays.co.uk

POLLOCK, Christopher Martin (Sept 2008)
(Director)
Pollock Fairbridge Schiavone Limited,
Glasgow. . . . .(p.1033)
T: 0141 7792577
E: Cp@pfssolicitors.co.uk

POLLOCK, George Edward (Oct 1976) (Partner)
Pollock, Ross & Co, Stirling . . . .(p.1167)
T: 01786 449933
E: george@pollockross.com

POLLOCK, Lorraine Anne (Oct 1987)
(Employee)
Morton Fraser LLP, Edinburgh . . . .(p.891)
T: 0131 2471000
E: Lorri.Pollock@morton-fraser.com

POLLOCK, Matthew David (Jul 2017)
(Employee)
Kirkland & Ellis International LLP, London
EC3 . . . .(p.1265)
T: 0207 4692000
E: matthew.pollock@kirkland.com

POLLOCK, Victoria Mary (Dec 2001)
(Employee)
Inverclyde Council, Greenock. . . . .(p.1246)
T: 01475 712180
E: vicky.pollock@inverclyde.gov.uk

POLOVINKINA, Valeria Pavlovna (Sept 2011)
(Employee)
DLA Piper, Sydney . . . .(p.1257)
T: +61 2 9286 8693
E: Valerie.Polovinkina@dlapiper.com

POLSON, Alison Elizabeth (Nov 1988)
(Associate)
Brodies LLP, Edinburgh . . . .(p.845)
T: 01312283777/07977182
E: alison.polson@brodies.com

POLSON, Jacqueline Alison (Jun 2005)
(Solicitor)
NO FIRM

POLSON, Michael Buchanan (Nov 1989)
(Employee)
Ashurst LLP, Glasgow . . . .(p.1237)
T: 0141 3754202
E: mike.polson@ashurst.com

POLSON, Niall David (Oct 2008) (Employee)
KCA Deutag Drilling Ltd,
Portlethen . . . .(p.1254)
T: 01224 987000
E: Niall.Polson@kcadeutag.com

POLSON, Sarah Louise (Sept 2012) (Employee)
Brodies LLP, Aberdeen . . . .(p.723)
　　T: 01224 392242
　　E: sarah.polson@brodies.com

PONNIAH, Fiona Janet Deas (Jul 2012)
(Employee)
Walter Scott & Partners Limited,
　　Edinburgh . . . .(p.1236)
　　T: (0131) 225 1357
　　E: fponniah@walterscott.com

POOLE, Richard Robert (Apr 2007) (Associate)
Thorntons Law LLP, Dundee . . . .(p.819)
　　T: 01382 229 111
　　E: rpoole@thorntons-law.co.uk

POPE, John Lewis (Apr 2008) (Employee)
Repsol Sinopec Resources UK Limited,
　　Aberdeen . . . .(p.1213)
　　T: 01224 352990
　　E: John.Pope@repsolsinopecuk.com

POPE, Margaret Cairine (Nov 1988) (Associate)
DLA Piper Scotland LLP, Edinburgh . . . .(p.863)
　　T: 0131 242 5515
　　E: maggie.pope@dlapiper.com

POPPIUS, Vilhelmina Irene Charlotta
(Oct 2009) (Employee)
Procurator Fiscal Service,
　　Edinburgh . . . .(p.1227)
　　T: 0300 0203168
　　E: vilhelmina.poppius@copfs.gov.uk

PORTEOUS, Indhumathi Nilakanthi
(May 1995) (Employee)
Sainsbury's Bank plc, Edinburgh . . . . . .(p.1230)
　　T: (0131) 286 0807
　　E: Indhu.Porteous@sainsburysbank.co.uk

PORTER, Campbell John (Oct 1982) (Partner)
Bilkus & Boyle, Glasgow . . . .(p.946)
　　T: 0141 8823221
　　E: cjporter2175@aol.com

PORTER, Cheryl Stewart (Jul 2020) (Employee)
Slater and Gordon Scotland Limited,
　　Edinburgh . . . .(p.903)
　　T: 0131 7184150
　　E: cporter@slatergordon.co.uk

PORTER, Frances Mary (Oct 1989) (Consultant)
Nicolson O'Brien, Airdrie . . . .(p.751)
　　T: 01236 751224
　　E: frances.porter@nicolsonobrien.co.uk

PORTER, Justine Jennifer (Mar 2014)
(Employee)
East Dunbartonshire Council,
　　Kirkintilloch . . . .(p.1249)
　　T: 0141 5788000
　　E: justine.porter@eastdunbarton.gov.uk

PORTER, Lewis (Oct 2007) (Employee)
TotalEnergies E&P UK Limited,
　　Westhill . . . .(p.1255)
　　T: 01224 297000
　　E: lewis.porter@totalenergies.com

PORTER, Louise Kathryn (Jun 2018) (Employee)
Burnett & Reid LLP, Aberdeen . . . .(p.726)
　　T: 01224 644333
　　E: louise.porter@burnett-reid.co.uk

PORTER, Simon Richard (Oct 2008) (Associate)
CMS Cameron McKenna Nabarro Olswang LLP,
　　Glasgow. . . . .(p.962)
　　T: 0141 2222200
　　E: Simon.Porter@cms-cmno.com

PORTER, Stuart Benjamin (Apr 2012) (Partner)
Bilkus & Boyle, Glasgow . . . .(p.946)
　　T: 0141 8823221

POSTLETHWAITE, Chloe Louise (Aug 2012)
(Employee)
DAC Beachcroft Scotland LLP,
　　Glasgow. . . . .(p.964)
　　T: 0141 2486688
　　E: cpostlethwaite@dacbeachcroft.com

POTHAN, Jane Lesley (Feb 2021) (Employee)
Anderson Strathern LLP, Edinburgh . . . .(p.839)
　　T: 0131 2707700
　　E: jane.pothan@andersonstrathern.co.uk

POTTINGER, Shona Ann (Sept 1996)
(Employee)
Highland Council, Dingwall . . . .(p.1216)
　　T: 01349 868 539
　　E: shona.pottinger@highland.gov.uk

POTTINGER, Tom Stuart (Oct 2008) (Employee)
A.M. Simpson & Son, Moffat . . . .(p.1124)
　　T: 01683 220118

POULLAIN, Julian Michael (Nov 2009)
(Employee)
Ocean Winds UK Limited,
　　Edinburgh . . . .(p.1227)
　　T: 0131 5567602
　　E: julian.poullain@oceanwinds.com

POUNDER, Jennie Katharine (Mar 2019)
(Employee)
Addleshaw Goddard LLP,
　　Edinburgh . . . .(p.835)
　　T: 0131 2282400
　　E: Jennie.Pounder@addleshawgoddard.com

POWELL, Sarah Elizabeth (Jan 2011)
(Employee)
Brazenall & Orr, Dumfries . . . .(p.800)
　　T: 01387 255695
　　E: sarah@brazenallandorr.co.uk

POWELL, Shauna Margaret (Oct 1999)
(Employee)
N4 Partners LLP, Glasgow . . . .(p.1241)
　　E: smp@n4partners.com

POWER, Michael Se n (Jul 2013) (Solicitor)
National Westminster Bank PLC,
   Edinburgh . . . .(p.1226)
   T: (0131) 626 2925
   E: Michael.power@natwest.com

PRAG, Veronika (Nov 2004) (Employee)
Renfrewshire Council, Paisley . . . .(p.1252)
   T: 0141 8403648
   E: veronika.prag@renfrewshire.gov.uk

PRATT, Aimee (Feb 2021) (Employee)
Shepherd and Wedderburn LLP,
   Edinburgh . . . .(p.900)
   T: 0131 2289900
   E: aimee.pratt@shepwedd.com

PRATT, Peter William David Alexan
   (Feb 1997) (Partner)
Kerr Stirling LLP, Stirling . . . .(p.1165)
   T: 01786 463414
   E: pp@kerrstirling.co.uk

PRATT, Stephanie Elizabeth (Apr 2013)
   (Partner)
Thorntons Law LLP, Cupar. . . . .(p.793)
   T: 01334 652285
   E: spratt@thorntons-law.co.uk

PREECE, Keri Jayne (Sept 2012) (Employee)
Harper Macleod LLP, Edinburgh . . . .(p.877)
   T: 0131 247 3331
   E: keri.preece@harpermacleod.co.uk

PRENDERGAST, Karen (Oct 2021) (Employee)
The McKinstry Company LLP, Ayr . . . . .(p.765)
   T: 01292 281711

PRENTICE, Alexander, QC (Sept 1983)
   (Employee)
Procurator Fiscal Service,
   Edinburgh . . . .(p.1227)
   T: 0300 0203469
   E: Alex.Prentice@copfs.gov.uk

PRENTICE, Hannah (Nov 2010) (Employee)
Wright, Johnston & Mackenzie LLP,
   Inverness . . . .(p.1083)
   T: 01463 234445
   E: hp@wjm.co.uk

PRENTICE, Helen Jane (Feb 2015) (Employee)
Hewats, Castle Douglas . . . .(p.784)
   T: 01556 502391
   E: helenprentice@hewats.co.uk

PRENTICE, Sarah Gyllian (Jul 2012) (Employee)
Scottish Social Services Council,
   Dundee . . . .(p.1218)
   T: 0345 6030 891
   E: sarah.prentice@sssc.uk.com

PRESLY, Victoria Katie (Sept 2013) (Employee)
NEO Energy, Aberdeen . . . .(p.1213)
   T: (01224) 659120
   E: Victoria.Presly@neweuropeanoffshore.com

PRESTON, Jennifer Emily Fiona (Nov 2018)
   (Associate)
JGW Legal Services Limited,
   Kinross . . . .(p.1098)
   T: 01577 862302
   E: j.preston@jgwilson.co.uk

PRESTON, Kirsty Louise (Nov 2014) (Employee)
Lindsays LLP, Dundee . . . .(p.814)
   T: 01382 224112
   E: kirstypreston@lindsays.co.uk

PRETORIUS, Elaine Buchanan (Jan 2001)
   (Employee)
Molson Coors Beverage Company,
   Milwaukee . . . .(p.1279)
   T: +1 414-931-2643
   E: elaine.pretorius1@molsoncoors.com

PRICE, Andrew Kevin (May 1985) (Director)
Andrew K. Price Limited, Kirkcaldy . . . .(p.1102)
   T: 01592 205151
   E: andrew@andrewkprice.co.uk

PRICE, Barry William (Jan 2007) (Director)
Latta Law Limited, Glasgow . . . .(p.998)
   T: 0141 222 2185
   E: barryprice@lattalaw.co.uk

PRICE, Donna Marie (Jul 1993) (Consultant)
Andrew K. Price Limited, Kirkcaldy . . . .(p.1102)
   T: 01592 205151
   E: donna@andrewkprice.co.uk

PRICE, Joanne (Jun 2005) (Employee)
RBS and NatWest Mentor,
   Glasgow. . . . .(p.1243)
   T: 0141 227 4590
   E: joanne.price@mentor.uk.com

PRICE, Kathleen Louise (Feb 1991) (Partner)
D'Arcy Price Law, Dundee . . . .(p.808)
   T: 01382 217999
   E: info@darcypricelaw.com

PRICE, Moira (Sept 1991) (Employee)
Procurator Fiscal Service, Glasgow . . . .(p.1242)
   E: Moira.Price@copfs.gov.uk

PRICE, Ross Eliot (Jan 2020) (Employee)
Procurator Fiscal Service,
   Edinburgh . . . .(p.1227)
   T: 0300 0203168
   E: ross.price@copfs.gov.uk

PRICE, Samuel Andrew (Dec 2004) (Employee)
Abellio ScotRail Limited, Glasgow . . . . .(p.1237)
   E: Sam.Price@scotrail.co.uk

PRICE, Sian (Oct 2016) (Director)
Andrew K. Price Limited, Kirkcaldy . . . .(p.1102)
   T: 01592 205151
   E: sianprice@andrewkprice.co.uk

PRIEST, Christina Ann Lorraine (Feb 2017)
(Employee)
SSE Plc, Perth . . . .(p.1253)
T: (01738) 453697
E: christina.priest@sse.com

PRIESTER, Katherine Elizabeth (Jul 2015)
(Employee)
Brodies LLP, Glasgow . . . .(p.948)
T: 0141 2484672
E: katie.priester@brodies.com

PRIESTLEY, Carolyn Ann (Sept 2010) (Partner)
Walker & Sharpe, Dumfries . . . .(p.803)
T: 01387 267222
E: carolyn.priestley@walker-sharpe.co.uk

PRIESTLEY, Christopher Severyn Somerville
(Jan 1995) (Employee)
Withers LLP, London EC4 . . . .(p.1269)
T: 0207 5976135
E: chris.priestley@withersworldwide.com

PRIESTLEY, Robin Andrew (Nov 1994) (Partner)
Whose Land Scotland, Linlithgow . . . . .(p.1117)
T: 07867 387591
E: whoselandscotland@gmail.com

PRIMROSE, Kate Marion (Mar 2013)
(Employee)
Burness Paull LLP, Glasgow . . . .(p.954)
T: 0141 2484933
E: Kate.Primrose@burnesspaull.com

PRINGLE, Amanda Mary (Jan 1990) (Solicitor)
NO FIRM

PRINGLE, Caroline Alexandra (Aug 2011)
(Associate)
Murray Beith Murray, Edinburgh . . . . . .(p.893)
T: 0131 2251200
E: caroline.pringle@murraybeith.co.uk

PRINGLE, Gregor James Lind (Oct 2018)
(Employee)
Shepherd and Wedderburn LLP,
Edinburgh . . . .(p.900)
T: 0131 2289900
E: Greg.Pringle@shepwedd.com

PRINGLE, Jacquelyne (Sept 1996) (Associate)
Allan McDougall McQueen LLP,
Penicuik . . . .(p.1144)
T: 01968 675694
E: jackiepringle@allanmcdougall.co.uk

PRINGLE, John Daniel Murray (Jul 2011)
(Partner)
Harper Macleod LLP, Glasgow . . . .(p.983)
T: 0141 2218888
E: john.pringle@harpermacleod.co.uk

PRINGLE, Kenneth Bryce (Oct 2009)
(Employee)
Scottish Legal Aid Board,
Edinburgh . . . .(p.1233)
T: 0131 2267061
E: PringleKe@slab.org.uk

PRIOR, Poppy Elizabeth Shepherd
(Aug 2019) (Employee)
Brodies LLP, Edinburgh . . . .(p.845)
T: 0131 2283777
E: poppy.prior@brodies.com

PRITCHARD, Jennifer Margaret (Aug 2016)
(Solicitor)
NO FIRM

PRITTY, Iain Walter (Oct 1999) (Employee)
Womble Bond Dickinson (UK) LLP, London
SE1 . . . .(p.1269)
T: 0345 4150000
E: Iain.Pritty@wbd-uk.com

PROCHALSKA, Katarzyna Alina (Nov 2017)
(Employee)
Brown & Co Legal LLP, Glasgow . . . . . .(p.950)
T: 0141 3533354
E: KasiaProchalska@lsa.org.uk

PROCTER, Thomas Nathan (Apr 2019)
(Employee)
Procurator Fiscal Service, Aberdeen . . .(p.1213)
T: 0300 0202336
E: Thomas.Procter@copfs.gov.uk

PROCTOR, Kathleen Docherty (Mar 2019)
(Employee)
Wright, Johnston & Mackenzie LLP,
Glasgow. . . . .(p.1054)
T: 0141 2483434
E: kdp@wjm.co.uk

PROCTOR, Lesley Stewart (Sept 2004)
(Associate)
Shepherd and Wedderburn LLP,
Glasgow. . . . .(p.1039)
T: 0141 5669900
E: Lesley.Proctor@shepwedd.com

PROUDFOOT, Alasdair John (Nov 2000)
(Partner)
Dickson Minto, Edinburgh . . . .(p.861)
T: 0131 2254455
E: alasdair.proudfoot@dmws.com

PROUDFOOT, Elaine Mary (Nov 1999)
(Employee)
Turcan Connell, Edinburgh . . . .(p.908)
T: 0131 2288111
E: elaine.proudfoot@turcanconnell.com

PROUDFOOT, Marc Douglas (Sept 2013)
(Employee)
Howard Kennedy LLP, London SE1 . . . .(p.1265)
E: Marc.Proudfoot@howardkennedy.com

PROVAN, Roy Craig (Sept 1998) (Employee)
Wheatley Housing Group Limited,
Glasgow. . . . .(p.1246)
T: 0845 9001001
E: roy.provan@wheatley-group.com

PROVAN, Victoria Ann (Feb 1992) (Employee)
ContractPod Technologies Limited,
   Glasgow . . . .(p.1238)
   T: 0141 280 1600

PRYDE, Denise Mary (Nov 1999) (Employee)
MBM Commercial LLP, Edinburgh . . . . .(p.889)
   T: 0131 2268200
   E: denise.pryde@mbmcommercial.co.uk

PRYDE, Helen Margaret Mary (Sept 1996)
   (Solicitor)
NO FIRM

PRYDE, Naomi Sarah Jane (Jan 2009) (Partner)
DWF LLP, Manchester . . . .(p.1270)
   T: 0161 6035000
   E: naomi.pryde@dwf.law

PRYOR, Rachael Elizabeth (Sept 2019)
   (Employee)
Scottish Social Services Council,
   Dundee . . . .(p.1218)
   T: 0345 6030 891
   E: Rachael.Pryor@sssc.uk.com

PULLAR, Thomas Lee (Feb 2021) (Employee)
CMS Cameron McKenna Nabarro Olswang LLP,
   Edinburgh . . . .(p.856)
   T: 0131 2288000
   E: Thomas.Pullar@cms-cmno.com

PURCELL, Cecily Grace (Aug 2019) (Employee)
DAC Beachcroft Scotland LLP,
   Glasgow . . . .(p.964)
   T: 0141 2486688
   E: cpurcell@dacbeachcroft.com

PURDIE, Andrew, WS (Oct 1982) (Director)
Purdie Maclean Limited, Livingston . . .(p.1119)
   T: 01506 420333
   E: andrew@purdiemaclean.co.uk

PURDIE, Dean (Jun 2003) (Partner)
DJP Solicitors, Aberdeen . . . .(p.730)
   T: 01224 590053
   E: dp@djpsolicitors.com

PURDIE, Douglas David (Nov 1989) (Partner)
Stewart & Watson, Turriff . . . .(p.1177)
   T: 01888 563773
   E: ddpurdie@stewartwatson.co.uk

PURDIE, Emma (Nov 2005) (Employee)
Peterkin & Kidd, Livingston . . . .(p.1119)
   T: 01506 880548
   E: epurdie@peterkinandkidd.co.uk

PURDIE, Fiona Louise (Aug 1993) (Partner)
Stewart & Watson, Turriff . . . .(p.1177)
   T: 01888 563773
   E: fpurdie@stewartwatson.co.uk

PURDY, Jamie Michael (Oct 2014) (Employee)
Nordic Capital Limited, St Helier . . . . .(p.1274)
   E: Jamie.Purdy@nordiccapital.je

PURDY, Susan (Oct 2014) (Employee)
Royal Bank of Scotland Int. Ltd, St
   Helier . . . .(p.1274)
   E: susan.purdy@rbsint.com

PUREWAL, Baljinder Kaur (Feb 2006)
   (Employee)
Hill & Robb Limited, Stirling . . . .(p.1164)
   T: 01786 450985
   E: baljinderpurewal@hillandrobb.co.uk

PURI, Puneet Kaur (Oct 2020) (Employee)
Inheritance Legal, Glasgow . . . .(p.989)
   T: 0800 404 5962
   E: puneetpuri@inheritancelegal.com

PURKIS, Linda Alison (Sept 2000) (Partner)
Peterkins, Inverurie . . . .(p.1085)
   T: 01467 672800
   E: lap@peterkins.com

PURVES, Kayleigh (Jul 2017) (Employee)
CMS Cameron McKenna Nabarro Olswang LLP,
   Edinburgh . . . .(p.856)
   T: 0131 2288000
   E: Kayleigh.purves@cms-cmno.com

PURVES, Laura Alexandra (Jul 2018) (Employee)
Morton Fraser LLP, Edinburgh . . . .(p.891)
   T: 0131 2471000
   E: laura.purves@morton-fraser.com

PURVES, Lynette Katherine Hamilton
   (Sept 2011) (Employee)
ERG UK Holding Ltd, Edinburgh . . . . . .(p.1223)
   T: +44 (0) 7815 513 163
   E: lpurves@erg.eu

PURVIS, Caroline Anne (Aug 2010) (Employee)
Brodies LLP, Edinburgh . . . .(p.845)
   T: 0131 2283777
   E: caroline.purvis@brodies.com

PURVIS, Susan Elizabeth Collin (Sept 1996)
   (Employee)
Ledingham Chalmers LLP,
   Aberdeen . . . .(p.734)
   T: 01224 408408
   E: susan.purvis@ledinghamchalmers.com

PYATT, Ruth Alison (Nov 2007) (Employee)
Thorntons Law LLP, Dundee . . . .(p.819)
   T: 01382 229 111
   E: rpyatt@thorntons-law.co.uk

PYPER, Dervile Monica (Jan 1993) (Employee)
Aegon UK, Edinburgh . . . .(p.1220)
   T: 0131 549 3530
   E: dervile.pyper@aegon.co.uk

PYPER, Emma Mackenzie (Nov 2012) (Partner)
Taylor & Henderson LLP, Saltcoats . . . .(p.1160)
   T: 01294 464341
   E: epyper@taylorandhenderson.co.uk

QUAIL, Thomas Lloyd (Aug 1983) (Partner)
Wright, Johnston & Mackenzie LLP,
Glasgow . . . .(p.1054)
T: 0141 2483434
E: tlq@wjm.co.uk

QUAR, Isabella Houston (Jan 2004) (Employee)
AMIS: Abused Men In Scotland,
Dalkeith . . . .(p.1216)
T: 0131 4477449
E: iris@amis.org.uk

QUEEN, Graham John Holland (Oct 1988)
(Director)
Clark Boyle Limited, Glasgow . . . .(p.960)
T: 0141 2272200
E: gq@clarkboyle.co.uk

QUEEN, Konrad (Jun 2020) (Employee)
Harter & Co., Glasgow . . . .(p.985)
T: 0141 4270901
E: hartersolicitors@tiscali.co.uk

QUEEN, Lauren Margaret Helen (Apr 2014)
(Employee)
Scottish Environment Protection Agency,
Edinburgh . . . .(p.1230)
T: 0131 4497296
E: Lauren.Queen@sepa.org.uk

QUEEN, Mairi Mackenzie (Mar 2011)
(Employee)
Life Technologies Limited, Paisley . . . . .(p.1252)
T: 0141 8146100
E: Mairi.Queen@thermofisher.com

QUEEN, Neil Thomas Hugh (Nov 2009)
(Partner)
Ross & Connel LLP, Dunfermline . . . . . .(p.825)
T: 01383 721156
E: nqueen@ross.connel.co.uk

QUICKFALL, Marie (Sept 2004) (Partner)
South Forrest, Inverness . . . .(p.1082)
T: 01463 237171
E: marie@southforrest.co.uk

QUIGG, Manus Martin (May 2003) (Partner)
Brodies LLP, Glasgow . . . .(p.948)
T: 0141 2484672
E: manus.quigg@brodies.com

QUIGLEY, Anthony John (Mar 2003)
(Employee)
Procurator Fiscal Service,
Edinburgh . . . .(p.1229)
T: 0300 0203000
E: anthony.quigley@copfs.gov.uk

QUIGLEY, Mary Patricia (May 2000) (Solicitor)
NO FIRM

QUIN, Adrienne Louise (Oct 1996) (Solicitor)
NO FIRM

QUIN, Anthony (Aug 1984) (Partner)
Aberdein Considine and Company,
Stirling . . . .(p.1163)
T: 01786 450944
E: aquin@acandco.com

QUIN, Karen Anne (Oct 1986) (Employee)
Falkirk Council, Falkirk . . . .(p.1236)
T: 01324 506070
E: karenanne.quin@falkirk.gov.uk

QUINN, Anne Elaine Frances (Jun 2009)
(Associate)
Stirling & Gilmour LLP, Clydebank . . . . .(p.785)
T: 0141 952 2669
E: a.quinn@stirlingandgilmour.co.uk

QUINN, Claire Louise (Sept 2014) (Associate)
CMS Cameron McKenna Nabarro Olswang LLP,
Aberdeen . . . .(p.727)
T: 01224 622002
E: claire.quinn@cms-cmno.com

QUINN, Daniel Marcus (Apr 2004) (Employee)
Akin Gump Strauss Hauer & Feld LLP, London
E1 . . . .(p.1261)
T: +44 20.7012.9842
E: Daniel.Quinn@akingump.com

QUINN, Eoin Malachy (Jan 2012) (Associate)
Keoghs Scotland LLP, Glasgow . . . .(p.996)
T: 0141 2380100
E: EQuinn@keoghs.co.uk

QUINN, Hazel Shakur (Feb 2003) (Employee)
Bryan Cave Leighton Paisner LLP, Abu
Dhabi . . . .(p.1277)
E: hazel.shakurquinn@bclplaw.com

QUINN, Jennifer (Jan 2001) (Partner)
The PRG Partnership, Glasgow . . . .(p.1045)
T: 0141 3530550
E: jenniferquinn@prg.co.uk

QUINN, John (Oct 1986) (Director)
Wallace Quinn & Co Limited,
Glasgow . . . .(p.1051)
T: 0141 7713911
E: john@wallacequinn.co.uk

QUINN, Judith Ann (Oct 2001) (Partner)
Blackwood Partners LLP, Aberdeen . . . . .(p.723)
T: 01224 446230
E: judith.quinn@blackwood-partners.com

QUINN, Lewis Alexander (May 2015) (Director)
Q&A Law Practice Limited,
Aberdeen . . . .(p.740)
T: 7770996601
E: lewis@qalawpractice.co.uk

QUINN, Marc Lowson (Dec 2013) (Partner)
Kerr Stirling LLP, Stirling . . . .(p.1165)
T: 01786 463414
E: marc.quinn@kerrstirling.co.uk

QUINN, Mark Alexander (Nov 2006) (Associate)
MacRoberts LLP, Glasgow . . . .(p.1015)
T: 0141 3031100
E: mark.quinn@macroberts.com

QUINN, Martha (Jan 1997) (Employee)
Pension Protection Fund, Croydon . . . .(p.1259)
T: 020 8633 4957
E: Martha.quinn@ppf.co.uk

QUINN, Martin Alexander (Dec 1998)
(Director)
Edinburgh Corporate Solicitors Limited,
Kinglassie . . . .(p.1098)
T: 01592 882205
E: martin@edinburghcorporate.com

QUINN, Paul James (Oct 1999) (Partner)
Dickson Minto, Edinburgh . . . .(p.861)
T: 0131 2254455
E: paul.quinn@dmws.com

QUINN, Suzanne (Aug 2016) (Employee)
Scottish Children's Reporter Administration,
Dumbarton . . . .(p.1217)
T: 01389 764268
E: Suzanne.Quinn@scra.gov.uk

QUINN, Wendy Jane (Oct 1989) (Associate)
Pinsent Masons LLP, Glasgow . . . .(p.1031)
T: 0141 567 8400
E: Wendy.Quinn@pinsentmasons.com

QUIRK, Fiona (Oct 1982) (Associate)
Paterson Holms, Glasgow . . . .(p.1029)
T: 0141 9428825
E: fiona@patersonholms.co.uk

QUIRK, Stanley Thomas (Nov 1982) (Employee)
Public Defence Solicitors Office,
Falkirk . . . .(p.1237)
T: 01324 631 475
E: squirk@pdso.org.uk

QUITHER, Steven Robert (Aug 1984)
(Employee)
Procurator Fiscal Service, Glasgow . . . .(p.1241)
T: 0300 0203000
E: steven.quither@copfs.gov.uk

QUMSIEH, Lee (Aug 2011) (Employee)
Paterson Bell Limited, Kirkcaldy . . . . . .(p.1102)
T: 01592 646600

R DAR S, Jacqueline Ruth (Feb 2010)
(Employee)
CMS Cameron McKenna Nabarro Olswang LLP,
Aberdeen . . . .(p.727)
T: 01224 622002
E: jacqueline.redares@cms-cmno.com

RADLOW, Allan (Sept 1979) (Partner)
McVey & Murricane, Glasgow . . . .(p.1017)
T: 0141 3339688
E: aradlow@mcvey-murricane.com

RADLOW, Morvyn Anne (Jul 2011) (Employee)
White & Case LLP, London EC2 . . . . . .(p.1269)
T: 0207 5321000
E: morvyn.radlow@whitecase.com

RAE, Christopher Neil (Oct 2004) (Partner)
CMS Cameron McKenna Nabarro Olswang LLP,
Glasgow . . . .(p.962)
T: 0141 2222200
E: chris.rae@cms-cmno.com

RAE, Christopher Robert (Jul 2019) (Employee)
Keoghs Scotland LLP, Glasgow . . . .(p.996)
T: 0141 2380100
E: CRae@keoghs.co.uk

RAE, Elaine Louise (Aug 2008) (Employee)
Gallen & Company Ltd, Glasgow . . . . . .(p.978)
T: 0141 4201441

RAE, Emma Jane (Feb 2020) (Employee)
Addleshaw Goddard LLP, Glasgow . . . . .(p.938)
T: 0141 2212300
E: Emma.Rae@addleshawgoddard.com

RAE, Evie Alexandra (May 2018) (Employee)
Brodies LLP, Edinburgh . . . .(p.845)
T: 0131 2283777
E: evie.rae@brodies.com

RAE, Jennifer (Sept 1997) (Employee)
Barclays Bank PLC, London E14 . . . . . .(p.1262)
E: jennifer.mennim@barclays.com

RAE, Jennifer Jane (Oct 2014) (Employee)
Burness Paull LLP, Edinburgh . . . .(p.850)
T: 0131 4736000
E: Jennifer.rae@burnesspaull.com

RAE, Lauren Janet (Jun 2011) (Partner)
Thorntons Law LLP, Dundee . . . .(p.819)
T: 01382 229 111
E: lrae@thorntons-law.co.uk

RAE, Lisa Jane (Aug 2009) (Partner)
Lisa Rae & Co Court Solicitors,
Edinburgh . . . .(p.898)
T: 0131 5503716
E: lr@lisaraeandco.co.uk

RAE, Nicola Helen (Aug 2010) (Employee)
Dentons UK and Middle East LLP,
Edinburgh . . . .(p.860)
T: 0330 2220050
E: Nicola.Rae@dentons.com

RAE, Paul Anthony (Oct 2008) (Employee)
Barclays Execution Services Limited, London
E14 . . . .(p.1262)
E: paul.rae@barclays.com

RAE, Simon Scott (Nov 1996) (Partner)
DLA Piper Scotland LLP, Edinburgh . . . .(p.863)
T: 08700 111111
E: simon.rae@dlapiper.com

RAE, Victoria Ann (Dec 2017) (Employee)
DWF LLP, Glasgow . . . . (p.973)
  T: 0141 228 8000
  E: victoria.rae@dwf.law

RAEBURN, Alexander Murray (Sept 2017)
  (Employee)
Collins & Co Defence Lawyers Ltd,
  Edinburgh . . . . (p.857)
  T: 0131 661 3210
  E: sraeburn@collinsandcolawyers.com

RAESIDE, Stewart John (Oct 2000) (Employee)
Agoda Company Pte Ltd, Bangkok . . . . (p.1277)
  T: + 6697 214 1176
  E: Stewart.Raeside@agoda.com

RAFFERTY, Martha Anne (Oct 1983)
  (Consultant)
Philip Rooney & Co., Glasgow . . . . (p.1036)
  T: 0141 423 0000
  E: m.rafferty@philiprooney.com

RAFFERTY, Zara Jenny (Feb 2016) (Employee)
Digby Brown LLP, Glasgow . . . . (p.970)
  T: 0333 200 5925
  E: zara.clark@digbybrown.co.uk

RAFI, Mudassar Husain (Oct 2020) (Employee)
JKR Law Ltd, Glasgow . . . . (p.992)
  T: 0141 473 3999
  E: mr@jklaws.co.uk

RAFTERY, Claire Elizabeth (Dec 2014)
  (Associate)
Clyde & Co (Scotland) LLP,
  Edinburgh . . . . (p.855)
  T: 0131 5571545
  E: Claire.Raftery@clydeco.com

RAFTERY, Matthew Bernard Kenneth
  (Jul 2015) (Associate)
BTO Solicitors LLP, Edinburgh . . . . (p.849)
  T: 0131 2222939
  E: mra@bto.co.uk

RAGHAVAN, Shalani (Feb 2003) (Employee)
Scottish Government, Edinburgh . . . . . (p.1232)
  E: Shalinay.Raghavan@gov.scot

RAHMAN, Nina (Jan 2013) (Employee)
NO FIRM

RAHMATULLAH, Nhabeela (Mar 2021)
  (Employee)
Procurator Fiscal Service,
  Edinburgh . . . . (p.1229)
  T: 0300 0203000
  E: Nhabeela.Rahmatullah@copfs.gov.uk

RAIKKONEN, Veli-Matti Antinpoika
  (Sept 2006) (Employee)
Ledingham Chalmers LLP,
  Aberdeen . . . . (p.734)
  T: 01224 408408
  E:
  Veli-Matti.Raikkonen@ledinghamchalmers.com

RAILTON, Karen (Jul 2007) (Employee)
DAC Beachcroft Scotland LLP,
  Glasgow. (p.964)
  T: 0141 2237842
  E: krailton@dacbeachcroft.com

RAINE, Calum Stephen Henry (Aug 2014)
  (Employee)
DWF LLP, Edinburgh . . . . (p.865)
  T: 0131 2265541
  E: calum.raine@dwf.law

RAINEY, Lauren Elizabeth (Oct 2014)
  (Employee)
Sainsbury's Bank plc, Edinburgh . . . . . . (p.1230)
  T: (0131) 286 0807

RAITT, Jacqueline Lesley (Nov 2004) (Partner)
Allan McDougall McQueen LLP,
  Edinburgh . . . . (p.837)
  T: 0131 2252121
  E: jackieraitt@allanmcdougall.co.uk

RAJA, Syema (Sept 2007) (Employee)
Wright, Johnston & Mackenzie LLP,
  Glasgow. (p.1054)
  T: 0141 2483434
  E: sr@wjm.co.uk

RAJGOPAUL, Simon (Jan 2015) (Employee)
Lloyds Banking Group Plc,
  Edinburgh . . . . (p.1224)
  T: 0131 222 0362
  E: simon.rajgopaul@lloydsbanking.com

RALEIGH, Hope Ellen (Dec 2019) (Employee)
Scullion Law Limited, Hamilton . . . . . . (p.1069)
  T: 01698 283265
  E: hope@scullionlaw.com

RALPH, Gillian Margaret (Oct 1999)
  (Employee)
Shoosmiths, Edinburgh . . . . (p.902)
  T: 03700 868000
  E: gillian.ralph@shoosmiths.co.uk

RALPH, Ivan Alexander (Jul 1992) (Consultant)
Hendrie Legal Limited, Edinburgh . . . . . (p.878)
  T: 0131 370 0470
  E: Ivan.Ralph@ralphhendrie.legal

RALPH, Paul William (Nov 1992) (Partner)
Paul W. Ralph, Torryburn . . . . (p.1175)
  T: 07986 431730
  E: paul.w.ralph@btinternet.com

RALPH, Scott David (Aug 1985) (Partner)
Scott Ralph, Dunfermline . . . . (p.825)
  T: 01383 626780
  E: sr@scottralph.co.uk

RALPH, Sharon Marie (Dec 1986) (Employee)
Procurator Fiscal Service, Inverness . . . . (p.1248)
  T: 0844 5612926
  E: sharon.ralph@copfs.gov.uk

RALSTON, Alan Mark (Oct 1991) (Director)
Wright & Crawford (1906) Limited,
Paisley . . . .(p.1142)
T: 0141 8876211
E: M.Ralston@wright-crawford.co.uk

RAM, Manjit Kaur (Oct 1999) (Partner)
East End Law, Glasgow . . . .(p.974)
T: 0141 554 4556
E: manjitram@eastendlaw.co.uk

RAM SANGRAY, Lauren (Jul 2019) (Employee)
Procurator Fiscal Service, Glasgow . . . .(p.1241)
T: 0300 0203000
E: lauren.ramsangray@copfs.gov.uk

RAMACHANDRAN, Kay Fiona (Sept 2004)
(Employee)
National Health Service Scotland,
Edinburgh . . . .(p.1225)
T: 0131 2757800
E: kay.ramachandran@nhs.scot

RAMAGE, Cameron (Feb 2020) (Employee)
Life Technologies Limited, Paisley . . . . .(p.1252)
T: 0141 8146100

RAMAGE, David James (Jun 2017) (Associate)
CMS Cameron McKenna Nabarro Olswang LLP,
Glasgow. . . . .(p.962)
T: 0141 2222200
E: david.ramage@cms-cmno.com

RAMAGE, Siobhan Louise (Aug 2006)
(Employee)
Procurator Fiscal Service, Glasgow . . . .(p.1241)
T: 0844 5612980
E: siobhan.ramge@copfs.gov.uk

RAMOS, Kirsten Jennifer (Sept 2018)
(Employee)
Procurator Fiscal Service, Dumfries . . . .(p.1217)
T: 01387 274585
E: Kirsten.Ramos@copfs.gov.uk

RAMSAY, Alaina (Sept 2009) (Employee)
Abu Dhabi National Oil Company, Abu
Dhabi . . . .(p.1277)
T: 971566963496
E: aramsay@adnoc.ae

RAMSAY, Alison Gail, M.B.E. (Sept 1983)
(Partner)
Jameson + Mackay LLP, Perth . . . .(p.1148)
T: 01738 631666
E: alison.ramsay@jamesonmackay.co.uk

RAMSAY, Caroline Tod (Sept 2004) (Partner)
TLT LLP, Glasgow . . . .(p.1048)
T: 0333 006 0400
E: Caroline.Ramsay@TLTsolicitors.com

RAMSAY, Catriona Michelle (Oct 2012)
(Employee)
Aberdein Considine and Company,
Glasgow. . . . .(p.937)
T: 0141 2278200
E: cmilne@acandco.com

RAMSAY, Craig William (Nov 2012) (Partner)
Harper Macleod LLP, Glasgow . . . .(p.983)
T: 0141 2218888
E: craig.ramsay@harpermacleod.co.uk

RAMSAY, Elizabeth Lydia (Nov 1998)
(Employee)
Procurator Fiscal Service, Glasgow . . . .(p.1241)
T: 0300 020 3000
E: Liz.Ramsay@copfs.gov.uk

RAMSAY, Jane Margaret (Apr 1995) (Partner)
MBM Commercial LLP, Edinburgh . . . . .(p.889)
T: 0131 2268200
E: jane.ramsay@mbmcommercial.co.uk

RAMSAY, Michael Harvie (Dec 1991) (Director)
Ramsay & Co. Solicitors Ltd,
Glasgow. . . . .(p.1034)
T: 0141 945 1917
E: info@ramsay-solicitors.com

RAMSAY, Michael John (Sept 1993) (Partner)
Morton Fraser LLP, Edinburgh . . . .(p.891)
T: 0131 2471000
E: michael.ramsay@morton-fraser.com

RAMSEY, Karen Elizabeth (Jun 2009) (Director)
Ennova Limited, Edinburgh . . . .(p.869)
T: 0131 510 4954
E: kramsey@ennova-law.com

RAMSEY, Katy Louise (Oct 2003) (Employee)
Sigma Capital Group plc,
Edinburgh . . . .(p.1234)
T: 0131 2209444
E: kramsey@sigmacapital.co.uk

RANALLI, Lorenzo Shaw (Feb 2019) (Employee)
Corrigall Black, Dunoon . . . .(p.828)
T: 01369 702941
E: lorenzo.ranalli@corrigallblack.com

RANI, Anna Louise Jean C. A. (Nov 2015)
(Employee)
Drummond Miller LLP, Edinburgh . . . . .(p.864)
T: 0131 2265151
E: arani@drummondmiller.co.uk

RANKIN, David Allan (Nov 1976) (Partner)
T.F. Reid & Donaldson, Paisley . . . .(p.1141)
T: 0141 8897531
E: allan.rankin@reidlaw.co.uk

RANKIN, Dorothy Crombie (Dec 1985)
(Partner)
Lindsays LLP, Edinburgh . . . .(p.882)
T: 0131 2291212
E: dorothyrankin@lindsays.co.uk

RANKIN, Jeffrey Colin (Mar 1985) (Employee)
Gallen & Company Ltd, Glasgow . . . . . .(p.978)
T: 0141 4201441
E: jeff.rankin@gallenandco.com

RANKIN, Laura Marie (Nov 2019) (Employee)
CMS Cameron McKenna Nabarro Olswang LLP,
Glasgow......................(p.962)
T: 0141 2222200
E: laura.rankin@cms-cmno.com

RANKIN, Michelle Dawn (Oct 2014) (Director)
Archibald Sharp & Son Limited,
Glasgow......................(p.1039)
T: 0141 3393036
E: mrankin@archibaldsharp.co.uk

RANKINE, Alison Kathryn (Nov 2006)
(Employee)
Pinsent Masons LLP, Edinburgh.......(p.895)
T: 0131 777 7000
E: alison.rankine@pinsentmasons.com

RANKINE, Fraser Donald Moore (Nov 2012)
(Employee)
Scottish Borders Council, Newtown St.
Boswells....................(p.1251)
T: 01835 825 225
E: Fraser.Rankine@scotborders.gov.uk

RANKINE, Neil Bromham (Jan 1980) (Partner)
Carruthers Gemmill, Glasgow........(p.958)
T: 0141 3330 033
E: nbr@carruthersgemmill.co.uk

RANKINE, Sandra (Jul 1987) (Employee)
Elliott Matthew Property Lawyers, London
W1......................(p.1264)
E: Sandra@EML.legal

RASHEED, Saima (Sept 2013) (Employee)
Procurator Fiscal Service, Dundee.....(p.1218)
T: 01382 342559
E: Saima.Rasheed@copfs.gov.uk

RASHID, Shazia (Nov 2011) (Employee)
Procurator Fiscal Service, Glasgow....(p.1241)
T: 0300 0203000
E: shazia.rashid@copfs.gov.uk

RASHID, Umera (Sept 2018) (Employee)
Scottish Hospital Inquiry, Glasgow....(p.1244)
E: umera.rashid@hospitalsinquiry.scot

RASMUSEN, Fiona Rosemary (Dec 1981)
(Director)
Gibson Kerr Limited, Edinburgh.......(p.872)
T: 0131 2257558
E: fiona.rasmusen@gibsonkerr.co.uk

RASMUSEN, Gordon Scott (Dec 1982)
(Director)
Gibson Kerr (incorporating Marwicks and
Grange), Edinburgh............(p.871)
T: 0131 2257558
E: scott.rasmusen@gibsonkerr.co.uk

RASMUSSEN, Joseph John Lamb (Jan 2019)
(Employee)
Maguire Solicitors, Glasgow.........(p.1017)
T: 0141 3312885

RASOOL, Ambreen Zahra (May 2021)
(Associate)
CMS Cameron McKenna Nabarro Olswang LLP,
Glasgow......................(p.962)
T: 0141 2222200
E: ambreen.rasool@cms-cmno.com

RASSOULI, Kaveh (Oct 2006) (Employee)
Subsea 7 (UK Service Company) Ltd,
Westhill....................(p.1255)
T: 01224 344308
E: kaveh.rassouli@subsea7.com

RATHORE, Afshan (Nov 2000) (Employee)
Aberdeen Corporate Services Limited,
Edinburgh..................(p.1220)
T: 0131 245 2228
E: afshan.rathore@abrdn.com

RATTER, Andrew William (Sept 2018)
(Employee)
Levy & McRae Solicitors LLP,
Glasgow....................(p.1000)
T: 0141 3072311
E: aratter@lemac.co.uk

RATTER, David Alexander (Apr 1990) (Partner)
DWF LLP, Edinburgh..............(p.865)
T: 0131 2265541
E: David.Ratter@dwf.law

RATTRAY, Howard John Charles (Jan 1992)
(Employee)
Scottish Courts and Tribunals Service,
Glasgow....................(p.1243)
T: 0141 4298888
E: hrattray@scotcourts.gov.uk

RATTRAY, Jane Elizabeth (Nov 2012)
(Employee)
Brodies LLP, Aberdeen.............(p.723)
T: 01224 392242
E: jane.rattray@brodies.com

RATTRAY, Kevin William (Oct 1990) (Partner)
Andersonbain LLP, Aberdeen.........(p.721)
T: 01224 456789
E: krattray@andersonbain.co.uk

RAWCLIFFE, Coral Ann (Oct 2021) (Employee)
James McKay Defence Solicitors Limited,
Elgin......................(p.917)
T: 01343 556500

RAWICZ, Konrad Pawel (Apr 2016) (Associate)
CMS Cameron McKenna Nabarro Olswang LLP,
London EC4..................(p.1263)
T: 0207 3673000
E: konrad.rawicz@cms-cmno.com

RAWLINSON, Keith James (Oct 2006)
(Associate)
Davidson Chalmers Stewart LLP,
Edinburgh..................(p.859)
T: 0131 6259191
E: Keith.Rawlinson@dcslegal.com

RAWLINSON, Mandy Louise (Nov 2008)
(Employee)
Standard Life Investments Limited,
Edinburgh ....(p.1234)
T: 0131 245 53601
E: Mandy.Rawlinson@aberdeenstandard.com

RAYMOND, Eilidh McIntyre (May 2014)
(Employee)
Primrose & Gordon, Dumfries ....(p.802)
T: 01387 267316
E: eilidh@primroseandgordon.co.uk

RAYNER, Lynn Elizabeth (Jan 1991) (Partner)
Patten & Prentice LLP, Greenock .....(p.1062)
T: 01475 720306
E: lynnr@patten.co.uk

RAZA, Ifet (Oct 2002) (Employee)
Pacitti Jones Legal Limited,
Glasgow.....................(p.1028)
T: 0141 5714444
E: ifet@pjglasgow.co.uk

RAZA, Shafana (Jan 2007) (Employee)
NORTH LANARKSHIREre Council,
Motherwell...................(p.1251)
T: 01698 302196
E: RazaS@northlan.gov.uk

RAZAQ, Sheereen (Mar 2021) (Employee)
Aberdeenshire Council, Aberdeen.....(p.1211)
T: 0345 608 1208
E: sheereen.razaq@aberdeenshire.gov.uk

RAZZAQ, Shazia Saiqa (Nov 1999) (Employee)
Scottish Government, Glasgow ......(p.1244)
T: 0131 244 0815
E: Shazia.razzaq@gov.scot

REA, Gino Mario Vittorio (Sept 2012) (Director)
Rea Law Ltd, Glasgow.............(p.1034)
T: 0141 3701241
E: gino@realaw.co.uk

READ, Campbell Calum (Nov 2001) (Director)
Stewart Balfour & Sutherland,
Campbeltown..................(p.783)
T: 01586 552871
E: CampbellR@sbslaw.co.uk

READ, Emma Jane (Aug 2017) (Employee)
Shepherd and Wedderburn LLP,
Edinburgh ....(p.900)
T: 0131 2289900
E: emma.read@shepwedd.co.uk

REAY, Christine Ann (Dec 2003) (Employee)
Scottish Government, Edinburgh .....(p.1231)
T: 0131 244 0815
E: christine.reay@gov.scot

REBELLO, Dr, Adrian Vernon Ashok
(Oct 2011) (Employee)
National Health Service Scotland,
Edinburgh ....(p.1225)
T: 0131 2757800
E: ash.rebello@nhs.scot

REBISZ-BAHRA, Michalina Pria Udhare
(Jan 2019) (Employee)
DWF Law LLP, London EC3 ....(p.1264)
T: 020 7645 9636
E: Michalina.Rebisz-Bahra@dwf.law

REDFORD, Kevin Philip (Nov 2012) (Partner)
Redford Robertson Solicitors,
Glasgow.....................(p.1034)
T: 0141 6485535
E: kpr@redfordrobertson.com

REDMOND, Claire (Aug 2015) (Employee)
Thorntons Law LLP, Dundee ....(p.819)
T: 01382 229 111
E: credmond@thorntons-law.co.uk

REDPATH, Colin (Oct 1987) (Director)
Allingham & Co (Solicitors) Limited,
Edinburgh ....(p.838)
T: 0131 4479341
E: colin@allingham.co.uk

REDPATH, Thomas Adam (Oct 2011)
(Employee)
Office of the Advocate General,
Edinburgh ....(p.1227)
T: 0131 2441635
E: thomas.redpath@advocategeneral.gov.uk

REEKIE, Christa Margaretha (Nov 1994)
(Employee)
Scottish Futures Trust, Edinburgh .....(p.1231)
T: 0131 5100803
E: christa.reekie@scottishfuturestrust.org.uk

REEKIE, Deborah Elizabeth (Jul 2011)
(Employee)
BTO Solicitors LLP, Edinburgh ....(p.849)
T: 0131 2222939
E: der@bto.co.uk

REEKIE, James Alexander (Sept 2011)
(Associate)
Brodies LLP, Edinburgh ....(p.845)
T: 0131 2283777
E: jamie.reekie@brodies.com

REEKIE, Kirsteen Margaret Louise
(Jun 2021) (Employee)
Mackenzie & Cormack, Tain ....(p.1173)
T: 01862 892046

REES, Emma Ann (Oct 1999) (Employee)
National Westminster Bank PLC,
Edinburgh ....(p.1226)
T: 0131 6264129
E: Emma.Rees@rbs.co.uk

REES, Jaimie Louise (Aug 2021) (Employee)
Dickson Minto, Edinburgh...........(p.861)
T: 0131 2254455
E: jaimie.rees@dmws.com

REES, Stephen Leslie (Nov 2000) (Employee)
Legal Secretariat to the Lord Advocate,
Edinburgh . . . . (p.1224)
T: (0300) 020 3364
E: stephen.rees@gov.scot

REGAN, Ewan McPherson (Nov 2001)
(Associate)
Anderson Strathern LLP, Edinburgh . . . . (p.839)
T: 0131 2707700
E: ewan.regan@andersonstrathern.co.uk

REGAN, Helen Therese (Nov 1985) (Employee)
Amber Fund Managers Ltd, London
SE1 . . . . (p.1261)
T: 0207 939 0550
E: Helen.Regan@amberinfrastructure.com

REHMAN, Shaista (Oct 2016) (Employee)
DAC Beachcroft Scotland LLP,
Glasgow. . . . . (p.964)
T: 0141 2486688
E: shrehman@dacbeachcroft.com

REID, Ainsley Macdonald (Nov 1999)
(Associate)
Morton Fraser LLP, Edinburgh . . . . (p.891)
T: 0131 2471000
E: ainsley.reid@morton-fraser.com

REID, Alan William (Nov 1977) (Partner)
Murray, Gillies & Wilson, Irvine . . . . . . (p.1087)
T: 01294 278355
E: awr@murraygillies.co.uk

REID, Alexander Charles (Nov 1975) (Director)
Reid Quarton Limited, Glasgow . . . . . . (p.1035)
T: 0141 354 7651
E: sandy.reid@reidquarton.co.uk

REID, Alison Jane (Nov 2001) (Employee)
Wright, Johnston & Mackenzie LLP,
Inverness . . . . (p.1083)
T: 01463 234445
E: ajr@wjm.co.uk

REID, Alison Patricia (Oct 1996) (Director)
Clan Childlaw Limited, Edinburgh . . . . . (p.854)
T: 0808 129 0522
E: alison.reid@clanchildlaw.org

REID, Alix Jean (Dec 2013) (Associate)
Raeburn Christie Clark & Wallace LLP,
Aberdeen . . . . (p.741)
T: 01224 332400
E: Alix.Reid@raeburns.co.uk

REID, Allan Christopher (Sept 1993) (Employee)
Vialex Limited, Edinburgh . . . . (p.1235)
T: 0333 2400127
E: allan.reid@vialex.co.uk

REID, Andrew James (Jan 2003) (Partner)
Reid Solicitors, Hamilton . . . . (p.1068)
T: 07394 150383
E: andrew.reidajrlaw@gmail.com

REID, Anna Christine (Oct 2002) (Employee)
Procurator Fiscal Service,
Edinburgh . . . . (p.1227)
T: 0300 0203168
E: anna.reid@civilrecoveryunit.gov.scot

REID, Anna Louise (Oct 2016) (Employee)
Burness Paull LLP, Edinburgh . . . . (p.850)
T: (0)1224 618 567
E: anna.reid@burnesspaull.com

REID, Catriona Gail Mackie (Oct 2017)
(Employee)
Rooney Nimmo Limited, London
EC2 . . . . (p.1267)
T: 0208 6292150
E: catriona.reid@rooneynimmo.co.uk

REID, Christopher James William (Aug 2017)
(Employee)
Turcan Connell, Edinburgh . . . . (p.908)
T: 0131 2288111
E: Christopher.Reid@turcanconnell.com

REID, Christopher Miller (Feb 2015) (Employee)
Levy & McRae Solicitors LLP,
Glasgow. (p.1000)
T: 0141 3072311
E: CReid@lemac.co.uk

REID, Claire Ann (Nov 2000) (Director)
Raeside Chisholm Solicitors Limited,
Glasgow. (p.1034)
T: 0141 2483456

REID, Claire Marie (Oct 2008) (Employee)
Brodies LLP, Edinburgh . . . . (p.845)
T: 0131 2283777
E: claire.reid@brodies.com

REID, David Peter Robertson (Jul 2005)
(Employee)
University of Strathclyde, Glasgow . . . . (p.1245)
T: 0141 548 4873
E: david.reid@strath.ac.uk

REID, David Wilkie (Jan 2005) (Employee)
Just Employment Law Ltd,
Glasgow. (p.1240)
T: 0141 3315150
E: davidreid@justemploymentlaw.co.uk

REID, Donald Bremner (Dec 1975) (Consultant)
Mitchells Roberton Ltd, Glasgow . . . . . (p.1020)
T: 0141 5523422
E: dbr@mitchells-roberton.co.uk

REID, Emma Elizabeth (Oct 2013) (Employee)
Pinsent Masons LLP, Glasgow . . . . (p.1031)
T: 0141 567 8400
E: emma.reid@pinsentmasons.com

REID, Emma Grace Cameron (Oct 2005)
(Director)
Ergo Law Limited, Edinburgh . . . . (p.869)
T: 0131 618 7007
E: emma.reid@ergolaw.co.uk

REID, Ewen Charles (Mar 2018) (Employee)
Digby Brown LLP, Inverness . . . . (p.1075)
T: 0333 200 5925
E: ewen.reid@digbybrown.co.uk

REID, Hannah Melanie (Sept 2018) (Employee)
Burness Paull LLP, Edinburgh . . . . (p.850)
T: 0131 4736000
E: hannah.reid@burnesspaull.com

REID, Isobell Ann (Mar 2003) (Partner)
Gillespie Macandrew LLP, Glasgow . . . . . (p.979)
T: 0141 4735555
E: Isobell.reid@gillespiemacandrew.co.uk

REID, Jacqualynn Margaret (Jul 2000)
(Employee)
Procurator Fiscal Service,
Edinburgh . . . . (p.1227)
T: 0300 0203168
E: jacqualynn.reid@copfs.gov.uk

REID, James Alexander Fergusson
(Dec 1975) (Partner)
Reid Cooper, Glasgow . . . . (p.1034)
T: 0141 4294656
E: jafr@reidcooper.co.uk

REID, James Robert (May 2017) (Director)
Wallace Quinn & Co Limited,
Glasgow . . . . (p.1051)
T: 0141 7713911
E: james@wallacequinn.co.uk

REID, Jamie Andrew (Oct 2015) (Associate)
Morton Fraser LLP, Edinburgh . . . . (p.891)
T: 0131 2471000
E: jamie.reid@morton-fraser.com

REID, Jennifer Kirsty (Aug 2015) (Employee)
Procurator Fiscal Service, Glasgow . . . . (p.1241)
T: 0300 020 3000
E: Jennifer.Reid@copfs.gov.uk

REID, Jill (Dec 1986) (Director)
Outside Inhouse Legal Limited,
Aberdeen . . . . (p.739)
T: 07927 560475
E: jill.reid@oilegal.com

REID, John Francis (Nov 2003) (Employee)
Scottish Power Limited, Glasgow . . . . . (p.1244)
T: 0141 6140000
E: john.reid@scottishpower.com

REID, Jordon Christopher (Jun 2017)
(Employee)
Brodies LLP, Glasgow . . . . (p.948)
T: 0141 2484672
E: jordon.reid@brodies.com

REID, Judith-Anne (Sept 2000) (Director)
Clyde Defence Lawyers Limited,
Clydebank . . . . (p.785)
T: 0141 9512211
E: jreid@clydedefencelawyers.com

REID, Kathryn Margaret (Aug 2019)
(Employee)
The Weir Group PLC, Glasgow . . . . (p.1245)
E: Katy.Reid@mail.weir

REID, Kurt John Ward (Feb 1990) (Director)
Galletly & Co Limited, Glasgow . . . . (p.978)
T: 0141 5530886
E: baillieandreid@btconnect.com

REID, Lauren Kay (Sept 2016) (Employee)
Jardine Phillips LLP, Edinburgh . . . . (p.879)
T: 0131 4466850
E: lauren.reid@jardinephillips.com

REID, Lauren Margaret Anne (Nov 2016)
(Employee)
Glasgow City Council, Glasgow . . . . . . (p.1240)
E: laurenmareid@gmail.com

REID, Lilias Carol (Oct 1985) (Partner)
KW Law, Livingston . . . . (p.1119)
T: 01506 415333
E: clr@kwlaw.co.uk

REID, Liusa (Sept 2018) (Employee)
MacRoberts LLP, Glasgow . . . . (p.1015)
T: 0141 3031100
E: liusa.reid@macroberts.com

REID, Louise Kathleen (Mar 2018) (Employee)
DLA Piper Middle East LLP, Dubai . . . . (p.1278)
T: (+971) (0)4 438 6315

REID, Lynsey Margaret (Apr 2016) (Employee)
Burges Salmon LLP, Edinburgh . . . . (p.850)
T: 0131 3142112
E: lynsey.reid@burges-salmon.com

REID, Margaret Mary (Jan 1991) (Director)
Macallans Limited, Glasgow . . . . (p.1005)
T: 0141 6131787/6474441
E: mr@macallans.co.uk

REID, Marieclaire Anne (Nov 1998) (Associate)
BTO Solicitors LLP, Glasgow . . . . (p.952)
T: 0141 2218012
E: mre@bto.co.uk

REID, Martin (Jan 1994) (Solicitor)
NO FIRM

REID, Mhairi Anne (Oct 2000) (Employee)
Scottish Government, Edinburgh . . . . . (p.1231)
T: 0131 244 0815
E: mhairi.reid@gov.scot

REID, Moira Simpson (Apr 2001) (Employee)
Aberdeenshire Council, Aberdeen . . . . . (p.1211)
T: 01467 535 704
E: mona.reid@aberdeenshire.gov.uk

REID, Nicola (Jan 2019) (Employee)
Scottish Courts and Tribunals Service,
Aberdeen . . . . (p.1214)
T: 01224 657248
E: nreid@scotcourts.gov.uk

REID, Nicola Margaret (Feb 2010) (Employee)
National Westminster Bank PLC,
Edinburgh . . . .(p.1226)
T: 0131 5568555
E: nicola.reid@natwest.com

REID, Nicola Wendy (Jun 2003) (Partner)
Ledingham Chalmers LLP,
Aberdeen . . . .(p.734)
T: 01224 408408
E: nicola.reid@ledinghamchalmers.com

REID, Nils Malcolm (May 2006) (Employee)
City Law Firm Limited, London
WC1 . . . .(p.1262)
E: Nils.Reid@stjohnlegal.co.uk

REID, Pauline Mary (Jul 1994) (Employee)
Procurator Fiscal Service,
Edinburgh . . . .(p.1227)
T: 0300 0203368
E: Pauline.Reid@copfs.gov.uk

REID, Peter Michael (Sept 2007) (Employee)
Procurator Fiscal Service, Glasgow . . . .(p.1241)
T: 0844 5614800
E: Peter.Reid@copfs.gov.uk

REID, Robert William (Nov 2007) (Partner)
McGovern Reid Court Lawyers,
Wishaw . . . .(p.1182)
T: 01698 359550
E: br@mcgovernreid.co.uk

REID, Thomas Graham (Oct 1986) (Employee)
Charles Wood & Son Limited,
Kirkcaldy . . . .(p.1103)
T: 01592 261621
E: graham@charleswoodlaw.co.uk

REID, Walter Macarthur, WS (Nov 1969)
(Consultant)
T.F. Reid & Donaldson, Paisley . . . .(p.1141)
T: 0141 8897531

REID, William Henry (Jun 2010) (Employee)
DLA Piper Scotland LLP, Edinburgh . . . .(p.863)
T: 0131 2425009
E: william.reid@dlapiper.com

REID, Zeenat Yasmeen (Apr 2021) (Employee)
Blackadders LLP, Dundee . . . .(p.805)
T: 01382 229222
E: zeenat.reid@blackadders.co.uk

REILLY, Anna (Sept 2021) (Employee)
Brodies LLP, Edinburgh . . . .(p.845)
T: 0131 2283777
E: anna.reilly@brodies.com

REILLY, Catherine Margaret (May 1995)
(Associate)
Brodies LLP, Glasgow . . . .(p.948)
T: 0141 2484672
E: catherine.reilly@brodies.com

REILLY, Claudia Jessica Rose (Aug 2019)
(Employee)
Thompson Family Law, Glasgow . . . . .(p.1046)
T: 0141 4046575
E: claudia@tflaw.co.uk

REILLY, Gabrielle Anna (Oct 2017) (Employee)
Miller Samuel Hill Brown LLP,
Glasgow . . . .(p.1020)
T: 0141 2211919
E: gar@mshblegal.com

REILLY, Gillian Sarah (Dec 2009) (Associate)
KW Law, Livingston . . . .(p.1119)
T: 01506 635533
E: gillianr@kwlaw.co.uk

REILLY, Hazel Aileen (Aug 2012) (Employee)
Scottish Government, Edinburgh . . . . .(p.1231)
T: 0131 244 0815
E: Hazel.Reilly@gov.scot

REILLY, James (Jan 1993) (Solicitor)
NO FIRM

REILLY, John Alan (Oct 1990) (Employee)
Raytheon Systems Limited,
Glenrothes . . . .(p.1246)
T: 01592 762336
E: john.reilly@raytheon.co.uk

REILLY, Justine Lianne (Sept 2011) (Employee)
DWF LLP, Glasgow . . . .(p.973)
T: 0141 2288000
E: Justine.Reilly@dwf.law

REILLY, Kieran John (Mar 2017) (Employee)
Anderson Strathern LLP, Edinburgh . . . .(p.839)
T: 0131 2707700
E: Kieran.reilly@andersonstrathern.co.uk

REILLY, Kirstie Courtney (Mar 2021)
(Employee)
Grigor & Young LLP, Elgin . . . .(p.916)
T: 01343 544077
E: kirstie@grigor-young.co.uk

REILLY, Laurence Vincent (Oct 1980) (Director)
Clark Boyle Limited, Glasgow . . . .(p.960)
T: 0141 2272200
E: Laurence.Reilly@clarkboyle.co.uk

REILLY, Lisa Marie (Mar 2018) (Employee)
Brodies LLP, Aberdeen . . . .(p.723)
T: 01224 392242
E: lisa.reilly@brodies.com

REILLY, Lynne Marie (Sept 2014) (Employee)
Procurator Fiscal Service,
Edinburgh . . . .(p.1227)
T: 0300 0203168
E: Lynne.Reilly@copfs.gov.uk

REILLY, Michael Francis (Jul 2018) (Employee)
Brodies LLP, Glasgow . . . .(p.948)
T: 0141 2484672
E: mike.reilly@brodies.com

RENFREW, Bruce Norman (Aug 1991) (Partner)
Thorntons Law LLP, Perth . . . .(p.1151)
  T: 01738 621212
  E: brenfrew@thorntons-law.co.uk

RENFREW, Pamela Jean (Mar 1995) (Employee)
McCash & Hunter LLP, Perth . . . .(p.1149)
  T: 01738 620451
  E: pamelarenfrew@mccash.co.uk

RENNET, Fiona (Sept 2011) (Employee)
Directorate of Army Legal Services,
  Andover . . . .(p.1258)
  T: 01980 615013

RENNET, Miriam Fraser (Apr 1987) (Employee)
Lindsays LLP, Dundee . . . .(p.814)
  T: 01382 346 404
  E: miriamrennet@lindsays.co.uk

RENNIE, Alison (Jul 2000) (Employee)
Scottish Courts and Tribunals Service,
  Perth . . . .(p.1253)
  T: 01738 492932
  E: arennie@scotcourts.gov.uk

RENNIE, Alison Claire (Sept 2003) (Employee)
Aberdeen Corporate Services Limited,
  Edinburgh . . . .(p.1220)
  T: 0131 245 7508
  E: alison.rennie@abrdn.com

RENNIE, Bruce Peter (Jun 2017) (Employee)
Allen & Overy LLP, London E1 . . . .(p.1261)
  T: 020 3088 0000
  E: Bruce.Rennie@AllenOvery.com

RENNIE, Christopher Gavin (Oct 2016)
  (Employee)
DLA Piper Scotland LLP, Edinburgh . . . .(p.863)
  T: 08700 111111
  E: Chris.Rennie@dlapiper.com

RENNIE, David Alan (Dec 1976) (Consultant)
Stronachs LLP, Aberdeen . . . .(p.744)
  T: 01224 845845
  E: david.rennie@stronachs.com

RENNIE, James Stewart (Mar 1989) (Partner)
Rennie McInnes LLP, Milngavie . . . . . .(p.1124)
  T: 0141 5629540
  E: stewart@renniemcinnes.co.uk

RENNIE, Jane Charlotte (Oct 2018) (Employee)
Procurator Fiscal Service,
  Livingston . . . .(p.1250)
  T: 0300 020 3696
  E: Jane.Rennie@copfs.gov.uk

RENNIE, Jennifer Anne (Jan 1983) (Associate)
R. & R.S. Mearns, Glasgow . . . .(p.1018)
  T: 0141 6326162
  E: jarmearns@gmail.com

RENNIE, Laura Katherine (Sept 2017)
  (Employee)
Shepherd and Wedderburn LLP,
  Edinburgh . . . .(p.900)
  T: 0131 2289900
  E: laura.rennie@shepwedd.com

RENNIE, Lesley Louise (Jul 2010) (Employee)
Law At Work Incorporating Empire,
  Aberdeen . . . .(p.1213)
  T: 01224 701383
  E: lesleyrennie@worknest.com

RENNIE, Rachel Annette (Sept 2011)
  (Employee)
Spirit Production (Services) Limited,
  Aberdeen . . . .(p.1214)
  T: 01224 415000
  E: rachel.rennie@spirit-energy.com

RENNIE, Richard Veitch (Oct 1994) (Partner)
Burness Paull LLP, Edinburgh . . . .(p.850)
  T: 0131 4736000
  E: Richard.Rennie@burnesspaull.com

RENNIE, Scott (Jul 2012) (Employee)
Raeburn Christie Clark & Wallace LLP,
  Aberdeen . . . .(p.741)
  T: 01224 332400
  E: scott.rennie@raeburns.co.uk

RENNIE, Thomas George (Jan 1971)
  (Consultant)
Burnett & Reid LLP, Aberdeen . . . .(p.726)
  T: 01224 644333
  E: TGRennie@burnett-reid.co.uk

RENNIE, William Jonathan (Oct 2005) (Partner)
TLT LLP, Glasgow . . . .(p.1048)
  T: 0333 006 0400
  E: Jonathan.Rennie@TLTsolicitors.com

RENNIE, William Pirie (Dec 1991) (Partner)
R. Bruce & Co., Arbroath . . . .(p.757)
  T: 01241 430660
  E: wrennie@bruce-co.co.uk

RENTON, Andrew Lamont (Oct 1986)
  (Director)
Castletown Law Limited,
  Edinburgh . . . .(p.853)
  T: 0131 2403880
  E: andrew.renton@castletownlaw.com

RENTON, Michele Louise (Oct 1992)
  (Employee)
Smith & Grant, Leven . . . .(p.1116)
  T: 01333 423441
  E: michele@smithandgrant.com

RENUCCI, Demi Marie (Aug 2019) (Employee)
Burness Paull LLP, Glasgow . . . .(p.954)
  T: 0141 2484933
  E: demi.renucci@burnesspaull.com

RENWICK, Lisa Kathryn (Apr 2005) (Employee)
Shepherd and Wedderburn LLP, London
    EC2 . . . .(p.1268)
    T: 020 74294900
    E: Lisa.Renwick@shepwedd.com

REOCH, Dawn (Oct 2001) (Partner)
Burness Paull LLP, Edinburgh . . . .(p.850)
    T: 0131 4736000
    E: dawn.reoch@burnesspaull.com

RETTIE, Christopher Graham Ross
    (Nov 2010) (Employee)
TAQA Bratani Limited, Aberdeen . . . . .(p.1214)
    T: 01224 275275
    E: Chris.Rettie@taqaglobal.com

REVILLE, Lucy Anne (Sept 2021) (Employee)
Dickson Minto, London EC2 . . . .(p.1263)
    T: 020 76284455
    E: lucy.reville@dmws.com

REVILLE, Philip (Mar 1983) (Partner)
Inheritance Legal, Glasgow . . . .(p.989)
    T: 0800 404 5962
    E: philreville@inheritancelegal.com

REYNOLDS, Anthony Vincent (Sept 2002)
    (Partner)
TLT LLP, Edinburgh . . . .(p.908)
    T: 0333 006 0500
    E: tony.reynolds@tltsolicitors.com

REYNOLDS, Donna (Sept 2004) (Partner)
Blackadders LLP, Edinburgh . . . .(p.843)
    T: 0131 2228000
    E: donna.reynolds@blackadders.co.uk

REYNOLDS, Lindsey Ann (Jun 2005) (Employee)
Equality and Human Rights Commission,
    Glasgow . . . .(p.1239)
    T: 0141 228 5967
    E: Lindsey.Reynolds@equalityhumanrights.com

REYNOLDS, Paul Henry (Sept 1998) (Employee)
Procurator Fiscal Service, Paisley . . . . . .(p.1252)
    T: 0141 8875225
    E: paul.reynolds@copfs.gov.uk

RHODES, James Scullion (Oct 1996) (Associate)
McClure Collins Limited, Glasgow . . . .(p.1007)
    T: 0141 4237181
    E: jim@mcclurecollins.com

RHODES, Jordan Nathan (Nov 2019)
    (Employee)
Paul Hastings (Europe) LLP, London
    EC2 . . . .(p.1267)
    T: 020 3023 5100
    E: jordanrhodes@paulhastings.com

RHYND, Shirley-Ann (Aug 2004) (Employee)
Glasgow City Council, Glasgow . . . . . .(p.1239)
    T: 0141 2874843
    E: shirley.rhynd@ced.glasgow.gov.uk

RIACH, Ian Hamish (Nov 1995) (Associate)
MacRoberts LLP, Edinburgh . . . .(p.887)
    T: 0131 2295046
    E: ian.riach@macroberts.com

RIAZ, Ziqyia (Sept 2006) (Associate)
Campbell & McCartney, Glasgow . . . . .(p.956)
    T: 0141 423 2222
    E: zr@patrickcampbellsolicitors.co.uk

RICE, Claire (Sept 2005) (Associate)
Brodies LLP, Glasgow . . . .(p.948)
    T: 0141 2484672
    E: claire.rice@brodies.com

RICE, Helen Mary (Sept 2001) (Employee)
Lloyds Banking Group Plc,
    Edinburgh . . . .(p.1224)
    T: (0131) 442 9579
    E: helen.rice@lloydsbanking.com

RICE, James Alexander (Sept 2005) (Associate)
Pinsent Masons LLP, Edinburgh . . . .(p.895)
    T: 0131 777 7000
    E: James.Rice@pinsentmasons.com

RICHARD, Tom Adam (Oct 2017) (Employee)
Burness Paull LLP, Edinburgh . . . .(p.850)
    T: 0131 4736000
    E: tom.richard@burnesspaull.com

RICHARDS, Carolyn Margaret (Oct 1991)
    (Associate)
Burness Paull LLP, Aberdeen . . . .(p.724)
    T: 01224 621621
    E: Carolyn.Richards@burnesspaull.com

RICHARDS, Eleanor Ramage Macdonald
    (Sept 1995) (Employee)
Glasgow City Council, Glasgow . . . . . .(p.1239)
    T: 0141 2875672
    E: eleanor.richards@glasgow.gov.uk

RICHARDS, Katherine Victoria (Nov 2012)
    (Employee)
Scottish Government, Edinburgh . . . . .(p.1231)
    T: 0131 2441403
    E: katy.richards@gov.scot

RICHARDS, Mark (Feb 1999) (Employee)
Scottish Government, Edinburgh . . . . .(p.1231)
    T: 0131 244 0815
    E: mark.richards@gov.scot

RICHARDS, Sheonagh Lesley (Nov 1989)
    (Partner)
Anderson Strathern LLP, Edinburgh . . . .(p.839)
    T: 0131 2707700
    E: sheonagh.richards@andersonstrathern.co.uk

RICHARDS, Simon James Barr (Sept 2008)
    (Partner)
Digby Brown LLP, Edinburgh . . . .(p.862)
    T: 0333 200 5925
    E: simon.richards@digbybrown.co.uk

RICHARDSON, Amanda Frances (Jun 2011)
(Partner)
McAndrew & Richardson,
Stranraer ....(p.1171)
T: 01776 704324
E: mail@mcandrewandrichardson.co.uk

RICHARDSON, Andrew John (Sept 1994)
(Employee)
Procurator Fiscal Service, Glasgow ....(p.1243)
T: (0300) 020 2944
E: andrew.richardson@copfs.gov.uk

RICHARDSON, Claire Lynn (Dec 2003)
(Employee)
Angus Council, Forfar ....(p.1237)
T: 01307 476228
E: richardsonC@angus.gov.uk

RICHARDSON, Jemma Rachel (Mar 2011)
(Partner)
Anderson Strathern LLP, Edinburgh ....(p.839)
T: 0131 2707700
E: jemma.richardson@andersonstrathern.co.uk

RICHARDSON, John Somerville (Dec 1987)
(Employee)
Procurator Fiscal Service, Dundee .....(p.1218)
T: 01382 342559
E: john.richardson@copfs.gov.uk

RICHARDSON, Kendra (Sept 2011) (Employee)
Brodies LLP, Glasgow ....(p.948)
T: 0141 428 3337
E: kendra.richardson@brodies.com

RICHARDSON, Lewis Robert John
(Oct 2011) (Employee)
BTO Solicitors LLP, Edinburgh ....(p.849)
T: 0131 2222939
E: lri@bto.co.uk

RICHARDSON, Marian Isabel Campbell
(Dec 1999) (Employee)
The Scottish Parliament, Edinburgh ...(p.1235)
T: 0131 348 6575
E: marian.richardson@parliament.scot

RICHARDSON, Neal Scott (May 2004) (Partner)
Brodies LLP, Aberdeen..............(p.723)
T: 01224 392242
E: neal.richardson@brodies.com

RICHARDSON, Sophie Elizabeth (Nov 2021)
(Employee)
Lindsays LLP, Glasgow.............(p.1001)
T: 0141 2216551
E: SophieRichardson@lindsays.co.uk

RICHARDSON, Wendy Margaret (Jan 1994)
(Employee)
West Lothian Council, Livingston .....(p.1250)
T: 01506 280000
E: wendy.richardson@westlothian.gov.uk

RICHMOND, Alison (Oct 1988) (Employee)
Shepherd and Wedderburn LLP,
Glasgow ....(p.1039)
T: 0141 5669900
E: alison.richmond@shepwedd.com

RICHMOND, Hannah Louise (Sept 2009)
(Partner)
Richmond Clark, Glasgow ....(p.1035)
T: 0141 9549550
E: h.richmond@richmondclark.co.uk

RICHMOND, Hugh Kelvin Murray
(Nov 1985) (Associate)
Ledingham Chalmers LLP,
Aberdeen ....(p.734)
T: 01224 408408
E: kelvin.richmond@ledinghamchalmers.com

RICHMOND, Karyn Anne (Sept 2016)
(Employee)
Stronachs LLP, Inverness ....(p.1082)
T: 01463 663382
E: karyn.richmond@stronachs.com

RICHMOND, Lynn (Nov 2005) (Partner)
BTO Solicitors LLP, Edinburgh ....(p.849)
T: 0131 2222939
E: lyr@bto.co.uk

RICHMOND, Susan Elizabeth (Dec 1980)
(Employee)
Ward & Co (Perth) Ltd, Perth ....(p.1152)
T: 01738 638461
E: SRichmond_WardCo@yahoo.co.uk

RICKERBY, Judith (Oct 2002) (Employee)
National Westminster Bank PLC,
Edinburgh ....(p.1226)
T: (0131) 626 2925
E: Judith.rickerby@natwest.com

RICKETT, Charles Christopher Hugh
(May 1993) (Partner)
Andrew Haddon & Crowe, Hawick....(p.1070)
T: 01450 372738
E: charlesrickett@ahcsolicitors.co.uk

RIDDELL, Lynne Elaine (Mar 2007) (Employee)
Jamieson Law Ltd, Giffnock ....(p.934)
T: 07703 569279
E: lynne@jamiesonlaw.legal

RIDDELL, Vivien Margaret (Oct 2009)
(Employee)
TC Young LLP, Edinburgh ....(p.914)
T: 0131 2207660
E: vmr@tcyoung.co.uk

RIDDIOUGH, Ralph Leigh (Feb 1999) (Director)
Holmes Mackillop Limited,
Glasgow....................(p.986)
T: 0141 226 4942
E: rriddiough@homack.co.uk

RIDLEY, Adam Porter (Feb 2021) (Employee)
Addleshaw Goddard LLP,
Edinburgh . . . .(p.835)
T: 0131 2282400
E: adam.ridley@addleshawgoddard.com

RIDLEY, David (Oct 2016) (Employee)
Womble Bond Dickinson (UK) LLP, Newcastle
Upon Tyne . . . .(p.1270)
T: 0345 4150000
E: david.ridley@wbd-uk.com

RIDLEY, Jacqueline Sara (Sept 2004) (Associate)
Blacklocks, Edinburgh . . . .(p.844)
T: 0131 5553888
E: jsr@blacklocks.co.uk

RIISE, Jan-Robert (Nov 1988) (Employee)
Shetland Islands Council, Lerwick . . . . .(p.1250)
T: 01595 744550
E: jan.riise@shetland.gov.uk

RIISE, Sophie Jade (Dec 2019) (Employee)
Anderson Strathern LLP, Edinburgh . . . .(p.839)
T: 0131 2707700
E: sophie.riise@andersonstrathern.co.uk

RILEY, Amy Martha (Jul 2017) (Employee)
Plexus Law LLP, Edinburgh . . . .(p.897)
T: 0344 2454802
E: amy.riley@plexuslaw.co.uk

RINALDI, Nicola Suzanne (Oct 2002)
(Employee)
National Health Service Scotland,
Edinburgh . . . .(p.1225)
T: 0131 275 7024
E: nicola.rinaldi@nhs.scot

RINALDI, Stefano Carlo Romeo (Jan 2001)
(Employee)
National Health Service Scotland,
Edinburgh . . . .(p.1225)
T: 0131 2757924
E: stefano.rinaldi@nhs.scot

RING-MACLEOD, Charlotte Claire
(Sept 2009) (Employee)
Standard Life Assets and Employee Services
Limited, Edinburgh . . . .(p.1234)
T: 0131 2457508
E: charlotte_ring-macleod@standardlife.com

RINTOUL, Lynsey (Apr 2007) (Partner)
Morgans, Dunfermline . . . .(p.824)
T: 01383 620222
E: lynseyrintoul@morganlaw.co.uk

RIPLEY, Peter Lawrence (Aug 2012) (Employee)
Premier Oil UK Limited, Aberdeen . . . .(p.1213)
T: 01224 618900
E: pripley@premier-oil.com

RISK, Robert Neil (Dec 1982) (Partner)
Anderson Strathern LLP, Lerwick . . . . .(p.1112)
T: 01595 695262
E: neil.risk@andersonstrathern.co.uk

RITCHIE, Ailsa (Sept 1995) (Partner)
CMS Cameron McKenna Nabarro Olswang LLP,
Glasgow. . . . .(p.962)
T: 0141 2222200
E: Ailsa.Ritchie@cms-cmno.com

RITCHIE, Amanda Denise (Oct 2010)
(Employee)
EthosEnergy (GBR) Limited,
Aberdeen . . . .(p.1212)
T: 01224 367206
E: Amanda.Ritchie@ethosenergygroup.com

RITCHIE, Andrew Alan (Feb 1988) (Employee)
RSB Lindsays, Dundee . . . .(p.818)
T: 01382 224112
E: andrewritchie@lindsays.co.uk

RITCHIE, Ann Margaret (Jun 1994) (Employee)
Moir and Sweeney LLP, Glasgow . . . . .(p.1021)
T: 0141 4292724

RITCHIE, Catriona (May 2021) (Employee)
CMS Cameron McKenna Nabarro Olswang LLP,
Edinburgh . . . .(p.856)
T: 0131 2288000
E: catriona.ritchie@cms-cmno.com

RITCHIE, Christopher Neil (Oct 2017)
(Employee)
Digby Brown LLP, Dundee . . . .(p.808)
T: 3332005925
E: chris.ritchie@digbybrown.co.uk

RITCHIE, David Alexander (Sept 2016)
(Employee)
William Grant & Sons Ltd., Bellshill . . .(p.1215)
T: 01698 843843
E: David.Ritchie@wgrant.com

RITCHIE, David Morrice (Dec 1982) (Partner)
F.T. & D.C. Wallace, Leven . . . .(p.1116)
T: 01333 423804
E: david@ft-dc-wallace.co.uk

RITCHIE, Denise Kathryn (Oct 2004)
(Employee)
The Medical & Dental Defence Union of
Scotland, Glasgow . . . .(p.1245)
T: 0845 2702034
E: dritchie@mddus.com

RITCHIE, Dominic (Sept 2014) (Associate)
Jones Whyte LLP, Glasgow. . . . .(p.993)
T: 0141 375 1222
E: dominic.ritchie@joneswhyte.co.uk

RITCHIE, Emma Jane (Aug 1999) (Employee)
Procurator Fiscal Service, Glasgow . . . .(p.1241)
T: 0300 0203000
E: emma.ritchie@copfs.gov.uk

RITCHIE, Graham Cordiner (Dec 1993)
(Partner)
Sneddon Morrison, Bathgate . . . .(p.772)
T: 01506 635590
E: gr@sneddons-ssc.co.uk

RITCHIE, Ian David (Aug 1977) (Employee)
Law Society of Scotland,
Edinburgh . . . .(p.1224)
T: 0131 2267411
E: ianritchie@lawscot.org.uk

RITCHIE, James (Oct 2018) (Employee)
Burness Paull LLP, Glasgow . . . .(p.954)
T: 0141 2484933
E: james.ritchie@burnesspaull.com

RITCHIE, Jennifer Elaine (Jan 2015) (Employee)
Dundee City Council, Dundee . . . .(p.1217)
T: 01382 434000
E: jen.ritchie@dundeecity.gov.uk

RITCHIE, Joanne Mary (Feb 2019) (Employee)
Procurator Fiscal Service, Perth. . . . . . .(p.1253)
T: 01738 637272
E: joanne.ritchie@copfs.gov.uk

RITCHIE, Karla Joy (Dec 2015) (Employee)
CMS Cameron McKenna Nabarro Olswang LLP,
Aberdeen . . . .(p.727)
T: 01224 622002
E: Karla.Ritchie@cms-cmno.com

RITCHIE, Kerry Christine Allan (Jul 2017)
(Employee)
Fulton's, Glasgow . . . .(p.1010)
T: 0141 6322248
E: kritchie@fultonslaw.co.uk

RITCHIE, Kerry Louise (Oct 2001) (Employee)
National Health Service Scotland,
Edinburgh . . . .(p.1225)
T: 0131 2757800
E: kerry.ritchie@nhs.scot

RITCHIE, Kirsteen Joan (Jul 2015) (Employee)
Philpott Platt Niblett & Wight,
Clydebank . . . .(p.785)
T: 0141 9529545
E: kritchie@ppnw.co.uk

RITCHIE, Lewis David Charles (Jun 2015)
(Associate)
Shoosmiths LLP, Glasgow . . . .(p.1040)
T: 0370 086 8300
E: lewis.ritchie@shoosmiths.co.uk

RITCHIE, Mhari Elizabeth (Aug 2017)
(Employee)
Brown & McRae LLP, Fraserburgh . . . . .(p.930)
T: 01346 514761
E: m.ritchie@brown-mcrae.co.uk

RITCHIE, Scott Paul (Sept 2004) (Partner)
Shepherd and Wedderburn LLP,
Edinburgh . . . .(p.900)
T: 0131 2289900
E: scott.ritchie@shepwedd.com

RITCHIE, Steven William (Oct 2009) (Employee)
DJP Solicitors, Aberdeen . . . .(p.730)
T: 01224 590053
E: sr@djpsolicitors.com

ROACH, Natalie Susan (Jun 2013) (Employee)
Andersonbain LLP, Aberdeen . . . .(p.721)
T: 01224 456789
E: Nroach@andersonbain.co.uk

ROACH, Olivia Christine Alexis (Aug 2006)
(Employee)
Facebook UK Limited, London
NW1 . . . .(p.1264)
E: oliviaroach@fb.com

ROARTY, Lesley Anne (Oct 2004) (Associate)
MacRoberts LLP, Edinburgh . . . .(p.887)
T: 0131 2295046

ROBB, Andrew Joseph Patrick (Oct 1990)
(Partner)
Stevenson & Marshall LLP,
Dunfermline . . . .(p.825)
T: 01383 721141
E: ajpr@stevenson-marshall.co.uk

ROBB, Eloise Ann (Sept 2006) (Employee)
University of Dundee, Dundee . . . .(p.1219)
T: (44) (0)1382 385340
E: ERobb001@dundee.ac.uk

ROBB, Fiona A. (Nov 1988) (Employee)
Law Society of Scotland,
Edinburgh . . . .(p.1224)
T: 0131 2267411
E: FionaA.Robb@lawscot.org.uk

ROBB, Fiona Jane (Nov 1990) (Employee)
Law Society of Scotland,
Edinburgh . . . .(p.1224)
T: 0131 2267411
E: fionaj.robb@lawscot.org.uk

ROBB, James Anthony (Aug 2011) (Associate)
BTO Solicitors LLP, Edinburgh . . . .(p.849)
T: 0131 2222939
E: jro@bto.co.uk

ROBB, John Andrew (Jan 1984) (Partner)
Fleetwood & Robb, Inverness . . . .(p.1076)
T: 01463 226232
E: John@fleetwoodandrobb.co.uk

ROBB, Katherine Jane (Nov 1997) (Employee)
East Renfrewshire Council, Giffnock . . .(p.1237)
T: 0141 5773000
E: katherine.robb@eastrenfrewshire.gov.uk

ROBB, Laura Elizabeth (Aug 2020) (Employee)
JHS Law, Dumfries . . . .(p.801)
T: 01387 739000
E: laura.robb@jhslaw.co.uk

ROBB, Lesley Diane (Jan 1996) (Partner)
Murphy, Robb + Sutherland,
Glasgow. . . . .(p.1025)
T: 0141 4182931
E: lr@murphyrobbsutherland.co.uk

ROBB, Neal Euan (Feb 2017) (Employee)
Gray & Co., Glasgow . . . .(p.981)
T: 0141 9467777

ROBB, Neil Beresford (Oct 1991) (Partner)
Blackadders LLP, Aberdeen . . . .(p.722)
T: 01224 588913
E: neil.robb@blackadders.co.uk

ROBB, Peigi Carrick (Jun 1987) (Partner)
Carrick Robb, Kilbirnie. . . . .(p.1092)
T: 01505 682408
E: carrickrobb@btconnect.com

ROBB, Susan (Oct 2005) (Employee)
Scottish Government, Edinburgh . . . . .(p.1231)
T: 0131 244 0815
E: susan.robb@gov.scot

ROBBINS, Mark John (Jan 2021) (Employee)
Bruce, Short & Co., Dundee . . . .(p.806)
T: 01382 223400

ROBERTON, James Gerard (Mar 1985) (Partner)
James G. Roberton, Glasgow . . . .(p.1036)
T: 0141 4451150
E: jimgroberton@msn.com

ROBERTS, Amy Drew (Sept 2017) (Solicitor)
CMS Cameron McKenna Nabarro Olswang LLP,
Glasgow. . . . .(p.962)
T: 0141 2222200
E: amy.roberts@cms-cmno.com

ROBERTS, Craig Davidson (Oct 2008) (Partner)
Dickson Minto, Edinburgh . . . .(p.861)
T: 0131 2001563
E: craig.roberts@dmws.com

ROBERTS, Douglas Andrew (Dec 1999)
(Partner)
Lindsays LLP, Edinburgh . . . .(p.882)
T: 0131 2291212
E: DouglasRoberts@lindsays.co.uk

ROBERTS, John Simpson (Jun 2002) (Director)
Austin Lafferty Limited, East
Kilbride . . . .(p.830)
T: 01355 263777
E: jroberts@laffertylaw.com

ROBERTS, Melanie (Sept 2009) (Director)
Melrose & Porteous Limited, Duns . . . . .(p.829)
T: 01361 882 752
E: mel.roberts@melroseporteous.co.uk

ROBERTS, Neil John (Jul 1990) (Employee)
Shell International Limited,
Aberdeen . . . .(p.1214)
T: 01224 882000
E: n.roberts@shell.com

ROBERTS, Nicola Louise (Nov 2009) (Employee)
Murray Beith Murray, Edinburgh . . . . . .(p.893)
T: 0131 2251200
E: nicola.roberts@murraybeith.co.uk

ROBERTS, Rebecca Jane (Sept 2015)
(Employee)
Burness Paull LLP, Edinburgh . . . .(p.850)
T: 0131 4736000
E: Rebecca.Roberts@burnesspaull.com

ROBERTS, Valerie Sandra (Sept 1994)
(Employee)
Parabis Scotland Limited,
Edinburgh . . . .(p.895)
T: 0131 3221268
E: val.roberts@friends-legal.co.uk

ROBERTS, Winston Alexander Montague
(Jul 2014) (Associate)
Harper Macleod LLP, Glasgow . . . .(p.983)
T: 0141 2218888
E: winston.roberts@harpermacleod.co.uk

ROBERTSON, Alan William (Feb 2006)
(Employee)
MBS Solicitors, Edinburgh . . . .(p.889)
T: 0131 3374100
E: alan@mbssolicitors.co.uk

ROBERTSON, Alexander John Ritchie
(Mar 2021) (Employee)
Gillespie Macandrew LLP, Glasgow. . . . .(p.979)
T: 0141 4735555
E:
alexander.robertson@gillespiemacandrew.co.uk

ROBERTSON, Alexander Ritchie (Jul 1983)
(Partner)
Robertson Smith, Dundee . . . .(p.818)
T: 01382 226602
E: r.robertson@rsdundee.f9.co.uk

ROBERTSON, Alexandra Dyce (Nov 2009)
(Employee)
Allan McDougall McQueen LLP,
Edinburgh . . . .(p.837)
T: 0131 2252121
E: alexandrarobertson@allanmcdougall.co.uk

ROBERTSON, Amy Jennifer (Oct 2020)
(Employee)
Ormistons Law Practice Limited,
Glenrothes . . . .(p.1057)
T: 0800 7810413
E: arobertson@ormistonslaw.co.uk

ROBERTSON, Andrew John (Oct 2019)
(Employee)
Turcan Connell, Edinburgh . . . .(p.908)
T: 0131 2288111
E: andrew.robertson@turcanconnell.com

ROBERTSON, Angela (Sept 2019) (Employee)
Thorntons Law LLP, Forfar . . . .(p.927)
T: 01307 466886
E: arobertson@thorntons-law.co.uk

ROBERTSON, Anna (Sept 2016) (Employee)
Procurator Fiscal Service,
Edinburgh . . . .(p.1229)
T: 0300 0203000
E: anna.robertson@copfs.gov.uk

ROBERTSON, Anne Macdonald (Jul 1978)
(Partner)
J.E.P. Robertson & Son, Stromness . . . . (p.1173)
T: 01856 850232
E: enquiries@jeprobertson.co.uk

ROBERTSON, Becky Elizabeth (Jan 2017)
(Employee)
Glasgow City Council, Glasgow . . . . . . (p.1239)
T: 0141 2872000
E: Becky.Robertson@glasgow.gov.uk

ROBERTSON, Blair Andrew (Jun 2011)
(Employee)
J. Myles & Co., Dundee . . . . (p.817)
T: 01382 204625
E: blairrobertson@jmylessols.co.uk

ROBERTSON, Bruce Gordon (Oct 1980)
(Partner)
Raeburn Christie Clark & Wallace LLP,
Aberdeen . . . . (p.741)
T: 01224 332400
E: bruce.robertson@raeburns.co.uk

ROBERTSON, Calum Alexander (Mar 2007)
(Employee)
Nintendo Europe GmbH, Frankfurt am
Main . . . . (p.1273)
E: calum.robertson@nintendo.de

ROBERTSON, Carrie (Dec 2019) (Employee)
Castle Water, Blairgowrie . . . . (p.1216)
T: 01250 718700
E: Carrie.Davidson@castlewater.co.uk

ROBERTSON, Catriona Morag (May 1989)
(Employee)
National Health Service Scotland,
Edinburgh . . . . (p.1225)
T: 0131 2757800
E: Catriona.Robertson2@nhs.scot

ROBERTSON, Chantelle Rachel (Sept 2018)
(Employee)
Digby Brown LLP, Glasgow . . . . (p.970)
T: 0333 200 5925
E: Chantelle.Robertson@digbybrown.co.uk

ROBERTSON, Ciaran (Jun 2015) (Employee)
Ellis Whittam Limited, Glasgow . . . . . . (p.1239)
T: (0345) 226 8393
E: ciaranrobertson@elliswhittam.com

ROBERTSON, Colin John (Oct 2004) (Partner)
Shepherd and Wedderburn LLP,
Glasgow . . . . (p.1039)
T: 0141 5669900
E: colin.robertson@shepwedd.com

ROBERTSON, Corinne (Jan 1989) (Employee)
Miller Homes Limited, Edinburgh . . . . . (p.1225)
T: 0870 336 5130
E: Corinne.Robertson@miller.co.uk

ROBERTSON, D H, BSc MRICS (Partner &
Director)
J & E Shepherd, Perth . . . . (p.1356)
T: (01738) 638188

ROBERTSON, Dawn Elizabeth (Oct 1998)
(Director)
Rooney Nimmo Limited,
Edinburgh . . . . (p.899)
T: 0131 220 9570
E: dawn.robertson@rooneynimmo.co.uk

ROBERTSON, Deborah Alison (Sept 1991)
(Employee)
Perth & Kinross Council, Perth . . . . (p.1253)
T: 01738 475 495
E: debbierobertson@pkc.gov.uk

ROBERTSON, Donald (Mar 1982) (Associate)
BTO Solicitors LLP, Glasgow . . . . (p.952)
T: 0141 2218012
E: dr@bto.co.uk

ROBERTSON, Edward Graham (Oct 2005)
(Employee)
Bruce McCormack Limited,
Motherwell . . . . (p.1127)
T: 01698 260033
E: admin@brucethelawyers.co.uk

ROBERTSON, Eilidh Catriona (Dec 2017)
(Employee)
Lindsays LLP, Edinburgh . . . . (p.882)
T: 0131 2291212
E: eilidhrobertson@lindsays.co.uk

ROBERTSON, Eilidh Fiona (Jul 2018) (Employee)
Burness Paull LLP, Edinburgh . . . . (p.850)
T: 0131 4736000
E: eilidh.robertson@burnesspaull.com

ROBERTSON, Eilidh Lesley (Jun 2012)
(Employee)
Procurator Fiscal Service, Dundee . . . . . (p.1218)
T: 01382 342559
E: Eilidh.Robertson@copfs.gov.uk

ROBERTSON, Elaine Mary (Mar 1983) (Partner)
Young, Robertson & Co., Thurso . . . . . (p.1174)
T: 01847 893247
E: EMR@youngrob.co.uk

ROBERTSON, Elizabeth (Aug 2012) (Employee)
Baillie Gifford & Co, Edinburgh . . . . . . (p.1220)
T: 0131 2752000
E: Elizabeth.Robertson@bailliegifford.com

ROBERTSON, Emma Jane (Nov 2003)
(Associate)
Shepherd and Wedderburn LLP,
Aberdeen . . . . (p.742)
T: 01224 621166
E: emma.robertson@shepwedd.com

ROBERTSON, Euan (Oct 2016) (Employee)
Digby Brown LLP, Dundee . . . .(p.808)
T: 3332005925
E: euan.robertson@digbybrown.co.uk

ROBERTSON, Euan David (Mar 1989) (Partner)
Euan Robertson, Glasgow . . . .(p.1036)
T: 0141 4237389
E: euanrobertsonsolicitors@gmail.com

ROBERTSON, Ewan Campbell (Nov 1994)
(Partner)
Pinsent Masons, Melbourne . . . .(p.1257)
T: +61 399 092 500
E: ewan.robertson@pinsentmasons.com

ROBERTSON, Ewen Graham (Dec 2002)
(Employee)
Fife Council, Glenrothes . . . .(p.1246)
T: 03451 550000
E: ewen.robertson@fife.gov.uk

ROBERTSON, Fiona Janet, WS (Dec 1980)
(Employee)
Office of the Advocate General,
Edinburgh . . . .(p.1227)
T: 0131 2441639
E: fiona.robertson@advocategeneral.gov.uk

ROBERTSON, Frazer Thomas (Mar 2021)
(Associate)
Shoosmiths LLP, Glasgow . . . .(p.1040)
T: 0370 086 8300
E: Frazer.Robertson@shoosmiths.co.uk

ROBERTSON, Georgina Marie (Sept 2008)
(Partner)
Masson Glennie LLP, Peterhead . . . . . .(p.1154)
T: 01779 474271
E: marie.robertson@massonglennie.co.uk

ROBERTSON, Gordon Thomas Hughes
(Sept 1978) (Partner)
Murray, Gillies & Wilson, Irvine . . . . . .(p.1087)
T: 01294 278355
E: gr@murraygillies.co.uk

ROBERTSON, Grazia Maria (Sept 1984)
(Director)
L & G Robertson Limited, Glasgow . . .(p.1036)
T: 0141 4297979
E: grazia@liamrobertsonsolicitors.co.uk

ROBERTSON, Greg James (Aug 2011) (Partner)
Grigor & Young LLP, Elgin . . . .(p.916)
T: 01343 544077
E: GregR@grigor-young.co.uk

ROBERTSON, Hayley (Jun 2008) (Employee)
Procurator Fiscal Service, Ayr . . . .(p.1215)
T: 03000 204268
E: Haley.Robertson@copfs.gov.uk

ROBERTSON, Hayley Alyson (Jul 2008) (Partner)
Brodies LLP, Edinburgh . . . .(p.845)
T: 0131 2283777
E: hayley.robertson@brodies.com

ROBERTSON, Hugh Stuart (Mar 1991) (Partner)
Gilson Gray LLP, Edinburgh . . . .(p.874)
T: 0131 5165354
E: srobertson@gilsongray.co.uk

ROBERTSON, Jaclyn Marie (Jun 2010)
(Employee)
Robertson Wyse, Cowdenbeath . . . .(p.788)
T: 01383 515020
E: info@robertsonwyse.co.uk

ROBERTSON, James (Dec 1983) (Director)
Davidson & Shirley Limited, Lanark . . .(p.1107)
T: 01555 662576/7
E: jim.robertson@davidsonandshirley.co.uk

ROBERTSON, James Keith (Sept 1974)
(Solicitor)
NO FIRM

ROBERTSON, Jamie Lee (Sept 2014) (Employee)
Blackadders LLP, Aberdeen . . . .(p.722)
T: 01224 588913
E: Jamie.Robertson@blackadders.co.uk

ROBERTSON, Jennifer (Nov 2005) (Employee)
Howden Group Limited, Renfrew . . . . .(p.1254)
T: 0141 885 7459
E: jennifer.robertson@howden.com

ROBERTSON, Jodie Ashleigh (Sept 2020)
(Employee)
Thompsons, Edinburgh . . . .(p.906)
T: 0131 2254297
E: jodie.robertson@thompsons-scotland.co.uk

ROBERTSON, John Paul (Dec 1993) (Employee)
Procurator Fiscal Service, Glasgow . . . .(p.1241)
T: 0300 0203000
E: john.robertson@copfs.gov.uk

ROBERTSON, Jonathan Mark, WS (Dec 1986)
(Partner)
Turcan Connell, Edinburgh . . . .(p.908)
T: 0131 2288111
E: jonathan.robertson@turcanconnell.com

ROBERTSON, Keith Coll (Jul 1980) (Employee)
Procurator Fiscal Service, Dundee . . . . .(p.1218)
T: 01382 342559
E: keith.robertson@copfs.gov.uk

ROBERTSON, Kenneth (Mar 2001) (Employee)
National Westminster Bank PLC,
Edinburgh . . . .(p.1226)
T: (0131) 626 2925
E: kenny.robertson@rbs.co.uk

ROBERTSON, Kenneth Stewart (Mar 1985)
(Partner)
Balfour + Manson LLP, Edinburgh . . . . .(p.841)
T: 0131 2001200
E: ken.robertson@balfour-manson.co.uk

ROBERTSON, Lee Elizabeth (Jul 2007)
(Employee)
Clackmannanshire Council, Alloa . . . . .(p.1215)
T: 01259 450000
E: leerobertson@clacks.gov.uk

ROBERTSON, Liam (Nov 1981) (Director)
L & G Robertson Limited, Glasgow . . .(p.1036)
T: 0141 4297979
E: liam@liamrobertsonsolicitors.co.uk

ROBERTSON, Lindsay Anne (Nov 2011)
(Employee)
Anderson Strathern LLP, Edinburgh . . . .(p.839)
T: 0131 2707802

ROBERTSON, Lisa Kelly (Nov 2018) (Employee)
Jones Whyte LLP, Glasgow. . . . .(p.993)
T: 0141 375 1222
E: lisa.robertson@joneswhyte.co.uk

ROBERTSON, Louise Emily (Jan 1977) (Partner)
The Kellas Partnership, Inverurie . . . . . .(p.1086)
T: 01467 627300
E: ler@kellas.biz

ROBERTSON, Mandy Jane (Nov 2018)
(Employee)
Procurator Fiscal Service, Paisley . . . . . .(p.1252)
T: 0141 8875225
E: mandy.robertson@copfs.gov.uk

ROBERTSON, Mark (Jun 2018) (Employee)
Redford Robertson Solicitors,
Glasgow. . . . .(p.1034)
T: 0141 6485535
E: mar@redfordrobertson.com

ROBERTSON, Michael Colin (Jun 2020)
(Employee)
J. Myles & Co., Dundee . . . .(p.817)
T: 01382 204625

ROBERTSON, Michael Jon (Sept 2006)
(Employee)
Dickson Minto, Edinburgh . . . .(p.861)
T: 0131 2254455
E: michael.robertson@dmws.com

ROBERTSON, Murray Stephen (Jan 1992)
(Partner)
RSC Solicitors, Edinburgh . . . .(p.899)
T: 0131 2207430
E: mrobertson@rscsolicitors.co.uk

ROBERTSON, Neil Douglas (May 2018)
(Associate)
Addleshaw Goddard LLP,
Edinburgh . . . .(p.835)
T: 0131 2282400
E: neil.robertson@addleshawgoddard.com

ROBERTSON, Neil James (Sept 1992) (Partner)
Central Court Lawyers, Livingston . . . .(p.1118)
T: 01506 416999
E: neilrobertson@centralcourtlawyers.co.uk

ROBERTSON, Neil John (Feb 2019) (Employee)
Jones Whyte LLP, Glasgow. . . . .(p.993)
T: 0141 375 1222
E: neil.robertson@@joneswhyte.co.uk

ROBERTSON, Nicola Claire (Jun 2019)
(Employee)
Wright, Johnston & Mackenzie LLP,
Glasgow. . . . .(p.1054)
T: 0141 2483434
E: ncr@wjm.co.uk

ROBERTSON, Peter Edwards (Jul 2009)
(Partner)
Robertson Wyse, Cowdenbeath . . . .(p.788)
T: 01383 515020
E: peter.e.robertson@gmail.com

ROBERTSON, Sheila Ann (Apr 1990)
(Employee)
Procurator Fiscal Service,
Edinburgh . . . .(p.1227)
T: 3000204184
E: sheila.robertson@copfs.gov.uk

ROBERTSON, Shiona Glen (Jun 2016)
(Employee)
Hill & Robb Limited, Stirling . . . .(p.1164)
T: 01786 450985
E: ShionaRobertson@hillandrobb.co.uk

ROBERTSON, Stephanie Elizabeth
(Jul 2010) (Partner)
Pike & Chapman, Selkirk . . . .(p.1162)
T: 01750 720271
E: Stephanie.robertson@douglasgilmour.co.uk

ROBERTSON, Steven Grant (Feb 2011)
(Employee)
Bannerman Burke Law, Hawick . . . . . .(p.1070)
T: 01450 372750
E: Steven@bannermanburke.co.uk

ROBERTSON, Stewart Miller (Nov 1989)
(Partner)
Peterkin & Kidd, Linlithgow . . . .(p.1116)
T: 01506 845191
E: srobertson@peterkinandkidd.co.uk

ROBERTSON, Struan James Alastair
(Sept 1997) (Employee)
Google UK Limited, London SW1 . . . . .(p.1264)
T: 020 7346 2927
E: struan@google.com

ROBERTSON, Suzanne (Oct 2012) (Employee)
Wood Group UK Limited,
Aberdeen . . . .(p.1214)
T: 01224 851000
E: suzanne.robertson@woodgroup.com

ROBERTSON, Vaila Marie (Jul 2010) (Employee)
Anderson & Goodlad, Lerwick . . . .(p.1112)
T: 01595 692297
E: vrobertson@anderson-goodlad.co.uk

ROBERTSON, Wai-Man Shek (Sept 2007)
(Employee)
Spirit Production (Services) Limited,
Aberdeen . . . .(p.1214)
T: 01224 415242
E: wai-man.robertson@spirit-energy.com

ROBERTSON, William Alexander (Nov 2005)
(Partner)
Burnett & Reid LLP, Aberdeen . . . .(p.726)
T: 01224 644333
E: warobertson@burnett-reid.co.uk

ROBERTSON, William Derek (Nov 1975)
(Partner)
Stirling & Gilmour LLP, Alexandria . . . . .(p.752)
T: 01389 752641
E: d.robertson@stirlingandgilmour.co.uk

ROBERTSON, Yve Dayna (Nov 2018)
(Employee)
Innes & Mackay Limited, Inverness. . . .(p.1078)
T: 01463 232273
E: yver@innesmackay.com

ROBERTSON, Yvonne Elaine (Oct 1990)
(Associate)
Jackson Boyd LLP, Glasgow . . . .(p.991)
T: 0141 2214325
E: yrobertson@jacksonboyd.co.uk

ROBINSON, Alasdair Nicholson (Feb 1995)
(Employee)
Gulf Keystone Petroleum Limited, London
EC4 . . . .(p.1265)

ROBINSON, Ellen Betty (Jun 2018) (Employee)
Morton Fraser LLP, Edinburgh . . . .(p.891)
T: 0131 2471000
E: ellen.robinson@morton-fraser.com

ROBINSON, Fiona Kirsty (Sept 2017)
(Employee)
Berrymans Lace Mawer LLP,
Glasgow. . . . .(p.945)
T: 0141 3532121
E: fiona.robinson@blmlaw.com

ROBINSON, Kathryn Agnes (Nov 1996)
(Employee)
Baillie Gifford & Co, Edinburgh . . . . . .(p.1220)
T: 0131 2752000
E: kate.robinson@bailliegifford.com

ROBINSON, Kristine Elizabeth (Jan 2006)
(Employee)
Glasgow City Council, Glasgow . . . . . .(p.1239)
T: 0141 287 0200
E: kristine.robinson@glasgow.gov.uk

ROBINSON, Lindsay Helen (Oct 2013)
(Associate)
Anderson Strathern LLP, Edinburgh . . . .(p.839)
T: 0131 2707700
E: lindsay.robinson@andersonstrathern.co.uk

ROBINSON, Rosemary Ann (Feb 2001)
(Partner)
R R Law, Hamilton . . . .(p.1069)
T: 01698 322475
E: rosemary@rrlaw.co.uk

ROBINSON, Victoria (Oct 2018) (Employee)
Harper Macleod LLP, Glasgow . . . .(p.983)
T: 0141 2218888
E: victoria.robinson@harpermacleod.co.uk

ROBISON, Jane Elizabeth (Mar 1997) (Director)
Smail & Ewart Ltd, Biggar . . . .(p.774)
T: 01899 220058
E: jrobison@smail-ewart.co.uk

ROBSON, Anthony David (Jan 2002)
(Employee)
Aegon Asset Management UK Plc,
Edinburgh . . . .(p.1220)
T: 0131 5493356
E: Anthony.Robson@aegonam.com

ROBSON, Gemma May (Oct 2010) (Solicitor)
The Edrington Group Limited,
Glasgow. . . . .(p.1245)
T: 0141 9404505
E: gemma.robson@edrington.com

ROBSON, Gordon William (Sept 1997)
(Associate)
Lambert & Co.,, Ayr . . . .(p.764)
T: 01292 282811
E: lambert.gr@btconnect.com

ROBSON, Lucy Clare (Jul 2011) (Associate)
Herbert Smith Freehills LLP, London
EC2 . . . .(p.1265)
T: 020 7466 2848
E: Lucy.Robson@hsf.com

ROBSON, Stuart Fraser (Sept 2007) (Employee)
KCA Deutag Drilling Ltd,
Portlethen . . . .(p.1254)
T: 01224 299638
E: Stuart.Robson@kcadeutag.com

ROBY, Bethany Anne (Jan 2007) (Employee)
Lawford Kidd, Edinburgh . . . .(p.881)
T: 0131 2255214
E: bethany.roby@lawfordkidd.co.uk

ROCHE, Hannah Louise (Dec 2002) (Partner)
MBM Commercial LLP, Edinburgh . . . . .(p.889)
T: 0131 226 8216
E: hannah.roche@mbmcommercial.co.uk

ROCHESTER, Alison Mary (Sept 2009)
(Employee)
Shepherd and Wedderburn LLP,
Edinburgh . . . .(p.900)
T: 0131 2289900
E: alison.rochester@shepwedd.com

ROCHFORD, Mikela Louise (Aug 2016)
(Employee)
DWF LLP, Glasgow . . . . (p.973)
T: 0141 228 8000
E: Mikela.Rochford@dwf.law

ROCKS, Zoe Annmarie (May 2019) (Employee)
MacRoberts LLP, Glasgow . . . . (p.1015)
T: 0141 3031100
E: zoe.rocks@macroberts.com

RODDEN, Claira Anne (Aug 2021) (Employee)
DWF LLP, Glasgow . . . . (p.973)
T: 0141 228 8000
E: claira.rodden@dwf.law

RODDEN, Kirsty (May 2019) (Employee)
Thompsons, Glasgow . . . . (p.1046)
T: 0141 2218840
E: kirsty.rodden@thompsons-scotland.co.uk

RODGER, Alan Jamieson (Sept 2006) (Director)
Hill & Robb Limited, Stirling . . . . (p.1164)
T: 01786 450985
E: alanrodger@hillandrobb.co.uk

RODGER, Ian Murphy (Jan 1998) (Partner)
Williamson & Henry LLP,
Kirkcudbright . . . . (p.1104)
T: 01557 330692
E: irodger@williamsonandhenry.co.uk

RODGER, Sarah-Louise (Sept 1995) (Employee)
Perth & Kinross Council, Perth . . . . (p.1253)
T: 01738 475177
E: srodger@pkc.gov.uk

RODGER, Scott Lindsay (Aug 2018) (Employee)
Shepherd and Wedderburn LLP,
Glasgow . . . . (p.1039)
T: 0141 5669900
E: Scott.Rodger@shepwedd.com

RODGER, Sheila (Dec 1986) (Employee)
Fife Council, Glenrothes . . . . (p.1246)
T: 03451 550000
E: sheila.rodger@fife.gov.uk

RODGERS, Alan James (Oct 2008) (Partner)
Thompsons, Glasgow . . . . (p.1046)
T: 0141 221 8840
E: alan.rodgers@thompsons-scotland.co.uk

RODGERS, Iona Joyce Bell (Jun 2010)
(Employee)
Falkirk Council, Falkirk . . . . (p.1236)
T: 01324 506070
E: Iona.Rodgers@falkirk.gov.uk

RODGERS, Jillian Amanda (Aug 2002)
(Employee)
Glasgow City Council, Glasgow . . . . . . (p.1239)
T: 0141 2875832
E: jillian.rodgers@ced.glasgow.gov.uk

RODGERS, Katherine Anne (Apr 2018)
(Employee)
Richmond Clark, Glasgow . . . . (p.1035)
T: 0141 9549550

RODGERS, Pamela (Mar 2016) (Employee)
PBW Law Solicitors, Glasgow . . . . (p.1030)
T: 0141 439 1990
E: pamela.rodgers@pbwlaw.co.uk

RODGERS, Rachel Elizabeth (Jun 2011)
(Director)
Linda George Family Law Limited,
Hamilton . . . . (p.1067)
T: 01698 459200
E: rrodgers@lgfamilylaw.co.uk

RODR GUEZ MOLINA, Silvia (Jun 2020)
(Solicitor)
NO FIRM

ROG LSKA, Natalia (Sept 2019) (Employee)
Mitchells Roberton Ltd, Glasgow . . . . . (p.1020)
T: 0141 5523422

ROGERS, Charles Oliver (Dec 2013) (Employee)
Financial Conduct Authority, London
E20 . . . . (p.1264)
E: charles.rogers@fca.org.uk

ROGERS, Christopher David (Nov 1979)
(Director)
Ross Rogers & Co Limited,
Rutherglen . . . . (p.1159)
T: 0141 6479771
E: chris@rossrogers.co.uk

ROGERS, Claire Margaret (Feb 1997)
(Employee)
SOUTH LANARKSHIREre Council,
Hamilton . . . . (p.1247)
T: 01698 454548
E: claire.rogers@southlanarkshire.gov.uk

ROGERS, David Graeme Stuart (Nov 2019)
(Employee)
Boyles Solicitors, Dundee . . . . (p.806)
T: 01382 221214
E: drogers@wgboyle.co.uk

ROGERSON, Jill (Jan 2014) (Employee)
NORTH LANARKSHIRERe Council,
Motherwell . . . . (p.1251)
T: 01698 302196
E: RogersonJ@northlan.gov.uk

ROGOLSKA, Dominika Aleksandra
(Sept 2017) (Employee)
Herbert Smith Freehills LLP, London
EC2 . . . . (p.1265)
T: (020) 7466 2422
E: Dominika.rogolska@hsf.com

ROLLINSON, William Benoit (Oct 2014)
(Employee)
Brodies LLP, Edinburgh . . . .(p.845)
T: 0131 2283777
E: will.rollinson@brodies.com

ROLLO, Fiona Dorothy Elizabeth (Oct 2006)
(Employee)
Diageo Scotland Limited,
Edinburgh . . . .(p.1222)
T: 0131 519 2261

ROLLO, Karon Helen (Dec 1991) (Employee)
Procurator Fiscal Service,
Edinburgh . . . .(p.1227)
T: 0300 0203168
E: Karon.Rollo@copfs.gov.uk

ROMAN, Emma Caroline (Sept 2017)
(Employee)
Aberdein Considine and Company,
Edinburgh . . . .(p.833)
T: 0131 2212424
E: eroman@acandco.com

ROMANIS, Joanne Christine (Aug 1987)
(Consultant)
Inksters, Forfar . . . .(p.927)
T: 01307 497008
E: joanne@inksters.com

ROMPCA, Justyna Katarzyna (Jun 2019)
(Employee)
Digby Brown LLP, Edinburgh . . . .(p.862)
T: 0333 200 5925
E: justyna.rompca@digbybrown.co.uk

RONALD, Alasdair Graham James
(Jul 2013) (Employee)
Eversheds Sutherland (International) LLP,
Edinburgh . . . .(p.869)
T: 0207 9194500
E: GrahamRonald@eversheds-Sutherland.com

RONALD, Andrew Stewart Niall (May 2013)
(Employee)
Harper Macleod LLP, Glasgow . . . .(p.983)
T: 0141 2218888
E: andrew.ronald@harpermacleod.co.uk

RONNEY, Rebecca Bethan (Nov 2018)
(Employee)
Dentons UK and Middle East LLP,
Glasgow. . . . .(p.968)
T: 0330 2220050
E: rebecca.ronney@dentons.com

RONSON, Gemma (May 2009) (Solicitor)
NO FIRM

ROOKES, Deborah (Nov 2018) (Employee)
Harper Macleod LLP, Glasgow . . . .(p.983)
T: 0141 2218888
E: Deborah.Rookes@harpermacleod.co.uk

ROONEY, Brian James (Oct 2009) (Director)
Rooney Family Law Limited,
Uddingston . . . .(p.1178)
T: 01698 815620
E: brian@rooneyfamilylaw.co.uk

ROONEY, Frances Anelia (Apr 2009) (Partner)
Lexares LLP, Glasgow . . . .(p.1001)
T: 0141 3780960
E: frances.rooney@lexares.co.uk

ROONEY, Lynsey Anne (Nov 2003) (Employee)
Procurator Fiscal Service,
Edinburgh . . . .(p.1229)
T: (0844) 561 3268
E: Lynsey.Rooney@copfs.gov.uk

ROONEY, Philip (Jul 1972) (Consultant)
Philip Rooney & Co., Glasgow . . . .(p.1036)
T: 0141 423 0000
E: a.hamid@philiprooney.com

ROPER, David John (Nov 2007) (Solicitor)
NO FIRM

ROPER, Max David (Sept 2021) (Employee)
DWF LLP, Edinburgh. . . . .(p.865)
T: 0131 2265541
E: max.roper@dwf.law

ROPER, Paul Frederick Allen, WS (Nov 1978)
(Director)
Paul Roper Associates Limited,
Kelso . . . .(p.1092)
T: 01573 225082
E: paul@pra.scot

RORE, Samantha Mone Har (Nov 2007)
(Employee)
Scottish Hospital Inquiry, Glasgow . . . .(p.1244)
E: samantha.rore@hospitalsinquiry.scot

ROSCOE, James Ian (Oct 1987) (Partner)
Brodies LLP, Edinburgh . . . .(p.845)
T: 0131 2283777
E: james.roscoe@brodies.com

ROSE, David Geddes (Sept 1992) (Partner)
Lindsays LLP, Dundee . . . .(p.814)
T: 01382 224112
E: davidrose@lindsays.co.uk

ROSE, Elizabeth Paterson (Apr 2012)
(Associate)
Levy & McRae Solicitors LLP,
Glasgow. . . . .(p.1000)
T: 0141 3072311
E: erose@lemac.co.uk

ROSE, Georgia Elizabeth Fraser (Oct 2017)
(Employee)
BTO Solicitors LLP, Edinburgh . . . .(p.849)
T: 0131 2222939
E: gro@bto.co.uk

ROSENSHINE, Suzanne Jane (Jun 2018)
(Employee)
Scottish Police Authority, Police Scotland,
Glasgow . . . .(p.1244)
 T: 01786 895727
 E: suzanne.rosenshine@scotland.pnn.police.uk

ROSOCHOWSKA, Karolina Malgorzata
(Aug 2007) (Employee)
Burness Paull LLP, Glasgow . . . .(p.954)
 T: 0141 2484933
 E: karolina.rosochowska@burnesspaull.com

ROSS, Alastair Crawford (Oct 1987) (Partner)
Pollock, Ross & Co, Stirling . . . .(p.1167)
 T: 01786 449933
 E: alastair@pollockross.com

ROSS, Andrea Laureen (Jun 2010) (Employee)
Harper Macleod LLP, Inverness . . . .(p.1077)
 T: 01463 798777
 E: Andrea.Ross@harpermacleod.co.uk

ROSS, Andrew David (Oct 2014) (Employee)
Holman Fenwick Willan LLP, London
 EC3 . . . .(p.1265)
 T: 020 7264 8000
 E: andrew.ross@hfw.com

ROSS, Andrew William (Jul 2014) (Employee)
Turcan Connell, Edinburgh . . . .(p.908)
 T: 0131 2288111
 E: andrew.ross@turcanconnell.com

ROSS, Betheney Anne (Aug 2016) (Employee)
Scottish Environment Protection Agency,
 Holytown . . . .(p.1248)
 T: (01698) 839 000
 E: betheney.ross@sepa.org.uk

ROSS, Calum Alexander (Nov 1991) (Partner)
Ross & Fox, Glasgow . . . .(p.1036)
 T: 0141 4291230
 E: calumross.rossfoxsolicitors@yahoo.co.uk

ROSS, Calum Morrison (Dec 2019) (Employee)
Highland Council, Inverness . . . .(p.1248)
 T: 01463 702000
 E: Calum.Ross@highland.gov.uk

ROSS, Carolyn Susan (Dec 2018) (Employee)
Burness Paull LLP, Glasgow . . . .(p.954)
 T: 0141 2484933
 E: Carolyn.Ross@burnesspaull.com

ROSS, Chelsey Jane (Sept 2016) (Employee)
CMS Cameron McKenna Nabarro Olswang LLP,
 Glasgow . . . .(p.962)
 T: 0141 2222200
 E: Chelsey.Ross@cms-cmno.com

ROSS, Dale (Jul 1996) (Associate)
Blackadders LLP, Dundee . . . .(p.805)
 T: 01382 229222
 E: Dale.Ross@blackadders.co.uk

ROSS, David Scott (Nov 2006) (Employee)
Pinsent Masons LLP, Glasgow . . . .(p.1031)
 T: 0141 567 8400
 E: david.ross@pinsentmasons.com

ROSS, Elizabeth Joan (Oct 1990) (Employee)
Inspectorate of Prosecution in Scotland,
 Glasgow . . . .(p.1240)
 E: elizabeth.ross@copfs.gov.uk

ROSS, Evelyn (Jan 2015) (Employee)
NORTH LANARKSHIRERe Council,
 Motherwell . . . .(p.1251)
 T: 01698 302695
 E: rossev@northlan.gov.uk

ROSS, Fiona (Feb 2008) (Associate)
Pinsent Masons LLP, London EC2 . . . . .(p.1267)
 T: 020 7418 7000
 E: fiona.ross@pinsentmasons.com

ROSS, Fiona Elizabeth (Sept 1997) (Employee)
Scottish Courts and Tribunals Service,
 Dumfries . . . .(p.1217)
 E: fross@scotcourts.gov.uk

ROSS, Fiona Emma (May 1994) (Employee)
City of Edinburgh Council,
 Edinburgh . . . .(p.1221)
 T: 0131 5294321
 E: fiona.ross@edinburgh.gov.uk

ROSS, Frances Elizabeth (Dec 2004) (Partner)
Clyde & Co (Scotland) LLP,
 Glasgow . . . .(p.961)
 T: 0141 2482666
 E: Frances.Ross@clydeco.com

ROSS, Gary (Oct 2012) (Employee)
Digby Brown LLP, Glasgow . . . .(p.970)
 T: 0333 200 5925
 E: gary.ross@digbybrown.co.uk

ROSS, Gary Francis (Feb 2008) (Partner)
Aberdein Considine and Company,
 Inverurie . . . .(p.1084)
 T: 01467 621263
 E: gross@acandco.com

ROSS, Gavin John (Sept 2010) (Employee)
Shell International Limited, London
 SE1 . . . .(p.1268)
 E: gavin.ross@shell.com

ROSS, Gillian Margaret (Oct 2005) (Employee)
Pinsent Masons LLP, Glasgow . . . .(p.1031)
 T: 0141 567 8400
 E: gillian.ross@pinsentmasons.com

ROSS, Graham John (Nov 2006) (Employee)
DOF Subsea UK Limited, Aberdeen . . . .(p.1212)
 T: 01224 614193
 E: Graham.Ross@dofsubsea.com

ROSS, Hannah Beverley (Oct 2001) (Employee)
City of Edinburgh Council,
Edinburgh . . . .(p.1221)
T: (0131) 5294145
E: hannah.ross@edinburgh.gov.uk

ROSS, Hilary Anne (Sept 1992) (Partner)
DWF LLP, Manchester . . . .(p.1270)
T: 0161 6035000
E: hilary.ross@dwf.law

ROSS, Jennifer Lois (Jun 2017) (Employee)
CMS Cameron McKenna Nabarro Olswang LLP,
Edinburgh . . . .(p.856)
T: 0131 200 7378
E: Jennifer.Ross@cms-cmno.com

ROSS, Julie Anne (Oct 1998) (Employee)
Buchanan Burton Limited, East
Kilbride . . . .(p.830)
T: 01355 249228
E: julier@buchananburton.co.uk

ROSS, Keith William Caldwell (Dec 1978)
(Solicitor)
NO FIRM

ROSS, Kenneth Alexander (Oct 1981) (Partner)
Brodies LLP, Edinburgh . . . .(p.845)
T: 0131 2283777
E: ken.ross@brodies.com

ROSS, Professor, Kenneth Clark (Dec 1982)
(Employee)
Loch Lomond and The Trossachs National Park
Authority, Balloch . . . .(p.1215)
T: 01389 722600
E: kenneth.ross@lochlomond-trossachs.org

ROSS, Kenneth William Coleman (Nov 1991)
(Partner)
Stewart & McIsaac, Elgin. . . . .(p.917)
T: 01343 544971
E: kenny@lexelgin.com

ROSS, Kirstie Ann (Feb 2001) (Employee)
TSB Bank Plc, Edinburgh . . . .(p.1235)
T: (0131) 260 0051
E: kirstie.ross@tsb.co.uk

ROSS, Lisa Miller (Aug 2016) (Employee)
Burness Paull LLP, Glasgow . . . .(p.954)
T: 0141 2484933
E: lisa.ross@burnesspaull.com

ROSS, Lynda Elizabeth (Dec 1990) (Employee)
Burness Paull LLP, Edinburgh . . . .(p.850)
T: 0131 4736000
E: Lynda.Ross@burnesspaull.com

ROSS, Margaret Morton Kennedy
(Dec 2004) (Associate)
Balfour + Manson LLP, Edinburgh . . . . .(p.841)
T: 0131 2001295
E: margaret.ross@balfour-manson.co.uk

ROSS, Michael Edward (Jul 2015) (Employee)
Brzoom Kadirgolam, Glasgow . . . .(p.952)
T: 0141 2042888
E: m.ross@emlc.org.uk

ROSS, Nicola (Oct 2003) (Partner)
Morton Fraser LLP, Glasgow . . . .(p.1022)
T: 0141 2741100
E: Nicola.Ross@morton-fraser.com

ROSS, Nicola Anne (Oct 2005) (Employee)
Scottish Solicitors' Discipline Tribunal,
Cupar . . . .(p.1216)
T: 01334 659088
E: enquiries@ssdt.org.uk

ROSS OF ROSS, Fiona Campbell (Jan 1990)
(Employee)
South Ayrshire Council, Ayr . . . .(p.1215)
T: 01292 612 126
E: fiona.ross2@south-ayrshire.gov.uk

ROSS, Owen Noel (Feb 2021) (Employee)
DJP Solicitors, Aberdeen . . . .(p.730)
T: 01224 590053
E: or@djpsolicitors.com

ROSS, Robert David (Nov 2000) (Employee)
Brodies LLP, Edinburgh . . . .(p.845)
T: 0131 2283777
E: robert.ross@brodies.com

ROSS, Sean David (Sept 2020) (Employee)
Burness Paull LLP, Edinburgh . . . .(p.850)
T: 0131 4736000
E: sean.ross@burnesspaull.com

ROSS, Stephanie Jayne (Jul 2010) (Employee)
Procurator Fiscal Service,
Edinburgh . . . .(p.1227)
T: 0300 0203168
E: Stephanie.Ross@copfs.gov.uk

ROSS, Suzanne Anderson (Mar 2010)
(Employee)
Midlothian Council, Dalkeith . . . .(p.1216)
T: 0131 2707500
E: Suzanne.Ross@midlothian.gov.uk

ROSS-DAVIE, Ruth Ann (May 2006) (Employee)
Procurator Fiscal Service, Glasgow . . . .(p.1241)
T: 0300 0203000
E: Ruth.RossDavie@copfs.gov.uk

ROSSETTER, Fiona Jane (Sept 2003) (Associate)
Pinsent Masons LLP, Glasgow . . . .(p.1031)
T: 0141 567 8400
E: Fiona.Rossetter@pinsentmasons.com

ROSSI, Michael Gerard (Jul 2017) (Employee)
Ferguson, MacSween & Stewart, Kyle of
Lochalsh. . . . .(p.1107)
T: 01599 534500
E: michael@fmslaw.co.uk

ROSSOR, Benjamin Michael (Jan 2017)
(Employee)
Which Ltd, Cardiff . . . .(p.1279)
E: ben.rossor@which.co.uk

ROTH, Carla Joy (Mar 2012) (Employee)
Stirling Council, Stirling. . . . .(p.1255)
T: 01786 233065
E: rothc@stirling.gov.uk

ROUGH, Rachel Jane (Aug 2002) (Employee)
DAC Beachcroft Scotland LLP,
Glasgow . . . .(p.964)
T: 0141 2486688
E: RachelRough@dacbeachcroft.com

ROUGHEAD, Alan (Mar 2012) (Partner)
Macnabs LLP, Perth . . . .(p.1150)
T: 01738 623432
E: alanroughead@macnabs-law.co.uk

ROULSTON, Catherine Ann (Jul 2009)
(Employee)
Scottish Widows Limited,
Edinburgh . . . .(p.1233)
T: 0131 300 8201
E: catherine.roulston@lloydsbanking.com

ROWAN, Claire (Oct 2018) (Employee)
Procurator Fiscal Service,
Edinburgh . . . .(p.1229)
T: 0300 0203000
E: claire.rowan@copfs.gov.uk

ROWANTREE, Catriona Anne (Jun 2018)
(Employee)
National Westminster Bank PLC,
Edinburgh . . . .(p.1226)
T: (0131) 626 2925
E: Catriona.Rowantree@natwest.com

ROWATT, Alison Isabel (Jun 2006) (Associate)
Connell & Connell, WS, Edinburgh . . . .(p.857)
T: 0131 5562993
E: air@connellws.co.uk

ROWLINSON, Jennifer Lee (Jun 2019)
(Employee)
Jackson Boyd LLP, Glasgow . . . .(p.991)
T: 0141 2214325
E: jrowlinson@jacksonboyd.co.uk

ROWNEY, Karen Anne (Jun 2012) (Employee)
Medical Protection Society, Leeds. . . . .(p.1260)
E: karen.rowney@medicalprotection.org

ROWNEY, Lynsey Catherine Dawn
(Apr 2007) (Partner)
Lockharts Law LLP, Ayr . . . .(p.764)
T: 01292 265045
E: lynseyrowney@lockhartslaw.com

ROWSON, Stuart John (Jan 1994) (Associate)
Brodies LLP, Edinburgh . . . .(p.845)
T: 0131 2283777
E: stuart.rowson@brodies.com

ROXBURGH, Annette Hughes (Oct 2002)
(Employee)
SSE Plc, Perth . . . .(p.1253)
T: 01738 516619
E: Annette.Roxburgh@sse.com

ROY, Ewen Patrick (Dec 1995) (Partner)
Adams Whyte, Edinburgh . . . .(p.835)
T: 0131 555 7220
E: ewenroy@adamswhyte.com

ROY, Lynsey Fiona (Apr 2016) (Employee)
Aberdeen Corporate Services Limited,
Edinburgh . . . .(p.1220)
T: 0131 245 7508
E: lynsey.roy@abrdn.com

ROYDEN, Michael (Dec 1991) (Partner)
Thorntons Law LLP, Dundee . . . .(p.819)
T: 01382 229 111
E: mroyden@thorntons-law.co.uk

ROYLE, Tania Margaret (Jul 2019) (Employee)
Gilson Gray LLP, Dundee. . . . .(p.812)
E: troyle@gilsongray.co.uk

ROYSTON, Jennifer Elizabeth (Oct 2008)
(Employee)
Scottish Children's Reporter Administration,
Edinburgh . . . .(p.1230)
T: 0131 6679431

RUDD, Malcolm Iain (Dec 2018) (Employee)
DWF LLP, Edinburgh. . . . .(p.865)
T: 0131 2265541
E: Malcolm.rudd@dwf.law

RUDDIMAN, Robert John Arthur (Mar 1989)
(Partner)
Burness Paull LLP, Aberdeen . . . .(p.724)
T: 01224 621621
E: Bob.Ruddiman@burnesspaull.com

RUDDY, Terence David (Sept 1994) (Partner)
Jain, Neil & Ruddy, Glasgow . . . .(p.992)
T: 0141 2218778
E: terry@jnrsolicitors.com

RUGGERI, Alejandra Carmela Julie
(Nov 2018) (Employee)
Digby Brown LLP, Edinburgh . . . .(p.862)
T: 0333 200 5925
E: alejandra.ruggeri@digbybrown.co.uk

RULE, Stephen (Sept 1987) (Director)
Watersrule Limited, Stirling . . . .(p.1167)
T: 01786 235 235
E: stephen.rule@watersrule.co.uk

RUNCIE, Colin Gordon (Aug 1983) (Partner)
Blackadders LLP, Aberdeen . . . .(p.722)
T: 01224 588913
E: colin.runcie@blackadders.co.uk

RUNCIE, Graeme George (Nov 1987) (Partner)
Graeme Runcie & Co, Edinburgh . . . . . .(p.899)
T: 07957 554958
E: graeme.runcie@btinternet.com

RUNCIMAN, Scott Ian (Dec 2015) (Employee)
Gilson Gray LLP, Edinburgh . . . .(p.874)
  T: 0131 5165354
  E: srunciman@gilsongray.co.uk

RUSHBURY, Gillian (Oct 1991) (Employee)
DAC Beachcroft Scotland LLP,
  Glasgow. . . . .(p.964)
  T: 0141 2486688
  E: GRushbury@dacbeachcroft.com

RUSHWORTH, Alistair James (Dec 2009)
  (Partner)
Turcan Connell, Edinburgh . . . .(p.908)
  T: 0131 2288111
  E: alistair.rushworth@turcanconnell.com

RUSSELL, Abby Jayne (Nov 2021) (Employee)
Graham Walker, Glasgow . . . .(p.1050)
  T: 0141 9460111
  E: ar@gwsolicitors.com

RUSSELL, Andrew Robert (Jun 2014)
  (Employee)
North Oil Company, Doha . . . .(p.1275)
  E: andy.russell@noc.qa

RUSSELL, Catherine Mary (Oct 1978)
  (Employee)
Law Society of Scotland,
  Edinburgh . . . .(p.1224)
  T: 0131 2267411
  E: cathrussell@lawscot.org.uk

RUSSELL, Clare Frances (Sept 2013) (Employee)
Craig Wood Solicitors Limited,
  Inverness . . . .(p.1083)
  T: 01463 225544
  E: clare.russell@craigwood.co.uk

RUSSELL, Claudia Ruth (Nov 2003) (Associate)
CMS Cameron McKenna Nabarro Olswang LLP,
  Edinburgh . . . .(p.856)
  T: 0131 2288000
  E: claudia.russell@cms-cmno.com

RUSSELL, Craig Scott (Apr 2007) (Employee)
City of Edinburgh Council,
  Edinburgh . . . .(p.1221)
  T: (0131) 5294145
  E: craig.russell@edinburgh.gov.uk

RUSSELL, Eilish (Jul 2018) (Associate)
Ashurst LLP, London E1 . . . .(p.1261)
  T: (020) 7859 2145
  E: Eilish.Russell@ashurst.com

RUSSELL, Emily Cleo (Aug 2021) (Employee)
Brodies LLP, Edinburgh . . . .(p.845)
  T: 0131 2283777
  E: emily.russell@brodies.com

RUSSELL, Emma Anne (Dec 2002) (Employee)
Haynes and Boone CDG, LLP, London
  EC4 . . . .(p.1265)
  T: 020 8734 2807
  E: Emma.Russell@haynesboone.com

RUSSELL, Gail Isobel (Nov 1997) (Employee)
Procurator Fiscal Service, Falkirk . . . . . .(p.1236)
  T: 0300 020 3000
  E: gail.russell@copfs.gov.uk

RUSSELL, Gillian Claire (Jun 2011) (Employee)
Livingstone Brown Limited,
  Glasgow . . . .(p.1004)
  T: 0141 7789657
  E: gr@livbrown.co.uk

RUSSELL, Jaclyn Elizabeth Petrie (Oct 2007)
  (Partner)
Stronachs LLP, Aberdeen . . . .(p.744)
  T: 01224 845845
  E: jaclyn.russell@stronachs.com

RUSSELL, James Brown (Jun 1974) (Partner)
James Patrick & Muir, Dalry . . . .(p.795)
  T: 01294 832442
  E: jbr@jpmlaw.co.uk

RUSSELL, Jamie Munro (Jun 2019) (Employee)
Gowling WLG (UK) LLP,
  Birmingham . . . .(p.1258)
  E: Jamie.Russell@gowlingwlg.com

RUSSELL, Kathleen Frances (Oct 2004)
  (Partner)
Burges Salmon LLP, Edinburgh . . . .(p.850)
  T: 0131 3142112
  E: katie.russell@burges-salmon.com

RUSSELL, Katie Elizabeth (Dec 2016)
  (Employee)
The McKinstry Company LLP, Ayr . . . . .(p.765)
  T: 01292 281711
  E: katie@mckinstry.co.uk

RUSSELL, Kimberley Anne (Oct 2008) (Solicitor)
NO FIRM

RUSSELL, Laura Jane (Jul 2008) (Employee)
Scottish Social Services Council,
  Dundee . . . .(p.1218)
  T: 0345 6030 891
  E: laura.russell@sssc.uk.com

RUSSELL, Paula Louise (Sept 2011) (Employee)
Procurator Fiscal Service, Hamilton . . . .(p.1247)
  T: 0844 5613245
  E: Paula.Russell@copfs.gov.uk

RUSSELL, Ryan Robert (Aug 2009) (Partner)
MML Legal, Dundee . . . .(p.817)
  T: 01382 206 000
  E: ryan@mmllaw.co.uk

RUSSELL, Stuart Fraser (Dec 2001) (Solicitor)
NO FIRM

RUSSO, Adrian (Mar 2013) (Partner)
East End Law, Glasgow . . . .(p.974)
  T: 0141 5544556
  E: adrianrusso@eastendlaw.co.uk

RUSSO, Niccola Luisa (Oct 1999) (Employee)
Bank of America Merrill Lynch, New
   York . . . .(p.1279)
   T: +1 646 855 3672
   E: niccola.russo@bofa.com

RUSSO, Sarah Jane Margaret (Jul 2001)
   (Employee)
T. Duncan & Co., Montrose . . . .(p.1125)
   T: 01674 672533
   E: Sarah@tduncan.com

RUST, Gillian Catherine (Sept 1994) (Employee)
Postcode Lottery Limited,
   Edinburgh . . . .(p.1227)
   T: 0131 555 (ext) 9558
   E: gillian.rust@postcodelottery.co.uk

RUST, Jason Geoffrey (Nov 2003) (Employee)
Scottish Land & Estates Limited,
   Musselburgh. . . . .(p.1251)
   T: 0131 6535400
   E: jason.rust@scottishlandandestates.co.uk

RUST, Malcolm Hamilton (Sept 1994) (Partner)
Shepherd and Wedderburn LLP,
   Edinburgh . . . .(p.900)
   T: 0131 2289900
   E: malcolm.rust@shepwedd.com

RUTH, Rachael Jane (Jul 2018) (Employee)
Brodies LLP, Glasgow . . . .(p.948)
   T: 0141 2484672
   E: rachaeljane.ruth@brodies.com

RUTHERFORD, Andrew (Jun 2017) (Employee)
Burness Paull LLP, Glasgow . . . .(p.954)
   T: 0141 2484933
   E: andrew.rutherford@burnesspaull.com

RUTHERFORD, Bernadette Niamh
   (Sept 2017) (Employee)
Harper Macleod LLP, Edinburgh . . . .(p.877)
   T: 0131 2472500
   E: bernadette.rutherford@harpermacleod.co.uk

RUTHERFORD, Harriet Grace Rebecca
   (Oct 2014) (Employee)
Brodies LLP, Edinburgh . . . .(p.845)
   T: 0131 2283777
   E: harriet.rutherford@brodies.com

RUTHERFORD, Iain James (Sept 2004) (Partner)
Brodies LLP, Edinburgh . . . .(p.845)
   T: 0131 2283777
   E: iain.rutherford@brodies.com

RUTHERFORD, Kerri Rebekah (Mar 2021)
   (Employee)
Ledingham Chalmers LLP,
   Aberdeen . . . .(p.734)
   T: 01224 408408
   E: kerri.rutherford@ledinghamchalmers.com

RUTHERFORD, Melissa (Nov 2009) (Director)
Rutherford Sheridan Ltd, Glasgow . . . .(p.1037)
   T: 0141 248 3320
   E: melissa@rutherfordsheridan.com

RUTHERFORD, Paul John William (Oct 1978)
   (Partner)
Harper Macleod LLP, Lerwick . . . .(p.1113)
   T: 01595 695583
   E: paul.rutherford@harpermacleod.co.uk

RUTHERFORD, Ross Samuel (Feb 2010)
   (Employee)
LDF Operations Limited, Chester . . . . .(p.1259)
   T: 01244 527300
   E: Ross.Rutherford@ldf.co.uk

RUXTON, Andrew Norman (Oct 2007)
   (Employee)
Legal Secretariat to the Lord Advocate,
   Edinburgh . . . .(p.1224)
   T: (0300) 020 3364
   E: andrew.ruxton@gov.scot

RYAN, Christopher (Mar 2007) (Associate)
Fiona McPhail Solicitors, Edinburgh . . . .(p.886)
   T: 0344 5152410
   E: Chris_Ryan@shelter.org.uk

RYAN, Clare Lorraine (Sept 1992) (Partner)
Clare Ryan, Bearsden . . . .(p.772)
   T: 0141 9315254
   E: clarelryan@aol.com

RYAN, Kirsty Anne Stead (Jan 2015) (Employee)
Office of the Advocate General,
   Edinburgh . . . .(p.1227)
   T: 0131 2441635
   E: Kirsty.Ryan@advocategeneral.gov.uk

RYAN-HUME, Kavin (Sept 2020) (Employee)
Procurator Fiscal Service, Glasgow . . . .(p.1241)
   T: 0300 0203000
   E: Kavin.ryan-hume@copfs.gov.uk

RYDER-FORMAN, Kimberley Leigh
   (May 2011) (Employee)
Brodies LLP, Edinburgh . . . .(p.845)
   T: 0131 2283777
   E: kimberley.forman@brodies.com

RYLATT, Nicola (Jun 2009) (Director)
Lanarkshire Community Law Centre Ltd,
   Airdrie . . . .(p.749)
   T: 01236 757 337
   E: Nicola.Rylatt@lclc.org.uk

RZEPKA, Sandra Monika (Jun 2021) (Employee)
Lindsays LLP, Edinburgh . . . .(p.882)
   T: 0131 2291212
   E: sandrarzepka@lindsays.co.uk

SABBA, Julie Claire (Sept 2003) (Employee)
MLP Law Ltd, Altrincham . . . .(p.1258)
   T: 0161 9261582
   E: julies@mlplaw.co.uk

SABIR, Mohammed (Nov 2005) (Partner)
MBS Solicitors, Edinburgh . . . . (p.889)
   T: 0131 3374100
   E: ali@mbssolicitors.co.uk

SACRANIE, Shehzaad (Sept 2000) (Solicitor)
NO FIRM

SADDIQ, Shabeilla (Feb 2011) (Employee)
TCH Law, Hamilton . . . . (p.1070)
   T: 01698 312080
   E: shs@tchlaw.co.uk

SADDLER, Beth (Jul 2006) (Employee)
Scottish Government, Edinburgh . . . . . (p.1231)
   T: 0131 244 2077
   E: beth.saddler@gov.scot

SADIQ, Muhammad Bilal (Sept 2014)
   (Employee)
Procurator Fiscal Service, Dundee . . . . . (p.1218)
   T: 01382 342559
   E: muhammad.sadiq@copfs.gov.uk

SADIQ, Muhammad Pervez (Jul 2020)
   (Employee)
Core Consultants (Immigration & Study Abroad)
   Limited, Glasgow . . . . (p.1238)
   E: mps@coreconsultant.co.uk

SADLER, Emma (Sept 2014) (Employee)
Blackadders LLP, Glasgow . . . . (p.946)
   T: 0141 2481888
   E: Emma.sadler@blackadders.co.uk

SAEED, Adil (Jun 2021) (Employee)
Maguire Solicitors, Glasgow . . . . (p.1017)
   T: 0141 3312885
   E: adil@maguiresolicitors.co.uk

SAGEWOOD, Donna Marie (Jan 2019) (Partner)
E. Thornton & Co., Oban . . . . (p.1135)
   T: 01631 566771
   E: donna@ethornton.co.uk

SAHA, Sheekha (Oct 2002) (Employee)
Comhairle Nan Eilean Siar,
   Stornoway . . . . (p.1255)
   T: 01851 822604
   E: s.saha@cne-siar.gov.uk

SAHEEL-IKRAM, Zenab (Nov 2021) (Employee)
Watt Law, Cumbernauld . . . . (p.791)
   T: 01236 787030
   E: zenab@wattlaw.co.uk

SAIGEON, Joanna Ruth (May 2019) (Employee)
Lindsays LLP, Dundee . . . . (p.814)
   T: 01382 224112
   E: JoannaSaigeon@lindsays.co.uk

SALEEM, Arif (Jul 2015) (Employee)
Bird & Bird LLP, London EC4 . . . . (p.1262)
   T: 0207 415 6000
   E: arif.saleem@twobirds.com

SALEH AL-OBAIDY, Rhian Elizabeth
   (Oct 2013) (Employee)
Senderwood Group Limited, London
   NW1 . . . . (p.1268)
   E: rhian@localglobe.vc

SALMON, Elizabeth Caroline (Oct 1994)
   (Employee)
Brodies LLP, Glasgow . . . . (p.948)
   T: 0141 2484672
   E: elizabeth.salmon@brodies.com

SALMON, John Alexander (Oct 1993)
   (Employee)
Hogan Lovells International LLP, London
   EC1 . . . . (p.1265)
   T: 020 7296 5017
   E: john.salmon@hoganlovells.com

SALMON, Victoria Kate (Mar 2002) (Employee)
National Westminster Bank PLC, London
   EC2 . . . . (p.1266)
   E: Victoria.Salmon@rbs.com

SALMOND, Laura Irene (Nov 2003) (Partner)
BTO Solicitors LLP, Glasgow . . . . (p.952)
   T: 0141 2218012
   E: lis@bto.co.uk

SALMOND, Rachel Alice (Mar 2020) (Employee)
Lindsays LLP, Edinburgh . . . . (p.882)
   T: 0131 2291212
   E: rachelsalmond@lindsays.co.uk

SALT, Agnieszka Maria (Oct 2015) (Associate)
Dentons UK and Middle East LLP,
   Edinburgh . . . . (p.860)
   T: 0330 2220050
   E: aggie.salt@dentons.com

SALTON, Catriona Morven (Aug 2021)
   (Employee)
Brodies LLP, Edinburgh . . . . (p.845)
   T: 0131 2283777
   E: catriona.salton@brodies.com

SALUJA, Sean Ajit (Aug 1991) (Partner)
Burness Paull LLP, Aberdeen . . . . (p.724)
   T: 01224 621621
   E: Sean.Saluja@burnesspaull.com

SAMPSON, Alasdair Colin (Sept 1977)
   (Director)
Financial Services Advocacy Ltd,
   Stewarton . . . . (p.1162)
   T: 01560 485225
   E: alasdair@fsalawyer.co.uk

SAMSON, Craig William (Feb 1995) (Partner)
Blackadders LLP, Dundee . . . . (p.805)
   T: 01382 229222
   E: craig.samson@blackadders.co.uk

SAMSON, Dawn (Dec 2000) (Employee)
Procurator Fiscal Service,
  Edinburgh . . . .(p.1229)
  T: 0300 0203000
  E: dawn.samson@copfs.gov.uk

SAMSON, Kym (Dec 2014) (Director)
Duncan & McConnell Solicitors Limited,
  Dundee . . . .(p.809)
  T: 07761 301390

SANDEMAN, Richard Allan (Jan 1977) (Partner)
Sandemans, Falkirk . . . .(p.925)
  T: 01324 633222
  E: dicksandeman@sandemans.co.uk

SANDEMAN, Robert Meldrum (Nov 2000)
(Employee)
Office of the Queen's and Lord Treasurer's
  Remembrancer, Edinburgh. . . . .(p.1227)
  T: 0300 0204356
  E: bobby.sandeman@qltr.gov.uk

SANDERS, Geoffrey Hugh (Dec 2009)
(Employee)
Law Society of Scotland,
  Edinburgh . . . .(p.1224)
  T: 0131 2267411
  E: hughsanders@lawscot.org.uk

SANDERS, Paul James (Oct 2021) (Employee)
Brodies LLP, Edinburgh . . . .(p.845)
  T: 0131 2283777
  E: paul.sanders@brodies.com

SANDERS, Shona Mary (Nov 1989)
(Consultant)
CMS Cameron McKenna Nabarro Olswang LLP,
  Edinburgh . . . .(p.856)
  T: 0131 2288000
  E: Shona.Sanders@cms-cmno.com

SANDHAM, Seonaid Margaret (Sept 2009)
(Employee)
Anderson Strathern LLP, Edinburgh . . . .(p.839)
  T: 0131 2707700
  E: seonaid.sandham@andersonstrathern.co.uk

SANDHU, Nikita Kaur (Jul 2021) (Employee)
MacRoberts LLP, Glasgow . . . .(p.1015)
  T: 0141 3031100
  E: nikita.sandhu@macroberts.com

SANDHU, Sonia (Nov 2020) (Employee)
DLA Piper Scotland LLP, Edinburgh . . . .(p.863)
  T: 08700 111111
  E: sonia.sandhu@dlapiper.com

SANDILANDS, Colin Alexander (Oct 2000)
(Partner)
Stronachs LLP, Inverness . . . .(p.1082)
  T: 01463 713225
  E: colin.sandilands@stronachs.com

SANDISON, Charles John (Nov 1995) (Director)
Sandison Kennedy Limited,
  Aberdeen . . . .(p.742)
  T: 01224 443555
  E: charles@sandisonkennedy.com

SANGSTER, David Alexander (Dec 1988)
(Associate)
Urquharts, Edinburgh . . . .(p.909)
  T: 0131 5562896
  E: davidsangster@urquharts.co.uk

SANTANDREU, Kirsty (Dec 2009) (Employee)
Balfour Beatty Regional Civil Engineering,
  Motherwell. . . . .(p.1251)
  T: 01698 647 983
  E: kirsty.santandreu@balfourbeatty.com

SANTONI, Paul (Nov 1982) (Consultant)
Freelands, Wishaw . . . .(p.1181)
  T: 01698 355936
  E: psantoni@freelands.co.uk

SARGENT, Alison Louise (Sept 1998)
(Employee)
National Health Service Scotland,
  Edinburgh . . . .(p.1225)
  T: 0131 2757800
  E: alison.sargent@nhs.scot

SARGENT, Neil Joseph William (Jul 2009)
(Employee)
VicAsset Advisors (UK) Limited, London
  SW1 . . . .(p.1269)
  T: 020 7429 2255
  E: Neil.Sargent@vicasset.com

SARGENT, Pamela May (Oct 2014) (Employee)
Ledingham Chalmers LLP,
  Aberdeen . . . .(p.734)
  T: 01224 408408
  E: pamela.sargent@ledinghamchalmers.com

SARWAR, Khadija (Jul 2018) (Employee)
Keoghs Scotland LLP, Glasgow. . . . .(p.996)
  T: 0141 2380100
  E: ksarwar@keoghs.co.uk

SARWAR, Mohammed (Dec 2013) (Solicitor)
NO FIRM

SARWAR, Mohammed Hamza (Oct 2013)
(Employee)
Procurator Fiscal Service, Hamilton . . . .(p.1247)
  T: 0844 5613245
  E: Mohammed.Sarwar@copfs.gov.uk

SARWAR, Sana (May 2019) (Employee)
The Moray Council, Elgin . . . .(p.1236)
  T: 01343 543451
  E: sana.sarwar@moray.gov.uk

SARWAR, Umran Ali (Mar 2004) (Employee)
University of Dundee, Dundee . . . .(p.1219)
  T: 44 (0)1382 385340
  E: u.z.sarwar@dundee.ac.uk

SASAN, Hazel Fiona (Sept 1986) (Partner)
Morton Fraser LLP, Glasgow . . . .(p.1022)
T: 0141 2741100
E: fiona.sasan@morton-fraser.com

SAUNDERS, Joanne (Sept 1993) (Employee)
NORTH LANARKSHIREre Council,
Motherwell . . . .(p.1251)
T: 01698 302196
E: saundersj@northlan.gov.uk

SAUNDERS, Lyndsey McLare Steele
(Sept 2009) (Solicitor)
NO FIRM

SAVAGE, Anna Christine (Oct 2012) (Employee)
WSP UK Limited, London WC2 . . . . . .(p.1269)
T: 0131 344 2300
E: anna.savage@wsp.com

SAVAGE, Fiona (Feb 2006) (Employee)
TLT LLP, Glasgow . . . .(p.1048)
T: 0333 006 0400
E: Fiona.Savage@TLTsolicitors.com

SAVAGE, Gillian (Jun 2021) (Employee)
Scottish Police Authority, Police Scotland,
Dundee . . . .(p.1218)
T: (0300) 1112222
E: gillian.savage@scotland.pnn.police.uk

SAVAGE, James Francis (Sept 1982) (Director)
Russel + Aitken (Falkirk + Alloa) Ltd,
Alloa . . . .(p.753)
T: 01259 723201
E: jamessavage@randa-fa.co.uk

SAVAGE, Victoria Louise (Aug 2009) (Associate)
Levy & McRae Solicitors LLP,
Glasgow . . . .(p.1000)
T: 0141 3072311
E: vsavage@lemac.co.uk

SAWERS, Helen Grace (Sept 2010) (Employee)
Russel + Aitken (Falkirk + Alloa) Ltd,
Falkirk . . . .(p.924)
T: 01324 622888
E: helensawers@randa-fa.co.uk

SAYER, Christopher John (Jan 1984) (Partner)
Sayer Burnett, Edinburgh . . . .(p.899)
T: 0131 225 5567
E: cs@sayerburnett.com

SCAIFE, Lindy-Rose (Nov 2003) (Employee)
Procurator Fiscal Service, Greenock . . . .(p.1246)
T: 0844 5613404
E: lindy.scaife@copfs.gov.uk

SCANLAN, Cathleen Louise (Oct 2016)
(Employee)
Pinsent Masons LLP, Glasgow . . . .(p.1031)
T: 0141 567 8400
E: cathleen.scanlan@pinsentmasons.com

SCANLON, Mairi (Oct 1983) (Director)
Scanlon Ewing Limited, Clydebank . . . . .(p.785)
T: 0141 9529297
E: mairi@scanlonewing.co.uk

SCHARBERT, Markus (Dec 2017) (Employee)
Anderson Strathern LLP, Edinburgh . . . .(p.839)
T: 0131 2707700
E: markus.scharbert@andersonstrathern.co.uk

SCHIAVONE, Laura Catherine (Sept 2011)
(Director)
Mitchells Roberton Ltd, Glasgow . . . . .(p.1020)
T: 0141 5523422
E: laura@mitchells-roberton.co.uk

SCHIAVONE, Paul Rossi (Mar 2009) (Director)
Pollock Fairbridge Schiavone Limited,
Glasgow . . . .(p.1033)
T: 0141 7792577
E: ps@pfssolicitors.co.uk

SCHMIDT, John Michael (Feb 1994) (Employee)
Arnold & Porter Kaye Scholer LLP, London
EC2 . . . .(p.1261)
E: john.schmidt@arnoldporter.com

SCHMIDT, Rhona Elizabeth (Oct 1996)
(Employee)
Dorsey & Whitney LLP,
Minneapolis . . . .(p.1279)
E: schmidt.rhona@dorsey.com

SCHMIDTOV, Dominika (Jun 2019) (Solicitor)
NO FIRM

SCHOFIELD, Kim Antoinette (Jun 2010)
(Employee)
Procurator Fiscal Service,
Edinburgh . . . .(p.1229)
T: 0300 0203000
E: Kim.Schofield@copfs.gov.uk

SCHOLARIOS, Nicos (Dec 1983) (Director)
MSM Solicitors Limited, Glasgow . . . . .(p.1024)
T: 0141 3395252
E: ns@msmlaw.co.uk

SCHOLEFIELD, Victoria Elizabeth (Dec 2002)
(Employee)
Arthur J Gallagher, Glasgow . . . .(p.1237)
T: 0141 285 3056
E: Victoria_Scholefield@ajg.com

SCHREIBER, Alasdair Campbell (May 2021)
(Employee)
Miller Hendry, Perth . . . .(p.1150)
T: 01738 637311
E: alasdairschreiber@millerhendry.co.uk

SCHUMACHER, Susanne Patricia (Feb 2018)
(Employee)
Flo Health UK Limited, London . . . . . .(p.1264)
E: s_schumacher@flo.health

SCHWINDT, Melanie Petra (Aug 2005)
(Employee)
Morton Fraser LLP, Edinburgh . . . .(p.891)
T: 0131 2471000
E: melanie.schwindt@morton-fraser.com

SCLARE, Laura Fiona (Sept 2012) (Employee)
Latta Law Limited, Glasgow . . . .(p.998)
T: 0141 222 2185
E: ls@lattalaw.co.uk

SCOBBIE, Eilidh Melvin (Dec 1977) (Solicitor)
NO FIRM

SCOBBIE, Mary Ellen (Jan 2018) (Employee)
Bruce McCormack Limited,
Motherwell . . . .(p.1127)
T: 01698 260033

SCOTT, Aileen (Sept 1989) (Employee)
The Moray Council, Elgin . . . .(p.1236)
T: 01343 563020
E: aileen.scott@moray.gov.uk

SCOTT, Aileen Isobel (Jun 2008) (Employee)
Miller Hendry, Perth . . . .(p.1150)
T: 01738 637311
E: aileenscott@millerhendry.co.uk

SCOTT, Aisling Sarah (Sept 2012) (Employee)
National Health Service Scotland,
Edinburgh . . . .(p.1225)
T: 0131 2757800
E: Aisling.Scott@nhs.scot

SCOTT, Alison Elizabeth (Dec 2002) (Associate)
DLA Piper Scotland LLP, Edinburgh . . . .(p.863)
T: 0131 345 5164
E: Alison.Scott@dlapiper.com

SCOTT, Alistair James (Sept 1999) (Employee)
Lloyds Banking Group Plc,
Edinburgh . . . .(p.1224)
T: (0131) 442 9579
E: alistair.scott@lloydsbanking.com

SCOTT, Amanda (Mar 2019) (Solicitor)
NO FIRM

SCOTT, Andrew (Nov 2000) (Employee)
Brodies LLP, Edinburgh . . . .(p.845)
T: 0131 2283777
E: andrew.scott@brodies.com

SCOTT, Angela Louise (Sept 1995) (Partner)
Wyllie & Henderson Solicitors,
Perth . . . .(p.1153)
T: 01738 638465
E: ascott@wyllie-henderson.co.uk

SCOTT, Antonia Rebecca (Jan 2013) (Employee)
Brodies LLP, Edinburgh . . . .(p.845)
T: 0131 2283777
E: antonia.scott@brodies.com

SCOTT, Brenda Catherine (Oct 1993) (Partner)
Brodies LLP, Edinburgh . . . .(p.845)
T: 0131 2283777
E: brenda.scott@brodies.com

SCOTT, Brianella Nikesha Samantha
(Dec 2020) (Employee)
Harper Macleod LLP, Glasgow . . . .(p.983)
T: 0141 2218888
E: brianella.scott@harpermacleod.co.uk

SCOTT, Callum Rankine (Nov 2011) (Employee)
Acteon Group Limited, London
EC1 . . . .(p.1260)
E: callum.scott@acteon.com

SCOTT, Caroline Ferrier (Jan 2009) (Employee)
Medtronic Limited, Watford . . . .(p.1272)
E: caroline.scott@medtronic.com

SCOTT, Cassandra Merete (Sept 2010)
(Employee)
Procurator Fiscal Service, Glasgow . . . .(p.1241)
T: 0300 0203000
E: cassandra.scott@copfs.gov.uk

SCOTT, Catherine Margaret (Nov 2001)
(Employee)
Scottish Government, Edinburgh . . . . .(p.1231)
T: 0131 244 6554
E: catherine.scott@gov.scot

SCOTT, Claire Louise (Jul 2018) (Employee)
Brodies LLP, Edinburgh . . . .(p.845)
T: 0131 2283777
E: claire.scott@brodies.com

SCOTT, Claire Michelle (Oct 2002) (Employee)
Pinsent Masons LLP, Aberdeen . . . .(p.739)
T: 01224 377900
E: Claire.Scott@pinsentmasons.com

SCOTT, Craig Colin (Jun 2015) (Employee)
Central Court Lawyers, Livingston . . . .(p.1118)
T: 01506 416999
E: craigscott@centralcourtlawyers.co.uk

SCOTT, David Jason (Dec 1991) (Partner)
Warners Solicitors LLP, Edinburgh . . . . . .(p.911)
T: 0131 6624747
E: jscott@warnersllp.com

SCOTT, David Stuart (Oct 2001) (Partner)
Ledingham Chalmers LLP,
Aberdeen . . . .(p.734)
T: 01224 408573
E: david.scott@ledinghamchalmers.com

SCOTT, Eric John, WS (Dec 1981) (Partner)
Campbell Smith LLP, Edinburgh . . . .(p.852)
T: 0131 5563737
E: eric.scott@camsmith.co.uk

SCOTT, Fiona Ann (Nov 1999) (Associate)
CMS Cameron McKenna Nabarro Olswang LLP,
Edinburgh . . . .(p.856)
T: 0131 2288000
E: Fiona.Scott@cms-cmno.com

SCOTT, Fiona Elen (Apr 2010) (Employee)
Brodies LLP, Edinburgh . . . . (p.845)
T: 0131 2283777
E: fiona.scott@brodies.com

SCOTT, Fraser Clark (Dec 2009) (Employee)
Murray Beith Murray, Edinburgh . . . . . . (p.893)
T: 0131 2251200
E: fraser.scott@murraybeith.co.uk

SCOTT, Gary James (Nov 2007) (Employee)
Subsea 7 (UK Service Company) Ltd,
Westhill . . . . (p.1255)
T: 01224 344308
E: gary.scott@subsea7.com

SCOTT, George John, SSC (Mar 1980)
(Associate)
TC Young LLP, Edinburgh . . . . (p.914)
T: 0131 2207660
E: gjs@tcyoung.co.uk

SCOTT, Ian Alexander (Sept 1992) (Director)
Bruce McCormack Limited,
Motherwell. . . . . (p.1127)
T: 01698 260033
E: admin@brucethelawyers.co.uk

SCOTT, Ian Brown Gilkison (Oct 2001)
(Associate)
Ledingham Chalmers LLP,
Edinburgh . . . . (p.881)
T: 0131 2001000
E: ian.scott@ledinghamchalmers.com

SCOTT, Jane (Nov 2014) (Employee)
The Medical & Dental Defence Union of
Scotland, Glasgow . . . . (p.1245)
T: 0845 2702034
E: jscott@mddus.com

SCOTT, Jenny Nevay (May 2019) (Employee)
Burness Paull LLP, Glasgow . . . . (p.954)
T: 0141 2484933
E: jenny.scott94@gmail.com

SCOTT, Jill Gwendoline (Oct 1985) (Employee)
University of Strathclyde, Glasgow . . . . (p.1245)
T: (0141) 5485905

SCOTT, John Alexander (Jan 1977) (Consultant)
Scott Alexander, Montrose . . . . (p.1125)
T: 01674 671477
E: john@scottalexandersolicitors.co.uk

SCOTT, John Dominic, QC (Dec 1986) (Partner)
John Scott QC, Edinburgh . . . . (p.900)
T: 07779 328656
E: johndscott@talk21.com

SCOTT, Julian McKenzie, WS (Dec 1985)
(Employee)
Gilson Gray LLP, Edinburgh . . . . (p.874)
T: 0131 5165354
E: jscott@gilsongray.co.uk

SCOTT, Julie-Marie (Nov 1997) (Employee)
Scottish Courts and Tribunals Service,
Paisley . . . . (p.1252)
T: 0141 8875291
E: jscott4@scotcourts.gov.uk

SCOTT, Kenneth Andrew (Sept 2004)
(Associate)
MacRoberts LLP, Edinburgh . . . . (p.887)
T: 0131 2295046
E: kenny.Scott@macroberts.com

SCOTT, Liam John (Aug 2021) (Employee)
The Kerr Brown Partnership,
Glasgow. (p.1044)
T: 0141 2214880

SCOTT LINTOTT, Sally Jane (Apr 2016)
(Employee)
Murray Beith Murray, Edinburgh . . . . . . (p.893)
T: 0131 2251200
E: Sally.Scottlintott@murraybeith.co.uk

SCOTT, Lorraine Lennox (Oct 2020)
(Employee)
Thompsons, Glasgow . . . . (p.1046)
T: 0141 2218840
E: lorraine.scott@thompsons-scotland.co.uk

SCOTT, Lynne Anne (Oct 1994) (Solicitor)
NO FIRM

SCOTT, Mark Wilburn (May 2011) (Employee)
Last Mile Infrastructure Limited,
Glasgow. (p.1240)
E: mark.scott@lastmile-group.com

SCOTT, Michael James (Dec 1980) (Employee)
The Institute and Faculty of Actuaries,
Edinburgh . . . . (p.1234)
T: 1312401307
E: Michael.Scott@actuaries.org.uk

SCOTT, Michael Sydney William (Jan 2000)
(Employee)
Orkney Islands Council, Kirkwall . . . . . . (p.1250)
T: 01856 873535
E: michael.scott@orkney.gov.uk

SCOTT, Mylene Helen Maxwell (Aug 1990)
(Associate)
Douglas Wright, Kilmarnock . . . . (p.1096)
T: 01563 532177
E: mscott@douglas-wright.co.uk

SCOTT, Myra (Aug 1990) (Partner)
Aberdein Considine and Company,
Glasgow. (p.937)
T: 0141 227 8200
E: mscott@acandco.com

SCOTT, Nicholas (May 2000) (Partner)
Brodies LLP, Edinburgh . . . . (p.845)
T: 0131 2283777
E: nick.scott@brodies.com

SCOTT, Nicola Clair (Jul 2008) (Partner)
Davidson Chalmers Stewart LLP,
 Glasgow . . . .(p.967)
 T: 0141 4283258
 E: nicola.scott@dcslegal.com

SCOTT, Norman John (Oct 1983) (Partner)
D. Douglas Mackie, Glasgow . . . .(p.971)
 T: 0141 3312882
 E: info@ddmackie.co.uk

SCOTT, Peter (Oct 1996) (Consultant)
Malcolm, Jack & Matheson Limited,
 Dunfermline . . . .(p.824)
 T: 01383 723444
 E: Peter@malcolmjack.co.uk

SCOTT, Rebecca Anne (Jan 2018) (Employee)
Harper Macleod LLP, Glasgow . . . .(p.983)
 T: 0141 2218888
 E: rebecca.scott@harpermacleod.co.uk

SCOTT, Rebecca Julie (Aug 2020) (Employee)
Procurator Fiscal Service,
 Edinburgh . . . .(p.1227)
 T: 0300 0203168
 E: rebecca.scott@copfs.gov.uk

SCOTT, Rebecca May (Sept 2012) (Employee)
Clan Childlaw Limited, Glasgow . . . .(p.959)
 T: (0808) 129 0522
 E: rebecca.scott@clanchildlaw.org

SCOTT, Richard Imray (Sept 2003) (Partner)
Pinsent Masons LLP, Aberdeen . . . .(p.739)
 T: 01224 377900
 E: richard.scott@pinsentmasons.com

SCOTT, Rosalind Louise (Oct 2003) (Employee)
Lloyds Banking Group Plc,
 Edinburgh . . . .(p.1224)
 T: 0131 442 9571
 E: rosalind.scott@lloydsbanking.com

SCOTT, Rosemary Anne (Dec 1982) (Associate)
Thorntons Law LLP, Perth . . . .(p.1151)
 T: 01738 621212
 E: rscott@thorntons-law.co.uk

SCOTT, Sara Noel MacKinnon (Nov 2000)
 (Employee)
Blackadders LLP, Dundee . . . .(p.805)
 T: 01382 229222
 E: sara.scott@blackadders.co.uk

SCOTT, Stephen Reader (Sept 1987)
 (Consultant)
Burness Paull LLP, Edinburgh . . . .(p.850)
 T: 0131 4736000
 E: stephen.scott@burnesspaull.com

SCOTT, Susan Jane (Jun 2006) (Associate)
McCash & Hunter LLP, Perth . . . .(p.1149)
 T: 01738 620451
 E: susanscott@mccash.co.uk

SCOTT, Tracey Marie (Feb 1995) (Employee)
Scottish Courts and Tribunals Service,
 Stirling . . . .(p.1255)
 T: 01786 462191
 E: TScott@scotcourts.gov.uk

SCOTT-DEMPSTER, Robert Andrew
 (Nov 1997) (Partner)
Gillespie Macandrew LLP,
 Edinburgh . . . .(p.872)
 T: 0131 2251677
 E:
 robert.scott-dempster@gillespiemacandrew.co.
 uk

SCOTT-GILROY, Julie (Sept 2008) (Associate)
Morton Fraser LLP, Edinburgh . . . .(p.891)
 T: 0131 2471000
 E: julie.scott-gilroy@morton-fraser.co.uk

SCOULLER, Karen Jane (Sept 1989) (Employee)
Dundee City Council, Dundee . . . .(p.1217)
 T: 01382 434813
 E: karen.scouller@dundeecity.gov.uk

SCRIMGEOUR, Gemma Louise (Oct 2018)
 (Employee)
MacRoberts LLP, Dundee. . . . .(p.815)
 T: 01382 339340
 E: gemma.scrimgeour@macroberts.com

SCRIMGEOUR, Stephanie Reith (Apr 2005)
 (Employee)
Standard Life Assets and Employee Services
 Limited, Edinburgh . . . .(p.1234)
 T: 0131 2457508
 E:
 stephanie.scrimgeour@aberdeenstandard.com

SCRYMGEOUR, Karen Christine (Feb 2012)
 (Employee)
Historic Environment Scotland,
 Edinburgh . . . .(p.1223)
 T: (0131) 6688987
 E: karen.scrymgeour@hes.scot

SCULLION, Alison Mary (Aug 2008) (Employee)
Highland Council, Inverness . . . .(p.1248)
 T: 01463 702000
 E: alison.scullion@highland.gov.uk

SCULLION, Louise Anne (Jan 2019) (Employee)
Hamilton Ross, Airdrie . . . .(p.749)
 T: 01236 627627
 E: louise@hamiltonross.co.uk

SCULLION, Nicholas James Martin Russell
 (Oct 1975) (Director)
Scullion Law Limited, Hamilton . . . . . .(p.1069)
 T: 01698 283265
 E: njs@scullionlaw.com

SCULLION, Nicholas Jonathan (Aug 2005)
 (Director)
Scullion Law Limited, Hamilton . . . . . .(p.1069)
 T: 01698 283265
 E: nicholas@scullionlaw.com

SCULLION, Nigel Russell (Nov 2006) (Partner)
Manus James, Glasgow . . . .(p.1018)
E: nigel@manusjames.com

SCULLION, Paul Michael (Oct 2009) (Partner)
Burness Paull LLP, Glasgow . . . .(p.954)
T: 0141 2736703
E: Paul.Scullion@burnesspaull.com

SCULLY, Rebecca (Dec 2001) (Employee)
Procurator Fiscal Service, Hamilton . . . .(p.1247)
T: 0844 5613245
E: rebecca.scully@copfs.gov.uk

SCULTHORPE, Erin Cameron (Aug 2020)
(Employee)
DLA Piper Scotland LLP, Edinburgh . . . .(p.863)
T: 08700 111111
E: Erin.Sculthrope@dlapiper.com

SEAGER, Kathleen Anne (Aug 1992) (Partner)
Fraser & Mulligan, Aberdeen . . . .(p.731)
T: 01224 646428
E: kas@fraser-mulligan.co.uk

SEAL, Abby Claire (Sept 2017) (Employee)
Procurator Fiscal Service, Hamilton . . . .(p.1247)
T: 0844 5613245
E: Abby.Seal@copfs.gov.uk

SEALEY, Pamela Jane (Sept 2013) (Employee)
Shockingly Fresh Limited,
Edinburgh . . . .(p.1234)
E: Pamela@shockinglyfresh.com

SEATH, Gordon Russell (Aug 1990) (Employee)
MacHardy, Alexander & Whyte, WS,
Forfar. . . . .(p.927)
T: 01307 463593
E: gseath@machardy.co.uk

SEATH, Jamie Scott (Oct 2019) (Employee)
Gillespie Macandrew LLP,
Edinburgh . . . .(p.872)
T: 0131 2251677
E: jamie.seath@gillespiemacandrew.co.uk

SEATON, Adelle Astra (Oct 2012) (Employee)
Turcan Connell, Edinburgh . . . .(p.908)
T: 0131 2288111
E: adelle.seaton@turcanconnell.com

SEATON, Robert Henderson (Jul 2004)
(Employee)
Directorate For Planning & Environmental
Appeals, Falkirk . . . .(p.1236)
T: 0131 244 6909

SEATON, William Gordon (Nov 1974) (Partner)
Anderson Banks, Oban . . . .(p.1134)
T: 01631 563158
E: gseaton@andersonbanks.co.uk

SEAWARD, Rose Alison (Jan 2013) (Employee)
Ennova Limited, Edinburgh . . . .(p.869)
T: 0131 6624555
E: rseaward@ennova-law.com

SEDDON, Emma Samantha (Nov 2006)
(Employee)
Vialex Limited, Edinburgh . . . .(p.1235)
T: 0333 2400127
E: emma.seddon@vialex.co.uk

SEDDON, Jonathan (Jan 1997) (Partner)
Morton Fraser LLP, Edinburgh . . . .(p.891)
T: 0131 2471000
E: jonathan.seddon@morton-fraser.com

SEDMAN JAENSSON, Caroline Birgitta
(Aug 2020) (Employee)
Burness Paull LLP, Glasgow . . . .(p.954)
T: 0141 2484933
E: caroline.sedmanjaensson@burnesspaull.com

SEENAN, Nicola Elaine (Dec 1996) (Employee)
Alexis Hunter Family Law, Glasgow . . . .(p.989)
T: 0141 4040124
E: nes@ahfamilylaw.co.uk

SEFTON, Laura Elizabeth (Jan 2016) (Associate)
CMS Cameron McKenna Nabarro Olswang LLP,
Edinburgh . . . .(p.856)
T: 0131 2288000
E: laura.sefton@cms-cmno.com

SEGAL, Gerald Robert Alfred (Oct 2008)
(Associate)
Drummond Miller LLP, Glasgow. . . . . . .(p.971)
T: 0141 3320086
E: GSegal@dm-property.com

SEGER, Tobias Max (Mar 2021) (Employee)
CMS Cameron McKenna Nabarro Olswang LLP,
Edinburgh . . . .(p.856)
T: 0131 2288000
E: tobias.seger@cms-cmno.com

SEGGIE, Andrew Thomas (May 2015)
(Employee)
MTM Defence Lawyers Limited,
Edinburgh . . . .(p.893)
T: 0131 3060115
E: aseggie@mtmdefence.co.uk

SEIDEL, Stephanie Alexandra (Oct 2013)
(Employee)
DWF LLP, Glasgow . . . .(p.973)
T: 0141 228 8000
E: steph.seidel@dwf.law

SEIVWRIGHT, Cara Fiona Iris (Aug 2009)
(Employee)
McEwan Fraser Legal, Edinburgh . . . . . .(p.885)
T: 0131 5249797
E: cara.seivwright@mcewanfraserlegal.co.uk

SELFRIDGE, Vhari Yvonne (May 2001)
(Employee)
Lindsays LLP, Edinburgh . . . .(p.882)
T: 0131 2291212

SELLA, Francesca (Jul 2020) (Employee)
JustRight Scotland LLP, Glasgow ......(p.994)
T: 0141 406 5350
E: francesca@justrightscotland.org.uk

SELLAR, Dominic Jonathan Keith (Jul 1996)
(Partner)
Dominic Sellar & Co, Glasgow.......(p.1038)
T: 0141 2551519
E: dominicsellar@hotmail.com

SELLAR, Donald Harper (Dec 2004) (Employee)
British Telecommunications PLC, London
EC4.......................(p.1262)
E: donald.sellar@bt.com

SELLAR, Gillian Christine (Oct 1994)
(Employee)
Scottish Borders Council, Newtown St.
Boswells....................(p.1251)
T: 01835 825 225
E: gillian.sellar@scotborders.gov.uk

SELLAR, Michael Stewart (Oct 1997)
(Employee)
Carpenters Scotland Limited,
Glasgow.....................(p.956)
T: 0141 3285452

SELMAN, Douglas George (Jun 2014)
(Employee)
Baillie Gifford & Co, Edinburgh ......(p.1220)
T: 0131 2752000
E: dougie.selman@bailliegifford.com

SELMAN, Natalie Rachael Hawes (Mar 2019)
(Employee)
Mills & Reeve LLP, London EC4 ......(p.1266)
E: Natalie.Selman@mills-reeve.com

SEMPLE, Heather Anne (Sept 2011) (Employee)
Renfrewshire Valuation Joint Board,
Paisley ....(p.1252)

SENDA, Francesca Maria (Aug 2006) (Solicitor)
NO FIRM

SERGEANT, Andrew Kevin (Jul 2019)
(Employee)
Thorntons Law LLP, Edinburgh ....(p.906)
T: 0131 2258705
E: asergeant@thorntons-law.co.uk

SERVICE, Kelly Frances (Sept 2007) (Employee)
National Health Service Scotland,
Edinburgh ....(p.1225)
T: 0131 2757800
E: kelly.service@nhs.scot

SEVERIN, Colin Crawford (Aug 2017)
(Employee)
Wardlaw Stephenson Allan,
Edinburgh ....(p.910)
T: 0131 5578020
E: colin@wsalawyers.com

SHABBIR, Muhammad Bilaal (Jul 2020)
(Associate)
Clyde & Co (Scotland) LLP,
Edinburgh ....(p.855)
T: 0131 5571545
E: Bilaal.Shabbir@clydeco.com

SHACKLETON, Alison Margaret (Nov 1994)
(Associate)
Pinsent Masons LLP, Glasgow ....(p.1031)
T: 0141 567 8400
E: alison.shackleton@pinsentmasons.com

SHADE, Pauline (Nov 1994) (Employee)
Procurator Fiscal Service,
Edinburgh ....(p.1227)
T: 0300 020725
E: pauline.shade@copfs.gov.uk

SHAFAATULLA, Shereen (Nov 2006) (Employee)
Five Star (International) Ltd,
Glasgow....................(p.1239)
T: 0141 3397373
E: info@fivestarinternational.co.uk

SHAFI, Mamoun Khaleel (Aug 2012) (Solicitor)
NO FIRM

SHAH-GAIR, Jessel Nazir (Oct 2005) (Employee)
Poseidon Enhanced Technologies Limited,
Dublin ....(p.1274)
E: j.gair@poseidonplastics.com

SHAHID, Sanaa (Mar 2016) (Employee)
Glasgow City Council, Glasgow ......(p.1239)
T: 0141 2872000
E: Sanaa.Shahid@ced.glasgow.gov.uk

SHAND, Amy Jane (Oct 2018) (Employee)
Digby Brown LLP, Aberdeen ....(p.729)
T: 0333 200 5925
E: amy.shand@digbybrown.co.uk

SHAND, Antonia Elizabeth (Apr 2007)
(Employee)
PTS Consulting, London EC3 ....(p.1267)
E: Antonia.Shand@ptsconsulting.com

SHAND, Caroline Falconer (Oct 2005) (Partner)
Shepherd and Wedderburn LLP,
Edinburgh ....(p.900)
T: 0131 2289900
E: Caroline.Shand@shepwedd.com

SHAND, Erin (Jan 2019) (Employee)
Aberdein Considine and Company,
Aberdeen....................(p.718)
T: 01224 589700
E: eshand@acandco.com

SHAND, Kenneth David (Oct 1984) (Solicitor)
NO FIRM

SHAND, Lewis Ian (Jun 2016) (Employee)
Angus Council, Forfar ....(p.1237)
T: 01307 476228
E: ShandL@angus.gov.uk

SHAND, Nicola Anne (Apr 2009) (Employee)
Scotia Gas Networks Limited,
Horley . . . .(p.1260)
T: 01293 818 217
E: nicola.shand@sgn.co.uk

SHAND, Peter Graham, WS (Nov 2001)
(Partner)
Murray Beith Murray, Edinburgh . . . . . .(p.893)
T: 0131 2251200
E: peter.shand@murraybeith.co.uk

SHANKS, Allan David (Apr 2015) (Employee)
University of Edinburgh, Edinburgh . . .(p.1235)
E: Allan.Shanks@ed.ac.uk

SHANKS, Andrew William (Sept 2001)
(Employee)
Procurator Fiscal Service, Elgin . . . .(p.1236)
T: 0844561 2670
E: andy.shanks@copfs.gov.uk

SHANKS, Lawri James (Jul 2008) (Employee)
Williamson & Henry LLP,
Kirkcudbright . . . .(p.1104)
T: 01557 330692
E: ljshanks@williamsonandhenry.co.uk

SHANKS, Ronald Alan (Nov 1999) (Partner)
Addleshaw Goddard LLP,
Edinburgh . . . .(p.835)
T: 0131 2282400
E: Alan.Shanks@addleshawgoddard.com

SHANNON, Christopher Johnstone
(Dec 1997) (Partner)
Harper, Robertson & Shannon,
Annan . . . .(p.754)
T: 01461 203418
E: christopher@hrands.co.uk

SHANNON, Julie (Feb 1991) (Employee)
Dumfries & Galloway Council,
Dumfries . . . .(p.1217)
T: 01387 260000
E: julie.shannon@dumgal.gov.uk

SHANNON, William Elliot (Mar 1993)
(Employee)
Anderson Strathern LLP, Edinburgh . . . .(p.839)
T: 0131 2707700
E: william.shannon@andersonstrathern.co.uk

SHARIF, Francesca Dominique (Aug 2016)
(Employee)
Scottish Government, Edinburgh . . . . .(p.1231)
T: 0131 244 0815
E: francesca.sharif@gov.scot

SHARIF, Nadia Kausar (Dec 2015) (Employee)
Allingham & Co (Solicitors) Limited,
Edinburgh . . . .(p.838)
T: 0131 4479341

SHARKEY, David Andrew (Aug 2021)
(Employee)
Burness Paull LLP, Edinburgh . . . .(p.850)
T: 0131 4736000
E: david.sharkey@burnesspaull.com

SHARKEY, Kenzie Anne (Jul 2014) (Employee)
Ofgem, Glasgow . . . .(p.1241)
T: (0141) 354 5425
E: kenzie.sharkey@ofgem.gov.uk

SHARKEY, Maria Therese (Dec 2008)
(Employee)
SOUTH LANARKSHIREre Council,
Hamilton . . . .(p.1247)
T: (01698) 454785
E: maria.sharkey@southlanarkshire.gov.uk

SHARKEY, Natalie Elizabeth (Jun 2016)
(Employee)
Reed Smith LLP, London EC2 . . . .(p.1267)
E: nsharkey@reedsmith.com

SHARMA, Savita (Aug 2015) (Employee)
Morton Fraser LLP, Edinburgh . . . .(p.891)
T: 0131 2471000
E: savita.sharma@morton-fraser.com

SHARMA, Vikas (Jan 2009) (Director)
The Chamber Practice Ltd,
Aberdeen . . . .(p.745)
T: 01224 433301
E: vikas@thechamberpractice.co.uk

SHARP, Fiona Bain (Dec 1996) (Associate)
Brodies LLP, Glasgow . . . .(p.948)
T: 0141 2484672
E: fiona.sharp@brodies.com

SHARP, Jennifer Agnes (Nov 1991) (Employee)
Wheatley Housing Group Limited,
Glasgow. . . . .(p.1246)
T: 0845 9001001
E: jennifer.sharp@wheatley-group.com

SHARP, Kate Anne (Oct 2013) (Employee)
Lloyds Banking Group Plc,
Edinburgh . . . .(p.1224)
T: (0131) 442 9579
E: kate.sharp@lloydsbanking.com

SHARP, Michelle Gillian (Sept 2006) (Employee)
Stronachs LLP, Aberdeen . . . .(p.744)
T: 01224 845845
E: Michelle.Sharp@stronachs.com

SHARP, Rona Marion Dennison (Oct 2005)
(Director)
Red Letter Law Limited, Edinburgh . . . . .(p.898)
T: 07712 052834
E: rona@redletterlaw.co.uk

SHARPE, Matthew David (Sept 2020)
(Employee)
Ashurst LLP, London E1 . . . .(p.1261)
T: (020) 7859 2145
E: matthew.sharpe@ashurst.com

SHAW, Aileen Cecilia (Sept 1984) (Employee)
Malcolm, Jack & Matheson Limited,
    Dunfermline . . . .(p.824)
    T: 01383 723444
    E: aileenshaw@malcolmjack.co.uk

SHAW, Alasdair James (Dec 2017) (Employee)
Procurator Fiscal Service,
    Edinburgh . . . .(p.1227)
    T: 0300 0203168
    E: Alasdair.Shaw@copfs.gov.uk

SHAW, Alison (Oct 2008) (Employee)
Procurator Fiscal Service, Aberdeen . . .(p.1213)
    T: 0300 0202336
    E: alison.shaw@copfs.gov.uk

SHAW, Alison Ballantyne (Oct 2019)
  (Employee)
Digby Brown LLP, Glasgow . . . .(p.970)
    T: 0333 200 5925
    E: alison.shaw@digbybrown.co.uk

SHAW, Alyson Anne (Oct 2018) (Employee)
Shepherd and Wedderburn LLP,
    Edinburgh . . . .(p.900)
    T: 0131 2289900

SHAW, Andrew Brian (Sept 2003) (Partner)
CMS Cameron McKenna Nabarro Olswang LLP,
    London EC4 . . . .(p.1263)
    T: 0207 3673000
    E: Andrew.Shaw@cms-cmno.com

SHAW, Andrew John (Sept 2019) (Employee)
Blackadders LLP, Glasgow . . . .(p.946)
    T: 0141 2481888
    E: andrew.shaw@blackadders.co.uk

SHAW, Arlene Martha Susan (Nov 2007)
  (Employee)
Procurator Fiscal Service,
    Edinburgh . . . .(p.1229)
    T: 0300 0203000
    E: arlene.shaw@copfs.gov.uk

SHAW, Cameron Andrew (Nov 2010)
  (Employee)
Jones Whyte LLP, Glasgow. . . . .(p.993)
    T: 0141 375 1222
    E: cameron.shaw@joneswhyte.co.uk

SHAW, Christopher Alexander (Jul 2018)
  (Employee)
Levy & McRae Solicitors LLP,
    Glasgow. . . . .(p.1000)
    T: 0141 3072311
    E: cshaw@lemac.co.uk

SHAW, Christopher Joseph Stuart
  (Oct 2007) (Employee)
Moody's Group Deutschland GmbH,
    Frankfurt . . . .(p.1273)
    T: +49 69 7370 0857
    E: Christopher.Shaw2@moodys.com

SHAW, Donald Gordon Brian, WS
  (Oct 1979) (Solicitor)
NO FIRM

SHAW, Elizabeth (Oct 2008) (Employee)
Bedell Cristin Jersey Partnership, St
    Helier . . . .(p.1274)
    T: 01534 814814
    E: elizabethshaw85@gmail.com

SHAW, Emily Harriette (Aug 2019) (Employee)
National Westminster Bank PLC,
    Edinburgh . . . .(p.1226)
    T: (0131) 626 2925
    E: Emily.Shaw@natwest.com

SHAW, Gillian (Nov 2001) (Employee)
Buchanan Shaw Consulting Ltd,
    Dingwall . . . .(p.1216)
    E: gill@buchananshaw.co.uk

SHAW, Heather Grace (Jan 2010) (Director)
Shaw's Law Ltd, Oban . . . .(p.1135)
    T: 01631 705007
    E: heather@shawslaw.co.uk

SHAW, James Alan George (Sept 2000)
  (Employee)
Withers LLP, London EC4 . . . .(p.1269)
    T: (0207) 5976135
    E: james.shaw@withersworldwide.com

SHAW, James Duncan (Aug 1993) (Employee)
The Scottish Parliament, Edinburgh . . .(p.1235)
    T: 0131 3486502
    E: james.shaw@parliament.scot

SHAW, Joel Julian Guise (Feb 2014) (Employee)
Thompsons, Glasgow . . . .(p.1046)
    T: 0141 2218840
    E: Joel.Shaw@thompsons-scotland.co.uk

SHAW, Karen Elizabeth (Oct 1996) (Director)
Renew Legal Limited, Edinburgh . . . . . .(p.898)
    E: shaw@renewlegal.com

SHAW, Kirsty (Jan 2018) (Employee)
Brodies LLP, Edinburgh . . . .(p.845)
    T: 0131 2283777
    E: kirsty.shaw@brodies.com

SHAW, Kirsty Jane (Dec 1984) (Employee)
Highland Council, Inverness. . . . .(p.1248)
    T: 01463 702108
    E: Kirsty.Shaw@highland.gov.uk

SHAW, Louise Ann (Oct 2014) (Employee)
Pinsent Masons LLP, Glasgow . . . .(p.1031)
    T: 0141 567 8400
    E: louise.shaw@pinsentmasons.com

SHAW, Martyn Thomson (Nov 1996) (Partner)
MacRoberts LLP, Glasgow . . . .(p.1015)
    T: 0141 3031100
    E: martyn.shaw@macroberts.com

SHAW, Rachel Elizabeth (Jan 2017) (Employee)
Dentons UK and Middle East LLP,
Glasgow . . . . (p.968)
T: 0330 2220050
E: Rachel.Shaw@dentons.com

SHAW, Sara Anne (Oct 2000) (Employee)
Procurator Fiscal Service,
Edinburgh . . . . (p.1227)
T: 0300 0203317
E: sara.shaw@copfs.gov.uk

SHAW, Sarah Catherine (Sept 2019)
(Employee)
Caesar & Howie, Bathgate . . . . (p.770)
T: 01506 815900
E: scs@caesar-howie.co.uk

SHAW, Steven Andrew (Sept 2009) (Employee)
TotalEnergies E&P UK Limited,
Westhill . . . . (p.1255)
T: 01224 297000
E: steven.shaw@totalenergies.com

SHAW, Susan Dorothy (Nov 2008) (Partner)
Living Law, Wester Inch Village . . . . . . (p.1178)
T: 07929 996105
E: susan@livinglaw.co.uk

SHAW, Thomas Elder (Sept 1981) (Solicitor)
NO FIRM

SHEACH, David Alexander (Sept 1988)
(Employee)
Siccar Point Energy Limited,
Aberdeen . . . . (p.1214)
T: 01224 678127
E: das@siccarpointenergy.co.uk

SHEARER, Aileen Fiona (Jun 2003) (Associate)
DWF LLP, Edinburgh . . . . (p.865)
T: 0131 2265541
E: Aileen.Shearer@dwf.law

SHEARER, Charles James Robert (Feb 2019)
(Employee)
Moir and Sweeney LLP, Glasgow . . . . . (p.1021)
T: 0141 4292724
E: Charlie@moirandsweeney.com

SHEARER, Fay Charteris (Jun 2017) (Associate)
Burges Salmon LLP, Edinburgh . . . . (p.850)
T: 0131 3142112
E: fay.shearer@burges-salmon.com

SHEARER, Kerry Anne (Nov 2019) (Employee)
Cadwalader, Wickersham & Taft LLP, London
EC2 . . . . (p.1262)
E: kerry.shearer@cwt.com

SHEARER, Louise (Nov 2012) (Employee)
East Lothian Council, Haddington . . . . (p.1246)
T: 01620 827827
E: lshearer1@eastlothian.gov.uk

SHEARER, Lynsey Marion Anne (Jul 2007)
(Associate)
Strefford Tulips Limited, Hamilton . . . . (p.1070)
T: 01698 429428
E: l.shearer@strefford-tulips.co.uk

SHEARER, Nicola Carson (Jul 1995) (Employee)
North Ayrshire Council, Irvine . . . . (p.1249)
T: 01294 310000
E: nshearer@north-ayrshire.gov.uk

SHEARER, Paul Alexander (Sept 2003)
(Employee)
TSB Bank Plc, Edinburgh . . . . (p.1235)
T: 0131 260 0491
E: Paul.Shearer@tsb.co.uk

SHEDDON, Harry Stewart Peter (Jul 2012)
(Employee)
Kilpatrick & Walker, Ayr . . . . (p.763)
T: 01292 618585
E: harry@kilpatrickwalker.com

SHEERAN, Edwin John (Oct 2019) (Employee)
Procurator Fiscal Service,
Kilmarnock . . . . (p.1249)
T: 01563 536211
E: edwin.sheeran@copfs.gov.uk

SHEILS, Dominic Ciaran (Nov 2000) (Solicitor)
Mubadala Investment Company PJSC, Abu
Dhabi . . . . (p.1277)

SHELDON, John Christopher Phelps
(Nov 2005) (Partner)
Turcan Connell, Edinburgh . . . . (p.908)
T: 0131 2288111
E: chris.sheldon@turcanconnell.com

SHELDON, Sarah-Jane Mary (Mar 2016)
(Employee)
Holmes Mackillop Limited,
Johnstone . . . . (p.1089)
T: 01505 328 271
E: ss@homack.co.uk

SHELTON, Laura Paton (Nov 2008) (Employee)
Ridouts Professional Services Plc, London
W1 . . . . (p.1267)
T: 020 7317 0354
E: laura@ridout-law.com

SHENKEN, Nicholas Simon (Mar 1999)
(Partner)
TLT LLP, Glasgow . . . . (p.1048)
T: 0333 006 0400
E: nick.shenken@tltsolicitors.com

SHEPHERD, Adrienne Rowan (Oct 2007)
(Employee)
Sterling & Sterling LLC, New York . . . . (p.1279)
E: adrienne2000_uk@yahoo.co.uk

SHEPHERD, Claire Elizabeth (Nov 2010)
(Employee)
Epigenetica Limited, Glasgow . . . . (p.1239)
E: claire@epigenetica.uk

SHEPHERD, Kirsty Robyn (Feb 2020)
(Employee)
Dentons UK and Middle East LLP,
Edinburgh . . . .(p.860)
T: 0330 2220050
E: kirsty.shepherd@dentons.com

SHEPHERD, Michael John (Sept 2006)
(Employee)
Pinsent Masons LLP, Aberdeen . . . .(p.739)
T: 01224 377900
E: Michael.shepherd@pinsentmasons.com

SHEPHERD, Morag (Dec 1996) (Employee)
National Health Service Scotland,
Edinburgh . . . .(p.1225)
T: 0131 2757800
E: Morag.Shepherd@nhs.scot

SHEPHERD, Peter Brakenridge (Dec 1970)
(Employee)
Gilson Gray LLP, Dundee . . . .(p.812)
E: pshepherd@gilsongray.co.uk

SHEPHERD, Richard Douglas McKenzie
(Nov 1989) (Employee)
NO FIRM

SHEPPARD, Benjamin Hugh (Sept 2015)
(Employee)
Eversheds Sutherland (International) LLP,
Edinburgh . . . .(p.869)
T: 0207 9194500
E: BenSheppard@eversheds-Sutherland.com

SHERIDAN, Christopher Paul (Jun 2004)
(Partner)
Sheridans, Glasgow . . . .(p.1040)
T: 0141 3323536
E: chris@sheridanssolicitors.co.uk

SHERIDAN, John Paul (Aug 1999) (Partner)
TLT LLP, Glasgow . . . .(p.1048)
T: 0333 006 0400
E: jp.Sheridan@tltsolicitors.com

SHERIDAN, Laura Ann (Jun 2011) (Employee)
Harper Macleod LLP, Glasgow . . . .(p.983)
T: 0141 2218888
E: lauraann.sheridan@harpermacleod.co.uk

SHERIDAN, Michael (Oct 1972) (Partner)
Sheridans, Glasgow . . . .(p.1040)
T: 0141 3323536
E: michael@sheridanssolicitors.co.uk

SHERIDAN, Paul Watt (Jun 2011) (Director)
Rutherford Sheridan Ltd, Glasgow . . . .(p.1037)
T: 0141 248 3320
E: paul@rutherfordsheridan.com

SHERIDAN, Robert John (Jun 2008) (Director)
Sheridan At Law Ltd., Glasgow . . . . . .(p.1040)
T: 0141 465 3333
E: robert@sheridanatlaw.com

SHERRIFF, Ewan Andrew John (Jan 1993)
(Solicitor)
NO FIRM

SHERRINGTON, Jennifer (Oct 2010) (Solicitor)
NO FIRM

SHERRY, Eileen Claire (Jul 2008) (Associate)
DWF LLP, Glasgow . . . .(p.973)
T: 0141 228 8000
E: Eileen.Sherry@dwf.law

SHEWAN, Emma Jennifer (Sept 2019)
(Employee)
Baillie Gifford & Co, Edinburgh . . . . . .(p.1220)
T: 0131 2752000
E: emma.shewan@bailliegifford.com

SHIELDS, Bruce Robert (Jul 1997) (Partner)
Thompsons, Glasgow . . . .(p.1046)
T: 0141 2218840
E: bruce.shields@thompsons-scotland.co.uk

SHIELDS, Chloe Anne (Sept 2018) (Employee)
Brodies LLP, Edinburgh . . . .(p.845)
T: 0131 2283777
E: chloe.shields@brodies.com

SHIELDS, Laraine (Nov 1997) (Employee)
Miller Beckett & Jackson Limited,
Glasgow . . . .(p.1019)
T: 0141 2042833
E: LShields@mbjsolicitors.co.uk

SHIELDS, Laura Margaret (Aug 2021)
(Employee)
Wright Hassall LLP, Warwick . . . .(p.1272)
E: laura.shields@wrighthassall.co.uk

SHIELDS, Sandi Marie Anne (Mar 2012)
(Partner)
Colledge & Shields LLP, Dumfries . . . . .(p.800)
T: 01387 240044
E: ss@colledgeandshields.co.uk

SHIELS, Louise (Sept 2004) (Partner)
Brodies LLP, Edinburgh . . . .(p.845)
T: 0131 2283777
E: Louise.Shiels@brodies.com

SHIELS, Sarah Ann (Oct 2006) (Partner)
Balfour + Manson LLP, Edinburgh . . . . .(p.841)
T: 0131 2001200
E: sarah.shiels@balfour-manson.co.uk

SHIPPIN, Katherine Mairi (Sept 2015)
(Employee)
National Health Service Scotland,
Edinburgh . . . .(p.1225)
T: 0131 2757800
E: kat.shippin@nhs.scot

SHIPPIN, Norma Anne (Dec 1983) (Employee)
National Health Service Scotland,
Edinburgh . . . .(p.1225)
T: 0131 2757800
E: Norma.Shippin@nhs.scot

SHOAIB, Muhammad (Mar 2017) (Employee)
Campbell & McCartney, Glasgow . . . . .(p.956)
T: 0141 4232222

SHORNEY, Philip Andrew (Feb 2020)
(Employee)
Burness Paull LLP, Edinburgh . . . .(p.850)
T: 0131 4736000
E: philip.shorney@burnesspaull.com

SHORT, Alexandra (Nov 2015) (Employee)
Bruce, Short & Co., Dundee . . . .(p.806)
T: 01382 223400
E: alexandrashort@bruceshort.co.uk

SHORT, David (Aug 1986) (Partner)
Balfour + Manson LLP, Edinburgh . . . . .(p.841)
T: 0131 2001200
E: david.short@balfour-manson.co.uk

SHORT, Hannah Sophie (Nov 2014) (Solicitor)
NO FIRM

SHORT, Michael (Nov 1986) (Partner)
Bruce, Short & Co., Dundee . . . .(p.806)
T: 01382 223400
E: contactus@bruceshort.co.uk

SHORT, Michael Kenneth (Sept 2021)
(Employee)
Clyde & Co (Scotland) LLP,
Edinburgh . . . .(p.855)
T: 0131 5571545
E: michael.short@clydeco.com

SIBBALD, Elainne Lea (Dec 2001) (Employee)
Procurator Fiscal Service, Glasgow . . . .(p.1241)
T: 0844 5612158
E: Elainne.Sibbald@copfs.gov.uk

SIBBALD, Greg Russell (Oct 2009) (Employee)
CMS Cameron McKenna Nabarro Olswang LLP,
Dubai . . . .(p.1278)
T: +971 4374 2813
E: greg.sibbald@cms-cmno.com

SICHI, Gemma Susan (Oct 2019) (Employee)
Mourant Ozannes, St Helier. . . . .(p.1274)
T: 1481731513

SIDDIQUE, Ayesha Aleem (Jul 2017) (Employee)
Drummond Miller LLP, Edinburgh . . . . .(p.864)
T: 0131 2265151

SIDEY, Gillian Rachael (Feb 2017) (Employee)
Clifford Chance LLP, Newcastle Upon
Tyne . . . .(p.1270)
T: +44 (020) 7006 3449
E: Gillian.Sidey@cliffordchance.com

SIDHU, Gurnish Kaur (Dec 2020) (Employee)
Glasgow City Council, Glasgow . . . . . .(p.1239)
T: 0141 2872000
E: gurnish.sidhu@glasgow.gov.uk

SIEDLECKI, Igor Grzegorz (Sept 2021)
(Employee)
Clyde & Co (Scotland) LLP,
Edinburgh . . . .(p.855)
T: 0131 5571545
E: igor.siedlecki@clydeco.com

SIEKMANN, Astrid Howden (Jan 2004)
(Employee)
Harper Macleod LLP, Glasgow . . . .(p.983)
T: 0141 2218888
E: Astrid.Siekmann@harpermacleod.co.uk

SIEVEWRIGHT, David James (Nov 1985)
(Partner)
Campbell Sievewright & Co.,
Hamilton . . . .(p.1066)
T: 01698 284994
E: djs@campbellsievewright.co.uk

SIEVWRIGHT, Ian Robert (Jul 1998) (Partner)
Graham Walker, Glasgow . . . .(p.1050)
T: 0141 946 0111
E: is@gwsolicitors.com

SIEVWRIGHT, Nigel (Oct 2003) (Partner)
Shepherd and Wedderburn LLP,
Edinburgh . . . .(p.900)
T: 0131 2289900
E: Nigel.Sievwright@shepwedd.com

SILLARS, Laura Ann (Nov 2006) (Associate)
Friends Legal, Glasgow . . . .(p.978)
T: 0844 8921250
E: laura.sillars@friends-legal.co.uk

SIM, Alison Jane (Apr 2005) (Solicitor)
NO FIRM

SIM, Callum Downie (Oct 1995) (Solicitor)
NO FIRM

SIM, Frances Elizabeth (Nov 1997) (Director)
Frances E Sim Ltd, Edinburgh . . . .(p.903)
T: 7547824773
E: francessim@hotmail.co.uk

SIM, Gillian Margaret (Sept 2009) (Solicitor)
The General Teaching Council for Scotland,
Edinburgh . . . .(p.1234)
T: 0131 314 6008
E: gillian.sim@gtcs.org.uk

SIM, Gregor Forbes (Jun 1987) (Employee)
Mackinnons Solicitors LLP,
Aberdeen . . . .(p.736)
T: 01224 632464
E: gregor@mackinnons.com

SIM, Jennifer Elizabeth (Oct 2018) (Employee)
Brodies LLP, Edinburgh . . . .(p.845)
T: 0131 656 3724
E: jennifer.sim@brodies.com

SIM, Kerry Anne (Jan 2020) (Employee)
Young, Robertson & Co., Thurso . . . . .(p.1174)
T: 01847 893247
E: kerry@youngrob.co.uk

SIM, Philip James George (Oct 1986) (Director)
Sim Legal Limited, Edinburgh . . . .(p.902)
  T: 07449 339046
  E: philip@simlegal.co.uk

SIMMONS, Karen Emily (Dec 1982) (Employee)
Shetland Islands Council, Lerwick . . . . .(p.1250)
  T: 01595 744550
  E: karen.simmons@shetland.gov.uk

SIMMONS, Natasha (Apr 2013) (Employee)
Adobe Systems Software Ireland,
  Dublin . . . .(p.1273)
  E: nsimmons@adobe.com

SIMMONS, Thomas Richard (Sept 2012)
  (Employee)
Trustpilot A/S, Copenhagen . . . .(p.1257)
  T: +45 31 676988
  E: tsi@trustpilot.com

SIMMONS, William Graeme, WS (Nov 1981)
  (Partner)
CMS Cameron McKenna Nabarro Olswang LLP,
  London EC4 . . . .(p.1263)
  T: 0207 3673000
  E: William.Simmons@cms-cmno.com

SIMONNET-LEFEVRE, Kirsten (Nov 1991)
  (Employee)
Scottish Government, Edinburgh . . . . .(p.1231)
  T: 0131 2440505
  E: kirsten.simonnet-lefevre@gov.scot

SIMPSON, Alan Gordon (Sept 2018)
  (Employee)
Gray & Gray LLP, Ellon . . . .(p.918)
  T: 01358 724455
  E: alan@graygraylaw.com

SIMPSON, Ashley Marie (Jun 2006) (Partner)
Patience & Buchan, Aberdeen . . . .(p.739)
  T: 01224 648222
  E: ashley@patienceandbuchan.com

SIMPSON, Brian (Mar 2010) (Employee)
Law Society of Scotland,
  Edinburgh . . . .(p.1224)
  T: 0131 2267411
  E: briansimpson@lawscot.org.uk

SIMPSON, Colin Mackie (Nov 1991) (Partner)
RSC Solicitors, Edinburgh . . . .(p.899)
  T: 0131 2207430
  E: csimpson@rscsolicitors.co.uk

SIMPSON, David (Jan 1981) (Partner)
Inverness Law, Inverness . . . .(p.1078)
  T: 01463 832818
  E: david@invernesslaw.co.uk

SIMPSON, David John (Mar 2013) (Employee)
Law Society of Scotland,
  Edinburgh . . . .(p.1224)
  T: 0131 2267411
  E: davidsimpson@lawscot.org.uk

SIMPSON, Donald William (Nov 2000)
  (Partner)
Turcan Connell, Edinburgh . . . .(p.908)
  T: 0131 2288111
  E: Donald.simpson@turcanconnell.com

SIMPSON, Douglas John (Nov 2012) (Solicitor)
NO FIRM

SIMPSON, Douglas Scott (Nov 2007) (Director)
Health Law Limited, Edinburgh . . . .(p.878)
  T: 0800 920 2080
  E: ds@health-law.uk

SIMPSON, Fiona May (Jan 2004) (Employee)
Glasgow City Council, Glasgow . . . . . .(p.1239)
  T: 0141 2874381
  E: fiona.simpson@ced.glasgow.gov.uk

SIMPSON, Fraser George James (Sept 2018)
  (Employee)
Pinsent Masons LLP, Edinburgh . . . .(p.895)
  T: 0131 777 7000
  E: fraser.simpson@pinsentmasons.com

SIMPSON, Fraser Malcolm (Oct 2005)
  (Employee)
AXA Investment Managers, London
  EC2 . . . .(p.1261)
  T: 07894 942894
  E: Fraser.Simpson@axa-im.com

SIMPSON, Fraser Wallace (Oct 1991) (Partner)
Digby Brown LLP, Glasgow . . . .(p.970)
  T: 0333 200 5925
  E: fraser.simpson@digbybrown.co.uk

SIMPSON, Frederick Stephen (Oct 1986)
  (Partner)
Fred Simpson, Glasgow . . . .(p.1041)
  T: 07557 916721
  E: simpsonfs63@aol.com

SIMPSON, Gavin John (Oct 2006) (Employee)
Lloyds Banking Group Plc,
  Edinburgh . . . .(p.1224)
  T: (0131) 442 9579
  E: gavinsimpson@lloydsbanking.com

SIMPSON, Gillian Buchan (Oct 1981)
  (Employee)
BAM Construct UK Ltd, Hemel
  Hempstead . . . .(p.1260)
  T: 01442 238394
  E: gsimpson@bam.co.uk

SIMPSON, Gillian Louise (Aug 2017)
  (Employee)
Wilson McLeod, Edinburgh . . . .(p.912)
  T: 0131 5560055

SIMPSON, James (Feb 2014) (Employee)
CMS Cameron McKenna Nabarro Olswang LLP,
  Edinburgh . . . .(p.856)
  T: 0131 2288000
  E: Jamie.Simpson@cms-cmno.com

SIMPSON, Jennifer Mairi (Oct 2008) (Director)
BBM Solicitors Limited, Wick . . . .(p.1180)
T: 01955 604188
E: jms@bbmsolicitors.co.uk

SIMPSON, Jordan Keith (Aug 2009) (Partner)
Dickson Minto, London EC2 . . . .(p.1263)
T: 020 76284455
E: jordan.simpson@dmws.com

SIMPSON, Joyce Denise (Oct 1993) (Director)
Jack Gowans & Marc Dickson Solicitors Limited,
Inverness . . . .(p.1076)
T: 01463 710677
E: joyce@gowansdickson.com

SIMPSON, Julie McIntyre (Aug 2007)
(Employee)
Heineken UK Limited, Edinburgh . . . . .(p.1223)
T: 0131 5281000
E: Julie.Simpson@heineken.co.uk

SIMPSON, Karen Patricia (Sept 2005) (Partner)
Peterkins, Aberdeen . . . .(p.739)
T: 01224 428000
E: ks@peterkins.com

SIMPSON, Keith Peter Malcolm (Sept 2002)
(Associate)
CMS Cameron McKenna Nabarro Olswang LLP,
Edinburgh . . . .(p.856)
T: 0131 2288000
E: Keith.Simpson@cms-cmno.com

SIMPSON, Kerry Louise (Oct 2017) (Employee)
Aberdein Considine and Company,
Edinburgh . . . .(p.833)
T: 0131 2229000
E: ksimpson@acandco.com

SIMPSON, Laura Marjory (Aug 2011)
(Employee)
Dailly, Walker and Co., Solicitors,
Glasgow. . . . .(p.965)
T: 0141 4402503
E: lsimpson@govanlc.com

SIMPSON, Lisa (Nov 1992) (Employee)
Perth & Kinross Council, Perth . . . .(p.1253)
T: 01738 475000
E: Llsimpson@pkc.gov.uk

SIMPSON, Louise (Jul 2008) (Employee)
Ledingham Chalmers LLP,
Aberdeen . . . .(p.734)
T: 01224 408408
E: louise.simpson@ledinghamchalmers.com

SIMPSON, Lucy (Jul 2018) (Employee)
Procurator Fiscal Service, Aberdeen . . .(p.1213)
T: 0300 0204165
E: lucy.simpson@copfs.gov.uk

SIMPSON, Lynn Rae (Feb 2008) (Employee)
Ennova Limited, Edinburgh . . . .(p.869)
T: 0131 6624555
E: lsimpson@ennova-law.com

SIMPSON, Rebecca Anne (Oct 2020)
(Employee)
Drummond Miller LLP, Edinburgh . . . . .(p.864)
T: 0131 2265151
E: rsimpson@drummondmiller.co.uk

SIMPSON, Ronald Alexander (Dec 2011)
(Employee)
Michael Lyon Solicitors Limited,
Glasgow. . . . .(p.1005)
T: 0141 550 1074
E: rs@theroadtrafficlawyer.com

SIMPSON, Ross Andrew (Sept 2004) (Partner)
Burges Salmon LLP, Bristol. . . . .(p.1258)
T: 0117 9392000
E: ross.simpson@burges-salmon.com

SIMPSON, Sarah Ann (Oct 2013) (Employee)
TLT LLP, Glasgow . . . .(p.1048)
T: 0333 006 0400
E: sarah.simpson@tltsolicitors.com

SIMPSON, Sarah Joanne (Jul 2004) (Associate)
James Guthrie & Company LLP,
Kilmarnock . . . .(p.1095)
T: 01563 525155
E: sarah@jamesguthrie.co.uk

SIMPSON, Susan Catherine (Oct 2012)
(Employee)
Scottish Government, Edinburgh . . . . .(p.1231)
T: 0131 244 0815
E: susan.simpson@gov.scot

SIMPSON, Tomas Michael (Jul 2017)
(Employee)
Macleod & MacCallum Limited,
Inverness . . . .(p.1080)
T: 01463 239393
E: tomas.simpson@macandmac.co.uk

SIMPSON, Victoria (Oct 2010) (Associate)
Shoosmiths, Edinburgh . . . .(p.902)
T: 03700 868036
E: victoria.simpson@shoosmiths.co.uk

SIMPSON, Victoria Joan Wendy (Sept 1998)
(Employee)
Anderson Strathern LLP, Edinburgh . . . .(p.839)
T: 0131 2707700
E: victoria.simpson@andersonstrathern.co.uk

SIMS, Elaine Elizabeth (Mar 2008) (Employee)
Valaris, Dubai . . . .(p.1278)
T: +971 4 403 7481
E: Elaine.Sims@valaris.com

SINCLAIR, Alan Gerard (Jan 2004) (Partner)
Addleshaw Goddard LLP, Glasgow . . . . .(p.938)
T: 0141 2212300
E: Alan.Sinclair@addleshawgoddard.com

SINCLAIR, Anne Margaret (Aug 1992)
(Employee)
Inverclyde Council, Greenock . . . .(p.1246)
T: 01475 717171
E: Anne.Sinclair@inverclyde.gov.uk

SINCLAIR, Callum Snowden (Sept 2001)
(Partner)
Burness Paull LLP, Glasgow . . . .(p.954)
T: 0141 273 6882
E: callum.sinclair@burnesspaull.com

SINCLAIR, Christina (Nov 2007) (Employee)
Shepherd and Wedderburn LLP,
Edinburgh . . . .(p.900)
T: 0131 2289900
E: christina.sinclair@shepwedd.com

SINCLAIR, Claire Anne (Nov 1992) (Employee)
Standard Life Assets and Employee Services
Limited, Edinburgh . . . .(p.1234)
T: 0131 2457508
E: claire_a_sinclair@standardlife.com

SINCLAIR, David Watson (Aug 2005)
(Employee)
Public Defence Solicitors Office,
Dundee . . . .(p.1218)
T: 01382 226051
E: dsinclair@pdso.org.uk

SINCLAIR, Douglas Cassie (Oct 2006) (Partner)
Shepherd and Wedderburn LLP,
Edinburgh . . . .(p.900)
T: 0131 2289900
E: douglas.sinclair@shepwedd.com

SINCLAIR, Elaine (May 2011) (Employee)
Ashurst LLP, Glasgow . . . .(p.1237)
T: (0141) 375 4242
E: elaine.sinclair@ashurst.com

SINCLAIR, Isla Christina (Nov 2021) (Employee)
KM Law, Glasgow. . . . .(p.997)
T: 07702 735440

SINCLAIR, Jill (Oct 2005) (Partner)
DWF LLP, Glasgow . . . .(p.973)
T: 0141 228 8000
E: Jill.Sinclair@dwf.law

SINCLAIR, John Douglas (Nov 1991)
(Consultant)
Burness Paull LLP, Edinburgh . . . .(p.850)
T: 0131 4736000
E: John.Sinclair@burnesspaull.com

SINCLAIR, Katherine (Feb 2016) (Employee)
Dickson Minto, London EC2 . . . .(p.1263)
T: 020 76284455
E: Katie.Sinclair@dmws.com

SINCLAIR, Kirsty MacLeod (Aug 2016)
(Employee)
Russel + Aitken Edinburgh LLP,
Edinburgh . . . .(p.899)
T: 0131 2285500
E: Kirsty.Sinclair@russelaitken-edinburgh.com

SINCLAIR, Laura Ann (Jul 2015) (Associate)
Anderson Strathern LLP, Lerwick . . . . .(p.1112)
T: 01595 695262
E: laura.sinclair@andersonstrathern.co.uk

SINCLAIR, Lady, Laura Cicely (Jan 2019)
(Solicitor)
NO FIRM

SINCLAIR, Lisa (May 1997) (Employee)
ContractPod Technologies Limited,
Glasgow . . . .(p.1238)
T: 0141 280 1600
E: lisa.sinclair@newgalexy.com

SINCLAIR, Margot (Apr 1984) (Employee)
Burnett & Reid LLP, Aberdeen . . . .(p.726)
T: 01224 644333
E: margot.sinclair@burnett-reid.co.uk

SINCLAIR, Martin Turner (Oct 1991) (Partner)
Mackinnons Solicitors LLP,
Aberdeen . . . .(p.736)
T: 01224 632464
E: martin@mackinnons.com

SINCLAIR, Michael Walter (Nov 1985) (Partner)
Aberdein Considine and Company,
Aberdeen . . . .(p.718)
T: 01224 267067
E: msinclair@acandco.com

SINCLAIR, Nina Elizabeth (Nov 2006)
(Associate)
Thorntons Law LLP, Dundee . . . .(p.819)
T: 01382 229 111
E: nsinclair@thorntons-law.co.uk

SINCLAIR, Patricia (Mar 1982) (Partner)
Pat Sinclair & Co., Stonehaven . . . . . .(p.1169)
T: 07483 304780
E: info@patsinclair.com

SINCLAIR, Peter Rae (Sept 1999) (Solicitor)
NO FIRM

SINCLAIR, Trina (Jul 2004) (Employee)
Procurator Fiscal Service, Dundee . . . . .(p.1218)
T: 0844 561 2856
E: trina.sinclair@copfs.gov.uk

SINCLAIR, William Hugh MacKay, WS
(May 1981) (Partner)
MacKay Sinclair, Edinburgh . . . .(p.886)
T: 0131 6521166
E: mackaysinclair@btconnect.com

SINGER, Richard Alan (Aug 2002) (Associate)
Thompsons, Edinburgh . . . .(p.906)
T: 0131 2254297
E: richard.singer@thompsons-scotland.co.uk

SINGERMAN, Jennifer Trudi (Oct 2012)
(Employee)
Scottish Government, Edinburgh . . . . .(p.1231)
T: (0131) 244 0815
E: Jennifer.Singerman@gov.scot

SINGH, Akemkar (Aug 2015) (Employee)
Angus Council, Forfar . . . . (p.1237)
T: 01307 476228
E: SinghTN@angus.gov.uk

SINGH, Gurcharanjeet (Oct 2015) (Employee)
Brzoom Kadirgolam, Glasgow . . . . (p.952)
T: 0141 2042888
E: gurcharanjeet.singh@live.com

SINGH, Rashpal (Oct 2013) (Director)
Maguire Solicitors, Glasgow . . . . (p.1017)
T: 0141 3312885
E: rashpal@maguiresolicitors.co.uk

SINGH, Sathpal (Jul 2015) (Employee)
Procurator Fiscal Service, Glasgow . . . . (p.1241)
T: 0300 0203000
E: sathpal.singh@copfs.gov.uk

SINGLETON, Louise (Jan 1993) (Employee)
Skills Development Scotland,
Glasgow . . . . (p.1244)
T: 0300 013 2120
E: Louise.Singleton@sds.co.uk

SIRC, Nadia Rebecca Nikolaya (Oct 2004)
(Employee)
Clydesdale Bank Plc, Glasgow . . . . (p.1238)
T: 0141 2423733
E: nadia.sirc@cybg.com

SIREL, Andrew James (Feb 2014) (Partner)
JustRight Scotland LLP, Glasgow . . . . . . (p.994)
T: 0141 406 5350
E: andy@justrightscotland.org.uk

SJ STEN, Eva Kristina Louise (Jun 2010)
(Employee)
Norges Bank Investment Management, London
W1 . . . . (p.1266)
T: 020 7534 9000
E: Louise.Sjosten@nbim.no

SKELLY, Donna Margaret (Nov 1997) (Partner)
Grigor & Young LLP, Elgin . . . . (p.916)
T: 01343 544077
E: donna@grigor-young.co.uk

SKELLY, Michelle Louise (Feb 2007) (Employee)
Berry, Poggi & Co, Glasgow . . . . (p.946)
T: 0141 4297211

SKELLY, Robert John Martin (Oct 1984)
(Director)
Injury Claims Services Ltd,
Glasgow . . . . (p.989)
T: 07738 884895
E: robertskelly@injuryclaimsservices.co.uk

SKELLY, Stuart Crawford (Aug 1993)
(Employee)
Birmingham 2022 Commonwealth Games,
Birmingham . . . . (p.1258)
E: stuart.skelly@birmingham2022.com

SKELTON, Corinne Louise (Oct 2021)
(Employee)
Thompsons, Edinburgh . . . . (p.906)
T: 0131 2254297
E: Corinne.Skelton@thompsons-scotland.co.uk

SKELTON, Niall Michael (Sept 2018)
(Employee)
Addleshaw Goddard LLP,
Edinburgh . . . . (p.835)
T: 0131 2282400
E: niall.skelton@addleshawgoddard.com

SKENE, Ayla (Oct 2012) (Employee)
TLT LLP, Glasgow . . . . (p.1048)
T: 0333 006 0400
E: ayla.skene@tltsolicitors.com

SKENE, Meryl Zoe (Sept 2011) (Employee)
Scottish Government's Parliamentary Counsel
Office, Edinburgh . . . . (p.1233)
T: 0131 244 6917
E: Meryl.Skene@gov.scot

SKEOCH, Alison Mary Margaret (Sept 2019)
(Solicitor)
NO FIRM

SKEOCH, Jennifer Carol (Nov 2007) (Partner)
Burness Paull LLP, Glasgow . . . . (p.954)
T: 0141 2484933
E: Jennifer.Skeoch@burnesspaull.com

SKETT, Emma Jane (Jun 2006) (Employee)
DAC Beachcroft Scotland LLP,
Glasgow . . . . (p.964)
T: 0141 2486688
E: eskett@dacbeachcroft.com

SKINNER, Iain MacLennan (Feb 2001)
(Associate)
DLA Piper Middle East LLP, Dubai . . . . (p.1278)
T: (+971) (0)4 438 6315
E: iain.skinner@dlapiper.com

SKINNER, Paula (Dec 2002) (Partner)
Harper Macleod LLP, Glasgow . . . . (p.983)
T: 0141 2218888
E: Paula.Skinner@harpermacleod.co.uk

SKIPPER, John Christopher (Oct 2006)
(Employee)
Squire Patton Boggs (MEA) LLP,
Dubai . . . . (p.1278)
T: +971 4 447 8761
E: christopher.skipper@squirepb.com

SKIPPER, John Craig (Sept 1983) (Solicitor)
NO FIRM

SKIPPER, Louise Emma (Oct 2010) (Employee)
Dubai Holding LLC, Dubai . . . . (p.1278)
E: louise.skipper@dubaiholding.com

SKIPPER, Sharon Elizabeth (Jun 2017)
(Employee)
Kirkland & Ellis International LLP, London
    EC3 . . . .(p.1265)
    T: 0207 4692000

SKIRVING-YOUNG, Sharon Ita (Apr 2010)
(Employee)
Berrymans Lace Mawer LLP,
    Edinburgh . . . .(p.842)
    T: 0131 2259855
    E: sharon.skirving-young@blmlaw.com

SLACK, David Isaac (Sept 2018) (Employee)
Pinsent Masons LLP, Glasgow . . . .(p.1031)
    T: 0141 567 8400
    E: david.slack@pinsentmasons.com

SLANE, Joseph Peter (Jul 2017) (Employee)
Shepherd and Wedderburn LLP,
    Glasgow. . . . .(p.1039)
    T: 0141 5669900
    E: Joseph.Slane@shepwedd.com

SLATER, Kay (Dec 2019) (Employee)
Procurator Fiscal Service, Glasgow . . . .(p.1241)
    T: 0300 0203000
    E: kay.slater@copfs.gov.uk

SLATER, Linda Jane (Apr 2003) (Solicitor)
NO FIRM

SLATER, Mark Sutherland (Mar 2014)
(Employee)
Carey Olsen, St Helier . . . .(p.1274)
    T: 01534 822240
    E: mark.slater@careyolsen.com

SLATER, Megan Anne (Sept 2021) (Employee)
Rea Law Ltd, Glasgow. . . . .(p.1034)
    T: 0141 3701241
    E: megan@realaw.co.uk

SLATER, Ross Alexander (Nov 1988) (Partner)
Oakwood Scotland Solicitors Limited,
    Glasgow. . . . .(p.1027)
    T: 0141 404 1181
    E: r.slater@oakwoodscotland.co.uk

SLAVEN, Janine Marie (Nov 2008) (Employee)
Thompsons, Edinburgh . . . .(p.906)
    T: 0131 2254297
    E: janine.slaven@thompsons-scotland.co.uk

SLEE, Kirsten Claire (Dec 2003) (Employee)
Scottish Government, Edinburgh . . . . .(p.1231)
    T: 0131 244 0815
    E: kirsty.slee@gov.scot

SLEIGH, Andrew Falconer (Nov 1981) (Partner)
BTO Solicitors LLP, Glasgow . . . .(p.952)
    T: 0141 2218012
    E: afs@bto.co.uk

SLESSOR, Calum Craig (Jul 2014) (Employee)
Grant Smith Law Practice Limited,
    Banff . . . .(p.769)
    T: 01261 815678
    E: calum.slessor@grantsmithlaw.co.uk

SLOAN, Catherine Jane (Jul 2018) (Employee)
Turcan Connell, Edinburgh . . . .(p.908)
    T: 0131 2288111
    E: catherine.sloan@turcanconnell.com

SLOAN, Edward Charles Paul (Mar 2011)
(Employee)
Mills & Reeve LLP, London EC4 . . . . . .(p.1266)
    E: edward.sloan@mills-reeve.com

SLOAN, Graeme Eoghan Campbell
(Feb 1987) (Solicitor)
NO FIRM

SLOAN, James Joseph (Feb 1991) (Partner)
Dunipace Brown, Cumbernauld . . . .(p.790)
    T: 01236 453004
    E: james@dunipacebrown.co.uk

SLOAN, Lesley Margaret (Sept 1985)
(Consultant)
Walter Gerrard & Co., Macduff . . . . . .(p.1122)
    T: 01261 832491
    E: lesley@waltergerrard.co.uk

SLOAN, Martin Andrew (Oct 2003) (Partner)
Brodies LLP, Edinburgh . . . .(p.845)
    T: 0131 2283777
    E: martin.sloan@brodies.com

SLOAN, Ryan (Jan 2009) (Associate)
Aamer Anwar & Co, Glasgow . . . .(p.941)
    T: 0141 4297090
    E: ryan@aameranwar.com

SLOANE, Andrew John (Aug 2002) (Employee)
Accelerated Digital Ventures Ltd,
    Sheffield. . . . .(p.1271)
    E: andrew.sloane@accelerated.ventures

SLOEY, Holly (Feb 2020) (Employee)
Dailly, Walker and Co., Solicitors,
    Glasgow. . . . .(p.965)
    T: 0141 4402503
    E: hsloey@govanlc.com

SLOSS, Alannah Sheila (Jul 2019) (Employee)
Gildeas Limited, Edinburgh . . . .(p.872)
    T: 0141 331 6079
    E: asloss@gildeas.net

SLOWEY, John Anthony (Oct 1991) (Employee)
Procurator Fiscal Service, Glasgow . . . .(p.1241)
    T: 8445612367
    E: john.slowey@copfs.gov.uk

SMAIL, Martin Gordon Edward (Jun 2017)
(Employee)
Brodies LLP, Edinburgh . . . .(p.845)
    T: 0131 2283777
    E: martin.smail@brodies.com

SMALL, Stephen Thomas (Mar 2002)
(Employee)
The National Trust for Scotland,
Edinburgh . . . .(p.1235)
T: 0844 4932100
E: ssmall@nts.org.uk

SMART, David John (Feb 1989) (Associate)
Miller Hendry, Crieff . . . .(p.789)
T: 01764 655151
E: davidsmart@millerhendry.co.uk

SMART, Ian Stewart (Nov 1980) (Consultant)
The Cumbernauld Law Practice,
Cumbernauld . . . .(p.791)
T: 01236 731911
E: iansmart@cumbernauldlaw.co.uk

SMART, John Douglas (Nov 1995) (Partner)
Wright, Johnston & Mackenzie LLP,
Inverness . . . .(p.1083)
T: 01463 234445
E: jds@wjm.co.uk

SMART, Kimberley Joan (Feb 2009) (Associate)
Raeburn Christie Clark & Wallace LLP,
Inverurie . . . .(p.1085)
T: 01467 629300
E: kimberley.smart@raeburns.co.uk

SMART, Steven James (Oct 2006) (Partner)
Horwich Farrelly Scotland,
Glasgow. . . . .(p.987)
T: 03300 240711
E: Steven.Smart@h-f.co.uk

SMARTT, Graham Peter (Jan 2007) (Associate)
Addleshaw Goddard LLP,
Edinburgh . . . .(p.835)
T: 0131 2282400
E: peter.smartt@addleshawgoddard.com

SMEATON, Clara Marie (Aug 2018) (Employee)
Burness Paull LLP, Glasgow . . . .(p.954)
T: 0141 2484933
E: clara.smeaton@burnesspaull.com

SMILEY, Alexander Hugh (Jul 2008) (Employee)
Chivas Brothers Limited, Glasgow . . . .(p.1238)
E: alexander.smiley@pernod-ricard.com

SMILLIE, Craig James (Feb 2012) (Partner)
Thompsons, Glasgow . . . .(p.1046)
T: 0141 2218840
E: craig.smillie@thompsons-scotland.co.uk

SMILLIE, Graeme Samuel (Sept 1991)
(Employee)
Dundee City Council, Dundee . . . .(p.1217)
T: 01382 434000
E: graeme.smillie@dundeecity.gov.uk

SMILLIE, Karen (Sept 1998) (Director)
The Conveyancing Practice Ltd,
Bathgate . . . .(p.772)
T: 01506 653 819
E: karen.smillie@theconveyancingpractice.com

SMILLIE, Maria Elena (Sept 2014) (Employee)
Levy & McRae Solicitors LLP,
Glasgow. . . . .(p.1000)
T: 0141 3072311
E: msmillie@lemac.co.uk

SMIT-HAFFMANS, Judith Theresia Maria
(Mar 2014) (Solicitor)
NO FIRM

SMITH, Adam Kennedy (Oct 2017) (Employee)
Gilson Gray LLP, Dundee. . . . .(p.811)
T: 01382 549321
E: asmith1@gilsongray.co.uk

SMITH, Adrian Charles Newlands
(Mar 1997) (Employee)
FMS Legal and Compliance Services Limited,
Edinburgh . . . .(p.1223)
E: acnsmith80@outlook.com

SMITH, Alan Barry William (Nov 2006)
(Partner)
Brown & McRae LLP, Fraserburgh . . . . .(p.930)
T: 01346 514761
E: B.Smith@brown-mcrae.co.uk

SMITH, Alasdair Angus (Jul 1997) (Partner)
Raeburn Christie Clark & Wallace LLP,
Aberdeen . . . .(p.741)
T: 01224 332400
E: Alasdair.Smith@raeburns.co.uk

SMITH, Alastair James (Nov 2006) (Associate)
Lindsays LLP, Edinburgh . . . .(p.882)
T: 0131 2291212
E: alastairsmith@lindsays.co.uk

SMITH, Alastair Melville John (Nov 1999)
(Employee)
Scottish Law Commission,
Edinburgh . . . .(p.1233)
T: 0131 6682131
E: alastair.smith@scotlawcom.gov.uk

SMITH, Alison Mary (Oct 2006) (Solicitor)
NO FIRM

SMITH, Amy Kathleen (Apr 2012) (Employee)
CIGNA International, Glasgow . . . .(p.1238)
T: 01475 492388
E: amy.smith4@cigna.com

SMITH, Andrew John (Sept 2011) (Employee)
Burness Paull LLP, Aberdeen . . . .(p.724)
T: 01224 621621

SMITH, Barry Colin (Sept 2011) (Employee)
Al Jazeera Media Network, Doha . . . . .(p.1275)
T: 97444897643
E: SmithBa@aljazeera.net

SMITH, Billie (Jul 2016) (Associate)
MacPhee & Partners LLP, Oban . . . . . .(p.1135)
T: 01631 562308
E: billiesmith@macphee.co.uk

SMITH, Caroline Leslie (Oct 1996) (Associate)
MTM Family Law LLP, Glasgow . . . . . .(p.1025)
   T: 0141 6117535
   E: cs@mtmfamilylaw.co.uk

SMITH, Catherine Marie (Nov 2009) (Director)
Lows Orkney Limited, Kirkwall . . . .(p.1106)
   T: 01856 873151
   E: Catherine.Smith@lowsorkney.co.uk

SMITH, Catriona Jane (Oct 2005) (Employee)
Lloyds Banking Group Plc,
   Edinburgh . . . .(p.1224)
   T: (0131) 442 9579
   E: catriona.smith@lloydsbanking.com

SMITH, Chloe Louise (Sept 2016) (Employee)
Clifford Chance LLP, London E14 . . . . .(p.1262)
   E: chloe.smith@cliffordchance.com

SMITH, Christina-Jo Macleod (Oct 2020)
(Employee)
Derek Mackenzie & Company Limited,
   Stornoway . . . .(p.1170)
   T: 01851 702211
   E: christina_smith080@hotmail.com

SMITH, Christine Anne (Nov 1985)
(Consultant)
Mike Smith & Co., Lenzie . . . .(p.1112)
   T: 0141 7762621
   E: sales@mikesmithproperties.co.uk

SMITH, Christopher Douglas (Oct 2009)
(Employee)
Baillie Gifford & Co, Edinburgh . . . . . .(p.1220)
   T: 0131 2753823
   E: Christopher.Smith@bailliegifford.com

SMITH, Colin Walker (Dec 2015) (Associate)
Burness Paull LLP, Glasgow . . . .(p.954)
   T: 0141 2484933
   E: colin.smith@burnesspaull.com

SMITH, Craig Joseph (Mar 2006) (Associate)
Young & Partners Business Lawyers Limited,
   Dunfermline . . . .(p.827)
   T: 01383 721621
   E: cjs@businesslaw.co.uk

SMITH, Craig William (Feb 2018) (Employee)
East Dunbartonshire Council,
   Kirkintilloch . . . .(p.1249)
   T: 0141 5788000
   E: Craig_Smith@eastdunbarton.gov.uk

SMITH, David Andrew Gordon (Nov 2018)
(Employee)
Turcan Connell, Edinburgh . . . .(p.908)
   T: 0131 2288111
   E: david.smith@turcanconnell.com

SMITH, David Christopher (Oct 1993) (Partner)
Gillespie Macandrew LLP,
   Edinburgh . . . .(p.872)
   T: 0131 2251677
   E: christopher.smith@gillespiemacandrew.co.uk

SMITH, David James William (Sept 2013)
(Employee)
Burness Paull LLP, Aberdeen . . . .(p.724)
   T: 01224 621621
   E: David.Smith@burnesspaull.com

SMITH, David John (Oct 2000) (Employee)
Scottish Government, Edinburgh . . . . .(p.1231)
   T: 0131 244 0815
   E: davidj.smith@gov.scot

SMITH, David Maughan (Jan 2010) (Employee)
Raeburn Christie Clark & Wallace LLP,
   Aberdeen . . . .(p.741)
   T: 01224 564636
   E: david.smith@raeburns.co.uk

SMITH, David William (Oct 2002) (Employee)
Creative Scotland, Edinburgh . . . .(p.1222)
   T: 0330 3332000
   E: david.smith@creativescotland.com

SMITH, Denise Michelle (Feb 1998) (Solicitor)
NO FIRM

SMITH, Donna (Aug 2017) (Employee)
Wilson McKendrick Solicitors Limited,
   Glasgow . . . .(p.1053)
   T: 0141 2227950
   E: donnasmith@wilsonmckendrick.co.uk

SMITH, Eilidh (Jul 2018) (Employee)
Brodies LLP, Edinburgh . . . .(p.845)
   T: 0131 2283777
   E: eilidh.smith@brodies.com

SMITH, Eilidh (Jan 2000) (Employee)
Procurator Fiscal Service, Falkirk . . . . . .(p.1236)
   T: 0300 020 3000
   E: eilidh.smith@copfs.gov.uk

SMITH, Eilidh Catherine (Jun 2008) (Employee)
Scottish Government, Edinburgh . . . . .(p.1231)
   T: 0131 244 0815
   E: Eilidh.Smith2@gov.scot

SMITH, Elizabeth Maria (May 2013) (Employee)
Embark Corporate Services Limited,
   Edinburgh . . . .(p.1223)
   T: (0131) 603 5899
   E: elizabeth.smith@embarkgroup.co.uk

SMITH, Ellen Jemima Stuart (Nov 2020)
(Employee)
Brodies LLP, Edinburgh . . . .(p.845)
   T: 0131 2283777
   E: ellen.smith@brodies.com

SMITH, Emma Joan (Oct 2007) (Director)
Connelly & Yeoman Law Limited,
   Arbroath . . . .(p.757)
   T: 01241 434200
   E: emma@connellyyeoman.com

SMITH, Euan Colm (Aug 2008) (Employee)
Navigator Employment Law Ltd,
  Edinburgh . . . .(p.1227)
  T: 0333 2400308
  E: euan.smith@navigatorlaw.co.uk

SMITH, Euan Mark Folan (Oct 1996) (Partner)
Eversheds Sutherland (International) LLP,
  Edinburgh . . . .(p.869)
  T: 0207 9194500
  E: euansmith@eversheds-sutherland.com

SMITH, Fearghas Edward Douglas
  (Jul 2021) (Employee)
Hughes Dowdall, Glasgow. . . . .(p.987)
  T: 0141 2407020
  E: fearghas.smith@hughesdowdall.com

SMITH, Gail Louise (Jan 1995) (Employee)
Brodies LLP, Glasgow . . . .(p.948)
  T: 0141 2484672
  E: gail.smith@brodies.com

SMITH, Gary (Jan 2013) (Employee)
EthosEnergy (GBR) Limited,
  Aberdeen . . . .(p.1212)
  T: 01224 291 764
  E: gary.smith@ethosenergygroup.com

SMITH, Gavin Gar-Wing (Sept 2018)
  (Employee)
Addleshaw Goddard LLP, Glasgow . . . . .(p.938)
  T: 0141 2212300
  E: gavin.smith@addleshawgoddard.com

SMITH, Geoffrey Neilson (Sept 2004)
  (Employee)
CMS Cameron McKenna Nabarro Olswang LLP,
  Dubai . . . .(p.1278)
  T: +971 4374 2813
  E: geoff.smith@cms-cmno.com

SMITH, Gillian Catherine Janet (Oct 1996)
  (Employee)
Raeburn Christie Clark & Wallace LLP,
  Aberdeen . . . .(p.741)
  T: 01224 332400
  E: gillian.smith@raeburns.co.uk

SMITH, Grace Mairi (Mar 2016) (Solicitor)
NO FIRM

SMITH, Gregor Wilkie (Oct 2008) (Partner)
Montgomery Smith Solicitors,
  Bishopbriggs . . . .(p.774)
  T: 0141 772 5344
  E: greg@montgomerysmith.co.uk

SMITH, Heather Jane (Sept 2009) (Employee)
Procurator Fiscal Service,
  Edinburgh . . . .(p.1227)
  T: 07423 000728
  E: Heather.Smith@copfs.gov.uk

SMITH, Henry Cannon (Jan 1989) (Partner)
Gillespie Macandrew LLP,
  Edinburgh . . . .(p.872)
  T: 0131 2400754
  E: Harry.Smith@gillespiemacandrew.co.uk

SMITH, Iain Henry Barclay (Nov 1994)
  (Partner)
Keegan Smith, SSC., Livingston . . . . . .(p.1119)
  T: 01506 497500
  E: iain@keegansmith.org

SMITH, Iain William Macdonald (Jun 2014)
  (Associate)
Brodies LLP, Glasgow . . . .(p.948)
  T: 0141 2484672
  E: iain.smith@brodies.com

SMITH, Jack Matthew (Sept 2020) (Employee)
Latta Law Limited, Glasgow. . . . .(p.998)
  T: 0141 222 2185
  E: js@lattalaw.co.uk

SMITH, Jennifer (Oct 2018) (Employee)
Burness Paull LLP, Glasgow . . . .(p.954)
  T: 0141 2484933
  E: jennifer.smith@burnesspaull.com

SMITH, Jennifer Chloe (Jan 2003) (Partner)
Harper Macleod LLP, Glasgow . . . .(p.983)
  T: 0141 2218888
  E: jenny.smith@harpermacleod.co.uk

SMITH, Jennifer Fiona (Jun 2012) (Employee)
The Moray Council, Elgin . . . .(p.1236)
  T: 01343 543451
  E: jennifer.smith@moray.gov.uk

SMITH, Joanne Rachel (Jun 2017) (Employee)
SSE PLC, Glasgow. . . . .(p.1244)
  T: 0141 224 7248
  E: Joanne.Smith3@sse.com

SMITH, Joanne Taylor (Sept 2004) (Employee)
Procurator Fiscal Service, Kirkcaldy . . . .(p.1249)
  T: 0300 0203000
  E: Joanne.Smith2@copfs.gov.uk

SMITH, John Macdonald Fraser (Oct 2007)
  (Employee)
Standard Life Investments Limited,
  Edinburgh . . . .(p.1234)
  T: 0131 312 6068
  E: iain.smith@abrdn.com

SMITH, Karen (Jan 2004) (Partner)
Moore & Partners LLP,
  Cumbernauld . . . .(p.790)
  T: 01236 727715
  E: ks@moorepartners.com

SMITH, Karen (Mar 2005) (Employee)
Procurator Fiscal Service,
  Stornoway . . . .(p.1255)
  E: karen.smith@copfs.gov.uk

SMITH, Karren (Nov 1995) (Partner)
Brodies LLP, Dingwall . . . .(p.796)
   T: 01349 860111
   E: karren.smith@brodies.com

SMITH, Kate (Jan 2021) (Employee)
Fiona McPhail Solicitors, Edinburgh . . . .(p.886)
   T: 0344 5152410

SMITH, Kate (Jul 2009) (Employee)
Scottish Children's Reporter Administration,
   Hamilton . . . .(p.1247)
   T: 0131 2448676
   E: Kate.Smith@scra.gov.uk

SMITH, Kate Susan (Jul 1996) (Employee)
National Westminster Bank PLC,
   Edinburgh . . . .(p.1226)
   E: Kate.Smith@natwest.com

SMITH, Katharine Louise (Oct 2003)
   (Employee)
Blackadders LLP, Glasgow . . . .(p.946)
   T: 0141 2481888
   E: katharine.smith@blackadders.co.uk

SMITH, Kathryn Jane (Aug 2019) (Employee)
Burges Salmon LLP, Bristol. . . . .(p.1258)
   T: 0117 9392000
   E: kathryn.smith@burges-salmon.com

SMITH, Katy Jane Lindsay (Sept 2021)
   (Employee)
DWF LLP, Glasgow . . . .(p.973)
   T: 0141 228 8000
   E: katy.smith@dwf.law

SMITH, Kieran Francis Stead (Jan 2015)
   (Employee)
Thompsons, Glasgow . . . .(p.1046)
   T: 0141 2218840
   E: Kieran.Smith@thompsons-scotland.co.uk

SMITH, Kirsty Alexandria Martin (Nov 2006)
   (Employee)
TLT LLP, Glasgow . . . .(p.1048)
   T: 0333 006 0400
   E: kirsty.smith@tltsolicitors.com

SMITH, Lauren (Mar 2021) (Employee)
Thorntons Law LLP, Dundee . . . .(p.819)
   T: 01382 229 111
   E: laurensmith@thorntons-law.co.uk

SMITH, Lauren (Oct 2011) (Employee)
Aberdeen Corporate Services Limited,
   Edinburgh . . . .(p.1220)
   T: 0131 245 3032
   E: lauren.x.smith@aberdeenstandard.com

SMITH, Lauren Aileen (Aug 2016) (Employee)
Standard Life Investments Limited,
   Edinburgh . . . .(p.1234)
   T: (0131) 245 4153
   E: Lauren.Smith@abrdn.com

SMITH, Lauren Hannah Braid (Jun 2019)
   (Employee)
Jas Campbell & Co Ltd, Saltcoats . . . . .(p.1160)
   T: 01294 464301
   E: l.smith@jascampbell.co.uk

SMITH, Lauren Hazel Hamilton (Aug 2017)
   (Employee)
Balfour + Manson LLP, Edinburgh . . . . .(p.841)
   T: 0131 2001200
   E: lauren.smith@balfour-manson.co.uk

SMITH, Lesley Claire (Oct 2009) (Employee)
Procurator Fiscal Service,
   Edinburgh . . . .(p.1229)
   T: (0844) 561 3268
   E: lesley.smith@copfs.gov.uk

SMITH, Prof Dr, Lesley Jane (Nov 1981)
(Consultant)
Weber-Steinhaus Smith & Klein,
   Bremen . . . .(p.1273)
   T: 0049 421 639360
   E: smith@weber-steinhaus.com

SMITH, Liam Anthony (Sept 2017) (Employee)
Anderson Strathern LLP, Edinburgh . . . .(p.839)
   T: 0131 2707700
   E: liam.smith@andersonstrathern.co.uk

SMITH, Liane (Nov 2007) (Employee)
Royal London, Edinburgh . . . .(p.1230)
   T: 0131 6726410
   E: liane.smith@royallondon.com

SMITH, Lucy Lindsay (Sept 2011) (Employee)
Blackadders LLP, Dundee. . . . .(p.805)
   T: 01382 229222
   E: Lucy.Smith@blackadders.co.uk

SMITH, Lynsey (Dec 2020) (Employee)
Brodies LLP, Edinburgh . . . .(p.845)
   T: 0131 2283777
   E: lynsey.smith@brodies.com

SMITH, Marianne (Sept 2012) (Associate)
Clyde & Co (Scotland) LLP,
   Glasgow. . . . .(p.961)
   T: 0141 2482666
   E: marianne.smith@clydeco.com

SMITH, Martin Alfred (Sept 1994) (Partner)
South Forrest, Inverness . . . .(p.1082)
   T: 01463 237171
   E: martin@southforrest.co.uk

SMITH, Matthew Barnett (Oct 2013) (Solicitor)
NO FIRM

SMITH, Matthew Bruce Kerr (Mar 2017)
   (Employee)
Harper Macleod LLP, Edinburgh . . . .(p.877)
   T: 0131 2472500
   E: matthew.smith@harpermacleod.co.uk

SMITH, Maureen Alice (Sept 2004) (Employee)
Angus McIntosh & Simon Hodge,
Glasgow . . . .(p.1012)
T: 0141 6340313
E: maureen.smith@castlemilklawcentre.co.uk

SMITH, Michael Duncan (Sept 2015)
(Employee)
Pinsent Masons LLP, Glasgow . . . .(p.1031)
T: 0141 567 8400
E: michael.d.smith@pinsentmasons.com

SMITH, Michael James Redman (Oct 1980)
(Partner)
Mike Smith & Co., Lenzie . . . .(p.1112)
T: 0141 7762621
E: law@mike-smith.co.uk

SMITH, Dr, Michael Peter Gordon, WS
(Oct 1982) (Employee)
University of Northumbria, Newcastle Upon
Tyne . . . .(p.1270)
T: 0191 3495534
E: michael.p.g.smith@northumbria.ac.uk

SMITH, Morag Jane (Mar 1996) (Employee)
The Moray Council, Elgin . . . .(p.1236)
T: 01343 563461
E: morag.smith@moray.gov.uk

SMITH, Morgan Rebecca (Aug 2018)
(Associate)
Addleshaw Goddard LLP,
Edinburgh . . . .(p.835)
T: 0131 2282400
E: morgan.smith@addleshawgoddard.com

SMITH, Neil Bryce (Oct 2001) (Partner)
Burness Paull LLP, Aberdeen . . . .(p.724)
T: 01224 621621
E: Neil.Smith@burnesspaull.com

SMITH, Nicholas Scott (Oct 1998) (Employee)
City of Edinburgh Council,
Edinburgh . . . .(p.1221)
T: 0131 529 4377
E: nick.smith@edinburgh.gov.uk

SMITH, Nicola Jane (Nov 1997) (Director)
Cairn Legal Ltd, Glasgow . . . .(p.955)
T: 0141 221 7948
E: nicola@cairnlegal.co.uk

SMITH, Olivia Sophie Abbott (Oct 2018)
(Employee)
Burness Paull LLP, Edinburgh . . . .(p.850)
T: 0131 4736000

SMITH, Paul David (Sept 1997) (Employee)
CN Defence Ltd, Edinburgh. . . . .(p.857)
T: 0131 5571000
E: Paul@cndefence.com

SMITH, Paul Forrester (Dec 1993) (Associate)
Turcan Connell, Edinburgh . . . .(p.908)
T: 0131 2288111
E: paul.forrestersmith@turcanconnell.com

SMITH, Peter Richard (Nov 2003) (Partner)
Burness Paull LLP, Aberdeen . . . .(p.724)
T: 01224 621621
E: Peter.Smith@burnesspaull.com

SMITH, Richard Bryan (Dec 1997) (Partner)
Brodies LLP, Edinburgh . . . .(p.845)
T: 0131 2283777
E: richard.b.smith@brodies.com

SMITH, Richard Ian Campbell (Sept 1993)
(Partner)
Brodies LLP, Glasgow . . . .(p.948)
T: 0141 2456284
E: richard.smith@brodies.com

SMITH, Robert Stewart (Jul 1980) (Employee)
Russel + Aitken (Falkirk + Alloa) Ltd,
Alloa . . . .(p.753)
T: 01259 723201
E: robertsmith@randa-fa.co.uk

SMITH, Rosie Elizabeth (Apr 2017) (Employee)
Burness Paull LLP, Edinburgh . . . .(p.850)
T: 0131 4736000
E: Rosie.Smith@burnesspaull.com

SMITH, Ryan (Jan 2015) (Employee)
Digby Brown LLP, Kirkcaldy . . . .(p.1099)
T: 0333 200 5925
E: ryan.smith@digbybrown.co.uk

SMITH, Sara Alicia (Aug 2008) (Partner)
Urquharts, Edinburgh . . . .(p.909)
T: 0131 5562896
E: sarasmith@urquharts.co.uk

SMITH, Sarah Benedicte (Dec 2010)
(Employee)
ATLEU Ltd, London SE1 . . . .(p.1261)
T: 0207 7007311
E: sarah@atleu.org.uk

SMITH, Sarah Kate (Aug 2015) (Employee)
Procurator Fiscal Service, Falkirk . . . . . .(p.1236)
T: 0300 020 3000
E: sarah.smith@copfs.gov.uk

SMITH, Scott John (Feb 1998) (Employee)
Spirit Production (Services) Limited,
Aberdeen . . . .(p.1214)
T: 01224 415000
E: scott.smith@spirit-energy.com

SMITH, Shona Houston (Sept 1991) (Partner)
Balfour + Manson LLP, Edinburgh . . . . .(p.841)
T: 0131 2001200
E: shona.smith@balfour-manson.co.uk

SMITH, Simon John (Dec 2020) (Solicitor)
Miller Hendry, Dundee . . . .(p.816)
T: 01382 200000
E: simonsmith@millerhendry.co.uk

SMITH, Stephanie Nicole (Oct 2012)
(Employee)
SKO Family Law Specialists LLP,
Edinburgh . . . . (p.903)
T: 0131 3226669
E: stephanie.smith@sko-family.co.uk

SMITH, Stephen George (Nov 2002)
(Employee)
Livingstone Brown Limited,
Glasgow. (p.1003)
T: 0141 4298166
E: sgs@livbrown.co.uk

SMITH, Stephen Thomas (Nov 2010) (Partner)
Davidson Chalmers Stewart LLP,
Glasgow. (p.967)
T: 0141 4283258
E: stephen.smith@dcslegal.com

SMITH, Stewart Park (Nov 2007) (Employee)
KW Law, Livingston . . . . (p.1119)
T: 01506 415333
E: stewarts@kwlaw.co.uk

SMITH, William James (Jul 2003) (Consultant)
McGreevy & Co Limited, Glasgow . . . . (p.1011)
T: 0141 2397407/0796880

SMITH, William Urquhart Proctor
(Jul 2006) (Director)
Clarity Simplicity Ltd, Glasgow. . . . . . . (p.960)
T: 0141 4332626
E: b.smith@claritysimplicity.co.uk

SMITHARD, Victoria Marie (Jun 2009)
(Employee)
Scottish Widows Limited,
Edinburgh . . . . (p.1233)
T: 0131 6557230
E: vicky.smithard@lloydsbanking.com

SMITHERAM, Jie (Jul 2020) (Employee)
Carr Berman Crichton Limited,
Rutherglen . . . . (p.1159)
T: 0141 6479851
E: jade@cbcsolicitors.co.uk

SMYLIE, Victoria Evelyn (Oct 2016) (Employee)
Al Tamimi & Company, Dubai . . . . (p.1277)
T: (+971) 4 364 1641
E: victoriasmylie@gmail.com

SMYTH, Jacqueline Mary (Aug 2006)
(Employee)
Procurator Fiscal Service, Hamilton . . . . (p.1247)
T: 0844 5613245
E: Jacqueline.Smyth@copfs.gov.uk

SMYTH, Maurice Thomas (Dec 1961) (Partner)
Gordon & Smyth, Bishopbriggs . . . . (p.774)
T: 0141 7724186
E: mslawman@hotmail.com

SMYTH, Pamela June (Jan 1989) (Employee)
Forth Ports Limited, Edinburgh . . . . . . (p.1223)
T: 0131 5558700
E: pamela.smyth@forthports.co.uk

SMYTH, Roland William (Feb 1999) (Associate)
CMS Cameron McKenna Nabarro Olswang LLP,
Edinburgh . . . . (p.856)
T: 0131 2288000
E: Roland.Smyth@cms-cmno.com

SMYTH, Sally Caroline (Jul 2010) (Associate)
CMS Cameron McKenna Nabarro Olswang LLP,
Edinburgh . . . . (p.856)
T: 0131 2288000
E: sally.smyth@cms-cmno.com

SNEDDON, Amanda Jane (Jan 2004)
(Employee)
BSW Solicitors LLP, Glenrothes . . . . (p.1056)
T: 01592 725130
E: amanda@bastensneddon.co.uk

SNEDDON, Christopher Alexander
(Nov 1998) (Partner)
BSW Solicitors LLP, Dunfermline . . . . . . (p.823)
T: 01383 621144
E: chris@bastensneddon.co.uk

SNEDDON, Douglas (Oct 1982) (Partner)
Blackadders LLP, Dundee. . . . . (p.805)
T: 01382 229222
E: douglas.sneddon@blackadders.co.uk

SNEDDON, Kerr Malcolm Grant (Sept 2004)
(Partner)
Robert F MacDonald Solicitors,
Kirkcaldy . . . . (p.1101)
T: 01592 643357
E: kerr@robertfmacdonald.org.uk

SNEDDON, Linda (Jan 1993) (Employee)
W L Gore & Associates, Livingston . . . . (p.1250)
T: 01506 678027
E: lsneddon@wlgore.com

SNEDDON, Nicola Christine (May 1999)
(Employee)
Aldermore Bank Plc, London EC2 . . . . . (p.1261)
T: 0203 553 4236
E: Nicola.Sneddon@aldermore.co.uk

SNEDDON, Sandra Anne (May 2001) (Partner)
Sneddon Morrison, Livingston . . . . (p.1120)
T: 01506 497160
E: Sandra@pcmcfarlane.co.uk

SNEDDON, Walter, SSC (Nov 1970) (Partner)
Sneddons SSC, Armadale . . . . (p.758)
T: 01501 733200
E: walter@sneddons.com

SNEDDON, Walter Scott (Aug 1997)
(Consultant)
Black and McCorry Limited,
Livingston . . . . (p.1118)
T: 01506 467823
E: scott@bmlegal.co.uk

SNEE, Craig Fraser (Nov 2012) (Employee)
Thompsons, Dundee . . . . (p.819)
E: craig.snee@thompsons-scotland.co.uk

SNELL, Philippa Mary Ordish, WS
(Jan 1984) (Associate)
MacRoberts LLP, Edinburgh . . . . (p.887)
T: 0131 2295046
E: pippa.snell@macroberts.com

SNOW, Carol Phyllis (Dec 2001) (Employee)
Office of the Advocate General,
Edinburgh . . . . (p.1227)
T: 07596 890200
E: carol.snow@advocategeneral.gov.uk

SOAL, Jeffrey Stuart Bertram (Nov 2000)
(Solicitor)
NO FIRM

SOCHA, Marjorie Janet (Oct 1985) (Employee)
Scottish Solicitors' Discipline Tribunal,
Cupar . . . . (p.1216)
T: 01334 659088
E: marjorie.socha@btinternet.com

SODERSTEN, Caroline Elizabeth (Nov 2007)
(Employee)
Brodies LLP, Aberdeen . . . . (p.723)
T: 01224 392242
E: caroline.sodersten@brodies.com

SOEDER, David Gordon Ramsay (Nov 1989)
(Partner)
Leyshon WS, Kelso . . . . (p.1092)
T: 01573 402520
E: david.soeder@leyshonws.co.uk

SOMERS, Gary (Mar 2013) (Employee)
MacPhee & Partners LLP, Fort
William . . . . (p.930)
T: 01397 701000
E: garysomers@macphee.co.uk

SOMERVILLE, Emma Catherine Reading
(Aug 2014) (Employee)
Ledingham Chalmers LLP,
Aberdeen . . . . (p.734)
T: 01224 408408
E: emma.somerville@ledinghamchalmers.com

SOMERVILLE, Molly Wendy Alice (Apr 2021)
(Employee)
Cairns Brown, Alexandria . . . . (p.751)
T: 01389 756979
E: M.Somerville@cairnsbrown.co.uk

SOMERVILLE, Robbie Hamish (Jun 2014)
(Employee)
Dorsey & Whitney (Europe) LLP, London
EC2 . . . . (p.1264)
E: somerville.robbie@dorsey.com

SOMERVILLE, Sharon Nicola (Mar 2017)
(Employee)
Miller Hendry, Dundee . . . . (p.816)
T: 01382 200000
E: sharonsomerville@millerhendry.co.uk

SOMERVILLE, William Geddas Young
(Sept 1979) (Director)
A.C. Miller & Mackay Limited,
Perth . . . . (p.1151)
T: 01738 620087
E: ws@acmm.co.uk

SOMMERVILLE, Andrew Gordon (Apr 1977)
(Partner)
Pomphreys, Wishaw . . . . (p.1182)
T: 01698 373365
E: ags@pomphreyslaw.com

SOMMERVILLE, Wendy Jane (Oct 2001)
(Employee)
Royal Mail Group Legal, London
EC1 . . . . (p.1267)
E: wendy.sommerville@royalmail.com

SOOD, Neha (Oct 2011) (Solicitor)
Kinetic Lawyers Ltd, Glasgow . . . . (p.997)
T: 01254 846561

SOPER, Kenneth James Haward (Mar 1983)
(Partner)
Campbell Boath, Dundee . . . . (p.808)
T: 01382 200110
E: ksoper@campbellboath.com

SOPPITT, Alan Henry (Nov 1990) (Partner)
Burness Paull LLP, Edinburgh . . . . (p.850)
T: 0131 4736000
E: Alan.Soppitt@burnesspaull.com

SOPPITT, Amanda Lindsay (Nov 1997)
(Employee)
Shoosmiths, Edinburgh . . . . (p.902)
T: 03700 868000
E: mandy.soppitt@shoosmiths.co.uk

SOPPITT, Ian Richard (Dec 1996) (Associate)
Shepherd and Wedderburn LLP,
Edinburgh . . . . (p.900)
T: 0131 2289900
E: ian.soppitt@shepwedd.com

SORRENTINO, Lorraine (Jul 2011) (Solicitor)
NO FIRM

SORRIE, Cherrisse (Dec 2017) (Employee)
Blackadders LLP, Dundee . . . . (p.805)
T: 01382 229222
E: cherrisse.sorrie@blackadders.co.uk

SOUNESS, Neil Brian (Sept 2013) (Employee)
Tesco Personal Finance Plc,
Edinburgh . . . . (p.1234)
T: (0131) 274 3426
E: neil.souness@tescobank.com

SOUTAR, Alasdair Charles Ogg (Oct 1984)
(Employee)
Lindsays LLP, Edinburgh ....(p.882)
T: 0131 2291212
E: alasdairsoutar@lindsays.co.uk

SOUTAR, Murray Duncan (Oct 2007) (Partner)
Gillespie Macandrew LLP,
Edinburgh ....(p.872)
T: 0131 2251677
E: murray.soutar@gillespiemacandrew.co.uk

SOUTER, Caitlin McDonald (Nov 2004)
(Employee)
National Health Service Scotland,
Edinburgh ....(p.1225)
T: 0131 2757800
E: caitlin.souter@nhs.scot

SOUTER, Lynzi Johnson (Oct 2009) (Employee)
Procurator Fiscal Service, Aberdeen ...(p.1213)
T: 0844 561 3660
E: Lynzi.Souter@copfs.gov.uk

SOUTER, Richard Alexander Kyle (Sept 1995)
(Partner)
George More & Company LLP,
Edinburgh ....(p.891)
T: 0131 2026552
E: richardsouter@hotmail.com

SOUTTER, Andrew Eliot (Sept 1999) (Director)
Miller Beckett & Jackson Limited,
Glasgow....................(p.1019)
T: 0141 2042833
E: asoutter@mbjsolicitors.co.uk

SOUTTER, Linsey Jane (Jul 2008) (Employee)
Fiona McPhail Solicitors, Edinburgh ....(p.886)
T: 0344 5152410
E: Linsey_Soutter@shelter.org.uk

SPADARO-DUTTURI, Lucia Giuseppa
(Aug 2021) (Employee)
Howden Group Limited, Renfrew .....(p.1254)
T: 0141 8852245
E: lucia.spadaro@howden.com

SPALDING, Pamela Mairi (Sept 1994)
(Employee)
Gavin Bain & Co., Aberdeen ....(p.721)
T: 01224 623040
E: p.spalding@gavin-bain.co.uk

SPARKS, Elizabeth Alexandra (Oct 2014)
(Employee)
Morton Fraser LLP, Edinburgh ....(p.891)
T: 0131 2471000
E: elizabeth.sparks@morton-fraser.com

SPEARMAN, Katie Diane (Aug 2015)
(Employee)
Brodies LLP, Aberdeen..............(p.723)
T: +44(0) 1224 392548
E: katie.spearman@brodies.com

SPEED, Blair James Matthew (Apr 2004)
(Employee)
Procurator Fiscal Service,
Edinburgh ....(p.1227)
T: 0300 0203168
E: Blair.Speed@copfs.gov.uk

SPEED, Janette (Oct 1990) (Partner)
Shoosmiths, Edinburgh ....(p.902)
T: 03700 868000
E: janette.speed@shoosmiths.co.uk

SPEED, Martha Rose (Aug 2021) (Employee)
Brodies LLP, Glasgow ....(p.948)
T: 0141 2484672
E: martha.speed@brodies.com

SPEEDIE, Ruth (Jul 2004) (Employee)
Sparrows Offshore Services Limited, Bridge of
Don........................(p.1216)
T: 01224 704868
E: Ruth.Speedie@sparrowsgroup.com

SPEIGHT, Fergus Harry (Oct 1996) (Employee)
Royal London Group, London EC3 ....(p.1267)
T: 020 75066787
E: fergus.speight@royallondon.com

SPEIGHT, Neil Brian (Nov 1991) (Employee)
Munro & Noble, Inverness ....(p.1080)
T: 01463 221727
E: Neils@munronoble.com

SPEIRS, Arlene Fiona (Jun 2007) (Employee)
Latta Law Limited, Glasgow..........(p.998)
T: 0141 222 2185
E: as@lattalaw.co.uk

SPEIRS, Thomas Sturrock Blair (Oct 1997)
(Partner)
Addleshaw Goddard LLP,
Edinburgh ....(p.835)
T: 0131 2282400
E: Tom.Speirs@addleshawgoddard.com

SPENCE, Anneli Wilma (Oct 2001) (Associate)
Eden Legal Limited, Perth ....(p.1147)
T: 01738 310047
E: annelispence@eden-legal.co.uk

SPENCE, David Russell (Dec 1983) (Partner)
A.C. Morrison & Richards LLP,
Aberdeen ....(p.737)
T: 01224 573321
E: rspence@acmr.co.uk

SPENCE, Gordon Dewar (Aug 1985) (Partner)
Dewar Spence, Leven ....(p.1114)
T: 01333 425200
E: dewar@dewarspence.co.uk

SPENCE, Stephen Russell (Mar 1980) (Partner)
Neilsons, Edinburgh ....(p.894)
T: 0131 3164444
E: stevespence@neilsons.co.uk

SPENCE, Stroma Elizabeth (Mar 1982)
(Consultant)
Buchanan Burton Limited, East
Kilbride . . . .(p.830)
T: 01355 249228
E: stromas@buchananburton.co.uk

SPENCER, Amy (Feb 2013) (Employee)
The Robert Kerr Partnership Limited,
Paisley . . . .(p.1141)
T: 0141 8896458

SPENCER, Fallon Sara (Feb 2017) (Associate)
McVey & Murricane, Glasgow . . . .(p.1017)
T: 0141 3339688
E: fspencer@mcvey-murricane.com

SPIERS, Adrienne Rama (Jan 2005) (Partner)
Addleshaw Goddard LLP,
Edinburgh . . . .(p.835)
T: 0131 2282400
E: Addi.Spiers@addleshawgoddard.com

SPIERS, Jacqueline Brown Hamilton
(Nov 2007) (Employee)
Procurator Fiscal Service, Glasgow . . . .(p.1241)
T: 0300 0203000
E: jacqueline.spiers@copfs.gov.uk

SPILG, Jillian Deborah (Oct 1992) (Employee)
NORTH LANARKSHIRERe Council,
Motherwell. . . . .(p.1251)
T: 01698 302196
E: Spilgj@northlan.gov.uk

SPILLER, Liesa Mary (Sept 1989) (Partner)
Drummond Miller LLP, Edinburgh . . . . .(p.864)
T: 0131 2265151
E: lspiller@drummondmiller.co.uk

SPINKS, Russell Martin (Oct 2007) (Partner)
Kerr Stirling LLP, Stirling . . . .(p.1165)
T: 01786 463414
E: rspinks@kerrstirling.co.uk

SPRANG, Alan Kenneth (Jan 1984) (Director)
Sprang Terras Limited, Ayr. . . . .(p.765)
T: 01292 288300
E: aks@sprangterras.co.uk

SPROAT, Monique (Jun 2007) (Employee)
Procurator Fiscal Service, Dumfries . . . .(p.1217)
T: 01387 274585
E: monique.sproat@copfs.gov.uk

SPROSON, Sienna Margaret Fernie
(Nov 2011) (Employee)
Blackadders LLP, Dundee. . . . .(p.805)
T: 01382 229222
E: sienna.sproson@blackadders.co.uk

SPROUL, Paola Maria (Nov 1994) (Employee)
Thompsons, Glasgow . . . .(p.1046)
T: 0141 2218840
E: paola.sproul@thompsons-scotland.co.uk

SPROULE, Graeme David (Oct 1999)
(Employee)
National Health Service Scotland,
Edinburgh . . . .(p.1225)
T: 0131 2757800
E: graeme.sproule@nhs.scot

SPROULE, Madelaine (Feb 2000) (Employee)
Church of Scotland, Edinburgh . . . . . .(p.1221)
T: 0131 2255722
E: msproule@cofscotland.org.uk

SPY, Jennifer Ann (Oct 2007) (Employee)
Scottish Government, Glasgow . . . . . .(p.1243)
T: (0141) 2727233
E: Jan.Spy@gov.scot

SRIVASTAVA, Anita (Nov 2003) (Solicitor)
NO FIRM

STACEY, Calum James (Jul 2012) (Employee)
Total UK Limited, London NW1 . . . . . .(p.1269)
T: 0207 3398024
E: calum.stacey@total.com

STACHURA, Karen Marie (Mar 2000)
(Employee)
Brodies LLP, Edinburgh . . . .(p.845)
T: 0131 2283777
E: karen.stachura@brodies.com

STACHURA, Peter Gregory (Oct 2000)
(Employee)
Carey Olsen, London EC2 . . . .(p.1262)
T: (020) 7614 5610
E: gregory.stachura@careyolsen.com

STAFFORD, Ewan (Oct 2009) (Associate)
Harper Macleod LLP, Inverness. . . . . . .(p.1077)
T: 01463 798777
E: ewan.stafford@harpermacleod.co.uk

STAKIM, Caroline (Oct 2007) (Employee)
Intel Ireland Ltd, Leixlip. . . . .(p.1274)
E: caroline.stakim@intel.com

STALKER, Alan Douglas (Nov 2001) (Director)
Young & Partners Business Lawyers Limited,
Dunfermline . . . .(p.827)
T: 01383 721621
E: ads@businesslaw.co.uk

STANKARD, Saoirse Antonia Susan
(Oct 2019) (Employee)
Davidson Chalmers Stewart LLP,
Edinburgh . . . .(p.859)
T: 0131 6259191
E: saoirse.stankard@dcslegal.co.uk

STANLEY, Kenneth Alan, WS (Nov 1981)
(Solicitor)
NO FIRM

STANNAGE, Rhona Henderson (Oct 1988)
(Employee)
Scottish Police Authority, Police Scotland,
　Glasgow . . . .(p.1244)
　T: 01786 895787
　E: Rhona.Stannage@scotland.pnn.police.uk

STANSFIELD, Geoffrey George (Oct 1994)
(Partner)
DWF LLP, Glasgow . . . .(p.973)
　T: 0141 228 8000
　E: geoff.stansfield@dwf.law

STAPLETON, Graeme Stuart (Sept 2011)
(Associate)
Pinsent Masons LLP, Edinburgh . . . .(p.895)
　T: 0131 777 7000
　E: graeme.stapleton@pinsentmasons.com

STARCZEWSKA, Agata Maria (Oct 2016)
(Employee)
Shepherd and Wedderburn LLP,
　Edinburgh . . . .(p.900)
　T: 0131 2289900
　E: Agata.Starczewska@shepwedd.com

STARK, James Gordon Croll (Sept 1988)
(Partner)
Burness Paull LLP, Aberdeen . . . .(p.724)
　T: 01224 621621
　E: jamie.stark@burnesspaull.com

STARK, Jason (Mar 2013) (Employee)
DAC Beachcroft Scotland LLP,
　Glasgow . . . .(p.964)
　T: 0141 2486688
　E: jstark@dacbeachcroft.com

STARK, Lindsay Margaret (Jul 2019) (Employee)
MacRoberts LLP, Glasgow . . . .(p.1015)
　T: 0141 3031100
　E: lindsay.burns@macroberts.com

STATHAM, Gemma Christine (Oct 2010)
(Employee)
National Westminster Bank PLC,
　Edinburgh . . . .(p.1227)
　T: 0131 5235185
　E: Gemma.Statham@rbs.com

STAUNTON, Lauren Alison (Jun 2014)
(Employee)
Procurator Fiscal Service, Glasgow . . . .(p.1241)
　T: 0300 0203000
　E: Lauren.Staunton@copfs.gov.uk

STEEDMAN, Kerry Christina Linda
(Mar 2021) (Employee)
Ormistons Law Practice Limited,
　Glenrothes . . . .(p.1057)
　T: 0800 7810413
　E: ksteedman@ormistonslaw.co.uk

STEEL, Alistair George (Jan 1989) (Employee)
Falkirk Council, Falkirk . . . .(p.1236)
　T: 01324 506070
　E: alistair.steel@falkirk.gov.uk

STEEL, David Alexander (Dec 1973) (Partner)
Harper Macleod LLP, Glasgow . . . .(p.983)
　T: 0141 2218888
　E: david.steel@harpermacleod.co.uk

STEEL, James (Dec 1968) (Solicitor)
NO FIRM

STEEL, Jamie Christina Elizabeth (Jul 2017)
(Employee)
Brodies LLP, Glasgow . . . .(p.948)
　T: 0141 2484672
　E: james.steel@brodies.com

STEEL, Jane Anne (Nov 1992) (Partner)
BTO Solicitors LLP, Glasgow . . . .(p.952)
　T: 0141 2218012
　E: js@bto.co.uk

STEEL, Tanya Louise (Aug 2013) (Partner)
Lindsay, Dumfries . . . .(p.801)
　T: 01387 259236
　E: tanya@lindsaysolicitors.co.uk

STEEL, Thomas Cunningham (Jan 1983)
(Partner)
Brunton Miller, Glasgow . . . .(p.951)
　T: 0141 3371199
　E: tomsteel@bruntonmiller.com

STEELE, Alasdair Montgomerie (Oct 1995)
(Partner)
CMS Cameron McKenna Nabarro Olswang LLP,
　London EC4 . . . .(p.1263)
　T: 0207 3673000
　E: alasdair.steele@cms-cmno.com

STEELE, Allan Richard Morison, WS
(Sept 1998) (Partner)
ARMS Legal Services WS, Glasgow . . . . .(p.942)
　T: 07954 188167
　E: allanrmsteele@armslegalservices.co.uk

STEELE, Andrew Gabriel (Oct 1995) (Employee)
Stevens & Bolton LLP, Guildford . . . . .(p.1259)
　T: 01483 302264
　E: Andrew.Steele@stevens-bolton.com

STEELE, Anne Elizabeth (Jan 1987) (Employee)
Church of Scotland, Edinburgh . . . . . .(p.1221)
　T: 0131 240 2218
　E: ASTEELE@churchofscotland.org.uk

STEELE, Anthony Paul (Jun 2014) (Employee)
Procurator Fiscal Service,
　Edinburgh . . . .(p.1227)
　T: 0300 0203168
　E: Anthony.Steele@copfs.gov.uk

STEELE, Catriona Morag (Aug 2004)
(Employee)
NO FIRM

STEELE, Helen Mary (Oct 2011) (Employee)
Williamson & Henry LLP,
　Kirkcudbright . . . .(p.1104)
　T: 01557 330692
　E: hsteele@williamsonandhenry.co.uk

STEELE, Hilary Anne (Jun 2004) (Director)
Starling Lawyers Limited,
Edinburgh . . . .(p.904)
T: 0131 581 8685
E: hilarysteele@starlinglawyers.com

STEELE, Kenneth Urquhart (Sept 1986)
(Partner)
Campbell Smith LLP, Edinburgh . . . .(p.852)
T: 0131 5563737
E: kenneth.steele@camsmith.co.uk

STEELE, Lauren (Jul 2019) (Employee)
Addleshaw Goddard LLP, Glasgow . . . . .(p.938)
T: 0141 2212300
E: lauren.steele@addleshawgoddard.com

STEELL, Richard David (Nov 2020) (Employee)
Harper Macleod LLP, Glasgow . . . .(p.983)
T: 0141 2218888
E: richard.steell@harpermacleod.co.uk

STEER, Jane Elizabeth (Dec 2003) (Employee)
Gair & Gibson LLP, Falkirk . . . .(p.922)
T: 01324 623928
E: JaneSteer@gairgibson.co.uk

STEFANIAK, Magdalena (May 2017) (Employee)
Scottish Government, Edinburgh . . . . .(p.1231)
T: 0131 244 0815
E: megan.stefaniak@gov.scot

STENHOUSE, Joanne (Jul 2017) (Employee)
Cirrus Logic International Semiconductor Ltd,
Edinburgh . . . .(p.1221)
T: 0131 2727000
E: Joanne.stenhouse@cirrus.com

STEPHEN, Andrew Johnston (Nov 1991)
(Partner)
Murray Beith Murray, Edinburgh . . . . . .(p.893)
T: 0131 225 1200
E: andrew.stephen@murraybeith.co.uk

STEPHEN, Bruce (Nov 1994) (Partner)
Brodies LLP, Edinburgh . . . .(p.845)
T: 0131 2283777
E: bruce.stephen@brodies.com

STEPHEN, Cameron Grant (Apr 1985) (Partner)
Cameron Stephen & Co.,
Edinburgh . . . .(p.852)
T: 0131 5551234
E: cameron@cameronstephen.co.uk

STEPHEN, Caroline Anne (Oct 2005) (Partner)
Laurie & Co Solicitors LLP,
Aberdeen . . . .(p.733)
T: 01224 645 085
E: caroline@laurieandco.co.uk

STEPHEN, Daniel Gordon (Jul 2019) (Employee)
Anderson Shaw & Gilbert Limited,
Inverness . . . .(p.1075)
T: 01463 236123
E: dgs@solicitorsinverness.com

STEPHEN, Emma (Aug 2007) (Partner)
Stronachs LLP, Aberdeen . . . .(p.744)
T: 01224 845845
E: emma.stephen@stronachs.com

STEPHEN, Fiona Margaret (Oct 1988) (Partner)
Anderson Strathern LLP, Edinburgh . . . .(p.839)
T: 0131 2707700
E: fiona.stephen@andersonstrathern.co.uk

STEPHEN, Heather Mari-Ann (Mar 2006)
(Partner)
Raeburn Christie Clark & Wallace LLP,
Aberdeen . . . .(p.741)
T: 01224 332400
E: heather.stephen@raeburns.co.uk

STEPHEN, Hilary Jane (Nov 1991) (Employee)
Scottish Courts and Tribunals Service,
Kirkcaldy . . . .(p.1249)
E: hstephen@scotcourts.gov.uk

STEPHEN, Jake Anthony Ross (Jun 2021)
(Employee)
Brodies LLP, Aberdeen. . . . .(p.723)
T: 01224 392242
E: jake.stephen@brodies.com

STEPHEN, James Alexander (Dec 2017)
(Employee)
Digby Brown LLP, Glasgow . . . .(p.970)
T: 0141 566 2355
E: james.stephen@digbybrown.co.uk

STEPHEN, John Alexander (Jun 2013)
(Employee)
Alston & Bird (London) LLP, London
EC2 . . . .(p.1261)
E: john.stephen@alston.com

STEPHEN, Lorna Helen (Jul 2019) (Employee)
Burness Paull LLP, Edinburgh . . . .(p.850)
T: 0131 4736000
E: lorna.stephen@burnesspaull.com

STEPHEN, Martin Sutherland (Oct 1979)
(Partner)
Wright, Johnston & Mackenzie LLP,
Glasgow. . . . .(p.1054)
T: 0141 2483434
E: mss@wjm.co.uk

STEPHEN, Michael David Peter (Apr 1989)
(Partner)
Brodies LLP, Edinburgh . . . .(p.845)
T: 0131 2283777
E: michael.stephen@brodies.com

STEPHEN, Nicola Ann (Dec 2016) (Employee)
Gillespie Gifford & Brown LLP, Castle
Douglas . . . .(p.783)
T: 01556 503744
E: nicola.stephen@ggblaw.co.uk

STEPHEN, Peter Desmond Jonathan, WS
(Nov 1975) (Partner)
Rae, Reid & Stephen WS,
Edinburgh . . . .(p.898)
T: 0131 337 0899
E: peter@raereidstephen.co.uk

STEPHEN, Ruth Mary (Aug 2014) (Associate)
Pinsent Masons LLP, Dubai . . . .(p.1278)
E: ruth.stephen@pinsentmasons.com

STEPHENSON, Heike (Jan 2009) (Employee)
The Scottish Parliament, Edinburgh . . .(p.1235)
T: 0131 3486580
E: heike.stephenson@parliament.scot

STEPHENSON, James Patrick (Aug 1989)
(Consultant)
Thorley Stephenson Ltd,
Edinburgh . . . .(p.906)
T: 0131 5569599
E: jps@thorleystephenson.com

STEPHENSON, Jonathan Mark (Sept 2018)
(Employee)
Scottish Government, Edinburgh . . . . .(p.1232)
T: 0131 244 0815
E: Jonathan.Stephenson@gov.scot

STEPHENSON, Judith Hilary (Dec 2003)
(Partner)
Shepherd and Wedderburn LLP,
Glasgow. . . . .(p.1039)
T: 0141 566 7208
E: Judith.Stephenson@shepwedd.com

STEVEN, Andrew Gordon (Nov 1986) (Partner)
Watters, Steven & Co., Motherwell . . .(p.1128)
T: 01698 276550
E: info@watterssteven.co.uk

STEVEN, Lorren Georgia (Apr 2021) (Employee)
Raeburn Christie Clark & Wallace LLP,
Aberdeen . . . .(p.741)
T: 01224 332400
E: lorren.steven@raeburns.co.uk

STEVENS, Carrie Lorraine (Jul 2018) (Employee)
Procurator Fiscal Service, Glasgow . . . .(p.1241)
T: 0300 0203000
E: carrie.stevens@copfs.gov.uk

STEVENS, Kirsty Elizabeth (Nov 1994)
(Employee)
Scottish Government, Edinburgh . . . . .(p.1231)
T: 0131 244 0815
E: Kirsty.Stevens@gov.scot

STEVENSON, Alison (Sept 1996) (Employee)
National Health Service Scotland,
Edinburgh . . . .(p.1225)
T: 0131 2757800
E: alison.stevenson4@nhs.scot

STEVENSON, Alison Mary (Jul 2001) (Associate)
Thorntons Law LLP, Dundee . . . .(p.819)
T: 01382 229 111
E: astevenson@thorntons-law.co.uk

STEVENSON, Alistair James (Aug 1990)
(Partner)
McJerrow & Stevenson, Lockerbie . . . .(p.1122)
T: 01576 202123
E: as@mcjerrowstevenson.co.uk

STEVENSON, Andrew Gordon (Aug 1990)
(Employee)
Waddell & Mackintosh Solicitors Ltd,
Troon. . . . .(p.1176)
T: 01292 312222
E: andrew@wmtroon.co.uk

STEVENSON, Caroline (Oct 2007) (Solicitor)
Burness Paull LLP, Edinburgh . . . .(p.850)
T: 0131 4736000
E: Caroline.Stevenson@burnesspaull.com

STEVENSON, Catherine (Jul 2021) (Solicitor)
NO FIRM

STEVENSON, Claire (Oct 1997) (Partner)
Cook, Stevenson & Co., Greenock . . . .(p.1061)
T: 01475 722100
E: cstevenson1973@gmail.com

STEVENSON, Claire (Feb 2015) (Assistant)
Carey Hughes Limited, High
Blantyre . . . .(p.1073)
T: 01698 404616
E: claire@careyhughes.co.uk

STEVENSON, Craig Forbes (Nov 1995)
(Employee)
Ernst and Young LLP, London SE1 . . . .(p.1264)
E: craig.stevenson@uk.ey.com

STEVENSON, Danielle Emma (Jun 2012)
(Employee)
Caritas Legal Limited, Dunfermline . . . . .(p.823)
T: 01383 431101
E: danielle@caritaslegal.co.uk

STEVENSON, Darren Douglas Hugh
(Jul 2010) (Employee)
Wiggin LLP, London W1 . . . .(p.1269)
E: Darren.stevenson@wiggin.co.uk

STEVENSON, Donna Lesley (Feb 1988)
(Employee)
Scottish Futures Trust, Edinburgh . . . . .(p.1231)
T: 0131 5100836
E: donna.stevenson@scottishfuturestrust.org.uk

STEVENSON, Emma Anne (Sept 2016)
(Employee)
Scottish Government, Edinburgh . . . . .(p.1231)
T: 0131 244 0815
E: emma.stevenson@gov.scot

STEVENSON, Emma Victoria Louise
(Jul 2014) (Employee)
South Ayrshire Council, Ayr . . . .(p.1215)
  T: 01292 612 762
  E: Emma.Stevenson@south-ayrshire.gov.uk

STEVENSON, George William (Jan 1981)
(Consultant)
Shepherd and Wedderburn LLP,
  Aberdeen . . . .(p.742)
  T: 01224 621166
  E: george.stevenson@shepwedd.com

STEVENSON, Gordon Douglas (Aug 2017)
(Employee)
Hann & Co Solicitors Ltd, Annan . . . . . .(p.754)
  T: 01461 203836
  E: gordon@hannandco.com

STEVENSON, Grant Tennant (May 1997)
(Partner)
Burness Paull LLP, Glasgow . . . .(p.954)
  T: 0141 2484933
  E: Grant.Stevenson@burnesspaull.com

STEVENSON, Jennifer Christine (Aug 2010)
(Employee)
Brodies LLP, Aberdeen. . . . .(p.723)
  T: 01224 392242
  E: jennifer.stevenson@brodies.com

STEVENSON, Jill (Oct 2001) (Employee)
Lloyds Banking Group Plc,
  Edinburgh . . . .(p.1224)
  T: (0131) 442 9579
  E: Jill.Stevenson@lloydsbanking.com

STEVENSON, Jodi Marie (Oct 2010) (Employee)
Ribnort Limited, Aberdeen. . . . .(p.1213)
  E: jodi@gss-developments.co.uk

STEVENSON, Judith Kathleen (Aug 1990)
(Employee)
Angus McIntosh & Simon Hodge,
  Glasgow. . . . .(p.1012)
  T: 0141 6340313

STEVENSON, Kate Frances Mary (Oct 2021)
(Employee)
John Kilcoyne & Co. Solicitors,
  Glasgow. . . . .(p.997)
  T: 0141 4231400
  E: ks@johnkilcoynesolicitors.co.uk

STEVENSON, Katie Maureen (Jul 2020)
(Employee)
McJerrow & Stevenson, Lockerbie . . . .(p.1122)
  T: 01576 202123
  E: ks@mcjerrowstevenson.co.uk

STEVENSON, Katy Anne (Aug 2017)
(Employee)
Addleshaw Goddard LLP, London
  EC1 . . . .(p.1261)
  T: 0207 6068855
  E: Katy.Stevenson@addleshawgoddard.com

STEVENSON, Lynne Joanne (Sept 1991)
(Associate)
Harper Macleod LLP, Glasgow . . . .(p.983)
  T: 0141 2218888
  E: lynne.stevenson@harpermacleod.co.uk

STEVENSON, Mark (Apr 2018) (Employee)
Addleshaw Goddard LLP,
  Edinburgh . . . .(p.835)
  T: 0131 2282400
  E: mark.stevenson@addleshawgoddard.com

STEVENSON, Martyn Glavin (Jan 2019)
(Associate)
CMS Cameron McKenna Nabarro Olswang LLP,
  Glasgow. . . . .(p.962)
  T: 0141 2222200
  E: martyn.stevenson@cms-cmno.com

STEVENSON, Maureen (Jul 1985) (Employee)
Gilson Gray LLP, Edinburgh . . . .(p.874)
  T: 0131 5165354
  E: mstevenson@gilsongray.co.uk

STEVENSON, Morag (Aug 1999) (Employee)
Murray Ormiston LLP, Aberdeen . . . . . .(p.738)
  T: 01224 478822
  E: morag@murrayormiston.com

STEVENSON, Pamela (Oct 1998) (Partner)
Weightmans (Scotland) LLP,
  Glasgow. . . . .(p.1051)
  T: 0345 073 9900
  E: Pamela.stevenson@weightmans.com

STEVENSON, Scott Fraser (Nov 2021)
(Employee)
Clarity Simplicity Ltd, Glasgow. . . . .(p.960)
  T: 0141 4332626
  E: s.stevenson@claritysimplicity.co.uk

STEVENSON, Seonaid Mary (Feb 2018)
(Solicitor)
NO FIRM

STEVENSON, Zoe Pauline (Sept 2008)
(Associate)
Thorntons Law LLP, Kirkcaldy. . . . .(p.1102)
  T: 01592 268608
  E: zstevenson@thorntons-law.co.uk

STEWART, Alan Breck (Oct 1997) (Employee)
Law Society of Scotland,
  Edinburgh . . . .(p.1224)
  T: 0131 2267411
  E: BreckStewart@lawscot.org.uk

STEWART, Alan George (Mar 1994) (Partner)
Morton Fraser LLP, Edinburgh . . . .(p.891)
  T: 0131 2471000
  E: alan.stewart@morton-fraser.com

STEWART, Alan James (Dec 1979) (Partner)
Davidson Chalmers Stewart LLP,
  Glasgow. . . . .(p.967)
  T: 0141 4283258
  E: alan.stewart@dcslegal.com

STEWART, Alan John (Dec 2015) (Employee)
Sainsbury's Bank plc, Edinburgh......(p.1230)
T: (0131) 286 0807
E: alan.stewart@sainsburysbank.co.uk

STEWART, Alec Dougal (Nov 2002) (Solicitor)
NO FIRM

STEWART, Alison Jane (Nov 1997) (Employee)
Office of the Advocate General,
Edinburgh ....(p.1227)
T: 07834 699872
E: Alison.Stewart@advocategeneral.gov.uk

STEWART, Alpin James Bruce (Oct 1990)
(Partner)
Munro & Noble, Dingwall...........(p.797)
T: 01349 866777
E: alpins@munronoble.com

STEWART, Amy Elizabeth (Jun 2021)
(Employee)
McLean & Stewart LLP, Dunblane .....(p.804)
T: 01786 823217
E: Amy@mcleanandstewart.co.uk

STEWART, Anca-Maria (Nov 2019) (Employee)
Cairns Brown, Alexandria ....(p.751)
T: 01389 756979
E: a.stewart@cairnsbrown.co.uk

STEWART, Ann Eileen Atkinson, WS
(Aug 1980) (Associate)
Shepherd and Wedderburn LLP,
Edinburgh ....(p.900)
T: 0131 4735380
E: ann.stewart@shepwedd.com

STEWART, Catriona (Jan 1986) (Associate)
Clyde & Co (Scotland) LLP,
Edinburgh ....(p.855)
T: 0131 5571545
E: catriona.stewart@clydeco.com

STEWART, Christopher Walter (Nov 2000)
(Partner)
Digby Brown LLP, Glasgow ....(p.970)
T: 0333 200 5925
E: chris.stewart@digbybrown.co.uk

STEWART, Claire Allison (Sept 2000)
(Employee)
Ocean Winds UK Limited,
Edinburgh ....(p.1227)
T: 0131 5567602
E: Claire.Stewart@oceanwinds.com

STEWART, David Alan (Nov 1980) (Partner)
Carruthers, Curdie, Sturrock & Co.,
Kilmarnock..................(p.1094)
T: 01563 572727
E:
DavidStewart@carrutherscurdiesturrock.co.uk

STEWART, David Ross (Dec 2002) (Partner)
Morton Fraser LLP, Edinburgh ....(p.891)
T: 0131 2471000
E: David.Stewart@morton-fraser.com

STEWART, Donald John (May 1988) (Employee)
Ruscombe Management Services Limited,
Ruscombe ....(p.1271)

STEWART, Douglas Iain Gilmour (Mar 2004)
(Employee)
Element Materials Technology Group,
Edinburgh ....(p.1222)
T: 0131 333 8053
E: doug.stewart@element.com

STEWART, Elizabeth Ann (Jan 2000) (Partner)
Stronachs LLP, Aberdeen ....(p.744)
T: 01224 845845
E: Liz.Stewart@stronachs.com

STEWART, Fiona Ann (Nov 2019) (Employee)
NORTH LANARKSHIREre Council,
Motherwell..................(p.1251)
T: 01698 302196
E: StewartFi@northlan.gov.uk

STEWART, Fiona Mary (Jan 1992) (Employee)
Aberdeenshire Council, Banff........(p.1215)
T: 01261 813200
E: Fiona.Stewart@aberdeenshire.gov.uk

STEWART, Fraser William McDonald
(May 2017) (Employee)
Harper Macleod LLP, Glasgow ....(p.983)
T: 0141 2218888
E: Fraser.Stewart@harpermacleod.co.uk

STEWART, Gillian Simpson (Nov 1999)
(Employee)
Aberdeen Corporate Services Limited,
Edinburgh ....(p.1220)
T: 0131 2455982
E: gillian.stewart@abrdn.com

STEWART, Gordon James (Apr 1999) (Director)
Good & Stewart Limited,
Edinburgh ....(p.875)
T: 0131 662 9177
E: goodandstewart@gmail.com

STEWART, Gordon John (Nov 2006)
(Employee)
SOUTH LANARKSHIREre Council,
Hamilton ....(p.1247)
T: (01698) 454785
E: Gordon.Stewart@southlanarkshire.gov.uk

STEWART, Gulam Karima (Aug 2020)
(Employee)
Procurator Fiscal Service,
Edinburgh ....(p.1229)
T: 0300 0203000
E: karima.stewart@copfs.gov.uk

STEWART, Hayley (Mar 2018) (Employee)
Ofgem, Glasgow . . . .(p.1241)
　T: 0141 354 5432
　E: Hayley.Stewart@ofgem.gov.uk

STEWART, Helen Maria (Sept 2015) (Employee)
Pinsent Masons Espana SLP,
　Madrid. . . . .(p.1276)
　E: Helen.M.Stewart@pinsentmasons.com

STEWART, Ishbel Miriam (Oct 1984)
　(Employee)
Liddle & Anderson LLP, Boness . . . .(p.777)
　T: 01506 822727
　E: ims@liddleandanderson.co.uk

STEWART, Isla Joy (Jul 2010) (Employee)
Aramark Ireland, Dublin . . . .(p.1274)

STEWART, James Andrew (Sept 2008)
　(Director)
Stewart and O'Neill Defence Limited,
　Edinburgh . . . .(p.904)
　T: 0131 225 2900
　E: stewartandoneill@gmail.com

STEWART, James Hymers Sutherland, WS
　(Jan 1970) (Consultant)
Inverness Law, Inverness . . . .(p.1078)
　T: 01463 832818

STEWART, James Morrison (Dec 2004)
　(Employee)
Brabners LLP, Manchester . . . .(p.1270)
　T: 0161 8368800
　E: James.Stewart@brabners.com

STEWART, Jennifer Helen (Nov 2014)
　(Associate)
CMS Cameron McKenna Nabarro Olswang LLP,
　Edinburgh . . . .(p.856)
　T: 0131 2007369
　E: Jennifer.Stewart@cms-cmno.com

STEWART, Jennifer Helen (Nov 2004)
　(Associate)
BTO Solicitors LLP, Glasgow . . . .(p.952)
　T: 0141 2218012
　E: jhs@bto.co.uk

STEWART, Joanna Jayne (Sept 2014)
　(Employee)
Davidson & Co, Dubai . . . .(p.1278)
　T: +971 4 3438897
　E: jstewart@davidsoncolaw.com

STEWART, Joseph Alan (Nov 2003) (Employee)
Procurator Fiscal Service,
　Edinburgh . . . .(p.1227)
　T: 0300 0203168
　E: Joe.Stewart@copfs.gov.uk

STEWART, Karen Ann (Nov 2007) (Partner)
Mackintosh & Wylie LLP,
　Kilmarnock. . . . .(p.1095)
　T: 01563 525104
　E: kstewart@mackwylie.com

STEWART, Karen Mary (Oct 2000) (Employee)
QBE Management Services (UK) Ltd, London
　EC3 . . . .(p.1267)
　T: 0207 105 5947
　E: karen.stewart@uk.qbe.com

STEWART, Kathleen (Oct 1986) (Employee)
Procurator Fiscal Service, Paisley . . . . . .(p.1252)
　T: 0141 8875225
　E: Katie.Stewart@copfs.gov.uk

STEWART, Kathleen Margaret, WS
　(Jan 1976) (Partner)
Kathleen Stewart, WS, Edinburgh . . . . . .(p.904)
　T: 0131 2259181
　E: kathleen@katws.co.uk

STEWART, Keir Andrew (May 2019) (Employee)
Capricorn Energy Ltd, Edinburgh . . . . .(p.1221)
　T: 0131 4753000
　E: keir.stewart@cairnenergy.com

STEWART, Kirsty (Jul 2013) (Employee)
Thorntons Law LLP, Dundee . . . .(p.819)
　T: 01382 229 111
　E: kstewart@thorntons-law.co.uk

STEWART, Lauren Dee (Feb 2006) (Employee)
TotalEnergies E&P UK Limited,
　Westhill . . . .(p.1255)
　T: 01224 297000
　E: Lauren.Stewart@totalenergies.com

STEWART, Lindsay Elaine (Oct 1987)
　(Employee)
Scottish Courts and Tribunals Service,
　Dundee . . . .(p.1218)

STEWART, Lisa Claire (Aug 2008) (Employee)
Scottish Social Services Council,
　Dundee . . . .(p.1218)
　T: 0345 6030 891
　E: lisa.stewart@sssc.uk.com

STEWART, Lucy (Jun 2011) (Employee)
Law Society of Scotland,
　Edinburgh . . . .(p.1224)
　T: 0131 2267411
　E: lucydurie@lawscot.org.uk

STEWART, Lynne Ann (Nov 1991) (Partner)
Ledingham Chalmers LLP,
　Aberdeen . . . .(p.733)
　T: 01224 622622
　E: Lynne.Stewart@ledinghamchalmers.com

STEWART, Margaret Anne (Aug 1986)
　(Employee)
Procurator Fiscal Service, Hamilton . . . .(p.1247)
　T: 0844 5613245
　E: margaret.stewart@copfs.gov.uk

STEWART, Mark Edward (Oct 1996) (Partner)
Brodies LLP, Aberdeen. . . . .(p.723)
　T: 01224 392 242
　E: mark.stewart@brodies.com

STEWART, Michael David (Apr 2015)
(Employee)
Burness Paull LLP, Edinburgh . . . .(p.850)
  T: 0131 4736000
  E: michael.stewart@burnesspaull.com

STEWART, Michael James (Oct 1996)
(Employee)
National Health Service Scotland,
  Edinburgh . . . .(p.1225)
  T: 0131 2757800
  E: Michael.Stewart5@nhs.scot

STEWART, Michael Patrick (Dec 2020)
(Employee)
McCusker McElroy & Gallanagh Solicitors,
  Paisley . . . .(p.1139)
  T: 0141 5619999
  E: michael.stewart@mccuskerlaw.co.uk

STEWART, Mimi (Dec 2001) (Associate)
Morton Fraser LLP, Edinburgh . . . .(p.891)
  T: 0131 2471000
  E: mimi.stewart@morton-fraser.com

STEWART, Murray (Aug 2005) (Partner)
Gilson Gray LLP, Edinburgh . . . .(p.874)
  T: 0131 516 5354
  E: mstewart@gilsongray.co.uk

STEWART, Nadya Leanne (Jul 2000) (Employee)
Procurator Fiscal Service,
  Edinburgh . . . .(p.1227)
  T: 1312438152
  E: Nadya.Stewart@copfs.gov.uk

STEWART, Natalie (Oct 1998) (Employee)
Scottish Government, Edinburgh . . . . .(p.1231)
  T: 0131 244 0815
  E: Natalie.Stewart@gov.scot

STEWART, Neil Conrad (Jul 2009) (Employee)
Public Defence Solicitors Office,
  Glasgow . . . .(p.1243)
  T: 0141 553 0794
  E: NStewart@pdso.org.uk

STEWART, Neil Iain (Oct 2008) (Partner)
Stewart Legal, Edinburgh . . . .(p.904)
  T: 0131 2352426
  E: neil@stewartlegal.co.uk

STEWART, Nicholas (Oct 2014) (Employee)
Standard Life Assets and Employee Services
  Limited, Edinburgh . . . .(p.1234)
  T: 0131 2457508
  E: nick_stewart@thephoenixgroup.com

STEWART, Nicola Louise (Jul 2018) (Employee)
Scottish Environment Protection Agency,
  Dingwall . . . .(p.1217)
  T: 01349 862021
  E: nikki.stewart@sepa.org.uk

STEWART, Patrick Charles Donald
(Jan 1997) (Employee)
Manchester United Limited,
  Manchester . . . .(p.1270)
  T: 0161 8688329
  E: patrick.stewart@manutd.co.uk

STEWART, Peter John (Oct 1999) (Partner)
Anderson Beaton Lamond, Perth . . . . .(p.1146)
  T: 01738 639999
  E: peterstewart@abl-law.co.uk

STEWART, Richard Harrison (Sept 2011)
(Employee)
Aberdeen Corporate Services Limited,
  Edinburgh . . . .(p.1220)
  T: 0131 245 7508
  E: Richard.Stewart@abrdn.com

STEWART, Robert Crombie (Aug 1984)
(Director)
Holmes Mackillop Limited,
  Giffnock . . . .(p.934)
  T: 0141 638 7405
  E: rstewart@homack.co.uk

STEWART, Ronald Alan (Sept 1983) (Director)
McCartney Stewart Limited,
  Renfrew . . . .(p.1159)
  T: 0141 8851858
  E: alan@mccartneystewart.co.uk

STEWART, Samantha (Aug 2017) (Employee)
Thompsons, Glasgow . . . .(p.1046)
  T: 0141 2218840
  E:
  samantha.stewart@thompsons-scotland.co.uk

STEWART, Sarah Amy Ruth (Sept 2015)
(Employee)
Burges Salmon LLP, Edinburgh . . . .(p.850)
  T: 0131 3142 112
  E: sarah.stewart@burges-salmon.com

STEWART, Sarah Anne (Sept 2014) (Employee)
Harper Macleod LLP, Glasgow . . . .(p.983)
  T: 0141 227 9611
  E: sarah.stewart@harpermacleod.co.uk

STEWART, Sarah Kirstin (Jan 2008) (Employee)
Brodies LLP, Aberdeen . . . .(p.723)
  T: 01224 392242
  E: Sarah.Stewart@brodies.com

STEWART, Steven Robert William
(Mar 2013) (Employee)
Burness Paull LLP, Glasgow . . . .(p.954)
  T: 0141 2484933
  E: Steven.Stewart@burnesspaull.com

STEWART, Susan Edith (Nov 2010) (Employee)
Anderson Strathern LLP, Edinburgh . . . .(p.839)
  T: 0131 2707700
  E: Susan.Stewart@andersonstrathern.co.uk

STEWART, Thomas Henry Gilmour
(Oct 1977) (Partner)
Thomas H.G. Stewart, Edinburgh . . . . . .(p.904)
T: 0131 2294939
E: tom@thomashgstewart.co.uk

STEWART, Victoria Louise (Sept 2004)
(Employee)
Partners Group AG, Baar-Zug. . . . .(p.1276)
T: +41 41784 6376
E: victoria.stewart@partnersgroup.com

STEWART-HART, Kathryn Jane (Sept 2011)
(Employee)
Scottish Widows Limited,
Edinburgh . . . .(p.1233)
T: 0131 6557230
E: kate.stewart-hart@lloydsbanking.com

STEWART-SMITH, Martin Charles (Nov 1987)
(Partner)
Addleshaw Goddard LLP, London
EC1 . . . .(p.1261)
T: 0207 6068855
E:
martin.stewart-smith@addleshawgoddard.com

STIHLER, David Thomas (Oct 2005) (Employee)
Church of Scotland, Edinburgh . . . . . .(p.1221)
T: 0131 2255722
E: dstihler@churchofscotland.org.uk

STILLIE, Derek Daniel (Jul 2013) (Director)
Wallace Hodge & Company Limited,
Ayr . . . .(p.766)
T: 01292 611177
E: derek.stillie@wallace-hodge.co.uk

STIMPSON, Lara Macaulay (Jan 1996)
(Employee)
Renfrewshire Council, Paisley . . . .(p.1252)
T: (0141) 6187172
E: lara.stimpson@renfrewshire.gov.uk

STIRLING, Amy Kate (Mar 2014) (Employee)
Pinsent Masons LLP, London EC2 . . . . .(p.1267)
T: 020 7418 7000
E: amy.stirling@pinsentmasons.com

STIRLING, Craig (Sept 1997) (Partner)
Davidson Chalmers Stewart LLP,
Edinburgh . . . .(p.859)
T: 0131 6259191
E: craig.stirling@dcslegal.com

STIRLING, Fiona Sanderson (Oct 1999)
(Employee)
EDF Energy Renewables,
Edinburgh . . . .(p.1222)
T: (0131) 460 3654
E: Fiona.stirling@edf-re.uk

STIRLING, John Boyd (Nov 1991) (Partner)
Gillespie Macandrew LLP,
Edinburgh . . . .(p.872)
T: 0131 2251677
E: john.stirling@gillespiemacandrew.co.uk

STIRLING, Lorraine (Jun 2003) (Employee)
Scottish Law Commission,
Edinburgh . . . .(p.1233)
T: 0131 6682131
E: lorraine.stirling@scotlawcom.gov.uk

STIRLING, Ross Francis (Jul 2014) (Employee)
Scott Alexander, Montrose . . . .(p.1125)
T: 01674 671477
E: ross@scottalexandersolicitors.co.uk

STIRLING, Shuna Margaret Elizabeth
(Oct 1996) (Partner)
Brodies LLP, Glasgow . . . .(p.948)
T: 0141 2484672
E: shuna.stirling@brodies.com

STIRRAT, David (Sept 2007) (Employee)
Burness Paull LLP, Edinburgh . . . .(p.850)
T: 0131 4736000
E: David.Stirrat@burnesspaull.com

STIRRAT, Euan Campbell (Aug 1976) (Director)
John Jackson & Dick Limited,
Hamilton . . . .(p.1067)
T: 01698 281747
E: estirrat@jacksondicklaw.com

STOBIE, Alistair James (Jan 1996) (Employee)
Aberdeenshire Council, Aberdeen . . . . .(p.1211)
T: 0345 608 1208
E: Alistair.Stobie@aberdeenshire.gov.uk

STOCK, Claire Anne (May 2018) (Employee)
SSE Plc, Perth . . . .(p.1253)
T: 07901 124391
E: claire.stock@sse.com

STOCKER, Thomas Stephen (Oct 1999)
(Partner)
Pinsent Masons LLP, Edinburgh . . . .(p.895)
T: 0131 777 7000
E: tom.stocker@pinsentmasons.com

STOCKEY, Leigh Alexandra (Jul 2012)
(Employee)
Travers Smith LLP, London EC1 . . . . . .(p.1269)
T: 020 7295 3412
E: Leigh.Stockey@traverssmith.com

STOKES, Hannah Rita (Sept 2018) (Employee)
Colledge & Shields LLP, Dumfries . . . . .(p.800)
T: 01387 240044
E: hs@colledgeandshields.co.uk

STONE, Alison Henderson (Nov 1985)
(Employee)
Scottish Courts and Tribunals Service,
Aberdeen . . . .(p.1214)
T: 01224 657258
E: astone@scotcourts.gov.uk

STONE, Catherine Rose (Jan 2001) (Employee)
Lloyds Banking Group Plc,
Edinburgh . . . .(p.1224)
T: (0131) 442 9579
E: Catherine.Stone@LloydsBanking.com

STONE, Fern Jamieson (Aug 2017) (Employee)
Wilsone & Duffus, Aberdeen . . . .(p.746)
T: 01224 651700
E: Fern.Stone@wilsoneduffus.co.uk

STONEHAM, Michael Peter, WS (Nov 1985)
(Partner)
Brodies LLP, Edinburgh . . . .(p.845)
T: 0131 2283777
E: michael.stoneham@brodies.com

STONEHAM, Richard William (Nov 2016)
(Employee)
PEAK6 Group LLC
E: rstoneham@peak6.com

STORRAR, Grant James Begbie (Jun 2016)
(Director)
Watersrule Limited, Stirling . . . .(p.1167)
T: 01786 235 235
E: grant.storrar@watersrule.co.uk

STORRIE, Alix Elizabeth (Sept 2004) (Partner)
Turcan Connell, Edinburgh . . . .(p.908)
T: 0131 2288111
E: alix.storrie@turcanconnell.com

STORRIE, Angus Kerr (Jan 1978) (Director)
Cochran Dickie, Paisley . . . .(p.1137)
T: 0141 8892245
E: aks@cochrandickie.co.uk

STORRIE, Caroline Victoria (Oct 2005)
(Employee)
National Westminster Bank PLC,
Edinburgh . . . .(p.1226)
T: (0131) 626 2925
E: caroline.storrie@natwest.com

STORRIE, David (Jul 2002) (Director)
Thorley Stephenson Ltd,
Edinburgh . . . .(p.906)
T: 0131 5569599
E: ds@thorleystephenson.com

STOTT, Andrew (Nov 2007) (Employee)
Ledingham Chalmers LLP,
Inverness . . . .(p.1078)
T: 01463 667412
E: andrew.stott@ledinghamchalmers.com

STRACHAN, Christopher Murray (Jul 2017)
(Employee)
Subsea 7 (UK Service Company) Ltd,
Westhill . . . .(p.1255)
T: 01224 526018
E: chris.strachan@subsea7.com

STRACHAN, Euan Allister (Sept 2011)
(Employee)
Akin Gump Strauss Hauer & Feld LLP,
Singapore. . . . .(p.1276)
E: estrachan@akingump.com

STRACHAN, Grant Finlayson (Dec 2008)
(Associate)
Brodies LLP, Edinburgh . . . .(p.845)
T: 0131 2283777
E: grant.strachan@brodies.com

STRACHAN, Iain David (Oct 1998) (Employee)
City of Edinburgh Council,
Edinburgh . . . .(p.1221)
T: (0131) 5294145
E: iain.strachan@edinburgh.gov.uk

STRACHAN, Jenny Leigh (Jun 2011) (Employee)
Office of the Advocate General,
Edinburgh . . . .(p.1227)
T: 0131 2441635
E: jenny.strachan@advocategeneral.gov.uk

STRACHAN, John Alan (Nov 2001) (Partner)
Burness Paull LLP, Aberdeen . . . .(p.724)
T: 01224 621621
E: John.Strachan@burnesspaull.com

STRACHAN, Kirsty Audrey Pauline
(Jul 2016) (Employee)
Lindsays LLP, Edinburgh . . . .(p.882)
T: 0131 2291212
E: kirstystrachan@lindsays.co.uk

STRACHAN, Lucy Jill (Mar 2006) (Employee)
The Malcolm Group, Paisley . . . .(p.1253)
E: strachanl@whm.co.uk

STRACHAN, Melissa Jayne (Nov 2017)
(Employee)
Gillespie Macandrew LLP,
Edinburgh . . . .(p.872)
T: 0131 2251677
E: Melissa.Strachan@gillespiemacandrew.co.uk

STRACHAN, Rebekah Louise (May 2021)
(Employee)
Loughran & Co Limited, Glasgow . . . .(p.1004)
T: 0141 3310374

STRACHAN, Richard Khalil (Dec 2010)
(Employee)
Weatherford, Aberdeen . . . .(p.1214)
T: 01224 380200
E: Richard.Strachan3@EU.Weatherford.com

STRACHAN, Taleen (Feb 2011) (Employee)
Gilson Gray LLP, Dundee. . . . .(p.811)
T: 01382 549321
E: tstrachan@gilsongray.co.uk

STRAIN, Alan (Aug 1990) (Consultant)
Davidson Chalmers Stewart LLP,
Edinburgh . . . .(p.859)
T: 0131 6259191
E: alan.strain@dcslegal.com

STRAIN, Lauren McCann (Feb 2021)
(Employee)
Thompsons, Glasgow . . . .(p.1046)
T: 0141 2218840
E: lauren.strain@thompsons-scotland.co.uk

STRAIN, Michael William (Mar 2019)
(Employee)
Keoghs Scotland LLP, Glasgow........(p.996)
T: 0141 2380100
E: mstrain@keoghs.co.uk

STRAITON, Victoria Janet (Jun 2009) (Director)
Clan Childlaw Limited, Glasgow.......(p.959)
T: 0808 129 0522
E: vicki.straiton@clanchildlaw.org

STRAND, Josef Tierney (Oct 2019) (Employee)
Watermans Legal Limited,
Edinburgh ....(p.911)
T: 0131 4675566
E: JosefStrand@watermanslegal.co.uk

STRANG, Douglas Alexander (Sept 1995)
(Associate)
BTO Solicitors LLP, Glasgow ....(p.952)
T: 0141 2218012
E: dst@bto.co.uk

STRANG, Fiona Marion (Jul 2014) (Employee)
Harper Macleod LLP, Glasgow ....(p.983)
T: 0141 2218888
E: fiona.strang@harpermacleod.co.uk

STRASSER, Ferdinand (Jan 2018) (Partner)
Greenberg Solicitors, Laurencekirk ....(p.1111)
T: 07415 135957
E: office@greenberg-law.co.uk

STRATFORD, Lynne (Nov 2003) (Partner)
Drummond Miller LLP, Dalkeith ....(p.794)
T: 0131 6639568
E: lstratford@drummondmiller.co.uk

STRATHDEE, Grant David (Mar 2010)
(Employee)
DAC Beachcroft Scotland LLP,
Glasgow....................(p.964)
T: 0141 2486688
E: gstrathdee@dacbeachcroft.com

STRATHDEE, Jaymie (Oct 2011) (Partner)
Allan, Black & McCaskie, Elgin ....(p.915)
T: 01343 543355
E: js@abmsols.co.uk

STRATHERN, Jane McNair (Jun 1987)
(Employee)
National Health Service Scotland,
Edinburgh ....(p.1225)
T: 0131 2757800
E: jane.strathern@nhs.scot

STREET, Richard (Jun 2003) (Employee)
Brewdog Plc, Ellon ....(p.1236)
T: 01358 724 924
E: richard.street@brewdog.com

STREFFORD, David Samuel (Nov 1981)
(Consultant)
Strefford Tulips Limited, Hamilton ....(p.1070)
T: 01698 429428
E: d.strefford@strefford-tulips.co.uk

STREFFORD, Greg David (Sept 2014)
(Employee)
Howden M&A Limited, London
SE1 ....(p.1265)

STRINGER, John Paul (Mar 2019) (Employee)
DAC Beachcroft Scotland LLP,
Glasgow....................(p.964)
T: 0141 2486688
E: jstringer@dacbeachcroft.com

STRINGER, Niall (Nov 1989) (Partner)
Turcan Connell, Edinburgh ....(p.908)
T: 0131 2288111
E: niall.stringer@turcanconnell.com

STRONG, Donna (Sept 2004) (Partner)
TLT LLP, Glasgow ....(p.1048)
T: 0333 006 0400
E: donna.strong@tltsolicitors.com

STRONG, Eleanor Zo (Jan 2020) (Associate)
Weightmans (Scotland) LLP,
Glasgow....................(p.1051)
T: 0345 073 9900
E: zoe.strong@weightmans.com

STROUD, Derek Andrew (Dec 1989) (Partner)
Brodies LLP, Glasgow ....(p.948)
T: 0141 2484672
E: derek.stroud@brodies.com

STROUD, Jacqueline Anne (Oct 1990) (Partner)
MacRoberts LLP, Edinburgh ....(p.887)
T: 0131 2295046
E: Jacqueline.Stroud@macroberts.com

STRUCKMEIER, Anne Christina (Oct 1995)
(Partner)
Addleshaw Goddard LLP,
Edinburgh ....(p.835)
T: 0131 2282400
E: Anne.Struckmeier@addleshawgoddard.com

STRUTH, Douglas Francis (Jan 2005)
(Employee)
Scottish Rugby, Edinburgh ....(p.1233)
T: 0131 3465000
E: douglas.struth@sru.org.uk

STRUTH, Jane Frances (Dec 2004) (Employee)
Zonal Retail Data Systems Limited,
Edinburgh ....(p.1236)
T: (07970) 172738
E: jane.struth@zonal.co.uk

STRUTHERS, Fiona Gillian (Aug 2008)
(Employee)
Standard Life Investments Limited,
Edinburgh ....(p.1234)
T: (0131) 245 4153
E: fiona.struthers@abrdn.com

STRUTHERS, Zoe Andrea (Aug 2019)
(Employee)
Banijay UK, Glasgow . . . . (p.1238)
T: 0141 3533222
E: zoe.struthers@banijayuk.com

STRZYZEWSKA, Angela (Feb 2018) (Employee)
Just Employment Law Ltd,
Glasgow . . . . (p.1240)
T: 0141 3315150
E: angelas@justemploymentlaw.co.uk

STUART, Aimee Christine (Aug 2019)
(Employee)
A D Stuart & Co. Limited,
Edinburgh . . . . (p.905)
T: 0845 056 3958
E: aimee.stuart@stuart-co.com

STUART, Alan Davidson (Dec 1988) (Director)
A D Stuart & Co. Limited,
Edinburgh . . . . (p.905)
T: 0845 056 3958
E: alan.stuart@stuart-co.com

STUART, Chloe (Jul 2019) (Employee)
Jones Whyte LLP, Glasgow . . . . (p.993)
T: 0141 375 1222
E: chloe.stuart@joneswhyte.co.uk

STUART, Christine Anne (Jan 1990) (Partner)
TC Young LLP, Edinburgh . . . . (p.914)
T: 0131 2207660
E: cas@tcyoung.co.uk

STUART, Christopher David Brown
(Apr 1981) (Partner)
Stuart & Co, Inverness . . . . (p.1083)
T: 01463 731582
E: chris@highlandsolicitor.com

STUART, Fiona Mary (Oct 2003) (Employee)
Fife Council, Glenrothes . . . . (p.1246)
T: 03451 550000
E: fiona.stuart@fife.gov.uk

STUART, John Forester, WS (Aug 1988)
(Solicitor)
Scottish Episcopal Church,
Edinburgh . . . . (p.1231)
T: 0131 2256357
E: johnstuart@breathemail.net

STUART, Rachel Louise (Oct 2006) (Employee)
Aker Solutions AS, Fornebu . . . . (p.1275)
T: 0047 406 43 475
E: rachel.stuart@akersolutions.com

STUART, Sarah Duncan (Jul 1997) (Partner)
Ledingham Chalmers LLP,
Aberdeen . . . . (p.734)
T: 01224 408 449
E: sarah.stuart@ledinghamchalmers.com

STUART, Vivienne Carol (Nov 1992) (Employee)
DWF LLP, Edinburgh . . . . (p.865)
T: 0131 2265541
E: vivienne.stuart@dwf.law

STUBING, Eliza Augusta (Sept 2020)
(Employee)
Shoosmiths, Edinburgh . . . . (p.902)
T: 03700 868000
E: Eliza.Stubing@shoosmiths.co.uk

STURDY, Paul (Oct 2012) (Director)
Livingstone Brown Limited,
Glasgow . . . . (p.1004)
T: 0141 7789657
E: ps@livbrown.co.uk

STURGEON, Kevin Buchanan (Sept 2018)
(Employee)
Gillespie Macandrew LLP,
Edinburgh . . . . (p.872)
T: 0131 2251677
E: kevin.sturgeon@gillespiemacandrew.co.uk

STURROCK, Ashley Fiona (Jul 2011) (Employee)
Digby Brown LLP, Edinburgh . . . . (p.862)
T: 0333 200 5925
E: ashley.sturrock@digbybrown.co.uk

STURROCK, Claire Mary (Dec 1988)
(Consultant)
Morton Fraser LLP, Edinburgh . . . . (p.891)
T: 0131 247 1202
E: Claire.Sturrock@morton-fraser.com

STURROCK, Garry John (Jul 2013) (Employee)
Brodies LLP, Aberdeen . . . . (p.723)
T: 01224 392242
E: garry.sturrock@brodies.com

STURROCK, Jenna (Feb 2020) (Employee)
Clyde & Co (Scotland) LLP,
Edinburgh . . . . (p.855)
T: 0131 5571545

STURROCK, Jennifer Zoe Elder (Aug 2013)
(Associate)
Drummond Miller LLP, Edinburgh . . . . . (p.864)
T: 0131 2265151
E: jsturrock@drummondmiller.co.uk

STURROCK, Lynne (Jun 2007) (Employee)
Thorntons Law LLP, Dundee . . . . (p.819)
T: 01382 229 111
E: lsturrock@thorntons-law.co.uk

STYGAL, Leigh (Oct 2017) (Employee)
Slater and Gordon Scotland Limited,
Edinburgh . . . . (p.903)
T: 0131 7184150
E: Leigh.Stygal@slatergordon.uk

STYLES, Colin John (Dec 1984) (Partner)
Cockburns, Forres . . . . (p.928)
T: 01309 673373
E: Colin.Styles@cockburns-solicitors.com

STYLES, Roderick Robertson (Dec 1983)
(Partner)
Walker & Sharpe, Dumfries . . . .(p.803)
T: 01387 267222
E: rod.styles@walker-sharpe.co.uk

SULLIVAN, Amy Louise (Sept 2020) (Employee)
Pomphreys, Wishaw . . . .(p.1182)
T: 01698 373365
E: amy@pomphreyslaw.com

SULLIVAN, John William (Nov 1982) (Partner)
The PRG Partnership, Kirkintilloch. . . . .(p.1105)
T: 0141 7762298
E: johnsullivan@prg.co.uk

SULLIVAN, Julie Kathryn (Sept 2002) (Associate)
Young & Partners Business Lawyers Limited,
Dunfermline . . . .(p.827)
T: 01383 721621
E: jks@businesslaw.co.uk

SULLIVAN, Dr, Laurence Michael (Sept 1995)
(Employee)
Legal Secretariat to the Lord Advocate,
Edinburgh . . . .(p.1224)
T: 0300 020 3364
E: laurence.sullivan@gov.scot

SUMAL, Paman Veer Singh (Nov 2017)
(Employee)
Law at Work Ltd, Glasgow . . . .(p.1240)
T: 0141 2715555
E: paman.singh@lawatwork.co.uk

SUMAL, Pavan Kaur (May 2012) (Associate)
Shoosmiths LLP, Glasgow . . . .(p.1040)
T: 0370 086 8300
E: pavan.sumal@shoosmiths.co.uk

SUMMERS, Andrea (Oct 1996) (Employee)
NO FIRM

SUMMERS, Caroline (Oct 1995) (Partner)
Harper Macleod LLP, Glasgow . . . .(p.983)
T: 0141 2218888
E: caroline.summers@harpermacleod.co.uk

SUMMERS, Courtney Jade (Aug 2021)
(Employee)
Brodies LLP, Aberdeen. . . . .(p.723)
T: 01224 392242
E: courtney.summers@brodies.com

SUMMERS, Kirsty Laidlaw (Oct 2019)
(Employee)
Campbell Smith LLP, Edinburgh . . . .(p.852)
T: 0131 5563737
E: kls@camsmith.co.uk

SUN, Lixia (Jun 2012) (Employee)
Procurator Fiscal Service, Aberdeen . . .(p.1213)
T: 0300 0202336
E: lixia.sun@copfs.gov.uk

SUPER, Matthew Paul (Mar 2021) (Employee)
Adams Whyte, Livingston . . . .(p.1117)
T: 01506 401999
E: matthewsuper@adamswhyte.com

SUTHERLAND, Alan James (Jul 2000)
(Employee)
Navigator Employment Law Ltd,
Edinburgh . . . .(p.1227)
T: 0333 2400308
E: alan.sutherland@navigatorlaw.co.uk

SUTHERLAND, Alasdair Oman (Feb 2008)
(Partner)
Burness Paull LLP, Edinburgh . . . .(p.850)
T: 0131 4736000

SUTHERLAND, Catriona Lindsay (Jun 2015)
(Solicitor)
NO FIRM

SUTHERLAND, Claire Mary (Jul 2005) (Partner)
Finnieston Franchi & McWilliams,
Glasgow. . . . .(p.976)
T: 0141 2263000
E: claire@ffmcw.co.uk

SUTHERLAND, David Eric (Sept 1982) (Partner)
David E Sutherland, Aberdeen . . . .(p.745)
T: 01224 857900
E: David.Sutherland@davidesutherland.com

SUTHERLAND, Garry Allan (Aug 2002)
(Partner)
Macnabs LLP, Perth . . . .(p.1150)
T: 01738 623 432
E: garrysutherland@macnabs-law.co.uk

SUTHERLAND, Iain Duncan (Jan 1995) (Partner)
Dentons UK and Middle East LLP,
Glasgow. . . . .(p.968)
T: 0330 2220050
E: Iain.Sutherland@dentons.com

SUTHERLAND, Jean Winifred (Aug 1999)
(Employee)
Health Law Limited, Edinburgh . . . .(p.878)
T: 0800 920 2080
E: jeanwin2005@yahoo.co.uk

SUTHERLAND, Karen Elizabeth (Apr 2003)
(Employee)
Gibson Kerr Limited, Edinburgh . . . .(p.872)
T: 0131 2257558
E: karen.sutherland@gibsonkerr.co.uk

SUTHERLAND, Karen Iona (Aug 2013)
(Employee)
Brodies LLP, Dingwall . . . .(p.796)
T: 01349 860111
E: karen.sutherland@brodies.com

SUTHERLAND, Kate Louise (Feb 2014)
(Employee)
Harper Macleod LLP, Edinburgh . . . .(p.877)
T: 0131 2472500
E: kate.sutherland@harpermacleod.co.uk

SUTHERLAND, Kathleen Joanne (Nov 2019)
(Employee)
Munro & Noble, Inverness . . . .(p.1080)
T: 1349866777
E: kathleens@munronoble.com

SUTHERLAND, Laura Jane (Jun 2005) (Partner)
Next Law (Scotland) LLP, Perth . . . . . .(p.1151)
T: 01738 707274
E: laura.sutherland@next-law.co.uk

SUTHERLAND, Marjorie Elizabeth
(Feb 1980) (Partner)
Masson Glennie LLP, Peterhead . . . . . .(p.1154)
T: 01779 474271
E: marjorie.sutherland@masson-glennie.co.uk

SUTHERLAND, Natalie (Mar 2016) (Employee)
Scottish Social Services Council,
   Dundee . . . .(p.1218)
T: 01382 721939
E: natalie.sutherland@sssc.uk.com

SUTHERLAND, Olivia Beth (Jan 2016)
(Employee)
Burness Paull LLP, Aberdeen . . . .(p.724)
T: 01224 261296
E: olivia.sutherland@burnesspaull.com

SUTHERLAND, Paul Dominic (Oct 2005)
(Partner)
Murphy, Robb + Sutherland,
   Glasgow. . . . .(p.1025)
T: 0141 4182931

SUTHERLAND, Paul John (Oct 1991)
(Employee)
Shetland Islands Council, Lerwick . . . . .(p.1250)
T: 01595 744550
E: paul.sutherland@shetland.gov.uk

SUTHERLAND, Rachel Ellen (Nov 2021)
(Solicitor)
NO FIRM

SUTHERLAND, Sandra Mary (Aug 1991)
(Partner)
Thorntons Law LLP, Arbroath . . . .(p.757)
T: 01241 872683
E: ssutherland@thorntons-law.co.uk

SUTHERLAND, Serena Kelly (Jun 2008)
(Director)
DANDHLAW LIMITED, Kirkwall. . . . . . .(p.1106)
T: 01856 872216
E: sks@dandhlaw.co.uk

SUTHERLAND, Sharron (Jul 2021) (Employee)
Innes Johnston LLP, Glenrothes . . . . . .(p.1057)
T: 01592 757114
E: ssutherland@innesjohnston.co.uk

SUTHERLAND, Suzanne Frances (Jan 2007)
(Employee)
Morton Fraser LLP, Edinburgh . . . .(p.891)
T: 0131 2471000
E: Suzanne.Sutherland@morton-fraser.com

SUTHERLAND, Wendy Joan (Aug 1993)
(Employee)
Scottish Police Authority, Police Scotland,
   Dundee . . . .(p.1218)
T: 0300 1112222
E: Wendy.Sutherland2@scotland.pnn.police.uk

SUTHERLAND, William Graham (Dec 1985)
(Employee)
Kerr Stirling LLP, Stirling . . . .(p.1165)
T: 01786 463414
E: gs@kerrstirling.co.uk

SUTHERLAND, Zoe (Jul 2019) (Employee)
Addleshaw Goddard LLP,
   Aberdeen . . . .(p.719)
T: (+44) (0) 1224 96 5410
E: Zoe.Sutherland@addleshawgoddard.com

SUTHERLAND-GEORGE, Kirsten Frances
(Aug 2012) (Employee)
Aberdeenshire Council, Aberdeen. . . . .(p.1211)
T: 0345 608 1208
E: kirsten.george@aberdeenshire.gov.uk

SUTTIE, Jaclyn Mary (Jan 2010) (Employee)
University of Dundee, Dundee . . . .(p.1219)
T: (44) (0)1382 385340
E: j.z.suttie@dundee.ac.uk

SUTTIE, Janine Alison (Nov 2010) (Employee)
Accel Partners Management LLP, London
   W1 . . . .(p.1260)

SUTTON, Brian (Jun 1997) (Partner)
James & George Collie LLP,
   Aberdeen . . . .(p.728)
T: 01224 581581
E: b.sutton@jgcollie.co.uk

SWAIN, Alexandra Eva (Dec 2014) (Employee)
Procurator Fiscal Service, Inverness . . . .(p.1248)
T: 0844 5612926
E: alex.swain@copfs.gov.uk

SWAN, Lynn Mary (Jun 2007) (Employee)
MTM Defence Lawyers Limited,
   Falkirk . . . .(p.923)
T: 01324 633221
E: lswan@mtmdefence.co.uk

SWAN, Stella Theresa (Dec 1997) (Employee)
Procurator Fiscal Service, Inverness . . . .(p.1248)
T: 0844 5612925
E: stella.swan@copfs.gov.uk

SWAN, Stephen Andrew (Nov 2000)
(Employee)
Edinburgh Airport Limited,
   Edinburgh . . . .(p.1222)
T: 07901 811 652
E: stephen_swan@edinburghairport.com

SWAN, Susan (Aug 2010) (Employee)
Shepherd and Wedderburn LLP,
Glasgow.....................(p.1039)
T: 0141 5668510
E: susan.swan@shepwedd.com

SWAN, Thomas William (Oct 2005) (Partner)
Shepherd and Wedderburn LLP,
Glasgow.....................(p.1039)
T: 0141 5669900
E: tom.swan@shepwedd.com

SWANKIE, Clare (Jun 2010) (Employee)
Baker Hughes Ltd., Portlethen ....(p.1254)
T: 01224 721845
E: clare.swankie@bakerhughes.com

SWANKIE, Scott (Aug 1999) (Partner)
Blackwood Partners LLP, Aberdeen . . . . .(p.723)
T: 01224 446230
E: Scott.Swankie@blackwood-partners.com

SWANNEY, Gillian Todd (Oct 2010) (Partner)
Allan Kerr Solicitors, Kilmarnock . . . . . .(p.1093)
T: 01563 571571
E: Gillian@allankerrsolicitors.co.uk

SWANSEY, Rebecca (Aug 2013) (Employee)
Procurator Fiscal Service,
Edinburgh ....(p.1230)
T: 0300 0204245
E: rebecca.swansey@copfs.gov.uk

SWANSON, Alasdair John (Aug 2015)
(Employee)
Howden Group Limited, Renfrew . . . . .(p.1254)
T: 0141 8852245

SWANSON, Ashley James (May 1979)
(Employee)
Fraser & Mulligan, Aberdeen . . . .(p.731)
T: 01224 646428
E: ajs@fraser-mulligan.co.uk

SWANSON, Callum David Kenneth
(Nov 2013) (Associate)
DLA Piper Scotland LLP, Edinburgh . . . .(p.863)
T: 08700 111111
E: Callum.Swanson@dlapiper.com

SWANSON, Hayley Marie (Aug 2015)
(Employee)
Morton Fraser LLP, Edinburgh . . . .(p.891)
T: 0131 2471000
E: hayley.Swanson@morton-fraser.com

SWANSON, Rory Neil (Oct 2019) (Employee)
British Business Bank, London EC4 . . . .(p.1262)

SWANSON, Ruth (Nov 2019) (Employee)
Scottish Government, Edinburgh . . . . .(p.1231)
T: 0131 244 0815
E: ruth.swanson@gov.scot

SWARBRICK, Duncan James (Jan 2004)
(Partner)
Swarbrick Law, Aviemore . . . .(p.759)
T: 01479 811180
E: duncan@swarbricklaw.co.uk

SWARBRICK, Emma Elizabeth (Sept 2013)
(Employee)
Dickson Minto, Edinburgh . . . .(p.861)
T: 0131 2254455
E: emma.swarbrick@dmws.com

SWAYNE, Adam Frederick (Aug 2019)
(Employee)
Murray Beith Murray, Edinburgh . . . . . .(p.893)
T: 0131 2251200
E: adam.swayne@murraybeith.co.uk

SWEENEY, Agnes Lisa Marie (Sept 2016)
(Employee)
Pinsent Masons LLP, Glasgow . . . .(p.1031)
T: 0141 567 8400
E: lisa.sweeney@pinsentmasons.com

SWEENEY, Allana Clair Breaden (Oct 2008)
(Employee)
Burness Paull LLP, Glasgow . . . .(p.954)
T: 0141 2484933
E: allana.sweeney@burnesspaull.com

SWEENEY, Anne Elizabeth (Sept 1997)
(Employee)
Procurator Fiscal Service,
Edinburgh . . . .(p.1229)
T: 0300 0203000
E: anne.sweeney@copfs.gov.uk

SWEENEY, Ashleigh (Jun 2016) (Employee)
Maguire Solicitors, Glasgow . . . .(p.1017)
T: 0141 3312885
E: ashleigh@maguiresolicitors.co.uk

SWEENEY, Calum (Sept 2011) (Associate)
BTO Solicitors LLP, Glasgow . . . .(p.952)
T: 0141 2218012
E: csw@bto.co.uk

SWEENEY, Edward Andrew (Mar 1998)
(Partner)
Sweeney Law, Greenock . . . .(p.1063)
T: 01475 892125
E: mail@sweeney-law.co.uk

SWEENEY, Gerard (Aug 1993) (Partner)
G. Sweeney Solicitors Limited,
Glasgow.....................(p.1042)
T: 0141 4290677
E: gerardsweeney@btconnect.com

SWEENEY, Hannah Ellen (Aug 2016)
(Employee)
Procurator Fiscal Service, Glasgow . . . .(p.1241)
T: 0300 0203000
E: Hannah.Sweeney@copfs.gov.uk

SWEENEY, Michael (Aug 2017) (Employee)
Procurator Fiscal Service, Perth . . . . . . (p.1253)
T: 01738 637272
E: michael.sweeney@copfs.gov.uk

SWEENEY, Michael Anthony (Sept 2009)
(Employee)
A.C. O'Neill & Co., Dumbarton . . . . (p.799)
T: 01389 762997
E: aconeillandco@btconnect.com

SWEENEY, Paul Gerard (Jul 2008) (Partner)
Moir and Sweeney LLP, Glasgow . . . . . (p.1021)
T: 0141 4292724
E: paul@moirandsweeney.com

SWEETLAND, Marion Frances (Jun 2021)
(Employee)
Aegon UK, Edinburgh . . . . (p.1220)
T: (+44) 131 549 3739
E: Marion.Sweetland@aegon.co.uk

SWIFT, Andrew Gordon (Jul 2013) (Employee)
Scotch Whisky Association,
Edinburgh . . . . (p.1230)
T: 0131 222 9200
E: aswift@swa.org.uk

SWINBURNE, James (Dec 1977) (Partner)
Swinburne & Co, Glasgow . . . . (p.1042)
T: 0141 2222213
E: swinburnejim@gmail.com

SWINDELL, Robert (Sept 1981) (Consultant)
Morton Fraser LLP, Glasgow . . . . (p.1022)
T: 0141 2741100
E: Robert.Swindell@morton-fraser.com

SWINLEY, Campbell Cairns (Sept 2018)
(Employee)
BTO Solicitors LLP, Glasgow . . . . (p.952)
T: 0141 2218012
E: ccs@bto.co.uk

SWINNEY, Sally Ann (Aug 1997) (Partner)
Blackwood & Smith LLP, Peebles . . . . . (p.1143)
T: 01721 720131/723313
E: sally@blackwoodsmith.com

SWINTON, Caroline Mary (Dec 2012)
(Employee)
Aegon Asset Management UK Plc,
Edinburgh . . . . (p.1220)
T: 0131 549 2588
E: caroline.swinton@aegonam.com

SWINTON, Hannah Louise (Mar 2011)
(Employee)
Shepherd and Wedderburn LLP,
Edinburgh . . . . (p.900)
T: 0131 4735105
E: hannah.swinton@shepwedd.com

SWINTON, Robert Stewart (Jul 2012)
(Employee)
Baillie Gifford & Co, Edinburgh . . . . . . (p.1220)
T: 0131 2752000
E: Robert.Swinton@bailliegifford.com

SWIRA, Monalisa (Jun 2021) (Employee)
Friends Legal, Glasgow . . . . (p.978)
T: 0844 8921250
E: monalisa.swira@friends-legal.co.uk

SYKES, Meredith Graham (Nov 1986) (Partner)
G S Legal, Glasgow . . . . (p.981)
T: 0141 2273995
E: mgs63@live.co.uk

SYM, Elaine Mary (Feb 1999) (Associate)
Thorntons Law LLP, Forfar . . . . (p.927)
T: 01307 466886
E: esym@thorntons-law.co.uk

SYM, Keith Archibald (Sept 1993) (Partner)
R. Bruce & Co., Arbroath . . . . (p.757)
T: 01241 430660
E: ksym@bruce-co.co.uk

SYME, David Wilson (Oct 2007) (Employee)
Scotsman Holdings Plc, Glasgow . . . . . (p.1243)
T: 0141 581 2416
E: davidsyme@scotsman.group

SYME, Gordon Michael (Jul 2009) (Employee)
Aegon Asset Management UK Plc,
Edinburgh . . . . (p.1220)
T: 0131 549 6461
E: Gordon.Syme@aegonam.com

SYMON, Fraser William John (Jul 2009)
(Partner)
Paris Steele, Dunbar . . . . (p.803)
T: 01368 862 746
E: fsymon@parissteele.com

SYMON, Philip William (May 2014) (Employee)
Holmes Mackillop Limited,
Glasgow . . . . (p.986)
T: 0141 226 4942
E: psymon@homack.co.uk

SZPERZYNSKA, Magdalena Lucyna
(Aug 2017) (Employee)
Simmons & Simmons, London
EC2 . . . . (p.1268)
T: +44 20 7825 3740
E:
Magdalena.Olesiewicz@simmons-simmons.
com

T RNES, Daniel MacIntyre (Sept 2020)
(Employee)
Clan Childlaw Limited, Glasgow . . . . . . (p.959)
T: 0808 129 0522
E: daniel.tornes@clanchildlaw.org

TAGGART, Lucy Jane (Sept 2000) (Partner)
Warners Solicitors LLP, Edinburgh . . . . . .(p.911)
   T: 0131 6624747
   E: ltaggart@warnersllp.com

TAGGART, Rachel Louise (May 2016)
(Employee)
Travers Smith LLP, London EC1 . . . . . .(p.1269)
   T: (0207) 2953387
   E: rachel.taggart@traverssmith.com

TAGGART, Ross (Feb 1980) (Partner)
Taggart Meil Mathers, Aberdeen . . . . . .(p.745)
   T: 01224 588020
   E: ross@tmmsolicitors.co.uk

TAINSH, Elizabeth Irene (Sept 2011)
(Employee)
Wright, Johnston & Mackenzie LLP,
   Edinburgh . . . .(p.913)
   T: 0131 5241500
   E: eit@wjm.co.uk

TAINSH, Jacqueline (Dec 2004) (Employee)
Blackadders LLP, Glasgow . . . .(p.946)
   T: 0141 2481888
   E: Jacqueline.Tainsh@blackadders.co.uk

TAINSH, Laura Louise (Sept 2004) (Partner)
Davidson Chalmers Stewart LLP,
   Edinburgh . . . .(p.859)
   T: 0131 6259191
   E: Laura.Tainsh@dcslegal.com

TAIT, Alice Stevenson (Oct 2019) (Employee)
Andersonbain LLP, Aberdeen . . . .(p.721)
   T: 01224 456789
   E: atait@andersonbain.co.uk

TAIT, Brian John (Oct 1991) (Partner)
Morgans, Dunfermline . . . .(p.824)
   T: 01383 620222
   E: briantait@morganlaw.co.uk

TAIT, Cameron James (Sept 2002) (Director)
Capital Defence Lawyers Ltd,
   Edinburgh . . . .(p.853)
   T: 07867 637638
   E: ctait@capdef.co.uk

TAIT, David William (Aug 1999) (Partner)
Clyde & Co (Scotland) LLP,
   Edinburgh . . . .(p.855)
   T: 0131 5571545
   E: david.tait@clydeco.com

TAIT, Elaine (Apr 1999) (Employee)
National Health Service Scotland,
   Edinburgh . . . .(p.1225)
   T: 0131 2757800
   E: Elaine.Tait@nhs.scot

TAIT, Fraser Calder (Sept 2018) (Employee)
W. & A.S. Bruce, Dundee . . . .(p.807)
   T: 01382 568188
   E: fraser@wasbruce.co.uk

TAIT, Graham Neil (Sept 2016) (Employee)
DWF LLP, Glasgow . . . .(p.973)
   T: 0141 228 8000
   E: Graham.Tait@dwf.law

TAIT, Hazel (Dec 2004) (Solicitor)
NO FIRM

TAIT, John Fraser (Oct 1993) (Partner)
Tait Macleod, Falkirk . . . .(p.925)
   T: 01324 888877
   E: fraser@taitmacleod.com

TAIT, Jonathan Johnstone (Sept 1981) (Partner)
Jonathan Tait & Co., Aberdeen . . . .(p.745)
   T: 01224 582211
   E: jjt@jonathantait.co.uk

TAIT, Jonathan Louden (May 2017) (Employee)
STV Group plc, Glasgow . . . .(p.1245)
   T: 0141 3003300
   E: Jonathan.Tait@stv.tv

TAIT, Lucy Fiona (Dec 2013) (Employee)
EDF Energy Renewables,
   Edinburgh . . . .(p.1222)
   T: (0131) 460 3654
   E: Lucy.Tait@edf-re.uk

TAIT, Luke Harrison (May 2018) (Solicitor)
NO FIRM

TAIT, Michael Andrew (Oct 2016) (Employee)
Lyons Davidson Ltd, Bristol . . . .(p.1259)
   T: 0117 9047740
   E: mtait@lyonsdavidson.co.uk

TAIT, Michael James (Oct 1989) (Solicitor)
NO FIRM

TAIT, Nikola June Mhairi (May 2018) (Solicitor)
NO FIRM

TAIT, Stuart Robert (Apr 1989) (Partner)
CMS Cameron McKenna Nabarro Olswang LLP,
   Edinburgh . . . .(p.856)
   T: 0131 2288000
   E: Stuart.Tait@cms-cmno.com

TALBOT, Alison Janet (Nov 1995) (Employee)
Induction Healthcare UK Limited, London
   EC3 . . . .(p.1265)
   E: alison.t@inductionhealthcare.com

TALBOT, Elspeth Joyce (Sept 1993) (Partner)
Ralstons Solicitors, Glasgow . . . .(p.1034)
   T: 7760196224
   E: ejt@ralstonssolicitors.co.uk

TALBOT, Jennifer (Oct 2012) (Employee)
DLA Piper Scotland LLP, Edinburgh . . . .(p.863)
   T: 08700 111111
   E: Jennifer.Talbot@dlapiper.com

TAMMES, Tamar (Jan 1997) (Partner)
Burness Paull LLP, Edinburgh . . . .(p.850)
   T: 0131 4736000
   E: Tamar.Tammes@burnesspaull.com

TAPLIN, Lynne Ann (Nov 2016) (Employee)
Addleshaw Goddard LLP,
Edinburgh . . . .(p.835)
T: 0131 2282400
E: Lynne.taplin@addleshawgoddard.com

TARIQ, Haseeba (Apr 2007) (Employee)
Scottish Legal Aid Board,
Edinburgh . . . .(p.1233)
T: 0131 2267061
E: tariqha@slab.org.uk

TARTAGLIA, Dianne Jane (Mar 2011)
(Associate)
Ashurst LLP, Glasgow . . . .(p.1237)
T: 0141 375 4453
E: Dianne.Tartaglia@ashurst.com

TASKER, Philip Sydney (Sept 1991) (Partner)
Duncan McLean & Co.,
Kilmarnock . . . .(p.1094)
T: 01563 524222
E: philip.tasker@duncanmcleanandco.co.uk

TASSELL, Jenna Helen (Oct 2010) (Solicitor)
NO FIRM

TATE, Rachel Charlotte (Jun 2014) (Employee)
Dalmore Executive Services Limited,
Edinburgh . . . .(p.1222)
E: Rachel.Tate@dalmorecapital.com

TATNELL, Gordon (Aug 2017) (Employee)
Dickson Minto, Edinburgh . . . .(p.861)
T: 0131 2254455
E: Gordon.Tatnell@dmws.com

TAVENDALE, Michael John (Mar 1982) (Partner)
Hodge Solicitors LLP, Blairgowrie . . . . . .(p.775)
T: 01250 874441
E: mjtavendale@hodgesolicitors.co.uk

TAYLOR, Aileen Norma (Oct 1998) (Employee)
HSBC Holdings Plc, London E14 . . . . .(p.1265)
T: 2079923637
E: aileen.taylor@hsbc.com

TAYLOR, Alan Scott (Sept 1991) (Employee)
DAC Beachcroft Scotland LLP,
Glasgow. . . . .(p.964)
T: 0141 223 8578
E: ataylor@dacbeachcroft.com

TAYLOR, Alasdair Ian (Oct 1989) (Associate)
Burnett & Reid LLP, Aberdeen . . . .(p.726)
T: 01224 644333
E: alasdair.taylor@burnett-reid.co.uk

TAYLOR, Andrew (Sept 1984) (Associate)
Murray Beith Murray, Edinburgh . . . . . .(p.893)
T: 0131 2251200
E: drew.taylor@murraybeith.co.uk

TAYLOR, Andrew James (Jul 2010) (Consultant)
Boyd Legal Limited, Edinburgh . . . .(p.845)
T: 0131 2267464
E: andrew.taylor@boydlegaluk.com

TAYLOR, Andrew Ross (Feb 2000) (Partner)
Wright, Johnston & Mackenzie LLP,
Dunfermline . . . .(p.826)
T: 01383 626666
E: art@wjm.co.uk

TAYLOR, Arlene Margaret (Jun 2012)
(Employee)
Gillespie Macandrew LLP, Glasgow. . . . .(p.979)
T: 0141 4735555
E: arlene.taylor@gillespiemacandrew.co.uk

TAYLOR, Brian (Aug 2010) (Employee)
Hymans Robertson LLP, Edinburgh . . . .(p.1223)
T: (0131) 656 5187
E: brian.taylor@hymans.co.uk

TAYLOR, Charlotte Ann Louise (Sept 2013)
(Employee)
Hymans Robertson LLP, Edinburgh . . . .(p.1223)
T: (0131) 656 5187
E: charlotte.taylor@hymans.co.uk

TAYLOR, Christopher James (Sept 2020)
(Employee)
Clyde & Co (Scotland) LLP,
Edinburgh . . . .(p.855)
T: 0131 5571545
E: christopher.taylor@clydeco.com

TAYLOR, Claire Marie (Aug 2004) (Employee)
Sparrows Offshore Services Limited, Bridge of
Don. . . . .(p.1216)
T: 01224 704868
E: claire.taylor@sparrowsgroup.com

TAYLOR, Danielle (Oct 2021) (Employee)
Levy & McRae Solicitors LLP,
Glasgow. . . . .(p.1000)
T: 0141 3072311
E: dtaylor@lemac.co.uk

TAYLOR, David Neil (Sept 1987) (Employee)
Berrymans Lace Mawer LLP,
Glasgow. . . . .(p.945)
T: 0141 3532121
E: David.Taylor@blmlaw.com

TAYLOR, David Scott (Jul 2010) (Employee)
Carey Olsen, St Helier . . . .(p.1274)
T: 01534 888900
E: David.Taylor@careyolsen.com

TAYLOR, Euan George (Sept 2011) (Associate)
Brodies LLP, Edinburgh . . . .(p.845)
T: 0131 2283777
E: Euan.Taylor@brodies.com

TAYLOR, Francesca Maria (Jan 2015)
(Employee)
Maguire Solicitors, Glasgow. . . . .(p.1017)
T: 0141 3312885

TAYLOR, Gordon Alexander (Nov 1994)
(Employee)
Baillie Gifford & Co, Edinburgh . . . . . .(p.1220)
T: 0131 2752000
E: gordon.taylor@bailliegifford.com

TAYLOR, Graham (Sept 2006) (Employee)
Thorntons Law LLP, Montrose . . . .(p.1125)
T: 01674 673 444
E: GTaylor@thorntons-law.co.uk

TAYLOR, Hayley (Mar 2014) (Employee)
Howden Group Limited, Renfrew . . . . .(p.1254)
T: 0141 3043549
E: Hayley.Taylor@howden.com

TAYLOR, Heather Mary Antoinette
(May 2021) (Employee)
Aberdein Considine and Company,
Aberdeen . . . .(p.718)
T: 01224 589700
E: htaylor@acandco.com

TAYLOR, Isla Ruth (Nov 2003) (Associate)
DAC Beachcroft Scotland LLP,
Glasgow. . . . .(p.964)
T: 0141 2486688
E: itaylor@dacbeachcroft.com

TAYLOR, Jacqueline Carol (Nov 1987)
(Associate)
Taylor & Henderson LLP, Irvine . . . . . .(p.1087)
T: 01294 278306
E: jtaylor@taylorandhenderson.co.uk

TAYLOR, Jenna Claire McArthur (Dec 2020)
(Employee)
TC Young LLP, Glasgow . . . .(p.1055)
T: 0141 2215562
E: jct@tcyoung.co.uk

TAYLOR, Joanna Judith Anderson (Nov 2014)
(Employee)
Pinsent Masons LLP, Edinburgh . . . .(p.895)
T: 0131 777 7000
E: joanna.taylor@pinsentmasons.com

TAYLOR, John (Nov 1978) (Director)
Chambers Legal Limited, Lauder . . . . .(p.1111)
T: 07921 850565
E: john.taylor@chamberslegallimited.co.uk

TAYLOR, Justine (Aug 2013) (Employee)
Procurator Fiscal Service,
Edinburgh . . . .(p.1227)
T: 0300 0203168
E: ustine.taylor@civilrecoveryunit.gov.scot

TAYLOR, Kevin John (Oct 1993) (Director)
Pacitti Jones Legal Limited,
Glasgow. . . . .(p.1028)
T: 0141 3346444
E: kevin@pjglasgow.co.uk

TAYLOR, Laura Chloe (Mar 2016) (Employee)
Brodies LLP, Aberdeen. . . . .(p.723)
T: 01224 392242
E: laura.taylor@brodies.com

TAYLOR, Lauren Anne (Jul 2018) (Associate)
Addleshaw Goddard LLP,
Aberdeen . . . .(p.719)
T: (+44) (0) 1224 96 5410
E: lauren.taylor@addleshawgoddard.com

TAYLOR, Linda Joyce (Sept 2004) (Employee)
North Ayrshire Council, Irvine . . . .(p.1249)
T: 01294 310000
E: lindataylor@north-ayrshire.gcsx.gov.uk

TAYLOR, Lindsey Anne (Jul 2017) (Employee)
TC Young LLP, Glasgow . . . .(p.1055)
T: 0141 2215562
E: lxj@tcyoung.co.uk

TAYLOR, Lisa (Jan 1996) (Employee)
Stirling Council, Stirling. . . . .(p.1255)
T: 01786 233065
E: taylorl@stirling.gov.uk

TAYLOR, Lisa Ann (Sept 2009) (Director)
Bell & Craig Limited, Falkirk. . . . .(p.920)
T: 01324 635257
E: lisataylor@bellandcraig.co.uk

TAYLOR, Marjory Elaine (Oct 1983) (Employee)
Procurator Fiscal Service, Paisley . . . . . .(p.1252)
T: 0141 8875225
E: elaine.taylor@copfs.gov.uk

TAYLOR, Martin Charles Henry (Jun 1998)
(Partner)
Tait & Peterson, Lerwick . . . .(p.1114)
T: 01595 693010
E: martin.taylor@tait-peterson.co.uk

TAYLOR, Natalie (Aug 2018) (Employee)
K&L Gates LLP, London EC4 . . . .(p.1265)
T: 020 7360 6367
E: Natalie.Taylor@klgates.com

TAYLOR, Natalie Margaret (Sept 2017)
(Employee)
Carey Hughes Limited, High
Blantyre . . . .(p.1073)
T: 01698 404616
E: natalie@careyhughes.co.uk

TAYLOR, Neil (Aug 2005) (Employee)
Michael Lott, Motherwell . . . .(p.1127)
T: 01698 252331
E: neil@taylordefenceservices.com

TAYLOR, Neil Simpson (Oct 1996) (Employee)
Office of the Advocate General,
Edinburgh . . . .(p.1227)
T: 0131 2441634
E: neil.taylor@advocategeneral.gov.uk

TAYLOR, Nicholas James Kerr (Jan 1996)
(Partner)
Addleshaw Goddard LLP, Glasgow . . . . .(p.938)
T: 0141 2212300
E: Nicholas.Taylor@addleshawgoddard.com

TAYLOR, Nina Ariella Salicath (Aug 1991)
(Partner)
Lindsays LLP, Edinburgh . . . .(p.882)
T: 0131 2291212
E: NinaTaylor@lindsays.co.uk

TAYLOR, Patricia Rachel Britainy (Dec 2019)
(Employee)
DWF LLP, Edinburgh . . . .(p.865)
T: 0131 2265541
E: Patricia.Taylor@dwf.law

TAYLOR, Paul (Feb 2013) (Director)
Paul Taylor Family & Civil Law Limited,
Edinburgh . . . .(p.905)
T: 0131 5500414
E: pt@ptlaw.co.uk

TAYLOR, Paul Alister Gerald (Jul 2006)
(Employee)
Teva UK Limited, Harlow . . . .(p.1260)
T: 020 75407489
E: paul.taylor@tevauk.com

TAYLOR, Richard Joseph (Jun 2010) (Director)
Time Legal Consulting Limited,
Glasgow. . . . .(p.1048)
T: 0141 4283488
E: richard@timelegalconsulting.co.uk

TAYLOR, Robert Stevenet (Jan 1981) (Partner)
Bannatyne, Kirkwood, France & Co.,
Glasgow. . . . .(p.943)
T: 0141 2216020
E: roberttaylor@bkf.co.uk

TAYLOR, Robin George (Oct 1989) (Employee)
Aberdeenshire Council, Aberdeen . . . . .(p.1211)
T: 0345 608 1208

TAYLOR, Samantha Caroline (Apr 2012)
(Associate)
Monteith Solicitors Limited, Nairn . . . .(p.1129)
T: (0141) 370 0900
E: sam@monteithsolicitors.com

TAYLOR, Sarah Mairi (Aug 2013) (Solicitor)
NO FIRM

TAYLOR, Stephen David Ruairidh (Nov 2007)
(Employee)
A.G. Barr P.l.c, Cumbernauld . . . .(p.1216)
T: 01236 852400
E: stephentaylor@agbarr.co.uk

TAYLOR, Timothy Douglas (May 2018)
(Employee)
Borders Legal Limited, Kelso . . . .(p.1091)
T: 01573 226999
E: tt@hastingslegal.co.uk

TAYLOR, Victoria Emma Harvey (Oct 2003)
(Employee)
Peterkin & Kidd, Linlithgow . . . .(p.1116)
T: 01506 845191
E: vtaylor@peterkinandkidd.co.uk

TEALE, David Sutherland (Aug 1981) (Director)
The MacIver Teale Law Practice Ltd,
Stornoway . . . .(p.1170)
T: 01851 706070
E: david@maciverteale.co.uk

TEALL, Sandra Anne (Jan 1989) (Director)
The Chamber Practice Ltd, Dundee . . . .(p.819)
T: 01382 203000
E: sandra@thechamberpractice.co.uk

TELFER, Alexander Robert (Sept 1993)
(Consultant)
DLA Piper Scotland LLP, Edinburgh . . . .(p.863)
T: 08700 111111
E: Sandy.Telfer@dlapiper.com

TELFER, Norman Douglas (Mar 2009) (Partner)
Aberdein Considine and Company,
Glasgow. . . . .(p.937)
T: 0141 636 4131
E: dtelfer@acandco.com

TELFER, Dr, Robert Thomas Currie
(Jul 2019) (Associate)
MacDonald Lynch Solicitors,
Glasgow. . . . .(p.1009)
T: 0141 6499552
E: robert.telfer@macdonaldlynch.co.uk

TELFORD, Colin Scott (Oct 2009) (Employee)
National Westminster Bank PLC,
Edinburgh . . . .(p.1226)
T: 0131 5568555
E: Colin.Telford@natwest.com

TEMBLETT, Jennifer Anne (Jan 2017)
(Employee)
J & H Mitchell LLP, Pitlochry . . . .(p.1155)
T: 01796 472606
E: jenny.temblett@hmitchell.co.uk

TEMPLE, Katherine Chantal Tatham
(Feb 2011) (Employee)
Scottish Enterprise, Glasgow . . . .(p.1243)
T: 0141 2482700
E: Kate.temple@scotent.co.uk

TEMPLE, Natasha Rosaline (Mar 2005)
(Director)
Temple & Co Solicitors Ltd,
Edinburgh . . . .(p.906)
T: 0131 2208218
E: nt@templeandco.co.uk

TEMPLETON, Emma (Aug 2009) (Partner)
Mannifield Templeton Defence,
Edinburgh . . . .(p.888)
T: 0131 3228777
E: e_henderson@live.co.uk

TEMPLETON, Mark Dominic (Oct 2003)
(Partner)
Quinn, Martin & Langan, Glasgow . . . . (p.1033)
T: 0141 332 3702
E: markdtqml@gmail.com

TEMPLETON, Philip John Anthony
(Oct 1999) (Partner)
Wilson McLeod, Edinburgh . . . . (p.912)
T: 0131 5560055
E: wilsonmcleod@btconnect.com

TEMPLETON, Richard Jonathan (Sept 2012)
(Associate)
Clyde & Co (Scotland) LLP,
Edinburgh . . . . (p.855)
T: 0131 5571545
E: richard.templeton@clydeco.com

TEMPLETON, Robert James (Jan 2016)
(Employee)
Aberdeen City Council, Aberdeen . . . . . (p.1211)
T: 01224 522 000
E: rtempleton@aberdeencity.gov.uk

TEMPLETON, Ryan (Aug 2010) (Solicitor)
NO FIRM

TEMPLETON, Shona Mary (Oct 1988) (Partner)
MTM Family Law LLP, Glasgow . . . . . . (p.1025)
T: 0141 6117535
E: smt@mtmfamilylaw.co.uk

TEMPLETON, Steven Robert (Mar 2009)
(Director)
Bellwether Green Limited, Glasgow . . . . (p.944)
T: 0141 2184900
E: steven.templeton@bellwethergreen.com

TENNANT, Alexander Clarkson (Dec 1981)
(Director)
Hill & Robb Limited, Stirling . . . . (p.1164)
T: 01786 450985
E: sandytennant@hillandrobb.co.uk

TENNANT, Shona Elizabeth (Aug 2008)
(Employee)
William Grant & Sons Ltd., Bellshill . . . (p.1215)
T: 01698 843843
E: shona.tennant@wgrant.com

TENNANT, Stuart Alexander (May 2013)
(Employee)
The Premier League, London W2 . . . . . (p.1269)
T: +44 (0) 20 7864 9000
E: STennant@premierleague.com

TENNANT, William (Jan 1978) (Director)
Davidson & Shirley Limited, Lanark . . . (p.1107)
T: 01555 662576/7
E: william.tennant@davidsonandshirley.co.uk

TENNER, Gareth Gerald (Oct 2005) (Associate)
Dentons UK and Middle East LLP,
Edinburgh . . . . (p.860)
T: 0330 2220050
E: Gareth.Tenner@dentons.com

TERRANCE, Hannah Ruth (Sept 2016)
(Employee)
Procurator Fiscal Service, Glasgow . . . . (p.1241)
T: 0300 0203000
E: hannah.terrance@copfs.gov.uk

TERRAS, Euan Maxwell (Nov 1993) (Director)
Sprang Terras Limited, Ayr . . . . (p.765)
T: 01292 288300
E: emt@sprangterras.co.uk

TERREY, Julie Irene MacDonald (Apr 1998)
(Director)
MTL Law, Glasgow . . . . (p.1024)
T: 0141 2225793
E: julie@mtllaw.co.uk

TERRY, Michael James (Jun 2017) (Associate)
Dickson Minto, Edinburgh . . . . (p.861)
T: 0131 2254455
E: michael.terry@dmws.com

TEVEN, Cara (Jul 2021) (Employee)
Jones Whyte LLP, Glasgow . . . . (p.993)
T: 0141 375 1222
E: cara.teven@joneswhyte.co.uk

THAIN, Gavin Macdonald (Feb 1992) (Partner)
Anderson Strathern LLP, Edinburgh . . . . (p.839)
T: 0131 2707700
E: gavin.thain@andersonstrathern.co.uk

THAPA-MAGAR, Gunga (Apr 2009) (Employee)
Ofgem, Glasgow . . . . (p.1241)
T: (0141) 354 5425
E: Gunga.Thapa-Magar@ofgem.gov.uk

THIAM, Donde Ba (Mar 2021) (Employee)
Lisa Rae & Co Court Solicitors,
Edinburgh . . . . (p.898)
T: 0131 5503716
E: dt@lisaraeandco.co.uk

THOM, Ben (May 2019) (Employee)
James McKay Defence Solicitors Limited,
Elgin . . . . (p.917)
T: 01343 556500
E: ben@jamesmckay.uk

THOM, Calum Blair (Oct 2010) (Associate)
McDermott Will & Emery UK LLP, London
EC2 . . . . (p.1266)
T: 0207 577 3494
E: cthom@mwe.com

THOM, Jennifer Anne (May 2015) (Employee)
Anderson Strathern LLP, Edinburgh . . . . (p.839)
T: 0131 2707700
E: jennifer.thom@andersonstrathern.co.uk

THOM, John Gibb (May 1987) (Partner)
Miller Hendry, Perth . . . . (p.1150)
T: 01738 637311
E: johnthom@millerhendry.co.uk

THOM, Patricia Louise (Oct 1991) (Solicitor)
NO FIRM

THOMAS, Alun, WS (Mar 1983) (Partner)
Anderson Strathern LLP, Edinburgh . . . .(p.839)
T: 0131 625 7245
E: alun.thomas@andersonstrathern.co.uk

THOMAS, Ben (Nov 2020) (Employee)
Addleshaw Goddard (Middle East) LLP,
Dubai . . . .(p.1277)
E: ben.thomas@addleshawgoddard.com

THOMAS, Brittany Grace (Aug 2018)
(Employee)
BTO Solicitors LLP, Edinburgh . . . .(p.849)
T: 0131 222 2939
E: bth@bto.co.uk

THOMAS, Claire Avril (Jul 2007) (Employee)
Beltrami & Co Limited, Glasgow . . . . . .(p.944)
T: 0141 4292262
E: claire.thomas@beltramiandcompany.co.uk

THOMAS, Gary George (Sept 1991) (Partner)
Thorntons Law LLP, Edinburgh . . . .(p.906)
T: 0131 2258705
E: gthomas@thorntons-law.co.uk

THOMAS, Neeraj (Sept 2009) (Employee)
CMS Cameron McKenna Nabarro Olswang LLP,
Glasgow. . . . .(p.962)
T: 0141 2222200
E: Neeraj.Thomas@CMS-CMNO.com

THOMAS, Nicholas (Oct 2011) (Employee)
Gilson Gray LLP, Glasgow . . . .(p.980)
T: 0141 5302021
E: nthomas@gilsongray.co.uk

THOMAS, Robert Brown (Sept 1977)
(Employee)
Campbell Sievewright & Co.,
Glasgow. . . . .(p.956)
T: 0141 4222642
E: rthomas@cs-homes.co.uk

THOMAS, Thomas Ifan Gwyn (May 2001)
(Partner)
Harper Macleod LLP, Glasgow . . . .(p.983)
T: 0141 227 9320
E: tom.thomas@harpermacleod.co.uk

THOMAS, Timothy Robert (Dec 2001) (Partner)
Ledingham Chalmers LLP,
Aberdeen . . . .(p.734)
T: 01224 408408
E: timothy.thomas@ledinghamchalmers.com

THOMPSON, Casey Elspeth (Aug 2008)
(Employee)
DAC Beachcroft Scotland LLP,
Glasgow. . . . .(p.964)
T: 0141 2486688
E: cthompson@dacbeachcroft.com

THOMPSON, Claire Sarah (Aug 2007)
(Employee)
Scottish Enterprise, Glasgow . . . .(p.1243)
T: 0141 2482700
E: Claire.Thompson@scotent.co.uk

THOMPSON, David Joseph (Mar 1993)
(Employee)
Angus Council, Forfar . . . .(p.1237)
T: 01307 476241
E: thompsond@angus.gov.uk

THOMPSON, David Ross (Oct 2001)
(Employee)
SL Capital Partners LLP, Edinburgh . . . .(p.1234)
T: 0131 245 1802
E: david.thompson@abrdn.com

THOMPSON, Euan Andrew (Sept 2020)
(Employee)
Burness Paull LLP, Edinburgh . . . .(p.850)
T: 0131 4736000
E: euan.thompson@burnesspaull.com

THOMPSON, Fiona Hazel (Nov 2007)
(Employee)
Dickson Minto, Edinburgh . . . .(p.861)
T: 0131 2254455
E: fiona.thompson@dmws.com

THOMPSON, Gary William (Jun 2013)
(Employee)
Thompson Family Law, Glasgow . . . . .(p.1046)
T: 0141 4046575
E: gary@tflaw.co.uk

THOMPSON, Heather (Dec 1990) (Partner)
Brodies LLP, Edinburgh . . . .(p.845)
T: 0131 2283777
E: heather.thompson@brodies.com

THOMPSON, John William (Jun 2015)
(Employee)
Thompson Family Law, Glasgow . . . . .(p.1046)
T: 0141 404 6575
E: johnny@tflaw.co.uk

THOMPSON, Kenneth Richard (Oct 2006)
(Solicitor)
NO FIRM

THOMPSON, Kevin (Dec 2003) (Director)
Holmes Mackillop Limited,
Glasgow. . . . .(p.986)
T: 0141 226 4942
E: kthompson@homack.co.uk

THOMPSON, Michael (Oct 2008) (Partner)
Thompson Family Law, Glasgow . . . . .(p.1046)
T: 0141 404 6575
E: michael@tflaw.co.uk

THOMPSON, Nicola Jane (Apr 2017)
(Employee)
Thompsons, Glasgow . . . .(p.1046)
T: 0141 2218840
E:
Nicola.Thompson@thompsons-scotland.co.uk

THOMPSON, Rebecca Alison (Aug 2016)
(Employee)
Procurator Fiscal Service, Aberdeen   . . .(p.1213)
T: 0300 0202336
E: rebecca.thompson@copfs.gov.uk

THOMPSON, Richard John (Jan 2011)
(Employee)
Clackmannanshire Council, Alloa . . . . .(p.1215)
T: 01259 450000
E: rthompson@clacks.gov.uk

THOMPSON, Ross Hodgson Allan
(Feb 2021) (Employee)
Burness Paull LLP, Edinburgh . . . .(p.850)
T: 0131 4736000
E: Ross.Thompson@burnesspaull.com

THOMPSON, Sarah Marie (Oct 2010)
(Employee)
Scottish Borders Council, Newtown St.
Boswells. . . . .(p.1251)
T: 01835 825 225
E: Sarah.Thompson@scotborders.gov.uk

THOMS, Ewan John (Nov 1983) (Partner)
Young, Robertson & Co., Thurso . . . . .(p.1174)
T: 01847 893247
E: EJT@youngrob.co.uk

THOMSON, Aileen Patricia (Sept 1991)
(Partner)
Miller Samuel Hill Brown LLP,
Glasgow. . . . .(p.1020)
T: 0141 2211919
E: at@mshblegal.com

THOMSON, Ailsa Carmichael (Aug 2021)
(Employee)
Brodies LLP, Glasgow . . . .(p.948)
T: 0141 2484672
E: ailsa.thomson@brodies.com

THOMSON, Alan Douglas (Aug 2011)
(Employee)
Aberdeen City Council, Aberdeen. . . . .(p.1211)
T: 01224 522000
E: alathomson@aberdeencity.gov.uk

THOMSON, Alan George (Aug 1999)
(Associate)
Thorntons Law LLP, Edinburgh . . . . . .(p.906)
T: 0131 2258705
E: athomson@thorntons-law.co.uk

THOMSON, Andrew (Sept 1988) (Director)
Guarino & Thomson Limited, East
Kilbride . . . .(p.831)
T: 01355 263848
E: admin@guarinothomson.co.uk

THOMSON, Andrew Alexander (Jul 2020)
(Employee)
Ashurst LLP, Glasgow . . . .(p.1237)
T: (0141) 375 4242
E: Andrew.thomson@ashurst.com

THOMSON, Andrew Michael MacGregor
(Dec 1991) (Director)
Macgregor Thomson Limited,
Stirling . . . .(p.1166)
T: 01786 406423
E: athomson@macgregorthomson.co.uk

THOMSON, Andrew William (Jun 2011)
(Employee)
Perth & Kinross Council, Perth . . . .(p.1253)
T: 01738 475000
E: AndrewThomson@pkc.gov.uk

THOMSON, Brodie Campbell (Nov 2018)
(Employee)
Macfarlanes LLP, London EC4 . . . .(p.1266)
T: (020) 7791 4044
E: brodie.thomson@macfarlanes.com

THOMSON, Callum MacEwan (Jan 2021)
(Employee)
Procurator Fiscal Service,
Edinburgh . . . .(p.1229)
T: 0300 020 3000
E: callum.thomson@copfs.gov.uk

THOMSON, Carole Ann (Dec 1987) (Employee)
MSM Solicitors Limited, Paisley . . . . . .(p.1140)
T: 0141 8896244
E: cat@msmlaw.co.uk

THOMSON, Ceilidh Dewar (Nov 2013)
(Employee)
TJX Europe, Watford . . . .(p.1272)
E: ceilidh_thomson@tjxeurope.com

THOMSON, Chloe Janet (Jul 2021) (Employee)
Good & Stewart Limited,
Edinburgh . . . .(p.875)
T: 0131 6629177

THOMSON, Christopher Robert McIntosh
(Oct 2008) (Partner)
J K Cameron, Glasgow . . . .(p.955)
T: 0141 2214787
E: chris.thomson@jkcameron.co.uk

THOMSON, Craig Alexander (Oct 1996)
(Employee)
FES Ltd, Stirling . . . .(p.1254)
T: 01786 819600
E: cThomson@fes.ltd.uk

THOMSON, Darren (Jul 2021) (Employee)
Brodies LLP, Edinburgh . . . .(p.845)
T: 0131 2283777
E: darren.thomson@brodies.com

THOMSON, David (Mar 1991) (Employee)
Keystone Law Limited, London
WC2 . . . .(p.1265)
T: 020 33193700
E: David.Thomson@keystonelaw.co.uk

THOMSON, Douglas James Campbell
(Jul 1985) (Employee)
J. Myles & Co., Carnoustie . . . .(p.783)
T: 01241 855769

THOMSON, Elizabeth Brown (Nov 2009)
(Director)
Anderson Shaw & Gilbert Limited,
Inverness . . . .(p.1075)
T: 01463 236123
E: ET@solicitorsinverness.com

THOMSON, Emily Rachel (Sept 2018)
(Employee)
NEO Energy, Aberdeen . . . .(p.1213)
T: (01224) 659120

THOMSON, Emma (Oct 2012) (Associate)
Gildeas Limited, Glasgow . . . .(p.979)
T: 0141 331 6071
E: EThomson@gildeas.net

THOMSON, Emma Louise (Mar 1998)
(Employee)
Scottish Government, Edinburgh . . . . .(p.1231)
T: 0131 244 0815
E: emma.thomson@gov.scot

THOMSON, Emma Louise (Feb 2015)
(Employee)
Procurator Fiscal Service, Paisley. . . . . .(p.1252)
T: 0300 020 3000
E: Emma.Thomson@copfs.gov.uk

THOMSON, Eoin James (Jul 2015) (Employee)
Lows Orkney Limited, Kirkwall . . . .(p.1106)
T: 01856 873151
E: eoin.thomson@lowsorkney.co.uk

THOMSON, Ewan Swanson (Oct 1990)
(Consultant)
CMS Cameron McKenna Nabarro Olswang LLP,
Edinburgh . . . .(p.856)
T: 0131 2288000
E: Ewan.Thomson@cms-cmno.com

THOMSON, Fergus Hugh (Sept 1998)
(Associate)
Gildeas Limited, Glasgow . . . .(p.979)
T: 0141 331 6071
E: FThomson@gildeas.net

THOMSON, Fiona (Sept 1981) (Consultant)
Mackinnons Solicitors LLP,
Aberdeen . . . .(p.736)
T: 01224 632464
E: fionat@mackinnons.com

THOMSON, Fiona Margaret (Nov 2001)
(Partner)
Ledingham Chalmers LLP,
Aberdeen . . . .(p.734)
T: 01224 408408
E: fiona.thomson@ledinghamchalmers.com

THOMSON, Frederick Davie (Dec 2012)
(Solicitor)
NO FIRM

THOMSON, Gavin David Barclay (Mar 2019)
(Employee)
Wood Group UK Limited,
Aberdeen . . . .(p.1214)
T: 01224 851000
E: gavin.thomson1@woodplc.com

THOMSON, Gavin Ross (Nov 2001) (Partner)
MacRoberts LLP, Edinburgh . . . .(p.887)
T: 0131 2295046
E: gavin.thomson@macroberts.com

THOMSON, Gemma Rose Macgregor
(Jul 2019) (Solicitor)
NO FIRM

THOMSON, Graeme Henry (Oct 2003)
(Partner)
Balfour + Manson LLP, Edinburgh . . . . .(p.841)
T: 0131 2001200
E: graeme.thomson@balfour-manson.co.uk

THOMSON, Greg William (Feb 2000)
(Employee)
Office of the Advocate General,
Edinburgh . . . .(p.1227)
T: 7551680050
E: greg.thomson@advocategeneral.gov.uk

THOMSON, Iain Dallas (Sept 2012) (Associate)
Balfour + Manson LLP, Edinburgh . . . . .(p.841)
T: 0131 2001200
E: iain.thomson@balfour-manson.co.uk

THOMSON, Jamie Colin (Sept 2016)
(Employee)
Kirkland & Ellis International LLP, London
EC3 . . . .(p.1265)
T: 0207 4692000
E: jamie.thomson@kirkland.com

THOMSON, Jenna (Jan 2009) (Director)
Macleod & MacCallum Limited,
Inverness . . . .(p.1080)
T: 01463 239393
E: jenna.thomson@macandmac.co.uk

THOMSON, Jennifer Anne (Oct 2007)
(Employee)
Dentons UK and Middle East LLP,
Glasgow. . . . .(p.968)
T: 0330 2220050
E: Jennifer.Thomson@dentons.com

THOMSON, Jennifer Dalrymple (Oct 2007)
(Associate)
Morton Fraser LLP, Edinburgh . . . .(p.891)
T: 0131 2471000
E: jennifer.thomson@morton-fraser.com

THOMSON, Jennifer Irene (Jul 2012)
(Employee)
Procurator Fiscal Service,
Edinburgh . . . .(p.1227)
T: 0300 0203168
E: Jennifer.Thomson2@copfs.gov.uk

THOMSON, Joanna (Sept 2010) (Employee)
Kirkland & Ellis International LLP, London
EC3 . . . .(p.1265)
T: 0207 4692000
E: joanna.thomson@kirkland.com

THOMSON, Joanna Izabela (Nov 2018)
(Employee)
Caesar & Howie, Boness . . . .(p.777)
T: 01506 826166
E: ait@Caesar-Howie.co.uk

THOMSON, John (Aug 1977) (Consultant)
WGM Legal Limited, Glasgow . . . .(p.1052)
T: 0141 6166655
E: john@wgmlegal.co.uk

THOMSON, John Edward Gallagher, WS
(Dec 1984) (Employee)
Scottish Government, Edinburgh . . . . .(p.1231)
T: 0131 244 0815
E: John.Thomson2@gov.scot

THOMSON, Julie (Sept 2006) (Employee)
Alexander Dennis Limited, Larbert . . . .(p.1250)
T: 01324 677942
E: julie.thomson@alexander-dennis.com

THOMSON, Juliet Elspeth (Feb 2011)
(Employee)
John Menzies Plc, Edinburgh . . . .(p.1224)
E: juliet.thomson@johnmenziesplc.com

THOMSON, Katarijna Bronia (Oct 2020)
(Employee)
Gilson Gray LLP, Dundee. . . . .(p.811)
T: 01382 549321
E: kthomson@gilsongray.co.uk

THOMSON, Katherine Rose (Sept 2020)
(Employee)
Burness Paull LLP, Edinburgh . . . .(p.850)
T: 0131 4736000
E: katy.thomson@burnesspaull.com

THOMSON, Katy Hazel (Oct 2013) (Employee)
Aldar Properties PJSC, Abu Dhabi . . . . .(p.1277)
E: kthomson@aldar.com

THOMSON, Kenneth William (Sept 1982)
(Partner)
Thorntons Law LLP, Dundee . . . .(p.819)
T: 01382 229 111
E: kthomson@thorntons-law.co.uk

THOMSON, Kirsten Johanna (Sept 2013)
(Employee)
Addleshaw Goddard LLP,
Edinburgh . . . .(p.835)
T: 0131 2282400

THOMSON, Kirsty (Feb 2006) (Partner)
JustRight Scotland LLP, Glasgow . . . . . .(p.994)
T: 0141 406 5350
E: kirsty@justrightscotland.org.uk

THOMSON, Lara Kathryn (Jan 2012)
(Employee)
Virgil M. Crawford, Stirling . . . .(p.1164)
T: 01786 464055

THOMSON, Laura Jane (Sept 2007) (Partner)
Sutherland Thomson Law Practice,
Forres . . . .(p.929)
T: 01309 752022
E: laura@st-law.co.uk

THOMSON, Lauren Elizabeth (Aug 2010)
(Partner)
Shepherd and Wedderburn LLP,
Edinburgh . . . .(p.900)
T: 0131 2289900
E: lauren.thomson@shepwedd.com

THOMSON, Leanne Maree (Sept 1993)
(Solicitor)
NO FIRM

THOMSON, Leonard John (Nov 1991) (Partner)
Sturrock, Armstrong & Thomson,
Edinburgh . . . .(p.905)
T: 0131 5560159
E: ljt@satsolicitors.co.uk

THOMSON, Lindsay George (Dec 2009)
(Employee)
Midlothian Council, Dalkeith . . . .(p.1216)
T: 0131 2707500
E: lindsay.thomson@midlothian.gov.uk

THOMSON, Lindsay Margaret (Jan 2006)
(Employee)
Fife Council, Glenrothes . . . .(p.1246)
T: 03451 550000
E: Lindsay.Thomson@fife.gov.uk

THOMSON, Lynne Janette (Dec 2017)
(Employee)
Aberdein Considine and Company,
Glasgow. . . . .(p.937)
T: 0141 2278200
E: lthomson@acandco.com

THOMSON, Malcolm Welsh (Feb 1989)
(Director)
Marshall Wilson Law Group Limited,
Falkirk . . . .(p.922)
T: 01324 612569
E: mthomson@marshallwilson.com

THOMSON, Margaret Craig (Dec 1966)
(Partner)
James Thomson & Son, Kirkcaldy . . . . .(p.1102)
T: 01592 268575
E: margaret@jamesthomsonandson.com

THOMSON, Martha Louisa Christina
(Dec 2004) (Solicitor)
Nellany & Company LLP, Saltcoats . . . . (p.1160)
T: 01294 464175
E: martha@nellanysols.co.uk

THOMSON, Matthew Frederick John
(Nov 2006) (Employee)
Lockton Companies LLP,
Edinburgh . . . . (p.1225)
T: 0131 345 5550
E: Matthew.Thomson@uk.lockton.com

THOMSON, Michael Philip (Jul 2009) (Partner)
Burness Paull LLP, Glasgow . . . . (p.954)
T: 0141 2484933
E: michael.thomson@burnesspaull.com

THOMSON, Moray Ewan Jacks (Sept 2001)
(Partner)
Shepherd and Wedderburn LLP,
Edinburgh . . . . (p.900)
T: 0131 2289900
E: moray.thomson@shepwedd.com

THOMSON, Neil Purves (Jul 2018) (Employee)
Procurator Fiscal Service, Hamilton . . . . (p.1247)
T: 0300 0201171
E: Neil.Thomson@copfs.gov.uk

THOMSON, Paul Alexander (Oct 2016)
(Employee)
Digby Brown LLP, Aberdeen . . . . (p.729)
T: 01224 608781
E: paul.thomson@digbybrown.co.uk

THOMSON, Rachael Stewart (May 2019)
(Employee)
Shepherd and Wedderburn LLP,
Edinburgh . . . . (p.900)
T: 0131 2289900
E: rachael.thomson@shepwedd.com

THOMSON, Rachel (May 2015) (Employee)
Weatherford, Aberdeen . . . . (p.1214)
T: 01224 380200
E: rachel.thomson1@weatherford.com

THOMSON, Rachel (Dec 2017) (Employee)
Friends Legal, Glasgow . . . . (p.978)
T: 0844 8921250
E: rachel.thomson@friends-legal.co.uk

THOMSON, Rebecca Mary (Oct 2015)
(Employee)
CMS Cameron McKenna Nabarro Olswang LLP,
London EC4 . . . . (p.1263)
T: 0207 3673000
E: Rebecca.Thomson@cms-cmno.com

THOMSON, Rory Donald (Jul 2009) (Employee)
CMS Cameron McKenna Nabarro Olswang LLP,
Edinburgh . . . . (p.856)
T: 0131 2288000
E: Rory.Thomson@cms-cmno.com

THOMSON, Rosalyn Patricia (Jun 2019)
(Employee)
Beveridge & Kellas, Edinburgh . . . . (p.843)
T: 0131 5546321
E: r.thomson@beveridgekellas.com

THOMSON, Ross Gordon (Aug 2004) (Partner)
Harper Macleod LLP, Inverness . . . . (p.1077)
T: 01463 798777
E: ross.thomson@harpermacleod.co.uk

THOMSON, Ruth Claire (Dec 2017) (Employee)
Brodies LLP, Edinburgh . . . . (p.845)
T: 0131 2283777
E: ruth.thomson@brodies.com

THOMSON, Samantha (Jun 2006) (Associate)
Connelly & Yeoman Law Limited,
Arbroath . . . . (p.757)
T: 01241 434200
E: samantha@connellyyeoman.com

THOMSON, Sarah Leanne (Nov 2009)
(Employee)
East Ayrshire Council, Kilmarnock . . . . . (p.1249)
T: 01563 576161
E: Leanne.Thomson@east-ayrshire.gov.uk

THOMSON, Sophie Rosalie Mary (Jan 2014)
(Employee)
Openreach Limited, London WC1 . . . . (p.1267)
T: 0207 8097460
E: sophie.thomson@openreach.co.uk

THOMSON, Stefanie (Oct 2007) (Employee)
City of Edinburgh Council,
Edinburgh . . . . (p.1221)
T: 0131 5293670
E: stefanie.thomson@edinburgh.gov.uk

THOMSON, Steven Lewis (Nov 2006)
(Employee)
Morton Fraser LLP, Edinburgh . . . . (p.891)
T: 0131 2471000
E: steven.thomson@morton-fraser.com

THOMSON, Wendy Jane (Sept 1997) (Partner)
BTO Solicitors LLP, Edinburgh . . . . (p.849)
T: 0131 2222939
E: wjt@bto.co.uk

THORBURN, Michael Henry (Jun 2017)
(Employee)
CMS Cameron McKenna Nabarro Olswang LLP,
Aberdeen . . . . (p.727)
T: 01224 622002
E: Michael.Thorburn@cms-cmno.com

THORLEY, Mark Richard (Dec 1987) (Director)
Thorley Stephenson Ltd,
Edinburgh . . . . (p.906)
T: 0131 5569599
E: mrt@thorleystephenson.com

THORNBER, Claire Elizabeth (Nov 2004)
(Partner)
Weightmans (Scotland) LLP,
Glasgow. . . . .(p.1051)
T: 0345 073 9900
E: claire.thornber@weightmans.com

THORNE, Christina Jane (Jun 2004) (Employee)
Scottish Enterprise, Glasgow . . . .(p.1243)
T: 0141 2482700
E: Christina.thorne@scotent.co.uk

THORNTON, Calum John (Sept 2020)
(Employee)
Ashurst LLP, Glasgow . . . .(p.1237)
T: (0141) 375 4242
E: calum.thornton@ashurst.com

THORNTON, David Alexander (May 2018)
(Employee)
The R & A
E: DavidThornton@randa.org

THORNTON, Edward (Sept 1977) (Partner)
E. Thornton & Co., Oban . . . .(p.1135)
T: 01631 566771
E: info@ethornton.co.uk

THORNTON, Lucy Clare (Jan 2015) (Associate)
Anderson Strathern LLP, Edinburgh . . . .(p.839)
T: 0131 2707700
E: lucy.thornton@andersonstrathern.co.uk

THOW, Kelly Deborah (Oct 2013) (Employee)
Dana Petroleum Limited, Aberdeen . . .(p.1212)
T: 01224 616000
E: kelly.thow@dana-petroleum.com

THRELFALL, Eileen Mary (Oct 2000) (Employee)
Scottish Government, Edinburgh . . . . .(p.1231)
T: 0131 244 0815
E: Eileen.threlfall@gov.scot

THUMATH, Brian Hugh (Nov 2006) (Employee)
Pinsent Masons LLP, Glasgow . . . .(p.1031)
T: 0141 567 8400
E: brian.thumath@pinsentmasons.com

THURSTON SMITH, Carolyn Fiona
(Sept 2012) (Employee)
Ernst & Young LLP, Edinburgh . . . .(p.1223)
E: Carolyn.Thurston.Smith@uk.ey.com

TIDMAN, Oliver James Andrew (Aug 2009)
(Director)
Tidman Legal Limited, Edinburgh. . . . . .(p.908)
T: 0131 5576450
E: oliver@tidmanlegal.com

TIERNEY, Heather Isabel Mary (Jul 2012)
(Employee)
Watermans Solicitors Limited,
Glasgow. . . . .(p.1051)
T: 0141 4307055
E: heathertierney@watermans.ws

TIERNEY, Michael Logan (Sept 2020)
(Employee)
Graham Walker, Glasgow . . . .(p.1050)
T: 0141 9460111
E: mt@gwsolicitors.com

TIERNEY, Peter Desmond (May 2016)
(Employee)
Procurator Fiscal Service,
Edinburgh . . . .(p.1227)
T: 0300 0203168
E: peter.tierney@copfs.gov.uk

TILL, Pamela Joan (Oct 2010) (Employee)
SSE PLC, Glasgow. . . . .(p.1244)
T: +44 (0) 7469 411 865
E: Pamela.Till@sse.com

TILL, Tessa (Aug 2002) (Employee)
BBM Solicitors Limited, Wick . . . .(p.1180)
T: 01955 604188
E: tt@bbmsolicitors.co.uk

TILLING, Simon Andrew (Sept 2016)
(Employee)
Steptoe & Johnson UK LLP, London
EC2 . . . .(p.1268)
E: stilling@steptoe.com

TIMLIN, Kevin Barry (Sept 2017) (Employee)
K&L Gates LLP, London EC4 . . . .(p.1265)
T: (0207) 360 8161
E: Kevin.Timlin@klgates.com

TIMMINS, Emma Louise (Nov 2017)
(Employee)
The Kerr Brown Partnership,
Glasgow. . . . .(p.1044)
T: 0141 2214880
E: emma@kerrbrown.co.uk

TIMMINS, Lynne Margaret Gillian
(Oct 2001) (Solicitor)
NO FIRM

TIMMONS, John Bernard (Oct 2012)
(Associate)
White & Case LLP, London EC2 . . . . . .(p.1269)
T: 0207 5321000
E: john.timmons@whitecase.com

TIMMS, Alison Margaret (Feb 2013)
(Consultant)
Castletown Law Limited,
Edinburgh . . . .(p.853)
T: 0131 2403880
E: ali.timms@castletownlaw.com

TINDALL, Sarah Marie (Oct 2011) (Employee)
DLA Piper UK LLP, London EC1 . . . . . .(p.1263)
T: 020 7796 6026
E: sarah.tindall@dlapiper.com

TINNEY, Stephanie Margaret (Aug 2020)
(Employee)
Morton Fraser LLP, Glasgow . . . .(p.1022)
T: 0141 2741100
E: stephanie.tinney@morton-fraser.com

TINSON, Linda Jane Aird (Oct 1989) (Partner)
Ledingham Chalmers LLP, Stirling . . . .(p.1165)
T: 01786 478100
E: linda.tinson@ledinghamchalmers.com

TINTO, Jo-anne (Apr 2015) (Employee)
Scottish Government, Edinburgh . . . . .(p.1231)
T: 0131 244 0815

TOAL, Danielle (Aug 2009) (Employee)
Sigma Capital Group plc,
Edinburgh . . . .(p.1234)
T: 0131 2209444
E: dtoal@sigmacapital.co.uk

TOAL, Scott Roderick (Sept 2001) (Employee)
Procurator Fiscal Service,
Kilmarnock . . . .(p.1249)
T: 01563 536211
E: scott.toal@copfs.gov.uk

TOBIAS, Ruth (Nov 1998) (Partner)
Pinsent Masons LLP, Glasgow . . . .(p.1031)
T: 0141 567 8400
E: ruth.tobias@pinsentmasons.com

TOBIN, Stephen Manus (Oct 1997) (Partner)
Pinsent Masons LLP, London EC2 . . . . .(p.1267)
T: 020 7418 7000
E: stephen.tobin@pinsentmasons.com

TOCH, Iulia (Jan 2016) (Employee)
Glasgow City Council, Glasgow . . . . . .(p.1239)
T: 0141 2872000
E: Iulia.Toch@glasgow.gov.uk

TOCHER, Linsey Jane (May 2017) (Employee)
Stevenson & Marshall LLP,
Dunfermline . . . .(p.825)
T: 01383 721141
E: ltocher@stevenson-marshall.co.uk

TOD, David John Roberts (Jan 1987) (Solicitor)
NO FIRM

TODD, Andrew George (Mar 1990) (Partner)
Dickson Minto, Edinburgh . . . .(p.861)
T: 0131 2254455
E: andrew.todd@dmws.com

TODD, Andrew Ross (Oct 2001) (Employee)
Springfield Properties Plc, Larbert . . . . .(p.1250)
T: 01324 555 536
E: Andrew.Todd@sremltd.co.uk

TODD, Christopher John (Jul 2007) (Partner)
Lindsays LLP, Dundee . . . .(p.814)
T: 01382 224112
E: christodd@lindsays.co.uk

TODD, Elaine Margaret (Nov 1989) (Partner)
Shepherd and Wedderburn LLP,
Edinburgh . . . .(p.900)
T: 0131 2289900
E: Elaine.Todd@shepwedd.com

TODD, Emma Louise (Jun 2007) (Associate)
V. Good & Co., Edinburgh . . . .(p.875)
T: 0131 6223349
E: vgoodlaw@hotmail.co.uk

TODD, Isabel Sandra (Dec 1981) (Director)
Fiducia-Legal Limited, Edinburgh . . . . . .(p.870)
T: 0131 6579197
E: isabel.todd@fiducialegal.co.uk

TODD, James Douglas William (Oct 2013)
(Employee)
Pinsent Masons LLP, Edinburgh . . . .(p.895)
T: 0131 777 7000
E: james.todd@pinsentmasons.com

TODD, Jennifer Aileen (Jul 2006) (Employee)
Freedom From Torture Scotland,
Glasgow . . . .(p.1239)
T: 0141 4203161
E: Jennifer.Todd@centralenglandlc.org.uk

TODD, Joanne Alison Scott (Nov 2009)
(Employee)
Blackadders LLP, Dundee . . . .(p.805)
T: 01382 229222
E: joanne.todd@blackadders.co.uk

TODD, Lesley-Anne Paton (Oct 2003)
(Employee)
Pinsent Masons LLP, Glasgow . . . .(p.1031)
T: 0141 567 8400
E: lesley-anne.todd@pinsentmasons.com

TODD, Lorne Catherine (Nov 2010) (Employee)
Clyde & Co (Scotland) LLP,
Edinburgh . . . .(p.855)
T: 0131 5571545
E: Lorne.Todd@clydeco.com

TODD, Melanie Dorey Jane (Oct 2006)
(Employee)
Ashurst LLP, Glasgow . . . .(p.1237)
T: (0141) 375 4242
E: melanie.todd@ashurst.com

TODD, Nadine (Dec 2020) (Employee)
Womble Bond Dickinson (UK) LLP,
Edinburgh . . . .(p.913)
T: 0345 415 0000
E: Nadine.todd@wbd-uk.com

TODD, Pamela Anne (Mar 1990) (Partner)
Harper Macleod LLP, Edinburgh . . . .(p.877)
T: 0131 2472509
E: pamela.todd@harpermacleod.co.uk

TODD, Rachel (Sept 2017) (Employee)
CMS Cameron McKenna Nabarro Olswang LLP,
Edinburgh . . . .(p.856)
T: 0131 2288000
E: rachel.todd@cms-cmno.com

TODD, Simon Daniel (Mar 2021) (Employee)
City of Edinburgh Council,
Edinburgh . . . .(p.1221)
T: (0131) 5294145
E: simon.todd@edinburgh.gov.uk

TOGHER, Joseph Garrett (Mar 2018) (Solicitor)
NO FIRM

TOLAND, Janine (Sept 2004) (Partner)
W. & A.S. Bruce, Broxburn . . . .(p.780)
T: 01506 855777
E: Janine@wasbruce.co.uk

TOLEDO, Alison (Mar 2012) (Employee)
Scottish Government, Edinburgh . . . . .(p.1231)
T: 0131 244 0815
E: alison.toledo@gov.scot

TOLLAN, Lorraine Elizabeth (Jan 1992)
(Partner)
MHD Law LLP, Edinburgh . . . .(p.890)
T: 0131 5550616
E: lorraine.tollan@mhdlaw.co.uk

TOLLAND, Gordon Cameron (Nov 1995)
(Employee)
Scottish Legal Aid Board,
Edinburgh . . . .(p.1233)
T: 0131 2267061
E: TollandGo@slab.org.uk

TOLLAND, Lindsay (Oct 2003) (Employee)
Scottish Environment Protection Agency,
Edinburgh . . . .(p.1230)
T: 0131 449 8589
E: lindsay.tolland@sepa.org.uk

TOLLAND, Manus Gerard (Feb 1981)
(Employee)
Graham Walker, Glasgow . . . .(p.1050)
T: 0141 9460111
E: manus@gwsolicitors.com

TOLLAND, Sarah (Feb 2021) (Employee)
Rutherford Sheridan Ltd, Glasgow . . . .(p.1037)
T: 0141 248 3320

TOLMIE, Andrew Charles Stewart
(Oct 2010) (Associate)
Clyde & Co (Scotland) LLP,
Edinburgh . . . .(p.855)
T: 0131 5571545
E: andrew.tolmie@clydeco.com

TOLMIE, Peter Fraser (Sept 2020) (Employee)
Brodies LLP, Dingwall . . . .(p.796)
T: 01349 860111
E: pete.tolmie@brodies.com

TOMINEY, Paul Christopher (Aug 2013)
(Employee)
DLA Piper Scotland LLP, Edinburgh . . . .(p.863)
T: 08700 111111
E: Paul.Tominey@dlapiper.com

TOMLINSON, Carole (Jan 2010) (Partner)
Anderson Strathern LLP, Edinburgh . . . .(p.839)
T: 0131 2707700
E: carole.tomlinson@andersonstrathern.co.uk

TOMLINSON, Paula (Sept 2012) (Employee)
Scottish Social Services Council,
Dundee . . . .(p.1218)
T: 0345 6030 891
E: paula.tomlinson@sssc.uk.com

TOMNAY, Jacob Anthony (Jul 2018) (Employee)
Procurator Fiscal Service, Glasgow . . . .(p.1241)
T: 0300 0203000
E: jacob.tomnay@copfs.gov.uk

TONER, Caley Jane (Aug 2016) (Employee)
NORTH LANARKSHIREre Council,
Motherwell. . . . .(p.1251)
T: 01698 302196
E: TonerC@northlan.gov.uk

TONER, James (Nov 1988) (Partner)
Cartys, Hamilton. . . . .(p.1066)
T: 01698 285432
E: jt@cartylaw.co.uk

TONER, Jamie Douglas (Oct 2012) (Employee)
McAfee, Coatbridge . . . .(p.787)
T: 01236 423437

TONNER, Damien Christopher (Sept 2004)
(Associate)
Clyde & Co, Edinburgh. . . . .(p.854)
T: 0131 5571545
E: damien.tonner@clydeco.com

TOOLEY, Harriet Jane (Jul 2018) (Employee)
DAC Beachcroft Scotland LLP,
Edinburgh . . . .(p.858)
T: 0131 5247790
E: htooley@dacbeachcroft.com

TOPPING, Ashley (Sept 2004) (Employee)
SSE Plc, Perth. . . . .(p.1253)
T: 01738 456 000
E: ashley.topping@sse.com

TORLEY, Julie Ann (Mar 2021) (Employee)
Public Defence Solicitors Office,
Edinburgh . . . .(p.1230)
T: 0131 557 1222
E: jtorley@pdso.org.uk

TORR, Louise (Oct 2014) (Solicitor)
NO FIRM

TORRANCE, Catriona Alice (Sept 2006)
(Employee)
ELP Arbuthnott McClanachan,
Edinburgh . . . .(p.867)
T: 0131 5548649
E: cat@elpamsolicitors.co.uk

TORRANCE, Neil Miller (Oct 1993) (Partner)
Mackinnons Solicitors LLP,
Aberdeen . . . .(p.736)
T: 01224 632464
E: neilt@mackinnons.com

TOSH, Andrew Nial Robert (Oct 1996)
(Employee)
Dickson Minto, Edinburgh . . . .(p.861)
T: 0131 2254455
E: nial.tosh@dmws.com

TOSH, Claire Murray (Aug 1993) (Employee)
Scottish Government, Edinburgh . . . . .(p.1231)
T: 0131 244 7943
E: Claire.Tosh@gov.scot

TOSH, Fiona Lennox (Oct 2013) (Employee)
Burness Paull LLP, Glasgow . . . .(p.954)
T: 0141 2484933
E: Fiona.Tosh@burnesspaull.com

TOSH, Gavin Charles (Nov 2001) (Director)
Clerwood Legal Services Ltd,
Edinburgh . . . .(p.854)
T: 0131 4677611
E: gavin.tosh@clerwoodlegal.com

TOTHILL, John Alan (Dec 1984) (Employee)
HSBC Bank Middle East Limited,
Dubai . . . .(p.1278)

TOUGH, Amy Fiona (Nov 2019) (Employee)
TLT LLP, Glasgow . . . .(p.1048)
T: 0333 006 0400
E: amy.tough@tltsolicitors.com

TOUGHER, Samantha (Jan 2016) (Employee)
Ness Gallagher Solicitors Limited,
Wishaw . . . .(p.1182)
T: 01698 355 525
E: st@nessgallagher.co.uk

TOWERS, Lynda Ann (Dec 1981) (Employee)
Morton Fraser LLP, Edinburgh . . . .(p.891)
T: 0131 2471000
E: Lynda.Towers@morton-fraser.com

TOWERS, Murray Ewan (Aug 2017) (Employee)
Tesla Motors Limited, West
Drayton . . . .(p.1272)
E: MTowers@tesla.com

TOWIE, Lauren (Oct 2016) (Employee)
Glasgow City Council, Glasgow . . . . . .(p.1239)
T: 0141 2872000
E: lauren.findlay@glasgow.gov.uk

TOWNEND, Callum Andrew (Nov 2017)
(Employee)
Turcan Connell, Glasgow . . . .(p.1049)
T: 0141 441 2111
E: callum.townend@turcanconnell.com

TOWNLEY, Lucy Hannah (Sept 2018)
(Employee)
Pinsent Masons LLP, Glasgow . . . .(p.1031)
T: 0141 567 8400
E: lucy.townley@pinsentmasons.com

TOWNSEND, Alan Cameron (Jan 2007)
(Employee)
Procurator Fiscal Service, Aberdeen . . .(p.1213)
T: 0844 561 2589
E: alan.townsend@copfs.gov.uk

TOWNSEND, Arlene Compton (Sept 2015)
(Employee)
Scottish Water, Dunfermline . . . .(p.1219)
T: 01383 667 815
E: Arlene.Townsend@scottishwater.co.uk

TOWNSEND, John Patrick (Nov 2012)
(Employee)
Shepherd and Wedderburn LLP,
Edinburgh . . . .(p.900)
T: 0131 2289900
E: John.Townsend@shepwedd.com

TOWNSEND, Laura Alice (Aug 2021)
(Employee)
Brodies LLP, Edinburgh . . . .(p.845)
T: 0131 2283777
E: laura.townsend@brodies.com

TOWNSEND, Marjorie Rose (Mar 1984)
(Partner)
Neilsons, Edinburgh . . . .(p.894)
T: 0131 5565522
E: mt@neilsons.co.uk

TOWNSEND, Rebecca Christine (Sept 2019)
(Employee)
Pinsent Masons LLP, London EC2 . . . . .(p.1267)
T: 020 7418 7000
E: rebecca.townsend@pinsentmasons.com

TOWSEY, Donald William (May 2017)
(Employee)
Allan McDougall McQueen LLP,
Penicuik . . . .(p.1144)
T: 01968 675694
E: donaldtowsey@mcdougallmcqueen.co.uk

TOYE, Anna Naomi (Aug 2017) (Employee)
Altera Infrastructure, Westhill . . . .(p.1255)
E: anna.toye@alterainfra.com

TRAIL, Daniel James (Jul 2014) (Employee)
Lyons Davidson Scotland LLP,
Edinburgh . . . .(p.883)
T: 0344 251 0070
E: dtrail@lyonsdavidson.co.uk

TRAILL, Alain Michael (Feb 2013) (Employee)
Latham & Watkins (London) LLP, London
EC2 . . . .(p.1266)
T: 020 7710 1000

TRAILL, Fiona Jane (Nov 2006) (Employee)
Glasgow City Council, Glasgow . . . . . .(p.1239)
T: 0141 2875205
E: fiona.traill@ced.glasgow.gov.uk

TRAINER, Derrick Michael (Aug 1990)
(Employee)
Cannons Law Practice LLP,
Glasgow. . . . .(p.956)
T: 0141 204 5115
E: derrick@cannonslaw.com

TRAINOR, Hugh (Apr 1974) (Director)
Trainor Alston Limited, Coatbridge . . . . .(p.787)
T: 01236 600600
E: cashroom@trainoralston.co.uk

TRAPP, Danielle Collette (Nov 2020)
(Employee)
Jones Whyte LLP, Glasgow. . . . .(p.993)
T: 0141 375 1222
E: danielle.trapp@joneswhyte.co.uk

TRAYNOR, Christopher Brian (Dec 2020)
(Employee)
Burness Paull LLP, Edinburgh . . . .(p.850)
T: 0131 4736000

TRAYNOR, Daniel Owen (Feb 2021) (Employee)
Sacker & Partners LLP, London
EC2 . . . .(p.1268)

TRAYNOR, Laurie Anne (Jan 2000) (Employee)
Plexus Law LLP, Edinburgh . . . .(p.897)
T: 0131 3229253
E: laurie.traynor@plexuslaw.co.uk

TRAYNOR, Scott (Dec 2020) (Employee)
DLA Piper Ireland LLP, Dublin . . . .(p.1274)
E: scott.traynor@dlapiper.com

TRAYNOR, Stephanie (Nov 2016) (Employee)
Postcode Lottery Limited,
Edinburgh . . . .(p.1227)
T: 0131 555 9558

TRAYNOR, Suzanne Jayne (Jul 2019) (Associate)
Shoosmiths LLP, Glasgow . . . .(p.1040)
T: 0370 086 8300

TREANOR, Caroline Anne (Sept 2007)
(Employee)
Dumfries & Galloway Council,
Dumfries . . . .(p.1217)
T: 01387 260000
E: Caroline.Treanor@dumgal.gov.uk

TREASE, Rachel Louise (Jan 2021) (Employee)
Pinsent Masons LLP, Aberdeen . . . .(p.739)
T: 01224 377900
E: rachel.trease@pinsentmasons.com

TREASURER, Gillian Claire (Jun 2011)
(Employee)
Scottish Rugby, Edinburgh . . . .(p.1233)
T: 0131 3465000
E: gillian.treasurer@sru.org.uk

TREHARNE, Gareth Ian Rome (Oct 2004)
(Employee)
Shell International Limited,
Aberdeen . . . .(p.1214)
T: 44 (0)1224 883239.
E: Gareth.Treharne@Shell.com

TREHARNE, Helen Jane (Jun 2004) (Employee)
Procurator Fiscal Service, Aberdeen . . .(p.1213)
T: 0300 0202336
E: helen.treharne@copfs.gov.uk

TRESCA, Katherine Anne (Jul 2010) (Employee)
Carey Olsen, St Helier . . . .(p.1274)
T: 01534 888900
E: Katherine.Tresca@careyolsen.com

TRIMBLE, Averil Marion (Sept 2010)
(Employee)
Morton Fraser LLP, Glasgow . . . .(p.1022)
T: 0141 274 1153
E: averil.trimble@morton-fraser.com

TRIMBLE, Nicole (Nov 2015) (Employee)
Burness Paull LLP, Edinburgh . . . .(p.850)
T: 0131 4736000
E: nicole.trimble@burnesspaull.com

TRIPP, Euan Charles Morgan (Aug 2002)
(Partner)
Anderson Strathern LLP, Edinburgh . . . .(p.839)
T: 0131 2707700
E: euan.tripp@andersonstrathern.co.uk

TRIZULIAK, Kamila (Sept 2018) (Employee)
Baillie Gifford & Co, Edinburgh . . . . . .(p.1220)
T: 0131 2752000
E: Kamila.trizuliak@bailliegifford.com

TRODDEN, Peter Francis (Nov 1987)
(Employee)
Orkney Islands Council, Kirkwall . . . . . .(p.1250)
T: 01856 873535
E: peter.trodden@orkney.gov.uk

TROMBALA, Stephen Andrew (Nov 1996)
(Partner)
Shepherd and Wedderburn LLP,
Edinburgh . . . .(p.900)
T: 0131 2289900
E: stephen.trombala@shepwedd.com

TROUP, Dr, Colin Andrew (Jun 1989)
(Employee)
Legal Secretariat to the Lord Advocate,
Edinburgh . . . .(p.1224)
T: 0300 0203363
E: colin.troup@gov.scot

TRUESDALE, Edwin Robert (Jun 2011)
(Associate)
DLA Piper Scotland LLP, Edinburgh ....(p.863)
T: 08700 111111
E: edwin.truesdale@dlapiper.com

TRUSS, Kathryn (Feb 2019) (Employee)
Rutherford Sheridan Ltd, Glasgow ....(p.1037)
T: 0141 248 3320
E: kathryn@rutherfordsheridan.com

TSANG, Gordon (May 2018) (Employee)
CMS Cameron McKenna Nabarro Olswang LLP,
Edinburgh ....(p.856)
T: 0131 2288000
E: gordon.tsang@cms-cmno.com

TSVETANOVA, Viktoria Orlinova (Jul 2018)
(Employee)
Dentons UK and Middle East LLP,
Glasgow.........................(p.968)
T: 0330 2220050
E: Viktoria.Tsvetanova@dentons.com

TUCK, Keith John (Oct 1986) (Partner)
Keith J. Tuck, Glasgow.............(p.1049)
T: 0141 3362020
E: ktuck@btconnect.com

TUDHOPE, William Kirkwood Mackenzie
(Nov 1990) (Partner)
Ledingham Chalmers LLP,
Inverness ....(p.1078)
T: 01463 667400
E: kirk.tudhope@ledinghamchalmers.com

TUFF, Hannah Louise (Sept 2018) (Employee)
Morison & Smith Limited, Carluke .....(p.783)
T: 01555 773146
E: hannah@morisonandsmith.com

TUGHAN, Linda Graham (Nov 2002)
(Employee)
Scottish Water, Dunfermline ....(p.1219)
T: (01383) 665410
E: linda.tughan@scottishwater.co.uk

TULIPS, William Christopher (Nov 1982)
(Consultant)
Strefford Tulips Limited, Hamilton ....(p.1070)
T: 01698 429428
E: c.tulips@strefford-tulips.co.uk

TULLOCH, Aim e Lindsey (Aug 2020)
(Employee)
Lisa Rae & Co Court Solicitors,
Edinburgh ....(p.898)
T: 0131 5503716

TULLOCH, Sheila Mary (Nov 2003) (Employee)
Orkney Islands Council, Kirkwall......(p.1250)
T: 01856 873535

TUOHY, Aidan Daniel (Jan 2020) (Associate)
Neilsons, Edinburgh ....(p.894)
T: 0131 3164444
E: aidantuohy@neilsons.co.uk

TURLEY, Brendan Bernard (Apr 1998)
(Employee)
Leidos Innovations UK Limited,
Glasgow.....................(p.1241)
T: 0141 8143700
E: brendan.turley@leidos.com

TURLEY, Jamie Douglas (Nov 2018) (Employee)
Shearman & Sterling (London) LLP, London
EC2.......................(p.1268)
E: jamie.turley@shearman.com

TURNBULL, Adam (Oct 2007) (Partner)
Gillespie Gifford & Brown LLP,
Kirkcudbright ....(p.1104)
T: 01557 330539
E: adam.turnbull@ggblaw.co.uk

TURNBULL, Darren Alexander (Feb 2020)
(Employee)
Watermans Solicitors Limited,
Glasgow.....................(p.1051)
T: 0141 4307055
E: darrenturnbull@watermans.co.uk

TURNBULL, David Alistair (Apr 1998)
(Employee)
D C Thomson & Co Ltd, Dundee.....(p.1217)
E: aturnbull@dcthomson.co.uk

TURNBULL, Donna Marie (Oct 2004)
(Employee)
Anesco Limited, Reading ....(p.1271)

TURNBULL, James Scobbie (Feb 1971)
(Director)
James Turnbull & Co Ltd, Larbert .....(p.1109)
T: 01324 552456
E: joan@jamesturnbullandco.co.uk

TURNBULL, Jill Louise (Mar 2002) (Employee)
Scottish Government, Edinburgh .....(p.1231)
T: 0131 244 0815
E: Jill.Turnbull@gov.scot

TURNBULL, Richard Jon (Sept 2004) (Partner)
Shepherd and Wedderburn LLP,
Edinburgh ....(p.900)
T: 0131 2289900
E: richard.turnbull@shepwedd.com

TURNBULL, Robin Jonathan Fidler
(Oct 2012) (Employee)
Anderson Strathern LLP, Edinburgh ....(p.839)
T: 0131 2707700
E: Robin.Turnbull@andersonstrathern.co.uk

TURNBULL, Tracey Amanda (Oct 1996)
(Employee)
National Health Service Scotland,
Edinburgh ....(p.1225)
T: 0131 2757800
E: Tracey.Turnbull@nhs.scot

TURNBULL, Tristan George (Oct 1996)
(Employee)
John Menzies Plc, Edinburgh . . . . (p.1224)
E: tristan.turnbull@menziesaviation.com

TURNER, Bruce Conroy (Jun 2010) (Employee)
Celeros Flow Technology,
Aberdeen . . . . (p.1212)
T: 0141 3082095

TURNER, Calum Leonard Dickson
(Jun 2015) (Employee)
Adams Whyte, Edinburgh . . . . (p.835)
T: 0131 555 7220
E: calumturner@adamswhyte.com

TURNER, Elise Jean (Mar 2011) (Employee)
Morton Fraser LLP, Glasgow . . . . (p.1022)
T: 0141 2741100
E: Elise.Turner@morton-fraser.com

TURNER, Gayle Louise Blaikie (Aug 2007)
(Employee)
Wheatley Housing Group Limited,
Glasgow . . . . (p.1246)
T: 0141 2745758
E: Gayle.Turner@wheatley-group.com

TURNER, Gillian Claire (Sept 2000) (Employee)
The Scottish Parliament, Edinburgh . . . (p.1235)
T: (0131) 3486653
E: gillian.turner@parliament.scot

TURNER, Irene Ethel (Nov 2005) (Associate)
ELP Arbuthnott McClanachan,
Edinburgh . . . . (p.867)
T: 0131 3127276
E: iet@elpamsolicitors.co.uk

TURNER, Jesse Arthur (Aug 2009) (Employee)
IQVIA Ltd, Livingston . . . . (p.1250)
T: 01506 814 622
E: Jesse.Turner@iqvia.com

TURNER, Dr, Jill Fraser (Oct 2002) (Employee)
TotalEnergies E&P UK Limited,
Westhill . . . . (p.1255)
T: 01224 297000
E: jill.turner@external.totalenergies.com

TURNER, Lesley-Ann McCluskie (Dec 2013)
(Employee)
Thorley Stephenson Ltd,
Edinburgh . . . . (p.906)
T: 0131 5569599
E: lt@thorleystephenson.com

TURNER, Lorna Ann (Oct 2008) (Director)
Leonards Solicitors Limited,
Hamilton . . . . (p.1067)
T: 01698 457313
E: lt@leonardslaw.com

TURNER, Regan Elizabeth (Jul 2018) (Associate)
Clifford Chance LLP, London E14 . . . . . (p.1262)
E: Regan.Turner@cliffordchance.com

TURPIE, Alan Leonard (Mar 1990) (Employee)
Midlothian Council, Dalkeith . . . . (p.1216)
T: 0131 2707500
E: alan.turpie@midlothian.gov.uk

TWEED, Victoria Nairne (Sept 2009)
(Employee)
Burness Paull LLP, Edinburgh . . . . (p.850)
T: 0131 4736000
E: Victoria.Tweed@burnesspaull.com

TWEEDIE, Andrew Peter Ross (Aug 2019)
(Employee)
Burness Paull LLP, Edinburgh . . . . (p.850)
T: 0131 4736000
E: andrew.tweedie@burnesspaull.com

TWEEDIE, Iain William (Nov 2003) (Partner)
Andrew T. Gilbertson, Dalkeith. . . . . . . (p.795)
T: 0131 6609888
E: gilbertsonsols@hotmail.com

TWEEDIE, Peter David (Nov 1984) (Partner)
Lindsays LLP, Edinburgh . . . . (p.882)
T: 0131 2291212
E: petertweedie@lindsays.co.uk

TWEEDIE, Susan Janette (Sept 2010)
(Employee)
Shepherd and Wedderburn LLP,
Glasgow. (p.1039)
T: 0141 5669900
E: susie.tweedie@shepwedd.com

TYLER, Alison Barbara (Sept 2010) (Associate)
Clyde & Co (Scotland) LLP,
Edinburgh . . . . (p.855)
T: 0131 5571545
E: alison.tyler@clydeco.com

TYLER, Andrew James (Mar 2012) (Associate)
Burness Paull LLP, Edinburgh . . . . (p.850)
T: 0131 4736000
E: Andy.Tyler@burnesspaull.com

TYSON, Peter Trygve (Sept 1999) (Employee)
Standard Life Assets and Employee Services
Limited, Edinburgh . . . . (p.1234)
T: 0131 2457508
E: peter_tyson@standardlife.com

TYTLER, Marian (Sept 2009) (Associate)
Clyde & Co (Scotland) LLP,
Edinburgh . . . . (p.855)
T: 0131 5571545
E: marian.tytler@clydeco.com

UGBOLUE, Eghosa Evhuowie Abieyuwa
(May 2016) (Employee)
Maguire Solicitors, Glasgow. . . . . (p.1017)
T: 0141 3312885
E: Eghosa@maguiresolicitors.co.uk

UL-HASSAN, Baqar Saud (Aug 2015)
(Employee)
Procurator Fiscal Service,
Edinburgh . . . .(p.1227)
T: 0844 561 3615
E: saud.ul-hassan@copfs.gov.uk

UL-HASSAN, Samerah (Sept 2008) (Employee)
Glasgow City Council, Glasgow . . . . . .(p.1239)
T: 0141 2872000
E: Samerah.Ul-Hassan@glasgow.gov.uk

UL-HASSAN, Ziad Ahmad Ullam (Nov 2007)
(Employee)
Procurator Fiscal Service, Paisley . . . . . .(p.1252)
T: 0141 8875225
E: ziad.ul-hassan@copfs.gov.uk

ULHAQ, Nilah (Oct 2019) (Employee)
Brodies LLP, Edinburgh . . . .(p.845)
T: 0131 2283777

ULLAH, Mohammed Ruhel (Jul 2019)
(Employee)
Aberdein Considine and Company,
Aberdeen . . . .(p.718)
T: 01224 589700

ULLAH, Rucsar Yasmeen (Jan 2018) (Associate)
Gunnercooke SCO LLP, Glasgow . . . . . .(p.982)
E: rucsar.ullah@gunnercooke.com

ULPH, Victoria Isabella (Oct 1991) (Consultant)
Logans, Cumnock . . . .(p.791)
T: 01290 424566
E: victoria@loganssolicitors.co.uk

UNDERDOWN, Nicola Edna (Jan 2011)
(Employee)
Highland Council, Inverness . . . .(p.1248)
T: 01463 254 960
E: Nicola.Underdown@highland.gov.uk

UPADHYAY, Manishkumar (Jan 2011) (Director)
Legal Eagle Scotland Ltd, Glasgow . . . . .(p.999)
T: 0141 275 4844
E: mu@normanlawsonsolicitors.co.uk

UPPAL, Gagandeep Kaur (Nov 2019)
(Employee)
Dunne Defence Lawyers,
Edinburgh . . . .(p.865)
T: 0131 466 5630
E: gagan@dunnedefence.com

UPPAL, Raj-Kiran Kaur (May 2017) (Employee)
Office of the Advocate General,
Edinburgh . . . .(p.1227)
T: 0131 244 0359
E: kiran.uppal@advocategeneral.gov.uk

UPTON, Andrew David (Sept 2010) (Partner)
Harper Macleod LLP, Glasgow . . . .(p.983)
T: 0141 2279522
E: andrew.upton@harpermacleod.co.uk

URIE, Marina McLeod (Oct 2004) (Employee)
Thompsons, Galashiels . . . .(p.933)
T: 0800 0015163
E: Marina.Urie@thompsons-scotland.co.uk

URQUHART, Alison Lambie (Oct 2011)
(Solicitor)
NO FIRM

URQUHART, Catriona Hazel (Oct 2018)
(Employee)
Carey Olsen, St Helier . . . .(p.1274)
T: 01534 888900
E: catriona.urquhart@careyolsen.com

URQUHART, Kirsty Nicola (Jun 2015)
(Employee)
Procurator Fiscal Service, Glasgow . . . .(p.1241)
T: 0300 0203000
E: Kirsty.Urquhart@copfs.gov.uk

URQUHART, Michael Gordon (Aug 2007)
(Employee)
CMS Cameron McKenna Nabarro Olswang LLP,
Edinburgh . . . .(p.856)
T: 0131 2288000

URQUHART, Roderick Williamson (Oct 1981)
(Employee)
Procurator Fiscal Service, Inverness . . . .(p.1248)
T: 0300 020 4078
E: roderick.urquhart@copfs.gov.uk

URQUHART, Vicki (Jun 2007) (Employee)
Brazenall & Orr, Dumfries . . . .(p.800)
T: 01387 255695
E: vicki.urquhart@brazenallandorr.co.uk

URWIN, Ashleigh Barbara (Aug 2016)
(Employee)
Blackadders LLP, Edinburgh . . . .(p.843)
T: 0131 2228000
E: ashleigh.urwin@blackadders.co.uk

USHER, Louise Mackay (May 2018) (Employee)
Brodies LLP, Edinburgh . . . .(p.845)
T: 0131 2283777
E: louise.usher@brodies.com

UTTLEY, Donald Michael (Dec 2001) (Partner)
Beveridge & Kellas, Edinburgh . . . .(p.843)
T: 0131 5546321
E: d.uttley@beveridgekellas.com

VAILLANCOURT, Meghan Elizabeth
(Nov 2020) (Employee)
Addleshaw Goddard LLP,
Edinburgh . . . .(p.835)
T: 0131 2282400
E:
meghan.vaillancourt@addleshawgoddard.com

VAL FERN NDEZ, Mar a Del Mar (Jan 2020)
(Employee)
University of Edinburgh, Edinburgh . . .(p.1235)

VALANSOT, Fiona (Sept 2004) (Employee)
UBS.AG, London EC2 . . . .(p.1269)
E: Fiona.valansot@ubs.com

VALENTINE, Jane (Oct 1999) (Employee)
Wheatley Housing Group Limited,
Glasgow. . . . .(p.1246)
T: 0141 2746317
E: jane.valentine@wheatley-group.com

VALENTINE, Jordan (Dec 2016) (Partner)
P.C. McFarlane & Co, Livingston . . . . .(p.1119)
T: 01506 497160
E: jv@sneddons-ssc.co.uk

VALENTINE, Katherine (Apr 2008) (Employee)
SSE Plc, Perth . . . .(p.1253)
T: 01738 456 000
E: katy.valentine@sse.com

VALENTINE, Robin Keith (May 1983)
(Consultant)
Thorntons Law LLP, Edinburgh . . . .(p.906)
T: 0131 2258705
E: rvalentine@thorntons-law.co.uk

VALLANCE, Stephen Julian (Jan 1984)
(Employee)
Harper Macleod LLP, Glasgow . . . .(p.983)
T: 0141 2218888
E: stephen.vallance@harpermacleod.co.uk

VALLARINO, Aulo Plauzio (Sept 2014)
(Employee)
Stronachs LLP, Aberdeen . . . .(p.744)
T: 01224 845845
E: Aulo.Vallarino@stronachs.com

VAN BEUSEKOM, Carol (Sept 2010) (Employee)
CalaChem Limited, Grangemouth . . . .(p.1246)
T: 01324 498300
E: carol.vanbeusekom@calachecm.com

VAN DER MERWE, Danielle (Nov 2009)
(Employee)
Latham & Watkins (London) LLP, London
EC2 . . . .(p.1266)
T: 020 7710 1000
E: Danielle.vanderMerwe@lw.com

VAN DER VELDE, Silvana Giulia (Jul 2008)
(Employee)
Travers Smith LLP, London EC1 . . . . . .(p.1269)
T: 020 7295 3151
E: silvana.vandervelde@traverssmith.com

VAN DIGGELEN, Shona Eilidh (Aug 2012)
(Employee)
Wood Group UK Limited,
Aberdeen . . . .(p.1214)
T: 01224 851000
E: shona.vandiggelen@woodplc.com

VAN LOOY, Marsaili Elisabeth (Jan 2021)
(Employee)
Pinsent Masons LLP, Glasgow . . . .(p.1031)
T: 0141 567 8400
E: marsaili.vanlooy@pinsentmasons.com

VAN TOOREN, Claudia Grace (Oct 2009)
(Employee)
Heineken UK Limited, Edinburgh . . . . .(p.1223)
T: 0131 5281000
E: claudia.vantooren@heineken.co.uk

VANCE, Margaret Agnes Jamieson
(Oct 1990) (Employee)
South Ayrshire Council, Ayr . . . .(p.1215)
T: 01292 612420
E: margaret.vance@south-ayrshire.gov.uk

VANDAL, Fraser William (Oct 2014) (Employee)
TLT LLP, Glasgow . . . .(p.1048)
T: 0333 006 0400
E: fraser.vandal@TLTsolicitors.com

VANDECASTEELE, Judith Mary (Sept 2007)
(Associate)
Rollos Law LLP, Cupar. . . . .(p.792)
T: 01334 654081
E: judithvandecasteele@rollos.co.uk

VANDERBURG SOLE, Keri Elizabeth
(Nov 2015) (Partner)
Blair Cadell, Edinburgh . . . .(p.844)
T: 0131 555 5800
E: Keri.VanderburgSole@blaircadell.com

VANHEGAN, Graham William Corbett
(Oct 1989) (Employee)
The Weir Group PLC, Glasgow . . . .(p.1245)
E: graham.vanhegan@mail.weir

VARELA, Danielle Suzanne (Jan 2009)
(Employee)
Berrymans Lace Mawer LLP,
Glasgow. . . . .(p.945)
T: 0141 3532121
E: danielle.varela@blmlaw.com

VARNEY, James Alan (Oct 2002) (Employee)
DAC Beachcroft Scotland LLP,
Glasgow. . . . .(p.964)
T: 0141 2486688
E: Jvarney@dacbeachcroft.com

VARTY, Victoria Annabel Helen (Oct 2005)
(Partner)
Drummond Miller LLP, Edinburgh . . . . .(p.864)
T: 0131 2265151
E: vvarty@drummondmiller.co.uk

VASS, Sarah Anne (Jun 2006) (Employee)
Total S.A., La Defence Cedex . . . .(p.1272)
E: sarah.vass@totalenergies.com

VASSENAIX-PAXTON, Anne-Sylvie
(Nov 1996) (Partner)
DWF (France) AARPI, Paris . . . .(p.1272)
T: +33 0140692650
E: as.vassenaix-paxton@dwf.law

VASSILIOU, John (Oct 2012) (Associate)
Shepherd and Wedderburn LLP,
　Edinburgh . . . .(p.900)
T: 0131 2289900
E: john.vassiliou@shepwedd.com

VAUGHAN, Lynda Jane Rosie (Aug 1998)
(Partner)
Grieve, Grierson, Moodie & Walker,
　Dumfries . . . .(p.801)
T: 01387 266250
E: Lynda.vaughan@ggmw.co.uk

VAUGHAN, Michael (Nov 2012) (Employee)
MacRoberts LLP, Edinburgh . . . .(p.887)
T: 0131 2295046
E: michael.vaughan@macroberts.com

VAUGHAN, Robert Smith (Nov 1977) (Partner)
R.S. Vaughan & Co, Glasgow. . . . .(p.1050)
T: 0141 2215482
E: rvaughan@rsvaughan.co.uk

VAUSE, David Matthew (Nov 1988) (Partner)
Peterkin & Kidd, Linlithgow . . . .(p.1116)
T: 01506 845191
E: DVause@peterkinandkidd.co.uk

VEITCH, Craig Alan (Mar 2002) (Employee)
Raeburn Christie Clark & Wallace LLP,
　Aberdeen . . . .(p.741)
T: 01224 332400
E: craig.veitch@raeburns.co.uk

VEITCH, Thomas Stewart (Dec 1989) (Partner)
Thomas S. Veitch & Son,
　Linlithgow . . . .(p.1117)
T: 01506 842100
E: stewart@tsveitch.com

VEITCH, Zoe Claire (May 2018) (Employee)
Scottish Children's Reporter Administration,
　Edinburgh . . . .(p.1230)
T: 0131 6679431
E: Claire.Veitch@scra.gsi.gov.uk

VELICHANSKY, Andrew Boris (Aug 2012)
(Employee)
Cochran Ltd, Edinburgh . . . .(p.1222)
T: 01461 200258
E: avelichansky@cochran.co.uk

VENABLES, Aileen Anderson (Aug 1983)
(Director)
Beveridge Philp & Ross Limited,
　Edinburgh . . . .(p.843)
T: 0131 554 6244
E: avenables@bprsolicitors.co.uk

VENMAN, Marion Shepherd (Feb 1992)
(Employee)
Scottish Power Limited, Glasgow . . . . .(p.1244)
T: 0141 6140000
E: marion.venman@scottishpower.com

VENNARD, Andrew Ross (Dec 2008)
(Employee)
E. Thornton & Co., Oban . . . .(p.1135)
T: 01631 566771
E: andrew@ethornton.co.uk

VENTERS, Katrina Elaine (Oct 2010) (Solicitor)
NO FIRM

VENTERS, William (Oct 1994) (Employee)
Midlothian Council, Dalkeith . . . .(p.1216)
T: 0131 2707500
E: william.venters@midlothian.gov.uk

VENTISEI, Giorgio Alessandro (Sept 2020)
(Employee)
Aberdein Considine and Company,
　Edinburgh . . . .(p.833)
T: 0131 2212424
E: gventisei@acandco.com

VENTRE, Laura Paton (Oct 2014) (Employee)
Walter Scott & Partners Limited,
　Edinburgh . . . .(p.1236)
T: (0131) 225 1357
E: lventre@walterscott.com

VERRECCHIA, Clare Louise (Oct 2019)
(Employee)
Optical Express Limited

VEZZA, Rachel Louise (Oct 2017) (Employee)
Scottish Government, Edinburgh . . . . .(p.1231)
T: 0131 244 0815
E: Rachel.Vezza@gov.scot

VICKERSTAFF, Ian Frank (Nov 1999) (Employee)
Lord President's Private Office,
　Edinburgh . . . .(p.1225)
T: 0131 240 6808
E: ivickerstaff@scotcourts.gov.uk

VINCENT, Isobel (Oct 2008) (Employee)
Procurator Fiscal Service, Dundee . . . . .(p.1218)
T: 01382 342559
E: Isobel.Vincent@copfs.gov.uk

VINCENT, Mary Claire (Feb 2011) (Employee)
National Westminster Bank PLC,
　Edinburgh . . . .(p.1226)
T: (0131) 626 2925
E: Claire.vincent@natwest.com

VINCENT-ELOAGU, Ngozi Elizabeth
(Jul 2019) (Employee)
Angus Council, Forfar . . . .(p.1237)
T: 01307 476228
E: Vincent-EloaguN1@angus.gov.uk

VIRLOGEUX, Stephanie Jane (Dec 2008)
(Employee)
Scottish Government, Edinburgh . . . . . .(p.1231)
T: 0131 244 0815
E: stephanie.virlogeux@gov.scot

VIRTUE, Melissa Janice (May 2015) (Employee)
George More & Company LLP,
Edinburgh . . . .(p.891)
T: 0131 2026552

VON POULTON, Scott David (Apr 2004)
(Employee)
Facebook UK Limited, London
NW1 . . . .(p.1264)
E: scottvonpoulton@fb.com

VOTYPKOVA, Lenka (May 2021) (Employee)
McEwan Fraser Legal, Edinburgh . . . . . .(p.885)
T: 0131 5249797
E: lenka@mcewanfraserlegal.co.uk

VOYSEY, Christopher Ross (Feb 2020)
(Employee)
National Westminster Bank PLC,
Edinburgh . . . .(p.1226)
T: (0131) 626 2925
E: christopher.voysey@natwest.com

WACHTEL, Raymond Grant (Dec 1977)
(Partner)
Jas. S. Grosset, Leven . . . .(p.1115)
T: 01333 426023
E: raymond.wachtel@grossets.co.uk

WACLAWSKI, Liana Esther (Oct 2011)
(Employee)
Office of the Advocate General,
Edinburgh . . . .(p.1227)
T: 0131 2441635
E: Liana.Waclawski@advocategeneral.gov.uk

WACLAWSKI, Stephen James (Oct 2006)
(Employee)
National Health Service Scotland,
Edinburgh . . . .(p.1225)
T: 0131 2757800
E: stephen.waclawski@nhs.scot

WADDELL, Andrea Isabella (Sept 2015)
(Partner)
Weaver & Waddell Solicitors,
Glasgow. . . . .(p.1051)
T: 0141 7396100
E:
andrea.waddell@weaverwaddellsolicitors.com

WADDELL, Christina Julie (Oct 2017)
(Employee)
McArthur Stanton, Dumbarton . . . .(p.798)
T: 01389 762266
E: cw@mcarthurstanton.co.uk

WADDELL, Colin John (Sept 2007) (Employee)
Clydesdale Bank Plc, Glasgow . . . .(p.1238)
T: 0141 2423728
E: colin.waddell@cybg.com

WADDELL, Douglas Robert (Oct 2013)
(Employee)
Brodies LLP, Edinburgh . . . .(p.845)
T: 0131 2283777
E: douglas.waddell@brodies.com

WADDELL, Gemma (Aug 2007) (Partner)
A.C. White, Ayr . . . .(p.766)
T: 01292 266900
E: Gemma.Waddell@acwhiteayr.co.uk

WADDELL, Joanna Collin (Nov 1998)
(Associate)
CMS Cameron McKenna Nabarro Olswang LLP,
Edinburgh . . . .(p.856)
T: 0131 2288000
E: Joanna.Waddell@cms-cmno.com

WADDELL, Kenneth James (Feb 1996) (Partner)
Peacock Johnston, Glasgow . . . .(p.1030)
T: 0141 3339505
E: kjw@peacockjohnston.co.uk

WADDELL, Marysia Margaret Michalina
(Oct 1990) (Partner)
Liddle & Anderson LLP, Boness . . . .(p.777)
T: 01506 822727
E: mw@liddleandanderson.co.uk

WADDELL, Ross David Kalusz (Jul 2016)
(Employee)
North of England Protecting and Indemnity
Association, Newcastle Upon
Tyne . . . .(p.1270)

WADDELL, Shona (Oct 2000) (Solicitor)
NO FIRM

WADDELL, Stuart Archie (Mar 2002)
(Employee)
SSE Plc, Perth. . . . .(p.1253)
T: 01738 456 000
E: stuart.waddell@sse.com

WADE, Katherine Elizabeth (Oct 2020)
(Employee)
Brechin Tindal Oatts, Glasgow . . . .(p.947)
T: 0141 2218012
E: kew@bto.co.uk

WADE, Louisa Jane (Sept 1995) (Director)
L J Wade Ltd, Perth. . . . .(p.1152)
T: 07310 164305
E: louisa@louisawade.co.uk

WADSWORTH, Ronald Stuart (Aug 1970)
(Consultant)
Boyd Legal Limited, Edinburgh . . . .(p.845)
T: 0131 2267464
E: Ron.Wadsworth@boydlegaluk.com

WAGNER, Sophia Jane (Jan 1985) (Partner)
A S Wagner Limited, Glasgow . . . .(p.1050)
T: 0141 332 0809
E: mail@aswagner.co.uk

WAHLE, Viktoria Claire (Dec 2001) (Associate)
Burnett & Reid LLP, Aberdeen . . . .(p.726)
T: 01224 644333
E: viktoria.wahle@burnett-reid.co.uk

WAINWRIGHT, Craig David (Sept 2018)
(Employee)
Procurator Fiscal Service,
Kilmarnock . . . .(p.1249)
T: 01563 536211
E: Craig.Wainwright@copfs.gov.uk

WAINWRIGHT, Lindsey Margaret (Sept 2011)
(Associate)
CMS Cameron McKenna Nabarro Olswang LLP,
Glasgow . . . .(p.962)
T: 0141 304 6262
E: lindsey.wainwright@cms-cmno.com

WAISS, Yuliia Alexeievna (Jul 2017) (Employee)
Fraser Shepherd, Falkirk . . . .(p.921)
T: 01324 630700
E: yuliia@frasershepherd.co.uk

WAITE, Jennifer (Nov 2017) (Employee)
Austin Lafferty Limited, East
Kilbride . . . .(p.830)
T: 01355 263777
E: jwaite@laffertylaw.com

WAKEFIELD, Christine Gibbs Elliot
(Nov 2005) (Solicitor)
NO FIRM

WALES, Chloe (Oct 2008) (Employee)
Brodies LLP, Edinburgh . . . .(p.845)
T: 0131 2283777
E: chloe.wales@brodies.com

WALI, Amar Farooq (Sept 2001) (Partner)
Morton Fraser LLP, Glasgow . . . .(p.1022)
T: 0141 2741100
E: amar.wali@morton-fraser.com

WALI, Khalda (Jul 2008) (Director)
LKW Solicitors Ltd, Glasgow . . . .(p.1004)
T: 0141 4236999
E: khalda.wali@lkwsolicitors.co.uk

WALKDEN, Sarah Anne (Jul 2009) (Employee)
Aberdeen City Council, Aberdeen . . . . .(p.1211)
T: 01224 522000
E: swalkden@aberdeencity.gov.uk

WALKER, Adelle Ashley (Jul 2013) (Employee)
Balfour + Manson LLP, Edinburgh . . . . .(p.841)
T: 0131 2001200
E: adelle.walker@balfour-manson.co.uk

WALKER, Alexander Andrew (Sept 2017)
(Employee)
Brodies LLP, Edinburgh . . . .(p.845)
T: 0131 2283777
E: alexander.walker@brodies.com

WALKER, Alexandra Elizabeth (May 1986)
(Partner)
Hughes Walker, Edinburgh . . . .(p.878)
T: 0131 6038676
E: swalker.hugheswalker@gmail.com

WALKER, Andrew Graham Alexander
(Oct 1993) (Partner)
Morton Fraser LLP, Edinburgh . . . .(p.891)
T: 0131 2471000
E: andrew.walker@morton-fraser.com

WALKER, Andrew Patrick Kearns (Mar 2018)
(Employee)
East Dunbartonshire Council,
Kirkintilloch . . . .(p.1249)
T: 0141 5788000
E: andrew.walker@eastdunbarton.gov.uk

WALKER, Anna (Oct 2006) (Employee)
Scottish Power Limited, Glasgow . . . . .(p.1244)
T: 0141 6140000
E: a.walker@scottishpower.com

WALKER, Barbara Margaret Ellen (Oct 2006)
(Employee)
Renfrewshire Council, Paisley . . . .(p.1252)
T: 0141 618 7156
E: barbara.walker@renfrewshire.gov.uk

WALKER, Carly Louise (Sept 2021) (Employee)
Gildeas Limited, Glasgow . . . .(p.979)
T: 0141 331 6071

WALKER, Carol Ann Hadden (Dec 1992)
(Employee)
Andersonbain LLP, Aberdeen . . . .(p.721)
T: 01224 456789
E: CWalker@andersonbain.co.uk

WALKER, David Andrew (Sept 2000)
(Employee)
Lindsays LLP, Edinburgh . . . .(p.882)
T: 0131 2291212
E: davidwalker@lindsays.co.uk

WALKER, David James (Nov 1984) (Partner)
Morton Fraser LLP, Edinburgh . . . .(p.891)
T: 0131 2471000
E: david.walker@morton-fraser.com

WALKER, Douglas Graeme (Dec 1978) (Partner)
Brown & McRae LLP, Fraserburgh . . . . .(p.930)
T: 01346 514761
E: dgw@brown-mcrae.co.uk

WALKER, Elizabeth Mary (Oct 1989) (Partner)
Ferguson Walker, Glenrothes . . . .(p.1056)
T: 01592 759600
E: fergusonwalker@btconnect.com

WALKER, Faye Ellen (Aug 2007) (Partner)
Andersonbain LLP, Aberdeen . . . .(p.721)
T: 01224 456789
E: fwalker@andersonbain.co.uk

WALKER, Grant Colin (Jun 2011) (Employee)
Dana Petroleum Limited, Aberdeen . . .(p.1212)
T: 01224 616000
E: grant.walker@dana-petroleum.com

WALKER, Grant Kyle (Feb 2000) (Employee)
Inverclyde Council, Greenock . . . .(p.1246)
T: 01475 717171
E: Grant.walker@Inverclyde.gov.uk

WALKER, Iain James (Jun 2014) (Employee)
Aberdeen Corporate Services Limited,
Edinburgh . . . .(p.1220)
T: 0131 245 7508
E: iain.walker@abrdn.com

WALKER, Irene (Oct 2002) (Employee)
Anderson Shaw & Gilbert Limited,
Inverness . . . .(p.1075)
T: 01463 236123
E: iw@solicitorsinverness.com

WALKER, James Ian (Jul 2018) (Employee)
Adams Whyte, Livingston . . . .(p.1117)
T: 01506 401999
E: jameswalker@adamswhyte.com

WALKER, Jennifer Caroline (Apr 2012)
(Employee)
Deans Solicitors and Estate Agents LLP,
Edinburgh . . . .(p.860)
T: 0131 6671900
E: jen.walker@deansproperties.co.uk

WALKER, John (Oct 1987) (Partner)
Kilpatrick & Walker, Ayr . . . .(p.763)
T: 01292 618585
E: john@kilpatrickwalker.com

WALKER, Julia Claire Donnetta (Nov 1995)
(Employee)
City of Edinburgh Council,
Edinburgh . . . .(p.1221)
T: 0131 5293637
E: Julia.Walker@edinburgh.gov.uk

WALKER, Karen Lynn (Jul 2000) (Partner)
Barnetts, Kilmarnock . . . .(p.1093)
T: 01563 522137
E: lynn@barnettslaw.co.uk

WALKER, Kathryn Claire (Nov 2008)
(Employee)
Scottish Government, Edinburgh . . . . .(p.1231)
T: 0131 244 0815
E: kate.walker@gov.scot

WALKER, Laura Jane (Aug 2007) (Partner)
Deans Solicitors and Estate Agents LLP,
Edinburgh . . . .(p.860)
T: 0131 6671900
E: laura.walker@deansproperties.co.uk

WALKER, Linda Ann (Oct 2005) (Associate)
Harper Macleod LLP, Edinburgh . . . .(p.877)
T: 0131 2472500
E: Linda.Walker@harpermacleod.co.uk

WALKER, Lorna Joyce (Nov 2008) (Partner)
Dailly, Walker and Co., Solicitors,
Glasgow . . . .(p.965)
T: 0141 4402503
E: lwalker@govanlc.com

WALKER, Louise Elizabeth (Aug 2011)
(Employee)
Just Employment Law Ltd,
Glasgow . . . .(p.1240)
T: 0141 331 5150
E: louisewalker@justemploymentlaw.co.uk

WALKER, Lynsey Clare (Oct 2009) (Partner)
Addleshaw Goddard LLP,
Edinburgh . . . .(p.835)
T: 0131 2282400
E: Lynsey.Walker@addleshawgoddard.com

WALKER, Mark Lee (Feb 1997) (Associate)
CMS Cameron McKenna Nabarro Olswang LLP,
Edinburgh . . . .(p.856)
T: 0131 2288000
E: Mark.Walker@cms-cmno.com

WALKER, Martin David (Sept 2016) (Partner)
Balfour + Manson LLP, Edinburgh . . . . .(p.841)
T: 0131 2001486
E: Martin.Walker@balfour-manson.co.uk

WALKER, Martine Sheena (Jan 1995) (Partner)
A.C. White, Ayr . . . .(p.766)
T: 01292 266900
E: martine.walker@acwhiteayr.co.uk

WALKER, Maxine Nicole (Nov 2020)
(Employee)
Addleshaw Goddard LLP,
Edinburgh . . . .(p.835)
T: 0131 2282400
E: Maxine.Walker@addleshawgoddard.com

WALKER, Michael (Dec 1999) (Employee)
Scottish Criminal Cases Review Commission,
Glasgow . . . .(p.1243)
T: 0141 2707030
E: mwalker@sccrc.org.uk

WALKER, Natalie Jane (Feb 2010) (Associate)
Pinsent Masons LLP, Aberdeen . . . .(p.739)
T: 01224 377966
E: Natalie.Walker@pinsentmasons.com

WALKER, Rachel Claire (Nov 2012) (Associate)
DJ Mackay and Partners LLP,
Glasgow . . . .(p.1012)
T: 0141 353 8700
E: rachel.walker@unionlinescotland.co.uk

WALKER, Rachel Mary-Norine (Aug 2017)
(Employee)
Stewart & Bennett, Dunoon . . . .(p.828)
T: 01369 702885
E: rwalker@stewartbennett.com

WALKER, Rachel Wilson (Oct 2015) (Partner)
Brown & Co Legal LLP, Glasgow . . . . . .(p.950)
T: 0141 3533354
E: rachelwalker@lsa.org.uk

WALKER, Rebecca Clare (Jan 2009) (Associate)
Ledingham Chalmers LLP,
Aberdeen . . . .(p.734)
T: 01224 408408
E: rebecca.walker@ledinghamchalmers.com

WALKER, Rosemary Clare (Dec 2003) (Partner)
Gilson Gray LLP, Edinburgh . . . .(p.874)
T: 0131 5165354
E: rwalker@gilsongray.co.uk

WALKER, Sarah Kate (Nov 2010) (Employee)
Shepherd and Wedderburn LLP, London
EC2 . . . .(p.1268)
T: 020 74294900
E: Sarah.Walker@shepwedd.com

WALKER, Sarah Sian (Oct 2008) (Solicitor)
NO FIRM

WALKER, Sophie Julia (Oct 2019) (Employee)
Turcan Connell, Edinburgh . . . .(p.908)
T: 0131 2288111
E: sophie.walker@turcanconnell.com

WALKER, Tricia Lyn (Nov 2003) (Partner)
Burness Paull LLP, Aberdeen . . . .(p.724)
T: 01224 621621
E: Tricia.Walker@burnesspaull.com

WALKINSHAW, Lorraine Janet (Oct 2005)
(Employee)
Scottish Government, Edinburgh . . . . .(p.1231)
T: 0131 244 0815
E: lorraine.walkinshaw@gov.scot

WALL, Jacqueline May (Sept 2016) (Employee)
John Brown (Scotland) Ltd,
Glasgow. . . . .(p.951)
T: 0141 7810000
E: office@browns-solicitors.co.uk

WALLACE, Andrew (Nov 1985) (Partner)
DLA Piper Scotland LLP, Edinburgh . . . .(p.863)
T: 08700 111111
E: drew.wallace@dlapiper.com

WALLACE, Andrew James (Sept 2014)
(Associate)
Thorntons Law LLP, Edinburgh . . . .(p.906)
T: 0131 2258705
E: awallace@thorntons-law.co.uk

WALLACE, Anthony Paul (Sept 1998) (Director)
The Building Law Practice Limited,
Glasgow. . . . .(p.1043)
T: 0141 3537655
E: anthony.wallace@buildinglawpractice.com

WALLACE, Carolyn Anne (Nov 1985)
(Employee)
North Ayrshire Council, Irvine . . . .(p.1249)
T: 01294 310000
E: cwallace@north-ayrshire.GCSX.gov.uk

WALLACE, Cheryl Samantha (Jun 2009)
(Associate)
Thorntons Law LLP, Cupar. . . . .(p.793)
T: 01334 652285
E: cherylwallace@thorntons-law.co.uk

WALLACE, Claire Richmond (Oct 2014)
(Employee)
Procurator Fiscal Service, Glasgow . . . .(p.1241)
T: 0300 0203000
E: Claire.Wallace@copfs.gov.uk

WALLACE, David Joseph (Nov 2013)
(Employee)
The Building Law Practice Limited,
Glasgow. . . . .(p.1043)
T: 0141 3537655
E: david.wallace@buildinglawpractice.com

WALLACE, Duncan Charles (Dec 1984)
(Solicitor)
NO FIRM

WALLACE, Emily Clare (Sept 2017) (Employee)
Shepherd and Wedderburn LLP,
Edinburgh . . . .(p.900)
T: 0131 2289900
E: emily.wallace@shepwedd.com

WALLACE, Eric Robert Carson (Nov 1980)
(Director)
Bell Russell & Company Limited,
Airdrie . . . .(p.748)
T: 01236 764781
E: ewallace@bell-russell.com

WALLACE, Euan Brodie (Jun 2016) (Employee)
Brodies LLP, Glasgow . . . .(p.948)
T: 0141 2484672
E: Euan.Wallace@brodies.com

WALLACE, Evelyn Anne (Aug 2011) (Employee)
TC Young LLP, Glasgow . . . .(p.1055)
T: 0141 2215562
E: eaw@tcyoung.co.uk

WALLACE, Gertrude Elizabeth (May 1994)
(Employee)
Procurator Fiscal Service,
Edinburgh . . . .(p.1229)
T: 0300 0203000
E: gertie.wallace@copfs.gov.uk

WALLACE, Gordon James (Dec 2012)
(Associate)
Raeburn Christie Clark & Wallace LLP,
Aberdeen . . . .(p.741)
T: 01224 332400
E: gordon.wallace@raeburns.co.uk

WALLACE, Graham Callan (Oct 2009)
(Associate)
Pinsent Masons LLP, Glasgow . . . .(p.1031)
T: 0141 567 8400
E: graham.wallace@pinsentmasons.com

WALLACE, Grant (Jun 2017) (Employee)
Burness Paull LLP, Edinburgh . . . .(p.850)
T: 0131 4736000
E: grant.wallace@burnesspaull.com

WALLACE, Iain Andrew (Dec 2015) (Employee)
City of Edinburgh Council,
Edinburgh . . . .(p.1221)
T: (0131) 5294145
E: Iain.Wallace@edinburgh.gov.uk

WALLACE, James Robertson (Jan 1988)
(Partner)
James R. Wallace, Glasgow . . . .(p.1051)
T: 07949 133123
E: james.robertson@wallace.ms

WALLACE, Jennifer Binnie (Nov 1978)
(Employee)
Wallace Hodge & Company Limited,
Ayr . . . .(p.766)
T: 01292 611177
E: jennifer.wallace@wallace-hodge.co.uk

WALLACE, Jennifer Elizabeth Margaret
(Nov 2007) (Employee)
SOUTH LANARKSHIREre Council,
Hamilton . . . .(p.1247)
E: jennifer.wallace@southlanarkshire.gov.uk

WALLACE, Jennifer Freeman (Nov 2009)
(Associate)
Dickson Minto, Edinburgh . . . .(p.861)
T: 0131 2254455
E: jennifer.wallace@dmws.com

WALLACE, Karen Dorothy (Aug 2012)
(Employee)
Irwin Mitchell Scotland LLP,
Glasgow. . . . .(p.991)
T: 0141 3004300
E: Karen.Wallace@IrwinMitchell.com

WALLACE, Lindsay Ann (Jan 1995) (Partner)
Burness Paull LLP, Edinburgh . . . .(p.850)
T: 0131 4736000
E: lindsay.wallace@burnesspaull.com

WALLACE, Mark Farrel (Nov 2001) (Employee)
Glasgow City Council, Glasgow . . . . . .(p.1239)
T: 0141 2874131
E: mark.wallace@ced.glasgow.gov.uk

WALLACE, Natalie (Dec 2020) (Employee)
The McKinstry Company LLP, Ayr . . . . .(p.765)
T: 01292 281711
E: natalie@mckinstry.co.uk

WALLACE, Natalie Coia (Mar 1999) (Employee)
Ashurst LLP, Glasgow . . . .(p.1237)
T: (0141) 375 4242
E: Natalie.Wallace@ashurst.com

WALLACE, Natalie Sarah (Oct 2017)
(Employee)
Harper Macleod LLP, Glasgow . . . .(p.983)
T: 0141 2218888
E: natalie.wallace@harpermacleod.co.uk

WALLACE, Paul David Walker (Sept 2001)
(Associate)
Brodies LLP, Edinburgh . . . .(p.845)
T: 0131 228 3777
E: paul.wallace@brodies.com

WALLACE, Rachel Russell (Mar 2021)
(Employee)
Procurator Fiscal Service,
Edinburgh . . . .(p.1229)
T: 0300 0203000
E: rachel.wallace@copfs.gov.uk

WALLACE, Rhona Emily (Dec 2020) (Employee)
Addleshaw Goddard LLP,
Edinburgh . . . .(p.835)
T: 0131 2282400
E: rhona.wallace@addleshawgoddard.com

WALLACE, Ross Thomas (Oct 2017) (Employee)
MacRoberts LLP, Glasgow . . . .(p.1015)
T: 0141 3031100
E: Ross.Wallace@macroberts.com

WALLACE, Ruth Anne (Sept 2018) (Employee)
Thompsons, Glasgow . . . .(p.1046)
T: 0141 2218840
E: ruth.wallace@thompsons-scotland.co.uk

WALLACE, Susan (Sept 2020) (Employee)
Hall Baird Solicitors Ltd, Castle
Douglas . . . .(p.784)
T: 01556 502764
E: suzy@hallbaird.co.uk

WALLACE, William (Oct 2018) (Employee)
Balfour + Manson LLP, Edinburgh . . . . .(p.841)
T: 0131 2001200
E: william.wallace@balfour-manson.co.uk

WALLER, Joanna Page (Sept 2019) (Employee)
Procurator Fiscal Service,
Edinburgh . . . .(p.1227)
T: 0300 0203168
E: joanna.waller@copfs.gov.uk

WALLER, John Richard (Nov 2007) (Employee)
Addleshaw Goddard LLP,
Edinburgh . . . .(p.835)
T: 0131 2282400
E: John.Waller@addleshawgoddard.com

WALLER, Morag Fiona Margaret (Sept 2007)
(Employee)
Vialex Limited, Edinburgh . . . .(p.1235)
T: 0333 2400127
E: morag.waller@vialex.co.uk

WALLIS, Claire Helen (Oct 2004) (Partner)
CMS Cameron McKenna Nabarro Olswang LLP,
Edinburgh . . . .(p.856)
T: 0131 2288000
E: claire.wallis@cms-cmno.com

WALLS, Charles Alastair (Oct 1997) (Employee)
Pinsent Masons LLP, Edinburgh . . . .(p.895)
T: 0131 777 7000
E: alastair.walls@pinsentmasons.com

WALLS, Ellis Gillespie (Mar 2015) (Employee)
Davidson Chalmers Stewart LLP,
Edinburgh . . . .(p.859)
T: 0131 6259191
E: ellis.walls@dcslegal.com

WALLS, Louisa-Jane (Oct 1998) (Employee)
Scottish Government, Edinburgh . . . . .(p.1231)
T: 0131 244 0815
E: Louisa.Walls@gov.scot

WALMSLEY, Thomas William (Oct 2014)
(Employee)
Addleshaw Goddard LLP, London
EC1 . . . .(p.1261)
T: 0207 6068855
E: Tom.Walmsley@addleshawgoddard.com

WALSH, Amy Helen (Jul 2009) (Partner)
Harper Macleod LLP, Glasgow . . . .(p.983)
T: 0141 2218888
E: amy.walsh@harpermacleod.co.uk

WALSH, Gavin (Feb 2002) (Employee)
WEST DUNBARTONSHIREhire Council,
Dumbarton . . . .(p.1217)
T: 01389 737000
E: gavin.walsh@west-dunbarton.gov.uk

WALSH, James Matthew (Mar 2011)
(Employee)
Ogier, St Peter Port. . . . .(p.1273)
T: (+44) 1481 752242
E: James.Walsh@ogier.com

WALSH, Kevin (Jan 1992) (Employee)
Scottish Courts and Tribunals Service,
Kilmarnock . . . .(p.1249)
E: kwalsh@scotcourts.gov.uk

WALSH, Megan (Jun 2019) (Employee)
DAC Beachcroft Scotland LLP,
Glasgow. . . . .(p.964)
T: 0141 2486688
E: mwalsh@dacbeachcroft.com

WALSH, Peter John (Feb 2008) (Employee)
Jas Campbell & Co Ltd, Saltcoats . . . . .(p.1160)
T: 01294 464301
E: p.walsh@jascampbell.co.uk

WALSH, Rosslyn (Sept 2020) (Employee)
Procurator Fiscal Service,
Edinburgh . . . .(p.1227)
T: 0300 0203168
E: rosslyn.walsh@copfs.gov.uk

WALTERS, Christopher Stewart (Nov 2010)
(Employee)
Herbert Smith Freehills LLP, Dubai . . . .(p.1278)
T: +971 4 428 6338
E: chris.walters@hsf.com

WALTON, Alice Jane (Oct 2014) (Employee)
Sky UK Ltd, Isleworth . . . .(p.1260)
T: (020) 7032 7085
E: alice.walton@sky.uk

WAMBERG, Elisa Ann (Oct 2008) (Employee)
Department For Business, Energy and Industrial
Strategy, Birmingham . . . .(p.1258)
E: elisa.wamberg@beis.gov.uk

WAN, Roddy Chun Pui (May 2012) (Employee)
Scottish Power Limited, Glasgow . . . . .(p.1244)
T: 0141 568 2000
E: roddy.wan@scottishpower.com

WANG, Sandie Yu-hsuan (Apr 2013) (Associate)
DLA Piper Scotland LLP, Edinburgh . . . .(p.863)
T: 08700 111111
E: sandie.wang@dlapiper.com

WANG, Tony (Oct 2009) (Employee)
Nomura Asset Management U.K. Limited,
London EC4 . . . .(p.1266)

WARBURTON, Sophia Rose (Sept 2015)
(Employee)
Burness Paull LLP, Edinburgh . . . .(p.850)
T: 0131 4736000
E: sophia.warburton@burnesspaull.com

WARD, Annette Marie (Mar 1991) (Employee)
Procurator Fiscal Service, Airdrie . . . . . .(p.1214)
T: 01236 747027
E: Annette.Ward@copfs.gov.uk

WARD, Catriona Margaret Anne (May 2018)
(Employee)
CMS Cameron McKenna Nabarro Olswang LLP,
Glasgow. . . . .(p.962)
T: 0141 2222200
E: Catriona.Ward@cms-cmno.com

WARD, Christy Catherine (Jun 2017)
(Employee)
Procurator Fiscal Service, Aberdeen . . .(p.1213)
T: 0300 020 4386
E: Christy.Ward@copfs.gov.uk

WARD, Corinne Denise (Jul 2015) (Employee)
Aviva, Perth . . . .(p.1253)
T: 01738 621202

WARD, Elaine Marie (Sept 2009) (Employee)
Procurator Fiscal Service, Aberdeen . . .(p.1213)
T: 01224 578965
E: elaine.ward@copfs.gov.uk

WARD, Elizabeth Katrien (Oct 2004) (Associate)
Brodies LLP, Edinburgh . . . .(p.845)
  T: 0131 2283777
  E: elizabeth.ward@brodies.com

WARD, Hannah (Mar 2018) (Associate)
MacRoberts LLP, Edinburgh . . . .(p.887)
  T: 0131 2295046
  E: hannah.ward@macroberts.com

WARD, Ian (Jul 2019) (Employee)
The Kerr Brown Partnership,
  Glasgow. . . . .(p.1044)
  T: 0141 2214880
  E: ian@kerrbrown.co.uk

WARD, John Aloysius (Mar 1973) (Partner)
Wilson Ward LLP, Edinburgh . . . .(p.913)
  T: 0131 4677550
  E: john@wilsonward.co.uk

WARD, John Michael (Jan 1988) (Director)
Ward & Co (Perth) Ltd, Perth . . . .(p.1152)
  T: 01738 638461
  E: jward_wardco@yahoo.co.uk

WARD, Joshua (Jan 2019) (Employee)
Primrose & Gordon, Dumfries . . . .(p.802)
  T: 01387 267316
  E: joshw@primroseandgordon.co.uk

WARD, Karly Louise (Mar 2021) (Solicitor)
NO FIRM

WARD, Lesley Anne (Sept 1991) (Solicitor)
NO FIRM

WARD, Louise (Jan 2016) (Employee)
TLT LLP, Glasgow . . . .(p.1048)
  T: 0333 006 0400
  E: Louise.Ward@TLTsolicitors.com

WARD, Melanie Mitchell (Oct 1994)
  (Employee)
Procurator Fiscal Service,
  Edinburgh . . . .(p.1227)
  T: 0300 0203168
  E: melanie.ward@copfs.gov.uk

WARD, Nathalie Joyce (Jun 2017) (Employee)
Burness Paull LLP, Glasgow . . . .(p.954)
  T: 0141 2484933
  E: nathalie.ward@burnesspaull.com

WARD, Pauline Isabella (Dec 2001) (Partner)
Neill Clerk & Murray, Greenock . . . . . .(p.1062)
  T: 01475 724522
  E: pw@neillclerkmurray.co.uk

WARD, Peter (Oct 2007) (Solicitor)
NO FIRM

WARD, Peter Mark (Nov 2006) (Partner)
Burness Paull LLP, Edinburgh . . . .(p.850)
  T: 0131 4736000
  E: Peter.Ward@burnesspaull.com

WARD, Stacey (Jul 2015) (Employee)
Fergusson Law, Edinburgh. . . . .(p.870)
  T: 0131 556 4044
  E: stacey@fergussonlaw.com

WARD, Suzanne Victoria (Mar 2005)
  (Employee)
Aberdeenshire Council, Inverurie . . . . .(p.1248)
  T: 01467 537421
  E: Suzanne.Ward@aberdeenshire.gov.uk

WARD, Victoria Joanne (Jul 2020) (Employee)
Davidson Chalmers Stewart LLP,
  Glasgow. . . . .(p.967)
  T: 0141 4283258
  E: vicky.ward@dcslegal.com

WARD, William Frederick (Oct 2019)
  (Employee)
Brodies LLP, Glasgow . . . .(p.948)
  T: 0141 2484672
  E: freddie.ward@brodies.com

WARDELL, Sarah Catherine (Nov 2008)
  (Associate)
Dentons UK and Middle East LLP,
  Edinburgh . . . .(p.860)
  T: 0330 2220050
  E: Sarah.Wardell@dentons.com

WARDEN, William (Jan 1993) (Partner)
Culley & McAlpine, Perth . . . .(p.1147)
  T: 01738 626644
  E: B.Warden@culleymcalpine.co.uk

WARDHAUGH, Frazer Hamilton (Apr 2001)
  (Employee)
BAM Construct UK Ltd, Edinburgh . . . .(p.1221)
  E: fwardhaugh@bam.co.uk

WARDROP, Amy Jean (Aug 2013) (Employee)
Friends Legal, Glasgow . . . .(p.978)
  T: 0844 8921250
  E: amy.wardrop@friends-legal.co.uk

WARDROP, Andrew David (Apr 2001)
  (Associate)
DLA Piper Scotland LLP, Edinburgh . . . .(p.863)
  T: 08700 111111
  E: andrew.wardrop@dlapiper.com

WARDROP, Patricia Frances (Jan 2008)
  (Employee)
McKinsey & Company Inc., Dubai . . . .(p.1278)
  T: +971 4 519 8073
  E: patricia_wardrop@mckinsey.com

WARDROP-SZILAGYI, Allan Clement Simpson
  (Nov 2002) (Employee)
Oaktree Capital Management, Hong
  Kong . . . .(p.1273)
  E: awardrop@oaktreecapital.com

WARDROPE, Sharlene Marie (May 1995)
(Associate)
Strefford Tulips Limited, Hamilton ....(p.1070)
T: 01698 429428
E: s.wardrope@strefford-tulips.co.uk

WARE, Gareth (Sept 1995) (Director)
Corries Solicitors (Scotland) Limited,
Glasgow......................(p.963)
T: 0141 2493400
E: gareth.ware@corries-g.co.uk

WARES, Sharon Mary (Oct 1988) (Employee)
Aberdeen City Council, Aberdeen.....(p.1211)
T: 01224 522000
E: swares@aberdeencity.gov.uk

WARK, Rhona Murray (Mar 1990) (Consultant)
BTO Solicitors LLP, Glasgow ....(p.952)
T: 0141 2218012
E: rmw@bto.co.uk

WARNE, Alice Shirley (Jul 2014) (Employee)
Turcan Connell, Edinburgh ....(p.908)
T: 0131 2288111
E: alice.warne@turcanconnell.com

WARNE, Susan Penelope (Sept 1992) (Partner)
CMS Cameron McKenna Nabarro Olswang LLP,
Aberdeen.....................(p.727)
T: 01224 622002
E: penelope.warne@cms-cmno.com

WARNER, Alison Jane (Mar 1999) (Employee)
Hunting Energy Services (UK) Limited,
Aberdeen....................(p.1212)
T: 01224 787000
E: alison.warner@hunting-intl.com

WARNER, Jeremy Andrew (Oct 1996)
(Employee)
Scottish Environment Protection Agency,
Dingwall ....(p.1217)
T: 01349 862021
E: jeremy.warner@sepa.org.uk

WARNER, Naomei Sophia (Sept 2013)
(Employee)
Procurator Fiscal Service,
Edinburgh ....(p.1227)
T: 0300 0203168
E: naomei.warner@copfs.gov.uk

WARNER, Rachel Mary (Nov 2003) (Employee)
Pinsent Masons LLP, Aberdeen........(p.739)
T: 01224 377900
E: rachel.warner@pinsentmasons.com

WARNOCK, James Archibald Kirkland, WS
(Apr 1977) (Consultant)
Davidson Chalmers Stewart LLP,
Edinburgh ....(p.859)
T: 0131 6259191
E: James.Warnock@dcslegal.com

WARNOCK, Laura Jane (Aug 2014) (Employee)
BAM PPP UK Limited, stepps ....(p.1254)
T: 0141 7798600
E: laura.warnock@bam.com

WARREN, Andrew Michael (May 1987)
(Partner)
Weightmans (Scotland) LLP,
Glasgow.....................(p.1051)
T: 0345 073 9900
E: andrew.warren@weightmans.com

WARREN, Graeme Duncan (Oct 2008)
(Employee)
Steadman Partners, Crieff ....(p.1216)
E: graeme.warren@steadmanpartners.com

WARRENDER, Leanne (Aug 2015) (Employee)
Aberdein Considine and Company,
Aberdeen ....(p.718)
T: 01224 589700
E: lwarrender@acandco.com

WARRILLOW, Nicholas Piers (Feb 2021)
(Associate)
Burness Paull LLP, Edinburgh ....(p.850)
T: 0131 4736000
E: nick.warrillow@burnesspaull.com

WASEEM, Nadia (Oct 2019) (Employee)
National Health Service Scotland,
Edinburgh ....(p.1225)
T: 0131 2757800
E: nadia.waseem@nhs.scot

WASILEWSKA, Klaudia (Aug 2020) (Employee)
Balfour + Manson LLP, Edinburgh .....(p.841)
T: 0131 2001200
E: Klaudia.Wasilewska@balfour-manson.co.uk

WASON, Christina Louise (Aug 2004)
(Associate)
Harper Macleod LLP, Glasgow ....(p.983)
T: 0141 2218888
E: christina.wason@harpermacleod.co.uk

WATERS, Eileen Annette (May 2001)
(Employee)
Government Legal Department,
Leeds......................(p.1260)

WATERS, Harriet Louise (Sept 2018) (Employee)
Lindsays LLP, Edinburgh ....(p.882)
T: 0131 2291212
E: HarrietWaters@lindsays.co.uk

WATERS, Joanne Margaret (Feb 1984)
(Employee)
Watersrule Limited, Stirling ....(p.1167)
T: 01786 235 235
E: joanne.waters@watersrule.co.uk

WATERS, Marc Anthony (Jan 2021) (Employee)
Jonathan Paul Solicitors, Alexandria ....(p.751)
T: 01389 756785

WATERS, Nicola Frances (Feb 2017) (Employee)
Jones Whyte LLP, Glasgow . . . .(p.993)
T: 0141 375 1222
E: nicola.waters@joneswhyte.co.uk

WATERS, Ruth (Nov 1990) (Director)
Young & Partners Business Lawyers Limited,
Glasgow . . . .(p.1056)
T: 01383 721621
E: rxw@businesslaw.co.uk

WATERS, Steven Robert (Sept 1983) (Director)
Watersrule Limited, Tillicoultry . . . .(p.1174)
T: 01259 753330
E: steven.waters@watersrule.co.uk

WATERS, Susan Margaret (Dec 1992)
(Employee)
James & George Collie LLP,
Aberdeen . . . .(p.728)
T: 01224 581581
E: s.waters@jgcollie.co.uk

WATKINS, Avril Elaine (Jul 2009) (Employee)
SOUTH LANARKSHIRERe Council,
Hamilton . . . .(p.1247)
T: 01698 454173
E: Avril.watkins@southlanarkshire.gov.uk

WATON, Ashlee (Dec 2018) (Employee)
Stirling & Mair Limited, Johnstone . . . .(p.1090)
T: 01505 329373
E: ashlee.waton@stirlingmair.com

WATSON, Adam Spencer (Aug 2009)
(Employee)
National Health Service Scotland,
Edinburgh . . . .(p.1225)
T: 0131 2757800
E: adam.watson@nhs.scot

WATSON, Aimee (Nov 2009) (Employee)
Skills Development Scotland,
Glasgow . . . .(p.1244)
T: 0141 343 9315
E: Aimee.Watson@sds.co.uk

WATSON, Alison (Nov 2004) (Employee)
Angus Council, Forfar . . . .(p.1237)
T: 01307 476228
E: WatsonA1@angus.gov.uk

WATSON, Amy Cecile Doris (Oct 2009)
(Partner)
Raeburn Christie Clark & Wallace LLP,
Aberdeen . . . .(p.741)
T: 01224 332400
E: amy.watson@raeburns.co.uk

WATSON, Amy Claire (Mar 2015) (Employee)
DWF LLP, Edinburgh . . . .(p.865)
T: 0131 2265541
E: Amy.Watson@dwf.law

WATSON, Audrey Frances (Jul 1985)
(Employee)
West Lothian Council, Livingston . . . . .(p.1250)
T: 01506 280000
E: audrey.watson@westlothian.gov.uk

WATSON, Barbara Jane (Sept 1983) (Associate)
ELP Arbuthnott McClanachan,
Edinburgh . . . .(p.867)
T: 0131 3127276
E: bw@elpamsolicitors.co.uk

WATSON, Campbell Colin (May 1978) (Partner)
Andersons LLP, Kinross . . . .(p.1098)
T: 01577 862405
E: campbellcwatson@yahoo.co.uk

WATSON, Colin Carrick (Oct 1985) (Employee)
Alba Power, Stonehaven . . . .(p.1255)
E: colin.watson@albapower.com

WATSON, David Beattie (Jul 1994) (Employee)
Wilson McKendrick Solicitors Limited,
Glasgow . . . .(p.1053)
T: 0141 2227950
E: davidwatson@wilsonmckendrick.co.uk

WATSON, Douglas Morgan (Oct 1990)
(Partner)
Ledingham Chalmers LLP,
Aberdeen . . . .(p.734)
T: 01224 408408
E: douglas.watson@ledinghamchalmers.com

WATSON, Duncan Forbes (Mar 2005)
(Employee)
Mayer Brown International LLP, London
EC2 . . . .(p.1266)
T: +44 20 3130 3033
E: dwatson@mayerbrown.com

WATSON, Erica (Apr 2004) (Employee)
Scottish Police Authority, Police Scotland,
Dundee . . . .(p.1218)
T: 0300 1112222
E: Erica.Watson@scotland.pnn.police.uk

WATSON, Fiona Jane (Jun 2008) (Partner)
Paris Steele, Dunbar . . . .(p.803)
T: 01620 820982
E: fwatson@parissteele.com

WATSON, Gillian Helen (Oct 2001) (Employee)
Brodies LLP, Edinburgh . . . .(p.845)
T: 0131 2283777
E: gillian.watson@brodies.com

WATSON, Gordon Scot (Aug 2017) (Employee)
Raeside Chisholm Solicitors Limited,
Glasgow . . . .(p.1034)
T: 0141 2483456
E: g.watson@raesidechisholm.co.uk

WATSON, Grace Helen (Oct 2015) (Associate)
Shoosmiths, Edinburgh . . . .(p.902)
T: 03700 868000
E: grace.watson@shoosmiths.co.uk

WATSON, Graeme Douglas (Oct 1999)
(Partner)
Clyde & Co (Scotland) LLP,
Edinburgh . . . .(p.855)
T: 0131 5571545
E: graeme.watson@clydeco.com

WATSON, Jane Elizabeth Anne (Nov 2007)
(Employee)
Lindsays LLP, Glasgow. . . . .(p.1001)
T: 0141 2216551
E: janewatson@lindsays.co.uk

WATSON, Janine (Jun 2009) (Solicitor)
NO FIRM

WATSON, Jennifer Gray (Dec 2004) (Associate)
Digby Brown LLP, Dundee . . . .(p.808)
T: 3332005925
E: jennifer.watson@digbybrown.co.uk

WATSON, Katherine Ann (Jul 2018) (Employee)
Addleshaw Goddard LLP, London
EC1 . . . .(p.1261)
T: 0207 6068855
E: katherine.watson@addleshawgoddard.com

WATSON, Kirsty Ann (Oct 2009) (Employee)
Civil Legal Assistance Office,
Edinburgh . . . .(p.1222)
T: 0131 2401960
E: WatsonKir@clao.org.uk

WATSON, Kirsty Stephenson (Dec 2020)
(Employee)
Harper Macleod LLP, Glasgow . . . .(p.983)
T: 0141 2218888
E: kirsty.watson@harpermacleod.co.uk

WATSON, Leisha Jayne (Oct 2014) (Employee)
The Institute and Faculty of Actuaries,
Edinburgh . . . .(p.1234)
T: (020) 7632 1488
E: Leisha.Watson@actuaries.org.uk

WATSON, Mark John Reid (Jun 2020)
(Employee)
Ogier, St Helier . . . .(p.1274)
T: 01534 504000
E: Mark.Watson@ogier.com

WATSON, Michael Gall (Oct 1994) (Partner)
Pinsent Masons LLP, Edinburgh . . . .(p.895)
T: 0131 7777000
E: michael.watson@pinsentmasons.com

WATSON, Morven Smith (Jul 2014) (Employee)
Scottish Government, Edinburgh . . . . .(p.1231)
T: 0131 244 0815
E: morven.davidson@gov.scot

WATSON, Nadia Egbujo (May 2013)
(Employee)
Morton Fraser LLP, Glasgow . . . .(p.1022)
T: 0141 2741100
E: nadia.watson@morton-fraser.com

WATSON, Nicky-Ray (Oct 2011) (Employee)
Harper Macleod LLP, Glasgow . . . .(p.983)
T: 0141 2218888
E: nicky-ray.watson@harpermacleod.co.uk

WATSON, Nicola (Jun 2014) (Employee)
Brodies LLP, Aberdeen. . . . .(p.723)
T: 01224 392242
E: nicola.watson@brodies.com

WATSON, Nicola (Feb 2015) (Employee)
Livingstone Brown Limited,
Glasgow. . . . .(p.1003)
T: 0141 4298166
E: nicola.watson@livbrown.co.uk

WATSON, Olivia Rose (Nov 2020) (Employee)
Addleshaw Goddard LLP,
Edinburgh . . . .(p.835)
T: 0131 2282400
E: olivia.watson@addleshawgoddard.com

WATSON, Professor, Peter Black (Sept 1981)
(Partner)
PBW Law Solicitors, Glasgow . . . .(p.1030)
T: 0141 439 1990
E: pbw@pbwlaw.co.uk

WATSON, Ryan David (Sept 2016) (Associate)
Clyde & Co (Scotland) LLP,
Glasgow. . . . .(p.961)
T: 0141 2482666
E: ryan.watson@clydeco.com

WATSON, Shona Mary (Nov 2003) (Employee)
Siemens Gamesa Renewable Energy,
Edinburgh . . . .(p.1234)
E: Shona.Watson@siemensgamesa.com

WATSON, Stephanie Margaret (Jul 2009)
(Employee)
Thorntons Law LLP, Dundee . . . .(p.819)
T: 01382 346276
E: swatson@thorntons-law.co.uk

WATSON, Susan Margaret (Feb 1984)
(Employee)
Scottish Environment Protection Agency,
Holytown. . . . .(p.1248)
T: (01698) 839 000
E: susan.watson@sepa.org.uk

WATSON-HILL, Chloe Lois (Jul 2017)
(Employee)
Ogier, St Helier . . . .(p.1274)
T: 01534 504000
E: Chloe.Watson-Hill@ogier.com

WATSON-ORR, Stephanie McKay (Oct 2014)
(Employee)
Pinsent Masons LLP, Glasgow . . . .(p.1031)
T: 0141 249 5476
E: Stephanie.watson-orr@pinsentmasons.com

WATT, Adriana Zdravkova (Sept 2016) (Employee)
Pinsent Masons LLP, Edinburgh . . . .(p.895)
T: 0131 777 7000
E: adriana.watt@pinsentmasons.com

WATT, Alan Robert Kennedy (Jan 1998) (Partner)
Watt Law, Cumbernauld . . . .(p.791)
T: 01236 787030
E: alan@wattlaw.co.uk

WATT, Alan Russell (Sept 1985) (Partner)
Hamilton Watt & Co, Aberdeen . . . .(p.731)
T: 01224 586685
E: alanhw@hamiltonwatt.co.uk

WATT, Alexander John (Jun 2016) (Associate)
Travers Smith LLP, London EC1 . . . . . .(p.1269)
T: 020 7295 3000
E: Alexander.Watt@traverssmith.com

WATT, Amy Jane (Jun 2013) (Employee)
Carruthers Gemmill, Glasgow . . . .(p.958)
T: 0141 3330 033
E: ajw@carruthersgemmill.co.uk

WATT, Anna Mhairi (Nov 2004) (Employee)
Ledingham Chalmers LLP,
Edinburgh . . . .(p.881)
T: 0131 2001000
E: anna.watt@ledinghamchalmers.com

WATT, Caroline Jane (Sept 1993) (Associate)
Wright & Crawford (1906) Limited,
Paisley . . . .(p.1142)
T: 0141 8876211
E: c.watt@wright-crawford.co.uk

WATT, Catriona Mackay (Oct 2001) (Partner)
Anderson Strathern LLP, Edinburgh . . . .(p.839)
T: 0131 2707700
E: catriona.watt@andersonstrathern.co.uk

WATT, Craig Ian, WS (Nov 2002) (Partner)
Brodies LLP, Edinburgh . . . .(p.845)
T: 0131 2283777
E: Craig.Watt@brodies.com

WATT, David MacLean (Oct 1974) (Employee)
Scottish Courts and Tribunals Service,
Paisley . . . .(p.1252)
T: 0141 8875291
E: dwatt4@scotcourts.gov.uk

WATT, Edward Bruce (Mar 1999) (Partner)
Addleshaw Goddard LLP,
Edinburgh . . . .(p.835)
T: 0131 2282400
E: Edward.Watt@addleshawgoddard.com

WATT, Erika Kennedy (Feb 2011) (Director)
MML (Scotland) Ltd, Glasgow . . . .(p.1021)
T: 0141 2642272
E: erika@mmlegal.co.uk

WATT, Gail (Aug 2005) (Associate)
Morton Fraser LLP, Edinburgh . . . .(p.891)
T: 0131 2471000
E: Gail.Watt@morton-fraser.com

WATT, Gregor John (Oct 2018) (Employee)
Lloyds Banking Group Plc, London
EC2 . . . .(p.1266)
E: gregor.watt@lloydsbanking.com

WATT, Jamie Douglas Sinclair (Feb 2006) (Partner)
Harper Macleod LLP, Edinburgh . . . .(p.877)
T: 0131 2472500
E: jamie.watt@harpermacleod.co.uk

WATT, Jennifer Elizabeth (Sept 2017) (Employee)
TotalEnergies E&P UK Limited,
Westhill . . . .(p.1255)
T: 01224 297000

WATT, Jordan Alexander (Apr 2019) (Employee)
Aberdein Considine and Company,
Peterhead. . . . .(p.1153)
T: 01779 475365
E: jwatt@acandco.com

WATT, Kara (Dec 2019) (Employee)
Procurator Fiscal Service,
Edinburgh . . . .(p.1227)
T: 0300 0203168

WATT, Karyn Marjorie, WS (Feb 1985) (Partner)
Anderson Strathern LLP, Edinburgh . . . .(p.839)
T: 0131 2707700
E: karyn.watt@andersonstrathern.co.uk

WATT, Kenneth William (Jan 1982) (Partner)
McEwan Fraser Legal, Edinburgh . . . . . .(p.885)
T: 0131 5249797
E: kenny.watt@mcewanfraserlegal.co.uk

WATT, Lara Katie (Aug 2014) (Employee)
Dickson Minto, London EC2 . . . .(p.1263)
T: 020 76284455
E: Lara.Watt@dmws.com

WATT, Robin James (Sept 2004) (Partner)
DWF LLP, Edinburgh . . . .(p.865)
T: 0131 2265541
E: Robin.Watt@dwf.law

WATT, Stephen Robert (Nov 1983) (Partner)
Carruthers Gemmill, Glasgow . . . .(p.958)
T: 0141 3330 033
E: srw@carruthersgemmill.co.uk

WATT, Stewart Allan (Nov 2019) (Employee)
CMS Cameron McKenna Nabarro Olswang LLP,
Aberdeen . . . .(p.727)
T: 01224 622002
E: stewart.watt@cms-cmno.com

WATT, Vikki (Oct 2002) (Partner)
BTO Solicitors LLP, Glasgow . . . .(p.952)
T: 0141 2218012
E: vwa@bto.co.uk

WATT, William Cameron (Feb 2009)
(Employee)
Caird & Vaughan, Dundee . . . .(p.807)
T: 01382 229399

WATTERS, Amy (Nov 2015) (Associate)
Malcolm & Hutchison, Airdrie . . . .(p.750)
T: 01236 755050
E: Amy@malcolmandhutchison.co.uk

WATTERS, Thomas Martin (Jan 1986) (Partner)
Watters, Steven & Co., Motherwell . . .(p.1128)
T: 01698 276550
E: info@watterssteven.co.uk

WATTS, Andrew Graham (Oct 2020) (Associate)
Addleshaw Goddard LLP,
Aberdeen . . . .(p.719)
T: (+44) (0) 1224 96 5410
E: andrew.watts@addleshawgoddard.com

WATTS, Michaela (Oct 2012) (Associate)
Pinsent Masons LLP, Aberdeen . . . .(p.739)
T: 01224 377900
E: Michaela.Watts@pinsentmasons.com

WAUGH, Angus John Somerville (Aug 1991)
(Employee)
First Milk Ltd, Paisley . . . .(p.1252)
T: 0141 8476895
E: anguswaugh@firstmilk.co.uk

WAUGH, Carol Stella Philomena (Mar 2001)
(Solicitor)
NO FIRM

WAUGHMAN, Kirsty Patricia (Nov 2018)
(Employee)
Thorntons Law LLP, Dundee . . . .(p.819)
T: 01382 229 111
E: KWaughman@thorntons-law.co.uk

WAYMAN, Fiona Hannah (Oct 1999)
(Employee)
Mitchells Roberton Ltd, Glasgow . . . . .(p.1020)
T: 0141 5523422
E: fhw@mitchells-roberton.co.uk

WEATHERHEAD, Alison Jane (Mar 2002)
(Partner)
Dentons UK and Middle East LLP,
Glasgow . . . .(p.968)
T: 0330 2220050
E: Alison.Weatherhead@dentons.com

WEATHERSTON, Graham (Aug 1994)
(Associate)
DWF LLP, Glasgow . . . .(p.973)
T: 07845 049249
E: Graham.Weatherston2@dwf.law

WEAVER, Annette Christiona (Nov 1987)
(Employee)
Argyll & Bute Council,
Lochgilphead . . . .(p.1251)
T: 01546 604 732
E: Annette.Weaver@argyll-bute.gov.uk

WEAVER, Lucrecia Marie (Jun 2006) (Partner)
Weaver & Waddell Solicitors,
Glasgow . . . .(p.1051)
T: 0141 7396100
E: lucy.weaver@weaverwaddellsolicitors.com

WEBB, Alison (Oct 2010) (Associate)
Clyde & Co (Scotland) LLP,
Edinburgh . . . .(p.855)
T: 0131 525 8603
E: Alison.webb@clydeco.com

WEBB, Johanne (Oct 2008) (Employee)
Procurator Fiscal Service, Glasgow . . . .(p.1242)
T: (0300) 020 3000
E: johanne.webb@copfs.gov.uk

WEBB, Roger Geoffrey (Oct 1993) (Partner)
Roger Webb, Inverness . . . .(p.1083)
T: 01463 234036
E: rogerwebbsolicitor@btinternet.com

WEBB, Ross Alan (Oct 2008) (Partner)
Aberdein Considine and Company,
Edinburgh . . . .(p.833)
T: 0131 2212424
E: rwebb@acandco.com

WEBBER, Ashley (Jun 2017) (Employee)
Paul Hastings (Europe) LLP, London
EC2 . . . .(p.1267)
T: 020 3023 5197
E: ashleywebber@paulhastings.com

WEBSTER, Diane Margaret Jane (Oct 2008)
(Employee)
Scottish Borders Council, Newtown St.
Boswells . . . .(p.1251)
T: 01835 825 225
E: jane.webster@scotborders.gov.uk

WEBSTER, Dylan James (Sept 2019) (Employee)
SSE PLC, Glasgow . . . .(p.1244)
T: 0141 224 7248
E: dylan.webster@sse.com

WEBSTER, Gareth Peter (Oct 2005) (Employee)
Premier Oil UK Limited, Aberdeen . . . .(p.1213)
T: 01224 618900
E: gwebster@premier-oil.com

WEBSTER, Gary Alexander (Nov 2004)
(Partner)
Ledingham Chalmers LLP,
Inverness . . . .(p.1078)
T: 01463 667400
E: gary.webster@ledinghamchalmers.com

WEBSTER, Kimberley (Mar 2021) (Employee)
DAC Beachcroft Scotland LLP,
Edinburgh . . . .(p.858)
T: 0131 5247790
E: kwebster@dacbeachcroft.com

WEBSTER, Mark James (Aug 2016) (Solicitor)
NO FIRM

WEBSTER, Martyn Timothy Keith (Dec 2005)
(Associate)
BTO Solicitors LLP, Glasgow . . . .(p.952)
T: 0141 2218012
E: twe@bto.co.uk

WEBSTER, Neil (Oct 1996) (Partner)
Walker & Sharpe, Dumfries . . . .(p.803)
T: 01387 267222
E: neil.webster@walker-sharpe.co.uk

WEBSTER, Sheila Mairead (Jan 1991) (Partner)
Davidson Chalmers Stewart LLP,
Edinburgh . . . .(p.859)
T: 0131 6259191
E: sheila.webster@dcslegal.com

WEBSTER, Stephen William (Dec 1989)
(Partner)
Urquharts, Edinburgh . . . .(p.909)
T: 0131 5562896
E: stephenwebster@urquharts.co.uk

WEDDERBURN, Kathryn Jean (Sept 1995)
(Partner)
MacRoberts LLP, Glasgow . . . .(p.1015)
T: 0141 3031100
E: katy.wedderburn@macroberts.com

WEIHE, Brynhild Dalsgaard (Aug 2021)
(Employee)
Turcan Connell, Edinburgh . . . .(p.908)
T: 0131 2288111
E: brynhild.weihe@turcanconnell.com

WEIR, Calum James Masson (Aug 1994)
(Partner)
Penmans, Glasgow . . . .(p.1031)
T: 0141 429 4489
E: cjmweir@hotmail.co.uk

WEIR, Caroline Jean (May 1993) (Partner)
Stirling & Gilmour LLP, Clydebank . . . . .(p.785)
T: 0141 9522669
E: c.weir@stirlingandgilmour.co.uk

WEIR, Catriona Leanne (Oct 2008) (Employee)
Mitie, London SE1 . . . .(p.1266)
E: Catriona.Weir@mitie.com

WEIR, Christopher Henry (Sept 2010)
(Employee)
Scottish Social Services Council,
Dundee . . . .(p.1218)
T: 0345 6030 891
E: christopher.weir@sssc.uk.com

WEIR, Emma Allison (Sept 2017) (Employee)
Carr & Co (Solicitors) Limited,
Glasgow. . . . .(p.957)
T: 0141 7794466
E: ew@theglasgowlawpractice.co.uk

WEIR, Hazel May (Dec 1993) (Associate)
DWF LLP, Glasgow . . . .(p.973)
T: 0141 228 8000
E: hazel.weir@dwf.law

WEIR, Jessica Grace (Nov 2015) (Employee)
Pinsent Masons LLP, Edinburgh . . . .(p.895)
T: 0131 777 7000
E: jessica.weir@pinsentmasons.com

WEIR, Nicola Jane (Aug 1994) (Employee)
SOUTH LANARKSHIRERe Council,
Hamilton . . . .(p.1247)
T: 01698 454694
E: nicola.weir@southlanarkshire.gov.uk

WEIR, Nicola Patricia (Jan 2009) (Associate)
Burness Paull LLP, Glasgow . . . .(p.954)
T: 0141 2484933
E: nikki.weir@burnesspaull.com

WEIR, Rachael Janet (Dec 1999) (Employee)
Procurator Fiscal Service,
Edinburgh . . . .(p.1227)
T: 0300 0203168
E: rachael.weir@fcdo.gov.uk

WEIR, Robert Gray (May 2017) (Employee)
Procurator Fiscal Service, Inverness . . . .(p.1248)
T: 0844 5612926
E: Robert.Weir@copfs.gov.uk

WEIR, Ruth (Sept 2011) (Associate)
Gillespie Macandrew LLP, Perth . . . . . .(p.1148)
T: 01738 231000
E: ruth.weir@gillespiemacandrew.co.uk

WEIR, Serena Evelyn (Sept 2010) (Employee)
Shepherd and Wedderburn LLP,
Edinburgh . . . .(p.900)
T: 0131 2289900
E: serena.weir@shepwedd.com

WEIR, Timothy Paul Anthony (Nov 2005)
(Director)
Weir Law Limited, Glasgow . . . .(p.1052)
T: 0141 6285544
E: tim.weir@weirlaw.co.uk

WEISSGERBER, Rebecca Jane (Oct 2008)
(Director)
RJW Defence Ltd, Dunbar . . . .(p.803)
T: 07719 272436
E: rebecca@rjwdefence.com

WELLBURN, John Stewart (Nov 2001) (Partner)
Andersons LLP, Kinross . . . .(p.1098)
T: 01577 862405
E: j_wellburn@andersons-kinross.co.uk

WELLS, Ian Matthew (Mar 2004) (Associate)
ELP Arbuthnott McClanachan,
   Edinburgh . . . .(p.867)
   T: 0131 5548649
   E: imw@elpamsolicitors.co.uk

WELLS, Michael Gavin (Oct 1992) (Employee)
Office of the Advocate General,
   Edinburgh . . . .(p.1227)
   T: 0131 2441635
   E: michael.wells@advocategeneral.gov.uk

WELSH, Lauren (Aug 2020) (Employee)
MacDonald, Maciver & Company Limited,
   Stornoway . . . .(p.1170)
   T: 01851 704343
   E: lauren.welsh@macdmac.co.uk

WELSH, Louise (Nov 2013) (Employee)
Weightmans (Scotland) LLP,
   Glasgow. . . . .(p.1051)
   T: 0345 073 9900
   E: Louise.Welsh@weightmans.com

WELSH, Lynn (Sept 1986) (Employee)
Equality and Human Rights Commission,
   Glasgow. . . . .(p.1239)
   T: 0141 2285968
   E: Lynn.Welsh@equalityhumanrights.com

WELSH, Nicola (Sept 2017) (Employee)
Pinsent Masons LLP, Glasgow . . . .(p.1031)
   T: 0141 567 8400
   E: nicola.welsh@pinsentmasons.com

WELSH, Stephen Barclay (Dec 1988)
   (Employee)
Ithaca Energy (Uk) Limited,
   Aberdeen . . . .(p.1213)
   T: 01224 334028
   E: swelsh@ithacaenergy.com

WELSH, Vivien Ailsa Roberta (Dec 2002)
   (Associate)
Pinsent Masons LLP, Edinburgh . . . .(p.895)
   T: 0131 7777000
   E: vivien.welsh@pinsentmasons.com

WEMYSS, Jonathan Mark (Mar 2019)
   (Employee)
Stronachs LLP, Aberdeen . . . .(p.744)
   T: 01224 845845
   E: jonathan.wemyss@stronachs.com

WERNHAM, Allan (Feb 1995) (Partner)
CMS Cameron McKenna Nabarro Olswang LLP,
   Glasgow. . . . .(p.962)
   T: 0141 2222200
   E: Allan.Wernham@cms-cmno.com

WEST, Aidan Nicholas (Jun 2008) (Employee)
Law Society of Scotland,
   Edinburgh . . . .(p.1224)
   T: 0131 2267411
   E: aidanwest@lawscot.org.uk

WEST, Gordon Mckenzie (Aug 2021)
   (Associate)
Addleshaw Goddard LLP,
   Edinburgh . . . .(p.835)
   T: 0131 2282400
   E: Gordon.West@addleshawgoddard.com

WEST, John William (Aug 2013) (Employee)
Procurator Fiscal Service,
   Edinburgh . . . .(p.1227)
   T: 0300 0203168
   E: john.west@civilrecoveryunit.gov.scot

WEST, Laura Jane (Nov 2013) (Associate)
CMS Cameron McKenna Nabarro Olswang LLP,
   Edinburgh . . . .(p.856)
   T: 0131 2288000
   E: Laura.West@cms-cmno.com

WEST, Micheila Constance Pritchard
   (Feb 2014) (Employee)
Scottish Government, Edinburgh . . . . .(p.1231)
   T: 0131 244 0815
   E: Micheila.West@gov.scot

WEST, Sheena Ann (Sept 1984) (Solicitor)
NO FIRM

WEST, Stuart Gordon (May 2019) (Employee)
Brodies LLP, Edinburgh . . . .(p.845)
   T: 0131 2283777
   E: stuart.west@brodies.com

WESTWOOD, Samuel Robert (May 1985)
   (Director)
Carr Berman Crichton Limited,
   Rutherglen . . . .(p.1159)
   T: 0141 6479851
   E: robert@cbcsolicitors.co.uk

WHALEY, Rosemary Celia Mackay
   (Oct 2001) (Employee)
Scottish Government, Edinburgh . . . . .(p.1231)
   T: 0131 2441424
   E: rosemary.whaley@gov.scot

WHEADON, Pamela Ross (Jan 2016) (Employee)
Aberdeen City Council, Aberdeen. . . . .(p.1211)
   T: 01224 522000
   E: pwheadon@aberdeencity.gov.uk

WHEAT, Neil Michael (Jul 2005) (Consultant)
Beckley Kenny & Co, Laurencekirk . . . .(p.1111)
   T: 01561 377188
   E: neil.wheat@beckleykenny.com

WHEATLEY, Laurel Ann (Jun 1998) (Employee)
Aberdeenshire Council, Aberdeen. . . . .(p.1211)
   T: 0345 608 1208
   E: laurel.wheatley@aberdeenshire.gov.uk

WHEELER, Joanne Elizabeth (Nov 1996)
   (Employee)
Alden Legal Limited, London WC2 . . . .(p.1261)
   E: joanne.wheeler@wearealden.com

WHEELER, Nadia Michelle (Oct 2015)
(Associate)
CMS Cameron McKenna Nabarro Olswang LLP,
London EC4 . . . .(p.1263)
T: 0207 3673000
E: nadia.wheeler@cms-cmno.com

WHEELER-OZANNE, Fritha Christina
(Feb 2008) (Employee)
Fluor Corporation, Texas . . . .(p.1279)
T: +469 3217860
E: Fritha.Wheeler-Ozanne@fluor.com

WHEELHOUSE, Emma Danielle (Nov 2019)
(Employee)
Thompsons, Glasgow . . . .(p.1046)
T: 0141 2218840
E:
emma.wheelhouse@thompsons-scotland.co.uk

WHELAN, Lynsey Susan (Oct 2008) (Employee)
Aegon UK, Edinburgh . . . .(p.1220)
T: 1315493986
E: lynsey.whelan@aegon.co.uk

WHELAN, Nicholas (Nov 2000) (Partner)
Whelan & Co, Arbroath . . . .(p.758)
T: 01241 431155
E: nwhelan@whelanandco.co.uk

WHELAN, Ryan Thomas (Feb 2013) (Employee)
Gibson, Dunn & Crutcher LLP,
Dubai . . . .(p.1278)
T: (+971) 4 318 4619
E: rwhelan@gibsondunn.com

WHELTON, Craig Michael (Nov 2003) (Partner)
Burges Salmon LLP, Edinburgh . . . .(p.850)
T: 0131 3142112
E: craig.whelton@burges-salmon.com

WHILLANS, Amanda Jane (Dec 2017)
(Employee)
TC Young LLP, Glasgow . . . .(p.1055)
T: 0141 2215562
E: ajw@tcyoung.co.uk

WHILLANS, Matthew (Apr 2010) (Employee)
Citizens Advice Bureau, Inverness . . . . .(p.1248)
E: matt.whillans@invernesscab.org

WHITAKER, Elizabeth Mary (Sept 2011)
(Employee)
Pinsent Masons LLP, Glasgow . . . .(p.1031)
T: 0141 567 8400
E: Elizabeth.Whitaker@pinsentmasons.com

WHITAKER, Kristian Yves (Oct 2012) (Solicitor)
NO FIRM

WHITE, Alan James (Mar 2002) (Partner)
Gillespie Macandrew LLP,
Edinburgh . . . .(p.872)
T: 0131 2251677

WHITE, Alison Jayne (Nov 1994) (Consultant)
Shepherd and Wedderburn LLP,
Edinburgh . . . .(p.900)
T: 0131 2289900
E: Alison.White@shepwedd.com

WHITE, Benjamin Edwin (Nov 2014)
(Employee)
Wright, Johnston & Mackenzie LLP,
Edinburgh . . . .(p.913)
T: 0131 5241500
E: bew@wjm.co.uk

WHITE, Bethan Lucy (Jan 2013) (Associate)
CMS Cameron McKenna Nabarro Olswang LLP,
Edinburgh . . . .(p.856)
T: 0131 2288000
E: bethan.white@cms-cmno.com

WHITE, Catherine Ann (Jan 1989) (Employee)
Procurator Fiscal Service,
Kilmarnock . . . .(p.1249)
T: 01563 536211
E: catherine.white@copfs.gov.uk

WHITE, Charlotte Joy (Jul 2020) (Employee)
Gilson Gray LLP, Glasgow . . . .(p.980)
T: 0141 5302021
E: lwhite@gilsongray.co.uk

WHITE, Christine Margaret (Oct 2011)
(Employee)
National Westminster Bank PLC,
Edinburgh . . . .(p.1226)
T: (0131) 626 2925
E: Christine.white@natwest.com

WHITE, Claire Esther Margaret (Oct 1996)
(Partner)
BTO Solicitors LLP, Glasgow . . . .(p.952)
T: 0141 2218012
E: cwh@bto.co.uk

WHITE, Damian Andrew (Sept 1993) (Partner)
Digby Brown LLP, Ayr . . . .(p.761)
T: 0333 200 59285
E: damian.white@digbybrown.co.uk

WHITE, David Ross (Oct 2017) (Employee)
BTO Solicitors LLP, Glasgow . . . .(p.952)
T: 0141 2218012
E: dwh@bto.co.uk

WHITE, Dominic Nathaniel (Feb 2003)
(Associate)
Addleshaw Goddard LLP, Glasgow . . . . .(p.938)
T: 0141 2212300
E: Dominic.White@addleshawgoddard.com

WHITE, Emma Louise (Oct 2009) (Employee)
Procurator Fiscal Service, Falkirk . . . . . .(p.1236)
T: 0300 020 3000
E: emma.white@copfs.gov.uk

WHITE, Jacqueline (May 2013) (Employee)
Ian C. McCarthy Ltd, Glasgow . . . .(p.1007)
T: 0141 7631366
E: jackie@iancmccarthy.co.uk

WHITE, Jennifer Margaret (Jul 2015)
(Employee)
Pinsent Masons LLP, Glasgow . . . .(p.1031)
T: 0141 567 8400
E: Jennifer.White@pinsentmasons.com

WHITE, Julie Anne (Dec 2001) (Employee)
Falkirk Council, Falkirk . . . .(p.1236)
T: 01324 506070
E: julie.white@falkirk.gov.uk

WHITE, Keith Robin Hughes (Jan 2003)
(Employee)
Scottish Government, Edinburgh . . . . .(p.1231)
T: 0131 244 0815
E: keith.white@gov.scot

WHITE, Liam Calum (Jun 2021) (Employee)
Harper Macleod LLP, Glasgow . . . .(p.983)
T: 0141 227 9559
E: liam.white@harpermacleod.co.uk

WHITE, Lyndsey (Oct 2011) (Associate)
Miller Hendry, Dundee . . . .(p.816)
T: 01382 200000
E: lyndseywhite@millerhendry.co.uk

WHITE, Morven Elizabeth (Jun 2020)
(Employee)
Stronachs LLP, Aberdeen . . . .(p.744)
T: 01224 845845
E: morven.white@stronachs.com

WHITE, Nadia Bridia (Oct 2021) (Employee)
Gillespie Macandrew LLP,
Edinburgh . . . .(p.872)
T: 0131 2251677
E: nadia.white@gillespiemacandrew.co.uk

WHITE, Rebecca Catherine (Jul 2019) (Solicitor)
Black Hay, Ayr . . . .(p.760)
T: 01292 268988
E: rebecca.white@blackhay.co.uk

WHITE, Robin William Lee (Jan 2013) (Solicitor)
Rradar (Scotland) Limited,
Glasgow. . . . .(p.1036)
E: robin.white@rradar.com

WHITE, Sean Mark (Oct 2016) (Employee)
Shepherd and Wedderburn LLP,
Edinburgh . . . .(p.900)
T: 0131 2289900
E: sean.white@shepwedd.com

WHITE, Shona Paxton (Jul 2011) (Employee)
Scottish Government's Parliamentary Counsel
Office, Edinburgh . . . .(p.1233)
T: 0131 244 1668
E: shona.white@gov.scot

WHITE, Stewart George (Jun 2004) (Associate)
Thompsons, Edinburgh . . . .(p.906)
T: 0131 2254297
E: stewart.white@thompsons-scotland.co.uk

WHITE, Sylvia (Oct 1997) (Employee)
Adhibeo Limited, Bedford . . . .(p.1258)

WHITEFORD, Martin William Robert
(May 2007) (Partner)
Anderson Strathern LLP, Edinburgh . . . .(p.839)
T: 0131 2707700
E: martin.whiteford@andersonstrathern.co.uk

WHITEHEAD, Jennifer Leigh (Nov 2003)
(Employee)
Argonon Ltd, Glasgow . . . .(p.1237)
E: jenny.whitehead@argonon.com

WHITELAW, Jennifer Margaret (Sept 1995)
(Partner)
BTO Solicitors LLP, Glasgow . . . .(p.952)
T: 0141 2218012
E: jmw@bto.co.uk

WHITELAW, Laura Currie Caldwell
(Oct 1999) (Employee)
Dumfries & Galloway Council,
Dumfries . . . .(p.1217)
T: 01387 260000
E: Laura.Whitelaw@dumgal.gov.uk

WHITELAW, Steven John (Jun 2000) (Employee)
JHS Law, Dumfries . . . .(p.801)
T: 01387 739000
E: steven.whitelaw@jhslaw.co.uk

WHITESIDE, James Henry (Dec 2016)
(Employee)
Ogier, St Helier . . . .(p.1274)
T: 01534 504000
E: james.whiteside@ogier.com

WHITTAKER, Catherine Anne (Jul 2016)
(Employee)
EDF Energy Renewables,
Edinburgh . . . .(p.1222)
T: (0131) 460 3654
E: catherine.whittaker@edf-re.uk

WHITTAKER, Conor Craig (Aug 2020)
(Employee)
Anderson Strathern LLP, Edinburgh . . . .(p.839)
T: 0131 2707700
E: conor.whittaker@andersonstrathern.co.uk

WHITTEN, Caroline Ann (Nov 2010)
(Employee)
Sainsbury's Bank plc, Edinburgh . . . . . .(p.1230)
T: (0131) 286 0807
E: caroline.whitten@sainsburysbank.co.uk

WHITTEN, Jennifer (Nov 2021) (Employee)
Jackson Boyd LLP, Glasgow . . . .(p.991)
T: 0141 2214325
E: jwhitten@jacksonboyd.co.uk

WHITTET, Neil Thomas (Nov 1988) (Partner)
Neil Whittet, Perth . . . . (p.1152)
T: 01738 628900
E: hs@neilwhittet.co.uk

WHITTLE, James Alexander Cameron
(Oct 2002) (Partner)
R & R Urquhart LLP, Forres . . . . (p.929)
T: 01309 672216
E: jamiewhittle@r-r-urquhart.com

WHITWELL-CLAYDON, Jennifer Rose
(Dec 2020) (Employee)
Addleshaw Goddard LLP,
Edinburgh . . . . (p.835)
T: 0131 2282400
E: jennifer.claydon@addleshawgoddard.com

WHORISKEY, Elise Kirsten (Nov 2014)
(Employee)
National Westminster Bank PLC,
Edinburgh . . . . (p.1226)
T: (0131) 626 2925
E: elise.whoriskey@natwest.com

WHYTE, Andrew (Oct 1978) (Partner)
Storie, Cruden & Simpson,
Aberdeen . . . . (p.743)
T: 01224 587261
E: aw@storiecs.co.uk

WHYTE, Calum (Aug 2021) (Employee)
Thermo Fisher Scientific, Paisley . . . . . . (p.1253)
T: 0141 814 6100

WHYTE, Carol Georgina (Sept 2006)
(Employee)
Procurator Fiscal Service, Perth . . . . . . (p.1253)
T: 0844 561 3000
E: Carol.Whyte@copfs.gov.uk

WHYTE, Claire Louise (May 1999) (Employee)
National Westminster Bank PLC,
Edinburgh . . . . (p.1226)
T: 7789652587
E: Claire.whyte@natwest.com

WHYTE, Clare (Jul 2004) (Employee)
Lord President's Private Office,
Edinburgh . . . . (p.1225)
T: 0131 2406701
E: cwhyte2@scotcourts.gov.uk

WHYTE, Douglas (Jan 1989) (Employee)
NO FIRM

WHYTE, Gavin Thomas (Sept 2016) (Employee)
South Ayrshire Council, Ayr . . . . (p.1215)
T: 01292 612420
E: gavin.whyte@south-ayrshire.gov.uk

WHYTE, Greg William Thomas (Dec 2008)
(Partner)
Jones Whyte LLP, Glasgow . . . . (p.993)
T: 0141 375 1222
E: greg.whyte@joneswhyte.co.uk

WHYTE, Hamish William (Jun 2014) (Partner)
MacHardy, Alexander & Whyte, WS,
Forfar . . . . (p.927)
T: 01307 463593
E: hwhyte@machardy.co.uk

WHYTE, Helen Margaret (Nov 1985) (Partner)
Ferguson Whyte, Glasgow . . . . (p.975)
T: 0141 3398432
E: hmw@fergusonwhyte.co.uk

WHYTE, Iain Stewart (Sept 1999) (Partner)
Stewart Whyte, Solicitor, Glasgow . . . . (p.1052)
T: 0141 2803737
E: swhyte@iswlegal.co.uk

WHYTE, Iona Mary Staggs (Oct 2020)
(Employee)
Wright, Johnston & Mackenzie LLP,
Glasgow . . . . (p.1054)
T: 0141 2483434
E: imw@wjm.co.uk

WHYTE, Jennifer Pyott (Dec 2013) (Employee)
Mental Health Tribunal for Scotland,
Hamilton . . . . (p.1247)
E: jwhyte3@scotcourtstribunals.gov.uk

WHYTE, Kerry Louise (Dec 2019) (Employee)
Digby Brown LLP, Aberdeen . . . . (p.729)
T: 0333 200 5925
E: kerry.whyte@digbybrown.co.uk

WHYTE, Laura Jayne (Sept 2019) (Employee)
Shepherd and Wedderburn LLP,
Edinburgh . . . . (p.900)
T: 0131 473 5178
E: laura.whyte@shepwedd.com

WHYTE, Marcus Fraser (Oct 2001) (Director)
Whyte Fraser & Co Limited,
Motherwell . . . . (p.1128)
T: 0141 3785711
E: mwh@whytefraser.co.uk

WHYTE, Nicholas Douglas, WS (Oct 1976)
(Partner)
MacHardy, Alexander & Whyte, WS,
Forfar . . . . (p.927)
T: 01307 463593
E: nwhyte@machardy.co.uk

WHYTE, Nicola Dorothy (Sept 2018)
(Employee)
Gillespie Macandrew LLP,
Edinburgh . . . . (p.872)
T: 0131 2251677
E: nicola.whyte@gillespiemacandrew.co.uk

WHYTE, Richard William (May 1999) (Partner)
Brodies LLP, Edinburgh . . . . (p.845)
T: 0131 2283777
E: richard.whyte@brodies.com

WHYTE, Ritchie Forbes (Feb 2007) (Partner)
Aberdein Considine and Company,
Aberdeen . . . .(p.718)
T: 01224 589700
E: rwhyte@acandco.com

WHYTE, Rodney Wallace (Feb 1991) (Partner)
Pinsent Masons LLP, Aberdeen . . . .(p.739)
T: 01224 377900
E: rodney.whyte@pinsentmasons.com

WHYTE, Scott Donald David (Apr 2009)
(Director)
Watermans Legal Limited,
Edinburgh . . . .(p.911)
T: 0131 4675566
E: scottwhyte@watermans.co.uk

WHYTE, Simon Thomas (Aug 2004) (Employee)
Beltrami & Co Limited, Glasgow . . . . . .(p.944)
T: 0141 4292262
E: simon.whyte@beltramiandcompany.co.uk

WHYTE, Suzanne Antonette (Sept 1994)
(Consultant)
Blackwater Law Limited, Glasgow . . . . . .(p.947)
T: 0141 404 7778
E: suzanne@iswlegal.co.uk

WHYTE, Vivien Alexandra (Dec 2009)
(Employee)
The General Teaching Council for Scotland,
Edinburgh . . . .(p.1234)
T: 0131 314 6076
E: Vivien.Whyte@gtcs.org.uk

WICKHAM, Alan Malachy (Jun 2016)
(Employee)
Procurator Fiscal Service,
Edinburgh . . . .(p.1227)
T: 0300 0203168
E: alan.wickham@copfs.gov.uk

WICKS, Steven Andrew (Oct 2008) (Employee)
Young & Partners Business Lawyers Limited,
Dunfermline . . . .(p.827)
T: 01383 721621
E: saw@businesslaw.co.uk

WIGGINS, Gail Ann (Nov 1985) (Consultant)
Grant Smith Law Practice Limited,
Aberdeen . . . .(p.743)
T: 01224 621620
E: gail.wiggins@grantsmithlaw.co.uk

WIGHT, Stephen John Robert (Jun 1985)
(Partner)
Freelands, Wishaw . . . .(p.1181)
T: 01698 355936
E: swight@freelands.co.uk

WIGHTMAN, Robert Kerr (Oct 1996)
(Employee)
National Health Service Scotland,
Edinburgh . . . .(p.1225)
T: 0131 2757800
E: Robbie.Wightman@nhs.scot

WIGHTMAN, Susan Jane (Nov 1987) (Partner)
Kippen Campbell LLP, Perth . . . .(p.1149)
T: 01738 635353
E: sw@kcllp.co.uk

WILCOX, Laura Louise (Sept 2014) (Employee)
Procurator Fiscal Service, Paisley . . . . . .(p.1252)
T: 0141 8875225
E: laura.wilcox@copfs.gov.uk

WILD, Jennifer Mackintosh (Apr 2010)
(Employee)
Peterkin & Kidd, Linlithgow . . . .(p.1116)
T: 01506 845191
E: jwild@peterkinandkidd.co.uk

WILD, Robert John (Apr 1989) (Consultant)
Inksters, Forfar . . . .(p.927)
T: 01307 497008
E: Robert@inksters.com

WILDE, David Michael (Jan 2004) (Employee)
Chilcotts, Tavistock . . . .(p.1272)
T: 01822 612535
E: dmw@chilcotts.co.uk

WILDE, Stephanie (Feb 2010) (Employee)
Macleod & MacCallum Limited,
Inverness . . . .(p.1080)
T: 01463 239393
E: stephanie.wilde@macandmac.co.uk

WILDGOOSE, Fiona (Sept 2000) (Partner)
Aberdein Considine and Company,
Aberdeen . . . .(p.717)
T: 01224 723737
E: fwildgoose@acandco.com

WILES, Karen Frances (Dec 1992) (Employee)
Aberdeenshire Council, Aberdeen . . . . .(p.1211)
T: +44(0)1467536160
E: karen.wiles@aberdeenshire.gov.uk

WILKIE, Adam John Christison (Jul 2004)
(Employee)
National Westminster Bank PLC,
Edinburgh . . . .(p.1226)
T: (0131) 626 2925
E: Adam.Wilkie@rbs.com

WILKIE, Jennifer (Feb 2008) (Partner)
Brodies LLP, Edinburgh . . . .(p.845)
T: 0131 526 4003
E: Jennifer.Wilkie@brodies.com

WILKIE, Karen (Aug 2009) (Employee)
Aberdeen City Council, Aberdeen . . . . .(p.1211)
T: 01224 522000
E: KWilkie@aberdeencity.gov.uk

WILKIE, Lisa Jaime (Apr 2003) (Employee)
Aegon UK, Edinburgh . . . .(p.1220)
T: 0870 2426610
E: lisa.wilkie@aegon.co.uk

WILKIE, Martin (Oct 2003) (Employee)
TSB Bank Plc, Edinburgh . . . .(p.1235)
T: 0131 260 0337
E: Martin.Wilkie@tsb.co.uk

WILKIE, Paula Barbara (Jan 2018) (Employee)
Scottish Social Services Council,
Dundee . . . .(p.1218)
T: 0345 6030 891
E: paula.wilkie@sssc.uk.com

WILKIE, Shannan (Mar 2018) (Employee)
Burness Paull LLP, Edinburgh . . . .(p.850)
T: 0131 4736000
E: shannan.wilkie@burnesspaull.com

WILKINSON, John Stephen (Jul 1997)
(Consultant)
Cannons Law Practice LLP,
Glasgow. . . . .(p.956)
T: 0141 2045115
E: John@cannonslaw.com

WILKINSON, Laura Jane (Oct 2006) (Employee)
Scottish Government, Edinburgh . . . . .(p.1231)
T: 0131 244 7950
E: Laura.wilkinson@gov.scot

WILKINSON, Riikka-Liisa (Feb 2011) (Employee)
Turcan Connell, Edinburgh . . . .(p.908)
T: 0131 2288111
E: riikka.wilkinson@turcanconnell.com

WILLAN, Victoria Jane (Mar 2019) (Employee)
Harper Macleod LLP, Glasgow . . . .(p.983)
T: 0141 2218888
E: victoria.willan@harpermacleod.co.uk

WILLETTS, Francesca Mhairi Bridgit
(Mar 2015) (Employee)
Lindsays LLP, Edinburgh . . . .(p.882)
T: 0131 2291212
E: francescawilletts@lindsays.co.uk

WILLIAMS BOYLSTON, Emily Cecilia
(Feb 2018) (Employee)
Scottish Government, Edinburgh . . . . .(p.1231)
T: 0131 244 0815
E: Emily.WilliamsBoylston@gov.scot

WILLIAMS, Christopher Stephen (Feb 2019)
(Employee)
DLA Piper Scotland LLP, Edinburgh . . . .(p.863)
T: 08700 111111
E: Christopher.Williams@dlapiper.com

WILLIAMS, Gordon Fleming (Jan 1980)
(Director)
Gordon Williams Limited, Glasgow . . . . .(p.981)
T: 0141 5853948
E: gordonfwilliams@hotmail.co.uk

WILLIAMS, Jennifer Ann (Nov 1995)
(Employee)
Clydesdale Bank Plc, Glasgow . . . .(p.1238)
T: 0141 2423725
E: jennifer.williams@cybg.com

WILLIAMS, Jonathan Graham Aitken
(Aug 1993) (Consultant)
Lindsays LLP, Glasgow . . . .(p.1001)
T: 0141 2216551
E: jonathanwilliams@lindsays.co.uk

WILLIAMS, Laura (Sept 2018) (Employee)
Law Society of Scotland,
Edinburgh . . . .(p.1224)
T: 0131 2267411
E: laurawilliams@lawscot.org.uk

WILLIAMS, Rowena Winifred (May 2016)
(Associate)
CMS Cameron McKenna Nabarro Olswang LLP,
Edinburgh . . . .(p.856)
T: 0131 2288000
E: rowena.williams@cms-cmno.com

WILLIAMS, Samuel (Sept 2019) (Employee)
Pinsent Masons LLP, Glasgow . . . .(p.1031)
T: 0141 567 8400
E: sam.williams@pinsentmasons.com

WILLIAMS, Simon Jonathan Conon
(Jan 2009) (Partner)
Gillespie Macandrew LLP,
Edinburgh . . . .(p.872)
T: 0131 260 7516
E: Simon.Williams@gillespiemacandrew.co.uk

WILLIAMS, Stephen (Apr 1982) (Associate)
McJerrow & Stevenson, Lockerbie . . . .(p.1122)
T: 01576 202123
E: sw@mcjerrowstevenson.co.uk

WILLIAMS, Suzanne (Oct 1999) (Associate)
Digby Brown LLP, Glasgow . . . .(p.970)
T: 0333 200 5925
E: suzanne.williams@digbybrown.co.uk

WILLIAMSON, Andrew Grant (Oct 1990)
(Employee)
City Law Firm Limited, London
WC1 . . . .(p.1262)
E: andrew.williamson@stjohnlegal.co.uk

WILLIAMSON, Charles Fraser Scott
(Nov 1978) (Consultant)
Blackadders LLP, Dundee. . . . .(p.805)
T: 01382 229222
E: scott.williamson@blackadders.co.uk

WILLIAMSON, Derick (Oct 1973) (Partner)
Derick Williamson & Co., East
Kilbride . . . .(p.832)
T: 01355 222337
E: derickwilliamsonandco@hotmail.co.uk

WILLIAMSON, Douglas Ian (Nov 2000)
(Partner)
Warners Solicitors LLP, Edinburgh. . . . . .(p.911)
T: 0131 6624747
E: dwilliamson@warnersllp.com

WILLIAMSON, Eric John, SSC (Dec 1981)
(Director)
JGW Legal Services Limited,
  Kinross . . . .(p.1098)
  T: 01577 862302
  E: e.williamson@jgwilson.co.uk

WILLIAMSON, John Greig (Dec 1996)
(Employee)
Vialex Limited, Edinburgh . . . .(p.1235)
  T: 0333 2400127
  E: greig.williamson@vialex.co.uk

WILLIAMSON, Lorna (Jul 2005) (Partner)
Energy Law Unlimited LLP,
  Glasgow. . . . .(p.974)
  T: 1412210276
  E: lwilliamson@elu-llp.com

WILLIAMSON, Nicholas David (Oct 2000)
(Employee)
Scottish Widows Limited,
  Edinburgh . . . .(p.1233)
  T: 0131 6557230
  E: nick.williamson@scottishwidows.co.uk

WILLIAMSON, Rachel Elizabeth (Aug 2019)
(Employee)
Red Rock Power Limited,
  Edinburgh . . . .(p.1230)
  T: 0131 5577101
  E: rachel.williamson@redrockpower.co.uk

WILLIAMSON, Simona Marie (Feb 2000)
(Employee)
Pinsent Masons LLP, Glasgow . . . .(p.1031)
  T: 0141 567 8400
  E: simona.williamson@pinsentmasons.com

WILLIAMSON, Stephen (Sept 1983)
(Consultant)
Holmes Mackillop Limited,
  Johnstone. . . . .(p.1089)
  T: 01505 328 271
  E: sw@homack.co.uk

WILLIAMSON, Thomas (Dec 1982) (Director)
Tom Williamson Limited, Paisley . . . . . .(p.1142)
  T: 0141 8899099
  E: tomwilliamson40@gmail.com

WILLIFORD, James Carlo (Jun 2004) (Employee)
Caesar & Howie, Alloa . . . .(p.752)
  T: 01259 815900
  E: jw@caesar-howie.co.uk

WILLOX, Keir (Aug 1994) (Partner)
Shepherd and Wedderburn LLP,
  Aberdeen . . . .(p.742)
  T: 01224 343542
  E: keir.willox@shepwedd.com

WILLS, Emma Marie (Jan 2021) (Employee)
SSE PLC, Glasgow . . . .(p.1244)
  T: 0141 224 7248
  E: emma.wills@sse.com

WILSON, Alan Alexander Slessor (Apr 1976)
(Consultant)
A.C. Morrison & Richards LLP,
  Aberdeen . . . .(p.737)
  T: 01224 573321
  E: awilson@acmr.co.uk

WILSON, Alexander Neil (Nov 1983)
(Associate)
Turcan Connell, Edinburgh . . . .(p.908)
  T: 0131 2288111
  E: Neil.Wilson@turcanconnell.com

WILSON, Alistair (Dec 2002) (Employee)
University of Glasgow, Glasgow . . . . . .(p.1245)
  T: (0141) 330 7725
  E: Alistair.Wilson@glasgow.ac.uk

WILSON, Amanda Anne (Aug 2006) (Partner)
Amanda Wilson Family Law,
  Dundee . . . .(p.821)
  T: 01382 219004
  E: amanda@amandawilsonfamilylaw.co.uk

WILSON, Andrew John Patterson (Dec 1985)
(Partner)
Wright, Johnston & Mackenzie LLP,
  Edinburgh . . . .(p.913)
  T: 0131 5241500
  E: ajpw@wjm.co.uk

WILSON, Anna May (Jul 2018) (Employee)
Office of the Advocate General,
  Edinburgh . . . .(p.1227)
  T: 0131 2441635
  E: anna.wilson@advocategeneral.gov.uk

WILSON, Aran Logan (Oct 2019) (Employee)
Bell & Craig Limited, Stirling . . . .(p.1164)
  T: 01786 470444
  E: aranwilson@bellandcraig.co.uk

WILSON, Bryan (Jun 2007) (Partner)
Brodies LLP, Aberdeen. . . . .(p.723)
  T: 01224 392242
  E: bryan.wilson@brodies.com

WILSON, Carol Ann (Sept 1996) (Employee)
National Westminster Bank PLC,
  Edinburgh . . . .(p.1226)
  T: (0131) 626 2925
  E: carol.c.wilson@rbs.co.uk

WILSON, Carole-Anne (Jan 2021) (Employee)
Moir and Sweeney LLP, Glasgow . . . . .(p.1021)
  T: 0141 4292724
  E: cwilson@moirandsweeney.com

WILSON, Caroline Macnee (Oct 1992)
(Associate)
CMS Cameron McKenna Nabarro Olswang LLP,
  Edinburgh . . . .(p.856)
  T: 0131 2288000
  E: Caroline.Wilson@cms-cmno.com

WILSON, Ciara Jane (Nov 2018) (Employee)
Turcan Connell, Edinburgh . . . .(p.908)
T: 0131 2288111
E: ciara.wilson@turcanconnell.com

WILSON, Claire Chisholm (Nov 2019)
(Employee)
Digby Brown LLP, Edinburgh . . . .(p.862)
T: 0333 200 5925
E: claire.wilson@digbybrown.co.uk

WILSON, Clare Louise (Aug 2009) (Associate)
Lindsays LLP, Glasgow . . . .(p.1001)
T: 0141 2216551
E: clarewilson@lindsays.co.uk

WILSON, Colin James (Sept 2017) (Employee)
Procurator Fiscal Service,
Edinburgh . . . .(p.1227)
T: 0300 0203168
E: Colin.Wilson@copfs.gov.uk

WILSON, Craig James (Jun 2010) (Associate)
CMS Cameron McKenna Nabarro Olswang LLP,
Aberdeen . . . .(p.727)
T: 01224 622002
E: Craig.wilson@cms-cmno.com

WILSON, Craig McKeever (Jan 2018)
(Employee)
DLA Piper Scotland LLP, Edinburgh . . . .(p.863)
T: 08700 111111
E: craig.wilson@dlapiper.com

WILSON, David (Oct 1984) (Employee)
Ennova Limited, Edinburgh . . . .(p.869)
T: 0131 6624555
E: dwilson@ennova-law.com

WILSON, David Alexander (Oct 1993) (Partner)
Digby Brown LLP, Glasgow . . . .(p.970)
T: 0333 200 5925
E: david.wilson@digbybrown.co.uk

WILSON, David Dalgleish (Oct 1996) (Partner)
MacRoberts LLP, Glasgow . . . .(p.1015)
T: 0141 3031100
E: david.wilson@macroberts.com

WILSON, Edward John (Nov 1988) (Partner)
Wilson McLeod, Edinburgh . . . .(p.912)
T: 0131 5560055
E: wilsonmcleod@btconnect.com

WILSON, Elizabeth Barbara (Jul 2017)
(Employee)
Murchison Law Limited, Inverness . . . .(p.1081)
T: 01463 709992
E: elizabeth@murchisonlaw.co.uk

WILSON, Euan Macdonald (Feb 1999)
(Employee)
Fitzpatrick & Co., Glasgow . . . .(p.976)
T: 0141 2042200
E: ew@fitzpatrickandco.co.uk

WILSON, Euan Robert (Oct 1994) (Partner)
Dentons UK and Middle East LLP,
Edinburgh . . . .(p.860)
T: 0330 2220050
E: Euan.Wilson@dentons.com

WILSON, Ewan Campbell (Oct 2019)
(Employee)
CMS Cameron McKenna Nabarro Olswang LLP,
Glasgow. . . . .(p.962)
T: 0141 2222200
E: ewan.wilson@cms-cmno.com

WILSON, Gillian Anne (Sept 2016) (Employee)
Gillespie Macandrew LLP,
Edinburgh . . . .(p.872)
T: 0131 2251677
E: Gillian.Wilson@gillespiemacandrew.co.uk

WILSON, Gina Mary (Nov 2003) (Employee)
Kellogg Brown & Root (U.K.) Limited,
Surrey . . . .(p.1272)

WILSON, Gordon Alexander (Nov 1990)
(Employee)
Office of the Advocate General,
Edinburgh . . . .(p.1227)
T: 0131 2441635
E: Gordon.Wilson@advocategeneral.gov.uk

WILSON, Gordon James (Jan 1992) (Employee)
Black & Veatch (UK) Limited,
Surrey . . . .(p.1272)
E: wilsong@bv.com

WILSON, Graham Alexander (Aug 1978)
(Partner)
Thorntons Law LLP, Dundee . . . .(p.819)
T: 01382 229 111
E: gwilson@thorntons-law.co.uk

WILSON, Graham James Arnott (Aug 2012)
(Employee)
Addleshaw Goddard LLP, Glasgow . . . . .(p.938)
T: 0141 2212300
E: Graham.Wilson@addleshawgoddard.com

WILSON, Hannah Elizabeth (Apr 2021)
(Employee)
Hunter & Robertson Limited,
Paisley . . . .(p.1138)
T: 0141 8893196
E: hannahwilson@hunter-robertson.co.uk

WILSON, Hayley Jane (Aug 2012) (Employee)
Farrer & Co LLP, London WC2. . . . . . .(p.1264)
E: hayley.wilson@farrer.co.uk

WILSON, Iain Collier (Oct 1995) (Partner)
Pomphreys, Wishaw . . . .(p.1182)
T: 01698 373365
E: icw@pomphreyslaw.com

WILSON, Iain Stuart (Dec 2004) (Employee)
Andersonbain LLP, Aberdeen . . . .(p.721)
T: 01224 456789
E: iain@andersonbain.co.uk

WILSON, James Gordon (Jan 2019) (Partner)
Dentons UK and Middle East LLP,
Edinburgh . . . . (p.860)
T: 0330 2220050
E: James.Wilson@dentons.com

WILSON, Jamie Campbell (Mar 2016)
(Employee)
Burness Paull LLP, Aberdeen . . . . (p.724)
T: 01224 618571
E: jamie.wilson@burnesspaull.com

WILSON, Jennifer Frances (Sept 2012)
(Employee)
Kirkland & Ellis International LLP, London
EC3 . . . . (p.1265)
T: 0207 4692000
E: jennifer.f.wilson@kirkland.com

WILSON, Joanne Lesley (Nov 2003) (Employee)
Morton Fraser LLP, Glasgow . . . . (p.1022)
T: 0141 2741100
E: Joanne.wilson@morton-Fraser.com

WILSON, John David (Mar 2010) (Solicitor)
NO FIRM

WILSON, Karen (Sept 2013) (Employee)
Procurator Fiscal Service,
Edinburgh . . . . (p.1227)
T: 0300 0203168
E: Karen.Wilson@copfs.gov.uk

WILSON, Katharine Anne (Sept 1998)
(Employee)
Primrose & Gordon, Dumfries . . . . (p.802)
T: 01387 267316
E: WilsonK@primroseandgordon.co.uk

WILSON, Katherine Jane (Aug 2009) (Partner)
Bilkus & Boyle, Glasgow . . . . (p.946)
T: 0141 8823221
E: kjwilson2101@yahoo.co.uk

WILSON, Kathryn Janet (Oct 1985) (Director)
Melrose & Porteous Limited, Duns . . . . . (p.829)
T: 01361 882 752
E: kathryn.wilson@melroseporteous.co.uk

WILSON, Kelsey Ann (Jul 2018) (Employee)
Andrew K. Price Limited, Kirkcaldy . . . . (p.1102)
T: 01592 205151
E: Kelsey@andrewkprice.co.uk

WILSON, Kirsty Anne (Feb 2010) (Employee)
Paris Steele, North Berwick . . . . (p.1133)
T: 01620 892138
E: kwilson@parissteele.com

WILSON, Kirsty Louisa (Feb 2020) (Employee)
Wavemaker UK, London SE1 . . . . (p.1269)

WILSON, Kristy Anne (Oct 2015) (Employee)
Aker Solutions Limited, Aberdeen . . . . . (p.1211)
T: 01224 255000
E: kristy.wilson@akersolutions.com

WILSON, Laura Ann (Jun 2010) (Employee)
Digby Brown LLP, Edinburgh . . . . (p.862)
T: 0333 200 5925
E: laura.wright@digbybrown.co.uk

WILSON, Laura Anne (Sept 2011) (Associate)
Pinsent Masons LLP, Edinburgh . . . . . . (p.895)
T: 0131 777 7000
E: Laura.Wilson@pinsentmasons.com

WILSON, Lauren (Jan 2020) (Employee)
Just Employment Law Ltd,
Glasgow . . . . (p.1240)
T: 0141 3315150

WILSON, Louise Elizabeth (Dec 2016)
(Employee)
McKean Gardner Limited, Perth . . . . . . (p.1150)
T: 01738 700240
E: louise@mckeangardner.co.uk

WILSON, Lynsey (Nov 2009) (Employee)
Virgin Money Plc, Edinburgh . . . . (p.1236)
T: 1316039349
E: Lynsey.Wilson@virginmoney.com

WILSON, Lynsey Jane (Mar 2016) (Employee)
BTO Solicitors LLP, Glasgow . . . . (p.952)
T: 0141 2218012

WILSON, Margaret Anne (Oct 1992) (Partner)
MacArthur Legal, Oban . . . . (p.1134)
T: 01631 562215
E: oban@macarthurstewart.co.uk

WILSON, Margaret Mary (Sept 1992)
(Employee)
SOUTH LANARKSHIREre Council,
Hamilton . . . . (p.1247)
T: 01698 454501
E:
margaretmary.cairns@southlanarkshire.gov.uk

WILSON, Mark Anthony (Oct 2002) (Employee)
Creative Scotland, Glasgow . . . . (p.1239)
T: 0330 3332000
E: Mark.Wilson@creativescotland.com

WILSON, Mark Jeremy (Aug 1990) (Director)
Wilson McKendrick Solicitors Limited,
Glasgow . . . . (p.1053)
T: 0141 2227950
E: markwilson@wilsonmckendrick.co.uk

WILSON, Melissa (Oct 2019) (Employee)
Patten & Prentice LLP, Greenock . . . . . (p.1062)
T: 01475 720306

WILSON, Michael Gordon (Sept 2010)
(Associate)
Keoghs Scotland LLP, Glasgow . . . . (p.996)
T: 0141 2380100
E: mwilson@keoghs.co.uk

WILSON, Natalie Aleesa (Jan 2003) (Employee)
Lloyds Banking Group Plc,
Edinburgh . . . .(p.1224)
T: (0131) 442 9579
E: natalie.wilson@lloydsbanking.com

WILSON, Neil Georg (Nov 1982) (Employee)
Kier Limited, Salford . . . .(p.1271)
E: neil.g.wilson@kier.co.uk

WILSON, Neil Munro (Sept 1996) (Partner)
Ferguson and Wilson, Inverness . . . . . .(p.1076)
T: 01463 222221
E: enquiries@fergusonandwilson.co.uk

WILSON, Peter George (Mar 1989) (Employee)
Sunny Hill Energy, London SW1 . . . . . .(p.1268)
E: Peter.Wilson@sunnyhillenergy.com

WILSON, Peter Urquhart (Nov 1989) (Partner)
Wilson Ward LLP, Edinburgh . . . .(p.913)
T: 0131 4677550
E: peter@wilsonward.co.uk

WILSON, Richard Laurie (Aug 2018)
(Employee)
Blackadders LLP, Dundee. . . . .(p.805)
T: 01382 229222
E: richard.wilson@blackadders.co.uk

WILSON, Robert Edward (Sept 2009)
(Associate)
Anderson Strathern LLP, Edinburgh . . . .(p.839)
T: 0131 2707700
E: robbie.wilson@andersonstrathern.co.uk

WILSON, Robert Patrick Malcolm, WS
(Apr 1993) (Partner)
CMS Cameron McKenna Nabarro Olswang LLP,
Edinburgh . . . .(p.856)
T: 0131 2288000
E: Rob.Wilson@cms-cmno.com

WILSON, Ruth Mary (Apr 2014) (Employee)
North Ayrshire Council, Irvine . . . .(p.1249)
T: 01294 324374
E: ruthwilson@north-ayrshire.gov.uk

WILSON, Simon Nicholas (Dec 1984)
(Employee)
Scottish National Investment Bank,
Edinburgh . . . .(p.1233)
E: simon.wilson@thebank.scot

WILSON, Siobhan (May 2014) (Employee)
East Renfrewshire Council, Giffnock . . .(p.1237)
T: 0141 5773040
E: Siobhan4.Wilson@eastrenfrewshire.gov.uk

WILSON, Stacey Louise (May 2014) (Director)
VMH Solicitors Limited, Edinburgh . . . . .(p.910)
T: 0131 6615911
E: stacey.wilson@vmh.co.uk

WILSON, Stuart Fraser (Nov 1989) (Director)
Macnairs & Wilson Limited, Paisley. . . .(p.1140)
T: 0141 887 5181
E: stuart.wilson@macnairswilson.co.uk

WILSON, Suzanne Elizabeth (Oct 1993)
(Employee)
Galliford Try, Edinburgh . . . .(p.1223)
T: 0131 3386002
E: Suzanne.Wilson@gallifordtry.co.uk

WILSON, Tracy Lynn (Aug 2001) (Partner)
Wilsons Solicitors, Inverkeithing . . . . . .(p.1075)
T: 01383 411533
E: admin@tlwilson.co.uk

WILSON, Wendy (Aug 2011) (Employee)
Procurator Fiscal Service, Glasgow . . . .(p.1241)
T: 0300 0203000
E: wendy.wilson@copfs.gov.uk

WILSON-MCCUISH, Deborah Anne
(Mar 1980) (Partner)
Wilson Defence, Banff . . . .(p.770)
T: 01261 819831
E: debbie@banffdefence.co.uk

WILTON, Owen Gibbons (Sept 2015)
(Employee)
Government Legal Department, London
SW1 . . . .(p.1264)
T: 020 7210 1476
E: Owen.Wilton@governmentlegal.gov.uk

WINDRAM, William James (Apr 1985) (Partner)
Pike & Chapman, Galashiels . . . .(p.933)
T: 01896 752379
E: gala@pikeandchapman.co.uk

WINDSOR, Sarah Rosalie (Sept 2009)
(Employee)
Inksters, Inverness . . . .(p.1078)
T: 01463 210333
E: sarah@inksters.com

WINNING, Peter (Feb 1990) (Partner)
Winning & Co, Edinburgh . . . .(p.913)
T: 07957 095973
E: winningpeter@gmail.com

WINSKILL, Donald (May 2001) (Associate)
Gillespie Macandrew LLP,
Edinburgh . . . .(p.872)
T: 0131 2251677
E: donald.winskill@gillespiemacandrew.co.uk

WINTER, Sarah Jane (Jan 2008) (Employee)
Blackadders LLP, Dundee. . . . .(p.805)
T: 01382 229222
E: sarah.winter@blackadders.co.uk

WINTERS, Graham Campbell (Oct 1999)
(Solicitor)
NO FIRM

WINTERS, Kevin John (Sept 2016) (Employee)
Brodies LLP, Glasgow . . . .(p.948)
T: 0141 2484672
E: kevin.winters@brodies.com

WINTERS, Lauren Ashley (Mar 2013)
(Associate)
Burges Salmon LLP, Edinburgh ....(p.850)
   T: 0131 3142112
   E: Lauren.Winters@burges-salmon.com

WINTON, Andrew Scott (Nov 2012)
(Employee)
Shepherd and Wedderburn LLP,
   Glasgow......................(p.1039)
   T: 0141 5669900
   E: andrew.winton@shepwedd.com

WIPAT, Angela Patricia (Mar 1996) (Associate)
Thorntons Law LLP, Perth ....(p.1151)
   T: 01738 621212
   E: awipat@thorntons-law.co.uk

WISCHIK, Marcus Augustine (Sept 2010)
(Employee)
TauRx Therapeutics Ltd, Aberdeen ....(p.1214)
   T: (01224) 440911
   E: marcus@taurx.com

WISE, Melvyn (Dec 1979) (Partner)
Mel Wise, Glasgow..............(p.1053)
   T: 0141 6393059
   E: melwise100@hotmail.com

WISELY, Iain Robertson (Sept 2002) (Employee)
Chivas Brothers Limited,
   Dumbarton ....(p.1217)
   T: 01389 723 425
   E: iain.wisely@pernod-ricard.com

WISELY, Lesley Ann (Sept 2000) (Employee)
Brodies LLP, Edinburgh ....(p.845)
   T: 0131 2283777
   E: lesley.wisely@brodies.com

WISELY, Norman Sinclair (Sept 2000) (Partner)
CMS Cameron McKenna Nabarro Olswang LLP,
   Aberdeen ....(p.727)
   T: 01224 622002
   E: norman.wisely@cms-cmno.com

WISEMAN, Eilidh Ann Campbell (Nov 1987)
(Solicitor)
NO FIRM

WISHART, Alan Michael (Sept 2010)
(Employee)
The Royal Bank of Scotland PLC,
   Edinburgh ....(p.1235)
   E: alan.wishart@natwesttds.com

WISHART, Frances Jane (Jan 2000) (Partner)
Wisharts Law LLP, Glasgow ....(p.1054)
   T: 0141 370 0342
   E: frances.wishart@wishartslaw.co.uk

WISHART, Iain Andrew Fraser (Sept 2005)
(Partner)
Shepherd and Wedderburn LLP,
   Edinburgh ....(p.900)
   T: 0131 2289900
   E: iain.wishart@shepwedd.com

WISHART, Jill Evelyn (Oct 2010) (Employee)
Clydesdale Bank Plc, Glasgow ....(p.1238)
   T: 0141 2423733
   E: jill.wishart@cybg.com

WISHART, Paul Edward Ferguson
(Oct 1999) (Employee)
Shetland Islands Council, Lerwick.....(p.1250)
   T: 01595 744550
   E: paul.wishart@shetland.gov.uk

WISHART, Robert Westwood (Nov 1978)
(Partner)
Wisharts Law LLP, Glasgow ....(p.1054)
   T: 0141 370 0342
   E: robbie.wishart@wishartslaw.co.uk

WITHERS, Claire Emma (Jul 2018) (Solicitor)
NO FIRM

WITHEYMAN, Iain Alvin (May 2014)
(Employee)
DAC Beachcroft Scotland LLP,
   Glasgow......................(p.964)
   T: 0141 2486688
   E: iwitheyman@dacbeachcroft.com

WITTY, Barbara (Oct 1985) (Associate)
McJerrow & Stevenson, Lockerbie ....(p.1122)
   T: 01576 202123
   E: bw@mcjerrowstevenson.co.uk

WLOCHAL, Magdalena Barbara (Sept 2017)
(Employee)
Digby Brown LLP, Edinburgh ....(p.862)
   T: 0333 200 5925
   E:
   magdalena.wlochal-suchara@digbybrown.co.
   uk

WOLFE, Limor (Apr 2012) (Partner)
Harper Macleod LLP, Glasgow ....(p.983)
   T: 0141 2218888
   E: limor.wolfe@harpermacleod.co.uk

WOLSTENHOLME, Catriona Louise
(Apr 2011) (Employee)
John Menzies Plc, Edinburgh ....(p.1224)
   E:
   catriona.wolstenholme@johnmenziesplc.com

WOLSTENHOLME, Suzanna Margaret
(Aug 2009) (Employee)
EDF Energy Renewables,
   Edinburgh ....(p.1222)
   T: 07875 112 317
   E: Suzanna.Wolstenholme@edf-re.uk

WOMERSLEY, Gary Stuart (Sept 1995)
(Employee)
Student Loans Company Limited,
   Glasgow....................(p.1245)
   T: 0141 306 2000
   E: Gary_Womersley@slc.co.uk

WONG, Anita Oi Liun (Jul 2016) (Employee)
CMS Cameron McKenna Nabarro Olswang LLP,
 Edinburgh ....(p.856)
 T: 0131 2288000
 E: Anita.Wong@cms-cmno.com

WONG, Jade Wendy (Jan 2020) (Employee)
Scottish Social Services Council,
 Dundee ....(p.1218)
 T: 0345 6030 891
 E: jade.wong@sssc.uk.com

WOOD, Alistair Kerr (Sept 2016) (Employee)
Pinsent Masons LLP, Edinburgh ....(p.895)
 T: 0131 777 7000
 E: alistair.wood@pinsentmasons.com

WOOD, Angus Robert (Oct 2008) (Partner)
BTO Solicitors LLP, Glasgow ....(p.952)
 T: 0141 2218012
 E: arw@bto.co.uk

WOOD, Benjamin David (Sept 2019) (Solicitor)
NO FIRM

WOOD, Beverley (Feb 2002) (Partner)
Morton Fraser LLP, Edinburgh ....(p.891)
 T: 0131 2471000
 E: beverley.wood@morton-fraser.com

WOOD, David George (Oct 1990) (Partner)
Lindsays LLP, Edinburgh ....(p.882)
 T: 0131 2291212
 E: davidwood@lindsays.co.uk

WOOD, David Gordon (Feb 1985) (Partner)
F.T. & D.C. Wallace, Leven..........(p.1116)
 T: 01333 423804
 E: g.wood@ft-dc-wallace.co.uk

WOOD, Eilidh Elspeth (Sept 2018) (Employee)
Burges Salmon LLP, Edinburgh ....(p.850)
 T: 0131 3142148
 E: Eilidh.Wood@burges-salmon.com

WOOD, Emma Jane (Jul 2013) (Associate)
Morton Fraser LLP, Edinburgh ....(p.891)
 T: 0131 2471000
 E: emma.wood@morton-fraser.com

WOOD, Gillian (Oct 2005) (Associate)
Shoosmiths, Edinburgh ....(p.902)
 T: 03700 868000
 E: gillian.wood@shoosmiths.co.uk

WOOD, Kieran Donald (Feb 2021) (Employee)
CMS Cameron McKenna Nabarro Olswang LLP,
 Glasgow....................(p.962)
 T: 0141 2222200
 E: kieran.wood@cms-cmno.com

WOOD, Kingsley William Alexander
 (Nov 1985) (Director)
Kingsley Wood & Co Solicitors Limited,
 Kilmacolm ....(p.1093)
 T: 01505 874114
 E: kw@kingsleywood.co.uk

WOOD, Michael Fenwick (Jan 2004) (Partner)
Burness Paull LLP, Glasgow ....(p.954)
 T: 0141 2484933
 E: Michael.Wood@burnesspaull.com

WOOD, Rachel Mary (Nov 1994) (Employee)
Law Society of Scotland,
 Edinburgh ....(p.1224)
 T: 0131 2267411
 E: rachelwood@lawscot.org.uk

WOOD, Robert Bruce, CVO, WS (Nov 1976)
 (Consultant)
Morton Fraser LLP, Edinburgh ....(p.891)
 T: 0131 2471000
 E: bruce.wood@morton-fraser.com

WOOD, Shawn Ross (Jul 2016) (Employee)
Watermans Legal Limited,
 Edinburgh ....(p.911)
 T: 0131 4675566
 E: ShawnWood@watermanslegal.co.uk

WOODBURN, Kenneth David (May 2011)
 (Employee)
Keith Leishman & Co Defence,
 Edinburgh ....(p.882)
 T: 07590 315434
 E: kwleishmandefence@outlook.com

WOODCOCK, Brian (Feb 1990) (Employee)
Dundee City Council, Dundee ....(p.1217)
 T: 01382 434000
 E: brian.woodcock@dundeecity.gov.uk

WOODGER, Cassandra Maisie (Sept 2020)
 (Employee)
Watermans Solicitors Limited,
 Edinburgh ....(p.912)
 T: 0131 5557055
 E: CassandraWoodger@watermans.co.uk

WOODS, Alison Helen (Aug 2001) (Partner)
CMS Cameron McKenna Nabarro Olswang LLP,
 Aberdeen ....(p.727)
 T: 01224 622002
 E: alison.woods@cms-cmno.com

WOODS, Dr, Brian Andrew (Jul 2021)
 (Employee)
Turcan Connell, Edinburgh ....(p.908)
 T: 0131 2288111
 E: brian.woods@turcanconnell.com

WOODS, David James (Jan 2001) (Partner)
Pinsent Masons LLP, Glasgow ....(p.1031)
 T: 0141 567 8400
 E: david.woods@pinsentmasons.com

WOODS, Dylan William (Jul 2021) (Employee)
Bell Legal Limited, Kilmarnock ....(p.1093)
 T: 01563 535545
 E: dwoods@bell-co.co.uk

WOODS, Kirsty Sarah (Nov 2007) (Employee)
Dickson Minto, Edinburgh . . . .(p.861)
　　T: 0131 2254455
　　E: kirsty.woods@dmws.com

WOODWARD, Claire Elizabeth (Sept 2009)
(Employee)
Ledingham Chalmers LLP,
　Aberdeen . . . .(p.734)
　　T: 01224 408408
　　E: claire.woodward@ledinghamchalmers.com

WOODWARD, Gillian Christine (Feb 2002)
(Associate)
Pinsent Masons LLP, Edinburgh . . . .(p.895)
　　T: 0131 777 7000
　　E: gillian.woodward@pinsentmasons.com

WOODWARD, James Stephen (Aug 2002)
(Associate)
Addleshaw Goddard LLP,
　Edinburgh . . . .(p.835)
　　T: 0131 2282400
　　E: james.woodward@addleshawgoddard.com

WOODWARD-NUTT, Ian James (Nov 1991)
(Partner)
Woodward Lawson, Aberdeen . . . .(p.747)
　　T: 01224 619330
　　E: ian@woodwardlawson.com

WOOLFSON, Giles Ian (Aug 1998) (Director)
McGrade & Co Limited, Glasgow . . . . .(p.1011)
　　T: 0141 2214488
　　E: gwoolfson@mcgrade.co.uk

WOOTON, Karen (Nov 2000) (Employee)
Gillespie Macandrew LLP, Glasgow . . . . .(p.979)
　　T: 0141 4735555
　　E: Karen.wooton@gillespiemacandrew.co.uk

WORTHINGTON, Christine Ellen (Jan 1998)
(Partner)
CMS Cameron McKenna Nabarro Olswang LLP,
　Glasgow. . . . .(p.962)
　　T: 0141 2222200
　　E: christine.worthington@cms-cmno.com

WORTLEY, Heather (May 2001) (Employee)
Scottish Government's Parliamentary Counsel
　Office, Edinburgh . . . .(p.1233)
　　T: 0131 244 2950
　　E: heather.wortley@gov.scot

WOSIAK, Izabela Dominika (Aug 2016)
(Employee)
Digby Brown LLP, Edinburgh . . . .(p.862)
　　T: 0333 200 5925
　　E: Izabela.Wosiak@digbybrown.co.uk

WOTHERSPOON, James Robert Edwards, WS
(Dec 1979) (Director)
Macandrew & Jenkins, WS Limited,
　Inverness . . . .(p.1079)
　　T: 01463 723500
　　E: james@macandrewjenkins.co.uk

WOTHERSPOON, Jonathan Lawrence Edwards
(Nov 1984) (Director)
Macandrew & Jenkins, WS Limited,
　Inverness . . . .(p.1079)
　　T: 01463 723500
　　E: Jonathan@macandrewjenkins.co.uk

WOTHERSPOON, Karen Isabella (Mar 2016)
(Employee)
McSherry Halliday LLP, Kilmarnock . . . .(p.1096)
　　T: 01563 533121
　　E: kw@mcsherryhalliday.co.uk

WOWK, Alison (Oct 2008) (Employee)
Barclays Bank PLC, London E14 . . . . . .(p.1262)
　　T: 020 7116 4355
　　E: alison.wowk@barclays.com

WOWK, Nicholas James Alexander
(Oct 2008) (Employee)
Deloitte LLP, London EC4 . . . .(p.1263)
　　T: 0207 0072147
　　E: jwowk@deloitte.co.uk

WRAIGHT, Wendy Anne (Oct 2008) (Associate)
Addleshaw Goddard LLP,
　Edinburgh . . . .(p.835)
　　T: 0131 2282400
　　E: Wendy.Wraight@addleshawgoddard.com

WRAY, Zoe Hunter (Mar 2009) (Employee)
Brodies LLP, Glasgow . . . .(p.948)
　　T: 0141 2484672
　　E: zoe.wray@brodies.com

WRIGHT, Alan Martin (Jul 2005) (Employee)
Glasgow City Council, Glasgow . . . . . .(p.1239)
　　T: 0141 2873892
　　E: alan.wright@ced.glasgow.gov.uk

WRIGHT, Amanda Deborah Tracey
(Sept 2006) (Employee)
Aberdeen Corporate Services Limited,
　Edinburgh . . . .(p.1220)
　　T: 0131 245 7508
　　E: amanda.wright@abrdn.com

WRIGHT, Andrew (Nov 2008) (Employee)
Glasgow City Council, Glasgow . . . . . .(p.1239)
　　T: 0141 2870483
　　E: andrew.wright@glasgow.gov.uk

WRIGHT, Caitlin Elizabeth (Aug 2021)
(Employee)
Brodies LLP, Edinburgh . . . .(p.845)
　　T: 0131 2283777
　　E: caitlin.wright@brodies.com

WRIGHT, Carrie (May 2016) (Employee)
Blackwood & Smith LLP, Peebles . . . . .(p.1143)
　　T: 01721 720131
　　E: carrie@blackwoodsmith.com

WRIGHT, Donald James (Sept 1983) (Partner)
Notary.Scot, Edinburgh . . . .(p.894)
　　T: 07947 232353
　　E: donaldwright@notary.scot

WRIGHT, Edmund (Sept 2004) (Director)
Black and McCorry Limited,
Livingston . . . . (p.1118)
T: 01506 467823
E: ed@blackandmccorry.co.uk

WRIGHT, Eilidh Ann (Oct 2008) (Employee)
Procurator Fiscal Service, Aberdeen . . . (p.1213)
T: 0300 0202336
E: eilidh.wright@copfs.gov.uk

WRIGHT, Emily Heather (Jan 2021) (Employee)
Stronachs LLP, Aberdeen . . . . (p.744)
T: 01224 845845
E: emily.wright@stronachs.com

WRIGHT, Emma Elizabeth (Nov 2020)
(Employee)
Scullion Law Limited, Hamilton . . . . . . (p.1069)
T: 01698 283265
E: emmaw@scullionlaw.com

WRIGHT, Fiona Marion (Dec 2003) (Employee)
Ofgem, Glasgow . . . . (p.1241)
T: (0141) 354 5425
E: fiona.wright@ofgem.gov.uk

WRIGHT, Gillian Jane (Oct 2012) (Partner)
Gillespie Macandrew LLP,
Edinburgh . . . . (p.872)
T: 0131 2251677
E: gillian.wright@gillespiemacandrew.co.uk

WRIGHT, Graeme (Jun 1993) (Director)
Westcourts Litigation Ltd,
Greenock . . . . (p.1063)
T: 01475 601999
E: info@westcourts.co.uk

WRIGHT, Jennifer Catherine (Nov 2011)
(Associate)
Shoosmiths LLP, Glasgow . . . . (p.1040)
T: 0370 086 8190
E: Jennifer.Wright@shoosmiths.co.uk

WRIGHT, Kathryn Alice (May 2021) (Employee)
Munro & Noble, Dingwall . . . . (p.797)
T: 01349 866777
E: kathrynw@munronoble.com

WRIGHT, Laura Fiona (Sept 2012) (Employee)
TSB Bank Plc, Edinburgh . . . . (p.1235)
T: 0131 260 5072
E: laura.wright@tsb.co.uk

WRIGHT, Lauren Marie (Dec 2012) (Associate)
Grigor & Young LLP, Elgin . . . . (p.916)
T: 01343 544077
E: Lauren@grigor-young.co.uk

WRIGHT, Maeve Flora Agnes (Sept 2020)
(Solicitor)
NO FIRM

WRIGHT, Stephanie Jennifer (Jun 2016)
(Solicitor)
NO FIRM

WRIGHT, Stephen (Sept 2010) (Employee)
The Scottish Parliament, Edinburgh . . . (p.1235)
T: 0131 348 6631
E: stephen.wright@parliament.scot

WRIGHT, Stephen Stewart (Oct 2007)
(Employee)
Wheatley Housing Group Limited,
Glasgow . . . . (p.1246)
T: 0845 9001001
E: Stephen.Wright@wheatley-group.com

WRIGHT, Thomas Ross (Nov 2020) (Employee)
Addleshaw Goddard LLP,
Edinburgh . . . . (p.835)
T: 0131 2282400
E: thomas.wright@addleshawgoddard.com

WRIGHT, Victoria Catherine (May 2018)
(Employee)
Thorntons Law LLP, Edinburgh . . . . (p.906)
T: 0131 2258705
E: vwright@thorntons-law.co.uk

WRIGHT-DAVIES, Shannon Louise
(Nov 2021) (Employee)
Innes Johnston LLP, Kirkcaldy . . . . (p.1100)
T: 01592 263455
E: swright-davies@innesjohnston.co.uk

WYATT, Katherine Jane (Feb 2013) (Partner)
Lindsays LLP, Dundee . . . . (p.814)
T: 01382 224112
E: katewyatt@lindsays.co.uk

WYLES, Shirley Anne (Nov 1994) (Employee)
Berrymans Lace Mawer LLP,
Edinburgh . . . . (p.842)
T: 0131 2259855
E: Shirley.Wyles@blmlaw.com

WYLIE, David John (Dec 2002) (Partner)
MacRoberts LLP, Edinburgh . . . . (p.887)
T: 0131 248 2228
E: david.wylie@macroberts.com

WYLIE, Duncan James (Aug 2008) (Employee)
Scottish Environment Protection Agency,
Edinburgh . . . . (p.1230)
T: 0131 4497296
E: Duncan.Wylie@sepa.org.uk

WYLIE, Jennifer Marie (Jun 2009) (Employee)
CALA Group Ltd, Edinburgh . . . . (p.1221)
T: 0131 4530075
E: jwylie@cala.co.uk

WYLIE, Karen Sandra (Sept 2005) (Associate)
Morton Fraser LLP, Glasgow . . . . (p.1022)
T: 0141 2741100
E: karen.wylie@morton-fraser.com

WYLIE, Laura Christina (Oct 2007) (Employee)
Sheku Bayoh Public Inquiry,
Edinburgh . . . . (p.1233)
E: laura.wylie@shekubayohinquiry.scot

WYLIE, Sarah Jane (Jul 2008) (Employee)
Dickson Minto, Edinburgh . . . . (p.861)
   T: 0131 2254455
   E: Sarah.Wylie@dmws.com

WYLLIE, Gordon Malcolm, WS (Nov 1974)
   (Solicitor)
NO FIRM

WYLLIE, Natasha Rosalind (Nov 2019)
   (Employee)
Ergo Law Limited, Edinburgh . . . . (p.869)
   T: 0131 618 7007

WYNN, Kathryn Ann (Feb 2003) (Partner)
Pinsent Masons LLP, Edinburgh . . . . (p.895)
   T: 0131 777 7000
   E: kathryn.wynn@pinsentmasons.com

WYNNE, Judith (Jan 1990) (Employee)
Wynne Associates Limited, Dalgety
   Bay . . . . (p.1216)
   T: 01383 829312
   E: jw3039@hotmail.co.uk

WYPER, Alastair Blackwood (Sept 1993)
   (Partner)
Blackwood Partners LLP, Aberdeen . . . . . (p.723)
   T: 01224 446230
   E: alastair.wyper@blackwood-partners.com

WYPER, James Scott (Oct 2005) (Partner)
BTO Solicitors LLP, Glasgow . . . . (p.952)
   T: 0141 2218012
   E: swy@bto.co.uk

WYPER, Stephen (Oct 2018) (Employee)
Morton Fraser LLP, Glasgow . . . . (p.1022)
   T: 0141 2741100
   E: stephen.wyper@morton-fraser.com

WYSE, Andrew George (Nov 1972) (Employee)
Angus Council, Forfar . . . . (p.1237)
   T: 01307 476228

XIA, Wenzhuo (Jul 2014) (Employee)
Pinsent Masons LLP, Edinburgh . . . . (p.895)
   T: 0131 777 7106
   E: Wenzhuo.Xia@pinsentmasons.com

YASIN, Aziz (Jan 2020) (Employee)
Morton Fraser LLP, Glasgow . . . . (p.1022)
   T: 0141 2741100
   E: Aziz.Yasin@morton-fraser.com

YASSIN, Omar Adam (Mar 2016) (Employee)
BNP Paribas, Glasgow . . . . (p.1238)

YASSIN, Rebecca Margaret Catherine
   (Sept 2015) (Associate)
MacRoberts LLP, Edinburgh . . . . (p.887)
   T: 0131 2295046
   E: rebecca.yassin@macroberts.com

YATES, Eilidh MacDougall (Jul 2010)
   (Employee)
Procurator Fiscal Service,
   Edinburgh . . . . (p.1229)
   T: 0300 0203000
   E: Eilidh.Yates@copfs.gov.uk

YEATS, Jennifer Alice (Mar 2013) (Employee)
Gilson Gray LLP, Edinburgh . . . . (p.874)
   T: 0131 5165354
   E: jyeats@gilsongray.co.uk

YELLOWLEES, Michael James (Jan 1995)
   (Partner)
Lindsays LLP, Edinburgh . . . . (p.882)
   T: 0131 2291212
   E: michaelyellowlees@lindsays.co.uk

YELLOWLEES, Morag Wilson (Dec 1990)
   (Partner)
Lindsays LLP, Edinburgh . . . . (p.882)
   T: 0131 2291212
   E: moragyellowlees@lindsays.co.uk

YEOMAN, Graeme Douglas (Nov 1984)
   (Partner)
Stirling & Gilmour LLP, Alexandria . . . . . (p.752)
   T: 01389 722700
   E: g.yeoman@stirlingandgilmour.co.uk

YEUNG, Fiona Pei Shan (Aug 2011) (Solicitor)
NO FIRM

YEUNG, Kwan-Nga (Nov 2006) (Associate)
Allingham & Co (Solicitors) Limited,
   Edinburgh . . . . (p.838)
   T: 0131 4479341
   E: kwannga@allingham.co.uk

YORK, Alison Margaret (Nov 1994) (Employee)
Scottish Environment Protection Agency,
   Edinburgh . . . . (p.1230)
   T: 0131 4497296
   E: alison.york@sepa.org.uk

YOUNES, Samir (Jul 2017) (Employee)
Burges Salmon LLP, Edinburgh . . . . (p.850)
   T: 0131 3142112
   E: samir.younes@burges-salmon.com

YOUNG, Aimee Louise (Nov 2021) (Employee)
Macnabs LLP, Perth . . . . (p.1150)
   T: 01738 623432
   E: aimeeyoung@macnabs-law.co.uk

YOUNG, Alexander Craig (Oct 1995)
   (Employee)
East Ayrshire Council, Kilmarnock . . . . . (p.1249)
   T: 01563 576161
   E: craig.young@east-ayrshire.gov.uk

YOUNG, Alison Elizabeth (Aug 1989)
   (Employee)
Procurator Fiscal Service, Inverness . . . . (p.1248)
   T: 0844 5612926
   E: Alison.Young@copfs.gov.uk

YOUNG, Amy Maree (Feb 2014) (Solicitor)
NO FIRM

YOUNG, Brian Alexander (Sept 2020)
(Employee)
Procurator Fiscal Service,
Edinburgh . . . . (p.1227)
T: 0300 0203168
E: brian.young@copfs.gov.uk

YOUNG, Ciara Jayne (Dec 2020) (Employee)
Clarity Simplicity Ltd, Glasgow . . . . (p.960)
T: 0141 4332626
E: c.young@claritysimplicity.co.uk

YOUNG, Colin Forrest Graham (Oct 1987)
(Partner)
Anderson Strathern LLP, Glasgow . . . . . . (p.940)
T: 0141 2426060
E: colin.young@andersonstrathern.co.uk

YOUNG, David Allan (Oct 2005) (Partner)
BTO Solicitors LLP, Glasgow . . . . (p.952)
T: 0141 2218012
E: dyo@bto.co.uk

YOUNG, David Andrew (Oct 2001) (Partner)
Pinsent Masons LLP, Edinburgh . . . . (p.895)
T: 0131 777 7000
E: david.young@pinsentmasons.com

YOUNG, Gordon Taylor (Jun 1975) (Employee)
Wilkie & Dundas, Kirriemuir . . . . (p.1107)
T: 01575 572608
E: gty@wdws.co.uk

YOUNG, Graeme Keith Perkin (Nov 1997)
(Partner)
CMS Cameron McKenna Nabarro Olswang LLP,
Edinburgh . . . . (p.856)
T: 0131 2288000
E: Graeme.Young@cms-cmno.com

YOUNG, Iain Mackenzie (May 2006) (Partner)
Morton Fraser LLP, Edinburgh . . . . (p.891)
T: 0131 2471000
E: iain.young@morton-fraser.com

YOUNG, Ian Brian (Sept 1995) (Employee)
Scottish Government's Parliamentary Counsel
Office, Edinburgh . . . . (p.1233)
T: 0131 244 7393
E: Ian.Young@gov.scot

YOUNG, Jacqueline May (Aug 1993) (Partner)
The MFY Partnership, Airdrie . . . . (p.751)
T: 01236 607180
E: jackie@mfypartnership.co.uk

YOUNG, James Hugh Durham (Oct 1974)
(Employee)
Charles Wood & Son Limited,
Kirkcaldy . . . . (p.1103)
T: 01592 261621
E: jim@charleswoodlaw.co.uk

YOUNG, Jane Elizabeth (Oct 1989) (Director)
Innes & Mackay Limited, Inverness . . . . (p.1078)
T: 01463 232273
E: janey@innesmackay.com

YOUNG, Jennifer Evelyn (Feb 1993) (Partner)
Ledingham Chalmers LLP,
Aberdeen . . . . (p.734)
T: 01224 408408
E: jennifer.young@ledinghamchalmers.com

YOUNG, John Craik (Jul 2015) (Associate)
Brodies LLP, Edinburgh . . . . (p.845)
T: 0131 2283777
E: john.young@brodies.com

YOUNG, Julie Margaret (Jul 2004) (Partner)
T. Duncan & Co., Montrose . . . . (p.1125)
T: 01674 672533
E: julie@tduncan.com

YOUNG, Kirsten (Aug 2020) (Employee)
Dentons UK and Middle East LLP,
Glasgow . . . . (p.968)
T: 0330 2220050
E: kirsten.young@dentons.com

YOUNG, Madeleine Clare (Oct 2007)
(Associate)
CMS Cameron McKenna Nabarro Olswang LLP,
Glasgow . . . . (p.962)
T: 0141 304 6295
E: madeleine.young@cms-cmno.com

YOUNG, Michelle (Jul 2021) (Associate)
Carey Olsen, St Peter Port . . . . (p.1273)
T: (+44) 1481 741505
E: michelle.young@careyolsen.com

YOUNG, Michelle Dunnington (Oct 2005)
(Employee)
Digby Brown LLP, Edinburgh . . . . (p.862)
T: 0333 200 5925
E: michelle.young@digbybrown.co.uk

YOUNG, Nairn Robert (Sept 2008) (Employee)
Renfrewshire Council, Paisley . . . . (p.1252)
T: 0141 8403648
E: nairn.young@renfrewshire.gov.uk

YOUNG, Nicholas James (Jun 2018) (Employee)
Vialex Limited, Edinburgh . . . . (p.1235)
T: 0333 2400127
E: nicky.young@vialex.co.uk

YOUNG, Paul James (Sept 2010) (Partner)
Dentons UK and Middle East LLP,
Glasgow . . . . (p.968)
T: 0330 2220050
E: paul.young@dentons.com

YOUNG, Peter McLew (Sept 1986) (Partner)
Wilsone & Duffus, Aberdeen . . . . (p.746)
T: 01224 251100
E: peter.young@key-moves.co.uk

YOUNG, Rebecca Louise (Apr 2009) (Employee)
Enquest Britain Limited, Aberdeen . . . . (p.1212)
T: 01224 975000
E: rebecca.young@enquest.com

YOUNG, Shona Anne (Sept 2016) (Employee)
Gilson Gray LLP, Edinburgh . . . . (p.874)
T: 0131 5165354
E: syoung@gilsongray.co.uk

YOUNG, Simone Gabriella (Nov 1994)
(Employee)
Davidson Chalmers Stewart LLP,
Edinburgh . . . . (p.859)
T: 0131 6259191
E: simone.young@dcslegal.com

YOUNG, Stephanie Louise (Aug 2017)
(Employee)
Thompsons, Glasgow . . . . (p.1046)
T: 0141 2218840
E: stephanie.young@thompsons-scotland.co.uk

YOUNG, Tamara Lawson (Oct 2017)
(Employee)
Burness Paull LLP, Glasgow . . . . (p.954)
T: 0141 2484933
E: tamara.young@burnesspaull.com

YOUNG, William Buchanan (Jul 1991) (Partner)
Alex. Brown & Co., Inverness . . . . . . (p.1075)
T: 01463 243450
E: mail@alexbrownandco.com

YOUNG, William David (Jan 2012) (Employee)
Solicitors Direct, Aberdeen. . . . . (p.743)
T: 01224 327 437
E: willie@solicitorsdirect.info

YOUNG, William James (Sept 2013) (Employee)
Burness Paull LLP, Edinburgh . . . . (p.850)
T: 0131 4736000
E: liam.young@burnesspaull.com

YOUNGER, Hugh Patrick, WS (Dec 1981)
(Partner)
Murray Beith Murray, Edinburgh . . . . . . (p.893)
T: 0131 2251200
E: hugh.younger@murraybeith.co.uk

YOUNGER, Jennifer (Nov 2005) (Associate)
Turcan Connell, Edinburgh . . . . (p.908)
T: 0131 2288111
E: jennifer.younger@turcanconnell.com

YOUNGER, Robert William (Mar 2009)
(Employee)
Fish Legal, Leominster. . . . . (p.1260)
T: 0131 5564462
E: robert.younger@fishlegal.net

YOUNGER, Rose Elizabeth (Aug 2021)
(Employee)
Turcan Connell, Edinburgh . . . . (p.908)
T: 0131 2288111
E: rose.younger@turcanconnell.com

YOUNGER, Susan Emma (Nov 1989) (Solicitor)
NO FIRM

YOUNGSON, Laura (Nov 2007) (Partner)
Andersonbain LLP, Aberdeen . . . . (p.721)
T: 01224 456789
E: lyoungson@andersonbain.co.uk

YOUNIE, Lindsay Claire (Sept 1999) (Employee)
National Westminster Bank PLC,
Edinburgh . . . . (p.1226)
T: (0131) 626 2925
E: lindsay.younie@rbs.co.uk

YOUSAF, Azrah (Dec 1996) (Employee)
Procurator Fiscal Service,
Dunfermline . . . . (p.1219)
T: 3000203000
E: azrah.yousaf@copfs.gov.uk

YOUSAF, Tahirah Khalid (Nov 2008)
(Employee)
Digby Brown LLP, Edinburgh . . . . (p.862)
T: 0333 200 5925
E: tahirah.yousaf@digbybrown.co.uk

YUILE, Zoe Cassandra (Jul 2018) (Employee)
Burness Paull LLP, Edinburgh . . . . (p.850)
T: 0131 4736000
E: zoe.yuile@burnesspaull.com

YUILL, Christine Wilson (Sept 2004) (Partner)
Pinsent Masons LLP, Glasgow . . . . . . (p.1031)
T: 0141 567 8400
E: christine.yuill@pinsentmasons.com

YUILL, Kirsty Anne (Jan 2003) (Associate)
Berrymans Lace Mawer LLP,
Glasgow. (p.945)
T: 0141 3532121
E: Kirsty.Yuill@blmlaw.com

YUILL, Ross John James (Aug 2002) (Director)
Carr & Co (Solicitors) Limited,
Glasgow. (p.957)
T: 0141 6412912/8346
E: ry@theglasgowlawpractice.co.uk

YUILLE, Alan David (Sept 2009) (Employee)
Baillie Gifford & Co, Edinburgh . . . . . . (p.1220)
T: 0131 2752000
E: Alan.Yuille@bailliegifford.com

YUILLE, Viki Louise (Oct 2000) (Employee)
Procurator Fiscal Service,
Edinburgh . . . . (p.1229)
T: 0300 0203000
E: viki.yuille@copfs.gov.uk

YULE, Andrew Derrick (Sept 2003) (Employee)
Blackadders LLP, Edinburgh . . . . (p.843)
T: 0131 2228000
E: andrew.yule@blackadders.co.uk

YULE, Christopher Liam (Jan 2018) (Employee)
Caritas Legal Limited, Dunfermline . . . . . (p.823)
T: 01383 431101
E: chris@caritaslegal.co.uk

YULE, Kathryn Elizabeth (Sept 2021)
(Employee)
Morton Fraser LLP, Edinburgh . . . .(p.891)
T: 0131 2471000
E: katie.yule@morton-fraser.com

ZABIR, Maaria Annam (Mar 2021) (Employee)
DAC Beachcroft Scotland LLP,
Glasgow. . . . .(p.964)
T: 0141 2486688
E: mzabir@dacbeachcroft.com

ZAK, Stephanie Francesca (Apr 2010) (Partner)
Balfour + Manson LLP, Edinburgh . . . . .(p.841)
T: 0131 2001200
E: Stephanie.Zak@balfour-manson.co.uk

ZAKRZEWSKI, Daniel Julian (Sept 2020)
(Employee)
Addleshaw Goddard LLP,
Edinburgh . . . .(p.835)
T: 0131 2282400
E: daniel.zakrzewski@addleshawgoddard.com

ZASINAITE, Agne (Oct 2018) (Employee)
MacRoberts LLP, Glasgow . . . .(p.1015)
T: 0141 3031100
E: agne.zasinaite@macroberts.com

ZAVARONI, Gianna (Oct 1989) (Employee)
Hannay Fraser & Co Ltd, Isle of
Bute . . . .(p.1088)
T: 01700 503112
E: gianna@hannayfraser.co.uk

ZEYBEK, Victoria Arlene (Sept 2020)
(Employee)
Brodies LLP, Edinburgh . . . .(p.845)
T: 0131 2283777
E: victoria.zeybek@brodies.com

ZHAROV, Ilya (Jul 2005) (Employee)
Police Investigations and Review Commissioner,
Hamilton . . . .(p.1247)
T: 01698 542900
E: Ilya.Zharov@gov.scot

ZHU, Xing (Jan 2015) (Associate)
Rea Law Ltd, Glasgow . . . .(p.1034)
T: 0141 3701241
E: xing@realaw.co.uk

ZIARKOWSKA, Anna (Jan 2021) (Employee)
Aberdeenshire Council, Aberdeen . . . . .(p.1211)
T: 01467 620981
E: anna.ziarkowska@aberdeenshire.gov.uk

ZIEGELMEYER, Livia (Jul 2018) (Solicitor)
NO FIRM

ZIELINSKI, Benjamin Thomas (Dec 2013)
(Employee)
Shoosmiths, Edinburgh . . . .(p.902)
T: 03700 868000
E: ben.zielinski@shoosmiths.co.uk

ZIOLO, Desmond Jan (Jun 2009) (Employee)
Fitzpatrick & Co., Glasgow . . . .(p.976)
T: 0141 2042200
E: dz@fitzpatrickandco.co.uk

ZVEREV MIRONYUK, Artem Sergeevich
(Aug 2019) (Employee)
Burness Paull LLP, Edinburgh . . . .(p.850)
T: 0131 4736000
E: archie.zverev@burnesspaull.com

Accredited Specialists

Accredited Specialists

The ACCREDITED Specialists' Scheme has been developed to provide a system of client referral from general practitioners to specialists. This is to enable difficult or complex cases to be referred to accredited specialists without the risk of the referring solicitor losing the client to the specialist. It is open to the referring and specialist solicitors to agree the specific terms of their own relationship and it is recommended that this be done clearly and unambiguously at the outset.

There are currently thirty-three areas of specialisation and specialists accredited to date are noted below.

Agricultural Law

BARCLAY-SMITH, Linsey Jane, Anderson Strathern LLP, 1 Rutland Court EDINBURGH EH3 8EY
DX: ED3 EDINBURGH
Tel: 0131 2707700
Email: linsey.barclay-smith@andersonstrathern.co.uk
Date Admitted: 27/11/1987

BLAIR, John Michael Greene, Gillespie Macandrew LLP, Broxden House, Lamberkine Drive, Broxden, PERTH PH1 1RA
Tel: 01738 231020
Email: Mike.Blair@gillespiemacandrew.co.uk
Date Admitted: 30/06/1982

BOWIE, Ryan, Brodies LLP, 110 Queen Street, GLASGOW G1 3BX
Tel: 0141 2484672
Email: ryan.bowie@brodies.com
Date Admitted: 09/12/2008

BRUCE, Heather Catherine, Turcan Connell, Princes Exchange, 1 Earl Grey Street, EDINBURGH EH3 9EE
Tel: 0131 2288111
Email: heather.bruce@turcanconnell.com
Date Admitted: 16/08/2007

BUCHAN, Alexander Dalrymple Stewart, Brodies LLP, 15 Atholl Crescent, EDINBURGH EH3 8HA
Tel: 0131 2283777
Email: alex.buchan@brodies.com
Date Admitted: 27/11/1996

BURY, Catherine Anne, Stewart & Watson, 59 High Street, TURRIFF AB53 4EL
Tel: 01888 63773
Email: cbury@stewartwatson.com
Date Admitted: 15/03/2004

DRYSDALE, WS, James Cunison, Ledingham Chalmers LLP, Suite A3, Stirling Agricultural Centre, STIRLING FK9 4RN
Tel: 01786 478100
Email: jim.drysdale@ledinghamchalmers.com
Date Admitted: 15/02/1982

FOTHERINGHAM, Lydia Margaret, Anderson Beaton Lamond, Bordeaux House, 31 Kinnoull Street, PERTH PH1 5EN
Tel: 01738 639999
Email: lydia@abl-law.co.uk
Date Admitted: 15/10/1996

GREENWOOD, Stuart Henry, Shepherd and Wedderburn LLP, 1 Exchange Crescent, Conference Square, EDINBURGH EH3 8UL
Tel: 0131 2289900
Email: stuart.greenwood@shepwedd.com
Date Admitted: 27/08/2010

GRUNENBERG, Petra Anna Frieda Cornelia, Blackadders LLP, 30/34 Reform Street, DUNDEE DD1 1RJ
Tel: 01382 229222
Email: petra.grunenberg@blackadders.co.uk
Date Admitted: 24/07/2000

LEAN, Hamish, Shepherd and Wedderburn LLP, Commercial House, 2 Rubislaw Terrace, ABERDEEN AB10 1XE
Tel: 01224 621166
Email: hamish.lean@shepwedd.com
Date Admitted: 30/10/1985

LINDLEY, Christopher Gerald, Thorntons Law LLP, 53 East High Street, FORFAR DD8 2EL
Tel: 01307 466886
Email: clindley@thorntons-law.co.uk
Date Admitted: 25/10/1990

LINEHAN, Andrew Dermot, Murray Beith Murray, 3 Glenfinlas Street, EDINBURGH EH3 6AQ
Tel: 0131 2251200
Email: andrew.linehan@murraybeith.co.uk
Date Admitted: 18/10/2002

MCGILL, Margo Kyle, Lockharts Law LLP, 12 Beresford Terrace, AYR KA7 2EG
Tel: 01292 265045
Email: MargoMcgill@lockhartslaw.com
Date Admitted: 13/09/1999

MCKAY, Lorna Agnes, Ledingham Chalmers LLP, Suite A3 Stirling Agricultural Centre, STIRLING FK9 4RN
Tel: 01786 478100
Email: lorna.mckay@ledinghamchalmers.com
Date Admitted: 21/08/2006

MCLEISH, Kathryn Ann, Brodies LLP, 15 Atholl Crescent, EDINBURGH EH3 8HA
Tel: 0131 2283777
Email: kate.mcleish@brodies.com
Date Admitted: 01/11/2012

MILNE, Odell Campbell, Brodies LLP, 15 Atholl Crescent, EDINBURGH EH3 8HA

Tel: 0131 2283777
Email: odell.milne@brodies.com
Date Admitted: 26/09/1984

MITCHELL, John Angus, Anderson Strathern LLP,
1 Rutland Court, EDINBURGH EH3 8EY
Tel: 0131 2707700
Email: john.mitchell@andersonstrathern.co.uk
Date Admitted: 06/10/1995

NICOL, Adele Jeanne, Anderson Strathern LLP, 1
Rutland Court, EDINBURGH EH3 8EY
Tel: 0131 2707700
Email: adele.nicol@andersonstrathern.co.uk
Date Admitted: 18/02/1983

PHILLIPS, Clive, Brodies LLP, Brodies House,
31-33 Union Grove, ABERDEEN AB10 6SD
Tel: 01224 392242
Email: clive.phillips@brodies.com
Date Admitted: 09/11/1992

ROBERTSON, Emma Jane, Shepherd and
Wedderburn LLP, Commercial House, 2
Rubislaw Terrace, ABERDEEN AB10 1XE
Tel: 01224 621166
Email: emma.robertson@shepwedd.com
Date Admitted: 17/11/2003

SCOTT-DEMPSTER, Robert Andrew, Gillespie
Macandrew LLP, 5 Atholl Crescent,
EDINBURGH EH3 8EJ
Tel: 0131 2251677
Email: robert.
scott-dempster@gillespiemacandrew.co.uk
Date Admitted: 13/11/1997

YELLOWLEES, Michael James, Lindsays LLP,
Caledonian Exchange, 19A Canning Street,
EDINBURGH EH3 8HE
Tel: 0131 2291212
Email: michaelyellowlees@lindsays.co.uk
Date Admitted: 12/01/1995

Arbitration Law

CONNAL, QC, Robert Craig
Date Admitted: 30/08/1977

FRAME, Shona McNae, CMS Cameron McKenna
Nabarro Olswang LLP, 1 West Regent Street,
GLASGOW G2 1AP
Tel: 0141 3046379
Email: Shona.Frame@cms-cmno.com
Date Admitted: 23/09/1993

KELLY, Neil Joseph, MacRoberts LLP, Excel House
30 Semple Street, EDINBURGH EH3 8BL
Tel: 0131 2295046
Email: neil.kelly@macroberts.com
Date Admitted: 09/11/1984

MALONE, Brandon James, Brandon Malone &
Company Limited, 83 Princes Street,
EDINBURGH EH2 2ER
Tel: 0131 3578549
Email: brandon@brandonmalone.com
Date Admitted: 16/08/1993

MCMILLAN, Alan Charles, Burness Paull LLP, 50
Lothian Road, Festival Square, EDINBURGH
EH3 9WJ
Tel: 0131 4736000

Email: Alan.McMillan@burnesspaull.com
Date Admitted: 27/10/1995

Charity Law

BROWN, Sarah Margaret, J & H Mitchell LLP, 51
Atholl Road, PITLOCHRY PH16 5BU
Tel: 01796 472606
Email: sarah.brown@hmitchell.co.uk
Date Admitted: 08/01/2013

DAVIS, Marion Elizabeth, BTO Solicitors LLP, 48
St. Vincent Street, GLASGOW G2 5HS
Tel: 0141 2218012
Email: mda@bto.co.uk
Date Admitted: 21/09/1998

EWING, Mark Espie, T.C. Young LLP, 7 West
George Street, GLASGOW G2 1BA
Tel: 0141 2215562
Email: mee@tcyoung.co.uk
Date Admitted: 28/11/1985

FALLAS, Robin Kenneth, MacRoberts LLP, Excel
House 30 Semple Street, EDINBURGH EH3 8BL
Tel: 0131 229 5046
Email: robin.fallas@macroberts.com
Date Admitted: 19/01/2004

GILFILLAN, Alan Robert John, Balfour + Manson
LLP, 56-66 Frederick Street, EDINBURGH EH2
1LS
Tel: 0131 2001200
Email: Alan.Gilfillan@balfour-manson.co.uk
Date Admitted: 16/07/2010

KEATINGE, WS, Alastair John, Lindsays LLP,
Caledonian Exchange, 19A Canning Street,
EDINBURGH EH3 8HE
Tel: 0131 6565746
Email: alastairkeatinge@lindsays.co.uk
Date Admitted: 03/12/1982

KIDD, Brodies LLP, 15 Atholl Crescent
EDINBURGH EH3 8HA
DX: ED10 EDINBURGH
Tel: 0131 2283777
Email: helen.kidd@brodies.com
Date Admitted: 19/07/2012

MCEWAN, Gavin Graham Robert, Turcan
Connell, Princes Exchange, 1 Earl Grey Street,
EDINBURGH EH3 9EE
Tel: 0131 2288111
Email: gavin.mcewan@turcanconnell.com
Date Admitted: 13/11/1997

MCGILL, Christopher Paul, Shepherd and
Wedderburn LLP, 1 Exchange Crescent,
Conference Square, EDINBURGH EH3 8UL
Tel: 0131 2289900
Email: christopher.mcgill@shepwedd.com
Date Admitted: 01/10/2001

RUST, Malcolm Hamilton, Shepherd and
Wedderburn LLP, 1 Exchange Crescent,
Conference Square, EDINBURGH EH3 8UL
Tel: 0131 2289900
Email: malcolm.rust@shepwedd.com
Date Admitted: 21/09/1994

SIMPSON, Victoria Joan Wendy, Anderson Strathern LLP, 1 Rutland Court, EDINBURGH EH3 8EY
Tel: 0131 2707700
Email: victoria.simpson@andersonstrathern.co.uk
Date Admitted: 17/09/1998

Child Law

ANDERSON, Lesley Bell, Lesley Anderson Law Ltd, 5 Manse Place, FALKIRK FK1 1JN
Tel: 07444 889193
Email: la@lesleyandersonlaw.co.uk
Date Admitted: 25/09/2006

ANDERSON, Lorna Jane, Kelly & Co, 184 Abercromby Street, Bridgeton, GLASGOW G40 2RZ
Tel: 0141 5544141
Email: gerry@kellysolicitors.com
Date Admitted: 23/09/1993

BAXTER, Bernadette Mary, Mellicks, Incorporating Naftalin Duncan & Co., 160 Hope Street, GLASGOW G2 2TL
Tel: 0141 3320902
Email: bernadette.baxter@mellicks.co.uk
Date Admitted: 02/10/1989

COLLINGHAM, Lynne, T.C. Young LLP, 7 West George Street, GLASGOW G2 1BA
Tel: 0141 2215562
Email: lyc@tcyoung.co.uk
Date Admitted: 25/10/1990

COMRIE, Eva Margaret, Comrie Law, 40 Stirling Street, ALVA FK12 5EB
Tel: 01259 235567
Email: eva@comrielaw.co.uk
Date Admitted: 25/08/1986

COUTTS, David Michael, Simpson & Marwick, 23 Alva Street, EDINBURGH EH2 4PS
Tel: 01224 606 210
Email: david.coutts@simpsonmarwick.com
Date Admitted: 26/10/2012

CRANSTON, Claire Margaret Helen, Macnabs LLP, 10 Barossa Place, PERTH PH1 5JX
Tel: 01738 623432
Email: claircranston@macnabs-law.co.uk
Date Admitted: 13/07/2012

CULLEN, Marisa Anne, Family Law Matters Scotland LLP, Queens House, 19 St. Vincent Place, GLASGOW G1 2DT
Tel: 0141 4202430
Email: marisa.cullen@flmscotland.co.uk
Date Admitted: 24/06/2005

DOWDALLS, Lesley, Mackintosh & Wylie LLP, 23 The Foregate, KILMARNOCK KA1 1LE
Tel: 01563 525104
Email: ldowdalls@mackwylie.com
Date Admitted: 15/08/1988

ELSBY, Donna Margaret, Galloway & Elsby Legal Limited, 37 Bank Street, KILMARNOCK KA1 1ER
Tel: 01563 527 564
Email: delsby@gallowayandelsby.co.uk

Date Admitted: 14/10/2011

FOWLER, Lauren, Frazer Coogans Ltd, Dalblair House 46 Dalblair Road, AYR KA7 1UQ
Tel: 01292 280499
Email: lauren.fowler@frazercoogans.co.uk
Date Admitted: 15/08/1988

FOWLER, Linda, The Scottish Parliament, Solicitor's Office, EDINBURGH EH99 1SP
Email: linda.fowler@parliament.scot
Date Admitted: 14/11/2008

GAILEY, Karen, Family Law Matters Scotland LLP, Queens House, 19 St. Vincent Place, GLASGOW G1 2DT
Tel: 0141 4202430
Email: karen.gailey@flmscotland.co.uk
Date Admitted: 28/09/1992

GALLAGHER, Jennifer, Lindsays LLP, Seabraes House, 18 Greenmarket, DUNDEE DD1 4QB
Tel: 01382 224112
Email: JenniferGallagher@lindsays.co.uk
Date Admitted: 16/11/1998

GIRDWOOD, Lisa Anne Irvine, Brodies LLP, 110 Queen Street, GLASGOW G1 3BX
Tel: 0141 2484672
Email: lisa.girdwood@brodies.com
Date Admitted: 02/10/1989

HIGSON, Judith May, Scullion Law Limited, 105 Cadzow Street, HAMILTON ML3 6HG
Tel: 01698 283265
Email: judith@scullionlaw.com
Date Admitted: 07/11/2001

HOGG, Nicola Marianne, West Lothian Council, Corporate/ Support / Legal Services, West Lothian Civic Centre, Howden South Road, LIVINGSTON EH54 6FF
Tel: 01506 280000
Email: Nicola.Hogg@westlothian.gov.uk
Date Admitted: 27/04/2001

JACK, Karen Margaret
Date Admitted: 21/11/1991

LANG, Louise Ruth Niven, Fife Community Law Limited, Units 4 and 5 Ore Valley Business Centre 93 Main Street, LOCHGELLY KY5 9AF
Tel: 01592 786710
Date Admitted: 14/08/2008

LILLEY, Sarah Ann, Brodies LLP, 3 Fodderty Way Dingwall Business Park, DINGWALL IV15 9XB
Tel: 01349 860111
Email: sarah.lilley@brodies.com
Date Admitted: 10/09/2007

MACANDREW, Hilary Anne Barrowman, Grant Smith Law Practice Limited, Old Bank Buildings, Balmellie Street, TURRIFF AB53 4DW
Tel: 01888 562245
Email: hilary.macandrew@grantsmithlaw.co.uk
Date Admitted: 01/10/1985

MACKINNON, Duncan William Neil, RSB Lindsays, 21 Crichton Street, DUNDEE DD1 3AR
Tel: 01382 802050
Date Admitted: 28/01/1993

MACKINTOSH, Caroline Ann, Scottish
Government, Legal Directorate Victoria Quay,
EDINBURGH EH6 6QQ
Tel: 0131 244 0815
Email: caroline.mackintosh@gov.scot
Date Admitted: 15/07/2011

MARTIN, Nadine, Gibson Kerr Limited, 46 India
Street, EDINBURGH EH3 6HJ
DX: 551100 EDINBURGH 7
Tel: 0131 2257558
Email: nadine.martin@gibsonkerr.co.uk
Date Admitted: 10/07/2006

MASSON, Amanda Elizabeth, Harper Macleod
LLP, The Ca'd'oro 45 Gordon Street,
GLASGOW G1 3PE
Tel: 0141 2218888
Email: Amanda.Masson@harpermacleod.co.uk
Date Admitted: 03/12/2002

MASSON, Gareth Antony, Blackadders LLP, 6 Bon
Accord Square, Aberdeen AB11 6XU
Tel: 01224 588913
Email: gareth.masson@blackadders.co.uk
Date Admitted: 07/10/1993

MCKEE, Alison Jayne, Lindsays LLP, 100 Queen
Street, Glasgow G1 3DN
Tel: 0141 2216551
Email: alisonmckee@lindsays.co.uk
Date Admitted: 18/02/1999

MILLARD, Lucy, Mill and Millard LLP, 69-71 Dalry
Road, EDINBURGH EH11 2AA
Tel: 0131 3227222
Email: lm@millardlaw.co.uk
Date Admitted: 23/11/2010

OGILVIE, Lindsey, Turcan Connell, Princes
Exchange, 1 Earl Grey Street, EDINBURGH
EH3 9EE
Tel: 0131 2288111
Email: lindsey.ogilvie@turcanconnell.com
Date Admitted: 05/08/2004

OSWALD, Susan Margaret, SKO Family Limited,
18 George Street, EDINBURGH EH2 2PF
Tel: 0131 3226669
Email: Susan.Oswald@sko-family.co.uk
Date Admitted: 16/10/1995

SIMPSON, Ashley Marie, Patience & Buchan, 10
Golden Square, ABERDEEN AB10 1RB
Tel: 01224 648222
Email: ashley@patienceandbuchan.com
Date Admitted: 21/06/2006

SMITH, Stephanie Nicole, SKO Family Law
Specialists LLP, 18 George Street, EDINBURGH
EH2 2PF

STURROCK, Garry John, Brodies LLP, Brodies
House, 31-33 Union Grove, ABERDEEN AB10
6SD
DX: AB10 ABERDEEN
Tel: 01224 392242
Email: garry.sturrock@brodies.com
Date Admitted: 12/07/2013

THOMSON, Elizabeth Brown, Anderson Shaw &
Gilbert Limited, York House, 20 Church Street
INVERNESS IV1 1ED
Tel: 01463 236123

Email: ET@solicitorsinverness.com
Date Admitted: 12/11/2009

WILKIE, Karen, Aberdeen City Council, Marischal
College, Broad Street, ABERDEEN AB10 1AB
Tel: 01224 522000
Email: KWilkie@aberdeencity.gov.uk
Date Admitted: 05/08/2009

WYLIE, Karen Sandra, Morton Fraser LLP, 145 St
Vincent Street, GLASGOW G2 5JF
DX: GW58 GLASGOW
Tel: 0141 2741100
Email: karen.wylie@morton-fraser.com
Date Admitted: 09/09/2005

Commercial Leasing

BELL, David William John, Harper Macleod LLP,
The Ca'd'oro, 45 Gordon Street, GLASGOW
G1 3PE
Tel: 0141 2218888
Email: david.bell@harpermacleod.co.uk
Date Admitted: 19/10/1988

BRADSHAW, Graeme Stuart, Burness Paull LLP,
120 Bothwell Street, GLASGOW G2 7JL
Tel: 0141 2484933
Email: Graeme.Bradshaw@burnesspaull.com
Date Admitted: 06/08/2001

GERBER, Kenneth Steven, Mitchells Roberton Ltd,
George House, 36 North Hanover Street,
GLASGOW G1 2AD
Tel: 0141 5523422
Email: ksg@mitchells-roberton.co.uk
Date Admitted: 04/12/1980

Commercial Mediation

FENDER-ALLISON, Jane Elizabeth, CMS Cameron
McKenna Nabarro Olswang LLP, 1 West
Regent Street, GLASGOW G2 1AP
Tel: 0141 2222200
Email: Jane.Fender-Allison@cms-cmno.com
Date Admitted: 22/02/2008

GRANT, Alison MacIntyre, DWF LLP, 110 Queen
Street, GLASGOW G1 3HD
Tel: 0141 2288000
Email: Alison.Grant@dwf.law
Date Admitted: 19/10/1984

HOSSACK, David, Morton Fraser LLP, Quartermile
Two 2 Lister Square, EDINBURGH EH3 9GL
Tel: 0131 2471000
Email: david.hossack@morton-fraser.com
Date Admitted: 06/11/1987

KIRKWOOD, Paul
Date Admitted: 27/09/1993

Construction Law

ALEXANDER, Sarah Louise, Dentons UK and
Middle East LLP, Quartermile One, 15
Lauriston Place, EDINBURGH EH3 9EP
Tel: 0330 2220050
Email: Sarah.Alexander@dentons.com
Date Admitted: 19/10/2007

ARNOTT, David Scott, Brodies LLP, Capital House, 2 Festival Square, EDINBURGH EH3 9SU
Tel: 0131 228 3777
Email: david.arnott@brodies.com
Date Admitted: 28/01/1993

BARLOW, Michael John, MacRoberts LLP, Excel House, 30 Semple Street, EDINBURGH EH3 8BL
Tel: 0131 2295046
Email: mike.barlow@macroberts.com
Date Admitted: 28/09/1998

BRADSHAW, Robert Craig, Dentons UK and Middle East LLP, 1 George Square, GLASGOW G2 1AL
DX: GW67 GLASGOW
Tel: 0330 2220050
Email: craig.bradshaw@dentons.com
Date Admitted: 13/08/1998

CONROY, Michael Christopher, Harper Macleod LLP, The Ca'd'oro, 45 Gordon Street, GLASGOW G1 3PE
Tel: 0141 2218888
Email: michael.conroy@harpermacleod.co.uk

CORMACK, Roderick Stewart, Wright, Johnston & Mackenzie LLP, The Green House Beechwood Park North, INVERNESS IV2 3BL
Tel: 01463 234445
Email: rsc@wjm.co.uk
Date Admitted: 20/08/1999

COWDEN, Davinia-Elizabeth, CMS Cameron McKenna Nabarro Olswang LLP, 1 West Regent Street, GLASGOW G2 1AP
Tel: 0141 2222200
Email: Davinia.Cowden@cms-cmno.com
Date Admitted: 24/10/2002

DORAN, Katherine Ellen Clarissa, Holman Fenwick Willan LLP, Friary Court 65 Crutched Friars, LONDON EC3N 2AE
Tel: 020 7264 8000
Email: katherine.doran@hfw.com
Date Admitted: 30/04/2007

DRUMMOND, Iain Kerr, Shepherd and Wedderburn LLP, 1 Exchange Crescent, Conference Square, EDINBURGH EH3 8UL
Tel: 0131 2289900
Email: iain.drummond@shepwedd.com
Date Admitted: 10/03/1995

DUFF, Christopher William, Brodies LLP, 15 Atholl Crescent, EDINBURGH EH3 8HA
Tel: 0131 2283777
Email: chris.duff@brodies.com
Date Admitted: 15/10/2009

FENDER-ALLISON, Jane Elizabeth, CMS Cameron McKenna Nabarro Olswang LLP, 1 West Regent Street, GLASGOW G2 1AP
Tel: 0141 2222200
Email: Jane.Fender-Allison@cms-cmno.com
Date Admitted: 22/02/2008

FORBES, James Bennie Cook, Burness Paull LLP, 120 Bothwell Street, GLASGOW G2 7JL
Tel: 0141 2484933
Email: James.Forbes@burnesspaull.com

Date Admitted: 01/10/1990

FRAME, Shona McNae, CMS Cameron McKenna Nabarro Olswang LLP, 1 West Regent Street, GLASGOW G2 1AP
Tel: 0141 3046379
Email: Shona.Frame@cms-cmno.com
Date Admitted: 23/09/1993

HALDANE, Juliet Lorna, Brodies LLP, 110 Queen Street, GLASGOW G1 3BX
Tel: 0141 2484672
Email: juliet.haldane@brodies.com
Date Admitted: 05/12/1991

HERD, Leigh Anne, Shepherd and Wedderburn LLP, 1 Exchange Crescent, Conference Square, EDINBURGH EH3 8UL
Tel: 0131 473 5182
Email: Leigh.Herd@shepwedd.com
Date Admitted: 19/09/2013

JACKSON, James Richard Graham, Thorntons Law LLP, Whitehall House, 33 Yeaman Shore, DUNDEE DD1 4BJ
Tel: 01382 229111
Email: gjackson@thorntons-law.co.uk
Date Admitted: 09/11/1998

JOHNSTON, Scott Forsyth, Pinsent Masons LLP, 13 Queen's Road, ABERDEEN AB15 4YL
Tel: 01224 377900
Email: scott.johnston@pinsentmasons.com
Date Admitted: 29/09/1994

JOHNSTONE, Eric, Brodies LLP, 15 Atholl Crescent, EDINBURGH EH3 8HA
DX: ED10 EDINBURGH
Tel: 0131 2283777
Email: eric.johnstone@brodies.com
Date Admitted: 13/09/2011

JONES, QC, Anthony Gerald Morrell, Brodies LLP, 15 Atholl Crescent, EDINBURGH EH3 8HA
Tel: 0131 2283777
Email: tony.jones@brodies.com
Date Admitted: 22/10/1991

KELLY, Neil Joseph, MacRoberts LLP, Excel House, 30 Semple Street, EDINBURGH EH3 8BL
Tel: 0131 2295046
Email: neil.kelly@macroberts.com
Date Admitted: 09/11/1984

KILBURN, Keith, Brodies LLP, 110 Queen Street, GLASGOW G1 3BX
Tel: 0141 2484672
Email: keith.kilburn@brodies.com
Date Admitted: 04/08/2006

KINNES, Margaret White, MacRoberts LLP, Excel House, 30 Semple Street, EDINBURGH EH3 8BL
Tel: 0131 2295046
Email: margaret.kinnes@macroberts.com
Date Admitted: 07/10/1993

KIRKE, Mark Jonathan, CMS Cameron McKenna Nabarro Olswang LLP, Saltire Court, 20 Castle Terrace, EDINBURGH EH1 2EN
Tel: 0131 2288000
Email: Mark.Kirke@cms-cmno.com
Date Admitted: 23/10/1996

LOFTUS, Patrick Joseph, Anderson Strathern LLP, 1 Rutland Court, EDINBURGH EH3 8EY
Tel: 0131 2707700
Email: pat.loftus@andersonstrathern.co.uk
Date Admitted: 10/02/2000

MALONE, Brandon James, Brandon Malone & Company Limited, 83 Princes Street, EDINBURGH EH2 2ER
Tel: 0131 3578549
Email: brandon@brandonmalone.com
Date Admitted: 16/08/1993

MCLAUGHLIN, Elizabeth Christine, Scottish Water, Castle House, 6 Castle Drive, Carnegie Campus, DUNFERMLINE KY11 8GG
Email: elizabeth.mclaughlin@scottishwater.co.uk
Date Admitted: 17/10/1994

MCMONAGLE, Jane Claire, Brodies LLP, 110 Queen Street, GLASGOW G1 3BX
Tel: 0141 2484672
Email: jane.mcmonagle@brodies.com
Date Admitted: 22/04/2004

MILNE, Kirsteen Elizabeth, Brodies LLP, 15 Atholl Crescent, EDINBURGH EH3 8HA
DX: ED10 EDINBURGH
Tel: 0131 2283777
Email: Kirsteen.Milne@brodies.com
Date Admitted: 21/12/2004

MORRISON, Philip, Clarion Solicitors Limited, Elizabeth House, 13-19 Queen Street, LEEDS LS1 2TW
Email: phil.morrison@clarionsolicitors.com
Date Admitted: 26/09/1991

PENGELLY, Sarah Mary Katherine, MacRoberts LLP, Excel House, 30 Semple Street, EDINBURGH EH3 8BL
Tel: 0131 2295046
Email: sarah.pengelly@macroberts.com
Date Admitted: 15/05/2003

PHILIP, Andrew David Pyka, Scottish Power Limited, Legal Team, 320 St Vincent Street, GLASGOW G2 5AD
Tel: 0141 6140000
Email: aphilip@ScottishPower.com
Date Admitted: 15/10/2002

PIRIE, Euan David Thomas, Harper Macleod LLP, Citypoint, 65 Haymarket Terrace, EDINBURGH EH12 5HD
DX: ED167 EDINBURGH
Tel: 0131 2472500
Email: euan.pirie@harpermacleod.co.uk
Date Admitted: 30/11/1995

ROSS, Lynda Elizabeth, Burness Paull LLP, 50 Lothian Road Festival Square, EDINBURGH EH3 9WJ
Tel: 0131 473 6000
Email: lynda.ross@burnesspaull.com
Date Admitted: 12/12/1990

RUSSELL, Claudia Ruth, CMS Cameron McKenna Nabarro Olswang LLP, Saltire Court, 20 Castle Terrace, EDINBURGH EH1 2EN
Tel: 0131 2288000
Date Admitted: 17/11/2003

SCOTT-GILROY, Julie, Morton Fraser LLP, Quartermile Two, 2 Lister Square, EDINBURGH EH3 9GL
Tel: 0131 2471000
Email: julie.scott-gilroy@morton-fraser.co.uk
Date Admitted: 25/09/2008

SHIELS, Louise, Brodies LLP, 15 Atholl Crescent, EDINBURGH EH3 8HA
Tel: 0131 2283777
Email: Louise.Shiels@brodies.com
Date Admitted: 06/09/2004

STRUCKMEIER, Anne Christina, Addleshaw Goddard LLP, Exchange Tower, 19 Canning Street, EDINBURGH EH3 8EH
Tel: 0131 2282400
Email: Anne.Struckmeier@addleshawgoddard.com
Date Admitted: 03/10/1995

THOMSON, Gavin Ross, MacRoberts LLP, Excel House, 30 Semple Street, EDINBURGH EH3 8BL
Tel: 0131 2295046
Email: gavin.thomson@macroberts.com
Date Admitted: 20/11/2001

WATT, WS, Karyn Marjorie, Anderson Strathern LLP, 1 Rutland Court, EDINBURGH EH3 8EY
Tel: 0131 2707700
Email: karyn.watt@andersonstrathern.co.uk
Date Admitted: 08/02/1985

WILSON, David Dalgleish, MacRoberts LLP, Capella, 60 York Street, GLASGOW G2 8JX
Tel: 0141 3031100
Email: david.wilson@macroberts.com
Date Admitted: 01/10/1996

YOUNG, Jennifer Evelyn, Ledingham Chalmers LLP, Johnstone House, 52-54 Rose Street, ABERDEEN AB10 1HA
Tel: 01224 408408
Email: jennifer.young@ledinghamchalmers.com
Date Admitted: 03/02/1993

YOUNG, Madeleine Clare, CMS Cameron McKenna Nabarro Olswang LLP, 1 West Regent Street, GLASGOW G2 1AP
Tel: 0141 304 6295
Email: madeleine.young@cms-cmno.com
Date Admitted: 23/10/2007

Crofting Law

BENFIELD, Jeremy Peter, MacPhee & Partners LLP, Airds House, An Aird, FORT WILLIAM PH33 6BL
Tel: 01397 701000
Email: jeremybenfield@macphee.co.uk
Date Admitted: 29/05/2001

MACLEOD, Calum Martin, Harper Macleod LLP, Alder House, Cradlehall Business Park, INVERNESS IV2 5GH
Tel: 01463 798777
Email: calum.macleod@harpermacleod.co.uk
Date Admitted: 24/11/2006

Debt and Asset Recovery

BASHIR, Zibya, Miller Samuel Hill Brown LLP, RWF House, 5 Renfield Street, GLASGOW G2 5EZ
DX: GW161 GLASGOW
Tel: 0141 2211919
Email: zba@mshblegal.com
Date Admitted: 05/08/2004

CONN, Joel Martin, Mitchells Roberton Ltd, George House, 36 North Hanover Street, GLASGOW G1 2AD
Tel: 0141 5523422
Email: jmc@mitchells-roberton.co.uk
Date Admitted: 21/09/1998

DISSAKE, Natalie, Harper Macleod LLP, The Ca'd'oro, 45 Gordon Street, GLASGOW G1 3PE
Tel: 0141 2218888
Email: natalie.dissake@harpermacleod.co.uk
Date Admitted: 19/09/2006

MCCLUSKEY, Gillian Bell, Moray Legal Limited, The Forsyth Building, 5 Renfield Street GLASGOW G2 5EZ
Tel: 0344 5715205
Email: gillian.mccluskey@alstonlaw.co.uk
Date Admitted: 13/08/2002

MCWILLIAMS, Helen Marie, Cowan & Co, 81 Berkeley Street, GLASGOW G3 7DX
Tel: 0141 221 1803
Email: hmcw@cowanandco.co.uk
Date Admitted: 14/12/1992

Discrimination Law

GILZEAN, Sarah Anne, Morton Fraser LLP, Quartermile Two 2 Lister Square, EDINBURGH EH3 9GL
Tel: 0131 247 1000
Email: sarah.gilzean@morton-fraser.com
Date Admitted: 27/10/2003

KING, Robert, Clyde & Co (Scotland) LLP, 144 West George Street, GLASGOW G2 2HG
Tel: 0141 2482666
Email: robert.king@clydeco.com
Date Admitted: 19/10/1988

LEE, John James Armstrong, Ledingham Chalmers LLP, 3rd Floor, 68-70 George Street, EDINBURGH EH2 2LR
Tel: 0131 2001000
Email: john.lee@ledinghamchalmers.com
Date Admitted: 20/10/2000

MILLER, Stephen Charles, Clyde & Co (Scotland) LLP, 144 West George Street, GLASGOW G2 2HG
Tel: 0141 2482666
Email: stephen.miller@clydeco.com
Date Admitted: 30/10/1989

MITCHELL, Graham Stuart, Clyde & Co (Scotland) LLP, 144 West George Street, GLASGOW G2 2HG
Tel: 0141 2482666
Email: graham.mitchell@clydeco.com
Date Admitted: 23/09/1997

REYNOLDS, Donna, Blackadders LLP, 40 Torphichen Street, EDINBURGH EH3 8JB
Tel: 0131 2228000
Email: donna.reynolds@blackadders.co.uk
Date Admitted: 22/09/2004

WEDDERBURN, Kathryn Jean, MacRoberts LLP, Capella, 60 York Street, GLASGOW G2 8JX
DX: GW70 GLASGOW
Tel: 0141 3031100
Email: katy.wedderburn@macroberts.com
Date Admitted: 04/09/1995

Employment Law

ALLISON, Simon David, Blackadders LLP, 30/34 Reform Street, DUNDEE DD1 1RJ
Tel: 01382 229222
Email: simon.allison@blackadders.co.uk
Date Admitted: 08/11/2001

ANDERSON, Laurie Gallacher, Ellis Whittam Limited, The Beacon 7th Floor, 176 St Vincent Street, GLASGOW G2 5SG
Email: laurieanderson@elliswhittam.com
Date Admitted: 24/09/2007

BOYLE, Jack Glass, Blackadders LLP, 30/34 Reform Street, DUNDEE DD1 1RJ
Tel: 01382 229222
Email: jack.boyle@blackadders.co.uk
Date Admitted: 04/11/2010

BROWN, Andrew James William, Anderson Strathern LLP, 1 Rutland Court, EDINBURGH EH3 8EY
Tel: 0131 20700
Email: andrew.brown@andersonstrathearn.co.uk
Date Admitted: 08/02/2007

BROWN, Kelly, Addleshaw Goddard LLP, Exchange Tower 19 Canning Street, EDINBURGH EH3 8EH
Tel: 0131 2282400
Email: Kelly.Brown@addleshawgoddard.com
Date Admitted: 13/09/2011

BROWN, Paul James, Glasgow Caledonian University, Law Division, City Campus, Cowcaddens Road, GLASGOW G4 0BA
Email: paul.brown@gcu.ac.uk
Date Admitted: 25/10/1990

CALDOW, Bruce Alan, Harper Macleod LLP, The Ca'd'oro, 45 Gordon Street, GLASGOW G1 3PE
Tel: 0141 2279339
Email: bruce.caldow@harpermacleod.co.uk
Date Admitted: 23/01/2003

CAMPBELL, Brian James, Brodies LLP, 110 Queen Street, GLASGOW G1 3BX
Tel: 0141 2484672
Email: brian.campbell@brodies.com
Date Admitted: 02/09/1996

CARR, Caroline Ann, BTO Solicitors LLP, 48 St. Vincent Street, GLASGOW G2 5HS
Tel: 0141 2218012
Email: cac@bto.co.uk
Date Admitted: 28/01/1993

CARTWRIGHT, Lindsey Jane, Morton Fraser LLP, 145 St Vincent Street, GLASGOW G2 5JF
Tel: 0141 2741100
Email: lindsey.cartwright@morton-fraser.com
Date Admitted: 12/02/1996

CLARK, Geoffrey Alan, Burness Paull LLP, Union Plaza, 1 Union Wynd, ABERDEEN AB10 1DQ
Tel: 01224 621621
Email: Geoffrey.Clark@burnesspaull.com
Date Admitted: 09/11/1998

CLARK, James Innes, Morton Fraser LLP, Quartermile Two, 2 Lister Square, EDINBURGH EH3 9GL
Tel: 0131 2471000
Email: innes.clark@morton-fraser.com
Date Admitted: 13/11/1997

COUTTS, Hazel Anne, Brodies LLP, 15 Atholl Crescent, EDINBURGH EH3 8HA
Tel: 0131 2283777
Email: hazel.coutts@brodies.com
Date Admitted: 18/10/2004

CRADDEN, Joan Mary, Brodies LLP, 110 Queen Street, GLASGOW G1 3BX
Tel: 0141 2484672
Email: joan.cradden@brodies.com
Date Admitted: 11/07/1994

DAVIS, Lorna, Harper Macleod LLP, The Ca'd'oro, 45 Gordon Street, GLASGOW G1 3PE
Tel: 0141 2218888
Email: lorna.davis@harpermacleod.co.uk
Date Admitted: 28/08/2002

DELANEY, Alan Joseph, Morton Fraser LLP, Quartermile Two, 2 Lister Square, EDINBURGH EH3 9GL
Tel: 0131 2471000
Email: Alan.Delaney@morton-fraser.com
Date Admitted: 13/08/2002

EWART, Laura Dawn, National Health Service Scotland, Anderson House, Breadalbane St Bonnington Road EDINBURGH EH6 5JR
Tel: 0131 2757800
Email: laura.ewart@nhs.net
Date Admitted: 28/02/2003

FELLOWS, Deborah, Thorntons Law LLP, Whitehall House, 33 Yeaman Shore, DUNDEE DD1 4BJ
Tel: 01382 229111
Email: dfellows@thorntons-law.co.uk
Date Admitted: 16/11/2000

GALLAGHER, Lindsay Catherine, National Health Service Scotland, Anderson House, Breadalbane St Bonnington Road, EDINBURGH EH6 5JR
Tel: 0131 2757800
Email: l.gallagher1@nhs.scot
Date Admitted: 15/10/2004

GIBSON, Andrew Robert, Morton Fraser LLP, 145 St Vincent Street, GLASGOW G2 5JF
Tel: 0141 2741100
Email: Andrew.Gibson@morton-fraser.com
Date Admitted: 01/10/2002

GILLIGAN, Eric John, CMS Cameron McKenna Nabarro Olswang LLP, 6 Queens Road, ABERDEEN AB15 4ZT
Tel: 01224 622002
Email: Eric.Gilligan@cms-cmno.com
Date Admitted: 05/11/1997

GILZEAN, Sarah Anne, Morton Fraser LLP, Quartermile Two, 2 Lister Square, EDINBURGH EH3 9GL
Tel: 0131 2471000
Email: sarah.gilzean@morton-fraser.com
Date Admitted: 27/10/2003

GREIG, Catherine Jean, Greig Employment Law Limited, 2 West Regent Street, GLASGOW G2 1RW
Tel: 07584 244565
Email: catherine@greigemploymentlaw.com
Date Admitted: 30/10/1991

HADDEN, Anthony Archibald, Brodies LLP, 15 Atholl Crescent, EDINBURGH EH3 8HA
Tel: 0131 2283777
Email: tony.hadden@brodies.com
Date Admitted: 01/02/1999

HEMSI, Musab, Anderson Strathern LLP, George House, 50 George Square, GLASGOW G2 1EH
DX: GW157 GLASGOW
Tel: 0141 242 7988
Email: Musab.hemsi@andersonstrathern.co.uk
Date Admitted: 14/10/2011

HOSSACK, David, Morton Fraser LLP, Quartermile Two, 2 Lister Square, EDINBURGH EH3 9GL
Tel: 0131 2471000
Email: david.hossack@morton-fraser.com
Date Admitted: 06/11/1987

HUGHES, David William, Addleshaw Goddard LLP, Exchange Tower, 19 Canning Street, EDINBURGH EH3 8EH
Tel: 0131 2282400
Date Admitted: 08/11/1991

HUNTER, Lucinda Jane, Rennie McInnes LLP, Douglas House, 42 Main Street, MILNGAVIE G62 6BU
Tel: 0141 5629540
Email: lucinda@renniemcinnes.co.uk
Date Admitted: 16/12/1992

HUTCHISON, David Martin, Dallas McMillan, 1st Floor, Regent Court, 70 West Regent Street, GLASGOW G2 2Q
Tel: 0141 3336750
Email: Davidhutchison@dallasmcmillan.co.uk
Date Admitted: 07/12/2012

JONES, Amy Carole, Thorntons Law LLP, Whitehall House 33 Yeaman Shore, DUNDEE DD1 4BJ
Tel: 01382 229 111
Email: ajones@thorntons-law.co.uk
Date Admitted: 09/02/2010

KERR, Matthew Liam Philip, Trinity Kerr Limited, 6 Oakdale Terrace, ABERDEEN AB15 7PJ
Tel: 01224 312767
Email: liam@trinitykerr.co.uk
Date Admitted: 18/01/2005

KING, Robert, Clyde & Co (Scotland) LLP, 144 West George Street, GLASGOW G2 2HG
Tel: 0141 2482666
Email: robert.king@clydeco.com
Date Admitted: 19/10/1988

LEE, John James Armstrong, Ledingham Chalmers LLP, 3rd Floor, 68-70 George Street, EDINBURGH EH2 2LR
Tel: 0131 2001000
Email: john.lee@ledinghamchalmers.com
Date Admitted: 20/10/2000

MACAULAY, Pamela Jayne, National Westminster Bank PLC, Group Legal Business House G P.O. Box 1000, EDINBURGH EH12 1HQ
Email: pamela.macaulay@rbs.co.uk
Date Admitted: 06/09/2004

MACDONALD, Marie Elizabeth, Miller Samuel Hill Brown LLP, RWF House, 5 Renfield Street, GLASGOW G2 5EZ
Tel: 0141 2211919
Email: mem@mshblegal.com
Date Admitted: 10/12/1985

MACKINNON, Donald John, Law at Work Ltd, Kintyre House, 205 West George Street, GLASGOW G2 2LW
Tel: 0141 2715555
Email: donald.mackinnon@lawatwork.co.uk
Date Admitted: 28/09/1995

MACLEAN, Neil John, Shepherd and Wedderburn LLP, 1 Exchange Crescent, Conference Square, EDINBURGH EH3 8UL
Tel: 0131 473 5181
Email: neil.maclean@shepwedd.com
Date Admitted: 01/10/1996

MACMILLAN, John Ernest Newall, MacRoberts LLP, River Court, 5 West Victoria Dock Road, DUNDEE DD1 3JT
Tel: 01382 339340
Email: john.macmillan@macroberts.com
Date Admitted: 20/10/1980

MANNION, Eleanor Margaret, MacRoberts LLP, Capella, 60 York Street, GLASGOW G2 8JX
Tel: 0141 3031100
Email: Eleanor.Mannion@macroberts.com
Date Admitted: 06/07/2011

MARR, Lynne Anne, Brodies LLP, 15 Atholl Crescent, EDINBURGH EH3 8HA
Tel: 0131 2283777
Email: lynne.marr@brodies.com
Date Admitted: 10/02/2000

MAYBERRY, Simon Jonathan Ross, Leyton UK Partners LLP, Harmsworth House, 13-15 Bouverie Street, LONDON EC4Y 8DP <comm>
Email: smayberry@lexleyton.co.uk
Date Admitted: 07/12/2012

MCCLELLAND, Noele Gillian, Thorntons Law LLP, Whitehall House, 33 Yeaman Shore, DUNDEE DD1 4BJ
Tel: 01382 229111
Email: nmcclelland@thorntons-law.co.uk
Date Admitted: 26/06/1998

MCCLUSKEY, Jacqueline Davidson, BTO Solicitors LLP, One Edinburgh Quay, 133 Fountainbridge, EDINBURGH EH3 9QG
Tel: 0131 2222939
Email: jmcc@bto.co.uk
Date Admitted: 07/10/1993

MCGRADE, Anthony Michael, McGrade & Co Limited, Standard Buildings, 94 Hope Street, GLASGOW G2 6PH
Tel: 0141 2214488
Email: tmcg@mcgrade.co.uk
Date Admitted: 18/12/1986

MCJANNETT, Marianne Sarah, T.C. Young LLP, 7 West George Street, GLASGOW G2 1BA
Tel: 01312207660
Email: msg@tcyoung.co.uk
DateAdmitted: 14/10/2011 Date

MCLAREN, Steven George, Kippen Campbell LLP, 48 Tay Street, PERTH PH1 5TR
Tel: 01738 635353
Email: sm@kcllp.co.uk
Date Admitted: 08/11/1983

MILLER, Deborah, Shepherd and Wedderburn LLP, 1 Exchange Crescent, Conference Square, EDINBURGH EH3 8UL
Tel: 0131 2289900
Email: Deborah.Miller@shepwedd.com
Date Admitted: 28/08/2002

MILLER, Stephen Charles, Clyde & Co (Scotland) LLP, 144 West George Street, GLASGOW G2 2HG
Tel: 0141 2482666
Email: stephen.miller@clydeco.com
Date Admitted: 30/10/1989

MILLIGAN, Scott Stewart, Harper Macleod LLP, The Ca'd'oro, 45 Gordon Street GLASGOW G1 3PE
Tel: 0141 2218888
Email: scott.milligan@harpermacleod.co.uk
Date Admitted: 04/12/2006

MITCHELL, Graham Stuart, Clyde & Co (Scotland) LLP, 144 West George Street, GLASGOW G2 2HG
Tel: 0141 2482666
Email: graham.mitchell@clydeco.com
Date Admitted: 23/09/1997

MORGAN, David, Burness Paull LLP, 120 Bothwell Street, GLASGOW G2 7JL
Tel: 0141 2484933
Email: David.Morgan@burnesspaull.com
Date Admitted: 26/09/1997

MOWAT, Ewan James Hay, A.C. White, 23 Wellington Square, AYR KA7 1HG
Tel: 01292 266900
Email: ewan.mowat@acwhiteayr.co.uk
Date Admitted: 20/08/1999

NICHOL, Barry Christopher, Anderson Strathern LLP, 1 Rutland Court, EDINBURGH EH3 8EY
Tel: 0131 625 7238
Email: barry.nichol@andersonstrathern.co.uk
Date Admitted: 28/03/2000

PHILLIPS, John Christian, Thorntons Law LLP, City Point, 3rd Floor, 65 Haymarket Terrace, EDINBURGH EH12 5HD
Tel: 0131 2258705
Email: cphillips@thorntons-law.co.uk
Date Admitted: 11/09/1997

PHILLIPS, Robert Gerald, Addleshaw Goddard LLP, Kingswells Causeway, ABERDEEN AB15 8PU
Tel: 01224 965410
Email: robert.phillips@addleshawgoddard.com
Date Admitted: 16/08/2007

REID, Alexander Charles, Reid Quarton Limited, 272 Bath Street, GLASGOW G2 4JR
Tel: 0141 354 7651
Email: sandy.reid@reidquarton.co.uk
Date Admitted: 11/11/1975

RENNIE, William Jonathan, TLT LLP, 140 West George Street, GLASGOW G2 2HG
Tel: 0333 006 0400
Email: Jonathan.Rennie@TLTsolicitors.com
Date Admitted: 15/10/2005

REYNOLDS, Donna, Blackadders LLP, 40 Torphichen Street EDINBURGH EH3 8JB
Tel: 0131 2228000
Email: donna.reynolds@blackadders.co.uk
Date Admitted: 22/09/2004

ROBERTSON, Dawn Elizabeth, Rooney Nimmo Limited, 8 Walker Street, EDINBURGH EH3 7LA
Tel: 0131 220 9570
Email: dawn.robertson@rooneynimmo.co.uk
Date Admitted: 06/10/1998

RUSSELL, Kathleen Frances, Burges Salmon LLP, Atria One 144 Morrison Street, EDINBURGH EH3 8EX
Tel: 0131 314 2112
Email: katie.russell@burges-salmon.com
Date Admitted: 15/10/2004

RUSSELL, Ryan Robert, MML Legal, Meadow Place Buildings Bell Street, DUNDEE DD1 1EJ
Tel: 01382 206 000
Email: ryan@mmllaw.co.uk
Date Admitted: 24/08/2009

SALMOND, Laura Irene, BTO Solicitors LLP, 48 St. Vincent Street, GLASGOW G2 5HS
DX: GW96 GLASGOW
Tel: 0141 2218012
Email: lis@bto.co.uk
Date Admitted: 24/11/2003

THOMAS, WS, Alun, Anderson Strathern LLP, 1 Rutland Court, EDINBURGH EH3 8EY
Tel: 0131 625 7245
Email: alun.thomas@andersonstrathern.co.uk
Date Admitted: 01/03/1983

TUDHOPE, William Kirkwood Mackenzie, Ledingham Chalmers LLP, Kintail House, Beechwood Business Park, INVERNESS IV2 3BW
Tel: 01463 667400
Email: kirk.tudhope@ledinghamchalmers.com
Date Admitted: 12/11/1990

WALKER, David James, Morton Fraser LLP, Quartermile Two, 2 Lister Square, EDINBURGH EH3 9GL
Tel: 0131 2471000
Email: david.walker@morton-fraser.com
Date Admitted: 09/11/1984

WEDDERBURN, Kathryn Jean, MacRoberts LLP, Capella, 60 York Street, GLASGOW G2 8JX
Tel: 0141 3031100
Email: katy.wedderburn@macroberts.com
Date Admitted: 04/09/1995

WILSON, Gina Mary, Kellogg Brown & Root (U.K.) Limited, Hill Park Court Springfield Drive Leatherhead, SURREY KT22 7NL
Date Admitted: 13/11/2003

WOOLFSON, Giles Ian, McGrade & Co Limited, Standard Buildings, 94 Hope Street, GLASGOW G2 6PH
Tel: 0141 2214488
Email: gwoolfson@mcgrade.co.uk
Date Admitted: 28/08/1998

Environmental Law

LOVE, Barry, Environmental Law Chambers Ltd, 700 Clarkston Road, GLASGOW G44 3YR
Tel: 0141 2256499
Email: barry.love@elchambers.com
Date Admitted: 09/09/1993

MCKENNA, Chala Siskin, Davidson Chalmers Stewart LLP, 163 Bath Street, GLASGOW G2 4SQ
Tel:: 0141 4283258
Email: chala.mckenna@dcslegal.com
Date Admitted: 19/12/2008

TAINSH, Laura Louise, Davidson Chalmers Stewart LLP, 12 Hope Street, EDINBURGH EH2 4DB
Tel: 0131 6259191
Email: Laura.Tainsh@dcslegal.com
Date Admitted: 06/09/2004

Family Law

ABERDEIN, Ruth Mary, Aberdein Considine and Company, 5-9 Bon Accord Crescent, ABERDEEN AB11 6DN
Tel: 01224 589700
Email: raberdein@acandco.com
Date Admitted: 14/08/2000

ANDERSON, Fiona Elizabeth, MTM Family Law LLP, 2nd Floor, 91 Mitchell Street, GLASGOW G1 3LN
Tel: 0141 6117535
Email: fea@mtmfamilylaw.co.uk
Date Admitted: 18/10/1995

ANDERSON, Lesley Bell, Lesley Anderson Law Ltd, 5 Manse Place, FALKIRK FK1 1JN
Tel: 07444 889193
Email: la@lesleyandersonlaw.co.uk
Date Admitted: 25/09/2006

BAXTER, Bernadette Mary, Mellicks, Incorporating Naftalin Duncan & Co., 160 Hope Street, GLASGOW G2 2TL

Tel: 0141 3320902
Email: bernadette.baxter@mellicks.co.uk
Date Admitted: 02/10/1989

BUCHAN, Lorna Gilmore, Patience & Buchan, 10 Golden Square, ABERDEEN AB10 1RB
Tel: 01224 648222
Email: lorna@patienceandbuchan.com
Date Admitted: 29/09/1994

BURKE, Leonie Sarah Rose, Aberdein Considine and Company, 2nd Floor, East Suite Elder House Multrees Walk EDINBURGH EH1 3DX
Tel: 0333 0044333
Email: lburke@acandco.com
Date Admitted: 25/09/2001

CAMPBELL, Ewan Mackenzie, SKO Family Law Specialists LLP, 18 George Street EDINBURGH EH2 2PF
Tel: 0131 3226669
Email: Ewan.Campbell@sko-family.co.uk
Date Admitted: 11/12/1991

CAMPBELL, Fiona Jane, Macleod & MacCallum Limited, 28 Queensgate, INVERNESS IV1 1DJ
Tel: 01463 239393
Email: fiona.campbell@macandmac.co.uk
Date Admitted: 20/11/1989

CAREY, Fiona Janet, Brophy Carey & Co Ltd, Mediacorp House, 2 Caird Park, HAMILTON ML3 0EU
Tel: 01698 200111
Email: fjc@brophycareylaw.com
Date Admitted: 11/07/1989

CARRICK, Jill Elizabeth, Blair & Bryden, 20A Union Street, GREENOCK PA16 8JL
Tel: 01475 888777
Email: jcarrick@blair-bryden.co.uk
Date Admitted: 05/10/1984

CHALMERS, Ann-Marie, Rooney Family Law Limited, 52 Main Street, UDDINGSTON G71 7LS
Tel: 01698 815 620
Email: amc@rooneyfamilylaw.co.uk
Date Admitted: 02/07/1993

CHRISTIE, Claire, SKO Family Lw Specialists LLP, 18 George Street, EDINBURGH EH2 2PF
Tel: 0131 3226669
Email: claire.christie@sko-family.co.uk
Date Admitted: 28/06/2007

CLARK, Lucia Elaine, Morton Fraser LLP, Quartermile Two, 2 Lister Square, EDINBURGH EH3 9GL
Tel: 0131 2471000
Email: lucia.clark@morton-fraser.com
Date Admitted: 06/09/2004

COLLEDGE, Jennifer Claire, Colledge & Shields LLP, 30 Castle Street, DUMFRIES DG1 1DU
Tel: 01387 240044
Email: jcc@colledgeandshields.co.uk
Date Admitted: 02/09/1996

COLLINGHAM, Lynne, T.C. Young LLP, 7 West George Street, GLASGOW G2 1BA
Tel: 0141 2215562
Email: lyc@tcyoung.co.uk
Date Admitted: 25/10/1990

COMRIE, Eva Margaret, Comrie Law, 40 Stirling Street, ALVA FK12 5EB
Tel: 01259 235567
Email: eva@comrielaw.co.uk
Date Admitted: 25/08/1986

COUTTS, David Michael, Simpson & Marwick, 23 Alva Street, EDINBURGH EH2 4PS
Tel: 01224 606210
Email: David.Coutts@simpsonmarwick.com
Date Admitted: 26/10/2012

CRANDLES, Gillian, Turcan Connell, Princes Exchange, 1 Earl Grey Street, EDINBURGH EH3 9EE
Tel: 0131 2288111
Email: gillian.crandles@turcanconnell.com
Date Admitted: 10/11/2000

CROMAN, Ruth Catriona, Macnabs LLP, 10 Barossa Place, PERTH PH1 5JX
Tel: 01738 623432
Email: ruthcroman@macnabs-law.co.uk
Date Admitted: 17/09/1998

CULLEN, Marisa Anne, Family Law Matters Scotland LLP, Queens House,19 St. Vincent Place, GLASGOW G1 2DT
Email: marisa.cullen@flmscotland.co.uk
Tel: 0141 4202430
Date Admitted: 24/06/2005

DAVIES, Alan Graham, McCash & Hunter LLP, 25 South Methven Street, PERTH PH1 5PE
Tel: 01738 620451
Email: alandavies@mccash.co.uk
Date Admitted: 29/11/1983

DOUGLAS, Morven Jean Kilpatrick, BTO Solicitors LLP, 48 St. Vincent Street, GLASGOW G2 5HS
Tel: 0141 2218012
Email: mjd@bto.co.uk
Date Admitted: 18/09/2002

DOWDALLS, Lesley, Mackintosh & Wylie LLP, 23 The Foregate, KILMARNOCK KA1 1LE
Tel: 01563 525104
Email: ldowdalls@mackwylie.com
Date Admitted: 15/08/1988

EDMONDSON, Alison Elizabeth Redpath, SKO Family Law Specialists LLP, 18 George Street, EDINBURGH EH2 2PF
Tel: 0131 3226669
Email: Alison.Edmondson@sko-family.co.uk
Date Admitted: 27/09/2004

ELSBY, Donna Margaret, Galloway & Elsby Legal Limited, 37 Bank Street, KILMARNOCK KA1 1ER
Tel: 01563 527 564
Email: delsby@gallowayandelsby.co.uk
Date Admitted: 14/10/2011

FORD, Michael Gregory, Ross, Strachan & Co., 2 India Buildings, 86 Bell Street, DUNDEE DD1 1JQ
Tel: 01382 201010
Email: mford@ross-strachan.co.uk
Date Admitted: 08/08/1986

FORSYTH, Ellen Anne, Forsyth WS Limited, 46 High Street, HADDINGTON EH41 3EE
Tel: 01620 824045

Email: af@forsythsolicitors.co.uk
Date Admitted: 28/09/1998

FOULIS, Jamie Munro, Balfour + Manson LLP, 56-66 Frederick Street, EDINBURGH EH2 1LS
Tel: 0131 2001200
Email: jamie.foulis@balfour-manson.co.uk
Date Admitted: 12/09/2012

FRANCESCHI, Marika Simona Leonora, MacRoberts LLP, Excel House, 30 Semple Street, EDINBURGH EH3 8BL
Tel: 0131 2295046
Email: marika.franceschi@macroberts.com
Date Admitted: 15/10/2003

FRASER, Morag, Fraser Shepherd, 39 Vicar Street, FALKIRK FK1 1LL
Tel: 01324 630700
Email: morag@frasershepherd.co.uk
Date Admitted: 28/09/1987

FRENZ, Richard Alan, Miller Hendry, 10 Blackfriars Street, PERTH PH1 5NS
Tel: 01738 637311
Email: richardfrenz@millerhendry.co.uk
Date Admitted: 21/10/1980

GAILEY, Karen, Family Law Matters Scotland LLP, Queens House, 19 St. Vincent Place, GLASGOW G1 2DT
Tel: 0141 4202430
Email: karen.gailey@flmscotland.co.uk
Date Admitted: 28/09/1992

GALLAGHER, Jennifer, Lindsays LLP, Seabraes House, 18 Greenmarket, DUNDEE DD1 4QB
Tel: 01382 224112
Email: JenniferGallagher@lindsays.co.uk
Date Admitted: 16/11/1998

GEAR, Jennifer Morag, Harper Macleod LLP, St Olaf's Hall Church Road Lerwick SHETLAND ZE1 0FD
Tel: 01595 695583
Email: jenni.gear@harpermacleod.co.uk
Date Admitted: 30/09/2009

GEORGE, Linda Elizabeth, Linda George Family Law Limited, Mediacorp House, 2 Caird Park, HAMILTON ML3 0EU
Tel: 01698 459200
Email: leg@lgfamilylaw.co.uk
Date Admitted: 08/10/1991

GEORGE, Shaun Arthur, Brodies LLP, Brodies House, 31-33 Union Grove, ABERDEEN AB10 6SD
Tel: 01224 392242
Email: shaun.george@brodies.com
Date Admitted: 18/10/1988

GIANNELLI, Paula Elaine, GWG Ltd, 81 St. Vincent Street, GLASGOW G2 5TF
Tel: 0141 7769960
Email: paula@gwg-ltd.com
Date Admitted: 19/09/2005

GIBBONS, Karen Louise, Harper Macleod LLP, Citypoint 65, Haymarket Terrace, EDINBURGH EH12 5HD
Tel: 0131 2472500
Email: Karen.Gibbons@harpermacleod.co.uk
Date Admitted: 22/09/2004

GILMOUR, Robert Lister, SKO Family Law Specialists LLP, 18 George Street, EDINBURGH EH2 2PF
Tel: 0131 3226669
Email: robert.gilmour@sko-family.co.uk
Date Admitted: 22/10/1996

GIRDWOOD, Lisa Anne Irvine, Brodies LLP, 110 Queen Street, GLASGOW G1 3BX
Tel: 0141 2484672
Email: lisa.girdwood@brodies.com
Date Admitted: 02/10/1989

GORDON, Lesley Jane, BTO Solicitors LLP, One Edinburgh Quay, 133 Fountainbridge, EDINBURGH EH3 9QG
Tel: 0131 2222939
Email: lxg@bto.co.uk
Date Admitted: 03/02/1995

HARPER, Alexis Rachel, Harper Macleod LLP, The Ca'd'oro, 45 Gordon Street, GLASGOW G1 3PE
Tel: 0141 2218888
Email: alexis.harper@harpermacleod.co.uk
Date Admitted: 06/06/2008

HARRISON, Lynn Louisa, Beveridge & Kellas, 52 Leith Walk, Leith, EDINBURGH EH6 5HW
Tel: 0131 5546321
Email: l.harrison@beveridgekellas.com
Date Admitted: 27/10/1987

HIGSON, Judith May, Scullion Law Limited, 105 Cadzow Street, HAMILTON ML3 6HG
Tel: 01698 283265
Email: judith@scullionlaw.com
Date Admitted: 07/11/2001

HINCHIN, Michaela Louise, MTM Family Law LLP, 2nd Floor, 91 Mitchell Street, GLASGOW G1 3LN
Tel: 0141 6117535
Email: mh@mtmfamilylaw.co.uk
Date Admitted: 06/11/1987

HOOPER, Denise, Wright & Crawford (1906) Limited, 11 Glasgow Road, PAISLEY PA1 3QS
Tel: 0141 8876211
Email: D.Hooper@wright-crawford.co.uk
Date Admitted: 23/02/1995

HUNTER, Stuart David, Macnabs LLP, 10 Barossa Place, PERTH PH1 5JX
Tel: 01738 623432
Email: stuarthunter@macnabs-law.co.uk
Date Admitted: 18/10/1988

JACK, Karen Margaret
Date Admitted: 21/11/1991

JONES, Janice, Anderson Strathern LLP, George House, 50 George Square, GLASGOW G2 1EH
Tel: 0141 2426060
Email: janice.jones@andersonstrathern.co.uk
Date Admitted: 31/07/1989

KARLIN, Catherine Margaret, Horchheim Ltd, 15/16 Queen Street, EDINBURGH EH2 1JE
Tel: 0131 2401213
Email: cath@cathkarlinfamilylaw.co.uk
Date Admitted: 02/12/1992

KELSEY, Rachael Joy Christina, SKO Family Law Specialists LLP, 18 George Street, EDINBURGH EH2 2PF
Tel: 0131 3226669
Email: Rachael.Kelsey@sko-family.co.uk
Date Admitted: 22/10/1996

KERR, Nicola Louise, Brodies LLP, 15 Atholl Crescent, EDINBURGH EH3 8HA
Tel: 0131 2283777
Email: nicola.kerr@brodies.com
Date Admitted: 26/02/2008

KNIGHT, Grant Alexander, T.C. Young LLP, Melrose House, 69A George Street, EDINBURGH EH2 2JG
Tel: 0131 2207660
Email: gak@tcyoung.co.uk
Date Admitted: 02/08/1985

KNIGHT, Kirsten Isobell, Balfour + Manson LLP, 42 Carden Place, ABERDEEN AB10 1UP
Tel: 01224 498080
Email: Kirsten.knight@balfour-manson.co.uk
Date Admitted: 25/09/2008

LAVERTY, Denise Karen, Gilson Gray LLP, 160 West George Street, GLASGOW G2 2HG
Tel: 0141 5302021
Email: dlaverty@gilsongray.co.uk
Date Admitted: 31/01/2005

LAW, Janie Kerr, Family Law Matters Scotland LLP, Queens House, 19 St. Vincent Place, GLASGOW G1 2DT
Tel: 0141 4202430
Email: janie.law@flmscotland.co.uk
Date Admitted: 16/11/1987

LEWIS, Vicky Lee, T.C. Young LLP, Melrose House, 69A George Street, EDINBURGH EH2 2JG
Tel: 0131 2207660
Email: vll@tcyoung.co.uk
Date Admitted: 01/10/2001

LILLEY, Sarah Ann, Brodies LLP, 3 Fodderty Way, Dingwall Business Park, DINGWALL IV15 9XB
Tel: 01349 860111
Email: sarah.lilley@brodies.com
Date Admitted: 10/09/2007

MACANDREW, Hilary Anne Barrowman, Grant Smith Law Practice Limited, Old Bank Buildings, Balmellie Street, TURRIFF AB53 4DW
Tel: 01888 562245
Email: hilary.macandrew@grantsmithlaw.co.uk
Date Admitted: 01/10/1985

MACBRIDE, Carolyn Margaret, MTM Family Law LLP, 2nd Floor, 91 Mitchell Street, GLASGOW G1 3LN
Tel: 0141 6117535
Email: cmm@mtmfamilylaw.co.uk
Date Admitted: 03/12/1979

MACDONALD, Ewen Joseph, Anderson Shaw & Gilbert Limited, York House, 20 Church Street, INVERNESS IV1 1ED
Tel: 01463 236123
Email: ejm@solicitorsinverness.com
Date Admitted: 13/09/1989

MACDONALD, Rachael Hannah, Macnabs LLP, 10 Barossa Place, PERTH PH1 5JX

DX: PE122 PERTH
Tel: 01738 623432
Email: rachaelmacdonald@macnabs-law.co.uk
Date Admitted: 30/09/2009

MACKENZIE, WS, John Alexander, Stuart & Stuart, 25 Rutland Street, EDINBURGH EH1 2RN
Tel: 0131 2286449
Email: jmackenzie@stuartandstuart.co.uk
Date Admitted: 08/03/1983

MAITLES, Anna Claire, Morton Fraser LLP, 145 St Vincent Street, GLASGOW G2 5JF
Tel: 0141 2741100
Date Admitted: 05/12/2013

MARTIN, Nadine, Gibson Kerr Limited, 46 India Street, EDINBURGH EH3 6HJ
DX: 551100 EDINBURGH 7
Tel: 0131 2257558
Email: nadine.martin@gibsonkerr.co.uk
Date Admitted: 10/07/2006

MASSON, Amanda Elizabeth, Harper Macleod LLP, The Ca'd'oro, 45 Gordon Street, GLASGOW G1 3PE
Tel: 0141 2218888
Email: Amanda.Masson@harpermacleod.co.uk
Date Admitted: 03/12/2002

MASSON, Gareth Antony, Blackadders LLP, 6 Bon Accord Square, ABERDEEN AB11 6XU
Tel: 01224 588913
Email: gareth.masson@blackadders.co.uk
Date Admitted: 07/10/1993

MCINTOSH, Rowena Marie, McIntosh Family Law, 52-54 Albert Street, ABERDEEN AB25 1XS
Tel: 01224 593100
Email: rowena@mcintoshfamilylaw.com
Date Admitted: 20/09/1985

MCKAY, Donna, Brodies LLP, Brodies House, 31-33 Union Grove, ABERDEEN AB10 6SD
Tel: 01224 392242
Email: donna.mckay@brodies.com
Date Admitted: 15/02/2002

MCKEE, Alison Jayne, Lindsays LLP, 100 Queen Street, GLASGOW G1 3DN
Tel: 0141 2216551
Email: alisonmckee@lindsays.co.uk
Date Admitted: 18/02/1999

MCKERROW, Isabella, Affinity Family Law, 4 The Chalet, Broomknowe Road, KILMACOLM PA13 4JG
Tel: 01505873751/07739 639337
Email: isabella@affinityfamilylaw.co.uk
Date Admitted: 29/10/1993

MCLACHLAN, Lydia Ishbel, Brodies LLP, Brodies House, 31-33 Union Grove, ABERDEEN AB10 6SD
Tel: 01224 392242
Email: lydia.mclachlan@brodies.com
Date Admitted: 16/10/2006

MEIL, Judith Anne, Taggart Meil Mathers, 20 Bon Accord Square, ABERDEEN AB11 6DJ
Tel: 01224 588020
Email: judith@tmmsolicitors.co.uk
Date Admitted: 22/09/1983

METCALF, Ann Lucy, Thorntons Law LLP, City Point, 3rd Floor, 65 Haymarket Terrace, EDINBURGH EH12 5HD
Tel: 0131 2258705
Email: lmetcalf@thorntons-law.co.uk
Date Admitted: 13/05/1994

MILLAR, Caroline, SKO Family Law Specialists LLP, 18 George Street, EDINBURGH EH2 2PF
Tel: 0131 3226669
Email: caroline.millar@sko-family.co.uk
Date Admitted: 27/10/2009

MITCHELL, Gillian Elizabeth Smith, Patience & Buchan, 10 Golden Square, ABERDEEN AB10 1RB
Tel: 01224 648222
Email:gillian@patienceandbuchan.com Email:
Date Admitted: 05/09/2012

MONAGHAN, Martin Francis, Caesar & Howie, 107 Almondvale South, Almondvale Centre, LIVINGSTON EH54 6QT
Tel: 01506 435271
Email: mfm@caesar-howie.co.uk
Date Admitted: 11/09/1991

MOUNTAIN, Susannah Elizabeth, Brodies LLP, Brodies House, 31-33 Union Grove, ABERDEEN AB10 6SD
Tel: 01224 392242
Email: susie.mountain@brodies.com
Date Admitted: 05/10/2010

MUNDY, Fiona Margaret, Johnson Legal, 22a Rutland Square, EDINBURGH EH1 2BB
Tel: 0131 6228477
Email: fiona@johnsonlegal.co.uk
Date Admitted: 19/09/1984

MURRAY, Joanne Ronna, Blackadders LLP, 6 Bon Accord Square, ABERDEEN AB11 6XU
DX: AB152 ABERDEEN
Tel: 01224 588913
Email: joanne.murray@blackadders.co.uk
Date Admitted: 22/02/2008

MURRAY, Lynsey Carol, Mackintosh & Wylie LLP, 23 The Foregate KILMARNOCK KA1 1LE
Tel: 01563 525104
Email: lmurray@mackwylie.com
Date Admitted: 12/06/2009

MURRAY, Sharon
Date Admitted: 14/04/1987

NASH, Sally Elizabeth, Gilson Gray LLP, 29 Rutland Square, EDINBURGH EH1 2BW
Tel: 0131 5165354
Email: snash@gilsongray.co.uk
Date Admitted: 06/09/2004

NICOL, Karen Lynsey, Scottish Social Services Council Compass House, Discovery Quay, 11 Riverside Drive, DUNDEE DD1 4NY
Tel: 01382 721658
Email: Karen.Nicol@sssc.uk.com
Date Admitted: 26/01/2010

NOBLE, Rachael Evalyn, Brodies LLP, Brodies House, 31-33 Union Grove, ABERDEEN AB10 6SD
DX: AB10 ABERDEEN
Tel: 01224 392242

Email: rachael.noble@brodies.com
Date Admitted:: 13/05/2014

OGILVIE, Lindsey, Turcan Connell, Princes Exchange, 1 Earl Grey Street, EDINBURGH EH3 9EE
Tel: 0131 2288111
Email: lindsey.ogilvie@turcanconnell.com
Date Admitted: 05/08/2004

PATON, Carolyn Jayne, Elizabeth Welsh Family Law Practice, 26 Miller Road, AYR KA7 2AY
Tel: 01292 284786
Email: carolyn.paton@familylawpractice.co.uk
Date Admitted: 11/09/1985

POLSON, Jacqueline Alison
Date Admitted: 24/06/2005

RASMUSEN, Fiona Rosemary, Gibson Kerr, 46 India Street, EDINBURGH EH3 6HJ
Tel: 0131 225 7558
Email: fiona.rasmusen@gibsonkerr.co.uk
Date Admitted: 02/12/1981

REEKIE, Deborah Elizabeth, BTO Solicitors LLP, One Edinburgh Quay, 133 Fountainbridge EDINBURGH EH3 9QG
Tel: 0131 2222939
Email: der@bto.co.uk
Date Admitted: 13/07/2011

ROMANIS, Joanne Christine, Inksters, Top Floor, 24 West High Street, FORFAR DD8 1BA
Tel: 01307 497008
Email: joanne@inksters.com
Date Admitted: 11/08/1987

ROONEY, Brian James, Rooney Family Law Limited, 52 Main Street, UDDINGSTON G71 7LS
DX: 501052 UDDINGSTON
Tel: 01698 815620
Email: brian@rooneyfamilylaw.co.uk
Date Admitted: 30/10/2009

SASAN, Hazel Fiona, Morton Fraser LLP, 145 St Vincent Street, GLASGOW G2 5JF
Tel: 0141 2741100
Email: fiona.sasan@morton-fraser.com
Date Admitted: 30/09/1986

SHARP, Fiona Bain, Brodies LLP, 110 Queen Street, GLASGOW G1 3BX
Tel: 0141 2484672
Email: fiona.sharp@brodies.com
Date Admitted: 20/12/1996

SIMPSON, Ashley Marie, Patience & Buchan, 10 Golden Square, ABERDEEN AB10 1RB
Tel: 01224 648222
Email: ashley@patienceandbuchan.com
Date Admitted: 21/06/2006

SIMPSON, Joyce Denise, Jack Gowans & Marc Dickson Solicitors Limited, 46 Church Street INVERNESS IV1 1EH
Tel: 01463 71067
Email: joyce@gowansdickson.com
Date Admitted: 01/10/1993

SMITH, Jennifer Chloe, Harper Macleod LLP, The Ca'd'oro, 45 Gordon Street, GLASGOW G1 3PE
Tel: 0141 2218888

Email: jenny.smith@harpermacleod.co.uk
Date Admitted: 06/01/2003
SMITH, Richard Bryan, Brodies LLP, 15 Atholl
Crescent, EDINBURGH EH3 8HA
Tel: 0131 2283777
Email: richard.b.smith@brodies.com
Date Admitted: 19/12/1997
SMITH, Shona Houston, Balfour + Manson LLP,
56-66 Frederick Street, EDINBURGH EH2 1LS
Tel: 0131 2001200
Email: shona.smith@balfour-manson.co.uk
Date Admitted: 05/09/1991
SOMERVILLE, Emma Catherine Reading,
Ledingham Chalmers LLP, Johnstone House,
52-54 Rose Street, ABERDEEN AB10 1HA
Tel: 01224 408408
Email: emma.somerville@ledinghamchalmers.
com
Date Admitted: 28/08/2014
STEVENSON, Andrew Gordon, Waddell &
Mackintosh Solicitors Ltd, 36 West Portland
Street, TROON KA10 6AB
Tel: 01292 312222
DX: 557804 TROON
Email: andrew@wmtroon.co.uk
Date Admitted: 14/08/1990
STRATFORD, Lynne, Drummond Miller LLP, 11
White Hart Street, DALKEITH EH22 1AE
Tel: 0131 6639568
Email: lstratford@drummondmiller.co.uk
Date Admitted: 17/11/2003
STROUD, Jacqueline Anne, MacRoberts LLP, Excel
House, 30 Semple Street, EDINBURGH EH3
8BL
Tel: 0131 2295046
Email: Jacqueline.Stroud@macroberts.com
Date Admitted: 25/10/1990
SUTHERLAND, Sandra Mary, Thorntons Law LLP,
Brothockbank House, ARBROATH DD11 1NE
Tel: 01241 872683
Email: ssutherland@thorntons-law.co.uk
Date Admitted: 27/08/1991
SYM, Elaine Mary, Thorntons Law LLP, 53 East
High Street, FORFAR DD8 2EL
Tel: 01307 466886
Email: esym@thorntons-law.co.uk
Date Admitted: 01/02/1999
TAYLOR, Nina Ariella Salicath, Lindsays LLP,
Caledonian Exchange, 19A Canning Street,
EDINBURGH EH3 8HE
Tel: 0131 2291212
Email: NinaTaylor@lindsays.co.uk
Date Admitted: 19/08/1991
TEMPLETON, Shona Mary, MTM Family Law LLP,
2nd Floor, 91 Mitchell Street, GLASGOW G1
3LN
Tel: 0141 6117535
Email: smt@mtmfamilylaw.co.uk
Date Admitted: 05/10/1988
THOMSON, Elizabeth Brown, Anderson Shaw &
Gilbert Limited, York House, 20 Church Street,
INVERNESS IV1 1ED
Tel: 01463 236123

Email: ET@solicitorsinverness.com
Date Admitted: 12/11/2009
THOMSON, Iain Dallas, Balfour + Manson LLP,
56-66 Frederick Street, EDINBURGH EH2 1LS
Tel: 0131 2001200
Email: iain.thomson@balfour-manson.co.uk
Date Admitted: 12/09/2012
THOMSON, Jenna, Macleod & MacCallum
Limited, 28 Queensgate, INVERNESS IV1 1DJ
Tel: 01463 239393
Email: jenna.thomson@macandmac.co.uk
Date Admitted: 15/01/2009
WALI, Khalda, LKW Solicitors Ltd, 414 Cathcart
Road, GLASGOW G42 7BZ
Tel: 0141 4236999
Email: khalda.wali@lkwsolicitors.co.uk
Date Admitted: 02/07/2008
WALKER, Linda Ann, Harper Macleod LLP,
Citypoint, 65 Haymarket Terrace, EDINBURGH
EH12 5HD
DX: ED167 EDINBURGH
Tel: 0131 2472500
Email: Linda.Walker@harpermacleod.co.uk
Date Admitted: 31/10/2005
WALLACE, Cheryl Samantha, Thorntons Law LLP,
49 Bonnygate, CUPAR KY15 4BY
Tel: 01334 652285
Email: cherylwallace@thorntons-law.co.uk
Date Admitted: 25/06/2009
WIGHTMAN, Susan Jane, Kippen Campbell LLP,
48 Tay Street, PERTH PH1 5TR
Tel: 01738 635353
Email: sw@kcllp.co.uk
Date Admitted: 24/11/1987
WILKIE, Jennifer, Brodies LLP, 15 Atholl Crescent,
EDINBURGH EH3 8HA
Tel: 0131 5264003
Email: Jennifer.Wilkie@brodies.com
Date Admitted: 26/02/2008
WILSON, Amanda Anne, Amanda Wilson Family
Law, Office 12, 4th Floor, Dundee One, 5
West Victoria Dock Road, DUNDEE DD1 3JT
Tel: 01382 219004
Email: amanda@amandawilsonfamilylaw.co.uk
Date Admitted: 04/08/2006
WIPAT, Angela Patricia, Thorntons Law LLP,
Whitefriars House, 7 Whitefriars Crescent,
PERTH PH2 0PA
Tel: 01738 621212
Email: awipat@thorntons-law.co.uk
Date Admitted: 05/03/1996
WRAY, Zoe Hunter, Brodies LLP, 110 Queen
Street, GLASGOW G1 3BX
Tel: 0141 2484672
Email: zoe.wray@brodies.com
Date Admitted: 16/03/2009
WYLIE, Karen Sandra, Morton Fraser LLP, 145 St
Vincent Street, GLASGOW G2 5JF
Tel: 0141 2741100
Email: karen.wylie@morton-fraser.com
Date Admitted: 09/09/2005
YOUNG, Jacqueline May, The MFY Partnership,
25 Stirling Street, AIRDRIE ML6 0AH

Tel: 01236 607180
Email: jackie@mfypartnership.co.uk
Date Admitted: 16/08/1993
YOUNG, Jane Elizabeth, Innes & Mackay Limited, Kintail House, Beechwood Business Park, INVERNESS IV2 3BW
Tel: 01463 232273
Email: janey@innesmackay.com
Date Admitted: 16/10/1989
YOUNG, Julie Margaret, T. Duncan & Co., 192 High Street, MONTROSE DD10 8NA
Tel: 01674 672533
Email: julie@tduncan.com
Date Admitted: 01/07/2004

Family Mediation

ABERDEIN, Ruth Mary, Aberdein Considine and Company, 5-9 Bon Accord Crescent, ABERDEEN AB11 6DN
Tel: 01224 589700
Email: raberdein@acandco.com
Date Admitted: 14/08/2000
ADAMS, Rhona Anne, Morton Fraser LLP, Quartermile Two, 2 Lister Square, EDINBURGH EH3 9GL
Tel: 0131 2471000
Email: rhona.adams@morton-fraser.com
Date Admitted: 26/04/1991
BARRETT, Angela O'Hara, Russel & Aitken Denny LLP, 22 & 24 Stirling Street, DENNY FK6 6AZ
Tel: 01324 822194
Email: ab@radenny.co.uk
Date Admitted: 09/11/1992
BLACKWOOD, Jane Alexandra, Harper Macleod LLP, The Ca'd'oro 45 Gordon Street, GLASGOW G1 3PE
Tel: 0141 2218888
Email: jane.blackwood@harpermacleod.co.uk
Date Admitted: 26/02/2010
BOWMAN, Gillian Louise, Cairns Brown, 112 Main Street, ALEXANDRIA G83 0NZ
Tel: 01389 756979
Email: g.bowman@cairnsbrown.co.uk
Date Admitted: 06/09/2013
BROPHY, Anne, Brophy Carey & Co Ltd, Mediacorp House, 2 Caird Park, HAMILTON ML3 0EU
Tel: 01698 200111
Email: ab@brophycareylaw.com
Date Admitted: 27/08/1991
BROWN, Cheryl Prentice, McWhinney Richards, 66 Stirling Street, AIRDRIE ML6 0AW
Tel: 01236 754571
Email: cheryl.brown@mcwhinneyrichards.com
Date Admitted: 21/10/1986
BUCHAN, Lorna Gilmore, Patience & Buchan, 10 Golden Square, ABERDEEN AB10 1RB
Tel: 01224 648222
Email: lorna@patienceandbuchan.com
Date Admitted: 29/09/1994
BUCHANAN, Nicola Jean, Berrymans Lace Mawer LLP, 13 Bath Street, GLASGOW G2 1HY

Tel: 0141 3532121
Email: Nicola.Buchanan@blmlaw.com
Date Admitted: 20/10/1994
BURKE, Leonie Sarah Rose, Aberdein Considine and Company, 2nd Floor, East Suite Elder House Multrees Walk, EDINBURGH EH1 3DX
Tel: 0333 0044333
Email: lburke@acandco.com
Date Admitted: 25/09/2001
BYTH, Sheila Janet, McKinnon Forbes, 54 High Street, TRANENT EH33 1HH
Tel: 01875 611211
Email: sheila.byth@mckinnonforbes.co.uk
Date Admitted: 20/06/1997
CAMPBELL, Fiona Jane, Macleod & MacCallum Limited, 28 Queensgate, INVERNESS IV1 1DJ
Tel: 01463 239393
Email: fiona.campbell@macandmac.co.uk
Date Admitted: 20/11/1989
CAREY, Fiona Janet, Brophy Carey & Co Ltd, Mediacorp House, 2 Caird Park, HAMILTON ML3 0EU
Tel: 01698 200111
Email: fjc@brophycareylaw.com
Date Admitted: 11/07/1989
CARTHY, Jade Elizabeth, A.C. O'Neill & Co., Second Floor, 32 High Street, DUMBARTON G82 1LL
Tel: 01389 762997
Date Admitted: 06/10/2011
CLARK, Lucia Elaine, Morton Fraser LLP, Quartermile Two, 2 Lister Square, EDINBURGH EH3 9GL
Tel: 0131 2471000
Email: lucia.clark@morton-fraser.com
Date Admitted: 06/09/2004
COLLEDGE, Jennifer Claire, Colledge & Shields LLP, 30 Castle Street, DUMFRIES DG1 1DU
Tel: 01387 240044
Email: jcc@colledgeandshields.co.uk
Date Admitted: 02/09/1996
DOCHERTY, Scott Charles, McArthur Stanton, 40 High Street, DUMBARTON G82 1LL
Tel: 01389 762266
Email: sd@mcarthurstanton.co.uk
Date Admitted: 25/09/2001
DONALD, Faye Louise, Raeburn Christie Clark & Wallace LLP, 12-16 Albyn Place, ABERDEEN AB10 1PS
Tel: 01224 332400
Email: faye.donald@raeburns.co.uk
Date Admitted: 24/04/2006
FEENEY, Sarah Louise Helen, Gilson Gray LLP, 160 West George Street, GLASGOW G2 2HG
Tel: 0141 5302021
Email: sfeeney@gilsongray.co.uk
Date Admitted: 16/01/2008
FERGUSON, Jane Margaret Wilson, R & R Urquhart LLP, 117-121 High Street, FORRES IV36 1AB
Tel: 01309 672216
Email: janeferguson@r-r-urquhart.com
Date Admitted: 27/11/1990

FRASER, Morag, Fraser Shepherd, 39 Vicar Street, FALKIRK FK1 1LL
Tel: 01324 630700
Email: morag@frasershepherd.co.uk
Date Admitted: 28/09/1987

GEORGE, Shaun Arthur, Brodies LLP, Brodies House, 31-33 Union Grove, ABERDEEN AB10 6SD
Tel: 01224 392242
Email: shaun.george@brodies.com
Date Admitted: 18/10/1988

GIBBONS, Karen Louise, Harper Macleod LLP, Citypoint, 65 Haymarket Terrace, EDINBURGH EH12 5HD
Tel: 0131 2472500
Email: Karen.Gibbons@harpermacleod.co.uk
Date Admitted: 22/09/2004

GILLIES, Louise Mary, Ness Gallagher Solicitors Limited, 358 Brandon Street, MOTHERWELL ML1 1XA
Tel: 01698 254644
Email: LG@nessgallagher.co.uk
Date Admitted: 16/08/2007

GILMOUR, Robert Lister, SKO Family Limited, 18 George Street, EDINBURGH EH2 2PF
Tel: 0131 3226669
Email: robert.gilmour@sko-family.co.uk
Date Admitted: 22/10/1996

GIRDWOOD, Lisa Marie Irvine, Brodies LLP, 110 Queen Street, GLASGOW G1 3BX
Tel: 0141 2484672
Email: lisa.girdwood@brodies.com
Date Admitted: 02/10/1989

GORDON, Lesley Jane, BTO Solicitors LLP, One Edinburgh Quay, 133 Fountainbridge, EDINBURGH EH3 9QG
Tel: 0131 2222939
Email: lxg@bto.co.uk
Date Admitted: 03/02/1995

GOSTELOW, Paul Gerard, Baker Gostelow Law Limited, 36 Cadzow Street, HAMILTON ML3 6DG
Tel: 01698 820700
Email: paul@bgfamilylaw.co.uk
Date Admitted: 10/03/1995

HIGSON, Judith May, Scullion Law Limited, 105 Cadzow Street, HAMILTON ML3 6HG
Tel: 01698 283265
Email: judith@scullionlaw.com
Date Admitted: 07/11/2001

HINCHIN, Michaela Louise, MTM Family Law LLP, 2nd Floor, 91 Mitchell Street, GLASGOW G1 3LN
Tel: 0141 6117535
Email: mh@mtmfamilylaw.co.uk
Date Admitted: 06/11/1987

HOOPER, Denise, Wright & Crawford (1906) Limited, 11 Glasgow Road, PAISLEY PA1 3QS
Tel: 0141 8876211
Email: D.Hooper@wright-crawford.co.uk
Date Admitted: 23/02/1995

HUGHES, Helen, McAuley, McCarthy & Co., 29 Moss Street, PAISLEY PA1 1DL
Tel: 0141 5617779
Email: h.hughes-paisley@btconnect.com
Date Admitted: 22/08/1988

HUNTER, Alexis Margaret, Alexis Hunter Family Law, Cartside House, 1/7 Clarkston Road Cathcart, GLASGOW G44 4EF
Tel: 0141 4040124
Email: amh@ahfamilylaw.co.uk
Date Admitted: 04/08/1977

KARLIN, Catherine Margaret, Horchheim Ltd, 15/16 Queen Street, EDINBURGH EH2 1JE
Tel: 0131 2401213
Email: cath@cathkarlinfamilylaw.co.uk
Date Admitted: 02/12/1992

KELSEY, Rachael Joy Christina, SKO Family Law Specialists LLP, 18 George Street, EDINBURGH EH2 2PF
Tel: 0131 3226669
Email: Rachael.Kelsey@sko-family.co.uk
Date Admitted: 22/10/1996

LANG, Margaret Jane, Russel & Aitken (Falkirk & Alloa) Ltd, Kings Court High Street, FALKIRK FK1 1PQ
Tel: 01324 622888
Email: margaretlang@russel-aitken.co.uk
Date Admitted: 30/10/1984

LAVERTY, Denise Karen, Gilson Gray LLP, 160 West George Street, GLASGOW G2 2HG
Tel: 0141 5302021
Email: dlaverty@gilsongray.co.uk
Date Admitted: 31/01/2005

LAW, Janie Kerr, Family Law Matters Scotland LLP, Queens House, 19 St. Vincent Place, GLASGOW G1 2DT
Tel: 0141 4202430
Email: janie.law@flmscotland.co.uk
Date Admitted: 16/11/1987

LIDDIARD, Simon James Carnegie, Stewart & Watson, 35 Queen Street, PETERHEAD AB42 1TP
Tel: 01779 476351
Email: sliddiard@stewartwatson.co.uk
Date Admitted: 02/07/1996

LOTHIAN, Ailie Joanna, Smail & Ewart, 68-70 High Street, LANARK ML11 7ES
Tel: 01555 666111
Email: alothian@smail-ewart.co.uk
Date Admitted: 06/09/2004

MACANDREW, Hilary Anne Barrowman, Grant Smith Law Practice Limited, Old Bank Buildings, Balmellie Street, TURRIFF AB53 4DW
Tel: 01888 562245
Email: hilary.macandrew@grantsmithlaw.co.uk
Date Admitted: 01/10/1985

MALLOY, Ann Jane Reid Watt, Lanarkshire Community Law Centre Ltd, C/o Airdrie Citizens Advice (First Floor), 61A Stirling Street, AIRDRIE ML6 0AS
Tel: 01236 757 337
Date Admitted: 09/07/2008

MARTIN, Nadine, Gibson Kerr Limited, 46 India Street, EDINBURGH EH3 6HJ
DX: 551100 EDINBURGH 7

Tel: 0131 2257558
Email: nadine.martin@gibsonkerr.co.uk
Date Admitted: 10/07/2006

MASSON, Amanda Elizabeth, Harper Macleod
LLP, The Ca'd'oro, 45 Gordon Street,
GLASGOW G1 3PE
Tel: 0141 2218888
Email: Amanda.Masson@harpermacleod.co.uk
Date Admitted: 03/12/2002

MCINTOSH, Rowena Marie, McIntosh Family
Law, 52-54 Albert Street, ABERDEEN AB25 1XS
Tel: 01224 593100
Email: rowena@mcintoshfamilylaw.com
Date Admitted: 20/09/1985

MCKAY, Donna, Brodies LLP, Brodies House,
31-33 Union Grove, ABERDEEN AB10 6SD
Tel: 01224 392242
Email: donna.mckay@brodies.com
Date Admitted: 15/02/2002

MCLACHLAN, Lindsey Ann, LAM Family Law,
Studio 3015, Mile End Mill Abbey Mill
Business Centre, 12 Seedhill Road, PAISLEY
PA1 1JS
Tel: 0141 8890101
Email: enquiry@lamfamilylaw.co.uk
Date Admitted: 04/02/1994

MCLACHLAN, Lydia Ishbel, Brodies LLP, Brodies
House, 31-33 Union Grove, ABERDEEN AB10
6SD
Tel: 01224 392242
Email: lydia.mclachlan@brodies.com
Date Admitted: 16/10/2006

MCLAUGHLAN, Lisa Marie, Stirling & Mair
Limited, 28 High Street, JOHNSTONE PA5 8AH
Tel: 01505 329373
Email: lisa.mclaughlan@stirlingmair.com
Date Admitted: 10/08/2004

MCWILLIAMS, Gerald Thomas, Cowan & Co., 81
Berkeley Street, GLASGOW G3 7DX
Tel: 0141 2211803
Email: gmcw@cowanandco.co.uk
Date Admitted: 16/10/1990

MEIL, Judith Anne, Taggart Meil Mathers, 20 Bon
Accord Square, ABERDEEN AB11 6DJ
Tel: 01224 588020
Email: judith@tmmsolicitors.co.uk
Date Admitted: 22/09/1983

MONAGHAN, Catherine Mary, Moore & Partners
LLP, Lennox House, Lennox Road, Seafar,
CUMBERNAULD G67 1LL
Tel: 01236 727715
Email: cmonaghan@moorepartners.com
Date Admitted: 18/09/1992

MURRAY, Joanne Ronna, Blackadders LLP, 6 Bon
Accord Square, ABERDEEN AB11 6XU
Tel: 01224 588913
Email: joanne.murray@blackadders.co.uk
Date Admitted: 22/02/2008

MURRAY, Sharon
Date Admitted: 14/04/1987

OSWALD, Susan Margaret, SKO Family Law
Specialists LLP, 18 George Street, EDINBURGH
EH2 2PF

Tel: 0131 3226669
Email: Susan.Oswald@sko-family.co.uk
Date Admitted: 16/10/1995

POLSON, Jacqueline Alison
Date Admitted: 24/06/2005

PURVIS, Susan Elizabeth Collin, Ledingham
Chalmers LLP, Johnstone House, 52-54 Rose
Street, ABERDEEN AB10 1HA
Tel: 01224 408408
Email: susan.purvis@ledinghamchalmers.com
Date Admitted: 23/09/1996

RASMUSEN, Fiona Rosemary, Gibson Kerr, 46
India Street, EDINBURGH EH3 6HJ
Tel: 0131 2257558
Email: fiona.rasmusen@gibsonkerr.co.uk
Date Admitted: 02/12/1981

REEKIE, Deborah Elizabeth, BTO Solicitors LLP,
One Edinburgh Quay, 133 Fountainbridge,
EDINBURGH EH3 9QG
Tel: 0131 2222939
Email: der@bto.co.uk
Date Admitted: 13/07/2011

RIDDELL, Vivien Margaret, T.C. Young LLP,
Melrose House, 69A George Street,
EDINBURGH EH2 2JG
Tel: 0131 2207660
Email: vmr@tcyoung.co.uk
Date Admitted: 20/10/2009

SCHOLARIOS, Nicos, MSM Solicitors Limited, 51
Moss Street, PAISLEY PA1 1DR
Tel: 0141 8896244
Email: ns@msmlaw.co.uk
Date Admitted: 05/12/1983

SHIELDS, Sandi Marie Anne, Colledge & Shields
LLP, 30 Castle Street, DUMFRIES DG1 1DU
Tel: 01387 240044
Email: ss@colledgeandshields.co.uk
Date Admitted: 23/03/2012

SIMPSON, Ashley Marie, Patience & Buchan, 10
Golden Square, ABERDEEN AB10 1RB
Tel: 01224 648222
Email: ashley@patienceandbuchan.com
Date Admitted: 21/06/2006

SMITH, Caroline Leslie, MTM Family Law LLP,
2nd Floor, 91 Mitchell Street, GLASGOW G1
3LN
Tel: 0141 6117535
Email: cs@mtmfamilylaw.co.uk
Date Admitted: 17/10/1996

SMITH, Jennifer Chloe, Harper Macleod LLP, The
Ca'd'oro 45 Gordon Street, GLASGOW G1
3PE
Tel: 0141 2218888
Email: jenny.smith@harpermacleod.co.uk
Date Admitted: 06/01/2003

SMITH, Richard Bryan, Brodies LLP, 15 Atholl
Crescent, EDINBURGH EH3 8HA
Tel: 0131 2283777
Email: richard.b.smith@brodies.com
Date Admitted: 19/12/1997

SMITH, Shona Houston, Balfour + Manson LLP,
56-66 Frederick Street, EDINBURGH EH2 1LS
Tel: 0131 2001200

Email: shona.smith@balfour-manson.co.uk
Date Admitted: 05/09/1991

STRATFORD, Lynne, Drummond Miller LLP, 11
White Hart Street, DALKEITH EH22 1AE
Tel: 0131 6639568
Email: lstratford@drummondmiller.co.uk
Date Admitted: 17/11/2003

STROUD, Jacqueline Anne, MacRoberts LLP, Excel
House, 30 Semple Street, EDINBURGH EH3
8BL
Tel: 0131 2295046
Email: Jacqueline.Stroud@macroberts.com
Date Admitted: 25/10/1990

STURROCK, Garry John, Brodies LLP, Brodies
House, 31-33 Union Grove, ABERDEEN AB10
6SD
Tel: 01224 392242
Email: garry.sturrock@brodies.com
Date Admitted: 12/07/2013

TEMPLETON, Shona Mary, MTM Family Law LLP,
2nd Floor, 91 Mitchell Street, GLASGOW G1
3LN
Tel: 0141 6117535
Email: smt@mtmfamilylaw.co.uk
Date Admitted: 05/10/1988

WILKIE, Jennifer, Brodies LLP, 15 Atholl Crescent,
EDINBURGH EH3 8HA
Tel: 0131 5264003
Email: Jennifer.Wilkie@brodies.com
Date Admitted: 26/02/2008

YOUNG, Jacqueline May, The MFY Partnership,
25 Stirling Street, AIRDRIE ML6 0AH
Tel: 01236 607180
Email: jackie@mfypartnership.co.uk
Date Admitted: 16/08/1993

Immigration Law

DUHERIC, Damir, D. Duheric & Co Solicitors, 23
Castle Street, Third Floor, EDINBURGH EH2
3DN
Tel: 0131 2255444
Email: damir.duheric@dduhericsolicitors.co.uk
Date Admitted: 18/01/2005

LATTA, Fraser Paterson, Latta Law Limited, 2nd
Floor, 137 Sauchiehall Street, GLASGOW G2
3EW
Tel: 0141 2222185
Email: fl@lattalaw.co.uk
Date Admitted: 13/11/2003

MCGILL, Grace Margaret, Burness Paull LLP, 50
Lothian Road, Festival Square, EDINBURGH
EH3 9WJ
DX: ED73 EDINBURGH
Tel: 0131 4736000
Email: grace.mcgill@burnesspaull.com

MCWILLIAMS, Stuart Alistair, Morton Fraser LLP,
145 St Vincent Street, GLASGOW G2 5JF
Tel: 0141 2741100
Email: Stuart.McWilliams@morton-fraser.com
Date Admitted: 15/10/2008

MOORE, Jacqueline Hazel, Shepherd and
Wedderburn LLP, 1 Exchange Crescent,
Conference Square, EDINBURGH EH3 8UL
Tel: 0131 2289900
Email: Jacqueline.Moore@shepwedd.com
Date Admitted: 13/09/1999

SPEIRS, Arlene Fiona, Latta Law Limited, 2nd
Floor, 137 Sauchiehall Street, GLASGOW G2
3EW
Tel: 0141 222 2185
Email: as@lattalaw.co.uk
Date Admitted: 14/06/2007

TODD, Jennifer Aileen, Freedom From Torture
Scotland, Room 24, The Adelphi Centre, 12
Commercial Road, GLASGOW G5 0PQ
Tel: 0141 4203161
Email: Jennifer.Todd@centralenglandlc.org.uk
Date Admitted: 10/07/2006

VASSILIOU, John, Shepherd and Wedderburn LLP,
1 Exchange Crescent, Conference Square,
EDINBURGH EH3 8UL
DX: 551971 EDINBURGH 53
Tel: 0131 2289900
Email: john.vassiliou@shepwedd.com
Date Admitted: 03/10/2012

Incapacity & Mental Disability Law

BROWN, Gillian Jane, Blackadders LLP, 53
Bothwell Street, GLASGOW G2 6TS
Tel: 0141 2481888
Email: gillian.brown@blackadders.co.uk
Date Admitted: 15/08/1988

FOWLER, The Scottish Parliament, Solicitor's
Office, EDINBURGH EH99 1SP
Email: linda.fowler@parliament.scot
Date Admitted: 14/11/2008

HURST, Lesley Anne, Macallans Limited, 236
Stonelaw Road, Burnside, GLASGOW G73 3SA
Tel: 0141 6131787/6474441
Email: lah@macallans.co.uk
Date Admitted: 05/10/1990

IRVINE, Francis Joseph, Frank Irvine Solicitors Ltd,
Carlton Buildings, 63 Carlton Place,
GLASGOW G5 9TW
Tel: 0141 3759000
Email: fji@frankirvine.com
Date Admitted: 18/10/1995

LAW, Elizabeth Jean Marie, Brodies LLP, 3
Fodderty Way, Dingwall Business Park,
DINGWALL IV15 9XB
Tel: 01349 860111
Email: lisa.law@brodies.com
Date Admitted: 08/02/2007

MCDOWALL, Laura, Blackadders LLP, 30/34
Reform Street, DUNDEE DD1 1RJ
Tel: 01382 229222
Email: laura.mcdowall@blackadders.co.uk
Date Admitted: 24/09/2007

MONAGHAN, Martin Francis, Caesar & Howie,
107 Almondvale South, Almondvale Centre,
LIVINGSTON EH54 6QT
Tel: 01506 435271

Email: mfm@caesar-howie.co.uk
Date Admitted: 11/09/1991

RALSTON, Alan Mark, Wright & Crawford (1906) Limited, 11 Glasgow Road, PAISLEY PA1 3QS
Tel: 0141 8876211
Email: M.Ralston@wright-crawford.co.uk
Date Admitted: 30/10/1991

WINSKILL, Donald, Gillespie Macandrew LLP, 5 Atholl Crescent, EDINBURGH EH3 8EJ
Tel: 0131 2251677
Email: donald.winskill@gillespiemacandrew.co.uk
Date Admitted: 29/05/2001

Insolvency Law

BAIJAL, Eric Marcus, BBM Solicitors Limited, Unit 5B, Wick Business Park, WICK KW1 4QR
Tel: 01955 604188
Email: emb@bbmsolicitors.co.uk
Date Admitted: 13/06/2005

BUCHANAN, Karen Elaine, Buchanan Macleod, 180 West Regent Street, GLASGOW G2 4RW
Tel: 0141 2214440
Email: KBuchanan@buchananmacleod.co.uk
Date Admitted: 28/09/1987

CARR, Stephanie Margaret Mary, Blackadders LLP, 53 Bothwell Street GLASGOW G2 6TS
Tel: 0141 2481888
Email: Stephanie.Carr@blackadders.co.uk
Date Admitted: 16/09/1999

CARTY, Gillian Anne, Shepherd and Wedderburn LLP, 1 Exchange Crescent, Conference Square, EDINBURGH EH3 8UL
Tel: 0131 2289900
Email: Gillian.Carty@shepwedd.com
Date Admitted: 08/02/1995

CLARKE, WS, John Bernard, Wright, Johnston & Mackenzie LLP, Crescent House, Carnegie Campus, DUNFERMLINE KY11 8GR
Tel: 01383 626666
Email: jbc@wjm.co.uk
Date Admitted: 23/11/1979

FREEMAN, Alasdair Charles, Burness Paull LLP, Union Plaza, 1 Union Wynd, ABERDEEN AB10 1DQ
Tel: 01224 621621
Email: Alasdair.Freeman@burnesspaull.com
Date Admitted: 13/02/1997

HOLLERIN, Gordon Craig Hollerin, Harper Macleod LLP, The Ca'd'oro 45 Gordon Street, GLASGOW G1 3PE
Tel: 0141 2218888
Email: gordon.hollerin@harpermacleod.co.uk
Date Admitted: 03/11/1980

JANSCH, Steven William, Gilson Gray LLP, 29 Rutland Square, EDINBURGH EH1 2BW
Tel: 0131 5165354
Email: sjansch@gilsongray.co.uk
Date Admitted: 29/10/2002

JONES, Calum Symon, Kepstorn Solicitors Limited, 7 St. James Terrace, Lochwinnoch Road, KILMACOLM PA13 4HB
Tel: 07935 228791
Email: calum.jones@kepstorn.co.uk
Date Admitted: 16/09/1988

LLOYD, James Semple, Harper Macleod LLP, The Ca'd'oro 45 Gordon Street GLASGOW G1 3PE
Tel: 0141 2218888
Email: james.lloyd@harpermacleod.co.uk
Date Admitted: 23/10/1989

MASSIE, Claire Catherine Lindsay, Pinsent Masons LLP, Level 7, 141 Bothwell Street, GLASGOW G2 7EQ
Tel: 0141 5678400
Email: claire.massie@pinsentmasons.com
Date Admitted: 02/10/1997

MOFFAT, Gary John, Burness Paull LLP, 120 Bothwell Street, GLASGOW G2 7JL
Tel: 0141 2484933
Email: Gary.Moffat@burnesspaull.com
Date Admitted: 17/09/1991

SWEENEY, Allana Clair Breaden, Burness Paull LLP, 120 Bothwell Street, GLASGOW G2 7JL
Tel: 0141 2484933
Email: allana.sweeney@burnesspaull.com
Date Admitted: 20/10/2008

THOMSON, Michael Philip, Burness Paull LLP, 120 Bothwell Street, GLASGOW G2 7JL
Tel: 0141 2484933
Email: michael.thomson@burnesspaull.com
Date Admitted: 24/07/2009

Intellectual Property

BOAG-THOMSON, Joanna Susan, Shepherd and Wedderburn LLP, 1 West Regent Street, GLASGOW G2 1RW
Tel: 0141 5669900
Email: joanna.bt@shepwedd.com
Date Admitted: 15/11/1990

CRUICKSHANK, Colin Mark, National Westminster Bank PLC, Group Legal, Business House G, P.O. Box 1000, EDINBURGH EH12 1HQ
Email: mark.cruickshank@rbs.co.uk
Date Admitted: 17/10/2005

DUNCAN, Euan Findlay, MacRoberts LLP, Capella, 60 York Street, GLASGOW G2 8JX
Tel: 0141 3031100
Email: euan.duncan@macroberts.com
Date Admitted: 04/01/1991

FERGUSON-SNEDDEN, Historic Environment Scotland, Longmore House, Salisbury Place, EDINBURGH EH9 1SH
Tel: 0131 6688987
Email: susan.ferguson-snedden@hes.scot
Date Admitted: 02/06/2003

FLINT, David, Inksters, The Exchange, 142 St. Vincent Street, GLASGOW G2 5LA
Tel: 0141 2290880
Email: david.flint@inksters.com
Date Admitted: 13/12/1979

FORSYTH, John Francis, Lloyds Banking Group
Plc, Sighthill North, Mail Area 38, Sighthill
North, 2 Bankhead Crossway North,
EDINBURGH EH11 4EF
Tel: 07824 320663
Email: John.Forsyth@lloydsbanking.com
Date Admitted: 02/10/1989
GOURLAY, David McRae, MacRoberts LLP, Excel
House, 30 Semple Street, EDINBURGH EH3
8BL
Tel: 0131 2295046
Email: david.gourlay@macroberts.com
Date Admitted: 29/09/1994
HARRIS, Andrew John Forsyth, MBM Commercial
LLP, 5th Floor, 125 Princes Street, EDINBURGH
EH2 4AD
Tel: 0131 2268200
Email: andy.harris@mbmcommercial.co.uk
Date Admitted: 21/10/1993
HULME, Colin James Kennedy, Burness Paull LLP,
120 Bothwell Street, GLASGOW G2 7JL
Tel: 0141 2484933
Email: Colin.Hulme@burnesspaull.com
Date Admitted: 23/09/1996
KERR, Scott Thomas Reid, Harper Macleod LLP,
Citypoint, 65 Haymarket Terrace, EDINBURGH
EH12 5HD
Tel: 0131 2472500
Email: scott.kerr@harpermacleod.co.uk
Date Admitted: 01/11/1988
LOW, Lindesay Matheson, Scotch Whisky
Association, 1st Floor, Quartermile, Two 2
Lister Square, EDINBURGH EH3 9GL
Tel: 0131 2229258
Email: llow@swa.org.uk
Date Admitted: 11/12/1991
MILNE, Claire Catherine, Appleby, 33 Athol
Street, DOUGLAS IM1 1LB ISLE OF MAN
Tel: 01624 647647
Email: cmilne@applebyglobal.com
Date Admitted: 14/12/1992
NICOLSON, Fiona Margaret McLean, Keystone
Law Limited, 48 Chancery Lane, LONDON
WC2A 1JF
Tel: 020 33193700
Email: fiona.nicolson@keystonelaw.co.uk
Date Admitted: 13/10/1986
RICHMOND, Lynn Richmond, BTO Solicitors LLP,
One Edinburgh Quay, 133 Fountainbridge,
EDINBURGH EH3 9QG
Tel: 0131 2222939
Email: lyr@bto.co.uk
Date Admitted: 07/11/2005
THOMAS, Neeraj, CMS Cameron McKenna
Nabarro Olswang LLP, 1 West Regent Street,
GLASGOW G2 1AP
Tel: 0141 2222200
Email: Neeraj.Thomas@cms-cmno.com
Date Admitted: 14/09/2009
WATT, Jamie Douglas Sinclair, Harper Macleod
LLP, Citypoint, 65 Haymarket Terrace,
EDINBURGH EH12 5HD
Tel: 0131 2472500
Email: jamie.watt@harpermacleod.co.uk
Date Admitted: 06/02/2006

Liquor Licensing Law
CUMMINS, John Carlisle, Hill Brown Licensing,
RWF House, 5 Renfield Street, GLASGOW G2
5EZ
Tel: 0141 221 1919
Email: JCC@mshblicensing.com
Date Admitted: 02/10/1978
DAWSON, Anthony James, James & George
Collie LLP, 1 East Craibstone Street, ABERDEEN
AB11 6YQ
Tel: 01224 581581
Email: a.dawson@jgcollie.co.uk
Date Admitted: 13/11/1975
HOOD, Janet Hebe, Janet Hood Training and
Consulting Limited, Kirkton of Balfour
Farmhouse, Edzell, BRECHIN DD9 7XU
Tel: 01356 648966
Email: janethood@me.com
Date Admitted: 09/01/1984
HUNTER, Andrew John, Harper Macleod LLP, The
Ca'd'oro, 45 Gordon Street, GLASGOW G1
3PE
Tel: 0141 2218888
Email: andrew.hunter@harpermacleod.co.uk
Date Admitted: 28/08/2002
JUNNER, Audrey Anne, Hill Brown Licensing,
RWF House, 5 Renfield Street, GLASGOW G2
5EZ
Tel: 0141 3323265
Email: AJunner@hillbrown.co.uk
Date Admitted: 0/08/2009
LOUDON, Caroline Kate Powlett, TLT LLP, Once
Redcliff Street, BRISTOL BS1 6TP
Tel: 0333 0060000
Email: Caroline.Loudon@TLTsolicitors.com
Date Admitted: 28/08/2002
MACIVER, Archibald Duncan, Brunton Miller,
Herbert House, 22 Herbert Street, GLASGOW
G20 6NB
Tel: 0141 3371199
Email: archiemaciver@bruntonmiller.com
Date Admitted: 20/10/1982
MCGOWAN, Stephen John, TLT LLP, 140 West
George Street, GLASGOW G2 2HG
Tel: 0333 0060400
Email: Stephen.McGowan@TLTsolicitors.com
Date Admitted: 27/08/2010

Medical Negligence
CERESA, Laura Viviana Maria, Peacock Johnston,
Ashfield House, 402 Sauchiehall Street,
GLASGOW G2 3JD
Tel: 0141 3339505
Email: lvmc@peacockjohnston.co.uk
Date Admitted: 16/11/1982
COULL, Elaine Rose, National Health Service
Scotland, Anderson House, Breadalbane St,
Bonnington Road, EDINBURGH EH6 5JR
Tel: 0131 2757800

Email: elaine.coull@nhs.scot
Date Admitted: 23/10/1989

DEERY, Darren James Crilley, Drummond Miller
LLP, Glenorchy House, 20 Union Street,
EDINBURGH EH1 3LR
DX: ED104 EDINBURGH
Tel: 0131 2265151
Email: DDeery@drummondmiller.co.uk
Date Admitted: 11/08/2008

GOSNEY, Joanne Margaret, Digby Brown LLP,
Causewayside House, 160 Causewayside,
EDINBURGH EH9 1PR
Tel: 0333 2005925
Email: Joanne.Gosney@digbybrown.co.uk
Date Admitted: 15/10/2009

GRIEG, Lynne Jenny Isobelle, National Health
Service Scotland, Anderson House,
Breadalbane St, Bonnington Road,
EDINBURGH EH6 5JR
Tel: 0131 2757800
Email: lynne.greig@nhs.net
Date Admitted: 06/03/1991

KANE, Dianne, National Health Service Scotland,
Anderson House, Breadalbane St, Bonnington
Road, EDINBURGH EH6 5JR
Tel: 0131 2757800
Email: dianne.kane@nhs.scot
Date Admitted: 05/03/1997

KELLIHER, Ruth Sarah Anne, Digby Brown LLP, 2
West Regent Street, GLASGOW G2 1RW
Tel: 0131 3198148
Email: ruth.kelliher@digbybrown.co.uk
Date Admitted: 24/04/2002

LANG, Kathleen Heather, Irwin Mitchell Scotland
LLP, 150 St Vincent Street, GLASGOW G2 5NE
Tel: 0141 3004300
Email: kathleen.lang@irwinmitchell.com
Date Admitted: 28/01/1983

LOGAN, Ann Agnes, Balfour + Manson LLP,
56-66 Frederick Street, EDINBURGH EH2 1LS
Tel: 0131 2001200
Email: ann.logan@balfour-manson.co.uk
Date Admitted: 15/02/1989

MCFADDEN, Patricia Mary, Digby Brown LLP,
Causewayside House, 160 Causewayside,
EDINBURGH EH9 1PR
Tel: 0333 2005925
Email: trish.mcfadden@digbybrown.co.uk
Date Admitted: 19/10/2000

ROSE, Elizabeth Paterson, Levy & McRae
Solicitors LLP, Pacific House, 70 Wellington
Street, GLASGOW G2 6UA
Tel: 0141 3072311
Email: erose@lemac.co.uk
Date Admitted: 05/04/2012

SERVICE, Kelly Frances, National Health Service
Scotland, Anderson House, Breadalbane St,
Bonnington Road, EDINBURGH EH6 5JR
Tel: 0131 2757800
Email: kelly.service@nhs.scot
Date Admitted: 24/09/2007

SOUTER, Caitlin McDonald, National Health
Service Scotland, Anderson House,
Breadalbane St, Bonnington Road,
EDINBURGH EH6 5JR
Tel: 0131 2757800
Email: caitlin.souter@nhs.scot
Date Admitted: 01/11/2004

SPILLER, Liesa Mary, Drummond Miller LLP,
Glenorchy House, 20 Union Street,
EDINBURGH EH1 3LR
Tel: 0131 2265151
Email: lspiller@drummondmiller.co.uk
Date Admitted: 06/09/1989

WILSON, Robert Edward, Anderson Strathern
LLP, 1 Rutland Court, EDINBURGH EH3 8EY
Tel: 0131 2707700
Email: robbie.wilson@andersonstrathern.co.uk
Date Admitted: 03/09/2009

Medical Negligence (Defender Only)

HOPKIN, Susan Anne, National Health Service
Scotland, Anderson House, Breadalbane St,
Bonnington Road, EDINBURGH EH6 5JR
DX: ED154 EDINBURGH
Tel: 0131 2757603
Email: susan.hopkin@nhs.net
Date Admitted: 18/12/1991

MAYBERRY, Hayley Jane, National Health Service
Scotland Anderson House, Breadalbane St
Bonnington Road EDINBURGH EH6 5JR
DX: ED154 EDINBURGH
Tel: 0131 2757800
Email: hayley.mayberry@nhs.scot
Date Admitted: 17/07/2013

MCCORMACK, Joanna, National Health Service
Scotland, Anderson House, Breadalbane St,
Bonnington Road, EDINBURGH EH6 5JR
<comm> DX: ED154 EDINBURGH
Tel: 0131 2757800
Email: Joanna.McCormack@nhs.scot
Date Admitted: 13/09/1999

MCCRAE, Lorna Elizabeth, National Health
Service Scotland, Anderson House,
Breadalbane St, Bonnington Road,
EDINBURGH EH6 5JR
DX: ED154 EDINBURGH
Tel: 0131 2757800
Email: lornamccrae@nhs.net
Date Admitted: 30/10/1991

RINALDI, Stefano Carlo ROMEO, National Health
Service Scotland, Anderson House,
Breadalbane St, Bonnington Road,
EDINBURGH EH6 5JR
DX: ED154 EDINBURGH
Tel: 0131 2757924
Email: stefano.rinaldi@nhs.net
Date Admitted: 25/01/2001

SHEPHERD, Morag, National Health Service
Scotland, Anderson House, Breadalbane St,
Bonnington Road, EDINBURGH EH6 5JR
DX: ED154 EDINBURGH
Tel: 0131 2757800

Email: morag.shepherd@nhs.net
Date Admitted: 20/12/1996
SHIPPIN, Norma Anne, National Health Service
Scotland, Anderson House, Breadalbane St,
Bonnington Road, EDINBURGH EH6 5JR
DX: ED154 EDINBURGH
Tel: 0131 2757892
Email: Norma.Shippin@nhs.net
Date Admitted: 07/12/1983
STEWART, Michael James, National Health
Service Scotland, Anderson House,
Breadalbane St, Bonnington Road,
EDINBURGH EH6 5JR
DX: ED154 EDINBURGH
Tel: 0131 2757800
Email: michaelj.stewart@nhs.net
Date Admitted: 17/10/1996

Mental Health Law

IRVINE, Francis Joseph, Frank Irvine Solicitors Ltd,
Carlton Buildings, 63 Carlton Place,
GLASGOW G5 9TW
Tel: 0141 3759000
Email: fji@frankirvine.com
Date Admitted: 18/10/1995
ORMISTON, Trevor Andrew, Ormistons Law
Practice Limited, Suite 5, Unit 3, Lomond
Business Park, Baltimore Road, GLENROTHES
KY6 2SU
Tel: 0800 7810413
Email: ormistonslaw@btconnect.com
Date Admitted: 27/05/1999

Pensions Law

CROMBIE, June, DWF LLP, 103 Waterloo Street,
GLASGOW G2 7BW
DX: GW9 GLASGOW
Tel: 0141 2288000
Email: june.crombie@dwf.law
Date Admitted: 20/01/1987
GREIG, Colin Gordon, DWF LLP, 103 Waterloo
Street, GLASGOW G2 7BW
DX: GW9 GLASGOW
Tel: 0141 2288000
Email: Colin.Greig@dwf.law
Date Admitted: 30/10/1991

Personal Injury Law

BARNES, Lianda Jane, Digby Brown LLP, 23
Whytescauseway, KIRKCALDY KY1 1XF
Tel: 0333 200 5925
Email: lianda.barnes@digbybrown.co.uk
Date Admitted: 28/06/2007
BARTON, Stuart Alastair, Digby Brown LLP, 2
West Regent Street, GLASGOW G2 1RW
Tel: 0333 200 5925
Email: stuart.barton@digbybrown.co.uk
Date Admitted: 02/07/2008
BECHER, Miranda Justine, Drummond Miller LLP,
Glenorchy House, 20 Union Street,
EDINBURGH EH1 3LR

Tel: 0131 2265151
Email: mbecher@drummondmiller.co.uk
Date Admitted: 24/04/1997
BELL, James Gordon, Dallas McMillan, 1st Floor,
Regent Court, 70 West Regent Street,
GLASGOW G2 2QZ
Tel: 0141 3336750
Email: gb@dallasmcmillan.co.uk
Date Admitted: 22/10/1991
BRASH, Peter Melrose, Grigor & Young LLP, 1
North Street, ELGIN IV30 1UA
Tel: 01343 544077
Email: peter@grigor-young.co.uk
Date Admitted: 24/09/1991
BROWN, Craig, Scottish Social Services Council,
Compass House, Discovery Quay, 11 Riverside
Drive, DUNDEE DD1 4NY
Tel: 0345 6030 891
Email: craig.brown@sssc.uk.com
Date Admitted: 29/08/2008
BUCHANAN, Victoria Anne, Jameson + Mackay
LLP, 1 Charlotte Street, PERTH PH1 5LP
Tel: 01738 631666
Email: victoria.buchanan@jamesonmackay.co.
uk
Date Admitted: 02/10/2008
CALDERWOOD, Heather Elizabeth, Harper
Macleod LLP, The Ca'd'oro, 45 Gordon Street,
GLASGOW G1 3PE
Tel: 0141 2279301
Email: heather.calderwood@harpermacleod.
co.uk
Date Admitted: 01/09/2006
CAMERON, Alastair, Gildeas Limited, 97-99 West
Regent Street, GLASGOW G2 2BA
DX: 561476 GLASGOW 16
Tel: 0141 331 6071
Email: acameron@gildeas.net
Date Admitted: 02/07/2008
CONNOR, Deborah Anne, DWF LLP, 110 Queen
Street, GLASGOW G1 3HD
Tel: 0141 228 8000
Email: debbie.connor@dwf.law
Date Admitted: 22/10/2001
CONNOR, Laura, Thompsons, Berkeley House,
285 Bath Street, GLASGOW G2 4HQ
Tel: 0141 2218840
Email: laura.connor@thompsons-scotland.co.uk
Date Admitted: 22/02/2008
CONSTABLE, Andrew Alan, Clyde & Co
(Scotland) LLP, Albany House, 58 Albany
Street, EDINBURGH EH1 3QR
Tel: 0131 5571545
Email: andrew.constable@clydeco.com
Date Admitted: 27/11/1996
CORNWELL, Jonathan Islay, Lindsays LLP, 100
Queen Street, GLASGOW G1 3DN
Tel: 0141 2216551
Email: jonathancornwell@linsdays.co.uk
Date Admitted: 04/03/1999
COWAN, Douglas John Lockhart, Keoghs
Scotland LLP, Office 107, 2 West Regent
Street, GLASGOW G2 1RW

Tel: 0141 2380100
Email: dcowan@keoghs.scot
Date Admitted: 06/10/1998

DALYELL, Gordon, Digby Brown LLP,
Causewayside House, 160 Causewayside,
EDINBURGH EH9 1PR
Tel: 0333 200 5925
Email: gordon.dalyell@digbybrown.co.uk
Date Admitted: 11/09/1990

DICKSON, Amy Vittoria, Harper Macleod LLP,
The Ca'd'oro, 45 Gordon Street, GLASGOW
G1 3PE
Tel: 0141 2218888
Email: amy.dickson@harpermacleod.co.uk
Date Admitted: 26/01/2009

DOUGLAS, Sarah, Digby Brown LLP, Caledonian
House, Greenmarket, DUNDEE DD1 4QB
Tel: 03332005925
Email: sarah.douglas@digbybrown.co.uk
Date Admitted: 24/11/2003

EDGAR, Nicola Mary, Morton Fraser LLP, 145 St
Vincent Street, GLASGOW G2 5JF
Tel: 0141 2741100
Email: nicola.edgar@morton-fraser.com
Date Admitted: 23/10/2008

EDWARD, Graeme Mark Kynoch, Ledingham
Chalmers LLP, Johnstone House, 52-54 Rose
Street, ABERDEEN AB10 1HA
Tel: 01224 408408
Email: graeme.edward@ledinghamchalmers.
com
Date Admitted: 01/10/1996

FIFE, Calum Andrew, Keoghs Scotland LLP, The
Forsyth Building, 5 Renfield Street, GLASGOW
G2 5EZ
Tel: 0141 2380100
Email: CFife@keoghs.co.uk
Date Admitted: 25/08/2005

GIBSON, Mark Dalziel, Digby Brown LLP, 2 West
Regent Street, GLASGOW G2 1RW
Tel: 0333 200 5925
Email: mark.gibson@digbybrown.co.uk
Date Admitted: 15/10/2004

GRAHAM, Gilles Robert, Clyde & Co (Scotland)
LLP, 144 West George Street, GLASGOW G2
2HG
Tel: 0141 2482666
Email: gilles.graham@clydeco.com
Date Admitted: 28/09/1992

GREGORY, Lisa Jane Gregory, Grant Smith Law
Practice Limited, Amicable House, 252 Union
Street ABERDEEN AB10 1TN
Tel: 01224 621620
E: lisa.gregory@grantsmithlaw.co.uk
Date Admitted: 29/08/1994

HARPER, Marina, Harper Macleod LLP, The
Ca'd'oro, 45 Gordon Street, GLASGOW G1
3PE
Tel: 0141 2218888
Email: marina.harper@harpermacleod.co.uk
Date Admitted: 03/03/2009

HARRIS, Julie Elizabeth, Allan McDougall
McQueen LLP, 3 Coates Crescent, EDINBURGH
EH3 7AL
Tel: 0131 2252121
Email: julieharris@allanmcdougall.co.uk
Date Admitted: 28/09/1995

HERD, James George, Scottish Fire and Rescue
Service, West Service Delivery Area HQ, 99
Bothwell Road, HAMILTON ML3 0EA
Tel: 0141 646 4699
Email: James.herd@firescotland.gov.uk
Date Admitted: 13/10/1986

HUGHES, Francis, Berrymans Lace Mawer LLP, 13
Bath Street, GLASGOW G2 1HY
Tel: 0141 3532121
Email: frank.hughes@blmlaw.com
Date Admitted: 16/09/1988

KAY, Moira Alison, Digby Brown LLP, 2 West
Regent Street, Glasgow, GLASGOW G2 1RW
Tel: 0333 200 5925
Email: moira.kay@digbybrown.co.uk
Date Admitted: 17/11/2003

KAYE, Darrell Elizabeth, Digby Brown LLP, 2 West
Regent Street, GLASGOW G2 1RW
Tel: 01463 227372
Email: darrell.kaye@digbybrown.co.uk
Date Admitted: 24/11/2003

KERNAGHAN, Robert Alexander, Digby Brown
LLP, Caledonian House, Greenmarket,
DUNDEE DD1 4QB
Tel: 01382 205917
Email: robert.kernaghan@digbybrown.co.uk
Date Admitted: 08/09/2000

LAING, Innes, Digby Brown LLP, 23
Whytescauseway, KIRKCALDY KY1 1XF
Tel: 0333 200 5925
Email: innes.laing@digbybrown.co.uk
Date Admitted: 18/12/1991

LECKIE, Matthew William, Digby Brown LLP, 2
West Regent Street, Glasgow, GLASGOW G2
1RW
Tel: 0141 566 9494
Email: matt.leckie@digbybrown.co.uk
Date Admitted: 15/10/2008

LESLIE, Kim Louise, Digby Brown LLP,
Causewayside House, 160 Causewayside,
EDINBURGH EH9 1PR
Tel: 0131 3198123
Email: kim.leslie@digbybrown.co.uk
Date Admitted: 19/10/1999

LESLIE, Victoria Jane, Ledingham Chalmers LLP,
Kintail House, Beechwood Business Park,
INVERNESS IV2 3BW
Tel: 01463 667400
Email: victoria.leslie@ledinghamchalmers.com
Date Admitted: 27/10/2003

MACFARLANE, Lynne Mhairi, DWF LLP, 110
Queen Street, GLASGOW G1 3HD
Tel: 0141 2288000
Email: lynne.macfarlane@dwf.law
Date Admitted: 16/10/2000

MANNION, Gary Ian, Thorntons Law LLP,
Whitehall House, 33 Yeaman Shore DUNDEE
DD1 4BJ
Tel: 01382 229111
Email: GMannion@thorntons-law.co.uk
Date Admitted: 16/08/2007

MCCAFFERTY, Dawn, Digby Brown LLP, 2 West
Regent Street, GLASGOW G2 1RW
Tel: 0333 200 5925
Email: dawn.mccafferty@digbybrown.co.uk
Date Admitted: 26/06/2002

MCCARTNEY, Natalie Elizabeth, BTO Solicitors
LLP, One Edinburgh Quay, 133
Fountainbridge, EDINBURGH EH3 9QG
Tel: 0131 2222939
Email: nem@bto.co.uk
Date Admitted: 09/05/2008

MCELROY, David James, Dallas McMillan, 1st
Floor, Regent Court, 70 West Regent Street,
GLASGOW G2 2QZ
Tel: 0141 3336750
Email: davidj.mcelroy@dallasmcmillan.co.uk
Date Admitted: 09/11/1998

MCGEE, Laura Jane, NewLaw Scotland LLP, 7th
Floor Delta House, 50 West Nile Street,
GLASGOW G1 2NP
Tel: 0845 225 4794
Email: laura.mcgee@newlaw-scotland.co.uk
Date Admitted: 02/10/2008

McGILLIVRAY, Ewan Boyd, Morton Fraser LLP,
Quartermile Two, 2 Lister Square, EDINBURGH
EH3 9GL
Tel: 0131 2471000
Email: ewan.mcgillivray@morton-fraser.com
Date Admitted: 17/02/2000

MCGRAW, Susanne Marie, Waterman's Solicitors
Limited, Fourth Floor, Festival House, 177
West George Street, GLASGOW G2 2LB
Tel: 0141 4307055
Email: SusanneMcgraw@watermans.ws
Date Admitted: 22/11/1999

MCINTOSH, David Stewart, Balfour + Manson
LLP, 56-66 Frederick Street, EDINBURGH EH2
1LS
Tel: 0131 2001200
Email: david.mcintosh@balfour-manson.co.uk
Date Admitted: 04/09/1984

MCINTYRE, Ewan Colin, Burges Salmon LLP, Atria
One, 144 Morrison Street, EDINBURGH EH3
8EX
Tel: 0131 3142112
Date Admitted: 14/10/1992

MCLAREN, Stephen Charles, Ledingham
Chalmers LLP, Johnstone House, 52-54 Rose
Street, ABERDEEN AB10 1HA
Tel: 01224 408408
Email: stephen.mclaren@ledinghamchalmers.
com
Date Admitted: 06/01/2003

MCLEAN, Michael John, Jones Whyte LLP, The
Connect Building, 3rd Floor, 59 Bath Street,
GLASGOW G2 2DH
Tel: 0141 375 1222

Email: michael.mclean@joneswhyte.co.uk
Date Admitted: 10/09/2008

MORRIS, Sarah Elizabeth, Ledingham Chalmers
LLP, 3rd Floor, 68-70 George Street,
EDINBURGH EH2 2LR
Tel: 0131 2001000
Email: sarah.morris@ledinghamchalmers.com
Date Admitted: 03/11/2003

NELLANEY, David, Digby Brown LLP, 2 West
Regent Street, GLASGOW G2 1RW
Tel: 0141 566 2353
Email: david.nellaney@digbybrown.co.uk
Date Admitted: 10/11/2005

NICOL, Iain William, Lefevres (Scotland) Ltd, 70
West Regent Street, GLASGOW G2 2QZ
Tel: 0845 3052555
Email: IWN@lefevres.law
Date Admitted: 29/07/1991

O'DONNELL, Kirsty Ann, Digby Brown LLP, 2
West Regent Street, GLASGOW G2 1RW
Tel: 0141 5660896
Email: kirsty.odonnell@digbybrown.co.uk
Date Admitted: 24/11/2009

PITT, Valerie Elizabeth, Horwich Farrelly Scotland,
Suite 5 & 6, Floor 6, 7 Buchanan Street,
GLASGOW G1 3HL
Tel: 03300 240711
Email: Val.Pitt@h-f.co.uk
Date Admitted: 19/10/2007

POOLE, Richard Robert, Thorntons Law LLP,
Whitehall House, 33 Yeaman Shore, DUNDEE
DD1 4BJ
Tel: 01382 229111
Email: rpoole@thorntons-law.co.uk
Date Admitted: 16/04/2007

RAITT, Jacqueline Lesley, Allan McDougall
McQueen LLP, 3 Coates Crescent, EDINBURGH
EH3 7AL
Tel: 0131 2252121
Email: jackieraitt@allanmcdougall.co.uk
Date Admitted: 01/11/2004

SCOTT, Ian Brown Gilkison, Ledingham Chalmers
LLP, 3rd Floor, 68-70 George Street,
EDINBURGH EH2 2LR
Tel: 0131 2001000
Email: ian.scott@ledinghamchalmers.com
Date Admitted: 11/10/2001

SHORT, David, Balfour + Manson LLP, 56-66
Frederick Street, EDINBURGH EH2 1LS
Tel: 0131 2001200
Email: david.short@balfour-manson.co.uk
Date Admitted: 26/08/1986

SIMPSON, Fraser Wallace, Digby Brown LLP, 2
West Regent Street, GLASGOW G2 1RW
Tel: 0333 200 5925
Email: fraser.simpson@digbybrown.co.uk
Date Admitted: 22/10/1991

SINCLAIR, Martin Turner, Mackinnons Solicitors
LLP, 14 Carden Place, ABERDEEN AB10 1UR
Tel: 01224 632464
Email: martin@mackinnons.com
Date Admitted: 22/10/1991

SINGER, Richard Alan, Thompsons, 16-20 Castle Street, EDINBURGH EH2 3AT
Tel: 0131 2254297
Email: richard.singer@thompsons-scotland.co.uk
Date Admitted: 28/08/2002

SMART, Steven James, Horwich Farrelly Scotland, Suite 5 & 6, Floor 6, 7 Buchanan Street, GLASGOW G1 3HL
Tel: 03300 240711
Email: steven.smart@h-f.co.uk
Date Admitted: 02/10/2006

SOUTER, Caitlin McDonald, National Health Service Scotland, Anderson House, Breadalbane St, Bonnington Road, EDINBURGH EH6 5JR
DX: ED154 EDINBURGH
Tel: 0131 2757800
Email: caitlin.souter@nhs.scot
Date Admitted: 01/11/2004

TAYLOR, Isla Ruth, DAC Beachcroft Scotland LLP, 125 West Regent Street, GLASGOW G2 2SA
DX: 512403 Glas Bath Street
Tel: 0141 2486688
Email: itaylor@dacbeachcroft.com
Date Admitted: 10/11/2003

THOMPSON, Casey Elspeth, DAC Beachcroft Scotland LLP, 125 West Regent Street, GLASGOW G2 2SA
DX: 512403 Glas Bath Street
Tel: 0141 2486688
Email: cthompson@dacbeachcroft.com
Date Admitted: 29/08/2008

THOMSON, Fergus Hugh, Gildeas Limited, 97-99 West Regent Street, GLASGOW G2 2BA
Tel: 0141 3316071
Email: FThomson@gildeas.net
Date Admitted: 17/09/1998

THOMSON, Jennifer Dalrymple, Morton Fraser LLP, Quartermile Two, 2 Lister Square, EDINBURGH EH3 9GL
Tel: 0131 2471000
Email: jennifer.thomson@morton-fraser.com
Date Admitted: 23/10/2007

TIERNEY, Heather Isabel Mary, Waterman's Solicitors Limited, Fourth Floor, Festival House, 177 West George Street, GLASGOW G2 2LB
Tel: 0141 4307055
Email: heathertierney@watermans.ws
Date Admitted: 25/07/2012

WATSON, Jennifer Gray, Digby Brown LLP, Caledonian House, Greenmarket, DUNDEE DD1 4QB
Tel: 03332005925
Email: jennifer.watson@digbybrown.co.uk
Date Admitted: 21/12/2004

WATT, Anna Mhairi, Ledingham Chalmers LLP, 3rd Floor, 68-70 George Street EDINBURGH EH2 2LR
Tel: 0131 2001000
Email: anna.watt@ledinghamchalmers.com
Date Admitted: 05/11/2004

WATT, WS, Craig Ian, Brodies LLP, Capital House, 2 Festival Square, EDINBURGH EH3 9SU
Tel: 0131 2283777
Email: Craig.Watt@brodies.com
Date Admitted: 13/11/2002

WHITE, Stewart George, Thompsons, 16-20 Castle Street, EDINBURGH EH2 3AT
Tel: 0131 2254297
Email: stewart.white@thompsons-scotland.co.uk
Date Admitted: 21/06/2004

WILLIAMS, Suzanne, Digby Brown LLP, 2 West Regent Street, GLASGOW G2 1RW
Tel: 0333 2005925
Email: suzanne.williams@digbybrown.co.uk
Date Admitted: 01/10/1999

Planning Law

BAILLIE, Sarah, Addleshaw Goddard LLP, Exchange Tower, 19 Canning Street, EDINBURGH EH3 8EH
Tel: 0131 2282400
Email: Sarah.Baillie@addleshawgoddard.com
Date Admitted: 18/09/2002

COLLAR, Neil Andrew, Brodies LLP, 15 Atholl Crescent, EDINBURGH EH3 8HA
Tel: 0131 2283777
Email: neil.collar@brodies.com
Date Admitted: 03/02/1993

FARQUHARSON-BLACK, Elaine, Brodies LLP, 15 Atholl Crescent, EDINBURGH EH3 8HA
Tel: 0131 2283777
Email: efb@brodies.com
Date Admitted: 12/12/1990

GILLIES, Fraser Anthony Brian, Wright, Johnston & Mackenzie LLP, The Capital Building, 12/13 St Andrew Square, EDINBURGH EH2 2AF
Tel: 0131 5241500
Email: fzg@wjm.co.uk
Date Admitted: 11/10/2001

INNES, Colin William, Shepherd and Wedderburn LLP, 1 Exchange Crescent, Conference Square, EDINBURGH EH3 8UL
Tel: 0131 2289900
Email: colin.innes@shepwedd.com
Date Admitted: 29/10/1993

MACLEOD, Ewan, Shepherd and Wedderburn LLP, 1 Exchange Crescent, Conference Square, EDINBURGH EH3 8UL
Tel: 0131 2289900
Email: Ewan.MacLeod@shepwedd.com
Date Admitted: 30/04/1998

MCKIE, Alastair John, Anderson Strathern LLP, 1 Rutland Court, EDINBURGH EH3 8EY
Tel: 0131 2707700
Email: alastair.mckie@andersonstrathern.co.uk
Date Admitted: 25/02/1986

TELFER, Alexander Robert, DLA Piper Scotland LLP, Collins House, Rutland Square, EDINBURGH EH1 2AA
Tel: 08700 111111
Email: Sandy.Telfer@dlapiper.com

Date Admitted: 09/09/1993

THOMSON, Moray Ewan Jacks, Shepherd and Wedderburn LLP, 1 Exchange Crescent, Conference Square, EDINBURGH EH3 8UL
Tel: 0131 2289900
Email: moray.thomson@shepwedd.co.uk
Date Admitted: 25/09/2001

Private Client Tax Law

CAMPBELL, Martin Stuart, Anderson Strathern LLP, 1 Rutland Court, EDINBURGH EH3 8EY
Tel: 0131 2707700
Email: martin.campbell@andersonstrathern.co.uk
Date Admitted: 02/06/2003

MACPHERSON, Claire Eileen, Burness Paull LLP, 120 Bothwell Street, GLASGOW G2 7JL
Tel: 0141 2484933
Email: claire.e.macpherson@burnesspaull.com
Date Admitted: 10/11/2003

MCDONALD, Fiona Fyfe, Fyfe McDonald Limited, 43a Argyle Street, ST. ANDREWS KY16 9BX
Tel: 01334 845197
Email: ffm@fyfemcdonald.co.uk
Date Admitted: 27/09/2004

MURRIN, Peter James, Turcan Connell, 180 St. Vincent Street, GLASGOW G2 5SG
Tel: 0141 4412111
Email: pete.murrin@turcanconnell.com
Date Admitted: 02/06/2010

Professional Negligence Law

ATKINSON, Beverley, DAC Beachcroft Scotland LLP, 24 Dublin Street, EDINBURGH EH1 3PP
Tel: 0131 5247790
Email: batkinson@dacbeachcroft.com
Date Admitted: 01/10/2001

BICKNELL, Rachael Louise
Date Admitted: 10/01/2007

BLANE, Stephen Martin, A. & W.M. Urquhart, 16 Heriot Row, EDINBURGH EH3 6HR
Tel: 0131 5562896
Email: stephenblane@urquharts.co.uk
Date Admitted: 02/11/1992

CARDOW, Lynne Margaret Wallace, BTO Solicitors LLP, 48 St. Vincent Street, GLASGOW G2 5HS
Tel: 0141 2218012
Email: lca@bto.co.uk
Date Admitted: 10/11/2000

CORNWELL, Karen Margaret, Thorntons Law LLP, Whitehall House, 33 Yeaman Shore, DUNDEE DD1 4BJ
Tel: 01382 229 111
Email: kcornwell@thorntons-law.co.uk
Date Admitted: 05/08/1999

EDWARD, Timothy James, MBM Commercial LLP, Suite 2, Orchard Brae House, 30 Queensferry Road, EDINBURGH EH4 2HS
Tel: 0131 2268200
Email: Tim.Edward@mbmcommercial.co.uk

Date Admitted: 24/11/1989

JONES, QC, Antony Gerald Morrell, Brodies LLP, 15 Atholl Crescent, EDINBURGH EH3 8HA
Tel: 0131 2283777
Email: tony.jones@brodies.com
Date Admitted: 22/10/1991

MATHESON, Alisdair Stuart, Brodies LLP, 110 Queen Street, GLASGOW G1 3BX
Tel: 0141 2484672
Email: alisdair.matheson@brodies.com
Date Admitted: 15/10/1996

MAWBY, Ashley Helen, Burness Paull LLP, 50 Lothian Road Festival Square, EDINBURGH EH3 9WJ
Tel: 0131 4736000
Email: ashley.mawby@burnesspaull.com
Date Admitted: 18/10/2002

ROBB, James Anthony, BTO Solicitors LLP, One Edinburgh Quay, 133 Fountainbridge, EDINBURGH EH3 9QG
DX: ED77 EDINBURGH
Tel: 0131 2222939
Email: jro@bto.co.uk
Date Admitted: 04/08/2011

SHERIDAN, John Paul, TLT LLP, 140 West George Street, GLASGOW G2 2HG
Tel: 0333 006 0400
Email: jp.Sheridan@tltsolicitors.com
Date Admitted: 20/08/1999

Public Procurement Law

LANE, Eleanor Rosamond Anne, CMS Cameron McKenna Nabarro Olswang LLP, 1 West Regent Street, GLASGOW G2 1AP
Tel: 0141 2222200
Email: Eleanor.Lane@cms-cmno.com
Date Admitted: 10/11/2000

MCGOWAN, David Thomas, Dentons UK and Middle East LLP, 1 George Square, GLASGOW G2 1AL
Tel: 0330 2220050
Email: David.McGowan@dentons.com
Date Admitted: 28/03/2000

MCLACHLAN, Douglas Walter, Anderson Strathern LLP, George House, 50 George Square, GLASGOW G2 1EH
Tel: 0141 2426060
Email: douglas.mclachlan@andersonstrathern.co.uk
Date Admitted: 15/03/2000

OSLER, Duncan Farnworth, MacRoberts LLP, Excel House, 30 Semple Street, EDINBURGH EH3 8BL
Tel: 0131 2295046
Email: duncan.osler@macroberts.com
Date Admitted: 13/01/1994

RITCHIE, Ailsa Ritchie, CMS Cameron McKenna Nabarro Olswang LLP, 1 West Regent Street, GLASGOW G2 1AP
Tel: 0141 2222200
Email: Ailsa.Ritchie@cms-cmno.com
Date Admitted: 04/09/1995

Trusts Law

BATCHELOR, Susanne Nicola, Brodies LLP, 15 Atholl Crescent, EDINBURGH EH3 8HA
Tel: 0131 2283777
Email: susanne.batchelor@brodies.com
Date Admitted: 13/08/1998

CAMPBELL, Martin Stuart, Anderson Strathern LLP, 1 Rutland Court, EDINBURGH EH3 8EY
Tel: 0131 2707700
Email: martin.campbell@andersonstrathern.co.uk
Date Admitted: 02/06/2003

GARDEN, Alexander Kenneth, Turcan Connell, Princes Exchange, 1 Earl Grey Street, EDINBURGH EH3 9EE
Tel: 0131 2288111
Email: alexander.garden@turcanconnell.com
Date Admitted: 25/10/1999

LESLIE, Jacqueline, Harper Macleod LLP, The Ca'd'oro, 45 Gordon Street, GLASGOW G1 3PE
Tel: 0141 2218888
Email: jacqueline.leslie@harpermacleod.co.uk
Date Admitted: 29/10/1993

MACPHERSON, Claire Eileen, Burness Paul LLP, 120 Bothwell Street, GLASGOW G2 7JL
Tel: 0141 2484933
Email: claire.e.macpherson@burnesspaull.com
Date Admitted: 10/11/2003

MURRIN, Peter James, Turcan Connell, 180 St. Vincent Street, GLASGOW G2 5SG
Tel: 0141 4412111
Email: pete.murrin@turcanconnell.com
Date Admitted: 02/06/2010

STEWART, Mark Edward, Brodies LLP, Brodies House, 31-33 Union Grove, ABERDEEN AB10 6SD
Tel: 01224 392 242
Email: mark.stewart@brodies.com
Date Admitted: 01/10/1996

TOMLINSON, Carole, Anderson Strathern LLP, 1 Rutland Court, EDINBURGH EH3 8EY
Tel: 0131 2707700
Email: carole.tomlinson@andersonstrathern.co.uk
Date Admitted: 21/01/2010

Arbitrators

CONNAL, QC, Robert Craig
Date Admitted: 30/08/1977

FRAME, Shona McNae, CMS Cameron McKenna Nabarro Olswang LLP, 1 West Regent Street, GLASGOW G2 1AP
Tel: 0141 304 6379
Email: Shona.Frame@cms-cmno.com
Date Admitted: 23/09/1993

KELLY, Neil Joseph, MacRoberts LLP, Excel House, 30 Semple Street, EDINBURGH EH3 8BL
Tel: 0131 2295046
Email: neil.kelly@macroberts.com
Date Admitted: 09/11/1984

MALONE, Brandon James, Brandon Malone & Company Limited, 83 Princes Street, EDINBURGH EH2 2ER
Tel: 0131 3578549
Email: brandon@brandonmalone.com
Date Admitted: 16/08/1993

MCMILLAN, Alan Charles, Burness Paull LLP, 50 Lothian Road, Festival Square, EDINBURGH EH3 9WJ
Tel: 0131 4736000
Email: Alan.McMillan@burnesspaull.com
Date Admitted: 27/10/1995

Freedom of Information & Data Protection

BLACK, Allison Elizabeth, Renfrewshire Council, Finance & Corporate Services, Renfrewshire House, Cotton, St. PAISLEY PA1 1TT
Tel: 0141 6187175
Email: Alison.Black@renfrewshire.gov.uk
Date Admitted: 22/08/1997

IRVINE, Laura Jane, Davidson Chalmers Stewart LLP, 12 Hope Street, EDINBURGH EH2 4DB
Tel: 0131 6259191
Email: laura.irvine@dcslegal.com
Date Admitted: 05/08/1999

MOTION, Paul Robert, BTO Solicitors LLP, One Edinburgh Quay, 133 Fountainbridge EDINBURGH EH3 9QG
Tel: 0131 2222932
Email: prm@bto.co.uk
Date Admitted: 14/05/1984

Housing and Residential Tenancy

BAULD, James, T.C. Young LLP, 7 West George Street, GLASGOW G2 1BA
Tel: 0141 2215562
Email: jdb@tcyoung.co.uk
Date Admitted: 30/10/1986

GRAHAM, Katherine Sarah Graham, Wheatley Housing Group Limited, Wheatley House, 25 Cochrane Street, GLASGOW G1 1HL
Tel: 0845 9001001
Email: Katie.Graham@wheatley-group.com
Date Admitted: 02/10/2008

HENRY, Catherine Dawn, TC Young LLP, 7 West George Street, GLASGOW G2 1BA
Tel: 0141 2215562
Email: cdm@tcyoung.co.uk
Date Admitted: 23/08/2013

KELLY, Mary-Claire, Clan Childlaw Limited, Unit S4B, Norton Park, 57 Albion Road, EDINBURGH EH7 5QY
Tel: 0808 129 0522
Email: Mary-Claire.kelly@clanchildlaw.org
Date Admitted: 30/05/2000

MCLEOD, Fiona, Brodies LLP, 110 Queen Street, GLASGOW G1 3BX
Tel: 0141 2484672
Email: fiona.mcleod@brodies.com
Date Admitted: 29/10/2008

MULLEN, Claire Anne, T.C. Young LLP, 7 West George Street, GLASGOW G2 1BA
Tel: 0141 2215562
Email: cag@tcyoung.co.uk
Date Admitted: 29/06/2010

Regulation of Professional Conduct

BURTON, Gary John, Anderson Strathearn LLP, 1 Rutland Court, EDINBURGH EH3 8EY
Tel: 0131 2707700
Email: gary.burton@andersonstrathearn.co.uk
Date Admitted: 26/10/2010

HENDERSON, Wendy Mari, The Law Society of Scotland, Atria One, 144 Morrison Street, EDINBURGH EH3 8EX
Tel: 0131 2267411
Email: wendyhenderson@lawscot.org.uk

Date Admitted: 25/10/1994

MOTION, Elaine Joyce, Balfour + Manson LLP, 56-66 Frederick Street, EDINBURGH EH2 1LS
Tel: 0131 2001200
Email: elaine.motion@balfour-manson.co.uk
Date Admitted: 08/08/1986

MUIRS, Fiona Kirsty, Balfour + Manson LLP, 56-66 Frederick Street, EDINBURGH EH2 1LS
Tel: 0131 2001200
Email: fiona.muirs@balfour-manson.co.uk
Date Admitted: 03/11/1998

RAFTERY, Claire Elizabeth, Clyde & Co (Scotland) LLP, Albany House, 58 Albany Street, EDINBURGH EH1 3QR
Tel: 0131 5571545
Email: Claire.Raftery@clydeco.com
Date Admitted: 09/12/2014

Commercial Mediators (Accord)

FENDER-ALLISON, Jane Elizabeth, CMS Cameron McKenna Nabarro Olswang LLP, 1 West Regent Street, GLASGOW G2 1AP
Tel: 0141 2222200
Email: Jane.Fender-Allison@cms-cmno.com
Date Admitted: 22/02/2008

GRANT, Alison MacIntyre, DWF LLP, 110 Queen Street, GLASGOW G1 3HD
Tel: 0141 2288000
Email: Alison.Grant@dwf.law
Date Admitted: 19/10/1984

HOSSACK, David, Morton Fraser LLP, Quartermile Two 2 Lister Square, EDINBURGH EH3 9GL
Tel: 0131 2471000
Email: david.hossack@morton-fraser.com
Date Admitted: 06/11/1987

KIRKWOOD, Paul
Date Admitted: 27/09/1993

Family Law Mediators

ABERDEIN, Ruth Mary, Aberdein Considine and
Company, 5-9 Bon Accord Crescent,
ABERDEEN AB11 6DN
Tel: 01224 589700
Email: raberdein@acandco.com
Date Admitted: 14/08/2000

ADAMS, Rhona Anne, Morton Fraser LLP,
Quartermile Two, 2 Lister Square, EDINBURGH
EH3 9GL
Tel: 0131 2471000
Email: rhona.adams@morton-fraser.com
Date Admitted: 26/04/1991

BARRETT, Angela O'Hara, Russel & Aitken Denny
LLP, 22 & 24 Stirling Street, DENNY FK6 6AZ
Tel: 01324 822194
Email: ab@radenny.co.uk
Date Admitted: 09/11/1992

BLACKWOOD, Jane Alexandra, Harper Macleod
LLP, The Ca'd'oro 45 Gordon Street,
GLASGOW G1 3PE
Tel: 0141 2218888
Email: jane.blackwood@harpermacleod.co.uk
Date Admitted: 26/02/2010

BOWMAN, Gillian Louise, Cairns Brown, 112
Main Street, ALEXANDRIA G83 0NZ
Tel: 01389 756979
Email: g.bowman@cairnsbrown.co.uk
Date Admitted: 06/09/2013

BROPHY, Anne, Brophy Carey & Co Ltd,
Mediacorp House, 2 Caird Park, HAMILTON
ML3 0EU
Tel: 01698 200111
Email: ab@brophycareylaw.com
Date Admitted: 27/08/1991

BROWN, Cheryl Prentice, McWhinney Richards,
66 Stirling Street, AIRDRIE ML6 0AW
Tel: 01236 754571
Email: cheryl.brown@mcwhinneyrichards.com
Date Admitted: 21/10/1986

BUCHAN, Lorna Gilmore, Patience & Buchan, 10
Golden Square, ABERDEEN AB10 1RB
Tel: 01224 648222
Email: lorna@patienceandbuchan.com
Date Admitted: 29/09/1994

BUCHANAN, Nicola Jean, Berrymans Lace Mawer
LLP, 13 Bath Street, GLASGOW G2 1HY
Tel: 0141 3532121
Email: Nicola.Buchanan@blmlaw.com
Date Admitted: 20/10/1994

BURKE, Leonie Sarah Rose, Aberdein Considine
and Company, 2nd Floor, East Suite Elder
House Multrees Walk, EDINBURGH EH1 3DX
Tel: 0333 0044333
Email: lburke@acandco.com
Date Admitted: 25/09/2001

BYTH, Sheila Janet, McKinnon Forbes, 54 High
Street, TRANENT EH33 1HH
Tel: 01875 611211

Email: sheila.byth@mckinnonforbes.co.uk
Date Admitted: 20/06/1997

CAMPBELL, Fiona Jane, Macleod & MacCallum
Limited, 28 Queensgate, INVERNESS IV1 1DJ
Tel: 01463 239393
Email: fiona.campbell@macandmac.co.uk
Date Admitted: 20/11/1989

CAREY, Fiona Janet, Brophy Carey & Co Ltd,
Mediacorp House, 2 Caird Park, HAMILTON
ML3 0EU
Tel: 01698 200111
Email: fjc@brophycareylaw.com
Date Admitted: 11/07/1989

CARTHY, Jade Elizabeth, A.C. O'Neill & Co.,
Second Floor, 32 High Street, DUMBARTON
G82 1LL
Tel: 01389 762997
Date Admitted: 06/10/2011

CLARK, Lucia Elaine, Morton Fraser LLP,
Quartermile Two, 2 Lister Square, EDINBURGH
EH3 9GL
Tel: 0131 2471000
Email: lucia.clark@morton-fraser.com
Date Admitted: 06/09/2004

COLLEDGE, Jennifer Claire, Colledge & Shields
LLP, 30 Castle Street, DUMFRIES DG1 1DU
Tel: 01387 240044
Email: jcc@colledgeandshields.co.uk
Date Admitted: 02/09/1996

DOCHERTY, Scott Charles, McArthur Stanton, 40
High Street, DUMBARTON G82 1LL
Tel: 01389 762266
Email: sd@mcarthurstanton.co.uk
Date Admitted: 25/09/2001

DONALD, Faye Louise, Raeburn Christie Clark &
Wallace LLP, 12-16 Albyn Place, ABERDEEN
AB10 1PS
Tel: 01224 332400
Email: faye.donald@raeburns.co.uk
Date Admitted: 24/04/2006

FEENEY, Sarah Louise Helen, Gilson Gray LLP, 160
West George Street, GLASGOW G2 2HG
Tel: 0141 5302021
Email: sfeeney@gilsongray.co.uk
Date Admitted: 16/01/2008

FERGUSON, Jane Margaret Wilson, R & R
Urquhart LLP, 117-121 High Street, FORRES
IV36 1AB
Tel: 01309 672216
Email: janeferguson@r-r-urquhart.com
Date Admitted: 27/11/1990

FRASER, Morag, Fraser Shepherd, 39 Vicar Street,
FALKIRK FK1 1LL
Tel: 01324 630700
Email: morag@frasershepherd.co.uk
Date Admitted: 28/09/1987

GEORGE, Shaun Arthur, Brodies LLP, Brodies House, 31-33 Union Grove, ABERDEEN AB10 6SD
Tel: 01224 392242
Email: shaun.george@brodies.com
Date Admitted: 18/10/1988

GIBBONS, Karen Louise, Harper Macleod LLP, Citypoint, 65 Haymarket Terrace, EDINBURGH EH12 5HD
Tel: 0131 2472500
Email: Karen.Gibbons@harpermacleod.co.uk
Date Admitted: 22/09/2004

GILLIES, Louise Mary, Ness Gallagher Solicitors Limited, 358 Brandon Street, MOTHERWELL ML1 1XA
Tel: 01698 254644
Email: LG@nessgallagher.co.uk
Date Admitted: 16/08/2007

GILMOUR, Robert Lister, SKO Family Limited, 18 George Street, EDINBURGH EH2 2PF
Tel: 0131 3226669
Email: robert.gilmour@sko-family.co.uk
Date Admitted: 22/10/1996

GIRDWOOD, Lisa Anne Irvine, Brodies LLP, 110 Queen Street, GLASGOW G1 3BX
Tel: 0141 2484672
Email: lisa.girdwood@brodies.com
Date Admitted: 02/10/1989

GORDON, Lesley Jane, BTO Solicitors LLP, One Edinburgh Quay, 133 Fountainbridge, EDINBURGH EH3 9QG
Tel: 0131 2222939
Email: lxg@bto.co.uk
Date Admitted: 03/02/1995

GOSTELOW, Paul Gerard, Baker Gostelow Law Limited, 36 Cadzow Street, HAMILTON ML3 6DG
Tel: 01698 820700
Email: paul@bgfamilylaw.co.uk
Date Admitted: 10/03/1995

HIGSON, Judith May, Scullion Law Limited, 105 Cadzow Street, HAMILTON ML3 6HG
Tel: 01698 283265
Email: judith@scullionlaw.com
Date Admitted: 07/11/2001

HINCHIN, Michaela Louise, MTM Family Law LLP, 2nd Floor, 91 Mitchell Street, GLASGOW G1 3LN
Tel: 0141 6117535
Email: mh@mtmfamilylaw.co.uk
Date Admitted: 06/11/1987

HOOPER, Denise, Wright & Crawford (1906) Limited, 11 Glasgow Road, PAISLEY PA1 3QS
Tel: 0141 8876211
Email: D.Hooper@wright-crawford.co.uk
Date Admitted: 23/02/1995

HUGHES, Helen, McAuley, McCarthy & Co., 29 Moss Street, PAISLEY PA1 1DL
Tel: 0141 5617779
Email: h.hughes-paisley@btconnect.com
Date Admitted: 22/08/1988

HUNTER, Alexis Margaret, Alexis Hunter Family Law, Cartside House, 1/7 Clarkston Road Cathcart, GLASGOW G44 4EF
Tel: 0141 4040124
Email: amh@ahfamilylaw.co.uk
Date Admitted: 04/08/1977

KARLIN, Catherine Margaret, Horchheim Ltd, 15/16 Queen Street, EDINBURGH EH2 1JE
Tel: 0131 2401213
Email: cath@cathkarlinfamilylaw.co.uk
Date Admitted: 02/12/1992

KELSEY, Rachael Joy Christina, SKO Family Law Specialists LLP, 18 George Street, EDINBURGH EH2 2PF
Tel: 0131 3226669
Email: Rachael.Kelsey@sko-family.co.uk
Date Admitted: 22/10/1996

LANG, Margaret Jane, Russel & Aitken (Falkirk & Alloa) Ltd, Kings Court High Street, FALKIRK FK1 1PQ
Tel: 01324 622888
Email: margaretlang@russel-aitken.co.uk
Date Admitted: 30/10/1984

LAVERTY, Denise Karen, Gilson Gray LLP, 160 West George Street, GLASGOW G2 2HG
Tel: 0141 5302021
Email: dlaverty@gilsongray.co.uk
Date Admitted: 31/01/2005

LAW, Janie Kerr, Family Law Matters Scotland LLP, Queens House, 19 St. Vincent Place, GLASGOW G1 2DT
Tel: 0141 4202430
Email: janie.law@flmscotland.co.uk
Date Admitted: 16/11/1987

LIDDIARD, Simon James Carnegie, Stewart & Watson, 35 Queen Street, PETERHEAD AB42 1TP
Tel: 01779 476351
Email: sliddiard@stewartwatson.co.uk
Date Admitted: 02/07/1996

LOTHIAN, Ailie Joanna, Smail & Ewart, 68-70 High Street, LANARK ML11 7ES
Tel: 01555 666111
Email: alothian@smail-ewart.co.uk
Date Admitted: 06/09/2004

MACANDREW, Hilary Anne Barrowman, Grant Smith Law Practice Limited, Old Bank Buildings, Balmellie Street, TURRIFF AB53 4DW
Tel: 01888 562245
Email: hilary.macandrew@grantsmithlaw.co.uk
Date Admitted: 01/10/1985

MALLOY, Ann Jane Reid Watt, Lanarkshire Community Law Centre Ltd, C/o Airdrie Citizens Advice (First Floor), 61A Stirling Street, AIRDRIE ML6 0AS
Tel: 01236 757 337
Date Admitted: 09/07/2008

MARTIN, Nadine, Gibson Kerr Limited, 46 India Street, EDINBURGH EH3 6HJ
DX: 551100 EDINBURGH 7
Tel: 0131 2257558
Email: nadine.martin@gibsonkerr.co.uk
Date Admitted: 10/07/2006

MASSON, Amanda Elizabeth, Harper Macleod LLP, The Ca'd'oro, 45 Gordon Street, GLASGOW G1 3PE
Tel: 0141 2218888
Email: Amanda.Masson@harpermacleod.co.uk
Date Admitted: 03/12/2002

MCINTOSH, Rowena Marie, McIntosh Family Law, 52-54 Albert Street, ABERDEEN AB25 1XS
Tel: 01224 593100
Email: rowena@mcintoshfamilylaw.com
Date Admitted: 20/09/1985

MCKAY, Donna, Brodies LLP, Brodies House, 31-33 Union Grove, ABERDEEN AB10 6SD
Tel: 01224 392242
Email: donna.mckay@brodies.com
Date Admitted: 15/02/2002

MCLACHLAN, Lindsey Ann, LAM Family Law, Studio 3015, Mile End Mill Abbey Mill Business Centre, 12 Seedhill Road, PAISLEY PA1 1JS
Tel: 0141 8890101
Email: enquiry@lamfamilylaw.co.uk
Date Admitted: 04/02/1994

MCLACHLAN, Lydia Ishbel, Brodies LLP, Brodies House, 31-33 Union Grove, ABERDEEN AB10 6SD
Tel: 01224 392242
Email: lydia.mclachlan@brodies.com
Date Admitted: 16/10/2006

MCLAUGHLAN, Lisa Marie, Stirling & Mair Limited, 28 High Street, JOHNSTONE PA5 8AH
Tel: 01505 329373
Email: lisa.mclaughlan@stirlingmair.com
Date Admitted: 10/08/2004

MCWILLIAMS, Gerald Thomas, Cowan & Co., 81 Berkeley Street, GLASGOW G3 7DX
Tel: 0141 2211803
Email: gmcw@cowanandco.co.uk
Date Admitted: 16/10/1990

MEIL, Judith Anne, Taggart Meil Mathers, 20 Bon Accord Square, ABERDEEN AB11 6DJ
Tel: 01224 588020
Email: judith@tmmsolicitors.co.uk
Date Admitted: 22/09/1983

MONAGHAN, Catherine Mary, Moore & Partners LLP, Lennox House, Lennox Road, Seafar, CUMBERNAULD G67 1LL
Tel: 01236 727715
Email: cmonaghan@moorepartners.com
Date Admitted: 18/09/1992

MURRAY, Joanne Ronna, Blackadders LLP, 6 Bon Accord Square, ABERDEEN AB11 6XU
Tel: 01224 588913
Email: joanne.murray@blackadders.co.uk
Date Admitted: 22/02/2008

MURRAY, Sharon
Date Admitted: 14/04/1987

OSWALD, Susan Margaret, SKO Family Law Specialists LLP, 18 George Street, EDINBURGH EH2 2PF
Tel: 0131 3226669
Email: Susan.Oswald@sko-family.co.uk
Date Admitted: 16/10/1995

POLSON, Jacqueline Alison
Date Admitted: 24/06/2005

PURVIS, Susan Elizabeth Collin, Ledingham Chalmers LLP, Johnstone House, 52-54 Rose Street, ABERDEEN AB10 1HA
Tel: 01224 408408
Email: susan.purvis@ledinghamchalmers.com
Date Admitted: 23/09/1996

RASMUSEN, Fiona Rosemary, Gibson Kerr, 46 India Street, EDINBURGH EH3 6HJ
Tel: 0131 2257558
Email: fiona.rasmusen@gibsonkerr.co.uk
Date Admitted: 02/12/1981

REEKIE, Deborah Elizabeth, BTO Solicitors LLP, One Edinburgh Quay, 133 Fountainbridge, EDINBURGH EH3 9QG
Tel: 0131 2222939
Email: der@bto.co.uk
Date Admitted: 13/07/2011

RIDDELL, Vivien Margaret, T.C. Young LLP, Melrose House, 69A George Street, EDINBURGH EH2 2JG
Tel: 0131 2207660
Email: vmr@tcyoung.co.uk
Date Admitted: 20/10/2009

SCHOLARIOS, Nicos, MSM Solicitors Limited, 51 Moss Street, PAISLEY PA1 1DR
Tel: 0141 8896244
Email: ns@msmlaw.co.uk
Date Admitted: 05/12/1983

SHIELDS, Sandi Marie Anne, Colledge & Shields LLP, 30 Castle Street, DUMFRIES DG1 1DU
Tel: 01387 240044
Email: ss@colledgeandshields.co.uk
Date Admitted: 23/03/2012

SIMPSON, Ashley Marie, Patience & Buchan, 10 Golden Square, ABERDEEN AB10 1RB
Tel: 01224 648222
Email: ashley@patienceandbuchan.com
Date Admitted: 21/06/2006

SMITH, Caroline Leslie, MTM Family Law LLP, 2nd Floor, 91 Mitchell Street, GLASGOW G1 3LN
Tel: 0141 6117535
Email: cs@mtmfamilylaw.co.uk
Date Admitted: 17/10/1996

SMITH, Jennifer Chloe, Harper Macleod LLP, The Ca'd'oro 45 Gordon Street, GLASGOW G1 3PE
Tel: 0141 2218888
Email: jenny.smith@harpermacleod.co.uk
Date Admitted: 06/01/2003

SMITH, Richard Bryan, Brodies LLP, 15 Atholl Crescent, EDINBURGH EH3 8HA
Tel: 0131 2283777
Email: richard.b.smith@brodies.com
Date Admitted: 19/12/1997

SMITH, Shona Houston, Balfour + Manson LLP, 56-66 Frederick Street, EDINBURGH EH2 1LS
Tel: 0131 2001200
Email: shona.smith@balfour-manson.co.uk
Date Admitted: 05/09/1991

STRATFORD, Lynne, Drummond Miller LLP, 11
White Hart Street, DALKEITH EH22 1AE
Tel: 0131 6639568
Email: lstratford@drummondmiller.co.uk
Date Admitted: 17/11/2003

STROUD, Jacqueline Anne, MacRoberts LLP, Excel
House, 30 Semple Street, EDINBURGH EH3
8BL
Tel: 0131 2295046
Email: Jacqueline.Stroud@macroberts.com
Date Admitted: 25/10/1990

STURROCK, Garry John, Brodies LLP, Brodies
House, 31-33 Union Grove, ABERDEEN AB10
6SD
Tel: 01224 392242
Email: garry.sturrock@brodies.com
Date Admitted: 12/07/2013

TEMPLETON, Shona Mary, MTM Family Law LLP,
2nd Floor, 91 Mitchell Street, GLASGOW G1
3LN
Tel: 0141 6117535
Email: smt@mtmfamilylaw.co.uk
Date Admitted: 05/10/1988

WILKIE, Jennifer, Brodies LLP, 15 Atholl Crescent,
EDINBURGH EH3 8HA
Tel: 0131 5264003
Email: Jennifer.Wilkie@brodies.com
Date Admitted: 26/02/2008

YOUNG, Jacqueline May, The MFY Partnership,
25 Stirling Street, AIRDRIE ML6 0AH
Tel: 01236 607180
Email: jackie@mfypartnership.co.uk
Date Admitted: 16/08/1993

CALM

ABERDEIN, Ruth, Aberdein Considine & Company, 5-9 Bon Accord Crescent, Aberdeen AB11 6DN
Tel: 01224 337471
Email: raberdein@acandco.com

ADAMS, Rhona, Morton Fraser LLP, Quartermile Two, 2 Lister Square, Edinburgh EH3 9GL
Tel: 0131 2471339
Email: rhona.adams@morton-fraser.com

BARRETT, Angela, Russel & Aitken LLP, 22-24 Stirling Street, Denny FK6 6AZ
Tel: 01324 822194
Email: ab@radenny.co.uk

BLACKWOOD, Jane, Family Law Matters LLP, Queens House, 19 St Vincent Pace, Glasgow G1 2DT
Tel: 0141 4202430
Email: jane.blackwood@flmscotland.co.uk

BOWMAN, Gillian, Cairns Brown, 112 Main Street, Alexandria G83 0NZ
Tel: 01389 756979
Email: g.bowman@cairnsbrown.co.uk

BROPHY, Anne, Brophy Carey & Co Limited, 2 Caird Park, Hamilton ML3 0EU
Tel: 01698 200111
Email: ab@brophycareylaw.com

BROWN, Cheryl, McWhinney Richards, 66 Stirling Street, Airdrie ML6 0AW
Tel: 01236 754571
Email: cheryl.brown@mcwhinneyrichards.com

BUCHAN, Lorna, Patience & Buchan, 10 Golden Square, Aberdeen AB10 1RB
Tel: 01224 648222
Email: lorna@patienceandbuchan.com

BUCHANAN, Nicola, BLM, 13 Bath Street, Glasgow G2 1HY
Tel: 0141 353 2121
Email: nicola.buchanan@blmlaw.com

BURKE, Leoni, Aberdein Considine & Co, Elder House, Multrees Walk, Edinburgh EH1 3DX
Tel: 03330 044333
Email: lburke@acandco.com

BYTH, Sheila, McKinnon Forbes, 54 High Street, Tranent EH34 1HH
Tel: 01875 611 211
Email: sheila.byth@mckinnonforbes.co.uk

CAMPBELL, Fiona, Macleod & MacCallum Inverness Limited, 28 Queensgate, Inverness IV1 1YN
Tel: 01463 239393
Email: fiona.campbell@macandmac.co.uk

CAREY, Fiona, Brophy Carey & Co Limited, Mediacorp House, 2 Caird Park, Hamilton ML3 0EU
Tel: 01698 200111
Email: fjc@brophycareylaw.com

CARTHY, Jade, A.C. O'Neill & Co, 32 High Street, Dumbarton G82 1LL

Tel: 01389 762997
Email: jade.carthy@hotmail.co.uk

CLARK, Lucia, Morton Fraser LLP, Quartermile Two, Lister Square, Edinburgh EH3 9GL
Tel: 0131 2471000
Email: lucia.clark@morton-fraser.com

COLLEDGE, Jennifer, Colledge & Shields, 30 Castle Street, Dumfries DG1 1DU
Tel: 01387 240044
Email: jcc@colledgeandshields.co.uk

DONALD, Faye, Raeburn Christie Clark and Wallace, 12-16 Albyn Place, Aberdeen AB10 1PS
Tel: 01224 332400
Email: faye.donald@raeburns.co.uk

FEENEY, Sarah, Gilson Gray LLP, 160 West George Street, Glasgow G2 2HG
Tel: 0141 530 2034
Email: sfeeney@gilsongray.co.uk

FERGUSON, Jane, R & R Urquhart LLP, 117-121 High Street, Forres IV36 1AB
Tel: 01309 672216
Email: janeferguson@r-r-urquhart.com

FRASER, Morag, Fraser Shepherd, 39 Vicar Street, Falkirk FK1 1LL
Tel: 01324 630700
Email: morag@frasershepherd.co.uk

GEORGE, Shaun, Brodies LLP, 31/33 Union Grove, Aberdeen, AB10 6SD
Tel: 01224 392531
Email: shaun.george@brodies.com

GIBBONS, Karen, Harper MacLeod, Citypoint, 65 Haymarket Terrace, Edinburgh
Tel: 0131 2472500
Email: karen.gibbons@harpermacleod.co.uk

GILLIES, Lousie, Ness Gallagher & Co, 358 Brandon Street, Motherwell ML1 1XA
Tel: 01698 254644
Email: lg@nessgallagher.co.uk

GILMOUR, Robert, SKO Family Law Limited, Forsyth House, 93 George Street, Edinburgh EH2 3ES
Tel: 0131 2432583
Email: robert.gilmour@sko-family.co.uk

GIRDWOOD, Lisa, Brodies LLP, 110 Queen Street, Glasgow G1 3BX
Tel: 0141 2484672
Email: lisa.girdwood@brodies.com

GORDON, Lesley, BTO Solicitors LLP, One Edinburgh Quay, 133 Fountainbridge, Edinburgh EH3 9QG
Tel: 0131 222 2959
Email: lxg@bto.co.uk

GOSTELOW, Paul, Baker Gostelow Law Limited, 16 Clydeview Shopping Centre, Blantyre G72 0QD
Tel: 01698 820700

Email: moyra.hotchkiss@bakergostelowlaw.co.
uk

HIGSON, Judith, Scullion Law, 105 Cadzow
Street, Hamilton ML3 6HG
Tel: 01698 283265
Email: judith@scullionlaw.com

HINCHIN, Michaela, Family Law Matters
Scotland LLP, 63 Carlton Place, Glasgow G5
9TW
Tel: 0141 4202430
Email: michaela.hinchin@flmscotland.co.uk

HOOPER, Denise, Wright & Crawford, 11
Glasgow Road, Paisley PA1 3QS
Tel: 0141 887 6211
Email: d.hooper@wright-crawford.co.uk

HUGHES, Helen, McAuley McCarthy & Co, 29
Moss Street, Paisley PA1 1DL
Tel: 0141 5617779
Email: h.hughes-paisley@btconnect.com

HUNTER, Alexis, Alexis Hunter Family Law,
Cartside House, 1/7 Clarkston Road, Cathcart,
Glasgow G44 4EF
Tel: 0141 4040124
Email: amh@ahfamilylaw.co.uk

KARLIN, Cath, Cath Karlin Family Law, 15/16
Queen Street, Edinburgh EH2 1JE
Tel: 0131 3571515
Email: cath@cathkarlinfamilylaw.co.uk

KELSEY, Rachael, SKO Family Law Limited,
Forsyth House, 93 George Street, Edinburgh
EH2 3ES
Tel: 0131 2432583
Email: Rachael.Kelsey@sko-family.co.uk

LAW, Janie, Family Law Matters Scotland LLP, 63
Carlton Place, Glasgow G5 9TW
Tel: 0141 4202430
Email: janie.law@flmscotland.co.uk

LIDDIARD, Simon, Stewart & Watson, 35 Queen
Street, Peterhead AB42 1TP
Tel: 01779 476351
Email: sliddiard@stewartwatson.co.uk

LOTHIAN, Ailie, Smail & Ewart, 70 High Street,
Lanark ML11 7ES
Tel: 01555 666111
Email: alothian@smail-ewart.co.uk

MACANDREW, Hilary, Grant Smith Law Practice
Limited, Old Bank Buildings, Balmellie Street,
Turriff, Aberdeenshire AB53 4DW
Tel: 01888 562245
Email: hilary.macandrew@grantsmithlaw.co.uk

MARTIN, Nadine, Gibson Kerr, 46 India Street,
Edinburgh EH3 6HJ
Tel: 0131 226 9161
Email: nadine.martin@gibsonkerr.co.uk

MASSON, Amanda, Harper MacLeod LLP, 45
Gordon Street, Glasgow G1 3PE
Tel: 0141 2279394
Email: amanda.masson@harpermacleod.co.uk

McINTOSH, Rowena, McIntosh Family Law,
52-54 Albert Street, Aberdeen AB25 1XS
Tel: 01224 593100
Email: rowena@mcintoshfamilylaw.com

McKAY, Donna, Brodies LLP, 31/33 Union Grove,
Aberdeen AB10 6SD
Tel: 01224 392532
Email: donna.mckay@brodies.com

McLACHLAN, Lindsay, LAM Family Law, Studio
3015, Mile End Mill, Abbey Mill Business
Centre, 12 Seedhill Road, Paisley PA1 1JS
Tel: 0141 889 0101
Email: lm@lamfamilylaw.co.uk

McLACHLAN, Lydia, Brodies LLP, 31/33 Union
Grove, Aberdeen AB10 6SD
Tel: 01224 392533
Email: lydia.mclachlan@brodies.com

McLAUGHLAN, Lisa, Stirling & Mair, 28 High
Street, Johnstone, Renfrewshire PA5 8AH
Tel: 01505 329373
Email: lisa.mclaughlan@stirlingmair.com

McWILLIAMS, Gerald, Cowan & Co, 81 Berkeley
Street, Glasgow G3 7DX
Tel: 0141 2211803
Email: gmcw@cowanandco.co.uk

MEIL, Judith, Taggart Meil Mathers, 20 Bon
Accord Square, Aberdeen AB11 6DJ
Tel: 01224 588020
Email: judy@tmmsolicitors.co.uk

MURRAY, Joanne, Blackadders, 6 Bon Accord
Square, Aberdeen AB11 6XU
Tel: 01224 588913
Email: joanne.murray@blackadders.co.uk

MURRAY, Sharon, Gillespie Macandrew LLP, 5
Atholl Crescent, Edinburgh EH3 8EJ
Tel: 0131 2251677
Email: sharon.murra@gillespiemacandrew.co.
uk

OSWALD, Susan, SKO Family Law Limited,
Forsyth House, 93 George Street, Edinburgh
EH2 3ES
Tel: 0131 2432583
Email: susan.oswald@sko-family.co.uk

POLSON, Jackie, PO Box 17495, Edinburgh EH12
1PG
Email: jackie.a.polson@outlook.com

PURVIS, Susan, Ledingham Chalmers LLP,
Johnstone House, 52-54 Rose Street, Aberdeen
AB10 1HA
Tel: 01224 408408
Email: susan.purvis@ledinghamchalmers.com

RASMUSEN, Fiona, Gibson Kerr, 46 India Street,
Edinburgh EH3 6HJ
Tel: 0131 2257558
Email: fiona.rasmusen@gibsonkerr.co.uk

REEKIE, Debbie, BTO Solicitors LLP, 1 Edinburgh
Quay, 133 Fountainbridge, Edinburgh EH3
9QG
Tel: 0131 2222939
Email: der@bto.co.uk

RIDDELL, Vivien, TC Young LLP, Melrose House,
69a George Street, Edinburgh EH2 2JG
Tel: 0131 2207660
Email: vmr@tcyoung.co.uk

SCHOLARIOS, Nicos, MSM Solicitors Limited, 51
Moss Street, Paisley PA1 1DR
Tel: 0141 8896244

Email: ns@msmlaw.co.uk

SHEILDS, Sandi, Colledge & Shields LLP, 30 Castle Street, Dumfries DG1 1DU
Tel: 01387 240044
Email: ss@colledgeandshields.co.uk

SIMPSON, Ashley, Patience and Buchan, 10 Golden Square, Aberdeen AB10 1RB
Tel: 01224 648222
Email: ashley@patienceandbuchan.com

SMITH, Caroline, MTM Family Law LLP, 2nd Floor, 91 Mitchell Street, Glasgow G1 3LN
Tel: 0141 6117535
Email: clsh@mtmfamilylaw.co.uk

SMITH, Jenny, Harper Macleod LLP, The Ca'd'oro, 45 Gordon Street, Glasgow G1 3PE
Tel: 0141 2218888
Email: jenny.smith@harpermacleod.co.uk

SMITH, Richard, Burness Paull LLP, 50 Lothian Road, Festival Square, Edinburgh EH3 9WJ
Tel: 0131 4736000
Email: richard.smith@burnesspaull.com

SMITH, Shona, Balfour & Manson LLP, 62 Frederick Street, Edinburgh EH2 1LS
Tel: 0131 200 1238
Email: shona.smith@balfour-manson.co.uk

STRATFORD, Lynn, Drummond Miller LLP, 11 White Hart Street, Dalkeith EH22 1AE
Tel: 0131 561 5918
Email: LStratford@drummondmiller.co.uk

STROUD, Jacqueline, MacRoberts LLP, Excel House, 30 Semple Street, Edinburgh EH3 8BL
Tel: 0131 248 2231
Email: jacqueline.stroud@macroberts.com

STURROCK, Garry, Brodies LLP, Brodies House, 31-33 Union Grove, Aberdeen AB10 6SD
Tel: 01224 392242
Email: garry.sturrock@brodies.com

TEMPLETON, Shona, MTM Family Law, 2nd Floor Front, 91 Mitchell Street, Glasgow G1 3LN
Tel: 0141 6117535
Email: smt@mtmfamilylaw.co.uk

WILKIE, Jennifer, Brodies LLP, 15 Atholl Crescent, Edinburgh EH3 8HA
Tel: 0131 5264003
Email: jennifer.wilkie@brodies.com

YOUNG, Jacqueline, The MFY Partnership, 22 Stirling Street, Airdrie ML6 0AH
Tel: 01236 6077180
Email: jackie@mfypartnership.co.uk

Alphabetical List of Law Firms

BLAIR & BRYDEN
Dunoon . . . . (p.827)
BLAIR & BRYDEN
Greenock . . . . (p.1059)
BLAIR & BRYDEN
Greenock . . . . (p.1060)
BLAIR & BRYDEN
Port Glasgow . . . . (p.1156)
BLAIR CADELL
Edinburgh EH11 . . . . (p.844)
BLAIR CADELL
Edinburgh EH6 . . . . (p.844)
BLANEY CARNAN
Glasgow G2 . . . . (p.947)
BMK (NOMINEES) LIMITED
Glasgow G2 . . . . (p.947)
C.T. BOLLEN LIMITED
Glasgow G3 . . . . (p.947)
BONACCORD ECOSSE LIMITED
Edinburgh EH10 . . . . (p.844)
ANTHONY BONE
Kilmarnock . . . . (p.1094)
BON LAW LTD
Edinburgh EH10 . . . . (p.845)
BONNAR ACCIDENT LAW LTD
Airdrie . . . . (p.748)
BONNAR ACCIDENT LAW LTD
Dunfermline . . . . (p.822)
BONNAR ACCIDENT LAW LTD
East Kilbride . . . . (p.830)
BONNAR ACCIDENT LAW LTD
Edinburgh EH2 . . . . (p.845)
BONNAR LAW LIMITED
East Kilbride . . . . (p.830)
SIMON D BOOKER-MILBURN
Nairn . . . . (p.1129)
BORDERS LEGAL LIMITED
Duns . . . . (p.828)
BORDERS LEGAL LIMITED
Kelso . . . . (p.1091)
BORDERS LEGAL LIMITED
Selkirk . . . . (p.1161)
BOWMANS
Dundee . . . . (p.806)
BOWMANS
Forfar . . . . (p.926)
JOSEPH G BOYD & CO COURT LAWYERS LTD
Edinburgh EH12 . . . . (p.845)
BOYD LEGAL LIMITED
Edinburgh EH2 . . . . (p.845)
BOYD LEGAL LIMITED
Kirkcaldy . . . . (p.1099)
BOYDS LAW
Forfar . . . . (p.926)
C.F. BOYLE & CO LIMITED
Glasgow G3 . . . . (p.947)
T BOYLE & CO LIMITED
Glasgow G5 . . . . (p.947)
BOYLES SOLICITORS
Dundee . . . . (p.806)

AJ BRADLEY & CO LTD
Glasgow G1 . . . . (p.947)
BRAIDWOODS
Dumfries . . . . (p.800)
BRAZENALL & ORR
Dumfries . . . . (p.800)
BREADY & CO.
Glasgow G5 . . . . (p.947)
BRECHIN TINDAL OATTS
Glasgow G2 . . . . (p.947)
BRIDGE EMPLOYMENT SOLICITORS LIMITED
Glasgow G2 . . . . (p.948)
BRIDGE LEGAL LIMITED
Glasgow G5 . . . . (p.948)
BRODIES LLP
Aberdeen AB10 . . . . (p.723)
BRODIES LLP
Dingwall . . . . (p.796)
BRODIES LLP
Edinburgh EH3 . . . . (p.845)
BRODIES LLP
Glasgow G1 . . . . (p.948)
ANDREW BROPHY
Hamilton . . . . (p.1066)
BROPHY CAREY & CO LTD
Hamilton . . . . (p.1066)
BROTHOCK TRUSTEES LIMITED
Dundee . . . . (p.806)
BROWN & CO LEGAL LLP
Edinburgh EH2 . . . . (p.848)
BROWN & CO LEGAL LLP
Glasgow G33 . . . . (p.950)
BROWN & CO LEGAL LLP
Glasgow G3 . . . . (p.950)
BROWN & CO LEGAL LLP
Glasgow G33 . . . . (p.951)
BROWN & CO LEGAL LLP
Greenock . . . . (p.1060)
JACK BROWN & COMPANY
Dundee . . . . (p.806)
BROWN & MCRAE LLP
Fraserburgh . . . . (p.930)
BROWN & MCRAE LLP
Turriff . . . . (p.1176)
JOHN BROWN (SCOTLAND) LTD
Glasgow G34 . . . . (p.951)
MICHAEL A BROWN SOLICITORS
Dundee . . . . (p.806)
M.J. BROWN, SON & CO.
Edinburgh EH3 . . . . (p.848)
R. BRUCE & CO.
Arbroath . . . . (p.757)
R. BRUCE & CO.
Forfar . . . . (p.926)
BRUCE MACDONALD & CO.
Aberdeen AB25 . . . . (p.724)
BRUCE, SHORT & CO.
Dundee . . . . (p.806)
BRUCE THE LAWYERS
Motherwell . . . . (p.1126)

GILLESPIE GIFFORD & BROWN LLP
Dumfries . . . .(p.800)
GILLESPIE GIFFORD & BROWN LLP
Kirkcudbright . . . .(p.1104)
GILLESPIE MACANDREW LLP
Edinburgh EH3 . . . .(p.872)
GILLESPIE MACANDREW LLP
Edinburgh EH10 . . . .(p.874)
GILLESPIE MACANDREW LLP
Glasgow G2 . . . .(p.979)
GILLESPIE MACANDREW LLP
Perth . . . .(p.1148)
GILLIES MAXWELL
Ayr . . . .(p.763)
BK GILL SOLICITORS
Bearsden . . . .(p.772)
DOUGLAS GILMOUR & SON
Selkirk . . . .(p.1162)
GILROY & CO
Glasgow G44 . . . .(p.980)
GILSON GRAY LLP
Dundee . . . .(p.811)
GILSON GRAY LLP
Dundee . . . .(p.812)
GILSON GRAY LLP
Edinburgh EH1 . . . .(p.874)
GILSON GRAY LLP
Glasgow G2 . . . .(p.980)
GILSON GRAY LLP
North Berwick . . . .(p.1132)
GLASGOW CITIZEN ADVICE BUREAUX
SPECIALIST SERVICES
Glasgow G40 . . . .(p.980)
GLASGOW DEFENCE LAWYERS LIMITED
Glasgow G2 . . . .(p.981)
GLEESON MCCAFFERTY LAW
Glenrothes . . . .(p.1057)
GMC CRIMINAL LAWYERS
Kilmarnock . . . .(p.1095)
GOLDEN SQUARE NOMINEES LIMITED
Aberdeen AB10 . . . .(p.731)
GOLDSMITH & HUGHES LTD
East Kilbride . . . .(p.831)
V. GOOD & CO.
Edinburgh EH1 . . . .(p.875)
GAIL GOODFELLOW, SOLICITOR ADVOCATE
Aberdeen AB11 . . . .(p.731)
GOOD & STEWART LIMITED
Edinburgh EH8 . . . .(p.875)
GORBALS LAW AND MONEY ADVICE CENTRE
Glasgow G5 . . . .(p.981)
A. J. GORDON & CO
Glasgow G20 . . . .(p.981)
GORDON & SMYTH
Bishopbriggs . . . .(p.774)
GORDON WILLIAMS LIMITED
Glasgow G43 . . . .(p.981)
W. & J.S. GORDON
Forfar . . . .(p.926)
GORRIE & DAVIDSON
Dunfermline . . . .(p.823)

LESLEY GOVAN ASSOCIATES
Glasgow G41 . . . .(p.981)
JACK GOWANS & MARC DICKSON
SOLICITORS LIMITED
Inverness . . . .(p.1076)
S. GRADY SOLICITORS
Glasgow G1 . . . .(p.981)
JACK GRANT & CO.
Motherwell . . . .(p.1127)
GRAY & CO.
Glasgow G20 . . . .(p.981)
GRAY & GRAY LLP
Ellon . . . .(p.918)
GRAY & GRAY LLP
Peterhead . . . .(p.1153)
LESLEY A. GRAY
Gullane . . . .(p.1063)
A. GRAY MUIR, WS LIMITED
Edinburgh EH17 . . . .(p.875)
GREAT STUART TRUSTEES LIMITED
Edinburgh EH3 . . . .(p.876)
GREENBERG SOLICITORS
Laurencekirk . . . .(p.1111)
KENNETH M. GREENER LIMITED
Stonehouse . . . .(p.1169)
GREENTREE LEGAL LIMITED
Glasgow G2 . . . .(p.981)
GREIG EMPLOYMENT LAW LIMITED
Glasgow G2 . . . .(p.981)
GREY & CO SOLICITORS LTD
Inverness . . . .(p.1076)
GRIEVE, GRIERSON, MOODIE & WALKER
Dumfries . . . .(p.801)
GRIGOR & YOUNG LLP
Elgin . . . .(p.916)
GRIGOR & YOUNG LLP
Forres . . . .(p.928)
JAS. S. GROSSET
Leven . . . .(p.1115)
G S LEGAL
Glasgow G1 . . . .(p.981)
GUARINO & THOMSON LIMITED
East Kilbride . . . .(p.831)
GUNNERCOOKE
Edinburgh EH2 . . . .(p.876)
GUNNERCOOKE SCO LLP
Edinburgh EH2 . . . .(p.876)
GUNNERCOOKE SCO LLP
Glasgow G1 . . . .(p.982)
JAMES GUTHRIE & COMPANY LLP
Kilmarnock . . . .(p.1095)
GWG LTD
Glasgow G2 . . . .(p.982)
HALL BAIRD SOLICITORS LTD
Castle Douglas . . . .(p.784)
HALL & HAUGHEY
Glasgow G5 . . . .(p.982)
HALLIDAY CAMPBELL W.S.
Edinburgh EH16 . . . .(p.876)
HALL NORRIE WARDEN LLP
Dundee . . . .(p.812)

LINDSAYS LLP
Dundee . . . .(p.814)
LINDSAYS LLP
Edinburgh EH3 . . . .(p.882)
LINDSAYS LLP
Glasgow G1 . . . .(p.1001)
LINDSAYS (PROPERTY)
Dundee . . . .(p.814)
LIU'S LEGAL SOLUTIONS LTD
Glasgow G4 . . . .(p.1002)
LIVING LAW
Wester Inch Village . . . .(p.1178)
LIVINGSTONE BROWN LIMITED
Glasgow G34 . . . .(p.1002)
LIVINGSTONE BROWN LIMITED
Glasgow G2 . . . .(p.1003)
LIVINGSTONE BROWN LIMITED
Glasgow G42 . . . .(p.1003)
LIVINGSTONE BROWN LIMITED
Glasgow G32 . . . .(p.1004)
LKW SOLICITORS LTD
Glasgow G42 . . . .(p.1004)
LOCKHARTS LAW LLP
Ayr . . . .(p.764)
LOGANS
Cumnock . . . .(p.791)
MICHAEL LOTT
Motherwell . . . .(p.1127)
LOUGHRAN & CO LIMITED
Glasgow G3 . . . .(p.1004)
LOW BEATON RICHMOND LLP
Glasgow G2 . . . .(p.1005)
LOW BEATON RICHMOND LLP
Largs . . . .(p.1110)
R A LOW & COMPANY
Musselburgh . . . .(p.1129)
LOWS ORKNEY LIMITED
Kirkwall . . . .(p.1106)
LOWS ORKNEY TRUSTEES LIMITED
Kirkwall . . . .(p.1106)
LUMSDEN CONSULTANCY LIMITED
Falkirk . . . .(p.922)
LUNNY & CO
Bellshill . . . .(p.773)
LYNCH & CO., SOLICITORS
Glasgow G51 . . . .(p.1005)
LYONS DAVIDSON SCOTLAND LLP
Edinburgh EH3 . . . .(p.883)
MICHAEL LYON SOLICITORS LIMITED
Dumfries . . . .(p.802)
MICHAEL LYON SOLICITORS LIMITED
Glasgow G1 . . . .(p.1005)
MCAFEE
Airdrie . . . .(p.749)
MCAFEE
Coatbridge . . . .(p.787)
MCAFEE
Lanark . . . .(p.1108)
MACALLANS LIMITED
Glasgow G73 . . . .(p.1005)

MACANDREW & JENKINS (TRUSTEES) LIMITED
Inverness . . . .(p.1079)
MACANDREW & JENKINS, WS LIMITED
Inverness . . . .(p.1079)
MCANDREW & RICHARDSON
Stranraer . . . .(p.1171)
MCARDLE
Glasgow G53 . . . .(p.1005)
MACARTHUR LEGAL
Oban . . . .(p.1134)
MCARTHUR STANTON
Dumbarton . . . .(p.798)
MCARTHUR STANTON
Helensburgh . . . .(p.1072)
MCARTHUR STANTON
Helensburgh . . . .(p.1072)
MACARTHUR STEWART, FORT WILLIAM
Fort William . . . .(p.929)
MCAULEY, MCCARTHY & CO.
Glasgow G51 . . . .(p.1005)
MCAULEY, MCCARTHY & CO.
Paisley . . . .(p.1139)
MCAULEY, MCCARTHY & CO.
Renfrew . . . .(p.1159)
STEPHEN J. MACBRIDE & CO
Wishaw . . . .(p.1181)
MCBRIDE KONDOL & CO.
Glasgow G42 . . . .(p.1006)
ALEXANDER MCBURNEY SOLICITORS
Glasgow G11 . . . .(p.1006)
MCCARRON & CO.
Airdrie . . . .(p.750)
MCCARRYS SOLICITORS
Glasgow G20 . . . .(p.1006)
MCCARTHY LAW
Glasgow G11 . . . .(p.1006)
IAN C. MCCARTHY LTD
Glasgow G11 . . . .(p.1006)
IAN C. MCCARTHY LTD
Glasgow G32 . . . .(p.1007)
MCCARTNEY STEWART LIMITED
Renfrew . . . .(p.1159)
MCCASH & HUNTER LLP
Perth . . . .(p.1149)
MCCLURE COLLINS LIMITED
Glasgow G42 . . . .(p.1007)
MCCLUSKEY BROWNE
Kilmarnock . . . .(p.1095)
WILLIAM MCCLUSKEY SOLICITORS LIMITED
Glasgow G5 . . . .(p.1007)
BRUCE MCCORMACK LIMITED
Glasgow G5 . . . .(p.1007)
BRUCE MCCORMACK LIMITED
Motherwell . . . .(p.1127)
MCCORMACKS SOLICITORS LIMITED
Glasgow G2 . . . .(p.1007)
JOHN N. MCCORMICK
Glasgow G2 . . . .(p.1007)
MCCORMICK & NICHOLSON
Girvan . . . .(p.935)

ANGUS MCINTOSH & SIMON HODGE
Glasgow G45 . . . .(p.1012)
MCINTYRE & CO.
Fort William . . . .(p.930)
MCINTYRES
Edinburgh EH15 . . . .(p.886)
MCJERROW & STEVENSON
Lockerbie . . . .(p.1122)
DJ MACKAY AND PARTNERS LLP
Glasgow G3 . . . .(p.1012)
JAMES MCKAY DEFENCE SOLICITORS LIMITED
Elgin . . . .(p.917)
MACKAY SINCLAIR
Edinburgh EH7 . . . .(p.886)
MCKEAN GARDNER LIMITED
Perth . . . .(p.1150)
MCKEE CAMPBELL MORRISON LIMITED
Glasgow G2 . . . .(p.1013)
RON MACKENNA DEFENCE LAWYERS LTD
Glasgow G5 . . . .(p.1013)
MCKENNAS LAW PRACTICE LIMITED
Glenrothes . . . .(p.1057)
DEREK MACKENZIE & COMPANY LIMITED
Stornoway . . . .(p.1170)
MACKENZIE & CORMACK
Tain . . . .(p.1173)
MACKENZIE LAW LTD
Inverness . . . .(p.1080)
MACKENZIE & MACKENZIE
Dundee . . . .(p.815)
MCKENZIES
Kirkcaldy . . . .(p.1101)
MACKIE & DEWAR
Aberdeen AB11 . . . .(p.736)
MACKINLAY & SUTTIE
Barrhead . . . .(p.770)
MCKINLEY & CO.
Glasgow G20 . . . .(p.1013)
MCKINNON & CO
Glasgow G33 . . . .(p.1013)
MCKINNON FORBES
Tranent . . . .(p.1175)
MCKINNON HEWITT
Irvine . . . .(p.1086)
MACKINNONS SOLICITORS LLP
Aberdeen AB10 . . . .(p.736)
MACKINNONS SOLICITORS LLP
Aberdeen AB15 . . . .(p.737)
MACKINNONS SOLICITORS LLP
Aboyne . . . .(p.748)
MACKINTOSH & WYLIE LLP
Irvine . . . .(p.1087)
MACKINTOSH & WYLIE LLP
Kilmarnock . . . .(p.1095)
MACKINTOSH & WYLIE LLP
Stewarton . . . .(p.1163)
MCLAUGHLIN & CO
Kirkcaldy . . . .(p.1101)
MCLAUGHLIN & CO
Leven . . . .(p.1116)

MACLAY MURRAY & SPENS
Glasgow G2 . . . .(p.1013)
MCLEAN & STEWART LLP
Dunblane . . . .(p.804)
MCLENNAN ADAM DAVIS
Ayr . . . .(p.764)
LORNA MACLEOD FAMILY LAW
East Kilbride . . . .(p.832)
JANE MACLEOD
Lochgilphead . . . .(p.1120)
MACLEOD & MACCALLUM LIMITED
Inverness . . . .(p.1080)
MACLEOD & MACCALLUM LIMITED
Portree . . . .(p.1157)
MCMAHON EMPLOYMENT LAW
Bearsden . . . .(p.772)
MCMAHON EMPLOYMENT LAW
Kirkintilloch . . . .(p.1105)
MACMILLAN & CO.
Alness . . . .(p.753)
MCMULLEN LAW LIMITED
Hamilton . . . .(p.1067)
MACNABS LLP
Auchterarder . . . .(p.759)
MACNABS LLP
Blairgowrie . . . .(p.776)
MACNABS LLP
Bridge of Allan . . . .(p.779)
MACNABS LLP
Perth . . . .(p.1150)
MACNABS LLP
Pitlochry . . . .(p.1155)
JAMES MCNAIR SOLICITORS
Glasgow G66 . . . .(p.1014)
MACNAIRS & WILSON LIMITED
Glasgow G31 . . . .(p.1014)
MACNAIRS & WILSON LIMITED
Paisley . . . .(p.1140)
GORDON MACNEIL
Cowdenbeath . . . .(p.788)
MCO DEFENCE SOLICITORS
Glasgow G1 . . . .(p.1014)
JAMES MCPARLAND
Glasgow G33 . . . .(p.1014)
IAIN A. MCPHAIL
Glasgow G3 . . . .(p.1014)
FIONA MCPHAIL SOLICITORS
Edinburgh EH2 . . . .(p.886)
MACPHEE & PARTNERS LLP
Fort William . . . .(p.930)
MACPHEE & PARTNERS LLP
Oban . . . .(p.1135)
MACPHERSON & DISSELDUFF
Greenock . . . .(p.1061)
MACPHERSON MAGUIRE COOK
Glasgow G2 . . . .(p.1015)
NEIL F. MCPHERSON
Kilmarnock . . . .(p.1096)
MCQUILLAN GLASSER & WAUGHMAN
Hamilton . . . .(p.1068)

MACRAE AND KAUR LLP
Glasgow G2 . . . .(p.1015)
GORDON MACRAE & CO LTD
Edinburgh EH7 . . . .(p.886)
GORDON MACRAE & CO LTD
Edinburgh EH3 . . . .(p.887)
MACRAE STEPHEN & CO.
Fraserburgh . . . .(p.931)
MACROBERTS CORPORATE SERVICES LIMITED
Glasgow G2 . . . .(p.1015)
MACROBERTS LLP
Dundee . . . .(p.815)
MACROBERTS LLP
Edinburgh EH2 . . . .(p.887)
MACROBERTS LLP
Glasgow G2 . . . .(p.1015)
MACROBERTS TRUSTEES LIMITED
Glasgow G2 . . . .(p.1016)
MCSHERRY HALLIDAY LLP
Kilmarnock . . . .(p.1096)
MCSHERRY HALLIDAY LLP
Troon . . . .(p.1175)
MCSPARRAN MCCORMICK
Glasgow G44 . . . .(p.1016)
MCSPARRAN MCCORMICK
Glasgow G2 . . . .(p.1016)
IAIN MCSPORRAN QC, SOLICITOR ADVOCATE
Edinburgh EH1 . . . .(p.888)
MCSPORRANS
Edinburgh EH2 . . . .(p.888)
C. & D. MACTAGGART
Campbeltown . . . .(p.782)
C. & D. MACTAGGART
Lochgilphead . . . .(p.1121)
MACTAGGART & CO LIMITED
Largs . . . .(p.1110)
MCVEY & MURRICANE
Glasgow G2 . . . .(p.1017)
MCVEY & MURRICANE NOMINEES LIMITED
Glasgow G2 . . . .(p.1017)
MCWHINNEY RICHARDS
Airdrie . . . .(p.750)
MAGUIRE SOLICITORS
Glasgow G20 . . . .(p.1017)
ANTHONY MAHON LIMITED
Glasgow G15 . . . .(p.1017)
ANTHONY MAHON LIMITED
Glasgow G2 . . . .(p.1018)
MAILERS
Alloa . . . .(p.753)
MAILERS
Bridge of Allan . . . .(p.780)
MAILERS
Stirling . . . .(p.1166)
MAINS SOLICITORS
East Kilbride . . . .(p.832)
MAIR MATHESON SOLICITORS LTD
Newmilns . . . .(p.1130)
MAITLAND & CO
Glasgow G1 . . . .(p.1018)

MAITLANDS
Greenock . . . .(p.1062)
CONNOR MALCOLM
Edinburgh EH3 . . . .(p.888)
MALCOLM & HUTCHISON
Airdrie . . . .(p.750)
MALCOLM, JACK & MATHESON LIMITED
Dunfermline . . . .(p.824)
MALOCO + ASSOCIATES LIMITED
Dunfermline . . . .(p.824)
MALOCO LETTINGS
Dunfermline . . . .(p.824)
BRANDON MALONE & COMPANY LIMITED
Edinburgh EH2 . . . .(p.888)
BRANDON MALONE & COMPANY LIMITED
Penicuik . . . .(p.1145)
ANDREW G. MANDERSON & CO.
Dundee . . . .(p.816)
MANINI BELARDO LIMITED
Airdrie . . . .(p.750)
MANINI BELARDO LIMITED
Coatbridge . . . .(p.787)
MANNIFIELD TEMPLETON DEFENCE
Edinburgh EH1 . . . .(p.888)
MANUS JAMES
Glasgow G3 . . . .(p.1018)
MARITIME TRUSTEES LIMITED
Glasgow G2 . . . .(p.1018)
MARSALI MURRAY
Edinburgh EH10 . . . .(p.888)
MARSHALL WILSON LAW GROUP LIMITED
Falkirk . . . .(p.922)
MARTIN, JOHNSTON & SOCHA LIMITED
Alloa . . . .(p.753)
MARTIN, JOHNSTON & SOCHA LIMITED
Dunfermline . . . .(p.824)
MARTIN, JOHNSTON & SOCHA LIMITED
Kirkcaldy . . . .(p.1102)
MASSON CAIRNS LIMITED
Grantown-on-Spey . . . .(p.1059)
MASSON GLENNIE LLP
Fraserburgh . . . .(p.931)
MASSON GLENNIE LLP
Peterhead . . . .(p.1154)
ALAN E. MASTERTON
Monifieth . . . .(p.1125)
GEORGE MATHERS & CO
Aberdeen AB11 . . . .(p.737)
MATHIE, LENNOX & CO.
Kilsyth . . . .(p.1097)
MATHIE-MORTON
Ayr . . . .(p.764)
MATTAC LIMITED
Edinburgh EH2 . . . .(p.888)
MATTHEW BROWN
Irvine . . . .(p.1087)
MATTHEWS LEGAL LIMITED
Dumfries . . . .(p.802)
MATTHEWS LEGAL LIMITED
Newton Stewart . . . .(p.1131)

Geographical List of Law Firms – Scotland

Aberdeen

ABERDEIN CONSIDINE
5-9 Bon Accord Crescent, Aberdeen
AB11 6DN
Tel: (01224) 589700
Categories of Work
Adjudication
Adoption
Advice the elderly & powers of attorney
Agriculture and estates
Agriculture, crofting and fishing
Alternative dispute resolution
Alternative investment market
Banking & finance
Charities
Children
Childrens
Civil court work
Civil legal aid
Commercial litigation
Commercial property
Competition
Construction
Consumer credit
Contract & property disputes
Copyright, trade marks and design
Corporate tax
Credit brokerage
Criminal court work
Criminal legal aid
Data protection
Debt
Debt adjusting and debt counselling
Debt collecting
Debt recovery, insolvency, bankruptcy
Disability
Discrimination
Education
Employment
Employment law
Environment
Environment (Business Premises)
EU / international
Family and divorce
Family business advice
Freedom of information
Health
Health and safety
Human rights
Insolvency & corporate recovery
Insurance
Joint venture
Landlord & tenant
Liquor licensing
Local government
Media and entertainment
Mental health

Mergers and acquisitions
Pensions (Company)
Pensions (Employment)
Personal injury
Personal tax
Planning (Business Premises)
Private equity
Professional negligence
Property litigation
Public finance initiative
Public sector
Residential property
SME business advice
Social housing
Telecoms
Unit Trusts, OEICs and investment trusts
Wills, executries and trusts

ABERDEIN CONSIDINE AND COMPANY
115 Victoria Street, Dyce, Aberdeen AB21 7AX
Tel: (01224) 723737
Fax: (01224) 724867
E-mail: dyce@acandco.com
Web: www.acandco.com
Categories of Work
Adjudication
Adoption
Advice the elderly & powers of attorney
Agriculture and estates
Agriculture, crofting and fishing
Alternative dispute resolution
Alternative investment market
Banking & finance
Charities
Children
Childrens
Civil court work
Civil legal aid
Commercial litigation
Commercial property
Competition
Construction
Consumer credit
Contract & property disputes
Copyright, trade marks and design
Corporate tax
Credit brokerage
Criminal court work
Criminal legal aid
Data protection
Debt
Debt adjusting and debt counselling
Debt collecting
Debt recovery, insolvency, bankruptcy
Disability
Discrimination
Education
Employment

► **Aberdeen continued**

Employment law
Environment
Environment (Business Premises)
EU / international
Family and divorce
Family business advice
Freedom of information
Health
Health and safety
Human rights
Insolvency & corporate recovery
Insurance
Joint venture
Landlord & tenant
Liquor licensing
Local government
Media and entertainment
Mental health
Mergers and acquisitions
Pensions (Company)
Pensions (Employment)
Personal injury
Personal tax
Planning (Business Premises)
Private equity
Professional negligence
Property litigation
Public finance initiative
Public sector
Residential property
SME business advice
Social housing
Telecoms
Unit Trusts, OEICs and investment trusts
Wills, executives and trusts
Partner
Fiona Wildgoose
Employee
Eleanor Clare Comfort

ABERDEIN CONSIDINE AND COMPANY
420-424 Union Street, Aberdeen AB10 1TQ
Tel: (01224) 267067
Fax: (01224) 267068
E-mail: 420@acandco.com
Web: www.acandco.com
Categories of Work
Adjudication
Adoption
Advice the elderly & powers of attorney
Agriculture and estates
Agriculture, crofting and fishing
Alternative dispute resolution
Alternative investment market
Banking & finance
Charities
Children
Childrens
Civil court work
Civil legal aid
Commercial litigation
Commercial property

Competition
Construction
Consumer credit
Contract & property disputes
Copyright, trade marks and design
Corporate tax
Credit brokerage
Criminal court work
Criminal legal aid
Data protection
Debt
Debt adjusting and debt counselling
Debt collecting
Debt recovery, insolvency, bankruptcy
Disability
Discrimination
Education
Employment
Employment law
Environment
Environment (Business Premises)
EU / international
Family and divorce
Family business advice
Freedom of information
Health
Health and safety
Human rights
Insolvency & corporate recovery
Insurance
Joint venture
Landlord & tenant
Liquor licensing
Local government
Media and entertainment
Mental health
Mergers and acquisitions
Pensions (Company)
Pensions (Employment)
Personal injury
Personal tax
Planning (Business Premises)
Private equity
Professional negligence
Property litigation
Public finance initiative
Public sector
Residential property
SME business advice
Social housing
Telecoms
Unit Trusts, OEICs and investment trusts
Wills, executives and trusts
Partners
Christopher Robert Comfort
Robert Malcolm Fraser
Michael Walter Sinclair

ABERDEIN CONSIDINE AND COMPANY
5-9 Bon Accord Crescent, Aberdeen
AB11 6DN
Tel: (01224) 589700
Fax: (01224) 288079

DX: AB46 ABERDEEN
E-mail: mail@acandco.com
Web: www.acandco.com
Categories of Work
Adjudication
Adoption
Advice the elderly & powers of attorney
Agriculture and estates
Agriculture, crofting and fishing
Alternative dispute resolution
Alternative investment market
Banking & finance
Charities
Children
Childrens
Civil court work
Civil legal aid
Commercial litigation
Commercial property
Competition
Construction
Consumer credit
Contract & property disputes
Copyright, trade marks and design
Corporate tax
Credit brokerage
Criminal court work
Criminal legal aid
Data protection
Debt
Debt adjusting and debt counselling
Debt collecting
Debt recovery, insolvency, bankruptcy
Disability
Discrimination
Education
Employment
Employment law
Environment
Environment (Business Premises)
EU / international
Family and divorce
Family business advice
Freedom of information
Health
Health and safety
Human rights
Insolvency & corporate recovery
Insurance
Joint venture
Landlord & tenant
Liquor licensing
Local government
Media and entertainment
Mental health
Mergers and acquisitions
Pensions (Company)
Pensions (Employment)
Personal injury
Personal tax
Planning (Business Premises)
Private equity
Professional negligence

Property litigation
Public finance initiative
Public sector
Residential property
SME business advice
Social housing
Telecoms
Unit Trusts, OEICs and investment trusts
Wills, executries and trusts
Partners
Ruth Mary Aberdein
Lynn Frances Bentley
Karl Alexander Brown
Margaret April Campbell
Isabelle Alexandra Douglas
Nicola Jane Gray
Jacqueline Law
Euan Ross Cunningham McSherry
Gemma Aitken Perfect
Ritchie Forbes Whyte
Consultant
David Melville Burnside
Associate
Paul Richard Hutcheson
Employees
Danny Sean Anderson
Natasha Mary Day
Elaine Elder
Samantha Diane Gilbert
Katie Louise Hutchinson
Mairi Rebecca Innes
Thomas Iain Main
Lindsey Olivia McDiarmid
Claire Louise Munro
Shaju Ahmed Noor
Erin Shand
Heather Mary Antoinette Taylor
Mohammed Ruhel Ullah
Leanne Warrender

ADDLESHAW GODDARD LLP
1st Floor North, Kingshill View, Prime Four
Business Park, Aberdeen AB15 8PU
Tel: (+44) (0) 1224 96 5410
Categories of Work
Adjudication
Adoption
Advice the elderly & powers of attorney
Agriculture and estates
Agriculture, crofting and fishing
Alternative dispute resolution
Alternative investment market
Banking & finance
Benefit advice
Betting & gaming
Charities
Children
Childrens
Civil court work
Civil legal aid
Commercial litigation
Commercial property
Competition

► **Aberdeen continued**

Construction
Consumer credit
Contract & property disputes
Copyright, trade marks and design
Corporate tax
Credit brokerage
Criminal court work
Criminal legal aid
Data protection
Debt
Debt adjusting and debt counselling
Debt administration
Debt collecting
Debt management
Debt recovery, insolvency, bankruptcy
Disability
Discrimination
Education
Employment
Employment law
Environment
Environment (Business Premises)
EU / international
Family and divorce
Family business advice
Fishing
Freedom of information
Health
Health and safety
Housing
Human rights
Immigration and asylum
Insolvency & corporate recovery
Insurance
IT and intellectual property
Joint venture
Landlord & tenant
Liquor licensing
Local government
Media and entertainment
Medical negligence – defender
Medical negligence – claimant
Mental health
Mergers and acquisitions
Mining
Oil & gas
Parliamentary
Pensions (Company)
Pensions (Employment)
Personal injury
Personal injury – defender
Personal tax
Planning
Planning (Business Premises)
Power and utilities
Private equity
Professional negligence
Projects
Property litigation
Provision of credit information services
Public finance initiative

Public sector
Residential property
Road traffic
Shipping
SME business advice
Social housing
Software licensing
Sport
Telecoms
Transport
Unit Trusts, OEICs and investment trusts
Wills, executries and trusts
Partners
David McEwing
Ross McKenzie
Associates
Connor Knowles
Lauren Anne Taylor
Andrew Graham Watts
Employees
Craig Stanley Falconer
Caroline Harwood
Cameron Alexander Johnstone
Robert Gerald Phillips
Zoe Sutherland

ALSTON LAW
66 Queen's Road, Aberdeen AB15 4YE
Tel: (01224) 606210
Web: www.alstonlaw.co.uk
Categories of Work
Adoption
Advice the elderly & powers of attorney
Agriculture and estates
Alternative dispute resolution
Banking & finance
Children
Civil court work
Commercial litigation
Commercial property
Consumer credit
Contract & property disputes
Debt
Debt collecting
Debt recovery, insolvency, bankruptcy
Disability
Discrimination
Employment
Employment law
EU / international
Family and divorce
Housing
Insolvency & corporate recovery
Insurance
Landlord & tenant
Local government
Medical negligence – claimant
Personal injury
Professional negligence
Property litigation
Public sector
Residential property
Road traffic

Wills, executries and trusts

ANDERSONBAIN LLP
6, 8 & 10 Thistle Street, Aberdeen AB10 1XZ
Tel: (01224) 456789
Fax: (01224) 646411
DX: AB36 ABERDEEN
Web: www.andersonbain.co.uk
Categories of Work
Adoption
Advice the elderly & powers of attorney
Banking & finance
Benefit advice
Charities
Children
Commercial property
Consumer credit
Contract & property disputes
Copyright, trade marks and design
Corporate tax
Debt collecting
Debt recovery, insolvency, bankruptcy
Employment
Employment law
Environment (Business Premises)
Family and divorce
Family business advice
Freedom of information
Health and safety
Housing
Insolvency & corporate recovery
Joint venture
Landlord & tenant
Liquor licensing
Medical negligence – defender
Medical negligence – claimant
Mental health
Mergers and acquisitions
Pensions (Company)
Pensions (Employment)
Personal injury
Personal injury – defender
Personal tax
Professional negligence
Residential property
Road traffic
SME business advice
Social housing
Sport
Wills, executries and trusts
Partners
Scott Allan
Stuart McDonald Bain
Calum Iain Bell
Alison Julie Jackson
Robin James Leith
Kevin William Rattray
Faye Ellen Walker
Laura Youngson
Consultant
Peter Duthie Anderson

Employees
Fiona Margaret Barker
Rebecca Louise Bett
Ashleigh Buchan
Paul Flecher-Herd
Natalie Susan Roach
Alice Stevenson Tait
Carol Ann Hadden Walker
Iain Stuart Wilson

GAVIN BAIN & CO.
432 Union Street, Aberdeen AB10 1TR
Tel: (01224) 623040
Fax: (01224) 623050
DX: AB40 ABERDEEN
E-mail: info@gavin-bain.co.uk
Web: www.gavin-bain.co.uk
Categories of Work
Commercial property
Criminal court work
Criminal legal aid
Residential property
Wills, executries and trusts
Partners
Gavin Murray Bain
Angela West Bruce
Stephen Glennie
John Robert Simpson Hardie
Neil Robert James Johnston
Graham Morrison
Employee
Pamela Mairi Spalding

BALFOUR + MANSON LLP
6 Albyn Terrace, Aberdeen AB10 1YP
Tel: (01224) 498080
Fax: (01224) 498081
DX: AB42 ABERDEEN
E-mail: info@balfour-manson.co.uk
Web: www.balfour-manson.co.uk
Categories of Work
Adoption
Advice the elderly & powers of attorney
Alternative dispute resolution
Banking & finance
Benefit advice
Charities
Children
Childrens
Civil court work
Civil legal aid
Commercial litigation
Commercial property
Consumer credit
Contract & property disputes
Copyright, trade marks and design
Corporate tax
Criminal court work
Data protection
Debt
Debt management
Disability
Discrimination
Education

▶ *Aberdeen continued*

Employment
Employment law
Environment
Family and divorce
Family business advice
Freedom of information
Health
Health and safety
IT and intellectual property
Joint venture
Landlord & tenant
Local government
Media and entertainment
Medical negligence – defender
Medical negligence – claimant
Mental health
Personal injury
Personal injury – defender
Personal tax
Planning (Business Premises)
Professional negligence
Property litigation
Residential property
Road traffic
SME business advice
Transport
Wills, executries and trusts
Partners
Julie Ann Clark-Spence
Kirsten Isobell Knight
Lynne Mulcahy
Associates
Amy Louise McKay
Sophie Elizabeth Hamilton Pike
Employees
Catherine Elizabeth Albiston
Iona Margaret Campbell
Diana Mackenzie

BLACKADDERS LLP
6 Bon Accord Square, Aberdeen AB11 6XU
Tel: (01224) 588913
Fax: (01224) 581149
DX: AB152 ABERDEEN
E-mail: enquiries@blackadders.co.uk
Categories of Work
Adoption
Advice the elderly & powers of attorney
Agriculture and estates
Agriculture, crofting and fishing
Alternative dispute resolution
Banking & finance
Charities
Children
Childrens
Civil court work
Civil legal aid
Commercial litigation
Commercial property
Competition
Construction
Consumer credit

Contract & property disputes
Copyright, trade marks and design
Data protection
Debt
Debt collecting
Debt recovery, insolvency, bankruptcy
Disability
Discrimination
Employment
Employment law
Environment
Environment (Business Premises)
EU / international
Family and divorce
Family business advice
Fishing
Freedom of information
Housing
Human rights
Insolvency & corporate recovery
IT and intellectual property
Joint venture
Landlord & tenant
Media and entertainment
Medical negligence – defender
Medical negligence – claimant
Mental health
Mergers and acquisitions
Pensions (Employment)
Personal injury
Personal injury – defender
Personal tax
Planning
Power and utilities
Private equity
Professional negligence
Property litigation
Public sector
Residential property
Road traffic
SME business advice
Software licensing
Sport
Telecoms
Wills, executries and trusts
Partners
John Arthur Dargie
Ellen Catherine Eunson
Gareth Antony Masson
Ryan Daniel McKay
John Charles Plenderleath
Neil Beresford Robb
Colin Gordon Runcie
Associates
Nicola Tamara Brown
Joanne Ronna Murray
Employees
Melanie Sarah Ballantyne
Emma Margaretha Grunenberg
Fiona Allan James
Jamie Lee Robertson

BLACKADDER TRUSTEES (ABERDEEN) LIMITED
6 Bon Accord Square, Aberdeen AB11 6XU
Tel: (01382) 229222

BLACKWOOD PARTNERS LLP
Blackwood House, Union Grove Lane,
Aberdeen AB10 6XU
Tel: (01224) 446230
Fax: (01224) 325 749
Web: www.blackwood-partners.com
Categories of Work
Adjudication
Alternative dispute resolution
Banking & finance
Civil court work
Commercial litigation
Data protection
Debt
Debt recovery, insolvency, bankruptcy
Disability
Discrimination
Employment
Employment law
Freedom of information
Health and safety
Human rights
Insolvency & corporate recovery
Insurance
Joint venture
Mergers and acquisitions
Oil & gas
Pensions (Employment)
Private equity
Shipping
SME business advice
Transport
Partners
Alasdair Ross Fair
Judith Ann Quinn
Scott Swankie
Alastair Blackwood Wyper
Employees
Jennifer Clark
Erica Joanne Kinmond
Lewis Scott Millar
George Pennel

BRODIES LLP
Brodies House, 31-33 Union Grove, Aberdeen
AB10 6SD
Tel: (01224) 392242
Fax: (01224) 392244
DX: AB10 ABERDEEN
E-mail: mailbox@brodies.com
Web: www.brodies.com
Categories of Work
Adjudication
Adoption
Advice the elderly & powers of attorney
Agriculture and estates
Agriculture, crofting and fishing
Alternative dispute resolution
Alternative investment market
Banking & finance

Charities
Children
Childrens
Civil court work
Civil legal aid
Commercial litigation
Commercial property
Competition
Construction
Consumer credit
Contract & property disputes
Copyright, trade marks and design
Corporate tax
Credit brokerage
Criminal court work
Criminal legal aid
Data protection
Debt
Debt adjusting and debt counselling
Debt administration
Debt collecting
Debt recovery, insolvency, bankruptcy
Disability
Discrimination
Education
Employment
Employment law
Environment
Environment (Business Premises)
EU / international
Family and divorce
Family business advice
Fishing
Freedom of information
Health
Health and safety
Housing
Human rights
Immigration and asylum
Insolvency & corporate recovery
Insurance
IT and intellectual property
Joint venture
Landlord & tenant
Liquor licensing
Local government
Media and entertainment
Medical negligence – defender
Medical negligence – claimant
Mental health
Mergers and acquisitions
Mining
Oil & gas
Parliamentary
Pensions (Company)
Pensions (Employment)
Personal injury
Personal injury – defender
Personal tax
Planning
Planning (Business Premises)
Power and utilities
Private equity

▶ *Aberdeen continued*

Professional negligence
Projects
Property litigation
Provision of credit information services
Public finance initiative
Public sector
Residential property
Road traffic
Shipping
SME business advice
Social housing
Software licensing
Sport
Telecoms
Transport
Unit Trusts, OEICs and investment trusts
Wills, executries and trusts

Partners
Thomas Owen Boulton-Jones
Douglas James Crawford
Martin William Ewan
Shaun Arthur George
Leigh Gould
Fiona Jane Herrell
Sonia Love
Kenneth John MacDonald
Malcolm Peter Miller Mackay
Nicholas Jonathan Marshall
Rhona Margaret McFarlane
Tracey Jayne Houston Menzies
David Mitchell Millar
Tamsin Clare Munro
Clive Phillips
Neal Scott Richardson
Mark Edward Stewart
Bryan Wilson

Consultant
Finlay George Crossan

Associates
Gillian Scott Donald
Sarah Victoria Peace Gall
Lydia Ishbel McLachlan
Lynne Murray

Employees
Andrew John Askew Blain
Kate Bradbury
Eilidh Marion Rarity Calvert
Chloe Ellen Fitzgerald
Stephen Gerard Flynn
Natalia Paulina Fraser
Ross James Gardiner
Ian James Gibson
Lucie Charlotte Hassell
Ailidh Margaret Hay
Gemma Kirsten Hills
Erin Macaulay Hunt
Graeme Mitchell Imrie
Margaret Louise Keir
Katharine Isabel Love
Matthew James Lyon
Fraser Hugh Mackay

Kirsten Lindsay MacRae
Rae-Anne Megan Marr
Jenna Eliza McCosh
Donna McKay
Susannah Elizabeth Mountain
Rachael Evalyn Noble
Ryan Mackenzie Openshaw
Laura Marie Petrie
Sarah Louise Polson
Jane Elizabeth Rattray
Lisa Marie Reilly
Caroline Elizabeth Sodersten
Katie Diane Spearman
Jake Anthony Ross Stephen
Jennifer Christine Stevenson
Sarah Kirstin Stewart
Garry John Sturrock
Courtney Jade Summers
Laura Chloe Taylor
Nicola Watson

BRUCE MACDONALD & CO.
6 Albert Place, Aberdeen AB25 1RG
Tel: (01224) 643332
Fax: (01224) 643334
E-mail: bruce@brucemacdonald.co.uk
Categories of Work
Criminal court work
Criminal legal aid
Partner
Bruce Dey MacDonald

BURNESS PAULL LLP
Union Plaza, 1 Union Wynd, Aberdeen
AB10 1DQ
Tel: (01224) 621621
Fax: (01224) 627437
DX: AB35 ABERDEEN
E-mail: info@burnesspaull.com
Web: www.burnesspaull.com
Categories of Work
Adjudication
Adoption
Advice the elderly & powers of attorney
Agriculture and estates
Agriculture, crofting and fishing
Alternative dispute resolution
Alternative investment market
Banking & finance
Betting & gaming
Charities
Civil court work
Commercial litigation
Commercial property
Competition
Construction
Consumer credit
Contract & property disputes
Copyright, trade marks and design
Corporate tax
Credit brokerage
Criminal court work
Data protection
Debt

Debt adjusting and debt counselling
Debt administration
Debt collecting
Debt recovery, insolvency, bankruptcy
Education
Employment
Employment law
Environment
Environment (Business Premises)
EU / international
Family business advice
Fishing
Freedom of information
Health
Health and safety
Housing
Human rights
Immigration and asylum
Insolvency & corporate recovery
Insurance
IT and intellectual property
Joint venture
Landlord & tenant
Liquor licensing
Local government
Media and entertainment
Medical negligence – claimant
Mergers and acquisitions
Mining
Oil & gas
Parliamentary
Pensions (Company)
Pensions (Employment)
Personal injury
Personal injury – defender
Personal tax
Planning
Planning (Business Premises)
Power and utilities
Private equity
Professional negligence
Projects
Property litigation
Provision of credit information services
Public finance initiative
Public sector
Residential property
Road traffic
Shipping
SME business advice
Social housing
Software licensing
Sport
Telecoms
Transport
Unit Trusts, OEICs and investment trusts
Wills, executories and trusts

Partners
Fiona Marie Clarke
Helen Mary Dickson
Alasdair Charles Freeman
Richard Goodfellow
Lynne Carol Gray

Steven James Guild
John Kennedy
Andrew Moray Knight
Colin Neil McKenzie
Alexander Michael Freeland Morrice
Robert John Arthur Ruddiman
Sean Ajit Saluja
Neil Bryce Smith
Peter Richard Smith
James Gordon Croll Stark
John Alan Strachan
Tricia Lyn Walker

Consultant
Geoffrey Alan Clark

Associates
Claire Louise Campbell
Stuart George Gardiner
Julie Helen Greig
Laura Ann Hay
Gillian Grace Irons
James William Lyall Jack
Kim Louise Johnston
Andrew Stuart Lyndon
Arran Lee Mackenzie
Lucy Jacqueline Mathers
Caroline Win McIntyre
Claire Christine McKay
Emma Louise Miller
Lynne Moss
Carolyn Margaret Richards

Employees
Victoria Ann Blair
Claire Patricia Bruce
Fiona Closs
Colin Scott Dalgarno
Victoria Anne Duthie
Laura Anne Fraser
Gillian Harrington
Samuel John Jones
Rebecca Hannah Kondol
Viktoria Katy Latham
Cara Louise Low
Natasha Mary MacDonald
Emma Rose MacFarland
Kal Masia
Grant Douglas McGregor
Louise Anne McKibben
Laura Milne
Lisa Florence Penny
Andrew John Smith
David James William Smith
Olivia Beth Sutherland
Jamie Campbell Wilson

BURNETT CRIMINAL DEFENCE
48A Union Street, Aberdeen AB10 1BB
Tel: (07515) 964194
E-mail: mike@burnettcriminaldefence.co.uk
Categories of Work
Criminal court work
Criminal legal aid
Partner
Michael Ian James Burnett

▶ Aberdeen continued

BURNETT LEGAL SERVICES LIMITED
6 King's Gate, Aberdeen AB15 4EJ
Tel: (01224) 648797
Fax: (01224) 647175
DX: AB54 ABERDEEN
E-mail: douglas@burnettandco.co.uk
Categories of Work
Children
Civil court work
Family and divorce
Mental health
Personal injury
Director
Douglas Burnett

BURNETT & REID LLP
Suite A Ground Floor, 9 Queens Road,
Aberdeen AB15 4YL
Tel: (01224) 644333
Fax: (01224) 632173
DX: AB19 ABERDEEN
E-mail: mail@burnett-reid.co.uk
Web: www.burnett-reid.co.uk
Categories of Work
Advice the elderly & powers of attorney
Agriculture and estates
Agriculture, crofting and fishing
Banking & finance
Civil court work
Civil legal aid
Commercial litigation
Commercial property
Construction
Contract & property disputes
Copyright, trade marks and design
Debt
Debt collecting
Debt recovery, insolvency, bankruptcy
Employment law
Environment
Family business advice
Fishing
Health and safety
Insolvency & corporate recovery
IT and intellectual property
Joint venture
Landlord & tenant
Mergers and acquisitions
Oil & gas
Personal tax
Power and utilities
Private equity
Projects
Property litigation
Residential property
SME business advice
Wills, executries and trusts
Partners
Colin Scott Bremner
James Herbertson
William Alexander Robertson

Consultants
Marichen Meyer
Thomas George Rennie
Associates
Stuart Edward Campbell
Michael James Douglas Kusznir
Rachael Margaret Mackay
Alasdair Ian Taylor
Viktoria Claire Wahle
Employees
Nicola Maureen Jamieson
Brittany Louise Kilner
Kathryn Mari Victoria Murdoch
Louise Kathryn Porter
Margot Sinclair

BURN & MCGREGOR
48A Union Street, Aberdeen AB10 1BB
Tel: (01224) 639660
Fax: (01224) 635525
Categories of Work
Criminal court work
Criminal legal aid
Partners
Alexander McLennan Burn
Iain Robert McGregor
Employee
Laura Sophia Gracie

CAMPBELL CONNON
36 Albyn Place, Aberdeen AB10 1YF
Tel: (01224) 585585
Fax: (01224) 580766
DX: AB14 ABERDEEN
E-mail: info@campbellconnon.co.uk
Categories of Work
Advice the elderly & powers of attorney
Debt
Residential property
Wills, executries and trusts
Partners
John Fraser Hendry
David Morrison

CLYDE & CO (SCOTLAND) LLP
Silver Fin Building, Orega, Office 106,
Aberdeen AB11 6DB
Tel: (01224) 624924
Fax: (01224) 626590
DX: AB6 ABERDEEN
E-mail: Enquiries.Scotland@clydeco.com
Web: www.clydeco.com
Categories of Work
Adjudication
Adoption
Alternative dispute resolution
Banking & finance
Children
Civil court work
Civil legal aid
Commercial litigation
Commercial property
Construction
Contract & property disputes

Copyright, trade marks and design
Criminal court work
Criminal legal aid
Data protection
Disability
Discrimination
Education
Employment
Employment law
Environment
Environment (Business Premises)
EU / international
Family and divorce
Freedom of information
Health
Health and safety
Human rights
Insurance
Joint venture
Landlord & tenant
Liquor licensing
Local government
Medical negligence – defender
Medical negligence – claimant
Mental health
Oil & gas
Parliamentary
Pensions (Employment)
Personal injury
Personal injury – defender
Power and utilities
Professional negligence
Property litigation
Public sector
Road traffic
Shipping
Sport
Transport
Partners
Henry Thompson Dalgety Boyle
Mark Mackenzie Donaldson
Associate
Kim McLeod
Employee
Andrew Logue

CMS CAMERON MCKENNA NABARRO OLSWANG LLP
6 Queens Road, Aberdeen AB15 4ZT
Tel: (01224) 622002
Fax: (01224) 622066
DX: AB64 ABERDEEN
Categories of Work
Adjudication
Agriculture and estates
Agriculture, crofting and fishing
Alternative dispute resolution
Alternative investment market
Banking & finance
Betting & gaming
Charities
Civil court work
Civil legal aid

Commercial litigation
Commercial property
Competition
Construction
Consumer credit
Contract & property disputes
Copyright, trade marks and design
Corporate tax
Credit brokerage
Data protection
Debt administration
Debt collecting
Debt recovery, insolvency, bankruptcy
Discrimination
Education
Employment
Employment law
Environment
Environment (Business Premises)
EU / international
Family business advice
Fishing
Freedom of information
Health
Health and safety
Housing
Human rights
Immigration and asylum
Insolvency & corporate recovery
Insurance
IT and intellectual property
Joint venture
Landlord & tenant
Liquor licensing
Local government
Media and entertainment
Mergers and acquisitions
Mining
Oil & gas
Parliamentary
Pensions (Company)
Pensions (Employment)
Personal injury
Personal injury – defender
Personal tax
Planning
Planning (Business Premises)
Power and utilities
Private equity
Professional negligence
Projects
Property litigation
Public finance initiative
Public sector
Residential property
Shipping
SME business advice
Social housing
Software licensing
Sport
Telecoms
Transport
Unit Trusts, OEICs and investment trusts

▶ **Aberdeen continued**

Partners
Valerie Louise Allan
Graeme Matheson Clubley
Frank Alexander Fowlie
Paula Suzanne Leslie Kidd
Helen Machin
Carol Margaret Nisbet
Susan Penelope Warne
Norman Sinclair Wisely
Alison Helen Woods
Consultant
Derek Robert Cameron
Associates
Maribel Barrag n de La Cruz
Sophie Brown
Mary Flora Muriel Forbes
Fiona Elizabeth Henderson
Cameron John Milne
Rosalind Carole Morgan
Claire Louise Quinn
Craig James Wilson
Employees
Kyle Michael James Allen
Sarah Jane Matheson Dobbie
Katie Louise Fleming
Ruth Margaret Gardiner
Eric John Gilligan
Natalie Jayde Haefner
Nadia Lucherini
Rachel Ann Macrae
Niamh Catherine Morrison
Finn O'Neill
Jacqueline Ruth R dar s
Karla Joy Ritchie
Michael Henry Thorburn
Stewart Allan Watt

JAMES & GEORGE COLLIE LLP
1 East Craibstone Street, Aberdeen AB11 6YQ
Tel: (01224) 945592
Fax: (01224) 580119
DX: AB43 ABERDEEN
E-mail: info@jgcollie.co.uk
Web: www.jgcollie.co.uk
Categories of Work
Adoption
Advice the elderly & powers of attorney
Alternative dispute resolution
Banking & finance
Betting & gaming
Charities
Children
Civil court work
Civil legal aid
Commercial litigation
Commercial property
Competition
Consumer credit
Contract & property disputes
Copyright, trade marks and design
Debt collecting
Debt recovery, insolvency, bankruptcy

Employment
Employment law
Family and divorce
Family business advice
Freedom of information
Housing
Insolvency & corporate recovery
Landlord & tenant
Liquor licensing
Local government
Media and entertainment
Medical negligence – claimant
Mental health
Mergers and acquisitions
Personal injury
Professional negligence
Property litigation
Residential property
Road traffic
SME business advice
Sport
Wills, executries and trusts
Partners
Mark William Allan
Steven Allan
Duncan Mackinnon Love
Forbes Fleming McLennan
Brian Sutton
Consultants
Anthony James Dawson
Elizabeth Jane Wilson Mackinnon
Employees
Nikita-Hedy Velvet Kimberly F Andrews
Marie-Louise Armstrong
Vivienne Margaret Bruce
Susan Margaret Waters

JAMES & GEORGE COLLIE LLP
450 Union Street, Aberdeen AB10 1TR
Tel: (01224) 039150
DX: AB43 ABERDEEN
E-mail: p.sales@jgcollie.co.uk
Web: www.jgcollie.co.uk
Categories of Work
Adoption
Advice the elderly & powers of attorney
Alternative dispute resolution
Banking & finance
Betting & gaming
Charities
Children
Civil court work
Civil legal aid
Commercial litigation
Commercial property
Competition
Consumer credit
Contract & property disputes
Copyright, trade marks and design
Debt collecting
Debt recovery, insolvency, bankruptcy
Employment
Employment law

Family and divorce
Family business advice
Freedom of information
Housing
Insolvency & corporate recovery
Landlord & tenant
Liquor licensing
Local government
Media and entertainment
Medical negligence – claimant
Mental health
Mergers and acquisitions
Personal injury
Professional negligence
Property litigation
Residential property
Road traffic
SME business advice
Sport
Wills, executries and trusts

DENTONS UK AND MIDDLE EAST LLP

The Capitol, 431 Union Street, Aberdeen
AB11 6DA
Tel: (0330) 2220050
Categories of Work
Adjudication
Adoption
Advice the elderly & powers of attorney
Agriculture and estates
Agriculture, crofting and fishing
Alternative dispute resolution
Alternative investment market
Banking & finance
Betting & gaming
Charities
Children
Civil court work
Civil legal aid
Commercial litigation
Commercial property
Competition
Construction
Contract & property disputes
Copyright, trade marks and design
Corporate tax
Data protection
Debt recovery, insolvency, bankruptcy
Disability
Discrimination
Education
Employment
Employment law
Environment
Environment (Business Premises)
EU / international
Family and divorce
Family business advice
Fishing
Freedom of information
Health
Health and safety
Housing

Human rights
Immigration and asylum
Insolvency & corporate recovery
Insurance
IT and intellectual property
Joint venture
Landlord & tenant
Liquor licensing
Local government
Media and entertainment
Medical negligence – defender
Medical negligence – claimant
Mergers and acquisitions
Mining
Oil & gas
Parliamentary
Pensions (Company)
Pensions (Employment)
Personal injury
Personal injury – defender
Personal tax
Planning
Planning (Business Premises)
Power and utilities
Private equity
Professional negligence
Projects
Property litigation
Public finance initiative
Public sector
Residential property
Shipping
SME business advice
Software licensing
Sport
Telecoms
Transport
Unit Trusts, OEICs and investment trusts
Wills, executries and trusts

DIGBY BROWN LLP

220 Union Street, Aberdeen AB10 1TL
Tel: (0333) 200 5925
DX: AB52 ABERDEEN
E-mail: enquiries@digbybrown.co.uk
Web: www.digbybrown.co.uk
Categories of Work
Advice the elderly & powers of attorney
Agriculture and estates
Agriculture, crofting and fishing
Alternative dispute resolution
Alternative investment market
Banking & finance
Benefit advice
Charities
Children
Civil court work
Civil legal aid
Commercial litigation
Commercial property
Competition
Construction
Contract & property disputes

► *Aberdeen continued*

Corporate tax
Criminal court work
Data protection
Debt
Debt adjusting and debt counselling
Debt collecting
Debt recovery, insolvency, bankruptcy
Disability
Discrimination
Employment
Employment law
Environment (Business Premises)
EU / international
Family and divorce
Family business advice
Freedom of information
Health and safety
Human rights
Immigration and asylum
Insolvency & corporate recovery
Insurance
Joint venture
Landlord & tenant
Medical negligence – defender
Medical negligence – claimant
Mental health
Mergers and acquisitions
Pensions (Company)
Personal injury
Personal injury – defender
Planning (Business Premises)
Private equity
Professional negligence
Property litigation
Provision of credit information services
Public finance initiative
Public sector
Residential property
Road traffic
SME business advice
Unit Trusts, OEICs and investment trusts
Wills, executries and trusts
Partner
Neil Christopher Cowins Davidson
Employees
Ciara Boyle
Kimberley Jane MacLennan
Amy Jane Shand
Paul Alexander Thomson
Kerry Louise Whyte

DJP SOLICITORS
226 Holburn Street, Aberdeen AB10 6DB
Tel: (01224) 590053
Fax: (01224) 592970
DX: AB154 ABERDEEN
E-mail: dp@djpsolicitors.com
Web: www.djpsolicitors.com
Categories of Work
Children
Civil court work
Civil legal aid

Commercial litigation
Contract & property disputes
Debt administration
Debt collecting
Employment law
Family and divorce
Landlord & tenant
Medical negligence – claimant
Personal injury
Property litigation
Road traffic
Partner
Dean Purdie
Employees
Steven William Ritchie
Owen Noel Ross

DUTHIE WARD
42 Carden Place, Aberdeen AB10 1UP
Tel: (01224) 621622
DX: AB156 ABERDEEN
Categories of Work
Adoption
Advice the elderly & powers of attorney
Alternative dispute resolution
Banking & finance
Benefit advice
Charities
Children
Childrens
Civil court work
Civil legal aid
Commercial litigation
Commercial property
Consumer credit
Contract & property disputes
Copyright, trade marks and design
Corporate tax
Criminal court work
Data protection
Debt
Debt management
Disability
Discrimination
Education
Employment
Employment law
Environment
Family and divorce
Family business advice
Freedom of information
Health
Health and safety
IT and intellectual property
Joint venture
Landlord & tenant
Local government
Media and entertainment
Medical negligence – defender
Medical negligence – claimant
Mental health
Personal injury
Personal injury – defender

Personal tax
Planning (Business Premises)
Professional negligence
Property litigation
Residential property
Road traffic
SME business advice
Transport
Wills, executives and trusts

ESSON ABERDEIN
66 Queen's Road, Aberdeen AB15 4YE
Tel: (01224) 606210
Fax: (01224) 606211
E-mail: info@essonaberdein.com
Categories of Work
Adoption
Advice the elderly & powers of attorney
Agriculture and estates
Alternative dispute resolution
Banking & finance
Children
Civil court work
Commercial litigation
Commercial property
Consumer credit
Contract & property disputes
Debt
Debt collecting
Debt recovery, insolvency, bankruptcy
Disability
Discrimination
Employment
Employment law
EU / international
Family and divorce
Housing
Insolvency & corporate recovery
Insurance
Landlord & tenant
Local government
Medical negligence – claimant
Personal injury
Professional negligence
Property litigation
Public sector
Residential property
Road traffic
Wills, executives and trusts
Director
Joni Esson
Employee
Julie Ann Hamill

FIRST EMPLOYMENT LAW LIMITED
7 Queens Gardens, Aberdeen AB15 4YD
Tel: (01224) 619 282
Web: www.felaw.co.uk
Categories of Work
Employment
Employment law
Immigration and asylum
Director
Linda Agnes Jane Beedie

FRASER & MULLIGAN
1 Carden Place, Aberdeen AB10 1UT
Tel: (01224) 646428
Fax: (01224) 643773
DX: AB23 ABERDEEN
E-mail: mail@fraser-mulligan.co.uk
Categories of Work
Advice the elderly & powers of attorney
Commercial property
Contract & property disputes
Landlord & tenant
Residential property
Wills, executives and trusts
Partners
Dawn Clark
Gordon Geddes Dominic Fraser
Kathleen Anne Seager
Consultants
Gordon Glen Cameron
James Roy McCulloch Grant
Employee
Ashley James Swanson

GOLDEN SQUARE NOMINEES LIMITED
Johnstone House, 52-54 Rose Street, Aberdeen
AB10 1HA
Tel: (01224) 408408

GAIL GOODFELLOW, SOLICITOR ADVOCATE
49 Castle Street, Aberdeen AB11 5BB
Tel: (01224) 878417
Fax: (01224) 896535
E-mail: info@gailgoodfellow.com
Categories of Work
Criminal court work
Criminal legal aid
Partner
Gail Goodfellow
Employee
Caitlin Mairi Pirie

HAMILTON WATT & CO
4 Bon Accord Crescent, Aberdeen AB11 6DH
Tel: (01224) 586685
Fax: (01224) 586686
DX: AB22 ABERDEEN
E-mail: alanhw@hamiltonwatt.co.uk
Web: www.hamiltonwatt.co.uk
Categories of Work
Adoption
Advice the elderly & powers of attorney
Children
Commercial property
Employment law
Family and divorce
Landlord & tenant
Residential property
Wills, executives and trusts
Partners
Hazel Jeanette Bone
Alan Russell Watt

ALASTAIR HART & CO.
76A Countesswells Road, Seafield Shopping
Centre, Aberdeen AB15 7YJ

► *Aberdeen continued*

Tel: (01224) 310600
Fax: (01224) 310604
E-mail: info@alastairhart.co.uk
Web: www.alastairhart.co.uk

Categories of Work
Advice the elderly & powers of attorney
Childrens
Commercial litigation
Debt collecting
Family and divorce
Landlord & tenant
Residential property
Wills, executries and trusts

Partner
Alastair Ralph Hart

HINGSTON'S LAW LIMITED
13 Marischal Street, Aberdeen AB11 5AD
Tel: (01224) 562300

Categories of Work
Criminal court work
Criminal legal aid

Director
Iain David Hingston

Employees
Shane Paul Campbell
Diane Findlay
Graeme Bruce Murray

MICHAEL HORSMAN & CO.
11 Back Wynd, Aberdeen AB10 1JN
Tel: (01224) 633333
Fax: (01224) 620099
E-mail: horsmanm@outlook.com

Categories of Work
Criminal court work
Criminal legal aid

Partner
Michael Kenneth Horsman

HOWIE (SCOTLAND) LIMITED
86 Hamilton Place, Aberdeen AB15 5BA
E-mail: ch@howieandco.com

Director
Colin Neville Howie

ALEX HUTCHEON & CO.
248 Union Street, Aberdeen AB10 1TN
Tel: (01224) 623423
Fax: (01224) 623422
DX: AB151 ABERDEEN
E-mail: mail@mortgageandproperty.co.uk
Web: www.mortgageandproperty.co.uk

Categories of Work
Advice the elderly & powers of attorney
Consumer credit
Debt adjusting and debt counselling
Debt administration
Debt collecting
Family and divorce
Housing
Residential property
Wills, executries and trusts

Partners
Fayona Ann Gordon
Alexander Buchan Hutcheon

INKSTERS
Citibase, 9 Queens Road, Aberdeen AB15 4YL
Tel: (01224) 252730
Fax: (01224) 252735
E-mail: aberdeen@inksters.com
Web: www.inksters.com

Categories of Work
Advice the elderly & powers of attorney
Agriculture and estates
Agriculture, crofting and fishing
Alternative dispute resolution
Children
Childrens
Civil court work
Civil legal aid
Commercial property
Consumer credit
Contract & property disputes
Criminal court work
Criminal legal aid
Data protection
Debt
Debt collecting
Debt recovery, insolvency, bankruptcy
Family and divorce
Family business advice
Landlord & tenant
Personal tax
Projects
Property litigation
Residential property
Road traffic
Wills, executries and trusts

Employee
Rory Cradock

JAMIESONS SOLICITORS LIMITED
16 North Silver Street, Aberdeen AB10 1RL
Tel: (01224) 443204
Fax: (01224) 634623
E-mail: mail@jamsolaw.com
Web: www.jamsolaw.com

Categories of Work
Advice the elderly & powers of attorney
Agriculture and estates
Agriculture, crofting and fishing
Civil court work
Commercial litigation
Commercial property
Contract & property disputes
Debt collecting
Employment law
Family and divorce
Family business advice
Fishing
IT and intellectual property
Joint venture
Landlord & tenant
Mergers and acquisitions
Residential property

SME business advice
Wills, executries and trusts
Director
William Miller Jamieson

JUST DEFENCE LAW PRACTICE
35a Union Street, Aberdeen AB11 5BN
Tel: (01224) 644999
Categories of Work
Criminal court work
Criminal legal aid
Partner
Anthony John Burgess
Employee
Deborah Elizabeth Alice Ginniver

KING STREET NOMINEES LIMITED
100 Union Street, Aberdeen AB10 1QR
Tel: (01224) 428000

LAURIE & CO SOLICITORS LLP
17 Victoria Street, Aberdeen AB10 1PU
Tel: (01224) 645 085
Fax: (01224) 645 114
DX: AB16 ABERDEEN
E-mail: info@laurieandco.co.uk
Web: www.laurieandco.co.uk
Categories of Work
Advice the elderly & powers of attorney
Children
Civil court work
Commercial litigation
Criminal court work
Debt collecting
Debt recovery, insolvency, bankruptcy
Employment law
Family and divorce
Insolvency & corporate recovery
Personal injury – defender
Property litigation
Wills, executries and trusts
Partners
Linda Kirstine Fyffe
Stephanie Mann
Caroline Anne Stephen
Employees
Anne Margaret Cassidy
Nicola Patricia Ewen
Lucy Louise Light

LC SECRETARIES LIMITED
Johnstone House, 52-54 Rose Street, Aberdeen
AB10 1HA
Tel: (01224) 408408

LEDINGHAM CHALMERS LLP
4 Alford Place, Aberdeen AB10 1YD
Tel: (01224) 622622
Fax: (01224) 646133
E-mail: mail@ledinghamchalmers.com
Web: www.ledinghamchalmers.com
Categories of Work
Adjudication
Adoption
Advice the elderly & powers of attorney

Agriculture and estates
Agriculture, crofting and fishing
Alternative dispute resolution
Alternative investment market
Banking & finance
Charities
Children
Childrens
Civil court work
Civil legal aid
Commercial litigation
Commercial property
Competition
Construction
Consumer credit
Contract & property disputes
Copyright, trade marks and design
Corporate tax
Credit brokerage
Criminal court work
Criminal legal aid
Data protection
Debt
Debt adjusting and debt counselling
Debt administration
Debt collecting
Debt management
Debt recovery, insolvency, bankruptcy
Disability
Discrimination
Education
Employment
Employment law
Environment
Environment (Business Premises)
EU / international
Family and divorce
Family business advice
Fishing
Freedom of information
Health and safety
Housing
Human rights
Immigration and asylum
Insolvency & corporate recovery
Insurance
IT and intellectual property
Joint venture
Landlord & tenant
Liquor licensing
Local government
Media and entertainment
Medical negligence – defender
Medical negligence – claimant
Mental health
Mergers and acquisitions
Oil & gas
Pensions (Company)
Pensions (Employment)
Personal injury
Personal injury – defender
Personal tax
Planning

▶ **Aberdeen continued**

Planning (Business Premises)
Power and utilities
Private equity
Professional negligence
Projects
Property litigation
Provision of credit information services
Public finance initiative
Public sector
Residential property
Road traffic
SME business advice
Software licensing
Telecoms
Transport
Unit Trusts, OEICs and investment trusts
Wills, executries and trusts
Partner
Lynne Ann Stewart
Associate
Claire Ogston

LEDINGHAM CHALMERS LLP

Johnstone House, 52-54 Rose Street, Aberdeen
AB10 1HA
Tel: (01224) 408408
Fax: (01224) 408400
DX: AB15 ABERDEEN
E-mail: mail@ledinghamchalmers.com
Web: www.ledinghamchalmers.com
Categories of Work
Adjudication
Adoption
Advice the elderly & powers of attorney
Agriculture and estates
Agriculture, crofting and fishing
Alternative dispute resolution
Alternative investment market
Banking & finance
Charities
Children
Childrens
Civil court work
Civil legal aid
Commercial litigation
Commercial property
Competition
Construction
Consumer credit
Contract & property disputes
Copyright, trade marks and design
Corporate tax
Credit brokerage
Criminal court work
Criminal legal aid
Data protection
Debt
Debt adjusting and debt counselling
Debt administration
Debt collecting
Debt management
Debt recovery, insolvency, bankruptcy

Disability
Discrimination
Education
Employment
Employment law
Environment
Environment (Business Premises)
EU / international
Family and divorce
Family business advice
Fishing
Freedom of information
Health and safety
Housing
Human rights
Immigration and asylum
Insolvency & corporate recovery
Insurance
IT and intellectual property
Joint venture
Landlord & tenant
Liquor licensing
Local government
Media and entertainment
Medical negligence – defender
Medical negligence – claimant
Mental health
Mergers and acquisitions
Oil & gas
Pensions (Company)
Pensions (Employment)
Personal injury
Personal injury – defender
Personal tax
Planning
Planning (Business Premises)
Power and utilities
Private equity
Professional negligence
Projects
Property litigation
Provision of credit information services
Public finance initiative
Public sector
Residential property
Road traffic
SME business advice
Software licensing
Telecoms
Transport
Unit Trusts, OEICs and investment trusts
Wills, executries and trusts
Partners
Graeme Mark Kynoch Edward
Phyllis Garden
Alasdair Eoin MacLure
Alan Johnston Michie
Jody Bruce Mitchell
John Gillan Mitchell
Hazel Marion Moir
Stephen James Morrice
Peter Murray
Craig Andrew Pike

Nicola Wendy Reid
David Stuart Scott
Sarah Duncan Stuart
Timothy Robert Thomas
Fiona Margaret Thomson
Douglas Morgan Watson
Jennifer Evelyn Young
Associates
Erica Buchan
Lynne Burke
Jennifer Cham
Sarah Louise Londragan
Stephen Charles McLaren
Hugh Kelvin Murray Richmond
Rebecca Clare Walker
Employees
Rosie Emily Allan
Hannah Emma Black
Hollie Kathleen Rose Cavanagh
Lois Craig
Lucy Ann Cran
Naomi Rhiannon Elspeth Davies
Laura-Anne Campbell Edmunds
James Andrew Florance
Jenna Erin Hendry
Dara Ann Kinloch
Emma Margaret McNay
Mhari Kirsten Michie
Alanah Beth Mills
Joanna Clare Milne
Fiona Neilson
Nicola Jo Nicolson
Susan Elizabeth Collin Purvis
Veli-Matti Antinpoika Raikkonen
Kerri Rebekah Rutherford
Pamela May Sargent
Louise Simpson
Emma Catherine Reading Somerville
Claire Elizabeth Woodward

LEDINGHAM CHALMERS LLP

Unit 1 Braehead Shopping Centre, Bridge of
Don, Aberdeen AB22 8RR
Tel: (01224) 823282
E-mail: mail@ledinghamchalmers.com
Web: www.ledinghamchalmers.com
Categories of Work
Adjudication
Adoption
Advice the elderly & powers of attorney
Agriculture and estates
Agriculture, crofting and fishing
Alternative dispute resolution
Alternative investment market
Banking & finance
Charities
Children
Childrens
Civil court work
Civil legal aid
Commercial litigation
Commercial property
Competition

Construction
Consumer credit
Contract & property disputes
Copyright, trade marks and design
Corporate tax
Credit brokerage
Criminal court work
Criminal legal aid
Data protection
Debt
Debt adjusting and debt counselling
Debt administration
Debt collecting
Debt management
Debt recovery, insolvency, bankruptcy
Disability
Discrimination
Education
Employment
Employment law
Environment
Environment (Business Premises)
EU / international
Family and divorce
Family business advice
Fishing
Freedom of information
Health and safety
Housing
Human rights
Immigration and asylum
Insolvency & corporate recovery
Insurance
IT and intellectual property
Joint venture
Landlord & tenant
Liquor licensing
Local government
Media and entertainment
Medical negligence – defender
Medical negligence – claimant
Mental health
Mergers and acquisitions
Oil & gas
Pensions (Company)
Pensions (Employment)
Personal injury
Personal injury – defender
Personal tax
Planning
Planning (Business Premises)
Power and utilities
Private equity
Professional negligence
Projects
Property litigation
Provision of credit information services
Public finance initiative
Public sector
Residential property
Road traffic
SME business advice
Software licensing

▶ **Aberdeen continued**

Telecoms
Transport
Unit Trusts, OEICs and investment trusts
Wills, executries and trusts

LEDINGHAM CHALMERS NOMINEES LIMITED
Johnstone House, 52-54 Rose Street, Aberdeen
AB10 1HA
Tel: (01224) 408408
DX: AB15 ABERDEEN

LEDINGHAM CHALMERS TRUSTEE COMPANY LIMITED
Johnstone House, 52-54 Rose Street, Aberdeen
AB10 1HA
Tel: (01224) 408408

LEFEVRE LITIGATION
40 Carden Place, Queen's Cross, Aberdeen
AB10 1UP
Tel: (01224) 657657
Fax: (01224) 626917
DX: AB79 ABERDEEN
E-mail: initials@lefevre-litigation.com
Categories of Work
Benefit advice
Criminal court work
Criminal legal aid
Fishing
Health and safety
Human rights
Medical negligence – defender
Medical negligence – claimant
Mental health
Personal injury
Personal injury – defender
Professional negligence
Road traffic
Partners
Gregor James Kelly
Liam Ross McAllister
Consultant
Lynne Alexander Freeland

MCFLS LIMITED
Ground Floor, 4 Golden Square, Aberdeen
AB10 1RD
Tel: (01224) 467266
Fax: (01224) 467266
DX: AB165 ABERDEEN
E-mail: mubasher@mcfls.co.uk
Categories of Work
Adoption
Children
Family and divorce
Director
Mubasher Latif Choudry

MCINTOSH FAMILY LAW
52-54 Albert Street, Aberdeen AB25 1XS
Tel: (01224) 593100
E-mail: rowena@mcintoshfamilylaw.com
Categories of Work
Adoption

Advice the elderly & powers of attorney
Children
Family and divorce
Partner
Rowena Marie McIntosh

MACKIE & DEWAR
18 Bon Accord Square, Aberdeen AB11 6YP
Tel: (01224) 596341
Fax: (01224) 574327
DX: AB11 ABERDEEN
E-mail: awm@mackieanddewar.co.uk
Categories of Work
Criminal court work
Criminal legal aid
Partners
Alistair William Marshall
Michael Eric Monro
Associate
Sharon Jane McKilligin

MACKINNONS SOLICITORS LLP
14 Carden Place, Aberdeen AB10 1UR
Tel: (01224) 632464
Fax: (01224) 632184
DX: AB34 ABERDEEN
E-mail: admin@mackinnons.com
Web: www.mackinnons.com
Categories of Work
Advice the elderly & powers of attorney
Agriculture and estates
Agriculture, crofting and fishing
Alternative dispute resolution
Banking & finance
Betting & gaming
Civil court work
Civil legal aid
Commercial litigation
Commercial property
Construction
Contract & property disputes
Debt
Debt recovery, insolvency, bankruptcy
Employment
Employment law
Environment (Business Premises)
Family and divorce
Family business advice
Fishing
Health and safety
Housing
Insolvency & corporate recovery
Landlord & tenant
Liquor licensing
Medical negligence – defender
Oil & gas
Personal injury
Personal injury – defender
Personal tax
Planning
Planning (Business Premises)
Power and utilities
Professional negligence
Projects

Property litigation
Residential property
Road traffic
Shipping
SME business advice
Transport
Wills, executives and trusts
Partners
Caroline Elspet Cumming
Graham Edward Jones
Martin Turner Sinclair
Neil Miller Torrance
Consultants
Hayley Bloodworth
Keith Gordon MacRae
Fiona Thomson
Employees
Rachael Catherine Bain
Fiona Elizabeth Copp
Angus David Easton
Kirstin Ejsmont
Anna Kaparaki
Gregor Forbes Sim

MACKINNONS SOLICITORS LLP
379 North Deeside Road, Cults, Aberdeen
AB15 9SX
Tel: (01224) 868687
Fax: (01224) 861012
DX: AB34 ABERDEEN
E-mail: admin@mackinnons.com
Web: www.mackinnons.com
Categories of Work
Advice the elderly & powers of attorney
Agriculture and estates
Agriculture, crofting and fishing
Alternative dispute resolution
Banking & finance
Betting & gaming
Civil court work
Civil legal aid
Commercial litigation
Commercial property
Construction
Contract & property disputes
Debt
Debt recovery, insolvency, bankruptcy
Employment
Employment law
Environment (Business Premises)
Family and divorce
Family business advice
Fishing
Health and safety
Housing
Insolvency & corporate recovery
Landlord & tenant
Liquor licensing
Medical negligence – defender
Oil & gas
Personal injury
Personal injury – defender
Personal tax

Planning
Planning (Business Premises)
Power and utilities
Professional negligence
Projects
Property litigation
Residential property
Road traffic
Shipping
SME business advice
Transport
Wills, executives and trusts
Partners
Patricia Joy Gray
Ashleigh McConnell
Associates
Pamela Winifred Sharon Bursill
Jane Florence Merson
Employee
Hollie Shona Hutchison

GEORGE MATHERS & CO
23 Adelphi, Aberdeen AB11 5BL
Tel: (01224) 588599
Fax: (01224) 584147
DX: AB158 ABERDEEN
E-mail: info@georgemathers.co.uk
Web: www.georgemathers.co.uk
Categories of Work
Civil court work
Civil legal aid
Criminal court work
Criminal legal aid
Human rights
Partners
Paul Scott Barnett
Christopher Maitland
John Alexander McLeod
Neil Ross McRobert
Consultant
George Frank MacGregor Mathers
Employee
Sian Marie Fish

A.C. MORRISON & RICHARDS LLP
18 Bon Accord Crescent, Aberdeen AB11 6XY
Tel: (01224) 573321
Fax: (01224) 576115
DX: AB50 ABERDEEN
Web: www.acmr.co.uk
Categories of Work
Advice the elderly & powers of attorney
Agriculture and estates
Agriculture, crofting and fishing
Children
Civil court work
Commercial property
Contract & property disputes
Debt recovery, insolvency, bankruptcy
Family and divorce
Family business advice
Landlord & tenant
Personal injury
Property litigation

▶ **Aberdeen continued**

Residential property
Wills, executories and trusts
Partners
Martin Alan Fraser
Fiona Milne
David Russell Spence
Consultant
Alan Alexander Slessor Wilson

MUIRHEAD BUCHANAN

7-9 Bon Accord Crescent, Aberdeen
AB11 6DN
Categories of Work
Adjudication
Adoption
Advice the elderly & powers of attorney
Agriculture and estates
Agriculture, crofting and fishing
Alternative dispute resolution
Alternative investment market
Banking & finance
Charities
Children
Childrens
Civil court work
Civil legal aid
Commercial litigation
Commercial property
Competition
Construction
Consumer credit
Contract & property disputes
Copyright, trade marks and design
Corporate tax
Credit brokerage
Criminal court work
Criminal legal aid
Data protection
Debt
Debt adjusting and debt counselling
Debt collecting
Debt recovery, insolvency, bankruptcy
Disability
Discrimination
Education
Employment
Employment law
Environment
Environment (Business Premises)
EU / international
Family and divorce
Family business advice
Freedom of information
Health
Health and safety
Human rights
Insolvency & corporate recovery
Insurance
Joint venture
Landlord & tenant
Liquor licensing
Local government

Media and entertainment
Mental health
Mergers and acquisitions
Pensions (Company)
Pensions (Employment)
Personal injury
Personal tax
Planning (Business Premises)
Private equity
Professional negligence
Property litigation
Public finance initiative
Public sector
Residential property
SME business advice
Social housing
Telecoms
Unit Trusts, OEICs and investment trusts
Wills, executories and trusts

MULLEN AND CO

1 Marischal Square, Broad Street, Aberdeen
AB10 1BL
Tel: (01224) 433938
Fax: (01224) 900317
DX: AB166 ABERDEEN
Web: www.mullenandco.co.uk
Categories of Work
Adoption
Alternative dispute resolution
Benefit advice
Children
Childrens
Civil court work
Civil legal aid
Commercial litigation
Contract & property disputes
Criminal court work
Debt
Debt collecting
Debt management
Debt recovery, insolvency, bankruptcy
Disability
Discrimination
Education
Employment law
Family and divorce
Human rights
Insolvency & corporate recovery
Mental health
Public sector
Social housing
Wills, executories and trusts
Partners
Hayley Louise Mullen
Thomas Anthony Mullen

MURRAY ORMISTON LLP

Union Chambers, 46a Union Street, Aberdeen
AB10 1BD
Tel: (01224) 478822
DX: AB167 ABERDEEN
Web: www.murrayormiston.com

Categories of Work
Adoption
Advice the elderly & powers of attorney
Children
Childrens
Civil court work
Civil legal aid
Criminal court work
Criminal legal aid
Family and divorce
Human rights
Mental health
Parliamentary
Partners
Stuart Murray
Andrew Ormiston
Associate
Sarah McPherson
Employee
Morag Stevenson

NORRIS EMPLOYMENT LIMITED
499 Union Street, Aberdeen AB11 6DB
Tel: (01224) 228100
Categories of Work
Alternative dispute resolution
Employment
Director
Ljiljana Vukadinovic Norris

NORTHERN LAW
1 Northburn Lane, Aberdeen AB15 6GB
Tel: (01224) 379440
E-mail: info@northernlaw.co.uk
Categories of Work
Adoption
Advice the elderly & powers of attorney
Children
Criminal court work
Criminal legal aid
Education
Family and divorce
Mental health
Wills, executries and trusts
Partner
Charles Benzies

OUTSIDE INHOUSE LEGAL LIMITED
29 Craigton Terrace, Aberdeen AB15 7RN
Tel: (07927) 560475
E-mail: jill.reid@oilegal.com
Director
Jill Reid

PATIENCE & BUCHAN
10 Golden Square, Aberdeen AB10 1RB
Tel: (01224) 648222
Fax: (01224) 648848
DX: AB169 ABERDEEN
E-mail: lorna@patienceandbuchan.com
Web: www.patienceandbuchan.com
Categories of Work
Adoption
Advice the elderly & powers of attorney
Alternative dispute resolution

Children
Childrens
Civil court work
Family and divorce
Wills, executries and trusts
Partners
Lorna Gilmore Buchan
Ashley Marie Simpson
Employee
Gillian Elizabeth Smith Mitchell

PETERKINS
100 Union Street, Aberdeen AB10 1QR
Tel: (01224) 428000
Fax: (01224) 626123
DX: AB3 ABERDEEN
E-mail: maildesk@peterkins.com
Web: www.peterkins.com
Categories of Work
Advice the elderly & powers of attorney
Agriculture and estates
Agriculture, crofting and fishing
Banking & finance
Charities
Commercial property
Construction
Criminal court work
Criminal legal aid
Debt recovery, insolvency, bankruptcy
Environment (Business Premises)
Family business advice
Housing
Insolvency & corporate recovery
Landlord & tenant
Liquor licensing
Local government
Pensions (Company)
Planning
Planning (Business Premises)
Power and utilities
Residential property
SME business advice
Wills, executries and trusts
Partners
Robert Gordon William Davidson
Hartley Wilson Lumsden
Alastair Currie MacDonald
Caren McNeil
Karen Patricia Simpson
Consultant
Thomas Wilson Duncan
Associates
Marcia Alexandra Johnstone
Greg Scott Lawson
Employees
Catriona Ann Barclay
Adam Brian Grant
Christopher David Ernest Lawson

PETERKINS TRUSTEES LIMITED
100 Union Street, Aberdeen AB10 1QR
Tel: (01224) 428000

PINSENT MASONS LLP
13 Queen's Road, Aberdeen AB15 4YL

▶ **Aberdeen continued**

Tel: (01224) 377900
Web: www.pinsentmasons.com
Categories of Work
Adjudication
Advice the elderly & powers of attorney
Agriculture and estates
Agriculture, crofting and fishing
Alternative dispute resolution
Alternative investment market
Banking & finance
Betting & gaming
Charities
Children
Civil court work
Commercial litigation
Commercial property
Competition
Construction
Contract & property disputes
Copyright, trade marks and design
Corporate tax
Criminal court work
Data protection
Debt
Debt adjusting and debt counselling
Debt administration
Debt collecting
Debt recovery, insolvency, bankruptcy
Disability
Discrimination
Education
Employment
Employment law
Environment
Environment (Business Premises)
EU / international
Family and divorce
Family business advice
Fishing
Freedom of information
Health
Health and safety
Housing
Human rights
Immigration and asylum
Insolvency & corporate recovery
Insurance
IT and intellectual property
Joint venture
Landlord & tenant
Liquor licensing
Local government
Media and entertainment
Medical negligence – defender
Medical negligence – claimant
Mental health
Mergers and acquisitions
Mining
Oil & gas
Parliamentary
Pensions (Company)

Pensions (Employment)
Personal injury
Personal injury – defender
Planning
Planning (Business Premises)
Power and utilities
Private equity
Professional negligence
Projects
Property litigation
Public finance initiative
Public sector
Residential property
Road traffic
Shipping
SME business advice
Software licensing
Sport
Telecoms
Transport
Unit Trusts, OEICs and investment trusts
Wills, executries and trusts
Partners
Shirley Jean Allen
Bruce Craig
Scott Forsyth Johnston
Bruce Martin Ronald McLeod
Richard Imray Scott
Rodney Wallace Whyte
Associates
Lisa Claire Byars
Susan Louise Hay Mackay
Fiona Helen Elizabeth Martin
William Michael Park
Natalie Jane Walker
Michaela Watts
Employees
Emma-Louise Mary Beadie
Charlotte Elizabeth Booth
Sara Louise Brazendale
Shonagh Margaret Brown
Lauren Clark
Jennifer Anne Colvin
Roger Gordon Connon
Amy Catherine Fordyce
Stuart Blair Fraser
Lucy Fiona Griffiths
Neil Graeme Douglas Hehir
Leanne Hill
Jaimie Jean Hunter
Fiona Claire Kindness
Joanna Linda Lang
Natalie Jean Emma McBride
Claire Michelle Scott
Michael John Shepherd
Rachel Louise Trease
Rachel Mary Warner

Q&A LAW PRACTICE LIMITED
Citibase, 9 Queen's Road, Aberdeen AB15 4YL
Tel: 7770996601
E-mail: mike@qalawpractice.co.uk

Categories of Work
Banking & finance
Commercial property
Employment
Employment law
Joint venture
Landlord & tenant
Planning (Business Premises)
SME business advice
Directors
Michael William Anderson
Lewis Alexander Quinn

RAEBURN CHRISTIE CLARK & WALLACE LLP
12-16 Albyn Place, Aberdeen AB10 1PS
Tel: (01224) 332400
Fax: (01224) 332401
DX: AB2 ABERDEEN
Web: www.raeburns.co.uk
Categories of Work
Adoption
Advice the elderly & powers of attorney
Agriculture and estates
Agriculture, crofting and fishing
Alternative dispute resolution
Banking & finance
Betting & gaming
Charities
Children
Civil court work
Civil legal aid
Commercial litigation
Commercial property
Competition
Construction
Contract & property disputes
Copyright, trade marks and design
Data protection
Debt
Disability
Discrimination
Employment
Employment law
Environment
EU / international
Family and divorce
Family business advice
Freedom of information
Health and safety
Housing
Human rights
IT and intellectual property
Joint venture
Landlord & tenant
Liquor licensing
Media and entertainment
Medical negligence – defender
Mergers and acquisitions
Oil & gas
Personal injury
Personal injury – defender
Planning
Planning (Business Premises)

Private equity
Professional negligence
Property litigation
Residential property
Road traffic
Shipping
SME business advice
Social housing
Sport
Wills, executries and trusts
Partners
Fiona Lynne Coutts
Douglas John Crombie
Faye Louise Donald
Neil Fraser
Callum Anderson McDonald
Bruce Gordon Robertson
Alasdair Angus Smith
Heather Mari-Ann Stephen
Amy Cecile Doris Watson
Consultants
Anne Boyd
Peter William Littlejohn
Associates
Aaron Charles Doran
Kirsten Annette Dunford
Amanda Jane Gibb
Teresa Anne Law
Anne Sandra Littlejohn
Anna Jane Moir
Ishbel Nunn
Alix Jean Reid
Gordon James Wallace
Employees
George Keith Allan
Alison Jane Cowperthwaite
Sarah Charlotte Innes
Kirsty May Irvine
Michael Leith
Ruth Lussier
Allan William Mackenzie
Grant George Mills
Scott Rennie
Gillian Catherine Janet Smith
Lorren Georgia Steven
Craig Alan Veitch

RAEBURN CHRISTIE CLARK & WALLACE LLP
399 Union Street, Aberdeen AB11 6BX
Tel: (01224) 564636
Fax: (01224) 564601
DX: AB2 ABERDEEN
Web: www.raeburns.co.uk
Categories of Work
Adoption
Advice the elderly & powers of attorney
Agriculture and estates
Agriculture, crofting and fishing
Alternative dispute resolution
Banking & finance
Betting & gaming
Charities
Children

► **Aberdeen continued**

Civil court work
Civil legal aid
Commercial litigation
Commercial property
Competition
Construction
Contract & property disputes
Copyright, trade marks and design
Data protection
Debt
Disability
Discrimination
Employment
Employment law
Environment
EU / international
Family and divorce
Family business advice
Freedom of information
Health and safety
Housing
Human rights
IT and intellectual property
Joint venture
Landlord & tenant
Liquor licensing
Media and entertainment
Medical negligence – defender
Mergers and acquisitions
Oil & gas
Personal injury
Personal injury – defender
Planning
Planning (Business Premises)
Private equity
Professional negligence
Property litigation
Residential property
Road traffic
Shipping
SME business advice
Social housing
Sport
Wills, executries and trusts
Partner
William Douglas Barclay
Associate
Gavin Bruce Cooper
Employee
David Maughan Smith

ROAD TRAFFIC ACCIDENT LAW (SCOTLAND) LLP
1 Marischal Square, Broad Street, Aberdeen AB10 1BL
Tel: (01721) 728238
Categories of Work
Civil court work
Personal injury
Professional negligence
Road traffic
Sport

Employee
Rozanne Choi Ling Boynton

SANDISON KENNEDY LIMITED
7 Queen's Gardens, Aberdeen AB15 4YD
Tel: (01224) 443555
E-mail: charles@sandisonkennedy.com
Director
Charles John Sandison

SHEPHERD AND WEDDERBURN LLP
Commercial House, 2 Rubislaw Terrace, Aberdeen AB10 1XE
Tel: (01224) 621166
Fax: (01224) 623103
DX: AB103 ABERDEEN 1
Web: www.shepwedd.co.uk
Categories of Work
Adjudication
Adoption
Advice the elderly & powers of attorney
Agriculture and estates
Agriculture, crofting and fishing
Alternative dispute resolution
Alternative investment market
Banking & finance
Betting & gaming
Charities
Civil court work
Commercial litigation
Commercial property
Competition
Construction
Consumer credit
Contract & property disputes
Copyright, trade marks and design
Corporate tax
Credit brokerage
Data protection
Debt
Debt adjusting and debt counselling
Debt administration
Debt collecting
Debt recovery, insolvency, bankruptcy
Disability
Discrimination
Education
Employment
Employment law
Environment
Environment (Business Premises)
EU / international
Family business advice
Fishing
Freedom of information
Health
Health and safety
Housing
Human rights
Immigration and asylum
Insolvency & corporate recovery
Insurance
IT and intellectual property
Joint venture

Landlord & tenant
Liquor licensing
Local government
Media and entertainment
Medical negligence – defender
Medical negligence – claimant
Mergers and acquisitions
Mining
Oil & gas
Parliamentary
Pensions (Company)
Pensions (Employment)
Personal injury
Personal injury – defender
Personal tax
Planning
Planning (Business Premises)
Power and utilities
Private equity
Professional negligence
Projects
Property litigation
Provision of credit information services
Public finance initiative
Public sector
Residential property
Road traffic
Shipping
SME business advice
Software licensing
Sport
Telecoms
Transport
Unit Trusts, OEICs and investment trusts
Wills, executries and trusts
Partners
Gillian Fay Campbell
Hamish Lean
Keir Willox
Consultant
George William Stevenson
Associate
Emma Jane Robertson
Employees
Christopher George Garden
Alexandra Mae Lane

GRANT SMITH LAW PRACTICE LIMITED
Amicable House, 252 Union Street, Aberdeen
AB10 1TN
Tel: (01224) 621620
Fax: (01224) 622621
DX: 529443 ABERDEEN 6
E-mail: andrew.duthie@grantsmithlaw.co.uk
Web: www.grantsmithlaw.co.uk
Categories of Work
Adoption
Advice the elderly & powers of attorney
Alternative dispute resolution
Children
Childrens
Civil court work
Civil legal aid

Commercial property
Contract & property disputes
Criminal court work
Criminal legal aid
Debt
Debt collecting
Debt recovery, insolvency, bankruptcy
Education
Family and divorce
Landlord & tenant
Mental health
Personal injury
Professional negligence
Property litigation
Residential property
Road traffic
Wills, executries and trusts
Directors
Stuart Gordon Nicholas Beveridge
Andrew Duthie
Consultants
Lisa Jane Gregory
Peter Francis Keene
Donald Forbes Macandrew
Gail Ann Wiggins
Employee
Nicholas James MacAndrew

SOLICITORS DIRECT
479 Great Western Road, Aberdeen AB10 6NN
Tel: (01224) 327 437
Fax: (01224) 314 485
DX: AB172 ABERDEEN
E-mail: joy@solicitorsdirect.info
Categories of Work
Commercial property
Family business advice
Joint venture
Landlord & tenant
Mergers and acquisitions
Oil & gas
Residential property
Wills, executries and trusts
Partners
Joanna Carolyn Pyper Dunbar
Joy Patricia Dunbar
Employee
William David Young

SPANISH + SCOTTISH LAW PRACTICE LIMITED
1 East Craibstone Street, Aberdeen AB11 6YQ
Tel: (01224) 581581
E-mail: ignacio@sslawpractice.co.uk
Web: www.sslawpractice.co.uk
Categories of Work
Contract & property disputes
EU / international
Residential property
Wills, executries and trusts
Director
Ignacio Chanz Jord n

STORIE, CRUDEN & SIMPSON
2 Bon Accord Crescent, Aberdeen AB11 6DH

▶ *Aberdeen continued*

Tel: (01224) 587261
Fax: (01224) 580850
DX: AB12 ABERDEEN
E-mail: aw@storiecs.co.uk
Web: www.storiecs.co.uk
Categories of Work
Advice the elderly & powers of attorney
Agriculture and estates
Commercial property
Family and divorce
Landlord & tenant
Residential property
Wills, executives and trusts
Partner
Andrew Whyte
Employees
Stephen Bland
Jessica Alexandra Dickson

STRONACHS LLP
28 Albyn Place, Aberdeen AB10 1YL
Tel: (01224) 845845
Fax: (01224) 845800
DX: AB41 ABERDEEN
E-mail: info@stronachs.com
Categories of Work
Adjudication
Adoption
Advice the elderly & powers of attorney
Agriculture and estates
Agriculture, crofting and fishing
Alternative dispute resolution
Alternative investment market
Banking & finance
Benefit advice
Charities
Children
Childrens
Civil court work
Civil legal aid
Commercial litigation
Commercial property
Competition
Construction
Consumer credit
Contract & property disputes
Copyright, trade marks and design
Corporate tax
Data protection
Debt
Debt collecting
Debt management
Debt recovery, insolvency, bankruptcy
Disability
Education
Employment
Employment law
Environment
Environment (Business Premises)
EU / international
Family and divorce
Family business advice

Freedom of information
Health
Health and safety
Housing
Insolvency & corporate recovery
IT and intellectual property
Joint venture
Landlord & tenant
Media and entertainment
Medical negligence – defender
Medical negligence – claimant
Mental health
Mergers and acquisitions
Oil & gas
Pensions (Company)
Pensions (Employment)
Personal injury
Personal injury – defender
Personal tax
Planning
Planning (Business Premises)
Power and utilities
Private equity
Professional negligence
Projects
Property litigation
Public finance initiative
Public sector
Residential property
Road traffic
Shipping
SME business advice
Social housing
Software licensing
Sport
Telecoms
Transport
Wills, executives and trusts
Partners
Duncan Craig Campbell
James David Chalmers
Malcolm James Robert Donald
James Forbes Downie
Anya Dorothy Duncan
Neil David Forbes
Ross Scott Gardner
David Keith Marshall
Robert Duncan McDiarmid
James Robertson Muir
Ewan Craig Neilson
Jaclyn Elizabeth Petrie Russell
Emma Stephen
Elizabeth Ann Stewart
Consultant
David Alan Rennie
Associates
Jamie David Hunter
Pauline Amanda Lukins
Joy Helen Mullin
Karen Jayne Oliver
Employees
Sarah Elizabeth Adams
Adele Anderson

Kirsten Louise Anderson
Callum Charles Armstrong
Lewis William Armstrong
Lindsay Diane Dron
Laura Charlotte Gray
Stefanie Rollan Hendry
Deborah Caroline Law
Raiya Law
Annika Neukirch
Patrick Jamie Norris
Michelle Gillian Sharp
Aulo Plauzio Vallarino
Jonathan Mark Wemyss
Morven Elizabeth White
Emily Heather Wright

DAVID E SUTHERLAND
10-16 Exchequer Row, Aberdeen AB11 5BW
Tel: (01224) 857900
Fax: (01224) 590317
DX: AB55 ABERDEEN
E-mail:
David.Sutherland@davidesutherland.com
Categories of Work
Criminal court work
Criminal legal aid
Partner
David Eric Sutherland

TAGGART MEIL MATHERS
20 Bon Accord Square, Aberdeen AB11 6DJ
Tel: (01224) 588020
Fax: (01224) 588030
DX: AB173 ABERDEEN
E-mail: info@tmmsolicitors.co.uk
Web: www.tmmsolicitors.co.uk
Categories of Work
Adoption
Advice the elderly & powers of attorney
Alternative dispute resolution
Banking & finance
Children
Childrens
Civil court work
Civil legal aid
Commercial litigation
Commercial property
Copyright, trade marks and design
Criminal court work
Criminal legal aid
Debt collecting
Debt recovery, insolvency, bankruptcy
Education
Employment
Family and divorce
Family business advice
Health and safety
Landlord & tenant
Medical negligence – defender
Medical negligence – claimant
Oil & gas
Personal injury – defender
Professional negligence
Property litigation

Residential property
Shipping
SME business advice
Sport
Wills, executries and trusts
Partners
Frank George Mathers
Judith Anne Meil
Ross Taggart
Associate
Catriona Mairi MacLeod

JONATHAN TAIT & CO.
9 Crown Street, Aberdeen AB11 6HA
Tel: (01224) 582211
Fax: (01224) 584729
DX: AB51 ABERDEEN
E-mail: info@jonathantait.co.uk
Web: www.jonathantait.co.uk
Categories of Work
Advice the elderly & powers of attorney
Commercial property
Contract & property disputes
Family and divorce
Family business advice
Landlord & tenant
Personal injury
Residential property
Wills, executries and trusts
Partner
Jonathan Johnstone Tait

THE CHAMBER PRACTICE LTD
269 Holburn Street, Aberdeen AB10 7FL
Tel: (01224) 433301
Fax: (01224) 433302
E-mail: enquiries@thechamberpractice.co.uk
Web: www.thechamberpractice.co.uk
Categories of Work
Commercial property
Family business advice
Human rights
Immigration and asylum
Landlord & tenant
Liquor licensing
Residential property
Wills, executries and trusts
Director
Vikas Sharma

THE LAW PRACTICE
3 Rubislaw Terrace, Aberdeen AB10 1XE
Tel: (01224) 562870
Fax: (01224) 621540
DX: AB53 ABERDEEN
E-mail: lmcknight@thelawpractice.org
Web: www.thelawpractice.org
Categories of Work
Advice the elderly & powers of attorney
Residential property
Wills, executries and trusts
Partner
Lesley McKnight

▶ **Aberdeen continued**

Employee
Sarah Anne Newnham

THE MORTGAGE & PROPERTY CENTRE
248 Union Street, Aberdeen AB10 1TN
Tel: (01224) 623443
E-mail: mail@mortgageandproperty.co.uk
Web: www.mortgageandproperty.co.uk
Categories of Work
Advice the elderly & powers of attorney
Consumer credit
Debt adjusting and debt counselling
Debt administration
Debt collecting
Family and divorce
Housing
Residential property
Wills, executries and trusts

THE REMORTGAGE COMPANY
393 Union Street, Aberdeen AB11 6BX
Tel: (01224) 623423
Categories of Work
Advice the elderly & powers of attorney
Consumer credit
Debt adjusting and debt counselling
Debt administration
Debt collecting
Family and divorce
Housing
Residential property
Wills, executries and trusts

WILSONE & DUFFUS
1 Watson Street, Rosemount Place, Aberdeen
AB25 2QB
Tel: (01224) 625032
E-mail: info@wilsoneduffus.co.uk
Web: www.key-moves.co.uk
Categories of Work
Advice the elderly & powers of attorney
Banking & finance
Commercial property
Construction
Landlord & tenant
Liquor licensing
Planning
Planning (Business Premises)
Residential property
SME business advice
Wills, executries and trusts

WILSONE & DUFFUS
14 Chapel Street, Aberdeen AB10 1SP
Tel: (01224) 251100
Fax: (01224) 251101
E-mail: info@wilsoneduffus.co.uk
Web: www.key-moves.co.uk
Categories of Work
Advice the elderly & powers of attorney
Banking & finance
Commercial property
Construction

Landlord & tenant
Liquor licensing
Planning
Planning (Business Premises)
Residential property
SME business advice
Wills, executries and trusts
Partners
Graham Harold Mountford
Peter McLew Young

WILSONE & DUFFUS
7 Golden Square, Aberdeen AB10 1RD
Tel: (01224) 651700
Fax: (01224) 647329
DX: AB24 ABERDEEN
E-mail: info@wilsoneduffus.co.uk
Web: www.key-moves.co.uk
Categories of Work
Advice the elderly & powers of attorney
Banking & finance
Commercial property
Construction
Landlord & tenant
Liquor licensing
Planning
Planning (Business Premises)
Residential property
SME business advice
Wills, executries and trusts
Partner
Lindsey Mary Fettes
Consultant
Fiona Janet Mitchell
Employees
Angela Hay
Stephanie Patricia Moir
Fern Jamieson Stone

WOMBLE BOND DICKINSON (UK) LLP
1st Floor, Silver Fin Building, Aberdeen
AB11 6DB
Tel: (0345) 4150000
DX: AB37 ABERDEEN
Categories of Work
Adjudication
Agriculture and estates
Alternative dispute resolution
Alternative investment market
Banking & finance
Civil court work
Commercial litigation
Commercial property
Competition
Construction
Contract & property disputes
Copyright, trade marks and design
Debt recovery, insolvency, bankruptcy
Environment
Environment (Business Premises)
EU / international
Insolvency & corporate recovery
IT and intellectual property
Joint venture

Landlord & tenant
Media and entertainment
Mergers and acquisitions
Oil & gas
Pensions (Company)
Planning
Planning (Business Premises)
Power and utilities
Private equity
Projects
Property litigation
Public finance initiative
Public sector
Shipping
SME business advice
Sport
Transport
Unit Trusts, OEICs and investment trusts

WOODWARD LAWSON
7 Queens Gardens, Aberdeen AB15 4YD
Tel: (01224) 619330
E-mail: info@woodwardlawson.com
Categories of Work
Civil court work
Commercial litigation
Construction
Contract & property disputes
Criminal court work
Criminal legal aid
Debt collecting
Debt recovery, insolvency, bankruptcy
Family and divorce
Mental health
Road traffic
Wills, executries and trusts
Partner
Ian James Woodward-Nutt
Consultant
Philip Andrew Lawson

Aberfeldy

IRVING GEDDES, WS LIMITED
6 The Square, Aberfeldy PH15 2DD
Tel: (01887) 822 722
DX: 566382 CRIEFF
E-mail: aberfeldy@irvinggeddes.co.uk
Web: www.irvinggeddes.co.uk
Categories of Work
Advice the elderly & powers of attorney
Agriculture and estates
Agriculture, crofting and fishing
Charities
Commercial property
Employment
Environment (Business Premises)
Family business advice
Landlord & tenant
Planning
Residential property
Unit Trusts, OEICs and investment trusts
Wills, executries and trusts

J & H MITCHELL LLP
The Square, Aberfeldy PH15 2DD
Tel: (01887) 820285
E-mail: j@hmitchell.co.uk
Web: www.jandhmitchell.com
Categories of Work
Advice the elderly & powers of attorney
Agriculture and estates
Agriculture, crofting and fishing
Charities
Commercial property
Contract & property disputes
Data protection
Employment
Environment
Family business advice
Housing
IT and intellectual property
Joint venture
Landlord & tenant
Liquor licensing
Mergers and acquisitions
Personal tax
Planning (Business Premises)
Private equity
Residential property
SME business advice
Wills, executries and trusts

Aberuthven

NEXT LAW LLP
Loanfoot, Main Road, Aberuthven PH3 1HB
Tel: (01764) 680525
Web: www.next-law.co.uk
Categories of Work
Advice the elderly & powers of attorney
Charities
Children
Civil legal aid
Commercial property
Family and divorce
Mental health
Residential property
Wills, executries and trusts

Aboyne

CAMPBELL CONNON
The Hall, Charleston Road, Aboyne AB34 5EJ
Tel: (013398) 86732
E-mail: info@campbellconnon.co.uk
Categories of Work
Advice the elderly & powers of attorney
Debt
Residential property
Wills, executries and trusts

DEESIDE DEFENCE
PO Box 68, Aboyne AB34 4WY
Tel: (0771) 2005551
E-mail: deesidedefence@gmail.com

▶ **Aboyne continued**

Categories of Work
Criminal court work
Criminal legal aid
Partner
Kevin Denis Longino

MACKINNONS SOLICITORS LLP
Ballater Road, Aboyne AB34 5HN
Tel: (01339) 887665
Web: www.mackinnons.com
Categories of Work
Advice the elderly & powers of attorney
Agriculture and estates
Agriculture, crofting and fishing
Alternative dispute resolution
Banking & finance
Betting & gaming
Civil court work
Civil legal aid
Commercial litigation
Commercial property
Construction
Contract & property disputes
Debt
Debt recovery, insolvency, bankruptcy
Employment
Employment law
Environment (Business Premises)
Family and divorce
Family business advice
Fishing
Health and safety
Housing
Insolvency & corporate recovery
Landlord & tenant
Liquor licensing
Medical negligence – defender
Oil & gas
Personal injury
Personal injury – defender
Personal tax
Planning
Planning (Business Premises)
Power and utilities
Professional negligence
Projects
Property litigation
Residential property
Road traffic
Shipping
SME business advice
Transport
Wills, executries and trusts

Airdrie

AIRDRIE LEGAL CHAMBERS LIMITED
89 Graham Street, Airdrie ML6 6DE
Tel: (01236) 779970
E-mail: admin@ocurry.net
Categories of Work
Criminal court work

Criminal legal aid
Mental health
Director
Luke Eugene O'Curry
Associate
Ceri Victoria Evans
Solicitor
Frank Samuel Nicol

ALEXANDER JOHNSTONE SOLICITORS AND NOTARIES
Penreoch, Forrest Street, Airdrie ML6 7BD
Tel: (01236) 897171
Categories of Work
Adjudication
Advice the elderly & powers of attorney
Alternative dispute resolution
Civil court work
Civil legal aid
Commercial litigation
Employment law
Family and divorce
Immigration and asylum
Landlord & tenant
Medical negligence – defender
Personal injury – defender
Road traffic
Wills, executries and trusts
Partner
Thomas Alexander Johnstone

BELL RUSSELL & COMPANY LIMITED
111/111a Graham Street, Airdrie ML6 6DE
Tel: (01236) 764781
Fax: (01236) 764009
DX: 570410 AIRDRIE
E-mail: ewallace@bell-russell.com
Categories of Work
Adoption
Advice the elderly & powers of attorney
Children
Childrens
Criminal court work
Criminal legal aid
Family and divorce
Residential property
Wills, executries and trusts
Directors
Collette Catherine Connell
Eric Robert Carson Wallace
Employee
Niamh Boyd Buschman

BONNAR ACCIDENT LAW LTD
83 Graham Street, Airdrie ML6 6DE
Tel: (01236) 756188
Fax: (01236) 761899
DX: 570411 AIRDRIE
Web: www.bonnarandco.com
Categories of Work
Civil court work
Civil legal aid
Health and safety
Personal injury

Professional negligence
Road traffic
Director
Veronica Mary McManus

CARTYS
10A Anderson Street, Airdrie ML6 0AA
Tel: (01236) 761127
Fax: (01236) 753858
DX: 570412 AIRDRIE
E-mail: airdrie@cartylaw.co.uk
Web: www.cartylaw.co.uk
Categories of Work
Adoption
Advice the elderly & powers of attorney
Agriculture and estates
Benefit advice
Children
Civil court work
Civil legal aid
Commercial property
Consumer credit
Criminal court work
Criminal legal aid
Debt adjusting and debt counselling
Debt administration
Debt collecting
Debt management
Disability
Discrimination
Education
Family and divorce
Freedom of information
Human rights
Landlord & tenant
Mental health
Pensions (Employment)
Personal injury
Residential property
Road traffic
Social housing
Wills, executries and trusts
Partner
Paula Joanne Lutton
Employee
Fraser Gordon McKinnon

HAMILTON ROSS
18 Anderson Street, Airdrie ML6 0AA
Tel: (01236) 627627
Fax: (01236) 627628
DX: 570431 AIRDRIE
E-mail: mail@hamiltonross.co.uk
Web: www.hamiltonross.co.uk
Categories of Work
Adoption
Advice the elderly & powers of attorney
Children
Childrens
Civil court work
Civil legal aid
Criminal court work
Criminal legal aid
Family and divorce

Landlord & tenant
Medical negligence – defender
Medical negligence – claimant
Personal injury
Personal injury – defender
Professional negligence
Residential property
Road traffic
Wills, executries and trusts
Partner
Mark James McGraw
Employees
Kaitlin Tress Boswell
Gary David Morton
Louise Anne Scullion

LANARKSHIRE COMMUNITY LAW CENTRE LTD
C/o Airdrie Citizens Advice, (First Floor),
Airdrie ML6 0AS
Tel: (01236) 757 337
E-mail: AIR-NLCLS@airdriecab.casonline.org.uk
Categories of Work
Adoption
Benefit advice
Children
Civil court work
Civil legal aid
Consumer credit
Criminal court work
Criminal legal aid
Debt
Debt management
Disability
Discrimination
EU / international
Family and divorce
Housing
Human rights
Immigration and asylum
Local government
Mental health
Social housing
Director
Nicola Rylatt
Employee
Ann Jane Reid Watt Malloy

MCAFEE
81 Graham Street, Airdrie ML6 6DE
Tel: (01236) 755339
DX: 570422 AIRDRIE
Categories of Work
Adoption
Advice the elderly & powers of attorney
Children
Childrens
Civil court work
Civil legal aid
Criminal court work
Criminal legal aid
Disability
Discrimination
Education
Employment

▶ **Airdrie continued**

Employment law
Family and divorce
Human rights
Immigration and asylum
Medical negligence – claimant
Mental health
Personal injury
Professional negligence
Wills, executives and trusts

MCCARRON & CO.
Bank House, 17 East High Street, Airdrie
ML6 6LF
Tel: (01236) 762012
Fax: (01236) 748459
DX: 570414 AIRDRIE
E-mail: eric@mccarronlaw.co.uk
Categories of Work
Banking & finance
Debt recovery, insolvency, bankruptcy
Insolvency & corporate recovery
Insurance
Pensions (Company)
Residential property
Unit Trusts, OEICs and investment trusts
Wills, executives and trusts
Partner
Eric Abercrombie

BRUCE MCCORMACK LIMITED
1st Floor, 91 Graham Street, Airdrie ML6 6DE
Tel: (01236) 767240
Categories of Work
Criminal court work
Criminal legal aid

MCWHINNEY RICHARDS
66 Stirling Street, Airdrie ML6 0AW
Tel: (01236) 754571
Fax: (01236) 765339
DX: 570434 AIRDRIE
E-mail: general@mcwhinneyrichards.com
Categories of Work
Adoption
Advice the elderly & powers of attorney
Alternative dispute resolution
Benefit advice
Children
Civil court work
Civil legal aid
Commercial litigation
Consumer credit
Criminal court work
Criminal legal aid
Debt
Debt collecting
Debt management
Debt recovery, insolvency, bankruptcy
Education
Family and divorce
Medical negligence – claimant
Mental health
Personal injury

Professional negligence
Road traffic
Social housing
Wills, executives and trusts
Partner
Cheryl Prentice Brown
Employee
Stephen Gerard Fagan

MALCOLM & HUTCHISON
34-36 Alexander Street, Airdrie ML6 0BA
Tel: (01236) 755050
Fax: (01236) 747470
DX: 570433 AIRDRIE
E-mail: richard@malcolmandhutchison.co.uk
Categories of Work
Adoption
Advice the elderly & powers of attorney
Children
Civil court work
Civil legal aid
Commercial litigation
Commercial property
Contract & property disputes
Criminal court work
Criminal legal aid
Debt
Family and divorce
Landlord & tenant
Residential property
Wills, executives and trusts
Partners
Richard Hutchison
Irene Margaret Lynn Malcolm
Associate
Amy Watters
Employee
Jennifer O'Brien

MANINI BELARDO LIMITED
35 Hallcraig Street, Airdrie ML6 6AH
Tel: (01236) 769 257
DX: 570437 AIRDRIE
Categories of Work
Criminal court work
Criminal legal aid

MORISON & SMITH LIMITED
16 Anderson Street, Airdrie ML6 0AA
Tel: (01236) 809000
Categories of Work
Advice the elderly & powers of attorney
Agriculture and estates
Agriculture, crofting and fishing
Charities
Children
Civil court work
Civil legal aid
Commercial property
Contract & property disputes
Debt collecting
Family and divorce
Landlord & tenant
Residential property

Wills, executries and trusts

NICOLSON O'BRIEN
12 Stirling Street, Airdrie ML6 0AH
Tel: (01236) 751224
Fax: (01236) 748205
DX: 570415 AIRDRIE
E-mail: paul.nicolson@nicolsonobrien.co.uk
Categories of Work
Adoption
Advice the elderly & powers of attorney
Children
Civil court work
Civil legal aid
Criminal court work
Criminal legal aid
Family and divorce
Residential property
Wills, executries and trusts
Partner
Paul Nicolson
Consultant
Frances Mary Porter

THE MFY PARTNERSHIP
25 Stirling Street, Airdrie ML6 0AH
Tel: (01236) 607180
Fax: (01236) 607181
DX: 570436 AIRDRIE
E-mail: office@mfypartnership.co.uk
Categories of Work
Adoption
Advice the elderly & powers of attorney
Children
Childrens
Civil court work
Civil legal aid
Criminal court work
Criminal legal aid
Education
Family and divorce
Partners
Andrew Fitzpatrick
Jacqueline May Young
Employee
Scott Forbes Blair

Alexandria

CAIRNS BROWN
112 Main Street, Alexandria G83 0NZ
Tel: (01389) 756979
Fax: (01389) 754281
DX: 501105 ALEXANDRIA
E-mail: g.bowman@cairnsbrown.co.uk
Web: www.cairnsbrown.co.uk
Categories of Work
Adoption
Children
Civil court work
Civil legal aid
Criminal court work
Criminal legal aid
Debt

Employment
Family and divorce
Personal injury
Personal injury – defender
Partners
Gillian Louise Bowman
Kenneth Owen McGowan
Employees
Amanda Kelly
Stephen Christopher Maguire
Molly Wendy Alice Somerville
Anca-Maria Stewart

MY LAWYERS
134 Main Street, Alexandria G83 0NZ
Tel: (01389) 755235
Fax: (01389) 755282
DX: 501102 ALEXANDRIA
E-mail: amurray@mylawyers.co.uk
Categories of Work
Advice the elderly & powers of attorney
Commercial property
Contract & property disputes
Family business advice
Landlord & tenant
Personal tax
Planning (Business Premises)
Residential property
Wills, executries and trusts
Partner
Andrew Peter Murray

JONATHAN PAUL SOLICITORS
102 Main Street, Alexandria G83 0PB
Tel: (01389) 756785
E-mail: office@jpslaw.co.uk
Categories of Work
Adoption
Advice the elderly & powers of attorney
Benefit advice
Children
Childrens
Civil court work
Civil legal aid
Contract & property disputes
Criminal court work
Criminal legal aid
Debt
Debt management
Debt recovery, insolvency, bankruptcy
Disability
Discrimination
Education
Family and divorce
Family business advice
Human rights
Landlord & tenant
Medical negligence – claimant
Mental health
Personal injury
Road traffic
Social housing
Sport
Wills, executries and trusts

▶ **Alexandria continued**

Partner
Jonathan William Paul
Consultant
Nadine Dorothy Dormer
Employees
Dean John Gallacher
Alan Murdoch
Marc Anthony Waters

STIRLING & GILMOUR LLP
24 Gilmour Street, Alexandria G83 0DB
Tel: (01389) 752641
Fax: (01389) 758258
DX: 501103 ALEXANDRIA
Categories of Work
Adoption
Advice the elderly & powers of attorney
Agriculture and estates
Agriculture, crofting and fishing
Alternative dispute resolution
Charities
Children
Civil court work
Civil legal aid
Commercial litigation
Commercial property
Consumer credit
Contract & property disputes
Copyright, trade marks and design
Criminal court work
Criminal legal aid
Debt
Debt collecting
Debt recovery, insolvency, bankruptcy
Discrimination
Employment law
Family and divorce
Family business advice
Landlord & tenant
Liquor licensing
Personal injury
Personal tax
Planning (Business Premises)
Property litigation
Residential property
Road traffic
Wills, executries and trusts
Partners
William Derek Robertson
Graeme Douglas Yeoman
Employee
Norma Mary Bell Alloubani

Alford

JOHN DAVIE & CO
Archballoch Business Centre, Alford AB33 8HP
Tel: (01224) 656356
Fax: (01975) 563 813
E-mail: mail@johndavieandco.com
Categories of Work
Advice the elderly & powers of attorney

Commercial property
Contract & property disputes
Debt collecting
Family business advice
Landlord & tenant
Private equity
Residential property
SME business advice
Wills, executries and trusts
Partner
John Robert Davie

Alloa

CAESAR & HOWIE
27 Mar Street, Alloa FK10 1HX
Tel: (01259) 723408
Fax: (01259) 217634
DX: 560434 ALLOA
E-mail: enquiries@caesar-howie.co.uk
Web: www.caesar-howie.co.uk
Categories of Work
Adoption
Advice the elderly & powers of attorney
Alternative dispute resolution
Children
Childrens
Civil court work
Civil legal aid
Commercial property
Debt
Debt collecting
Debt recovery, insolvency, bankruptcy
Disability
Education
Employment law
Family and divorce
Family business advice
Landlord & tenant
Mental health
Personal injury
Residential property
Road traffic
Wills, executries and trusts
Partners
Rachel Camilleri-Brennan
Carmen Elizabeth MacIver
Employees
Emilia Patrycja McCleary
James Carlo Williford

JARDINE DONALDSON
18/22 Bank Street, Alloa FK10 1HP
Tel: (01259) 724411
Fax: (01259) 213064
DX: 560430 ALLOA
E-mail: bert.cullens@jardinedonaldson.co.uk
Categories of Work
Adoption
Advice the elderly & powers of attorney
Agriculture and estates
Charities
Children

Civil court work
Civil legal aid
Commercial property
Debt
Family and divorce
Family business advice
Landlord & tenant
Liquor licensing
Residential property
Wills, executries and trusts
Partners
Albert John Cullens
Andrew John Cullens
Associate
Mhairi McCallum

MAILERS
70 Drysdale Street, Alloa FK10 1JA
Tel: (01259) 217009
Fax: (01259) 219346
DX: 560453 ALLOA
E-mail: mail@mailers.co.uk
Categories of Work
Advice the elderly & powers of attorney
Children
Childrens
Civil court work
Civil legal aid
Commercial litigation
Commercial property
Contract & property disputes
Criminal court work
Criminal legal aid
Debt
Debt collecting
Debt recovery, insolvency, bankruptcy
Family and divorce
Family business advice
Joint venture
Landlord & tenant
Liquor licensing
Personal injury
Property litigation
Residential property
Road traffic
Wills, executries and trusts
Consultant
Gordon McIntyre

MARTIN, JOHNSTON & SOCHA LIMITED
Top Floor, 2 Candleriggs, Alloa FK10 1EA
Tel: (01259) 725922
Fax: (01259) 725923
DX: 560454 ALLOA
Categories of Work
Children
Civil court work
Civil legal aid
Criminal court work
Criminal legal aid
Data protection
Family and divorce
Human rights

Directors
Kelly-Anne Howe
Krista Isabel Johnston

RUSSEL + AITKEN (FALKIRK + ALLOA) LTD
19 Mar Street, Alloa FK10 1HR
Tel: (01259) 723201
Fax: (01259) 219398
Categories of Work
Adoption
Advice the elderly & powers of attorney
Alternative dispute resolution
Children
Civil court work
Civil legal aid
Commercial litigation
Commercial property
Consumer credit
Contract & property disputes
Criminal court work
Criminal legal aid
Debt
Debt administration
Debt collecting
Debt recovery, insolvency, bankruptcy
Discrimination
Education
Employment
Employment law
Family and divorce
Family business advice
Human rights
Landlord & tenant
Medical negligence – defender
Medical negligence – claimant
Personal injury
Personal injury – defender
Professional negligence
Property litigation
Residential property
Road traffic
SME business advice
Social housing
Wills, executries and trusts
Director
James Francis Savage
Employees
Philip Peter Bonnar
Robert Stewart Smith

Alness

MACMILLAN & CO.
87/89 High Street, Alness IV17 0SH
Tel: (01349) 883338
Fax: (01349) 883338
DX: 556021 ALNESS
E-mail: macmillanandco@btconnect.com
Categories of Work
Advice the elderly & powers of attorney
Commercial property
Landlord & tenant
Residential property

▶ *Alness continued*

Wills, executives and trusts
Partner
Karen Fiona MacGregor

MIDDLETON ROSS & ARNOT LIMITED
76 High Street, Alness IV17 0SG
Tel: (01349) 882870
E-mail: mail@middletonross.co.uk
Web: www.middletonross.co.uk
Categories of Work
Advice the elderly & powers of attorney
Agriculture and estates
Agriculture, crofting and fishing
Commercial property
Landlord & tenant
Residential property
Wills, executives and trusts

Alva

COMRIE LAW
40 Stirling Street, Alva FK12 5EB
Tel: (01259) 235567
Fax: (01259) 235568
DX: 560452 ALLOA
E-mail: eva@comrielaw.co.uk
Partner
Eva Margaret Comrie

Annan

HANN & CO SOLICITORS LTD
1 Bridgend, High Street, Annan DG12 6AG
Tel: (01461) 203836
Fax: (01461) 205634
DX: 580401 ANNAN
E-mail: joe@hannandco.com
Web: www.hannandco.com
Categories of Work
Adoption
Advice the elderly & powers of attorney
Alternative dispute resolution
Banking & finance
Benefit advice
Charities
Children
Civil court work
Civil legal aid
Commercial litigation
Commercial property
Competition
Consumer credit
Contract & property disputes
Copyright, trade marks and design
Corporate tax
Criminal court work
Criminal legal aid
Data protection
Debt
Debt adjusting and debt counselling
Debt collecting

Debt management
Debt recovery, insolvency, bankruptcy
Disability
Discrimination
Education
Employment
Employment law
Environment
Environment (Business Premises)
Family and divorce
Family business advice
Freedom of information
Health and safety
Human rights
Insolvency & corporate recovery
Insurance
IT and intellectual property
Joint venture
Landlord & tenant
Liquor licensing
Medical negligence – defender
Medical negligence – claimant
Mental health
Mergers and acquisitions
Oil & gas
Pensions (Company)
Pensions (Employment)
Personal injury
Personal injury – defender
Personal tax
Private equity
Professional negligence
Projects
Property litigation
Residential property
Road traffic
SME business advice
Social housing
Software licensing
Unit Trusts, OEICs and investment trusts
Wills, executives and trusts
Director
Joseph Timothy Hann
Employee
Gordon Douglas Stevenson

HARPER, ROBERTSON & SHANNON
100 High Street, Annan DG12 6EH
Tel: (01461) 203418
Fax: (01461) 205057
DX: 580400 ANNAN
E-mail: office@hrands.co.uk
Web: www.hrands.co.uk
Categories of Work
Adoption
Advice the elderly & powers of attorney
Alternative dispute resolution
Children
Civil court work
Civil legal aid
Commercial litigation
Criminal court work
Criminal legal aid

Debt
Debt adjusting and debt counselling
Debt collecting
Debt recovery, insolvency, bankruptcy
Education
Employment
Employment law
Family and divorce
Health and safety
Landlord & tenant
Liquor licensing
Medical negligence – claimant
Pensions (Employment)
Personal injury
Professional negligence
Property litigation
Residential property
Road traffic
Wills, executries and trusts
Partners
Murray Mackay Bolling
Christopher Johnstone Shannon

MURRAY, LITTLE & KNOX
27 Bank Street, Annan DG12 6AU
Tel: (01461) 202866
Fax: (01461) 205995
DX: 580402 ANNAN
E-mail: frances.campbell@mlandk.co.uk
Web: www.mlandk.co.uk
Categories of Work
Advice the elderly & powers of attorney
Alternative dispute resolution
Civil court work
Civil legal aid
Commercial property
Criminal court work
Criminal legal aid
Employment law
Family business advice
Landlord & tenant
Liquor licensing
Personal injury
Professional negligence
Residential property
Road traffic
Wills, executries and trusts
Partners
Janet Frances Campbell
Norman Scott Johnston

JOHN RODDICK & SON (SOLICITORS) LTD
Royal Bank Buildings, 52 High Street, Annan
DG12 6AL
Tel: (01461) 202822
Fax: (01461) 201822
DX: 580403 ANNAN
E-mail: office@roddicks.co.uk
Web: www.roddicks.co.uk
Categories of Work
Advice the elderly & powers of attorney
Agriculture, crofting and fishing
Commercial property
Corporate tax

Family business advice
Landlord & tenant
Personal tax
Residential property
SME business advice
Wills, executries and trusts
Director
Alistair Iain Beckett

Anstruther

COCKBURN MCGRANE
P.O. Box 14271, Anstruther KY10 9AD
Tel: (01333) 730 803
E-mail: barbara@cockburnmcgrane.co.uk
Categories of Work
Adoption
Children
Civil legal aid
Contract & property disputes
Family and divorce
Health and safety
Housing
Medical negligence – defender
Medical negligence – claimant
Mental health
Personal injury
Personal injury – defender
Personal tax
Road traffic
Partner
Barbara Susan Cockburn

THORNTONS LAW LLP
5a Shore Street, Anstruther KY10 3EA
Tel: (01333) 314395
Fax: (01334) 476862
E-mail: anstruther@thorntons-law.co.uk
Categories of Work
Adjudication
Adoption
Advice the elderly & powers of attorney
Agriculture and estates
Agriculture, crofting and fishing
Alternative dispute resolution
Alternative investment market
Banking & finance
Benefit advice
Betting & gaming
Charities
Children
Childrens
Civil court work
Civil legal aid
Commercial litigation
Commercial property
Competition
Construction
Consumer credit
Contract & property disputes
Copyright, trade marks and design
Corporate tax
Credit brokerage

▶ *Anstruther continued*

Criminal court work
Criminal legal aid
Data protection
Debt
Debt adjusting and debt counselling
Debt administration
Debt collecting
Debt recovery, insolvency, bankruptcy
Disability
Discrimination
Education
Employment
Employment law
Environment
Environment (Business Premises)
EU / international
Family and divorce
Family business advice
Fishing
Freedom of information
Health
Health and safety
Housing
Human rights
Immigration and asylum
Insolvency & corporate recovery
Insurance
IT and intellectual property
Joint venture
Landlord & tenant
Liquor licensing
Local government
Media and entertainment
Medical negligence – defender
Medical negligence – claimant
Mental health
Mergers and acquisitions
Oil & gas
Parliamentary
Pensions (Company)
Pensions (Employment)
Personal injury
Personal injury – defender
Personal tax
Planning
Planning (Business Premises)
Power and utilities
Private equity
Professional negligence
Projects
Property litigation
Public sector
Residential property
Road traffic
SME business advice
Social housing
Software licensing
Sport
Telecoms
Unit Trusts, OEICs and investment trusts
Wills, executries and trusts

Associate
Susan Dunn

Arbroath

BLACKADDERS LLP
129 High Street, Arbroath DD11 1DP
Tel: (01241) 876620
DX: 530456 ARBROATH
E-mail: enquiries@blackadders.co.uk
Categories of Work
Adoption
Advice the elderly & powers of attorney
Agriculture and estates
Agriculture, crofting and fishing
Alternative dispute resolution
Banking & finance
Charities
Children
Childrens
Civil court work
Civil legal aid
Commercial litigation
Commercial property
Competition
Construction
Consumer credit
Contract & property disputes
Copyright, trade marks and design
Data protection
Debt
Debt collecting
Debt recovery, insolvency, bankruptcy
Disability
Discrimination
Employment
Employment law
Environment
Environment (Business Premises)
EU / international
Family and divorce
Family business advice
Fishing
Freedom of information
Housing
Human rights
Insolvency & corporate recovery
IT and intellectual property
Joint venture
Landlord & tenant
Media and entertainment
Medical negligence – defender
Medical negligence – claimant
Mental health
Mergers and acquisitions
Pensions (Employment)
Personal injury
Personal injury – defender
Personal tax
Planning
Power and utilities
Private equity
Professional negligence

Property litigation
Public sector
Residential property
Road traffic
SME business advice
Software licensing
Sport
Telecoms
Wills, executries and trusts

R. BRUCE & CO.
89/91 High Street, Arbroath DD11 1DP
Tel: (01241) 430660
Fax: (01241) 430144
E-mail: info@bruce-co.co.uk
Web: www.bruce-co.co.uk
Categories of Work
Adoption
Advice the elderly & powers of attorney
Children
Childrens
Civil court work
Civil legal aid
Criminal court work
Criminal legal aid
Debt
Education
Family and divorce
Landlord & tenant
Mental health
Personal injury
Road traffic
Social housing
Wills, executries and trusts
Partners
William Pirie Rennie
Keith Archibald Sym
Employee
David Grant Bruce

CONNELLY & YEOMAN LAW LIMITED
78 High Street, Arbroath DD11 1HL
Tel: (01241) 434200
Fax: (01241) 434100
DX: 530458 ARBROATH
Web: www.connellyyeoman.com
Categories of Work
Advice the elderly & powers of attorney
Civil legal aid
Criminal court work
Criminal legal aid
Landlord & tenant
Residential property
Wills, executries and trusts
Directors
Nicola Jane Davidson
Barry George Dewar
Emma Joan Smith
Associates
Pamela Ann Gaffar
Samantha Thomson
Employee
Ainsley Leigh Al-Saffar

CONNELLY & YEOMAN NOMINEES LIMITED
78 High Street, Arbroath DD11 1HL
Tel: (01241) 434200

THORNTONS LAW LLP
Brothockbank House, Arbroath DD11 1NE
Tel: (01241) 872683
Fax: (01241) 871541
DX: 530464 ARBROATH
E-mail: arbroath@thorntons-law.co.uk
Web: www.thorntons-law.co.uk
Categories of Work
Adjudication
Adoption
Advice the elderly & powers of attorney
Agriculture and estates
Agriculture, crofting and fishing
Alternative dispute resolution
Alternative investment market
Banking & finance
Benefit advice
Betting & gaming
Charities
Children
Childrens
Civil court work
Civil legal aid
Commercial litigation
Commercial property
Competition
Construction
Consumer credit
Contract & property disputes
Copyright, trade marks and design
Corporate tax
Credit brokerage
Criminal court work
Criminal legal aid
Data protection
Debt
Debt adjusting and debt counselling
Debt administration
Debt collecting
Debt recovery, insolvency, bankruptcy
Disability
Discrimination
Education
Employment
Employment law
Environment
Environment (Business Premises)
EU / international
Family and divorce
Family business advice
Fishing
Freedom of information
Health
Health and safety
Housing
Human rights
Immigration and asylum
Insolvency & corporate recovery
Insurance

▶ **Arbroath continued**

IT and intellectual property
Joint venture
Landlord & tenant
Liquor licensing
Local government
Media and entertainment
Medical negligence – defender
Medical negligence – claimant
Mental health
Mergers and acquisitions
Oil & gas
Parliamentary
Pensions (Company)
Pensions (Employment)
Personal injury
Personal injury – defender
Personal tax
Planning
Planning (Business Premises)
Power and utilities
Private equity
Professional negligence
Projects
Property litigation
Public sector
Residential property
Road traffic
SME business advice
Social housing
Software licensing
Sport
Telecoms
Unit Trusts, OEICs and investment trusts
Wills, executures and trusts
Partners
Robin Malcolm Dickson Beattie
David Ian Mathieson
Sandra Mary Sutherland
Employee
Stacey Grace Jackson

WHELAN & CO
105 High Street, Arbroath DD11 1DP
Tel: (01241) 431155
Fax: (01241) 431166
DX: 530463 ARBROATH
E-mail: nwhelan@whelanandco.co.uk
Categories of Work
Criminal court work
Criminal legal aid
Partner
Nicholas Whelan
Employee
Angela McLardy

Ardrossan

JAS CAMPBELL & CO LTD
76 Princes Street, Ardrossan KA22 8DF
Tel: (01294) 464131
E-mail: mail@jascampbell.co.uk
Web: www.jascampbell.co.uk

Categories of Work
Adoption
Advice the elderly & powers of attorney
Agriculture and estates
Children
Civil court work
Civil legal aid
Commercial property
Construction
Contract & property disputes
Environment (Business Premises)
Family and divorce
Family business advice
Landlord & tenant
Liquor licensing
Personal injury
Planning (Business Premises)
Property litigation
Residential property
SME business advice
Wills, executures and trusts

Armadale

SNEDDONS SSC
47/49 West Main Street, Armadale EH48 3PZ
Tel: (01501) 733200
Fax: (01501) 733155
DX: 556041 ARMADALE
E-mail: walter@sneddons.com
Web: www.sneddons.com
Categories of Work
Contract & property disputes
Employment law
Landlord & tenant
Residential property
Wills, executures and trusts
Partner
Walter Sneddon
Employee
Jennifer Keane

Auchterarder

JAMESON + MACKAY LLP
71 High Street, Auchterarder PH3 1BN
Tel: (01764) 663830
DX: 556060 AUCHTERARDER
E-mail: mail@jamesonmackay.co.uk
Web: www.jamesonmackay.co.uk
Categories of Work
Advice the elderly & powers of attorney
Agriculture and estates
Civil court work
Commercial property
Family business advice
Landlord & tenant
Medical negligence – claimant
Personal injury
Residential property
Road traffic
Wills, executures and trusts

MACNABS LLP
Mullion House, Maidenplain Place,
Auchterarder PH3 1EL
Tel: (01738) 623432
E-mail: mail@macnabs-law.co.uk
Categories of Work
Adjudication
Adoption
Advice the elderly & powers of attorney
Agriculture and estates
Agriculture, crofting and fishing
Alternative dispute resolution
Children
Childrens
Civil court work
Civil legal aid
Commercial litigation
Commercial property
Construction
Consumer credit
Contract & property disputes
Criminal court work
Criminal legal aid
Debt
Debt adjusting and debt counselling
Debt administration
Debt collecting
Debt recovery, insolvency, bankruptcy
Disability
Education
Employment
Employment law
Family and divorce
Family business advice
Health and safety
Insolvency & corporate recovery
Insurance
Landlord & tenant
Medical negligence – defender
Medical negligence – claimant
Mental health
Personal injury
Personal injury – defender
Planning
Planning (Business Premises)
Professional negligence
Property litigation
Residential property
Road traffic
Wills, executries and trusts

NEXT LAW (SCOTLAND) LLP
Loanfoot, Main Road, Auchterarder PH3 1HB
Tel: (01764) 680525
Web: www.next-law.co.uk
Categories of Work
Advice the elderly & powers of attorney
Charities
Children
Civil legal aid
Commercial property
Family and divorce
Mental health

Residential property
Wills, executries and trusts

Auchtermuchty

ROLLOS LAW LLP
36 Cupar Road, Auchtermuchty KY14 7DD
Tel: (01337) 828775
Web: www.rollos.co.uk
Categories of Work
Adoption
Advice the elderly & powers of attorney
Agriculture and estates
Agriculture, crofting and fishing
Banking & finance
Children
Civil court work
Civil legal aid
Commercial property
Construction
Contract & property disputes
Criminal court work
Criminal legal aid
Debt
Disability
Discrimination
Employment
Employment law
Environment
Family and divorce
Family business advice
Fishing
Joint venture
Landlord & tenant
Mental health
Mergers and acquisitions
Personal injury
Projects
Residential property
Road traffic
SME business advice
Wills, executries and trusts

Aviemore

SWARBRICK LAW
Unit 18/5 Spey Valley Business Park, Dalfaber
Industrial Estate, Aviemore PH22 1ST
Tel: (01479) 811180
E-mail: duncan@swarbricklaw.co.uk
Categories of Work
Civil court work
Commercial litigation
Contract & property disputes
Debt collecting
Debt recovery, insolvency, bankruptcy
Employment
Employment law
Family and divorce
Landlord & tenant
Medical negligence – claimant
Personal injury

► *Aviemore continued*

Professional negligence
Property litigation
Partner
Duncan James Swarbrick

Ayr

1ST LEGAL LIMITED
62 Fort Street, Ayr KA
Tel: (01292) 290666
E-mail: arlene@1stlegal.co.uk
Categories of Work
Children
Civil court work
Civil legal aid
Criminal court work
Criminal legal aid
Debt
Family and divorce
Medical negligence – claimant
Personal injury
Professional negligence
Road traffic
Social housing

1ST LEGAL LIMITED
68 Kyle Street, Ayr KA7 1RJ
Tel: (01292) 290666
Fax: (01292) 290 688
E-mail: arlene@1stlegal.co.uk
Categories of Work
Children
Civil court work
Civil legal aid
Criminal court work
Criminal legal aid
Debt
Family and divorce
Medical negligence – claimant
Personal injury
Professional negligence
Road traffic
Social housing
Director
Anthony David Currie
Associate
Claire Elizabeth Currie
Employees
Deborah Edgar
Angela Ruth Goldie

ACCIDENTCLAIMS.COM
Dalblair House, 46 Dalblair Road, Ayr
KA7 1UQ
Tel: (01292) 280499
Web: www.accidentclaims.com
Categories of Work
Adoption
Advice the elderly & powers of attorney
Agriculture and estates
Agriculture, crofting and fishing
Banking & finance

Children
Childrens
Commercial property
Contract & property disputes
Criminal court work
Criminal legal aid
Family and divorce
Family business advice
Landlord & tenant
Personal injury
Personal tax
Residential property
Road traffic
SME business advice
Wills, executries and trusts

BLACK HAY
16c Beresford Terrace, Ayr KA7 2EG
Tel: (01292) 283606
DX: AY61 AYR
Web: www.blackhay.co.uk
Categories of Work
Adoption
Advice the elderly & powers of attorney
Alternative dispute resolution
Betting & gaming
Children
Childrens
Civil court work
Civil legal aid
Commercial property
Contract & property disputes
Criminal court work
Criminal legal aid
Family and divorce
Family business advice
Human rights
Immigration and asylum
Landlord & tenant
Liquor licensing
Mental health
Personal injury
Personal injury – defender
Personal tax
Residential property
Wills, executries and trusts

BLACK HAY
5 Wellington Square, Ayr KA7 1EN
Tel: (01292) 268988
Fax: (01292) 610353
DX: AY61 AYR
Web: www.blackhay.co.uk
Categories of Work
Adoption
Advice the elderly & powers of attorney
Alternative dispute resolution
Betting & gaming
Children
Childrens
Civil court work
Civil legal aid
Commercial property
Contract & property disputes

Criminal court work
Criminal legal aid
Family and divorce
Family business advice
Human rights
Immigration and asylum
Landlord & tenant
Liquor licensing
Mental health
Personal injury
Personal injury – defender
Personal tax
Residential property
Wills, executries and trusts
Partners
David James Leishman
Gillian Irvine Carruthers McBlane
Solicitor
Rebecca Catherine White
Employees
Keir Diarmid Gilius
Margaret Mary Macinnes
Stephen James Neillie

R.B. CAMPBELL & CO
7 Wellington Square, Ayr KA7 1EN
Tel: (01292) 261125
Fax: (01292) 283755
DX: AY71 AYR
Categories of Work
Adjudication
Adoption
Advice the elderly & powers of attorney
Agriculture and estates
Agriculture, crofting and fishing
Alternative dispute resolution
Banking & finance
Benefit advice
Children
Childrens
Civil court work
Civil legal aid
Commercial litigation
Commercial property
Contract & property disputes
Criminal court work
Criminal legal aid
Debt
Debt adjusting and debt counselling
Debt administration
Debt collecting
Debt management
Debt recovery, insolvency, bankruptcy
Employment
Employment law
Family and divorce
Family business advice
Human rights
Immigration and asylum
Landlord & tenant
Liquor licensing
Medical negligence – claimant
Mental health

Personal injury
Personal injury – defender
Personal tax
Professional negligence
Property litigation
Residential property
Road traffic
Wills, executries and trusts
Partner
Robert Bamford Campbell

TONY CURRIE SOLICITORS
62 Fort Street, Ayr KA
Tel: (01292) 290666
Categories of Work
Children
Civil court work
Civil legal aid
Criminal court work
Criminal legal aid
Debt
Family and divorce
Medical negligence – claimant
Personal injury
Professional negligence
Road traffic
Social housing

TONY CURRIE SOLICITORS
68 Kyle Street, Ayr KA7 1RZ
Tel: (01292) 290666
DX: AY26 AYR
Categories of Work
Children
Civil court work
Civil legal aid
Criminal court work
Criminal legal aid
Debt
Family and divorce
Medical negligence – claimant
Personal injury
Professional negligence
Road traffic
Social housing

DIGBY BROWN LLP
24 Sandgate, Ayr KA7 1BW
Tel: (0333) 200 59285
DX: AY6L AYR
E-mail: enquiries@digbybrown.co.uk
Web: www.digbybrown.co.uk
Categories of Work
Advice the elderly & powers of attorney
Agriculture and estates
Agriculture, crofting and fishing
Alternative dispute resolution
Alternative investment market
Banking & finance
Benefit advice
Charities
Children
Civil court work
Civil legal aid

► *Ayr continued*

Commercial litigation
Commercial property
Competition
Construction
Contract & property disputes
Corporate tax
Criminal court work
Data protection
Debt
Debt adjusting and debt counselling
Debt collecting
Debt recovery, insolvency, bankruptcy
Disability
Discrimination
Employment
Employment law
Environment (Business Premises)
EU / international
Family and divorce
Family business advice
Freedom of information
Health and safety
Human rights
Immigration and asylum
Insolvency & corporate recovery
Insurance
Joint venture
Landlord & tenant
Medical negligence – defender
Medical negligence – claimant
Mental health
Mergers and acquisitions
Pensions (Company)
Personal injury
Personal injury – defender
Planning (Business Premises)
Private equity
Professional negligence
Property litigation
Provision of credit information services
Public finance initiative
Public sector
Residential property
Road traffic
SME business advice
Unit Trusts, OEICs and investment trusts
Wills, executries and trusts

Partner
Damian Andrew White
Associate
Iona Jane Brown
Employees
Saima Ali
Lee Alexander Murray

D. & J. DUNLOP
2 Barns Street, Ayr KA7 1XD
Tel: (01292) 264091
Fax: (01292) 289856
DX: AY3 AYR
E-mail: gah@djdunlop.co.uk
Web: https://www.djdunlop-ayr.co.uk

Categories of Work
Adjudication
Adoption
Advice the elderly & powers of attorney
Agriculture and estates
Agriculture, crofting and fishing
Alternative dispute resolution
Banking & finance
Benefit advice
Betting & gaming
Charities
Children
Civil court work
Civil legal aid
Commercial litigation
Commercial property
Construction
Consumer credit
Contract & property disputes
Copyright, trade marks and design
Criminal court work
Criminal legal aid
Data protection
Debt
Debt adjusting and debt counselling
Debt administration
Debt collecting
Debt management
Debt recovery, insolvency, bankruptcy
Disability
Discrimination
Education
Employment
Employment law
Environment
Family and divorce
Family business advice
Fishing
Freedom of information
Health and safety
Housing
Human rights
Immigration and asylum
Insolvency & corporate recovery
Insurance
IT and intellectual property
Landlord & tenant
Liquor licensing
Local government
Media and entertainment
Medical negligence – defender
Medical negligence – claimant
Mental health
Personal injury
Personal injury – defender
Personal tax
Planning
Planning (Business Premises)
Professional negligence
Property litigation
Residential property
Road traffic
Social housing

Sport
Wills, executives and trusts
Partners
George Alexander Hay
John Andrew Hay
Quinton Muir

FRAZER COOGANS COMMERCIAL
Dalblair House, 46 Dalblair Road, Ayr
KA7 1UQ
Tel: (01292) 280499
Categories of Work
Adoption
Advice the elderly & powers of attorney
Agriculture and estates
Agriculture, crofting and fishing
Banking & finance
Children
Childrens
Commercial property
Contract & property disputes
Criminal court work
Criminal legal aid
Family and divorce
Family business advice
Landlord & tenant
Personal injury
Personal tax
Residential property
Road traffic
SME business advice
Wills, executives and trusts

FRAZER COOGANS LTD
Dalblair House, 46 Dalblair Road, Ayr
KA7 1UQ
Tel: (01292) 280499
Fax: (01292) 272 601
DX: AY29 AYR
Web: www.frazercoogans.co.uk
Categories of Work
Adoption
Advice the elderly & powers of attorney
Agriculture and estates
Agriculture, crofting and fishing
Banking & finance
Children
Childrens
Commercial property
Contract & property disputes
Criminal court work
Criminal legal aid
Family and divorce
Family business advice
Landlord & tenant
Personal injury
Personal tax
Residential property
Road traffic
SME business advice
Wills, executives and trusts
Directors
Carly Brodie
Norman George Geddes

Peter David McNamara
Associates
Susan Elizabeth Forbes
Lauren Fowler
Stuart James Gibson
Employees
Anoop Christi
Gemma Fulton
Kimberley Christina Helen Hainey
Linzi Jane Harper
Beth Anne Kelly
Victoria Anne Kerr

GILLIES MAXWELL
Wellington Chambers, 64/70 Fort Street, Ayr
KA7 1EH
Tel: (01292) 288860
Fax: (01292) 282887
DX: AY5 AYR
E-mail: jig@iangillies.com
Categories of Work
Criminal court work
Criminal legal aid
Partners
John Ian Gillies
Steven Bowman Maxwell

KILPATRICK & WALKER
4 Wellington Square, Ayr KA7 1EN
Tel: (01292) 618585
Fax: (01292) 885678
DX: AY45 AYR
E-mail: john@kilpatrickwalker.com
Web: www.k-and-w.com
Categories of Work
Adjudication
Advice the elderly & powers of attorney
Agriculture and estates
Agriculture, crofting and fishing
Alternative dispute resolution
Banking & finance
Charities
Children
Commercial property
Contract & property disputes
Copyright, trade marks and design
Criminal court work
Criminal legal aid
Discrimination
Education
Employment
Employment law
Environment
Family business advice
Housing
Joint venture
Landlord & tenant
Liquor licensing
Local government
Mental health
Mergers and acquisitions
Mining
Personal tax
Planning (Business Premises)

▶ *Ayr continued*

Power and utilities
Private equity
Residential property
SME business advice
Wills, executries and trusts
Partners
Jennifer Sarah Gray
John Walker
Consultant
Alastair Martin Annan
Employee
Harry Stewart Peter Sheddon

LAMBERT & CO.,
12 Cathcart Street, Ayr KA7 1BJ
Tel: (01292) 282811
Fax: (01292) 288028
DX: AY38 AYR
E-mail: lambert.asl1@btconnect.com
Categories of Work
Adoption
Advice the elderly & powers of attorney
Children
Civil court work
Civil legal aid
Consumer credit
Contract & property disputes
Credit brokerage
Criminal court work
Criminal legal aid
Debt
Debt adjusting and debt counselling
Debt administration
Debt collecting
Family and divorce
Landlord & tenant
Medical negligence – claimant
Personal injury
Professional negligence
Provision of credit information services
Residential property
Road traffic
Wills, executries and trusts
Partner
Alistair Scott Lambert
Associate
Gordon William Robson

LOCKHARTS LAW LLP
12 Beresford Terrace, Ayr KA7 2EG
Tel: (01292) 265045
Fax: (01292) 270112
DX: AY2 AYR
E-mail: info@lockhartslaw.com
Web: www.lockhartslaw.com
Categories of Work
Advice the elderly & powers of attorney
Commercial property
Criminal court work
Criminal legal aid
Landlord & tenant
Personal tax

Residential property
Wills, executries and trusts
Partners
Stephen Bradford
Peter McIlwraith Stevenson Lockhart
Robert Nigel Martin
Margo Kyle McGill
Lynsey Catherine Dawn Rowney
Associate
Dianne Rachel Kay

MCLENNAN ADAM DAVIS
13 Alloway Place, Ayr KA7 2AA
Tel: (01292) 289584
Fax: (01292) 611034
DX: AY68 AYR
E-mail: administrator@mad-law.co.uk
Categories of Work
Adoption
Children
Civil court work
Civil legal aid
Commercial litigation
Criminal court work
Criminal legal aid
Debt
Debt collecting
Employment law
Family and divorce
Human rights
Medical negligence – claimant
Personal injury
Professional negligence
Road traffic
Partners
Colin George Adam
Alexander Glenn Davis
John Robert Gallagher
Alan Stuart Paterson
Associate
James Leonard Petticrew

MATHIE-MORTON
4 Alloway Place, Ayr KA7 2AD
Tel: (01292) 263549
Fax: (01292) 264944
Categories of Work
Adoption
Advice the elderly & powers of attorney
Agriculture and estates
Agriculture, crofting and fishing
Banking & finance
Children
Civil court work
Civil legal aid
Commercial litigation
Commercial property
Consumer credit
Contract & property disputes
Debt
Debt adjusting and debt counselling
Debt collecting
Debt recovery, insolvency, bankruptcy
Disability

Discrimination
Education
Employment law
Family and divorce
Family business advice
Human rights
Insolvency & corporate recovery
Landlord & tenant
Liquor licensing
Medical negligence – defender
Medical negligence – claimant
Mergers and acquisitions
Personal injury
Personal injury – defender
Professional negligence
Property litigation
Residential property
Road traffic
Wills, executries and trusts
Partners
Kevin John Boyd
Carl Alexander Crone
John Patrick McPartlin
Employee
Kenneth William Donnelly

D.W. SHAW
34a Sandgate, Ayr KA7 1BX
Tel: (01292) 265033
Fax: (01292) 284906
DX: AY9 AYR
E-mail: ayrreception@dwshaw.co.uk
Web: www.dwshaw.co.uk
Categories of Work
Adoption
Advice the elderly & powers of attorney
Agriculture and estates
Agriculture, crofting and fishing
Children
Civil court work
Civil legal aid
Commercial property
Criminal court work
Criminal legal aid
Family and divorce
Family business advice
Landlord & tenant
Medical negligence – defender
Medical negligence – claimant
Personal injury
Personal injury – defender
Power and utilities
Professional negligence
Residential property
Road traffic
SME business advice
Wills, executries and trusts
Partner
Morven Fiona Howell
Employee
Shona Gallagher

SPRANG TERRAS LIMITED
64 Kyle Street, Ayr KA7 1RZ
Tel: (01292) 288300
Fax: (01292) 288400
DX: AY34 AYR
E-mail: mail@sprangterras.co.uk
Categories of Work
Adoption
Advice the elderly & powers of attorney
Agriculture and estates
Banking & finance
Charities
Children
Civil court work
Commercial property
Consumer credit
Contract & property disputes
Credit brokerage
Data protection
Debt
Debt adjusting and debt counselling
Debt collecting
Debt recovery, insolvency, bankruptcy
Disability
Discrimination
Education
Employment
Employment law
Environment (Business Premises)
Family and divorce
Family business advice
Freedom of information
Health and safety
Housing
Landlord & tenant
Local government
Media and entertainment
Mergers and acquisitions
Personal injury
Planning (Business Premises)
Property litigation
Provision of credit information services
Residential property
Road traffic
SME business advice
Wills, executries and trusts
Directors
Alan Kenneth Sprang
Euan Maxwell Terras

THE MCKINSTRY COMPANY LLP
Queens Court House, 39 Sandgate, Ayr
KA7 1BE
Tel: (01292) 281711
Fax: (01292) 610206
DX: AY8 AYR
E-mail: enquiries@mckinstry.co.uk
Web: www.mckinstry.co.uk
Categories of Work
Adjudication
Adoption
Advice the elderly & powers of attorney
Alternative dispute resolution
Charities
Children

► **Ayr continued**

Civil court work
Commercial litigation
Commercial property
Construction
Contract & property disputes
Criminal court work
Debt
Debt administration
Debt collecting
Debt recovery, insolvency, bankruptcy
Education
Employment
Employment law
Family and divorce
Family business advice
Freedom of information
Insolvency & corporate recovery
Insurance
Landlord & tenant
Medical negligence – defender
Medical negligence – claimant
Personal injury
Personal injury – defender
Personal tax
Planning (Business Premises)
Professional negligence
Property litigation
Residential property
Road traffic
SME business advice
Social housing
Sport
Wills, executries and trusts
Partners
Robert Neville Honeyman
Thiona Anne McQuiston
Solicitors
Nathaniel Duncan Alexander
Eleanor Clarke
Employees
Colin Jamie Duck
Kirsty Sarah Jane Leitch
Karen Prendergast
Katie Elizabeth Russell
Natalie Wallace

WALLACE HODGE & COMPANY LIMITED
6 Killoch Place, Ayr KA7 2EA
Tel: (01292) 611177
Fax: (01292) 611977
DX: AY49 AYR
E-mail: mail@wallace-hodge.co.uk
Web: www.wallace-hodge.co.uk
Categories of Work
Advice the elderly & powers of attorney
Commercial property
Landlord & tenant
Residential property
Wills, executries and trusts
Directors
Thomas Colvin Houston
Derek Daniel Stillie

Employees
Norman John Fraser
Jennifer Binnie Wallace

ELIZABETH WELSH FAMILY LAW PRACTICE
26 Miller Road, Ayr KA7 2AY
Tel: (01292) 284786
Fax: (01292) 283739
DX: AY63 AYR
E-mail: lizw@familylawpractice.co.uk
Web: elizabethwelshfamilylaw.co.uk
Categories of Work
Adoption
Advice the elderly & powers of attorney
Benefit advice
Children
Civil court work
Civil legal aid
Commercial litigation
Contract & property disputes
Criminal court work
Criminal legal aid
Debt
Debt management
Debt recovery, insolvency, bankruptcy
Disability
Discrimination
Education
Employment
Employment law
Family and divorce
Human rights
Immigration and asylum
Landlord & tenant
Liquor licensing
Medical negligence – claimant
Mental health
Personal injury
Professional negligence
Property litigation
Road traffic
Social housing
Partners
Penelope Elizabeth Galloway
Carolyn Jayne Paton
Employee
Rebecca Auld

A.C. WHITE
23 Wellington Square, Ayr KA7 1HG
Tel: (01292) 266900
Fax: (01292) 610152
DX: AY10 AYR
E-mail: mail@acwhiteayr.co.uk
Categories of Work
Adoption
Advice the elderly & powers of attorney
Agriculture and estates
Benefit advice
Children
Childrens
Civil court work
Civil legal aid
Commercial property

Contract & property disputes
Criminal court work
Criminal legal aid
Debt collecting
Debt management
Disability
Discrimination
Education
Employment
Employment law
Family and divorce
Human rights
Landlord & tenant
Liquor licensing
Mental health
Residential property
Road traffic
Social housing
Wills, executries and trusts
Partners
Gregor David Edward Forbes
Fiona Jane MacDonald
David Paul Mitchell
Ewan James Hay Mowat
Gemma Waddell
Martine Sheena Walker
Employee
Laura Margaret Crawford

Balivanich

FERGUSON, MACSWEEN & STEWART
College House, Balivanich HS7 5LA
Tel: (01870) 602865
E-mail: uist@fmslaw.co.uk
Categories of Work
Adoption
Advice the elderly & powers of attorney
Agriculture and estates
Agriculture, crofting and fishing
Alternative dispute resolution
Children
Civil court work
Civil legal aid
Commercial property
Debt
Debt collecting
Debt recovery, insolvency, bankruptcy
Education
Family and divorce
Family business advice
Landlord & tenant
Personal injury
Property litigation
Residential property
Road traffic
Wills, executries and trusts
Associate
Lesley Susan McFall

Ballater

FRASER & MULLIGAN
24 Bridge Street, Ballater AB35 5QP

Tel: (013397) 55633
Categories of Work
Advice the elderly & powers of attorney
Commercial property
Contract & property disputes
Landlord & tenant
Residential property
Wills, executries and trusts

LAURIE & CO SOLICITORS LLP
4 Bridge Street, Ballater AB35 5QP
Tel: (01339) 755535
Fax: (01339) 755217
DX: AB16 ABERDEEN
E-mail: ballater@laurieandco.co.uk
Categories of Work
Advice the elderly & powers of attorney
Children
Civil court work
Commercial litigation
Criminal court work
Debt collecting
Debt recovery, insolvency, bankruptcy
Employment law
Family and divorce
Insolvency & corporate recovery
Personal injury – defender
Property litigation
Wills, executries and trusts
Associate
Mary-Jay Clark Morton

Banchory

ABERDEIN CONSIDINE AND COMPANY
8 Dee Street, Banchory AB31 5ST
Tel: (01330) 824646
E-mail: banchory@acandco.com
Web: www.acandco.com
Categories of Work
Adjudication
Adoption
Advice the elderly & powers of attorney
Agriculture and estates
Agriculture, crofting and fishing
Alternative dispute resolution
Alternative investment market
Banking & finance
Charities
Children
Childrens
Civil court work
Civil legal aid
Commercial litigation
Commercial property
Competition
Construction
Consumer credit
Contract & property disputes
Copyright, trade marks and design
Corporate tax
Credit brokerage
Criminal court work

▶ **Banchory continued**

Criminal legal aid
Data protection
Debt
Debt adjusting and debt counselling
Debt collecting
Debt recovery, insolvency, bankruptcy
Disability
Discrimination
Education
Employment
Employment law
Environment
Environment (Business Premises)
EU / international
Family and divorce
Family business advice
Freedom of information
Health
Health and safety
Human rights
Insolvency & corporate recovery
Insurance
Joint venture
Landlord & tenant
Liquor licensing
Local government
Media and entertainment
Mental health
Mergers and acquisitions
Pensions (Company)
Pensions (Employment)
Personal injury
Personal tax
Planning (Business Premises)
Private equity
Professional negligence
Property litigation
Public finance initiative
Public sector
Residential property
SME business advice
Social housing
Telecoms
Unit Trusts, OEICs and investment trusts
Wills, executories and trusts
Employee
Stevie Margaret Kelman

BURNETT & REID LLP
Banchory Business Centre, Burn O'Bennie
Road, Banchory AB31 5ZU
Tel: (01330) 828684
E-mail: mail@burnett-reid.co.uk
Categories of Work
Advice the elderly & powers of attorney
Agriculture and estates
Agriculture, crofting and fishing
Banking & finance
Civil court work
Civil legal aid
Commercial litigation
Commercial property

Construction
Contract & property disputes
Copyright, trade marks and design
Debt
Debt collecting
Debt recovery, insolvency, bankruptcy
Employment law
Environment
Family business advice
Fishing
Health and safety
Insolvency & corporate recovery
IT and intellectual property
Joint venture
Landlord & tenant
Mergers and acquisitions
Oil & gas
Personal tax
Power and utilities
Private equity
Projects
Property litigation
Residential property
SME business advice
Wills, executories and trusts
Employee
Victoria Elizabeth Burnett

FERGUSON LEGAL LIMITED
Corner Cottage, Inchmarlo, Banchory
AB31 4AP
Tel: (07917) 848453
E-mail: ferguson.legal@icloud.com
Categories of Work
Adjudication
Alternative dispute resolution
Charities
Civil court work
Commercial litigation
Commercial property
Construction
Contract & property disputes
Copyright, trade marks and design
Criminal court work
Data protection
Environment
Environment (Business Premises)
Freedom of information
Health and safety
Insurance
IT and intellectual property
Liquor licensing
Mergers and acquisitions
Oil & gas
Personal injury
Personal injury – defender
Planning
Planning (Business Premises)
Power and utilities
Road traffic
Shipping
SME business advice
Sport

Telecoms
Transport
Director
Carole Anne Ferguson

RAEBURN CHRISTIE CLARK & WALLACE LLP
75 High Street, Banchory AB31 5TJ
Tel: (01330) 822931
Fax: (01330) 824799
DX: AB2 ABERDEEN
Web: www.raeburns.co.uk
Categories of Work
Adoption
Advice the elderly & powers of attorney
Agriculture and estates
Agriculture, crofting and fishing
Alternative dispute resolution
Banking & finance
Betting & gaming
Charities
Children
Civil court work
Civil legal aid
Commercial litigation
Commercial property
Competition
Construction
Contract & property disputes
Copyright, trade marks and design
Data protection
Debt
Disability
Discrimination
Employment
Employment law
Environment
EU / international
Family and divorce
Family business advice
Freedom of information
Health and safety
Housing
Human rights
IT and intellectual property
Joint venture
Landlord & tenant
Liquor licensing
Media and entertainment
Medical negligence – defender
Mergers and acquisitions
Oil & gas
Personal injury
Personal injury – defender
Planning
Planning (Business Premises)
Private equity
Professional negligence
Property litigation
Residential property
Road traffic
Shipping
SME business advice
Social housing

Sport
Wills, executries and trusts
Associate
Shona Ann Morrison

Banff

GRANT SMITH LAW PRACTICE LIMITED
25 High Street, Banff AB45 1AN
Tel: (01261) 815678
Fax: (01261) 818825
E-mail: info@grantsmithlaw.co.uk
Web: www.grantsmithlaw.co.uk
Categories of Work
Adoption
Advice the elderly & powers of attorney
Alternative dispute resolution
Children
Childrens
Civil court work
Civil legal aid
Commercial property
Contract & property disputes
Criminal court work
Criminal legal aid
Debt
Debt collecting
Debt recovery, insolvency, bankruptcy
Education
Family and divorce
Landlord & tenant
Mental health
Personal injury
Professional negligence
Property litigation
Residential property
Road traffic
Wills, executries and trusts
Director
Margaret Janet Mair Nash
Associate
Derek George Alexander Caseby
Employee
Calum Craig Slessor

STEWART & WATSON
65 High Street, Banff AB45 1AN
Tel: (01261) 818883
Fax: (01261) 818005
DX: 521337 BANFF
E-mail: info@stewartwatson.co.uk
Web: www.stewartwatson.co.uk
Categories of Work
Adoption
Advice the elderly & powers of attorney
Agriculture and estates
Agriculture, crofting and fishing
Alternative dispute resolution
Charities
Children
Civil court work
Civil legal aid
Commercial property

▶ *Banff continued*

Contract & property disputes
Criminal court work
Criminal legal aid
Debt
Debt collecting
Debt recovery, insolvency, bankruptcy
Employment
Environment
Environment (Business Premises)
Family and divorce
Housing
Immigration and asylum
Landlord & tenant
Mental health
Personal injury
Projects
Residential property
Road traffic
Wills, executries and trusts
Partner
Alan Duffill

WILSON DEFENCE
17 Low Street, Banff AB45 1AU
Tel: (01261) 819831
Fax: (01261) 819835
DX: 521339 BANFF
E-mail: debbiefornow@icloud.com
Web: www.wilsondefence.com
Categories of Work
Criminal court work
Criminal legal aid
Partner
Deborah Anne Wilson-McCuish

Barrhead

MACKINLAY & SUTTIE
The Centre, 48 Cross Arthurlie Street,
Barrhead G78 1QU
Tel: (0141) 8811572
Fax: (0141) 8818269
DX: 501316 BARRHEAD
E-mail: m.lynch@mackinlay-suttie.co.uk
Categories of Work
Adoption
Benefit advice
Childrens
Civil court work
Civil legal aid
Criminal court work
Criminal legal aid
Disability
Discrimination
Employment
Employment law
Family and divorce
Human rights
Immigration and asylum
Local government
Medical negligence – claimant
Mental health

Personal injury
Road traffic
Social housing
Partner
Matthew Gerard Lynch

Bathgate

BATHGATE FAMILY LAW PRACTICE LIMITED
1 Bloomfield Place, Bathgate EH48 1PB
Tel: (01506) 656820
Fax: (01506) 655620
DX: 540467 BATHGATE
Web: www.bathgateflp.co.uk
Categories of Work
Adoption
Advice the elderly & powers of attorney
Children
Civil legal aid
Family and divorce
Wills, executries and trusts
Director
Martin David Cameron Burns

CAESAR & HOWIE
29 George Street, Bathgate EH48 1PG
Tel: (01506) 815900
Fax: (01506) 815928
DX: 540460 BATHGATE
E-mail: enquiries@caesar-howie.co.uk
Web: www.caesar-howie.co.uk
Categories of Work
Adoption
Advice the elderly & powers of attorney
Alternative dispute resolution
Children
Childrens
Civil court work
Civil legal aid
Commercial property
Debt
Debt collecting
Debt recovery, insolvency, bankruptcy
Disability
Education
Employment law
Family and divorce
Family business advice
Landlord & tenant
Mental health
Personal injury
Residential property
Road traffic
Wills, executries and trusts
Partner
Graham Pattison Irvine
Employees
Raymond Innis Francis
Kerry Lees

CAESAR & HOWIE
64 George Street, Bathgate EH48 1PD
Tel: (01506) 815900
Fax: (01506) 815930

DX: 540460 BATHGATE
Categories of Work
Adoption
Advice the elderly & powers of attorney
Alternative dispute resolution
Children
Childrens
Civil court work
Civil legal aid
Commercial property
Debt
Debt collecting
Debt recovery, insolvency, bankruptcy
Disability
Education
Employment law
Family and divorce
Family business advice
Landlord & tenant
Mental health
Personal injury
Residential property
Road traffic
Wills, executries and trusts
Partner
Lesley Susan Cunningham
Associate
John Hector Robert Macadam
Employee
Sarah Catherine Shaw

CENTRAL SCOTLAND LAW GROUP
27/29 & 64 George Street, Bathgate
EH48 1PG
Tel: (01506) 655211
E-mail: enquiries@caesar-howie.co.uk
Web: www.caesar-howie.co.uk
Categories of Work
Adoption
Advice the elderly & powers of attorney
Alternative dispute resolution
Children
Childrens
Civil court work
Civil legal aid
Commercial property
Debt
Debt collecting
Debt recovery, insolvency, bankruptcy
Disability
Education
Employment law
Family and divorce
Family business advice
Landlord & tenant
Mental health
Personal injury
Residential property
Road traffic
Wills, executries and trusts

DRUMMOND MILLER LLP
64 South Bridge Street, Bathgate EH48 1TL
Tel: (01506) 656645

Fax: (01506) 652347
DX: 540462 BATHGATE
E-mail: reception@drummondmiller.co.uk
Web: www.drummondmiller.co.uk
Categories of Work
Adjudication
Adoption
Advice the elderly & powers of attorney
Alternative dispute resolution
Charities
Children
Childrens
Civil court work
Civil legal aid
Commercial litigation
Commercial property
Contract & property disputes
Criminal court work
Data protection
Debt recovery, insolvency, bankruptcy
Discrimination
Education
Employment
Employment law
Environment
EU / international
Family and divorce
Family business advice
Health
Health and safety
Human rights
Immigration and asylum
Landlord & tenant
Medical negligence – defender
Medical negligence – claimant
Mental health
Oil & gas
Personal injury
Personal injury – defender
Personal tax
Professional negligence
Property litigation
Residential property
Road traffic
Wills, executries and trusts
Partner
Sharon Eddington Fleming
Employees
Lindsay Alice Hamilton
Melissa Elizabeth Gordon Inman

KW LAW
12 Whitburn Road, Bathgate EH48 1HH
Tel: (01506) 635533
DX: 540469 BATHGATE
E-mail: bathgate@kwlaw.co.uk
Web: www.kwlaw.co.uk
Categories of Work
Adoption
Advice the elderly & powers of attorney
Children
Civil court work
Civil legal aid

► *Bathgate continued*

Employment
Employment law
Family and divorce
Personal injury
Residential property
Road traffic
Wills, executries and trusts

SNEDDON MORRISON
36-46 North Bridge Street, Bathgate EH48 4PP
Tel: (01506) 635590
Fax: (01501) 745 440
Categories of Work
Advice the elderly & powers of attorney
Charities
Commercial property
Contract & property disputes
Education
Employment law
Family business advice
Landlord & tenant
Liquor licensing
Mental health
Mergers and acquisitions
Residential property
Wills, executries and trusts
Partner
Graham Cordiner Ritchie
Employee
Lewis Greig Bryan

THE CONVEYANCING PRACTICE LTD
69 South Bridge Street, Bathgate EH48 1TJ
Tel: (01506) 653 819
Fax: (01506) 653 719
DX: 540472 BATHGATE
E-mail:
karen.smillie@theconveyancingpractice.com
Categories of Work
Residential property
Director
Karen Smillie

Bearsden

G A FORDYCE & CO
28 Iain Road, Bearsden G61 4PA
Tel: (0141) 9423538
Fax: (0141) 404 2629
E-mail: mail@gafordyce.com
Categories of Work
Children
Civil court work
Civil legal aid
Contract & property disputes
Debt
Debt collecting
Debt recovery, insolvency, bankruptcy
Family and divorce
Partner
Graham Alexander Fordyce

BK GILL SOLICITORS
1 Rannoch Drive, Bearsden G61 2JW
Tel: (0141) 9423007
Fax: (0141) 6261404
DX: 556100 BEARSDEN
E-mail: bel@bkgillsolicitors.com
Web: www.bkgillsolicitors.com
Categories of Work
Commercial property
Landlord & tenant
Residential property
Wills, executries and trusts
Partner
Beljit Kaur Gill
Employee
Edward Thomas Daly

MCMAHON EMPLOYMENT LAW
The Exchange House, 50 Drymen Road,
Bearsden G61 2RH
Tel: (0141) 447 0438
Fax: (0141) 7778639
Web: www.mcmahonlaw.co.uk
Categories of Work
Adjudication
Civil court work
Commercial litigation
Consumer credit
Data protection
Debt
Debt adjusting and debt counselling
Debt administration
Debt collecting
Debt management
Debt recovery, insolvency, bankruptcy
Employment
Employment law
Insolvency & corporate recovery
IT and intellectual property
Professional negligence
Property litigation
Road traffic
Director
Paul Dominic McMahon

CLARE RYAN
2 Douglas Gardens, Bearsden G61 2SJ
Tel: (0141) 9315254
Categories of Work
Criminal court work
Criminal legal aid
Mental health
Partner
Clare Lorraine Ryan

Beith

STEWART & OSBORNE LEGAL LLP
37 Eglinton Street, Beith KA15 1AE
Tel: (01505) 503345
Fax: (01505) 503345
DX: 556122 BEITH
E-mail: main@stewartandosborne.co.uk

Categories of Work
Adoption
Advice the elderly & powers of attorney
Agriculture and estates
Children
Civil court work
Civil legal aid
Debt management
Family and divorce
Residential property
Wills, executries and trusts
Partner
Louis Gregory Capaldi

Bellshill

BELL SOLICITORS LIMITED
17 Hamilton Road, Bellshill ML4 1AF
Tel: (01698) 749977
Fax: (01698) 748847
Categories of Work
Criminal court work
Criminal legal aid
Director
James Michael O'Dowd

LANARKSHIRE LAW PRACTICE LIMITED
228 Main Street, Bellshill ML4 1AB
Tel: (01698) 747171
Fax: (01698) 749733
DX: 556141 BELLSHILL
E-mail: Bellshill@lanarkshirelaw.co.uk
Web: www.lanarkshirelawpractice.co.uk
Categories of Work
Adoption
Advice the elderly & powers of attorney
Children
Childrens
Civil court work
Criminal court work
Criminal legal aid
Education
Family and divorce
Personal injury
Wills, executries and trusts
Director
Lynsey Jane Millar
Employees
Claire Donnelly
Frances Konopka

LUNNY & CO
PO Box 8778, Bellshill ML4 9AS
Tel: (01698) 269387
Fax: (01698) 537974
E-mail: mark@lunny.co.uk
Web: www.lunny.co.uk
Categories of Work
Advice the elderly & powers of attorney
Children
Civil court work
Civil legal aid
Contract & property disputes
Criminal court work

Criminal legal aid
Debt
Debt collecting
Debt recovery, insolvency, bankruptcy
Disability
Discrimination
Education
Family and divorce
Human rights
Landlord & tenant
Mental health
Personal injury
Personal injury – defender
Property litigation
Road traffic
Wills, executries and trusts
Partner
Mark Gerald Lunny

MURRAY, HAMILTON & CHALMERS
66 Hamilton Road, Bellshill ML4 1AG
Tel: (01698) 327488
Fax: (01698) 327491
DX: 556142 BELLSHILL
E-mail: mhc@mhcsol.co.uk
Categories of Work
Adoption
Advice the elderly & powers of attorney
Children
Childrens
Civil court work
Civil legal aid
Commercial property
Criminal court work
Criminal legal aid
Debt
Debt administration
Debt collecting
Disability
Discrimination
Education
Family and divorce
Housing
Human rights
Landlord & tenant
Medical negligence – defender
Medical negligence – claimant
Mental health
Personal injury
Personal injury – defender
Professional negligence
Residential property
Road traffic
Social housing
Wills, executries and trusts
Partners
Margaret Claire Chalmers
Alan Blair Murray
Employees
Gavin Ferguson Lawson
Fiona Marie Norris

Biggar

SMAIL & EWART LTD
79 High Street, Biggar ML12 6DE
Tel: (01899) 220058
Fax: (01899) 221269
E-mail: enquiry@smail-ewart.co.uk
Categories of Work
Adoption
Advice the elderly & powers of attorney
Agriculture and estates
Agriculture, crofting and fishing
Alternative investment market
Banking & finance
Benefit advice
Charities
Children
Childrens
Civil court work
Civil legal aid
Commercial litigation
Commercial property
Competition
Contract & property disputes
Corporate tax
Debt
Debt collecting
Debt recovery, insolvency, bankruptcy
Education
Employment
Environment (Business Premises)
EU / international
Family and divorce
Family business advice
Housing
Insolvency & corporate recovery
Insurance
Joint venture
Landlord & tenant
Mental health
Mergers and acquisitions
Pensions (Company)
Private equity
Public finance initiative
Public sector
Residential property
SME business advice
Social housing
Unit Trusts, OEICs and investment trusts
Wills, executries and trusts
Directors
John Bryson Armstrong
Jane Elizabeth Robison
Employee
Lesley Ann Armstrong

Bishopbriggs

S.P. FLANAGAN
6 Boclair Road, Bishopbriggs G64 2NA
Tel: (0141) 5630553
E-mail: seanpflanagan@hotmail.com

Categories of Work
Criminal court work
Criminal legal aid
Partner
Sean Paul Flanagan

GORDON & SMYTH
24 Cadder Road, Bishopbriggs G64 3JJ
Tel: (0141) 7724186
Fax: (0141) 4293110
Categories of Work
Criminal court work
Criminal legal aid
Partner
Maurice Thomas Smyth

HENNESSY, BOWIE & CO.
2 Kenmure Lane, Bishopbriggs G64 2RA
Tel: (0141) 7624040
Fax: (0141) 7620742
DX: 556160 BISHOPBRIGGS 3
E-mail: smg@hennessybowie.co.uk
Web: www.hennessybowie.co.uk
Categories of Work
Commercial property
Residential property
Wills, executries and trusts
Partner
Stephen McGuire

MACFARLANE & CO.
4 Kenmure Avenue, Bishopbriggs G64 2RE
Tel: (0141) 7726063
Fax: (0141) 7622621
DX: 556161 BISHOPBRIGGS 3
E-mail: jmk@macfarlane-law.co.uk
Web: www.macfarlane-law.co.uk
Categories of Work
Advice the elderly & powers of attorney
Residential property
Wills, executries and trusts
Associate
Jan Mitchell Kerr

MONTGOMERY SMITH SOLICITORS
128 Kirkintilloch Road, Bishopbriggs G64 2AB
Tel: (0141) 772 5344
E-mail: greg@montgomerysmith.co.uk
Web: www.montgomerysmith.co.uk
Categories of Work
Criminal court work
Criminal legal aid
Health and safety
Personal injury
Personal injury – defender
Road traffic
Partner
Gregor Wilkie Smith

PACITTI JONES LEGAL LIMITED
175 Kirkintilloch Road, Bishopbriggs G64 2LS
Tel: (0141) 7722211
Fax: (0141) 6480908
DX: 556162 BISHOPBRIGGS 3
Web: https://www.pacittijones.co.uk/

Categories of Work
Adoption
Advice the elderly & powers of attorney
Banking & finance
Children
Civil court work
Civil legal aid
Commercial property
Construction
Corporate tax
Criminal court work
Criminal legal aid
Education
Employment law
Environment
Family and divorce
Health and safety
Housing
Joint venture
Landlord & tenant
Mergers and acquisitions
Personal injury
Power and utilities
Private equity
Professional negligence
Projects
Residential property
Road traffic
SME business advice
Wills, executives and trusts
Director
Moira Gardner

Blackburn

ALAN MEECHAN SOLICITORS
C/o 19 Bathgate Road, Blackburn EH47 7LN
Tel: (07878) 159264
E-mail: ameechansolicitors@outlook.com
Categories of Work
Advice the elderly & powers of attorney
Benefit advice
Civil court work
Civil legal aid
Commercial litigation
Criminal court work
Criminal legal aid
Disability
Discrimination
Employment
Employment law
Family and divorce
Health and safety
Housing
Human rights
Landlord & tenant
Medical negligence – defender
Medical negligence – claimant
Mental health
Pensions (Employment)
Personal injury
Personal injury – defender
Professional negligence

Road traffic
Social housing
Wills, executives and trusts
Partner
Alan Reuben Meechan

Blairgowrie

HODGE SOLICITORS LLP
28 Wellmeadow, Blairgowrie PH10 6AX
Tel: (01250) 874441
Fax: (01250) 873998
DX: 531158 BLAIRGOWRIE
E-mail: info@hodgesolicitors.co.uk
Web: www.hodgesolicitors.co.uk
Categories of Work
Adjudication
Adoption
Advice the elderly & powers of attorney
Agriculture, crofting and fishing
Alternative dispute resolution
Benefit advice
Children
Civil court work
Civil legal aid
Commercial litigation
Consumer credit
Criminal court work
Criminal legal aid
Debt
Debt adjusting and debt counselling
Debt collecting
Debt recovery, insolvency, bankruptcy
Disability
Discrimination
Education
Employment
Employment law
Family and divorce
Freedom of information
Health and safety
Human rights
Immigration and asylum
Insolvency & corporate recovery
Landlord & tenant
Medical negligence – defender
Medical negligence – claimant
Mental health
Personal injury
Personal injury – defender
Professional negligence
Property litigation
Residential property
Road traffic
Social housing
Sport
Wills, executives and trusts
Partners
Andrew Davidson Hodge
Stephen James Lafferty
Michael John Tavendale
Employee
Ryan James Aitken

► *Blairgowrie continued*

MACNABS LLP
21 Allan Street, Blairgowrie PH10 6AB
Tel: (01738) 623432
Fax: (01738) 638 594
DX: 531159 BLAIRGOWRIE
E-mail: mail@macnabs-law.co.uk
Categories of Work
Adjudication
Adoption
Advice the elderly & powers of attorney
Agriculture and estates
Agriculture, crofting and fishing
Alternative dispute resolution
Children
Childrens
Civil court work
Civil legal aid
Commercial litigation
Commercial property
Construction
Consumer credit
Contract & property disputes
Criminal court work
Criminal legal aid
Debt
Debt adjusting and debt counselling
Debt administration
Debt collecting
Debt recovery, insolvency, bankruptcy
Disability
Education
Employment
Employment law
Family and divorce
Family business advice
Health and safety
Insolvency & corporate recovery
Insurance
Landlord & tenant
Medical negligence – defender
Medical negligence – claimant
Mental health
Personal injury
Personal injury – defender
Planning
Planning (Business Premises)
Professional negligence
Property litigation
Residential property
Road traffic
Wills, executries and trusts
Consultant
James Baxter

MILLER GERRARD LIMITED
The Studio, 13 High Street, Blairgowrie
PH10 6ET
Tel: (01250) 873468
Fax: (01250) 875257
DX: 531160 BLAIRGOWRIE
Web: www.millergerrard.com

Categories of Work
Advice the elderly & powers of attorney
Family and divorce
Landlord & tenant
Residential property
Wills, executries and trusts
Directors
David Millar Hart
Richard Gordon Hartley-Zels

WATSON & LYALL BOWIE
Union Bank Buildings, Calton Street,
Blairgowrie PH13 9AJ
Tel: (01828) 628395
Fax: (01828) 627147
DX: 566340 COUPAR ANGUS
E-mail: legalservices@wandlb.co.uk
Web: www.watson-lyall-bowie.co.uk
Categories of Work
Adoption
Advice the elderly & powers of attorney
Agriculture and estates
Benefit advice
Charities
Children
Civil court work
Civil legal aid
Commercial litigation
Commercial property
Consumer credit
Contract & property disputes
Criminal court work
Criminal legal aid
Debt
Debt collecting
Debt recovery, insolvency, bankruptcy
Education
Employment
Employment law
Family and divorce
Family business advice
Landlord & tenant
Liquor licensing
Personal injury
Personal tax
Property litigation
Residential property
Road traffic
Wills, executries and trusts
Partners
Alison Margaret Hodge
Kevin Edward Lancaster

Blantyre

BAKER GOSTELOW LAW
261 Glasgow Road, Blantyre G72 0YS
Tel: (01698) 820700
Web: www.bgfamilylaw.co.uk
Categories of Work
Adoption
Advice the elderly & powers of attorney
Alternative dispute resolution

Children
Childrens
Civil court work
Civil legal aid
Discrimination
Education
Family and divorce
Human rights
Landlord & tenant
Property litigation
Residential property
Wills, executives and trusts
Director
Gillian Catherine Baker

CARTYS
Unit 2, Clydeview Centre, Blantyre G72 0QD
Tel: (01698) 820896
Fax: (01698) 823866
DX: 501900 BLANTYRE
Web: www.cartylaw.co.uk
Categories of Work
Adoption
Advice the elderly & powers of attorney
Agriculture and estates
Benefit advice
Children
Civil court work
Civil legal aid
Commercial property
Consumer credit
Criminal court work
Criminal legal aid
Debt adjusting and debt counselling
Debt administration
Debt collecting
Debt management
Disability
Discrimination
Education
Family and divorce
Freedom of information
Human rights
Landlord & tenant
Mental health
Pensions (Employment)
Personal injury
Residential property
Road traffic
Social housing
Wills, executives and trusts
Partner
Andrew Fraser Iles
Employee
Lisa Rose Abena Agyako

ALISTAIR MURRAY SOLICITOR ADVOCATE
261 Glasgow Road, Blantyre G72 0YS
Tel: (01698) 721999
Fax: (01698) 721888
DX: 501906 BLANTYRE
E-mail: blantyrecriminallawyers@gmail.com
Categories of Work
Criminal court work

Criminal legal aid
Partner
Alistair Gerard Murray

STIRLING DUNLOP
261 Glasgow Road, Blantyre G72 0YS
Tel: 1698820700
E-mail: enquiries@stirlingdunlop.co.uk
Web: www.bgfamilylaw.co.uk
Categories of Work
Adoption
Advice the elderly & powers of attorney
Alternative dispute resolution
Children
Childrens
Civil court work
Civil legal aid
Discrimination
Education
Family and divorce
Human rights
Landlord & tenant
Property litigation
Residential property
Wills, executives and trusts

Boness

CAESAR & HOWIE
54 South Street, Boness EH51 9HA
Tel: (01506) 826166
Fax: (01506) 823019
E-mail: enquiries@caesar-howie.co.uk
Categories of Work
Adoption
Advice the elderly & powers of attorney
Alternative dispute resolution
Children
Childrens
Civil court work
Civil legal aid
Commercial property
Debt
Debt collecting
Debt recovery, insolvency, bankruptcy
Disability
Education
Employment law
Family and divorce
Family business advice
Landlord & tenant
Mental health
Personal injury
Residential property
Road traffic
Wills, executives and trusts
Partner
Alison Crane Macphee
Employee
Joanna Izabela Thomson

LIDDLE & ANDERSON LLP
2 Market Street, Boness EH51 9AD
Tel: (01506) 822727

▶ **Boness continued**

Fax: (01506) 828066
DX: 541180 BONESS
Web: www.liddleandanderson.co.uk
Categories of Work
Advice the elderly & powers of attorney
Agriculture and estates
Children
Civil court work
Commercial litigation
Commercial property
Construction
Contract & property disputes
Debt collecting
Debt recovery, insolvency, bankruptcy
Employment
Employment law
Family and divorce
Family business advice
Landlord & tenant
Mental health
Mergers and acquisitions
Property litigation
Residential property
SME business advice
Wills, executries and trusts
Partners
Joyce Emma Hobbs
Fiona Calder MacDonald
William James MacRae
Marysia Margaret Michalina Waddell
Employee
Ishbel Miriam Stewart

SNEDDONS SSC
1/3 South Street, Boness EH51 0EA
Tel: (01506) 826232
Fax: (01506) 824810
E-mail: boness@sneddons.com
Web: www.sneddons.com
Categories of Work
Contract & property disputes
Employment law
Landlord & tenant
Residential property
Wills, executries and trusts
Partner
Brian Daniel Lawson

Bonnyrigg

ALLAN MCDOUGALL MCQUEEN LLP
2 Lothian Street, Bonnyrigg EH19 3AD
Tel: (0131) 666 2424
E-mail: info@mcdougallmcqueen.co.uk
Web: www.mcdougallmcqueen.co.uk
Categories of Work
Adoption
Advice the elderly & powers of attorney
Charities
Children
Childrens
Civil court work

Civil legal aid
Commercial litigation
Commercial property
Contract & property disputes
Criminal court work
Criminal legal aid
Disability
Discrimination
Employment
Employment law
Family and divorce
Health and safety
Landlord & tenant
Medical negligence – claimant
Personal injury
Personal injury – defender
Personal tax
Professional negligence
Residential property
Road traffic
Wills, executries and trusts

MCDOUGALL MCQUEEN LLP
2 Lothian Street, Bonnyrigg EH19 3AD
Tel: (0131) 666 2424
Fax: (0131) 663 3418
E-mail: info@mcdougallmcqueen.co.uk
Web: www.mcdougallmcqueen.co.uk
Categories of Work
Adoption
Advice the elderly & powers of attorney
Charities
Children
Childrens
Civil court work
Civil legal aid
Commercial litigation
Commercial property
Contract & property disputes
Criminal court work
Criminal legal aid
Disability
Discrimination
Employment
Employment law
Family and divorce
Health and safety
Landlord & tenant
Medical negligence – claimant
Personal injury
Personal injury – defender
Personal tax
Professional negligence
Residential property
Road traffic
Wills, executries and trusts
Associate
Linsey Elizabeth Dagger

NEILSONS
72 High Street, Bonnyrigg EH19 2AE
Tel: (0131) 6639988
Categories of Work
Benefit advice

Commercial property
Debt management
Landlord & tenant
Mental health
Residential property
Wills, executries and trusts

STUART & STUART
7 High Street, Bonnyrigg EH19 2DA
Tel: (0131) 6637135
Fax: (0131) 6637501
DX: 551350 BONNYRIGG
E-mail: bonnyrigg@stuartandstuart.co.uk
Web: www.stuartandstuart.co.uk
Categories of Work
Advice the elderly & powers of attorney
Agriculture and estates
Alternative dispute resolution
Civil court work
Commercial property
Family and divorce
Immigration and asylum
Landlord & tenant
Liquor licensing
Mental health
Residential property
Unit Trusts, OEICs and investment trusts
Wills, executries and trusts
Employee
Rachel Emily Davies

Brechin

SHIELLS
31A St. David Street, Brechin DD9 6EG
Tel: (01356) 622171
Fax: (01356) 625232
DX: 556202 BRECHIN
E-mail: shiells@shiells-law.co.uk
Web: www.shiellslaw.co.uk
Categories of Work
Advice the elderly & powers of attorney
Family business advice
Landlord & tenant
Residential property
Wills, executries and trusts
Partners
Robert James Gair Couston
Stephen Renny Middleton

THE CHAMBER PRACTICE LTD
28 Clerk Street, Brechin DD9 6AY
Tel: (01356) 622289
E-mail: enquiries@thechamberpractice.co.uk
Web: www.thechamberpractice.co.uk
Categories of Work
Commercial property
Family business advice
Human rights
Immigration and asylum
Landlord & tenant
Liquor licensing
Residential property
Wills, executries and trusts

Bridge of Allan

AMI LAW
44a Henderson Street, Bridge of Allan
FK9 4HS
Tel: (07910) 858 077
E-mail: Allan.macintyre@amilaw.co.uk
Categories of Work
Civil court work
Civil legal aid
Mental health
Wills, executries and trusts
Partner
Allan Keith MacIntyre

MACNABS LLP
40 Henderson Street, Bridge of Allan FK9 4HS
Tel: (01738) 623432
E-mail: mail@macnabs-law.co.uk
Categories of Work
Adjudication
Adoption
Advice the elderly & powers of attorney
Agriculture and estates
Agriculture, crofting and fishing
Alternative dispute resolution
Children
Childrens
Civil court work
Civil legal aid
Commercial litigation
Commercial property
Construction
Consumer credit
Contract & property disputes
Criminal court work
Criminal legal aid
Debt
Debt adjusting and debt counselling
Debt administration
Debt collecting
Debt recovery, insolvency, bankruptcy
Disability
Education
Employment
Employment law
Family and divorce
Family business advice
Health and safety
Insolvency & corporate recovery
Insurance
Landlord & tenant
Medical negligence – defender
Medical negligence – claimant
Mental health
Personal injury
Personal injury – defender
Planning
Planning (Business Premises)
Professional negligence
Property litigation
Residential property
Road traffic
Wills, executries and trusts

▶ **Bridge of Allan continued**

MAILERS
88 Henderson Street, Bridge of Allan FK9 4HA
Tel: (01786) 832314
Fax: (01786) 834114
DX: 556211 BRIDGE OF ALLAN
E-mail: mail@mailers.co.uk
Categories of Work
Advice the elderly & powers of attorney
Children
Childrens
Civil court work
Civil legal aid
Commercial litigation
Commercial property
Contract & property disputes
Criminal court work
Criminal legal aid
Debt
Debt collecting
Debt recovery, insolvency, bankruptcy
Family and divorce
Family business advice
Joint venture
Landlord & tenant
Liquor licensing
Personal injury
Property litigation
Residential property
Road traffic
Wills, executives and trusts
Partner
Alasdair David Mackie

Bridge of Weir

COCHRAN DICKIE
3 Neva Place, Bridge of Weir PA11 3PN
Tel: (01505) 613807
Fax: (01505) 615682
E-mail: bridgeofweir@cochrandickie.com

COCKBURN & CO.
Burngill Place, Main Street, Bridge of Weir
PA11 3PF
Tel: (01505) 690500
Fax: (01505) 690235
E-mail: admin@cockburnandco.com
Web: www.cockburnandco.com
Categories of Work
Advice the elderly & powers of attorney
Civil court work
Family and divorce
Residential property
Wills, executives and trusts
Partners
Elizabeth Ross Cockburn
Grace Kelly Greene

Brodick

JAS CAMPBELL & CO LTD
Unit 2, Douglas Centre, Brodick KA27 8AJ

Tel: (01770) 302027
E-mail: mail@jascampbell.co.uk
Web: www.jascampbell.co.uk
Categories of Work
Adoption
Advice the elderly & powers of attorney
Agriculture and estates
Children
Civil court work
Civil legal aid
Commercial property
Construction
Contract & property disputes
Environment (Business Premises)
Family and divorce
Family business advice
Landlord & tenant
Liquor licensing
Personal injury
Planning (Business Premises)
Property litigation
Residential property
SME business advice
Wills, executives and trusts

Broughty Ferry

LESLEY MACDONALD FAMILY LAW
Spalding House, 90/92 Queen Street,
Broughty Ferry DD5 1AJ
Tel: (01382) 698600
E-mail: lesley@lesleymacdonaldfamilylaw.co.uk
Categories of Work
Family and divorce
Partner
Lesley Madeline Macdonald

Broxburn

W. & A.S. BRUCE
50 East Main Street, Broxburn EH52 5AE
Tel: (01506) 855777
Fax: (01506) 854368
DX: 556220 BROXBURN 2
Categories of Work
Adoption
Advice the elderly & powers of attorney
Agriculture and estates
Children
Childrens
Civil court work
Civil legal aid
Commercial property
Consumer credit
Contract & property disputes
Criminal court work
Criminal legal aid
Debt
Debt adjusting and debt counselling
Debt collecting
Debt recovery, insolvency, bankruptcy
Employment

Employment law
Family and divorce
Family business advice
Landlord & tenant
Liquor licensing
Medical negligence – claimant
Mental health
Pensions (Company)
Personal injury
Personal injury – defender
Personal tax
Professional negligence
Property litigation
Residential property
Road traffic
SME business advice
Wills, executives and trusts
Partner
Janine Toland

Buckie

GRANT SMITH LAW PRACTICE LIMITED
16 East Church Street, Buckie AB56 1AE
Tel: (01542) 831307
Fax: (01542) 833856
E-mail: info@grantsmithlaw.co.uk
Web: www.grantsmithlaw.co.uk
Categories of Work
Adoption
Advice the elderly & powers of attorney
Alternative dispute resolution
Children
Childrens
Civil court work
Civil legal aid
Commercial property
Contract & property disputes
Criminal court work
Criminal legal aid
Debt
Debt collecting
Debt recovery, insolvency, bankruptcy
Education
Family and divorce
Landlord & tenant
Mental health
Personal injury
Professional negligence
Property litigation
Residential property
Road traffic
Wills, executives and trusts
Associate
Christina Fiona Matthews

STEWART & WATSON
42/44 East Church Street, Buckie AB56 1AB
Tel: (01542) 833255
Fax: (01542) 834611
DX: 556243 BUCKIE
E-mail: info@stewartwatson.co.uk
Web: www.stewartwatson.co.uk

Categories of Work
Adoption
Advice the elderly & powers of attorney
Agriculture and estates
Agriculture, crofting and fishing
Alternative dispute resolution
Charities
Children
Civil court work
Civil legal aid
Commercial property
Contract & property disputes
Criminal court work
Criminal legal aid
Debt
Debt collecting
Debt recovery, insolvency, bankruptcy
Employment
Environment
Environment (Business Premises)
Family and divorce
Housing
Immigration and asylum
Landlord & tenant
Mental health
Personal injury
Projects
Residential property
Road traffic
Wills, executives and trusts
Partners
Samantha Jane Scott Bennion
Hugh Patrick Herries Cumming

Burntisland

W. & A.S. BRUCE
6 Kirkgate, Burntisland KY3 9DB
Tel: (01592) 873501
DX: 556262 BURNTISLAND
Categories of Work
Adoption
Advice the elderly & powers of attorney
Agriculture and estates
Children
Childrens
Civil court work
Civil legal aid
Commercial property
Consumer credit
Contract & property disputes
Criminal court work
Criminal legal aid
Debt
Debt adjusting and debt counselling
Debt collecting
Debt recovery, insolvency, bankruptcy
Employment
Employment law
Family and divorce
Family business advice
Landlord & tenant
Liquor licensing

▶ **Burntisland continued**

Medical negligence – claimant
Mental health
Pensions (Company)
Personal injury
Personal injury – defender
Personal tax
Professional negligence
Property litigation
Residential property
Road traffic
SME business advice
Wills, executries and trusts

Cambuslang

DEVINE & CO.
238 Hamilton Road, Halfway, Cambuslang
G72 7PF
Tel: (0141) 6460911
E-mail: devineandco@btconnect.com
Categories of Work
Criminal court work
Criminal legal aid
Partner
Christopher Edward Devine

DUFFY TOSHNER & CO LIMITED
23 Main Street, Cambuslang G72 7EX
Tel: (0141) 6418081
Fax: (0141) 6410091
Web: www.duffytoshner.co.uk
Categories of Work
Adoption
Advice the elderly & powers of attorney
Benefit advice
Children
Civil court work
Civil legal aid
Commercial litigation
Commercial property
Consumer credit
Criminal court work
Criminal legal aid
Debt
Debt adjusting and debt counselling
Debt collecting
Debt management
Debt recovery, insolvency, bankruptcy
Employment
Employment law
Family and divorce
Health and safety
Insurance
Medical negligence – claimant
Mental health
Pensions (Employment)
Personal injury
Professional negligence
Property litigation
Residential property
Road traffic
Social housing

Wills, executries and trusts
Directors
Claire Helen Crawford
Kenneth Scott Finnie

HEPWORTH & CO.
235 Hamilton Road, Halfway, Cambuslang
G72 7PH
Tel: (0141) 6410089
Fax: (0141) 6419538
E-mail: admin@hepworthsolicitors.co.uk
Categories of Work
Advice the elderly & powers of attorney
Criminal court work
Criminal legal aid
Family and divorce
Wills, executries and trusts
Partner
Alan Neil Hepworth

Campbeltown

C. & D. MACTAGGART
Castlehill, Campbeltown PA28 6AR
Tel: (01586) 552317
Fax: (01586) 554719
E-mail: mail@cdm-law.co.uk
Web: mactaggart-law.co.uk/
Categories of Work
Adoption
Advice the elderly & powers of attorney
Agriculture and estates
Agriculture, crofting and fishing
Betting & gaming
Children
Civil court work
Civil legal aid
Commercial litigation
Commercial property
Consumer credit
Contract & property disputes
Criminal court work
Criminal legal aid
Debt
Debt collecting
Debt recovery, insolvency, bankruptcy
Disability
Discrimination
Education
Employment
Employment law
Family and divorce
Family business advice
Housing
Human rights
Insolvency & corporate recovery
Landlord & tenant
Liquor licensing
Media and entertainment
Medical negligence – defender
Medical negligence – claimant
Mental health
Personal injury

Personal injury – defender
Professional negligence
Property litigation
Residential property
Road traffic
Social housing
Transport
Wills, executives and trusts
Partners
Christian Edmiston Kane
Stephen MacSporran
Associate
Keren Vaughan Mitchell

STEWART BALFOUR & SUTHERLAND
Kinloch Hall, Lochend Street, Campbeltown
PA28 6DL
Tel: (01586) 552871
DX: 556280 CAMPBELTOWN 2
E-mail: mail@sbslaw.co.uk
Categories of Work
Advice the elderly & powers of attorney
Residential property
Wills, executives and trusts
Director
Campbell Calum Read

Carluke

FORREST CAMPBELL & ANDERSON
23 Kirkton Street, Carluke ML8 4AB
Tel: (01555) 771383
Fax: (01555) 773421
DX: 570472 CARLUKE
E-mail: enquiries@fcasolicitors.co.uk
Categories of Work
Criminal court work
Criminal legal aid
Partner
Douglas Bruce Forrest

MORISON & SMITH LIMITED
39 High Street, Carluke ML8 4AL
Tel: (01555) 773146
Web: www.morisonandsmith.com
Categories of Work
Advice the elderly & powers of attorney
Agriculture and estates
Agriculture, crofting and fishing
Charities
Children
Civil court work
Civil legal aid
Commercial property
Contract & property disputes
Debt collecting
Family and divorce
Landlord & tenant
Residential property
Wills, executives and trusts
Employee
Hannah Louise Tuff

Carnoustie

CONNELLY & YEOMAN LAW LIMITED
31 High Street, Carnoustie DD7 6AG
Tel: (01241) 859500
E-mail: carnoustie@connellyyeoman.com
Web: www.connellyyeoman.com
Categories of Work
Advice the elderly & powers of attorney
Civil legal aid
Criminal court work
Criminal legal aid
Landlord & tenant
Residential property
Wills, executives and trusts

J. MYLES & CO.
63 High Street, Carnoustie DD7 6AD
Tel: (01241) 855769
Fax: (01241) 859775
DX: 556300 CARNOUSTIE
E-mail: carnoustie@jmylessols.co.uk
Categories of Work
Adoption
Advice the elderly & powers of attorney
Children
Childrens
Civil court work
Civil legal aid
Commercial litigation
Commercial property
Contract & property disputes
Criminal court work
Criminal legal aid
Debt
Debt collecting
Debt recovery, insolvency, bankruptcy
Employment
Employment law
Family and divorce
Human rights
Landlord & tenant
Medical negligence – claimant
Personal injury
Personal injury – defender
Professional negligence
Property litigation
Residential property
Road traffic
Wills, executives and trusts
Employee
Douglas James Campbell Thomson

Castle Douglas

GILLESPIE GIFFORD & BROWN LLP
135 King Street, Castle Douglas DG7 1NA
Tel: (01556) 503744
Fax: (01556) 503094
DX: 580493 CASTLE DOUGLAS
E-mail: mail@ggblaw.co.uk
Categories of Work
Adoption

► **Castle Douglas continued**

Advice the elderly & powers of attorney
Agriculture and estates
Agriculture, crofting and fishing
Children
Civil court work
Civil legal aid
Commercial property
Construction
Contract & property disputes
Debt
Debt collecting
Employment
Environment (Business Premises)
Family and divorce
Family business advice
Freedom of information
Landlord & tenant
Liquor licensing
Planning (Business Premises)
Residential property
Wills, executives and trusts
Consultant
Iain William McDonald
Associate
Kay Diane Bird
Employees
Victoria Evans
Nicola Ann Stephen

HALL BAIRD SOLICITORS LTD
The Old Exchange, Castle Douglas DG7 1TJ
Tel: (01556) 502764
DX: 580494 CASTLE DOUGLAS
E-mail: enquiries@hallbaird.co.uk
Web: www.hallbaird.co.uk
Categories of Work
Advice the elderly & powers of attorney
Agriculture and estates
Agriculture, crofting and fishing
Banking & finance
Commercial property
Contract & property disputes
Family business advice
Fishing
Landlord & tenant
Power and utilities
Residential property
Telecoms
Wills, executives and trusts
Directors
Karen Louise Baird
David Robert Fredrick Hall
Employee
Susan Wallace

HEWATS
63 King Street, Castle Douglas DG7 1AG
Tel: (01556) 502391
Fax: (01556) 504171
DX: 590495 CASTLE DOUGLAS
E-mail: scotslaw@hewats.co.uk
Web: www.hewats.co.uk

Categories of Work
Advice the elderly & powers of attorney
Agriculture and estates
Agriculture, crofting and fishing
Commercial property
Family business advice
Landlord & tenant
Personal tax
Residential property
SME business advice
Wills, executives and trusts
Partner
Andrew James Malone
Employees
David John Currie
Helen Jane Prentice

Clydebank

BLAIR & BRYDEN
23 Kilbowie Road, Clydebank G81 1TL
Tel: (0141) 9523322
Fax: (0141) 9523232
DX: 500502 CLYDEBANK
E-mail: 23@blair-bryden.co.uk
Web: www.blairbryden.co.uk
Categories of Work
Adoption
Advice the elderly & powers of attorney
Benefit advice
Charities
Children
Civil court work
Civil legal aid
Commercial litigation
Commercial property
Consumer credit
Contract & property disputes
Criminal court work
Criminal legal aid
Debt collecting
Debt recovery, insolvency, bankruptcy
Education
Employment
Employment law
Family and divorce
Family business advice
Housing
Immigration and asylum
Landlord & tenant
Liquor licensing
Medical negligence – claimant
Personal injury
Personal injury – defender
Planning (Business Premises)
Professional negligence
Property litigation
Residential property
Road traffic
Transport
Wills, executives and trusts
Partner
John Lawrie Kindness

Employee
Rabia Isha Ashraf

CLYDE DEFENCE LAWYERS LIMITED
30 Alexander Street, Clydebank G81 1RZ
Tel: (0141) 9512211
Fax: (0141) 9512233
E-mail: clydebank@clydedefencelawyers.com
Categories of Work
Criminal court work
Criminal legal aid
Directors
Philip Andrew Lafferty
Judith-Anne Reid

FMC LEGAL LIMITED
499 Kilbowie Road, Clydebank G81 2AX
Tel: (01389) 879791
Fax: (01389) 879005
DX: 500507 CLYDEBANK
E-mail:
fionacairnsfmcsolicitors@btconnect.com
Categories of Work
Advice the elderly & powers of attorney
Children
Civil court work
Civil legal aid
Family and divorce
Residential property
Wills, executries and trusts
Director
Fiona Marie Cairns

FMC SOLICITORS INCORPORATING JAMES A. MCCANN & CO
499 Kilbowie Road, Clydebank G81 2AX
Tel: (01389) 879791
DX: 500507 CLYDEBANK
Categories of Work
Advice the elderly & powers of attorney
Children
Civil court work
Civil legal aid
Family and divorce
Residential property
Wills, executries and trusts

PHILPOTT PLATT NIBLETT & WIGHT
4 Miller Street, Clydebank G81 1UQ
Tel: (0141) 9529545
Fax: (0141) 9528333
DX: 500509 CLYDEBANK
E-mail: aniblett@ppnw.co.uk
Web: www.ppmw.co.uk
Categories of Work
Children
Childrens
Civil legal aid
Commercial property
Contract & property disputes
Criminal court work
Criminal legal aid
Family and divorce
Immigration and asylum
Landlord & tenant

Personal injury
Residential property
Road traffic
Wills, executries and trusts
Associate
Gail Campbell
Employees
Hannah Claire Jones
Kirsteen Joan Ritchie

SCANLON EWING LIMITED
78 Dumbarton Road, Clydebank G81 1UG
Tel: (0141) 9529297
Fax: (0141) 9511002
DX: 500510 CLYDEBANK
E-mail: mail@scanlonewing.co.uk
Web: www.scanlonewing.co.uk
Categories of Work
Advice the elderly & powers of attorney
Commercial property
Residential property
Wills, executries and trusts
Directors
Maureen Frances Ewing
Mairi Scanlon
Employee
Hannah Ruth Higton

STIRLING & GILMOUR LLP
16 Alexander Street, Clydebank G81 1RZ
Tel: (0141) 9522669
Fax: (0141) 951 2088
DX: 500492 CLYDEBANK
Categories of Work
Adoption
Advice the elderly & powers of attorney
Agriculture and estates
Agriculture, crofting and fishing
Alternative dispute resolution
Charities
Children
Civil court work
Civil legal aid
Commercial litigation
Commercial property
Consumer credit
Contract & property disputes
Copyright, trade marks and design
Criminal court work
Criminal legal aid
Debt
Debt collecting
Debt recovery, insolvency, bankruptcy
Discrimination
Employment law
Family and divorce
Family business advice
Landlord & tenant
Liquor licensing
Personal injury
Personal tax
Planning (Business Premises)
Property litigation
Residential property

► *Clydebank continued*

Road traffic
Wills, executries and trusts
Partner
Caroline Jean Weir
Associate
Anne Elaine Frances Quinn

THE PRG PARTNERSHIP

1 Kilbowie Road, Clydebank G81 1TL
Tel: (0141) 9520019
Fax: (0141) 9524957
DX: 500491 CLYDEBANK
E-mail: scotslaw@prg.co.uk
Web: www.prg.co.uk
Categories of Work
Adjudication
Advice the elderly & powers of attorney
Alternative dispute resolution
Charities
Children
Civil court work
Civil legal aid
Commercial litigation
Commercial property
Competition
Contract & property disputes
Copyright, trade marks and design
Criminal court work
Criminal legal aid
Data protection
Debt
Debt collecting
Debt recovery, insolvency, bankruptcy
Disability
Discrimination
Employment
Employment law
Family and divorce
Family business advice
Health and safety
Human rights
Insolvency & corporate recovery
IT and intellectual property
Joint venture
Landlord & tenant
Media and entertainment
Medical negligence – defender
Medical negligence – claimant
Mergers and acquisitions
Pensions (Employment)
Personal injury
Personal injury – defender
Professional negligence
Property litigation
Residential property
Road traffic
SME business advice
Social housing
Software licensing
Wills, executries and trusts
Partner
Eugene Francis Boyle

Employee
Hannah Nicola Pearson

Coatbridge

FRIELS SOLICITORS LIMITED
180 Bank Street, Coatbridge ML5 1ET
Tel: (01236) 421 136
Fax: (01236) 429 890
DX: 570512 COATBRIDGE
Categories of Work
Adjudication
Advice the elderly & powers of attorney
Alternative dispute resolution
Banking & finance
Children
Civil court work
Civil legal aid
Commercial litigation
Commercial property
Competition
Construction
Consumer credit
Contract & property disputes
Copyright, trade marks and design
Credit brokerage
Criminal court work
Criminal legal aid
Debt
Debt adjusting and debt counselling
Debt administration
Debt collecting
Debt recovery, insolvency, bankruptcy
Disability
Discrimination
Employment
Employment law
Family and divorce
Family business advice
Housing
Human rights
Insolvency & corporate recovery
IT and intellectual property
Joint venture
Landlord & tenant
Liquor licensing
Mergers and acquisitions
Private equity
Property litigation
Provision of credit information services
Residential property
Software licensing
Wills, executries and trusts
Director
Asma Munir
Associate
Paul Martin McDermott
Employee
John Robin Wilson Carson

E.F. KELLY LIMITED
11B Academy Street, Coatbridge ML5 3AU
Tel: (01236) 434347

DX: 570511 COATBRIDGE
E-mail: kelly.e@btconnect.com
Categories of Work
Criminal court work
Criminal legal aid
Personal injury
Road traffic
Director
Edward Francis Kelly

LANARKSHIRE ACCIDENT LAW
Unit 23, Coatbank Business Centre,
Coatbridge ML5 3AG
Tel: (01236) 222888
Fax: (01236) 222889
DX: 570513 COATBRIDGE
E-mail: peter.crooks@lanaccidentlaw.co.uk
Web: www.lanaccidentlaw.co.uk
Categories of Work
Civil court work
Civil legal aid
Landlord & tenant
Personal injury
Road traffic
Partner
Peter Crooks

LINDEN LAW PRACTICE LTD
315 Muiryhall Street, Coatbridge ML5 3RY
Tel: (01236) 449921
Fax: (01236) 449921
E-mail: lindenlawpractice@gmail.com
Categories of Work
Criminal court work
Criminal legal aid
Director
Anthony John Linden

MCAFEE
83D Main Street, Coatbridge ML5 3EH
Tel: (01236) 423437
Fax: (01236) 440507
DX: 570506 COATBRIDGE
E-mail: mcafeelawyers@yahoo.co.uk
Categories of Work
Adoption
Advice the elderly & powers of attorney
Children
Childrens
Civil court work
Civil legal aid
Criminal court work
Criminal legal aid
Disability
Discrimination
Education
Employment
Employment law
Family and divorce
Human rights
Immigration and asylum
Medical negligence – claimant
Mental health
Personal injury

Professional negligence
Wills, executries and trusts
Partner
Rowan Gerard Myles
Employees
Mark Lutton
Carly Macleod
Jamie Douglas Toner

MANINI BELARDO LIMITED
7 Academy Street, Coatbridge ML5 3AU
Tel: (01236) 426070
Fax: (01236) 426088
DX: 570514 COATBRIDGE
Categories of Work
Criminal court work
Criminal legal aid
Directors
Paul Michael Belardo
Roberto Manini
Nicandro Matteo

THOMPSON FAMILY LAW
Unit 12, Coatbridge Business Centre,
Coatbridge ML5 3RB
Tel: (0141) 4046575
Categories of Work
Adoption
Advice the elderly & powers of attorney
Alternative dispute resolution
Children
Civil court work
Civil legal aid
Commercial litigation
Commercial property
Consumer credit
Criminal court work
Criminal legal aid
Data protection
Debt
Debt collecting
Debt recovery, insolvency, bankruptcy
Disability
Discrimination
Education
Family and divorce
Freedom of information
Housing
Human rights
Insolvency & corporate recovery
Insurance
IT and intellectual property
Medical negligence – defender
Medical negligence – claimant
Mental health
Personal injury
Professional negligence
Residential property
Road traffic
Wills, executries and trusts

TRAINOR ALSTON LIMITED
18 Academy Street, Coatbridge ML5 3AU
Tel: (01236) 600600

► *Coatbridge continued*

Fax: (01236) 600666
DX: 570500 COATBRIDGE
E-mail: megan@trainoralston.co.uk
Categories of Work
Adoption
Advice the elderly & powers of attorney
Children
Childrens
Civil court work
Civil legal aid
Commercial litigation
Commercial property
Consumer credit
Contract & property disputes
Criminal court work
Criminal legal aid
Debt
Discrimination
Employment
Employment law
Family and divorce
Family business advice
Health and safety
Insolvency & corporate recovery
Landlord & tenant
Liquor licensing
Medical negligence – claimant
Personal injury
Professional negligence
Residential property
Road traffic
Wills, executives and trusts
Directors
John Paul Gallacher
Theresa Mary McWilliams
Barry Charles Murphy
Hugh Trainor

Comrie

IRVING GEDDES, WS LIMITED
1 Drummond Street, Comrie PH6 2DW
Tel: (01764) 670325
E-mail: enquiries@irvinggeddes.co.uk
Web: www.irvinggeddes.co.uk
Categories of Work
Advice the elderly & powers of attorney
Agriculture and estates
Agriculture, crofting and fishing
Charities
Commercial property
Employment
Environment (Business Premises)
Family business advice
Landlord & tenant
Planning
Residential property
Unit Trusts, OEICs and investment trusts
Wills, executives and trusts

Cowdenbeath

BLACK & MARKIE
239 High Street, Cowdenbeath KY4 9QF
Tel: (01383) 610547
E-mail: blackandmarkie@hotmail.com
Web: www.blackandmarkiesolicitors.com
Categories of Work
Adoption
Advice the elderly & powers of attorney
Children
Civil court work
Civil legal aid
Criminal court work
Criminal legal aid
Mental health

GORDON MACNEIL
198 High Street, Cowdenbeath KY4 9NP
Tel: (01383) 515717
Fax: (01383) 515818
DX: 566363 COWDENBEATH
E-mail: gordon@gmacneil.co.uk
Categories of Work
Betting & gaming
Commercial property
Liquor licensing
Residential property
Wills, executives and trusts
Partner
Gordon David MacNeil

ROBERTSON WYSE
450 High Street, Cowdenbeath KY4 8LR
Tel: (01383) 515020
DX: : 566365 COWDENBEATH
E-mail: peter.e.robertson@gmail.com
Categories of Work
Adoption
Advice the elderly & powers of attorney
Children
Childrens
Civil court work
Civil legal aid
Criminal court work
Criminal legal aid
Education
Employment law
Family and divorce
Liquor licensing
Medical negligence – claimant
Residential property
Wills, executives and trusts
Partner
Peter Edwards Robertson
Employees
Christopher James Large
Jaclyn Marie Robertson

Crieff

IRVING GEDDES, WS LIMITED
25 West High Street, Crieff PH7 4AU
Tel: (01764) 653771

Fax: (01764) 654 654
E-mail: enquiries@irvinggeddes.co.uk
Web: www.irvinggeddes.co.uk
Categories of Work
Advice the elderly & powers of attorney
Agriculture and estates
Agriculture, crofting and fishing
Charities
Commercial property
Employment
Environment (Business Premises)
Family business advice
Landlord & tenant
Planning
Residential property
Unit Trusts, OEICs and investment trusts
Wills, executries and trusts
Director
David James Irving Geddes
Employee
Claire Marie Pirie

MILLER HENDRY
21 Comrie Street, Crieff PH7 4AX
Tel: (01764) 655151
Fax: (01764) 652903
DX: 566384 CRIEFF
E-mail: info@millerhendry.co.uk
Web: www.millerhendry.co.uk
Categories of Work
Adoption
Advice the elderly & powers of attorney
Agriculture and estates
Agriculture, crofting and fishing
Banking & finance
Charities
Children
Childrens
Civil court work
Civil legal aid
Commercial litigation
Commercial property
Contract & property disputes
Copyright, trade marks and design
Data protection
Debt collecting
Debt recovery, insolvency, bankruptcy
Employment
Employment law
Environment
Environment (Business Premises)
Family and divorce
Family business advice
Fishing
Housing
Immigration and asylum
Insolvency & corporate recovery
IT and intellectual property
Joint venture
Landlord & tenant
Media and entertainment
Medical negligence – claimant
Mental health

Mergers and acquisitions
Personal injury
Personal tax
Power and utilities
Professional negligence
Projects
Property litigation
Residential property
Road traffic
SME business advice
Social housing
Software licensing
Wills, executries and trusts
Associate
David John Smart
Employee
Julie Louise Darroch

Cromarty

CDA LAW
Unit 4, Cromarty Links Hub, Cromarty
IV11 8XZ
Tel: (01381) 625259
Web: www.cdalaw.co.uk
Categories of Work
Children
Civil court work
Civil legal aid
Debt
Family and divorce
Medical negligence – claimant
Personal injury
Road traffic
Wills, executries and trusts
Partner
Christopher Douglas Allan

Cullen

STEWART & WATSON
25 Grant Street, Cullen AB56 4RS
Tel: (01542) 840408
E-mail: info@stewartwatson.co.uk
Web: www.stewartwatson.co.uk
Categories of Work
Adoption
Advice the elderly & powers of attorney
Agriculture and estates
Agriculture, crofting and fishing
Alternative dispute resolution
Charities
Children
Civil court work
Civil legal aid
Commercial property
Contract & property disputes
Criminal court work
Criminal legal aid
Debt
Debt collecting
Debt recovery, insolvency, bankruptcy

► **Cullen** *continued*
Employment
Environment
Environment (Business Premises)
Family and divorce
Housing
Immigration and asylum
Landlord & tenant
Mental health
Personal injury
Projects
Residential property
Road traffic
Wills, executries and trusts

Cumbernauld

BARTON & HENDRY
Fleming House, Tryst Road, Cumbernauld
G67 1JW
Tel: (01236) 735466
Fax: (01236) 735451
DX: 500521 CUMBERNAULD
E-mail: info@bartonandhendry.co.uk
Web: www.bartonandhendry.co.uk
Categories of Work
Advice the elderly & powers of attorney
Children
Civil court work
Civil legal aid
Commercial property
Criminal court work
Criminal legal aid
Environment
Family and divorce
Landlord & tenant
Medical negligence – claimant
Personal injury
Power and utilities
Projects
Residential property
Wills, executries and trusts
Partners
Eric James Barton
Theresa Ann Beattie
Employees
Antonio Gerardo Cacace
Gillian Anne Gaffney
Natasha Racheal Pitt

DUNIPACE BROWN
12 Clyde Walk, Town Centre, Cumbernauld
G67 1BH
Tel: (01236) 453004
Fax: (01236) 458989
DX: 500534 CUMBERNAULD
E-mail: admin@dunipacebrown.co.uk
Web: www.dunipacebrown.co.uk
Categories of Work
Criminal court work
Criminal legal aid
Human rights

Partner
James Joseph Sloan

HAMILTON ROSS
The Muirfield Centre, 1A South Muirhead
Road, Cumbernauld G67 1AX
Tel: (01236) 550044
E-mail: mail@hamiltonross.co.uk
Web: www.hamiltonross.co.uk
Categories of Work
Adoption
Advice the elderly & powers of attorney
Children
Childrens
Civil court work
Civil legal aid
Criminal court work
Criminal legal aid
Family and divorce
Landlord & tenant
Medical negligence – defender
Medical negligence – claimant
Personal injury
Personal injury – defender
Professional negligence
Residential property
Road traffic
Wills, executries and trusts

MOORE & PARTNERS LLP
Office 4-5, 1st Floor Carron House,
Cumbernauld G67 1ER
Tel: (01236) 727715
Fax: (01236) 730570
DX: 500523 CUMBERNAULD
E-mail: ks@moorepartners.com
Categories of Work
Adoption
Advice the elderly & powers of attorney
Alternative dispute resolution
Children
Childrens
Civil court work
Civil legal aid
Commercial litigation
Education
Family and divorce
Partners
Catherine Mary Monaghan
Karen Smith

NORRIE MOORE LIMITED
Office 11, Muirfield Business Centre,
Cumbernauld G67 1AX
Tel: (01236) 729868
Fax: (0330) 2232574
DX: 500537 CUMBERNAULD
E-mail: norrie@nmlegal.co.uk
Categories of Work
Advice the elderly & powers of attorney
Banking & finance
Commercial property
Family business advice
Landlord & tenant

Planning (Business Premises)
Residential property
Wills, executries and trusts
Directors
Lindsey Fiona Devine
Norman William Moore
Employee
Kerrie Boyd

THE CUMBERNAULD LAW PRACTICE
28/30 Ettrick Walk, Town Centre,
Cumbernauld G67 1NE
Tel: (01236) 731911
Fax: (01236) 730038
DX: 500520 CUMBERNAULD
Web: www.cumbernauldlaw.co.uk
Categories of Work
Adoption
Advice the elderly & powers of attorney
Alternative dispute resolution
Benefit advice
Children
Childrens
Civil court work
Civil legal aid
Commercial property
Copyright, trade marks and design
Criminal court work
Criminal legal aid
Debt
Debt adjusting and debt counselling
Debt collecting
Family and divorce
Housing
Landlord & tenant
Medical negligence – claimant
Personal injury
Professional negligence
Residential property
Road traffic
Social housing
Wills, executries and trusts
Partners
Sharon Gardner
Lisa Marie O'Neil
Consultant
Ian Stewart Smart
Employee
Amrit Singh Pawar

WATT LAW
3 Leven Way, Town Centre, Cumbernauld
G67 1DY
Tel: (01236) 787030
Fax: (01236) 726814
DX: 500536 CUMBERNAULD
E-mail: alan@wattlaw.co.uk
Categories of Work
Adoption
Advice the elderly & powers of attorney
Alternative dispute resolution
Children
Childrens
Civil court work

Civil legal aid
Commercial litigation
Commercial property
Criminal court work
Criminal legal aid
Debt adjusting and debt counselling
Education
Employment
Employment law
Family and divorce
Landlord & tenant
Medical negligence – defender
Medical negligence – claimant
Personal injury
Personal injury – defender
Professional negligence
Property litigation
Road traffic
Wills, executries and trusts
Partner
Alan Robert Kennedy Watt
Employee
Zenab Saheel-Ikram

Cumnock

LOGANS
1 Ayr Road, Cumnock KA18 1DT
Tel: (01290) 424566
Fax: (01290) 426263
DX: 566422 CUMNOCK
E-mail: rlogan@loganssolicitors.co.uk
Categories of Work
Adoption
Advice the elderly & powers of attorney
Benefit advice
Children
Childrens
Civil court work
Civil legal aid
Commercial property
Criminal court work
Criminal legal aid
Debt recovery, insolvency, bankruptcy
Disability
Discrimination
Employment law
Family and divorce
Landlord & tenant
Medical negligence – claimant
Mental health
Personal injury
Residential property
Road traffic
Wills, executries and trusts
Partner
Robert Andrew Logan
Consultant
Victoria Isabella Ulph
Employee
Mhairi Elizabeth Logan

D.W. SHAW
1 The Square, Cumnock KA18 1BQ

► **Cumnock continued**

Tel: (01290) 421185
Fax: (01290) 428548
DX: 566421 CUMNOCK
E-mail: ayrreception@dwshaw.co.uk
Web: www.dwshaw.co.uk
Categories of Work
Adoption
Advice the elderly & powers of attorney
Agriculture and estates
Agriculture, crofting and fishing
Children
Civil court work
Civil legal aid
Commercial property
Criminal court work
Criminal legal aid
Family and divorce
Family business advice
Landlord & tenant
Medical negligence – defender
Medical negligence – claimant
Personal injury
Personal injury – defender
Power and utilities
Professional negligence
Residential property
Road traffic
SME business advice
Wills, executives and trusts
Partner
Lynne Jeffery

Cupar

LESLIE LAW PRACTICE
11 St. Catherine Street, Cupar KY15 4LS
Tel: (01334) 650166
Fax: (01334) 656066
Categories of Work
Adoption
Children
Childrens
Civil court work
Civil legal aid
Family and divorce
Medical negligence – claimant
Personal injury
Professional negligence
Wills, executives and trusts
Partner
Douglas Grant Leslie

PATERSON BELL LIMITED
11 – 13 St Catherine Street, Cupar KY15 4LS
Tel: (01334) 657310
DX: 560566 CUPAR
E-mail: crime@patersonbell.co.uk
Categories of Work
Criminal court work
Criminal legal aid

ROLLOS LAW LLP
67 Crossgate, Cupar KY15 5AS
Tel: (01334) 654081
Fax: (01334) 656 350
DX: 560567 CUPAR
E-mail: cupar@rollos.co.uk
Web: www.rollos.co.uk
Categories of Work
Adoption
Advice the elderly & powers of attorney
Agriculture and estates
Agriculture, crofting and fishing
Banking & finance
Children
Civil court work
Civil legal aid
Commercial property
Construction
Contract & property disputes
Criminal court work
Criminal legal aid
Debt
Disability
Discrimination
Employment
Employment law
Environment
Family and divorce
Family business advice
Fishing
Joint venture
Landlord & tenant
Mental health
Mergers and acquisitions
Personal injury
Projects
Residential property
Road traffic
SME business advice
Wills, executives and trusts
Partners
Anthony Karl Anderson
Fiona Kathleen Black
David James Bryce Harley
Associate
Judith Mary Vandecasteele
Employees
Charlotte Margaret Daly
Alice Catherine Hegarty
Donna Imrie
Jack McCrae Macpherson

THE CHAMBER PRACTICE LTD
Law House, Ferguson Square, Cupar KY15 5JU
Tel: (01334) 658222
Categories of Work
Commercial property
Family business advice
Human rights
Immigration and asylum
Landlord & tenant
Liquor licensing
Residential property

Wills, executries and trusts

THORNTONS LAW LLP
49 Bonnygate, Cupar KY15 4BY
Tel: (01334) 652285
Fax: (01334) 656331
DX: 560572 CUPAR
E-mail: cupar@thorntons-law.co.uk
Web: www.thorntons-law.co.uk
Categories of Work
Adjudication
Adoption
Advice the elderly & powers of attorney
Agriculture and estates
Agriculture, crofting and fishing
Alternative dispute resolution
Alternative investment market
Banking & finance
Benefit advice
Betting & gaming
Charities
Children
Childrens
Civil court work
Civil legal aid
Commercial litigation
Commercial property
Competition
Construction
Consumer credit
Contract & property disputes
Copyright, trade marks and design
Corporate tax
Credit brokerage
Criminal court work
Criminal legal aid
Data protection
Debt
Debt adjusting and debt counselling
Debt administration
Debt collecting
Debt recovery, insolvency, bankruptcy
Disability
Discrimination
Education
Employment
Employment law
Environment
Environment (Business Premises)
EU / international
Family and divorce
Family business advice
Fishing
Freedom of information
Health
Health and safety
Housing
Human rights
Immigration and asylum
Insolvency & corporate recovery
Insurance
IT and intellectual property
Joint venture

Landlord & tenant
Liquor licensing
Local government
Media and entertainment
Medical negligence – defender
Medical negligence – claimant
Mental health
Mergers and acquisitions
Oil & gas
Parliamentary
Pensions (Company)
Pensions (Employment)
Personal injury
Personal injury – defender
Personal tax
Planning
Planning (Business Premises)
Power and utilities
Private equity
Professional negligence
Projects
Property litigation
Public sector
Residential property
Road traffic
SME business advice
Social housing
Software licensing
Sport
Telecoms
Unit Trusts, OEICs and investment trusts
Wills, executries and trusts
Partners
Margaret Jean Allan
Susan Margaret Duff
Stephanie Elizabeth Pratt
Associate
Cheryl Samantha Wallace
Employee
Lisa May Hainey

WILLIAMSGRAYWILLIAMS LTD
10 St. Catherine Street, Cupar KY15 4HH
Tel: (01334) 656644
Fax: (01334) 655333
DX: 560573 CUPAR
Categories of Work
Advice the elderly & powers of attorney
Agriculture and estates
Agriculture, crofting and fishing
Banking & finance
Commercial property
Family business advice
Health
Joint venture
Landlord & tenant
Liquor licensing
Local government
Residential property
Wills, executries and trusts
Directors
Douglas Iain Gilfillan Gray
Kenneth Whitton Gray

► *Cupar continued*

WILLIAMSGRAYWILLIAMS LTD
7 St. Catherine Street, Cupar KY15 4LS
Tel: (01334) 656644
DX: 560573 CUPAR
E-mail: dgray@williamsgraywilliams.co.uk
Web: www.williamsgraywilliams.co.uk
Categories of Work
Advice the elderly & powers of attorney
Agriculture and estates
Agriculture, crofting and fishing
Banking & finance
Commercial property
Family business advice
Health
Joint venture
Landlord & tenant
Liquor licensing
Local government
Residential property
Wills, executries and trusts

WILLIAMS MCRAE
Law House, Ferguson Square, Cupar KY15 5JU
Tel: (01334) 658222
Categories of Work
Commercial property
Family business advice
Human rights
Immigration and asylum
Landlord & tenant
Liquor licensing
Residential property
Wills, executries and trusts

Dalbeattie

GILLESPIE GIFFORD & BROWN LLP
33 High Street, Dalbeattie DG5 4AD
Tel: (01556) 611247
Fax: (01556) 611626
DX: 556442 DALBEATTIE
E-mail: mail@ggblaw.co.uk
Categories of Work
Adoption
Advice the elderly & powers of attorney
Agriculture and estates
Agriculture, crofting and fishing
Children
Civil court work
Civil legal aid
Commercial property
Construction
Contract & property disputes
Debt
Debt collecting
Employment
Environment (Business Premises)
Family and divorce
Family business advice
Freedom of information
Landlord & tenant
Liquor licensing

Planning (Business Premises)
Residential property
Wills, executries and trusts
Partner
Abby Claire McAteer

Dalkeith

ALLAN MCDOUGALL MCQUEEN LLP
93 High Street, Dalkeith EH22 1JA
Tel: (0131) 6637261
DX: 540573 DALKEITH
E-mail: info@mcdougallmcqueen.co.uk
Web: www.mcdougallmcqueen.co.uk
Categories of Work
Adoption
Advice the elderly & powers of attorney
Charities
Children
Childrens
Civil court work
Civil legal aid
Commercial litigation
Commercial property
Contract & property disputes
Criminal court work
Criminal legal aid
Disability
Discrimination
Employment
Employment law
Family and divorce
Health and safety
Landlord & tenant
Medical negligence – claimant
Personal injury
Personal injury – defender
Personal tax
Professional negligence
Residential property
Road traffic
Wills, executries and trusts

DRUMMOND MILLER LLP
11 White Hart Street, Dalkeith EH22 1AE
Tel: (0131) 6639568
Fax: (0131) 6542676
DX: 540570 DALKEITH
E-mail: reception@drummondmiller.co.uk
Web: www.drummondmiller.co.uk
Categories of Work
Adjudication
Adoption
Advice the elderly & powers of attorney
Alternative dispute resolution
Charities
Children
Childrens
Civil court work
Civil legal aid
Commercial litigation
Commercial property
Contract & property disputes

Criminal court work
Data protection
Debt recovery, insolvency, bankruptcy
Discrimination
Education
Employment
Employment law
Environment
EU / international
Family and divorce
Family business advice
Health
Health and safety
Human rights
Immigration and asylum
Landlord & tenant
Medical negligence – defender
Medical negligence – claimant
Mental health
Oil & gas
Personal injury
Personal injury – defender
Personal tax
Professional negligence
Property litigation
Residential property
Road traffic
Wills, executries and trusts
Partner
Lynne Stratford

ANDREW T. GILBERTSON
112 High Street, Dalkeith EH22 1HZ
Tel: (0131) 6609888
DX: 540575 DALKEITH
E-mail: tweediw@aol.com
Categories of Work
Criminal court work
Criminal legal aid
Partners
Graeme Johnson Clark
Iain William Tweedie

HAUGHNEY SOLICITORS
17 Magpie Gardens, Dalkeith EH22 2RA
Tel: (0131) 6632132
E-mail: khaughney@hotmail.co.uk
Categories of Work
Advice the elderly & powers of attorney
Personal tax
Wills, executries and trusts
Partner
Kenneth Mark Paul Haughney

MCDOUGALL MCQUEEN
93 High Street, Dalkeith EH22 1JA
Tel: (0131) 6637261
DX: : 540573 DALKEITH
Web: www.mcdougallmcqueen.co.uk
Categories of Work
Adoption
Advice the elderly & powers of attorney
Charities
Children

Childrens
Civil court work
Civil legal aid
Commercial litigation
Commercial property
Contract & property disputes
Criminal court work
Criminal legal aid
Disability
Discrimination
Employment
Employment law
Family and divorce
Health and safety
Landlord & tenant
Medical negligence – claimant
Personal injury
Personal injury – defender
Personal tax
Professional negligence
Residential property
Road traffic
Wills, executries and trusts

Dalry

JAMES PATRICK & MUIR
44 New Street, Dalry KA24 5AE
Tel: (01294) 832442
Fax: (01294) 833415
DX: 556842 DALRY
E-mail: jbr@jpmlaw.co.uk
Categories of Work
Advice the elderly & powers of attorney
Agriculture and estates
Agriculture, crofting and fishing
Commercial property
Copyright, trade marks and design
Family and divorce
Family business advice
Liquor licensing
Personal injury
Personal tax
Residential property
SME business advice
Wills, executries and trusts
Partner
James Brown Russell

J. & J. MCCOSH
Clydesdale Bank Chambers, The Cross, Dalry
KA24 5AB
Tel: (01294) 832112
Fax: (01294) 833350
DX: 556481 DALRY
E-mail: info@jjmccosh.co.uk
Categories of Work
Advice the elderly & powers of attorney
Civil court work
Civil legal aid
Commercial property
Debt
Family and divorce

► **Dalry continued**

Family business advice
Mental health
Residential property
Wills, executives and trusts
Partner
Ian Briggs
Employee
Christian Macdonald Dickson

Denny

RUSSEL + AITKEN DENNY LLP
22 + 24 Stirling Street, Denny FK6 6AZ
Tel: (01324) 822194
Fax: (01324) 824560
E-mail: mail@radenny.co.uk
Web: www.radenny.co.uk
Categories of Work
Adoption
Advice the elderly & powers of attorney
Charities
Children
Civil court work
Civil legal aid
Commercial property
Contract & property disputes
Criminal court work
Criminal legal aid
Disability
Education
Employment law
Family and divorce
Landlord & tenant
Mental health
Personal injury
Residential property
Road traffic
Wills, executives and trusts
Partners
Angela O'Hara Barrett
David Elliott McClements
William Houston Simpson McIntyre
Employee
Georgia May Carey

Dingwall

BRODIES LLP
3 Fodderty Way, Dingwall Business Park,
Dingwall IV15 9XB
Tel: (01349) 860111
Fax: (01349) 860112
E-mail: mailbox@brodies.com
Categories of Work
Adjudication
Adoption
Advice the elderly & powers of attorney
Agriculture and estates
Agriculture, crofting and fishing
Alternative dispute resolution
Alternative investment market

Banking & finance
Charities
Children
Childrens
Civil court work
Civil legal aid
Commercial litigation
Commercial property
Competition
Construction
Consumer credit
Contract & property disputes
Copyright, trade marks and design
Corporate tax
Credit brokerage
Criminal court work
Criminal legal aid
Data protection
Debt
Debt adjusting and debt counselling
Debt administration
Debt collecting
Debt recovery, insolvency, bankruptcy
Disability
Discrimination
Education
Employment
Employment law
Environment
Environment (Business Premises)
EU / international
Family and divorce
Family business advice
Fishing
Freedom of information
Health
Health and safety
Housing
Human rights
Immigration and asylum
Insolvency & corporate recovery
Insurance
IT and intellectual property
Joint venture
Landlord & tenant
Liquor licensing
Local government
Media and entertainment
Medical negligence – defender
Medical negligence – claimant
Mental health
Mergers and acquisitions
Mining
Oil & gas
Parliamentary
Pensions (Company)
Pensions (Employment)
Personal injury
Personal injury – defender
Personal tax
Planning
Planning (Business Premises)
Power and utilities

Private equity
Professional negligence
Projects
Property litigation
Provision of credit information services
Public finance initiative
Public sector
Residential property
Road traffic
Shipping
SME business advice
Social housing
Software licensing
Sport
Telecoms
Transport
Unit Trusts, OEICs and investment trusts
Wills, executries and trusts
Partners
Elizabeth Jean Marie Law
Karren Smith
Associate
Sarah Ann Lilley
Employees
Adam Peter Brooks
Eildh Jayne Conacher
Karen Iona Sutherland
Peter Fraser Tolmie

MIDDLETON ROSS & ARNOT LIMITED
Mansefield House, 7 High Street, Dingwall
IV15 9HJ
Tel: (01349) 862214
Fax: (01349) 863819
DX: 520582 DINGWALL
E-mail: mail@middletonross.co.uk
Web: www.middletonross.co.uk
Categories of Work
Advice the elderly & powers of attorney
Agriculture and estates
Agriculture, crofting and fishing
Commercial property
Landlord & tenant
Residential property
Wills, executries and trusts
Director
John Alexander Maxwell
Associates
Fiona Elizabeth Fraser
Ian Rannochan Hanvidge
Sheena May MacLeod

MUNRO & NOBLE
4 Church Street, Dingwall IV15 9SB
Tel: (01349) 866777
Fax: (01349) 866888
Categories of Work
Adoption
Advice the elderly & powers of attorney
Agriculture and estates
Agriculture, crofting and fishing
Alternative dispute resolution
Children
Civil court work

Civil legal aid
Commercial litigation
Commercial property
Consumer credit
Copyright, trade marks and design
Criminal court work
Criminal legal aid
Data protection
Debt
Debt adjusting and debt counselling
Debt collecting
Debt recovery, insolvency, bankruptcy
Discrimination
Education
Employment
Employment law
Family and divorce
Freedom of information
Health
Health and safety
Housing
Landlord & tenant
Liquor licensing
Local government
Medical negligence – defender
Medical negligence – claimant
Mental health
Personal injury
Personal injury – defender
Personal tax
Professional negligence
Property litigation
Residential property
Road traffic
Social housing
Wills, executries and trusts
Partner
Alpin James Bruce Stewart
Employee
Kathryn Alice Wright

P BLACK SOLICITORS LIMITED
2 Park Street, Dingwall IV15 9JJ
Tel: (01349) 863222
Fax: (01349) 869839
Categories of Work
Advice the elderly & powers of attorney
Agriculture and estates
Agriculture, crofting and fishing
Commercial property
Family business advice
Landlord & tenant
Planning
Planning (Business Premises)
Residential property
Wills, executries and trusts
Director
Patricia Black

Dornoch

ARTHUR & CARMICHAEL LLP
Cathedral Square, Dornoch IV25 3SW

▶ *Dornoch continued*

Tel: (01862) 810202
Fax: (01862) 810166
DX: 557900 DORNOCH
E-mail: mail@arthur-carmichael.co.uk
Categories of Work
Agriculture and estates
Alternative dispute resolution
Commercial property
Contract & property disputes
Employment
Employment law
Family business advice
Residential property
SME business advice
Wills, executries and trusts
Partners
Daniel John Gunn
Colin James Milligan

Dufftown

STEPHEN & ROBB LLP
Royal Bank Buildings, 2 & 4 Fife Street,
Dufftown AB55 4AL
Tel: (01340) 820101
E-mail: dufftown@stephenrobb.co.uk
Web: www.stephenrobb.co.uk
Categories of Work
Advice the elderly & powers of attorney
Landlord & tenant
Residential property
Wills, executries and trusts

Dumbarton

ADAIRS
3 Castle Street, Dumbarton G82 1QS
Tel: (01389) 767625
Fax: (01389) 730606
DX: 500591 DUMBARTON
E-mail: mail@adairssolicitors.com
Web: www.adairssolicitors.com
Categories of Work
Adoption
Advice the elderly & powers of attorney
Children
Childrens
Civil court work
Civil legal aid
Commercial property
Contract & property disputes
Criminal court work
Criminal legal aid
Debt
Debt adjusting and debt counselling
Debt collecting
Debt recovery, insolvency, bankruptcy
Family and divorce
Human rights
Landlord & tenant
Medical negligence – claimant

Personal injury
Professional negligence
Residential property
Road traffic
Wills, executries and trusts
Partners
Jack Scott Adair
Michael James McGovern
Associate
Jill Glen Allan Foggo
Employee
Leo John McGinn

CAIRNS BROWN
45 High Street, Dumbarton G82 1LS
Tel: (01389) 742777
DX: 500571 DUMBARTON
E-mail: mail@cairnsbrown.co.uk
Web: www.cairnsbrown.co.uk
Categories of Work
Adoption
Children
Civil court work
Civil legal aid
Criminal court work
Criminal legal aid
Debt
Employment
Family and divorce
Personal injury
Personal injury – defender

CLYDE DEFENCE LAWYERS LIMITED
16 Station Road, Dumbarton G82 1QB
Tel: (01389) 730666
Fax: (01389) 761567
DX: 500572 DUMBARTON
E-mail: dumbarton@clydedefencelawyers.com
Categories of Work
Criminal court work
Criminal legal aid
Director
Brian John Colm McGuire

L KERR SOLICITORS
97-99 Glasgow Road, Dumbarton G82 1RE
Tel: (07393) 746024
E-mail: lk@lkerrsolicitors.com
Categories of Work
Adjudication
Children
Civil court work
Civil legal aid
Criminal court work
Criminal legal aid
Family and divorce
Personal injury
Road traffic
Partner
Lauren Maria Kerr

MCARTHUR STANTON
40 High Street, Dumbarton G82 1LL
Tel: (01389) 762266
Fax: (01389) 742282

DX: 500590 DUMBARTON
E-mail: dumbarton@mcarthurstanton.co.uk
Categories of Work
Adoption
Advice the elderly & powers of attorney
Agriculture and estates
Children
Civil court work
Civil legal aid
Commercial property
Criminal court work
Criminal legal aid
Debt collecting
Employment law
Family and divorce
Landlord & tenant
Liquor licensing
Medical negligence – claimant
Personal injury
Personal injury – defender
Power and utilities
Residential property
Road traffic
Telecoms
Wills, executries and trusts
Partner
Scott Charles Docherty
Employee
Christina Julie Waddell

MACINTOSH HUMBLE
21 High Street, Dumbarton G82 1LT
Tel: (01389) 763491
Fax: (01389) 742240
DX: 500596 DUMBARTON
E-mail: jem@macintosh-humble.co.uk
Categories of Work
Advice the elderly & powers of attorney
Children
Childrens
Civil court work
Civil legal aid
Education
Family and divorce
Residential property
Wills, executries and trusts
Partners
Kenneth Douglas MacRae
Jennifer Elizabeth Mansley

O'HARES
15 Station Road, Dumbarton G82 1SA
Tel: (01389) 742346
Fax: (01389) 743959
DX: 500582 DUMBARTON
E-mail: gerry@oharessolicitors.co.uk
Categories of Work
Residential property
Wills, executries and trusts
Partner
Gerard John O'Hare

A.C. O'NEILL & CO.
Second Floor, 32 High Street, Dumbarton
G82 1LL

Tel: (01389) 762997
Fax: (01389) 739006
DX: 500570 DUMBARTON
E-mail: aconeillandco@btconnect.com
Web: www.aconeill.com
Categories of Work
Adoption
Advice the elderly & powers of attorney
Alternative dispute resolution
Children
Childrens
Civil court work
Civil legal aid
Criminal court work
Criminal legal aid
Debt
Debt collecting
Debt recovery, insolvency, bankruptcy
Disability
Employment
Employment law
Family and divorce
Health and safety
Human rights
Landlord & tenant
Medical negligence – defender
Medical negligence – claimant
Mental health
Personal injury
Personal injury – defender
Road traffic
Social housing
Wills, executries and trusts
Partners
Jade Elizabeth Carthy
Alison Christina O'Neill
Employee
Michael Anthony Sweeney

PHILPOTT PLATT NIBLETT & WIGHT
103/105 Glasgow Road, Dumbarton G82 1RE
Tel: (01389) 733777
Fax: (01389) 734363
DX: 500575 DUMBARTON
E-mail: aniblett@ppnw.co.uk
Web: www.ppmw.co.uk
Categories of Work
Children
Childrens
Civil legal aid
Commercial property
Contract & property disputes
Criminal court work
Criminal legal aid
Family and divorce
Immigration and asylum
Landlord & tenant
Personal injury
Residential property
Road traffic
Wills, executries and trusts
Partner
Alan Bryce Niblett

Dumfries

BRAIDWOODS
1 Charlotte Street, Dumfries DG1 2AG
Tel: (01387) 257272
Fax: (01387) 257282
DX: 580626 DUMFRIES
E-mail: web@braidwoods.com
Web: www.braidwoods.com
Categories of Work
Advice the elderly & powers of attorney
Agriculture and estates
Commercial property
Residential property
Wills, executries and trusts
Partners
Catherine Emily Braidwood
Peter Maxwell Braidwood
Robert Maxwell Braidwood
Employee
Matthew Campbell Braidwood

BRAZENALL & ORR
104 Irish Street, Dumfries DG1 2PB
Tel: (01387) 255695
Fax: (01387) 252036
DX: 580652 DUMFRIES
E-mail: info@brazenallandorr.co.uk
Categories of Work
Children
Criminal court work
Criminal legal aid
Residential property
Wills, executries and trusts
Partners
Roger Parker Colledge
Elizabeth Dougan
Jill Jackson Irvine
Andrew Bernard Maxwell
Gavin John Stewart Orr
Employees
Cameron Ross Smillie McCartney
Amy Francis Rosemary Orr
David Thomas Hunter Orr
Sarah Elizabeth Powell
Vicki Urquhart

CHAMPION MACPHERSON SOLICITORS
66 Nunholm Road, Dumfries DG1 1JW
Tel: (07775) 072765
E-mail: info@scottishdrivinglaw.co.uk
Categories of Work
Road traffic
Partner
Joseph Oliver Champion MacPherson

CLARITY SIMPLICITY LTD
19 Bank Street, Dumfries DG1 2NX
E-mail: legalteam@claritysimplicity.co.uk
Categories of Work
Adoption
Advice the elderly & powers of attorney
Children
Childrens

Civil court work
Commercial litigation
Commercial property
Contract & property disputes
Debt
Debt recovery, insolvency, bankruptcy
Education
Family and divorce
Family business advice
Insolvency & corporate recovery
Landlord & tenant
Medical negligence – defender
Medical negligence – claimant
Personal injury
Personal injury – defender
Professional negligence
Property litigation
Residential property
Wills, executries and trusts
Employee
Lauren Dalgleish

COLLEDGE & SHIELDS LLP
30 Castle Street, Dumfries DG1 1DU
Tel: (01387) 240044
Fax: (01387) 254144
E-mail: info@colledgeandshields.co.uk
Categories of Work
Alternative dispute resolution
Children
Civil court work
Civil legal aid
Employment law
Family and divorce
Residential property
Partners
Jennifer Claire Colledge
Sandi Marie Anne Shields
Employee
Hannah Rita Stokes

GILLESPIE GIFFORD & BROWN LLP
135 Irish Street, Dumfries DG1 2NT
Tel: (01387) 255351
Fax: (01387) 257306
DX: 580663 DUMFRIES
E-mail: mail@ggblaw.co.uk
Categories of Work
Adoption
Advice the elderly & powers of attorney
Agriculture and estates
Agriculture, crofting and fishing
Children
Civil court work
Civil legal aid
Commercial property
Construction
Contract & property disputes
Debt
Debt collecting
Employment
Environment (Business Premises)
Family and divorce
Family business advice

Freedom of information
Landlord & tenant
Liquor licensing
Planning (Business Premises)
Residential property
Wills, executives and trusts
Partner
Valerie Anne McElroy

GRIEVE, GRIERSON, MOODIE & WALKER
14 Castle Street, Dumfries DG1 1DR
Tel: (01387) 266250
Fax: (01387) 257950
DX: 580664 DUMFRIES
E-mail: enquiries@ggmw.co.uk
Categories of Work
Advice the elderly & powers of attorney
Civil legal aid
Commercial property
Family and divorce
Landlord & tenant
Residential property
Wills, executives and trusts
Partners
Mhairi Elaine Dickson
Lynda Jane Rosie Vaughan

JHS LAW
8 Bank Street, Dumfries DG1 2NS
Tel: (01387) 739000
Categories of Work
Adoption
Advice the elderly & powers of attorney
Agriculture and estates
Agriculture, crofting and fishing
Alternative dispute resolution
Children
Civil court work
Civil legal aid
Commercial property
Contract & property disputes
Debt
Debt collecting
Disability
Family and divorce
Family business advice
Housing
Human rights
Landlord & tenant
Liquor licensing
Medical negligence – claimant
Mental health
Personal injury
Personal tax
Professional negligence
Property litigation
Residential property
Road traffic
Social housing
Wills, executives and trusts

JHS LAW
8/10 Bank Street, Dumfries DG1 2NS
Tel: (01387) 739000

Fax: (01387) 251320
DX: 580612 DUMFRIES
E-mail: info@jhslaw.co.uk
Web: www.jhslaw.co.uk
Categories of Work
Adoption
Advice the elderly & powers of attorney
Agriculture and estates
Agriculture, crofting and fishing
Alternative dispute resolution
Children
Civil court work
Civil legal aid
Commercial property
Contract & property disputes
Debt
Debt collecting
Disability
Family and divorce
Family business advice
Housing
Human rights
Landlord & tenant
Liquor licensing
Medical negligence – claimant
Mental health
Personal injury
Personal tax
Professional negligence
Property litigation
Residential property
Road traffic
Social housing
Wills, executives and trusts
Partners
Sharon Ann Galloway
Mark Kevin Marshall
Iain Sinclair Murray
Rebecca Joyce Ada Pickering
Consultant
Nicholas St. John Gordon
Employees
Simon William Milne
Lorraine Nicol
Laura Elizabeth Robb
Steven John Whitelaw

LATHAM & CO.
197 High Street, Dumfries DG1 2QT
Tel: (01387) 252888
Fax: (01387) 257747
DX: 580629 DUMFRIES
E-mail: office1@lathamandco.com
Categories of Work
Criminal court work
Criminal legal aid
Partner
Jacqueline Shirley Latham

LINDSAY
75 Buccleuch Street, Dumfries DG1 2AB
Tel: (01387) 259236
Fax: (01387) 267747
DX: 580639 DUMFRIES

▶ Dumfries continued

E-mail: info@lindsaysolicitors.co.uk
Categories of Work
Adoption
Advice the elderly & powers of attorney
Children
Childrens
Civil court work
Civil legal aid
Commercial litigation
Contract & property disputes
Criminal court work
Criminal legal aid
Family and divorce
Immigration and asylum
Property litigation
Road traffic
Partners
Ranald Bruce Lindsay
Tanya Louise Steel

MICHAEL LYON SOLICITORS LIMITED
43 Buccleuch Street, Dumfries DG1 2AB
Tel: (01387) 252 777
E-mail: ml@theroadtrafficlawyer.com
Web: www.theroadtrafficlawyer.com
Categories of Work
Criminal court work
Road traffic

MATTHEWS LEGAL LIMITED
The Old Bank, Buccleuch Street Bridge,
Dumfries DG2 7TJ
Tel: (01387) 257300
Fax: (01387) 257333
DX: 580637 DUMFRIES
E-mail: enquiries@abamatthews.com
Web: www.abamatthews.com
Categories of Work
Criminal court work
Criminal legal aid
Director
Neil John Da Prato

POLLOCK & MCLEAN
41 Castle Street, Dumfries DG1 1DU
Tel: (01387) 255414
E-mail: mail@pollockmclean.co.uk
Web: www.pollockmclean.co.uk
Categories of Work
Adoption
Advice the elderly & powers of attorney
Children
Civil court work
Civil legal aid
Commercial litigation
Consumer credit
Contract & property disputes
Criminal court work
Criminal legal aid
Debt
Debt collecting
Debt recovery, insolvency, bankruptcy
Disability

Discrimination
Employment
Employment law
Family and divorce
Housing
Human rights
Insolvency & corporate recovery
Landlord & tenant
Liquor licensing
Property litigation
Residential property
Road traffic
Wills, executries and trusts
Partners
Alasdair David Bryce
Lynn Lillian McMurchie

PRIMROSE & GORDON
1 Newall Terrace, Dumfries DG1 1LN
Tel: (01387) 267316
Fax: (01387) 269747
DX: 580670 DUMFRIES
E-mail: enquiries@primroseandgordon.co.uk
Web: www.primroseandgordon.co.uk
Categories of Work
Adoption
Advice the elderly & powers of attorney
Agriculture and estates
Agriculture, crofting and fishing
Charities
Children
Civil court work
Civil legal aid
Commercial property
Consumer credit
Contract & property disputes
Debt collecting
Debt recovery, insolvency, bankruptcy
Education
Employment
Employment law
Family and divorce
Family business advice
Freedom of information
Housing
Immigration and asylum
Landlord & tenant
Planning
Property litigation
Residential property
Wills, executries and trusts
Partner
John Francis Lawson
Employees
Eilidh McIntyre Raymond
Joshua Ward
Katharine Anne Wilson

SCOTTISH DRIVING LAW
1 Charlotte Street, Dumfries DG1 2AG
Tel: (01387) 640415
E-mail: info@scottishdrivinglaw.co.uk
Web: www.scottishdrivinglaw.co.uk

Categories of Work
Road traffic

WALKER & SHARPE
37 George Street, Dumfries DG1 1EB
Tel: (01387) 267222
Fax: (01387) 254775
DX: 580619 DUMFRIES
E-mail: law@walker-sharpe.co.uk
Web: www.walker-sharpe.co.uk
Categories of Work
Adoption
Advice the elderly & powers of attorney
Agriculture and estates
Agriculture, crofting and fishing
Alternative dispute resolution
Children
Childrens
Civil court work
Civil legal aid
Commercial litigation
Commercial property
Contract & property disputes
Criminal court work
Criminal legal aid
Debt
Debt collecting
Debt recovery, insolvency, bankruptcy
Employment
Employment law
Environment
Environment (Business Premises)
Family and divorce
Family business advice
Fishing
Health and safety
Landlord & tenant
Liquor licensing
Local government
Medical negligence – claimant
Mental health
Personal injury
Personal injury – defender
Property litigation
Residential property
Road traffic
Wills, executries and trusts
Partners
Shannon Kerry Joanne Gibson
Dominic Matthew Kearney
Lister Myles McKiddie
Carolyn Ann Priestley
Roderick Robertson Styles
Neil Webster
Consultant
Graham Fleming Law
Employee
Mitchel Kyle Bell

Dunbar
GARDEN STIRLING BURNET SOLICITORS LIMITED
39 High Street, Dunbar EH42 1EW

Tel: (01368) 862376
DX: 541197 DUNBAR
Categories of Work
Adoption
Advice the elderly & powers of attorney
Children
Commercial property
Criminal court work
Criminal legal aid
Education
Employment law
Family and divorce
Family business advice
Joint venture
Landlord & tenant
Liquor licensing
Residential property
Wills, executries and trusts

PARIS STEELE
116 High Street, Dunbar EH42 1JJ
Tel: (01368) 862 746
Fax: (01368) 864150
DX: 541196 DUNBAR
E-mail: dunbar@parissteele.com
Categories of Work
Advice the elderly & powers of attorney
Agriculture and estates
Betting & gaming
Civil court work
Civil legal aid
Commercial property
Contract & property disputes
Debt
Debt recovery, insolvency, bankruptcy
Disability
Employment
Employment law
Family and divorce
Family business advice
Human rights
Landlord & tenant
Liquor licensing
Medical negligence – claimant
Mental health
Personal injury
Personal tax
Property litigation
Residential property
Social housing
Wills, executries and trusts
Partners
Fiona Jane Watson
Fraser William John Symon

RJW DEFENCE LTD
10 Duke Street, Belhaven, Dunbar EH42 1NT
Tel: (07719) 272436
E-mail: rebecca@rjwdefence.com
Categories of Work
Criminal court work
Criminal legal aid
Director
Rebecca Jane Weissgerber

Dunblane

BARTYS
61 High Street, Dunblane FK15 0EH
Tel: (01786) 822296
Fax: (01786) 824249
Categories of Work
Adjudication
Adoption
Advice the elderly & powers of attorney
Agriculture and estates
Agriculture, crofting and fishing
Alternative dispute resolution
Alternative investment market
Banking & finance
Betting & gaming
Charities
Children
Childrens
Civil court work
Commercial litigation
Commercial property
Competition
Construction
Consumer credit
Contract & property disputes
Copyright, trade marks and design
Corporate tax
Criminal court work
Data protection
Debt
Debt collecting
Debt recovery, insolvency, bankruptcy
Disability
Discrimination
Education
Employment
Employment law
Environment
Environment (Business Premises)
EU / international
Family and divorce
Family business advice
Fishing
Freedom of information
Health and safety
Housing
Human rights
Insolvency & corporate recovery
Insurance
IT and intellectual property
Joint venture
Landlord & tenant
Liquor licensing
Local government
Media and entertainment
Medical negligence – defender
Medical negligence – claimant
Mergers and acquisitions
Mining
Oil & gas
Parliamentary
Pensions (Company)
Pensions (Employment)
Personal injury
Personal injury – defender
Personal tax
Planning
Planning (Business Premises)
Power and utilities
Private equity
Professional negligence
Projects
Property litigation
Public finance initiative
Public sector
Residential property
Road traffic
SME business advice
Software licensing
Sport
Telecoms
Transport
Unit Trusts, OEICs and investment trusts
Wills, executries and trusts
Partner
Bethia Mary Hamilton
Employee
Karen Crothers

MCLEAN & STEWART LLP
51/53 High Street, Dunblane FK15 0EG
Tel: (01786) 823217
Fax: (01786) 822575
DX: 560631 DUNBLANE
E-mail: mail@mcleanandstewart.co.uk
Web: www.mcleanandstewart.co.uk
Categories of Work
Adoption
Advice the elderly & powers of attorney
Agriculture and estates
Agriculture, crofting and fishing
Children
Childrens
Commercial property
Debt recovery, insolvency, bankruptcy
Family and divorce
Family business advice
Landlord & tenant
Residential property
Wills, executries and trusts
Partners
Gemma Clare Baillie
Hazel Joyce Selena Langan
Employee
Amy Elizabeth Stewart

Dundee

ANDREW FLEETWOOD
11 Park Place, Dundee DD2 2HS
Tel: (07801) 581765
E-mail: andrew@fleetwoodlegal.com
Categories of Work
Agriculture and estates
Banking & finance

Commercial property
Construction
Environment
Environment (Business Premises)
Landlord & tenant
Mergers and acquisitions
Planning
Power and utilities
Private equity
Projects
SME business advice
Partner
Andrew Beathan Fleetwood

KIM BARCLAY

9 South Tay Street, Dundee DD1 1NU
Tel: (01382) 228722
Fax: (01382) 224248
DX: DD129 DUNDEE
E-mail: law@kimbarclay.co.uk
Web: www.kimbarclay.co.uk
Categories of Work
Commercial property
Housing
Planning
Residential property
Wills, executries and trusts
Partner
Kim Barclay

BLACKADDERS LLP

30/34 Reform Street, Dundee DD1 1RJ
Tel: (01382) 229222
Fax: (01382) 342220
DX: DD108 DUNDEE
E-mail: enquiries@blackadders.co.uk
Categories of Work
Adoption
Advice the elderly & powers of attorney
Agriculture and estates
Agriculture, crofting and fishing
Alternative dispute resolution
Banking & finance
Charities
Children
Childrens
Civil court work
Civil legal aid
Commercial litigation
Commercial property
Competition
Construction
Consumer credit
Contract & property disputes
Copyright, trade marks and design
Data protection
Debt
Debt collecting
Debt recovery, insolvency, bankruptcy
Disability
Discrimination
Employment
Employment law
Environment

Environment (Business Premises)
EU / international
Family and divorce
Family business advice
Fishing
Freedom of information
Housing
Human rights
Insolvency & corporate recovery
IT and intellectual property
Joint venture
Landlord & tenant
Media and entertainment
Medical negligence – defender
Medical negligence – claimant
Mental health
Mergers and acquisitions
Pensions (Employment)
Personal injury
Personal injury – defender
Personal tax
Planning
Power and utilities
Private equity
Professional negligence
Property litigation
Public sector
Residential property
Road traffic
SME business advice
Software licensing
Sport
Telecoms
Wills, executries and trusts
Partners
Simon David Allison
Campbell John Scott Clark
Johnston Peter Campbell Clark
Kirk Anthony Dailly
Emma Louise Gray
Petra Anna Frieda Cornelia Grunenberg
Stuart David McCallum King
Laura McDowall
Susan Lea McFadyen
Lynn Melville
Craig William Samson
Douglas Sneddon
Consultant
Charles Fraser Scott Williamson
Associates
Claire Newton
Dale Ross
Employees
Hazel Lynne Barclay Anderson
Stephen David Annis
Tabitha Kate McGregor Bell
Jack Glass Boyle
Bethany Buchanan
Victoria Yvonne Christie
Rachel Elizabeth Crighton
Rachael Joanne Delaney
Blair Ian James Duncan
Corah Joanne Franco

▶ *Dundee continued*

Hamish Montgomery Fyfe
Gillian Ann Gibbons
Camilla Rose Griffiths
Megan Torano Hainey
Fiona Patricia Knox
Robyn Freda Lee
Faye Elizabeth Lipton
Suzi Low
James Douglas Martin
Blythe Helen Petrie
Zeenat Yasmeen Reid
Sara Noel MacKinnon Scott
Lucy Lindsay Smith
Cherrisse Sorrie
Sienna Margaret Fernie Sproson
Joanne Alison Scott Todd
Richard Laurie Wilson
Sarah Jane Winter

BOWMANS
27 Bank Street, Dundee DD1 1RP
Tel: (01382) 322267
Fax: (01382) 225000
DX: 110 DUNDEE
E-mail: enquiries@bowmansolicitors.co.uk
Web: www.bowmansolicitors.co.uk
Categories of Work
Advice the elderly & powers of attorney
Charities
Residential property
Wills, executries and trusts
Partner
Elizabeth Norma McGillivray
Employees
Donna Hampton
Sonja Yvonne Kidd

BOYLES SOLICITORS
Boyle Chambers, 15 Albert Square, Dundee
DD1 1DJ
Tel: (01382) 221214
Fax: (01382) 527 195
DX: DD127 DUNDEE
E-mail: enquiries@boylesolicitors.co.uk
Categories of Work
Adoption
Advice the elderly & powers of attorney
Alternative dispute resolution
Children
Childrens
Civil court work
Civil legal aid
Criminal court work
Criminal legal aid
Education
Family and divorce
Medical negligence – claimant
Personal injury
Professional negligence
Residential property
Road traffic
Wills, executries and trusts

Partners
John Ross Boyle
Elizabeth Fiona Scotland Macdonald
Employees
Susie Clark
David Graeme Stuart Rogers

BROTHOCK TRUSTEES LIMITED
Whitehall House, 33 Yeaman Shore, Dundee
DD1 4BJ
Tel: (01382) 229111
Web: www.thorntons-law.co.uk

JACK BROWN & COMPANY
7 Ward Road, Dundee DD1 1LP
Tel: (01382) 200411
DX: DD126 DUNDEE
E-mail: EDarroch@jackbrownsolicitors.co.uk
Categories of Work
Residential property
Wills, executries and trusts

MICHAEL A BROWN SOLICITORS
17 South Tay Street, Dundee DD1 1NR
Tel: (01382) 204242
E-mail: carol@michaelabrown.co.uk
Categories of Work
Advice the elderly & powers of attorney
Civil court work
Commercial litigation
Commercial property
Contract & property disputes
Debt
Employment
Family and divorce
Family business advice
Landlord & tenant
Personal injury
Property litigation
Residential property
Wills, executries and trusts
Partner
Michael Andrew Brown

BRUCE, SHORT & CO.
3 Rattray Street, Dundee DD1 1NA
Tel: (01382) 223400
Fax: (01382) 224550
DX: DD112 DUNDEE
E-mail: contactus@bruceshort.co.uk
Categories of Work
Children
Civil court work
Civil legal aid
Criminal court work
Criminal legal aid
Family and divorce
Partners
Gary Souter Foulis
Gordon Paul Parker-Smith
Michael Short
Consultant
John James Ferrie

Employees
Elizabeth Ann Hodgson
Ian James Houston
Mark John Robbins
Alexandra Short

W. & A.S. BRUCE
Unit 1 Lindsay Court, Gemini Crescent,
Technology Pk, Dundee DD2 1SW
Tel: (01382) 568188
Fax: (01382) 561768
DX: DD158 DUNDEE
Categories of Work
Adoption
Advice the elderly & powers of attorney
Agriculture and estates
Children
Childrens
Civil court work
Civil legal aid
Commercial property
Consumer credit
Contract & property disputes
Criminal court work
Criminal legal aid
Debt
Debt adjusting and debt counselling
Debt collecting
Debt recovery, insolvency, bankruptcy
Employment
Employment law
Family and divorce
Family business advice
Landlord & tenant
Liquor licensing
Medical negligence – claimant
Mental health
Pensions (Company)
Personal injury
Personal injury – defender
Personal tax
Professional negligence
Property litigation
Residential property
Road traffic
SME business advice
Wills, executries and trusts
Partner
Peter Denis McDevitt
Employee
Fraser Calder Tait

BRYMER LEGAL LIMITED
Verdant Works, West Henderson's Wynd,
Dundee DD1 5BT
DX: ED510 EDINBURGH
Categories of Work
Charities
Commercial property
Contract & property disputes
Copyright, trade marks and design
IT and intellectual property
Landlord & tenant
Media and entertainment

Private equity
Professional negligence
Residential property
SME business advice
Software licensing

CAIRD & VAUGHAN
1 Bank Street, Dundee DD1 1RL
Tel: (01382) 229399
Fax: (01382) 322003
E-mail: cairdvaughan@btconnect.com
Categories of Work
Adoption
Advice the elderly & powers of attorney
Benefit advice
Children
Childrens
Civil court work
Civil legal aid
Criminal court work
Criminal legal aid
Data protection
Debt
Debt management
Education
Employment law
Family and divorce
Freedom of information
Health
Human rights
Liquor licensing
Local government
Parliamentary
Social housing
Sport
Partners
James Ronald Archibald Caird
Alexis Boylan McVicar
Employees
Jane Elizabeth Caird
William Cameron Watt

CALDERS
10 Whitehall Street, Dundee DD1 4AQ
Tel: (01382) 224391
Fax: (01382) 202924
DX: DD4 DUNDEE
E-mail: admin@calders.com
Categories of Work
Advice the elderly & powers of attorney
Civil court work
Civil legal aid
Commercial property
Contract & property disputes
Debt
Debt collecting
Debt recovery, insolvency, bankruptcy
Disability
Discrimination
Employment
Employment law
Family and divorce
Health and safety
Landlord & tenant

▶ *Dundee continued*

Liquor licensing
Local government
Pensions (Employment)
Personal injury
Personal injury – defender
Personal tax
Property litigation
Residential property
Wills, executries and trusts
Partners
Mary Agnes Duffy Finlay Crighton
Emma Ethel Bennett De Vos

CAMPBELL BOATH
Bank House, 1 Stirling Street, Dundee
DD3 6PJ
Tel: (01382) 200110
Fax: (01382) 201078
DX: DD18 DUNDEE
Web: www.campbellboath.com
Categories of Work
Advice the elderly & powers of attorney
Commercial property
Contract & property disputes
Criminal court work
Criminal legal aid
Family business advice
Housing
Insurance
Residential property
Wills, executries and trusts
Partners
Ross Thomas Bennett
Ewan George Moffat
Kenneth James Haward Soper

CARLTON GILRUTH NOMINEES LIMITED
30/34 Reform Street, Dundee DD1 1RJ
Tel: (01382) 229222

D'ARCY PRICE LAW
Flour Mill, 34 Commercial Street, Dundee
DD1 3EJ
Tel: (01382) 217999
E-mail: info@darcypricelaw.com
Categories of Work
Criminal court work
Criminal legal aid
Partner
Kathleen Louise Price

DIGBY BROWN LLP
16-18 Whitehall Street, Dundee DD1 4AF
Tel: 3332005925
DX: DD26 DUNDEE
E-mail: enquiries@digbybrown.co.uk
Web: www.digbybrown.co.uk
Categories of Work
Advice the elderly & powers of attorney
Agriculture and estates
Agriculture, crofting and fishing
Alternative dispute resolution
Alternative investment market

Banking & finance
Benefit advice
Charities
Children
Civil court work
Civil legal aid
Commercial litigation
Commercial property
Competition
Construction
Contract & property disputes
Corporate tax
Criminal court work
Data protection
Debt
Debt adjusting and debt counselling
Debt collecting
Debt recovery, insolvency, bankruptcy
Disability
Discrimination
Employment
Employment law
Environment (Business Premises)
EU / international
Family and divorce
Family business advice
Freedom of information
Health and safety
Human rights
Immigration and asylum
Insolvency & corporate recovery
Insurance
Joint venture
Landlord & tenant
Medical negligence – defender
Medical negligence – claimant
Mental health
Mergers and acquisitions
Pensions (Company)
Personal injury
Personal injury – defender
Planning (Business Premises)
Private equity
Professional negligence
Property litigation
Provision of credit information services
Public finance initiative
Public sector
Residential property
Road traffic
SME business advice
Unit Trusts, OEICs and investment trusts
Wills, executries and trusts
Partners
Brian Christopher Castle
Robert Alexander Kernaghan
Associate
Jennifer Gray Watson
Employees
Claudia Jane McEachen
Christopher Neil Ritchie
Euan Robertson

DNLC LLP
163 Albert Street, Dundee DD4 6PX
Tel: (01382) 918230
E-mail: enquiries@dundeelaw.org
Web: www.dundeelaw.org
Categories of Work
Alternative dispute resolution
Benefit advice
Civil court work
Civil legal aid
Debt
Debt management
Disability
Discrimination
Housing
Human rights
Social housing
Partners
Joyce Anne Horsman
Rebecca Ann Menzies

DUNCAN & MCCONNELL SOLICITORS LIMITED
1st Floor, 6 Panmure Street, Dundee
DD1 2BW
Tel: (01382) 225823
E-mail: enquiries@duncanandmcconnell.com
Categories of Work
Adoption
Advice the elderly & powers of attorney
Alternative dispute resolution
Benefit advice
Children
Childrens
Civil court work
Civil legal aid
Criminal court work
Criminal legal aid
Debt
Debt management
Disability
Discrimination
Education
Employment
Employment law
Family and divorce
Health
Human rights
Medical negligence – claimant
Mental health
Personal injury
Road traffic
Social housing
Directors
David William Duncan
Douglas Iain Graham McConnell
Kym Samson
Employees
Lisa Jane Campbell
Holly Rachel Morrison

ENNOVA LAW
8 South Tay Street, Dundee DD1 1PA
Tel: (01382) 938118

Categories of Work
Adjudication
Adoption
Advice the elderly & powers of attorney
Agriculture and estates
Agriculture, crofting and fishing
Alternative dispute resolution
Banking & finance
Benefit advice
Betting & gaming
Charities
Children
Civil court work
Commercial litigation
Commercial property
Construction
Consumer credit
Contract & property disputes
Copyright, trade marks and design
Corporate tax
Debt
Debt adjusting and debt counselling
Debt collecting
Debt recovery, insolvency, bankruptcy
Disability
Discrimination
Education
Employment
Employment law
Environment (Business Premises)
Family and divorce
Family business advice
Freedom of information
Health and safety
Housing
Human rights
Insolvency & corporate recovery
Insurance
IT and intellectual property
Joint venture
Landlord & tenant
Liquor licensing
Media and entertainment
Medical negligence – claimant
Mental health
Mergers and acquisitions
Mining
Personal injury
Personal tax
Planning
Planning (Business Premises)
Power and utilities
Private equity
Professional negligence
Property litigation
Public sector
Residential property
Road traffic
SME business advice
Software licensing
Sport
Telecoms
Wills, executries and trusts

▶ *Dundee continued*

ENNOVA LIMITED
8 South Tay Street, Dundee DD1 1PA
Tel: (01382) 938118
Fax: (0131) 6677938
Categories of Work
Adjudication
Adoption
Advice the elderly & powers of attorney
Agriculture and estates
Agriculture, crofting and fishing
Alternative dispute resolution
Banking & finance
Benefit advice
Betting & gaming
Charities
Children
Civil court work
Commercial litigation
Commercial property
Construction
Consumer credit
Contract & property disputes
Copyright, trade marks and design
Corporate tax
Debt
Debt adjusting and debt counselling
Debt collecting
Debt recovery, insolvency, bankruptcy
Disability
Discrimination
Education
Employment
Employment law
Environment (Business Premises)
Family and divorce
Family business advice
Freedom of information
Health and safety
Housing
Human rights
Insolvency & corporate recovery
Insurance
IT and intellectual property
Joint venture
Landlord & tenant
Liquor licensing
Media and entertainment
Medical negligence – claimant
Mental health
Mergers and acquisitions
Mining
Personal injury
Personal tax
Planning
Planning (Business Premises)
Power and utilities
Private equity
Professional negligence
Property litigation
Public sector
Residential property

Road traffic
SME business advice
Software licensing
Sport
Telecoms
Wills, executries and trusts
Director
Fraser Morrison
Employee
Emma Louise Forrester

FENTONS
38 Elliot Road, Dundee DD2 1TB
Tel: (01382) 848458
E-mail: tfenton@plainenglish.law
Categories of Work
Contract & property disputes
Data protection
Discrimination
Employment law
Family business advice
IT and intellectual property
Joint venture
Mergers and acquisitions
SME business advice

MIKE FERRIE SOLICITOR
4 Chalmers Street, Dundee DD4 7EZ
Tel: (01382) 523977
Fax: (01382) 000053
DX: DD136 DUNDEE
E-mail: mikeferrie@outlook.com
Categories of Work
Adoption
Advice the elderly & powers of attorney
Benefit advice
Children
Civil court work
Civil legal aid
Contract & property disputes
Criminal court work
Criminal legal aid
Disability
Discrimination
Family and divorce
Fishing
Housing
Human rights
Landlord & tenant
Media and entertainment
Mental health
Property litigation
Road traffic
Social housing
Sport
Partner
Michael John Ferrie

FLYNN & CO.
1 West Bell Street, Dundee DD1 1EX
Tel: (01382) 223145
Fax: (01382) 322019
DX: DD121 DUNDEE
E-mail: flynn.legalteam@btconnect.com

Categories of Work

Adoption
Benefit advice
Children
Civil court work
Civil legal aid
Criminal court work
Criminal legal aid
Debt
Family and divorce
Mental health
Personal injury
Road traffic
Partner
Laurence Flynn

GFM LAW

13 Cowgate, Dundee DD1 2HS
Tel: (01382) 223505
Fax: (01382) 223504
DX: DD120 DUNDEE
E-mail: info@gfmlaw.co.uk
Web: www.gfmlaw.co.uk

Categories of Work

Adoption
Advice the elderly & powers of attorney
Alternative dispute resolution
Benefit advice
Charities
Children
Childrens
Civil court work
Civil legal aid
Commercial litigation
Consumer credit
Contract & property disputes
Criminal court work
Criminal legal aid
Data protection
Debt
Debt administration
Debt collecting
Debt management
Debt recovery, insolvency, bankruptcy
Disability
Discrimination
Education
Employment
Employment law
Family and divorce
Health
Housing
Human rights
Immigration and asylum
Landlord & tenant
Local government
Medical negligence – claimant
Mental health
Parliamentary
Personal injury
Property litigation
Residential property
Road traffic

Social housing
Partners
Theo William Finlay
Iain Michael MacRae
Employee
Carolyn Leckie

GILSON GRAY LLP

11 South Tay Street, Dundee DD1 1NU
Tel: (01382) 549321
Fax: (01382) 549322
E-mail: info@gilsongray.co.uk
Web: www.gilsongray.co.uk

Categories of Work

Adjudication
Adoption
Advice the elderly & powers of attorney
Agriculture and estates
Alternative dispute resolution
Banking & finance
Betting & gaming
Charities
Children
Childrens
Civil court work
Civil legal aid
Commercial litigation
Commercial property
Competition
Construction
Consumer credit
Contract & property disputes
Copyright, trade marks and design
Data protection
Debt
Debt administration
Debt collecting
Debt recovery, insolvency, bankruptcy
Disability
Discrimination
Education
Employment
Employment law
Environment
EU / international
Family and divorce
Family business advice
Freedom of information
Health and safety
Housing
Immigration and asylum
Insolvency & corporate recovery
Insurance
IT and intellectual property
Joint venture
Landlord & tenant
Liquor licensing
Local government
Media and entertainment
Medical negligence – defender
Medical negligence – claimant
Mergers and acquisitions
Mining

► **Dundee continued**

Oil & gas
Pensions (Company)
Personal injury
Personal injury – defender
Personal tax
Planning
Planning (Business Premises)
Power and utilities
Private equity
Professional negligence
Projects
Property litigation
Public sector
Residential property
Road traffic
Shipping
SME business advice
Social housing
Software licensing
Sport
Telecoms
Transport
Wills, executives and trusts
Partner
Lindsay Duncan Gunn Darroch
Associate
Lisa Martin
Employees
Karin Gwynneth Bousie
Adam Kennedy Smith
Taleen Strachan
Katarijna Bronia Thomson

GILSON GRAY LLP
37 Union Street, Dundee DD1 4BS
Categories of Work
Adjudication
Adoption
Advice the elderly & powers of attorney
Agriculture and estates
Alternative dispute resolution
Banking & finance
Betting & gaming
Charities
Children
Childrens
Civil court work
Civil legal aid
Commercial litigation
Commercial property
Competition
Construction
Consumer credit
Contract & property disputes
Copyright, trade marks and design
Data protection
Debt
Debt administration
Debt collecting
Debt recovery, insolvency, bankruptcy
Disability
Discrimination

Education
Employment
Employment law
Environment
EU / international
Family and divorce
Family business advice
Freedom of information
Health and safety
Housing
Immigration and asylum
Insolvency & corporate recovery
Insurance
IT and intellectual property
Joint venture
Landlord & tenant
Liquor licensing
Local government
Media and entertainment
Medical negligence – defender
Medical negligence – claimant
Mergers and acquisitions
Mining
Oil & gas
Pensions (Company)
Personal injury
Personal injury – defender
Personal tax
Planning
Planning (Business Premises)
Power and utilities
Private equity
Professional negligence
Projects
Property litigation
Public sector
Residential property
Road traffic
Shipping
SME business advice
Social housing
Software licensing
Sport
Telecoms
Transport
Wills, executives and trusts
Employees
Alan John Baillie
Kenneth Mitchell Glass
Alison Ann Mitchell
Tania Margaret Royle
Peter Brakenridge Shepherd

HALL NORRIE WARDEN LLP
Brook House, 86 Brook Street, Dundee
DD5 1DQ
Tel: (07752) 457043
E-mail: contact@hnwlegal.co.uk
Categories of Work
Adoption
Advice the elderly & powers of attorney
Benefit advice
Children

Childrens
Civil court work
Civil legal aid
Commercial property
Criminal court work
Criminal legal aid
Debt
Debt adjusting and debt counselling
Debt management
Education
Family and divorce
Landlord & tenant
Medical negligence – claimant
Mental health
Personal injury
Professional negligence
Residential property
Road traffic
Wills, executries and trusts
Partners
Andrew Finlayson Dunnet Lyall
Scott Keith Sreenan Norrie
Employee
Heather Anderson Glen

HENDRIE LEGAL LIMITED
20 Dock Street, Dundee DD1 3DP
Tel: (01382) 918418
Categories of Work
Commercial property
Landlord & tenant
Residential property
Wills, executries and trusts

JAB LEGAL LTD
7 Ward Road, Dundee DD1 1LP
Tel: (01382) 200411
Fax: (01382) 203033
E-mail: EDarroch@jackbrownsolicitors.co.uk
Categories of Work
Residential property
Wills, executries and trusts
Director
Elinor Morag Darroch

ANIKA JETHWA & CO
7 West Bell Street, Dundee DD1 1EX
Tel: (01382) 223399
Fax: (01382) 228833
DX: DD105 DUNDEE
E-mail: anikajethwa@btconnect.com
Categories of Work
Adjudication
Adoption
Advice the elderly & powers of attorney
Alternative dispute resolution
Children
Childrens
Civil court work
Civil legal aid
Commercial litigation
Criminal court work
Criminal legal aid
Education

Family and divorce
Medical negligence – defender
Personal injury – defender
Wills, executries and trusts
Partner
Anika Jethwa
Employees
Morgan Day
Eve Louise McKaig

KRIS GILMARTIN SOLICITOR ADVOCATE LTD
Chapelshade House, 84 Bell Street, Dundee
DD1 1RQ
Tel: (07540) 400871
Categories of Work
Criminal court work
Criminal legal aid
Director
Kristofer Gerald Gilmartin

LAMONTS LAW LIMITED
7 South Tay Street, Dundee DD1 1NU
Tel: (01382) 220202
Fax: (01382) 220203
E-mail: stevelamont@lamontsols.com
Web: www.lamontsols.com
Categories of Work
Advice the elderly & powers of attorney
Residential property
Wills, executries and trusts
Director
Steven Lamont

LAWSON COULL & DUNCAN
136/138 Nethergate, Dundee DD1 4PA
Tel: (01382) 227555
Fax: (01382) 200978
DX: DD131 DUNDEE
Web: www.lawsoncoull.co.uk
Categories of Work
Adoption
Advice the elderly & powers of attorney
Charities
Children
Childrens
Civil court work
Civil legal aid
Commercial property
Contract & property disputes
Criminal court work
Criminal legal aid
Debt
Disability
Discrimination
Education
Employment
Employment law
Family and divorce
Health and safety
Human rights
Landlord & tenant
Medical negligence – claimant
Mental health
Personal injury

▶ *Dundee continued*

Professional negligence
Residential property
Road traffic
Wills, executries and trusts
Partners
Campbell Victor Donaldson
Laura Catherine McDonald
Gary McIlravey
Hugh Derek McKay
Consultant
George Cullerton Donnelly
Employees
Amy Natasha Paula Black
Ross David Donnelly
Robyn Sarah MacNeil
Alison Morris

LINDSAYS LLP
Seabraes House, 18 Greenmarket, Dundee
DD1 4QB
Tel: (01382) 224112
Fax: (01382) 200109
E-mail: dundee@lindsays.co.uk
Categories of Work
Adjudication
Adoption
Advice the elderly & powers of attorney
Agriculture and estates
Agriculture, crofting and fishing
Alternative dispute resolution
Banking & finance
Betting & gaming
Charities
Children
Childrens
Civil court work
Civil legal aid
Commercial litigation
Commercial property
Construction
Consumer credit
Contract & property disputes
Copyright, trade marks and design
Corporate tax
Criminal court work
Criminal legal aid
Data protection
Debt
Debt adjusting and debt counselling
Debt administration
Debt collecting
Debt recovery, insolvency, bankruptcy
Discrimination
Education
Employment
Employment law
Environment
Environment (Business Premises)
EU / international
Family and divorce
Family business advice
Fishing

Freedom of information
Health
Health and safety
Housing
Human rights
Insolvency & corporate recovery
IT and intellectual property
Joint venture
Landlord & tenant
Liquor licensing
Local government
Media and entertainment
Medical negligence – defender
Medical negligence – claimant
Mergers and acquisitions
Oil & gas
Parliamentary
Pensions (Employment)
Personal injury
Personal injury – defender
Personal tax
Planning
Planning (Business Premises)
Power and utilities
Private equity
Professional negligence
Projects
Property litigation
Public finance initiative
Public sector
Residential property
Road traffic
SME business advice
Software licensing
Sport
Telecoms
Transport
Wills, executries and trusts
Partners
Caroline Allison Fraser
Jennifer Gallagher
Ian Grant Johnson
David Geddes Rose
Christopher John Todd
Katherine Jane Wyatt
Employees
Catriona Black
Lindsay Nicol Carr
Emma Louise Conway
Katherine Jennifer McAlpine
Erin Louise Peoples
Michael Piggot
Kirsty Louise Preston
Miriam Fraser Rennet
Joanna Ruth Saigeon

LINDSAYS (PROPERTY)
21 Crichton Street, Dundee DD1 3AR
Tel: (01382) 802050
Fax: (01382) 868109
DX: DD143 DUNDEE
E-mail: dundeeproperty@lindsays.co.uk

Categories of Work
Adjudication
Adoption
Advice the elderly & powers of attorney
Agriculture and estates
Agriculture, crofting and fishing
Alternative dispute resolution
Banking & finance
Betting & gaming
Charities
Children
Childrens
Civil court work
Civil legal aid
Commercial litigation
Commercial property
Construction
Consumer credit
Contract & property disputes
Copyright, trade marks and design
Corporate tax
Criminal court work
Criminal legal aid
Data protection
Debt
Debt adjusting and debt counselling
Debt administration
Debt collecting
Debt recovery, insolvency, bankruptcy
Discrimination
Education
Employment
Employment law
Environment
Environment (Business Premises)
EU / international
Family and divorce
Family business advice
Fishing
Freedom of information
Health
Health and safety
Housing
Human rights
Insolvency & corporate recovery
IT and intellectual property
Joint venture
Landlord & tenant
Liquor licensing
Local government
Media and entertainment
Medical negligence – defender
Medical negligence – claimant
Mergers and acquisitions
Oil & gas
Parliamentary
Pensions (Employment)
Personal injury
Personal injury – defender
Personal tax
Planning
Planning (Business Premises)
Power and utilities

Private equity
Professional negligence
Projects
Property litigation
Public finance initiative
Public sector
Residential property
Road traffic
SME business advice
Software licensing
Sport
Telecoms
Transport
Wills, executries and trusts
Partners
Duncan William Neil Mackinnon
Angela Jane Morrison

MACKENZIE & MACKENZIE
24 Abercorn Street, Dundee DD4 7FA
Tel: (01382) 455263
Fax: (01382) 454 822
DX: DD133 DUNDEE
E-mail: suzie_mackenzie@hotmail.com
Categories of Work
Advice the elderly & powers of attorney
Residential property
Wills, executries and trusts
Partners
Duncan Randell Mackenzie
Suzanne Margaret Mackenzie

MACROBERTS LLP
River Court, 5 West Victoria Dock Road,
Dundee DD1 3JT
Tel: (01382) 339340
Categories of Work
Adjudication
Adoption
Advice the elderly & powers of attorney
Agriculture and estates
Agriculture, crofting and fishing
Alternative dispute resolution
Alternative investment market
Banking & finance
Betting & gaming
Charities
Children
Civil court work
Commercial litigation
Commercial property
Competition
Construction
Consumer credit
Contract & property disputes
Copyright, trade marks and design
Data protection
Debt
Debt adjusting and debt counselling
Debt administration
Debt collecting
Debt recovery, insolvency, bankruptcy
Disability
Discrimination

▶ **Dundee continued**

Education
Employment
Employment law
Environment
Environment (Business Premises)
EU / international
Family and divorce
Family business advice
Fishing
Freedom of information
Health
Health and safety
Housing
Human rights
Immigration and asylum
Insolvency & corporate recovery
Insurance
IT and intellectual property
Joint venture
Landlord & tenant
Liquor licensing
Local government
Media and entertainment
Mergers and acquisitions
Mining
Oil & gas
Parliamentary
Pensions (Company)
Pensions (Employment)
Personal injury
Personal injury – defender
Personal tax
Planning
Planning (Business Premises)
Power and utilities
Private equity
Professional negligence
Projects
Property litigation
Public finance initiative
Public sector
Residential property
Road traffic
Shipping
SME business advice
Software licensing
Sport
Telecoms
Transport
Unit Trusts, OEICs and investment trusts
Wills, executries and trusts
Partners
David John Milne
Kyle Frank Strachan Moir
Consultant
John Ernest Newall Macmillan
Associate
Christopher Peter John Gardiner
Employees
Kim Jacqueline De-Smid
Derek Allan Petrie

Gemma Louise Scrimgeour

ANDREW G. MANDERSON & CO.
51 Reform Street, Dundee DD1 1SL
Tel: (01382) 200840
Fax: (01382) 200486
DX: DD95 DUNDEE
E-mail: andrewgmanderson@btconnect.com
Categories of Work
Commercial property
Landlord & tenant
Residential property
Wills, executries and trusts
Partner
Andrew George Manderson

MILLER HENDRY
13 Ward Road, Dundee DD1 1LU
Tel: (01382) 200000
Fax: (01382) 200098
E-mail: info@millerhendry.co.uk
Web: www.millerhendry.co.uk
Categories of Work
Adoption
Advice the elderly & powers of attorney
Agriculture and estates
Agriculture, crofting and fishing
Banking & finance
Charities
Children
Childrens
Civil court work
Civil legal aid
Commercial litigation
Commercial property
Contract & property disputes
Copyright, trade marks and design
Data protection
Debt collecting
Debt recovery, insolvency, bankruptcy
Employment
Employment law
Environment
Environment (Business Premises)
Family and divorce
Family business advice
Fishing
Housing
Immigration and asylum
Insolvency & corporate recovery
IT and intellectual property
Joint venture
Landlord & tenant
Media and entertainment
Medical negligence – claimant
Mental health
Mergers and acquisitions
Personal injury
Personal tax
Power and utilities
Professional negligence
Projects
Property litigation
Residential property

Road traffic
SME business advice
Social housing
Software licensing
Wills, executives and trusts
Solicitor
Simon John Smith
Partners
Ernest Sinclair Boath
Alistair Ross Duncan
Alison Louise Fitzgerald
Associate
Lyndsey White
Employees
Adam Stewart Hoggan
Fiona Alexandra Kelly
Lindsay Kirkwood
Catriona Ann Leuchars
Sharon Nicola Somerville

MML LEGAL
Meadow Place Buildings, Bell Street, Dundee
DD1 1EJ
Tel: (01382) 206 000
Fax: (01382) 206 012
DX: DD140 DUNDEE
Web: www.mmllegal.co.uk
Categories of Work
Adoption
Advice the elderly & powers of attorney
Benefit advice
Children
Civil court work
Civil legal aid
Commercial litigation
Commercial property
Contract & property disputes
Criminal court work
Criminal legal aid
Debt
Debt collecting
Debt recovery, insolvency, bankruptcy
Education
Employment
Employment law
Family and divorce
Health and safety
Housing
Human rights
Joint venture
Landlord & tenant
Mental health
Mergers and acquisitions
Pensions (Employment)
Property litigation
Residential property
Social housing
Wills, executives and trusts
Partners
Stephen James Forsyth
Alan Fraser
Kevin Hampton
James Laverty

John Clarke Muir
Ryan Robert Russell
Employees
John Tosh Clancy
Amy Elspeth Fox
Jay Lawson
Niamh Orla Lee

J. MYLES & CO.
7-9 South Tay Street, Dundee DD1 1NU
Tel: (01382) 204625
Fax: (01382) 227972
DX: DD125 DUNDEE
E-mail: jmylessols@btopenworld.com
Categories of Work
Adoption
Advice the elderly & powers of attorney
Children
Childrens
Civil court work
Civil legal aid
Commercial litigation
Commercial property
Contract & property disputes
Criminal court work
Criminal legal aid
Debt
Debt collecting
Debt recovery, insolvency, bankruptcy
Employment
Employment law
Family and divorce
Human rights
Landlord & tenant
Medical negligence – claimant
Personal injury
Personal injury – defender
Professional negligence
Property litigation
Residential property
Road traffic
Wills, executives and trusts
Partner
Joseph Myles
Associate
Jane Elizabeth Cumming
Employees
Blair Andrew Robertson
Michael Colin Robertson

PLAIN ENGLISH LAW LIMITED
Flour Mill, Unit 4.6.2, 34 Commercial Street,
Dundee DD1 3EJ
Tel: (01382) 848458
E-mail: tfenton@plainenglish.law
Categories of Work
Contract & property disputes
Data protection
Discrimination
Employment law
Family business advice
IT and intellectual property
Joint venture
Mergers and acquisitions

817

▶ *Dundee continued*

SME business advice
Director
Trevor Earl Fenton

RICHMOND & CO.
26 Commercial Street, Dundee DD1 3EJ
Tel: (01382) 201964
Fax: (01382) 224214
DX: DD53 DUNDEE
E-mail: richmondco@btconnect.com
Categories of Work
Adoption
Benefit advice
Children
Civil legal aid
Commercial property
Family and divorce
Housing
Landlord & tenant
Residential property
Wills, executries and trusts
Partner
Carol Ann Parratt

ROBERTSON SMITH
18B West Marketgait, Dundee DD1 1QR
Tel: (01382) 226602
Fax: (01382) 322884
DX: DD150 DUNDEE
E-mail: r.robertson@rsdundee.f9.co.uk
Categories of Work
Commercial property
Family business advice
Landlord & tenant
Mergers and acquisitions
Residential property
Wills, executries and trusts
Partner
Alexander Ritchie Robertson

ROSS, STRACHAN & CO.
2 India Buildings, 86 Bell Street, Dundee
DD1 1JQ
Tel: (01382) 201010
Fax: (01382) 202368
DX: DD151 DUNDEE
E-mail: mford@ross-strachan.co.uk
Web: www.ross-strachan.co.uk
Categories of Work
Adoption
Advice the elderly & powers of attorney
Children
Civil court work
Civil legal aid
Commercial property
Contract & property disputes
Debt
Education
Family and divorce
Family business advice
Landlord & tenant
Mental health
Property litigation

Residential property
SME business advice
Wills, executries and trusts
Partners
Michael Gregory Ford
Valerie Jane Lyall
Stephen Martyn Muir

RSB LINDSAYS
Seabraes House, 18 Greenmarket, Dundee
DD1 4QB
Tel: (01382) 224112
Fax: (01382) 200109
DX: DD143 DUNDEE
E-mail: dundee@lindsays.co.uk
Categories of Work
Adjudication
Adoption
Advice the elderly & powers of attorney
Agriculture and estates
Agriculture, crofting and fishing
Alternative dispute resolution
Banking & finance
Betting & gaming
Charities
Children
Childrens
Civil court work
Civil legal aid
Commercial litigation
Commercial property
Construction
Consumer credit
Contract & property disputes
Copyright, trade marks and design
Corporate tax
Criminal court work
Criminal legal aid
Data protection
Debt
Debt adjusting and debt counselling
Debt administration
Debt collecting
Debt recovery, insolvency, bankruptcy
Discrimination
Education
Employment
Employment law
Environment
Environment (Business Premises)
EU / international
Family and divorce
Family business advice
Fishing
Freedom of information
Health
Health and safety
Housing
Human rights
Insolvency & corporate recovery
IT and intellectual property
Joint venture
Landlord & tenant

Liquor licensing
Local government
Media and entertainment
Medical negligence – defender
Medical negligence – claimant
Mergers and acquisitions
Oil & gas
Parliamentary
Pensions (Employment)
Personal injury
Personal injury – defender
Personal tax
Planning
Planning (Business Premises)
Power and utilities
Private equity
Professional negligence
Projects
Property litigation
Public finance initiative
Public sector
Residential property
Road traffic
SME business advice
Software licensing
Sport
Telecoms
Transport
Wills, executies and trusts

Partners
John Derek Duncan
Darren John Leahy
Employees
Leann Marie Brown
Julie Malone
Andrew Alan Ritchie

THE CHAMBER PRACTICE LTD
30 Whitehall Street, Dundee DD1 4AF
Tel: (01382) 203000
Fax: (01382) 723756
DX: DD115 DUNDEE
E-mail: scott@thechamberpractice.co.uk
Web: www.thechamberpractice.co.uk
Categories of Work
Commercial property
Family business advice
Human rights
Immigration and asylum
Landlord & tenant
Liquor licensing
Residential property
Wills, executies and trusts
Directors
Scott Campbell
Sandra Anne Teall

THOMPSONS
4 Whitehall Crescent, Dundee DD1 4AU
Categories of Work
Adoption
Advice the elderly & powers of attorney
Agriculture and estates
Alternative dispute resolution

Charities
Children
Childrens
Civil court work
Civil legal aid
Commercial litigation
Consumer credit
Criminal court work
Disability
Discrimination
Education
Employment
Employment law
Family and divorce
Health
Health and safety
Human rights
Immigration and asylum
Insurance
Medical negligence – claimant
Personal injury
Personal injury – defender
Professional negligence
Residential property
Road traffic
Social housing
Wills, executies and trusts
Employee
Craig Fraser Snee

THORNTONS LAW LLP
Whitehall House, 33 Yeaman Shore, Dundee
DD1 4BJ
Tel: (01382) 229 111
Fax: (01382) 202 288
DX: DD157 DUNDEE
E-mail: dundee@thorntons-law.co.uk
Web: www.thorntons-law.co.uk
Categories of Work
Adjudication
Adoption
Advice the elderly & powers of attorney
Agriculture and estates
Agriculture, crofting and fishing
Alternative dispute resolution
Alternative investment market
Banking & finance
Benefit advice
Betting & gaming
Charities
Children
Childrens
Civil court work
Civil legal aid
Commercial litigation
Commercial property
Competition
Construction
Consumer credit
Contract & property disputes
Copyright, trade marks and design
Corporate tax
Credit brokerage

► *Dundee continued*

Criminal court work
Criminal legal aid
Data protection
Debt
Debt adjusting and debt counselling
Debt administration
Debt collecting
Debt recovery, insolvency, bankruptcy
Disability
Discrimination
Education
Employment
Employment law
Environment
Environment (Business Premises)
EU / international
Family and divorce
Family business advice
Fishing
Freedom of information
Health
Health and safety
Housing
Human rights
Immigration and asylum
Insolvency & corporate recovery
Insurance
IT and intellectual property
Joint venture
Landlord & tenant
Liquor licensing
Local government
Media and entertainment
Medical negligence – defender
Medical negligence – claimant
Mental health
Mergers and acquisitions
Oil & gas
Parliamentary
Pensions (Company)
Pensions (Employment)
Personal injury
Personal injury – defender
Personal tax
Planning
Planning (Business Premises)
Power and utilities
Private equity
Professional negligence
Projects
Property litigation
Public sector
Residential property
Road traffic
SME business advice
Social housing
Software licensing
Sport
Telecoms
Unit Trusts, OEICs and investment trusts
Wills, executories and trusts

Partners
Christopher David Allan
Nicholas Barclay
Gillian Coutts Buchanan
Christopher James Byrne
Lorna Margaret Christine
Steven Drake
David Murray Etherington
Deborah Fellows
Robin James Douglas Francis
Colin Thomas Graham
Jacqueline Henderson
Caroline Patricia Kelly
John William Crighton Kydd
Lesley Ann Larg
Gary Ian Mannion
Loretta Angela Maxfield
Gordon Graham McBean
Noele Gillian McClelland
Janet Helen McIntyre
Liam James McMonagle
Ewan Kenneth Miller
Scott Charles Milne
Craig Orr Nicol
Lauren Janet Rae
Michael Royden
Kenneth William Thomson
Graham Alexander Wilson
Associates
Christina Hill Baillie
Graeme Ross Campbell Dickson
James Richard Graham Jackson
Sylvia Marion Johnstone
Nicola Louise McCafferty
Lynsay Margaret McFarlane
Shirley Margaret Phillips
Richard Robert Poole
Nina Elizabeth Sinclair
Alison Mary Stevenson
Solicitors
Gemma Louise Hardie
Lisa Ann Mannion
Employees
Vicki Alexander
Chlo Rose Anderson
Rachel Anderson
Aadil Shamoon Anwar
Hayley Maree Blackman
Iain James Buchan
Michelle Burns
Kim Campbell
Ross Ian Cargill
Danielle Mari Connell
Sarah Cooper
Karen Margaret Cornwell
Lee Corr
Ling Shan Deng
Katharine Rose Dow
Aimee Louise Gibbons
Maria Christine Gravelle
Donna Louise Gray
Rachel Joy High
Sarah Ruth High

Alex May Patricia Hirst Dawson
Amy Carole Jones
Michael William Kemp
Jamie Kenneth Lyons
Alison Goodwin Marks
Daniel Patrick McGinn
Kerri Anne McIver
Jillian Vaughan McLaughlan
Neil Alistair McWilliam
Anne Margaret Miller
Stephen Patrick O'Hare
Ruth Alison Pyatt
Claire Redmond
Lauren Smith
Kirsty Stewart
Lynne Sturrock
Stephanie Margaret Watson
Kirsty Patricia Waughman

THORNTONS PROPERTY SERVICES
Whitehall House, 33 Yeaman Shore, Dundee
DD1 4BJ
Tel: (01382) 229111
Web: www.thorntons-law.co.uk
Categories of Work
Adjudication
Adoption
Advice the elderly & powers of attorney
Agriculture and estates
Agriculture, crofting and fishing
Alternative dispute resolution
Alternative investment market
Banking & finance
Benefit advice
Betting & gaming
Charities
Children
Childrens
Civil court work
Civil legal aid
Commercial litigation
Commercial property
Competition
Construction
Consumer credit
Contract & property disputes
Copyright, trade marks and design
Corporate tax
Credit brokerage
Criminal court work
Criminal legal aid
Data protection
Debt
Debt adjusting and debt counselling
Debt administration
Debt collecting
Debt recovery, insolvency, bankruptcy
Disability
Discrimination
Education
Employment
Employment law
Environment

Environment (Business Premises)
EU / international
Family and divorce
Family business advice
Fishing
Freedom of information
Health
Health and safety
Housing
Human rights
Immigration and asylum
Insolvency & corporate recovery
Insurance
IT and intellectual property
Joint venture
Landlord & tenant
Liquor licensing
Local government
Media and entertainment
Medical negligence – defender
Medical negligence – claimant
Mental health
Mergers and acquisitions
Oil & gas
Parliamentary
Pensions (Company)
Pensions (Employment)
Personal injury
Personal injury – defender
Personal tax
Planning
Planning (Business Premises)
Power and utilities
Private equity
Professional negligence
Projects
Property litigation
Public sector
Residential property
Road traffic
SME business advice
Social housing
Software licensing
Sport
Telecoms
Unit Trusts, OEICs and investment trusts
Wills, executries and trusts

WHITEHALL CHAMBERS TRUSTEES LIMITED
Whitehall House, 33 Yeaman Shore, Dundee
DD1 4BJ
Tel: (01382) 229111
Web: www.thorntons-law.co.uk

AMANDA WILSON FAMILY LAW
Office 12, 4th Floor, Dundee One, 5 West
Victoria Dock Road, Dundee DD1 3JT
Tel: (01382) 219004
Categories of Work
Adoption
Alternative dispute resolution
Children
Civil court work
Family and divorce

▶ **Dundee continued**

Partner
Amanda Anne Wilson

Dunfermline

ARLOW BROWN
26a East Port, Dunfermline KY12 7JB
Tel: (01383) 626626
Fax: (01383) 626627
DX: DF51 DUNFERMLINE
E-mail: arlowbrownlegal@gmail.com
Categories of Work
Advice the elderly & powers of attorney
Residential property
Wills, executives and trusts
Partner
Christine Isabel Arlow

BASTEN SNEDDON COURT SOLICITORS
20 Douglas Street, Dunfermline KY12 7EB
Tel: (01383) 621144
DX: DFS4 DUNFERMLINE
Categories of Work
Criminal court work
Criminal legal aid

IAN BEATSON
30 Headwell Road, Dunfermline KY12 0PW
Tel: 7762412943
E-mail: ibeatson@hotmail.co.uk
Categories of Work
Criminal court work
Criminal legal aid
Partner
Ian Beatson

BLACK & MARKIE
12 Douglas Street, Dunfermline KY12 7EB
Tel: (01383) 610 547
Fax: (01383) 732 246
DX: 560450 ALLOA
E-mail: bbblackandmarkie@hotmail.co.uk
Web: www.blackandmarkiesolicitors.com
Categories of Work
Adoption
Advice the elderly & powers of attorney
Children
Civil court work
Civil legal aid
Criminal court work
Criminal legal aid
Mental health
Partner
Brian Black
Consultant
Brian George Thomas Allison
Employee
Elaine Marie Buist

BONNAR ACCIDENT LAW LTD
8 New Row, Dunfermline KY12 7EF
Tel: (01383) 604110
Fax: (01383) 604113

DX: DF20 DUNFERMLINE
E-mail: findout@bonnarandco.com
Web: www.bonnarandco.com
Categories of Work
Civil court work
Civil legal aid
Health and safety
Personal injury
Professional negligence
Road traffic
Associate
Julian Paul Hanrahan

W. & A.S. BRUCE
80 St Margarets Street, Dunfermline KY12 7PE
Tel: (01383) 738000
Fax: (01383) 729105
DX: DF86 DUNFERMLINE
E-mail: pmcd@wasbruce.co.uk
Categories of Work
Adoption
Advice the elderly & powers of attorney
Agriculture and estates
Children
Childrens
Civil court work
Civil legal aid
Commercial property
Consumer credit
Contract & property disputes
Criminal court work
Criminal legal aid
Debt
Debt adjusting and debt counselling
Debt collecting
Debt recovery, insolvency, bankruptcy
Employment
Employment law
Family and divorce
Family business advice
Landlord & tenant
Liquor licensing
Medical negligence – claimant
Mental health
Pensions (Company)
Personal injury
Personal injury – defender
Personal tax
Professional negligence
Property litigation
Residential property
Road traffic
SME business advice
Wills, executives and trusts
Partners
Charles Berry Campbell
Sarah Josephine Jordan
Keith Robert William Kordula
Selina Mackay
Employees
Christopher Edward Campbell
Barbara Anne Collie
Catherine Howitt

BSW SOLICITORS LLP
20 Douglas Street, Dunfermline KY12 7EB
Tel: (01383) 621144
Fax: (01383) 621133
Categories of Work
Criminal court work
Criminal legal aid
Partners
Graham John Basten
Christopher Alexander Sneddon
Employees
Gwen Patricia Haggerty
James William Moncrieff
Stephen Gordon Morrison

CARITAS LEGAL LIMITED
Unit 10, Dunfermline Business Centre,
Dunfermline KY11 3BZ
Tel: (01383) 431101
DX: DFS7 DUNFERMLINE
E-mail: lornabrown@caritaslegal.co.uk
Web: www.caritaslegal.co.uk
Categories of Work
Adoption
Advice the elderly & powers of attorney
Children
Childrens
Civil court work
Civil legal aid
Family and divorce
Mental health
Director
Lorna Harriet Brown
Employees
Danielle Emma Stevenson
Christopher Liam Yule

CARITAS MENTAL HEALTH LAW
Unit 3, Dunfermline Business Centre,
Dunfermline KY11 3BZ
Tel: (01383) 431101
Categories of Work
Adoption
Advice the elderly & powers of attorney
Children
Childrens
Civil court work
Civil legal aid
Family and divorce
Mental health

CLICK4CONVEYANCING LIMITED
East Port House, 12 East Port, Dunfermline
KY12 7JB
Tel: (01383) 667550
E-mail: kyle.peddie@yourconveyancer.co.uk

DINGWALL SOLICITORS LTD
24 Chalmers Street, Dunfermline KY12 8DF
Tel: (01383) 808198
Fax: (01383) 729429
DX: DF71 DUNFERMLINE
E-mail: fdingwall@ds-solicitors.co.uk
Categories of Work
Alternative dispute resolution

Civil court work
Commercial litigation
Contract & property disputes
Debt
Debt recovery, insolvency, bankruptcy
Landlord & tenant
Property litigation
Residential property
Employee
Elizabeth Deborah Carole Milligan

DONNACHIE LAW
15 Pitreavie Court, Pitreavie Business Park,
Dunfermline KY11 8UU
Tel: (0800) 678 5167
DX: DF14 DUNFERMLINE
E-mail: Hello@DonnachieLaw.com
Web: www.DonnachieLaw.com
Categories of Work
Civil court work
Commercial litigation
Contract & property disputes
Criminal court work
Debt collecting
Debt recovery, insolvency, bankruptcy
Family and divorce
Health and safety
Professional negligence
Property litigation
Road traffic
Partner
Paul Kenneth Donnachie

GORRIE & DAVIDSON
26 Viewfield Terrace, Dunfermline KY12 7LB
Tel: (01383) 723618
Fax: (01383) 620367
DX: DF66 DUNFERMLINE
E-mail: iwd@gorriedavidson.co.uk
Categories of Work
Adoption
Advice the elderly & powers of attorney
Alternative investment market
Betting & gaming
Children
Commercial litigation
Commercial property
Contract & property disputes
Debt recovery, insolvency, bankruptcy
Employment
Family and divorce
Health and safety
Housing
Liquor licensing
Personal injury
Personal injury – defender
Public sector
Residential property
Road traffic
SME business advice
Transport
Wills, executries and trusts
Partner
Ian William Donaldson

► *Dunfermline continued*

MALCOLM, JACK & MATHESON LIMITED
Walmer House, Walmer Drive, Dunfermline
KY12 7LH
Tel: (01383) 723444
Fax: (01383) 730672
DX: DF8 DUNFERMLINE
E-mail: enquiries@malcolmjack.co.uk
Web: www.malcolmjack.co.uk
Categories of Work
Adjudication
Adoption
Advice the elderly & powers of attorney
Alternative dispute resolution
Children
Civil court work
Civil legal aid
Commercial litigation
Commercial property
Contract & property disputes
Criminal court work
Criminal legal aid
Debt
Debt collecting
Debt recovery, insolvency, bankruptcy
Disability
Discrimination
Education
Employment law
Family and divorce
Family business advice
Housing
Human rights
Insolvency & corporate recovery
Landlord & tenant
Medical negligence – defender
Personal injury – defender
Property litigation
Residential property
Road traffic
Sport
Wills, executries and trusts
Directors
Steven James Fell
Ralph Douglas McCran
Consultant
Peter Scott
Employees
Lyndsey Sophia McCran
Lynsey Pender
Aileen Cecilia Shaw

MALOCO + ASSOCIATES LIMITED
6-8 Bonnar Street, Dunfermline KY12 7JR
Tel: (01383) 629720
Fax: (01383) 621333
DX: DF69 DUNFERMLINE
E-mail: jim@maloco.co.uk
Web: www.maloco.co.uk
Categories of Work
Children
Civil court work
Family and divorce
Residential property
Wills, executries and trusts
Directors
Michael Joseph Maloco
Laura Mowat
Stacey Parker

MALOCO LETTINGS
6-8 Bonnar Street, Dunfermline KY12 7JR
Tel: (01383) 629720
Categories of Work
Children
Civil court work
Family and divorce
Residential property
Wills, executries and trusts

MARTIN, JOHNSTON & SOCHA LIMITED
11 Maygate, Dunfermline KY12 7NE
Tel: (01383) 730466
Fax: (01383) 621440
DX: DF70 DUNFERMLINE
E-mail: dunfermline1@btconnect.com
Categories of Work
Children
Civil court work
Civil legal aid
Criminal court work
Criminal legal aid
Data protection
Family and divorce
Human rights
Directors
Alexander Flett
Gordon Martin
Employees
Aime Allan
Maureen Duffy
Calum Harris

MORGANS
33 East Port, Dunfermline KY12 7JE
Tel: (01383) 620222
Fax: (01383) 621213
E-mail: info@morganlaw.co.uk
Web: www.morganlaw.co.uk
Categories of Work
Adoption
Advice the elderly & powers of attorney
Children
Civil court work
Civil legal aid
Commercial litigation
Consumer credit
Contract & property disputes
Criminal court work
Criminal legal aid
Debt
Debt collecting
Debt recovery, insolvency, bankruptcy
Employment
Employment law
Family and divorce
Landlord & tenant

Medical negligence – claimant
Personal injury
Professional negligence
Residential property
Road traffic
Wills, executries and trusts
Partners
Craig Bennet
Russel McPhate
Claire Louise Morgan
John Mitchell Morris
Lynsey Rintoul
Brian John Tait
Consultant
John Randal Bain
Associate
Alan Desmond Baxter
Employees
Susan Margaret Alexander
Jordan William Hay
Claire Victoria Fernie Hooper

ROSS & CONNEL LLP
18 Viewfield Terrace, Dunfermline KY12 7JH
Tel: (01383) 721156
Fax: (01383) 721150
DX: DF11 DUNFERMLINE
Web: www.rossconnel.co.uk
Categories of Work
Advice the elderly & powers of attorney
Alternative dispute resolution
Children
Civil court work
Civil legal aid
Commercial litigation
Commercial property
Contract & property disputes
Criminal court work
Criminal legal aid
Debt
Debt collecting
Debt recovery, insolvency, bankruptcy
Family and divorce
Insolvency & corporate recovery
Landlord & tenant
Medical negligence – claimant
Personal injury
Property litigation
Residential property
Road traffic
Wills, executries and trusts
Partners
Alastair Bracken
Edward Norman Christie Christie
Neil Thomas Hugh Queen
Employees
Thomas Hempleman
Susan Ann Berry Hill

SCOTT RALPH
31 Chalmers Street, Dunfermline KY12 8AT
Tel: (01383) 626780
Fax: (01383) 623564
DX: DF77 DUNFERMLINE

E-mail: sr@scottralph.co.uk
Categories of Work
Advice the elderly & powers of attorney
Alternative dispute resolution
Children
Civil court work
Civil legal aid
Commercial litigation
Commercial property
Contract & property disputes
Debt recovery, insolvency, bankruptcy
Employment law
Family and divorce
Family business advice
Landlord & tenant
Personal injury
Property litigation
Residential property
Road traffic
SME business advice
Wills, executries and trusts
Partner
Scott David Ralph

STENHOUSE, HUSBAND & IRVINE
3 East Port, Dunfermline KY12 7JG
Tel: (01383) 724949
Fax: (01383) 620643
DX: DF79 DUNFERMLINE
E-mail: ian@shisolicitors.co.uk
Categories of Work
Agriculture and estates
Agriculture, crofting and fishing
Commercial property
Personal injury
Residential property
Wills, executries and trusts
Partner
Ian MacLachlan Allan

STEVENSON & MARSHALL LLP
41 East Port, Dunfermline KY12 7LG
Tel: (01383) 721141
Fax: (01383) 723779
DX: DF80 DUNFERMLINE
E-mail: reception@stevenson-marshall.co.uk
Web: www.stevenson-marshall.co.uk
Categories of Work
Adoption
Advice the elderly & powers of attorney
Agriculture and estates
Alternative dispute resolution
Children
Civil court work
Civil legal aid
Commercial litigation
Commercial property
Construction
Contract & property disputes
Criminal court work
Criminal legal aid
Debt
Debt collecting
Debt recovery, insolvency, bankruptcy

▶ *Dunfermline continued*

Employment
Employment law
Family and divorce
Family business advice
Human rights
Landlord & tenant
Medical negligence – claimant
Mental health
Personal injury
Personal injury – defender
Professional negligence
Property litigation
Residential property
Road traffic
SME business advice
Wills, executives and trusts
Partners
Jillian Barnes
Andrew Thomas Brown
Angela Cameron Fyfe
Pauline Eleanor Kennedy
Andrew Joseph Patrick Robb
Associates
Gillian Margaret MacNulty
Angela McFarlane
Employees
Mathew Balfour Anderson
Alexandra Rachelle Imrie
Michelle Mary Moran
June Elizabeth Paterson
Linsey Jane Tocher

THE MORGAN LAW PARTNERSHIP
33 East Port, Dunfermline KY12 7JE
Tel: (01383) 620222
Fax: (01383) 621213
Categories of Work
Adoption
Advice the elderly & powers of attorney
Children
Civil court work
Civil legal aid
Commercial litigation
Consumer credit
Contract & property disputes
Criminal court work
Criminal legal aid
Debt
Debt collecting
Debt recovery, insolvency, bankruptcy
Employment
Employment law
Family and divorce
Landlord & tenant
Medical negligence – claimant
Personal injury
Professional negligence
Residential property
Road traffic
Wills, executives and trusts
Employee
Robin Joseph Jesse Grace

WRIGHT, JOHNSTON & MACKENZIE LLP
Crescent House, Carnegie Campus,
Dunfermline KY11 8GR
Tel: (01383) 626666
Fax: (01383) 626111
E-mail: enquiries@wjm.co.uk
Web: www.wjm.co.uk
Categories of Work
Adjudication
Adoption
Advice the elderly & powers of attorney
Agriculture and estates
Agriculture, crofting and fishing
Alternative dispute resolution
Alternative investment market
Banking & finance
Betting & gaming
Charities
Children
Childrens
Civil court work
Commercial litigation
Commercial property
Competition
Construction
Consumer credit
Contract & property disputes
Copyright, trade marks and design
Corporate tax
Criminal court work
Data protection
Debt
Debt collecting
Debt recovery, insolvency, bankruptcy
Disability
Discrimination
Education
Employment
Employment law
Environment
Environment (Business Premises)
EU / international
Family and divorce
Family business advice
Fishing
Freedom of information
Health and safety
Housing
Human rights
Insolvency & corporate recovery
Insurance
IT and intellectual property
Joint venture
Landlord & tenant
Liquor licensing
Local government
Media and entertainment
Medical negligence – defender
Medical negligence – claimant
Mergers and acquisitions
Mining
Oil & gas
Parliamentary

Pensions (Company)
Pensions (Employment)
Personal injury
Personal injury – defender
Personal tax
Planning
Planning (Business Premises)
Power and utilities
Private equity
Professional negligence
Projects
Property litigation
Public finance initiative
Public sector
Residential property
Road traffic
SME business advice
Software licensing
Sport
Telecoms
Transport
Unit Trusts, OEICs and investment trusts
Wills, executries and trusts
Partners
John Bernard Clarke
Alison Marshall
Andrew Ross Taylor

YOUNG & PARTNERS BUSINESS LAWYERS LIMITED

1 George Square, Castle Brae, Dunfermline
KY11 8QF
Tel: (01383) 721621
Fax: (01383) 722080
DX: 556507 DUNFERMLINE 8
E-mail: rxw@businesslaw.co.uk
Web: www.businesslaw.co.uk
Categories of Work
Agriculture and estates
Alternative dispute resolution
Banking & finance
Charities
Civil court work
Commercial litigation
Commercial property
Construction
Consumer credit
Contract & property disputes
Credit brokerage
Debt adjusting and debt counselling
Debt administration
Debt collecting
Debt recovery, insolvency, bankruptcy
Employment law
Environment
Environment (Business Premises)
Family business advice
Housing
IT and intellectual property
Joint venture
Landlord & tenant
Liquor licensing
Mergers and acquisitions

Planning (Business Premises)
Property litigation
Provision of credit information services
Public sector
Residential property
SME business advice
Directors
John Graham Cassells
Stephen Richard Lochrie
Alan Douglas Stalker
Associates
Craig Joseph Smith
Julie Kathryn Sullivan
Employee
Steven Andrew Wicks

YOUR CONVEYANCER LIMITED

East Port House, 12 East Port, Dunfermline
KY12 7JB
Tel: (01383) 667550
Fax: (01383) 663800
DX: 550420 DUNFERMLINE 4
E-mail: enquiries@yourconveyancer.co.uk
Web: www.yourconveyancer.co.uk
Categories of Work
Agriculture, crofting and fishing
Residential property
Directors
Neil Crockatt
Nicola Hannah Elliott
Employees
Joshua Andrew Gray
Carys Elin Magee

Dunoon

BLAIR & BRYDEN

47 Argyll Street, Dunoon PA23 7HG
Tel: (01369) 704037
DX: 591660 DUNOON
E-mail: dunoon@blair-bryden.co.uk
Web: www.blairbryden.co.uk
Categories of Work
Adoption
Advice the elderly & powers of attorney
Benefit advice
Charities
Children
Civil court work
Civil legal aid
Commercial litigation
Commercial property
Consumer credit
Contract & property disputes
Criminal court work
Criminal legal aid
Debt collecting
Debt recovery, insolvency, bankruptcy
Education
Employment
Employment law
Family and divorce
Family business advice

► **Dunoon** *continued*

Housing
Immigration and asylum
Landlord & tenant
Liquor licensing
Medical negligence – claimant
Personal injury
Personal injury – defender
Planning (Business Premises)
Professional negligence
Property litigation
Residential property
Road traffic
Transport
Wills, executives and trusts

CORRIGALL BLACK
20 John Street, Dunoon PA23 8BN
Tel: (01369) 702941
Fax: (01369) 704304
DX: 591651 DUNOON
E-mail: elspeth.black@corrigallblack.com
Web: www.corrigallblack.com
Categories of Work
Adoption
Advice the elderly & powers of attorney
Agriculture and estates
Children
Civil court work
Civil legal aid
Commercial property
Contract & property disputes
Debt
Debt collecting
Disability
Discrimination
Education
Family and divorce
Family business advice
Joint venture
Landlord & tenant
Liquor licensing
Mental health
Personal injury
Property litigation
Residential property
Wills, executives and trusts
Partner
Elspeth Catherine Black
Employee
Lorenzo Shaw Ranalli

STEWART & BENNETT
82 Argyll Street, Dunoon PA23 7NJ
Tel: (01369) 702885
Fax: (01369) 706695
DX: 591650 DUNOON
E-mail: EMacDonald@stewartbennett.com
Categories of Work
Adoption
Advice the elderly & powers of attorney
Agriculture and estates
Alternative dispute resolution

Civil court work
Civil legal aid
Commercial property
Contract & property disputes
Environment
Landlord & tenant
Power and utilities
Property litigation
Residential property
Wills, executives and trusts
Partner
Euan Joseph Macdonald
Consultant
Dorothy McGhie
Employee
Rachel Mary-Norine Walker

THE LAW COTTAGE
The Cottage, Orange Bank, Wyndham Road,
Dunoon PA23 7SH
Tel: (01369) 830007
Fax: (01369) 830003
E-mail: law@lawcottage.co.uk
Web: www.lawcottage.co.uk
Categories of Work
Advice the elderly & powers of attorney
Residential property
Wills, executives and trusts
Partner
Alexandra Macinnes

Duns

BORDERS LEGAL LIMITED
11-13 Murray Street, Duns TD11 3DF
Tel: (01361) 883222
Fax: (01361) 883517
E-mail: legal@hastingslegal.co.uk
Categories of Work
Adoption
Advice the elderly & powers of attorney
Agriculture and estates
Civil court work
Commercial property
Contract & property disputes
Copyright, trade marks and design
Debt adjusting and debt counselling
Debt administration
Debt collecting
Debt management
Debt recovery, insolvency, bankruptcy
Employment law
Environment
Family and divorce
Family business advice
Health
Health and safety
Housing
Landlord & tenant
Liquor licensing
Mental health
Personal injury
Personal tax

Planning
Planning (Business Premises)
Property litigation
Public sector
Residential property
SME business advice
Wills, executives and trusts
Director
Ricky Thomas Hope

J.D. CLARK & ALLAN LIMITED
Tolbooth House, Market Square, Duns
TD11 3DR
Tel: (01361) 882501
Fax: (01361) 883130
DX: 556521 DUNS
E-mail: property@jdca.co.uk
Web: www.jdca.co.uk
Categories of Work
Advice the elderly & powers of attorney
Agriculture and estates
Agriculture, crofting and fishing
Banking & finance
Children
Civil court work
Civil legal aid
Commercial litigation
Contract & property disputes
Criminal court work
Criminal legal aid
Debt
Debt collecting
Debt recovery, insolvency, bankruptcy
Family and divorce
Landlord & tenant
Medical negligence – claimant
Personal injury
Planning (Business Premises)
Power and utilities
Property litigation
Residential property
Road traffic
Wills, executives and trusts
Directors
Amy Dickson
Elliot Kinnear McQuarrie
Employees
Sara Lisa Hall
Patricia Hunter King

HASTINGS LEGAL
11-13 Murray Street, Duns TD11 3DF
Tel: (01361) 883222
E-mail: legal@hastingslegal.co.uk
Web: www.hastingslegal.co.uk
Categories of Work
Adoption
Advice the elderly & powers of attorney
Agriculture and estates
Civil court work
Commercial property
Contract & property disputes
Copyright, trade marks and design
Debt adjusting and debt counselling

Debt administration
Debt collecting
Debt management
Debt recovery, insolvency, bankruptcy
Employment law
Environment
Family and divorce
Family business advice
Health
Health and safety
Housing
Landlord & tenant
Liquor licensing
Mental health
Personal injury
Personal tax
Planning
Planning (Business Premises)
Property litigation
Public sector
Residential property
SME business advice
Wills, executives and trusts

MELROSE & PORTEOUS LIMITED
47 Market Square, Duns TD11 3BX
Tel: (01361) 882 752
Fax: (01361) 883 950
DX: 556522 DUNS
E-mail: mel.roberts@melroseporteous.co.uk
Categories of Work
Adoption
Advice the elderly & powers of attorney
Children
Commercial litigation
Debt
Employment law
Family and divorce
Directors
Melanie Roberts
Kathryn Janet Wilson

Dyce

WILSONE & DUFFUS
75 Victoria Street, Dyce AB21 7AX
Tel: (01224) 797979
E-mail: info@wilsoneduffus.co.uk
Web: www.key-moves.co.uk
Categories of Work
Advice the elderly & powers of attorney
Banking & finance
Commercial property
Construction
Landlord & tenant
Liquor licensing
Planning
Planning (Business Premises)
Residential property
SME business advice
Wills, executives and trusts

East Kilbride

AUSTIN LAFFERTY LIMITED
213 Edinburgh House, East Kilbride G74 1LJ
Tel: (01355) 263777
Fax: (01355) 263886
DX: 500649 East Kilbride
Web: www.austinlafferty.co.uk
Categories of Work
Adoption
Advice the elderly & powers of attorney
Alternative dispute resolution
Banking & finance
Children
Childrens
Civil court work
Civil legal aid
Commercial property
Consumer credit
Contract & property disputes
Credit brokerage
Criminal court work
Criminal legal aid
Data protection
Debt adjusting and debt counselling
Debt administration
Debt collecting
Education
Family and divorce
Family business advice
Freedom of information
Health and safety
Human rights
Landlord & tenant
Media and entertainment
Medical negligence – claimant
Mergers and acquisitions
Personal injury
Personal tax
Professional negligence
Property litigation
Provision of credit information services
Residential property
Road traffic
SME business advice
Wills, executries and trusts
Director
John Simpson Roberts
Consultant
Ian McKillop
Employees
Omair Maubeen Ahmed
Dominic Paul Coyle
Gayle Joan Heeps
Jennifer Waite

BONNAR ACCIDENT LAW LTD
319 Edinburgh House, Princes Square, East
Kilbride G74 1LJ
Tel: (0800) 163978
DX: 500646 EAST KILBRIDE
Categories of Work
Civil court work
Civil legal aid

Health and safety
Personal injury
Professional negligence
Road traffic

BONNAR LAW LIMITED
E216, Second Floor, Edinburgh House,
Righead Gate, East Kilbride G74 1LS
Tel: (01355) 268866
Fax: (01355) 268868
E-mail: bonnar.law@tiscali.co.uk
Web: www.bonnarlaw-eastkilbride.co.uk
Categories of Work
Advice the elderly & powers of attorney
Children
Commercial property
Construction
Contract & property disputes
Family and divorce
Landlord & tenant
Residential property
Wills, executries and trusts
Director
Damian Colin Bonnar

BUCHANAN BURTON LIMITED
2 Strathmore House, Princes Square, East
Kilbride G74 1LQ
Tel: (01355) 249228
Fax: (01355) 265535
DX: 500648 EAST KILBRIDE
E-mail: mailbox@buchananburton.co.uk
Web: www.buchananburton.co.uk
Categories of Work
Adoption
Advice the elderly & powers of attorney
Children
Civil court work
Civil legal aid
Commercial property
Criminal court work
Criminal legal aid
Debt
Debt recovery, insolvency, bankruptcy
Employment law
Family and divorce
Landlord & tenant
Mental health
Personal injury
Residential property
Social housing
Wills, executries and trusts
Directors
John Buchanan
Alexandria Catherine Thorburn Burton
Consultant
Stroma Elizabeth Spence
Associates
Pauline Geraghty
Rhona Anne Murray
Employees
Nadene Miller
Julie Anne Ross

CLARITY SIMPLICITY LTD
2 Main Street, The Village, East Kilbride
G74 4JH
Tel: (0141) 4332626
Fax: (0141) 423 7648
E-mail: legalteam@claritysimplicity.co.uk
Categories of Work
Adoption
Advice the elderly & powers of attorney
Children
Childrens
Civil court work
Commercial litigation
Commercial property
Contract & property disputes
Debt
Debt recovery, insolvency, bankruptcy
Education
Family and divorce
Family business advice
Insolvency & corporate recovery
Landlord & tenant
Medical negligence – defender
Medical negligence – claimant
Personal injury
Personal injury – defender
Professional negligence
Property litigation
Residential property
Wills, executives and trusts
Director
Emma Mary Christina King
Employee
Shannon Michelle Gaughan

COMPLETE CLARITY SOLICITORS
2 Main Street, The Village, East Kilbride
G74 4JH
Tel: (0141) 4332626
DX: : 500642 EAST KILBRIDE
Categories of Work
Adoption
Advice the elderly & powers of attorney
Children
Childrens
Civil court work
Commercial litigation
Commercial property
Contract & property disputes
Debt
Debt recovery, insolvency, bankruptcy
Education
Family and divorce
Family business advice
Insolvency & corporate recovery
Landlord & tenant
Medical negligence – defender
Medical negligence – claimant
Personal injury
Personal injury – defender
Professional negligence
Property litigation
Residential property

Wills, executives and trusts
THOMAS DUNCAN SOLICITOR
19 Mackenzie Gardens, East Kilbride G74 4SA
Tel: (07939) 340170
Fax: (01355) 200145
E-mail: fiona@scotlandlegal.co.uk
Categories of Work
Advice the elderly & powers of attorney
Commercial property
Contract & property disputes
Landlord & tenant
Local government
Planning (Business Premises)
Public sector
Residential property
Wills, executives and trusts
Consultant
Fiona Jean Hannay

GOLDSMITH & HUGHES LTD
51 Strathmore House, Princes Square, East
Kilbride G74 1LF
Tel: (01355) 260602
Fax: (01355) 260603
DX: 500685 EAST KILBRIDE
E-mail: goldsmith@goldsmithhughes.co.uk
Categories of Work
Adoption
Children
Employment law
Family and divorce
Directors
Mary Patricia Goldsmith
Eileen Mary Hughes
Employees
Kevin John Hughes
Stephen Sutherland McLean

GUARINO & THOMSON LIMITED
E201 Edinburgh House, Town Centre, East
Kilbride G74 1LJ
Tel: (01355) 263848
Fax: (01355) 237029
DX: 500647 EAST KILBRIDE
E-mail: admin@guarinothomson.co.uk
Categories of Work
Children
Civil court work
Civil legal aid
Commercial property
Criminal court work
Criminal legal aid
Debt collecting
Employment law
Family and divorce
Landlord & tenant
Medical negligence – claimant
Personal injury
Residential property
Road traffic
Wills, executives and trusts
Directors
Marco Filippo Guarino
Andrew Thomson

► *East Kilbride continued*

HUTCHESONS

324 Edinburgh House, East Kilbride G74 1LJ
Tel: (01355) 224545
DX: 500660 EAST KILBRIDE
E-mail: alan@hutchesonlaw.co.uk
Web: www.ahutcheson.co.uk
Categories of Work
Advice the elderly & powers of attorney
Civil court work
Commercial litigation
Commercial property
Contract & property disputes
Employment
Landlord & tenant
Mental health
Personal injury
Property litigation
Residential property
Road traffic
Sport
Wills, executories and trusts
Partner
Alan James Hutcheson

GERARD MCGUIRE & CO.

115 Strathmore House, Town Centre, East
Kilbride G74 1LF
Tel: (01355) 225322
Fax: (01355) 279350
Categories of Work
Criminal court work
Criminal legal aid
Partner
Gerard McGuire
Employee
Deborah Louise McGuire

LORNA MACLEOD FAMILY LAW

36 Strathmore House, Town Centre, East
Kilbride G74 1LQ
Tel: (01355) 261361
Fax: (01355) 261453
DX: 500662 EAST KILBRIDE
E-mail: ljm@lornamacleod.co.uk
Partner
Lorna Janet MacLeod

MAINS SOLICITORS

55 Strathmore House, East Kilbride G74 1LF
Tel: (01355) 225111
Fax: (01355) 225964
DX: 500663 EAST KILBRIDE
E-mail: mohanlon@mainslegal.com
Web: www.mains-sols.co.uk
Categories of Work
Adoption
Advice the elderly & powers of attorney
Agriculture and estates
Benefit advice
Children
Childrens
Civil court work
Civil legal aid

Commercial litigation
Consumer credit
Contract & property disputes
Copyright, trade marks and design
Criminal court work
Criminal legal aid
Data protection
Debt
Debt adjusting and debt counselling
Debt collecting
Debt management
Debt recovery, insolvency, bankruptcy
Education
Family and divorce
Family business advice
Housing
Landlord & tenant
Media and entertainment
Personal injury
Residential property
Road traffic
Social housing
Partner
Mark O'Hanlon

SIMPLICITY LEGAL

2 Main Street, The Village, East Kilbride
G74 4JH
Tel: (0141) 4332626
Categories of Work
Adoption
Advice the elderly & powers of attorney
Children
Childrens
Civil court work
Commercial litigation
Commercial property
Contract & property disputes
Debt
Debt recovery, insolvency, bankruptcy
Education
Family and divorce
Family business advice
Insolvency & corporate recovery
Landlord & tenant
Medical negligence – defender
Medical negligence – claimant
Personal injury
Personal injury – defender
Professional negligence
Property litigation
Residential property
Wills, executories and trusts

DERICK WILLIAMSON & CO.

1 Faichney Fields, The Village, East Kilbride
G74 4GZ
Tel: (01355) 222337
E-mail: derickwilliamsonandco@hotmail.co.uk
Categories of Work
Criminal court work
Criminal legal aid
Partner
Derick Williamson

Edinburgh

1234PROPERTY
14 Constitution Street, Edinburgh EH6 7BT
Tel: (0131) 5551234
DX: 550870 LEITH
Categories of Work
Advice the elderly & powers of attorney
Commercial property
Landlord & tenant
Liquor licensing
Residential property
Wills, executries and trusts

26GS (SECRETARIES) LIMITED
26 George Square, Edinburgh EH8 9LD
Tel: (0131) 6624747

ABERDEIN CONSIDINE AND COMPANY
2nd Floor, East Suite, Elder House, Edinburgh
EH1 3DX
Tel: (0131) 2212424
Fax: (0131) 2290731
Categories of Work
Adjudication
Adoption
Advice the elderly & powers of attorney
Agriculture and estates
Agriculture, crofting and fishing
Alternative dispute resolution
Alternative investment market
Banking & finance
Charities
Children
Childrens
Civil court work
Civil legal aid
Commercial litigation
Commercial property
Competition
Construction
Consumer credit
Contract & property disputes
Copyright, trade marks and design
Corporate tax
Credit brokerage
Criminal court work
Criminal legal aid
Data protection
Debt
Debt adjusting and debt counselling
Debt collecting
Debt recovery, insolvency, bankruptcy
Disability
Discrimination
Education
Employment
Employment law
Environment
Environment (Business Premises)
EU / international
Family and divorce
Family business advice
Freedom of information
Health
Health and safety
Human rights
Insolvency & corporate recovery
Insurance
Joint venture
Landlord & tenant
Liquor licensing
Local government
Media and entertainment
Mental health
Mergers and acquisitions
Pensions (Company)
Pensions (Employment)
Personal injury
Personal tax
Planning (Business Premises)
Private equity
Professional negligence
Property litigation
Public finance initiative
Public sector
Residential property
SME business advice
Social housing
Telecoms
Unit Trusts, OEICs and investment trusts
Wills, executries and trusts
Partners
Sally-Anne Anderson
Leonie Sarah Rose Burke
James David MacKinnon
Paul McIntosh
Ross Alan Webb
Associate
Karen Joan Harvie
Employees
Euan Scott Forbes
Rebecca Chloe Elizabeth Gray
Emma Caroline Roman
Giorgio Alessandro Ventisei

ABERDEIN CONSIDINE AND COMPANY
47 Lothian Road, Edinburgh EH1 2DJ
Tel: (0131) 2229000
Fax: (0131) 2282970
DX: ED502 EDINBURGH
E-mail: lothianroad@acandco.com
Categories of Work
Adjudication
Adoption
Advice the elderly & powers of attorney
Agriculture and estates
Agriculture, crofting and fishing
Alternative dispute resolution
Alternative investment market
Banking & finance
Charities
Children
Childrens
Civil court work
Civil legal aid
Commercial litigation

▶ **Edinburgh continued**

Commercial property
Competition
Construction
Consumer credit
Contract & property disputes
Copyright, trade marks and design
Corporate tax
Credit brokerage
Criminal court work
Criminal legal aid
Data protection
Debt
Debt adjusting and debt counselling
Debt collecting
Debt recovery, insolvency, bankruptcy
Disability
Discrimination
Education
Employment
Employment law
Environment
Environment (Business Premises)
EU / international
Family and divorce
Family business advice
Freedom of information
Health
Health and safety
Human rights
Insolvency & corporate recovery
Insurance
Joint venture
Landlord & tenant
Liquor licensing
Local government
Media and entertainment
Mental health
Mergers and acquisitions
Pensions (Company)
Pensions (Employment)
Personal injury
Personal tax
Planning (Business Premises)
Private equity
Professional negligence
Property litigation
Public finance initiative
Public sector
Residential property
SME business advice
Social housing
Telecoms
Unit Trusts, OEICs and investment trusts
Wills, executries and trusts
Partner
Sean Alexander MacMillan
Employee
Kerry Louise Simpson

ABERDEIN CONSIDINE AND COMPANY
6 Rutland Square, Edinburgh EH1 2AS
Tel: (0131) 2212424

DX: ED 501 EDINBURGH
E-mail: exchangetower@acandco.com
Categories of Work
Adjudication
Adoption
Advice the elderly & powers of attorney
Agriculture and estates
Agriculture, crofting and fishing
Alternative dispute resolution
Alternative investment market
Banking & finance
Charities
Children
Childrens
Civil court work
Civil legal aid
Commercial litigation
Commercial property
Competition
Construction
Consumer credit
Contract & property disputes
Copyright, trade marks and design
Corporate tax
Credit brokerage
Criminal court work
Criminal legal aid
Data protection
Debt
Debt adjusting and debt counselling
Debt collecting
Debt recovery, insolvency, bankruptcy
Disability
Discrimination
Education
Employment
Employment law
Environment
Environment (Business Premises)
EU / international
Family and divorce
Family business advice
Freedom of information
Health
Health and safety
Human rights
Insolvency & corporate recovery
Insurance
Joint venture
Landlord & tenant
Liquor licensing
Local government
Media and entertainment
Mental health
Mergers and acquisitions
Pensions (Company)
Pensions (Employment)
Personal injury
Personal tax
Planning (Business Premises)
Private equity
Professional negligence
Property litigation

Public finance initiative
Public sector
Residential property
SME business advice
Social housing
Telecoms
Unit Trusts, OEICs and investment trusts
Wills, executories and trusts

ADAMS LEGAL SOLUTIONS LIMITED
11 Kingsknowe Park, Edinburgh EH14 2JQ
Tel: (0131) 4434436
Fax: (0844) 484 4345
DX: 531155 BLAIRGOWRIE
E-mail: farah@adams-law.co.uk
Web: www.adams-law.co.uk
Categories of Work
Advice the elderly & powers of attorney
Alternative dispute resolution
Commercial property
Contract & property disputes
Employment
Employment law
Family business advice
Landlord & tenant
Liquor licensing
Residential property
Wills, executories and trusts
Director
Farhat Kauser Adams

ADAMS WHYTE
20 Leith Walk, Edinburgh EH6 5AA
Tel: (0131) 555 7220
Fax: (0131) 5557021
DX: 550864 LEITH
E-mail: edinburgh@adamswhyte.com
Web: www.adamswhyte.com
Categories of Work
Criminal court work
Criminal legal aid
Human rights
Road traffic
Partners
Nigel Bruce
Ross Alan Gardner
Ewen Patrick Roy
Associate
Jennifer Ann Cameron
Employee
Calum Leonard Dickson Turner

ADDLESHAW GODDARD LLP
Exchange Tower, 19 Canning Street,
Edinburgh EH3 8EH
Tel: (0131) 2282400
Fax: (0131) 2229800
Categories of Work
Adjudication
Adoption
Advice the elderly & powers of attorney
Agriculture and estates
Agriculture, crofting and fishing
Alternative dispute resolution

Alternative investment market
Banking & finance
Benefit advice
Betting & gaming
Charities
Children
Childrens
Civil court work
Civil legal aid
Commercial litigation
Commercial property
Competition
Construction
Consumer credit
Contract & property disputes
Copyright, trade marks and design
Corporate tax
Credit brokerage
Criminal court work
Criminal legal aid
Data protection
Debt
Debt adjusting and debt counselling
Debt administration
Debt collecting
Debt management
Debt recovery, insolvency, bankruptcy
Disability
Discrimination
Education
Employment
Employment law
Environment
Environment (Business Premises)
EU / international
Family and divorce
Family business advice
Fishing
Freedom of information
Health
Health and safety
Housing
Human rights
Immigration and asylum
Insolvency & corporate recovery
Insurance
IT and intellectual property
Joint venture
Landlord & tenant
Liquor licensing
Local government
Media and entertainment
Medical negligence – defender
Medical negligence – claimant
Mental health
Mergers and acquisitions
Mining
Oil & gas
Parliamentary
Pensions (Company)
Pensions (Employment)
Personal injury
Personal injury – defender

► **Edinburgh** continued

Personal tax
Planning
Planning (Business Premises)
Power and utilities
Private equity
Professional negligence
Projects
Property litigation
Provision of credit information services
Public finance initiative
Public sector
Residential property
Road traffic
Shipping
SME business advice
Social housing
Software licensing
Sport
Telecoms
Transport
Unit Trusts, OEICs and investment trusts
Wills, executries and trusts

Partners
Neil Michael Addis
David Jack Noble Anderson
Caroline Kathreen Macdonald Armstrong
Sarah Baillie
Anna Bridgetta Brown
Helena Anne Brown
Gaenor Judith Cassell
Simon James Dawson Catto
Euan Alastair Cluness
Timothy Cooper
Alastair Lindsay Cowan
Miles Jonathan Ede
Paul Ewing
Lorna Helen Finlayson
David William Murray Horne
David William Hughes
David Michael Kirchin
Andrew Charles Ley
Jamie Laurence McIntosh
Suzanne Dorothy Moir
Kirsty Jane Nicholson
Heather Brodie Pearson
Ronald Alan Shanks
Thomas Sturrock Blair Speirs
Adrienne Rama Spiers
Anne Christina Struckmeier
Lynsey Clare Walker
Edward Bruce Watt
Consultant
Malcolm Henry McPherson
Associates
Sarah Alexandra Dick
Katrina Margaret Durie
Laura Sian Falls
Rachel Anne Fisher
Yavor Miroslavov Georgiev
Fiona Gordon
Edward Stuart Gratwick

Zoe Elizabeth Jarvis
Nicholas James Kelly
Barry McHugh
Daniel Matthew McKinney
Joanne Elizabeth McLean
Joanne Helen Moynan
Chloe Alexandra De Falaise Oakshett
Neil Douglas Robertson
Graham Peter Smartt
Morgan Rebecca Smith
Gordon Mckenzie West
James Stephen Woodward
Wendy Anne Wraight
Employees
Euan Graham Anderson
Coral Bain
Julia Audrey Barette
Patrick Ronald Barnett
Martin John Methven Bogie
Kelly Brown
Colette Catherine Maria Burden
Roger Carr
Peter Ian Clyde
Mhairi Fiona Cruickshank
Rachel Mae Christina Davies
Elaine Deuchars
Jennifer Ross Donaldson
Kyla Jean Donaldson
Jodie Emma Nicola Dunz
Matthew Kenneth Finnie
Kirsten Fleming
James Michael Patrick Flett
Kathleen Frances Gallacher
Erin Louise Grieve
Bryony Elizabeth Hart
David James Harvey
Lauren Hill
Abigail Morven Housego
Gillian Louise Hutchison
Samuel Robert Lawson
Finlay Euan Cameron MacDougall
Colin John Maciver
Caitlin Janet MacMillan
Zaema Majeed
Andrew David McClean
Gillian McMillan
Lisa Jan McNeill
Sean Patrick Morris
Martin Robert Pirret
Jennie Katharine Pounder
Adam Porter Ridley
Niall Michael Skelton
Mark Stevenson
Lynne Ann Taplin
Kirsten Johanna Thomson
Meghan Elizabeth Vaillancourt
Maxine Nicole Walker
Rhona Emily Wallace
John Richard Waller
Olivia Rose Watson
Jennifer Rose Whitwell-Claydon
Thomas Ross Wright
Daniel Julian Zakrzewski

AIKMAN BELL LIMITED
19 Cadzow Place, Edinburgh EH7 5SN
Tel: (0131) 6610015
Fax: (0131) 661 0150
DX: 551158 EDINBURGH 8
E-mail: peter@aikmanbell.co.uk
Director
Peter Mackintosh Aikman

AIRDS & CO LIMITED
PO Box 28673, Edinburgh EH4 9FY
Tel: (0131) 3328411
Fax: (0131) 3328411
DX: ED614 EDINBURGH
E-mail: lja@airdsandco.co.uk
Web: www.airdsandco.co.uk
Director
Lorna Janette Aird

ALLAN MCDOUGALL MCQUEEN LLP
103-105 Bruntsfield Place, Edinburgh
EH10 4EQ
Tel: (0131) 2281926
Fax: (0131) 2289193
E-mail: info@mcdougallmcqueen.co.uk
Web: www.mcdougallmcqueen.co.uk
Categories of Work
Adoption
Advice the elderly & powers of attorney
Charities
Children
Childrens
Civil court work
Civil legal aid
Commercial litigation
Commercial property
Contract & property disputes
Criminal court work
Criminal legal aid
Disability
Discrimination
Employment
Employment law
Family and divorce
Health and safety
Landlord & tenant
Medical negligence – claimant
Personal injury
Personal injury – defender
Personal tax
Professional negligence
Residential property
Road traffic
Wills, executries and trusts
Partners
Craig Mercer Forster
Mary Robinson McQueen
Employee
Gerard Martin Davis

ALLAN MCDOUGALL MCQUEEN LLP
2b New Mart Road, Edinburgh EH14 1RL
Tel: (0131) 6221771
Fax: (0131) 4777052

E-mail: info@mcdougallmcqueen.co.uk
Web: www.mcdougallmcqueen.co.uk
Categories of Work
Adoption
Advice the elderly & powers of attorney
Charities
Children
Childrens
Civil court work
Civil legal aid
Commercial litigation
Commercial property
Contract & property disputes
Criminal court work
Criminal legal aid
Disability
Discrimination
Employment
Employment law
Family and divorce
Health and safety
Landlord & tenant
Medical negligence – claimant
Personal injury
Personal injury – defender
Personal tax
Professional negligence
Residential property
Road traffic
Wills, executries and trusts
Partner
Dorothy Elizabeth Mullally
Employee
Noele Ellen Harraghy

ALLAN MCDOUGALL MCQUEEN LLP
3 Coates Crescent, Edinburgh EH3 7AL
Tel: (0131) 2252121
Fax: (0131) 2258659
DX: ED32 EDINBURGH
E-mail: info@mcdougallmcqueen.co.uk
Web: www.allanmcdougall.co.uk
Categories of Work
Adoption
Advice the elderly & powers of attorney
Charities
Children
Childrens
Civil court work
Civil legal aid
Commercial litigation
Commercial property
Contract & property disputes
Criminal court work
Criminal legal aid
Disability
Discrimination
Employment
Employment law
Family and divorce
Health and safety
Landlord & tenant
Medical negligence – claimant

▶ **Edinburgh continued**

Personal injury
Personal injury – defender
Personal tax
Professional negligence
Residential property
Road traffic
Wills, executries and trusts
Partners
Gordon Foggo Bathgate
Julie Elizabeth Harris
Stephen Irvine
Ruaraidh McVicar Lawson
Johnson MacIntyre
Pamela Louise McKeand
Jacqueline Lesley Raitt
Consultants
David John Campbell Harris
Niall Peter Henderson
David John Caldwell Nicol
Associate
Emily Frances Allan
Employees
Alice Evelyn Bowman
Gordon Robert Milligan
Alexandra Dyce Robertson

ALLAN MCDOUGALL MCQUEEN LLP
55 Mayfield Road, Edinburgh EH9 3AA
Tel: (0131) 666 2424
DX: 551660 LIBERTON
Web: www.mcdougallmcqueen.co.uk
Categories of Work
Adoption
Advice the elderly & powers of attorney
Charities
Children
Childrens
Civil court work
Civil legal aid
Commercial litigation
Commercial property
Contract & property disputes
Criminal court work
Criminal legal aid
Disability
Discrimination
Employment
Employment law
Family and divorce
Health and safety
Landlord & tenant
Medical negligence – claimant
Personal injury
Personal injury – defender
Personal tax
Professional negligence
Residential property
Road traffic
Wills, executries and trusts

ALLINGHAM & CO (SOLICITORS) LIMITED
134 Marchmont Road, Edinburgh EH9 1AQ

Tel: (0131) 4479341
Fax: (0131) 4529383
DX: ED225 EDINBURGH
E-mail: info@allingham.co.uk
Web: www.allingham.co.uk
Categories of Work
Advice the elderly & powers of attorney
Landlord & tenant
Mental health
Personal injury
Personal tax
Residential property
Road traffic
Wills, executries and trusts
Employee
Joan Onyebuchi Kokovworho

ALLINGHAM & CO (SOLICITORS) LIMITED
4a Buckstone Terrace, Edinburgh EH10 6PZ
Tel: (0131) 4479341
Fax: (0131) 4455551
E-mail: info@allingham.co.uk
Web: www.allingham.co.uk
Categories of Work
Advice the elderly & powers of attorney
Landlord & tenant
Mental health
Personal injury
Personal tax
Residential property
Road traffic
Wills, executries and trusts
Director
Colin Redpath
Employee
Jennifer Catherine Mackintosh

ALLINGHAM & CO (SOLICITORS) LIMITED
9-15 Bridge Road, Colinton, Edinburgh
EH13 0LQ
Tel: (0131) 4479341
Fax: (0131) 4414517
E-mail: info@allingham.co.uk
Web: www.allingham.co.uk
Categories of Work
Advice the elderly & powers of attorney
Landlord & tenant
Mental health
Personal injury
Personal tax
Residential property
Road traffic
Wills, executries and trusts
Director
Duncan John Collinson
Associate
Kwan-Nga Yeung
Employees
Elaine Arnott
Hilary Louise Peppiette
Nadia Kausar Sharif

ALSTON LAW
23 Alva Street, Edinburgh EH2 4PS

Tel: (0131) 581 5700
E-mail: property@simpsonmarwick.com
Web: www.alstonlaw.co.uk
Categories of Work
Adoption
Advice the elderly & powers of attorney
Agriculture and estates
Alternative dispute resolution
Banking & finance
Children
Civil court work
Commercial litigation
Commercial property
Consumer credit
Contract & property disputes
Debt
Debt collecting
Debt recovery, insolvency, bankruptcy
Disability
Discrimination
Employment
Employment law
EU / international
Family and divorce
Housing
Insolvency & corporate recovery
Insurance
Landlord & tenant
Local government
Medical negligence – claimant
Personal injury
Professional negligence
Property litigation
Public sector
Residential property
Road traffic
Wills, executries and trusts
Director
Jill Shaw Andrew

ANDERSONBAIN LLP
125 Bruntsfield Place, Edinburgh EH10 4EQ
Tel: (0131) 2282000
Fax: (0131) 2281111
DX: ED654 EDINBURGH
Web: www.andersonbain.co.uk
Categories of Work
Adoption
Advice the elderly & powers of attorney
Banking & finance
Benefit advice
Charities
Children
Commercial property
Consumer credit
Contract & property disputes
Copyright, trade marks and design
Corporate tax
Debt collecting
Debt recovery, insolvency, bankruptcy
Employment
Employment law
Environment (Business Premises)

Family and divorce
Family business advice
Freedom of information
Health and safety
Housing
Insolvency & corporate recovery
Joint venture
Landlord & tenant
Liquor licensing
Medical negligence – defender
Medical negligence – claimant
Mental health
Mergers and acquisitions
Pensions (Company)
Pensions (Employment)
Personal injury
Personal injury – defender
Personal tax
Professional negligence
Residential property
Road traffic
SME business advice
Social housing
Sport
Wills, executries and trusts
Partner
Neil Kerr Finlayson

ANDERSON STRATHERN LLP
1 Rutland Court, Edinburgh EH3 8EY
Tel: (0131) 2707700
Fax: (0131) 2707788
DX: ED3 EDINBURGH
E-mail: info@andersonstrathern.co.uk
Web: www.andersonstrathern.co.uk
Categories of Work
Adjudication
Adoption
Advice the elderly & powers of attorney
Agriculture and estates
Agriculture, crofting and fishing
Alternative dispute resolution
Banking & finance
Betting & gaming
Charities
Children
Childrens
Civil court work
Civil legal aid
Commercial litigation
Commercial property
Competition
Construction
Consumer credit
Contract & property disputes
Copyright, trade marks and design
Corporate tax
Criminal court work
Data protection
Debt
Debt administration
Debt collecting
Debt recovery, insolvency, bankruptcy

▶ **Edinburgh** continued

Disability
Discrimination
Education
Employment
Employment law
Environment
Environment (Business Premises)
EU / international
Family and divorce
Family business advice
Fishing
Freedom of information
Health
Health and safety
Housing
Human rights
Immigration and asylum
Insolvency & corporate recovery
IT and intellectual property
Joint venture
Landlord & tenant
Liquor licensing
Local government
Media and entertainment
Medical negligence – defender
Medical negligence – claimant
Mental health
Mergers and acquisitions
Mining
Oil & gas
Parliamentary
Pensions (Employment)
Personal injury
Personal injury – defender
Personal tax
Planning
Planning (Business Premises)
Power and utilities
Private equity
Professional negligence
Projects
Property litigation
Public finance initiative
Public sector
Residential property
Road traffic
Shipping
SME business advice
Social housing
Software licensing
Sport
Telecoms
Transport
Wills, executries and trusts
Partners
Gillian Anne Anderson
Linsey Jane Barclay-Smith
Robin Douglas Beattie
Andrew James William Brown
Simon Thomas David Brown
David Haddow Campbell

Martin Stuart Campbell
Robert Carr
Anne Margaret Chapman
Alistair Fraser Dean
Bruce Farquhar
Neil Robert Farrell
Fiona Helen Gibb
Nicholas Alexander Howie
Sara Marziyeh Jalicy
Alasdair Scott Johnstone
Patrick Joseph Loftus
Deborah Anne Lovell
Katrina Louise Lumsdaine
Ruth Petricia Anne Maclean
Stephen James McDonagh
Alastair John McKie
Euan Andrew Mellor
John Angus Mitchell
Barry Christopher Nichol
Adele Jeanne Nicol
John Douglas Willison Peutherer
Sheonagh Lesley Richards
Jemma Rachel Richardson
Fiona Margaret Stephen
Gavin Macdonald Thain
Alun Thomas
Carole Tomlinson
Euan Charles Morgan Tripp
Catriona Mackay Watt
Karyn Marjorie Watt
Martin William Robert Whiteford
Consultants
James Don Blair
Alexander David Gunn
Colin Bruce Henderson
Sarah McKinlay
Andrew John Morris
Associates
Kate Denise Bond
Gary John Burton
Karen Yvonne Craig
Rowan Douglas
Claire Danielle Edgar
Shirley Patricia Evans
Lesley Alexander Fitzgerald
Scott Charles Flannigan
Neil Duncan Fraser
Scott Andrew Fyfe
Guy Maximilian George Grant
Anne Pamela Henderson
Russell Stuart Laughland
Robert Andrew Lawless
Sophia Yukyee Li
Jamie Graeme Marwick
Sophie Lucinda Noble
Sarah Ann Phillips
Ewan McPherson Regan
Lindsay Helen Robinson
Lucy Clare Thornton
Robert Edward Wilson
Employees
Megan Anderson
Mandy Armstrong

Lucy May Arthur
Greg Robb Barr
Laura Julie Bowen
Daniel John Considine
Christopher Devlin
Jamie Devlin
Nicholas Paul Dobbs
Sarah Donnachie
Leona Jane Duff
Lisa Flaherty
Emily Monica Margaret Flett-Grant
Laura Jane Flounders
Hamish Douglas John Forbes
Gregory Blair Calderwood Gardiner
Francesca Ellen Glendinning
Christina Balmain Heard
Anna Alice Hills
Alexandru Damaris Iliescu
William Lewis Jamieson
Julia Louise Kidd
Anne Scott Lawrie
Sarah Frances Lonie
Catherine Macdonald
Laura Anne McCabe
Molly McGrady
Niall McIntosh
Sarah Frances Monan
Laura Elizabeth Murray
Kirsty May Nicoll
Stuart Gordon Orr
Lara Claudia Pedreschi
Jane Lesley Pothan
Kieran John Reilly
Sophie Jade Riise
Lindsay Anne Robertson
Seonaid Margaret Sandham
Markus Scharbert
William Elliot Shannon
Victoria Joan Wendy Simpson
Liam Anthony Smith
Susan Edith Stewart
Jennifer Anne Thom
Robin Jonathan Fidler Turnbull
Conor Craig Whittaker

ANNAN SOLICITORS AND ESTATE AGENTS
44 Palmerston Place, Edinburgh EH12 5BJ
Tel: (0131) 2255484
Categories of Work
Advice the elderly & powers of attorney
Commercial property
Landlord & tenant
Residential property
Wills, executries and trusts

ARBUTHNOTT & MCCLANACHAN
89 Main Street, Davidson Mains, Edinburgh
EH4 5AD
Tel: (0131) 3127276
E-mail: enquiries@elpamsolicitors.co.uk
Categories of Work
Advice the elderly & powers of attorney
Charities
Civil court work

Commercial litigation
Commercial property
Contract & property disputes
Debt
Debt collecting
Debt recovery, insolvency, bankruptcy
Disability
Discrimination
Employment
Employment law
Health and safety
Landlord & tenant
Parliamentary
Personal tax
Property litigation
Residential property
Wills, executries and trusts

ASTON GOWMAN LIMITED
83 Princes Street, Edinburgh EH2 2ER
Categories of Work
Civil court work
Medical negligence – claimant
Personal injury
Professional negligence
Road traffic

BALFOUR + MANSON LLP
56-66 Frederick Street, Edinburgh EH2 1LS
Tel: (0131) 2001200
Fax: 0131-608-1004
E-mail: info@balfour-manson.co.uk
Web: www.balfour-manson.co.uk
Categories of Work
Adoption
Advice the elderly & powers of attorney
Alternative dispute resolution
Banking & finance
Benefit advice
Charities
Children
Childrens
Civil court work
Civil legal aid
Commercial litigation
Commercial property
Consumer credit
Contract & property disputes
Copyright, trade marks and design
Corporate tax
Criminal court work
Data protection
Debt
Debt management
Disability
Discrimination
Education
Employment
Employment law
Environment
Family and divorce
Family business advice
Freedom of information
Health

▶ *Edinburgh continued*

Health and safety
IT and intellectual property
Joint venture
Landlord & tenant
Local government
Media and entertainment
Medical negligence – defender
Medical negligence – claimant
Mental health
Personal injury
Personal injury – defender
Personal tax
Planning (Business Premises)
Professional negligence
Property litigation
Residential property
Road traffic
SME business advice
Transport
Wills, executives and trusts
Partners
Hugh Donald Walter Angus
Shona Margaret Brown
Gordon Fletcher Deane
Jamie Munro Foulis
Alan Robert John Gilfillan
Robert Andrew James Holland
Ann Agnes Logan
David Stewart McIntosh
Elaine Joyce Motion
Fiona Kirsty Muirs
Sindi Mules
Karen Elizabeth Phillips
Kenneth Stewart Robertson
Sarah Ann Shiels
David Short
Shona Houston Smith
Graeme Henry Thomson
Martin David Walker
Stephanie Francesca Zak
Associates
Russell John Eadie
Michaela Jill Guthrie
James Robert Hyams
Stephanie Nichol
Margaret Morton Kennedy Ross
Iain Dallas Thomson
Employees
Emily Mary Deans
Taylor Henry
Carolyn Sophie Jackson
Martin Lavery
Peter James Littlefair
Sylvia Claire McCullagh
Lauren Hazel Hamilton Smith
Adelle Ashley Walker
William Wallace
Klaudia Wasilewska

WSA BANNERMANBURKE DEFENCE LAWYERS
28 Albany Street, Edinburgh EH1 3QH
Tel: (0131) 5578020

Categories of Work
Criminal court work
Criminal legal aid
Human rights
Employee
Liam Alexander

BBM SOLICITORS LIMITED
1st Floor, 27 George Street, Edinburgh
EH2 2PA
Tel: (0131) 526 3280
Fax: (0131) 629 8878
DX: ED582 EDINBURGH
Web: www.bbmsolicitors.co.uk
Categories of Work
Adoption
Advice the elderly & powers of attorney
Agriculture and estates
Alternative dispute resolution
Charities
Children
Childrens
Civil court work
Commercial litigation
Contract & property disputes
Criminal court work
Debt collecting
Debt recovery, insolvency, bankruptcy
Employment
Family and divorce
Family business advice
Insolvency & corporate recovery
Landlord & tenant
Personal injury
Personal tax
Property litigation
Road traffic
Wills, executives and trusts
Employees
Ewan Alistair Hazelton
Thomas Daniel Holligan
Joanna Wilson Hunter Morris

NIGEL BEAUMONT & CO.
30 Annandale Street, Edinburgh EH7 4AN
Tel: (0131) 5573565
Fax: (0131) 5564273
E-mail: office@nigelbeaumont.co.uk
Categories of Work
Criminal court work
Criminal legal aid
Partner
Nigel James Bruce Beaumont
Employees
Gillian Law
Neil George David Martin

BERRYMANS LACE MAWER LLP
18 George Street, Edinburgh EH2 2PF
Tel: (0131) 2259855
Fax: (0131) 2267677
DX: 76 EDINBURGH
Categories of Work
Adjudication

Alternative dispute resolution
Banking & finance
Children
Civil court work
Civil legal aid
Commercial litigation
Commercial property
Construction
Contract & property disputes
Copyright, trade marks and design
Criminal court work
Criminal legal aid
Data protection
Debt
Debt collecting
Debt recovery, insolvency, bankruptcy
Employment
Employment law
Environment
Environment (Business Premises)
Family and divorce
Fishing
Freedom of information
Health
Health and safety
Housing
Human rights
Insurance
IT and intellectual property
Joint venture
Landlord & tenant
Medical negligence – defender
Medical negligence – claimant
Mergers and acquisitions
Mining
Oil & gas
Parliamentary
Personal injury
Personal injury – defender
Personal tax
Planning
Planning (Business Premises)
Power and utilities
Professional negligence
Projects
Property litigation
Road traffic
Transport
Partners
Ian Paul Leach
Greg Stuart MacDougall
Associate
Catriona Margaret MacLean
Employees
Rory William Anderson
Calum Graeme Murray
Sharon Ita Skirving-Young
Shirley Anne Wyles

BEVERIDGE & KELLAS
52 Leith Walk, Leith, Edinburgh EH6 5HW
Tel: (0131) 5546321
Fax: (0131) 5535319

DX: 550850 LEITH
E-mail: mail@beveridgekellas.com
Categories of Work
Adoption
Advice the elderly & powers of attorney
Children
Civil court work
Civil legal aid
Commercial property
Contract & property disputes
Debt
Debt recovery, insolvency, bankruptcy
Family and divorce
Landlord & tenant
Medical negligence – claimant
Personal injury
Personal injury – defender
Professional negligence
Property litigation
Residential property
Road traffic
Wills, executries and trusts
Partners
John Alexander Campbell
Gillian Frances Conlon
Graeme Lindesay Duncan
Lynn Louisa Harrison
Donald Michael Uttley
Employee
Rosalyn Patricia Thomson

BEVERIDGE PHILP & ROSS LIMITED
22 Bernard Street, Leith, Edinburgh EH6 6PS
Tel: (0131) 5546244
Fax: (0131) 553 2988
DX: 550851 LEITH
E-mail: avenables@bprsolicitors.co.uk
Categories of Work
Advice the elderly & powers of attorney
Commercial property
Family and divorce
Landlord & tenant
Wills, executries and trusts
Director
Aileen Anderson Venables

BLACKADDERS LLP
40 Torphichen Street, Edinburgh EH3 8JB
Tel: (0131) 2228000
Fax: (0131) 2228008
DX: ED508 EDINBURGH
E-mail: enquiries@blackadders.co.uk
Categories of Work
Adoption
Advice the elderly & powers of attorney
Agriculture and estates
Agriculture, crofting and fishing
Alternative dispute resolution
Banking & finance
Charities
Children
Childrens
Civil court work
Civil legal aid

▶ **Edinburgh continued**

Commercial litigation
Commercial property
Competition
Construction
Consumer credit
Contract & property disputes
Copyright, trade marks and design
Data protection
Debt
Debt collecting
Debt recovery, insolvency, bankruptcy
Disability
Discrimination
Employment
Employment law
Environment
Environment (Business Premises)
EU / international
Family and divorce
Family business advice
Fishing
Freedom of information
Housing
Human rights
Insolvency & corporate recovery
IT and intellectual property
Joint venture
Landlord & tenant
Media and entertainment
Medical negligence – defender
Medical negligence – claimant
Mental health
Mergers and acquisitions
Pensions (Employment)
Personal injury
Personal injury – defender
Personal tax
Planning
Power and utilities
Private equity
Professional negligence
Property litigation
Public sector
Residential property
Road traffic
SME business advice
Software licensing
Sport
Telecoms
Wills, executries and trusts
Partners
Richard Anthony James Godden
James Fraser McBride Hardie
Donna Reynolds
Employees
Philip Stanley Buchan
Stewart John Dunbar
Lesley Ann Iannarelli
Louise Emma Patterson
Ashleigh Barbara Urwin
Andrew Derrick Yule

BLACKLOCKS
First Floor, 34 Bernard Street, Edinburgh
EH6 7AS
Tel: (0131) 5553888
Fax: (0131) 5555535
DX: 550863 LEITH
E-mail: info@blacklocks.co.uk
Web: www.blacklocks.co.uk
Categories of Work
Civil court work
Commercial litigation
Debt collecting
Debt recovery, insolvency, bankruptcy
Landlord & tenant
Partner
Telfer George Blacklock
Associate
Jacqueline Sara Ridley

BLAIR CADELL
Property Sales Centre, 1 Harrison Gardens,
Edinburgh EH11 1SJ
Tel: (0131) 3371800
DX: ED92 EDINBURGH
E-mail: office@blaircadell.com
Web: www.blaircadell.com
Categories of Work
Advice the elderly & powers of attorney
Banking & finance
Charities
Commercial property
Family business advice
Landlord & tenant
Residential property
Wills, executries and trusts

BLAIR CADELL
The Bond House, 5 Breadalbane Street,
Edinburgh EH6 5JH
Tel: (0131) 555 5800
Fax: (0131) 555 1022
DX: ED92 EDINBURGH
E-mail: office@blaircadell.com
Web: www.blaircadell.com
Categories of Work
Advice the elderly & powers of attorney
Banking & finance
Charities
Commercial property
Family business advice
Landlord & tenant
Residential property
Wills, executries and trusts
Partners
Donald Jardine
Andrew Norman Grainger Macdonald
Susan Margaret Masterton
Keri Elizabeth Vanderburg Sole
Consultant
Kenneth Dick Brydon

BONACCORD ECOSSE LIMITED
31 Merchiston Park, Edinburgh EH10 4PW
Tel: (0131) 2026527

E-mail: enquiries@bonaccord.law
Web: www.bonaccord.law

Categories of Work
Alternative dispute resolution
Charities
Copyright, trade marks and design
Data protection
Employment law
EU / international
Family business advice
Freedom of information
IT and intellectual property
Joint venture
Media and entertainment
Mergers and acquisitions
Private equity
SME business advice
Software licensing
Director
Patricia Barbara Ann Barclay

BON LAW LTD
Level 2, 44 Biggar Road, Edinburgh EH10 7BJ
Tel: (0131) 5641460
E-mail: neil@bon-law.co.uk

Categories of Work
Banking & finance
Commercial property
Landlord & tenant
Public sector
Director
Neil John Bon

BONNAR ACCIDENT LAW LTD
27 Alva Street, Edinburgh EH2 4PS
Tel: (0131) 2207690
DX: ED121 EDINBURGH
E-mail: findout@bonnarandco.com
Web: www.bonnarandco.com

Categories of Work
Civil court work
Civil legal aid
Health and safety
Personal injury
Professional negligence
Road traffic

JOSEPH G BOYD & CO COURT LAWYERS LTD
Citypoint, 65 Haymarket Terrace, Edinburgh
EH12 5HD
Tel: (07746) 767776
E-mail: jboydlawyers@gmail.com

Categories of Work
Adoption
Advice the elderly & powers of attorney
Benefit advice
Children
Childrens
Civil court work
Civil legal aid
Commercial litigation
Contract & property disputes
Criminal court work
Criminal legal aid

Debt
Debt recovery, insolvency, bankruptcy
Family and divorce
Freedom of information
Housing
Human rights
Landlord & tenant
Liquor licensing
Local government
Media and entertainment
Mental health
Director
Joseph George Boyd

BOYD LEGAL LIMITED
21-22 Queensferry Street, Edinburgh EH2 4RD
Tel: (0131) 2267464
Fax: (0131) 2267242
E-mail: newenquiries@boydlegaluk.com

Categories of Work
Advice the elderly & powers of attorney
Agriculture and estates
Charities
Commercial property
Contract & property disputes
Copyright, trade marks and design
Employment law
Family and divorce
Family business advice
Housing
Joint venture
Landlord & tenant
Mergers and acquisitions
Residential property
SME business advice
Wills, executives and trusts
Directors
Diana Glennie Boyd
William Peter Boyd
Rachael Anne Brandon
Consultants
Donald Reid McKinnon
Andrew James Taylor
Ronald Stuart Wadsworth
Employees
Rona Estelle Burns
Susan Janet Clementine Malin

BRODIES LLP
15 Atholl Crescent, Edinburgh EH3 8HA
Tel: (0131) 2283777
Fax: (0131) 2283878
DX: ED10 EDINBURGH
E-mail: mailbox@brodies.com
Web: www.brodies.com

Categories of Work
Adjudication
Adoption
Advice the elderly & powers of attorney
Agriculture and estates
Agriculture, crofting and fishing
Alternative dispute resolution
Alternative investment market
Banking & finance

▶ **Edinburgh continued**

Charities
Children
Childrens
Civil court work
Civil legal aid
Commercial litigation
Commercial property
Competition
Construction
Consumer credit
Contract & property disputes
Copyright, trade marks and design
Corporate tax
Credit brokerage
Criminal court work
Criminal legal aid
Data protection
Debt
Debt adjusting and debt counselling
Debt administration
Debt collecting
Debt recovery, insolvency, bankruptcy
Disability
Discrimination
Education
Employment
Employment law
Environment
Environment (Business Premises)
EU / international
Family and divorce
Family business advice
Fishing
Freedom of information
Health
Health and safety
Housing
Human rights
Immigration and asylum
Insolvency & corporate recovery
Insurance
IT and intellectual property
Joint venture
Landlord & tenant
Liquor licensing
Local government
Media and entertainment
Medical negligence – defender
Medical negligence – claimant
Mental health
Mergers and acquisitions
Mining
Oil & gas
Parliamentary
Pensions (Company)
Pensions (Employment)
Personal injury
Personal injury – defender
Personal tax
Planning
Planning (Business Premises)

Power and utilities
Private equity
Professional negligence
Projects
Property litigation
Provision of credit information services
Public finance initiative
Public sector
Residential property
Road traffic
Shipping
SME business advice
Social housing
Software licensing
Sport
Telecoms
Transport
Unit Trusts, OEICs and investment trusts
Wills, executives and trusts

Partners

Helen Cecilia Abrams
Andrew Abayomi Akintewe
David Scott Arnott
Alan Roderic Barr
Susanne Nicola Batchelor
Juliet Miranda Lomax Bayne
Alexander Dalrymple Stewart Buchan
Allan Steven Cairns
Alan Donald Calvert
Grant Stewart Campbell
Neil Andrew Collar
Roger Hamish Cotton
Joyce Cullen
Laurence William Douglas
Christopher William Duff
Christopher Peter Dun
Elaine Farquharson-Black
Stephen Malcolm Goldie
Leslie Drysdale Graham
Anthony Archibald Hadden
Philip John Hunter
Antony Gerald Morrell Jones
Louise Margaret Kelso
Alan Keith Knowles
Graeme William Leith
David James Lightbody
Marion Ann MacInnes
Alexander Duncan MacLean
Tanya Jane MacLeod
Kirsty Louise Macpherson
Lynne Anne Marr
John Paul Marshall
Duncan Mawby
Lucy Jane McCann
Jacqueline Margaret McGuire
William Alexander McIntosh
Paul William McLaughlin
Alistair Gordon McLean
Niall McLean
Kathryn Ann McLeish
Laura Ruth McMillan
Mark James Meiklejohn
Colin James Morrison

Andrew William Nolan
Christine Mary O'Neill
Keith Leslie Patterson
Hayley Alyson Robertson
James Ian Roscoe
Kenneth Alexander Ross
Iain James Rutherford
Brenda Catherine Scott
Nicholas Scott
Louise Shiels
Martin Andrew Sloan
Richard Bryan Smith
Bruce Stephen
Michael David Peter Stephen
Michael Peter Stoneham
Heather Thompson
Craig Ian Watt
Richard William Whyte
Jennifer Wilkie
Consultants
Alistair Carnegie Campbell
Odell Campbell Milne
Associates
Elizabeth Janette Simpson Bruce
Donna Marie Cooper
Hazel Anne Coutts
Clare Margaret Henderson Dewar
Kathryn Donachie
Aileen-Clare Dunlop
Alasdair Robin Fleming
Jessica Kate Flowerdew
Lisa Grace Gibson
Fehmida Hanif
Jill Louise Harris
David Ashley Jack
Erica Margaret Hatton Johnston
Anna Grace Martin
Jennifer Matthew
Sarah Louise McCormick
Douglas Peter McGregor
Calum Ross McKenzie
Jennifer Louise Murphy
Callum Donald Murray
Sarah Catherine Noble
Kenneth James Pinkerton
Alison Elizabeth Polson
James Alexander Reekie
Stuart John Rowson
Grant Finlayson Strachan
Euan George Taylor
Paul David Walker Wallace
Elizabeth Katrien Ward
John Craik Young
Employees
Ellen Jane Andrew
Miriam Eileen Rose Armstrong
David Bales
Emma Victoria Barnett
Stephanie Barratt
Peter Alexander Begbie
Jessica Ruth Bonar
Johanna Catherine Boyd
Peter Edward Brading

Paul Douglas Breen
Claire Elizabeth Anne Brown
Matthew Alexander Bruce
Eilidh Morag Campbell
Duncan Craig Cathie
Fiona Mary Jervis Chute
Hannah Clark
Kirsty Emma Cooper
Greg Costello
Amy Elise Cugini
Andrew Harry Deans
Breda Martina Deeley
Jemma Ann Deeney
Clare Elizabeth Devlin
Amerdeep Dhami
Lucy Georgina Duff
Jennifer Amanda Dunlop
James Stephen Dunne
Emma Caitlin Dyson
Rebecca Helen Easton
Laura Jane Fell
Hannah Margaret Fergusson
Eilidh Grant Findlay
Mark Ernest Finlay
Rory Alasdair Gordon Forbes
David Allan Ford
Lauren Muriel Gibson
Stewart Gibson
Stacey Elizabeth Gourley
Kirsty Elizabeth Graham
Steven John Graham
Andrew Charles Groom
Edward John Philip Grundy
Victoria Guild
Keith Ramsay Hall
Tracy Margaret Hall
Craig Andrew Henry
Katie Higgins
Malcolm Brian Holmes
Thomas William Horton
Roslyn Mitchell James
Shumail Javed
James Samuel John Jerman
Kathryn Anne Johnston
Eric Johnstone
Rouzana Kasem
Julie Elizabeth Keir
Clare Kelly
Helen Claire Kidd
Lisa Paterson Kinroy
Monika Barbara Koczwara
Hannah Louise Lamont
Victoria Miller Lane
Robert Matthew Langridge
Sara Isabel Lannigan
Naiomi India Law
Rachel Linda Lawson
Evalyn Lee
Lindsay Isobel Lee
Scott Alexander Logan
Kirsty Ramsay MacAulay
Finlay Eric Alasdair MacKenzie
Lesley Margaret Mackenzie

▶ **Edinburgh continued**

Robin Alexander Simon Mackintosh
Alasdair William Madden
Melissa Claire Mavor
Lucy Charlotte McCracken
Bruce Hamilton McEwen
Jacqueline Ann McFarlane
Eilidh McMillan
Jennifer Anne Mhairi Darcy Mellor
Kathryn Grace Ann Merchant
Samantha Louise Millar
Christopher David Miller
Kirsteen Elizabeth Milne
Ross Andrew James Mitchell
Blair Ian James Munro
Gregor Neil Murphy
Nicola Jane Neal
David Alexander Nelson
Gemma Nicholson
Emily Rose O'Sullivan
Kirsten Elaine Ogg
Amy Louise Pairman
Iain McKie Penman
Poppy Elizabeth Shepherd Prior
Caroline Anne Purvis
Evie Alexandra Rae
Claire Marie Reid
Anna Reilly
William Benoit Rollinson
Robert David Ross
Emily Cleo Russell
Harriet Grace Rebecca Rutherford
Kimberley Leigh Ryder-Forman
Catriona Morven Salton
Paul James Sanders
Andrew Scott
Antonia Rebecca Scott
Claire Louise Scott
Fiona Elen Scott
Kirsty Shaw
Chloe Anne Shields
Jennifer Elizabeth Sim
Martin Gordon Edward Smail
Eilidh Smith
Ellen Jemima Stuart Smith
Lynsey Smith
Karen Marie Stachura
Darren Thomson
Ruth Claire Thomson
Laura Alice Townsend
Nilah Ulhaq
Louise Mackay Usher
Douglas Robert Waddell
Chloe Wales
Alexander Andrew Walker
Gillian Helen Watson
Stuart Gordon West
Lesley Ann Wisely
Caitlin Elizabeth Wright
Victoria Arlene Zeybek

BROWN & CO LEGAL LLP
15 Alva Street, Edinburgh EH2 4PH

Tel: (0131) 2289993
E-mail: mail@lsa.org.uk
Web: www.lsa.org.uk
Categories of Work
Adoption
Advice the elderly & powers of attorney
Alternative dispute resolution
Benefit advice
Charities
Children
Childrens
Civil court work
Civil legal aid
Commercial litigation
Contract & property disputes
Criminal court work
Criminal legal aid
Debt
Debt management
Debt recovery, insolvency, bankruptcy
Disability
Discrimination
Family and divorce
Human rights
Immigration and asylum
Landlord & tenant
Medical negligence – claimant
Mental health
Personal injury
Professional negligence
Property litigation
Social housing
Wills, executries and trusts

M.J. BROWN, SON & CO.
Deanbank Lodge, 10 Deanbank Lane,
Edinburgh EH3 5BS
Tel: (0131) 3321200
Fax: (0131) 332 4600
DX: ED 122 EDINBURGH
E-mail: jmat985725@aol.com
Partner
Joan Frances Matthew

BRYMER LEGAL LIMITED
8b Rutland Square, Edinburgh EH1 2AS
Tel: (0131) 2292158
DX: ED510 EDINBURGH
E-mail: stewart@brymerlegal.co.uk
Web: www.brymerlegal.co.uk
Categories of Work
Charities
Commercial property
Contract & property disputes
Copyright, trade marks and design
IT and intellectual property
Landlord & tenant
Media and entertainment
Private equity
Professional negligence
Residential property
SME business advice
Software licensing

Director
Stewart Brymer

BRZOOM KADIRGOLAM
Ethnic Minorities Law Centre, 103-5 Morrison Street, Edinburgh EH3 8BX
Categories of Work
Children
Civil court work
Civil legal aid
Disability
Discrimination
Employment
Employment law
Human rights
Immigration and asylum
Medical negligence – defender
Personal injury – defender

BTO SOLICITORS LLP
One Edinburgh Quay, 133 Fountainbridge, Edinburgh EH3 9QG
Tel: (0131) 2222939
Fax: (0131) 2222949
DX: ED77 EDINBURGH
E-mail: lawyers@bto.co.uk
Web: www.bto.co.uk
Categories of Work
Adjudication
Adoption
Advice the elderly & powers of attorney
Agriculture and estates
Agriculture, crofting and fishing
Alternative dispute resolution
Alternative investment market
Banking & finance
Benefit advice
Charities
Children
Childrens
Civil court work
Civil legal aid
Commercial litigation
Commercial property
Competition
Construction
Consumer credit
Contract & property disputes
Copyright, trade marks and design
Corporate tax
Criminal court work
Data protection
Debt
Debt collecting
Debt recovery, insolvency, bankruptcy
Disability
Discrimination
Employment
Employment law
Environment
Environment (Business Premises)
EU / international
Family and divorce
Family business advice
Freedom of information
Health
Health and safety
Housing
Insolvency & corporate recovery
Insurance
IT and intellectual property
Joint venture
Landlord & tenant
Liquor licensing
Media and entertainment
Medical negligence – defender
Medical negligence – claimant
Mental health
Mergers and acquisitions
Oil & gas
Pensions (Company)
Pensions (Employment)
Personal injury
Personal injury – defender
Personal tax
Planning
Planning (Business Premises)
Power and utilities
Private equity
Professional negligence
Projects
Property litigation
Provision of credit information services
Public finance initiative
Public sector
Residential property
Road traffic
Shipping
SME business advice
Social housing
Software licensing
Sport
Transport
Unit Trusts, OEICs and investment trusts
Wills, executries and trusts
Partners
William Pitkaithley Cole
Laura Jane Donald
Lesley Jane Gordon
Graeme Alistair Kelly
Jacqueline Davidson McCluskey
Gregor John Mitchell
Paul Robert Motion
Lynn Richmond
Wendy Jane Thomson
Associates
Mark James Colquhoun
Michael Andrew Cox
Claire Elizabeth Logue
Matthew Bernard Kenneth Raftery
James Anthony Robb
Employees
Sara Elena Albizzati
Piers Alexander Sebastian Baylis
Sandra Natalia Jurak
Sophie Lennox
Natalie Elizabeth McCartney

▶ *Edinburgh continued*

Lauren Allison McFarlane
Deborah Elizabeth Reekie
Lewis Robert John Richardson
Georgia Elizabeth Fraser Rose
Brittany Grace Thomas

BURGES SALMON LLP

Atria One, 144 Morrison Street, Edinburgh
EH3 8EX
Tel: (0131) 3142112
Categories of Work
Agriculture and estates
Agriculture, crofting and fishing
Alternative dispute resolution
Banking & finance
Civil court work
Commercial litigation
Commercial property
Contract & property disputes
Data protection
Debt recovery, insolvency, bankruptcy
Employment
Employment law
Environment
Environment (Business Premises)
EU / international
Fishing
Freedom of information
Health
Health and safety
Housing
Insolvency & corporate recovery
IT and intellectual property
Joint venture
Landlord & tenant
Local government
Media and entertainment
Mergers and acquisitions
Mining
Oil & gas
Parliamentary
Personal injury
Personal injury – defender
Planning
Planning (Business Premises)
Power and utilities
Private equity
Professional negligence
Projects
Property litigation
Public finance initiative
Public sector
Residential property
Road traffic
Shipping
SME business advice
Software licensing
Telecoms
Transport
Unit Trusts, OEICs and investment trusts

Partners
Robert Andrew Forman
Daniel Thomas Lee
Stuart McMillan
Kathleen Frances Russell
Craig Michael Whelton
Consultant
Ewan Colin McIntyre
Associates
Amy Elizabeth McVey
Fay Charteris Shearer
Lauren Ashley Winters
Employees
Natalie Elizabeth Victoria Bennett
Sophie Louise Black
Laura Margaret Craig
Amy Louise Ferguson
Matthew James Henson
Stephanie Jessica Anne Lynch
Victoria Macaulay
Niall Mackle
Claire Linsey MacLean
Amy McPherson
Joanna Louise Monaghan
Patrick Alan Munro
Lynsey Margaret Reid
Sarah Amy Ruth Stewart
Eilidh Elspeth Wood
Samir Younes

BURNESS PAULL LLP

50 Lothian Road, Festival Square, Edinburgh
EH3 9WJ
Tel: (0131) 4736000
Fax: (0131) 4736006
DX: ED 73 EDINBURGH
E-mail: info@burnesspaull.com
Web: www.burnesspaull.com
Categories of Work
Adjudication
Adoption
Advice the elderly & powers of attorney
Agriculture and estates
Agriculture, crofting and fishing
Alternative dispute resolution
Alternative investment market
Banking & finance
Betting & gaming
Charities
Civil court work
Commercial litigation
Commercial property
Competition
Construction
Consumer credit
Contract & property disputes
Copyright, trade marks and design
Corporate tax
Credit brokerage
Criminal court work
Data protection
Debt
Debt adjusting and debt counselling

Debt administration
Debt collecting
Debt recovery, insolvency, bankruptcy
Education
Employment
Employment law
Environment
Environment (Business Premises)
EU / international
Family business advice
Fishing
Freedom of information
Health
Health and safety
Housing
Human rights
Immigration and asylum
Insolvency & corporate recovery
Insurance
IT and intellectual property
Joint venture
Landlord & tenant
Liquor licensing
Local government
Media and entertainment
Medical negligence – claimant
Mergers and acquisitions
Mining
Oil & gas
Parliamentary
Pensions (Company)
Pensions (Employment)
Personal injury
Personal injury – defender
Personal tax
Planning
Planning (Business Premises)
Power and utilities
Private equity
Professional negligence
Projects
Property litigation
Provision of credit information services
Public finance initiative
Public sector
Residential property
Road traffic
Shipping
SME business advice
Social housing
Software licensing
Sport
Telecoms
Transport
Unit Trusts, OEICs and investment trusts
Wills, executries and trusts

Solicitor
Caroline Stevenson

Partners
Neil Thomas Bruce
Robert Burns
Peter Martin Antony Chambers
Andrew John Christie

Walter James Clark
Nicola Jane Clemence
Ruaridh Mark Cole
David William Davidson
Mark Julian Ellis
Andrew Campbell Forsyth
Joanna Margaret Fulton
David James Goodbrand
Christopher Phillip Gotts
Jonathan Heaney
Morag Hutchison
Paula Elaine Kennedy
Fiona Killen
Amanda-Jane Laurie
Peter Alexander Lawson
Caroline Louise Margaret Maciver
Christopher Neil Mackay
Fenella Mary Mason
Ashley Helen Mawby
Grace Margaret McGill
Alan Charles McMillan
Colin Barrie Miller
Hazel Elaine Moffat
Scott Campbell Neilson Peterkin
Sarah Jane Robertson Phillips
Richard Veitch Rennie
Dawn Reoch
Alan Henry Soppitt
Alasdair Oman Sutherland
Tamar Tammes
Lindsay Ann Wallace
Peter Mark Ward

Consultants
Philip Mackay
Stephen Reader Scott
John Douglas Sinclair

Associates
Rachel Louise Allan
David Antonelli
Colin Reid Brown
Natasha Brownlee
Sophie Coffey
Murray James Cree
Emma Morag Dewar
Sophia Victoria Harrison
Audrey Georgina Kennedy Harrow
Anna Maria Kandris
Kerry Jane Norval
Andrew James Tyler
Nicholas Piers Warrillow

Employees
Deborah Mary Adam
Sophie Katherine Ainslie
Kendall Duncan Allan
Amanda Jordan Armstrong
Hamaira Kausar Aslam
Martin Drew Balfour
Caroline Jane Bone
Alison Brunger
Kieran David Alexander Buxton
Victoria Stefanie Cole
Martin John Connelly
Paul Coyle

▶ **Edinburgh continued**

David George Cuthill
Rhona Delaney
Stuart Robert Dickie
Sarah Michelle Dilley
Callum Donald
Laura Charlotte Donohoe
Douglas Mitchell Dunbar
Kristen Lauren Eadie
Stephen James Farrell
Donald Fraser Findlay
Georgia Rossetta Fotheringham
Shelby Alana Gemmell
Alan David Gibson
Colin Alexander Gillies
Kirsty Glennan
Hilary McKee Gordon
Daniel Jamie Hannah
Sonja Hannele Hart
Joshua Alexander Harvey
Rory Andrew Henretty
Barry Graeme Herbertson
Edward Mark Hunter
Paul Andrew Iannetta
Alan David James Innes
Amanda Rose Jack
Dominique Alison Jamieson
Ross Crawford Jamieson
Anton Jasin
Daniele Johnston
Michael James Johnston
William Gordon James Kay
Won Lim
Andrew John Little
Victoria Macdonald
Pauline McCulloch
Leigh Kathryn McDonald
Louise Veronica McErlean
Benjamin Scott McGlinchey
Marcus Robbie McLaren
Richard Conor McLaren
James Michael McMahon
Robert Duncan McNab
Meriel Jane Miller
Hayley Gillian Montgomery
Jillian Mary Moore
Douglas Lawrie McGregor Morton
Hannah Mary Morton
Jacqueline Murray
Beth Maya Wallace Nandwani
Victoria Jane Nicholson
Daniela Cristina Pallucci
Nicola Frances Pascoe
Jennifer Jane Rae
Anna Louise Reid
Hannah Melanie Reid
Tom Adam Richard
Rebecca Jane Roberts
Eilidh Fiona Robertson
Lynda Elizabeth Ross
Sean David Ross
David Andrew Sharkey

Philip Andrew Shorney
Olivia Sophie Abbott Smith
Rosie Elizabeth Smith
Lorna Helen Stephen
Michael David Stewart
David Stirrat
Euan Andrew Thompson
Ross Hodgson Allan Thompson
Katherine Rose Thomson
Christopher Brian Traynor
Nicole Trimble
Victoria Nairne Tweed
Andrew Peter Ross Tweedie
Grant Wallace
Sophia Rose Warburton
Shannan Wilkie
William James Young
Zoe Cassandra Yuile
Artem Sergeevich Zverev Mironyuk

BURNETT CHRISTIE KNOWLES MCCOURTS
53 George IV Bridge, Edinburgh EH1 1YH
Tel: (0131) 2253456
Fax: (0131) 2256543
DX: ED597 EDINBURGH
Categories of Work
Adoption
Children
Childrens
Civil court work
Civil legal aid
Criminal court work
Criminal legal aid
Family and divorce
Human rights
Partners
Fergus John Francis Christie
Stephen Vincent Knowles
Employees
Edward Arthur George Cadden
Eilidh Heather Campbell
Mairead Clare Corrigan
Liam John Kildare
Alistair Ian Murphy

CAMERON STEPHEN & CO.
14 Constitution Street, Edinburgh EH6 7BT
Tel: (0131) 5551234
Fax: (0131) 5552299
E-mail: cameron@cameronstephen.co.uk
Web: www.cameronstephen.co.uk
Categories of Work
Advice the elderly & powers of attorney
Commercial property
Landlord & tenant
Liquor licensing
Residential property
Wills, executries and trusts
Partners
Fiona Margaret Elizabeth Duff
Cameron Grant Stephen

CAMPBELL SMITH LLP
21 York Place, Edinburgh EH1 3EN

Tel: (0131) 5563737
Fax: (0131) 4737700
DX: ED51 EDINBURGH
E-mail: info@camsmith.co.uk
Web: www.camsmith.co.uk
Categories of Work
Advice the elderly & powers of attorney
Alternative dispute resolution
Alternative investment market
Betting & gaming
Charities
Civil court work
Commercial litigation
Criminal legal aid
Data protection
Debt recovery, insolvency, bankruptcy
Discrimination
Education
Employment
Employment law
Family and divorce
Insolvency & corporate recovery
Insurance
Medical negligence – defender
Medical negligence – claimant
Pensions (Company)
Pensions (Employment)
Personal injury
Personal injury – defender
Professional negligence
Residential property
Unit Trusts, OEICs and investment trusts
Wills, executries and trusts
Partners
John Gerard Cavanagh
Helen Gilmour Ferguson
Julia Maria MacConnachie
Eric John Scott
Kenneth Urquhart Steele
Employees
Sarah Catherine Guthrie Connon
Robert Latta Dobie
Elisabeth Louise Innes
Kirsty Laidlaw Summers

CAMPBELL SMITH LLP
33 York Place, Edinburgh EH1 3HP
Tel: (0131) 5563737
DX: ED 51 EDINBURGH
E-mail: property@camsmith.co.uk
Web: www.camsmith.co.uk
Categories of Work
Advice the elderly & powers of attorney
Alternative dispute resolution
Alternative investment market
Betting & gaming
Charities
Civil court work
Commercial litigation
Criminal legal aid
Data protection
Debt recovery, insolvency, bankruptcy
Discrimination

Education
Employment
Employment law
Family and divorce
Insolvency & corporate recovery
Insurance
Medical negligence – defender
Medical negligence – claimant
Pensions (Company)
Pensions (Employment)
Personal injury
Personal injury – defender
Professional negligence
Residential property
Unit Trusts, OEICs and investment trusts
Wills, executries and trusts

CAPITAL DEFENCE LAWYERS LTD
Room 418, Regus, 9-10 St. Andrew Square,
Edinburgh EH2 2AF
Tel: (07867) 637638
E-mail: ctait@capdef.co.uk
Categories of Work
Criminal court work
Criminal legal aid
Directors
Jonathan James Marley Campbell
Cameron James Tait

CASTLE STREET TRUSTEES LIMITED
3 Glenfinlas Street, Edinburgh EH3 6AQ
Tel: (0131) 2251200

CASTLETOWN LAW LIMITED
23 Melville Street, Edinburgh EH3 7PE
Tel: (0131) 2403880
Categories of Work
Banking & finance
Charities
Family business advice
Insolvency & corporate recovery
Joint venture
Mergers and acquisitions
Oil & gas
Planning
Power and utilities
Private equity
Projects
Public finance initiative
Public sector
Shipping
SME business advice
Transport
Solicitor
David William Gilchrist
Director
Andrew Lamont Renton
Consultant
Alison Margaret Timms

CHANZA JORDAN LAW LIMITED
93 George Street, Edinburgh EH2 3ES
Tel: (0131) 2401285
E-mail: ignacio@sslawpractice.co.uk
Web: www.sslawpractice.co.uk

▶ **Edinburgh** *continued*

Categories of Work
Contract & property disputes
EU / international
Residential property
Wills, executries and trusts

CLAN CHILDLAW LIMITED
Unit S4B, Norton Park, 57 Albion Road,
Edinburgh EH7 5QY
Tel: (0808) 129 0522
Categories of Work
Adoption
Benefit advice
Children
Childrens
Civil court work
Civil legal aid
Debt
Debt management
Disability
Discrimination
Family and divorce
Housing
Human rights
Immigration and asylum
Landlord & tenant
Local government
Mental health
Social housing
Directors
Julia Elisabeth Donnelly
Mary-Claire Kelly
Alison Patricia Reid
Employees
Lucy Alexandra Frazer
Jenna Hall
Louise Mary Herd
Claire Louise Osborne

CLANCYS SOLICITORS AND ESTATE AGENTS LIMITED
89-91 Morrison Street, Edinburgh EH3 8BU
Tel: (0131) 337 7771
Fax: (0131) 510 9282
DX: ED432 EDINBURGH
E-mail: info@clancys-solicitors.co.uk
Web: www.clancys-solicitors.co.uk
Categories of Work
Commercial property
Landlord & tenant
Residential property
Wills, executries and trusts
Director
Paul Harvey Clancy
Employees
Rebeca Claire Marshall
Katie Jayne Milner

CLERWOOD LEGAL SERVICES LTD
51 Clermiston Road, Edinburgh EH12 6XD
Tel: (0131) 4677611
Fax: (0131) 4677273
E-mail: gavin.tosh@clerwoodlegal.com

Web: www.clerwoodlegal.com
Categories of Work
Copyright, trade marks and design
Data protection
EU / international
Family business advice
Freedom of information
IT and intellectual property
Joint venture
Landlord & tenant
Mergers and acquisitions
Public sector
SME business advice
Software licensing
Director
Gavin Charles Tosh

CLYDE & CO
Albany House, 58 Albany Street, Edinburgh
EH1 3QR
Tel: (0131) 5571545
DX: ED513 EDINBURGH
E-mail: Enquiries.Scotland@clydeco.com
Web: www.clydeco.com
Categories of Work
Adjudication
Adoption
Alternative dispute resolution
Banking & finance
Children
Civil court work
Civil legal aid
Commercial litigation
Commercial property
Construction
Contract & property disputes
Copyright, trade marks and design
Criminal court work
Criminal legal aid
Data protection
Disability
Discrimination
Education
Employment
Employment law
Environment
Environment (Business Premises)
EU / international
Family and divorce
Freedom of information
Health
Health and safety
Human rights
Insurance
Joint venture
Landlord & tenant
Liquor licensing
Local government
Medical negligence – defender
Medical negligence – claimant
Mental health
Oil & gas
Parliamentary

Pensions (Employment)
Personal injury
Personal injury – defender
Power and utilities
Professional negligence
Property litigation
Public sector
Road traffic
Shipping
Sport
Transport
Associate
Damien Christopher Tonner

CLYDE & CO (SCOTLAND) LLP
Albany House, 58 Albany Street, Edinburgh
EH1 3QR
Tel: (0131) 5571545
Fax: (0131) 5258651
DX: 550480 EDINBURGH 45
E-mail: Enquiries.Scotland@clydeco.com
Web: www.clydeco.com
Categories of Work
Adjudication
Adoption
Alternative dispute resolution
Banking & finance
Children
Civil court work
Civil legal aid
Commercial litigation
Commercial property
Construction
Contract & property disputes
Copyright, trade marks and design
Criminal court work
Criminal legal aid
Data protection
Disability
Discrimination
Education
Employment
Employment law
Environment
Environment (Business Premises)
EU / international
Family and divorce
Freedom of information
Health
Health and safety
Human rights
Insurance
Joint venture
Landlord & tenant
Liquor licensing
Local government
Medical negligence – defender
Medical negligence – claimant
Mental health
Oil & gas
Parliamentary
Pensions (Employment)
Personal injury

Personal injury – defender
Power and utilities
Professional negligence
Property litigation
Public sector
Road traffic
Shipping
Sport
Transport
Partners
Toni Louise Ashby
Duncan James Batchelor
Andrew Alan Constable
Sarah Helen Crewes
Andrew Bruce Goodbrand
Tanya Ann Gordon
Gavin Paul Henderson
Anne Kentish
Victoria Marchbank Melville
David William Tait
Graeme Douglas Watson
Consultant
Gordon Stuart Keyden
Associates
Rachel Elizabeth Carr
Lyndsey Helen Janet Combe
Abigail Louise Cooke
Kay Anne Darling
Ross Fyfe Fairweather
Colette Marie Finnieston
Natalie Leslie Gibb
Jennifer Eilise McKeown
Graeme Milloy
Kimberley Jane Mitchell
Robert Faulkner Murray
Gary Christopher Nicholls
Claire Elizabeth Raftery
Muhammad Bilaal Shabbir
Catriona Stewart
Richard Jonathan Templeton
Andrew Charles Stewart Tolmie
Alison Barbara Tyler
Marian Tytler
Alison Webb
Employees
John Munro Callender
Kirsty Louise Cassidy
Madelaine Cassidy
Bethany Norma Dodds
Christopher Martin Dunn
Bronagh Ann Finlay
Jennifer Elaine Proudfoot Harvie
Camilla Heidi Karin Horneman
Louise Anne Mackinnon
Lauren Helen McLaughlin
Rachael Elizabeth Miller
Michael Kenneth Short
Igor Grzegorz Siedlecki
Jenna Sturrock
Christopher James Taylor
Lorne Catherine Todd

▶ *Edinburgh continued*

CMS CAMERON MCKENNA NABARRO OLSWANG LLP

Saltire Court, 20 Castle Terrace, Edinburgh
EH1 2EN
Tel: (0131) 2288000
Fax: (0131) 2288888
DX: 553001 Edinburgh

Categories of Work

Adjudication
Agriculture and estates
Agriculture, crofting and fishing
Alternative dispute resolution
Alternative investment market
Banking & finance
Betting & gaming
Charities
Civil court work
Civil legal aid
Commercial litigation
Commercial property
Competition
Construction
Consumer credit
Contract & property disputes
Copyright, trade marks and design
Corporate tax
Credit brokerage
Data protection
Debt administration
Debt collecting
Debt recovery, insolvency, bankruptcy
Discrimination
Education
Employment
Employment law
Environment
Environment (Business Premises)
EU / international
Family business advice
Fishing
Freedom of information
Health
Health and safety
Housing
Human rights
Immigration and asylum
Insolvency & corporate recovery
Insurance
IT and intellectual property
Joint venture
Landlord & tenant
Liquor licensing
Local government
Media and entertainment
Mergers and acquisitions
Mining
Oil & gas
Parliamentary
Pensions (Company)
Pensions (Employment)
Personal injury

Personal injury – defender
Personal tax
Planning
Planning (Business Premises)
Power and utilities
Private equity
Professional negligence
Projects
Property litigation
Public finance initiative
Public sector
Residential property
Shipping
SME business advice
Social housing
Software licensing
Sport
Telecoms
Transport
Unit Trusts, OEICs and investment trusts

Partners

Sian Elizabeth Margaret Aitken
Catriona Jan Aldridge
Jennifer Mary Allan
Marc James Armstrong
Darren Alexander Craig
Alan David Crowther Fulton
Karagh Elisabeth Scott Gilliatt
Alison Margaret Gow
Gordon Douglas Hay
Robin William Hutchison
Colin John George Hutton
Mark Jonathan Kirke
Colin Thomas Lawrie
Graeme Bruce MacLeod
Michael Ian McCann
Laura Margaret McIntosh
Finlay Alexander McKay
Margaret McLean
Mark McMurray
Amanda Russell Methven
Caryn Lynn Miller
Harriet Anne Munro
Stephen James Phillips
Timothy Michael Pitt
Stuart Robert Tait
Claire Helen Wallis
Robert Patrick Malcolm Wilson
Graeme Keith Perkin Young

Consultants

Donald Ian Cumming
Cynthia Louise Johnson
Shona Mary Sanders
Ewan Swanson Thomson

Associates

Jennifer Margaret Antonelli
Paul John Baird
Caroline Sinclair Barr
Katherine Ann Becher
Fraser William Blair
Christopher John Bowie
Tak Lan Teresa Bradshaw-Wong
Amy Leigh Campbell

Keith Fraser Campbell
Jeanette Ann Chalmers
John Simon Craske
Jennifer Darling
Eilidh Sharrod Douglas
James Andrew Dundas
Jennifer Mary Robertson Durie
Charlotte Mary Edgar
Jennefer Charlotte Fusaro
Catriona Lesley Shirreffs Garcia-Alis
Gary Peter Georgeson
Alice Elizabeth Hardy
Abbie Harley
Bruce Douglas Harvie
Catherine Howie
Laura Amie King
Piotr Jozef Klaskala
Gavin Niall MacGregor
Louise Rae Macleod
Cara Elizabeth McGlynn
Amy Rebecca Wright Norton
Claudia Ruth Russell
Fiona Ann Scott
Laura Elizabeth Sefton
Keith Peter Malcolm Simpson
Roland William Smyth
Sally Caroline Smyth
Jennifer Helen Stewart
Joanna Collin Waddell
Mark Lee Walker
Laura Jane West
Bethan Lucy White
Rowena Winifred Williams
Caroline Macnee Wilson
Solicitor
Rachel Gillan
Employees
Sidrah Amin
Eilidh Jane Beveridge
Kirsty Margaret Blance
Joy Margaret Calder
Joanna Christine Clark
Katriona Rosemary Dunn
Jessica Eaton
Fanny S ra Fecskovics
Stephen James Fitzpatrick
Kirsty Robyn Fryer
June Valerie Gilles
Leanne Marion Hammell
Clare Mary Heggie
Dimitar Ivanov Kadiyski
Jamie William Kelman
Jack Robert Laidlaw
Melissa Lugton Laurie
Matthew Pablo Andrew Leon
Lee Anne Lothian
Jennifer Love
Amina Arshad Mahmood
James Thomas Marshall
Amy Mary Corcoran Mathewson
Laura Amber McArdle
Rebecca Anne-Marie McGladrigan
Claire Ann Miller

Kathryn Bea Nolin
Kirsty Shona Nurse
Kirsty April Margaret Paterson-Hunter
Elaine Fiona Piggot
Thomas Lee Pullar
Kayleigh Purves
Catriona Ritchie
Jennifer Lois Ross
Tobias Max Seger
James Simpson
Rory Donald Thomson
Rachel Todd
Gordon Tsang
Michael Gordon Urquhart
Anita Oi Liun Wong

CN DEFENCE LTD
55 St. Leonard's Street, Edinburgh EH8 9QN
Tel: (0131) 5571000
Fax: (0131) 5573443
E-mail: mail@cndefence.com
Categories of Work
Criminal court work
Criminal legal aid
Director
Matthew Nicholson
Employees
Hannah Baxter
Paul David Smith

COLLINS & CO DEFENCE LAWYERS LTD
18 Cadzow Place, Edinburgh EH7 5SN
Tel: (0131) 661 3210
DX: 551159 EDINBURGH 8
E-mail: mail@collinsandcolawyers.com
Web: www.collinsandcolawyers.com
Categories of Work
Criminal court work
Criminal legal aid
Director
Simon Gerard Corrieri Collins
Employees
Peter Robin Barr
Christopher Andrew MacFarlane
Alexander Murray Raeburn

CONNELL & CONNELL, WS
10 Dublin Street, Edinburgh EH1 3PR
Tel: (0131) 5562993
Fax: (0131) 5575542
DX: ED184 EDINBURGH
E-mail: enquiries@connellws.co.uk
Web: www.connellws.co.uk
Categories of Work
Advice the elderly & powers of attorney
Children
Commercial property
Family business advice
Landlord & tenant
Personal tax
Residential property
SME business advice
Wills, executries and trusts

▶ **Edinburgh continued**

Partners
Lesley Macpherson Elrick
Anne Morag McKenzie
Richard James Murray
Andrew James Ogilvie
Consultant
Gordon Douglas Cairns
Associate
Alison Isabel Rowatt
Employees
Jennifer Lynn Boyle
Ailie Elizabeth Christie
Chloe Davidson

COOMBS SOLICITORS AND NOTARIES LIMITED
160 Mayfield Road, Edinburgh EH9 3AP
Tel: (07764) 186588
Categories of Work
Advice the elderly & powers of attorney
Agriculture and estates
Charities
Family business advice
Landlord & tenant
Mental health
Personal tax
Residential property
Wills, executives and trusts
Director
Maria Francesca Coombs

COOPER JOHNSON LAW LTD
6 Redheughs Rigg, Edinburgh EH12 9DQ
Tel: (01577) 840213
Director
Hazel Anderson Johnson

COULTERS LEGAL LLP
Lochside House, 3 Lochside Way, Edinburgh
EH12 9DT
Tel: (0131) 603 7333
Fax: (0131) 339 6802
DX: ED550451 EDIN44
E-mail: enquiries@coultersproperty.co.uk
Categories of Work
Residential property
Partners
Wilson Forbes Browne
Ross Alexander MacKay
Associates
Graham David Keith
Jean McAlpine
Employee
Elaine Isobel Imlach

CURRIE, GILMOUR & CO.
41/43 Warrender Park Road, Edinburgh
EH9 1EU
Tel: (0131) 2295304
Fax: (0131) 2285112
DX: ED150 EDINBURGH
E-mail: enquiries@curriegilmour.co.uk
Web: www.curriegilmour.co.uk

Categories of Work
Advice the elderly & powers of attorney
Civil court work
Commercial property
Family and divorce
Landlord & tenant
Residential property
Wills, executives and trusts
Partner
Neil Campbell

CYCLE LAW SCOTLAND
16-20 Castle Street, Edinburgh EH2 3AT
Tel: (0131) 4736626
E-mail: edinburgh@cyclelawscotland.co.uk
Categories of Work
Civil court work
Personal injury
Professional negligence
Road traffic
Sport

DAC BEACHCROFT SCOTLAND LLP
24 Dublin Street, Edinburgh EH1 3PP
Tel: (0131) 5247790
Fax: (0131) 5247791
DX: 551112 EDINBURGH 7
E-mail: scottishclaims@dacbeachcroft.com
Web: https://www.dacbeachcroft.com/
Categories of Work
Adjudication
Adoption
Advice the elderly & powers of attorney
Agriculture and estates
Agriculture, crofting and fishing
Alternative dispute resolution
Alternative investment market
Banking & finance
Benefit advice
Betting & gaming
Charities
Children
Childrens
Civil court work
Civil legal aid
Commercial litigation
Commercial property
Competition
Construction
Consumer credit
Contract & property disputes
Copyright, trade marks and design
Corporate tax
Credit brokerage
Criminal court work
Criminal legal aid
Data protection
Debt
Debt adjusting and debt counselling
Debt administration
Debt collecting
Debt management
Debt recovery, insolvency, bankruptcy
Disability

Education
Employment
Employment law
Environment
Environment (Business Premises)
EU / international
Family and divorce
Family business advice
Fishing
Freedom of information
Health
Health and safety
Housing
Human rights
Immigration and asylum
Insolvency & corporate recovery
Insurance
IT and intellectual property
Joint venture
Landlord & tenant
Liquor licensing
Local government
Media and entertainment
Medical negligence – defender
Medical negligence – claimant
Mental health
Mergers and acquisitions
Mining
Oil & gas
Parliamentary
Pensions (Company)
Pensions (Employment)
Personal injury
Personal injury – defender
Personal tax
Planning
Planning (Business Premises)
Power and utilities
Private equity
Professional negligence
Projects
Property litigation
Provision of credit information services
Public finance initiative
Public sector
Road traffic
Shipping
SME business advice
Social housing
Software licensing
Sport
Telecoms
Transport
Unit Trusts, OEICs and investment trusts
Associate
Beverley Atkinson
Employees
Claire Elizabeth Newcombe
Andrew Campbell Normand
Harriet Jane Tooley
Kimberley Webster

DAVIDSON CHALMERS (NOMINEES) LIMITED
12 Hope Street, Edinburgh EH2 4DB
Tel: (0131) 6259191

DAVIDSON CHALMERS (SECRETARIAL SERVICES) LTD.
12 Hope Street, Edinburgh EH2 4DB
Tel: (0131) 6259191

DAVIDSON CHALMERS STEWART LLP
12 Hope Street, Edinburgh EH2 4DB
Tel: (0131) 6259191
Fax: (0131) 6259 192
DX: ED408 EDINBURGH
Web: www.dcslegal.com
Categories of Work
Adjudication
Adoption
Advice the elderly & powers of attorney
Agriculture and estates
Agriculture, crofting and fishing
Alternative dispute resolution
Alternative investment market
Banking & finance
Charities
Civil court work
Commercial litigation
Commercial property
Competition
Construction
Contract & property disputes
Copyright, trade marks and design
Corporate tax
Criminal court work
Data protection
Debt
Debt collecting
Debt recovery, insolvency, bankruptcy
Disability
Discrimination
Employment
Environment
Environment (Business Premises)
EU / international
Family and divorce
Family business advice
Fishing
Freedom of information
Health
Health and safety
Housing
Human rights
Insolvency & corporate recovery
Insurance
IT and intellectual property
Joint venture
Landlord & tenant
Liquor licensing
Local government
Medical negligence – defender
Medical negligence – claimant
Mergers and acquisitions
Mining
Oil & gas

► **Edinburgh continued**

Parliamentary
Personal injury
Personal injury – defender
Planning
Planning (Business Premises)
Power and utilities
Private equity
Professional negligence
Projects
Property litigation
Public finance initiative
Public sector
Residential property
Road traffic
Shipping
SME business advice
Telecoms
Transport
Wills, executries and trusts

Partners
Andrew Simon Chalmers
Caroline Isobel Court
Andrew James Jonathan Drane
Stuart Duncan
Greg Flett
Laura Jane Irvine
Bruce Donald Tyrie Lancaster
Gavin Iain Campbell Maclean
Craig Stirling
Laura Louise Tainsh
Sheila Mairead Webster

Consultants
Alan Strain
James Archibald Kirkland Warnock

Associates
Arveen Arabshahi
Lisa Christine Graham
Lisa Kitson
Steven Ryan McAllister
Magnus James William Miller
Keith James Rawlinson

Employees
Alexander James Murray Campbell
Jacqueline Elizabeth Cook
Elizabeth Enayati
Niall George Hughieson
Alexandra Emma Irwin
Louise Marie Jones
Stephanie Jane Mackenzie
Caroline Mary Matthews
Andrew McDonald
Antony Gerard Millar
Saoirse Antonia Susan Stankard
Ellis Gillespie Walls
Simone Gabriella Young

DAVIDSONS
35 Albany Street, Edinburgh EH1 3QN
Tel: (0131) 5589999
Fax: (0131) 5573139
DX: 551061 EDINBURGH 6
E-mail: iainhaigh@davidsons-solicitors.co.uk

Categories of Work
Advice the elderly & powers of attorney
Commercial property
Joint venture
Landlord & tenant
Residential property
Wills, executries and trusts

Partner
Iain Davidson Haigh

DEANS SOLICITORS AND ESTATE AGENTS LLP
135-137 St. Johns Road, Edinburgh EH12 7SB
Tel: (0131) 6671900
DX: 82 Edinburgh
Categories of Work
Residential property
Wills, executries and trusts

DEANS SOLICITORS AND ESTATE AGENTS LLP
3 St Patrick Street, Edinburgh EH8 9ES
Tel: (0131) 6671900
Fax: (0131) 6624815
DX: 82 Edinburgh
E-mail: mail@deansproperties.co.uk
Web: www.deansproperties.co.uk
Categories of Work
Residential property
Wills, executries and trusts

Partners
Graeme Alexander Laird
Laura Jane Walker

Consultant
Leslie George Deans

Employee
Jennifer Caroline Walker

DENTONS UK AND MIDDLE EAST LLP
Quartermile One, 15 Lauriston Place,
Edinburgh EH3 9EP
Tel: (0330) 2220050
Fax: (0330) 2220052
Categories of Work
Adjudication
Adoption
Advice the elderly & powers of attorney
Agriculture and estates
Agriculture, crofting and fishing
Alternative dispute resolution
Alternative investment market
Banking & finance
Betting & gaming
Charities
Children
Civil court work
Civil legal aid
Commercial litigation
Commercial property
Competition
Construction
Contract & property disputes
Copyright, trade marks and design
Corporate tax
Data protection
Debt recovery, insolvency, bankruptcy

Disability
Discrimination
Education
Employment
Employment law
Environment
Environment (Business Premises)
EU / international
Family and divorce
Family business advice
Fishing
Freedom of information
Health
Health and safety
Housing
Human rights
Immigration and asylum
Insolvency & corporate recovery
Insurance
IT and intellectual property
Joint venture
Landlord & tenant
Liquor licensing
Local government
Media and entertainment
Medical negligence – defender
Medical negligence – claimant
Mergers and acquisitions
Mining
Oil & gas
Parliamentary
Pensions (Company)
Pensions (Employment)
Personal injury
Personal injury – defender
Personal tax
Planning
Planning (Business Premises)
Power and utilities
Private equity
Professional negligence
Projects
Property litigation
Public finance initiative
Public sector
Residential property
Shipping
SME business advice
Software licensing
Sport
Telecoms
Transport
Unit Trusts, OEICs and investment trusts
Wills, executives and trusts

Partners
Claire Armstrong
William Fowler
Malcolm John Gunnyeon
Mark Russell Hamilton
Susan Mary Kelly
Ian Stewart Maciver
David Alexander McGrory
Brian Hugh Moore

Lyndsey Anne O'Connor
Kirsti Mary Olson
Andrew Alexander Orr
Euan Robert Wilson
James Gordon Wilson
Consultant
Catriona Mary Munro
Associates
Sarah Louise Alexander
Alexis Kasia Condie
Stuart Michael Gillies
Adam John Knowles
Kirsty Robertson McBirnie
Owen Daniel McLennan
Diana Leslie Mennie
Laura Louise Morrison
Elspeth Mary Grace Nuttall
Sarah Lynn Peock
Agnieszka Maria Salt
Gareth Gerald Tenner
Sarah Catherine Wardell
Employees
Aileen Catherine Banks
Sorcha Elizabeth Cierans
Gillian Catherine Cole
Emily Chrisanne Cranston
Lisa Anne Cruickshank
Hannah Frances Currie
Kaitlyn Emery Denham
Nicola Harvey
Christie Janet Jamieson
Steven Mark King
Lorna Jane MacFarlane
Claire Victoria Maclean
Lisa Jane McCreath
Louise McDaid
Sarah Mohammed Milne
Alice Mitchell Minick
Jack Mullen
Murray Angus McClements Newell
Nicola Helen Rae
Kirsty Robyn Shepherd

DICKSON MINTO
16 Charlotte Square, Edinburgh EH2 4DF
Tel: (0131) 2254455
Fax: (0131) 2252712
DX: ED199 EDINBURGH
E-mail: Private.CLR@DMWS.COM
Web: www.dicksonminto.co.uk
Categories of Work
Alternative investment market
Banking & finance
Commercial property
Construction
Debt recovery, insolvency, bankruptcy
Employment
Employment law
Environment (Business Premises)
EU / international
Family business advice
Insolvency & corporate recovery
Joint venture

► **Edinburgh continued**

Landlord & tenant
Mergers and acquisitions
Pensions (Employment)
Planning (Business Premises)
Private equity
Projects
Public finance initiative
SME business advice
Unit Trusts, OEICs and investment trusts
Partners
Douglas Alexander Armstrong
Catherine Mary Christie
Allan Fraser
Ewan Caldwell Gilchrist
Colin James MacNeill
Colin James McHale
Nicola Ann Mitchell
Andrew Alexander Nicolson
John Barry Pentland
Alasdair John Proudfoot
Paul James Quinn
Craig Davidson Roberts
Andrew George Todd
Associates
Fiona Jacqueline Carlin
Richard William Hothersall
Michael James Terry
Jennifer Freeman Wallace
Employees
Susannah May Aitken
Belinda Hannah Mary Beresford
Emma Rachel Bilotti
Catriona Elizabeth Campbell
Duncan Iain Christison
Andrew Jamie Clark
David Andrew Clark
Jamie Alexander Rushford Crook
Neil Alexander Daubney
Ione Skye Edmundson
Kerry Fraser
Lindsay Margaret Fraser
Nicholas Roy Grant
Claire Mary Henderson
Adam Matthew Howie
Calum William Melville Humphrey
Sylwia Jakuczun
Maryia Alexandrovna Lahatskaya
Kirsty Anne Maciver
Rhoda Annabel MacLennan
Eilidh Marnoch
Aim e Louise McArthur
Michelle Rose McCabe
David James McCaul
Fraser David McKay
Ross Guthrie Euan Michie
Bruce Watson Minto
Ronald Arthur Mosedale
Robert Adam Norman
Emma Louise O'Rourke
Jaimie Louise Rees
Michael Jon Robertson

Emma Elizabeth Swarbrick
Gordon Tatnell
Fiona Hazel Thompson
Andrew Nial Robert Tosh
Kirsty Sarah Woods
Sarah Jane Wylie

DIGBY BROWN LLP
Causewayside House, 160 Causewayside,
Edinburgh EH9 1PR
Tel: (0333) 200 5925
Fax: (0131) 319 8111
DX: ED182 EDINBURGH
E-mail: enquiries@digbybrown.co.uk
Web: www.digbybrown.co.uk
Categories of Work
Advice the elderly & powers of attorney
Agriculture and estates
Agriculture, crofting and fishing
Alternative dispute resolution
Alternative investment market
Banking & finance
Benefit advice
Charities
Children
Civil court work
Civil legal aid
Commercial litigation
Commercial property
Competition
Construction
Contract & property disputes
Corporate tax
Criminal court work
Data protection
Debt
Debt adjusting and debt counselling
Debt collecting
Debt recovery, insolvency, bankruptcy
Disability
Discrimination
Employment
Employment law
Environment (Business Premises)
EU / international
Family and divorce
Family business advice
Freedom of information
Health and safety
Human rights
Immigration and asylum
Insolvency & corporate recovery
Insurance
Joint venture
Landlord & tenant
Medical negligence – defender
Medical negligence – claimant
Mental health
Mergers and acquisitions
Pensions (Company)
Personal injury
Personal injury – defender
Planning (Business Premises)

Private equity
Professional negligence
Property litigation
Provision of credit information services
Public finance initiative
Public sector
Residential property
Road traffic
SME business advice
Unit Trusts, OEICs and investment trusts
Wills, executries and trusts
Partners
Gordon Dalyell
Mairi Jean Day
Simon John Hammond
Kim Louise Leslie
Patricia Mary McFadden
Simon James Barr Richards
Associates
Hollie Dilasser
Rona Jean Hayworth
Helen Anne Lawrence
Richard Dorian Pitts
Employees
Saira Ahmed
Constantin Bedrule
Rachel Margaret Black
Rory David Brown
Kim Catterall
Simon Matthew Dempsey
Lisa Chalmers Gaule
Justyna Dominika Gibb
Joanne Margaret Gosney
Maite Gurpegui Garcia
Catherine Frances Hammond
Catriona Alexandra Montgomery Headley
Claire Louise Innes
Donald Andrew Somhairle Mackay
Fern Mapp
Louise Anne Moffat
Theresa Mandisiya Mutapi
Justyna Katarzyna Rompca
Alejandra Carmela Julie Ruggeri
Ashley Fiona Sturrock
Claire Chisholm Wilson
Laura Ann Wilson
Magdalena Barbara Wlochal
Izabela Dominika Wosiak
Michelle Dunnington Young
Tahirah Khalid Yousaf

DLA PIPER SCOTLAND LLP
Collins House, Rutland Square, Edinburgh
EH1 2AA
Tel: (08700) 111111
Fax: (0131) 2425523
DX: ED271 EDINBURGH
Web: www.dlapiper.com
Categories of Work
Adjudication
Alternative dispute resolution
Alternative investment market
Banking & finance

Betting & gaming
Childrens
Civil court work
Commercial litigation
Commercial property
Competition
Construction
Consumer credit
Contract & property disputes
Copyright, trade marks and design
Data protection
Debt
Debt collecting
Debt recovery, insolvency, bankruptcy
Employment
Employment law
Environment
Environment (Business Premises)
EU / international
Family business advice
Fishing
Freedom of information
Health and safety
Housing
Human rights
Insolvency & corporate recovery
Insurance
IT and intellectual property
Joint venture
Landlord & tenant
Local government
Media and entertainment
Mergers and acquisitions
Mining
Oil & gas
Parliamentary
Pensions (Company)
Pensions (Employment)
Personal injury
Planning
Planning (Business Premises)
Power and utilities
Private equity
Professional negligence
Projects
Property litigation
Provision of credit information services
Public sector
Residential property
SME business advice
Software licensing
Telecoms
Transport
Unit Trusts, OEICs and investment trusts
Partners
Alistair David Drummond
Steven Graeme Edgecombe
Sharon Lesley Fitzgerald
Carolyne Jane Hair
Allan David Leal
Lillian Karen Mackenzie
John Christopher McKinlay
Stuart Alan Wilson Murdoch

▶ *Edinburgh continued*

Simon Scott Rae
Andrew Wallace
Consultants
Sheila Anne Irvine
Alexander Robert Telfer
Associates
Scott David Ferrier
Nadia Neelum Gehlen
Michael Kennedy Greig
Anthony Dean Holloran
Guy Anthony Irving
Lisa Kerr
James Christopher McGachie
Charlene McLaughlan
Catriona Lesley Melton
Margaret Cairine Pope
Alison Elizabeth Scott
Callum David Kenneth Swanson
Edwin Robert Truesdale
Sandie Yu-hsuan Wang
Andrew David Wardrop
Employees
Iain Mackenzie Brown
Euan Alan Bruce
Finlay Norman Campbell
Ross Donald Campbell
Thomas Peter Carr
Mark Davenport
Gavin Montgomery Sutherlan Deeprose
Stephen Robert Dick
Gale Marion Ervine
Patrick Struan Fulton
Sebastiano Lorenzo Galastro
Kirsty Margaret Campbell Gray
Craig Alexander Hunter
Rhea McNulty Ingram-Smith
Ross Indergaard Jespersen
Laura Anne Maclennan
Eilis Hetty McDonald
Eilidh Rae Moncrieff
Jamie Tazare O'Neill
Linzi Penman
Emma Louise Peveril
William Henry Reid
Christopher Gavin Rennie
Sonia Sandhu
Erin Cameron Sculthorpe
Jennifer Talbot
Paul Christopher Tominey
Christopher Stephen Williams
Craig McKeever Wilson

DMD LAW LLP

22 St. John's Road, Corstorphine, Edinburgh
EH12 6NZ
Tel: (0131) 3164666
Fax: (0131) 5397035
DX: 550440 EDINBURGH 44
E-mail: mail@dmdpartnership.co.uk
Categories of Work
Adoption
Advice the elderly & powers of attorney

Children
Family and divorce
Residential property
Wills, executries and trusts
Partners
Gordon MacDonald Anderson
Ivor Iain Mitchell Armstrong
Associate
Harold Henry Clark
Employee
Samantha Baird

STEVEN DONALD & CO

13 Gracemount Drive, Edinburgh EH16 6RR
Tel: (0131) 664 6777
Fax: (0131) 664
E-mail: steve.donald@btconnect.com
Categories of Work
Criminal court work
Criminal legal aid
Partner
Steven Reginald Donald

DRUMMOND MILLER LLP

Glenorchy House, 20 Union Street, Edinburgh
EH1 3LR
Tel: (0131) 2265151
Fax: (0131) 2252608
DX: ED104 EDINBURGH
E-mail: reception@drummondmiller.co.uk
Web: www.drummondmiller.co.uk
Categories of Work
Adjudication
Adoption
Advice the elderly & powers of attorney
Alternative dispute resolution
Charities
Children
Childrens
Civil court work
Civil legal aid
Commercial litigation
Commercial property
Contract & property disputes
Criminal court work
Data protection
Debt recovery, insolvency, bankruptcy
Discrimination
Education
Employment
Employment law
Environment
EU / international
Family and divorce
Family business advice
Health
Health and safety
Human rights
Immigration and asylum
Landlord & tenant
Medical negligence – defender
Medical negligence – claimant
Mental health
Oil & gas

Personal injury
Personal injury – defender
Personal tax
Professional negligence
Property litigation
Residential property
Road traffic
Wills, executives and trusts
Partners
Miranda Justine Becher
Alexander David Brown
Darren James Crilley Deery
Sarah Anne Jack
Laura Ann McDonagh
Ailsa Louise Preston Meiklejohn
Chigbo Humphrey Ndubuisi
Charles Stephen Ogilvie
Liesa Mary Spiller
Victoria Annabel Helen Varty
Consultant
Fiona Isabel Moore
Associates
Lynn Jane Bryson
Anna Davidson
Jennifer Zoe Elder Sturrock
Employees
Samirah Tariq Ahmed
Natalia Eve Bell
Ashley Louise Brolly
Caroline Sarah Burrows
Lorna Alison Hale
Michael Hutchison
Kirstyn Logan
Lindsay Macdonald
Eluned Lucy Elizabeth McHardy
ine Louise McShane
Lauren Jane Clarke Mizen
Iain James Moore
Anna Louise Jean C. A. Rani
Ayesha Aleem Siddique
Rebecca Anne Simpson

DS LAW
PO Box 28612, Edinburgh EH4 9BX
Tel: (0800) 920 2080
Categories of Work
Adoption
Advice the elderly & powers of attorney
Alternative dispute resolution
Children
Civil court work
Civil legal aid
Disability
Health
Human rights
Mental health

D. DUHERIC & CO SOLICITORS
23 Castle Street, Third Floor, Edinburgh
EH2 3DN
Tel: (0131) 2255444
Web: www.dduhericsolicitors.co.uk
Categories of Work
Employment law

Human rights
Immigration and asylum
Partner
Damir Duheric
Employee
Roderick Bruce Gibb

DUNNE DEFENCE LAWYERS
2a Randolph Place, Edinburgh EH3 7TQ
Tel: (0131) 466 5630
E-mail: paul@dunnedefence.com
Categories of Work
Criminal court work
Criminal legal aid
Immigration and asylum
Partner
Paul Joseph Dunne
Employee
Gagandeep Kaur Uppal

DWF LLP
No.2 Lochrin Square, 96 Fountainbridge,
Edinburgh EH3 9QA
Tel: (0131) 2265541
Fax: (0131) 2262278
DX: 15 EDINBURGH
Categories of Work
Adjudication
Agriculture and estates
Alternative dispute resolution
Alternative investment market
Banking & finance
Charities
Civil court work
Civil legal aid
Commercial litigation
Commercial property
Competition
Construction
Contract & property disputes
Copyright, trade marks and design
Corporate tax
Data protection
Debt
Debt collecting
Debt recovery, insolvency, bankruptcy
Disability
Discrimination
Education
Employment
Employment law
Environment
Environment (Business Premises)
EU / international
Family business advice
Freedom of information
Health
Health and safety
Housing
Insolvency & corporate recovery
Insurance
IT and intellectual property
Joint venture
Landlord & tenant

► **Edinburgh continued**

Liquor licensing
Local government
Media and entertainment
Medical negligence – defender
Medical negligence – claimant
Mergers and acquisitions
Oil & gas
Parliamentary
Pensions (Company)
Pensions (Employment)
Personal injury
Personal injury – defender
Personal tax
Planning
Planning (Business Premises)
Power and utilities
Private equity
Professional negligence
Projects
Property litigation
Public finance initiative
Public sector
Residential property
Road traffic
SME business advice
Social housing
Software licensing
Sport
Telecoms
Unit Trusts, OEICs and investment trusts
Wills, executries and trusts
Partners
Caroline Anne Watt Colliston
Wayne Lawrence
Andrew William Lothian
Gary John Macdonald
Kevin Douglas McGlone
Iain Reid Innes McHardy
Iain Robert McLean
Alasdair Graham Peacock
David Alexander Ratter
Robin James Watt
Associates
David Neil Gray
Rachel Claire Heathcote
Douglas Graham Buchanan Jefferies
Julia McDonald
Jamie McGiffen McLean
Aileen Fiona Shearer
Employees
Jonathan Frederick Arthur Barron
Sara May Bastekin
Sarah Louise Cunningham
Ursula Sophie Currie
Jonathan Edwin Gaskell
Alan Boyd Glen
Jordan Murray Gray
Nicole Michelle Hannah
Elisabeth Louise Harkness
Orla Elizabeth Kerr
David Ewan McNeish

Calum Stephen Henry Raine
Max David Roper
Malcolm Iain Rudd
Vivienne Carol Stuart
Patricia Rachel Britainy Taylor
Amy Claire Watson

EFFICAX LIMITED
32-1 Stafford Street, Edinburgh EH3 7BD
Tel: (07917) 817584
Categories of Work
Alternative dispute resolution
Banking & finance
Commercial litigation
Competition
Construction
Copyright, trade marks and design
Corporate tax
Data protection
Debt recovery, insolvency, bankruptcy
Employment law
EU / international
Freedom of information
Health and safety
Insolvency & corporate recovery
IT and intellectual property
Joint venture
Media and entertainment
Mergers and acquisitions
Mining
Oil & gas
Private equity
Public sector
Telecoms
Transport
Director
Rosemary Margaret Garrigan

ELMSLIE'S LTD
86 Haymarket Terrace, Edinburgh EH12 5LQ
Tel: (0131) 2255484
Fax: (0131) 2263543/ 34
E-mail: mail@elmslies.co.uk
Web: www.elmslies.co.uk
Categories of Work
Advice the elderly & powers of attorney
Commercial property
Landlord & tenant
Residential property
Wills, executries and trusts
Director
Derek James Elmslie

ELP-AM SOLICITORS LIMITED
89 Main Street, Davidsons Mains, Edinburgh
EH4 5AD
Tel: (0131) 3127276
E-mail: enquiries@elpamsolicitors.co.uk
Categories of Work
Advice the elderly & powers of attorney
Charities
Civil court work
Commercial litigation
Commercial property

Contract & property disputes
Debt
Debt collecting
Debt recovery, insolvency, bankruptcy
Disability
Discrimination
Employment
Employment law
Health and safety
Landlord & tenant
Parliamentary
Personal tax
Property litigation
Residential property
Wills, executries and trusts

ELP-AM SOLICITORS LIMITED
98 Ferry Road, Leith, Edinburgh EH6 4PG
Tel: (0131) 5548649
E-mail: enquiries@elpamsolicitors.co.uk
Web: www.elpamsolicitors.co.uk
Categories of Work
Advice the elderly & powers of attorney
Charities
Civil court work
Commercial litigation
Commercial property
Contract & property disputes
Debt
Debt collecting
Debt recovery, insolvency, bankruptcy
Disability
Discrimination
Employment
Employment law
Health and safety
Landlord & tenant
Parliamentary
Personal tax
Property litigation
Residential property
Wills, executries and trusts

ELP ARBUTHNOTT MCCLANACHAN
89 Main Street, Davidsons Mains, Edinburgh
EH4 5AD
Tel: (0131) 3127276
Fax: (0131) 3126029
DX: ED657 EDINBURGH
Categories of Work
Advice the elderly & powers of attorney
Charities
Civil court work
Commercial litigation
Commercial property
Contract & property disputes
Debt
Debt collecting
Debt recovery, insolvency, bankruptcy
Disability
Discrimination
Employment
Employment law
Health and safety

Landlord & tenant
Parliamentary
Personal tax
Property litigation
Residential property
Wills, executries and trusts
Director
Catherine McClanachan
Associates
Irene Ethel Turner
Barbara Jane Watson
Employee
Paul Anand Halliday

ELP ARBUTHNOTT MCCLANACHAN
98 Ferry Road, Leith, Edinburgh EH6 4PG
Tel: (0131) 5548649
Fax: (0131) 5548648
E-mail: enquiries@elpamsolicitors.co.uk
Categories of Work
Advice the elderly & powers of attorney
Charities
Civil court work
Commercial litigation
Commercial property
Contract & property disputes
Debt
Debt collecting
Debt recovery, insolvency, bankruptcy
Disability
Discrimination
Employment
Employment law
Health and safety
Landlord & tenant
Parliamentary
Personal tax
Property litigation
Residential property
Wills, executries and trusts
Directors
Duncan Ruaridh McFadzean
Laura Melanie McFadzean
Lisbeth-Ann Pay
Consultant
James Roy Aitken
Associate
Ian Matthew Wells
Employees
Duncan Martin Reid Hamilton
Catriona Alice Torrance

ELP SOLICITORS
98 Ferry Road, Edinburgh EH6 4PG
Tel: (0131) 5548649
E-mail: enquiries@elpamsolicitors.co.uk
Categories of Work
Advice the elderly & powers of attorney
Charities
Civil court work
Commercial litigation
Commercial property
Contract & property disputes
Debt

▶ **Edinburgh** *continued*

Debt collecting
Debt recovery, insolvency, bankruptcy
Disability
Discrimination
Employment
Employment law
Health and safety
Landlord & tenant
Parliamentary
Personal tax
Property litigation
Residential property
Wills, executries and trusts

EMPLOYMENT LAW PRACTICE
89 Main Street, Davidsons Mains, Edinburgh
EH4 5AD
Tel: (0131) 3127276
Categories of Work
Advice the elderly & powers of attorney
Charities
Civil court work
Commercial litigation
Commercial property
Contract & property disputes
Debt
Debt collecting
Debt recovery, insolvency, bankruptcy
Disability
Discrimination
Employment
Employment law
Health and safety
Landlord & tenant
Parliamentary
Personal tax
Property litigation
Residential property
Wills, executries and trusts

EMPLOYMENT LAW PRACTICE
99 Ferry Road, Edinburgh EH6 4ET
Tel: (0131) 5548649
E-mail: enquiries@elpamsolicitors.co.uk
Web: www.elp.solicitors.com
Categories of Work
Advice the elderly & powers of attorney
Charities
Civil court work
Commercial litigation
Commercial property
Contract & property disputes
Debt
Debt collecting
Debt recovery, insolvency, bankruptcy
Disability
Discrimination
Employment
Employment law
Health and safety
Landlord & tenant
Parliamentary

Personal tax
Property litigation
Residential property
Wills, executries and trusts

ENNOVA LAW
26 George Square, Edinburgh EH8 9LD
Tel: (0131) 6624555
Categories of Work
Adjudication
Adoption
Advice the elderly & powers of attorney
Agriculture and estates
Agriculture, crofting and fishing
Alternative dispute resolution
Banking & finance
Benefit advice
Betting & gaming
Charities
Children
Civil court work
Commercial litigation
Commercial property
Construction
Consumer credit
Contract & property disputes
Copyright, trade marks and design
Corporate tax
Debt
Debt adjusting and debt counselling
Debt collecting
Debt recovery, insolvency, bankruptcy
Disability
Discrimination
Education
Employment
Employment law
Environment (Business Premises)
Family and divorce
Family business advice
Freedom of information
Health and safety
Housing
Human rights
Insolvency & corporate recovery
Insurance
IT and intellectual property
Joint venture
Landlord & tenant
Liquor licensing
Media and entertainment
Medical negligence – claimant
Mental health
Mergers and acquisitions
Mining
Personal injury
Personal tax
Planning
Planning (Business Premises)
Power and utilities
Private equity
Professional negligence
Property litigation

Public sector
Residential property
Road traffic
SME business advice
Software licensing
Sport
Telecoms
Wills, executries and trusts

ENNOVA LIMITED

26 George Square, Edinburgh EH8 9LD
Tel: (0131) 6624555
Fax: (0131) 6677938
DX: ED 39 EDINBURGH
E-mail: mail@ennova-law.com
Web: www.ennova-law.com
Categories of Work
Adjudication
Adoption
Advice the elderly & powers of attorney
Agriculture and estates
Agriculture, crofting and fishing
Alternative dispute resolution
Banking & finance
Benefit advice
Betting & gaming
Charities
Children
Civil court work
Commercial litigation
Commercial property
Construction
Consumer credit
Contract & property disputes
Copyright, trade marks and design
Corporate tax
Debt
Debt adjusting and debt counselling
Debt collecting
Debt recovery, insolvency, bankruptcy
Disability
Discrimination
Education
Employment
Employment law
Environment (Business Premises)
Family and divorce
Family business advice
Freedom of information
Health and safety
Housing
Human rights
Insolvency & corporate recovery
Insurance
IT and intellectual property
Joint venture
Landlord & tenant
Liquor licensing
Media and entertainment
Medical negligence – claimant
Mental health
Mergers and acquisitions
Mining

Personal injury
Personal tax
Planning
Planning (Business Premises)
Power and utilities
Private equity
Professional negligence
Property litigation
Public sector
Residential property
Road traffic
SME business advice
Software licensing
Sport
Telecoms
Wills, executries and trusts
Directors
John Matheson Macleod Cumming
Keith Martin Dunlop
William George Gibson
Karen Elizabeth Ramsey
Employees
Randolph Wemyss Lawrence Hardie
Christian Kenneth Bowring Melville
Rose Alison Seaward
Lynn Rae Simpson
David Wilson

ERGO LAW LIMITED

26 Alva Street, Edinburgh EH2 4PY
Tel: (0131) 618 7007
E-mail: info@ergolaw.co.uk
Web: www.ergolaw.co.uk
Categories of Work
Employment
Employment law
Directors
Kathleen Elizabeth Donald
Emma Grace Cameron Reid
Employees
Claire Patricia Henderson
Natasha Rosalind Wyllie

EVERSHEDS SUTHERLAND (INTERNATIONAL) LLP

3-5 Melville Street, Edinburgh EH3 7PE
Tel: (0207) 9194500
Fax: (0845) 4980371
DX: ED24 EDINBURGH
Web: www.eversheds-sutherland.com
Categories of Work
Adjudication
Agriculture and estates
Agriculture, crofting and fishing
Alternative dispute resolution
Alternative investment market
Banking & finance
Betting & gaming
Charities
Civil court work
Civil legal aid
Commercial litigation
Commercial property
Competition

► **Edinburgh continued**

Construction
Consumer credit
Contract & property disputes
Copyright, trade marks and design
Corporate tax
Data protection
Debt
Debt collecting
Debt recovery, insolvency, bankruptcy
Education
Employment
Employment law
Environment
Environment (Business Premises)
EU / international
Family business advice
Fishing
Freedom of information
Housing
Immigration and asylum
Insolvency & corporate recovery
Insurance
IT and intellectual property
Joint venture
Landlord & tenant
Local government
Media and entertainment
Medical negligence – defender
Medical negligence – claimant
Mergers and acquisitions
Mining
Oil & gas
Parliamentary
Pensions (Company)
Pensions (Employment)
Personal injury
Personal injury – defender
Planning
Planning (Business Premises)
Power and utilities
Private equity
Professional negligence
Projects
Property litigation
Public finance initiative
Public sector
Residential property
Road traffic
Shipping
SME business advice
Software licensing
Sport
Telecoms
Transport
Unit Trusts, OEICs and investment trusts
Wills, executries and trusts
Partners
Steven Marshall Dick
Dawn Dickson
Alastair McGarva Frood
Euan Mark Folan Smith

Associates
Heidi Louise Archibald
Christine Frances Barnsley
Amanda Jayne Cooke
Csilla Zsuzsanna Gy ri
Employees
Jenny Marion Ione Burn
Sarah Elizabeth Stewart Burnside
Margaret Frances Coady
Dixcee Rae Fast
Sarah Victoria Holwill
Alisdair Tannahill Jamieson
Dean Mark Johnson
Martin Love
Lauren Helen Lynch
Christopher Andrew Thomas Murray
Alasdair Graham James Ronald
Benjamin Hugh Sheppard

FERGUSSON LAW
25-27 Barony Street, Edinburgh EH3 6PD
Tel: (0131) 556 4044
Fax: (0131) 5100663
E-mail: law@fergussonlaw.com
Web: www.fergussonlaw.com
Categories of Work
Advice the elderly & powers of attorney
Benefit advice
Charities
Health and safety
Personal tax
Residential property
Wills, executries and trusts
Partner
Janice Fergusson Nisbet
Employees
Katherine Olivia Hood
Cara Jacqueline Lawson
Stacey Ward

FIDUCIA-LEGAL LIMITED
10/5 Joppa Station Place, Edinburgh
EH15 2QU
Tel: (0131) 6579197
Categories of Work
Commercial property
Family business advice
Landlord & tenant
Liquor licensing
SME business advice
Director
Isabel Sandra Todd

FLEMINGS
8 Albany Street, Edinburgh EH1 3QB
Tel: (0131) 473 2343
Categories of Work
Alternative dispute resolution
Children
Civil court work
Commercial litigation
Contract & property disputes
Debt collecting
Debt recovery, insolvency, bankruptcy

Discrimination
Employment law
Insurance
Landlord & tenant
Medical negligence – defender
Medical negligence – claimant
Parliamentary
Personal injury
Personal injury – defender
Professional negligence
Property litigation
Public sector
Road traffic
Wills, executries and trusts

FLEMINGS LEGAL SERVICES LIMITED
8 Albany Street, Edinburgh EH1 3QB
Tel: (0131) 473 2343
Categories of Work
Alternative dispute resolution
Children
Civil court work
Commercial litigation
Contract & property disputes
Debt collecting
Debt recovery, insolvency, bankruptcy
Discrimination
Employment law
Insurance
Landlord & tenant
Medical negligence – defender
Medical negligence – claimant
Parliamentary
Personal injury
Personal injury – defender
Professional negligence
Property litigation
Public sector
Road traffic
Wills, executries and trusts
Director
Christopher James Fleming

FLEXLAW LTD
C B C House, 24 Canning Street, Edinburgh
EH3 8EG
Tel: (0131) 2026363
Fax: (0870) 6221138
E-mail: contact@flexlaw.co.uk
Web: www.flexlaw.co.uk
Categories of Work
Alternative dispute resolution
Civil court work
Commercial litigation
Consumer credit
Contract & property disputes
Debt
Debt collecting
Debt recovery, insolvency, bankruptcy
Disability
Discrimination
Employment
Employment law
Health and safety

Human rights
Insurance
Landlord & tenant
Medical negligence – defender
Medical negligence – claimant
Mental health
Personal injury
Personal injury – defender
Professional negligence
Property litigation
Residential property
Road traffic
Director
Mark Nicholas Harrison
Consultant
Claire Marion Maguire

FRASER BROOKS & COMPANY WS LIMITED
45 Frederick Street, Edinburgh EH2 1ES
Tel: (0131) 2256226
Fax: (0131) 2200651
DX: ED 111 Edinburgh
E-mail: Kenneth.cameron@fraserbrooks.com
Categories of Work
Agriculture and estates
Agriculture, crofting and fishing
Commercial property
Contract & property disputes
Family and divorce
Family business advice
Landlord & tenant
Pensions (Company)
Professional negligence
Property litigation
Residential property
Wills, executries and trusts
Director
Richard Kenneth Cameron

GIBSON KERR (INCORPORATING MARWICKS AND GRANGE)
40 Dundas Street, Edinburgh EH3 6JN
Tel: (0131) 2257558
Fax: (0131) 2251108
Categories of Work
Adoption
Advice the elderly & powers of attorney
Alternative dispute resolution
Children
Childrens
Civil court work
Civil legal aid
Commercial property
Education
Family and divorce
Family business advice
Landlord & tenant
Mental health
Personal tax
Residential property
Wills, executries and trusts
Director
Gordon Scott Rasmusen

▶ *Edinburgh continued*

Employees
Beverley Susan Cottrell
Gregor Kerr Robertson Mair

GIBSON KERR LIMITED
40 Dundas Street, Edinburgh EH3 6JN
Tel: (0131) 226 9167
Categories of Work
Adoption
Advice the elderly & powers of attorney
Alternative dispute resolution
Children
Childrens
Civil court work
Civil legal aid
Commercial property
Education
Family and divorce
Family business advice
Landlord & tenant
Mental health
Personal tax
Residential property
Wills, executries and trusts

GIBSON KERR LIMITED
46 India Street, Edinburgh EH3 6HJ
Tel: (0131) 2257558
Fax: (0131) 2251108
E-mail: edinburgh@gibsonkerr.co.uk
Categories of Work
Adoption
Advice the elderly & powers of attorney
Alternative dispute resolution
Children
Childrens
Civil court work
Civil legal aid
Commercial property
Education
Family and divorce
Family business advice
Landlord & tenant
Mental health
Personal tax
Residential property
Wills, executries and trusts
Directors
Lindsay Margaret Maclean
Fiona Rosemary Rasmusen
Associate
Nadine Martin
Employees
Louise Catherine Clark
Katie Helen Fulton
Caroline Jane MacBeath
Catriona Sarah Marshall
Stuart Graham Millar
Karen Elizabeth Sutherland

GIBSON KERR LIMITED TRADING AS GIBSON KERR
46 India Street, Edinburgh EH3 6HJ

Tel: (0131) 2257558
Categories of Work
Adoption
Advice the elderly & powers of attorney
Alternative dispute resolution
Children
Childrens
Civil court work
Civil legal aid
Commercial property
Education
Family and divorce
Family business advice
Landlord & tenant
Mental health
Personal tax
Residential property
Wills, executries and trusts

GILDEAS LIMITED
30 Melville Street, Edinburgh EH3 7HA
Tel: (0141) 331 6079
Fax: (0131) 4766742
DX: ED520 EDINBURGH
E-mail: mail@gildeas.net
Web: www.gildeas.net
Categories of Work
Civil court work
Commercial litigation
Contract & property disputes
Criminal court work
Debt collecting
Debt recovery, insolvency, bankruptcy
Health and safety
Landlord & tenant
Medical negligence – claimant
Personal injury
Professional negligence
Property litigation
Residential property
Road traffic
Associate
David McKee
Employees
Mohammed Sohail Amjad
Elizabeth Olofsson
Alannah Sheila Sloss

GILFEDDER & MCINNES LIMITED
149 Cowgate, Edinburgh EH1 1JS
Tel: (0131) 5543550
Fax: (0131) 5542718
E-mail: gilfedder@btconnect.com
Categories of Work
Criminal court work
Criminal legal aid
Director
Brian Gerard Gilfedder
Employee
William Ruairidh Mulheron

GILLESPIE MACANDREW LLP
5 Atholl Crescent, Edinburgh EH3 8EJ
Tel: (0131) 2251677

Fax: (0131) 2254519
DX: ED113 EDINBURGH
Web: www.gillespiemacandrew.co.uk
Categories of Work
Adjudication
Adoption
Advice the elderly & powers of attorney
Agriculture and estates
Agriculture, crofting and fishing
Alternative dispute resolution
Banking & finance
Benefit advice
Charities
Children
Civil court work
Civil legal aid
Commercial litigation
Commercial property
Competition
Construction
Consumer credit
Contract & property disputes
Copyright, trade marks and design
Corporate tax
Criminal court work
Data protection
Debt
Debt administration
Debt collecting
Debt recovery, insolvency, bankruptcy
Disability
Discrimination
Employment
Employment law
Environment
Environment (Business Premises)
EU / international
Family and divorce
Family business advice
Fishing
Freedom of information
Housing
Human rights
Insolvency & corporate recovery
IT and intellectual property
Joint venture
Landlord & tenant
Local government
Media and entertainment
Medical negligence – defender
Medical negligence – claimant
Mental health
Mergers and acquisitions
Mining
Parliamentary
Pensions (Employment)
Personal injury
Personal injury – defender
Personal tax
Planning
Planning (Business Premises)
Power and utilities
Private equity

Professional negligence
Projects
Property litigation
Public sector
Residential property
Road traffic
SME business advice
Software licensing
Wills, executries and trusts
Partners
Fiona Jane Cameron
Nicola Jane Dundas
Christopher Duncan Gibson
Colin Stuart Hamilton
Kenneth Wyness Irons
Fraser Gordon Leslie
Lianne Margaret Lodge
Agnes Mallon
John McArthur
Derek Ashley James McCulloch
Amy Joy McDowell
Robert Andrew Scott-Dempster
David Christopher Smith
Henry Cannon Smith
Murray Duncan Soutar
John Boyd Stirling
Alan James White
Simon Jonathan Conon Williams
Gillian Jane Wright
Associates
Lorna Margaret Claire Balfour
Elizabeth Anne Bremner
Judith Lesley Clark
Stewart James Crosbie
Victoria Curren
Margaret Lancaster Day
Elaine Reilly Del Valle
John Stephen Gamba
Helen Louise Kelly
Sarah-Jane Macdonald
Murray Ross MacRae
Doran Douglas Mitchell
Nicola Shona Elizabeth Murray
Lois Elizabeth Anne Newton
Tessa Jayne Petrides
Donald Winskill
Solicitor
Susan Elizabeth Henretty
Employees
Ana s Gw naelle Christine Banag Mongo
Ross Baron
Colin John Bathgate
Natalie Lauren Brooks
Katie Brown
Austen Purdie Burns
Rachael Marie Church
Gordon William Clark
Sam Patrick Conington
Laura Jane Fairgrieve
Hannah Janet Patricia Gaddie
Rachel Marion Gilchrist
David Timóthy Paul Doherty Halligan
Cheryl Susan Hogg

▶ *Edinburgh continued*

Kirsten Margaret Holmes
Zoe Inkster
Caitlin Mary Keegan
Elaine Kennedy-Walton
Laura Annetta Kirkman
Andrew Stuart Leslie
Scott Alexander Mackie
Ross Lawrie Matthew
Ashley Marie McCann
Conner McConnell
Margaret Louise Mitchelson
Jamie Scott Seath
Melissa Jayne Strachan
Kevin Buchanan Sturgeon
Nadia Bridia White
Nicola Dorothy Whyte
Gillian Anne Wilson

GILLESPIE MACANDREW LLP

76-80 Morningside Road, Edinburgh
EH10 4BY
Tel: (0131) 447 4747
Web:
www.residential.gillespiemacandrew.co.uk
Categories of Work
Adjudication
Adoption
Advice the elderly & powers of attorney
Agriculture and estates
Agriculture, crofting and fishing
Alternative dispute resolution
Banking & finance
Benefit advice
Charities
Children
Civil court work
Civil legal aid
Commercial litigation
Commercial property
Competition
Construction
Consumer credit
Contract & property disputes
Copyright, trade marks and design
Corporate tax
Criminal court work
Data protection
Debt
Debt administration
Debt collecting
Debt recovery, insolvency, bankruptcy
Disability
Discrimination
Employment
Employment law
Environment
Environment (Business Premises)
EU / international
Family and divorce
Family business advice
Fishing
Freedom of information

Housing
Human rights
Insolvency & corporate recovery
IT and intellectual property
Joint venture
Landlord & tenant
Local government
Media and entertainment
Medical negligence – defender
Medical negligence – claimant
Mental health
Mergers and acquisitions
Mining
Parliamentary
Pensions (Employment)
Personal injury
Personal injury – defender
Personal tax
Planning
Planning (Business Premises)
Power and utilities
Private equity
Professional negligence
Projects
Property litigation
Public sector
Residential property
Road traffic
SME business advice
Software licensing
Wills, executives and trusts

GILSON GRAY LLP

29 Rutland Square, Edinburgh EH1 2BW
Tel: (0131) 5165354
Fax: (0131) 5165378
DX: 5 EDINBURGH
E-mail: info@gilsongray.co.uk
Web: www.gilsongray.co.uk
Categories of Work
Adjudication
Adoption
Advice the elderly & powers of attorney
Agriculture and estates
Alternative dispute resolution
Banking & finance
Betting & gaming
Charities
Children
Childrens
Civil court work
Civil legal aid
Commercial litigation
Commercial property
Competition
Construction
Consumer credit
Contract & property disputes
Copyright, trade marks and design
Data protection
Debt
Debt administration
Debt collecting

Debt recovery, insolvency, bankruptcy
Disability
Discrimination
Education
Employment
Employment law
Environment
EU / international
Family and divorce
Family business advice
Freedom of information
Health and safety
Housing
Immigration and asylum
Insolvency & corporate recovery
Insurance
IT and intellectual property
Joint venture
Landlord & tenant
Liquor licensing
Local government
Media and entertainment
Medical negligence – defender
Medical negligence – claimant
Mergers and acquisitions
Mining
Oil & gas
Pensions (Company)
Personal injury
Personal injury – defender
Personal tax
Planning
Planning (Business Premises)
Power and utilities
Private equity
Professional negligence
Projects
Property litigation
Public sector
Residential property
Road traffic
Shipping
SME business advice
Social housing
Software licensing
Sport
Telecoms
Transport
Wills, executries and trusts
Partners
David William Alexander
Keith Downie Anderson
Calum George Crighton
Philippa Jayne Cunniff
Craig Charles Darling
Euan Kenneth James Fleming
John Paul Fulton
Alexander Garioch
Glen Douglas Gilson
Steven William Jansch
Deborah Ann McCathie
Sally Elizabeth Nash
Hugh Stuart Robertson

Murray Stewart
Rosemary Clare Walker
Consultants
Alasdair John Loudon
Gillian Frances Maclean
Associate
Eilidh Alison Jane MacEwan
Employees
Michael Alexander George Anderson
Caitlin Marie Ferguson Bell
Laura Margaret Brennan
Lianne Connell
Joe Alexander Davies
Edward Fitzgerald
Iain Harry Grant
Kenneth William Lauder
Scott Ian Runciman
Julian McKenzie Scott
Maureen Stevenson
Jennifer Alice Yeats
Shona Anne Young

V. GOOD & CO.
24-26 West Port, Grassmarket, Edinburgh
EH1 2JE
Tel: (0131) 6223349
Fax: (0131) 4663495
E-mail: vgoodlaw@hotmail.co.uk
Categories of Work
Criminal court work
Criminal legal aid
Partner
Victoria Jayne Good
Associate
Emma Louise Todd

GOOD & STEWART LIMITED
77-79 St Leonard's Street, Edinburgh EH8 9QR
Tel: (0131) 6629177
Fax: (0131) 6629188
DX: ED600 EDINBURGH
E-mail: goodandstewart@btconnect.com
Categories of Work
Criminal court work
Criminal legal aid
Personal injury
Road traffic
Directors
John Andrew Good
Gordon James Stewart
Employees
Simon Gregor
Chloe Janet Thomson

A. GRAY MUIR, WS LIMITED
89 Ravenscroft Street, Edinburgh EH17 8QS
Tel: (0131) 6643320
Fax: (0131) 6217006
E-mail: andrew@graymuir.co.uk
Categories of Work
Commercial property
Residential property
Director
Andrew Gray Muir

▶ *Edinburgh continued*

GREAT STUART TRUSTEES LIMITED
3 Glenfinlas Street, Edinburgh EH3 6AQ
Tel: (0131) 2255095

GUNNERCOOKE
80 George Street, Edinburgh EH2 3BU
Categories of Work
Alternative dispute resolution
Commercial property
Competition
EU / international
Family business advice
Joint venture
Landlord & tenant
Mergers and acquisitions
Oil & gas
Projects
SME business advice

GUNNERCOOKE SCO LLP
80 George Street, Edinburgh EH2 3BU
Categories of Work
Alternative dispute resolution
Commercial property
Competition
EU / international
Family business advice
Joint venture
Landlord & tenant
Mergers and acquisitions
Oil & gas
Projects
SME business advice
Partner
Simon Paul Etchells
Consultants
Roderick Stewart Lambert
John James McMuldroch

HALLIDAY CAMPBELL W.S.
7 Crawfurd Road, Edinburgh EH16 5PQ
Tel: (0131) 6683000
Fax: (0131) 5107113
E-mail: david.halliday@hallidaycampbell.com
Web: www.hallidaycampbell.com
Categories of Work
Alternative dispute resolution
Betting & gaming
Civil court work
Civil legal aid
Commercial litigation
Consumer credit
Contract & property disputes
Copyright, trade marks and design
Data protection
Debt
Debt collecting
Debt recovery, insolvency, bankruptcy
Freedom of information
Insolvency & corporate recovery
IT and intellectual property
Landlord & tenant
Liquor licensing

Local government
Media and entertainment
Professional negligence
Property litigation
Partner
David James Finlay Halliday
Employee
Lynn Littlejohn McMahon

HANN & CO SOLICITORS LTD
83 Princes Street, Edinburgh EH2 2ER
Tel: (0131) 2352100
Fax: (0131) 2020911
DX: ED17 EDINBURGH
E-mail: info@hannandco.com
Categories of Work
Adoption
Advice the elderly & powers of attorney
Alternative dispute resolution
Banking & finance
Benefit advice
Charities
Children
Civil court work
Civil legal aid
Commercial litigation
Commercial property
Competition
Consumer credit
Contract & property disputes
Copyright, trade marks and design
Corporate tax
Criminal court work
Criminal legal aid
Data protection
Debt
Debt adjusting and debt counselling
Debt collecting
Debt management
Debt recovery, insolvency, bankruptcy
Disability
Discrimination
Education
Employment
Employment law
Environment
Environment (Business Premises)
Family and divorce
Family business advice
Freedom of information
Health and safety
Human rights
Insolvency & corporate recovery
Insurance
IT and intellectual property
Joint venture
Landlord & tenant
Liquor licensing
Medical negligence – defender
Medical negligence – claimant
Mental health
Mergers and acquisitions
Oil & gas

Pensions (Company)
Pensions (Employment)
Personal injury
Personal injury – defender
Personal tax
Private equity
Professional negligence
Projects
Property litigation
Residential property
Road traffic
SME business advice
Social housing
Software licensing
Unit Trusts, OEICs and investment trusts
Wills, executries and trusts
Director
Benjamin Nephi Hann

HARPER MACLEOD LLP
Citypoint, 65 Haymarket Terrace, Edinburgh
EH12 5HD
Tel: (0131) 2472500
Fax: (0131) 2472501
DX: ED167 EDINBURGH
E-mail: info@harpermacleod.co.uk
Web: www.harpermacleod.co.uk
Categories of Work
Adjudication
Adoption
Advice the elderly & powers of attorney
Agriculture and estates
Agriculture, crofting and fishing
Alternative dispute resolution
Alternative investment market
Banking & finance
Betting & gaming
Charities
Children
Childrens
Civil court work
Civil legal aid
Commercial litigation
Commercial property
Competition
Construction
Consumer credit
Contract & property disputes
Copyright, trade marks and design
Corporate tax
Criminal court work
Criminal legal aid
Data protection
Debt
Debt administration
Debt collecting
Debt recovery, insolvency, bankruptcy
Disability
Discrimination
Education
Employment
Employment law
Environment

Environment (Business Premises)
EU / international
Family and divorce
Family business advice
Fishing
Freedom of information
Health
Health and safety
Housing
Human rights
Immigration and asylum
Insolvency & corporate recovery
Insurance
IT and intellectual property
Joint venture
Landlord & tenant
Liquor licensing
Local government
Media and entertainment
Medical negligence – defender
Medical negligence – claimant
Mental health
Mergers and acquisitions
Mining
Oil & gas
Parliamentary
Pensions (Company)
Pensions (Employment)
Personal injury
Personal injury – defender
Personal tax
Planning
Planning (Business Premises)
Power and utilities
Private equity
Professional negligence
Projects
Property litigation
Public finance initiative
Public sector
Residential property
Road traffic
Shipping
SME business advice
Social housing
Software licensing
Sport
Telecoms
Transport
Unit Trusts, OEICs and investment trusts
Wills, executries and trusts
Partners
Stephen Ka Leung Chan
Karen Louise Gibbons
Alexander Young Hastie
Jennifer Lorna Jack
Scott Thomas Reid Kerr
Laura Anne McCorquodale
John Miller McHugh
Christopher Alexander Noble
Fiona Jane Pask
Euan David Thomas Pirie
Pamela Anne Todd

▶ **Edinburgh continued**
Jamie Douglas Sinclair Watt
Associates
Martin David Bennett
Calum Gee
Cameron Lewis MacDonald Kemp
Lucy Rachel Mosedale
Linda Ann Walker
Employees
Sascha Jane Cochran
Richard Fenwick Gallen
Kate Louise Gillies
Michael Alexander Stuart Gilmartin
Gayle Tegen Hogwood
Alastair Iain Samuel Johnston
Catriona Leask Kemp
Paul-Silviu Manolache
Rory Edward Liston Paterson
Keri Jayne Preece
Bernadette Niamh Rutherford
Matthew Bruce Kerr Smith
Kate Louise Sutherland

HEALTH LAW LIMITED
21 Young Street, Edinburgh EH2 4HU
Tel: (0800) 920 2080
Fax: (0800) 920 2081
E-mail: ds@health-law.uk
Web: www.health-law.uk
Categories of Work
Adoption
Advice the elderly & powers of attorney
Alternative dispute resolution
Children
Civil court work
Civil legal aid
Disability
Health
Human rights
Mental health
Director
Douglas Scott Simpson
Employees
Ross Andrew Crawford
William Gilmour
Jean Winifred Sutherland

HENDRIE LEGAL LIMITED
Murrayburgh House, 17 Corstorphine Road,
Edinburgh EH12 6DD
Tel: (0131) 370 0470
Fax: (0131) 370 0471
Categories of Work
Commercial property
Landlord & tenant
Residential property
Wills, executries and trusts
Directors
Mark Eric Hendrie
Janette Margaret Kenny
Louise McLaren
Jadiene Valerie Rosemary Morison
Consultant
Ivan Alexander Ralph

Associate
Innes John Cradock
Employee
Mirella Marchini

RALPH HENDRIE LEGAL
Murrayburgh House, 17 Corstorphine Road,
Edinburgh EH12 6DD
Tel: (0131) 370 0470
Categories of Work
Commercial property
Landlord & tenant
Residential property
Wills, executries and trusts

HOOD CORPORATE
19 Rutland Square, Edinburgh EH1 2BB
Tel: (0131) 2125888
E-mail: legal@hoodcorporate.com
Web: www.hoodcorporate.com
Categories of Work
Alternative investment market
Banking & finance
Charities
Copyright, trade marks and design
Data protection
EU / international
Family business advice
Insolvency & corporate recovery
IT and intellectual property
Joint venture
Mergers and acquisitions
Oil & gas
Private equity
SME business advice
Sport
Partner
Ross Farr Hood

HORCHHEIM LTD
15/16 Queen Street, Edinburgh EH2 1JE
Tel: (0131) 2401213
E-mail: cath@cathkarlinfamilylaw.co.uk
Categories of Work
Adoption
Alternative dispute resolution
Children
Civil court work
Education
Family and divorce
Human rights
Director
Catherine Margaret Karlin

HUGHES WALKER
43 Bread Street, Edinburgh EH3 9AH
Tel: (0131) 6038676
E-mail: court@hugheswalkerlaw.com
Categories of Work
Criminal court work
Criminal legal aid
Mental health
Partner
Alexandra Elizabeth Walker

Employee
Julia Lucy McPartlin

G J HUNTER & CO LIMITED
26-28 Meadowbank Terrace, Edinburgh
EH8 7AS
Tel: (0131) 6613414
Fax: (0131) 6611305
DX: 551160 EDINBURGH 8
E-mail: ross@gjhunter.co.uk
Categories of Work
Advice the elderly & powers of attorney
Commercial property
Landlord & tenant
Residential property
Wills, executries and trusts
Director
Cameron Elliot Ross Hunter

INKSTERS
Spaces, 1 Lochrin Square, Edinburgh EH3 9QA
Tel: (0131) 357 5620
Fax: (0131) 357 5622
E-mail: edinburgh@inksters.com
Web: www.inksters.com
Categories of Work
Advice the elderly & powers of attorney
Agriculture and estates
Agriculture, crofting and fishing
Alternative dispute resolution
Children
Childrens
Civil court work
Civil legal aid
Commercial property
Consumer credit
Contract & property disputes
Criminal court work
Criminal legal aid
Data protection
Debt
Debt collecting
Debt recovery, insolvency, bankruptcy
Family and divorce
Family business advice
Landlord & tenant
Personal tax
Projects
Property litigation
Residential property
Road traffic
Wills, executries and trusts
Employee
Steven Boyd McDonald

INVESTMENT PROPERTY AGENCY
22a Rutland Square, Edinburgh EH1 2BB
Tel: (0131) 6229222
Categories of Work
Adoption
Advice the elderly & powers of attorney
Children
Civil court work
Commercial property

Contract & property disputes
Family and divorce
Landlord & tenant
Liquor licensing
Medical negligence – claimant
Personal injury
Professional negligence
Residential property

JARDINE PHILLIPS LLP
205 Morningside Road, Edinburgh EH10 4QP
Tel: (0131) 4466850
Fax: (0131) 4466859
DX: ED634 EDINBURGH
E-mail: info@jardinephillips.com
Categories of Work
Advice the elderly & powers of attorney
Commercial property
Contract & property disputes
Landlord & tenant
Residential property
Wills, executries and trusts
Partner
Gordon Alexander Phillips
Consultant
James Patrick Maguire
Employees
Samantha Lillian Joan Kennedy
Lauren Kay Reid

JARDINE PHILLIPS (SCOTLAND) LTD
205 Morningside Road, Edinburgh EH10 4QP
Tel: (0131) 4466850
E-mail: gordon.phillips@jardinephillips.com

JOHNSON FAMILY AND PROPERTY LAW LTD
1 Lynedoch Place, Edinburgh EH3 7PX
Tel: (0131) 622 9222
Categories of Work
Adoption
Advice the elderly & powers of attorney
Children
Civil court work
Commercial property
Contract & property disputes
Family and divorce
Landlord & tenant
Liquor licensing
Medical negligence – claimant
Personal injury
Professional negligence
Residential property
Associate
Kimberley Mackay

JOHNSON FAMILY AND PROPERTY LAW LTD
22a Rutland Square, Edinburgh EH1 2BB
Tel: (0131) 6229222
Fax: (0131) 6227922
DX: 401 EDINBURGH
E-mail: david@johnsonlegal.co.uk
Categories of Work
Adoption
Advice the elderly & powers of attorney
Children

▶ **Edinburgh continued**

Civil court work
Commercial property
Contract & property disputes
Family and divorce
Landlord & tenant
Liquor licensing
Medical negligence – claimant
Personal injury
Professional negligence
Residential property
Directors
Beverley Anne Johnson
David Ingram Johnson

JOHNSON LEGAL

22a Rutland Square, Edinburgh EH1 2BB
Tel: (0131) 6229222
Fax: (0131) 6227922
Categories of Work
Adoption
Advice the elderly & powers of attorney
Children
Civil court work
Commercial property
Contract & property disputes
Family and divorce
Landlord & tenant
Liquor licensing
Medical negligence – claimant
Personal injury
Professional negligence
Residential property
Consultant
Fiona Margaret Mundy
Associates
Pamela Jane McGowan
Hayley Jane Mitchell

CATH KARLIN FAMILY LAW

15/16 Queen Street, Edinburgh EH2 1JE
Tel: (0131) 2401213
Categories of Work
Adoption
Alternative dispute resolution
Children
Civil court work
Education
Family and divorce
Human rights

KENNEDYS

Baird House, 4 Lower Gilmore Bank,
Edinburgh EH3 9QP
Tel: (0131) 2256145
Categories of Work
Alternative dispute resolution
Civil court work
Commercial litigation
Criminal court work
Criminal legal aid
Data protection
Employment
Freedom of information

Health and safety
Insurance
IT and intellectual property
Local government
Media and entertainment
Medical negligence – defender
Medical negligence – claimant
Personal injury
Personal injury – defender
Power and utilities
Professional negligence
Road traffic

KENNEDYS SCOTLAND

Baird House, 4 Lower Gilmore Bank,
Edinburgh EH3 9QP
Tel: (0131) 2256145
Fax: (0131) 2264543
DX: ED 19 EDINBURGH
Web: www.kennedyslaw.com
Categories of Work
Alternative dispute resolution
Civil court work
Commercial litigation
Criminal court work
Criminal legal aid
Data protection
Employment
Freedom of information
Health and safety
Insurance
IT and intellectual property
Local government
Media and entertainment
Medical negligence – defender
Medical negligence – claimant
Personal injury
Personal injury – defender
Power and utilities
Professional negligence
Road traffic
Partners
Peter Adrian Demick
Roderick Andrew Stuart Jackson
Associate
Stephanie Martina Canda
Employees
Deborah Jane Clark
Ross Anthony Forrest
Stephen MacCallum Hill
Louise Claire Houliston
Kristopher Thomas Kane
Stephanie Mary Law

KERR LAW GROUP LIMITED

15 Ewerland, Edinburgh EH4 6DH
Tel: (07990) 734814
E-mail: kerrg@btinternet.com
Categories of Work
Advice the elderly & powers of attorney
Mental health
Wills, executives and trusts
Director
Gerard William Kerr

Employee
Amy Elizabeth Kerr

STUART KIDD WS
11 Strathalmond Green, Edinburgh EH4 8AG
Tel: (07764) 884103
E-mail: mkidd@stuartkiddws.co.uk
Categories of Work
Advice the elderly & powers of attorney
Agriculture and estates
Landlord & tenant
Residential property
Wills, executries and trusts
Partner
Mary Ainslie Kidd

LAWFORD KIDD
19 West Tollcross, Edinburgh EH3 9QN
Tel: (0131) 2255214
Fax: (0131) 2262069
DX: ED159 EDINBURGH
E-mail: Derek.Carrigan@lawfordkidd.co.uk
Web: www.lawfordclaims.com
Categories of Work
Civil court work
Medical negligence – claimant
Personal injury
Road traffic
Partner
Derek Carrigan
Employee
Bethany Anne Roby

LEDINGHAM CHALMERS LLP
3rd Floor, 68-70 George Street, Edinburgh
EH2 2LR
Tel: (0131) 2001000
Fax: (0131) 2001060
E-mail: mail@ledinghamchalmers.com
Web: www.ledinghamchalmers.com
Categories of Work
Adjudication
Adoption
Advice the elderly & powers of attorney
Agriculture and estates
Agriculture, crofting and fishing
Alternative dispute resolution
Alternative investment market
Banking & finance
Charities
Children
Childrens
Civil court work
Civil legal aid
Commercial litigation
Commercial property
Competition
Construction
Consumer credit
Contract & property disputes
Copyright, trade marks and design
Corporate tax
Credit brokerage
Criminal court work

Criminal legal aid
Data protection
Debt
Debt adjusting and debt counselling
Debt administration
Debt collecting
Debt management
Debt recovery, insolvency, bankruptcy
Disability
Discrimination
Education
Employment
Employment law
Environment
Environment (Business Premises)
EU / international
Family and divorce
Family business advice
Fishing
Freedom of information
Health and safety
Housing
Human rights
Immigration and asylum
Insolvency & corporate recovery
Insurance
IT and intellectual property
Joint venture
Landlord & tenant
Liquor licensing
Local government
Media and entertainment
Medical negligence – defender
Medical negligence – claimant
Mental health
Mergers and acquisitions
Oil & gas
Pensions (Company)
Pensions (Employment)
Personal injury
Personal injury – defender
Personal tax
Planning
Planning (Business Premises)
Power and utilities
Private equity
Professional negligence
Projects
Property litigation
Provision of credit information services
Public finance initiative
Public sector
Residential property
Road traffic
SME business advice
Software licensing
Telecoms
Transport
Unit Trusts, OEICs and investment trusts
Wills, executries and trusts
Partners
John Alexander Gunn Chalmers
John James Armstrong Lee

▶ **Edinburgh continued**

Sarah Elizabeth Morris
Associate
Ian Brown Gilkison Scott
Employees
Marie Patricia Cartney
Amy Dawn Dignan
Lauren Doherty
Anna Mhairi Watt

LEFEVRES (SCOTLAND) LIMITED
4 Randolph Place, Edinburgh EH3 7TQ
Tel: (0845) 305 2555
Fax: (0141) 226 5738
Web: www.lefevres.law
Categories of Work
Alternative dispute resolution
Civil court work
Civil legal aid
Commercial litigation
Discrimination
Employment
Employment law
Medical negligence – claimant
Personal injury
Professional negligence
Property litigation
Road traffic
Directors
Lindsay Davidson
Frank Hartley Lefevre
Consultant
Richard Christopher Frew
Associates
Lindsay Jane Bruce
Sarah Elizabeth McKinnon

KEITH LEISHMAN & CO DEFENCE
16 Forth Street, Edinburgh EH1 3LH
Tel: (07590) 315434
E-mail: leishmandefence@outlook.com
Categories of Work
Criminal court work
Criminal legal aid
Human rights
Mental health
Partner
Keith Robert Buchanan Leishman
Employee
Kenneth David Woodburn

LESLIE & CO. SSC
Blackrock House, 2-8 Millar Crescent,
Edinburgh EH10 5HW
Tel: (0131) 4478182
Fax: (0131) 4472274
E-mail: iain@leslieandco.co.uk
Categories of Work
Adoption
Advice the elderly & powers of attorney
Children
Civil court work
Commercial litigation
Commercial property

Contract & property disputes
Debt
Debt adjusting and debt counselling
Debt administration
Debt collecting
Debt recovery, insolvency, bankruptcy
Employment
Employment law
Family and divorce
Family business advice
Housing
Immigration and asylum
Insolvency & corporate recovery
Joint venture
Landlord & tenant
Medical negligence – claimant
Mental health
Mergers and acquisitions
Personal injury
Personal injury – defender
Property litigation
Residential property
Sport
Wills, executries and trusts
Partner
Iain Alexander Leslie

LINDSAYS LLP
Caledonian Exchange, 19A Canning Street,
Edinburgh EH3 8HE
Tel: (0131) 2291212
Fax: (0131) 2295611
DX: ED25 EDINBURGH
E-mail: edinburgh@lindsays.co.uk
Web: www.lindsays.co.uk
Categories of Work
Adjudication
Adoption
Advice the elderly & powers of attorney
Agriculture and estates
Agriculture, crofting and fishing
Alternative dispute resolution
Banking & finance
Betting & gaming
Charities
Children
Childrens
Civil court work
Civil legal aid
Commercial litigation
Commercial property
Construction
Consumer credit
Contract & property disputes
Copyright, trade marks and design
Corporate tax
Criminal court work
Criminal legal aid
Data protection
Debt
Debt adjusting and debt counselling
Debt administration
Debt collecting

Debt recovery, insolvency, bankruptcy
Discrimination
Education
Employment
Employment law
Environment
Environment (Business Premises)
EU / international
Family and divorce
Family business advice
Fishing
Freedom of information
Health
Health and safety
Housing
Human rights
Insolvency & corporate recovery
IT and intellectual property
Joint venture
Landlord & tenant
Liquor licensing
Local government
Media and entertainment
Medical negligence – defender
Medical negligence – claimant
Mergers and acquisitions
Oil & gas
Parliamentary
Pensions (Employment)
Personal injury
Personal injury – defender
Personal tax
Planning
Planning (Business Premises)
Power and utilities
Private equity
Professional negligence
Projects
Property litigation
Public finance initiative
Public sector
Residential property
Road traffic
SME business advice
Software licensing
Sport
Telecoms
Transport
Wills, executives and trusts

Partners
Gavin James Alexander Buchan
Alasdair William Donald Cummings
Andrew Russell Diamond
Kenneth David Gray
Alastair Paul Ludovic Harper
Brent William Haywood
Alastair John Keatinge
Callum Stuart Kennedy
Lynsey Christine Kerr
Susan Jane Law
Clare Margaret McCarroll
Derek Andrew Nash
Louise Dorothy Norris

Dorothy Crombie Rankin
Douglas Andrew Roberts
Nina Ariella Salicath Taylor
Peter David Tweedie
David George Wood
Michael James Yellowlees
Morag Wilson Yellowlees
Consultant
David Ness Dunsire
Associates
Vanessa Margaret Beattie
Kirsty Anne Cooper
Sharon Kristina Drysdale
Andrew James Duff
Kerry Gallagher
Scott Miller Geekie
Fiona Margaret Linklater
Gregor John MacEwan
Anna Mary McLaggan
Alastair James Smith
Employees
Dawn Melrose Anderson
Andrew Boccoli
Claire Marie Wills Brown
Jonathan George Woodd Cahusac
Nimarta Kaur Cheema
Caitlin Connolly
Lewis Crofts
Molly Grace Duncan
Adam Daniel Gardiner
Leanne Gordon
Michael John Gordon
Caroline Rebecca Grubb
Rebecca Healy
Rachel Louise Holt
Mumotaz Hossain
Katherine Elizabeth Irvine
Mohammed Hamaad Khalid
Darren Andrew Lightfoot
Timothy James Roxburgh Macdonald
Alison Anne Mackay
Sally Louise MacLean
Amy Mayberry
Se n Michael McEntee
James Alexander McGill
Lesley Anne McKinlay
Laura McKinnon
Alexandria Emily McNeill
Nicole Laura Noble
Eilidh Catriona Robertson
Sandra Monika Rzepka
Rachel Alice Salmond
Vhari Yvonne Selfridge
Alasdair Charles Ogg Soutar
Kirsty Audrey Pauline Strachan
David Andrew Walker
Harriet Louise Waters
Francesca Mhairi Bridgit Willetts

LYONS DAVIDSON SCOTLAND LLP
Enterprise House, 34 Earl Grey Street,
Edinburgh EH3 9BN
Tel: (0344) 251 0070

► **Edinburgh** continued

DX: ED31 EDINBURGH
Web: www.lyonsdavidson.co.uk
Categories of Work
Adoption
Advice the elderly & powers of attorney
Alternative dispute resolution
Charities
Children
Childrens
Civil court work
Civil legal aid
Commercial litigation
Criminal court work
Criminal legal aid
Data protection
Debt
Debt administration
Debt management
Debt recovery, insolvency, bankruptcy
Disability
Discrimination
Education
Family and divorce
Freedom of information
Health and safety
Housing
Insolvency & corporate recovery
Insurance
Media and entertainment
Medical negligence – claimant
Mental health
Personal injury
Professional negligence
Residential property
Road traffic
Social housing
Partner
Katherine Howells
Associates
Caroline Lorna Fraser
Elaine Marshall
Tanya Jane Murray
Employees
Kimberly Alison Kane
Daniel James Trail

MCDOUGALL MCQUEEN
103-105 Bruntsfield Place, Edinburgh
EH10 4EQ
Tel: (0131) 2281926
DX: : ED655 EDINBURGH
Web: www.mcdougallmcqueen.co.uk
Categories of Work
Adoption
Advice the elderly & powers of attorney
Charities
Children
Childrens
Civil court work
Civil legal aid
Commercial litigation
Commercial property

Contract & property disputes
Criminal court work
Criminal legal aid
Disability
Discrimination
Employment
Employment law
Family and divorce
Health and safety
Landlord & tenant
Medical negligence – claimant
Personal injury
Personal injury – defender
Personal tax
Professional negligence
Residential property
Road traffic
Wills, executries and trusts

MCDOUGALL MCQUEEN
2B New Mart Road, Edinburgh EH14 1RL
Tel: (0131) 6221771
Fax: (0131) 4777052
DX: : ED605 EDINBURGH
Web: www.mcdougallmcqueen.co.uk
Categories of Work
Adoption
Advice the elderly & powers of attorney
Charities
Children
Childrens
Civil court work
Civil legal aid
Commercial litigation
Commercial property
Contract & property disputes
Criminal court work
Criminal legal aid
Disability
Discrimination
Employment
Employment law
Family and divorce
Health and safety
Landlord & tenant
Medical negligence – claimant
Personal injury
Personal injury – defender
Personal tax
Professional negligence
Residential property
Road traffic
Wills, executries and trusts
Associate
Susan Jane Oates

MCDOUGALL MCQUEEN
3 Coates Crescent, Edinburgh EH3 7AL
Tel: (0131) 2252121
E-mail: info@mcdougallmcqueen.co.uk
Web: www.mcdougallmcqueen.co.uk
Categories of Work
Adoption
Advice the elderly & powers of attorney

Charities
Children
Childrens
Civil court work
Civil legal aid
Commercial litigation
Commercial property
Contract & property disputes
Criminal court work
Criminal legal aid
Disability
Discrimination
Employment
Employment law
Family and divorce
Health and safety
Landlord & tenant
Medical negligence – claimant
Personal injury
Personal injury – defender
Personal tax
Professional negligence
Residential property
Road traffic
Wills, executries and trusts

MCEWAN FRASER LEGAL
Claremont House, 130 East Claremont Street,
Edinburgh EH7 4LB
Tel: (0131) 5249797
Fax: (0131) 5570561
DX: ED650 Edinburgh
E-mail: email@mcewanfraserlegal.co.uk
Web: www.mcewanfraserlegal.co.uk
Categories of Work
Adoption
Advice the elderly & powers of attorney
Agriculture and estates
Agriculture, crofting and fishing
Charities
Children
Childrens
Civil court work
Commercial property
Contract & property disputes
Debt recovery, insolvency, bankruptcy
Family and divorce
Family business advice
Landlord & tenant
Property litigation
Residential property
Wills, executries and trusts
Partners
Artur Lasisz
Magnus Knowles Moodie
Kenneth William Watt
Employees
Richard Oliver Frederick Adams
Natalie Linda Urquhart Allan
Katie Isabella Burns
Sarah Kirsten Douglas
Anne Catherine Graham
Adeeb Al Mostafa

Cara Fiona Iris Seivwright
Lenka Votypkova

HELEN MCGINTY & COMPANY
1 St Colme Street, Edinburgh EH3 6AA
Tel: (0131) 2208380
E-mail: info@helenmcginty.com
Web: www.helenmcginty.com
Categories of Work
Adoption
Advice the elderly & powers of attorney
Children
Civil court work
Civil legal aid
Debt
Debt adjusting and debt counselling
Debt management
Disability
Discrimination
Family and divorce
Human rights
Medical negligence – claimant
Mental health
Personal injury
Professional negligence
Social housing
Wills, executries and trusts
Partner
Helen Frances McGinty

MACGREGOR BOWMAN WS
31 Winton Park, Edinburgh EH10 7EX
Tel: (0131) 4454177
E-mail: mail@macgregorbowman.co.uk
Web: www.macgregorbowman.co.uk
Categories of Work
Advice the elderly & powers of attorney
Personal tax
Wills, executries and trusts
Partner
Alistair MacGregor Bowman

MACGREGOR THOMSON LIMITED
50 Albany Street, Edinburgh EH1 3QR
Tel: (0131) 5561115
DX: ED562 EDINBURGH
E-mail: athomson@macgregorthomson.co.uk
Web: www.macgregorthomson.co.uk
Categories of Work
Banking & finance
Betting & gaming
Commercial property
Contract & property disputes
Debt
Debt recovery, insolvency, bankruptcy
Family business advice
Insolvency & corporate recovery
Joint venture
Landlord & tenant
Liquor licensing
Local government
Mergers and acquisitions
Private equity
Residential property

▶ **Edinburgh continued**

SME business advice
Sport
Wills, executries and trusts

MCINTYRES
158 Portobello High Street, Portobello,
Edinburgh EH15 1AH
Tel: (0131) 6697218
E-mail: property@mcintyresproperty.co.uk
Web: www.mcintyresproperty.co.uk
Categories of Work
Advice the elderly & powers of attorney
Charities
Civil court work
Commercial litigation
Commercial property
Contract & property disputes
Debt
Debt collecting
Debt recovery, insolvency, bankruptcy
Disability
Discrimination
Employment
Employment law
Health and safety
Landlord & tenant
Parliamentary
Personal tax
Property litigation
Residential property
Wills, executries and trusts

MACKAY SINCLAIR
11-15 Easter Road, Edinburgh EH7 5PJ
Tel: (0131) 6521166
Fax: (0131) 6521199
E-mail: mackaysinclair@btconnet.com
Web: www.mackaysinclair.co.uk
Categories of Work
Commercial property
Landlord & tenant
Residential property
Wills, executries and trusts
Partner
William Hugh MacKay Sinclair

FIONA MCPHAIL SOLICITORS
4th Floor, Scotiabank House, Edinburgh
EH2 4AW
Tel: (0344) 5152410
Fax: (0344) 5152904
Web: www.shelter.org.uk
Categories of Work
Alternative dispute resolution
Benefit advice
Charities
Civil court work
Civil legal aid
Commercial litigation
Consumer credit
Criminal court work
Data protection
Debt

Debt administration
Debt management
Debt recovery, insolvency, bankruptcy
Disability
Discrimination
Employment
Employment law
Freedom of information
Housing
Human rights
Immigration and asylum
Insolvency & corporate recovery
Landlord & tenant
Local government
Mental health
Parliamentary
Property litigation
Residential property
Social housing
Partner
Fiona Marie McPhail
Associate
Christopher Ryan
Employees
Lynne Cunningham
Trudy Ann Gill
Calvin Andrew Manson Gordon
Andrew Munro Knox
Vicki Louise McLanders
Vicki Heather Pirie
Kate Smith
Linsey Jane Soutter

GORDON MACRAE & CO LTD
15/8 Wellington Street, Hillside, Edinburgh
EH7 5EE
Tel: (0131) 6296355
E-mail: chris.macrae@gordonmacraeip.com
Categories of Work
Alternative dispute resolution
Banking & finance
Betting & gaming
Charities
Commercial litigation
Competition
Copyright, trade marks and design
Data protection
Education
EU / international
Family business advice
Freedom of information
Human rights
IT and intellectual property
Joint venture
Media and entertainment
Mergers and acquisitions
Power and utilities
Public sector
Shipping
SME business advice
Software licensing
Sport
Telecoms

Transport

GORDON MACRAE & CO LTD
C/o David Marshall Associates, CBC House,
Edinburgh EH3 8EG
Tel: (0131) 6296355
E-mail: chris.macrae@gordonmacraeip.com
Categories of Work
Alternative dispute resolution
Banking & finance
Betting & gaming
Charities
Commercial litigation
Competition
Copyright, trade marks and design
Data protection
Education
EU / international
Family business advice
Freedom of information
Human rights
IT and intellectual property
Joint venture
Media and entertainment
Mergers and acquisitions
Power and utilities
Public sector
Shipping
SME business advice
Software licensing
Sport
Telecoms
Transport
Director
Christopher James MacRae

MACROBERTS LLP
10 George Street, Edinburgh EH2 2PF
Tel: (0131) 2295046
Fax: (0131) 2290849
Categories of Work
Adjudication
Adoption
Advice the elderly & powers of attorney
Agriculture and estates
Agriculture, crofting and fishing
Alternative dispute resolution
Alternative investment market
Banking & finance
Betting & gaming
Charities
Children
Civil court work
Commercial litigation
Commercial property
Competition
Construction
Consumer credit
Contract & property disputes
Copyright, trade marks and design
Data protection
Debt
Debt adjusting and debt counselling
Debt administration
Debt collecting
Debt recovery, insolvency, bankruptcy
Disability
Discrimination
Education
Employment
Employment law
Environment
Environment (Business Premises)
EU / international
Family and divorce
Family business advice
Fishing
Freedom of information
Health
Health and safety
Housing
Human rights
Immigration and asylum
Insolvency & corporate recovery
Insurance
IT and intellectual property
Joint venture
Landlord & tenant
Liquor licensing
Local government
Media and entertainment
Mergers and acquisitions
Mining
Oil & gas
Parliamentary
Pensions (Company)
Pensions (Employment)
Personal injury
Personal injury – defender
Personal tax
Planning
Planning (Business Premises)
Power and utilities
Private equity
Professional negligence
Projects
Property litigation
Public finance initiative
Public sector
Residential property
Road traffic
Shipping
SME business advice
Software licensing
Sport
Telecoms
Transport
Unit Trusts, OEICs and investment trusts
Wills, executories and trusts
Partners
Michael John Barlow
Gillian Aida Campbell
Robin Kenneth Fallas
Marika Simona Leonora Franceschi
Elizabeth Margaret Frost
David McRae Gourlay
Julie Patricia Hamilton

▶ **Edinburgh continued**

Nicholas William Jones
Alan Andrew Kelly
Neil Joseph Kelly
Ainsley Grace Maclaren
Lisa Maguire
Norman Maclean Martin
Jennifer Reid McKay
Duncan Farnworth Osler
Jacqueline Anne Stroud
Gavin Ross Thomson
David John Wylie
Consultants
John Robert Neil Macleod
Gordon Lindsay Kevan Murray
Associates
Alan George Robert Burns
Lynsay Katherine Cargill
Gail Anne Clarke
James David Duff
Laura Elizabeth Gilbert
Rosalind Sarah Kelly
Margaret White Kinnes
Dorothy Lawrence
Susan Anne MacAulay
Dawn Crystal MacPherson
Pauline McLachlan
Bonar James Lamond Mercer
Sarah Mary Katherine Pengelly
Lynn Anne Pentland
Ian Hamish Riach
Lesley Anne Roarty
Kenneth Andrew Scott
Philippa Mary Ordish Snell
Hannah Ward
Rebecca Margaret Catherine Yassin
Employees
Emma Roberta Marjory Aitken
Brian Scott Barbour
Amy Boyce
Christie Rose Carswell
Amanda Claire Haynes
Kamila Julia Kaminska
Martin Krasimirov Kotsev
Calum Euan Lavery
Maya Elizabeth Lee Allen
Michael Vaughan

IAIN MCSPORRAN QC, SOLICITOR ADVOCATE
SSC Library, 11 Parliament Square, Edinburgh
EH1 1RF
Tel: (07891) 529849
E-mail: iainmcsporran@btinternet.com
Categories of Work
Criminal court work
Criminal legal aid
Partner
Iain McSporran

MCSPORRANS
45 Frederick Street, Edinburgh EH2 1ES
Tel: (0131) 5579151
Categories of Work
Criminal court work

Criminal legal aid
Partner
Andrew William Houston

CONNOR MALCOLM
1 Inverleith Terrace, Edinburgh EH3 5NS
Tel: (0131) 5576566
Fax: (0131) 5576561
DX: ED188 EDINBURGH
E-mail: mailroom@connormalcolm.com
Web: www.connormalcolm.com
Categories of Work
Advice the elderly & powers of attorney
Commercial property
Landlord & tenant
Residential property
Wills, executries and trusts
Partners
David Robert Lewis Henry Devlin
John Gillies Hughes

BRANDON MALONE & COMPANY LIMITED
83 Princes Street, Edinburgh EH2 2ER
Tel: (0131) 357 8549
Fax: (0131) 777 2609
E-mail: info@brandonmalone.com
Categories of Work
Adjudication
Alternative dispute resolution
Civil court work
Commercial litigation
Construction
Contract & property disputes
EU / international
Landlord & tenant
Oil & gas
Parliamentary
Power and utilities
Projects
Property litigation
Director
Brandon James Malone

MANNIFIELD TEMPLETON DEFENCE
23 (Middle Floor) Blair Street, Edinburgh
EH1 1QR
Tel: (0131) 3228777
E-mail: mail@mtdefence.com
Categories of Work
Criminal court work
Criminal legal aid
Partners
Stephen Royston Mannifield
Emma Templeton

MARSALI MURRAY
16 Merchiston Avenue, Edinburgh EH10 4NY
Tel: (0131) 2281109
Partner
Marsali Claire Murray

MATTAC LIMITED
93 George Street, Edinburgh EH2 3ES
Tel: (0131) 510 8740
Fax: (0131) 510 8750

E-mail: info@mattac.legal
Web: www.mattac.legal
Categories of Work
Advice the elderly & powers of attorney
Alternative dispute resolution
Civil court work
Commercial litigation
Commercial property
Health and safety
Medical negligence – claimant
Personal injury
Professional negligence
Residential property
Road traffic
Sport
Wills, executries and trusts
Director
Paul McIntosh
Consultant
David Graeme Dougall Ellis

MBM BOARD NOMINEES LIMITED
3 Glenfinlas Street, Edinburgh EH3 6AQ
Tel: (0131) 2251200

MBM COMMERCIAL LLP
Suite 2, Orchard Brae House, Edinburgh
EH4 2HS
Tel: (0131) 2268200
Fax: (0131) 2268240
E-mail: info@mbmcommercial.co.uk
Web: www.mbmcommercial.co.uk
Categories of Work
Alternative dispute resolution
Alternative investment market
Banking & finance
Betting & gaming
Charities
Civil court work
Commercial litigation
Commercial property
Contract & property disputes
Copyright, trade marks and design
Corporate tax
Data protection
Debt
Debt collecting
Debt recovery, insolvency, bankruptcy
Disability
Discrimination
Employment
Employment law
Environment
Environment (Business Premises)
EU / international
Family business advice
Freedom of information
Human rights
Insolvency & corporate recovery
IT and intellectual property
Joint venture
Landlord & tenant
Media and entertainment
Mergers and acquisitions

Oil & gas
Pensions (Employment)
Power and utilities
Private equity
Professional negligence
Projects
Property litigation
Public sector
Residential property
SME business advice
Software licensing
Sport
Unit Trusts, OEICs and investment trusts
Partners
Timothy James Edward
Tracey Margaret Ginn
Andrew John Forsyth Harris
Stuart James Falconer Hendry
Catriona Joan MacLean
Kenneth Mumford
Jane Margaret Ramsay
Hannah Louise Roche
Associates
Lynne Kathryn Telford Arnott
Craig James Edward
Alexander James Lamley
Employees
Jamie Apted
Hannah Louise Brazel
Ross Alan Byford
Greg Coats
Lucy Catherine Drury
Anelda Grov Dempster
Morgan Scott Landels
Madeleine Clare Macphail
Iain David McDougall
Helen McGrath
Jennifer Margaret McNichol
Mark Milne
Ruairidh Duncan Morrison
Kayleigh Palmer
Laura Elizabeth Peachey
Denise Mary Pryde

MBM TRUSTEE COMPANY LIMITED
3 Glenfinlas Street, Edinburgh EH3 6AQ
Tel: (0131) 2251200

MBS SOLICITORS
150-152 Gorgie Road, Edinburgh EH11 2NT
Tel: (0131) 3374100
Fax: (0131) 3373200
E-mail: office@mbssolicitors.co.uk
Web: www.mbssolicitors.co.uk
Categories of Work
Adoption
Charities
Children
Childrens
Civil court work
Civil legal aid
Commercial litigation
Commercial property
Contract & property disputes

▶ *Edinburgh continued*

Criminal court work
Criminal legal aid
Debt
Debt collecting
Debt management
Education
EU / international
Family and divorce
Family business advice
Freedom of information
Health
Human rights
Immigration and asylum
Insurance
Landlord & tenant
Local government
Medical negligence – claimant
Mental health
Parliamentary
Personal injury
Personal injury – defender
Professional negligence
Property litigation
Public sector
Road traffic
Wills, executives and trusts
Partner
Mohammed Sabir
Employees
Paige Anne Burton
Alan William Robertson

MHD LAW LLP
45 Queen Charlotte Street, Leith, Edinburgh
EH6 7HT
Tel: (0131) 5550616
Fax: (0131) 5531523
DX: 550856 LEITH
E-mail: edinburgh@mhdlaw.co.uk
Web: www.mhdlaw.co.uk
Categories of Work
Adoption
Advice the elderly & powers of attorney
Children
Civil court work
Civil legal aid
Commercial property
Education
Family and divorce
Family business advice
Landlord & tenant
Medical negligence – claimant
Mental health
Personal injury
Personal tax
Professional negligence
Residential property
Wills, executives and trusts
Partners
Christopher Derek Benson
Raymond George Fairgrieve
Kieran Gerard Fitzpatrick

Lorraine Elizabeth Tollan
Employees
Helen Jane Cormack
Fergus Henry Morris Johnston

MILL AND MILLARD LLP
69-71 Dalry Road, Edinburgh EH11 2AA
Tel: (0131) 3227222
Categories of Work
Adoption
Advice the elderly & powers of attorney
Children
Childrens
Civil court work
Civil legal aid
Education
Family and divorce
Wills, executives and trusts
Partners
Richard George Mill
Lucy Millard
Employees
Sarah Diana Kavanagh
Iain James Leiper

MILNE & CO. WS
7 Hopetoun Crescent, Edinburgh EH7 4AY
Tel: (0131) 5581441
Fax: (0131) 4455514
DX: ED435 EDINBURGH
E-mail: rorymilne@irishosted.co.uk
Categories of Work
Commercial property
Landlord & tenant
Residential property
Partner
Rhoderick Michael Stuart Milne
Consultant
Andrew John Mitchell

MOONEYS
3/4 Fettes Court, Craigleith Road, Edinburgh
EH4 2DL
Tel: (07711) 510816
E-mail: mooneys.solicitors@hotmail.co.uk
Categories of Work
Criminal court work
Criminal legal aid
Partner
Joseph Mooney

ROBERT MORE AND COMPANY
106 Duke Street, Edinburgh EH6 8HL
Tel: (0131) 5571110
E-mail: moreandco01@outlook.com
Categories of Work
Criminal court work
Criminal legal aid
Partners
Stephanie Louise Clinkscale
Robert Edwards More
Employee
Ian Ruaridh Anderson

GEORGE MORE & COMPANY LLP
145 Great Junction Street, Edinburgh EH6 5LG
Tel: (0131) 2026552
Fax: (0131) 2026096
E-mail: office@moreandcompany.com
Categories of Work
Advice the elderly & powers of attorney
Children
Childrens
Civil court work
Civil legal aid
Criminal court work
Criminal legal aid
Family and divorce
Personal injury
Wills, executries and trusts
Partner
Richard Alexander Kyle Souter
Employees
Richard William James Gray
Melissa Janice Virtue

MORGAN CUNNINGHAM SOLICITORS
Ground Floor, 1 Rutland Square, Edinburgh
EH1 2AS
Tel: (0131) 6239323
Fax: (0131) 6239322
DX: ED446 EDINBURGH
E-mail: info@morgancunningham.com
Categories of Work
Agriculture and estates
Commercial property
Contract & property disputes
Residential property
Wills, executries and trusts
Partner
Fiona Ellen Margaret Cunningham

MORTON FRASER LLP
Quartermile Two, 2 Lister Square, Edinburgh
EH3 9GL
Tel: (0131) 2471000
Fax: (0131) 2471007
DX: ED119 EDINBURGH
Web: www.morton-fraser.com
Categories of Work
Adjudication
Adoption
Advice the elderly & powers of attorney
Agriculture and estates
Agriculture, crofting and fishing
Alternative dispute resolution
Alternative investment market
Banking & finance
Betting & gaming
Charities
Children
Childrens
Civil court work
Civil legal aid
Commercial litigation
Commercial property
Competition
Construction

Consumer credit
Contract & property disputes
Copyright, trade marks and design
Corporate tax
Credit brokerage
Criminal court work
Criminal legal aid
Data protection
Debt
Debt adjusting and debt counselling
Debt administration
Debt collecting
Debt recovery, insolvency, bankruptcy
Disability
Discrimination
Education
Employment
Employment law
Environment
Environment (Business Premises)
EU / international
Family and divorce
Family business advice
Fishing
Freedom of information
Health
Health and safety
Housing
Human rights
Immigration and asylum
Insolvency & corporate recovery
Insurance
IT and intellectual property
Joint venture
Landlord & tenant
Liquor licensing
Local government
Media and entertainment
Medical negligence – defender
Medical negligence – claimant
Mental health
Mergers and acquisitions
Mining
Oil & gas
Parliamentary
Pensions (Company)
Pensions (Employment)
Personal injury
Personal injury – defender
Personal tax
Planning
Planning (Business Premises)
Power and utilities
Private equity
Professional negligence
Projects
Property litigation
Provision of credit information services
Public finance initiative
Public sector
Residential property
Road traffic
Shipping

▶ **Edinburgh continued**

SME business advice
Software licensing
Sport
Telecoms
Transport
Unit Trusts, OEICs and investment trusts
Wills, executives and trusts

Partners
Rhona Anne Adams
Rory Drummond Alexander
Matthew Alexander Barclay
Adrian Edward Robert Bell
Carryl Mairi Anna Beveridge
Ross Graham Caldwell
Kenneth William Carruthers
Sandra Isobel McDonald Cassels
James Innes Clark
Lucia Elaine Clark
Jennifer Alison Dickson
Amy Anne Entwistle
Austin Flynn
Paul James Thomas Geoghegan
Suzanne Claire Hardie
Christopher Joseph Harte
David Hossack
Sue Elizabeth Hunter
Jack McLauchlan Kerr
John Alexander Lunn
Catriona Mhairi Robertson MacPhail
Richard George McMeeken
Andrew Scott Meakin
Douglas Neil Milne
Michael John Ramsay
Jonathan Seddon
Alan George Stewart
David Ross Stewart
Andrew Graham Alexander Walker
David James Walker
Beverley Wood
Iain Mackenzie Young

Consultants
Alistair Robert Anderson
Nicholas John Atkins
John Gallacher
Karen Grace McGill
Iain Maury Campbell Meiklejohn
Carolyn Mary Mitchell
Robin James Scott Morton
Claire Mary Sturrock
Robert Bruce Wood

Associates
Fiona Jane Byron
Emma Louise Carmichael
Stephen John Clark
Derek Grant Couper
Caroline Rose Earnshaw
Sarah Anne Gilzean
Cameron James Greig
Lauren Elizabeth Hart
Fiona Margaret Hogg
Bess Macleod Innes

Susan Jane Leslie
Catherine Mary MacPherson
Ewan Boyd McGillivray
Kirsten Anne McManus
Angela Myles
Julie Elizabeth Jane Nixon
Ainsley Macdonald Reid
Jamie Andrew Reid
Julie Scott-Gilroy
Mimi Stewart
Jennifer Dalrymple Thomson
Gail Watt
Emma Jane Wood

Employees
Sally Jane MacRae Anthony
Isabelle Eliza Bain
Judith Liadhan Baxter
Yvonne Therese Brady
Trudy Eva Burns
Ying On Anthea Chan
Kitty Alexa Cowan
Ellen Crofts
Alan Joseph Delaney
Stuart David James Dick
Helen Mary Donnelly
David James Forrester
Mhairi Clare Foye
Chloe Margaret Gentle
Douglas James Harvey
Elizabeth Rebecca Holehouse
Robert Iain Jessiman
Robyn Alexandra Keay
Hannah Shyamali Lawrence
Finlay Crawford Leggat
Isabel Marie Momoko MacSwan
Caroline Maher
Katrina Emily Mahony
Hannah Felicity Kate Marshall
Ruth McCallister
Fiona Anne Meek
Stephen William Moffat
Craig David Muir
David Gordon Amcotts Murdie
Marianne Joy Miranda Murnin
Hazel Janet Noble
Kiril Georgiev Pehlivanov
Mark John Pelosi
Lorraine Anne Pollock
Laura Alexandra Purves
Ellen Betty Robinson
Melanie Petra Schwindt
Savita Sharma
Elizabeth Alexandra Sparks
Suzanne Frances Sutherland
Hayley Marie Swanson
Steven Lewis Thomson
Lynda Ann Towers
Kathryn Elizabeth Yule

MOTORCYCLE LAW SCOTLAND
16-20 Castle Street, Edinburgh EH2 3AT
Tel: (0131) 4736616

E-mail:
edinburgh@motorcyclelawscotland.co.uk
Categories of Work
Civil court work
Personal injury
Professional negligence
Road traffic
Sport

MOV8 REAL ESTATE LIMITED
6 Redheughs Rigg, Edinburgh EH12 9DQ
Tel: (0345) 646 0208
Fax: (0131) 777 2642
DX: 550449 EDINBURGH 44
E-mail: legal@mov8realestate.com
Web: www.mov8realestate.com
Categories of Work
Advice the elderly & powers of attorney
Agriculture and estates
Agriculture, crofting and fishing
Banking & finance
Charities
Commercial property
Contract & property disputes
Family business advice
Housing
Landlord & tenant
Property litigation
Residential property
SME business advice
Wills, executries and trusts
Directors
Robert Adamson Carroll
Gavin James Pearson
Employees
Stephen George Dickson
Mairi Louise Kennedy
Collette Frances McFarlane
Omar Hassan Mohammed

MSM TRUSTEES LIMITED
10 George Street, Edinburgh EH2 2PF

MTM DEFENCE LAWYERS LIMITED
Exchange Place 2, 5 Semple Street, Edinburgh
EH3 8BL
Tel: (0131) 3060115
Categories of Work
Adoption
Children
Childrens
Civil court work
Civil legal aid
Criminal court work
Criminal legal aid
Education
Family and divorce
Medical negligence – defender
Personal injury – defender
Director
Neil David Hay
Employee
Andrew Thomas Seggie

MUIRS
13 Alva Street, Edinburgh EH2 4PH
Tel: (0131) 2263058
Fax: (0131) 2202565
DX: ED186 EDINBURGH
E-mail: neilmuir@muirsws.com
Categories of Work
Commercial property
Residential property
Wills, executries and trusts
Partner
Neil Marshall Muir

MURRAY BEITH MURRAY
3 Glenfinlas Street, Edinburgh EH3 6AQ
Tel: (0131) 2251200
Fax: (0131) 2254412
DX: ED40 EDINBURGH
E-mail: mbm@murraybeith.co.uk
Web: www.murraybeith.co.uk
Categories of Work
Adjudication
Advice the elderly & powers of attorney
Agriculture and estates
Agriculture, crofting and fishing
Alternative dispute resolution
Banking & finance
Charities
Civil court work
Commercial litigation
Commercial property
Construction
Consumer credit
Contract & property disputes
Credit brokerage
Criminal court work
Criminal legal aid
Data protection
Debt
Debt adjusting and debt counselling
Debt administration
Debt collecting
Debt recovery, insolvency, bankruptcy
Disability
Discrimination
Employment
Employment law
Family business advice
Freedom of information
Health and safety
Human rights
Landlord & tenant
Medical negligence – claimant
Mergers and acquisitions
Personal injury
Personal injury – defender
Personal tax
Professional negligence
Property litigation
Provision of credit information services
Residential property
Road traffic
Wills, executries and trusts

▶ **Edinburgh** continued

Partners
William Ruthven Gemmell
Andrew Dermot Linehan
William Meldrum
Andrew John Neill Paterson
Peter Graham Shand
Andrew Johnston Stephen
Hugh Patrick Younger
Consultant
Carole Hope
Associates
Charles Richard Black
Sophie Elizabeth Napier
Caroline Alexandra Pringle
Andrew Taylor
Employees
Simon Andrew Boendermaker
Anna Lindsay MacLeod
Alastair Hannah Marshall
Nicola Louise Roberts
Fraser Clark Scott
Sally Jane Scott Lintott
Adam Frederick Swayne

NEILSONS
138 St. Johns Road, Edinburgh EH12 8AY
Tel: (0131) 3164444
Fax: (0131) 3348003
DX: 550441 EDINBURGH 44
E-mail: mail@neilsons.co.uk
Categories of Work
Benefit advice
Commercial property
Debt management
Landlord & tenant
Mental health
Residential property
Wills, executries and trusts
Partners
David John Douglas Marshall
Stephen Russell Spence
Associate
Aidan Daniel Tuohy
Employees
Yvonne Louise Blakeley
Claire McGilvary Corrieri
Chellsey Margaret Jane Fallon

NEILSONS
2a Picardy Place, Edinburgh EH1 3JT
Tel: (0131) 5565522
Fax: (0131) 5563666
DX: 551051 EDINBURGH 6
E-mail: mail@neilsons.co.uk
Categories of Work
Benefit advice
Commercial property
Debt management
Landlord & tenant
Mental health
Residential property
Wills, executries and trusts

Partner
Marjorie Rose Townsend
Employee
Kara Marie Marriott

NEILSONS
Property Centre, 142 St. Johns Road,
Edinburgh EH12 8AY
Tel: (0131) 6252222
DX: 550441 EDINBURGH 44
Categories of Work
Benefit advice
Commercial property
Debt management
Landlord & tenant
Mental health
Residential property
Wills, executries and trusts

NISBETS SOLICITORS LIMITED
30 Woodburn Terrace, Edinburgh EH10 4SS
Tel: (07967) 754488
E-mail: jn@nisbetssolicitors.com
Categories of Work
Agriculture, crofting and fishing
Alternative dispute resolution
Betting & gaming
Civil court work
Commercial litigation
Commercial property
Construction
Contract & property disputes
Debt recovery, insolvency, bankruptcy
Landlord & tenant
Liquor licensing
Power and utilities
Property litigation
Residential property
Telecoms
Director
Jonathan Alexander Foster Nisbet

NOTARY.SCOT
1/2 Walker Street, Edinburgh EH3 7JY
Tel: (07947) 232353
E-mail: donaldwright@notary.scot
Categories of Work
Advice the elderly & powers of attorney
Childrens
Civil court work
Commercial property
Family and divorce
Residential property
Wills, executries and trusts
Partner
Donald James Wright

ANN OGG
27/13 West Bryson Road, Edinburgh
EH11 1BN
Tel: (0131) 3370912
Fax: (0131) 3460588
Categories of Work
Criminal court work
Criminal legal aid

Partner
Ann Ogg

PARABIS SCOTLAND LIMITED
Bonnington Road, Suite 29, 2 Anderson
Square, Edinburgh EH6 5NP
Tel: (0131) 3221268
Categories of Work
Advice the elderly & powers of attorney
Alternative dispute resolution
Civil court work
Commercial litigation
Commercial property
Consumer credit
Contract & property disputes
Debt
Debt collecting
Disability
Discrimination
Employment
Employment law
Health
Health and safety
Human rights
Local government
Medical negligence – claimant
Personal injury
Professional negligence
Property litigation
Residential property
Road traffic
Wills, executries and trusts
Employee
Valerie Sandra Roberts

PATERSON BELL LIMITED
34 Blair Street, Edinburgh EH1 1QR
Tel: (0131) 2256111
Fax: (0131) 2263209
DX: ED602 EDINBURGH
E-mail: crime@patersonbell.co.uk
Categories of Work
Criminal court work
Criminal legal aid
Director
Iain Michael Paterson
Employee
Heather Morrison

PEDESTRIAN LAW SCOTLAND
16-20 Castle Street, Edinburgh EH2 3AT
Tel: (0131) 4736616
E-mail: edinburgh@pedestrianlaw.co.uk
Categories of Work
Civil court work
Personal injury
Professional negligence
Road traffic
Sport

PINSENT MASONS LLP
Princes Exchange, 1 Earl Grey Street,
Edinburgh EH3 9AQ
Tel: (0131) 777 7000
Fax: (0131) 7777003

Web: www.pinsentmasons.com
Categories of Work
Adjudication
Advice the elderly & powers of attorney
Agriculture and estates
Agriculture, crofting and fishing
Alternative dispute resolution
Alternative investment market
Banking & finance
Betting & gaming
Charities
Children
Civil court work
Commercial litigation
Commercial property
Competition
Construction
Contract & property disputes
Copyright, trade marks and design
Corporate tax
Criminal court work
Data protection
Debt
Debt adjusting and debt counselling
Debt administration
Debt collecting
Debt recovery, insolvency, bankruptcy
Disability
Discrimination
Education
Employment
Employment law
Environment
Environment (Business Premises)
EU / international
Family and divorce
Family business advice
Fishing
Freedom of information
Health
Health and safety
Housing
Human rights
Immigration and asylum
Insolvency & corporate recovery
Insurance
IT and intellectual property
Joint venture
Landlord & tenant
Liquor licensing
Local government
Media and entertainment
Medical negligence – defender
Medical negligence – claimant
Mental health
Mergers and acquisitions
Mining
Oil & gas
Parliamentary
Pensions (Company)
Pensions (Employment)
Personal injury
Personal injury – defender

► **Edinburgh continued**

Planning
Planning (Business Premises)
Power and utilities
Private equity
Professional negligence
Projects
Property litigation
Public finance initiative
Public sector
Residential property
Road traffic
Shipping
SME business advice
Software licensing
Sport
Telecoms
Transport
Unit Trusts, OEICs and investment trusts
Wills, executries and trusts

Partners
Ewan Grant Alexander
James Shearer Cormack
Alan Lindsay Diamond
Gavin Blair Farquhar
Louise Mary Forster
Gillian Elizabeth Frew
Matthew Charles Richard Godfrey-Faussett
Jacqueline Marie Harris
Richard Kerr Linton
Iain Angus Macaulay
John Angus Maciver
Duncan Iain Thomas Macphail
Julia Mary Maguire
Christopher Derek Martin
Ian Bryson McCarlie
Gary Peter McGovern
Victoria Anne Speirs Miller
Russell William Munro
Thomas Stephen Stocker
Michael Gall Watson
Kathryn Ann Wynn
David Andrew Young

Consultant
Euan Forbes McVicar

Associates
Fiona Caroline Alexander
Steven James Blane
Neil Alexander Carslaw
Stacey Graham Christie
James Douglas Cran
Andrew James Graham Fleming
James Stuart Gibson
John Mark Gillespie
Dawn Elizabeth Houston
Yasmin Hunter
Pamela Laird
Natalie Durie Manson
Mhairi Daniella Mival
Rosanne Dorothy Ogden
Rachel Jane Oliphant
Christopher Owens

Mark Iain Passant
James Alexander Rice
Graeme Stuart Stapleton
Vivien Ailsa Roberta Welsh
Laura Anne Wilson
Gillian Christine Woodward

Solicitor
Timothy Daniel Dale

Employees
Madeleine Barratt
Holly Margaret Brannan
David James Bryden
George Alexander Campbell
Hamish William Gordon Campbell
Lucy Mary Chambers
Rebecca Susan Clark
Peter Healy Miller Clelland
Rachel Jane Coleman
Eilidh Jane Collins
Sarah Anne Combe
Andrew John Young Crichton
Laura Margaret Crilly
Claudia Catherine Anne Dean
Michael John Duffy
Howat Douglas Duncan
Scott George Duncan
Arlene Margaret Eves
James Alexander Ferguson
Fiona Iona Heather Fingland
Lauren Margaret Fowler
Kirsty Gallacher
Alexandra Jane Gibb
Pamela Marie Gilmour
Brian John Grierson
Joanne Louise Isobel Harrison
Kenneth Thomas Hill
David Andrew Jeffries
Jasmine Johnson
Emma Mary Johnston
Jonathan Candlish Kirkwood
Carolyn Jane Lang
Lucy Emma Lawrie
Rachel Anne Leggett
Gemma Hope Lennie
Joanne Kelly McIntosh
Lyndsey Christina Elizabeth Mitchell
Scott Andrew Moir
Robert Angus Morrison
Poppy Elisabeth Mulligan
Sarah Lucy Muncer
Sarah Helen Munro
Kathryn Melissa O'Brien
Alexandra Janey O'Mara
Kyung Jae Park
Alison Kathryn Rankine
Fraser George James Simpson
Joanna Judith Anderson Taylor
James Douglas William Todd
Charles Alastair Walls
Adriana Zdravkova Watt
Jessica Grace Weir
Alistair Kerr Wood
Wenzhuo Xia

PINSENT MASONS LLP
Third Floor, Quay 2, 139 Fountainbridge,
Edinburgh EH3 9QG
Tel: (0131) 2250000
Fax: (0131) 2250099
Web: www.pinsentmasons.com
Categories of Work
Adjudication
Advice the elderly & powers of attorney
Agriculture and estates
Agriculture, crofting and fishing
Alternative dispute resolution
Alternative investment market
Banking & finance
Betting & gaming
Charities
Children
Civil court work
Commercial litigation
Commercial property
Competition
Construction
Contract & property disputes
Copyright, trade marks and design
Corporate tax
Criminal court work
Data protection
Debt
Debt adjusting and debt counselling
Debt administration
Debt collecting
Debt recovery, insolvency, bankruptcy
Disability
Discrimination
Education
Employment
Employment law
Environment
Environment (Business Premises)
EU / international
Family and divorce
Family business advice
Fishing
Freedom of information
Health
Health and safety
Housing
Human rights
Immigration and asylum
Insolvency & corporate recovery
Insurance
IT and intellectual property
Joint venture
Landlord & tenant
Liquor licensing
Local government
Media and entertainment
Medical negligence – defender
Medical negligence – claimant
Mental health
Mergers and acquisitions
Mining
Oil & gas

Parliamentary
Pensions (Company)
Pensions (Employment)
Personal injury
Personal injury – defender
Planning
Planning (Business Premises)
Power and utilities
Private equity
Professional negligence
Projects
Property litigation
Public finance initiative
Public sector
Residential property
Road traffic
Shipping
SME business advice
Software licensing
Sport
Telecoms
Transport
Unit Trusts, OEICs and investment trusts
Wills, executries and trusts
Employee
Lindsay Edwards

PLEXUS LAW LLP
Exchange Place 2, 5 Semple Street, Edinburgh
EH3 8BL
Tel: (0131) 3229 250
Web: www.plexuslaw.co.uk
Categories of Work
Adjudication
Civil court work
Commercial litigation
Criminal court work
Health and safety
Insurance
Medical negligence – defender
Medical negligence – claimant
Personal injury
Personal injury – defender
Professional negligence
Property litigation
Residential property
Road traffic
Partners
Calum Andrew Mathieson
Cameron John McNaught
Associates
Julie Fisher
Stuart John Mackie
Employees
John Barrie
Victoria Anne Howatson
Erica Margaret Jones
James Peden
Amy Martha Riley
Laurie Anne Traynor

JOHN PRYDE, SSC   ...nburgh EH3 9AR
1A Grindlay Street
Tel: (0131) 2?

► **Edinburgh** continued

Fax: (0131) 2202170
E-mail: jmccoll@hotmail.co.uk
Categories of Work
Criminal court work
Criminal legal aid
Partner
Jacqueline Grace McColl
Employees
Daniel Graham Cameron
Christopher Mark Fehilly
Mark Stephen Hutchison

PURDIE & CO LTD
69 Haymarket Terrace, Edinburgh EH12 5HD
Tel: (0131) 3467240
Fax: (0131) 3467707
DX: 557300 EDINBURGH 60
E-mail: struan@purdiesolicitors.co.uk
Web: www.purdiesolicitors.co.uk
Categories of Work
Advice the elderly & powers of attorney
Agriculture, crofting and fishing
Charities
Commercial property
Parliamentary
Residential property
Wills, executries and trusts
Directors
Bruce Cameron Beveridge
Alexander Struan Douglas

QUILL LEGAL
Hudson House, 8 Albany Street, Edinburgh
EH1 3QB
Tel: (0131) 5641044
E-mail: kay@quilllegal.co.uk
Categories of Work
Advice the elderly & powers of attorney
Wills, executries and trusts
Partner
Kathryn Mary Blaikie

LISA RAE & CO COURT SOLICITORS
16 Forth Street, Edinburgh EH1 3LH
Tel: (0131) 5503716
Fax: (0131) 5503701
E-mail: lr@lisaraeandco.co.uk
Web: www.lisaraelaw.com
Categories of Work
Adoption
Advice the elderly & powers of attorney
Children
Childrens
Civil court work
Civil legal aid
Criminal court work
Education legal aid
Family and dir
Mental health
Partner
Lisa Jane Rae

Employees
Donde Ba Thiam
Aim e Lindsey Tulloch

RAE, REID & STEPHEN WS
Stanhope House, 12 Stanhope Place,
Edinburgh EH12 5HH
Tel: (0131) 337 0899
Fax: (0131) 346 8290
DX: 557304 EDINBURGH 60
E-mail: peter@raereidstephen.co.uk
Web: www.raereidstephen.co.uk
Categories of Work
Adoption
Advice the elderly & powers of attorney
Agriculture, crofting and fishing
Commercial property
Contract & property disputes
Family and divorce
Landlord & tenant
Residential property
Wills, executries and trusts
Partner
Peter Desmond Jonathan Stephen

RED LETTER LAW LIMITED
Ground Floor, 11-15 Thistle Street, Edinburgh
EH2 1DF
Tel: (07712) 052834
Web: www.redletterlaw.co.uk
Categories of Work
Family business advice
Joint venture
Mergers and acquisitions
Private equity
SME business advice
Director
Rona Marion Dennison Sharp

RENEW LEGAL LIMITED
Exchange Place 2, 5 Semple Street, Edinburgh
EH3 8BL
Web: www.renewlegal.com
Categories of Work
Commercial property
Landlord & tenant
Residential property
Director
Karen Elizabeth Shaw

RICHMOND NOMINEES LIMITED
54-66 Frederick Street, Edinburgh EH2 1LS
Tel: (0131) 2001200

**ROAD TRAFFIC ACCIDENT LAW (SCOTLAND)
LLP**
16-20 Castle Street, Edinburgh EH2 3AT
Tel: (01721) 728238
Categories of Work
Civil court work
Personal injury
Professional negligence
Road traffic
Sport

ROAD TRAFFIC ACCIDENT LAW (SCOTLAND) LLP

83 Princes Street, Edinburgh EH2 2ER
Tel: (01721) 728238
Categories of Work
Civil court work
Personal injury
Professional negligence
Road traffic
Sport

ROONEY NIMMO LIMITED

8 Walker Street, Edinburgh EH3 7LA
Tel: (0131) 220 9570
E-mail: www.rooneynimmo.com
Categories of Work
Agriculture, crofting and fishing
Banking & finance
Competition
Copyright, trade marks and design
Data protection
Debt recovery, insolvency, bankruptcy
Disability
Discrimination
Employment
Employment law
Environment
EU / international
Family business advice
Fishing
Freedom of information
Insolvency & corporate recovery
Insurance
IT and intellectual property
Joint venture
Local government
Media and entertainment
Mergers and acquisitions
Oil & gas
Power and utilities
Private equity
Projects
Public finance initiative
Public sector
Shipping
SME business advice
Software licensing
Telecoms
Transport
Unit Trusts, OEICs and investment trusts
Directors
Grant Euan Turner Docherty
Thomas William John Nimmo
Dawn Elizabeth Robertson
Consultant
Neil Robert Anderson

RSC SOLICITORS

1A Hill Street, Edinburgh EH2 3JP
Tel: (0131) 2207430
Fax: (0131) 2257582
DX: ED587 EDINBURGH
E-mail: csimpson@rscsolicitors.co.uk

Categories of Work
Adoption
Children
Civil court work
Civil legal aid
Criminal court work
Criminal legal aid
Debt
Debt collecting
Debt recovery, insolvency, bankruptcy
Family and divorce
Partners
Murray Stephen Robertson
Colin Mackie Simpson

RS LEGAL SERVICES LIMITED

145 Great Junction Street, Edinburgh EH6 5LG
Tel: (0131) 2026552
E-mail: office@moreandcompany.com

GRAEME RUNCIE & CO

12 South Charlotte Street, Edinburgh EH2 4AX
Tel: (07957) 554958
Fax: (0131) 2288999
Categories of Work
Criminal court work
Criminal legal aid
Partner
Graeme George Runcie

RUSSEL + AITKEN EDINBURGH LLP

27 Rutland Square, Edinburgh EH1 2BU
Tel: (0131) 2285500
Fax: (0131) 4607333
E-mail: enquiries@russelaitken-edinburgh.com
Web: www.russelaitken-edinburgh.com
Categories of Work
Advice the elderly & powers of attorney
Agriculture and estates
Civil court work
Commercial litigation
Debt
Debt collecting
Medical negligence – claimant
Personal injury
Professional negligence
Residential property
Road traffic
Wills, executries and trusts
Partners
Alan Hugh Jones
Dianne Elizabeth Paterson
Associate
Emma Louise Parris
Employees
Michelle Marie McManus
Kirsty MacLeod Sinclair

SAYER BURNETT

43-45 Circus Lane, Edinburgh EH3 6SU
Tel: (0131) 2255567
Fax: (0131) 2253300
DX: ED632 EDINBURGH
E-mail: cs@sayerburnett.com

▶ **Edinburgh continued**

Categories of Work
Advice the elderly & powers of attorney
Agriculture and estates
Agriculture, crofting and fishing
Landlord & tenant
Residential property
Wills, executices and trusts
Partner
Christopher John Sayer

JOHN SCOTT QC
SSC Library, Parliament House, Edinburgh
EH1 1RF
Tel: (07779) 328656
E-mail: admin@johnscottqc.co.uk
Categories of Work
Criminal court work
Criminal legal aid
Human rights
Partner
John Dominic Scott

SHEPHERD AND WEDDERBURN LLP
1 Exchange Crescent, Conference Square,
Edinburgh EH3 8UL
Tel: (0131) 2289900
Fax: (0131) 2289900
DX: 551971 EDINBURGH 53
E-mail: info@shepwedd.com
Web: www.shepwedd.co.uk
Categories of Work
Adjudication
Adoption
Advice the elderly & powers of attorney
Agriculture and estates
Agriculture, crofting and fishing
Alternative dispute resolution
Alternative investment market
Banking & finance
Betting & gaming
Charities
Civil court work
Commercial litigation
Commercial property
Competition
Construction
Consumer credit
Contract & property disputes
Copyright, trade marks and design
Corporate tax
Credit brokerage
Data protection
Debt
Debt adjusting and debt counselling
Debt administration
Debt collecting
Debt recovery, insolvency, bankruptcy
Disability
Discrimination
Education
Employment
Employment law

Environment
Environment (Business Premises)
EU / international
Family business advice
Fishing
Freedom of information
Health
Health and safety
Housing
Human rights
Immigration and asylum
Insolvency & corporate recovery
Insurance
IT and intellectual property
Joint venture
Landlord & tenant
Liquor licensing
Local government
Media and entertainment
Medical negligence – defender
Medical negligence – claimant
Mergers and acquisitions
Mining
Oil & gas
Parliamentary
Pensions (Company)
Pensions (Employment)
Personal injury
Personal injury – defender
Personal tax
Planning
Planning (Business Premises)
Power and utilities
Private equity
Professional negligence
Projects
Property litigation
Provision of credit information services
Public finance initiative
Public sector
Residential property
Road traffic
Shipping
SME business advice
Software licensing
Sport
Telecoms
Transport
Unit Trusts, OEICs and investment trusts
Wills, executices and trusts
Partners
David John William Anderson
Colin John Archibald
Andrew John Blain
Elaine Nicola Brailsford
Fiona Murray Buchanan
Paul Haining Carlyle
Gillian Anne Carty
Kevin John Clancy
Stephen David Colliston
Paul Robert Alexander Donald
Gordon Harry Downie
Iain Kerr Drummond

Clare Elizabeth Foster
Stephen John Gibb
Stuart Henry Greenwood
Colin William Innes
Andrew Mackenzie Kinnes
Louisa Stewart Knox
Richard Dunbar Leslie
John Swanson MacKenzie
Neil John Maclean
Ewan MacLeod
Anthony Vincent McEwan
Christopher Paul McGill
Euan Alasdair McLeod
Stephen James Miller
David George Mitchell
John Morrison
Euan Murray
Edwin Andrew Mustard
Gareth Robert Parry
Hamish Andrew Patrick
Matthew Phillip
Scott Paul Ritchie
Malcolm Hamilton Rust
Caroline Falconer Shand
Nigel Sievwright
Douglas Cassie Sinclair
Lauren Elizabeth Thomson
Moray Ewan Jacks Thomson
Elaine Margaret Todd
Stephen Andrew Trombala
Richard Jon Turnbull
Iain Andrew Fraser Wishart

Consultants
John Macrae Caldwell
James Alexander Dobie
Andrew Neville Holehouse
Greig Honeyman
Deborah Miller
Peter Misselbrook
Alison Jayne White

Associates
Peter James Alderdice
Andrew Neil Cowan
Natasha Durkin
Fiona Elizabeth Foster
Thomas Philip Harris
Gregor Robert Hayworth
Richard Lloyd Jones
David William Lewis
Rhona Ann McGregor
Ian Richard Soppitt
Ann Eileen Atkinson Stewart
John Vassiliou

Employees
Lisa Jane Alexander
Lisa Ambrus
Alasdair Forrest Anderson
Marion Flora Celia Asplin
Anna Sophie Bailey
Daniel Clark Bain
Lynn Jennifer Beaumont
Heather Christina Bird
Kenna Charlotte Bisset

Alison Blair
Daniel Stuart Boynton
Gillian May Buchanan
Nathaniel Thomas Buckingham
James Edward Bulpitt
Euan Colin Campbell
Neil Colin Campbell
Christopher Louis Clark
Ian Crombie
Emma Christian Davidson
Timothy John Davidson
Tara Davison
Emma Mary De Sailly
Eilidh May Dobson
Carly Suzanne Duckett
Siobhan Dunphy
James Alexander Fair
Richard Alexander Farquhar
Lauren Finlay
Kathryn Margaret Fitzpatrick
Roderick Watson McDougal Forgie
Jack Alexander Freeland
Kara Gallagher
Eleanor Rachel Gannon
Ross Balfour Gibson
Aileen Elizabeth Gordon
Emma Fiona Helen Guthrie
Kirsty Sinclair Headden
Vikki Sara Henderson
Stephanie Frances Hepburn
Leigh Anne Herd
Sarah Charlotte Holmes
Natasha Louise Houghton
Georgina Mary Johnston
Kristina Orianne Jones
Alistair James Kennedy
Fiona Margaret Mary Kennedy
Suzanne Lee Knowles
Ruairidh James McIlroy Leishman
Sarah Victoria Leslie
Marion Joyce MacDonald
Iain Lewis Mackay
Magdalena MacLean
Catherine Aileen MacRae
Jessica Amy Maskrey
Liam Alexander McCabe
Justine Hannah McCluskey
Hannah Rebecca McFadden
Thomas Kerr McFarlane
Nicole Anne McGarty
Caroline Alys McGregor
Ella Lois McIntosh-Farrelly
Kirsten McKinnon
Melanie Alicia McLachlan
Keith Anthony McLaren
Ashley Elizabeth McLean
Laura McMillan
Katherine Louise McNab
Harriet Ann McRae
Corin Benedict Monaghan Metcalfe
Jane Mill
Jacqueline Hazel Moore
Gwen Rachel Napier

▶ **Edinburgh** *continued*

Rebecca Kirstine Nicholson
Harry Douglas Oliff
Daniel Stephen Parcell
Emma Barbara Paton
Jennifer Paton
Chiara Pieri
Aimee Pratt
Gregor James Lind Pringle
Emma Jane Read
Laura Katherine Rennie
Alison Mary Rochester
Alyson Anne Shaw
Christina Sinclair
Agata Maria Starczewska
Hannah Louise Swinton
Rachael Stewart Thomson
John Patrick Townsend
Emily Clare Wallace
Serena Evelyn Weir
Sean Mark White
Laura Jayne Whyte

SHOOSMITHS

2nd Floor North, Saltire Court, Edinburgh
EH1 2EN
Tel: (03700) 868000
Fax: (0131) 270 8008
E-mail:
accountspayablequerysection@schoosmiths.co.
uk

Categories of Work
Alternative dispute resolution
Banking & finance
Civil court work
Commercial litigation
Commercial property
Construction
Consumer credit
Contract & property disputes
Credit brokerage
Debt
Debt collecting
Debt recovery, insolvency, bankruptcy
Discrimination
Employment
Employment law
Environment
Environment (Business Premises)
Housing
Human rights
Immigration and asylum
Insolvency & corporate recovery
IT and intellectual property
Joint venture
Landlord & tenant
Local government
Mergers and acquisitions
Oil & gas
Parliamentary
Pensions (Company)
Pensions (Employment)
Personal injury – defender

Planning
Planning (Business Premises)
Power and utilities
Private equity
Professional negligence
Projects
Property litigation
Public sector
Residential property
SME business advice
Social housing
Partners
Stuart Alexander Clubb
Sheelagh Cooley
Andrew Joseph Foyle
Alison Mary Gilson
Fraser Jon Mitchell
Robin Hamish George Mitchell
Kim Suzanne Pattullo
Janette Speed
Associates
Courtney Margaret Scott Clelland
Victoria Simpson
Grace Helen Watson
Gillian Wood
Employees
Kirsten Joanne Belk
Kay Cuthbertson
Liana Di Ciacca
John William Dunlop
Samantha Jane Hamilton Mackie
Rachael Ann McCallum
Stuart Ritchie Murray
Gillian Margaret Ralph
Amanda Lindsay Soppitt
Eliza Augusta Stubing
Benjamin Thomas Zielinski

SIM LEGAL LIMITED

64a Cumberland Street, Edinburgh EH3 6RE
Tel: (07449) 339046
E-mail: philip@simlegal.co.uk
Web: www.simlegal.co.uk
Categories of Work
Agriculture and estates
Agriculture, crofting and fishing
Banking & finance
Commercial property
Construction
Contract & property disputes
Environment
Environment (Business Premises)
Family business advice
Housing
Joint venture
Landlord & tenant
Liquor licensing
Planning
Planning (Business Premises)
Power and utilities
Property litigation
Residential property
SME business advice

Transport
Wills, executives and trusts
Director
Philip James George Sim

FRANCES E SIM LTD
3/2 North Werber Road, Edinburgh EH4 1TA
Tel: 7547824773
E-mail: Frances@restitutionltd.co.uk
Categories of Work
Adjudication
Alternative dispute resolution
Banking & finance
Charities
Civil court work
Civil legal aid
Commercial litigation
Commercial property
Contract & property disputes
Landlord & tenant
Professional negligence
Property litigation
SME business advice
Director
Frances Elizabeth Sim

SIMPSON & MARWICK
23 Alva Street, Edinburgh EH2 4PS
Tel: (01224) 606210
Fax: 1224606211
Categories of Work
Adoption
Advice the elderly & powers of attorney
Agriculture and estates
Alternative dispute resolution
Banking & finance
Children
Civil court work
Commercial litigation
Commercial property
Consumer credit
Contract & property disputes
Debt
Debt collecting
Debt recovery, insolvency, bankruptcy
Disability
Discrimination
Employment
Employment law
EU / international
Family and divorce
Housing
Insolvency & corporate recovery
Insurance
Landlord & tenant
Local government
Medical negligence – claimant
Personal injury
Professional negligence
Property litigation
Public sector
Residential property
Road traffic
Wills, executives and trusts

Directors
David Michael Coutts
Robert Allan Fife
Associates
Suzanne Chitty
Georgina Kit Yin Li
Employees
Moira Alexandra Lauder Johnston
Katherine Ann Jean MacDonald

SINCLAIRS
207 Pleasance, Edinburgh EH8 9RU
Tel: (0131) 662 4205
E-mail: admin@sinclairscdl.co.uk
Categories of Work
Criminal court work
Criminal legal aid
Partners
George Bruce Henry
James Philip Martin Moore

SKO FAMILY LAW SPECIALISTS LLP
18 George Street, Edinburgh EH2 2PF
Tel: (0131) 3226669
Fax: (0131) 2258803
E-mail: info@sko-family.co.uk
Web: www.sko-family.co.uk
Categories of Work
Adoption
Advice the elderly & powers of attorney
Alternative dispute resolution
Children
Childrens
Civil court work
Commercial litigation
Education
Family and divorce
Family business advice
Partners
Alison Elizabeth Redpath Edmondson
Robert Lister Gilmour
Rachael Joy Christina Kelsey
Susan Margaret Oswald
Associate
Claire Christie
Employees
Ewan Mackenzie Campbell
Seonaid Claire Cochrane
Roisin Elizabeth Kerr
Catriona Ann Laidlaw
Caroline Millar
Stephanie Nicole Smith

SLATER AND GORDON SCOTLAND LIMITED
1 Lochrin Square, 92-98 Foutainbridge,
Edinburgh EH3 9QA
Tel: (0131) 7184150
Fax: (0131) 2203386
Web: www.slatergordon.co.uk
Categories of Work
Civil court work
Civil legal aid
Criminal court work
Insurance

▶ *Edinburgh continued*

Medical negligence – claimant
Personal injury
Professional negligence
Road traffic
Director
Alasdair Stuart Cochran
Associates
Andrew Duncan Bird
Elaine McCulloch
Sarah Ann McWhirter
Employees
Charlotte Naomi McTavish
Claire Elizabeth Paterson
Cheryl Stewart Porter
Leigh Stygal

SMART PROPERTY SALES
1 St. Colme Street, Edinburgh EH3 6AA
Tel: (0131) 2208218
Categories of Work
Civil legal aid
Commercial property
Public sector
Residential property
Social housing

SPENCER WEST SCO LIMITED
57-59 Bread Street, Edinburgh EH3 9AH
Categories of Work
Adjudication
Alternative dispute resolution
Banking & finance
Commercial litigation
Construction
Contract & property disputes
Insolvency & corporate recovery
IT and intellectual property
Oil & gas
Power and utilities
Projects
Property litigation
Public sector
Transport
Director
Jonathan James Christian More
Employee
David Ewan Morton

STARLING LAWYERS LIMITED
8 Albany Street, Edinburgh EH1 3QB
Tel: (0131) 2857499
Categories of Work
Civil court work
Civil legal aid
Medical negligence – claimant
Mental health
Personal injury
Road traffic
Director
Hilary Anne Steele

STEWART AND O'NEILL DEFENCE LIMITED
74 Rose Street, North Lane, Edinburgh
EH2 3DX

Tel: (0131) 225 2900
E-mail: office@stewartandoneill.co.uk
Categories of Work
Criminal court work
Criminal legal aid
Directors
Peter Alexander O'Neill
James Andrew Stewart
Employee
Nicola Haston

STEWART LEGAL
Hudson House, 8 Albany Street, Edinburgh
EH1 3QB
Tel: (0131) 2352426
E-mail: info@stewartlegal.co.uk
Categories of Work
Civil court work
Commercial litigation
Landlord & tenant
Medical negligence – claimant
Personal injury
Professional negligence
Road traffic
Partner
Neil Iain Stewart

THOMAS H.G. STEWART
41 Barclay Place, Bruntsfield, Edinburgh
EH10 4HW
Tel: (0131) 2294939
Fax: (0131) 656 0689
DX: ED434 EDINBURGH
E-mail: tom@thomashgstewart.co.uk
Web: www.thomashgstewart.co.uk
Categories of Work
Advice the elderly & powers of attorney
Commercial property
Family business advice
Landlord & tenant
Residential property
Wills, executives and trusts
Partner
Thomas Henry Gilmour Stewart
Associate
Fiona Robertson Mason

KATHLEEN STEWART, WS
13 Alva Street, Edinburgh EH2 4PH
Tel: (0131) 2259181
Fax: (0131) 2258001
E-mail: Kathleen@katws.co.uk
Categories of Work
Banking & finance
Employment
Employment law
Family business advice
IT and intellectual property
Joint venture
Mergers and acquisitions
Private equity
SME business advice
Partner
Kathleen Margaret Stewart

STUART & CO
16 Ravelston House Park, Edinburgh EH4 3LU
Tel: (0845) 056 3958
Categories of Work
Betting & gaming
Commercial property
Contract & property disputes
Copyright, trade marks and design
Data protection
EU / international
Freedom of information
IT and intellectual property
Joint venture
Landlord & tenant
Media and entertainment
Mergers and acquisitions
SME business advice
Software licensing
Sport
Telecoms

A D STUART & CO. LIMITED
16 Ravelston House Park, Edinburgh EH4 3LU
Tel: (0845) 056 3958
E-mail: contact@stuart-co.com
Web: www.stuart-co.com
Categories of Work
Betting & gaming
Commercial property
Contract & property disputes
Copyright, trade marks and design
Data protection
EU / international
Freedom of information
IT and intellectual property
Joint venture
Landlord & tenant
Media and entertainment
Mergers and acquisitions
SME business advice
Software licensing
Sport
Telecoms
Director
Alan Davidson Stuart
Consultant
Mark Crawford Lawson
Employee
Aimee Christine Stuart

STUART & STUART
25 Rutland Street, Edinburgh EH1 2RN
Tel: (0131) 2286449
Fax: (0131) 2296987
DX: ED54 EDINBURGH
E-mail: mailbox@stuartandstuart.co.uk
Web: www.stuartandstuart.co.uk
Categories of Work
Advice the elderly & powers of attorney
Agriculture and estates
Alternative dispute resolution
Civil court work
Commercial property
Family and divorce

Immigration and asylum
Landlord & tenant
Liquor licensing
Mental health
Residential property
Unit Trusts, OEICs and investment trusts
Wills, executries and trusts
Solicitor
Angela Agrawal
Partners
Christopher James Anderson
Emma Ashley Horne
Kenneth Corson Lauder
John Alexander MacKenzie
Fergus Stewart Macmillan
Consultant
Joseph Gordon Cameron
Employees
James Arthur Brogan
Hannah Louise Fitzgibbon
Carlene Louise Gibson

STURROCK, ARMSTRONG & THOMSON
7a Dundas Street, Edinburgh EH3 6QG
Tel: (0131) 5560159
Fax: (0131) 5562079
DX: ED109 EDINBURGH 1
E-mail: ad@satsolicitors.co.uk
Web: www.satsolicitors.co.uk
Categories of Work
Advice the elderly & powers of attorney
Charities
Commercial property
Immigration and asylum
Landlord & tenant
Residential property
SME business advice
Wills, executries and trusts
Partners
Alan James Davidson
Nicola Kay Gibson
Leonard John Thomson

SW (SCOTLAND) GROUP LIMITED
5-10 Dock Place, Edinburgh EH6 6LU

SW (SCOTLAND) HOLDINGS LIMITED
5-10 Dock Place, Edinburgh EH6 6LU
Tel: (0131) 5557055

PAUL TAYLOR FAMILY & CIVIL LAW LIMITED
8 Albany Street, Edinburgh EH1 3QB
Tel: (0131) 5500414
E-mail: pt@ptlaw.co.uk
Categories of Work
Children
Civil court work
Civil legal aid
Commercial litigation
Education
Family and divorce
Housing
Human rights
Director
Paul Taylor

► *Edinburgh continued*

TEMPLE & CO SOLICITORS LTD
1 St. Colme Street, Edinburgh EH3 6AA
Tel: (0131) 2208218
Fax: (0131) 202 0647
E-mail: nt@templeandco.co.uk
Categories of Work
Civil legal aid
Commercial property
Public sector
Residential property
Social housing
Director
Natasha Rosaline Temple

THOMPSONS
16-20 Castle Street, Edinburgh EH2 3AT
Tel: (0131) 2254297
Fax: (0131) 2259591
DX: ED101 EDINBURGH
E-mail: mail@thompsons-scotland.co.uk
Web: www.thompsons-scotland.co.uk
Categories of Work
Adoption
Advice the elderly & powers of attorney
Agriculture and estates
Alternative dispute resolution
Charities
Children
Childrens
Civil court work
Civil legal aid
Commercial litigation
Consumer credit
Criminal court work
Disability
Discrimination
Education
Employment
Employment law
Family and divorce
Health
Health and safety
Human rights
Immigration and asylum
Insurance
Medical negligence – claimant
Personal injury
Personal injury – defender
Professional negligence
Residential property
Road traffic
Social housing
Wills, executries and trusts
Partners
Jayne Crawford
Derek Robert McLean
Glen Archibald Millar
Associates
Richard Alan Singer
Stewart George White

Employees
Emma Kristina Nathalie Axelsson
Alan Calderwood
Robert Coutts Cranston
Paul Michael Deans
Clare Marie McDairmant
Catherine Frances McGarrell
Jodie Ashleigh Robertson
Corinne Louise Skelton
Janine Marie Slaven

THORLEY STEPHENSON LTD
20 Hopetoun Street, Edinburgh EH7 4GH
Tel: (0131) 5569599
Fax: (0131) 5561321
DX: ED604 EDINBURGH
E-mail: admin@thorleystephenson.com
Categories of Work
Adoption
Advice the elderly & powers of attorney
Alternative dispute resolution
Benefit advice
Children
Childrens
Civil court work
Civil legal aid
Contract & property disputes
Criminal court work
Criminal legal aid
Debt
Debt management
Education
Family and divorce
Health and safety
Human rights
Mental health
Road traffic
Social housing
Directors
Nicole Conroy
Nyree Mary Conway
Euan Gosney
David Storrie
Mark Richard Thorley
Consultants
James Douglas Keegan
James Patrick Stephenson
Employees
Eilidh Margaret Coltman
Nicola Margaret Dorina Hadden
Emma Margaret Martin
Emma Jane Elizabeth Murdoch
Lesley-Ann McCluskie Turner

THORNTONS LAW LLP
City Point, 3rd Floor, 65 Haymarket Terrace,
Edinburgh EH12 5HD
Tel: (0131) 2258705
Fax: (0131) 2267077
E-mail: edinburgh@thorntons-law.co.uk
Web: www.thorntons-law.co.uk
Categories of Work
Adjudication
Adoption

Advice the elderly & powers of attorney
Agriculture and estates
Agriculture, crofting and fishing
Alternative dispute resolution
Alternative investment market
Banking & finance
Benefit advice
Betting & gaming
Charities
Children
Childrens
Civil court work
Civil legal aid
Commercial litigation
Commercial property
Competition
Construction
Consumer credit
Contract & property disputes
Copyright, trade marks and design
Corporate tax
Credit brokerage
Criminal court work
Criminal legal aid
Data protection
Debt
Debt adjusting and debt counselling
Debt administration
Debt collecting
Debt recovery, insolvency, bankruptcy
Disability
Discrimination
Education
Employment
Employment law
Environment
Environment (Business Premises)
EU / international
Family and divorce
Family business advice
Fishing
Freedom of information
Health
Health and safety
Housing
Human rights
Immigration and asylum
Insolvency & corporate recovery
Insurance
IT and intellectual property
Joint venture
Landlord & tenant
Liquor licensing
Local government
Media and entertainment
Medical negligence – defender
Medical negligence – claimant
Mental health
Mergers and acquisitions
Oil & gas
Parliamentary
Pensions (Company)
Pensions (Employment)

Personal injury
Personal injury – defender
Personal tax
Planning
Planning (Business Premises)
Power and utilities
Private equity
Professional negligence
Projects
Property litigation
Public sector
Residential property
Road traffic
SME business advice
Social housing
Software licensing
Sport
Telecoms
Unit Trusts, OEICs and investment trusts
Wills, executries and trusts

Partners
Michelle Adam
Hugo John Allan
Morna Jane Coutts
Brian Arthur Fairgrieve
Ian Karlheinz Fraser
David John Jennings
Andrew Kirkhope
Kenneth Richard Mackay
Clare Susan Macpherson
Alexander Hugh McCreath
Ann Lucy Metcalf
Catriona Margaret Binnie Miller
John Christian Phillips
Gary George Thomas

Consultants
Susan Jane Calder
Robin Keith Valentine

Associates
Neil Andrew Darling
Nicholas Thornton Hooke
Kathleen-Erin Lawson
Gurjit Singh Pall
Alan George Thomson
Andrew James Wallace

Employees
Sabihah Ahmed
Iain Alexander Boyd
Jennifer Susan Broatch
Roisin Colleen Donnelly
Hannah Jean Dossett
Michaela Dougan
Scott Simpson Douglas
Robin John Muir Dunlop
Neil Beattie Manzie Falconer
Lauren Jane Marr Fettes
Simon Christopher Holbrey
Kirsty Alison Lynch
Megan Maclean
Cameron Robert Mathieson
Victoria Lindsay Margaret McLaren
Lydia Papandrianou
Charlotte May Parker-Smith

▶ **Edinburgh continued**

Emily Anna Rebecca Eliza Pepin
David Perdikou
Thea Elizabeth Pock
Andrew Kevin Sergeant
Victoria Catherine Wright

TIDMAN LEGAL LIMITED

6 St. Colme Street, Edinburgh EH3 6AD
Tel: (0131) 5576450
E-mail: oliver@tidmanlegal.com
Web: www.tidmanlegal.com
Categories of Work
Alternative dispute resolution
Betting & gaming
Commercial litigation
Copyright, trade marks and design
Data protection
Family business advice
Freedom of information
IT and intellectual property
Media and entertainment
SME business advice
Software licensing
Sport
Telecoms
Director
Oliver James Andrew Tidman

TLT LLP

3rd Floor, Hobart House, 80 Hanover Street,
Edinburgh EH2 1EL
Tel: (0333) 006 0500
Fax: (0333) 006 0511
Web: www.tltsolicitors.com
Categories of Work
Adjudication
Agriculture and estates
Alternative dispute resolution
Alternative investment market
Banking & finance
Betting & gaming
Civil court work
Commercial litigation
Commercial property
Construction
Consumer credit
Contract & property disputes
Debt
Debt adjusting and debt counselling
Debt administration
Debt collecting
Debt recovery, insolvency, bankruptcy
Disability
Discrimination
Education
Employment
Employment law
Environment
Environment (Business Premises)
EU / international
Family and divorce
Freedom of information

Health
Housing
Immigration and asylum
Insolvency & corporate recovery
Joint venture
Landlord & tenant
Liquor licensing
Local government
Medical negligence – defender
Medical negligence – claimant
Mergers and acquisitions
Mining
Parliamentary
Pensions (Employment)
Personal injury
Planning
Planning (Business Premises)
Power and utilities
Professional negligence
Projects
Property litigation
Public finance initiative
Public sector
Residential property
SME business advice
Partner
Anthony Vincent Reynolds
Employee
Niall John Norman Hassard

TLT LLP

369 High Street, Edinburgh EH1 1PW
Tel: (0131) 2207460
Fax: (0131) 2609571
Employee
Peter Andrew McGladrigan

TURCAN CONNELL

Princes Exchange, 1 Earl Grey Street,
Edinburgh EH3 9EE
Tel: (0131) 2288111
Fax: (0131) 2288118
DX: 723300 EDINBURGH 43
E-mail: enquiries@turcanconnell.com
Web: www.turcanconnell.com
Categories of Work
Adoption
Advice the elderly & powers of attorney
Agriculture and estates
Agriculture, crofting and fishing
Alternative dispute resolution
Alternative investment market
Banking & finance
Charities
Children
Childrens
Civil court work
Commercial litigation
Commercial property
Construction
Contract & property disputes
Employment
Employment law
Environment

Environment (Business Premises)
EU / international
Family and divorce
Family business advice
Fishing
Housing
Insolvency & corporate recovery
Joint venture
Landlord & tenant
Medical negligence – claimant
Mental health
Mergers and acquisitions
Mining
Pensions (Employment)
Personal tax
Planning (Business Premises)
Power and utilities
Private equity
Professional negligence
Property litigation
Residential property
SME business advice
Wills, executives and trusts
Assistant
Alexander David Iain Middleton
Partners
Ian Robert Clark
Gillian Crandles
Tom Duguid
Grierson Robert Dunlop
Alexander Kenneth Garden
Graeme Rodger Gass
Louise Margaret Johnston
Michael Anthony Kane
Peter Southern Littlefield
Paul Macaulay
Donald Frank Glendinning MacLeod
Gavin Graham Robert McEwan
Lindsey Ogilvie
David Cameron Ogilvy
Jonathan Mark Robertson
Alistair James Rushworth
John Christopher Phelps Sheldon
Donald William Simpson
Alix Elizabeth Storrie
Niall Stringer
Associates
Paula Anne Arnott
Alastair Buchan Collin
Richard Douglas-Home
Yvonne Elizabeth Littlefield
Rona Margaret Macdonald
Sarah Jane Macleod
David Lonsdale Mowlem
Paul Forrester Smith
Alexander Neil Wilson
Jennifer Younger
Employees
Holly Archibald
Juliet Catriona Louise Barker
Duncan Alan Chambers-Hunter Bauchop
Kirsty Margaret Bell
Amy Ann Benfield

Walter Duncan Biggar
Victoria Brown
Heather Catherine Bruce
Heather Elizabeth Burnett
Hilary Clare Busby
Alexander Dexter James O. R. Critchley
Moyra Lucia Diaz Limaco
Karen Christine Dixon
Hannah Katharina Duguid
Amy Catherine Eakin
Bethan Frances Evans
Graham Fisken
Alexandra Gell
Katherine Elizabeth Gillies
Catherine Joan Guthrie
Scott William Hunter
Sarah Victoria Jackson
Emma Louise Jordan
Jennifer Margaret Macdonald
David Andrew George McBurnie
Lindsay May Elizabeth McCulloch
Lauren Louise McDonach
Fraser Lewis McDonald
Lynne McLaren McElroy
Debbie Anne McIlwraith Cameron
Mark Philip McKeown
Caroline Ilse McMillan
Jamie Fraser McNish
Emma Morrison McWhirter
Sarah Megan Myles
Kirsty Laura Nelson
Andrew Gordon Tynam Nicholson
Joshua William Nutton
Holly Claire O'Hara
Eleanor Boyd Picken
Elaine Mary Proudfoot
Christopher James William Reid
Andrew John Robertson
Andrew William Ross
Adelle Astra Seaton
Catherine Jane Sloan
David Andrew Gordon Smith
Sophie Julia Walker
Alice Shirley Warne
Brynhild Dalsgaard Weihe
Riikka-Liisa Wilkinson
Ciara Jane Wilson
Brian Andrew Woods
Rose Elizabeth Younger

URQUHARTS
16 Heriot Row, Edinburgh EH3 6HR
Tel: (0131) 5562896
Fax: (0131) 5560046
DX: ED206 EDINBURGH
E-mail: enquiries@urquharts.co.uk
Web: www.urquharts.co.uk
Categories of Work
Alternative dispute resolution
Civil court work
Commercial litigation
Commercial property
Construction

▶ **Edinburgh continued**

Contract & property disputes
Environment
Environment (Business Premises)
Joint venture
Landlord & tenant
Mining
Planning
Planning (Business Premises)
Power and utilities
Professional negligence
Property litigation
Residential property
Telecoms
Wills, executries and trusts
Partners
Gillian Stewart Black
Stephen Martin Blane
Alison Murray Grandison
Sara Alicia Smith
Stephen William Webster
Associate
David Alexander Sangster
Employees
Ashley Marshall French
Sharon Gordon
Andrew Colin Graham-Smith
Thea Jo-Ann Doran Jackson

VIALEX WS
Floor 3, 1-4 Atholl Crescent, Edinburgh
EH3 8HA
Tel: (03332) 400 306
E-mail: keith.anderson@vialex.co.uk
Categories of Work
Agriculture, crofting and fishing
Alternative investment market
Banking & finance
Betting & gaming
Charities
Commercial property
Competition
Copyright, trade marks and design
Corporate tax
Data protection
Debt recovery, insolvency, bankruptcy
Employment
Employment law
Environment
EU / international
Family business advice
Freedom of information
Health and safety
Insolvency & corporate recovery
Insurance
IT and intellectual property
Joint venture
Landlord & tenant
Media and entertainment
Mergers and acquisitions
Oil & gas
Pensions (Employment)
Personal tax

Power and utilities
Private equity
Public sector
SME business advice
Software licensing
Sport
Telecoms
Partners
Keith Thomas Anderson
Keith Charles Dinsmore

VMH SOLICITORS
10 South Clerk Street, Edinburgh EH8 9JE
Tel: (0131) 6222626
Web: www.vmh.co.uk
Categories of Work
Advice the elderly & powers of attorney
Residential property
Wills, executries and trusts

VMH SOLICITORS LIMITED
10 South Clerk Street, Edinburgh EH8 9JE
Tel: (0131) 6222626
Fax: (0131) 6222627
DX: 553160 EDINBURGH ST PATRICK SQUARE
E-mail: cmc@vmh.co.uk
Web: www.vmh.co.uk
Categories of Work
Advice the elderly & powers of attorney
Residential property
Wills, executries and trusts
Directors
Robin John Hill
Mary Patricia McFarlane

VMH SOLICITORS LIMITED
43/45 Easter Road, Edinburgh EH7 5PL
Tel: (0131) 6615911
Fax: (0131) 6610193
DX: 551153 EDINBURGH 8
E-mail: accounts@vmh.co.uk
Web: www.vmh.co.uk
Categories of Work
Advice the elderly & powers of attorney
Residential property
Wills, executries and trusts
Directors
Kevin McLuskey
Stacey Louise Wilson
Associate
Michelle Louise Murdoch

WARDLAW STEPHENSON ALLAN
28 Albany Street, Edinburgh EH1 3QH
Tel: (0131) 5578020
Fax: (0131) 5579622
E-mail: admin@wsalawyers.com
Categories of Work
Criminal court work
Criminal legal aid
Human rights
Partners
David William Tait Allan
Mark Alexander Harrower
Mathew James Patrick

Employees
Kevin Paul Connor
Colin Crawford Severin

WARNERS SOLICITORS LLP
176 Portobello High Street, Edinburgh
EH15 1EX
Tel: (0131) 6624747
DX: 553168 EDINBURGH
E-mail: mail@warnersllp.com
Web: www.warnersllp.com
Categories of Work
Advice the elderly & powers of attorney
Banking & finance
Children
Civil court work
Civil legal aid
Commercial property
Criminal legal aid
Employment
Employment law
Family and divorce
Landlord & tenant
Liquor licensing
Medical negligence – claimant
Personal injury
Power and utilities
Professional negligence
Residential property
Road traffic
Wills, executries and trusts

WARNERS SOLICITORS LLP
22 & 24 St. Patrick Square, Edinburgh
EH8 9EY
Tel: (0131) 6624747
Fax: (0131) 6624117
DX: 553168 EDINBURGH
E-mail: mail@warnersllp.com
Web: www.warnersllp.com
Categories of Work
Advice the elderly & powers of attorney
Banking & finance
Children
Civil court work
Civil legal aid
Commercial property
Criminal legal aid
Employment
Employment law
Family and divorce
Landlord & tenant
Liquor licensing
Medical negligence – claimant
Personal injury
Power and utilities
Professional negligence
Residential property
Road traffic
Wills, executries and trusts
Partners
Scott Alexander Brown
George Scott Craig
James Martin MacLachlan

David Jason Scott
Lucy Jane Taggart
Douglas Ian Williamson
Consultant
Craig Scott Innes
Associate
Alison Mary Gordon
Employees
Leigh Gargan
Jazmin Hazel MacPherson
Ellen Frances McWhirter

WARNERS SOLICITORS LLP
247B St. John's Road, Corstorphine, Edinburgh
EH12 7XD
Tel: (0131) 6624747
DX: 553168 EDINBURGH
E-mail: mail@warnersllp.com
Web: www.warnersllp.com
Categories of Work
Advice the elderly & powers of attorney
Banking & finance
Children
Civil court work
Civil legal aid
Commercial property
Criminal legal aid
Employment
Employment law
Family and divorce
Landlord & tenant
Liquor licensing
Medical negligence – claimant
Personal injury
Power and utilities
Professional negligence
Residential property
Road traffic
Wills, executries and trusts

WATERMANS LEGAL LIMITED
5-10 Dock Place, Edinburgh EH6 6LU
Tel: (0131) 4675566
Fax: (0131) 4673344
DX: 550861 LEITH
E-mail: admin@watermans.co.uk
Web: watermanslegal.co.uk
Categories of Work
Adoption
Advice the elderly & powers of attorney
Alternative dispute resolution
Children
Childrens
Civil court work
Civil legal aid
Commercial property
Debt
Debt collecting
Disability
Education
Family and divorce
Health and safety
Human rights
Landlord & tenant

▶ **Edinburgh continued**

Medical negligence – claimant
Mental health
Personal injury
Professional negligence
Residential property
Road traffic
Wills, executives and trusts
Director
Scott Donald David Whyte
Employees
Sarah Isabel Hay
Catherine Dianne Millen
Josef Tierney Strand
Shawn Ross Wood

WATERMANS SOLICITORS LIMITED
5-10 Dock Place, Edinburgh EH6 6LU
Tel: (0131) 5557055
DX: 550855 LEITH
E-mail: admin@watermans.co.uk
Web: www.watermans.co.uk
Categories of Work
Civil court work
Data protection
Debt
Disability
Freedom of information
Health and safety
Medical negligence – claimant
Personal injury
Professional negligence
Road traffic
Employees
Lauren Louise Alexander-Smith
John Paul Dillon
Stacey Louise McDiarmid
Cassandra Maisie Woodger

STEWART WATT & CO.
202 Dalry Road, Edinburgh EH11 2ES
Tel: (0131) 3379692
Fax: (0844) 6825529
DX: ED166 EDINBURGH
E-mail: jennifer@stewartwatt.co.uk
Categories of Work
Advice the elderly & powers of attorney
Commercial property
Employment law
Personal tax
Residential property
Wills, executives and trusts
Partners
Jennifer Mair
Zara Mair

WEIGHTMANS (SCOTLAND) LLP
93 George Street, Edinburgh EH2 3ES
Tel: (0131) 2401200
Web: www.weightmans.com
Categories of Work
Adoption
Agriculture, crofting and fishing
Alternative dispute resolution

Alternative investment market
Banking & finance
Charities
Children
Civil court work
Commercial litigation
Commercial property
Competition
Construction
Consumer credit
Contract & property disputes
Copyright, trade marks and design
Corporate tax
Credit brokerage
Data protection
Debt
Debt adjusting and debt counselling
Debt administration
Debt collecting
Debt recovery, insolvency, bankruptcy
Discrimination
Employment
Employment law
Environment
Environment (Business Premises)
EU / international
Family and divorce
Family business advice
Human rights
Immigration and asylum
Insolvency & corporate recovery
Insurance
IT and intellectual property
Joint venture
Landlord & tenant
Local government
Media and entertainment
Medical negligence – defender
Mergers and acquisitions
Pensions (Company)
Personal injury
Personal injury – defender
Personal tax
Planning (Business Premises)
Power and utilities
Private equity
Professional negligence
Projects
Property litigation
Provision of credit information services
Public finance initiative
Public sector
Road traffic
SME business advice
Sport
Transport
Unit Trusts, OEICs and investment trusts

WILSON MCLEOD
44 St Mary's Street, Edinburgh EH1 1SX
Tel: (0131) 5560055
Fax: (0131) 5588680
DX: ED605 EDINBURGH

E-mail: wilsonmcleod@btconnect.com
Web: www.wilsonmcleod.co.uk
Categories of Work
Criminal court work
Criminal legal aid
Partners
Stuart Graham Carson
Philip John Anthony Templeton
Edward John Wilson
Employees
Elaine Margaret Carson
Gillian Louise Simpson

WILSON WARD LLP
131 Newhaven Road, Edinburgh EH6 4NP
Tel: (0131) 4677550
Fax: (0131) 4677553
DX: 550852 LEITH
E-mail: john@wilsonward.co.uk
Web: www.solicitoredinburgh.co.uk
Categories of Work
Charities
Commercial property
Family business advice
Landlord & tenant
Residential property
SME business advice
Wills, executries and trusts
Partners
John Aloysius Ward
Peter Urquhart Wilson
Employee
Joanne Louise McCann

WINNING & CO
6/18 Wharton Square, Edinburgh EH3 9FJ
Tel: (07957) 095973
E-mail: winningpeter@gmail.com
Categories of Work
Criminal court work
Criminal legal aid
Partner
Peter Winning

WOMBLE BOND DICKINSON (UK) LLP
2 Semple Street, Edinburgh EH3 8BL
Tel: (0345) 415 0000
Categories of Work
Adjudication
Agriculture and estates
Alternative dispute resolution
Alternative investment market
Banking & finance
Civil court work
Commercial litigation
Commercial property
Competition
Construction
Contract & property disputes
Copyright, trade marks and design
Debt recovery, insolvency, bankruptcy
Environment
Environment (Business Premises)
EU / international

Insolvency & corporate recovery
IT and intellectual property
Joint venture
Landlord & tenant
Media and entertainment
Mergers and acquisitions
Oil & gas
Pensions (Company)
Planning
Planning (Business Premises)
Power and utilities
Private equity
Projects
Property litigation
Public finance initiative
Public sector
Shipping
SME business advice
Sport
Transport
Unit Trusts, OEICs and investment trusts
Partners
Richard James Cockburn
Philip Charles Andrew Knight
Paul Mason
Associates
Paul James Kenneth
Ewelina Joanna Kurek
Clare Elizabeth Lamond
Employees
Lisa Dromgoole
Rosie Grace Gollan
Christopher Alan McLauchlan
Jessica Nunes
Nadine Todd

WRIGHT, JOHNSTON & MACKENZIE LLP
The Capital Building, 12/13 St Andrew
Square, Edinburgh EH2 2AF
Tel: (0131) 5241500
Fax: (0131) 5241529
DX: ED26 EDINBURGH
E-mail: enquiries@wjm.co.uk
Web: www.wjm.co.uk
Categories of Work
Adjudication
Adoption
Advice the elderly & powers of attorney
Agriculture and estates
Agriculture, crofting and fishing
Alternative dispute resolution
Alternative investment market
Banking & finance
Betting & gaming
Charities
Children
Childrens
Civil court work
Commercial litigation
Commercial property
Competition
Construction
Consumer credit

► **Edinburgh continued**

Contract & property disputes
Copyright, trade marks and design
Corporate tax
Criminal court work
Data protection
Debt
Debt collecting
Debt recovery, insolvency, bankruptcy
Disability
Discrimination
Education
Employment
Employment law
Environment
Environment (Business Premises)
EU / international
Family and divorce
Family business advice
Fishing
Freedom of information
Health and safety
Housing
Human rights
Insolvency & corporate recovery
Insurance
IT and intellectual property
Joint venture
Landlord & tenant
Liquor licensing
Local government
Media and entertainment
Medical negligence – defender
Medical negligence – claimant
Mergers and acquisitions
Mining
Oil & gas
Parliamentary
Pensions (Company)
Pensions (Employment)
Personal injury
Personal injury – defender
Personal tax
Planning
Planning (Business Premises)
Power and utilities
Private equity
Professional negligence
Projects
Property litigation
Public finance initiative
Public sector
Residential property
Road traffic
SME business advice
Software licensing
Sport
Telecoms
Transport
Unit Trusts, OEICs and investment trusts
Wills, executries and trusts

Partners
Stephen Michael Cotton
Michael James Dewar
Fraser Anthony Brian Gillies
Roderick Alexander Louden Harrison
Kenneth Burnie Long
Nicola Jane Martin
Andrew John Patterson Wilson
Associate
Emma Geraldine Arcari
Employees
Alan Chambers-Hunter Bauchop
Susannah Green
Fergus William Sinclair Hollins
Lyndsey Christine Mackay
Stuart Kevin Donald McDonald
Elizabeth Irene Tainsh
Benjamin Edwin White

YORK TRUSTEES LIMITED
Quartermile Two, 2 Lister Square, Edinburgh
EH3 9GL
Tel: (0131) 2471000

TC YOUNG LLP
Melrose House, 69A George Street, Edinburgh
EH2 2JG
Tel: (0131) 2207660
Fax: (0131) 2207661
DX: ED112 EDINBURGH
Web: www.tcyoung.co.uk
Categories of Work
Adjudication
Adoption
Advice the elderly & powers of attorney
Agriculture and estates
Alternative dispute resolution
Banking & finance
Charities
Children
Childrens
Civil court work
Civil legal aid
Commercial litigation
Commercial property
Construction
Consumer credit
Contract & property disputes
Credit brokerage
Criminal court work
Criminal legal aid
Data protection
Debt
Debt adjusting and debt counselling
Debt administration
Debt collecting
Debt recovery, insolvency, bankruptcy
Disability
Discrimination
Education
Employment
Employment law
Environment
Environment (Business Premises)

Family and divorce
Family business advice
Health and safety
Housing
Human rights
Insolvency & corporate recovery
Joint venture
Landlord & tenant
Mental health
Mergers and acquisitions
Pensions (Employment)
Personal tax
Planning
Planning (Business Premises)
Power and utilities
Private equity
Professional negligence
Projects
Property litigation
Public finance initiative
Public sector
Residential property
Road traffic
SME business advice
Social housing
Sport
Wills, executives and trusts
Partners
Grant Alexander Knight
Vicky Lee Lewis
Alastair Wood McKendrick
Christine Anne Stuart
Associate
George John Scott
Employees
Ian Webster Black
Nina Mary Derrin
Neil Rennie Matheson
Fiona Margaret McGougan
Vivien Margaret Riddell

Elgin

ALLAN, BLACK & MCCASKIE
151 High Street, Elgin IV30 1DX
Tel: (01343) 543355
Fax: (01343) 549667
DX: 520650 ELGIN
E-mail: GF@abmsols.co.uk
Web: www.abmsols.co.uk
Categories of Work
Adoption
Advice the elderly & powers of attorney
Children
Civil court work
Civil legal aid
Commercial property
Criminal court work
Criminal legal aid
Family and divorce
Residential property
Wills, executives and trusts

Partners
Robert Magnus Cruickshank
Lesley Johnston
Iain Ross Maltman
Jaymie Strathdee
Employee
Kevin Gerrard Anderson

LESLEY CLARK & CO LIMITED
The Park House Business Centre, South Street,
Elgin IV30 1JB
Tel: (01343) 553 950
DX: 520677 ELGIN
E-mail: lesleyclark@lesleyclarkandco.com
Web: www.lesleyclarkandco.com
Categories of Work
Adoption
Advice the elderly & powers of attorney
Children
Childrens
Civil court work
Civil legal aid
Commercial litigation
Contract & property disputes
Debt
Family and divorce
Family business advice
Landlord & tenant
Property litigation
Residential property
Wills, executives and trusts
Director
Lesley Helen Clark

COCKBURNS
82 High Street, Elgin IV30 1BL
Tel: (01343) 542684
Fax: (01343) 540024
DX: 520651 ELGIN
E-mail: elgin@cockburns-solicitors.com
Categories of Work
Adoption
Advice the elderly & powers of attorney
Agriculture and estates
Children
Civil court work
Commercial property
Criminal court work
Criminal legal aid
Debt
Debt collecting
Debt recovery, insolvency, bankruptcy
Employment
Employment law
Family and divorce
Landlord & tenant
Medical negligence – claimant
Personal injury
Property litigation
Residential property
Road traffic
Wills, executives and trusts
Partner
David William John Adams

► *Elgin continued*

Employees
Ashleigh Macgregor
Henrietta Edith Matheson Macpherson

GRIGOR & YOUNG LLP

1 North Street, Elgin IV30 1UA
Tel: (01343) 544077
Fax: (01343) 548523
DX: 520656 ELGIN
E-mail: mail@grigor-young.co.uk
Web: www.grigor-young.co.uk
Categories of Work
Adoption
Advice the elderly & powers of attorney
Agriculture and estates
Agriculture, crofting and fishing
Alternative dispute resolution
Benefit advice
Children
Civil court work
Civil legal aid
Commercial property
Contract & property disputes
Debt
Debt adjusting and debt counselling
Debt administration
Debt management
Debt recovery, insolvency, bankruptcy
Disability
Discrimination
Education
Employment
Employment law
Environment
Environment (Business Premises)
Family and divorce
Human rights
Landlord & tenant
Medical negligence – claimant
Mental health
Personal injury
Planning
Planning (Business Premises)
Property litigation
Residential property
Road traffic
Social housing
Wills, executives and trusts
Partners
Peter Melrose Brash
Ann Cruickshank
Richard Alexander Miller
Greg James Robertson
Donna Margaret Skelly
Associates
Cherry Zivia Fairley
Katie Ann Kennedy
Marie Helen Morrison
Lauren Marie Wright
Employees
Rhian-Elin Jones
Kirstie Courtney Reilly

HARPER MACLEOD LLP

The Old Station, Maisondieu Road, Elgin
IV30 1RH
Tel: (01343) 542623
Fax: (01343) 540775
Categories of Work
Adjudication
Adoption
Advice the elderly & powers of attorney
Agriculture and estates
Agriculture, crofting and fishing
Alternative dispute resolution
Alternative investment market
Banking & finance
Betting & gaming
Charities
Children
Childrens
Civil court work
Civil legal aid
Commercial litigation
Commercial property
Competition
Construction
Consumer credit
Contract & property disputes
Copyright, trade marks and design
Corporate tax
Criminal court work
Criminal legal aid
Data protection
Debt
Debt administration
Debt collecting
Debt recovery, insolvency, bankruptcy
Disability
Discrimination
Education
Employment
Employment law
Environment
Environment (Business Premises)
EU / international
Family and divorce
Family business advice
Fishing
Freedom of information
Health
Health and safety
Housing
Human rights
Immigration and asylum
Insolvency & corporate recovery
Insurance
IT and intellectual property
Joint venture
Landlord & tenant
Liquor licensing
Local government
Media and entertainment
Medical negligence – defender
Medical negligence – claimant
Mental health

Mergers and acquisitions
Mining
Oil & gas
Parliamentary
Pensions (Company)
Pensions (Employment)
Personal injury
Personal injury – defender
Personal tax
Planning
Planning (Business Premises)
Power and utilities
Private equity
Professional negligence
Projects
Property litigation
Public finance initiative
Public sector
Residential property
Road traffic
Shipping
SME business advice
Social housing
Software licensing
Sport
Telecoms
Transport
Unit Trusts, OEICs and investment trusts
Wills, executries and trusts
Partner
Ian Graham Davidson
Associates
Annabelle Louise Gow
Peter Alexander McLuckie

JAMES MCKAY DEFENCE SOLICITORS LIMITED
Criminal Defence Solicitors, 17 High Street,
Elgin IV30 1EQ
Tel: (01343) 556500
Fax: (01343) 556501
DX: 520670 ELGIN
E-mail: info@jamesmckay.uk
Web: www.jamesmckay.uk
Categories of Work
Criminal court work
Criminal legal aid
Director
Brent Robert Wilson Lockie
Employees
Stephen Patrick Carty
Grant Stephen Daglish
Coral Ann Rawcliffe
Ben Thom

GRANT SMITH LAW PRACTICE LIMITED
7 Mayne Road, Elgin IV30 1NY
Tel: (01343) 544466
Fax: (01343) 541999
E-mail: info@grantsmithlaw.co.uk
Web: www.grantsmithlaw.co.uk
Categories of Work
Adoption
Advice the elderly & powers of attorney
Alternative dispute resolution

Children
Childrens
Civil court work
Civil legal aid
Commercial property
Contract & property disputes
Criminal court work
Criminal legal aid
Debt
Debt collecting
Debt recovery, insolvency, bankruptcy
Education
Family and divorce
Landlord & tenant
Mental health
Personal injury
Professional negligence
Property litigation
Residential property
Road traffic
Wills, executries and trusts
Director
Matthew Derek O'Neill

STEWART & MCISAAC
50 High Street, Elgin IV30 1BU
Tel: (01343) 544971
Fax: (01343) 541205
DX: 520657 ELGIN
E-mail: kenny@lexelgin.com
Web: www.stewart-and-mcisaac.co.uk
Categories of Work
Advice the elderly & powers of attorney
Commercial property
Landlord & tenant
Residential property
Wills, executries and trusts
Partner
Kenneth William Coleman Ross

Ellon

ABERDEIN CONSIDINE AND COMPANY
57 Bridge Street, Ellon AB41 9AA
Tel: (01358) 721893
E-mail: ellon@acandco.com
Web: www.acandco.com
Categories of Work
Adjudication
Adoption
Advice the elderly & powers of attorney
Agriculture and estates
Agriculture, crofting and fishing
Alternative dispute resolution
Alternative investment market
Banking & finance
Charities
Children
Childrens
Civil court work
Civil legal aid
Commercial litigation
Commercial property

▶ **Ellon** *continued*

Competition
Construction
Consumer credit
Contract & property disputes
Copyright, trade marks and design
Corporate tax
Credit brokerage
Criminal court work
Criminal legal aid
Data protection
Debt
Debt adjusting and debt counselling
Debt collecting
Debt recovery, insolvency, bankruptcy
Disability
Discrimination
Education
Employment
Employment law
Environment
Environment (Business Premises)
EU / international
Family and divorce
Family business advice
Freedom of information
Health
Health and safety
Human rights
Insolvency & corporate recovery
Insurance
Joint venture
Landlord & tenant
Liquor licensing
Local government
Media and entertainment
Mental health
Mergers and acquisitions
Pensions (Company)
Pensions (Employment)
Personal injury
Personal tax
Planning (Business Premises)
Private equity
Professional negligence
Property litigation
Public finance initiative
Public sector
Residential property
SME business advice
Social housing
Telecoms
Unit Trusts, OEICs and investment trusts
Wills, executries and trusts

GRAY & GRAY LLP
69 Station Road, Ellon AB41 9AR
Tel: (01358) 724455
Fax: (01779) 470741
E-mail: accounts@graygraylaw.com
Web: www.grayandgraysolicitors.com
Categories of Work
Adjudication

Adoption
Advice the elderly & powers of attorney
Agriculture and estates
Agriculture, crofting and fishing
Alternative dispute resolution
Alternative investment market
Banking & finance
Charities
Children
Childrens
Civil court work
Civil legal aid
Commercial litigation
Commercial property
Competition
Construction
Contract & property disputes
Corporate tax
Criminal court work
Criminal legal aid
Debt
Debt recovery, insolvency, bankruptcy
Education
Environment
Environment (Business Premises)
EU / international
Family and divorce
Family business advice
Fishing
Housing
Insolvency & corporate recovery
Insurance
Joint venture
Landlord & tenant
Liquor licensing
Medical negligence – defender
Medical negligence – claimant
Mental health
Mergers and acquisitions
Mining
Oil & gas
Pensions (Company)
Personal injury
Personal injury – defender
Planning
Planning (Business Premises)
Power and utilities
Private equity
Projects
Property litigation
Public finance initiative
Public sector
Residential property
Road traffic
Shipping
SME business advice
Social housing
Transport
Unit Trusts, OEICs and investment trusts
Wills, executries and trusts
Partner
Brian Alexander Jamieson

918

Employee
Alan Gordon Simpson

RAEBURN CHRISTIE CLARK & WALLACE LLP
7 The Square, Ellon AB41 9JB
Tel: (01358) 720777
Fax: (01358) 724401
Web: www.raeburns.co.uk
Categories of Work
Adoption
Advice the elderly & powers of attorney
Agriculture and estates
Agriculture, crofting and fishing
Alternative dispute resolution
Banking & finance
Betting & gaming
Charities
Children
Civil court work
Civil legal aid
Commercial litigation
Commercial property
Competition
Construction
Contract & property disputes
Copyright, trade marks and design
Data protection
Debt
Disability
Discrimination
Employment
Employment law
Environment
EU / international
Family and divorce
Family business advice
Freedom of information
Health and safety
Housing
Human rights
IT and intellectual property
Joint venture
Landlord & tenant
Liquor licensing
Media and entertainment
Medical negligence – defender
Mergers and acquisitions
Oil & gas
Personal injury
Personal injury – defender
Planning
Planning (Business Premises)
Private equity
Professional negligence
Property litigation
Residential property
Road traffic
Shipping
SME business advice
Social housing
Sport
Wills, executries and trusts

Partner
James Henry Joseph Nixon
Consultant
Jennifer Ann Burnett
Associate
Andrew Buchan Bruce

Erskine

THE PRG PARTNERSHIP
12a Bridgewater, Erskine PA8 7AA
Tel: (0141) 812 4325
DX: 512215 SANDYFORD PLACE
E-mail: scotslaw@prg.co.uk
Web: www.prg.co.uk
Categories of Work
Adjudication
Advice the elderly & powers of attorney
Alternative dispute resolution
Charities
Children
Civil court work
Civil legal aid
Commercial litigation
Commercial property
Competition
Contract & property disputes
Copyright, trade marks and design
Criminal court work
Criminal legal aid
Data protection
Debt
Debt collecting
Debt recovery, insolvency, bankruptcy
Disability
Discrimination
Employment
Employment law
Family and divorce
Family business advice
Health and safety
Human rights
Insolvency & corporate recovery
IT and intellectual property
Joint venture
Landlord & tenant
Media and entertainment
Medical negligence – defender
Medical negligence – claimant
Mergers and acquisitions
Pensions (Employment)
Personal injury
Personal injury – defender
Professional negligence
Property litigation
Residential property
Road traffic
SME business advice
Social housing
Software licensing
Wills, executries and trusts

VINCENT BROWN ASSOCIATES
9 Garnie Lane, Erskine PA8 7BQ

▶ *Erskine continued*
Tel: (07740) 877627
Categories of Work
Construction
Contract & property disputes
Environment
Environment (Business Premises)
EU / international

VINCENT BROWN LAW
9 Garnie Lane, Erskine PA8 7BQ
Tel: (07740) 877627
Categories of Work
Construction
Contract & property disputes
Environment
Environment (Business Premises)
EU / international

VINCENT BROWN LIMITED
9 Garnie Lane, Erskine PA8 7BQ
Tel: (07740) 877627
E-mail: vincent@vincentbrown.eu
Web: www.vincentbrown.eu
Categories of Work
Construction
Contract & property disputes
Environment
Environment (Business Premises)
EU / international
Director
Vincent Brown

Eyemouth

CURRIE JOHNSTON & CO
7 Market Place, Eyemouth TD14 5HE
Tel: (018907) 50218

HASTINGS LEGAL INCORPORATING DOUGHTYS
3 & 7 Church Street, Eyemouth TD14 5DH
Tel: (018907) 51100
Fax: (018907) 51105
E-mail: legal@hastingslegal.co.uk
Web: www.hastingslegal.co.uk
Categories of Work
Adoption
Advice the elderly & powers of attorney
Agriculture and estates
Civil court work
Commercial property
Contract & property disputes
Copyright, trade marks and design
Debt adjusting and debt counselling
Debt administration
Debt collecting
Debt management
Debt recovery, insolvency, bankruptcy
Employment law
Environment
Family and divorce
Family business advice

Health
Health and safety
Housing
Landlord & tenant
Liquor licensing
Mental health
Personal injury
Personal tax
Planning
Planning (Business Premises)
Property litigation
Public sector
Residential property
SME business advice
Wills, executries and trusts
Consultant
Marina Beatrice Kerr

MELROSE & PORTEOUS LIMITED
1 Manse Road, Eyemouth TD14 5JE
Tel: (01890) 751557
DX: 556542 EYEMOUTH
E-mail: info@melroseporteous.co.uk
Categories of Work
Adoption
Advice the elderly & powers of attorney
Children
Commercial litigation
Debt
Employment law
Family and divorce

Falkirk

LESLEY ANDERSON LAW LTD
5 Manse Place, Falkirk FK1 1JN
Tel: (01324) 278 565
E-mail: enquiries@lesleyandersonlaw.co.uk
Categories of Work
Adoption
Advice the elderly & powers of attorney
Children
Childrens
Civil court work
Commercial litigation
Contract & property disputes
Debt collecting
Debt recovery, insolvency, bankruptcy
Family and divorce
Landlord & tenant
Property litigation
Wills, executries and trusts
Director
Lesley Bell Anderson

BELL & CRAIG LIMITED
12 Vicar Street, Falkirk FK1 1JL
Tel: (01324) 635257
Fax: (01324) 612350
E-mail: enquiries@bellandcraig.co.uk
Web: www.bellandcraig.co.uk
Categories of Work
Advice the elderly & powers of attorney
Commercial property

Employment
Family business advice
Joint venture
Landlord & tenant
Residential property
SME business advice
Wills, executives and trusts
Director
Lisa Ann Taylor

BLACKADDER & MCMONAGLE
41 High Street, Falkirk FK1 1EN
Tel: (01324) 612999
Fax: (01324) 612026
DX: FA4 FALKIRK
E-mail: maildesk@blackandmac.com
Web: www.blackadderandmcmonagle.com
Categories of Work
Adoption
Advice the elderly & powers of attorney
Children
Civil court work
Commercial litigation
Commercial property
Debt recovery, insolvency, bankruptcy
Employment law
Family and divorce
Landlord & tenant
Planning
Power and utilities
Projects
Property litigation
Residential property
Wills, executives and trusts
Partners
Graham Blyth
John William Keene Dickie
Catriona Ruth MacDonald
Consultant
Manus Joseph McMonagle

CAESAR & HOWIE
29 Upper Newmarket Street, Falkirk FK1 1JH
Tel: (01324) 628332
DX: FA24 FALKIRK
E-mail: enquiries@caesar-howie.co.uk
Web: www.caesar-howie.co.uk
Categories of Work
Adoption
Advice the elderly & powers of attorney
Alternative dispute resolution
Children
Childrens
Civil court work
Civil legal aid
Commercial property
Debt
Debt collecting
Debt recovery, insolvency, bankruptcy
Disability
Education
Employment law
Family and divorce
Family business advice

Landlord & tenant
Mental health
Personal injury
Residential property
Road traffic
Wills, executives and trusts
Partner
Sarah Helen Swan Patrick

THOMAS DOCHERTY SOLICITORS
3/10 Falkirk Business Hub, 45 Vicar Street,
Falkirk FK1 1LL
Tel: (01324) 875870
Fax: (01324) 614 054
E-mail: mail@tdlaw.co.uk
Categories of Work
Adoption
Advice the elderly & powers of attorney
Benefit advice
Children
Civil court work
Civil legal aid
Commercial property
Contract & property disputes
Debt
Family and divorce
Family business advice
Housing
Landlord & tenant
Liquor licensing
Medical negligence – defender
Medical negligence – claimant
Personal injury
Personal injury – defender
Residential property
SME business advice
Wills, executives and trusts
Partner
Thomas Edward Docherty
Consultant
Leigh Sarah Harris

DWJ LAW
75 Waggon Road, Brightons, Falkirk FK2 0EJ
Tel: (01324) 710137

FRASER SHEPHERD
39 Vicar Street, Falkirk FK1 1LL
Tel: (01324) 630700
Fax: (01324) 630225
DX: FA16 FALKIRK
E-mail: morag@frasershepherd.co.uk
Web: www.frasershepherd.co.uk
Categories of Work
Adoption
Advice the elderly & powers of attorney
Alternative dispute resolution
Children
Childrens
Civil court work
Civil legal aid
Family and divorce
Wills, executives and trusts

▶ **Falkirk** continued

Partner
Morag Fraser
Employee
Yuliia Alexeievna Waiss

GAIR & GIBSON LLP
9 & 11 Newmarket Street, Falkirk FK1 1JY
Tel: (01324) 623928
Fax: (01324) 611697
DX: FA7 FALKIRK
E-mail: andrewcraig@gairgibson.co.uk
Web:
www.lawscot.org.uk/firms/gairgibson.html
Categories of Work
Adoption
Advice the elderly & powers of attorney
Alternative dispute resolution
Benefit advice
Children
Civil court work
Civil legal aid
Commercial property
Debt
Debt management
Family and divorce
Landlord & tenant
Residential property
Wills, executries and trusts
Partner
William Andrew Craig
Employee
Jane Elizabeth Steer

HENDRY LAW
Former Camelon Police Office, 354 Main
Street, Falkirk FK1 4EG
Tel: (01324) 227273
Fax: (01324) 630322
E-mail: hendrylaw@outlook.com
Categories of Work
Criminal court work
Criminal legal aid
Partner
William Hendry

JAAPLAW LIMITED
75 Waggon Road, Brightons, Falkirk FK2 0EJ
Tel: (01324) 710137
E-mail: dwj@dwjlaw.com
Web: www.jaaplaw.com
Categories of Work
Adjudication
Alternative dispute resolution
Civil court work
Commercial litigation
Contract & property disputes
Debt
Debt administration
Debt collecting
Debt recovery, insolvency, bankruptcy
Disability
Discrimination
Employment

Employment law
Family business advice
Human rights
Insolvency & corporate recovery
Media and entertainment
Property litigation
Sport
Director
Douglas William Jaap

**KERR STIRLING LLP TRADING AS GIBSON &
KENNEDY WS**
Benview, Wellside Place, Falkirk FK1 5RP
Tel: (01324) 622741
E-mail: enquiries@kerrstirling.co.uk
Categories of Work
Advice the elderly & powers of attorney
Agriculture and estates
Agriculture, crofting and fishing
Banking & finance
Commercial property
Construction
Contract & property disputes
Debt
Debt recovery, insolvency, bankruptcy
Employment law
Family and divorce
Family business advice
Housing
Joint venture
Landlord & tenant
Liquor licensing
Mergers and acquisitions
Planning
Planning (Business Premises)
Power and utilities
Residential property
SME business advice
Wills, executries and trusts
Associate
David Alastair Barclay

LUMSDEN CONSULTANCY LIMITED
1 Greencraig Cottages, Avonbridge, Falkirk
FK1 2JD
Tel: (07831) 707525
E-mail: roy@rdllaw.co.uk
Categories of Work
Adoption
Advice the elderly & powers of attorney
Children
Childrens
Civil court work
Civil legal aid
Education
Employment
Family and divorce
Mental health
Wills, executries and trusts
Director
Roy Donald Lumsden

MARSHALL WILSON LAW GROUP LIMITED
2 High Street, Falkirk FK1 1EZ

Tel: (01324) 612569
Fax: (01324) 623512
DX: FA10 FALKIRK
E-mail: falkirk@marshallwilson.com
Web: www.marshallwilson.com
Categories of Work
Adoption
Advice the elderly & powers of attorney
Children
Childrens
Civil court work
Civil legal aid
Criminal court work
Criminal legal aid
Education
Employment
Employment law
Family and divorce
Health and safety
Liquor licensing
Local government
Mental health
Personal injury
Residential property
Road traffic
Wills, executuries and trusts
Directors
Stephen James Biggam
Fiona MacKay MacDonald Munn
Malcolm Welsh Thomson
Consultant
John Mark Mulholland
Employees
Emma Carter
Shelby Rose Johnstone

MOOREMARSHALL LIMITED
Office 1/9, Falkirk Business Hub, Falkirk
FK1 1LL
Tel: (01324) 614020
Fax: (0844) 2448679
E-mail: info@mooremarshall.co.uk
Web: www.mooremarshall.com
Categories of Work
Advice the elderly & powers of attorney
Children
Civil court work
Commercial property
Contract & property disputes
Employment law
Family and divorce
Family business advice
Landlord & tenant
Residential property
Wills, executuries and trusts
Director
Kenneth Robert James Marshall
Employees
Jasmine Ferguson
Judith Shaw Marshall

MORTON BRODY LAW
PO Box 21768, Falkirk FK1 9GQ
Tel: (07368) 136435

E-mail: info@mortonbrodylaw.co.uk
Categories of Work
Adoption
Advice the elderly & powers of attorney
Children
Childrens
Civil court work
Civil legal aid
Debt
Family and divorce
Partner
Ashleigh Margaret Morton

MORTON PACITTI LLP
5 Newmarket Street, Falkirk FK1 1JY
Tel: (01324) 679030
Fax: (01324) 626263
E-mail: info@mortonpacitti.com
Web: www.mortonpacitti.com
Categories of Work
Advice the elderly & powers of attorney
Commercial property
Residential property
Wills, executuries and trusts
Partner
Linda Anne Pacitti

MTM DEFENCE LAWYERS LIMITED
Campfield House, Wellside Place, Falkirk
FK1 5RL
Tel: (01324) 633221
Fax: (01324) 611694
Categories of Work
Adoption
Children
Childrens
Civil court work
Civil legal aid
Criminal court work
Criminal legal aid
Education
Family and divorce
Medical negligence – defender
Personal injury – defender
Directors
Murray Watson Aitken
Martin Thomas Morrow
Consultant
Simon John Black Hutchison
Employees
Ross John McGowan
Lynn Mary Swan

NELSONS SOLICITORS FALKIRK LIMITED
326 Main Street, Camelon, Falkirk FK1 4EG
Tel: (01324) 613316
Fax: (01324) 613317
E-mail: gordon@nelsonslawyers.co.uk
Web: www.nelsonslawyers.co.uk
Categories of Work
Advice the elderly & powers of attorney
Children
Civil court work
Civil legal aid

▶ *Falkirk continued*

Criminal court work
Criminal legal aid
Disability
Discrimination
Family and divorce
Human rights
Mental health
Personal injury
Professional negligence
Road traffic
Wills, executives and trusts
Directors
Gordon Addison
Andrew John Bryson
Employee
Mark Fallon

ORME LAW-A TRADING NAME OF KIRKLANDS
20 Meeks Road, Falkirk FK2 7ES
Tel: (01324) 882551
Fax: (01324) 882553
Web: www.kirklands-law.co.uk
Categories of Work
Commercial property
Family business advice
Landlord & tenant
Mergers and acquisitions
Residential property
SME business advice
Wills, executives and trusts
Directors
Amy Louise Bisset
Alan Stewart McLaren Orme

ROONEY FAMILY LAW LIMITED
Suite 1/10b, Falkirk Business Hub, Falkirk
FK1 1LL
Tel: (01324) 227027
Categories of Work
Adoption
Advice the elderly & powers of attorney
Alternative dispute resolution
Benefit advice
Charities
Children
Childrens
Civil court work
Civil legal aid
Commercial litigation
Consumer credit
Contract & property disputes
Copyright, trade marks and design
Criminal court work
Criminal legal aid
Debt
Debt collecting
Debt management
Debt recovery, insolvency, bankruptcy
Disability
Discrimination
Education
Employment law

Family and divorce
Family business advice
Human rights
Landlord & tenant
Medical negligence – claimant
Mental health
Personal injury
Private equity
Professional negligence
Property litigation
Road traffic
Social housing
Wills, executives and trusts

RUSSEL + AITKEN (FALKIRK + ALLOA) LTD
Unit 5 The Courtyard, Callender Business Park,
Falkirk FK1 1XR
Tel: (01324) 622888
Fax: (01324) 620994
E-mail: info@russel-aitken.co.uk
Categories of Work
Adoption
Advice the elderly & powers of attorney
Alternative dispute resolution
Children
Civil court work
Civil legal aid
Commercial litigation
Commercial property
Consumer credit
Contract & property disputes
Criminal court work
Criminal legal aid
Debt
Debt administration
Debt collecting
Debt recovery, insolvency, bankruptcy
Discrimination
Education
Employment
Employment law
Family and divorce
Family business advice
Human rights
Landlord & tenant
Medical negligence – defender
Medical negligence – claimant
Personal injury
Personal injury – defender
Professional negligence
Property litigation
Residential property
Road traffic
SME business advice
Social housing
Wills, executives and trusts
Director
Karen Elizabeth McLachlan
Consultant
Margaret Jane Lang
Employees
Marc Convery
Craig Dunbar

Michael John Lowrie
Helen Grace Sawers

SANDEMANS
34 Union Road, Camelon, Falkirk FK1 4PG
Tel: (01324) 633222
Fax: (01324) 630322
E-mail: dicksandeman@sandemans.co.uk
Web: www.sandemans.co.uk
Categories of Work
Advice the elderly & powers of attorney
Betting & gaming
Children
Civil court work
Civil legal aid
Commercial litigation
Commercial property
Contract & property disputes
Criminal court work
Criminal legal aid
Debt recovery, insolvency, bankruptcy
Family and divorce
Family business advice
Landlord & tenant
Liquor licensing
Local government
Property litigation
Residential property
Wills, executries and trusts
Partner
Richard Allan Sandeman

TAIT MACLEOD
Eilean Chambers, 6 Park Street, Falkirk
FK1 1RE
Tel: (01324) 888877
Fax: (01324) 411607
DX: FA67 FALKIRK
E-mail: fraser@taitmacleod.com
Web: www.taitmacleod.com
Categories of Work
Adoption
Advice the elderly & powers of attorney
Charities
Children
Civil court work
Civil legal aid
Commercial litigation
Commercial property
Contract & property disputes
Data protection
Debt recovery, insolvency, bankruptcy
Disability
Discrimination
Employment
Employment law
Family and divorce
Family business advice
Freedom of information
Human rights
IT and intellectual property
Landlord & tenant
Medical negligence – defender
Medical negligence – claimant

Personal injury
Personal injury – defender
Planning (Business Premises)
Professional negligence
Property litigation
Public sector
Residential property
SME business advice
Wills, executries and trusts
Partner
John Fraser Tait
Employee
Fraser Ronald Comrie-Bryant

TAYLOR & KELLY
Suites 2/1 & 2/2, Falkirk Business Hub, Falkirk
FK1 1LL
Tel: (01324) 614015
Fax: (01324) 614025
E-mail: tony@taylorkelly.co.uk
Web: www.taylorkelly.co.uk
Categories of Work
Civil court work
Civil legal aid
Criminal court work
Criminal legal aid
Discrimination
Human rights
Partner
Laura Elizabeth Milite

Forfar

BELL BRODIE LTD
77 Castle Street, Forfar DD8 3AG
Tel: (01307) 475320
Fax: (01307) 475321
E-mail: brian@bellbrodie.com
Categories of Work
Adoption
Advice the elderly & powers of attorney
Children
Civil court work
Criminal court work
Criminal legal aid
Family and divorce
Human rights
Medical negligence – claimant
Personal injury
Road traffic
Wills, executries and trusts
Director
Ernest Brian Bell

BLACKADDERS LLP
128 Castle Street, Forfar DD8 3HS
Tel: (01307) 461234
E-mail: enquiries@blackadders.co.uk
Categories of Work
Adoption
Advice the elderly & powers of attorney
Agriculture and estates
Agriculture, crofting and fishing
Alternative dispute resolution

▶ **Forfar continued**

Banking & finance
Charities
Children
Childrens
Civil court work
Civil legal aid
Commercial litigation
Commercial property
Competition
Construction
Consumer credit
Contract & property disputes
Copyright, trade marks and design
Data protection
Debt
Debt collecting
Debt recovery, insolvency, bankruptcy
Disability
Discrimination
Employment
Employment law
Environment
Environment (Business Premises)
EU / international
Family and divorce
Family business advice
Fishing
Freedom of information
Housing
Human rights
Insolvency & corporate recovery
IT and intellectual property
Joint venture
Landlord & tenant
Media and entertainment
Medical negligence – defender
Medical negligence – claimant
Mental health
Mergers and acquisitions
Pensions (Employment)
Personal injury
Personal injury – defender
Personal tax
Planning
Power and utilities
Private equity
Professional negligence
Property litigation
Public sector
Residential property
Road traffic
SME business advice
Software licensing
Sport
Telecoms
Wills, executries and trusts

BOWMANS
37 East High Street, Forfar DD8 2EL
Tel: (01307) 464088
E-mail: forfar@bowmansolicitors.co.uk
Web: www.bowmansolicitors.co.uk

Categories of Work
Advice the elderly & powers of attorney
Charities
Residential property
Wills, executries and trusts
Associate
Jacqueline Sarah Millar

BOYDS LAW
36 West High Street, Forfar DD8 1BA
Tel: (01307) 460499
Fax: (0800) 6681198
E-mail: mboyd@boydslaw.co.uk
Partner
Michael William Boyd

R. BRUCE & CO.
24 West High Street, Forfar DD8 1BA
Tel: (01307) 460666
DX: 530684 FORFAR
Web: www.bruce-co.co.uk
Categories of Work
Adoption
Advice the elderly & powers of attorney
Children
Childrens
Civil court work
Civil legal aid
Criminal court work
Criminal legal aid
Debt
Education
Family and divorce
Landlord & tenant
Mental health
Personal injury
Road traffic
Social housing
Wills, executries and trusts

W. & J.S. GORDON
Albion House, 52 East High Street, Forfar
DD8 2EG
Tel: (01307) 462188
Fax: (01307) 467571
E-mail: info@wjsgordon.co.uk
Web: www.wjsgordon.co.uk
Categories of Work
Adjudication
Alternative dispute resolution
Commercial litigation
Construction
Environment (Business Premises)
EU / international
Planning
Planning (Business Premises)
Residential property
Partner
William John Adam Hardie
Consultant
John Michael Ewart Hardie
Employee
Paul Lawrence Brown

INKSTERS
Top Floor, 24 West High Street, Forfar
DD8 1BA
Tel: (01307) 497008
Fax: (01307) 497009
E-mail: forfar@inksters.com
Web: www.inksters.com
Categories of Work
Advice the elderly & powers of attorney
Agriculture and estates
Agriculture, crofting and fishing
Alternative dispute resolution
Children
Childrens
Civil court work
Civil legal aid
Commercial property
Consumer credit
Contract & property disputes
Criminal court work
Criminal legal aid
Data protection
Debt
Debt collecting
Debt recovery, insolvency, bankruptcy
Family and divorce
Family business advice
Landlord & tenant
Personal tax
Projects
Property litigation
Residential property
Road traffic
Wills, executries and trusts
Consultants
Joanne Christine Romanis
Robert John Wild

MACHARDY, ALEXANDER & WHYTE, WS
71 Castle Street, Forfar DD8 3AG
Tel: (01307) 463593
Fax: (01307) 468507
E-mail: forfar@machardy.co.uk
Web: www.machardy.co.uk
Categories of Work
Advice the elderly & powers of attorney
Agriculture and estates
Agriculture, crofting and fishing
Civil court work
Commercial property
Employment law
Family and divorce
Family business advice
Landlord & tenant
Personal tax
Planning
Residential property
SME business advice
Wills, executries and trusts
Partners
Hamish William Whyte
Nicholas Douglas Whyte

Employees
Tina Magson
Gordon Russell Seath

MACHARDY LAW LIMITED
71 Castle Street, Forfar DD8 3AG
Tel: (01307) 463593
E-mail: nwhyte@machardy.co.uk
Categories of Work
Advice the elderly & powers of attorney
Agriculture and estates
Agriculture, crofting and fishing
Civil court work
Commercial property
Employment law
Family and divorce
Family business advice
Landlord & tenant
Personal tax
Planning
Residential property
SME business advice
Wills, executries and trusts

THORNTONS LAW LLP
53 East High Street, Forfar DD8 2EL
Tel: (01307) 466886
Fax: (01307) 464643
E-mail: forfar@thorntons-law.co.uk
Web: www.thorntons-law.co.uk
Categories of Work
Adjudication
Adoption
Advice the elderly & powers of attorney
Agriculture and estates
Agriculture, crofting and fishing
Alternative dispute resolution
Alternative investment market
Banking & finance
Benefit advice
Betting & gaming
Charities
Children
Childrens
Civil court work
Civil legal aid
Commercial litigation
Commercial property
Competition
Construction
Consumer credit
Contract & property disputes
Copyright, trade marks and design
Corporate tax
Credit brokerage
Criminal court work
Criminal legal aid
Data protection
Debt
Debt adjusting and debt counselling
Debt administration
Debt collecting
Debt recovery, insolvency, bankruptcy
Disability

▶ **Forfar continued**

Discrimination
Education
Employment
Employment law
Environment
Environment (Business Premises)
EU / international
Family and divorce
Family business advice
Fishing
Freedom of information
Health
Health and safety
Housing
Human rights
Immigration and asylum
Insolvency & corporate recovery
Insurance
IT and intellectual property
Joint venture
Landlord & tenant
Liquor licensing
Local government
Media and entertainment
Medical negligence – defender
Medical negligence – claimant
Mental health
Mergers and acquisitions
Oil & gas
Parliamentary
Pensions (Company)
Pensions (Employment)
Personal injury
Personal injury – defender
Personal tax
Planning
Planning (Business Premises)
Power and utilities
Private equity
Professional negligence
Projects
Property litigation
Public sector
Residential property
Road traffic
SME business advice
Social housing
Software licensing
Sport
Telecoms
Unit Trusts, OEICs and investment trusts
Wills, executries and trusts
Partners
Christopher Gerald Lindley
Anne Janette McKeown
Associates
Lynne Macintyre
Elaine Mary Sym
Employee
Angela Robertson

Forres

COCKBURNS
100c High Street, Forres IV36 1NX
Tel: (01309) 673373
Fax: (01309) 676336
DX: 520698 FORRES
E-mail: forres@cockburns-solicitors.com
Categories of Work
Adoption
Advice the elderly & powers of attorney
Agriculture and estates
Children
Civil court work
Commercial property
Criminal court work
Criminal legal aid
Debt
Debt collecting
Debt recovery, insolvency, bankruptcy
Employment
Employment law
Family and divorce
Landlord & tenant
Medical negligence – claimant
Personal injury
Property litigation
Residential property
Road traffic
Wills, executries and trusts
Partner
Colin John Styles

GRIGOR & YOUNG LLP
100 High Street, Forres IV36 1PD
Tel: (01309) 672126
E-mail: mail@grigor-young.co.uk
Web: www.grigor-young.co.uk
Categories of Work
Adoption
Advice the elderly & powers of attorney
Agriculture and estates
Agriculture, crofting and fishing
Alternative dispute resolution
Benefit advice
Children
Civil court work
Civil legal aid
Commercial property
Contract & property disputes
Debt
Debt adjusting and debt counselling
Debt administration
Debt management
Debt recovery, insolvency, bankruptcy
Disability
Discrimination
Education
Employment
Employment law
Environment
Environment (Business Premises)
Family and divorce
Human rights

Landlord & tenant
Medical negligence – claimant
Mental health
Personal injury
Planning
Planning (Business Premises)
Property litigation
Residential property
Road traffic
Social housing
Wills, executives and trusts
Associate
Lindsey Marie Carroll

ST LAW
PO Box 5918, Forres IV36 9AY
Tel: (01309) 752022
Categories of Work
Adoption
Advice the elderly & powers of attorney
Mental health
Wills, executives and trusts

SUTHERLAND THOMSON LAW PRACTICE
PO Box 5918, Forres IV36 9AY
Tel: (01309) 752022
E-mail: info@st-law.co.uk
Web: www.st-law.co.uk
Categories of Work
Adoption
Advice the elderly & powers of attorney
Mental health
Wills, executives and trusts
Partner
Laura Jane Thomson

R & R URQUHART LLP
117-121 High Street, Forres IV36 1AB
Tel: (01309) 672216
Fax: (01309) 673161
DX: 520690 FORRES
E-mail: info.forres@r-r-urquhart.com
Web: www.r-r-urquhart.com
Categories of Work
Adoption
Advice the elderly & powers of attorney
Agriculture and estates
Agriculture, crofting and fishing
Alternative dispute resolution
Banking & finance
Charities
Children
Civil court work
Commercial litigation
Commercial property
Contract & property disputes
Copyright, trade marks and design
Debt collecting
Debt recovery, insolvency, bankruptcy
Disability
Discrimination
Employment
Employment law
Environment

Environment (Business Premises)
EU / international
Family and divorce
Family business advice
Fishing
Human rights
Insolvency & corporate recovery
Joint venture
Landlord & tenant
Media and entertainment
Medical negligence – defender
Medical negligence – claimant
Pensions (Company)
Personal injury
Personal injury – defender
Planning
Planning (Business Premises)
Power and utilities
Professional negligence
Property litigation
Residential property
SME business advice
Telecoms
Unit Trusts, OEICs and investment trusts
Wills, executives and trusts
Partners
William Roger Murray Cowie
Jane Margaret Wilson Ferguson
James Alexander Cameron Whittle
Employee
Samantha Middleton

Fort William

JONATHAN BELL
Ben Nevis Auction Mart, Torlundy, Fort
William PH33 6SW
Tel: (07740) 110202
E-mail: johnnybell@twindeerlaw.co.uk
Web: www.twindeerlaw.co.uk

DEWAR & MURRAY
87 High Street, Fort William PH33 6DG
Tel: (01397) 702455
Fax: (01397) 705949
DX: 531402 FORT WILLIAM
E-mail: craig@macarthurstewart.co.uk
Web: www.macarthurstewart.co.uk
Categories of Work
Criminal court work
Criminal legal aid
Residential property
Wills, executives and trusts
Partners
David Peter Dewar
Craig Gordon Murray

MACARTHUR STEWART, FORT WILLIAM
87 High Street, Fort William PH33 6DG
Tel: (01397) 702455
E-mail: fortwilliam@macarthurstewart.co.uk
Web: www.macarthurstewart.co.uk
Categories of Work
Criminal court work

▶ **Fort William** continued

Criminal legal aid
Residential property
Wills, executives and trusts

MCINTYRE & CO.
38 High Street, Fort William PH33 6AT
Tel: (01397) 703231
Fax: (01397) 705070
DX: 531403 FORT WILLIAM
E-mail: law@solicitors-scotland.com
Web: www.solicitors-scotland.com
Categories of Work
Adoption
Advice the elderly & powers of attorney
Children
Civil court work
Civil legal aid
Commercial property
Contract & property disputes
Criminal court work
Criminal legal aid
Debt
Debt recovery, insolvency, bankruptcy
Family and divorce
Landlord & tenant
Personal injury
Residential property
Wills, executives and trusts
Partner
Stephen Douglas Kennedy
Associate
Colin Donald Mackay
Employees
Niall Alisdair MacBeath
Marie-Luise Christa MacDonald

MACPHEE & PARTNERS LLP
Airds House, An Aird, Fort William PH33 6BL
Tel: (01397) 701000
Fax: (01397) 701777
DX: 531408 FORT WILLIAM
E-mail: law@macphee.co.uk
Web: www.macphee.co.uk
Categories of Work
Adoption
Advice the elderly & powers of attorney
Agriculture and estates
Banking & finance
Children
Childrens
Civil court work
Civil legal aid
Commercial litigation
Commercial property
Consumer credit
Contract & property disputes
Copyright, trade marks and design
Data protection
Debt
Debt management
Debt recovery, insolvency, bankruptcy
Education

Employment
Employment law
Family and divorce
Family business advice
Freedom of information
Insolvency & corporate recovery
IT and intellectual property
Joint venture
Landlord & tenant
Liquor licensing
Media and entertainment
Mental health
Mergers and acquisitions
Property litigation
Residential property
SME business advice
Software licensing
Telecoms
Wills, executives and trusts
Partners
Jeremy Peter Benfield
Keith Diarmid Falconer
Claire Frances MacAlpin
Christine Jane MacKay
Employees
Olivia Frances Bridge
Rebecca Louise Fraser
Heather Elaine MacArthur
Ciara McCartney
Gary Somers

TWIN DEER LAW
TDL HQ, Lochaber Rural Complex, Fort
William PH33 6SQ
Tel: (07740) 110202
Fax: (01397) 608 555
DX: 531400 Fort William
E-mail: johnnybell@twindeerlaw.co.uk
Web: www.twindeerlaw.co.uk
Partner
Jonathan Richard Miles Bell

Fraserburgh

BROWN & MCRAE LLP
Anderson House, 9-11 Frithside Street,
Fraserburgh AB43 9AB
Tel: (01346) 514761
E-mail: property@brown-mcrae.co.uk
Categories of Work
Adoption
Advice the elderly & powers of attorney
Agriculture and estates
Agriculture, crofting and fishing
Charities
Civil court work
Commercial property
Criminal court work
Criminal legal aid
Debt
Debt recovery, insolvency, bankruptcy
Family and divorce
Family business advice

Insolvency & corporate recovery
Joint venture
Landlord & tenant
Mergers and acquisitions
Public sector
Residential property
SME business advice
Wills, executives and trusts
Partners
Steven Ian Gauld
Alan Barry William Smith
Douglas Graeme Walker
Director
Karen Stedward Paterson
Employees
Rachel Bruce
Staci Ann Buchan
Mhari Elizabeth Ritchie

MACRAE STEPHEN & CO.

57 High Street, Fraserburgh AB43 9ET
Tel: (01346) 514545
Fax: (01346) 510147
E-mail: archie@macraestephen.co.uk
Web: www.macraestephen.co.uk
Categories of Work
Adoption
Advice the elderly & powers of attorney
Alternative investment market
Benefit advice
Betting & gaming
Children
Civil court work
Commercial property
Consumer credit
Contract & property disputes
Credit brokerage
Debt adjusting and debt counselling
Debt administration
Debt collecting
Employment
Employment law
Family and divorce
Fishing
Health and safety
Housing
Landlord & tenant
Liquor licensing
Medical negligence – claimant
Mental health
Personal injury
Personal injury – defender
Personal tax
Property litigation
Provision of credit information services
Public sector
Residential property
Road traffic
Shipping
SME business advice
Wills, executives and trusts
Partner
Archibald James Millar

Employee
Donna Elaine Finnie

MASSON GLENNIE LLP

83 Broad Street, Fraserburgh AB43 9AX
Tel: (01346) 513338
DX: 521361 FRASERBURGH
E-mail: mail@masson-glennie.co.uk
Web: www.masson-glennie.co.uk
Categories of Work
Adoption
Advice the elderly & powers of attorney
Children
Childrens
Civil court work
Commercial litigation
Commercial property
Contract & property disputes
Criminal court work
Debt
Debt management
Employment
Employment law
Family and divorce
Family business advice
Immigration and asylum
Landlord & tenant
Mental health
Property litigation
Residential property
Shipping
Wills, executives and trusts

SAM MILLIGAN & CO.

38 Frithside Street, Fraserburgh AB43 9AR
Tel: (01346) 511966
Fax: (01346) 511977
E-mail: s.milligan@sammilligan.com
Categories of Work
Criminal court work
Criminal legal aid
Partner
Samuel Douglas Milligan
Employees
Marianne Milligan
Stephanie-Lynn Milligan

STEWART & WATSON

38 Broad Street, Fraserburgh AB43 9AH
Tel: (01346) 514443
E-mail: info@stewartwatson.co.uk
Web: www.stewartwatson.co.uk
Categories of Work
Adoption
Advice the elderly & powers of attorney
Agriculture and estates
Agriculture, crofting and fishing
Alternative dispute resolution
Charities
Children
Civil court work
Civil legal aid
Commercial property
Contract & property disputes

▶ **Fraserburgh continued**

Criminal court work
Criminal legal aid
Debt
Debt collecting
Debt recovery, insolvency, bankruptcy
Employment
Environment
Environment (Business Premises)
Family and divorce
Housing
Immigration and asylum
Landlord & tenant
Mental health
Personal injury
Projects
Residential property
Road traffic
Wills, executries and trusts
Employee
Alison Jean MacDonald

Galashiels

BURKE LEGAL
72 Bank Street, Galashiels TD1 1EL
Tel: (01896) 750350
Fax: (01896) 750360
E-mail: enquiries@burkelegal.co.uk
Categories of Work
Adoption
Advice the elderly & powers of attorney
Children
Civil court work
Civil legal aid
Commercial property
Contract & property disputes
Criminal court work
Criminal legal aid
Debt management
Debt recovery, insolvency, bankruptcy
Discrimination
Employment
Employment law
Family and divorce
Family business advice
Human rights
Liquor licensing
Local government
Mental health
Personal injury
Residential property
Road traffic
SME business advice
Wills, executries and trusts
Partner
Iain Thomas Burke

CULLEN KILSHAW
27 Market Street, Galashiels TD1 3AF
Tel: (01896) 758311
DX: 581240 Melrose
E-mail: gala@cullenkilshaw.com

Web: www.cullenkilshaw.com
Categories of Work
Adoption
Advice the elderly & powers of attorney
Agriculture and estates
Agriculture, crofting and fishing
Alternative dispute resolution
Children
Childrens
Civil court work
Civil legal aid
Commercial property
Contract & property disputes
Criminal court work
Criminal legal aid
Debt
Debt collecting
Debt recovery, insolvency, bankruptcy
Employment
Employment law
Environment (Business Premises)
Family and divorce
Family business advice
Fishing
Landlord & tenant
Liquor licensing
Local government
Personal injury
Planning (Business Premises)
Property litigation
Residential property
Road traffic
Wills, executries and trusts

CULLEN KILSHAW
Bank Close, Galashiels TD1 1BG
Tel: (01896) 752231
Fax: (01896) 754469
Categories of Work
Adoption
Advice the elderly & powers of attorney
Agriculture and estates
Agriculture, crofting and fishing
Alternative dispute resolution
Children
Childrens
Civil court work
Civil legal aid
Commercial property
Contract & property disputes
Criminal court work
Criminal legal aid
Debt
Debt collecting
Debt recovery, insolvency, bankruptcy
Employment
Employment law
Environment (Business Premises)
Family and divorce
Family business advice
Fishing
Landlord & tenant
Liquor licensing

Local government
Personal injury
Planning (Business Premises)
Property litigation
Residential property
Road traffic
Wills, executries and trusts
Associate
Greig Thomas McDonell
Employee
Sebastian Ireneusz Janus

CULLEN KILSHAW
Waverley Chambers, Ladhope Vale, Galashiels TD1 1BW
Tel: (01896) 800 800
Fax: (01896) 824 488
DX: 580700 GALASHIELS
E-mail: waverlychambers@cullenkilshaw.com
Web: www.cullenkilshaw.com
Categories of Work
Adoption
Advice the elderly & powers of attorney
Agriculture and estates
Agriculture, crofting and fishing
Alternative dispute resolution
Children
Childrens
Civil court work
Civil legal aid
Commercial property
Contract & property disputes
Criminal court work
Criminal legal aid
Debt
Debt collecting
Debt recovery, insolvency, bankruptcy
Employment
Employment law
Environment (Business Premises)
Family and divorce
Family business advice
Fishing
Landlord & tenant
Liquor licensing
Local government
Personal injury
Planning (Business Premises)
Property litigation
Residential property
Road traffic
Wills, executries and trusts
Partners
David Andrew George Kilshaw
Ross David Kilshaw
Consultant
Roderick James McGeoch
Employees
Kevin Robert Currie
Zoe Emma Duff
Anna Helen Duncan
Ruth Catherine Montgomery

EDINGTON LAW LIMITED
88/90 High Street, Galashiels TD1 1SQ
Tel: (01896) 756161
Fax: (01896) 751919
DX: 580710 GALASHIELS
E-mail: info@edingtonlaw.co.uk
Web: www.edingtonlaw.co.uk
Categories of Work
Advice the elderly & powers of attorney
Residential property
Wills, executries and trusts
Director
Susan Jane Edington

PIKE & CHAPMAN
36 Bank Street, Galashiels TD1 1ER
Tel: (01896) 752379
Fax: (01896) 754439
DX: 580701 GALASHIELS
E-mail: gala@pikeandchapman.co.uk
Categories of Work
Advice the elderly & powers of attorney
Agriculture, crofting and fishing
Charities
Commercial property
Landlord & tenant
Residential property
Wills, executries and trusts
Partner
William James Windram

THOMPSONS
84 Channel Street, Galashiels TD1 1BD
Tel: (0800) 0015163
Fax: (01896) 754636
Categories of Work
Adoption
Advice the elderly & powers of attorney
Agriculture and estates
Alternative dispute resolution
Charities
Children
Childrens
Civil court work
Civil legal aid
Commercial litigation
Consumer credit
Criminal court work
Disability
Discrimination
Education
Employment
Employment law
Family and divorce
Health
Health and safety
Human rights
Immigration and asylum
Insurance
Medical negligence – claimant
Personal injury
Personal injury – defender
Professional negligence
Residential property

► **Galashiels continued**

Road traffic
Social housing
Wills, executries and trusts
Employees
Natalie Susan Donald
Marina McLeod Urie

WARDLAW STEPHENSON ALLAN
The Lodge, 53 Market Street, Galashiels
TD1 3AF
Tel: (01896) 668669
Fax: (01896) 756900
Categories of Work
Criminal court work
Criminal legal aid
Human rights
Partners
Ross Michael Dow
Edward Thomson Hulme

Galston

DALES SOLICITORS LLP
18 Wallace Street, Galston KA4 8HP
Tel: (01563) 820216
Fax: (01563) 822188
E-mail: info@dalesllp.co.uk
Categories of Work
Advice the elderly & powers of attorney
Family and divorce
Residential property
Wills, executries and trusts
Partners
Alastair John Dale
John Mungall Dale
Jennifer Elizabeth McFadzean
Employees
Jacqueline Mary Campbell
Robert James Craig Cunningham
Jean Young Forrest
Thomas Charles Jordan
Suzanne McDonald

Gatehouse-of-Fleet

WILLIAMSON & HENRY LLP
32 High Street, Gatehouse-of-Fleet DG7 2HP
Tel: (01557) 814293
E-mail: enquiries@williamsonandhenry.co.uk
Web: www.williamsonandhenry.co.uk
Categories of Work
Advice the elderly & powers of attorney
Family business advice
Landlord & tenant
Personal tax
Residential property
Wills, executries and trusts

Giffnock

HOLMES MACKILLOP LIMITED
229 Fenwick Road, Giffnock G46 6JQ

Tel: (0141) 638 7405
Fax: (0141) 638 2512
Categories of Work
Adjudication
Advice the elderly & powers of attorney
Agriculture and estates
Agriculture, crofting and fishing
Alternative dispute resolution
Banking & finance
Charities
Children
Civil court work
Commercial litigation
Commercial property
Construction
Contract & property disputes
Data protection
Debt recovery, insolvency, bankruptcy
Employment
Employment law
Family and divorce
Family business advice
Freedom of information
Joint venture
Landlord & tenant
Liquor licensing
Mergers and acquisitions
Professional negligence
Property litigation
Public sector
Residential property
SME business advice
Wills, executries and trusts
Director
Robert Crombie Stewart
Associate
Kenneth John Clunie Hay

JAMIESON LAW LTD
G/2 2 Milverton Road, Giffnock G46 7AU
Tel: (07703) 569279
E-mail: babs@jamiesonlaw.legal
Categories of Work
Agriculture, crofting and fishing
Alternative investment market
Banking & finance
Charities
Commercial property
Competition
Corporate tax
Debt recovery, insolvency, bankruptcy
EU / international
Family business advice
Insolvency & corporate recovery
Insurance
Joint venture
Landlord & tenant
Mergers and acquisitions
Pensions (Company)
Private equity
Public finance initiative
Public sector
SME business advice

Unit Trusts, OEICs and investment trusts
Director
Barbara Jane Jamieson
Employee
Lynne Elaine Riddell

Girvan

GALLOWAY & AYRSHIRE PARTNERSHIP LLP
34 Dalrymple Street, Girvan KA26 9AE
Tel: (01465) 712345
Fax: (01465) 712346
E-mail: mail@smithvalentine.co.uk
Web: www.smithvalentine.co.uk
Categories of Work
Advice the elderly & powers of attorney
Agriculture and estates
Agriculture, crofting and fishing
Commercial property
Contract & property disputes
Debt collecting
Debt recovery, insolvency, bankruptcy
Employment law
Family and divorce
Family business advice
Housing
Insolvency & corporate recovery
Landlord & tenant
Liquor licensing
Personal tax
Planning
Planning (Business Premises)
Power and utilities
Residential property
SME business advice
Wills, executries and trusts
Partners
Craig Stewart William Currie
Shirley Corrinne McNeill
Employee
Alasdair Calum Craig

LAMBERT & CO.,
1 Hamilton Street, Girvan KA26 9EY
Tel: (01465) 715434
E-mail: Lambertco@btinternet.com
Categories of Work
Adoption
Advice the elderly & powers of attorney
Children
Civil court work
Civil legal aid
Consumer credit
Contract & property disputes
Credit brokerage
Criminal court work
Criminal legal aid
Debt
Debt adjusting and debt counselling
Debt administration
Debt collecting
Family and divorce
Landlord & tenant

Medical negligence – claimant
Personal injury
Professional negligence
Provision of credit information services
Residential property
Road traffic
Wills, executries and trusts

MCCORMICK & NICHOLSON
34 Dalrymple Street, Girvan KA26 9AE
Tel: (01465) 712345
E-mail: mail@smithvalentine.co.uk
Categories of Work
Advice the elderly & powers of attorney
Agriculture and estates
Agriculture, crofting and fishing
Commercial property
Contract & property disputes
Debt collecting
Debt recovery, insolvency, bankruptcy
Employment law
Family and divorce
Family business advice
Housing
Insolvency & corporate recovery
Landlord & tenant
Liquor licensing
Personal tax
Planning
Planning (Business Premises)
Power and utilities
Residential property
SME business advice
Wills, executries and trusts

SMITH & VALENTINE
34 Dalrymple Street, Girvan KA26 9AE
Tel: (01465) 712345
E-mail: mail@smithvalentine.co.uk
Web: www.smithvalentine.co.uk
Categories of Work
Advice the elderly & powers of attorney
Agriculture and estates
Agriculture, crofting and fishing
Commercial property
Contract & property disputes
Debt collecting
Debt recovery, insolvency, bankruptcy
Employment law
Family and divorce
Family business advice
Housing
Insolvency & corporate recovery
Landlord & tenant
Liquor licensing
Personal tax
Planning
Planning (Business Premises)
Power and utilities
Residential property
SME business advice
Wills, executries and trusts

THE MCKINSTRY COMPANY LLP
146 Dalrymple Street, Girvan KA26 9BQ

▶ **Girvan** continued

Tel: (01465) 713118
E-mail: enquiries@mckinstry.co.uk
Web: www.mckinstry.co.uk
Categories of Work
Adjudication
Adoption
Advice the elderly & powers of attorney
Alternative dispute resolution
Charities
Children
Civil court work
Commercial litigation
Commercial property
Construction
Contract & property disputes
Criminal court work
Debt
Debt administration
Debt collecting
Debt recovery, insolvency, bankruptcy
Education
Employment
Employment law
Family and divorce
Family business advice
Freedom of information
Insolvency & corporate recovery
Insurance
Landlord & tenant
Medical negligence – defender
Medical negligence – claimant
Personal injury
Personal injury – defender
Personal tax
Planning (Business Premises)
Professional negligence
Property litigation
Residential property
Road traffic
SME business advice
Social housing
Sport
Wills, executives and trusts
Partner
Deborah Dunlop

Glasgow

ABERDEIN CONSIDINE AND COMPANY
108 Byres Road, Glasgow G12 8TB
Tel: (0141) 3425570
Fax: (0141) 342 5575
Categories of Work
Adjudication
Adoption
Advice the elderly & powers of attorney
Agriculture and estates
Agriculture, crofting and fishing
Alternative dispute resolution
Alternative investment market
Banking & finance

Charities
Children
Childrens
Civil court work
Civil legal aid
Commercial litigation
Commercial property
Competition
Construction
Consumer credit
Contract & property disputes
Copyright, trade marks and design
Corporate tax
Credit brokerage
Criminal court work
Criminal legal aid
Data protection
Debt
Debt adjusting and debt counselling
Debt collecting
Debt recovery, insolvency, bankruptcy
Disability
Discrimination
Education
Employment
Employment law
Environment
Environment (Business Premises)
EU / international
Family and divorce
Family business advice
Freedom of information
Health
Health and safety
Human rights
Insolvency & corporate recovery
Insurance
Joint venture
Landlord & tenant
Liquor licensing
Local government
Media and entertainment
Mental health
Mergers and acquisitions
Pensions (Company)
Pensions (Employment)
Personal injury
Personal tax
Planning (Business Premises)
Private equity
Professional negligence
Property litigation
Public finance initiative
Public sector
Residential property
SME business advice
Social housing
Telecoms
Unit Trusts, OEICs and investment trusts
Wills, executives and trusts
Partner
William Bryden Crearie

ABERDEIN CONSIDINE AND COMPANY
18 Waterloo Street, Glasgow G2 6DB
Tel: (0141) 2278200
Fax: (0141) 2278219
Categories of Work
Adjudication
Adoption
Advice the elderly & powers of attorney
Agriculture and estates
Agriculture, crofting and fishing
Alternative dispute resolution
Alternative investment market
Banking & finance
Charities
Children
Childrens
Civil court work
Civil legal aid
Commercial litigation
Commercial property
Competition
Construction
Consumer credit
Contract & property disputes
Copyright, trade marks and design
Corporate tax
Credit brokerage
Criminal court work
Criminal legal aid
Data protection
Debt
Debt adjusting and debt counselling
Debt collecting
Debt recovery, insolvency, bankruptcy
Disability
Discrimination
Education
Employment
Employment law
Environment
Environment (Business Premises)
EU / international
Family and divorce
Family business advice
Freedom of information
Health
Health and safety
Human rights
Insolvency & corporate recovery
Insurance
Joint venture
Landlord & tenant
Liquor licensing
Local government
Media and entertainment
Mental health
Mergers and acquisitions
Pensions (Company)
Pensions (Employment)
Personal injury
Personal tax
Planning (Business Premises)
Private equity

Professional negligence
Property litigation
Public finance initiative
Public sector
Residential property
SME business advice
Social housing
Telecoms
Unit Trusts, OEICs and investment trusts
Wills, executries and trusts
Partners
Laura Margaret Browne
Michael Fraser Currie
Aileen Margaret Entwistle
Paul Knight Jennings
David Patrick Orr
Myra Scott
Consultant
Gavin John Finlay Crowe
Associates
Dalene Joyce Lyle
Joelle Nicole Neep
Employees
Jacqueline Lees Alleyne
John Joseph Di Paola
Megan Jayne Hannah
Sarah Christine Elizabeth Jack
Ellen Ruth Masters
Catriona Michelle Ramsay
Lynne Janette Thomson

ABERDEIN CONSIDINE AND COMPANY
251 Kilmarnock Road, Glasgow G41 3JF
Tel: (0141) 636 4131
Fax: (0141) 632 7136
E-mail: glasgow@acandco.com
Categories of Work
Adjudication
Adoption
Advice the elderly & powers of attorney
Agriculture and estates
Agriculture, crofting and fishing
Alternative dispute resolution
Alternative investment market
Banking & finance
Charities
Children
Childrens
Civil court work
Civil legal aid
Commercial litigation
Commercial property
Competition
Construction
Consumer credit
Contract & property disputes
Copyright, trade marks and design
Corporate tax
Credit brokerage
Criminal court work
Criminal legal aid
Data protection
Debt

▶ **Glasgow continued**

Debt adjusting and debt counselling
Debt collecting
Debt recovery, insolvency, bankruptcy
Disability
Discrimination
Education
Employment
Employment law
Environment
Environment (Business Premises)
EU / international
Family and divorce
Family business advice
Freedom of information
Health
Health and safety
Human rights
Insolvency & corporate recovery
Insurance
Joint venture
Landlord & tenant
Liquor licensing
Local government
Media and entertainment
Mental health
Mergers and acquisitions
Pensions (Company)
Pensions (Employment)
Personal injury
Personal tax
Planning (Business Premises)
Private equity
Professional negligence
Property litigation
Public finance initiative
Public sector
Residential property
SME business advice
Social housing
Telecoms
Unit Trusts, OEICs and investment trusts
Wills, executries and trusts
Partner
Norman Douglas Telfer

ACCIDENTS WILL HAPPEN
1007 Tollcross Road, Glasgow G32 8UQ
Tel: (0141) 7786500
Categories of Work
Adoption
Advice the elderly & powers of attorney
Benefit advice
Children
Childrens
Civil court work
Civil legal aid
Criminal court work
Criminal legal aid
Debt
Debt administration
Debt collecting
Debt management

Education
Family and divorce
Medical negligence – claimant
Mental health
Personal injury
Personal injury – defender
Provision of credit information services
Residential property
Road traffic
Social housing

ADDLESHAW GODDARD LLP
Cornerstone, 107 West Regent Street,
Glasgow G2 2BA
Tel: (0141) 2212300
Fax: (0141) 2215800
Categories of Work
Adjudication
Adoption
Advice the elderly & powers of attorney
Agriculture and estates
Agriculture, crofting and fishing
Alternative dispute resolution
Alternative investment market
Banking & finance
Benefit advice
Betting & gaming
Charities
Children
Childrens
Civil court work
Civil legal aid
Commercial litigation
Commercial property
Competition
Construction
Consumer credit
Contract & property disputes
Copyright, trade marks and design
Corporate tax
Credit brokerage
Criminal court work
Criminal legal aid
Data protection
Debt
Debt adjusting and debt counselling
Debt administration
Debt collecting
Debt management
Debt recovery, insolvency, bankruptcy
Disability
Discrimination
Education
Employment
Employment law
Environment
Environment (Business Premises)
EU / international
Family and divorce
Family business advice
Fishing
Freedom of information
Health

Health and safety
Housing
Human rights
Immigration and asylum
Insolvency & corporate recovery
Insurance
IT and intellectual property
Joint venture
Landlord & tenant
Liquor licensing
Local government
Media and entertainment
Medical negligence – defender
Medical negligence – claimant
Mental health
Mergers and acquisitions
Mining
Oil & gas
Parliamentary
Pensions (Company)
Pensions (Employment)
Personal injury
Personal injury – defender
Personal tax
Planning
Planning (Business Premises)
Power and utilities
Private equity
Professional negligence
Projects
Property litigation
Provision of credit information services
Public finance initiative
Public sector
Residential property
Road traffic
Shipping
SME business advice
Social housing
Software licensing
Sport
Telecoms
Transport
Unit Trusts, OEICs and investment trusts
Wills, executries and trusts
Partners
Joan Gabrielle Devine
Murray Alistair Jack
Alison Sarah Newton
Paul Ockrim
Alan Gerard Sinclair
Nicholas James Kerr Taylor
Consultant
Neil Hogg
Associates
Caroline Coulter
Karen Louise Crichton
Corrie Alexandra Kelso Ewing
Malcolm Hugh Fisher
Olivia Margaret Keary
Anita Maria Mulholland
Dominic Nathaniel White

Employees
Laurie Erin Anderson
Hannah Erin Brown
Allison Margaret Campbell
Matthew Stewart Campbell
James Patrick Campbell Corcoran
Andrea Victoria Hunter
Nicola McCluskie
Clare Louise McDevitt
Hannah Christie Moore
Mairi Nolan
Emma Jane Rae
Gavin Gar-Wing Smith
Lauren Steele
Graham James Arnott Wilson

ALBANY FRASER LIMITED
PO Box 2868, Glasgow G61 9EN
Tel: (0141) 4637065
E-mail: andrew@albanyfraser.com
Categories of Work
Copyright, trade marks and design
IT and intellectual property
Media and entertainment
SME business advice
Software licensing
Partner
Andrew Douglas James Fraser

ALEXANDER BOYD SOLICITORS
93 High Street, Merchant City, Glasgow
G1 1NB
Tel: (0141) 2373137
E-mail: alexanderboydsolicitors@gmail.com
Categories of Work
Benefit advice
Civil legal aid
Commercial property
Debt management
Discrimination
Employment law
Human rights
Immigration and asylum
Liquor licensing
Residential property
Social housing
Partner
Alexander Vitalievich Boyd

ALI & CO SOLICITORS
Suite 540, 103 Byres Road, Glasgow
G11 5HW
Tel: (07849) 007162
E-mail: S.ali@ali-legal.co.uk
Categories of Work
Adoption
Advice the elderly & powers of attorney
Children
Criminal court work
Criminal legal aid
Debt
Employment law
Family and divorce
Wills, executries and trusts

▶ *Glasgow continued*

Partner
Sidra Ali
Employee
Kelly-Anne Harkins

RICHARD JOHN ALLAN SOLICITOR

Festival Business Centre, Units 21 & 23,
Glasgow G51 1DH
Tel: (0141) 3399444
E-mail: info@richardjohnallan.co.uk
Categories of Work
Adoption
Advice the elderly & powers of attorney
Children
Civil court work
Civil legal aid
Consumer credit
Criminal court work
Criminal legal aid
Disability
Education
Family and divorce
Mental health
Personal injury
Road traffic
Social housing
Wills, executives and trusts
Partner
Richard John Allan

ALSTON LAW

The Forsyth Building, 5 Renfield Street,
Glasgow G2 5EZ
Tel: (0330) 127 2605
E-mail: info@alstonlaw.co.uk
Web: www.alstonlaw.co.uk
Categories of Work
Adoption
Advice the elderly & powers of attorney
Agriculture and estates
Alternative dispute resolution
Banking & finance
Children
Civil court work
Commercial litigation
Commercial property
Consumer credit
Contract & property disputes
Debt
Debt collecting
Debt recovery, insolvency, bankruptcy
Disability
Discrimination
Employment
Employment law
EU / international
Family and divorce
Housing
Insolvency & corporate recovery
Insurance
Landlord & tenant
Local government

Medical negligence – claimant
Personal injury
Professional negligence
Property litigation
Public sector
Residential property
Road traffic
Wills, executives and trusts
Director
Robert Douglas Aberdein
Employee
Gillian Bell McCluskey

ANDERSON STRATHERN LLP

George House, 50 George Square, Glasgow
G2 1EH
Tel: (0141) 2426060
Fax: (0141) 2214733
DX: GW157 GLASGOW
E-mail: info@andersonstrathern.co.uk
Web: www.andersonstrathern.co.uk
Categories of Work
Adjudication
Adoption
Advice the elderly & powers of attorney
Agriculture and estates
Agriculture, crofting and fishing
Alternative dispute resolution
Banking & finance
Betting & gaming
Charities
Children
Childrens
Civil court work
Civil legal aid
Commercial litigation
Commercial property
Competition
Construction
Consumer credit
Contract & property disputes
Copyright, trade marks and design
Corporate tax
Criminal court work
Data protection
Debt
Debt administration
Debt collecting
Debt recovery, insolvency, bankruptcy
Disability
Discrimination
Education
Employment
Employment law
Environment
Environment (Business Premises)
EU / international
Family and divorce
Family business advice
Fishing
Freedom of information
Health
Health and safety

Housing
Human rights
Immigration and asylum
Insolvency & corporate recovery
IT and intellectual property
Joint venture
Landlord & tenant
Liquor licensing
Local government
Media and entertainment
Medical negligence – defender
Medical negligence – claimant
Mental health
Mergers and acquisitions
Mining
Oil & gas
Parliamentary
Pensions (Employment)
Personal injury
Personal injury – defender
Personal tax
Planning
Planning (Business Premises)
Power and utilities
Private equity
Professional negligence
Projects
Property litigation
Public finance initiative
Public sector
Residential property
Road traffic
Shipping
SME business advice
Social housing
Software licensing
Sport
Telecoms
Transport
Wills, executries and trusts
Partners
Audrey Clare Cameron
Fraser Alexander John Geddes
Gillian Margaret Sharp Jamieson
Janice Jones
Paul Cyril Lombardi
Murray McCall
Christopher Leslie McDowall
Anne Campbell McGregor
Siobhan Clare McGuigan
Fiona Mary McKinnon
Douglas Walter McLachlan
Colin Forrest Graham Young
Consultants
James Alister Aitkenhead
Neil McDonald Amner
Associates
Ross Robert Cameron
Thomas Martin Docherty
Steven Dickson Dunn
Alasdair Henry Gillies
Stewart Henry Gordon
Jon Joseph McGee

Gillian Marion Murray
Employees
Emily Louise Campbell
Mohammed Ebrahim Desai
Jemma Margaret Forrest
Rachel Alice Frew
Elaine Goodwin
Gillian Anne Harkness-McKinlay
Musab Hemsi
Eilidh Patricia Knox
Rory Knox
Elizabeth Chalmers MacGregor
Kimberley Jane MacNeil
Julie Grace Macphail
James Harris McMillan
Anna O'Neil

**ANDREWS IMMIGRATION SOLICITORS
LIMITED**
4 Woodside Place, Charing Cross, Glasgow
G3 7QF
Tel: (0141) 3535026
Fax: (0141) 5309974
E-mail:
enquiries@andrewsimmigrationlaw.co.uk
Web: www.andrewsimmigrationlaw.co.uk
Categories of Work
Employment
Human rights
Immigration and asylum
Personal injury
Director
Peter Andrew Maguire

AAMER ANWAR & CO
21 Blythswood Square, Glasgow G2 4BL
Tel: (0141) 4297090
Fax: (0141) 4297025
E-mail: office@aameranwar.com
Web: www.aameranwar.co.uk
Categories of Work
Civil legal aid
Criminal court work
Criminal legal aid
Human rights
Immigration and asylum
Media and entertainment
Partner
Mohammed Aamer Anwar
Consultant
April Agnes Cowan Meechan
Associates
Sarah Jayne Murray
Ryan Sloan
Employee
Erin Monaghan

ARCHER COYLE
513 Clarkston Road, Muirend, Glasgow
G44 3PN
Tel: (0141) 6372434
Fax: (0141) 2373473
E-mail: enqs@archercoyle.co.uk

▶ **Glasgow** continued

Categories of Work
Advice the elderly & powers of attorney
Benefit advice
Civil court work
Civil legal aid
Consumer credit
Contract & property disputes
Criminal court work
Criminal legal aid
Data protection
Debt
Discrimination
Employment law
Family and divorce
Freedom of information
Human rights
Landlord & tenant
Media and entertainment
Medical negligence – claimant
Personal injury
Personal injury – defender
Residential property
Social housing
Wills, executives and trusts
Partner
Elizabeth June Coyle
Consultant
Gordon Dangerfield

ARGUE & CO LEGAL
First Floor, 9 George Square, Glasgow
G2 1QQ
Tel: (0141) 3784145
Categories of Work
Adjudication
Alternative dispute resolution
Civil court work
Civil legal aid
Commercial litigation
Employment
Employment law
Health
Health and safety
Local government
Medical negligence – defender
Medical negligence – claimant
Pensions (Employment)
Personal injury
Personal injury – defender
Professional negligence
Road traffic
Partner
Allan John Argue

ARMS LEGAL SERVICES WS
22 Forres Avenue, Giffnock, Glasgow G46 6LQ
Tel: (07954) 188167
E-mail: allanrmsteele@armslegalservices.co.uk
Web: www.armslegalservices.co.uk
Categories of Work
Data protection
Employment

Freedom of information
Human rights
Media and entertainment
Partner
Allan Richard Morison Steele

ASCENT LEGAL SCOTLAND
5th Floor, 150 St Vincent Street, Glasgow
G2 5NE
Tel: (0141) 3004300
Categories of Work
Banking & finance
Childrens
Civil court work
Civil legal aid
Commercial litigation
Consumer credit
Debt recovery, insolvency, bankruptcy
Family and divorce
Health and safety
Landlord & tenant
Medical negligence – claimant
Personal injury
Professional negligence
Property litigation
Residential property
Road traffic
Wills, executives and trusts
Employee
Eleanor Hamilton

AUSTIN LAFFERTY LIMITED
118 Ayr Road, Newton Mearns, Glasgow
G77 6EG
Tel: (0141) 6115221
Fax: (0141) 6393654
Categories of Work
Adoption
Advice the elderly & powers of attorney
Alternative dispute resolution
Banking & finance
Children
Childrens
Civil court work
Civil legal aid
Commercial property
Consumer credit
Contract & property disputes
Credit brokerage
Criminal court work
Criminal legal aid
Data protection
Debt adjusting and debt counselling
Debt administration
Debt collecting
Education
Family and divorce
Family business advice
Freedom of information
Health and safety
Human rights
Landlord & tenant
Media and entertainment
Medical negligence – claimant

Mergers and acquisitions
Personal injury
Personal tax
Professional negligence
Property litigation
Provision of credit information services
Residential property
Road traffic
SME business advice
Wills, executries and trusts
Consultant
Gary Simon Landa
Employee
Lisa Craig McCall

AUSTIN LAFFERTY LIMITED
213 Fenwick Road, Giffnock, Glasgow
G46 6JD
Tel: (0141) 6212212
Fax: (0141) 6211342
E-mail: enquiry@laffertylaw.com
Web: www.austinlafferty.co.uk
Categories of Work
Adoption
Advice the elderly & powers of attorney
Alternative dispute resolution
Banking & finance
Children
Childrens
Civil court work
Civil legal aid
Commercial property
Consumer credit
Contract & property disputes
Credit brokerage
Criminal court work
Criminal legal aid
Data protection
Debt adjusting and debt counselling
Debt administration
Debt collecting
Education
Family and divorce
Family business advice
Freedom of information
Health and safety
Human rights
Landlord & tenant
Media and entertainment
Medical negligence – claimant
Mergers and acquisitions
Personal injury
Personal tax
Professional negligence
Property litigation
Provision of credit information services
Residential property
Road traffic
SME business advice
Wills, executries and trusts
Director
Austin Joseph Lafferty

Employees
Jane Barrie
Louise Malone
Michelle Ann Orchard

BAKER HARDMAN LIMITED
Lime Tree Business Centre, 557 Sauchiehall
Street, Glasgow G3 7PQ

BANNATYNE, KIRKWOOD, FRANCE & CO.
Exchange House, 16 Royal Exchange Square,
Glasgow G1 3AG
Tel: (0141) 2216020
Fax: (0141) 2215120
DX: GW7 GLASGOW
E-mail: info@bkf.co.uk
Categories of Work
Advice the elderly & powers of attorney
Alternative dispute resolution
Banking & finance
Charities
Civil court work
Commercial litigation
Commercial property
Construction
Contract & property disputes
Copyright, trade marks and design
Criminal court work
Data protection
Debt collecting
Debt recovery, insolvency, bankruptcy
Employment
Employment law
Family business advice
Freedom of information
Insolvency & corporate recovery
IT and intellectual property
Joint venture
Landlord & tenant
Local government
Media and entertainment
Mental health
Mergers and acquisitions
Personal tax
Private equity
Professional negligence
Property litigation
Public sector
Residential property
SME business advice
Social housing
Wills, executries and trusts
Partners
Rory Andrew Burriss Cowan
Campbell Strachan Deane
Alan William Eccles
Alison Wendy McKenna
Brian Charles Meldrum
Robert Stevenet Taylor
Consultants
David William Deane
Angela McCracken
Employee
Euphemia Matheson

▶ *Glasgow continued*

BARTYS TRUSTEES LIMITED
302 St. Vincent Street, Glasgow G2 5RZ
Tel: (0141) 2483434

BELLWETHER GREEN LIMITED
225 West George Street, Glasgow G2 2ND
Tel: (0141) 2184900
Fax: (0141) 229 0640
E-mail: info@bellwethergreen.com
Web: www.bellwethergreen.com
Categories of Work
Alternative dispute resolution
Banking & finance
Betting & gaming
Charities
Commercial litigation
Competition
Consumer credit
Copyright, trade marks and design
Corporate tax
Credit brokerage
Data protection
Debt adjusting and debt counselling
Debt administration
Debt collecting
Debt recovery, insolvency, bankruptcy
Family business advice
Freedom of information
Insolvency & corporate recovery
IT and intellectual property
Joint venture
Liquor licensing
Media and entertainment
Mergers and acquisitions
Mining
Private equity
Provision of credit information services
Public finance initiative
Public sector
Shipping
SME business advice
Software licensing
Sport
Telecoms
Transport
Directors
April Bingham
John Paul Bingham
Frances Margaret Ennis
Steven Robert Templeton
Consultants
Caroline Mary Clark
Euan Allan Faulds
Associate
Stephanie Elizabeth Farrell
Employee
Eve Margaret Mundell

BELMONT LEGAL LTD
Spaces, 1 West Regent Street, Glasgow
G2 1RW
Tel: (0141) 7298848

E-mail: info@belmontsolicitors.co.uk
Director
Kirsten Elizabeth Morrison

BELTRAMI & CO LIMITED
83 Carlton Place, Glasgow G5 9TD
Tel: (0141) 4292262
Fax: (0141) 4292526
E-mail: enquiries@beltramiandcompany.co.uk
Categories of Work
Adoption
Advice the elderly & powers of attorney
Children
Childrens
Civil court work
Civil legal aid
Commercial litigation
Commercial property
Contract & property disputes
Criminal court work
Criminal legal aid
Data protection
Debt
Debt collecting
Debt management
Debt recovery, insolvency, bankruptcy
Disability
Discrimination
Education
Employment
Employment law
Family and divorce
Family business advice
Freedom of information
Health
Health and safety
Housing
Human rights
Landlord & tenant
Liquor licensing
Local government
Media and entertainment
Medical negligence – defender
Medical negligence – claimant
Mental health
Personal injury
Personal injury – defender
Professional negligence
Property litigation
Residential property
Road traffic
SME business advice
Social housing
Transport
Wills, executries and trusts
Assistant
Alistair Campbell McGarvey
Director
James Gary McAteer
Consultant
John David Murray Macara

Employees
Craig Philip Alexander Broadley
Augustine Michael Cortney Casiday
Antonia McCarry Crawford
Sebastien Marc Flowerdew
Alan Joseph Gravelle
Stephanie Kathleen Laura Grieve
Nicholas Michael Melville Nimmo
Claire Avril Thomas
Simon Thomas Whyte

BENTLEY LAW
4th Floor, 52 St Enoch Square, Glasgow
G1 4AA
Tel: (07713) 403020
E-mail: Stephen@bentleylaw.co.uk
Categories of Work
Criminal court work
Criminal legal aid
Partner
Stephen Thomas Wilson Bentley
Employee
Sarah Frances McIlwham

BERLOW RAHMAN SOLICITORS
Ground Floor, 40 Carlton Place, Glasgow
G5 9TW
Tel: (0141) 8901999
Fax: (0141) 429 4225
E-mail: info@brlaw.uk
Categories of Work
Adoption
Children
Childrens
Civil court work
Civil legal aid
Criminal court work
Criminal legal aid
Education
Family and divorce
Human rights
Immigration and asylum
Partner
Jelina Raheema Berlow-Rahman
Associate
Haseeb Ul Hassan

BERRYMANS LACE MAWER LLP
G1, 1 George Square, Glasgow G2 1DY
Tel: (0141) 3532121
Fax: (0141) 3532181
Categories of Work
Adjudication
Alternative dispute resolution
Banking & finance
Children
Civil court work
Civil legal aid
Commercial litigation
Commercial property
Construction
Contract & property disputes
Copyright, trade marks and design
Criminal court work

Criminal legal aid
Data protection
Debt
Debt collecting
Debt recovery, insolvency, bankruptcy
Employment
Employment law
Environment
Environment (Business Premises)
Family and divorce
Fishing
Freedom of information
Health
Health and safety
Housing
Human rights
Insurance
IT and intellectual property
Joint venture
Landlord & tenant
Medical negligence – defender
Medical negligence – claimant
Mergers and acquisitions
Mining
Oil & gas
Parliamentary
Personal injury
Personal injury – defender
Personal tax
Planning
Planning (Business Premises)
Power and utilities
Professional negligence
Projects
Property litigation
Road traffic
Transport
Partners
Karen Dance
Andrew Kenneth Gilmour
Francis Hughes
Consultant
George Kuthy Moore
Associates
Kelly Marie Brotherhood
Lorna Roseanne Ferguson
Zoe McDonnell
Kirsty Anne Yuill
Employees
Julie Anne Brodtkorb
Caroline Gillespie
Rachel Anne Henry
Wan-Ting Hwang
Mark Douglas Jamieson
Cheryl Liddell
Grant Ross Maclean
Steven Henry McDonagh
Fiona McEwan
Anthony James Murray
Alison Morag Nicol
Kirsteen Picken
Fiona Kirsty Robinson
David Neil Taylor

▶ *Glasgow continued*

Danielle Suzanne Varela

BERRY, POGGI & CO
3rd Floor, 46 Carlton Place, Glasgow G5 9TW
Tel: (0141) 4297211
Fax: 1414297453
DX: 500532 CUMBERNAULD
E-mail: mail@berrypoggi.co.uk
Categories of Work
Criminal court work
Criminal legal aid
Partner
Michael Joseph Poggi
Employee
Michelle Louise Skelly

BILKUS & BOYLE
2175 Paisley Road West, Cardonald, Glasgow
G52 3PF
Tel: (0141) 8823221
Fax: (0141) 8834848
DX: 500300 CARDONALD
E-mail: law@bilkusandboyle.com
Categories of Work
Adoption
Children
Civil court work
Civil legal aid
Criminal court work
Criminal legal aid
Family and divorce
Residential property
Wills, executives and trusts
Partners
Campbell John Porter
Stuart Benjamin Porter
Katherine Jane Wilson
Consultant
Margaret Mary Boyle

BLACKADDERS LLP
53 Bothwell Street, Glasgow G2 6TS
Tel: (0141) 2481888
Fax: (0141) 248 2030
E-mail: enquiries@blackadders.co.uk
Categories of Work
Adoption
Advice the elderly & powers of attorney
Agriculture and estates
Agriculture, crofting and fishing
Alternative dispute resolution
Banking & finance
Charities
Children
Childrens
Civil court work
Civil legal aid
Commercial litigation
Commercial property
Competition
Construction
Consumer credit
Contract & property disputes

Copyright, trade marks and design
Data protection
Debt
Debt collecting
Debt recovery, insolvency, bankruptcy
Disability
Discrimination
Employment
Employment law
Environment
Environment (Business Premises)
EU / international
Family and divorce
Family business advice
Fishing
Freedom of information
Housing
Human rights
Insolvency & corporate recovery
IT and intellectual property
Joint venture
Landlord & tenant
Media and entertainment
Medical negligence – defender
Medical negligence – claimant
Mental health
Mergers and acquisitions
Pensions (Employment)
Personal injury
Personal injury – defender
Personal tax
Planning
Power and utilities
Private equity
Professional negligence
Property litigation
Public sector
Residential property
Road traffic
SME business advice
Software licensing
Sport
Telecoms
Wills, executives and trusts
Partners
Gillian Jane Brown
Stephanie Margaret Mary Carr
Stephen David Connolly
Peter Duff
Karen Elizabeth Fulton
Lucy Rae Gannon
Consultant
John Kerrigan
Employees
Mohammad Azeem Arshad
Natalia Jade Bell
Susan Elizabeth Currie
Dario Demarco
Stefan Edward Docherty
Richard Thomas Duffy
Paul Francis Nash
Emma Sadler
Andrew John Shaw

Katharine Louise Smith
Jacqueline Tainsh

BLACKWATER LAW LIMITED
46A Carlton Place, Glasgow G5 9TW
Tel: (0141) 404 7778
E-mail:
graham.mann@blackwaterlawlimited.co.uk
Categories of Work
Adoption
Advice the elderly & powers of attorney
Children
Childrens
Civil court work
Criminal court work
Criminal legal aid
Education
Family and divorce
Wills, executries and trusts
Director
Graham Andrew Mann
Consultant
Suzanne Antonette Whyte

BLANEY CARNAN
5th Floor, Standard Buildings, Glasgow
G2 6PH
Tel: (0141) 2488111
Fax: (0141) 2218420
E-mail: mail@blaneycarnan.com
Categories of Work
Advice the elderly & powers of attorney
Commercial property
Contract & property disputes
Family business advice
Landlord & tenant
Residential property
SME business advice
Wills, executries and trusts
Partner
Paul Blaney Carnan

BMK (NOMINEES) LIMITED
302 St. Vincent Street, Glasgow G2 5RZ
Tel: (0141) 2483434

C.T. BOLLEN LIMITED
Suite 5, 98 Woodlands Road, Charing Cross,
Glasgow G3 6HB
Tel: (07702) 031976
E-mail: chris@ctbollensolicitors.co.uk
Web: www.ctbollensolicitors.co.uk
Director
Christopher Thomas Bollen

C.F. BOYLE & CO LIMITED
10 Newton Place, Glasgow G3 7PR
Tel: (0141) 2043897
Fax: (0141) 2482729
Categories of Work
Criminal court work
Criminal legal aid
Director
Christopher Francis Boyle

T BOYLE & CO LIMITED
C/o L & G Robertson Solicitors, 46 Carlton
Place, Glasgow G5 9TD
Tel: (07752) 266001
Fax: (0141) 4297453
E-mail: terry_boyle@btinternet.com
Categories of Work
Criminal court work
Criminal legal aid
Director
Terence Boyle

AJ BRADLEY & CO LTD
Floor 4, Suite 13, 111 Union Street, Glasgow
G1 3TA
Tel: (0141) 374 0474
Categories of Work
Criminal court work
Criminal legal aid
Immigration and asylum
Director
Andrew John Bradley
Employee
Kylie Lau

BREADY & CO.
First Floor, 40 Carlton Place, Glasgow G5 9TW
Tel: (0141) 334 2265
Fax: (0141) 3343284
DX: 513223 Glasgow Carlton Place
E-mail: info@breadyandco.com
Web: www.breadyandco.com
Categories of Work
Advice the elderly & powers of attorney
Criminal court work
Criminal legal aid
Landlord & tenant
Residential property
Road traffic
Wills, executries and trusts
Partner
James Bready
Employees
Sabrina Baig
Eileen Maeve Bready

BRECHIN TINDAL OATTS
48 St. Vincent Street, Glasgow G2 5HS
Tel: (0141) 2218012
Categories of Work
Adjudication
Adoption
Advice the elderly & powers of attorney
Agriculture and estates
Agriculture, crofting and fishing
Alternative dispute resolution
Alternative investment market
Banking & finance
Benefit advice
Charities
Children
Childrens
Civil court work
Civil legal aid

▶ **Glasgow** continued

Commercial litigation
Commercial property
Competition
Construction
Consumer credit
Contract & property disputes
Copyright, trade marks and design
Corporate tax
Criminal court work
Data protection
Debt
Debt collecting
Debt recovery, insolvency, bankruptcy
Disability
Discrimination
Employment
Employment law
Environment
Environment (Business Premises)
EU / international
Family and divorce
Family business advice
Freedom of information
Health
Health and safety
Housing
Insolvency & corporate recovery
Insurance
IT and intellectual property
Joint venture
Landlord & tenant
Liquor licensing
Media and entertainment
Medical negligence – defender
Medical negligence – claimant
Mental health
Mergers and acquisitions
Oil & gas
Pensions (Company)
Pensions (Employment)
Personal injury
Personal injury – defender
Personal tax
Planning
Planning (Business Premises)
Power and utilities
Private equity
Professional negligence
Projects
Property litigation
Provision of credit information services
Public finance initiative
Public sector
Residential property
Road traffic
Shipping
SME business advice
Social housing
Software licensing
Sport
Transport

Unit Trusts, OEICs and investment trusts
Wills, executries and trusts
Employee
Katherine Elizabeth Wade

BRIDGE EMPLOYMENT SOLICITORS LIMITED
Ground Floor, Regent Court, 70 West Regent
Street, Glasgow G2 2QZ
Tel: (0141) 4292181
E-mail: mgribbon@bridgeemplaw.com
Web: www.bridgeemplaw.com
Categories of Work
Employment
Employment law
Director
Margaret Gribbon

BRIDGE LEGAL LIMITED
Carlton Building, 4th Floor, 63 Carlton Place,
Glasgow G5 9TW
Tel: (0141) 4293100
E-mail: info@bridgelegalglasgow.co.uk
Categories of Work
Criminal court work
Criminal legal aid
Human rights
Directors
Marisa Borland
William Moore Lavelle
Consultants
Graeme Robert Brown
Peter Thomas Malone
John-Paul Mowberry
Employees
Lauren Aitchison
Laura Frances Boyd
Atlanta Tazmin Jack

BRODIES LLP
110 Queen Street, Glasgow G1 3BX
Tel: (0141) 2484672
Fax: (0141) 2219270
DX: GW11 GLASGOW
E-mail: mailbox@brodies.com
Web: www.brodies.co.uk
Categories of Work
Adjudication
Adoption
Advice the elderly & powers of attorney
Agriculture and estates
Agriculture, crofting and fishing
Alternative dispute resolution
Alternative investment market
Banking & finance
Charities
Children
Childrens
Civil court work
Civil legal aid
Commercial litigation
Commercial property
Competition
Construction
Consumer credit

Contract & property disputes
Copyright, trade marks and design
Corporate tax
Credit brokerage
Criminal court work
Criminal legal aid
Data protection
Debt
Debt adjusting and debt counselling
Debt administration
Debt collecting
Debt recovery, insolvency, bankruptcy
Disability
Discrimination
Education
Employment
Employment law
Environment
Environment (Business Premises)
EU / international
Family and divorce
Family business advice
Fishing
Freedom of information
Health
Health and safety
Housing
Human rights
Immigration and asylum
Insolvency & corporate recovery
Insurance
IT and intellectual property
Joint venture
Landlord & tenant
Liquor licensing
Local government
Media and entertainment
Medical negligence – defender
Medical negligence – claimant
Mental health
Mergers and acquisitions
Mining
Oil & gas
Parliamentary
Pensions (Company)
Pensions (Employment)
Personal injury
Personal injury – defender
Personal tax
Planning
Planning (Business Premises)
Power and utilities
Private equity
Professional negligence
Projects
Property litigation
Provision of credit information services
Public finance initiative
Public sector
Residential property
Road traffic
Shipping
SME business advice

Social housing
Software licensing
Sport
Telecoms
Transport
Unit Trusts, OEICs and investment trusts
Wills, executries and trusts

Partners
Alix Joan Bearhop
Neil Ross Burgess
Joan Mary Cradden
Karen Jane Davidson
Matthew Farrell
William Alasdair Fleming
Carly Louise Forrest
Eric Roger Galbraith
Lisa Anne Irvine Girdwood
Gareth Jonathan Hale
Karen Lesley Hamilton
Colin Christopher Keenan
Peter Robert Kelly
Norman Kennedy
Charles David Livingstone
Alisdair Stuart Matheson
Sarah-Jane McArthur
Angela Dale McCulloch
Christopher McDaid
Elaine Christina McIlroy
Jane Claire McMonagle
Jack Moir
Johane Macmillan Murray
Elaine Claire Petterson
Manus Martin Quigg
Richard Ian Campbell Smith
Shuna Margaret Elizabeth Stirling
Derek Andrew Stroud

Consultant
Frank Raine Johnstone

Associates
Victoria Louise Anderson
Kirstyn Faye Burke
Maureen Anne Burns
Heather Gibson
Lorne Campbell Graham
Marianne Robinson Griffin
Charles Wilson Hay
Caroline Joanna Dunn Kennedy
Keith Kilburn
Jennifer Macdonald Laurie
Shirley Li-Ting
Michael Andrew McQuade
Sarah Louise Miller
Jenna Alison Monteith
Stuart John Murray
Jamie Stewart Nellany
Catherine Margaret Reilly
Claire Rice
Fiona Bain Sharp
Iain William Macdonald Smith

Solicitor
Carly Nicola Mason

▶ **Glasgow** continued

Employees
Sophie Elizabeth Airth
Kathryn Charlotte Angus
Craig James Asbury
Iain Alastair Baird
Ryan William Bell
Lori Beveridge
Nicola Claire Fiona Boardley
Ryan Bowie
Brian James Campbell
Ross Donald Campbell
Joanna Mary Campbell-Smith
Mairi Taylor Carlin
Stephanie Carole Clarke
Monica Louise Connolly
Anthony Peter Convery
Jennifer Laura Clare Crawford
Giulia De Marco
Craig Thomas Donnelly
Fiona Mhairi Dromgoole
Louise Elizabeth Duffy
Alasdair Ian Dunn
Eilidh Louise Dunn
Isla Alexandra McIntosh Fern
Christy Foster
David Ewart Gallagher
Owen Daniel George
Kirstin Fiona Gillespie
Eoghann David MacLeod Green
Connor James Guinea
Jennifer Elizabeth Guy
Juliet Lorna Haldane
Jordan Thomas Halliday
Elizabeth Metcalfe Heaney
Catriona May Coom Heggie
Ashley Hollis
Joanne Louise Kelbrick
Lauren Margaret Kerr
Louise Anne Laing
Lynn Martin Livesey
Stuart William Logan
Callum David MacKinnon
Calum Michael MacPherson
Gillian Anne Mair
Alison Colette McAteer
Sarah Marie McConnell
Hannah McGurk
Cameron James McKay
Erin Anne McLafferty
Kirsty Hastings McLeish
Fiona McLeod
Hannah Alison McMurray
Claire Ruth Mills
Kathleen Anne Morrison
Donald Vladimir Muir
Niamh Murray-Sheridan
Rachel E.N.R. O'Reilly
Eilidh Sarah Jean Paterson
Jayne Macdonald Paterson
Emma Jayne Paul
Katherine Elizabeth Priester

Jordon Christopher Reid
Michael Francis Reilly
Kendra Richardson
Rachael Jane Ruth
Elizabeth Caroline Salmon
Gail Louise Smith
Martha Rose Speed
Jamie Christina Elizabeth Steel
Ailsa Carmichael Thomson
Euan Brodie Wallace
William Frederick Ward
Kevin John Winters
Zoe Hunter Wray

BROWN & CO LEGAL LLP
At Legal Services Agency, 1169 Royston Road,
Glasgow G33 1EY
Tel: (0141) 7707869
Web: www.lsa.org.uk
Categories of Work
Adoption
Advice the elderly & powers of attorney
Alternative dispute resolution
Benefit advice
Charities
Children
Childrens
Civil court work
Civil legal aid
Commercial litigation
Contract & property disputes
Criminal court work
Criminal legal aid
Debt
Debt management
Debt recovery, insolvency, bankruptcy
Disability
Discrimination
Family and divorce
Human rights
Immigration and asylum
Landlord & tenant
Medical negligence – claimant
Mental health
Personal injury
Professional negligence
Property litigation
Social housing
Wills, executives and trusts

BROWN & CO LEGAL LLP
Legal Services Agency, Fleming House,
Glasgow G3 6ST
Tel: (0141) 3533354
Fax: (0141) 3530354
E-mail: mail@lsa.org.uk
Web: www.lsa.org.uk
Categories of Work
Adoption
Advice the elderly & powers of attorney
Alternative dispute resolution
Benefit advice
Charities
Children

Childrens
Civil court work
Civil legal aid
Commercial litigation
Contract & property disputes
Criminal court work
Criminal legal aid
Debt
Debt management
Debt recovery, insolvency, bankruptcy
Disability
Discrimination
Family and divorce
Human rights
Immigration and asylum
Landlord & tenant
Medical negligence – claimant
Mental health
Personal injury
Professional negligence
Property litigation
Social housing
Wills, executories and trusts
Partners
Paul David Brown
Alastair David Houston
Rachel Wilson Walker
Employees
Benjamin David Gliori-Christman
Hannah Katherine Goldsmith
Rona Macleod
Helen McHugh
Shaun Lee McPhee
Aileen Frances Miller
Mhairi Elizabeth Anne Miller
Katarzyna Alina Prochalska

BROWN & CO LEGAL LLP
North Glasgow Advice Centre, 1169 Royston
Road, Glasgow G33 1EY
Tel: (0141) 7707869
Web: www.lsa.org.uk
Categories of Work
Adoption
Advice the elderly & powers of attorney
Alternative dispute resolution
Benefit advice
Charities
Children
Childrens
Civil court work
Civil legal aid
Commercial litigation
Contract & property disputes
Criminal court work
Criminal legal aid
Debt
Debt management
Debt recovery, insolvency, bankruptcy
Disability
Discrimination
Family and divorce
Human rights

Immigration and asylum
Landlord & tenant
Medical negligence – claimant
Mental health
Personal injury
Professional negligence
Property litigation
Social housing
Wills, executories and trusts

JOHN BROWN (SCOTLAND) LTD
48 Shandwick Square, Easterhouse, Glasgow
G34 9DT
Tel: (0141) 7810000
Fax: (0141) 7811708
E-mail: browns.solicitors@hotmail.co.uk
Categories of Work
Adoption
Advice the elderly & powers of attorney
Children
Civil court work
Civil legal aid
Criminal court work
Criminal legal aid
Family and divorce
Director
Alison Margaret Heron
Consultant
John Brown
Employee
Jacqueline May Wall

BRUNTON MILLER
Herbert House, 22 Herbert Street, Glasgow
G20 6NB
Tel: (0141) 3371199
Fax: (0141) 3373300
E-mail: info@bruntonmiller.com
Web: www.bruntonmiller.com
Categories of Work
Advice the elderly & powers of attorney
Banking & finance
Betting & gaming
Children
Civil court work
Civil legal aid
Commercial litigation
Commercial property
Construction
Consumer credit
Contract & property disputes
Copyright, trade marks and design
Credit brokerage
Criminal court work
Criminal legal aid
Debt
Debt adjusting and debt counselling
Debt administration
Debt collecting
Debt recovery, insolvency, bankruptcy
Employment
Employment law
Family and divorce
Family business advice

▶ **Glasgow continued**

Joint venture
Landlord & tenant
Liquor licensing
Local government
Mergers and acquisitions
Personal injury
Planning (Business Premises)
Provision of credit information services
Residential property
Road traffic
Wills, executries and trusts
Partners
Francis Collins
Edward Alexander Doull
Archibald Duncan Maciver
Thomas Cunningham Steel

BRYSON'S LEGAL SERVICES
3-Jan, 1534 Maryhill Road, Glasgow G20 9AD
Tel: (07841) 875853
E-mail: Brysonlegal@aol.com
Categories of Work
Children
Childrens
Civil court work
Civil legal aid
Criminal court work
Criminal legal aid
Employment
Family and divorce
Landlord & tenant
Road traffic
Partner
Graham Robert Bryson

BRZOOM KADIRGOLAM
Ethnic Minorities Law Centre, 41 St. Vincent
Place, Glasgow G1 2ER
Tel: (0141) 2042888
Fax: (0141) 2042006
E-mail: admin@emlc.org.uk
Web: www.emlc.org.uk
Categories of Work
Children
Civil court work
Civil legal aid
Disability
Discrimination
Employment
Employment law
Human rights
Immigration and asylum
Medical negligence – defender
Personal injury – defender
Partner
Brzoom Hassan Kadirgolam
Employees
Michael Edward Ross
Gurcharanjeet Singh

BTO SOLICITORS LLP
48 St. Vincent Street, Glasgow G2 5HS
Tel: (0141) 2218012

Fax: (0141) 2217803
DX: GW96 GLASGOW
E-mail: lawyers@bto.co.uk
Web: www.bto.co.uk
Categories of Work
Adjudication
Adoption
Advice the elderly & powers of attorney
Agriculture and estates
Agriculture, crofting and fishing
Alternative dispute resolution
Alternative investment market
Banking & finance
Benefit advice
Charities
Children
Childrens
Civil court work
Civil legal aid
Commercial litigation
Commercial property
Competition
Construction
Consumer credit
Contract & property disputes
Copyright, trade marks and design
Corporate tax
Criminal court work
Data protection
Debt
Debt collecting
Debt recovery, insolvency, bankruptcy
Disability
Discrimination
Employment
Employment law
Environment
Environment (Business Premises)
EU / international
Family and divorce
Family business advice
Freedom of information
Health
Health and safety
Housing
Insolvency & corporate recovery
Insurance
IT and intellectual property
Joint venture
Landlord & tenant
Liquor licensing
Media and entertainment
Medical negligence – defender
Medical negligence – claimant
Mental health
Mergers and acquisitions
Oil & gas
Pensions (Company)
Pensions (Employment)
Personal injury
Personal injury – defender
Personal tax
Planning

Planning (Business Premises)
Power and utilities
Private equity
Professional negligence
Projects
Property litigation
Provision of credit information services
Public finance initiative
Public sector
Residential property
Road traffic
Shipping
SME business advice
Social housing
Software licensing
Sport
Transport
Unit Trusts, OEICs and investment trusts
Wills, executries and trusts

Partners
Emma Robertson Barclay
Clare Jane Bone
Karen Susan Brodie
Ross Alexander Brown
Stephen Charles Bryceland
John Scott Buchan
Lynne Margaret Wallace Cardow
Caroline Ann Carr
Angus Kirkwood Crawford
Catherine Ann Currie
Alastair Kenneth Dunn
Alan William Eadie
Garry William Ferguson
David Bisset Gibson
Alasdair Duncan Gillies
Jeremy Stewart Glen
Peter Graham
Fraser Hopkins
Grant Martin Hunter
Karina Manson
Nicolas Richard McBride
Mark Alistair Craig Morton
Jillian Joanne Petrie
Laura Irene Salmond
Andrew Falconer Sleigh
Jane Anne Steel
Vikki Watt
Claire Esther Margaret White
Jennifer Margaret Whitelaw
Angus Robert Wood
James Scott Wyper
David Allan Young

Consultant
Rhona Murray Wark

Associates
Bruce Battersby
Audrey Sanderson Blair
Marjory Elizabeth Blair
Marion Elizabeth Davis
Lesley Helen Gray
Mark Francis Hastings
Kirsteen Margaret Maclean
Kirsty Elizabeth McGuinness

Stephanie Elizabeth Gillespie McLaughlan
Marieclaire Anne Reid
Donald Robertson
Jennifer Helen Stewart
Douglas Alexander Strang
Calum Sweeney
Martyn Timothy Keith Webster

Employees
Beverley May Addison
Siobhan Rhonwen Agosti
Amy Anderson
Alistair William Barbour
Katie Louise Coates
Stuart Andrew Craig
Cara Elizabeth Docherty
Emma Elizabeth Donaldson
Morven Jean Kilpatrick Douglas
Charles Wesley Eadie
Miriam Farooq
Charlotte Alexandra Fleming
Sean Patrick Folan
Morag Agnes Gibb
Angus Macdonald Gillies
Natasha Louise Goldman
Lesley Jane Grant
Keira Greer
Gillian Allison Harman
Katie Hendry
Michael Higgins
Aaron Alexander Hanson Kane
Jennifer Joyce King
Charlotte Mary Larkin
Neil David Macdonald
Jennifer Margaret Mackenzie
Lindsay MacLeod MacNeill
Fergus Samuel Torrance McColm
Mark Thomas McEvinney
Jaimie Margaret McGready
Rhona Mary McKerracher
Sophie Rebecca Mills
Jamie Alexander Caddis Murray
Rebecca O'Hear
Campbell Cairns Swinley
David Ross White
Lynsey Jane Wilson

BUCHANAN MACLEOD
180 West Regent Street, Glasgow G2 4RW
Tel: (0141) 2214440
Fax: (0141) 2212343
DX: GW62 GLASGOW
E-mail: mail@buchananmacleod.co.uk
Categories of Work
Advice the elderly & powers of attorney
Civil court work
Commercial litigation
Commercial property
Construction
Consumer credit
Contract & property disputes
Landlord & tenant
Residential property
Wills, executries and trusts

▶ *Glasgow continued*

Partner
Karen Elaine Buchanan
Employee
Patricia Ann Doogan

BURNESS PAULL LLP
120 Bothwell Street, Glasgow G2 7JL
Tel: (0141) 2484933
Fax: (0141) 2041601
DX: GW154 GLASGOW
E-mail: info@burnesspaull.com
Web: www.burnesspaull.com
Categories of Work
Adjudication
Adoption
Advice the elderly & powers of attorney
Agriculture and estates
Agriculture, crofting and fishing
Alternative dispute resolution
Alternative investment market
Banking & finance
Betting & gaming
Charities
Civil court work
Commercial litigation
Commercial property
Competition
Construction
Consumer credit
Contract & property disputes
Copyright, trade marks and design
Corporate tax
Credit brokerage
Criminal court work
Data protection
Debt
Debt adjusting and debt counselling
Debt administration
Debt collecting
Debt recovery, insolvency, bankruptcy
Education
Employment
Employment law
Environment
Environment (Business Premises)
EU / international
Family business advice
Fishing
Freedom of information
Health
Health and safety
Housing
Human rights
Immigration and asylum
Insolvency & corporate recovery
Insurance
IT and intellectual property
Joint venture
Landlord & tenant
Liquor licensing
Local government
Media and entertainment

Medical negligence – claimant
Mergers and acquisitions
Mining
Oil & gas
Parliamentary
Pensions (Company)
Pensions (Employment)
Personal injury
Personal injury – defender
Personal tax
Planning
Planning (Business Premises)
Power and utilities
Private equity
Professional negligence
Projects
Property litigation
Provision of credit information services
Public finance initiative
Public sector
Residential property
Road traffic
Shipping
SME business advice
Social housing
Software licensing
Sport
Telecoms
Transport
Unit Trusts, OEICs and investment trusts
Wills, executries and trusts
Partners
Graeme Stuart Bradshaw
Ronald Walter Brown
Jody Stephen Crockett
James Bennie Cook Forbes
Colin James Kennedy Hulme
Jamie Kerr
Ronald Mackay
Claire Eileen Macpherson
Steven McKinlay
Margaret Meehan
Gary John Moffat
Morag Woodburn Moffett
David Morgan
Nicholas Paul Naddell
Graeme Thomas Palmer
Gavin Hugh Paton
Paul Michael Scullion
Callum Snowden Sinclair
Jennifer Carol Skeoch
Grant Tennant Stevenson
Michael Philip Thomson
Michael Fenwick Wood
Consultant
Jennifer Margaret Adams
Associates
Caroline Robertson Allan
Amna Ashraf
Steven Chesney
Colin McArthur Clelland
Louise Kathleen Conroy
Gaelen Jenniffer Jamieson Doherty

Kirsteen Anne MacDonald
Barbara Louise Mayne
Kathleen McAnea
Laura Ann Millar
Mark Ian Patterson
Colin Walker Smith
Nicola Patricia Weir
Employees
Rebecca Fiona Ablett
Deborah Jane Allan
Kirstin Beattie
Shabnam Ellahie Bhatti
Andrew Peter Black
Megan Alison Briggs
Adam Nicholas Iain Bushnell
Yvonne Byrne
Roddy Gordon Cairns
Louise Chambers
Lewis Andrew Clark
Alison Clarke
Christopher Clarkson
Victoria Elizabeth Cowan
Sarah Allison Curran
Victoria Jacqueline Davis
Erica Joan Dickson
Leslie James Dickson
Laura Jane Fitzpatrick
Ashley Kim Flanagan
Fiona Fowle
Claire Margaret Hawthorne
Morven Grace Helen Hopper
Laurie Elizabeth Houston
Hannah Dilys Jenkins
Stephanie Louise Kyle
Ka Pui Cathy Lau
Kirsten Alana Leckie
Fiona Mairi MacLellan
Eilidh Anne Macleod
Karen Margaret Manning
Andrew John Martin
Emma Maxwell
Laura Ellen Victoria McClinton
Kevin McDade
James Stephen Hugh McFarlane
Scott John McGeachy
Rachel Louise McKay
Ruth Mary McNaught
Gavin McQueen
Jamie Meechan
Gillian Middleton
Ilaria Moretti
Kate Marion Primrose
Demi Marie Renucci
James Ritchie
Karolina Malgorzata Rosochowska
Carolyn Susan Ross
Lisa Miller Ross
Andrew Rutherford
Jenny Nevay Scott
Caroline Birgitta Sedman Jaensson
Clara Marie Smeaton
Jennifer Smith
Steven Robert William Stewart

Allana Clair Breaden Sweeney
Fiona Lennox Tosh
Nathalie Joyce Ward
Tamara Lawson Young

CAIRN LEGAL LTD
First Floor, Regent House, Glasgow G2 2RU
Tel: (0141) 221 7948
E-mail: nicola@cairntrusts.co.uk
Categories of Work
Advice the elderly & powers of attorney
Children
Civil court work
Civil legal aid
Disability
Discrimination
Education
Human rights
Mental health
Wills, executries and trusts
Director
Nicola Jane Smith
Consultant
Iain Alister Nisbet

CALLAN & CO (GLASGOW) LIMITED
157 Cumbernauld Road, Muirhead, Glasgow
G69 9AF
Tel: (0141) 7792114
Fax: (0141) 7791470
DX: 501700 MUIRHEAD
E-mail: CALLAN2114@aol.com
Categories of Work
Advice the elderly & powers of attorney
Commercial property
Residential property
Wills, executries and trusts
Director
Martin James Callan
Employee
Margaret Ann Callan

J K CAMERON
St. George's Buildings, 5 St Vincent Place,
Glasgow G1 2DH
Tel: (0141) 2214787
Fax: (0141) 2210701
E-mail: info@jkcameron.co.uk
Web: www.jkcameron.co.uk
Categories of Work
Adoption
Advice the elderly & powers of attorney
Children
Civil legal aid
Criminal court work
Criminal legal aid
Family and divorce
Wills, executries and trusts
Partners
Ross Charles Mackenzie
Claire Anne McFadden
Christopher Robert McIntosh Thomson
Employee
Joanna MacPherson

▶ *Glasgow continued*

CAMERON MACAULAY
107-109 Baltic Chambers, 50 Wellington
Street, Glasgow G2 6HJ
Tel: (0141) 204 7844
Fax: (0141) 6261455
E-mail: mail@cameronmacaulay.co.uk
Web: www.cameronmacaulay.co.uk
Categories of Work
Adoption
Civil legal aid
Employment
Employment law
Family and divorce
Residential property
Wills, executries and trusts
Partner
Malcolm Keith MacAulay Cameron
Employee
Vivien Ho

CAMPBELL & MCCARTNEY
430 Victoria Road, Glasgow G42 8YU
Tel: (0141) 4232222
Fax: (0141) 423 2424
E-mail: pc@patrickcampbellsolicitors.co.uk
Categories of Work
Adoption
Advice the elderly & powers of attorney
Benefit advice
Children
Childrens
Civil court work
Civil legal aid
Consumer credit
Credit brokerage
Criminal court work
Criminal legal aid
Debt
Debt adjusting and debt counselling
Debt administration
Debt collecting
Debt management
Disability
Discrimination
Education
Employment law
Family and divorce
Human rights
Landlord & tenant
Medical negligence – claimant
Mental health
Personal injury
Personal tax
Professional negligence
Provision of credit information services
Residential property
Road traffic
Social housing
Wills, executries and trusts
Partner
Patrick Ian Campbell

Associate
Ziqyia Riaz
Employees
Lesley Anne Graham
Muhammad Shoaib

CAMPBELL SIEVEWRIGHT & CO.
357 Victoria Road, Glasgow G42 8YZ
Tel: (0141) 4222642
Fax: (0141) 4236726
Web: www.campbellsievewrightsolicitors.co.uk
Categories of Work
Commercial property
Residential property
Wills, executries and trusts
Partner
Kenneth Hill
Employee
Robert Brown Thomas

CANNONS LAW PRACTICE LLP
158 Hyndland Road, Glasgow G12 9HZ
Tel: (0141) 2045115
Fax: (0141) 2262221
E-mail: office@cannonslaw.com
Categories of Work
Charities
Civil court work
Civil legal aid
Commercial litigation
Commercial property
Contract & property disputes
Criminal court work
Debt recovery, insolvency, bankruptcy
Employment
Employment law
Family business advice
Human rights
Insolvency & corporate recovery
Joint venture
Landlord & tenant
Medical negligence – defender
Medical negligence – claimant
Mergers and acquisitions
Personal injury
Professional negligence
Property litigation
Residential property
Road traffic
Wills, executries and trusts
Partners
Francis Cannon
Nicola Simone Cannon
Consultant
John Stephen Wilkinson
Employees
Hazel Dunsmuir
Derrick Michael Trainer

CARPENTERS SCOTLAND LIMITED
Third Floor Office Suite, 147 Blythswood
Street, Glasgow G2 4EN
Tel: (0141) 3285452
Fax: (0141) 3285313

Web: www.carpentersgroup.co.uk
Categories of Work
Alternative dispute resolution
Civil court work
Civil legal aid
Medical negligence – claimant
Personal injury
Personal injury – defender
Professional negligence
Road traffic
Director
Calum Stewart MacGregor
Employees
Andrew Graham Agnew
Simon David Campbell
Josh Alexander Dowie
Camilla Ann Greenhorn
Oliver James Hughes Harper
Osman Saeed Khan
Kirsty Angela Nicoletti
Michael Stewart Sellar

CARR & CO (SOLICITORS) LIMITED
100 Cumbernauld Road, Muirhead, Glasgow
G69 9AB
Tel: (0141) 7794466
Fax: (0141) 7792683
Categories of Work
Adoption
Advice the elderly & powers of attorney
Alternative dispute resolution
Banking & finance
Children
Civil court work
Civil legal aid
Commercial property
Contract & property disputes
Criminal court work
Criminal legal aid
Debt
Debt recovery, insolvency, bankruptcy
Disability
Discrimination
Employment
Employment law
Family and divorce
Family business advice
Human rights
Landlord & tenant
Medical negligence – defender
Medical negligence – claimant
Personal injury
Personal injury – defender
Planning (Business Premises)
Professional negligence
Property litigation
Residential property
Road traffic
SME business advice
Wills, executries and trusts
Director
Robert Fitzpatrick

Employees
Jacqueline Anne Harkins
Emma Allison Weir

CARR & CO (SOLICITORS) LIMITED
124 Main Street, Cambuslang, Glasgow
G72 7EL
Tel: (0141) 6412912/8346
Fax: (0141) 6433780
Categories of Work
Adoption
Advice the elderly & powers of attorney
Alternative dispute resolution
Banking & finance
Children
Civil court work
Civil legal aid
Commercial property
Contract & property disputes
Criminal court work
Criminal legal aid
Debt
Debt recovery, insolvency, bankruptcy
Disability
Discrimination
Employment
Employment law
Family and divorce
Family business advice
Human rights
Landlord & tenant
Medical negligence – defender
Medical negligence – claimant
Personal injury
Personal injury – defender
Planning (Business Premises)
Professional negligence
Property litigation
Residential property
Road traffic
SME business advice
Wills, executries and trusts
Director
Ross John James Yuill
Associate
Paul John Gallagher
Employee
Louise Marie Bain

CARR & CO (SOLICITORS) LIMITED
81 Main Street, Baillieston, Glasgow G69 6AD
Tel: (0141) 7732145
Fax: (0141) 7717246
E-mail: pm@theglasgowlawpractice.co.uk
Categories of Work
Adoption
Advice the elderly & powers of attorney
Alternative dispute resolution
Banking & finance
Children
Civil court work
Civil legal aid
Commercial property
Contract & property disputes

► **Glasgow continued**

Criminal court work
Criminal legal aid
Debt
Debt recovery, insolvency, bankruptcy
Disability
Discrimination
Employment
Employment law
Family and divorce
Family business advice
Human rights
Landlord & tenant
Medical negligence – defender
Medical negligence – claimant
Personal injury
Personal injury – defender
Planning (Business Premises)
Professional negligence
Property litigation
Residential property
Road traffic
SME business advice
Wills, executives and trusts
Director
Peter Charles Maley

CARR & CO (SOLICITORS) LIMITED
Curated House, 1/1 Gordon Chambers,
Glasgow G1 3NQ
Tel: (0141) 5528553
Categories of Work
Adoption
Advice the elderly & powers of attorney
Alternative dispute resolution
Banking & finance
Children
Civil court work
Civil legal aid
Commercial property
Contract & property disputes
Criminal court work
Criminal legal aid
Debt
Debt recovery, insolvency, bankruptcy
Disability
Discrimination
Employment
Employment law
Family and divorce
Family business advice
Human rights
Landlord & tenant
Medical negligence – defender
Medical negligence – claimant
Personal injury
Personal injury – defender
Planning (Business Premises)
Professional negligence
Property litigation
Residential property
Road traffic
SME business advice

Wills, executives and trusts

CARRUTHERS GEMMILL
81 Bath Street, Glasgow G2 2EH
Tel: (0141) 3330 033
Fax: (0141) 3321072
E-mail: twg@carruthersgemmill.co.uk
Web: www.carruthersgemmill.co.uk
Categories of Work
Advice the elderly & powers of attorney
Family and divorce
Family business advice
Media and entertainment
Residential property
Wills, executives and trusts
Partners
Thomas William Gemmill
Neil Bromham Rankine
Stephen Robert Watt
Employees
Thomas Mackintosh Miller
Amy Jane Watt

CASSIDYS' ADVICE & SOLICITOR SERVICES
1st Floor, 40 Carlton Place, Glasgow G5 9TW
Tel: (0141) 3532195
E-mail: info@cassidysolicitors.co.uk
Web: www.cassidysolicitors.co.uk
Categories of Work
Criminal court work
Criminal legal aid
Partner
Lindsay Ann Gaughan
Consultant
Kevin Francis Cassidy

CASTLEMILK LAW & MONEY ADVICE CENTRE
155 Castlemilk Drive, Castlemilk, Glasgow
G45 9UG
Tel: (0141) 6340313
E-mail: mail@castlemilklawcentre.co.uk
Categories of Work
Benefit advice
Consumer credit
Debt
Debt adjusting and debt counselling
Debt management
Disability
Discrimination
Employment law
Human rights
Mental health
Residential property
Social housing

CCMC LIMITED
322a, Pentagon Centre, 36 Washington Street,
Glasgow G3 8AZ
Tel: (0141) 2482204
Fax: (0141) 2482527
Categories of Work
Adoption
Advice the elderly & powers of attorney
Children
Childrens

Civil court work
Commercial property
Criminal court work
Criminal legal aid
Education
Family and divorce
Human rights
Immigration and asylum
Landlord & tenant
Medical negligence – claimant
Personal injury
Personal tax
Professional negligence
Residential property
Road traffic
Wills, executries and trusts
Director
Yumann Murray Chung

CCW SECRETARIES LIMITED
302 St. Vincent Street, Glasgow G2 5RZ
Tel: (0141) 2483434

CCW TRUSTEES LIMITED
302 St. Vincent Street, Glasgow G2 5RZ
Tel: (0141) 2483434

CHUNG & REA
322a, Pentagon Centre, 36 Washington Street,
Glasgow G3 8AZ
Tel: (0141) 2482204
Categories of Work
Adoption
Advice the elderly & powers of attorney
Children
Childrens
Civil court work
Commercial property
Criminal court work
Criminal legal aid
Education
Family and divorce
Human rights
Immigration and asylum
Landlord & tenant
Medical negligence – claimant
Personal injury
Personal tax
Professional negligence
Residential property
Road traffic
Wills, executries and trusts

CHUNG SOLICITORS
322a, Pentagon Centre, 36 Washington Street,
Glasgow G3 8AZ
Tel: (0141) 2482204
Categories of Work
Adoption
Advice the elderly & powers of attorney
Children
Childrens
Civil court work
Commercial property
Criminal court work

Criminal legal aid
Education
Family and divorce
Human rights
Immigration and asylum
Landlord & tenant
Medical negligence – claimant
Personal injury
Personal tax
Professional negligence
Residential property
Road traffic
Wills, executries and trusts

CITYWIDE ESTATES AND LETTING
1016 Cathcart Road, Mount Florida, Glasgow
G42 9XL
Categories of Work
Commercial property
Landlord & tenant
Residential property
Wills, executries and trusts

CLAN CHILDLAW LIMITED
Wellpark Enterprise Centre, 120 Sydney Street,
Glasgow G31 1JF
Tel: (0808) 129 0522
Categories of Work
Adoption
Benefit advice
Children
Childrens
Civil court work
Civil legal aid
Debt
Debt management
Disability
Discrimination
Family and divorce
Housing
Human rights
Immigration and asylum
Landlord & tenant
Local government
Mental health
Social housing
Director
Victoria Janet Straiton
Employees
Sarah Louise Bannerman
Rebecca May Scott
Daniel MacIntyre T rnes

CLAPHAMS
1B Helena House, Busby Road, Glasgow
G76 7RA
Tel: (0141) 6200800
Fax: (0141) 6200089
DX: 556320 CLARKSTON
E-mail: lawagents@davidcclapham.co.uk
Categories of Work
Advice the elderly & powers of attorney
Civil court work
Civil legal aid

▶ **Glasgow continued**

Commercial property
Employment law
Family and divorce
Landlord & tenant
Residential property
Wills, executries and trusts
Partner
Debra Harriet Clapham
Consultant
David Charles Clapham
Associate
Stacey McIntyre

CLARITY SIMPLICITY LTD
34 Woodlands Road, Glasgow G3 6UR
Tel: (0141) 4332626
Fax: (0141) 423 7648
DX: 512208 NEWTON
E-mail: legalteam@claritysimplicity.co.uk
Web: www.completeclaritysolicitors.com
Categories of Work
Adoption
Advice the elderly & powers of attorney
Children
Childrens
Civil court work
Commercial litigation
Commercial property
Contract & property disputes
Debt
Debt recovery, insolvency, bankruptcy
Education
Family and divorce
Family business advice
Insolvency & corporate recovery
Landlord & tenant
Medical negligence – defender
Medical negligence – claimant
Personal injury
Personal injury – defender
Professional negligence
Property litigation
Residential property
Wills, executries and trusts
Director
William Urquhart Proctor Smith
Employees
Siobhan Catherine Brown
Craig James McIntosh Chisholm
Susan Leigh Grierson
Dionne Maria Hunter
Sinead Anne Machin
Scott Fraser Stevenson
Ciara Jayne Young

CLARK BOYLE LIMITED
33a Gordon Street, Glasgow G1 3PF
Tel: (0141) 2272200
Fax: (0141) 2272222
E-mail: mail@clarkboyle.co.uk
Web: www.clarkboyle.co.uk
Categories of Work
Advice the elderly & powers of attorney

Commercial property
Contract & property disputes
Family business advice
Landlord & tenant
Mergers and acquisitions
Residential property
Wills, executries and trusts
Directors
Derek Wright Bell
Lauren Anne Heaney
Graham John Holland Queen
Laurence Vincent Reilly
Employee
Katherine Jane McMichael-Phillips

CLOCH SOLICITORS LIMITED
First Floor, Standard Buildings, Glasgow
G2 6PH
Tel: (0141) 221 8029
E-mail: info@cloch.co.uk
Web: www.cloch.co.uk
Categories of Work
Adjudication
Agriculture and estates
Agriculture, crofting and fishing
Alternative dispute resolution
Alternative investment market
Banking & finance
Betting & gaming
Charities
Civil court work
Commercial litigation
Commercial property
Competition
Construction
Contract & property disputes
Copyright, trade marks and design
Corporate tax
Data protection
Debt recovery, insolvency, bankruptcy
Employment
Employment law
Environment
Environment (Business Premises)
EU / international
Family business advice
Fishing
Freedom of information
Housing
Insolvency & corporate recovery
Insurance
IT and intellectual property
Joint venture
Landlord & tenant
Media and entertainment
Mergers and acquisitions
Mining
Oil & gas
Planning (Business Premises)
Power and utilities
Private equity
Projects
Property litigation

Public sector
SME business advice
Software licensing
Sport
Telecoms
Transport
Director
Philip Adamson Hannay
Employee
Laura Anne Scanlan Hannay

CLYDE & CO (SCOTLAND) LLP
144 West George Street, Glasgow G2 2HG
Tel: (0141) 2482666
Fax: (0141) 2489590
DX: GW377 GLASGOW
E-mail: Enquiries.Scotland@clydeco.com
Web: www.clydeco.com
Categories of Work
Adjudication
Adoption
Alternative dispute resolution
Banking & finance
Children
Civil court work
Civil legal aid
Commercial litigation
Commercial property
Construction
Contract & property disputes
Copyright, trade marks and design
Criminal court work
Criminal legal aid
Data protection
Disability
Discrimination
Education
Employment
Employment law
Environment
Environment (Business Premises)
EU / international
Family and divorce
Freedom of information
Health
Health and safety
Human rights
Insurance
Joint venture
Landlord & tenant
Liquor licensing
Local government
Medical negligence – defender
Medical negligence – claimant
Mental health
Oil & gas
Parliamentary
Pensions (Employment)
Personal injury
Personal injury – defender
Power and utilities
Professional negligence
Property litigation

Public sector
Road traffic
Shipping
Sport
Transport
Partners
Lesley Allan
Daniela Leda Fusi
Gilles Robert Graham
Robert King
Stephen Charles Miller
Graham Stuart Mitchell
Frances Elizabeth Ross
Associates
Ann Bonomy
Kirsty Anne Graydon
Miranda Faye Hughes
Nicola Julie Macara
Ameeta Panesar
Marianne Smith
Ryan David Watson
Employees
David Simpson Hutchison
Lynn Macdonald
Alanna Davidson McQueen

CMC LAW LLP
497 Duke Street, Glasgow G31 1DL
Tel: 7731536911
Categories of Work
Adoption
Advice the elderly & powers of attorney
Benefit advice
Children
Childrens
Civil court work
Civil legal aid
Consumer credit
Credit brokerage
Criminal court work
Criminal legal aid
Debt
Debt adjusting and debt counselling
Debt administration
Debt collecting
Debt management
Education
Family and divorce
Medical negligence – claimant
Mental health
Personal injury
Personal tax
Provision of credit information services
Residential property
Road traffic
Social housing
Wills, executries and trusts
Partners
Lorna Esther Clark
Joanne Louise McMillan
Employee
Yvette Fiona McCormick

▶ Glasgow continued

CMS CAMERON MCKENNA NABARRO OLSWANG LLP
1 West Regent Street, Glasgow G2 1AP
Tel: (0141) 2222200
Fax: (0141) 2222201
Categories of Work
Adjudication
Agriculture and estates
Agriculture, crofting and fishing
Alternative dispute resolution
Alternative investment market
Banking & finance
Betting & gaming
Charities
Civil court work
Civil legal aid
Commercial litigation
Commercial property
Competition
Construction
Consumer credit
Contract & property disputes
Copyright, trade marks and design
Corporate tax
Credit brokerage
Data protection
Debt administration
Debt collecting
Debt recovery, insolvency, bankruptcy
Discrimination
Education
Employment
Employment law
Environment
Environment (Business Premises)
EU / international
Family business advice
Fishing
Freedom of information
Health
Health and safety
Housing
Human rights
Immigration and asylum
Insolvency & corporate recovery
Insurance
IT and intellectual property
Joint venture
Landlord & tenant
Liquor licensing
Local government
Media and entertainment
Mergers and acquisitions
Mining
Oil & gas
Parliamentary
Pensions (Company)
Pensions (Employment)
Personal injury
Personal injury – defender
Personal tax

Planning
Planning (Business Premises)
Power and utilities
Private equity
Professional negligence
Projects
Property litigation
Public finance initiative
Public sector
Residential property
Shipping
SME business advice
Social housing
Software licensing
Sport
Telecoms
Transport
Unit Trusts, OEICs and investment trusts
Partners
Graeme Murray Bruce
Aidan George Campbell
Paul Barry Carter
Shona McNae Frame
Carina Pearl Healy
Alistair Ramsay Hill
Darina Catherine Kerr
Eleanor Rosamond Anne Lane
Jack Stewart Letson
Gillian Claire MacLellan
Michael Gerard McAuley
Michael Kenneth Edward McColl
Christopher Francis McGarvey
David James McGowan
Alan Fraser Nelson
Kirsten Marion Partridge
Christopher Neil Rae
Ailsa Ritchie
Allan Wernham
Christine Ellen Worthington
Consultants
Iain Arthur Doran
Alexander Douglas Mathie
Associates
Alana Jessica Sieczkowska Barker
Jennifer Margaret Elizabeth Barr
Martin Jacob Beveridge
Alexandra Hannah Bradley
Louise Jane Brymer
Karen Anne Cossar
Davinia-Elizabeth Cowden
Anita Ingrid Crozier
David William Ramsay Dennis
Julie Maura Devlin
Christopher John Dickson
Lindsay June Dougall
Jane Elizabeth Fender-Allison
Frances Elizabeth Garratt
Alan David Hughes
Iona Louise Arrol Hunter
Lisa Ann Kinloch
Eileen Mary MacMahon
Alan Andrew McDonald
Megan Rea McDonald

Alastair Daniel McNaughton
Kirsty Beth Mitchell
Simon Richard Porter
David James Ramage
Ambreen Zahra Rasool
Martyn Glavin Stevenson
Lindsey Margaret Wainwright
Madeleine Clare Young
Solicitors
Sanaa Hussain Akhtar
Amy Drew Roberts
Employees
Mitchell Robert Abbott
Zain Tarim Bin Tariq Akhtar
Rowan James Alexander
Scott Malcolm Allison
Amy Elizabeth Brown
Nicholas Steven Carroll
Kimberley Anne Cross
Valerie Anne Dougan
Eilidh Ann Fitzgibbon
Jordan Michael Galbraith
Hannah Elizabeth Gibson
Nicola Louise Halliday
Jordan Fraser Kerr
Moritz Kopka
Fiona Letham
Gillian Lorna McCulloch
Megan Rae McCulloch
Katherine McDougall
Katherine Sarah McInnes
Calum John McSporran
Kathryn Margaret Moffett
Rachel Anne Morrison
Laura Marie Rankin
Chelsey Jane Ross
Neeraj Thomas
Catriona Margaret Anne Ward
Ewan Campbell Wilson
Kieran Donald Wood

PHILIP COHEN SOLICITORS LIMITED
First Floor, 40 Carlton Place, Glasgow G5 9TW
Tel: (0141) 6312412
Fax: (0141) 6301814
E-mail: lawyer@philipcohen.co.uk
Categories of Work
Children
Criminal court work
Criminal legal aid
Family and divorce
Director
Philip Harris Cohen
Employee
Lisa Samantha Glass

COMPLETE CLARITY SOLICITORS
34 Woodlands Road, Glasgow G3 6UR
Tel: (0141) 4332626
DX: : 512208 NEWTON
Categories of Work
Adoption
Advice the elderly & powers of attorney
Children

Childrens
Civil court work
Commercial litigation
Commercial property
Contract & property disputes
Debt
Debt recovery, insolvency, bankruptcy
Education
Family and divorce
Family business advice
Insolvency & corporate recovery
Landlord & tenant
Medical negligence – defender
Medical negligence – claimant
Personal injury
Personal injury – defender
Professional negligence
Property litigation
Residential property
Wills, executives and trusts

CONROY MCINNES LIMITED
268 Kilmarnock Road, Shawlands, Glasgow
G43 2XS
Tel: (0141) 6166622
Fax: (0141) 6166633
DX: 501171 SHAWLANDS
E-mail: mail@conroymcinnes.co.uk
Categories of Work
Advice the elderly & powers of attorney
Residential property
Wills, executives and trusts
Solicitor
Edith Elizabeth Grant
Director
Alan Conroy

CORPORATE DEFENCE LTD
65 Bath Street, Glasgow G2 2BX
Tel: (0141) 3031274
E-mail: info@corporatedefence.co.uk
Categories of Work
Construction
Criminal court work
Health and safety
Human rights
Professional negligence
Road traffic
Director
John Martin McGovern

CORRIES SOLICITORS (SCOTLAND) LIMITED
40 Hillend Road, Burnside, Glasgow G73 4JX
Tel: (0141) 2493400
Fax: (0141) 2493401
DX: GW410 GLASGOW
E-mail: Gareth.Ware@corries-g.co.uk
Web: www.corries.co.uk
Categories of Work
Civil legal aid
Health and safety
Personal injury
Personal injury – defender
Road traffic

▶ *Glasgow continued*

Director
Gareth Ware

CORRIGAN LAW
486 Dumbarton Road, Glasgow G11 6SL
Tel: (07763) 704253
E-mail: mail@corriganlaw.co.uk
Categories of Work
Advice the elderly & powers of attorney
Children
Criminal court work
Criminal legal aid
Education
Residential property
Partner
Sin ad Corrigan

COWAN & CO.
81 Berkeley Street, Glasgow G3 7DX
Tel: (0141) 2211803
Fax: (0141) 2041650
Categories of Work
Advice the elderly & powers of attorney
Alternative dispute resolution
Children
Civil court work
Commercial litigation
Consumer credit
Contract & property disputes
Debt
Debt collecting
Debt recovery, insolvency, bankruptcy
Family and divorce
Insolvency & corporate recovery
Landlord & tenant
Medical negligence – claimant
Personal injury
Residential property
Road traffic
Wills, executries and trusts
Partners
Gerald Thomas McWilliams
Helen Marie McWilliams

CON CUNNINGHAM LEGAL SERVICES LTD
The Pentagon Centre, Suite 4, Glasgow
G3 8AZ
Tel: (077447) 446188
E-mail: info@concunningham.com
Categories of Work
Benefit advice
Disability
Discrimination
Human rights
Immigration and asylum
Social housing
Partner
Con Cunningham

CURLE STEWART LIMITED
189 St. Vincent Street, Glasgow G2 5QD
Tel: (0141) 227 6200
Fax: (0141) 227 6219

E-mail: pc@curlestewart.co.uk
Web: www.curlestewart.co.uk
Categories of Work
Banking & finance
Commercial property
Construction
Contract & property disputes
Copyright, trade marks and design
Data protection
Debt recovery, insolvency, bankruptcy
Employment
Employment law
Environment (Business Premises)
EU / international
Family business advice
Insolvency & corporate recovery
IT and intellectual property
Joint venture
Landlord & tenant
Media and entertainment
Mergers and acquisitions
Planning (Business Premises)
Private equity
Residential property
SME business advice
Software licensing
Sport
Directors
Elspeth Curle
Philip Curle
Bryan George Finlayson
Laura Mary McArthur
Employees
Mandy Lees Breen
Gerard Durkan
Lauren Isobel McLeod

DAC BEACHCROFT SCOTLAND LLP
125 West Regent Street, Glasgow G2 2SA
Tel: (0141) 2486688
Fax: (0141) 2489697
DX: 512403 Glas Bath Street
E-mail: scottishclaims@dacbeachcroft.com
Web: https://www.dacbeachcroft.com/
Categories of Work
Adjudication
Adoption
Advice the elderly & powers of attorney
Agriculture and estates
Agriculture, crofting and fishing
Alternative dispute resolution
Alternative investment market
Banking & finance
Benefit advice
Betting & gaming
Charities
Children
Childrens
Civil court work
Civil legal aid
Commercial litigation
Commercial property
Competition

Construction
Consumer credit
Contract & property disputes
Copyright, trade marks and design
Corporate tax
Credit brokerage
Criminal court work
Criminal legal aid
Data protection
Debt
Debt adjusting and debt counselling
Debt administration
Debt collecting
Debt management
Debt recovery, insolvency, bankruptcy
Disability
Education
Employment
Employment law
Environment
Environment (Business Premises)
EU / international
Family and divorce
Family business advice
Fishing
Freedom of information
Health
Health and safety
Housing
Human rights
Immigration and asylum
Insolvency & corporate recovery
Insurance
IT and intellectual property
Joint venture
Landlord & tenant
Liquor licensing
Local government
Media and entertainment
Medical negligence – defender
Medical negligence – claimant
Mental health
Mergers and acquisitions
Mining
Oil & gas
Parliamentary
Pensions (Company)
Pensions (Employment)
Personal injury
Personal injury – defender
Personal tax
Planning
Planning (Business Premises)
Power and utilities
Private equity
Professional negligence
Projects
Property litigation
Provision of credit information services
Public finance initiative
Public sector
Road traffic
Shipping

SME business advice
Social housing
Software licensing
Sport
Telecoms
Transport
Unit Trusts, OEICs and investment trusts
Partner
John Parker Maillie
Associates
Kathryn Jane Graham Gavin
Annis Mackay
Isla Ruth Taylor
Employees
Katherine Jane Anderson
Antony George Bateman
Ebony Jane Bennett
Mhairi Margaret Brown
Jenna Louise Campbell
Shuk Chun Catherine Chung
Nadia Ann Cook
April Alison Craine
Emma Francesca Crilley
Mohsen Saleem Din
Fiona Macdonald Dorman
Darran Elhami-Khorasani
Iain Christopher Franklin
Lara Lesley Frostwick
Louise Alison Gallagher
Linda Jane Gillespie
Andrew Roberts Ireland
Alasdair James MF Irvine
Michael Allan Jefferies
Anne Logan
David James Moy Magee
Caitlin McNiven
Steven Neil McTaggart
Chloe Louise Postlethwaite
Cecily Grace Purcell
Karen Railton
Shaista Rehman
Rachel Jane Rough
Gillian Rushbury
Emma Jane Skett
Jason Stark
Grant David Strathdee
John Paul Stringer
Alan Scott Taylor
Casey Elspeth Thompson
James Alan Varney
Megan Walsh
Iain Alvin Witheyman
Maaria Annam Zabir

DAILLY, WALKER AND CO., SOLICITORS
Govan Law Centre, Orkney St. Enterprise
Centre, Glasgow G51 2BX
Tel: (0141) 4402503
Fax: (0141) 4453934
E-mail: m@govanlc.com
Web: www.govanlc.com
Categories of Work
Adoption

▶ *Glasgow continued*

Advice the elderly & powers of attorney
Alternative dispute resolution
Banking & finance
Benefit advice
Children
Childrens
Civil court work
Civil legal aid
Consumer credit
Criminal legal aid
Debt
Debt adjusting and debt counselling
Debt management
Disability
Discrimination
Education
Employment
Employment law
EU / international
Family and divorce
Human rights
Immigration and asylum
Landlord & tenant
Local government
Mental health
Parliamentary
Personal injury
Personal injury – defender
Property litigation
Residential property
Social housing
Wills, executries and trusts
Partners
Michael Ronald Dailly
Lorna Joyce Walker
Employees
Jennifer Claire Barr
Sophie Catriona Boyd Berry
Claire Elizabeth Cochrane
Christine Long McKellar
Chloe Minto
Laura Marjory Simpson
Holly Sloey

DAILLY, WALKER AND CO., SOLICITORS
Govan Law Centre, Samaritan House, Lower
Ground, Glasgow G42 7JG
Tel: (0141) 433 2665
Categories of Work
Adoption
Advice the elderly & powers of attorney
Alternative dispute resolution
Banking & finance
Benefit advice
Children
Childrens
Civil court work
Civil legal aid
Consumer credit
Criminal legal aid
Debt
Debt adjusting and debt counselling

Debt management
Disability
Discrimination
Education
Employment
Employment law
EU / international
Family and divorce
Human rights
Immigration and asylum
Landlord & tenant
Local government
Mental health
Parliamentary
Personal injury
Personal injury – defender
Property litigation
Residential property
Social housing
Wills, executries and trusts
Employee
Rachel Macmillan Moon

DALLAS MCMILLAN
1st Floor, Regent Court, 70 West Regent
Street, Glasgow G2 2QZ
Tel: (0141) 3336750
Fax: (0141) 3336777
DX: GW30 GLASGOW
E-mail: mail@dallasmcmillan.co.uk
Web: www.dallasmcmillan.co.uk
Categories of Work
Advice the elderly & powers of attorney
Agriculture and estates
Alternative dispute resolution
Civil court work
Civil legal aid
Commercial litigation
Commercial property
Construction
Consumer credit
Contract & property disputes
Debt
Debt administration
Debt collecting
Debt recovery, insolvency, bankruptcy
Discrimination
Employment
Employment law
Environment (Business Premises)
Human rights
Insolvency & corporate recovery
Joint venture
Landlord & tenant
Medical negligence – defender
Medical negligence – claimant
Mergers and acquisitions
Personal injury
Personal injury – defender
Planning (Business Premises)
Professional negligence
Property litigation
Residential property

Road traffic
SME business advice
Wills, executries and trusts
Partners
James Gordon Bell
David Martin Hutchison
Forbes Gillies Leslie
David James McElroy
Consultant
Joyce Amanda Marshall
Associates
Richard Robert Andrew
Rosslyn Iona Margaret Milligan
Employees
Rachel Louise Hendry
Liam James Nicholas McKay
Craig David Muirhead

DAVIDSON CHALMERS STEWART LLP
163 Bath Street, Glasgow G2 4SQ
Tel: (0141) 4283258
Categories of Work
Adjudication
Adoption
Advice the elderly & powers of attorney
Agriculture and estates
Agriculture, crofting and fishing
Alternative dispute resolution
Alternative investment market
Banking & finance
Charities
Civil court work
Commercial litigation
Commercial property
Competition
Construction
Contract & property disputes
Copyright, trade marks and design
Corporate tax
Criminal court work
Data protection
Debt
Debt collecting
Debt recovery, insolvency, bankruptcy
Disability
Discrimination
Employment
Environment
Environment (Business Premises)
EU / international
Family and divorce
Family business advice
Fishing
Freedom of information
Health
Health and safety
Housing
Human rights
Insolvency & corporate recovery
Insurance
IT and intellectual property
Joint venture
Landlord & tenant

Liquor licensing
Local government
Medical negligence – defender
Medical negligence – claimant
Mergers and acquisitions
Mining
Oil & gas
Parliamentary
Personal injury
Personal injury – defender
Planning
Planning (Business Premises)
Power and utilities
Private equity
Professional negligence
Projects
Property litigation
Public finance initiative
Public sector
Residential property
Road traffic
Shipping
SME business advice
Telecoms
Transport
Wills, executries and trusts
Partners
David Stewart Allan
Catherine Mary Feechan
Fiona Margaret Piper
Nicola Clair Scott
Stephen Thomas Smith
Alan James Stewart
Employees
Craig Jackson
Elizabeth Anita Kennedy
Chala Siskin McKenna
Victoria Joanne Ward

DAVIDSON & COMPANY
26 Manse Brae, Glasgow G44 5UG
Tel: (0141) 6335600
Categories of Work
Banking & finance
Commercial property
Contract & property disputes
Debt
Landlord & tenant
Residential property

DAVIDSON & COMPANY SOLICITORS LIMITED
26 Manse Brae, Glasgow G44 5UG
Tel: (0141) 6335600
Web: www.dcosolicitors.co.uk
Categories of Work
Banking & finance
Commercial property
Contract & property disputes
Debt
Landlord & tenant
Residential property
Director
Neil Gillespie Davidson

► *Glasgow continued*

DEAN & CO
PO Box 7541, Glasgow G42 2BG
Tel: (0141) 6494159
Fax: (0141) 6494159
E-mail: deanandco@btinternet.com
Categories of Work
Criminal court work
Criminal legal aid
Partner
Kieran William Dean

DEBT GUARD
150 St Vincent Street, Glasgow G2 5NE
Tel: (0141) 3004300
Categories of Work
Banking & finance
Childrens
Civil court work
Civil legal aid
Commercial litigation
Consumer credit
Debt recovery, insolvency, bankruptcy
Family and divorce
Health and safety
Landlord & tenant
Medical negligence – claimant
Personal injury
Professional negligence
Property litigation
Residential property
Road traffic
Wills, executries and trusts

DEBT GUARD SCOTLAND
150 St Vincent Street, Glasgow G2 5NE
Tel: (0141) 3004300
Categories of Work
Banking & finance
Childrens
Civil court work
Civil legal aid
Commercial litigation
Consumer credit
Debt recovery, insolvency, bankruptcy
Family and divorce
Health and safety
Landlord & tenant
Medical negligence – claimant
Personal injury
Professional negligence
Property litigation
Residential property
Road traffic
Wills, executries and trusts

DELANEY GRAHAM LIMITED
196 Bath Street, Glasgow G2 4HG
Tel: (0141) 4834450
Fax: (0141) 4834455
E-mail: enquiries@delaneygraham.co.uk
Web: www.delaneygraham.co.uk
Categories of Work
Advice the elderly & powers of attorney

Family and divorce
Wills, executries and trusts
Directors
Sian Marie Delaney
Michael Joseph Graham
Employee
Patricia Jane Collins-Whyte

DENTONS UK AND MIDDLE EAST LLP
1 George Square, Glasgow G2 1AL
Tel: (0330) 2220050
Fax: (0330) 2220053
Categories of Work
Adjudication
Adoption
Advice the elderly & powers of attorney
Agriculture and estates
Agriculture, crofting and fishing
Alternative dispute resolution
Alternative investment market
Banking & finance
Betting & gaming
Charities
Children
Civil court work
Civil legal aid
Commercial litigation
Commercial property
Competition
Construction
Contract & property disputes
Copyright, trade marks and design
Corporate tax
Data protection
Debt recovery, insolvency, bankruptcy
Disability
Discrimination
Education
Employment
Employment law
Environment
Environment (Business Premises)
EU / international
Family and divorce
Family business advice
Fishing
Freedom of information
Health
Health and safety
Housing
Human rights
Immigration and asylum
Insolvency & corporate recovery
Insurance
IT and intellectual property
Joint venture
Landlord & tenant
Liquor licensing
Local government
Media and entertainment
Medical negligence – defender
Medical negligence – claimant
Mergers and acquisitions

Mining
Oil & gas
Parliamentary
Pensions (Company)
Pensions (Employment)
Personal injury
Personal injury – defender
Personal tax
Planning
Planning (Business Premises)
Power and utilities
Private equity
Professional negligence
Projects
Property litigation
Public finance initiative
Public sector
Residential property
Shipping
SME business advice
Software licensing
Sport
Telecoms
Transport
Unit Trusts, OEICs and investment trusts
Wills, executries and trusts
Partners
Douglas John Blyth
Alison Helen Bryce
Michael John Dean
Barry Edgar
Stuart Thomas Fitzsimmons
Paul Sydney Haniford
Brian Alexander Hutcheson
Craig David Kennedy
Mark Loudon Macaulay
Lorna Margaret McCaa
Derek Thomas McCombe
Ross James Nicol
Iain Duncan Sutherland
Alison Jane Weatherhead
Paul James Young
Consultants
Thomas Wilson Aitken
Morag Campbell
Associates
Yvonne Allan
Carolyn Helen Burns
Pamela Clare Coulthard
Elizabeth Louise Darley
Susan Christine Gillon
Kimberley Goh
Armando Denis Gon alves
Lindsey Emma Hamill
Lorna Henderson
Jayne Agnes Macfarlane
Sheena Mackintosh
Melanie Ann Martin
David Thomas McGowan
Employees
Lamia Lorraine Al-Lamki
Ian Fraser Barrie
Eileen Beaton

Gethin Bowen
Robert Craig Bradshaw
Daniel Peter Brown
Ally Jordan Burr
Fiona Lindsay Caldow
Ashley Jane Carter
Paul Macintyre Connolly
Amy Audrey Cornelius
Elouisa Margaret Leonard Crichton
Fraser William Crombie
Sophie Marie Davies
Rory James Donaldson
Lorelle Doyle
Rachel Elizabeth Dunn
Laura Margaret Edgar
Karen Farrell
Rachel Gibb
Kirsty Helen Madeline Girvan
Carmen Kahmun Goh
Amanda Gordon
Amy Catherine Gordon
Scott Alexander Greaves
Linzi Grace Hedalen
Gordon William Herd
Fiona Caroline Holmes
Sarah Sinclair Jackman
Colm Kerr
Afshan Sarwar Khan
Fergus Gordon Lawrie
Katy Elizabeth MacAskill
Fiona Sophia Macgregor
Liam Doherty McFadyen
John Denis McGonagle
Thembelihle Blessing McInnes
Kenneth Smith McLaren
Ross William McLelland
Rachel Jane McNeill
Lianne McPherson
Madeleine Louise Miller
Charmaine Anne Murdoch
Claire Nisbet
Anna Rose Owens
Emily Perrett
Giuseppe Pia
Rebecca Bethan Ronney
Rachel Elizabeth Shaw
Jennifer Anne Thomson
Viktoria Orlinova Tsvetanova
Kirsten Young

DAVID DEVINE & CO.
Strathearn House, 211 Hope Street, Glasgow
G2 2UW
Tel: (0141) 3527230
Fax: (0141) 3321437
E-mail: mail@daviddevine.co.uk
Categories of Work
Advice the elderly & powers of attorney
Banking & finance
Commercial property
Family business advice
Landlord & tenant
Mergers and acquisitions

► **Glasgow continued**

Residential property
SME business advice
Wills, executives and trusts
Partner
David Martin Devine

DIAKONEO LEGAL SERVICES LIMITED
48 Speirs Wharf, Glasgow G4 9TH
Tel: (07534) 143293
E-mail: alan@diakoneolegal.co.uk
Web: www.diakoneolegal.com
Categories of Work
Charities
Commercial property
Residential property
Director
Alan Holloway

DIGBY BROWN LLP
2 West Regent Street, Glasgow G2 1RW
Tel: (0333) 200 5925
Fax: (0870) 1911 249
DX: GW17 GLASGOW
E-mail: enquiries@digbybrown.co.uk
Web: https://www.digbybrown.co.uk
Categories of Work
Advice the elderly & powers of attorney
Agriculture and estates
Agriculture, crofting and fishing
Alternative dispute resolution
Alternative investment market
Banking & finance
Benefit advice
Charities
Children
Civil court work
Civil legal aid
Commercial litigation
Commercial property
Competition
Construction
Contract & property disputes
Corporate tax
Criminal court work
Data protection
Debt
Debt adjusting and debt counselling
Debt collecting
Debt recovery, insolvency, bankruptcy
Disability
Discrimination
Employment
Employment law
Environment (Business Premises)
EU / international
Family and divorce
Family business advice
Freedom of information
Health and safety
Human rights
Immigration and asylum
Insolvency & corporate recovery

Insurance
Joint venture
Landlord & tenant
Medical negligence – defender
Medical negligence – claimant
Mental health
Mergers and acquisitions
Pensions (Company)
Personal injury
Personal injury – defender
Planning (Business Premises)
Private equity
Professional negligence
Property litigation
Provision of credit information services
Public finance initiative
Public sector
Residential property
Road traffic
SME business advice
Unit Trusts, OEICs and investment trusts
Wills, executives and trusts
Partners
Stuart Alastair Barton
Gavin Daniel Brogan
Mark Dalziel Gibson
Catherine Ballingall Hart
Moira Alison Kay
Darrell Elizabeth Kaye
Ruth Sarah Anne Kelliher
Matthew William Leckie
Euan David Robert Love
Dawn McCafferty
David Nellaney
Fraser Charles Oliver
Fraser Wallace Simpson
Christopher Walter Stewart
David Alexander Wilson
Associates
Diane Caroline Cooper
Sarah Douglas
David Riddick McGowan
Colin Michael Moffat
Kirsty Ann O'Donnell
Suzanne Williams
Employees
Joy Bell
Ruthven Colin Bell
Linzi Boland
Samuel Alexander Boyce
Lisa Byrne
Rachel Sarah Campbell
Katherine Briege Cloherty
Stephen Henry Duff
Sarah Frances Ennis
Fiona Margaret Fowle
Amy Gannon
Lara Graham
Joanne Marlene Margaret Gray
David William Henderson
Sarah Hobkirk
Kaye Amanda Lyon
Caitlyn Maccabe

Andrew MacDonald
Stacey Martin
Jordan Stuart McCarter
Louise McCulloch
Megan Claire McGuire
Nathan Shmuel Ripley McHardy
Emma Jane McKenzie
Isla-Dawn McKnight
Ross John Milvenan
Elizabeth Anne Morrison
Siobhan Mary Mortimer
Neil Paterson
Zara Jenny Rafferty
Chantelle Rachel Robertson
Gary Ross
Alison Ballantyne Shaw
James Alexander Stephen

DMO OLABAMIJI SOLICITORS
Office 107, Abercromby Business Centre,
Glasgow G40 2DD
Tel: (0141) 2311650

ROISIN DOCHERTY SOLICITORS
15 Tavistock Drive, Newlands, Glasgow
G43 2SJ
Tel: (0141) 571 9193
E-mail: roisin.docherty@live.co.uk
Categories of Work
Adoption
Advice the elderly & powers of attorney
Children
Childrens
Civil court work
Civil legal aid
Criminal court work
Criminal legal aid
Debt recovery, insolvency, bankruptcy
Family and divorce
Family business advice
Insolvency & corporate recovery
Joint venture
Mergers and acquisitions
Road traffic
SME business advice
Wills, executives and trusts
Partner
Roisin Marie Docherty

D. DOUGLAS MACKIE
29 Park Circus, Glasgow G3 6AP
Tel: (0141) 3312882
Fax: (0141) 3311873
E-mail: info@ddmackie.co.uk
Partner
Norman John Scott

JACQUELINE DOYLE & CO.
1 Tollcross Road, Parkhead, Glasgow G31 4UG
Tel: (0141) 5502333
Fax: (0141) 5508008
E-mail: jacqueline.doyle@jdsolicitors.co.uk
Categories of Work
Adoption
Advice the elderly & powers of attorney
Benefit advice
Children
Childrens
Civil court work
Civil legal aid
Criminal court work
Criminal legal aid
Debt
Disability
Discrimination
Family and divorce
Personal injury
Personal injury – defender
Residential property
Road traffic
Wills, executives and trusts
Partner
Jacqueline Doyle

JACQUELINE DOYLE & CO.
Ladywell, Unit 7, 94 Duke Street, Glasgow
G4 0UW
Tel: (0141) 5481000
Categories of Work
Adoption
Advice the elderly & powers of attorney
Benefit advice
Children
Childrens
Civil court work
Civil legal aid
Criminal court work
Criminal legal aid
Debt
Disability
Discrimination
Family and divorce
Personal injury
Personal injury – defender
Residential property
Road traffic
Wills, executives and trusts

LEE DOYLE, SOLICITORS
Unit 5, 9 Budhill Avenue, Glasgow G32 0PW
Tel: (0141) 3704161
E-mail: admin@leedoylesolicitor.com
Web: https://www.leedoylesolicitor.com
Categories of Work
Adoption
Children
Civil court work
Civil legal aid
Criminal court work
Criminal legal aid
Family and divorce
Medical negligence – claimant
Personal injury
Road traffic
Partner
Lee Jane Doyle

DRUMMOND MILLER LLP
Tara House, 4th Floor East, Glasgow G2 1HG

▶ **Glasgow continued**

Tel: (0141) 3320086
Fax: (0141) 3328295
DX: 512813 GLASGOW CENTRAL
E-mail: reception@drummondmiller.co.uk
Web: www.drummondmiller.co.uk
Categories of Work
Adjudication
Adoption
Advice the elderly & powers of attorney
Alternative dispute resolution
Charities
Children
Childrens
Civil court work
Civil legal aid
Commercial litigation
Commercial property
Contract & property disputes
Criminal court work
Data protection
Debt recovery, insolvency, bankruptcy
Discrimination
Education
Employment
Employment law
Environment
EU / international
Family and divorce
Family business advice
Health
Health and safety
Human rights
Immigration and asylum
Landlord & tenant
Medical negligence – defender
Medical negligence – claimant
Mental health
Oil & gas
Personal injury
Personal injury – defender
Personal tax
Professional negligence
Property litigation
Residential property
Road traffic
Wills, executries and trusts
Partner
Camille Janey Armstrong
Associates
Julie Ann McMahon
Alison Mary Murphy
Gerald Robert Alfred Segal
Employees
Anne-Louise Bradshaw
Craig Jamieson Christie
Lindsay Alison Cumming
Laura-Ann Duddy
Cheryl Marie Gallagher
Grace Christina Harbison
Pamela Jean Booth Lamb
Gillian Christina Lolic

Lauryn Stephanie McCrorie

STEPHEN DRYDEN, SOLICITOR ADVOCATE
PO Box 26556, Glasgow G74 9GG
Tel: (07802) 449390
E-mail: stephen.dryden@sky.com
Categories of Work
Criminal court work
Criminal legal aid
Partner
Stephen Thomas Dryden

DUNLOP, ALLEN & CO.
177 Saltmarket, Glasgow G1 5LG
Tel: (0141) 5521726
Fax: 1412376169
E-mail: jrdunlopallen@gmail.com
Categories of Work
Adoption
Advice the elderly & powers of attorney
Children
Criminal court work
Criminal legal aid
Education
Family and divorce
Partner
Mark Francis Paul Allen

DUNLOP, ALLEN & CO.
29 Burleigh Street, Glasgow G51 3LA
Tel: (0141) 5521726
Categories of Work
Adoption
Advice the elderly & powers of attorney
Children
Criminal court work
Criminal legal aid
Education
Family and divorce

DUPONT ASSOCIATES
Gordon Chambers, Third Floor, Glasgow
G1 3LY
Tel: (07861) 401760
Categories of Work
Charities
Commercial property
Contract & property disputes
Debt
Debt administration
Debt recovery, insolvency, bankruptcy
Family business advice
Insolvency & corporate recovery
Joint venture
Landlord & tenant
Liquor licensing
Mental health
Mergers and acquisitions
Personal tax
Residential property
SME business advice
Wills, executries and trusts

DUPONT LEGAL SOLUTIONS LIMITED
Gordon Chambers, Third Floor, Glasgow
G1 3LY

Tel: (0141) 221 1403
Fax: (0141) 221 8177
E-mail: jade@dupontassociates.co.uk
Web: www.dupontassociates.co.uk
Categories of Work
Charities
Commercial property
Contract & property disputes
Debt
Debt administration
Debt recovery, insolvency, bankruptcy
Family business advice
Insolvency & corporate recovery
Joint venture
Landlord & tenant
Liquor licensing
Mental health
Mergers and acquisitions
Personal tax
Residential property
SME business advice
Wills, executries and trusts
Director
Jade Heloise Dupont

DWF LLP
103 Waterloo Street, Glasgow G2 7BW
Tel: (0141) 228 8000
Fax: (0141) 228 8310
DX: GW9 GLASGOW
Categories of Work
Adjudication
Agriculture and estates
Alternative dispute resolution
Alternative investment market
Banking & finance
Charities
Civil court work
Civil legal aid
Commercial litigation
Commercial property
Competition
Construction
Contract & property disputes
Copyright, trade marks and design
Corporate tax
Data protection
Debt
Debt collecting
Debt recovery, insolvency, bankruptcy
Disability
Discrimination
Education
Employment
Employment law
Environment
Environment (Business Premises)
EU / international
Family business advice
Freedom of information
Health
Health and safety
Housing

Insolvency & corporate recovery
Insurance
IT and intellectual property
Joint venture
Landlord & tenant
Liquor licensing
Local government
Media and entertainment
Medical negligence – defender
Medical negligence – claimant
Mergers and acquisitions
Oil & gas
Parliamentary
Pensions (Company)
Pensions (Employment)
Personal injury
Personal injury – defender
Personal tax
Planning
Planning (Business Premises)
Power and utilities
Private equity
Professional negligence
Projects
Property litigation
Public finance initiative
Public sector
Residential property
Road traffic
SME business advice
Social housing
Software licensing
Sport
Telecoms
Unit Trusts, OEICs and investment trusts
Wills, executries and trusts
Partners
Richard Cannon
Ann Frances Cooney
June Crombie
Alison MacIntyre Grant
Colin Gordon Greig
Paul Francis Pignatelli
Jill Sinclair
Geoffrey George Stansfield
Associates
Deborah Anne Connor
Ashleigh Farrell
Nichola McAtier
Daniel Mark McClymont
Lindsay Marie Ogunyemi
Eileen Claire Sherry
Graham Weatherston
Hazel May Weir
Employees
Siobhan Marina Cameron
Caroline Louise Coyle
Hope Catherine Donnachie
Ross Graham Ferguson
Gemma Helen Gallagher
Freya Fiona Gibb
Rebecca Duncan Gowans
Katherine Alison Lynch

▶ *Glasgow continued*

Kirsty Jane MacCorquodale
Lynne Mhairi Macfarlane
Andrew David McConnell
Ferga Claire McKay
Lucy McMeekin
Nicole McQuilken
Lucy Elizabeth Muir
Victoria Ann Rae
Justine Lianne Reilly
Mikela Louise Rochford
Claira Anne Rodden
Stephanie Alexandra Seidel
Katy Jane Lindsay Smith
Graham Neil Tait

EAST END LAW
1-3 Cumbernauld Road, Glasgow G31 2SW
Tel: (0141) 5544556
E-mail: adrianrusso@eastendlaw.co.uk
Categories of Work
Children
Civil court work
Civil legal aid
Commercial litigation
Contract & property disputes
Criminal court work
Criminal legal aid
Debt recovery, insolvency, bankruptcy
Family and divorce
Human rights
Landlord & tenant
Medical negligence – claimant
Personal injury
Personal injury – defender
Property litigation
Road traffic
Partners
Manjit Kaur Ram
Adrian Russo

EASTERHOUSE LAW PRACTICE LIMITED
48 Shandwick Square, Easterhouse, Glasgow
G34 9DT
Tel: (0141) 7810000
E-mail: alison.heron86@gmail.com

EASTONS SCOTLAND
The Pentagon Centre, Washington Street,
Glasgow G3 8AZ
Tel: (0141) 5331976

EASTONS SOLICITORS LIMITED
The Pentagon Centre, Washington Street,
Glasgow G3 8AZ
Tel: (0141) 5331976
Fax: (0141) 5331976
E-mail: mail@eastonssolicitors.co.uk
Categories of Work
Advice the elderly & powers of attorney
Charities
Commercial property
Family business advice
Mental health

Residential property
Wills, executries and trusts
Director
Stuart William Easton
Consultant
Mhairi Theresa McAllister
Employee
Karen Ann Murray

EMC SOLICITORS
Sheddens Mews,, 119A Busby Road, Glasgow
G76 8BD
Tel: (0141) 644 2865
Fax: (0141) 2020677
E-mail: paul@emcsolicitors.co.uk
Categories of Work
Employment
Employment law
Partner
Paul Gerard McGowan

EMERGENCY LAWYERS
40 New City Road, Glasgow G4 9JT
Tel: (0141) 2268825
Categories of Work
Criminal court work
Criminal legal aid

EMW LAW (SCOTLAND) LLP
272 Bath Street, Glasgow G2 4JR
Partner
Shabnam Hanif

ENERGY LAW UNLIMITED LLP
231 St Vincent Street, Glasgow G2 5QY
Tel: (0141) 2210276
E-mail: enquiries@ru-llp.com
Categories of Work
Agriculture, crofting and fishing
Commercial property
Copyright, trade marks and design
Data protection
Employment
Environment
Freedom of information
Housing
Human rights
IT and intellectual property
Oil & gas
Parliamentary
Planning
Power and utilities
Projects
Public sector
Software licensing
Telecoms
Partners
Deirdre Helen Anderson
Mark Anthony McFarlane O'Dowd
Lorna Williamson
Associate
Angus Reay Milne Mackay
Employees
David James Anderson
Janette Foster

Rhian Louise Griffiths
Laura Anne Hooman

ENVIRONMENTAL LAW CHAMBERS LTD
700 Clarkston Road, Glasgow G44 3YR
Tel: (0141) 354 7620
Fax: (0141) 354 7621
E-mail: barry.love@elchambers.com
Web: www.elchambers.com
Categories of Work
Criminal court work
Environment
Environment (Business Premises)
Fishing
Mining
Oil & gas
Planning
Power and utilities
Projects
Shipping
Transport
Director
Barry Love

ESTATES TEAM
1619 Great Western Road, Glasgow G13 1LT
Tel: (0141) 9549550
Categories of Work
Advice the elderly & powers of attorney
Family and divorce
Mental health
Residential property
Wills, executries and trusts

FAMILY LAW MATTERS SCOTLAND LLP
Queens House, 19 St. Vincent Place, Glasgow
G1 2DT
Tel: (0141) 4202430
Fax: (0141) 4202431
E-mail: louise.steel@flmscotland.co.uk
Categories of Work
Adjudication
Adoption
Alternative dispute resolution
Children
Childrens
Civil court work
Education
Family and divorce
Family business advice
Partners
Marisa Anne Cullen
Karen Gailey
Janie Kerr Law

FARHAN & CO SOLICITORS LIMITED
6 Bankhall Street, Glasgow G42 8JR
Tel: (0141) 2378787
E-mail: info@farhanlaw.co.uk
Web: www.farhanlaw.co.uk
Categories of Work
Benefit advice
Childrens
Family and divorce
Human rights

Immigration and asylum
Director
Nowsheen Farhan

PETER G. FARRELL
70 Royston Road, Glasgow G21 2NT
Tel: (0141) 5520033
Fax: (0141) 5520333
E-mail: paton.farrell@btconnect.com
Categories of Work
Criminal court work
Criminal legal aid
Immigration and asylum
Partner
Peter Gerard Farrell
Employee
Frances Peel Farrell

FERGUSON WHYTE
185 Byres Road, Glasgow G12 8TS
Tel: (0141) 3398432
Fax: (0141) 3394393
DX: 500202 HILLHEAD
E-mail: info@fergusonwhyte.co.uk
Web: www.fergusonwhyte.co.uk
Categories of Work
Residential property
Wills, executries and trusts
Partners
Martin Ferguson
Helen Margaret Whyte
Consultant
Kenneth Brown MacRae
Employee
Kenneth Craig Cook

FIELDING, MCLEAN & CO.
1986 Great Western Road, Glasgow G13 2SW
Tel: (0141) 9591674
Fax: (0141) 9540113
DX: 501430 ANNIESLAND
E-mail: nicola.fielding@fieldingmclean.co.uk
Categories of Work
Advice the elderly & powers of attorney
Commercial property
Contract & property disputes
Family and divorce
Landlord & tenant
Personal injury
Residential property
Wills, executries and trusts
Partners
Nicola Anne Fielding
Ross Douglas Fielding
Consultant
Douglas Harvey Fielding

FINLAYSON WISE
917 Shettleston Road, Shettleston, Glasgow
G32 7NU
Tel: (0141) 7631337
E-mail: enquiries@finlaysonswise.co.uk
Categories of Work
Adoption
Advice the elderly & powers of attorney

► **Glasgow continued**

Benefit advice
Children
Civil court work
Civil legal aid
Consumer credit
Criminal court work
Criminal legal aid
Debt
Debt adjusting and debt counselling
Debt administration
Debt collecting
Debt management
Debt recovery, insolvency, bankruptcy
Disability
Discrimination
Education
Employment
Employment law
Family and divorce
Human rights
Immigration and asylum
Medical negligence – claimant
Mental health
Personal injury
Residential property
Road traffic
Social housing
Wills, executries and trusts

FINNIESTON FRANCHI & MCWILLIAMS

24 St. Enoch Square, Glasgow G1 4DB
Tel: (0141) 2263000
Fax: (0141) 248 2003
DX: GW146 GLASGOW
E-mail: lawyers@ffmcw.co.uk
Categories of Work
Advice the elderly & powers of attorney
Criminal court work
Criminal legal aid
Residential property
Wills, executries and trusts
Partners
Philip Martin McWilliams
Claire Mary Sutherland
Employee
Poppy Catherine Fitzpatrick

FITZPATRICK & CO.

135 Wellington Street, Glasgow G2 2XD
Tel: (0141) 2042200
Fax: (0141) 2043204
DX: 512052 GLASGOW CENTRAL
E-mail: rf@fitzpatrickandco.co.uk
Categories of Work
Commercial property
Criminal court work
Criminal legal aid
Landlord & tenant
Residential property
Road traffic
Wills, executries and trusts

Partners
Brian James Fitzpatrick
David Bernard John Fitzpatrick
Richard Fitzpatrick
Employees
Mhairi Patricia Harkins
Euan Macdonald Wilson
Desmond Jan Ziolo

FITZPATRICK & CO.

875 Govan Road, Glasgow G51 3DL
Tel: (0141) 4453355
E-mail: mail.glasgow@fitzpatrickandco.co.uk
Categories of Work
Commercial property
Criminal court work
Criminal legal aid
Landlord & tenant
Residential property
Road traffic
Wills, executries and trusts

FLANAGAN & CO

357 Dumbarton Road, Partick, Glasgow
G11 6AL
Tel: (0141) 334 7686
Fax: (0141) 328 2894
E-mail: johngflanagan1@yahoo.co.uk
Web: www.flanagansolicitors.com
Categories of Work
Advice the elderly & powers of attorney
Benefit advice
Charities
Children
Civil court work
Civil legal aid
Commercial litigation
Consumer credit
Contract & property disputes
Credit brokerage
Criminal court work
Criminal legal aid
Data protection
Debt
Debt adjusting and debt counselling
Debt administration
Debt collecting
Debt management
Disability
Discrimination
Education
Employment
Employment law
Family and divorce
Freedom of information
Health
Health and safety
Human rights
Immigration and asylum
Landlord & tenant
Local government
Medical negligence – claimant
Parliamentary
Personal injury

Planning (Business Premises)
Property litigation
Provision of credit information services
Residential property
Road traffic
SME business advice
Social housing
Wills, executives and trusts
Partner
John Gerard Flanagan

FLEMING & REID
180 Hope Street, Glasgow G2 2UE
Tel: (0141) 3311144
Fax: (0141) 3311800
DX: 561463 GLASGOW 16
E-mail: em@flemingandreid.co.uk
Categories of Work
Adoption
Benefit advice
Children
Childrens
Civil court work
Civil legal aid
Criminal court work
Criminal legal aid
Family and divorce
Housing
Mental health
Personal injury
Social housing
Partners
Brian Cooney
Michael John Gallen
Employees
Ciara Claire Pia Bradley
Megan McAllister

FRANCHI LAW LLP
Queens House, 19 St Vincent Place, Glasgow
G1 2DT
Tel: (0141) 225 3810
Fax: (0141) 2041199
E-mail: leandro@franchilaw.co.uk
Categories of Work
Commercial property
Landlord & tenant
Residential property
Wills, executives and trusts
Partners
Leandro Ottavio Franchi
Peter Reidie Jack
Frances Alexa King

FRAZER COOGANS LTD
1 Woodside Place, Glasgow G3 7QF
Tel: (0141) 2121535
Categories of Work
Adoption
Advice the elderly & powers of attorney
Agriculture and estates
Agriculture, crofting and fishing
Banking & finance
Children

Childrens
Commercial property
Contract & property disputes
Criminal court work
Criminal legal aid
Family and divorce
Family business advice
Landlord & tenant
Personal injury
Personal tax
Residential property
Road traffic
SME business advice
Wills, executives and trusts

FREDERICK & CO (SANDYFORD) LIMITED
19 Sandyford Place, Glasgow G3 7NQ
Tel: (0141) 2215575
E-mail: info@frederickandco.co.uk
Categories of Work
Adoption
Advice the elderly & powers of attorney
Agriculture and estates
Children
Childrens
Education
Family and divorce
Residential property

FREDERICK & CO SOLICITORS LIMITED
1622 Paisley Road West, Glasgow G52 3QN
Tel: (0141) 8105283
DX: 512204 GLASGOW SANDYFORD
E-mail: info@frederickandco.co.uk
Web: www.frederickandco.co.uk
Categories of Work
Civil court work
Commercial litigation
Commercial property
Criminal court work
Criminal legal aid
Employment
Landlord & tenant
Medical negligence – claimant
Personal injury – defender
Professional negligence
Property litigation
Residential property
Wills, executives and trusts

FREDERICK & CO SOLICITORS LIMITED
19 Sandyford Place, Glasgow G3 7NQ
Tel: (0141) 2215575
Fax: (0141) 2211161
E-mail: info@frederickandco.co.uk
Web: www.frederickandco.co.uk
Categories of Work
Civil court work
Commercial litigation
Commercial property
Criminal court work
Criminal legal aid
Employment
Landlord & tenant

▶ **Glasgow continued**

Medical negligence – claimant
Personal injury – defender
Professional negligence
Property litigation
Residential property
Wills, executries and trusts
Directors
Sabina Donegan
Michael Jackson
Consultant
Saul Kleinglass
Employees
Nicola-Jane Campbell
Karen McFarlane

RICHARD FREEMAN & CO.
40 New City Road, Glasgow G4 9JT
Tel: (0141) 353 2223
Fax: (0141) 353 3280
Categories of Work
Criminal court work
Criminal legal aid
Partner
Richard Aaron Freeman
Employee
William James Mackay

JIM FRIEL SOLICITORS
Ground Floor, Oxford House, Glasgow G5 9EP
Tel: (0141) 4201234
Fax: (0141) 4203966
Categories of Work
Criminal court work
Criminal legal aid
Partners
John Scott McQuire
David Andrew O'Hagan
Consultant
Gary William Victor Miller

FRIENDS LEGAL
5th Floor, The Centrum Building, Glasgow
G1 3DX
Tel: (0844) 8921250
Fax: (0844) 8921251
Categories of Work
Advice the elderly & powers of attorney
Alternative dispute resolution
Civil court work
Commercial litigation
Commercial property
Consumer credit
Contract & property disputes
Debt
Debt collecting
Disability
Discrimination
Employment
Employment law
Health
Health and safety
Human rights
Local government

Medical negligence – claimant
Personal injury
Professional negligence
Property litigation
Residential property
Road traffic
Wills, executries and trusts
Associates
Lyndsey Bell
Dawn Louise Carlin
Laura Ann Sillars
Employees
Ellyn Sarah Fyvie
Suzanne Mackay Lloyd
Monalisa Swira
Rachel Thomson
Amy Jean Wardrop

GALLEN & COMPANY LTD
40 Carlton Place, Glasgow G5 9TW
Tel: (0141) 4201441
Fax: (0141) 4208258
DX: GW204 GLASGOW
Web: www.gallenandco.com
Categories of Work
Criminal court work
Criminal legal aid
Personal injury
Director
John Desmond McGuire
Employees
Linsey Bryson
Amy Margaret Liddell
Elaine Louise Rae
Jeffrey Colin Rankin

GALLEN & COMPANY LTD
419 Nitshill Road, Glasgow G53 7BN
Tel: (0141) 8807148
Web: www.gallenandco.com
Categories of Work
Criminal court work
Criminal legal aid
Personal injury
Employee
Jennifer Enid Liddell

GALLEN & COMPANY LTD
879 Govan Road, Glasgow G51 3DL
Tel: (0141) 4452949
Web: www.gallenandco.com
Categories of Work
Criminal court work
Criminal legal aid
Personal injury

GALLETLY & CO LIMITED
175 Saltmarket, Glasgow G1 5LG
Tel: (0141) 5530886
Fax: (0141) 4291100
E-mail: info@roberts-law.co.uk
Categories of Work
Criminal court work
Criminal legal aid

Director
Kurt John Ward Reid

GHAFAR & CO LTD
538 Cathcart Road, Glasgow G42 8YG
Tel: (0141) 4237800
Fax: (0141) 4231600
E-mail: info@ghafarandco.co.uk
Categories of Work
Commercial property
Human rights
Immigration and asylum
Landlord & tenant
Residential property
Wills, executries and trusts
Director
Shagufta Ghafar

GILDEAS LIMITED
97-99 West Regent Street, Glasgow G2 2BA
Tel: (0141) 331 6071
Fax: (0141) 3316079
E-mail: mail@gildeas.net
Web: www.gildeas.net
Categories of Work
Civil court work
Commercial litigation
Contract & property disputes
Criminal court work
Debt collecting
Debt recovery, insolvency, bankruptcy
Health and safety
Landlord & tenant
Medical negligence – claimant
Personal injury
Professional negligence
Property litigation
Residential property
Road traffic
Directors
Sanjeev Bali
Colin Ferguson
Lindsay Hare
Stephen James Hay
Associates
Emma Thomson
Fergus Hugh Thomson
Employees
Alastair Cameron
Carly Louise Walker

GILLESPIE MACANDREW LLP
163 West George Street, Glasgow G2 2JJ
Tel: (0141) 4735555
Fax: (0131) 2254519
Web: www.gillespiemacandrew.co.uk
Categories of Work
Adjudication
Adoption
Advice the elderly & powers of attorney
Agriculture and estates
Agriculture, crofting and fishing
Alternative dispute resolution
Banking & finance
Benefit advice
Charities
Children
Civil court work
Civil legal aid
Commercial litigation
Commercial property
Competition
Construction
Consumer credit
Contract & property disputes
Copyright, trade marks and design
Corporate tax
Criminal court work
Data protection
Debt
Debt administration
Debt collecting
Debt recovery, insolvency, bankruptcy
Disability
Discrimination
Employment
Employment law
Environment
Environment (Business Premises)
EU / international
Family and divorce
Family business advice
Fishing
Freedom of information
Housing
Human rights
Insolvency & corporate recovery
IT and intellectual property
Joint venture
Landlord & tenant
Local government
Media and entertainment
Medical negligence – defender
Medical negligence – claimant
Mental health
Mergers and acquisitions
Mining
Parliamentary
Pensions (Employment)
Personal injury
Personal injury – defender
Personal tax
Planning
Planning (Business Premises)
Power and utilities
Private equity
Professional negligence
Projects
Property litigation
Public sector
Residential property
Road traffic
SME business advice
Software licensing
Wills, executries and trusts

▶ Glasgow continued

Partners
Gregor Kenneth John Peebles
Isobell Ann Reid
Associate
Keith Robert Emmerson
Employees
Marcus MacKenzie Downie
Alexander John Ritchie Robertson
Arlene Margaret Taylor
Karen Wooton

GILROY & CO
15 Holmhead Road, Glasgow G44 3AS
Tel: (0141) 4293344
E-mail: gilroyandco@btconnect.com
Categories of Work
Criminal court work
Criminal legal aid
Partner
Edward Gilroy

GILSON GRAY LLP
160 West George Street, Glasgow G2 2HG
Tel: (0141) 5302021
Fax: (0141) 5302035
DX: 10 GLASGOW
Web: www.gilsongray.co.uk
Categories of Work
Adjudication
Adoption
Advice the elderly & powers of attorney
Agriculture and estates
Alternative dispute resolution
Banking & finance
Betting & gaming
Charities
Children
Childrens
Civil court work
Civil legal aid
Commercial litigation
Commercial property
Competition
Construction
Consumer credit
Contract & property disputes
Copyright, trade marks and design
Data protection
Debt
Debt administration
Debt collecting
Debt recovery, insolvency, bankruptcy
Disability
Discrimination
Education
Employment
Employment law
Environment
EU / international
Family and divorce
Family business advice
Freedom of information

Health and safety
Housing
Immigration and asylum
Insolvency & corporate recovery
Insurance
IT and intellectual property
Joint venture
Landlord & tenant
Liquor licensing
Local government
Media and entertainment
Medical negligence – defender
Medical negligence – claimant
Mergers and acquisitions
Mining
Oil & gas
Pensions (Company)
Personal injury
Personal injury – defender
Personal tax
Planning
Planning (Business Premises)
Power and utilities
Private equity
Professional negligence
Projects
Property litigation
Public sector
Residential property
Road traffic
Shipping
SME business advice
Social housing
Software licensing
Sport
Telecoms
Transport
Wills, executives and trusts
Partners
Iain Kemley Clark
Derek Hamill
Donna Marie Kelly-Gilmour
Denise Karen Laverty
Graham Ramsay Millar
Associate
Gregor Ian Duthie
Employees
Connor Kenneth Bowie
Fraser Alexander Cameron
Laura Ray Campbell
Francesca Marianna Capaldi
Lorna Davidson
Sarah Louise Helen Feeney
Alasdair William Fraser
Melissa June McIntyre
Joanna Wendy Elizabeth Millar
Nicholas Thomas
Charlotte Joy White

GLASGOW CITIZEN ADVICE BUREAUX SPECIALIST SERVICES
27 Main Street, Bridgeton, Glasgow G40 1QB
Tel: (07966) 005866

GLASGOW DEFENCE LAWYERS LIMITED
3rd Floor, 93 Hope Street, Glasgow G2 6LD
Tel: (0141) 4297677
E-mail: info@glasgowdefencelawyers.com
Categories of Work
Criminal court work
Criminal legal aid
Director
Raymond Cahal McIlwham

GORBALS LAW AND MONEY ADVICE CENTRE
72 Commercial Road, Twomax Rear Annexe,
Glasgow G5 0QZ
Categories of Work
Benefit advice
Consumer credit
Debt
Debt adjusting and debt counselling
Debt management
Disability
Discrimination
Employment law
Human rights
Mental health
Residential property
Social housing

A. J. GORDON & CO
2 Botanic Crescent, Glasgow G20 8QQ
Tel: (07812) 000554
E-mail: al@algordonlawyers.co.uk
Categories of Work
Adoption
Children
Civil court work
Civil legal aid
Criminal legal aid
Family and divorce
Partner
Alisdair Gordon

GORDON WILLIAMS LIMITED
38 Briar Road, Newlands, Glasgow G43 2TX
Tel: (0141) 5853948
Fax: (0141) 5838508
E-mail: gordonfwilliams@hotmail.co.uk
Categories of Work
Criminal court work
Criminal legal aid
Director
Gordon Fleming Williams

LESLEY GOVAN ASSOCIATES
Suite 123, Claymore House, 145-149
Kilmarnock Road, Glasgow G41 3JA
Tel: (07983) 811298
E-mail: lg@lesleygovanassociates.uk
Partner
Lesley Anne Govan
Employee
Carrie-Anne Clifford

S. GRADY SOLICITORS
40 St.Enoch Square, Glasgow G1 4DH
Tel: (0141) 2214000

E-mail: stephen_grady@hotmail.co.uk
Categories of Work
Children
Criminal court work
Criminal legal aid
Education
Family and divorce
Partner
Stephen Martin Grady
Consultant
Claire Margaret Donoghue

GRAY & CO.
16 Bilsland Drive, Glasgow G20 9TH
Tel: (0141) 9467777
Fax: (0141) 9469402
E-mail: info@grayandcoglasgow.co.uk
Categories of Work
Criminal court work
Criminal legal aid
Human rights
Immigration and asylum
Partners
Roisin Anne Kieran
Charles McGinley
Employee
Neal Euan Robb

GREENTREE LEGAL LIMITED
Spaces, 1 West Regent Street, Glasgow
G2 1RW
Categories of Work
Landlord & tenant
Personal injury
Residential property
Road traffic
Director
Beverley Tara McMahon

GREIG EMPLOYMENT LAW LIMITED
9 George Square, Glasgow G2 1QQ
Tel: (07584) 244565
E-mail: catherine@greigemploymentlaw.com
Categories of Work
Employment
Employment law
Director
Catherine Jean Greig

G S LEGAL
Unit 3.8, Forsyth House, 111 Union Street,
Glasgow G1 3TA
Tel: (0141) 2273995
E-mail: mgs63@live.co.uk
Categories of Work
Adoption
Advice the elderly & powers of attorney
Agriculture and estates
Alternative dispute resolution
Banking & finance
Benefit advice
Betting & gaming
Children
Childrens
Civil court work

▶ **Glasgow continued**

Civil legal aid
Commercial litigation
Commercial property
Copyright, trade marks and design
Criminal court work
Criminal legal aid
Data protection
Debt
Debt collecting
Debt management
Debt recovery, insolvency, bankruptcy
Disability
Discrimination
Education
Employment
Employment law
Family and divorce
Freedom of information
Health
Health and safety
Housing
Human rights
IT and intellectual property
Joint venture
Landlord & tenant
Local government
Media and entertainment
Medical negligence – defender
Medical negligence – claimant
Mental health
Mergers and acquisitions
Personal injury
Personal injury – defender
Planning
Professional negligence
Residential property
Social housing
Software licensing
Sport
Telecoms
Unit Trusts, OEICs and investment trusts
Wills, executives and trusts
Partner
Meredith Graham Sykes

GUNNERCOOKE SCO LLP
The Garment Factory, 2-10 Montrose Street,
Glasgow G1 1RE
Categories of Work
Alternative dispute resolution
Commercial property
Competition
EU / international
Family business advice
Joint venture
Landlord & tenant
Mergers and acquisitions
Oil & gas
Projects
SME business advice
Associate
Rucsar Yasmeen Ullah

Employee
Morven Anne Badger Finlayson

GWG LTD
81 St Vincent Street, Glasgow G2 5TF
Tel: (0141) 7769960
Fax: (0871) 2229066
Categories of Work
Adoption
Advice the elderly & powers of attorney
Children
Childrens
Civil court work
Civil legal aid
Commercial property
Contract & property disputes
Debt
Debt management
Family and divorce
Housing
Landlord & tenant
Local government
Mental health
Planning (Business Premises)
Residential property
Social housing
Wills, executives and trusts
Directors
Paula Elaine Giannelli
Eric Dodson Miller

HALL & HAUGHEY
87 Carlton Place, Glasgow G5 9TD
Tel: (0141) 4180505
Fax: (0141) 4293131
E-mail: david@hall-haughey.co.uk
Categories of Work
Criminal court work
Criminal legal aid
Partner
David Warrack Hall

PAUL HANNAH SOLICITORS
261 Springburn Way, Glasgow G21 1DX
Tel: (0141) 5587433
Fax: (0141) 5574300
E-mail: sp@paulhannah.org
Web: www.paulhannah.org
Categories of Work
Adoption
Advice the elderly & powers of attorney
Benefit advice
Children
Childrens
Civil court work
Civil legal aid
Consumer credit
Criminal court work
Criminal legal aid
Data protection
Debt
Debt management
Disability
Discrimination

Employment
Employment law
Family and divorce
Medical negligence – defender
Medical negligence – claimant
Personal injury
Personal injury – defender
Professional negligence
Residential property
Road traffic
Wills, executries and trusts
Partner
Paul Martin Jennings Hannah
Employees
Hazel Rebecca Kerr
Tracey Louise Mulholland

PAUL HANNAH SOLICITORS
478 Dumbarton Road, Partick, Glasgow
G11 6SQ
Tel: (0141) 4838888
E-mail: sp@paulhannah.org
Categories of Work
Adoption
Advice the elderly & powers of attorney
Benefit advice
Children
Childrens
Civil court work
Civil legal aid
Consumer credit
Criminal court work
Criminal legal aid
Data protection
Debt
Debt management
Disability
Discrimination
Employment
Employment law
Family and divorce
Medical negligence – defender
Medical negligence – claimant
Personal injury
Personal injury – defender
Professional negligence
Residential property
Road traffic
Wills, executries and trusts

HANNAY FRASER & CO LTD
95 Douglas Street, Glasgow G2 4EU
Tel: (0141) 2211381
Fax: (0141) 2040277
E-mail: calum@hannayfraser.co.uk
Categories of Work
Adoption
Advice the elderly & powers of attorney
Children
Civil court work
Civil legal aid
Commercial property
Consumer credit
Contract & property disputes

Criminal court work
Criminal legal aid
Debt
Debt adjusting and debt counselling
Debt recovery, insolvency, bankruptcy
Employment law
Family and divorce
Housing
Human rights
Landlord & tenant
Medical negligence – claimant
Mental health
Personal injury
Property litigation
Residential property
Road traffic
Wills, executries and trusts
Directors
Calum Donald Fraser
James Samuel Hannay

HARDING & CO.
79 Saltmarket, Glasgow G1 5LE
Tel: (0141) 5528880
Fax: (0141) 5528864
Categories of Work
Children
Criminal court work
Criminal legal aid
Mental health
Road traffic
Partner
Craig McInnes Dewar
Consultant
Matthew Ian Harding

HARPER MACLEOD LLP
The Ca'd'oro, 45 Gordon Street, Glasgow
G1 3PE
Tel: (0141) 2218888
Fax: (0141) 2264198
DX: GW86 GLASGOW
E-mail: info@harpermacleod.co.uk
Web: www.harpermacleod.co.uk
Categories of Work
Adjudication
Adoption
Advice the elderly & powers of attorney
Agriculture and estates
Agriculture, crofting and fishing
Alternative dispute resolution
Alternative investment market
Banking & finance
Betting & gaming
Charities
Children
Childrens
Civil court work
Civil legal aid
Commercial litigation
Commercial property
Competition
Construction
Consumer credit

► *Glasgow continued*

Contract & property disputes
Copyright, trade marks and design
Corporate tax
Criminal court work
Criminal legal aid
Data protection
Debt
Debt administration
Debt collecting
Debt recovery, insolvency, bankruptcy
Disability
Discrimination
Education
Employment
Employment law
Environment
Environment (Business Premises)
EU / international
Family and divorce
Family business advice
Fishing
Freedom of information
Health
Health and safety
Housing
Human rights
Immigration and asylum
Insolvency & corporate recovery
Insurance
IT and intellectual property
Joint venture
Landlord & tenant
Liquor licensing
Local government
Media and entertainment
Medical negligence – defender
Medical negligence – claimant
Mental health
Mergers and acquisitions
Mining
Oil & gas
Parliamentary
Pensions (Company)
Pensions (Employment)
Personal injury
Personal injury – defender
Personal tax
Planning
Planning (Business Premises)
Power and utilities
Private equity
Professional negligence
Projects
Property litigation
Public finance initiative
Public sector
Residential property
Road traffic
Shipping
SME business advice
Social housing

Software licensing
Sport
Telecoms
Transport
Unit Trusts, OEICs and investment trusts
Wills, executries and trusts
Partners
Omar Farooq Ali
David William John Bell
David James Bone
Heather Elizabeth Calderwood
Bruce Alan Caldow
Anthony James William Cameron
Michael Christopher Conroy
Lorne Donald Crerar
Lorna Davis
Natalie Dissake
David Eason
Peter Joseph Ferguson
E-Ming Fong
Jacqueline Christina Fraser
Alexis Rachel Harper
Marina Harper
Derek William Hogg
Gordon Craig Hollerin
Andrew John Hunter
David Stanley Kaye
Christopher James Kerr
David John Kerr
Karen Lang
Jacqueline Leslie
James Semple Lloyd
Anne Louise Macdonald
Paul Michael MacDonald
James George Nisbet MacGregor
Andrew William MacKenzie
Kathleen Mary Martin
Amanda Elizabeth Masson
Suzanne Margaret McGarrigle
David McIndoe
Craig Nicholas McKerracher
James Scott William McMorrow
John Gerard Meehan
Collette Tracey Miller
Scott Stewart Milligan
Elizabeth Anne Mitchell
Carolyn Nicola Morgan
Donald John Munro
Graeme Barry Nisbet
Jo-Anne Margaret Nisbet
Pamela Jane Niven
John Daniel Murray Pringle
Craig William Ramsay
Paula Skinner
Jennifer Chloe Smith
David Alexander Steel
Caroline Summers
Thomas Ifan Gwyn Thomas
Andrew David Upton
Amy Helen Walsh
Limor Wolfe

Associates
Kathryn Louise Black
David Allan Boag
Lauren Grant
Paul Harris Greenhill
Lewis Andrew Hendry
Lindsay Anne MacEwen
Jacqueline Elizabeth Meikle
Laura Marie Meldrum
Winston Alexander Montague Roberts
Lynne Joanne Stevenson
Christina Louise Wason
Employees
Christopher Thomas Agnew
Lauren Jane Anderson
Leigh Sorcha Beirne
Jane Alexandra Blackwood
Euan Forbes Bowie
Lynsey Brown
Rory James Lambert Byrom
Keni Campbell Carmichael
Eilidh Lindsay Crawford
Adam McAinsh de Ste Croix
Amy Vittoria Dickson
Sara Douglas-Smith
Blair Duffy
Megan Dunbar
Cinzia Chiara Duncan
Joanne Finlayson
Ellen Francksen
Kelly Moyra Fraser
Ann Gallagher
Jocelyn Louise Gilda
Angela Gizzi
Hannah Sarah Grace
Thomas Stephen Gray
Jennifer Grosvenor
Ross Hugh Hampsey
Graham William Horsman
Anisha Kaura
Laura Kerr
Scott Alexander King
Lila Nicole MacFarlane
Amy Elizabeth Mackenzie
Ricardo Angelo Matteo
Andrew Stuart Maxwell
Robert Scott McConnell
Clare Louise McGeough
Craig Christopher McKellar
Lyndsay Anne McMahon
Rachel Jane Miele
Kerri Paula Nicoll
Stephen Paul Nicolson
Sharon Nisbet
Grant Stephen O'Neill
Victoria Robinson
Andrew Stewart Niall Ronald
Deborah Rookes
Brianella Nikesha Samantha Scott
Rebecca Anne Scott
Laura Ann Sheridan
Astrid Howden Siekmann
Richard David Steell

Fraser William McDonald Stewart
Sarah Anne Stewart
Fiona Marion Strang
Stephen Julian Vallance
Natalie Sarah Wallace
Kirsty Stephenson Watson
Nicky-Ray Watson
Liam Calum White
Victoria Jane Willan

HARTER & CO.
4 Midlock Street, Glasgow G51 1SL
Tel: (0141) 4270901
Fax: (0141) 4277446
DX: 500607 GOVAN
E-mail: hartersolicitors@tiscali.co.uk
Categories of Work
Advice the elderly & powers of attorney
Civil court work
Civil legal aid
Commercial property
Criminal court work
Criminal legal aid
Family and divorce
Residential property
Wills, executries and trusts
Partner
Sally Gwen Harter
Employee
Konrad Queen

HASTIES
10 Newton Place, Glasgow G3 7PR
Tel: (0141) 3321454
Fax: (0141) 3324652
DX: 512217 GLAS SANDYFORD PL
E-mail: dgordon@hasties.co.uk
Categories of Work
Advice the elderly & powers of attorney
Charities
Commercial property
Debt collecting
Family business advice
Landlord & tenant
Liquor licensing
Local government
Residential property
Road traffic
Wills, executries and trusts
Partner
David Cargill Gordon

HENDRIE LEGAL LIMITED
17 Fitzroy Lane, Finnieston, Glasgow G3 8PL
Tel: (0141) 4655370
Categories of Work
Commercial property
Landlord & tenant
Residential property
Wills, executries and trusts

HIGHLAND TRUSTEES LIMITED
302 St. Vincent Street, Glasgow G2 5RZ
Tel: (0141) 2483434

▶ **Glasgow continued**

R & J M HILL BROWN & CO LIMITED
RWF House, 5 Renfield Street, Glasgow
G2 5EZ
Tel: (0141) 2211919
DX: 512207 Glasgow Sandyford Place
E-mail: DShaw@hillbrown.co.uk
Categories of Work
Betting & gaming
Commercial property
Liquor licensing
Residential property

HILL BROWN LICENSING
RWF House, 5 Renfield Street, Glasgow
G2 5EZ
Tel: (0141) 3323265
Fax: (0141) 332 0414
Categories of Work
Betting & gaming
Commercial property
Liquor licensing
Residential property
Directors
Audrey Anne Junner
Peter John Lawson
Consultant
John Carlisle Cummins

HM NOMINATIONS LIMITED
The Ca'd'oro, 45 Gordon Street, Glasgow
G1 3PE
Tel: (0141) 2218888

HMS DIRECTORS LIMITED
The Ca'd'oro, 45 Gordon Street, Glasgow
G1 3PE
Tel: (0141) 2218888

HMS SECRETARIES LIMITED
The Ca'd'oro, 45 Gordon Street, Glasgow
G1 3PE
Tel: (0141) 2218888

HM TRUSTEES LIMITED
The Ca'd'oro, 45 Gordon Street, Glasgow
G1 3PE
Tel: (0141) 2218888

HOLMES MACKILLOP LIMITED
109 Douglas Street, Glasgow G2 4HB
Tel: (0141) 226 4942
Fax: (0844) 824 1930
DX: GW50 GLASGOW
E-mail: general@homack.co.uk
Categories of Work
Adjudication
Advice the elderly & powers of attorney
Agriculture and estates
Agriculture, crofting and fishing
Alternative dispute resolution
Banking & finance
Charities
Children
Civil court work

Commercial litigation
Commercial property
Construction
Contract & property disputes
Data protection
Debt recovery, insolvency, bankruptcy
Employment
Employment law
Family and divorce
Family business advice
Freedom of information
Joint venture
Landlord & tenant
Liquor licensing
Mergers and acquisitions
Professional negligence
Property litigation
Public sector
Residential property
SME business advice
Wills, executries and trusts
Directors
Karen Tracey Condie
Amir Mohamed Ismail
Ralph Leigh Riddiough
Kevin Thompson
Associate
Yvonne Glenison Burnham
Employees
Cameron Macleod Kane
Philip William Symon

HOLMES MACKILLOP LIMITED
21 Stewart Street, Milngavie, Glasgow
G62 6BW
Tel: (0141) 956 5454
Fax: (0141) 956 6594
Categories of Work
Adjudication
Advice the elderly & powers of attorney
Agriculture and estates
Agriculture, crofting and fishing
Alternative dispute resolution
Banking & finance
Charities
Children
Civil court work
Commercial litigation
Commercial property
Construction
Contract & property disputes
Data protection
Debt recovery, insolvency, bankruptcy
Employment
Employment law
Family and divorce
Family business advice
Freedom of information
Joint venture
Landlord & tenant
Liquor licensing
Mergers and acquisitions
Professional negligence

Property litigation
Public sector
Residential property
SME business advice
Wills, executries and trusts
Director
Richard Leggett

HORWICH FARRELLY SCOTLAND
2nd Floor, 39 St. Vincent Place, Glasgow
G1 2ER
Tel: (03300) 240711
Fax: (03300) 240712
Web: www. h-f.co.uk
Categories of Work
Civil court work
Health
Health and safety
Insurance
Medical negligence – defender
Personal injury
Personal injury – defender
Road traffic
Partner
Steven James Smart
Employees
Lyndsey Anne McLean
Valerie Elizabeth Pitt

HOUSTON LAW
Clyde Offices, 2nd Floor, 48 West George
Street, Glasgow G2 1BP
Tel: (07834) 626890
E-mail: info@houstonlaw.co.uk
Categories of Work
Criminal court work
Criminal legal aid
Partner
Rebecca Jane Houston

HUGHES DOWDALL
James Miller House, Suite 3, 3rd Floor,
Glasgow G2 1PJ
Tel: (0141) 2407020
Fax: (0141) 2407058
DX: GW51 GLASGOW
E-mail: enquiries@hughesdowdall.com
Categories of Work
Adoption
Advice the elderly & powers of attorney
Benefit advice
Children
Childrens
Civil court work
Civil legal aid
Commercial litigation
Contract & property disputes
Criminal court work
Criminal legal aid
Debt
Debt collecting
Debt recovery, insolvency, bankruptcy
Disability
Discrimination

Education
Employment
Employment law
Family and divorce
Family business advice
Health and safety
Housing
Human rights
Landlord & tenant
Liquor licensing
Medical negligence – claimant
Personal injury
Personal injury – defender
Professional negligence
Residential property
Road traffic
Social housing
Wills, executries and trusts
Partner
Michael Anthony Foster
Employees
Ruth Gilfillan
Fearghas Edward Douglas Smith

HUGHES SHAUGHNESSY MCFARLANE LIMITED
216 Kilmarnock Road, Shawlands, Glasgow
G43 1TY
Tel: (0141) 6365115
Fax: (0141) 6365673
E-mail: paulhughes@hsmsolicitors.co.uk
Categories of Work
Advice the elderly & powers of attorney
Agriculture and estates
Agriculture, crofting and fishing
Charities
Children
Civil court work
Civil legal aid
Commercial property
Contract & property disputes
Debt recovery, insolvency, bankruptcy
Disability
Family and divorce
Family business advice
Insolvency & corporate recovery
Joint venture
Landlord & tenant
Mental health
Mergers and acquisitions
Personal injury
Planning (Business Premises)
Residential property
Wills, executries and trusts
Director
Paul Denis Hughes

HUGHES SHAUGHNESSY MCFARLANE LIMITED
256 Castlemilk Road, Glasgow G44 4LB
Tel: (0141) 6499772
Fax: (0141) 6320777
E-mail: ian@hsmsolicitors.co.uk

▶ *Glasgow continued*

Categories of Work
Advice the elderly & powers of attorney
Agriculture and estates
Agriculture, crofting and fishing
Charities
Children
Civil court work
Civil legal aid
Commercial property
Contract & property disputes
Debt recovery, insolvency, bankruptcy
Disability
Family and divorce
Family business advice
Insolvency & corporate recovery
Joint venture
Landlord & tenant
Mental health
Mergers and acquisitions
Personal injury
Planning (Business Premises)
Residential property
Wills, executries and trusts
Director
Ian Alexander Nicholas McFarlane

JC HUGHES SOLICITORS LIMITED
1007 Tollcross Road, Glasgow G32 8UW
Tel: (0141) 7785585
Categories of Work
Adoption
Advice the elderly & powers of attorney
Benefit advice
Children
Childrens
Civil court work
Civil legal aid
Criminal court work
Criminal legal aid
Debt
Debt administration
Debt collecting
Debt management
Education
Family and divorce
Medical negligence – claimant
Mental health
Personal injury
Personal injury – defender
Provision of credit information services
Residential property
Road traffic
Social housing

JC HUGHES SOLICITORS LIMITED
1028 Tollcross Road, Glasgow G32 8UW
Tel: (0141) 7782468
Fax: (0141) 7788883
Categories of Work
Adoption
Advice the elderly & powers of attorney
Benefit advice

Children
Childrens
Civil court work
Civil legal aid
Criminal court work
Criminal legal aid
Debt
Debt administration
Debt collecting
Debt management
Education
Family and divorce
Medical negligence – claimant
Mental health
Personal injury
Personal injury – defender
Provision of credit information services
Residential property
Road traffic
Social housing
Director
Ian Mark McClelland
Associate
Stephen Scott Hotchkiss
Employee
Joseph Keenan

JC HUGHES SOLICITORS LIMITED
55A Main Street, Glasgow G73 2JH
Tel: (0141) 6470700
Fax: (0141) 6479800
Categories of Work
Adoption
Advice the elderly & powers of attorney
Benefit advice
Children
Childrens
Civil court work
Civil legal aid
Criminal court work
Criminal legal aid
Debt
Debt administration
Debt collecting
Debt management
Education
Family and divorce
Medical negligence – claimant
Mental health
Personal injury
Personal injury – defender
Provision of credit information services
Residential property
Road traffic
Social housing
Director
Mark Connolly

JC HUGHES SOLICITORS LIMITED
721 Springfield Road, Parkhead, Glasgow
G31 8JU
Tel: (0141) 5508080
Fax: (0141) 5508585

Categories of Work
Adoption
Advice the elderly & powers of attorney
Benefit advice
Children
Childrens
Civil court work
Civil legal aid
Criminal court work
Criminal legal aid
Debt
Debt administration
Debt collecting
Debt management
Education
Family and divorce
Medical negligence – claimant
Mental health
Personal injury
Personal injury – defender
Provision of credit information services
Residential property
Road traffic
Social housing
Director
John Anthony McLaughlin

JC HUGHES SOLICITORS LIMITED
Carlton Buildings, 63 Carlton Place, Glasgow
G5 9TW
Tel: (0141) 4201000
Categories of Work
Adoption
Advice the elderly & powers of attorney
Benefit advice
Children
Childrens
Civil court work
Civil legal aid
Criminal court work
Criminal legal aid
Debt
Debt administration
Debt collecting
Debt management
Education
Family and divorce
Medical negligence – claimant
Mental health
Personal injury
Personal injury – defender
Provision of credit information services
Residential property
Road traffic
Social housing

ALEXIS HUNTER FAMILY LAW
Caledonia House, Evanton Drive, Glasgow
G46 8AJ
Tel: (0141) 4040124
Fax: (0141) 6366792
E-mail: mail@ahfamilylaw.co.uk
Web: www.ahfamilylaw.co.uk

Categories of Work
Alternative dispute resolution
Children
Childrens
Civil court work
Civil legal aid
Family and divorce
Partner
Alexis Margaret Hunter
Employee
Nicola Elaine Seenan

INCE GORDON DADDS (SCOTLAND) LLP
Tay House, 300 Bath Street, Glasgow G2 4JR
Partner
Stefanie Johnston

INHERITANCE LEGAL
Tay House (2nd Floor), 300 Bath Street,
Glasgow G2 4JR
Tel: (0800) 404 5962
E-mail: philreville@inheritancelegal.com
Web: www.inheritancelegal.com
Categories of Work
Advice the elderly & powers of attorney
Residential property
Wills, executries and trusts
Partner
Philip Reville
Employee
Puneet Kaur Puri

INJURY CLAIMS SERVICES LTD
272 Bath Street, Glasgow G2 4JR
Tel: (07738) 884895
E-mail: robertskelly@injuryclaimsservices.co.uk
Categories of Work
Adoption
Advice the elderly & powers of attorney
Children
Civil court work
Civil legal aid
Contract & property disputes
Criminal court work
Criminal legal aid
Debt
Disability
Discrimination
Family and divorce
Health and safety
Human rights
Immigration and asylum
Landlord & tenant
Medical negligence – defender
Medical negligence – claimant
Personal injury
Personal injury – defender
Professional negligence
Property litigation
Wills, executries and trusts
Director
Robert John Martin Skelly

INJURY CLAIMS SERVICES LTD
48 West George Street, Glasgow G2 1BP

▶ *Glasgow continued*

Tel: (07738) 884895
E-mail: robertskelly@injuryclaimsservices.co.uk

INJURY TIME CLAIMS

Centenary House, 69 Wellington Street,
Glasgow G2 6HG
Tel: (0141) 2214325
E-mail: Enquiries@jacksonboyd.co.uk
Web: www.injurytimeclaims.co.uk
Categories of Work
Adjudication
Alternative dispute resolution
Civil court work
Civil legal aid
Commercial litigation
Contract & property disputes
Criminal court work
Debt
Debt collecting
Debt recovery, insolvency, bankruptcy
Discrimination
Employment law
Insolvency & corporate recovery
Landlord & tenant
Medical negligence – defender
Medical negligence – claimant
Personal injury
Personal injury – defender
Professional negligence
Property litigation
Residential property
Road traffic

INKSTERS

The Exchange, 142 St Vincent Street, Glasgow
G2 5LA
Tel: (0141) 2290880
Fax: (0141) 2290550
DX: GW28 GLASGOW
E-mail: glasgow@inksters.com
Web: www.inksters.com
Categories of Work
Advice the elderly & powers of attorney
Agriculture and estates
Agriculture, crofting and fishing
Alternative dispute resolution
Children
Childrens
Civil court work
Civil legal aid
Commercial property
Consumer credit
Contract & property disputes
Criminal court work
Criminal legal aid
Data protection
Debt
Debt collecting
Debt recovery, insolvency, bankruptcy
Family and divorce
Family business advice
Landlord & tenant

Personal tax
Projects
Property litigation
Residential property
Road traffic
Wills, executries and trusts
Partner
Brian Hunter Inkster
Consultants
Steven Andrew Boyd Aitken
Stephanie Louise Christie-Carmichael
David Flint
Jacqueline Elizabeth Jobson
Laura King

IRESOLVELEGAL

5th Floor, The Centrum Building, Glasgow
G1 3DX
Tel: (0844) 8921250
Categories of Work
Advice the elderly & powers of attorney
Alternative dispute resolution
Civil court work
Commercial litigation
Commercial property
Consumer credit
Contract & property disputes
Debt
Debt collecting
Disability
Discrimination
Employment
Employment law
Health
Health and safety
Human rights
Local government
Medical negligence – claimant
Personal injury
Professional negligence
Property litigation
Residential property
Road traffic
Wills, executries and trusts

FRANK IRVINE SOLICITORS LTD

Carlton Buildings, 63 Carlton Place, Glasgow
G5 9TW
Tel: (0141) 3759000
Fax: (0141) 7734111
DX: 513224 GLASGOW CARLTON PLACE
E-mail: mail@frankirvine.com
Web: www.frankirvine.com
Categories of Work
Adjudication
Adoption
Advice the elderly & powers of attorney
Alternative dispute resolution
Benefit advice
Children
Childrens
Civil court work
Civil legal aid
Contract & property disputes

Criminal court work
Criminal legal aid
Data protection
Debt
Debt adjusting and debt counselling
Debt collecting
Debt management
Debt recovery, insolvency, bankruptcy
Disability
Discrimination
Education
Family and divorce
Freedom of information
Health
Human rights
Immigration and asylum
Local government
Mental health
Parliamentary
Personal injury
Professional negligence
Social housing
Wills, executries and trusts
Directors
Nicole Valerie Guidi
Francis Joseph Irvine
Employees
Nadia Orlando
Stewart William Pettigrew

IRWIN MITCHELL SCOTLAND LLP
150 St Vincent Street, Glasgow G2 5NE
Tel: (0141) 3004300
Fax: (01142) 753 306
DX: 320701 GLASGOW 56
Web: www.irwinmitchell.com
Categories of Work
Banking & finance
Childrens
Civil court work
Civil legal aid
Commercial litigation
Consumer credit
Debt recovery, insolvency, bankruptcy
Family and divorce
Health and safety
Landlord & tenant
Medical negligence – claimant
Personal injury
Professional negligence
Property litigation
Residential property
Road traffic
Wills, executries and trusts
Partners
Mark Andrew Higgins
Craig Alexander Marshall
Associate
Michael Andrew Callaghan
Employees
David Bryce Bell
John James Connelly
Lucy Claire Dunlop

Kathleen Heather Lang
Nicola McCartney
Mary Josephine McKenna
Karen Dorothy Wallace

ISW LEGAL
26 Netherpark Avenue, Netherlee, Glasgow
G44 3XW
Tel: (0141) 280 3737
E-mail: swhyte@iswlegal.co.uk
Categories of Work
Banking & finance
Charities
Copyright, trade marks and design
Data protection
Family business advice
Insolvency & corporate recovery
IT and intellectual property
Joint venture
Mergers and acquisitions
Private equity
SME business advice
Software licensing

JAAPLAW LIMITED
1/2 15 North Claremont Street, Glasgow
G3 7NR
Tel: (07709) 343201

JACKSON BOYD LLP
Centenary House, 69 Wellington Street,
Glasgow G2 6HG
Tel: (0141) 2214325
E-mail: kbruce@jacksonboyd.co.uk
Web: www.jacksonboyd.co.uk
Categories of Work
Adjudication
Alternative dispute resolution
Civil court work
Civil legal aid
Commercial litigation
Contract & property disputes
Criminal court work
Debt
Debt collecting
Debt recovery, insolvency, bankruptcy
Discrimination
Employment law
Insolvency & corporate recovery
Landlord & tenant
Medical negligence – defender
Medical negligence – claimant
Personal injury
Personal injury – defender
Professional negligence
Property litigation
Residential property
Road traffic
Partners
Alan Ian Cameron
Alan Macdonald
Laura Margaret Macdonald
Vannan Fraser McKellar
David Jonathan McKinney

► *Glasgow continued*

Deborah Weir Milne
Associates
Pamela Katy Bradshaw
Samuel Alan McCormack
Yvonne Elaine Robertson
Employees
Qurra-Tulain Mughal Amir
David Richard Berry
James Halley
Sarah Blythe McNicol
Fraser Robert Thomson Scott Napier
Jennifer Lee Rowlinson
Jennifer Whitten

JAIN, NEIL & RUDDY
1869 Great Western Road, Anniesland,
Glasgow G13 2UX
Tel: (0141) 9504672
Fax: (0141) 9504673
DX: 512214 GLAS SANDYFORD PL
E-mail: info@jnrsolicitors.com
Web: www.jnrsolicitors.com
Categories of Work
Advice the elderly & powers of attorney
Agriculture and estates
Benefit advice
Children
Childrens
Civil court work
Civil legal aid
Commercial litigation
Commercial property
Contract & property disputes
Criminal court work
Criminal legal aid
Data protection
Debt
Debt management
Debt recovery, insolvency, bankruptcy
Discrimination
Education
Employment
Employment law
EU / international
Family and divorce
Family business advice
Freedom of information
Health and safety
Human rights
Immigration and asylum
Landlord & tenant
Local government
Medical negligence – claimant
Mental health
Personal injury
Professional negligence
Property litigation
Residential property
Road traffic
SME business advice
Social housing
Wills, executrices and trusts

Partner
Pravin Jain
Employee
Ir n Fekete

JAIN, NEIL & RUDDY
The Town House,12 Sandyford Pl, Sauchiehall
Street, Glasgow G3 7NB
Tel: (0141) 2218778
Fax: (0141) 2218338
DX: 512214 GLAS SANDYFORD PL
E-mail: terry@jnrsolicitors.com
Web: www.jnrsolicitors.com
Categories of Work
Advice the elderly & powers of attorney
Agriculture and estates
Benefit advice
Children
Childrens
Civil court work
Civil legal aid
Commercial litigation
Commercial property
Contract & property disputes
Criminal court work
Criminal legal aid
Data protection
Debt
Debt management
Debt recovery, insolvency, bankruptcy
Discrimination
Education
Employment
Employment law
EU / international
Family and divorce
Family business advice
Freedom of information
Health and safety
Human rights
Immigration and asylum
Landlord & tenant
Local government
Medical negligence – claimant
Mental health
Personal injury
Professional negligence
Property litigation
Residential property
Road traffic
SME business advice
Social housing
Wills, executrices and trusts
Partners
Scott Martin
Terence David Ruddy
Employee
Derek Beagrie

JKC ATLANTIC LIMITED
Atlantic House, 6th Floor, 45 Hope Street,
Glasgow G2 6AE

JKR LAW LTD
103 West Regent Street, Glasgow G2 2DQ

Tel: (0141) 473 3999
Fax: (0141) 332 5252
E-mail: SK@jklaws.co.uk
Web: www.JKLaws.co.uk
Categories of Work
Commercial property
Contract & property disputes
Family and divorce
Residential property
Wills, executives and trusts
Director
Saaima Khalid
Employee
Mudassar Husain Rafi

JKR LAW SOLICITORS & NOTARIES PUBLIC
103 West Regent Street, Glasgow G2 2DQ
Categories of Work
Commercial property
Contract & property disputes
Family and divorce
Residential property
Wills, executives and trusts

JONES WHYTE LLP
105 West George Street, Glasgow G2 2DH
Tel: (0141) 375 1222
Fax: (0141) 375 1333
Web: www.joneswhyte.co.uk
Categories of Work
Adjudication
Adoption
Advice the elderly & powers of attorney
Alternative dispute resolution
Children
Childrens
Civil court work
Civil legal aid
Commercial litigation
Commercial property
Construction
Contract & property disputes
Copyright, trade marks and design
Criminal court work
Criminal legal aid
Data protection
Debt
Debt collecting
Debt recovery, insolvency, bankruptcy
Education
Family and divorce
Freedom of information
Housing
Human rights
Immigration and asylum
Insolvency & corporate recovery
Landlord & tenant
Medical negligence – claimant
Mental health
Pensions (Company)
Personal injury
Personal injury – defender
Professional negligence
Property litigation

Residential property
Road traffic
SME business advice
Social housing
Wills, executives and trusts
Partner
Charles Robertson Brown
Employees
Nadia Arshad
Tanya Bagri
Daniel Canning
Nicola Jane Cathcart
Claudia Maria Ayre Hoey

JONES WHYTE LLP
The Connect Building, 3rd Floor, Glasgow
G2 2DH
Tel: (0141) 375 1222
Fax: (0141) 375 1333
E-mail: info@joneswhyte.co.uk
Web: www.joneswhyte.co.uk
Categories of Work
Adjudication
Adoption
Advice the elderly & powers of attorney
Alternative dispute resolution
Children
Childrens
Civil court work
Civil legal aid
Commercial litigation
Commercial property
Construction
Contract & property disputes
Copyright, trade marks and design
Criminal court work
Criminal legal aid
Data protection
Debt
Debt collecting
Debt recovery, insolvency, bankruptcy
Education
Family and divorce
Freedom of information
Housing
Human rights
Immigration and asylum
Insolvency & corporate recovery
Landlord & tenant
Medical negligence – claimant
Mental health
Pensions (Company)
Personal injury
Personal injury – defender
Professional negligence
Property litigation
Residential property
Road traffic
SME business advice
Social housing
Wills, executives and trusts

▶ *Glasgow continued*

Partners
Deborah Louise Carmichael
Stephanie Claire Grace Hutton
Ross Alexander Jones
Michael John McLean
Greg William Thomas Whyte
Associates
Matthew John Currie
Ruth McIntosh
Dominic Ritchie
Employees
Ross Anderson
Steven James Bain
Chloe Melissa Barr
John Dominic Bayne
Laura Mary Christine
Nicole De-Pellette
Rebecca Devine
Roisin Eleanor Gunn
Nicholas William Hay
Lauren Elizabeth Hazlie
Ronan James Jackson-Platt
Amy Margaret Kelly
Kiera Rae Lambie
Heather Lillis
Matthew Ogilvie McCabe
Angela Mary McMahon
Katie Morgan
Ryan Morton
Bryan Michael O'Donnell
Marc Anthony Onorati
Phulah Singh Mouchull Pall
Lisa Kelly Robertson
Neil John Robertson
Cameron Andrew Shaw
Chloe Stuart
Cara Teven
Danielle Collette Trapp
Nicola Frances Waters

HAROLD W. JOSEPH
54 Carlton Place, Glasgow G5 9TW
Tel: (0141) 4201896
Fax: (0141) 4206795
E-mail: harold@hwjoseph.com
Categories of Work
Children
Civil court work
Civil legal aid
Commercial litigation
Contract & property disputes
Debt
Debt collecting
Debt recovery, insolvency, bankruptcy
Employment law
Family and divorce
Housing
Insurance
Landlord & tenant
Medical negligence – claimant
Personal injury
Personal injury – defender

Professional negligence
Partner
Harold William Joseph
Employee
Sharon Louise Collins

JUSTRIGHT SCOTLAND LLP
Room 1, 1st Floor, Libertas House, Glasgow
G1 2ER
Tel: (0141) 406 5350
Fax: (0141) 406 5351
Categories of Work
Adjudication
Adoption
Alternative dispute resolution
Benefit advice
Children
Childrens
Civil court work
Civil legal aid
Discrimination
Employment law
Family and divorce
Human rights
Immigration and asylum
Personal injury – defender
Social housing
Partners
Andrew James Sirel
Kirsty Thomson
Associates
Jennifer Su-lan Ang
Farida Elfallah
Anushya Thejamali Kulupana
Employees
Gwyneth King
Megan Claire Lafferty
Maria Macleod
Lyndsay Monaghan
Elaine Ann Nelson
Francesca Sella

KATANI & CO. LTD
Ground Floor, Sycamore House, Glasgow
G2 4JR
Tel: (0141) 2217788
Fax: (0141) 2217787
E-mail: reception@kataniandco.com
Web: www.kataniandco.com
Categories of Work
Civil court work
Civil legal aid
Discrimination
Human rights
Immigration and asylum
Director
Kamyar Katani
Associate
Darius Behreg Katani
Employees
Caitlin Jessica McEwan Alexander
Elisabetta Borla
Douglas Mitchell Britton
David Peter Corrigall

Colette Judith Keogh
Sarah Holt McKeeve
Barry Anthony Murphy

KAVANAGH COYLE LIMITED
21 West Nile Street, Glasgow G1 2PS
Tel: (0141) 2265500
Fax: (0141) 2265505
E-mail: pat@kavanaghcoyle.co.uk
Categories of Work
Criminal court work
Criminal legal aid
Residential property
Wills, executives and trusts
Directors
Patricia Ann Coyle
Paul Vincent Coyle
Employee
Michael John Northcote Coyle

KEE SOLICITORS LTD
Suite 5, Buchanan Business Centre,
Cumbernauld Road, Glasgow G33 6HZ
Tel: (0141) 478 9090
E-mail: jonathan@keesolicitors.co.uk
Categories of Work
Adoption
Advice the elderly & powers of attorney
Children
Civil court work
Civil legal aid
Debt
Family and divorce
Human rights
Medical negligence – defender
Medical negligence – claimant
Mental health
Personal injury
Personal injury – defender
Professional negligence
Wills, executives and trusts
Director
Jonathan Joseph Kee
Employee
Ainslie Jayne Morrison

KELLY & CO.
184 Abercromby Street, Bridgeton, Glasgow
G40 2RZ
Tel: (0141) 5544141
Fax: (0141) 5542288
DX: 500418 DENNISTOUN 2
E-mail: gerry-kelly@live.co.uk
Categories of Work
Adoption
Advice the elderly & powers of attorney
Benefit advice
Children
Civil court work
Civil legal aid
Criminal court work
Criminal legal aid
Debt
Education

Family and divorce
Housing
Landlord & tenant
Medical negligence – claimant
Personal injury
Road traffic
Social housing
Wills, executives and trusts
Partners
Lorna Jane Anderson
Gerard Anthony Kelly

KELLY LAW LIMITED
213 St Vincent Street, Glasgow G2 5QY
Tel: (0141) 6441116
Categories of Work
Adoption
Advice the elderly & powers of attorney
Benefit advice
Children
Civil court work
Civil legal aid
Criminal court work
Criminal legal aid
Debt
Education
Family and divorce
Housing
Landlord & tenant
Medical negligence – claimant
Personal injury
Road traffic
Social housing
Wills, executives and trusts

NEIL R. KELLY
Centrum House, 38 Queen Street, Glasgow
G1 3DX
Tel: (0141) 378 1111
E-mail: mail@neilrkelly.com
Web: www.neilrkelly.com
Categories of Work
Transport
Partner
Neil Raymond Kelly

KENNEDYS SCOTLAND
Mercantile Building, 53 Bothwell Street,
Glasgow G2 6TS
Tel: (0141) 433 7115
Fax: (0131) 226 4543
DX: GW101 GLASGOW
Web: www.kennedyslaw.com
Categories of Work
Alternative dispute resolution
Civil court work
Commercial litigation
Criminal court work
Criminal legal aid
Data protection
Employment
Freedom of information
Health and safety
Insurance

► **Glasgow continued**

IT and intellectual property
Local government
Media and entertainment
Medical negligence – defender
Medical negligence – claimant
Personal injury
Personal injury – defender
Power and utilities
Professional negligence
Road traffic
Employees
Amina Amin
Clare Louise Crawford
Timothy John William Lennox

KEOGHS SCOTLAND LLP
The Forsyth Building, 5 Renfield Street,
Glasgow G2 5EZ
Tel: (0141) 2380100
Fax: (0141) 2380101
Web: www.keoghs.co.uk
Categories of Work
Adjudication
Alternative dispute resolution
Civil court work
Civil legal aid
Commercial litigation
Construction
Contract & property disputes
Criminal court work
Debt collecting
Debt recovery, insolvency, bankruptcy
Health and safety
Human rights
Insurance
Liquor licensing
Local government
Medical negligence – defender
Oil & gas
Personal injury
Personal injury – defender
Power and utilities
Professional negligence
Property litigation
Public sector
Residential property
Road traffic
Shipping
Transport
Partners
Douglas John Lockhart Cowan
Calum Andrew Fife
David John Hennessy
Emily Kathryn Jeffrey
Peter Mark McCluskie
Associates
Eoin Malachy Quinn
Michael Gordon Wilson
Employees
Laura Jane Naismith Baxendale
Scott Alexander Johnston
David James McLeod

Mohammed Balal Pervaiz
Christopher Robert Rae
Khadija Sarwar
Michael William Strain

KERSLANDS SOLICITORS LIMITED
307 West George Street, Glasgow G2 4LF
Tel: (0333) 600 8000
Categories of Work
Advice the elderly & powers of attorney
Commercial property
Family business advice
Landlord & tenant
Mergers and acquisitions
Residential property
Wills, executries and trusts

KHAN LAW LIMITED
12 Fitzroy Place, Glasgow G3 7RW
Tel: (0141) 3780514
E-mail: info@khanlaw.co.uk
Categories of Work
Medical negligence – claimant
Personal injury
Road traffic
Director
Ra'ees-Mehran Kaif Sagar Khan

NEIL KILCOYNE & CO.
1st Floor, 38 Queen Street, Glasgow G1 3DX
Tel: (0141) 4332700
E-mail: nkilcoyne@kilcoyne-solicitors.co.uk
Categories of Work
Adoption
Advice the elderly & powers of attorney
Children
Childrens
Civil court work
Civil legal aid
Commercial property
Criminal court work
Criminal legal aid
Family and divorce
Residential property
Road traffic
Wills, executries and trusts

NEIL KILCOYNE & CO.
345 Victoria Road, Glasgow G42 7SA
Tel: (0141) 4332700
Fax: (0141) 4332705
E-mail: nkilcoyne@kilcoyne-solicitors.co.uk
Categories of Work
Adoption
Advice the elderly & powers of attorney
Children
Childrens
Civil court work
Civil legal aid
Commercial property
Criminal court work
Criminal legal aid
Family and divorce
Residential property
Road traffic

Wills, executories and trusts
Partner
Neil Martin Kilcoyne
Employees
Jennifer Anne Harkin
Abbie Kate Hunter

JOHN KILCOYNE & CO. SOLICITORS
270 Allison Street, Glasgow G42 8HD
Tel: (0141) 4231400
Fax: (0141) 4238987
Categories of Work
Adoption
Advice the elderly & powers of attorney
Benefit advice
Children
Childrens
Civil court work
Civil legal aid
Criminal court work
Criminal legal aid
Debt management
Education
Family and divorce
Mental health
Personal injury
Residential property
Road traffic
Social housing
Wills, executories and trusts
Partner
John Anthony Kilcoyne
Associate
Lisa Marshall-Kilcoyne
Employee
Kate Frances Mary Stevenson

JOHN KILCOYNE & CO. SOLICITORS
2nd Floor, 69 Buchanan Street, Glasgow
G1 3HL
Tel: (0141) 4238986
Categories of Work
Adoption
Advice the elderly & powers of attorney
Benefit advice
Children
Childrens
Civil court work
Civil legal aid
Criminal court work
Criminal legal aid
Debt management
Education
Family and divorce
Mental health
Personal injury
Residential property
Road traffic
Social housing
Wills, executories and trusts

KINETIC LAWYERS LTD
Unit 2.7, The Hub, 70 Pacific Quay, Glasgow
G51 1EA

Tel: (01254) 846561
E-mail: info@kineticlaw.co.uk
Categories of Work
Civil court work
Criminal court work
Criminal legal aid
Debt collecting
Personal injury
Road traffic
Solicitor
Neha Sood

DAVID KINLOCH & CO.
149 High Street, Glasgow G1 1PH
Tel: (0141) 552 6382
E-mail: info@childlaw.me
Categories of Work
Adoption
Children
Civil court work
Civil legal aid
Criminal court work
Criminal legal aid
Employee
Gayle Elizabeth Middleton

DAVID KINLOCH & CO.
211 Saracen Street, Glasgow G22 5JN
Tel: (0141) 3363000
Fax: (0141) 3362005
E-mail: info@kinlochlawyers.co.uk
Categories of Work
Adoption
Children
Civil court work
Civil legal aid
Criminal court work
Criminal legal aid
Partner
David Arthur Kinloch
Employee
Ross David Jenkins

KIRK HANLON
PO Box 3614, Glasgow G73 9FG
Tel: (0141) 3786653
E-mail: contact@kirkhanlon.com
Partners
Deirdre Elizabeth Hanlon
Karen Kirk

KM LAW
18 London Road, Glasgow G1 5NB
Tel: (07702) 735440
Categories of Work
Criminal court work
Criminal legal aid
Discrimination
Health and safety
Human rights
Partners
Paul George Kavanagh
Neal McShane

▶ **Glasgow continued**

Employees
George Collins Kavanagh
Isla Christina Sinclair

KUDOS LEGAL LIMITED
Spaces, 100 West George Street, Glasgow
G2 1PJ
Tel: (0141) 739 6606

LAMBIE LAW PARTNERSHIP
2345 Dumbarton Road, Yoker, Glasgow
G14 0NN
Tel: (0141) 9597000
Fax: (0141) 9501441
DX: 500508 CLYDEBANK
E-mail: enquiries@lambielaw.co.uk
Categories of Work
Criminal court work
Criminal legal aid
Family and divorce
Partner
Andrew Lambie
Employee
Anne Rose Lambie

B.J. LANIGAN & CO
14 Drumchapel Road, Glasgow G15 6QE
Tel: (0141) 9440671
E-mail: brian.lanigan@btinternet.com
Categories of Work
Advice the elderly & powers of attorney
Children
Civil court work
Civil legal aid
Criminal court work
Criminal legal aid
Family and divorce
Road traffic
Partner
Brian Joseph Lanigan

LATTA LAW LIMITED
2nd Floor, 137 Sauchiehall Street, Glasgow
G2 3EW
Tel: (0141) 222 2185
Fax: (0141) 222 2186
E-mail: info@lattalaw.co.uk
Web: www.lattalaw.co.uk
Categories of Work
Adoption
Alternative dispute resolution
Benefit advice
Children
Childrens
Civil court work
Civil legal aid
Consumer credit
Criminal court work
Criminal legal aid
Data protection
Debt
Debt management
Disability

Discrimination
Employment
Employment law
EU / international
Family and divorce
Family business advice
Freedom of information
Housing
Human rights
Immigration and asylum
Landlord & tenant
Liquor licensing
Local government
Media and entertainment
Mental health
Parliamentary
Public sector
SME business advice
Social housing
Directors
Fraser Paterson Latta
Barry William Price
Employees
Monica Rani Anand
Megan Ailsa Anderson
Ruzena Martina Benes
Andrew James Burns
Emily Morrison Carmichael
Jalal Noor Chaudry
Hannah Louise Cosgrove
Jennifer Scott Cowan
William Lawson Criggie
Kathryn Louise Dingwall
Robert James Forsyth Gibb
Tuyub Mukhtar
Laura Fiona Sclare
Jack Matthew Smith
Arlene Fiona Speirs

PAULA LAVELLE SOLICITOR
Clyde Offices, 2nd Floor, 48 West George
Street, Glasgow G2 1BP
Tel: (07710) 251587
E-mail: paulalavelle@yahoo.co.uk
Categories of Work
Criminal court work
Criminal legal aid
Partner
Paula Lavelle

LAWRIE JACKSON
13 Granville Street, Glasgow G3 7EE
Tel: (0141) 2481111
Fax: (0141) 5642993
E-mail: andrewlawrie@lawriejackson.co.uk
Categories of Work
Commercial property
Personal injury
Residential property
Wills, executories and trusts
Partner
Andrew Livingstone Lawrie
Employee
Fraser Livingstone Lawrie

NORMAN LAWSON & CO SOLICITORS
St George's Building, 3rd Floor, George
Square, Glasgow G1 2DH
Tel: (0141) 275 4844
Categories of Work
Adoption
Advice the elderly & powers of attorney
Benefit advice
Children
Childrens
Civil court work
Civil legal aid
Debt management
Disability
Discrimination
Education
Family and divorce
Housing
Human rights
Immigration and asylum
Landlord & tenant
Medical negligence – claimant
Mental health
Personal injury
Professional negligence
Road traffic
Social housing
Wills, executries and trusts

LB & CO.
Unit 6,42-46 New City Road, Glasgow G4 9JT
Tel: (0141) 3320047
Categories of Work
Advice the elderly & powers of attorney
Betting & gaming
Civil court work
Civil legal aid
Commercial property
Contract & property disputes
Copyright, trade marks and design
Criminal court work
Criminal legal aid
Data protection
Debt
Debt recovery, insolvency, bankruptcy
Discrimination
EU / international
Family and divorce
Freedom of information
Human rights
Immigration and asylum
IT and intellectual property
Joint venture
Landlord & tenant
Media and entertainment
Property litigation
Residential property
Road traffic
Social housing
Software licensing
Sport
Telecoms
Wills, executries and trusts

LEFEVRES (SCOTLAND) LIMITED
70 West Regent Street, Glasgow G2 2QZ
Tel: (0845) 3052555
Fax: (0131) 220 4374
Web: www.lefevres.law
Categories of Work
Alternative dispute resolution
Civil court work
Civil legal aid
Commercial litigation
Discrimination
Employment
Employment law
Medical negligence – claimant
Personal injury
Professional negligence
Property litigation
Road traffic
Employee
Iain William Nicol

LEGAL AND LEGAL SOLICITORS & NOTARIES
62 Nithsdale Road, Glasgow G41 2AN
Tel: (0141) 4240500
Fax: (0141) 4231604
E-mail: info@legalandlegalsolicitors.com
Partner
Asif Jilani Hussain
Employee
Mohammed Kashif Hussain

LEGAL EAGLE SCOTLAND LTD
St George's Building, 3rd Floor, George
Square, Glasgow G1 2DH
Tel: (0141) 275 4844
Fax: (0141) 4130555
E-mail: mu@normanlawsonsolicitors.co.uk
Categories of Work
Adoption
Advice the elderly & powers of attorney
Benefit advice
Children
Childrens
Civil court work
Civil legal aid
Debt management
Disability
Discrimination
Education
Family and divorce
Housing
Human rights
Immigration and asylum
Landlord & tenant
Medical negligence – claimant
Mental health
Personal injury
Professional negligence
Road traffic
Social housing
Wills, executries and trusts
Director
Manishkumar Upadhyay

▶ *Glasgow continued*

LEGAL SPARK
Savoy Tower, 77 Renfrew Street, Glasgow
G2 3BZ
Tel: (0141) 2800330
Categories of Work
Benefit advice
Charities
Children
Civil court work
Civil legal aid
Commercial litigation
Data protection
Disability
Discrimination
Education
Employment
Employment law
EU / international
Freedom of information
Health
Health and safety
Human rights
IT and intellectual property
Landlord & tenant
Liquor licensing
Local government
Media and entertainment
Mental health
Parliamentary
Personal injury
Professional negligence
Public sector
SME business advice
Social housing

**LEGAL SPARK SOLICITORS AND NOTARIES
LTD**
SPACES, 100 West George Street, Glasgow
G2 1PJ
Tel: (0141) 2800330
E-mail: DanielD@legalspark.co.uk
Categories of Work
Benefit advice
Charities
Children
Civil court work
Civil legal aid
Commercial litigation
Data protection
Disability
Discrimination
Education
Employment
Employment law
EU / international
Freedom of information
Health
Health and safety
Human rights
IT and intellectual property
Landlord & tenant
Liquor licensing

Local government
Media and entertainment
Mental health
Parliamentary
Personal injury
Professional negligence
Public sector
SME business advice
Social housing
Director
Daniel James Donaldson
Employee
Damian Hoggan-Radu

LEVY & MCRAE SOLICITORS LLP
Pacific House, 70 Wellington Street, Glasgow
G2 6UA
Tel: (0141) 3072311
Fax: (0141) 3076857
DX: GW149 GLASGOW
E-mail: info@lemac.co.uk
Web: lemac.co.uk/
Categories of Work
Adjudication
Advice the elderly & powers of attorney
Agriculture and estates
Alternative dispute resolution
Banking & finance
Children
Childrens
Civil court work
Commercial litigation
Commercial property
Construction
Contract & property disputes
Copyright, trade marks and design
Criminal court work
Criminal legal aid
Data protection
Debt
Debt administration
Debt collecting
Debt recovery, insolvency, bankruptcy
Disability
Discrimination
Education
Employment
Employment law
Environment
Environment (Business Premises)
Family and divorce
Family business advice
Fishing
Freedom of information
Health
Health and safety
Housing
Human rights
Insolvency & corporate recovery
Insurance
IT and intellectual property
Landlord & tenant
Liquor licensing

Local government
Media and entertainment
Medical negligence – defender
Medical negligence – claimant
Mergers and acquisitions
Mining
Oil & gas
Parliamentary
Personal injury
Personal injury – defender
Personal tax
Planning
Planning (Business Premises)
Power and utilities
Professional negligence
Projects
Property litigation
Public finance initiative
Public sector
Residential property
Road traffic
Shipping
SME business advice
Social housing
Sport
Transport
Wills, executries and trusts
Partners
Callum George Anderson
Richard Alexander Barrie
Anthony Max Caplan
Graham Duncan Dunbar Craik
David Robert McKie
Consultants
Michael Peter Anderson
Stephen John Giusti
William Couperthwaite Macreath
Leo Martin
Associates
Sandra Elizabeth Biggart
Donna Lee Carson
Raymond Scott Gribben
Elizabeth Paterson Rose
Victoria Louise Savage
Employees
Christopher Stephen Barnes
Carol Jane Boyd
Amanda Mary Buchanan
Iain Patrick Cahill
Sofia Rosa-Maria Crolla
Francis McKnight
Jack David McLarty
Caitlin Anne O'Hare
Andrew Graeme Park
Andrew William Ratter
Christopher Miller Reid
Christopher Alexander Shaw
Maria Elena Smillie
Danielle Taylor

LEXARES LLP
Centrum House, 38 Queen Street, Glasgow
G1 3DX

Tel: (0141) 3780960
E-mail: frances.rooney@lexares.co.uk
Categories of Work
Agriculture and estates
Commercial property
Construction
Contract & property disputes
Landlord & tenant
Property litigation
Residential property
Partner
Frances Anelia Rooney

LEXARES SCOTLAND LIMITED
Centrum House, 38 Queen Street, Glasgow
G1 3DX
Tel: (0141) 3780960

LINDSAYS LLP
100 Queen Street, Glasgow G1 3DN
Tel: (0141) 2216551
Fax: (0141) 2040507
DX: GW531 GLASGOW
E-mail: glasgow@lindsays.co.uk
Web: www.lindsays.co.uk
Categories of Work
Adjudication
Adoption
Advice the elderly & powers of attorney
Agriculture and estates
Agriculture, crofting and fishing
Alternative dispute resolution
Banking & finance
Betting & gaming
Charities
Children
Childrens
Civil court work
Civil legal aid
Commercial litigation
Commercial property
Construction
Consumer credit
Contract & property disputes
Copyright, trade marks and design
Corporate tax
Criminal court work
Criminal legal aid
Data protection
Debt
Debt adjusting and debt counselling
Debt administration
Debt collecting
Debt recovery, insolvency, bankruptcy
Discrimination
Education
Employment
Employment law
Environment
Environment (Business Premises)
EU / international
Family and divorce
Family business advice
Fishing

► *Glasgow continued*

Freedom of information
Health
Health and safety
Housing
Human rights
Insolvency & corporate recovery
IT and intellectual property
Joint venture
Landlord & tenant
Liquor licensing
Local government
Media and entertainment
Medical negligence – defender
Medical negligence – claimant
Mergers and acquisitions
Oil & gas
Parliamentary
Pensions (Employment)
Personal injury
Personal injury – defender
Personal tax
Planning
Planning (Business Premises)
Power and utilities
Private equity
Professional negligence
Projects
Property litigation
Public finance initiative
Public sector
Residential property
Road traffic
SME business advice
Software licensing
Sport
Telecoms
Transport
Wills, executries and trusts
Partners
David James Armstrong
John Alexander Bett
Jonathan Islay Cornwell
Benjamin John Doherty
Alastair Gordon Goodman
Alexander McDougal Lamb
Alison Jayne McKee
Alan Cunningham McLaren
Ian Robert Mitchell
Lauren Ann Pasi
Consultant
Jonathan Graham Aitken Williams
Associates
Garry Gibson
Lynne McLean
Clare Louise Wilson
Employees
Philippa Rose Abernethy
Qasim Hussain Ali
Ka Man Au-Yeung
Kathleen Gaughan
Kirsty Caitlin Macleod Martin

Maeve McCorry
Alison Doreen McKay
Samantha Alexandra Miller
Brian Pollock
Sophie Elizabeth Richardson
Jane Elizabeth Anne Watson

LIU'S LEGAL SOLUTIONS LTD
Unit 6,42-46 New City Road, Glasgow G4 9JT
Tel: (0141) 3320047
Fax: (0709) 2094561
E-mail: liu@liuslaw.co.uk
Web: www.liuslaw.co.uk
Categories of Work
Advice the elderly & powers of attorney
Betting & gaming
Civil court work
Civil legal aid
Commercial property
Contract & property disputes
Copyright, trade marks and design
Criminal court work
Criminal legal aid
Data protection
Debt
Debt recovery, insolvency, bankruptcy
Discrimination
EU / international
Family and divorce
Freedom of information
Human rights
Immigration and asylum
IT and intellectual property
Joint venture
Landlord & tenant
Media and entertainment
Property litigation
Residential property
Road traffic
Social housing
Software licensing
Sport
Telecoms
Wills, executries and trusts
Director
Lihe Liu
Employee
Heather Haiyan Du

LIVINGSTONE BROWN LIMITED
15 Shandwick Square, Easterhouse, Glasgow
G34 9DT
Tel: (0141) 7732010
E-mail: cp@livbrown.co.uk
Web: www.livbrown.co.uk
Categories of Work
Adoption
Advice the elderly & powers of attorney
Alternative dispute resolution
Benefit advice
Children
Childrens
Civil court work
Civil legal aid

Commercial litigation
Contract & property disputes
Copyright, trade marks and design
Criminal court work
Criminal legal aid
Data protection
Debt recovery, insolvency, bankruptcy
Disability
Discrimination
Education
Employment
Employment law
Family and divorce
Family business advice
Freedom of information
Housing
Human rights
Immigration and asylum
Insolvency & corporate recovery
IT and intellectual property
Landlord & tenant
Media and entertainment
Medical negligence – defender
Medical negligence – claimant
Mental health
Personal injury
Personal injury – defender
Professional negligence
Property litigation
Residential property
Road traffic
SME business advice
Software licensing
Sport
Wills, executries and trusts

LIVINGSTONE BROWN LIMITED
250 West George Street, Glasgow G2 4QY
Tel: (0141) 4298166
Fax: (0141) 4201337
E-mail: cp@livbrown.co.uk
Web: www.livbrown.co.uk
Categories of Work
Adoption
Advice the elderly & powers of attorney
Alternative dispute resolution
Benefit advice
Children
Childrens
Civil court work
Civil legal aid
Commercial litigation
Contract & property disputes
Copyright, trade marks and design
Criminal court work
Criminal legal aid
Data protection
Debt recovery, insolvency, bankruptcy
Disability
Discrimination
Education
Employment
Employment law

Family and divorce
Family business advice
Freedom of information
Housing
Human rights
Immigration and asylum
Insolvency & corporate recovery
IT and intellectual property
Landlord & tenant
Media and entertainment
Medical negligence – defender
Medical negligence – claimant
Mental health
Personal injury
Personal injury – defender
Professional negligence
Property litigation
Residential property
Road traffic
SME business advice
Software licensing
Sport
Wills, executries and trusts
Directors
Julia Rosalind Donnelly
Stuart Kenneth Munro
Kevin John Pike
Consultant
Gerard Anthony Brown
Employees
Nicole April Brodie
Robbie Brodie
Lynsey Meiklem Brown
Danielle Gail Evans
Mairead Frances McCrossan
Jenna McKinley
Sarah Anne Munro
Stephen George Smith
Nicola Watson

LIVINGSTONE BROWN LIMITED
365 Victoria Road, Glasgow G42 8YZ
Tel: (0141) 3759090
E-mail: cp@livbrown.co.uk
Web: www.livbrown.co.uk
Categories of Work
Adoption
Advice the elderly & powers of attorney
Alternative dispute resolution
Benefit advice
Children
Childrens
Civil court work
Civil legal aid
Commercial litigation
Contract & property disputes
Copyright, trade marks and design
Criminal court work
Criminal legal aid
Data protection
Debt recovery, insolvency, bankruptcy
Disability
Discrimination

▶ *Glasgow continued*

Education
Employment
Employment law
Family and divorce
Family business advice
Freedom of information
Housing
Human rights
Immigration and asylum
Insolvency & corporate recovery
IT and intellectual property
Landlord & tenant
Media and entertainment
Medical negligence – defender
Medical negligence – claimant
Mental health
Personal injury
Personal injury – defender
Professional negligence
Property litigation
Residential property
Road traffic
SME business advice
Software licensing
Sport
Wills, executives and trusts

LIVINGSTONE BROWN LIMITED
775 Shettleston Road, Glasgow G32 7NN
Tel: (0141) 7789657
Fax: (0141) 7784331
E-mail: cp@livbrown.co.uk
Web: www.livbrown.co.uk
Categories of Work
Adoption
Advice the elderly & powers of attorney
Alternative dispute resolution
Benefit advice
Children
Childrens
Civil court work
Civil legal aid
Commercial litigation
Contract & property disputes
Copyright, trade marks and design
Criminal court work
Criminal legal aid
Data protection
Debt recovery, insolvency, bankruptcy
Disability
Discrimination
Education
Employment
Employment law
Family and divorce
Family business advice
Freedom of information
Housing
Human rights
Immigration and asylum
Insolvency & corporate recovery
IT and intellectual property

Landlord & tenant
Media and entertainment
Medical negligence – defender
Medical negligence – claimant
Mental health
Personal injury
Personal injury – defender
Professional negligence
Property litigation
Residential property
Road traffic
SME business advice
Software licensing
Sport
Wills, executives and trusts
Directors
Paul Joseph Mullen
Paul Sturdy
Employees
Amy Dobbin
Darren Fleming
Alison Miller
Gillian Claire Russell

LKW SOLICITORS LTD
414 Cathcart Road, Glasgow G42 7BZ
Tel: (0141) 4236999
Fax: (0141) 4236444
E-mail: contact@lkwsolicitors.co.uk
Categories of Work
Adoption
Children
Childrens
Civil court work
Civil legal aid
Commercial litigation
Debt recovery, insolvency, bankruptcy
Discrimination
Family and divorce
Housing
Human rights
Immigration and asylum
Landlord & tenant
Medical negligence – defender
Personal injury
Personal injury – defender
Professional negligence
Property litigation
Residential property
Director
Khalda Wali
Employees
Zahra Yasmin Bhatti
Sofia Liaquat

LOUGHRAN & CO LIMITED
4 Somerset Place, Glasgow G3 7JT
Tel: (0141) 3310374
Fax: (0141) 6261494
E-mail: info@loughransolicitors.com
Categories of Work
Human rights
Immigration and asylum

Director
Nicola Loughran
Employees
Robert Andrew Middleton
Rebekah Louise Strachan

LOW BEATON RICHMOND LLP
Sterling House, 20 Renfield Street, Glasgow
G2 5AP
Tel: (0141) 2218931
Fax: (0141) 2484411
DX: GW83 GLASGOW
E-mail: City@lbr-law.co.uk
Web: www.lbr-law.co.uk
Categories of Work
Advice the elderly & powers of attorney
Agriculture and estates
Charities
Commercial property
Contract & property disputes
Family business advice
Landlord & tenant
Mental health
Mergers and acquisitions
Personal injury
Residential property
Wills, executries and trusts
Partners
Melissa Jane Gilmour
Ronald Charles Gordon Munton
Consultant
Murdoch Charles Beaton
Employees
Alastair MacBeath MacDonald
Neil Charles McKinlay

LYNCH & CO., SOLICITORS
5 North Gower Street, Ibrox, Glasgow
G51 1PW
Tel: (0141) 4276162
Fax: (0141) 4271888
E-mail: frankmcauley@hotmail.com
Categories of Work
Adoption
Advice the elderly & powers of attorney
Children
Civil court work
Civil legal aid
Criminal court work
Criminal legal aid
Family and divorce
Residential property
Wills, executries and trusts
Partner
Francis Anthony McAuley

MICHAEL LYON SOLICITORS LIMITED
165 High Street, Glasgow G1 1QN
Tel: (0141) 550 1074
Fax: (0141) 4042554
E-mail: ml@theroadtrafficlawyer.com
Web: www.theroadtrafficlawyer.com
Categories of Work
Criminal court work

Road traffic
Director
Michael Caithness Malcolm Lyon
Employee
Ronald Alexander Simpson

MACALLANS LIMITED
236 Stonelaw Road, Burnside, Glasgow
G73 3SA
Tel: (0141) 6131787/6474441
Fax: (0141) 6131431
E-mail: mr@macallans.co.uk
Web: www.macallans.co.uk
Categories of Work
Advice the elderly & powers of attorney
Agriculture and estates
Civil legal aid
Mental health
Residential property
Wills, executries and trusts
Directors
Lesley Anne Hurst
Margaret Mary Reid
Employees
David James Drain
Eleanor Frances Fitzsimmons

MCARDLE
116 Levernside Road, Pollok, Glasgow
G53 5NH
Tel: (0141) 8101001
Fax: (0141) 8915390
Categories of Work
Children
Criminal court work
Criminal legal aid
Family and divorce
Partner
Edward Garvey McArdle
Employee
John Paul Dunne

MCAULEY, MCCARTHY & CO.
417 Paisley Road West, Glasgow G51 1LS
Tel: (0141) 427 7150
Categories of Work
Adoption
Advice the elderly & powers of attorney
Alternative dispute resolution
Children
Childrens
Civil court work
Civil legal aid
Commercial property
Environment (Business Premises)
Family and divorce
Family business advice
Landlord & tenant
Mental health
Planning (Business Premises)
Private equity
Public sector
Residential property
SME business advice

▶ *Glasgow continued*

Wills, executries and trusts

MCBRIDE KONDOL & CO.
35 Glenmore Avenue, Glasgow G42 0EH
Tel: (0141) 6476400
Fax: (0141) 6476416
E-mail: mail@mcbridekondol.co.uk
Web: www.mcbridekondol.co.uk
Categories of Work
Adoption
Advice the elderly & powers of attorney
Benefit advice
Children
Civil court work
Civil legal aid
Criminal court work
Criminal legal aid
Debt
Family and divorce
Medical negligence – claimant
Personal injury
Road traffic
Wills, executries and trusts
Partner
Leon Kondol

ALEXANDER MCBURNEY SOLICITORS
338 Dumbarton Road, Glasgow G11 6TG
Tel: (0141) 5764808
DX: 500908 PARTICK
E-mail: lawatwork7@hotmail.com
Categories of Work
Civil legal aid
Disability
Employment
Employment law
Partner
Alexander John McBurney

MCCARRYS SOLICITORS
1944A Maryhill Road, Glasgow G20 0EQ
Tel: (0141) 9451911
Fax: (0141) 9464705
E-mail: mail@mccarrys.com
Web: www.mccarrys.com
Categories of Work
Advice the elderly & powers of attorney
Children
Civil court work
Civil legal aid
Criminal court work
Criminal legal aid
Human rights
Mental health
Residential property
Wills, executries and trusts
Partners
Colin Grant Adam
Moira Grant
Paul Charles McCormick
Associate
Richard Iain McKay

MCCARTHY LAW
243-245 Crow Road, Broomhill, Glasgow
G11 7BE
Tel: (0141) 3376678
E-mail: k@mccarthylaw.co.uk
Categories of Work
Adoption
Advice the elderly & powers of attorney
Children
Childrens
Civil court work
Civil legal aid
Commercial litigation
Consumer credit
Contract & property disputes
Criminal court work
Criminal legal aid
Debt
Family and divorce
Family business advice
Landlord & tenant
Medical negligence – claimant
Mental health
Personal injury
Professional negligence
Property litigation
Road traffic
Wills, executries and trusts
Partner
Kathleen McCarthy
Employee
Kathryn Judith Cochrane

IAN C. MCCARTHY LTD
306 Dumbarton Road, Partick, Glasgow
G11 6TD
Tel: (0141) 3392929
Categories of Work
Adoption
Advice the elderly & powers of attorney
Children
Childrens
Commercial property
Contract & property disputes
Criminal court work
Criminal legal aid
Debt
Education
Family and divorce
Freedom of information
Health
Human rights
Landlord & tenant
Local government
Medical negligence – claimant
Mental health
Personal injury
Professional negligence
Residential property
Road traffic
Social housing
Wills, executries and trusts

IAN C. MCCARTHY LTD
905 Shettleston Road, Glasgow G32 7NU
Tel: (0141) 7631366
Fax: (0141) 7780675
E-mail: info@iancmccarthy.co.uk
Categories of Work
Adoption
Advice the elderly & powers of attorney
Children
Childrens
Commercial property
Contract & property disputes
Criminal court work
Criminal legal aid
Debt
Education
Family and divorce
Freedom of information
Health
Human rights
Landlord & tenant
Local government
Medical negligence – claimant
Mental health
Personal injury
Professional negligence
Residential property
Road traffic
Social housing
Wills, executives and trusts
Director
Ian Christopher McCarthy
Employees
Paul Anthony Cruikshank
Jacqueline White

MCCLURE COLLINS LIMITED
139 Allison Street, Glasgow G42 8RY
Tel: (0141) 4237181
Categories of Work
Adoption
Advice the elderly & powers of attorney
Benefit advice
Children
Civil court work
Civil legal aid
Criminal court work
Criminal legal aid
Debt
Debt management
Disability
Family and divorce
Human rights
Immigration and asylum
Landlord & tenant
Mental health
Road traffic
Social housing
Directors
Anne Marie Bolger
Gerald McClure
Associate
James Scullion Rhodes

WILLIAM MCCLUSKEY SOLICITORS LIMITED
46a Carlton Place, Glasgow G5 9TW
Tel: (0141) 4180418
Fax: (0141) 4180518
E-mail: wmccluskey@hotmail.co.uk
Categories of Work
Criminal court work
Criminal legal aid
Education
Local government
Director
William McCluskey

BRUCE MCCORMACK LIMITED
78 Nicholson Street, Glasgow G5 9ER
Tel: (0141) 429 0010
Fax: (0141) 429 8222
E-mail: brucemccormackltd@hotmail.co.uk
Categories of Work
Criminal court work
Criminal legal aid
Employees
Gerard John Devaney
Marcell Horvath

MCCORMACKS SOLICITORS LIMITED
Waterloo Chambers, 19 Waterloo Street,
Glasgow G2 6AY
Tel: (0141) 404 0438
E-mail: mccormacks@live.co.uk
Categories of Work
Commercial property
Criminal court work
Criminal legal aid
Director
Robert Edward McCormack
Employee
Mark McCormack

JOHN N. MCCORMICK
Waterloo Chambers, 19 Waterloo Street,
Glasgow G2 6AH
Tel: (0141) 2487962
Categories of Work
Adoption
Advice the elderly & powers of attorney
Charities
Children
Commercial property
Criminal court work
Criminal legal aid
Data protection
Disability
Discrimination
Education
Employment
Employment law
Family business advice
Freedom of information
Health
Health and safety
Insurance
Local government
Personal injury

► Glasgow continued

Personal injury – defender
Professional negligence
Residential property
Wills, executives and trusts

PAUL MCCUE & CO LIMITED

2nd Floor, 46 Carlton Place, Glasgow G5 9TW
Tel: (07872) 835546
E-mail: paul.mccue@gmail.com
Categories of Work
Criminal court work
Criminal legal aid
Director
Paul Michael McCue

MCCUSKER, COCHRANE & GUNN

1242 Shettleston Road, Glasgow G32 7PG
Tel: (0141) 7782222
E-mail: jmccusker@prp-legal.co.uk
Categories of Work
Advice the elderly & powers of attorney
Children
Civil court work
Commercial litigation
Commercial property
Criminal court work
Criminal legal aid
Data protection
Disability
Employment
Employment law
Family and divorce
Immigration and asylum
IT and intellectual property
Landlord & tenant
Medical negligence – claimant
Mergers and acquisitions
Personal injury
Professional negligence
Property litigation
Residential property
Wills, executives and trusts
Director
James Anthony McCusker

MCDAID FARRELL

20 Croftfoot Road, Glasgow G44 5JT
Tel: (0141) 6340437
Fax: (0141) 6313675
DX: 566400 CROFTFOOT
E-mail: info@mcdaidfarrell.com
Categories of Work
Advice the elderly & powers of attorney
Children
Civil legal aid
Criminal court work
Criminal legal aid
Family and divorce
Personal injury
Residential property
Road traffic
Wills, executives and trusts

Partner
Christopher McDaid

MACDONALD & CO

1607 Great Western Road, Glasgow G13 1LT
Tel: (0141) 9591999
Fax: (0141) 9506252
E-mail: graeme@macdonald-solicitors.co.uk
Categories of Work
Advice the elderly & powers of attorney
Commercial property
Landlord & tenant
Residential property
Wills, executives and trusts
Partner
Graeme John MacDonald
Employee
Gina Cameron Macfarlane

MACDONALD HENDERSON LIMITED

Standard Buildings, 94 Hope Street, Glasgow
G2 6PH
Tel: (0141) 2484957
Fax: (0141) 2488455
DX: GW255 GLASGOW
E-mail: info@macdonaldhenderson.co.uk
Web: www.macdonaldhenderson.co.uk
Categories of Work
Advice the elderly & powers of attorney
Alternative dispute resolution
Banking & finance
Betting & gaming
Civil court work
Commercial litigation
Commercial property
Competition
Construction
Consumer credit
Contract & property disputes
Copyright, trade marks and design
Data protection
Debt collecting
Debt recovery, insolvency, bankruptcy
Employment
Employment law
Environment (Business Premises)
Family and divorce
Family business advice
Insolvency & corporate recovery
IT and intellectual property
Joint venture
Landlord & tenant
Media and entertainment
Mergers and acquisitions
Personal injury
Planning (Business Premises)
Property litigation
Public finance initiative
Residential property
Road traffic
SME business advice
Software licensing
Sport
Wills, executives and trusts

Directors
Ian Robert Edgar Anderson
David Brannigan Beveridge
Michael Richard Hankinson
Laura Maureen McKnight
Associate
Callum Farquhar McInnes
Employees
William Gordon Lennox
Ryan James Macready
Hilary Jane Malone
Peter William McEwan

MACDONALD LYNCH SOLICITORS
15/17 Carmunnock Road, Mount Florida,
Glasgow G44 4TZ
Tel: (0141) 6499552
Fax: (0141) 6324682
E-mail: hello@macdonaldlynch.co.uk
Web: www.macdonaldlynch.co.uk
Categories of Work
Advice the elderly & powers of attorney
Banking & finance
Children
Childrens
Civil court work
Civil legal aid
Commercial litigation
Commercial property
Contract & property disputes
Debt adjusting and debt counselling
Debt collecting
Debt management
Debt recovery, insolvency, bankruptcy
Family and divorce
Family business advice
Insolvency & corporate recovery
Personal injury
Personal injury – defender
Property litigation
Residential property
Road traffic
Wills, executries and trusts
Partners
Colin Peter Carr
Elaine MacDonald
Consultant
Gerard Paul Lynch
Associate
Robert Thomas Currie Telfer

BOB MCDOWALL
15 Tollcross Road, Glasgow G31 4UG
Tel: (0141) 7749996
Fax: (0141) 7740100
E-mail: law@bobmcdowall.com
Categories of Work
Criminal court work
Criminal legal aid
Partner
Robert McDowall

MACFARLANE & CO.
142 St Vincent Street, Glasgow G2 5LA

Tel: (0141) 2483307
Fax: (0141) 221 2713
DX: GW66 GLASGOW
E-mail: city@macfarlane-law.co.uk
Web: www.macfarlane-law.co.uk
Categories of Work
Advice the elderly & powers of attorney
Residential property
Wills, executries and trusts
Partners
April Anne Cuthbert
Alison Mary Macfarlane
Ian Greig McPhail

IAN A MCFARLANE & CO
216 Kilmarnock Road, Shawlands, Glasgow
G43 1TY
Tel: (0141) 6365115
Categories of Work
Advice the elderly & powers of attorney
Agriculture and estates
Agriculture, crofting and fishing
Charities
Children
Civil court work
Civil legal aid
Commercial property
Contract & property disputes
Debt recovery, insolvency, bankruptcy
Disability
Family and divorce
Family business advice
Insolvency & corporate recovery
Joint venture
Landlord & tenant
Mental health
Mergers and acquisitions
Personal injury
Planning (Business Premises)
Residential property
Wills, executries and trusts

IAN A MCFARLANE & CO.
256 Castlemilk Road, Kings Park, Glasgow
G44 4LB
Tel: (0141) 6499772
Categories of Work
Advice the elderly & powers of attorney
Agriculture and estates
Agriculture, crofting and fishing
Charities
Children
Civil court work
Civil legal aid
Commercial property
Contract & property disputes
Debt recovery, insolvency, bankruptcy
Disability
Family and divorce
Family business advice
Insolvency & corporate recovery
Joint venture
Landlord & tenant
Mental health

▶ Glasgow continued

Mergers and acquisitions
Personal injury
Planning (Business Premises)
Residential property
Wills, executries and trusts

MURNIN MCCLUSKEY
24 Sandyford Place, Glasgow G3 7NG
Tel: (0141) 2221760
Fax: (0141) 2216940
DX: 512219 GLAS SANDYFORD PL
E-mail: pm@murnin.co.uk
Categories of Work
Civil court work
Commercial litigation
Contract & property disputes
Debt recovery, insolvency, bankruptcy
Personal injury
Property litigation
SME business advice
Partner
Philip Brendan Murnin
Employee
Alistair John Murdoch

MACFARLANE LAW LIMITED
Caledonia House, 89 Seaward Street, Glasgow
G41 1HJ
Tel: (07808) 331224
E-mail: stuart.macfarlane@macfarlanelaw.co.uk
Director
Stuart Gordon Macfarlane

FULTON'S
1087 Cathcart Road, Mount Florida, Glasgow
G42 9XP
Tel: (0141) 6322248
Fax: (0141) 6490301
E-mail: mail@fultonslaw.co.uk
Categories of Work
Adjudication
Adoption
Advice the elderly & powers of attorney
Alternative dispute resolution
Children
Childrens
Civil court work
Civil legal aid
Commercial litigation
Commercial property
Contract & property disputes
Copyright, trade marks and design
Data protection
Disability
Discrimination
Education
Employment
Employment law
Family and divorce
Freedom of information
Health and safety
Human rights
IT and intellectual property

Landlord & tenant
Medical negligence – defender
Medical negligence – claimant
Pensions (Company)
Pensions (Employment)
Personal injury
Personal injury – defender
Professional negligence
Property litigation
Residential property
Road traffic
Wills, executries and trusts
Associate
Paul Steven Ferrie
Employees
Katie Elizabeth Kerr
Carly Alana MacDonough
Lauren Anne McGhie
Kerry Christine Allan Ritchie

FULTON'S
4 Howie Buildings, Mearns Road, Glasgow
G76 7ET
Tel: (0141) 6211816
Categories of Work
Adjudication
Adoption
Advice the elderly & powers of attorney
Alternative dispute resolution
Children
Childrens
Civil court work
Civil legal aid
Commercial litigation
Commercial property
Contract & property disputes
Copyright, trade marks and design
Data protection
Disability
Discrimination
Education
Employment
Employment law
Family and divorce
Freedom of information
Health and safety
Human rights
IT and intellectual property
Landlord & tenant
Medical negligence – defender
Medical negligence – claimant
Pensions (Company)
Pensions (Employment)
Personal injury
Personal injury – defender
Professional negligence
Property litigation
Residential property
Road traffic
Wills, executries and trusts
Employee
Claire Frances McNaught

MCGINN SOLICITORS LIMITED

4 Woodside Place, Glasgow G3 7QF
Tel: (0141) 3535355
Fax: (0141) 3535356
E-mail: admin@mcginnsolicitors.co.uk
Web: www.mcginnsolicitors.co.uk
Categories of Work
Alternative investment market
Banking & finance
Charities
Copyright, trade marks and design
Data protection
EU / international
Family business advice
Insolvency & corporate recovery
IT and intellectual property
Joint venture
Media and entertainment
Mergers and acquisitions
Private equity
Projects
Public finance initiative
Public sector
SME business advice
Software licensing
Telecoms
Director
James Waugh McGinn

MCGLASHAN MACKAY SOLICITORS

5-Jan, 146 Argyle Street, Glasgow G2 8BL
Tel: (0141) 3757557
Fax: (0141) 4042633
E-mail: reception@mcglashanmackay.com
Web: www.mcglashanmackay.com
Categories of Work
Civil legal aid
Criminal court work
Criminal legal aid
Human rights
Immigration and asylum
Partner
Euan Stewart MacKay
Employees
Andrew Robert Urquhart Fyffe
Alexander John Heeps
Lisa Jane McGuigan
Denize Ann Okan

MCGRADE & CO LIMITED

Standard Buildings, 94 Hope Street, Glasgow
G2 6PH
Tel: (0141) 2214488
Fax: (0141) 2213200
E-mail: info@mcgrade.co.uk
Web: www.mcgrade.co.uk
Categories of Work
Alternative dispute resolution
Disability
Discrimination
Employment
Employment law
Health and safety
Human rights

Pensions (Employment)
Directors
Anthony Michael McGrade
Giles Ian Woolfson
Employees
Morag Dalziel
Alison Mary Peat

MCGREEVY & CO LIMITED

370 Victoria Road, Govanhill, Glasgow
G42 8YW
Tel: (0141) 4222220/0795179
E-mail: mcgreevyandco@btinternet.com
Categories of Work
Criminal court work
Criminal legal aid
Human rights
Director
Robina Tina McGreevy
Consultant
William James Smith
Employee
Umar Farooq Hussain

MCGREGOR MACLEOD LTD

14 Carmyle Avenue, Glasgow G32 8HJ
Tel: (0141) 7789292
Categories of Work
Commercial property
Housing
Insolvency & corporate recovery
Landlord & tenant
Residential property
Wills, executries and trusts

MCINTOSH & MACLACHLAN

917 Shettleston Road, Shettleston, Glasgow
G32 7NU
Tel: (0141) 7631337/ 77
E-mail: mcinandmacl@msn.com
Categories of Work
Adoption
Advice the elderly & powers of attorney
Benefit advice
Children
Civil court work
Civil legal aid
Consumer credit
Criminal court work
Criminal legal aid
Debt
Debt adjusting and debt counselling
Debt administration
Debt collecting
Debt management
Debt recovery, insolvency, bankruptcy
Disability
Discrimination
Education
Employment
Employment law
Family and divorce
Human rights
Immigration and asylum

▶ **Glasgow** continued

Medical negligence – claimant
Mental health
Personal injury
Residential property
Road traffic
Social housing
Wills, executives and trusts

MCINTOSH MCCANN LTD
486 Dumbarton Road, Glasgow G11 6SL
Tel: (0141) 212 2222
Categories of Work
Adoption
Advice the elderly & powers of attorney
Alternative dispute resolution
Benefit advice
Children
Civil court work
Civil legal aid
Consumer credit
Criminal court work
Criminal legal aid
Debt
Debt adjusting and debt counselling
Debt collecting
Debt management
Debt recovery, insolvency, bankruptcy
Disability
Discrimination
Education
Family and divorce
Human rights
Medical negligence – defender
Medical negligence – claimant
Mental health
Personal injury
Personal injury – defender
Professional negligence
Residential property
Road traffic
Social housing
Wills, executives and trusts
Directors
Lorna McCann
Michelle McIntosh
Employee
Stuart Andrew Craig

ANGUS MCINTOSH & SIMON HODGE
Castlemilk Law & Money Advice Centre, 155
Castlemilk Drive, Castlemilk, Glasgow
G45 9UG
Tel: (0141) 6340313
Fax: (0141) 6341944
E-mail: castlemilklawcentre@tiscali.co.uk
Categories of Work
Benefit advice
Consumer credit
Debt
Debt adjusting and debt counselling
Debt management
Disability

Discrimination
Employment law
Human rights
Mental health
Residential property
Social housing
Partners
John Simon Hodge
Gerrard Loughery
Angus McIntosh
Employees
Peter Mark Benham
Angela Duncan
Abdullah Khalid
Maureen Alice Smith
Judith Kathleen Stevenson

DJ MACKAY AND PARTNERS LLP
4th Floor, Fountain House, 1-3 Woodside
Cresent, Glasgow G3 7UJ
Tel: (0141) 353 8700
DX: 512210 Sandyford Place,Glasgow
E-mail: enquiries@djmp-solicitors.co.uk
Web: www.djmp-solicitors.co.uk
Categories of Work
Adjudication
Adoption
Advice the elderly & powers of attorney
Alternative dispute resolution
Betting & gaming
Children
Childrens
Civil court work
Civil legal aid
Commercial litigation
Copyright, trade marks and design
Data protection
Education
Employment
Employment law
Family and divorce
Freedom of information
Health and safety
IT and intellectual property
Media and entertainment
Medical negligence – defender
Medical negligence – claimant
Pensions (Employment)
Personal injury
Personal injury – defender
Professional negligence
Road traffic
Software licensing
Sport
Telecoms
Partner
Mary Biggam
Associates
Laura Ann Fleming McManus
Rachel Claire Walker
Employees
Kathleen Janet Bolt
Mariam Zohra Javed

Harbir Kaur Singh
Tracy Catherine McKenzie
Brian McLaughlin
Vanessa Charlotte O'Connor

MCKEE CAMPBELL MORRISON LIMITED
The Hatrack, 144 St Vincent Street, Glasgow
G2 5LQ
Tel: (0141) 4883680
Fax: (0203) 318 4190
E-mail: mail@mcmsolicitors.co.uk
Web: www.mcmsolicitors.co.uk
Categories of Work
Alternative dispute resolution
Banking & finance
Children
Civil court work
Commercial litigation
Consumer credit
Contract & property disputes
Copyright, trade marks and design
Criminal court work
Data protection
Debt
Debt administration
Debt collecting
Debt recovery, insolvency, bankruptcy
Family and divorce
Family business advice
Freedom of information
Housing
Insolvency & corporate recovery
IT and intellectual property
Joint venture
Landlord & tenant
Medical negligence – claimant
Mergers and acquisitions
Personal injury
Private equity
Property litigation
Residential property
Road traffic
SME business advice
Software licensing
Sport
Wills, executives and trusts
Directors
Stacy Elise Campbell
Maureen McKee Matheson
Alan James McKee
Fraser Lewis Morrison

RON MACKENNA DEFENCE LAWYERS LTD
First Floor, 40 Carlton Place, Glasgow G5 9TW
Tel: (07990) 910295
E-mail: ronmackennadefence@gmail.com
Categories of Work
Criminal court work
Criminal legal aid
Director
Ronald James MacKenna

MCKINLEY & CO.
7 Jedburgh Gardens, Glasgow G20 6BP

Tel: (0141) 5761984
E-mail: ann.mckinley@ntlworld.com
Categories of Work
Criminal court work
Criminal legal aid
Partner
Ann Marie McKinley

MCKINNON & CO
51 Gartcraig Road, Carntyne, Glasgow
G33 2NW
Tel: (0141) 770 8777/4111
Fax: (0141) 770 8400
E-mail: mail@mckinnonlaw.co.uk
Web: www.mckinnonlaw.co.uk
Categories of Work
Children
Civil court work
Civil legal aid
Criminal court work
Criminal legal aid
Debt
Family and divorce
Personal injury
Road traffic
Partner
Fiona McKinnon

MACLAY MURRAY & SPENS
5 George Square, Glasgow G2 1AL
Tel: (0330) 2220050
Categories of Work
Adjudication
Adoption
Advice the elderly & powers of attorney
Agriculture and estates
Agriculture, crofting and fishing
Alternative dispute resolution
Alternative investment market
Banking & finance
Betting & gaming
Charities
Children
Civil court work
Civil legal aid
Commercial litigation
Commercial property
Competition
Construction
Contract & property disputes
Copyright, trade marks and design
Corporate tax
Data protection
Debt recovery, insolvency, bankruptcy
Disability
Discrimination
Education
Employment
Employment law
Environment
Environment (Business Premises)
EU / international
Family and divorce
Family business advice

► *Glasgow continued*

Fishing
Freedom of information
Health
Health and safety
Housing
Human rights
Immigration and asylum
Insolvency & corporate recovery
Insurance
IT and intellectual property
Joint venture
Landlord & tenant
Liquor licensing
Local government
Media and entertainment
Medical negligence – defender
Medical negligence – claimant
Mergers and acquisitions
Mining
Oil & gas
Parliamentary
Pensions (Company)
Pensions (Employment)
Personal injury
Personal injury – defender
Personal tax
Planning
Planning (Business Premises)
Power and utilities
Private equity
Professional negligence
Projects
Property litigation
Public finance initiative
Public sector
Residential property
Shipping
SME business advice
Software licensing
Sport
Telecoms
Transport
Unit Trusts, OEICs and investment trusts
Wills, executories and trusts

JAMES MCNAIR SOLICITORS
P.O. Box 3426, Glasgow G66 4EL
Tel: (07847) 466951
E-mail: jmcnairsol@gmail.com
Categories of Work
Children
Childrens
Criminal court work
Criminal legal aid
Family and divorce
Mental health
Road traffic
Partner
James McLaughlin McNair

MACNAIRS & WILSON LIMITED
662 Alexandra Parade, Glasgow G31 3BU

Tel: (0141) 5518185
Fax: (0141) 5546235
E-mail: glasgow@macnairswilson.co.uk
Categories of Work
Adoption
Advice the elderly & powers of attorney
Alternative dispute resolution
Children
Childrens
Civil court work
Civil legal aid
Commercial property
Contract & property disputes
Criminal court work
Criminal legal aid
Discrimination
Education
Employment
Employment law
Family and divorce
Housing
Human rights
Landlord & tenant
Mental health
Personal injury
Personal injury – defender
Property litigation
Residential property
Road traffic
Wills, executories and trusts
Director
Lesley Catherine Mathieson
Employees
Louise Morgan Jones
Amy-Louise Martha Pollock

MCO DEFENCE SOLICITORS
Floor 5 (Room 6), 41 St Vincent Place,
Glasgow G1 2ER
Tel: (07908) 167227
E-mail: mail@mcosolicitors.co.uk
Categories of Work
Criminal court work
Criminal legal aid
Partner
Haroun Tunweer Malik

JAMES MCPARLAND
PO Box 2306, Glasgow G33 9PB
Tel: (07811) 633581
E-mail: mcparland1710@aol.com
Categories of Work
Criminal court work
Criminal legal aid
Partner
James McParland

IAIN A. MCPHAIL
7 Royal Terrace, Glasgow G3 7NT
Tel: (0141) 3312166
E-mail: iain.mcphail@btinternet.com
Categories of Work
Advice the elderly & powers of attorney
Landlord & tenant

Residential property
Wills, executives and trusts
Partner
Iain Arnott McPhail

MACPHERSON MAGUIRE COOK
19 Waterloo Street, Glasgow G2 6BP
Tel: (0141) 221 6913
Fax: (0141) 221 9659
E-mail: mail@mgmc.o.uk
Categories of Work
Children
Civil court work
Commercial litigation
Commercial property
Construction
Contract & property disputes
Criminal court work
Criminal legal aid
Debt recovery, insolvency, bankruptcy
Employment law
Family and divorce
Family business advice
Landlord & tenant
Medical negligence – claimant
Personal injury
Professional negligence
Residential property
Road traffic
Wills, executives and trusts
Partner
John Napier McKissock

MACRAE AND KAUR LLP
45 Hope Street (6th Floor), Glasgow G2 6AE
Tel: (0141) 6116000
Fax: (0141) 3198702
E-mail: admin@mackaur.co.uk
Categories of Work
Banking & finance
Commercial property
Landlord & tenant
Residential property
Partner
Jatinder Kaur Chall

MACROBERTS CORPORATE SERVICES LIMITED
Capella, 60 York Street, Glasgow G2 8JX
Tel: (0141) 3031100

MACROBERTS LLP
Capella, 60 York Street, Glasgow G2 8JX
Tel: (0141) 3031100
Fax: (0141) 3328886
DX: GW70 GLASGOW
Web: www.macroberts.com
Categories of Work
Adjudication
Adoption
Advice the elderly & powers of attorney
Agriculture and estates
Agriculture, crofting and fishing
Alternative dispute resolution
Alternative investment market
Banking & finance

Betting & gaming
Charities
Children
Civil court work
Commercial litigation
Commercial property
Competition
Construction
Consumer credit
Contract & property disputes
Copyright, trade marks and design
Data protection
Debt
Debt adjusting and debt counselling
Debt administration
Debt collecting
Debt recovery, insolvency, bankruptcy
Disability
Discrimination
Education
Employment
Employment law
Environment
Environment (Business Premises)
EU / international
Family and divorce
Family business advice
Fishing
Freedom of information
Health
Health and safety
Housing
Human rights
Immigration and asylum
Insolvency & corporate recovery
Insurance
IT and intellectual property
Joint venture
Landlord & tenant
Liquor licensing
Local government
Media and entertainment
Mergers and acquisitions
Mining
Oil & gas
Parliamentary
Pensions (Company)
Pensions (Employment)
Personal injury
Personal injury – defender
Personal tax
Planning
Planning (Business Premises)
Power and utilities
Private equity
Professional negligence
Projects
Property litigation
Public finance initiative
Public sector
Residential property
Road traffic
Shipping

► *Glasgow continued*

SME business advice
Software licensing
Sport
Telecoms
Transport
Unit Trusts, OEICs and investment trusts
Wills, executries and trusts
Partners
Valerie Muriel Armstrong-Surgenor
Gary Alexander Baines
Ian Martin Bowie
Leon Breakey
Euan Findlay Duncan
Kelsey Thomson Gibson
James Inglis
James Kilpatrick Keith
Michael John Kelly
Neil Andrew Findlay Kennedy
Douglas Cameron Lamb
Louise Antonia Mahon
Carole Matheson Gemmell McAlpine-Scott
David Andrew McGuire
John Olav McQuillan
Roderick Neil Munro
Martyn Thomson Shaw
Kathryn Jean Wedderburn
David Dalgleish Wilson
Consultant
John Stewart Crawford
Associates
Fiona Frances Armour
Rebecca Mary Barrass
Amie Brown
Jennifer Louise Burns
Nicole Louise Cook
Rebecca Antonia Cox
Louise Gibson
Melissa Hall
Graeme Stephen James Harrison
Rebecca Marie Henderson
Graham Charles Horn
Richard David MacDonald
Eleanor Margaret Mannion
Jenna Louise Graham McLean
Victoria Christina McMurray
Gwendoline Murphy
Susan Carol O'Farrell
Mark Alexander Quinn
Employees
Barbara Elizabeth Dow
Edward Ferguson
Michael Joseph Gallagher
Sumaira Zanib Iqbal
Meghan Rachael Jenkins
Nicola Jane Kelly
Douglas Stuart Leslie
Joseph James Macfarlane
Ryan James McLaughlin
Sarah Lucy Milne
Rupneet Kaur Mooker
Christopher David Murphy

Salome Maria Jessica Nilsson
Liusa Reid
Zoe Annmarie Rocks
Nikita Kaur Sandhu
Lindsay Margaret Stark
Ross Thomas Wallace
Agne Zasinaite

MACROBERTS TRUSTEES LIMITED
Capella, 60 York Street, Glasgow G2 8JX
Tel: (0141) 3031100

MCSPARRAN MCCORMICK
663 Clarkston Road, Netherlee, Glasgow
G44 3SE
Tel: (0141) 6331557
Fax: (0141) 6330061
DX: 556323 CLARKSTON
E-mail: clarkston@mcsparranmccormick.co.uk
Web: www.mcsparranmccormick.co.uk
Categories of Work
Adoption
Advice the elderly & powers of attorney
Charities
Children
Commercial property
Criminal court work
Criminal legal aid
Data protection
Disability
Discrimination
Education
Employment
Employment law
Family business advice
Freedom of information
Health
Health and safety
Insurance
Local government
Personal injury
Personal injury – defender
Professional negligence
Residential property
Wills, executries and trusts
Associate
Hilary Doreen Denholm

MCSPARRAN MCCORMICK
Waterloo Chambers, 19 Waterloo Street,
Glasgow G2 6AH
Tel: (0141) 2487962
Fax: (0141) 2042232
E-mail: mail@mcsparranmccormick.co.uk
Web: www.mcsparranmccormick.co.uk
Categories of Work
Adoption
Advice the elderly & powers of attorney
Charities
Children
Commercial property
Criminal court work
Criminal legal aid
Data protection

Disability
Discrimination
Education
Employment
Employment law
Family business advice
Freedom of information
Health
Health and safety
Insurance
Local government
Personal injury
Personal injury – defender
Professional negligence
Residential property
Wills, executives and trusts
Partners
Francis Paul McCormick
Frank Paul McCormick
Associate
Lynsey Ross Clelland
Employee
Matthew Donald McCormick

MCVEY & MURRICANE
Fifth Floor, Albert Chambers, 13 Bath Street,
Glasgow G2 1HY
Tel: (0141) 3339688
Fax: (0845) 0582541/0141 25
DX: GW71 GLASGOW
E-mail: mail@mcvey-murricane.com
Categories of Work
Advice the elderly & powers of attorney
Alternative dispute resolution
Banking & finance
Commercial litigation
Commercial property
Consumer credit
Contract & property disputes
Corporate tax
Data protection
Debt recovery, insolvency, bankruptcy
Employment law
Family business advice
Insolvency & corporate recovery
IT and intellectual property
Joint venture
Landlord & tenant
Mergers and acquisitions
Private equity
Public finance initiative
Residential property
SME business advice
Wills, executives and trusts
Partner
Allan Radlow
Consultant
Jonathan Philip Edwards
Associate
Fallon Sara Spencer
Employees
Bethany Anne Beattie
John Mair Clyde

Andrew Robin Craig
Laura Gunn
Claire McLauchlan
Tay Carmichael Montgomery

MCVEY & MURRICANE NOMINEES LIMITED
Fifth Floor, Albert Chambers, 13 Bath Street,
Glasgow G2 1HY
Tel: (0141) 3339688

MAGUIRE SOLICITORS
2 Clarendon Place, Glasgow G20 7PY
Tel: (0141) 3312885
Fax: (0141) 3530104
E-mail: enquiries@maguiresolicitors.co.uk
Categories of Work
Adoption
Advice the elderly & powers of attorney
Children
Childrens
Criminal court work
Discrimination
Education
Employment law
EU / international
Family and divorce
Health
Human rights
Immigration and asylum
Medical negligence – defender
Directors
Adeel Raza Hussain
Rashpal Singh
Employees
Daniah Aboud
Zarah Anwar
Louise Heather Crichton
Emma Frotan
Kirsty Catherine Anne Hird Gemmell
Rana Abid Haq
Ahmed Shihab Eldin Osman Khogali
Connor Peter Philip Ledger
Ningzhou Lemon Li
Linzi McQuade
Joseph John Lamb Rasmussen
Adil Saeed
Ashleigh Sweeney
Francesca Maria Taylor
Eghosa Evhuowie Abieyuwa Ugbolue

ANTHONY MAHON LIMITED
10 Rozelle Avenue, Glasgow G15 7QR
Tel: (0141) 9441001
E-mail: office@a-man-cofsnet.co.uk
Categories of Work
Adoption
Advice the elderly & powers of attorney
Alternative dispute resolution
Benefit advice
Children
Civil court work
Civil legal aid
Consumer credit
Criminal court work

▶ *Glasgow continued*

Criminal legal aid
Debt
Debt adjusting and debt counselling
Debt administration
Debt collecting
Debt management
Disability
Discrimination
Education
Family and divorce
Human rights
Medical negligence – claimant
Mental health
Personal injury
Professional negligence
Road traffic
Social housing
Employee
Elaine Mary O'Connell

ANTHONY MAHON LIMITED

48 West George Street, Glasgow G2 1BP
Tel: (0141) 3321587
Fax: (0141) 3321585
E-mail: amahon@btconnect.com
Categories of Work
Adoption
Advice the elderly & powers of attorney
Alternative dispute resolution
Benefit advice
Children
Civil court work
Civil legal aid
Consumer credit
Criminal court work
Criminal legal aid
Debt
Debt adjusting and debt counselling
Debt administration
Debt collecting
Debt management
Disability
Discrimination
Education
Family and divorce
Human rights
Medical negligence – claimant
Mental health
Personal injury
Professional negligence
Road traffic
Social housing
Director
Owen Anthony Mahon

MAITLAND & CO

34 St Enoch Square, Station House 3:2,
Glasgow G1 4DF
Tel: (07714) 615845
E-mail: donnamaitland@hotmail.co.uk
Categories of Work
Criminal court work

Criminal legal aid
Partner
Donna Maitland

MANUS JAMES

1/2 50 Kelvingrove Street, Glasgow G3 7RZ
E-mail: nigel@manusjames.com
Categories of Work
Criminal court work
Criminal legal aid
Partner
Nigel Russell Scullion

MARITIME TRUSTEES LIMITED

302 St. Vincent Street, Glasgow G2 5RZ
Tel: (0141) 2483434

R. & R.S. MEARNS

2 Carment Drive, Shawlands, Glasgow
G41 3PR
Tel: (0141) 6326162
Fax: (0141) 6322490
Categories of Work
Adoption
Advice the elderly & powers of attorney
Alternative dispute resolution
Commercial property
Contract & property disputes
Copyright, trade marks and design
Corporate tax
Debt recovery, insolvency, bankruptcy
Family and divorce
Family business advice
Freedom of information
Housing
Immigration and asylum
IT and intellectual property
Joint venture
Landlord & tenant
Mergers and acquisitions
Personal tax
Residential property
SME business advice
Sport
Wills, executives and trusts
Partners
William Samuel Beresford
Donald Alexander David Henderson
Consultant
Donald Norman McGillivray
Associate
Jennifer Anne Rennie
Employees
Elspeth Catherine Doig
Abrar Hameed
Antonia Elizabeth McPike Jones
Fiona Clare O'Donnell

MELIORA

9 George Square, Glasgow G2 1DY
Tel: (0141) 266 0270
Fax: (0141) 626 6961
E-mail: info@melioralegal.com
Categories of Work
Human rights

Immigration and asylum
Partner
Gulfraz Ahmed

MELLICKS, INCORPORATING NAFTALIN DUNCAN & CO.
160 Hope Street, Glasgow G2 2TL
Tel: (0141) 3320902
Fax: (0141) 3339125
DX: GW23 GLASGOW
E-mail: mail@mellicks.co.uk
Categories of Work
Adoption
Advice the elderly & powers of attorney
Alternative dispute resolution
Children
Civil court work
Civil legal aid
Commercial litigation
Commercial property
Contract & property disputes
Debt recovery, insolvency, bankruptcy
Family and divorce
Family business advice
Insolvency & corporate recovery
Landlord & tenant
Liquor licensing
Media and entertainment
Medical negligence – claimant
Mental health
Personal injury
Professional negligence
Residential property
Road traffic
Social housing
Wills, executries and trusts
Partners
Bernadette Mary Baxter
Steven Kane
Kenneth Balfour Lang
Consultant
Pauline Marie Maclean
Associate
Sophie Margaret Cargill
Employees
Eidann Carina Campbell
James Scotland Dickson
Christopher James Naddell

MILLEN SOLICITORS
46 Carlton Place, Glasgow G5 9TW
Tel: (0141) 9590055
Fax: (0141) 9502122
E-mail: jm@millensolicitors.co.uk
Categories of Work
Adoption
Advice the elderly & powers of attorney
Benefit advice
Children
Civil court work
Civil legal aid
Criminal court work
Criminal legal aid
Debt

Education
Family and divorce
Residential property
Social housing
Wills, executries and trusts
Partner
Julie Millen
Employee
Lora Johnstone

MILLER BECKETT & JACKSON LIMITED
190 St Vincent Street, Glasgow G2 5SP
Tel: (0141) 2042833
Fax: (0141) 2487185
DX: GW20 GLASGOW
E-mail: mail@millerbj.co.uk
Categories of Work
Adjudication
Adoption
Advice the elderly & powers of attorney
Alternative dispute resolution
Charities
Children
Childrens
Civil court work
Commercial litigation
Commercial property
Consumer credit
Contract & property disputes
Criminal court work
Data protection
Debt
Debt collecting
Debt recovery, insolvency, bankruptcy
Employment
Employment law
Family and divorce
Family business advice
Freedom of information
Housing
Immigration and asylum
IT and intellectual property
Joint venture
Landlord & tenant
Mergers and acquisitions
Personal injury
Professional negligence
Property litigation
Residential property
Road traffic
SME business advice
Wills, executries and trusts
Directors
Robert Fulton Frame
Norman Alexander Fyfe
Jwad Hanif
Charles David Jackson
Victoria Elizabeth Mitchell
Andrew Eliot Soutter
Consultant
John Columba Bowie

▶ *Glasgow continued*

Employees
Ashley Jane MacLachlan
Laraine Shields

MILLER SAMUEL HILL BROWN LLP
RWF House, 5 Renfield Street, Glasgow
G2 5EZ
Tel: (0141) 2211919
Fax: (0141) 2213796
DX: GW161 GLASGOW
E-mail: ljb@mshblegal.com
Web: www.mshblegal.com
Categories of Work
Adoption
Advice the elderly & powers of attorney
Agriculture and estates
Alternative dispute resolution
Children
Civil court work
Commercial litigation
Commercial property
Consumer credit
Criminal court work
Criminal legal aid
Debt
Debt recovery, insolvency, bankruptcy
Disability
Discrimination
Education
Employment
Employment law
Family and divorce
Human rights
Landlord & tenant
Liquor licensing
Residential property
Wills, executives and trusts
Partners
Diane Christine Cairney
John Blyth Cowan
Robert Graham Richmond Davidson
Laura Ann Jamieson
Edward Lawrence Laverty
Marie Elizabeth Macdonald
Aileen Patricia Thomson
Consultants
Siobhan Catriona Therese Kelly
Christine Heather MacDiarmid
Employees
Lewis Fraser Barn
Zibya Bashir
Katie Cabrey
Calum Ruairidh John Maclean
Laura Jeffrey MacSporran
Sylvia Joyce Matheson
Claire Margaret McCulloch
Eilidh Marion McGuire
David Phillip Phinn
Gabrielle Anna Reilly

MINSTER LAW SCOTLAND
97-99 West Regent Street, Glasgow G2 2BA

Tel: (0141) 331 6071
Categories of Work
Civil court work
Commercial litigation
Contract & property disputes
Criminal court work
Debt collecting
Debt recovery, insolvency, bankruptcy
Health and safety
Landlord & tenant
Medical negligence – claimant
Personal injury
Professional negligence
Property litigation
Residential property
Road traffic

MITCHELLS ROBERTON LTD
George House, 36 North Hanover Street,
Glasgow G1 2AD
Tel: (0141) 5523422
Fax: (0141) 552 2935
DX: GW77 GLASGOW
E-mail: info@mitchells-roberton.co.uk
Web: www.mitchells-roberton.co.uk
Categories of Work
Adjudication
Adoption
Advice the elderly & powers of attorney
Agriculture and estates
Alternative dispute resolution
Banking & finance
Benefit advice
Charities
Children
Civil court work
Civil legal aid
Commercial litigation
Commercial property
Construction
Consumer credit
Contract & property disputes
Criminal court work
Data protection
Debt
Debt collecting
Debt management
Debt recovery, insolvency, bankruptcy
Disability
Discrimination
Education
Employment
Employment law
Environment (Business Premises)
Family and divorce
Family business advice
Freedom of information
Human rights
Insolvency & corporate recovery
Landlord & tenant
Liquor licensing
Local government
Media and entertainment

Medical negligence – defender
Medical negligence – claimant
Mental health
Mergers and acquisitions
Personal injury
Personal injury – defender
Personal tax
Planning (Business Premises)
Professional negligence
Property litigation
Residential property
Road traffic
SME business advice
Social housing
Wills, executries and trusts
Directors
Joel Martin Conn
Ian Cameron Ferguson
Kenneth Steven Gerber
Allyson Gilchrist
Mary Morag Inglis
Ronald James Inglis
Ross James Leatham
Heather Michele McKee
Martin David McLellan
Joyce Mary Moss
Paul David Neilly
Laura Catherine Schiavone
Consultants
William Marr Couper Grant
Neil James Mackenzie
Roderick Ruthven Mackenzie Paisley
Donald Bremner Reid
Associates
Lauren Nicola Booth
Euan Fearon David
Employees
Marie Angela Bradbury
Kathryn Anne Bready
Catherine Fiona Downie Fleming
Hugh Jamison Grant
Janet McLean Hynd
Sitara Batul Kausar
Andrew Lindsay
Sophie Jane Mason
Kim Jane Naismith
Natalia Rog Iska
Fiona Hannah Wayman

MMI LAW LLP
Fifth Floor, Albert Chambers, 13 Bath Street,
Glasgow G2 1HY
Tel: (0141) 3339688

MM LEGAL
The Pentagon Centre, 36 – 38 Washington
Street, Glasgow G3 8AZ
Tel: (0141) 2642272
Fax: (0141) 4048181
E-mail: ramiza@mmlegal.co.uk
Web: www.mmlegal.co.uk
Categories of Work
Advice the elderly & powers of attorney
Civil court work

Civil legal aid
Commercial litigation
Contract & property disputes
Disability
Discrimination
Employment
Employment law
Human rights
Landlord & tenant
Mental health
Pensions (Employment)
Property litigation
Residential property
Wills, executries and trusts
Director
Ramiza Mohammed

MML (SCOTLAND) LTD
The Pentagon Centre, 36 – 38 Washington
Street, Glasgow G3 8AZ
Tel: (0141) 2642272
Fax: (0141) 4048181
E-mail: ramiza@mmlegal.co.uk
Web: www.mmlegal.co.uk
Categories of Work
Advice the elderly & powers of attorney
Civil court work
Civil legal aid
Commercial litigation
Contract & property disputes
Disability
Discrimination
Employment
Employment law
Human rights
Landlord & tenant
Mental health
Pensions (Employment)
Property litigation
Residential property
Wills, executries and trusts
Director
Erika Kennedy Watt

MOIR AND SWEENEY LLP
457 Duke Street, Glasgow G31 1RD
Tel: (0141) 4292724
Fax: (0141) 4291711
E-mail: enquiries@moirandsweeny.com
Web: www.moirandsweeny.com
Categories of Work
Adoption
Advice the elderly & powers of attorney
Benefit advice
Children
Childrens
Civil court work
Civil legal aid
Consumer credit
Criminal court work
Criminal legal aid
Debt
Debt administration
Debt management

► *Glasgow continued*

Debt recovery, insolvency, bankruptcy
Education
Family and divorce
Landlord & tenant
Medical negligence – claimant
Mental health
Personal injury
Personal injury – defender
Road traffic
Social housing
Wills, executives and trusts
Partners
Ian Richard Moir
Paul Gerard Sweeney
Consultant
Michael O'Neill
Employees
Danielle Sharon Docherty
Yvonne Finlay
Keith Hamilton Mackenzie
Douglas James McAllister
Ann Margaret Ritchie
Charles James Robert Shearer
Carole-Anne Wilson

MOIR AND SWEENEY LLP
879 Govan Road, Glasgow G51 3DL
Tel: (0141) 4292724
E-mail: enquiries@moirandsweeny.com
Web: www.moirandsweeny.com
Categories of Work
Adoption
Advice the elderly & powers of attorney
Benefit advice
Children
Childrens
Civil court work
Civil legal aid
Consumer credit
Criminal court work
Criminal legal aid
Debt
Debt administration
Debt management
Debt recovery, insolvency, bankruptcy
Education
Family and divorce
Landlord & tenant
Medical negligence – claimant
Mental health
Personal injury
Personal injury – defender
Road traffic
Social housing
Wills, executives and trusts

MORAN & CO.
1/1, 102 Lancefield Quay, Glasgow G3 8HF
Tel: (0141) 221 7479
Categories of Work
Advice the elderly & powers of attorney
Commercial property

Contract & property disputes
Landlord & tenant
Residential property
Wills, executives and trusts
Partner
Ann Moran

MORGAN LEGAL SOLUTIONS LIMITED
Regent House, 113 West Regent Street,
Glasgow G2 2RU
Tel: (0141) 2584117
E-mail: yvonnemorgan@morganlegal.uk.com
Categories of Work
Alternative dispute resolution
Civil court work
Commercial litigation
Consumer credit
Contract & property disputes
Copyright, trade marks and design
Debt collecting
Debt recovery, insolvency, bankruptcy
Employment law
Insolvency & corporate recovery
Landlord & tenant
Property litigation
Director
Yvonne Elizabeth Morgan

MORTON FRASER LLP
145 St Vincent Street, Glasgow G2 5JF
Tel: (0141) 2741100
Fax: (0141) 2741129
DX: GW58 GLASGOW
Web: www.morton-fraser.com
Categories of Work
Adjudication
Adoption
Advice the elderly & powers of attorney
Agriculture and estates
Agriculture, crofting and fishing
Alternative dispute resolution
Alternative investment market
Banking & finance
Betting & gaming
Charities
Children
Childrens
Civil court work
Civil legal aid
Commercial litigation
Commercial property
Competition
Construction
Consumer credit
Contract & property disputes
Copyright, trade marks and design
Corporate tax
Credit brokerage
Criminal court work
Criminal legal aid
Data protection
Debt
Debt adjusting and debt counselling
Debt administration

Debt collecting
Debt recovery, insolvency, bankruptcy
Disability
Discrimination
Education
Employment
Employment law
Environment
Environment (Business Premises)
EU / international
Family and divorce
Family business advice
Fishing
Freedom of information
Health
Health and safety
Housing
Human rights
Immigration and asylum
Insolvency & corporate recovery
Insurance
IT and intellectual property
Joint venture
Landlord & tenant
Liquor licensing
Local government
Media and entertainment
Medical negligence – defender
Medical negligence – claimant
Mental health
Mergers and acquisitions
Mining
Oil & gas
Parliamentary
Pensions (Company)
Pensions (Employment)
Personal injury
Personal injury – defender
Personal tax
Planning
Planning (Business Premises)
Power and utilities
Private equity
Professional negligence
Projects
Property litigation
Provision of credit information services
Public finance initiative
Public sector
Residential property
Road traffic
Shipping
SME business advice
Software licensing
Sport
Telecoms
Transport
Unit Trusts, OEICs and investment trusts
Wills, executries and trusts
Partners
Robert Macdonald Bree
Lindsey Jane Cartwright
Brian Stuart Macfarlane

Fergus Archibald McDiarmid
Christopher James McLeish
Stuart Alistair McWilliams
Alan Crawford Meek
Nicola Ross
Hazel Fiona Sasan
Amar Farooq Wali
Consultant
Robert Swindell
Associates
Jennifer Andrew
Donna Bryson
Nicola Mary Edgar
Andrew Robert Gibson
Lesley Anne Holloway
Nikki Hunter
Sandra Hunter
Laura Ann McKenna
Stewart David Moy
Karen Sandra Wylie
Employees
Lisa Ann Blackwood
Debbie Morag Brogan
Matthew Alan Gray
Emma Marian Keil
Anna Claire Maitles
Martin MacDonald Minton
Nicole Maria Moscardini
Stephanie Margaret Tinney
Averil Marion Trimble
Elise Jean Turner
Nadia Egbujo Watson
Joanne Lesley Wilson
Stephen Wyper
Aziz Yasin

MOSS AND KELLY SOLICITORS LIMITED
Suite 5, Legal House, 101 Gorbals Street,
Glasgow G5 9DW
Tel: (0141) 2311605
Fax: (0141) 4298471
DX: 513225 GLASGOW
E-mail: lkelly@mossandkelly.co.uk
Categories of Work
Adoption
Advice the elderly & powers of attorney
Children
Family and divorce
Mental health
Wills, executries and trusts
Directors
Lorraine Ann Kelly
Garry Christopher Moss

MOV8 REAL ESTATE LIMITED
77 Renfrew Street, Glasgow G2 3BZ
Tel: (0345) 646 0208
Fax: (0131) 777 2642
E-mail: legal@mov8realestate.com
Categories of Work
Advice the elderly & powers of attorney
Agriculture and estates
Agriculture, crofting and fishing
Banking & finance

▶ *Glasgow continued*

Charities
Commercial property
Contract & property disputes
Family business advice
Housing
Landlord & tenant
Property litigation
Residential property
SME business advice
Wills, executives and trusts
Employees
Nigel Bailey
Hajira Noreen Nisa

MSM SOLICITORS LIMITED
2 Bridgeton Cross, Glasgow G40 1BW
Tel: (0141) 5548111
Fax: (0141) 5546566
E-mail: mail@msmlaw.co.uk
Web: www.msmlaw.co.uk
Categories of Work
Adoption
Advice the elderly & powers of attorney
Alternative dispute resolution
Benefit advice
Children
Childrens
Civil court work
Civil legal aid
Commercial litigation
Commercial property
Consumer credit
Contract & property disputes
Criminal court work
Criminal legal aid
Debt
Debt adjusting and debt counselling
Debt administration
Debt collecting
Debt management
Debt recovery, insolvency, bankruptcy
Disability
Discrimination
Education
Employment
Employment law
Family and divorce
Family business advice
Joint venture
Landlord & tenant
Liquor licensing
Medical negligence – claimant
Mental health
Personal injury
Personal injury – defender
Professional negligence
Property litigation
Residential property
Road traffic
SME business advice
Social housing
Wills, executives and trusts

Director
Mark Morrison Dunbar
Consultant
Jason Joseph Beltrami

MSM SOLICITORS LIMITED
43 Crow Road, Glasgow G11 7SH
Tel: (0141) 3395252
Fax: (0141) 3394617
Categories of Work
Adoption
Advice the elderly & powers of attorney
Alternative dispute resolution
Benefit advice
Children
Childrens
Civil court work
Civil legal aid
Commercial litigation
Commercial property
Consumer credit
Contract & property disputes
Criminal court work
Criminal legal aid
Debt
Debt adjusting and debt counselling
Debt administration
Debt collecting
Debt management
Debt recovery, insolvency, bankruptcy
Disability
Discrimination
Education
Employment
Employment law
Family and divorce
Family business advice
Joint venture
Landlord & tenant
Liquor licensing
Medical negligence – claimant
Mental health
Personal injury
Personal injury – defender
Professional negligence
Property litigation
Residential property
Road traffic
SME business advice
Social housing
Wills, executives and trusts
Director
Nicos Scholarios

MTL LAW
The Nexus Business Space, 126 West Regent
Street, Glasgow G2 2RQ
Tel: (0141) 2225793
E-mail: enquiries@mtllaw.co.uk
Web: www.mtllaw.co.uk
Categories of Work
Adoption
Advice the elderly & powers of attorney
Charities

Children
Childrens
Commercial property
Construction
Contract & property disputes
Family and divorce
Insolvency & corporate recovery
IT and intellectual property
Joint venture
Landlord & tenant
Mergers and acquisitions
Personal tax
Private equity
Projects
Residential property
Wills, executries and trusts
Directors
David Morris
Julie Irene MacDonald Terrey
Employee
Ella Bulchenko

MTM FAMILY LAW LLP
2nd Floor, 91 Mitchell Street, Glasgow
G1 3LN
Tel: (0141) 6117535
Fax: (0141) 2215501
E-mail: general@mtmfamilylaw.co.uk
Web: www.mtmfamilylaw.co.uk
Categories of Work
Adoption
Alternative dispute resolution
Children
Childrens
Civil court work
Education
Family and divorce
Family business advice
Wills, executries and trusts
Partners
Carolyn Margaret MacBride
Shona Mary Templeton
Associates
Fiona Elizabeth Anderson
Michaela Louise Hinchin
Caroline Leslie Smith

MTM SPECIALIST FAMILY LAWYERS
2nd Floor, 91 Mitchell Street, Glasgow G1 3LY
Tel: (0141) 6117535
E-mail: info@mtmfamilylaw.co.uk
Categories of Work
Adoption
Alternative dispute resolution
Children
Childrens
Civil court work
Education
Family and divorce
Family business advice
Wills, executries and trusts

MURDOCH STEWARTS LIMITED
Suite 4/2 Merchants House, 7 West George
Street, Glasgow G2 1BA

Tel: (0141) 226 3333
Fax: (0141) 221 2381
DX: GW19 GLASGOW
Web: www.murdochstewarts.co.uk
Categories of Work
Advice the elderly & powers of attorney
Charities
Debt management
Personal tax
Residential property
Wills, executries and trusts
Directors
Cecilia Mary Brough
Lesley Scott Wilson Forrest
Employee
Helen Anne MacCuish

MURPHY & CO.
10 Newton Place, Glasgow G3 7PR
Tel: (0141) 3322804
Fax: (0141) 3322299
E-mail: murphyandco@hotmail.com
Categories of Work
Criminal court work
Criminal legal aid
Partner
Joseph Brendan Murphy

MURPHY, ROBB + SUTHERLAND
1st Floor, 46 Carlton Place, Glasgow G5 9TW
Tel: (0141) 4182931
Fax: (0141) 4296100
E-mail: murphyrobbsutherland@gmail.com
Categories of Work
Adoption
Advice the elderly & powers of attorney
Benefit advice
Children
Childrens
Civil court work
Civil legal aid
Criminal court work
Criminal legal aid
Education
Family and divorce
Medical negligence – claimant
Mental health
Personal injury
Road traffic
Social housing
Wills, executries and trusts
Partners
David McNicol Fisken
Kevin Murphy
Lesley Diane Robb
Paul Dominic Sutherland

MURRAY LAW LTD
3 Oakfield Avenue, Glasgow G12 8JF
Tel: (0141) 3575151
Fax: (0141) 3573573
E-mail: mail@murraylaw.co.uk
Categories of Work
Advice the elderly & powers of attorney

► **Glasgow continued**

Children
Civil court work
Civil legal aid
Criminal court work
Criminal legal aid
Family and divorce
Personal injury
Personal injury – defender
Residential property
Road traffic
Wills, executries and trusts
Director
Stewart Murray

MURRAY SNELL
Capella, 60 York Street, Glasgow G2 8JX
Tel: (0141) 3031100
Categories of Work
Adjudication
Adoption
Advice the elderly & powers of attorney
Agriculture and estates
Agriculture, crofting and fishing
Alternative dispute resolution
Alternative investment market
Banking & finance
Betting & gaming
Charities
Children
Civil court work
Commercial litigation
Commercial property
Competition
Construction
Consumer credit
Contract & property disputes
Copyright, trade marks and design
Data protection
Debt
Debt adjusting and debt counselling
Debt administration
Debt collecting
Debt recovery, insolvency, bankruptcy
Disability
Discrimination
Education
Employment
Employment law
Environment
Environment (Business Premises)
EU / international
Family and divorce
Family business advice
Fishing
Freedom of information
Health
Health and safety
Housing
Human rights
Immigration and asylum
Insolvency & corporate recovery
Insurance

IT and intellectual property
Joint venture
Landlord & tenant
Liquor licensing
Local government
Media and entertainment
Mergers and acquisitions
Mining
Oil & gas
Parliamentary
Pensions (Company)
Pensions (Employment)
Personal injury
Personal injury – defender
Personal tax
Planning
Planning (Business Premises)
Power and utilities
Private equity
Professional negligence
Projects
Property litigation
Public finance initiative
Public sector
Residential property
Road traffic
Shipping
SME business advice
Software licensing
Sport
Telecoms
Transport
Unit Trusts, OEICs and investment trusts
Wills, executries and trusts

NERO LEGAL
81 St Vincent Street, Glasgow G2 5TF
Tel: (0141) 230 7080
Web: www.nerolegal.com
Categories of Work
Adoption
Advice the elderly & powers of attorney
Children
Childrens
Civil court work
Civil legal aid
Commercial property
Contract & property disputes
Debt
Debt management
Family and divorce
Housing
Landlord & tenant
Local government
Mental health
Planning (Business Premises)
Residential property
Social housing
Wills, executries and trusts

NEWFORD LAW
101 Eaglesham Road, Clarkston, Glasgow
G76 8RF
Tel: (0141) 6441792

E-mail: mcbride4law@gmail.com
Categories of Work
Adoption
Advice the elderly & powers of attorney
Children
Civil court work
Civil legal aid
Commercial litigation
Commercial property
Construction
Criminal court work
Criminal legal aid
Debt
Mental health
Personal injury
Professional negligence
Road traffic
Wills, executries and trusts
Partner
John Gerard McBride

NEWLAW SCOTLAND LLP
7th Floor, Delta House, Glasgow G1 2NP
Tel: (0333) 0030655
DX: 561482 GLASGOW 16
Web: www.newlaw-scotland.co.uk
Categories of Work
Alternative dispute resolution
Civil court work
Medical negligence – claimant
Personal injury
Personal injury – defender
Professional negligence
Road traffic
Partner
Paula Christina McMillan
Employees
Lesley-Anne Jack
Linda McClymont
Laura Jane McGee
David Grant McGilp

OAKWOOD SCOTLAND SOLICITORS LIMITED
1 West Regent Street, Glasgow G2 1RW
Tel: (0141) 4063324
Categories of Work
Civil court work
Civil legal aid
Medical negligence – claimant
Personal injury
Professional negligence
Road traffic
Partner
Ross Alexander Slater

O'DONNELL & CO.
79 Kinfauns Drive, Drumchapel, Glasgow
G15 7TG
Tel: (0141) 9441441
Fax: (0141) 9446631
E-mail: odonnelllaw@btconnect.com
Categories of Work
Criminal court work
Criminal legal aid

Partner
Gerald Anthony O'Donnell

OJ SOLICITORS LTD
Lime Tree Business Centre, 551 Sauchiehall
Street, Glasgow G3 7PQ
Tel: (07842) 507897
E-mail: contact@oj-solicitors.co.uk
Categories of Work
Children
Civil court work
Commercial litigation
Criminal court work
Employment
Employment law
Family and divorce
Health and safety
Immigration and asylum
Personal injury
Road traffic
SME business advice
Directors
Ioan Oltean
Oana-Iuliana Petre

OLABAMIJI & CO LIMITED
79 West Street, Glasgow G5 8BA
Tel: (0141) 2311650
Fax: (0141) 5565587
E-mail: mail@dmoolabamiji-solicitors.co.uk
Web: www.dmoolabamijisolicitors.co.uk
Director
Olawale Olabamiji

ORACLELAW LIMITED
1A Helena House, Clarkston Toll, Glasgow
G76 7RA
Tel: (0141) 4041091
Fax: (0141) 404 8212
DX: 556324 Clarkston
E-mail: info@oraclelaw.com
Web: www.oraclelaw.com
Categories of Work
Adjudication
Adoption
Advice the elderly & powers of attorney
Agriculture and estates
Agriculture, crofting and fishing
Alternative dispute resolution
Children
Civil court work
Commercial litigation
Commercial property
Competition
Construction
Contract & property disputes
Criminal court work
Debt
Debt collecting
Debt recovery, insolvency, bankruptcy
Employment
Employment law
Family and divorce
Family business advice

▶ *Glasgow continued*

Insolvency & corporate recovery
Joint venture
Landlord & tenant
Medical negligence – defender
Medical negligence – claimant
Mergers and acquisitions
Personal injury
Personal injury – defender
Planning
Planning (Business Premises)
Professional negligence
Property litigation
Residential property
SME business advice
Wills, executries and trusts
Directors
John Carruthers
Colette Marie Kerr
Employees
Jenna Louise McLaughlan
Zara Nisa Mohamed
Stephen Mullan

PACITTI JONES LEGAL LIMITED
2-6 Havelock Street, Glasgow G11 5JA
Tel: (0141) 3346444
Fax: (0141) 6480908
E-mail: kevin@pjglasgow.co.uk
Web: https://www.pacittijones.co.uk/
Categories of Work
Adoption
Advice the elderly & powers of attorney
Banking & finance
Children
Civil court work
Civil legal aid
Commercial property
Construction
Corporate tax
Criminal court work
Criminal legal aid
Education
Employment law
Environment
Family and divorce
Health and safety
Housing
Joint venture
Landlord & tenant
Mergers and acquisitions
Personal injury
Power and utilities
Private equity
Professional negligence
Projects
Residential property
Road traffic
SME business advice
Wills, executries and trusts
Director
Kevin John Taylor

Employee
Malgorzata Chylinska

PACITTI JONES LEGAL LIMITED
206 Kilmarnock Road, Shawlands, Glasgow
G43 1TY
Tel: (0141) 5714444
Fax: (0141) 6480908
Web: https://www.pacittijones.co.uk/
Categories of Work
Adoption
Advice the elderly & powers of attorney
Banking & finance
Children
Civil court work
Civil legal aid
Commercial property
Construction
Corporate tax
Criminal court work
Criminal legal aid
Education
Employment law
Environment
Family and divorce
Health and safety
Housing
Joint venture
Landlord & tenant
Mergers and acquisitions
Personal injury
Power and utilities
Private equity
Professional negligence
Projects
Residential property
Road traffic
SME business advice
Wills, executries and trusts
Employees
Irim Hussain
Ifet Raza

PACITTI JONES LEGAL LIMITED
218 Stonelaw Road, Burnside, Glasgow
G73 3SA
Tel: (0141) 6473322
Fax: (0141) 6480908
Web: https://www.pacittijones.co.uk/
Categories of Work
Adoption
Advice the elderly & powers of attorney
Banking & finance
Children
Civil court work
Civil legal aid
Commercial property
Construction
Corporate tax
Criminal court work
Criminal legal aid
Education
Employment law
Environment

Family and divorce
Health and safety
Housing
Joint venture
Landlord & tenant
Mergers and acquisitions
Personal injury
Power and utilities
Private equity
Professional negligence
Projects
Residential property
Road traffic
SME business advice
Wills, executives and trusts
Employee
Lauren Grace Mitchell

PACITTI JONES LEGAL LIMITED
648 Alexandra Parade, Dennistoun, Glasgow
G31 3BU
Tel: (0141) 611 8881
Fax: (0141) 648 0908
E-mail: dennistoun@pacittijones.co.uk
Categories of Work
Adoption
Advice the elderly & powers of attorney
Banking & finance
Children
Civil court work
Civil legal aid
Commercial property
Construction
Corporate tax
Criminal court work
Criminal legal aid
Education
Employment law
Environment
Family and divorce
Health and safety
Housing
Joint venture
Landlord & tenant
Mergers and acquisitions
Personal injury
Power and utilities
Private equity
Professional negligence
Projects
Residential property
Road traffic
SME business advice
Wills, executives and trusts
Consultant
William Nugent

PARABIS SCOTLAND LIMITED
5th Floor, The Centrum Building, Glasgow
G1 3DX
Tel: (0844) 8921250
Fax: (0844) 8921251
E-mail: tony.omalley@friends-legal.co.uk

Categories of Work
Advice the elderly & powers of attorney
Alternative dispute resolution
Civil court work
Commercial litigation
Commercial property
Consumer credit
Contract & property disputes
Debt
Debt collecting
Disability
Discrimination
Employment
Employment law
Health
Health and safety
Human rights
Local government
Medical negligence – claimant
Personal injury
Professional negligence
Property litigation
Residential property
Road traffic
Wills, executives and trusts
Director
Anthony John O'Malley
Employee
Louise Cameron

PATERSON HOLMS
3 Springfield Road, Bishopbriggs, Glasgow
G64 1PD
Tel: (0141) 772 0074
Fax: (0141) 942 4457
Categories of Work
Advice the elderly & powers of attorney
Civil court work
Civil legal aid
Commercial property
Debt
Debt collecting
Family and divorce
Landlord & tenant
Residential property
Employee
Maureen Angela Nicolson

PATERSON HOLMS
4 Roman Road, Bearsden, Glasgow G61 2SW
Tel: (0141) 9428825
Fax: (0141) 9424457
DX: 556105 BEARSDEN
E-mail: scott@patersonholms.co.uk
Web: www.patersonholms.co.uk
Categories of Work
Advice the elderly & powers of attorney
Civil court work
Civil legal aid
Commercial property
Debt
Debt collecting
Family and divorce
Landlord & tenant

► *Glasgow continued*

Residential property
Partners
Scott Russell Cowie
Brenda McCamley
Associate
Fiona Quirk

TRACY E PATERSON SOLICITORS
222 Crofthill Road, Glasgow G44 5NN
Tel: (07804) 149 942
E-mail: tracy.e.paterson@hotmail.co.uk
Categories of Work
Criminal court work
Criminal legal aid
Partner
Tracy Elizabeth Paterson

PATTISON & CO.
117 Byres Road, Glasgow G12 8TT
Tel: (0141) 3347706
Fax: (0141) 3572871
E-mail: hello@pattisonandcompany.com
Web: www.pattisonandcompany.com
Categories of Work
Adoption
Advice the elderly & powers of attorney
Children
Civil court work
Commercial litigation
Contract & property disputes
Criminal court work
Debt collecting
Debt recovery, insolvency, bankruptcy
Employment law
Family and divorce
Family business advice
Personal injury
Planning (Business Premises)
Professional negligence
Property litigation
Residential property
Road traffic
Wills, executries and trusts
Employee
Melanie Caitlin Paterson

PBW LAW SOLICITORS
18 Woodside Place, Glasgow G3 7QF
Tel: (0141) 439 1990
DX: 512203 Glasgow
E-mail: pbw@pbwlaw.co.uk
Categories of Work
Alternative dispute resolution
Charities
Civil court work
Commercial litigation
Copyright, trade marks and design
Criminal court work
Data protection
Disability
Discrimination
Employment
Employment law

Family business advice
Freedom of information
Health and safety
Human rights
Insurance
IT and intellectual property
Media and entertainment
Medical negligence – defender
Medical negligence – claimant
Personal injury
Personal injury – defender
Planning (Business Premises)
Professional negligence
Property litigation
Road traffic
SME business advice
Sport
Partner
Peter Black Watson
Employees
Thomas Stewart McMurtrie
Pamela Rodgers

PEACOCK JOHNSTON
Ashfield House, 402 Sauchiehall Street,
Glasgow G2 3JD
Tel: (0141) 3339505
Fax: (0141) 3312823
DX: GW165 GLASGOW
E-mail: info@peacockjohnston.co.uk
Web: www.peacockjohnston.co.uk
Categories of Work
Advice the elderly & powers of attorney
Children
Civil court work
Civil legal aid
Commercial litigation
Contract & property disputes
Criminal court work
Criminal legal aid
Data protection
Debt
Debt adjusting and debt counselling
Debt collecting
Debt recovery, insolvency, bankruptcy
Discrimination
Employment
Employment law
Family and divorce
Health and safety
Medical negligence – defender
Medical negligence – claimant
Personal injury
Personal injury – defender
Professional negligence
Road traffic
Wills, executries and trusts
Partners
Andrew Simon Pollock
Kenneth James Waddell
Consultant
Laura Viviana Maria Ceresa

Employees
Susith Dilanka Dematagoda
Saima Khatija Faheem

PENMANS
201 Saracen Street, Possilpark, Glasgow
G22 5JN
Tel: (0141) 3366646
Fax: (0141) 3366345
Categories of Work
Criminal court work
Criminal legal aid
Partner
Linda Kathleen Findlay
Consultant
Brian Greig
Employee
Susan Elizabeth Gibson

PENMANS
57 Kyleakin Road, Arden, Glasgow G46 8DE
Categories of Work
Criminal court work
Criminal legal aid

PENMANS
87 Carlton Place, Glasgow G5 9TD
Tel: (0141) 429 4489
Fax: (0141) 429 3971
Categories of Work
Criminal court work
Criminal legal aid
Partner
Calum James Masson Weir

KATE PHILLIPS
Carlton Buildings, 63 Carlton Place, Glasgow
G5 9TW
Tel: (0141) 4206120
Fax: (0141) 4293110
E-mail: katephillips21@yahoo.co.uk
Categories of Work
Criminal court work
Criminal legal aid
Partner
Catherine Mary Phillips

PIERI GRAHAM LTD
98 West George Street, Glasgow G2 1PJ
Tel: (0141) 3322525
Fax: (0141) 3312858
DX: GW218 GLASGOW
E-mail: kathleen@pierigraham.com
Categories of Work
Advice the elderly & powers of attorney
Commercial property
Family and divorce
Family business advice
Landlord & tenant
Residential property
Wills, executries and trusts
Directors
Kathleen Anne Graham
Dorothy Pieri

PINSENT MASONS LLP
Level 7, 141 Bothwell Street, Glasgow G2 7EQ
Tel: (0141) 567 8400
Fax: (0141) 567 8401
DX: GW74 GLASGOW
Web: www.pinsentmasons.com
Categories of Work
Adjudication
Advice the elderly & powers of attorney
Agriculture and estates
Agriculture, crofting and fishing
Alternative dispute resolution
Alternative investment market
Banking & finance
Betting & gaming
Charities
Children
Civil court work
Commercial litigation
Commercial property
Competition
Construction
Contract & property disputes
Copyright, trade marks and design
Corporate tax
Criminal court work
Data protection
Debt
Debt adjusting and debt counselling
Debt administration
Debt collecting
Debt recovery, insolvency, bankruptcy
Disability
Discrimination
Education
Employment
Employment law
Environment
Environment (Business Premises)
EU / international
Family and divorce
Family business advice
Fishing
Freedom of information
Health
Health and safety
Housing
Human rights
Immigration and asylum
Insolvency & corporate recovery
Insurance
IT and intellectual property
Joint venture
Landlord & tenant
Liquor licensing
Local government
Media and entertainment
Medical negligence – defender
Medical negligence – claimant
Mental health
Mergers and acquisitions
Mining
Oil & gas

▶ **Glasgow** *continued*

Parliamentary
Pensions (Company)
Pensions (Employment)
Personal injury
Personal injury – defender
Planning
Planning (Business Premises)
Power and utilities
Private equity
Professional negligence
Projects
Property litigation
Public finance initiative
Public sector
Residential property
Road traffic
Shipping
SME business advice
Software licensing
Sport
Telecoms
Transport
Unit Trusts, OEICs and investment trusts
Wills, executives and trusts

Partners

Michael Iain Allan
Stacey Bairner
Jennifer Anne Ballantyne
Stuart John Barr
Laura Elaine Cameron
Nicholas Charles Carlin
Alan McLeod Cassels
Rosalie Madeleine Chadwick
Paul Anthony Connolly
Alan Russell Cook
Kevin Alexander Devanny
Martin Gerard Devine
Yvonne Louise Dunn
Thomas Neil Ferrier
Colin John Fraser
Joanne Gillies
Ian Gordon
Katharine Helen Hardie
Claire Catherine Lindsay Massie
Barry John McCaig
Gordon Speirs McCreath
Alastair John MacKinnon Morrison
Craig Edward Morrison
Stuart William Neilson
Diane Elizabeth Nicol
Ruth Tobias
David James Woods
Christine Wilson Yuill

Associates

Gillian Catherine Anderson
Kevin James Beattie
Natalie Colaluca
Michael Alan Collins
Greg Stewart Dingwall
Joanna Rachel Donnelly
Zara Rachel Early

Kathleen Ann Fallon
Susan Gilchrist
Philippa Grace Rozelle Godwin
Heather Anne Hutcheon
Lauren Cheryl Jones
Elaine Elizabeth MacGregor
Craig David Macphee
Jennifer Catherine Helen McCormick
Sarah Margaret McNeil
Sian Phillipa McNiff
Wendy Suzanne Nicolson
Ashley Nimmo
Charlotte Louise O'Kane
Jennifer Margaret Oliver
Wendy Jane Quinn
Fiona Jane Rossetter
Alison Margaret Shackleton
Graham Callan Wallace

Solicitor

Emma Louise Blundell

Employees

Amnah Sehar Ahmed
Beth Anne Alexander
Christie Margaret Allan
Neal David Anderson
Miriam Ashraf
Holly Beaton
Hannah Louise Beaumont
Isla Russell Urquhart Burns
Fiona Jane Cameron
Louise Anne Cent
Lewis William Cheyne
Connor Scott Clark
Anthony Convery
Samantha Cooney
Ross Filshie Cooper
David James Crossan
Zita Louise Dempsey
Imogen Ruth Dewar
Katherine Maria Docherty
Ledia Doci
Susannah Elizabeth Donaldson
Jennifer Helen Dool
Lloyd Railton Embleton
Audrey Jane Ferrie
Lesley Michelle Finlayson
William Andrew Fordyce
Lindsey Arlene Franklin
Ben Robert Fulton
Graeme Douglas John Fyfe
Wendy Ann Gillan
Kirstyn Bald Gleeson
Jack Andrew Hamilton
Kirsty Anne Hannigan
Sinead Eveleen Hastings
Jacob David Hay
Joanne Elizabeth Hennessy
Alice Margaret Hepburn
Gemma Catherine Herbertson
Cameron John Ireland
Ailie Laura Isdale
Teuta Jahdaut Nerjovaj
Bethan Jones

Stacy Keen
Geraldine Patricia Kelm
James Laird
Michael Livingston
Alasdair MacDonald
Hannah Matthew
Ross James Fraser McAlister
David Edwin McAlpine
Deborah McCormack
Rachel McCourt
Alasdair Iain McCrone
Cameron Lars McCulloch
James Charles Fullarton McDonald
Ross Hamilton McDowall
Louise McKee
Steven McKinley
Kara Irena Marya McLaren
Elaine Johan McLean
Andrea Jane McLellan
Katherine Metcalfe
Kevin Michael Mulligan
Stuart Andrew Newlands
Emily Nicholl
Bernadine Mary Nordmann
Alexandra Jane Orr
Stephanie Jane Paton
Kathryn Louise Peoples
Christine Jane Pirie
Emma Elizabeth Reid
David Scott Ross
Gillian Margaret Ross
Cathleen Louise Scanlan
Louise Ann Shaw
David Isaac Slack
Michael Duncan Smith
Agnes Lisa Marie Sweeney
Brian Hugh Thumath
Lesley-Anne Paton Todd
Lucy Hannah Townley
Marsaili Elisabeth Van Looy
Stephanie McKay Watson-Orr
Nicola Welsh
Elizabeth Mary Whitaker
Jennifer Margaret White
Samuel Williams
Simona Marie Williamson

POLLOCK FAIRBRIDGE SCHIAVONE LIMITED
Pavilion 5, Buchanan Court, Cumbernauld
Road, Glasgow G33 6HZ
Tel: (0141) 7792577
Fax: (0141) 7793618
DX: 501702 MUIRHEAD
E-mail: info@pfssolicitors.co.uk
Web: www.pfssolicitors.co.uk
Categories of Work
Advice the elderly & powers of attorney
Civil court work
Commercial property
Contract & property disputes
Environment (Business Premises)
Family and divorce
Landlord & tenant

Pensions (Company)
Pensions (Employment)
Residential property
Wills, executries and trusts
Directors
Paul David Fairbridge
Christopher Martin Pollock
Paul Rossi Schiavone
Employee
Andrew Frew

PROPERTY SPOT
32 Main Street, Cambuslang, Glasgow
G72 7ER
Tel: (0141) 6419001
Categories of Work
Advice the elderly & powers of attorney
Criminal court work
Criminal legal aid
Family and divorce
Wills, executries and trusts

PRP LEGAL LIMITED
Kensington House, 227 Sauchiehall Street,
Glasgow G2 3EX
Tel: (0141) 3311050
Fax: (0141) 3326847
E-mail: enquiries@prp-legal.co.uk
Web: www.prp-legal.co.uk
Categories of Work
Advice the elderly & powers of attorney
Children
Civil court work
Commercial litigation
Commercial property
Criminal court work
Criminal legal aid
Data protection
Disability
Employment
Employment law
Family and divorce
Immigration and asylum
IT and intellectual property
Landlord & tenant
Medical negligence – claimant
Mergers and acquisitions
Personal injury
Professional negligence
Property litigation
Residential property
Wills, executries and trusts
Directors
Gordon Andrew Fraser
Donald Roderick Murray
Consultant
Douglas Kilpatrick
Associate
Tracy Jane Milligan

QUINN, MARTIN & LANGAN
68 Maryhill Road, Glasgow G20 7QB
Tel: (0141) 332 3702
Fax: (0141) 4296826

► *Glasgow continued*

E-mail: enquiries@qmlsolicitors.com
Web: www.qmlsolicitors.com
Categories of Work
Advice the elderly & powers of attorney
Criminal court work
Criminal legal aid
Family and divorce
Immigration and asylum
Partners
Paul Damien Langan
Gregory Patrick McGowan
Mark Dominic Templeton

RAESIDE CHISHOLM SOLICITORS LIMITED
Tontine House, 8 Gordon Street, Glasgow
G1 3PL
Tel: (0141) 2483456
Fax: (0141) 248 8116
DX: GW211 GLASGOW
E-mail: legal@raesidechisholm.co.uk
Web: www.raesidechisholm.co.uk
Categories of Work
Adoption
Advice the elderly & powers of attorney
Childrens
Civil court work
Civil legal aid
Commercial property
Contract & property disputes
Family and divorce
Family business advice
Landlord & tenant
Mental health
Residential property
SME business advice
Wills, executries and trusts
Directors
Kay Barr
Alison Mary Chisholm
William David Forrester Doig
Malcolm James Buchanan Goddard
Claire Ann Reid
Associate
Alison Janet Gourley
Employees
Ailsa Catherine Doig
Gordon Scot Watson

RALSTONS SOLICITORS
PO Box 2866, Glasgow G61 9EJ
Tel: 7760196224
E-mail: info@ralstonssolicitors.co.uk
Categories of Work
Advice the elderly & powers of attorney
Personal tax
SME business advice
Wills, executries and trusts
Partner
Elspeth Joyce Talbot

RAMSAY & CO. SOLICITORS LTD
974 Maryhill Road, Glasgow G20 7TA
Tel: (0141) 9451917

Fax: (0141) 945 5080
E-mail: info@ramsay-solicitors.com
Web: www.ramsayandcoglasgow.co.uk
Categories of Work
Advice the elderly & powers of attorney
Children
Civil legal aid
Family and divorce
Residential property
Wills, executries and trusts
Director
Michael Harvie Ramsay

REA LAW LTD
116 Blythswood Street, Glasgow G2 4EG
Tel: (0141) 3701241
Fax: (0141) 3701238
E-mail: info@realaw.co.uk
Categories of Work
Civil court work
Civil legal aid
Copyright, trade marks and design
Discrimination
EU / international
Human rights
Immigration and asylum
IT and intellectual property
Personal injury
Personal injury – defender
Private equity
Wills, executries and trusts
Director
Gino Mario Vittorio Rea
Associate
Xing Zhu
Employees
Muhammad Usman Aslam
Hazel Imrie
Megan Anne Slater

REDFORD ROBERTSON SOLICITORS
1 West Regent Street, Glasgow G2 1RW
Tel: (0141) 6485535
E-mail: info@redfordrobertson.com
Categories of Work
Civil court work
Civil legal aid
Mental health
Personal injury
Road traffic
Partner
Kevin Philip Redford
Employee
Mark Robertson

KURT REID AND COMPANY
175 Saltmarket, Glasgow G1 5LG
Tel: (0141) 5530886
E-mail: info@roberts-law.co.uk
Categories of Work
Criminal court work
Criminal legal aid

REID COOPER
Suite 1.3, Queens House, Glasgow G1 2DT

Tel: (0141) 4294656
Fax: (0141) 2041362
DX: GW94 GLASGOW
Web: www.reidcooper.co.uk
Categories of Work
Civil court work
Commercial litigation
Employment
Employment law
Health and safety
Personal injury
Personal injury – defender
Professional negligence
Road traffic
Partners
Louise Catherine Cooper
James Alexander Fergusson Reid
Employee
Emma McNulty

REID QUARTON LIMITED
272 Bath Street, Glasgow G2 4JR
Tel: (0141) 3547651
Fax: (0141) 354 7652
E-mail: sandy.reid@reidquarton.co.uk
Categories of Work
Alternative dispute resolution
Commercial litigation
Debt recovery, insolvency, bankruptcy
Discrimination
Employment
Employment law
Director
Alexander Charles Reid

RH & CO LTD
327-329 Paisley Road West, Glasgow G51 1LU
Tel: (0141) 4190897
Fax: (0141) 427 9293
E-mail: raiahmadkhan@hotmail.co.uk
Categories of Work
Benefit advice
Commercial property
Human rights
Immigration and asylum
Landlord & tenant
Residential property
Directors
Samina Kausar Hussain
Rai Ahmad Khan

RICHMOND CLARK
1619 Great Western Road, Glasgow G13 1LT
Tel: (0141) 9549550
DX: 501432 ANNIESLAND
E-mail: h.richmond@richmondclark.co.uk
Web: www.richmondclark.co.uk
Categories of Work
Advice the elderly & powers of attorney
Family and divorce
Mental health
Residential property
Wills, executries and trusts

Partner
Hannah Louise Richmond
Employee
Katherine Anne Rodgers

RIGHTWAY LEGAL
669 Pollokshaws Road, Glasgow G41 2AB
Tel: (0141) 4238920
Fax: (0141) 4238920
E-mail: rightwaylegal@hotmail.co.uk
Categories of Work
Adoption
Children
Childrens
Civil court work
Civil legal aid
Commercial litigation
Construction
Contract & property disputes
Criminal court work
Criminal legal aid
Education
Family and divorce
Health and safety
Human rights
Immigration and asylum
Landlord & tenant
Liquor licensing
Local government
Property litigation
Road traffic
Wills, executries and trusts
Partner
Munawar Ali

ROAD TRAFFIC ACCIDENT LAW (SCOTLAND) LLP
1 West Regent Street, Glasgow G2 1RW
Tel: (01721) 728238
Categories of Work
Civil court work
Personal injury
Professional negligence
Road traffic
Sport

ROADTRAFFIC EXPERT
40 New City Road, Glasgow G4 9JT
Tel: (0141) 2268825
Categories of Work
Criminal court work
Criminal legal aid

ROAD TRAFFIC LAW.COM LIMITED
Skypark Business Centre, Suite 10, The Hub, Glasgow G3 8EP
Tel: (0141) 2214645
Fax: (0141) 2372331
E-mail: sf@roadtrafficlaw.com
Web: www.roadtrafficlaw.com
Categories of Work
Criminal court work
Criminal legal aid
Director
Steven Thomas Farmer

▶ *Glasgow continued*

JAMES G. ROBERTON
895 Govan Road, Glasgow G51 3DN
Tel: (0141) 4451150
Categories of Work
Criminal court work
Criminal legal aid
Partner
James Gerard Roberton

EUAN ROBERTSON
254 Clarkston Road, Glasgow G44 3EA
Tel: (0141) 4237389
Fax: (0141) 4238041
E-mail: euanrobertsonsolicitors@gmail.com
Categories of Work
Criminal court work
Criminal legal aid
Partner
Euan David Robertson

L & G ROBERTSON LIMITED
46 Carlton Place, Glasgow G5 9TW
Tel: (0141) 4297979
Fax: (0141) 4297453
Categories of Work
Criminal court work
Criminal legal aid
Directors
Grazia Maria Robertson
Liam Robertson

PHILIP ROONEY & CO.
320 Langside Road, Glasgow G42 8XW
Tel: (0141) 423 0000
Fax: (0141) 423 0300
Categories of Work
Criminal court work
Criminal legal aid
Partner
Abdullah Faisal Hamid
Consultants
Martha Anne Rafferty
Philip Rooney

ROONEY FAMILY LAW LIMITED
Spiersbridge House, 1 Spiersbridge Way,
Glasgow G46 8NG
Tel: (0141) 2588685
E-mail: info@rooneyfamilylaw.co.uk
Categories of Work
Adoption
Advice the elderly & powers of attorney
Alternative dispute resolution
Benefit advice
Charities
Children
Childrens
Civil court work
Civil legal aid
Commercial litigation
Consumer credit
Contract & property disputes
Copyright, trade marks and design

Criminal court work
Criminal legal aid
Debt
Debt collecting
Debt management
Debt recovery, insolvency, bankruptcy
Disability
Discrimination
Education
Employment law
Family and divorce
Family business advice
Human rights
Landlord & tenant
Medical negligence – claimant
Mental health
Personal injury
Private equity
Professional negligence
Property litigation
Road traffic
Social housing
Wills, executives and trusts

ROSS & FOX
1st Floor, 87 Carlton Place, Glasgow G5 9TD
Tel: (0141) 4291230
Fax: (0141) 4203441
E-mail: rossfoxsolicitors@yahoo.co.uk
Categories of Work
Criminal court work
Criminal legal aid
Partner
Calum Alexander Ross

RRADAR (SCOTLAND) LIMITED
145 St. Vincent Street, Glasgow G2 5JF
Categories of Work
Adjudication
Alternative dispute resolution
Children
Childrens
Civil court work
Civil legal aid
Commercial litigation
Criminal court work
Criminal legal aid
Data protection
Debt
Debt collecting
Debt recovery, insolvency, bankruptcy
Employment
Employment law
Family and divorce
Health
Health and safety
Medical negligence – defender
Medical negligence – claimant
Pensions (Employment)
Personal injury
Personal injury – defender
Professional negligence
Road traffic

Solicitors
Alastair Neil Gray
Robin William Lee White
Employees
Laura Greta Brennen
Robbie Cole
Claire Lynch

RUSSELLS GIBSON MCCAFFREY
13 Bath Street, Glasgow G2 1HY
Tel: (0141) 271 1000
Fax: (0141) 3327908
DX: GW24 GLASGOW
E-mail: info@russellsgm.co.uk
Web: www.russellsgm.co.uk
Categories of Work
Adoption
Advice the elderly & powers of attorney
Benefit advice
Children
Civil court work
Civil legal aid
Commercial litigation
Commercial property
Contract & property disputes
Criminal court work
Criminal legal aid
Debt
Debt administration
Debt collecting
Debt recovery, insolvency, bankruptcy
Family and divorce
Family business advice
Human rights
Landlord & tenant
Mental health
Mergers and acquisitions
Personal injury
Professional negligence
Property litigation
Residential property
Road traffic
Wills, executries and trusts
Partners
Nicola Alison Irvine
Clair Janet McLachlan
Francis Gerald Moore
James John Mulgrew
Associate
Carla Louise Boylan
Employee
Taylor Muir

RUTHERFORD SHERIDAN LTD
5th Floor, 52 St Enoch Square, Glasgow
G1 4AA
Tel: (0141) 248 3320
Fax: (0141) 248 3320
E-mail: melissa@rutherfordsheridan.com
E-mail: paul@rutherfordsheridan.com
Web: www.rutherfordsheridan.co.uk
Categories of Work
Adoption
Alternative dispute resolution

Benefit advice
Charities
Children
Childrens
Civil court work
Civil legal aid
Consumer credit
Contract & property disputes
Criminal court work
Criminal legal aid
Data protection
Debt
Debt management
Debt recovery, insolvency, bankruptcy
Disability
Discrimination
Family and divorce
Freedom of information
Human rights
Immigration and asylum
Landlord & tenant
Medical negligence – claimant
Mental health
Personal injury
Personal injury – defender
Professional negligence
Property litigation
Road traffic
Social housing
Directors
Melissa Rutherford
Paul Watt Sheridan
Employees
Mark Peter Johnstone
Barry James Moir
Sarah Tolland
Kathryn Truss

RUTHVEN, KEENAN, POLLOCK & CO.
371 Victoria Road, Queens Park, Glasgow
G42 8YY
Tel: (0141) 4238951
Fax: (0141) 4241955
DX: 502000 QUEENS PARK
Categories of Work
Adoption
Advice the elderly & powers of attorney
Children
Civil court work
Civil legal aid
Commercial property
Contract & property disputes
Criminal court work
Criminal legal aid
Debt
Employment law
Family and divorce
Landlord & tenant
Personal injury
Residential property
Road traffic
Wills, executries and trusts

▶ *Glasgow continued*

Partner
Shabana Beg

RUTHVEN, KEENAN, POLLOCK & CO.
832 Crow Road, Anniesland, Glasgow
G13 1HB
Tel: (0141) 9542901
Fax: (0141) 9547296
DX: 501422 ANNIESLAND
Web: www.rkpsolicitors-glasgow.co.uk
Categories of Work
Adoption
Advice the elderly & powers of attorney
Children
Civil court work
Civil legal aid
Commercial property
Contract & property disputes
Criminal court work
Criminal legal aid
Debt
Employment law
Family and divorce
Landlord & tenant
Personal injury
Residential property
Road traffic
Wills, executries and trusts
Partners
John Kevin Duffy
Peter Fitzpatrick
Employee
Liza-Ann Henry

SCULLION LAW LIMITED
130 Saltmarket, Glasgow G1 5LB
Tel: (0141) 374 2121
E-mail: info@scullionlaw.com
Web: www.scullionlaw.com
Categories of Work
Adoption
Advice the elderly & powers of attorney
Alternative dispute resolution
Children
Civil court work
Commercial property
Contract & property disputes
Criminal court work
Criminal legal aid
Data protection
Employment
Employment law
Family and divorce
Family business advice
Health and safety
Human rights
Landlord & tenant
Liquor licensing
Pensions (Employment)
Property litigation
Residential property
Road traffic

Wills, executries and trusts

SCULLION LAW LIMITED
730 Dumbarton Road, Partick, Glasgow
G11 6RD
Tel: (0141) 3742121
E-mail: info@scullionlaw.com
Categories of Work
Adoption
Advice the elderly & powers of attorney
Alternative dispute resolution
Children
Civil court work
Commercial property
Contract & property disputes
Criminal court work
Criminal legal aid
Data protection
Employment
Employment law
Family and divorce
Family business advice
Health and safety
Human rights
Landlord & tenant
Liquor licensing
Pensions (Employment)
Property litigation
Residential property
Road traffic
Wills, executries and trusts

DOMINIC SELLAR & CO
First Floor, 102 Bath Street, Glasgow G2 2EP
Tel: (0141) 2551519
Fax: (0141) 2551499
Categories of Work
Criminal court work
Criminal legal aid
Partner
Dominic Jonathan Keith Sellar

SERENITY FAMILY LAW LTD
36 Fenwick Drive, Barrhead, Glasgow G78 2LB
Tel: (07557) 885013
Web: www.serenityfamilylaw.co.uk
Categories of Work
Adoption
Advice the elderly & powers of attorney
Children
Childrens
Civil court work
Education
Family and divorce
Wills, executries and trusts
Director
Michael Patrick George Hughes

SHAKESPEARE MARTINEAU (GLASGOW) LLP
272 Bath Street, Glasgow G2 4JR
Tel: (0121) 214 0000
Partners
Amal Kaur Dhesi
James Robert Gooch

ARCHIBALD SHARP & SON LIMITED
270 Dumbarton Road, Partick, Glasgow
G11 6TX
Tel: (0141) 3393036
Fax: (0141) 3416317
DX: 500904 PARTICK
E-mail: info@archibaldsharp.co.uk
Web: www.archibaldsharp.co.uk
Categories of Work
Advice the elderly & powers of attorney
Banking & finance
Civil court work
Commercial litigation
Commercial property
Consumer credit
Contract & property disputes
Copyright, trade marks and design
Data protection
Debt recovery, insolvency, bankruptcy
Family and divorce
Freedom of information
Insolvency & corporate recovery
IT and intellectual property
Landlord & tenant
Liquor licensing
Media and entertainment
Mental health
Property litigation
Residential property
Software licensing
Wills, executries and trusts
Directors
Barbara Anne Anderson
James William Craig
Michelle Dawn Rankin
Associate
Frances Yvonne Blair
Employees
David Michael Leishman
Monica Mary McCann

SHEPHERD AND WEDDERBURN LLP
1 West Regent Street, Glasgow G2 1RW
Tel: (0141) 5669900
Fax: (0141) 5651222
DX: GW409 GLASGOW
E-mail: info@shepwedd.com
Web: www.shepwedd.co.uk
Categories of Work
Adjudication
Adoption
Advice the elderly & powers of attorney
Agriculture and estates
Agriculture, crofting and fishing
Alternative dispute resolution
Alternative investment market
Banking & finance
Betting & gaming
Charities
Civil court work
Commercial litigation
Commercial property
Competition

Construction
Consumer credit
Contract & property disputes
Copyright, trade marks and design
Corporate tax
Credit brokerage
Data protection
Debt
Debt adjusting and debt counselling
Debt administration
Debt collecting
Debt recovery, insolvency, bankruptcy
Disability
Discrimination
Education
Employment
Employment law
Environment
Environment (Business Premises)
EU / international
Family business advice
Fishing
Freedom of information
Health
Health and safety
Housing
Human rights
Immigration and asylum
Insolvency & corporate recovery
Insurance
IT and intellectual property
Joint venture
Landlord & tenant
Liquor licensing
Local government
Media and entertainment
Medical negligence – defender
Medical negligence – claimant
Mergers and acquisitions
Mining
Oil & gas
Parliamentary
Pensions (Company)
Pensions (Employment)
Personal injury
Personal injury – defender
Personal tax
Planning
Planning (Business Premises)
Power and utilities
Private equity
Professional negligence
Projects
Property litigation
Provision of credit information services
Public finance initiative
Public sector
Residential property
Road traffic
Shipping
SME business advice
Software licensing
Sport

▶ **Glasgow continued**

Telecoms
Transport
Unit Trusts, OEICs and investment trusts
Wills, executries and trusts
Partners
Joanna Susan Boag-Thomson
Rodger William Cairns
George William Frier
John Andrew Dominic Grady
Alexis Irene Graham
James Russell Grant
Andrew William Macdonald Hall
Michael Gordon Henderson
Elaine Ann Hunter
Eleanor Mary Kerr
Roderick Mungall MacLeod
Scott McCallum
Fiona McKerrell
Elizabeth Margaret Miller McRobb
Colin John Robertson
Judith Hilary Stephenson
Thomas William Swan
Consultant
Lilian Patricia Hawthorn
Associates
Richard Gordon Hart
John McKie
George Lauchlan McKinlay
Lesley Stewart Proctor
Solicitor
Philippa Clare Haughney
Employees
Jacqueline Arthur
Amie Sutherland Bain
Marrya Anwar Bashir
Pamela Elizabeth Binnie
Craig Murdoch Brodie
Hannah May Bruce
Cornelius Kevin Casey
Gavin Iain Charlton
Sarah Marie Dippenaar
Abby MacKinnon Doig
John Whyte Elder
Joseph Maurice Patrick Fitzgibbon
Lorna Charlotte Hewitt
Alison Edna Horner
Elaine Joanne Kirk
Lucy Rachel Knox
Lisa Woods Lennox
Oonagh Kathleen Macdonald
Daniel MacKinnon
Claire McCarte
Pamela Sally McMillan
Gillian Ward Moore
Lucy Karen Mulreany
Rachel Erin Munro
Alison Richmond
Scott Lindsay Rodger
Joseph Peter Slane
Susan Swan
Susan Janette Tweedie

Andrew Scott Winton

SHERIDAN AT LAW LTD.
81 High Street, Glasgow G1 1NB
Tel: (0141) 465 3333
DX: 557587 SALTMARKET
E-mail: enquiries@sheridanatlaw.com
Web: www.sheridanatlaw.com
Categories of Work
Criminal court work
Criminal legal aid
Director
Robert John Sheridan

SHERIDANS
166 Buchanan Street, Glasgow G1 2LW
Tel: (0141) 3323536
Fax: (0141) 3533819
DX: GW266 GLASGOW
E-mail: michael@sheridanssolicitors.co.uk
Web: www.sheridanssolicitors.co.uk
Categories of Work
Criminal court work
Criminal legal aid
Partners
Christopher Paul Sheridan
Michael Sheridan

SHOOSMITHS LLP
5th Floor, The Garment Factory, Glasgow
G1 1RE
Tel: (0370) 086 8300
Categories of Work
Alternative dispute resolution
Banking & finance
Civil court work
Commercial litigation
Commercial property
Construction
Consumer credit
Contract & property disputes
Credit brokerage
Debt
Debt collecting
Debt recovery, insolvency, bankruptcy
Discrimination
Employment
Employment law
Environment
Environment (Business Premises)
Housing
Human rights
Immigration and asylum
Insolvency & corporate recovery
IT and intellectual property
Joint venture
Landlord & tenant
Local government
Mergers and acquisitions
Oil & gas
Parliamentary
Pensions (Company)
Pensions (Employment)
Personal injury – defender

Planning
Planning (Business Premises)
Power and utilities
Private equity
Professional negligence
Projects
Property litigation
Public sector
Residential property
SME business advice
Social housing
Partners
Fiona Cameron
Barry Alexander McKeown
Michael Joseph McLaughlin
Associates
Collette Gibson
Geraint James Gordon Hughes
Thomas Maxwell
Lewis David Charles Ritchie
Frazer Thomas Robertson
Pavan Kaur Sumal
Suzanne Jayne Traynor
Jennifer Catherine Wright
Employees
Eilidh Molly Durkin
Lauren Miller

SIMPLICITY LEGAL
34 Woodlands Road, Glasgow G3 6UR
Tel: (0141) 4332626
DX: : 512208 NEWTON
Categories of Work
Adoption
Advice the elderly & powers of attorney
Children
Childrens
Civil court work
Commercial litigation
Commercial property
Contract & property disputes
Debt
Debt recovery, insolvency, bankruptcy
Education
Family and divorce
Family business advice
Insolvency & corporate recovery
Landlord & tenant
Medical negligence – defender
Medical negligence – claimant
Personal injury
Personal injury – defender
Professional negligence
Property litigation
Residential property
Wills, executries and trusts

SIMPLICITY LEGAL
8 Regwood Street, Shawlands, Glasgow
G41 3JG
Tel: (0141) 433 2626
Categories of Work
Adoption
Advice the elderly & powers of attorney

Children
Childrens
Civil court work
Commercial litigation
Commercial property
Contract & property disputes
Debt
Debt recovery, insolvency, bankruptcy
Education
Family and divorce
Family business advice
Insolvency & corporate recovery
Landlord & tenant
Medical negligence – defender
Medical negligence – claimant
Personal injury
Personal injury – defender
Professional negligence
Property litigation
Residential property
Wills, executries and trusts

FRED SIMPSON
120F Southbrae Drive, Glasgow G13 1TZ
Tel: (07557) 916721
E-mail: simpsonfs63@aol.com
Categories of Work
Civil court work
Commercial litigation
Partner
Frederick Stephen Simpson

SIMPSON & MARWICK
The Forsyth Building, 5 Renfield Street,
Glasgow G2 5EZ
Tel: (0344) 5715205
E-mail: info@simpsonmarwick.com
Categories of Work
Adoption
Advice the elderly & powers of attorney
Agriculture and estates
Alternative dispute resolution
Banking & finance
Children
Civil court work
Commercial litigation
Commercial property
Consumer credit
Contract & property disputes
Debt
Debt collecting
Debt recovery, insolvency, bankruptcy
Disability
Discrimination
Employment
Employment law
EU / international
Family and divorce
Housing
Insolvency & corporate recovery
Insurance
Landlord & tenant
Local government
Medical negligence – claimant

► *Glasgow continued*

Personal injury
Professional negligence
Property litigation
Public sector
Residential property
Road traffic
Wills, executries and trusts

SINGH AND HUSSAIN LTD
2 Clarendon Place, Glasgow G20 7PY
Tel: (0141) 331 2885
E-mail: enquiries@maguiresolicitors.co.uk
Categories of Work
Adoption
Advice the elderly & powers of attorney
Children
Childrens
Criminal court work
Discrimination
Education
Employment law
EU / international
Family and divorce
Health
Human rights
Immigration and asylum
Medical negligence – defender

SINGH & CO SOLICITORS LTD
93 Middleton Street, Flat 3/1, Glasgow
G51 1AF
Tel: (07541) 950585
E-mail: info@singhandcosolicitors.com
Web: www.singhandcosolicitors.com

SJK LEGAL LTD
4-10 Darnley Street, 1st Floor, Glasgow
G41 2SE
Tel: (0141) 6482500
E-mail: info@sjksols.co.uk
Web: www.sjksols.co.uk
Categories of Work
Alternative dispute resolution
Employment law
EU / international
Human rights
Immigration and asylum
Director
Gurpreet Singh Johal
Employee
Said Jamil Khan

SKELLY AND COMPANY
272 Bath Street, Glasgow G2 4JR
Tel: (07738) 884895
E-mail: robertskelly@injuryclaimsservices.co.uk

J.B. SOUTTER, SON & MAIN
190 St. Vincent Street, Glasgow G2 5SP
Tel: (0141) 2042833
E-mail: mail@millerbj.co.uk
Categories of Work
Adjudication
Adoption

Advice the elderly & powers of attorney
Alternative dispute resolution
Charities
Children
Childrens
Civil court work
Commercial litigation
Commercial property
Consumer credit
Contract & property disputes
Criminal court work
Data protection
Debt
Debt collecting
Debt recovery, insolvency, bankruptcy
Employment
Employment law
Family and divorce
Family business advice
Freedom of information
Housing
Immigration and asylum
IT and intellectual property
Joint venture
Landlord & tenant
Mergers and acquisitions
Personal injury
Professional negligence
Property litigation
Residential property
Road traffic
SME business advice
Wills, executries and trusts

G. SWEENEY SOLICITORS LIMITED
2nd Floor, 87 Carlton Place, Glasgow G5 9TD
Tel: (0141) 4290677
Fax: (0141) 4290677
Categories of Work
Criminal court work
Criminal legal aid
Partner
Gerard Sweeney

SWINBURNE & CO
Oxford House, 71 Oxford Street, Glasgow
G5 9EP
Tel: (0141) 2222213
E-mail: swinburnejim@gmail.com
Categories of Work
Criminal court work
Criminal legal aid
Partner
James Swinburne
Employee
Harvie Samuel Diamond

TEMPLE & CO SOLICITORS LTD
Blue Square, 272 Bath Street, Glasgow G2 4JR
Tel: (0141) 4283979
Categories of Work
Civil legal aid
Commercial property
Public sector

Residential property
Social housing

TENEU LEGAL
2-Feb, 21 Thistle Terrace, Glasgow G5 0SJ
Tel: (07877) 347695
Categories of Work
Civil court work
Commercial litigation
Debt recovery, insolvency, bankruptcy
Human rights
Immigration and asylum
Public sector
Partner
Blair Melville

THE BUILDING LAW PRACTICE LIMITED
272 Bath Street, Glasgow G2 4JR
Tel: (0141) 3537655
Fax: (0141) 3547656
Categories of Work
Adjudication
Alternative dispute resolution
Commercial litigation
Construction
Health and safety
Housing
Insolvency & corporate recovery
Landlord & tenant
Power and utilities
Projects
Property litigation
SME business advice
Director
Anthony Paul Wallace
Employee
David Joseph Wallace

THE CAR ACCIDENT LAW PRACTICE
71 Oxford Street, Glasgow G5 9EP
Tel: (0141) 2286035
Categories of Work
Personal injury
Road traffic

THE CONWAY ACCIDENT LAW PRACTICE LTD
71 Oxford Street, Glasgow G5 9EP
Tel: (0141) 319 8240
E-mail: info@accidentlawscotland.com
Categories of Work
Personal injury
Road traffic
Director
Ronald Edward Conway
Employee
Rachel Anne Conway

THE GLASGOW LAW PRACTICE
100 Cumbernauld Road, Muirhead, Glasgow
G69 9AB
Tel: (0141) 7794466
Categories of Work
Adoption
Advice the elderly & powers of attorney
Alternative dispute resolution

Banking & finance
Children
Civil court work
Civil legal aid
Commercial property
Contract & property disputes
Criminal court work
Criminal legal aid
Debt
Debt recovery, insolvency, bankruptcy
Disability
Discrimination
Employment
Employment law
Family and divorce
Family business advice
Human rights
Landlord & tenant
Medical negligence – defender
Medical negligence – claimant
Personal injury
Personal injury – defender
Planning (Business Premises)
Professional negligence
Property litigation
Residential property
Road traffic
SME business advice
Wills, executries and trusts

THE GLASGOW LAW PRACTICE
124 Main Street, Cambuslang, Glasgow
G72 7EL
Tel: (0141) 6412912
E-mail: ry@theglasgowlawpractice.co.uk
Categories of Work
Adoption
Advice the elderly & powers of attorney
Alternative dispute resolution
Banking & finance
Children
Civil court work
Civil legal aid
Commercial property
Contract & property disputes
Criminal court work
Criminal legal aid
Debt
Debt recovery, insolvency, bankruptcy
Disability
Discrimination
Employment
Employment law
Family and divorce
Family business advice
Human rights
Landlord & tenant
Medical negligence – defender
Medical negligence – claimant
Personal injury
Personal injury – defender
Planning (Business Premises)
Professional negligence

▶ *Glasgow continued*

Property litigation
Residential property
Road traffic
SME business advice
Wills, executries and trusts
Consultant
Ian Brechany

THE GLASGOW LAW PRACTICE
81 Main Street, Baillieston, Glasgow G69 6AD
Tel: (0141) 7732145
Categories of Work
Adoption
Advice the elderly & powers of attorney
Alternative dispute resolution
Banking & finance
Children
Civil court work
Civil legal aid
Commercial property
Contract & property disputes
Criminal court work
Criminal legal aid
Debt
Debt recovery, insolvency, bankruptcy
Disability
Discrimination
Employment
Employment law
Family and divorce
Family business advice
Human rights
Landlord & tenant
Medical negligence – defender
Medical negligence – claimant
Personal injury
Personal injury – defender
Planning (Business Premises)
Professional negligence
Property litigation
Residential property
Road traffic
SME business advice
Wills, executries and trusts

THEGLASGOWLAWPRACTICE.COM
1 St. Margarets Place, Glasgow G1 5JY
Tel: (0141) 5528553
DX: 500100 BAILLIESTON
Categories of Work
Adoption
Advice the elderly & powers of attorney
Alternative dispute resolution
Banking & finance
Children
Civil court work
Civil legal aid
Commercial property
Contract & property disputes
Criminal court work
Criminal legal aid
Debt

Debt recovery, insolvency, bankruptcy
Disability
Discrimination
Employment
Employment law
Family and divorce
Family business advice
Human rights
Landlord & tenant
Medical negligence – defender
Medical negligence – claimant
Personal injury
Personal injury – defender
Planning (Business Premises)
Professional negligence
Property litigation
Residential property
Road traffic
SME business advice
Wills, executries and trusts

THE GLASGOW LAW PRACTICE (HOLDINGS) LTD
81 Main Street, Baillieston, Glasgow G69 6AD
Tel: (0141) 7732145

THE KERR BROWN PARTNERSHIP
Suite 312-315, Baltic Chambers, 50
Wellington Street, Glasgow G2 6HJ
Tel: (0141) 2214880
Fax: (0141) 2219669
DX: www.kerrbrown.co.uk
E-mail: enquiries@kerrbrown.co.uk
Categories of Work
Civil court work
Medical negligence – claimant
Personal injury
Professional negligence
Road traffic
Partners
Monica Anne Brown
Robert Peter Kerr
Associate
Mark John MacMillan
Employees
Ciaran Francis Dougherty
Deborah Louise Morris
Stephanie Petropoulos
Liam John Scott
Emma Louise Timmins
Ian Ward

THE MMFW PARTNERSHIP
917 Shettleston Road, Shettleston, Glasgow
G32 7NU
Tel: (0141) 7631337/ 77
DX: 501164 SHAWLANDS
E-mail: mcinandmacl@msn.com
Web: www.mmfw.weebly.com
Categories of Work
Adoption
Advice the elderly & powers of attorney
Benefit advice
Children

Civil court work
Civil legal aid
Consumer credit
Criminal court work
Criminal legal aid
Debt
Debt adjusting and debt counselling
Debt administration
Debt collecting
Debt management
Debt recovery, insolvency, bankruptcy
Disability
Discrimination
Education
Employment
Employment law
Family and divorce
Human rights
Immigration and asylum
Medical negligence – claimant
Mental health
Personal injury
Residential property
Road traffic
Social housing
Wills, executries and trusts
Partner
Steven Archibald Murray

THE PRG PARTNERSHIP
12 Royal Crescent, Glasgow G3 7SL
Tel: (0141) 3530550
Fax: (0141) 3312231
DX: 512215 GLAS SANDYFORD PL
E-mail: scotslaw@prg.co.uk
Web: www.prg.co.uk
Categories of Work
Adjudication
Advice the elderly & powers of attorney
Alternative dispute resolution
Charities
Children
Civil court work
Civil legal aid
Commercial litigation
Commercial property
Competition
Contract & property disputes
Copyright, trade marks and design
Criminal court work
Criminal legal aid
Data protection
Debt
Debt collecting
Debt recovery, insolvency, bankruptcy
Disability
Discrimination
Employment
Employment law
Family and divorce
Family business advice
Health and safety
Human rights

Insolvency & corporate recovery
IT and intellectual property
Joint venture
Landlord & tenant
Media and entertainment
Medical negligence – defender
Medical negligence – claimant
Mergers and acquisitions
Pensions (Employment)
Personal injury
Personal injury – defender
Professional negligence
Property litigation
Residential property
Road traffic
SME business advice
Social housing
Software licensing
Wills, executries and trusts
Partners
David John Oliver Dickson
John Gordon Alexander Mackie
Jennifer Quinn
Consultants
James McEwan Cassels
George Gilfillan Hunter

THE PRG PARTNERSHIP
208 Saracen Street, Glasgow G22 5EP
Tel: (0141) 3363241
E-mail: scotslaw@prg.co.uk
Web: www.prg.co.uk
Categories of Work
Adjudication
Advice the elderly & powers of attorney
Alternative dispute resolution
Charities
Children
Civil court work
Civil legal aid
Commercial litigation
Commercial property
Competition
Contract & property disputes
Copyright, trade marks and design
Criminal court work
Criminal legal aid
Data protection
Debt
Debt collecting
Debt recovery, insolvency, bankruptcy
Disability
Discrimination
Employment
Employment law
Family and divorce
Family business advice
Health and safety
Human rights
Insolvency & corporate recovery
IT and intellectual property
Joint venture
Landlord & tenant

▶ **Glasgow** continued

Media and entertainment
Medical negligence – defender
Medical negligence – claimant
Mergers and acquisitions
Pensions (Employment)
Personal injury
Personal injury – defender
Professional negligence
Property litigation
Residential property
Road traffic
SME business advice
Social housing
Software licensing
Wills, executries and trusts

**THE SHAREHOLDING & INVESTMENT
(PROPERTY) LIMITED**
Capella, 60 York Street, Glasgow G2 8JX
Tel: (0141) 3031100

**THE SHAREHOLDING & INVESTMENT TRUST
LIMITED**
Capella, 60 York Street, Glasgow G2 8JX
Tel: (0141) 3031100

THOMAS, CARLIN & PENDER
1490 Paisley Road West, Glasgow G52 1SP
Tel: (0141) 8836227
Fax: (0141) 8105346
DX: 500309 CARDONALD
E-mail: Carlin.Pender@btconnect.com
Categories of Work
Advice the elderly & powers of attorney
Criminal court work
Employment
Employment law
Landlord & tenant
Residential property
Wills, executries and trusts
Partner
Anne Mary Pender
Consultant
Michael Thomas Carlin

THOMPSON FAMILY LAW
Suite 200, Central Chambers, Glasgow
G2 6LD
Tel: (0141) 4046575
Fax: (0141) 4042582
E-mail: info@tflaw.co.uk
Web: www.tfamlaw.co.uk
Categories of Work
Adoption
Advice the elderly & powers of attorney
Alternative dispute resolution
Children
Civil court work
Civil legal aid
Commercial litigation
Commercial property
Consumer credit
Criminal court work

Criminal legal aid
Data protection
Debt
Debt collecting
Debt recovery, insolvency, bankruptcy
Disability
Discrimination
Education
Family and divorce
Freedom of information
Housing
Human rights
Insolvency & corporate recovery
Insurance
IT and intellectual property
Medical negligence – defender
Medical negligence – claimant
Mental health
Personal injury
Professional negligence
Residential property
Road traffic
Wills, executries and trusts
Partner
Michael Thompson
Employees
Abby Connor
Sylvia Noami Line
Melissa Anna Phillips
Claudia Jessica Rose Reilly
Gary William Thompson
John William Thompson

THOMPSONS
Berkeley House, 285 Bath Street, Glasgow
G2 4HQ
Tel: (0141) 2218840
Fax: (0141) 2265738
DX: GW162 GLASGOW
E-mail: mail@thompsons-scotland.co.uk
Web: www.thompsons-scotland.co.uk
Categories of Work
Adoption
Advice the elderly & powers of attorney
Agriculture and estates
Alternative dispute resolution
Charities
Children
Childrens
Civil court work
Civil legal aid
Commercial litigation
Consumer credit
Criminal court work
Disability
Discrimination
Education
Employment
Employment law
Family and divorce
Health
Health and safety
Human rights

Immigration and asylum
Insurance
Medical negligence – claimant
Personal injury
Personal injury – defender
Professional negligence
Residential property
Road traffic
Social housing
Wills, executries and trusts
Partners
Hannah Lucy Bennett
Laura Anne Blane
Seonaid Catriona Brophy
Claire Louise Campbell
Laura Connor
Wendy Durie
Andrew David Henderson
David Andrew Martyn
Patrick Gregory McGuire
Jillian Louise Merchant
Alan James Rodgers
Bruce Robert Shields
Craig James Smillie
Associates
Lynn Morton Fraser
Joanne Goodwin
Eilish Elizabeth Lindsay
Jillian Cheshire Mackenzie
Employees
David Adams
Hayden Thomas Bain
Ailidh Catherine Ballantyne
Michael Ballantyne
Shona Louise Cocksedge
Elspeth Fiona Drysdale
Deirdre Christine Flanigan
Mhari Gallacher
Amy Elizabeth Haughton
Jonathan Hay Howat
Conor Kenny
Zoheb Mohammed Khalid
Jennifer Hannah Lilly
William Donald McParland
Courtney Elizabeth McQuiston
Kirsty Elizabeth Moran
Chloe Elizabeth Neil
Lucy Bishop Neil
Kirsty Rodden
Lorraine Lennox Scott
Joel Julian Guise Shaw
Kieran Francis Stead Smith
Paola Maria Sproul
Samantha Stewart
Lauren McCann Strain
Nicola Jane Thompson
Ruth Anne Wallace
Emma Danielle Wheelhouse
Stephanie Louise Young

THORNTONS LAW LLP
Spaces, 1 West Regent Street, Glasgow
G2 1RW

Tel: (03330) 430350
Fax: (0131) 226 7077
E-mail: glasgow@thorntons-law.co.uk
Categories of Work
Adjudication
Adoption
Advice the elderly & powers of attorney
Agriculture and estates
Agriculture, crofting and fishing
Alternative dispute resolution
Alternative investment market
Banking & finance
Benefit advice
Betting & gaming
Charities
Children
Childrens
Civil court work
Civil legal aid
Commercial litigation
Commercial property
Competition
Construction
Consumer credit
Contract & property disputes
Copyright, trade marks and design
Corporate tax
Credit brokerage
Criminal court work
Criminal legal aid
Data protection
Debt
Debt adjusting and debt counselling
Debt administration
Debt collecting
Debt recovery, insolvency, bankruptcy
Disability
Discrimination
Education
Employment
Employment law
Environment
Environment (Business Premises)
EU / international
Family and divorce
Family business advice
Fishing
Freedom of information
Health
Health and safety
Housing
Human rights
Immigration and asylum
Insolvency & corporate recovery
Insurance
IT and intellectual property
Joint venture
Landlord & tenant
Liquor licensing
Local government
Media and entertainment
Medical negligence – defender
Medical negligence – claimant

▶ *Glasgow continued*

Mental health
Mergers and acquisitions
Oil & gas
Parliamentary
Pensions (Company)
Pensions (Employment)
Personal injury
Personal injury – defender
Personal tax
Planning
Planning (Business Premises)
Power and utilities
Private equity
Professional negligence
Projects
Property litigation
Public sector
Residential property
Road traffic
SME business advice
Social housing
Software licensing
Sport
Telecoms
Unit Trusts, OEICs and investment trusts
Wills, executries and trusts
Partner
Pamela Elizabeth Muir
Employee
Ryan James McCuaig

TIME LEGAL CONSULTING LIMITED

1 Spiersbridge Business Park, Thornliebank,
Glasgow G46 8NG
Tel: (0141) 4283488
E-mail: richard@timelegalconsulting.co.uk
Categories of Work
Alternative dispute resolution
Civil court work
Contract & property disputes
Debt collecting
Debt management
Debt recovery, insolvency, bankruptcy
Family business advice
Housing
Insolvency & corporate recovery
Landlord & tenant
Property litigation
Residential property
Social housing
Director
Richard Joseph Taylor

TLT LLP

140 West George Street, Glasgow G2 2HG
Tel: (0333) 006 0400
Fax: (0333) 006 0411
Web: www.tltsolicitors.com
Categories of Work
Adjudication
Agriculture and estates
Alternative dispute resolution

Alternative investment market
Banking & finance
Betting & gaming
Civil court work
Commercial litigation
Commercial property
Construction
Consumer credit
Contract & property disputes
Debt
Debt adjusting and debt counselling
Debt administration
Debt collecting
Debt recovery, insolvency, bankruptcy
Disability
Discrimination
Education
Employment
Employment law
Environment
Environment (Business Premises)
EU / international
Family and divorce
Freedom of information
Health
Housing
Immigration and asylum
Insolvency & corporate recovery
Joint venture
Landlord & tenant
Liquor licensing
Local government
Medical negligence – defender
Medical negligence – claimant
Mergers and acquisitions
Mining
Parliamentary
Pensions (Employment)
Personal injury
Planning
Planning (Business Premises)
Power and utilities
Professional negligence
Projects
Property litigation
Public finance initiative
Public sector
Residential property
SME business advice
Partners
Brian Oetegenn Armour
Howard Jeremy Beach
Damien Paul Bechelli
Stacey-Anne Cassidy
Louise Chopra
Douglas John Gourlay
Andrew Christopher McCowan
Thomas Peter McEntegart
Stephen John McGowan
Kenneth Turnbull Meldrum
Alan Turner Munro
Caroline Tod Ramsay
William Jonathan Rennie

Nicholas Simon Shenken
John Paul Sheridan
Donna Strong
Associates
Ainslie Ann Ginn Benzie
Allison Elizabeth Bruce
Alyson Lyndsay Cowan
Lucy Aline Harington
Employees
Philippa Louise Beveridge
Michael Philip Collins
Emma Christina Finch
Shaunagh Mairead Gilchrist
Declan William Grimason
Joanna Hamilton
Stephanie Lindsay Hands
Kris Robert Jenkins
Catharine Ann Beaton MacDonald
Michael McDougall
Lorna Forbes McWilliams
Laura-Kate O'Brien
Fiona Savage
Sarah Ann Simpson
Ayla Skene
Kirsty Alexandria Martin Smith
Amy Fiona Tough
Fraser William Vandal
Louise Ward

KEITH J. TUCK
254 Saracen Street, Possilpark, Glasgow
G22 5LF
Tel: (0141) 3362020
Fax: (0141) 3471000
Categories of Work
Criminal court work
Criminal legal aid
Partner
Keith John Tuck
Employee
Charles William Drummond

KEITH J. TUCK
68 Huntingdon Square, Sighthill, Glasgow
G21 1LR
Tel: (0141) 5588888
Categories of Work
Criminal court work
Criminal legal aid

TURCAN CONNELL
180 St Vincent Street, Glasgow G2 5SG
Tel: (0141) 441 2111
Fax: (0141) 221 9218
DX: GW4 GLASGOW
E-mail: enquiries@turcanconnell.com
Web: www.turcanconnell.com
Categories of Work
Adoption
Advice the elderly & powers of attorney
Agriculture and estates
Agriculture, crofting and fishing
Alternative dispute resolution
Alternative investment market

Banking & finance
Charities
Children
Childrens
Civil court work
Commercial litigation
Commercial property
Construction
Contract & property disputes
Employment
Employment law
Environment
Environment (Business Premises)
EU / international
Family and divorce
Family business advice
Fishing
Housing
Insolvency & corporate recovery
Joint venture
Landlord & tenant
Medical negligence – claimant
Mental health
Mergers and acquisitions
Mining
Pensions (Employment)
Personal tax
Planning (Business Premises)
Power and utilities
Private equity
Professional negligence
Property litigation
Residential property
SME business advice
Wills, executries and trusts
Partners
John Gardiner
Peter James Murrin
Associate
Stuart Hamilton Ferguson Gibb
Employees
Zaynab Al-Nasser
Jillian Bynoth
Simran Kaur Panesar
Callum Andrew Townend

TURNER & WHITE LIMITED
93 West Regent Street, Glasgow G2 2BA
Tel: (0141) 4654555
E-mail: info@turnerandwhite.co.uk
Categories of Work
Alternative dispute resolution
Civil court work
Civil legal aid
Personal injury
Personal injury – defender
Professional negligence
Road traffic

UNIONLINE SCOTLAND
4th Floor, Fountain House, 1-3 Woodside
Cresent, Glasgow G3 7UJ
Tel: (0141) 353 8700

▶ **Glasgow continued**

Categories of Work
Adjudication
Adoption
Advice the elderly & powers of attorney
Alternative dispute resolution
Betting & gaming
Children
Childrens
Civil court work
Civil legal aid
Commercial litigation
Copyright, trade marks and design
Data protection
Education
Employment
Employment law
Family and divorce
Freedom of information
Health and safety
IT and intellectual property
Media and entertainment
Medical negligence – defender
Medical negligence – claimant
Pensions (Employment)
Personal injury
Personal injury – defender
Professional negligence
Road traffic
Software licensing
Sport
Telecoms

R.S. VAUGHAN & CO
114 Union Street, Glasgow G1 3QQ
Tel: (0141) 2215482
Fax: (0141) 2217066
DX: GW198 GLASGOW
E-mail: rvaughan@rsvaughan.co.uk
Categories of Work
Adjudication
Adoption
Advice the elderly & powers of attorney
Alternative dispute resolution
Children
Childrens
Civil court work
Civil legal aid
Commercial litigation
Consumer credit
Contract & property disputes
Criminal court work
Criminal legal aid
Data protection
Debt
Debt collecting
Debt recovery, insolvency, bankruptcy
Education
Employment law
Family and divorce
Media and entertainment
Medical negligence – defender
Medical negligence – claimant

Personal injury
Personal injury – defender
Professional negligence
Road traffic
Wills, executries and trusts
Partner
Robert Smith Vaughan
Employee
Jonathan James Greenhorn

A S WAGNER LIMITED
The Connal Building, 34 West George Street,
Glasgow G2 1DA
Tel: (0141) 332 0809
Fax: (0870) 4469332
DX: 207 GLASGOW
E-mail: mail@aswagner.co.uk
Web: www.aswagner.co.uk
Categories of Work
Advice the elderly & powers of attorney
Commercial property
Family and divorce
Landlord & tenant
Residential property
Wills, executries and trusts
Partner
Sophia Jane Wagner

WA LEGAL LTD
Floor 4, Room 3, 41 St Vincent Place, Glasgow
G1 2ER
Tel: (0330) 1334563
Categories of Work
Criminal court work
Criminal legal aid
Director
Waqqas Abrar Ashraf

GRAHAM WALKER
1300 Shettleston Road, Glasgow G32 7YQ
Tel: (0141) 378 2560
E-mail: shettleston@@gwsolicitors.com
Web: www.gwsolicitors.com
Categories of Work
Criminal court work
Criminal legal aid

GRAHAM WALKER
1584 Maryhill Road, Maryhill, Glasgow
G20 0HL
Tel: (0141) 9460111
Fax: (0141) 945 6298
E-mail: maryhill@gwsolicitors.com
Web: www.gwsolicitors.com
Categories of Work
Criminal court work
Criminal legal aid
Partner
Ian Robert Sievwright
Consultant
Matthew Philip Berlow
Employees
Kevin James Corr
Abby Jayne Russell
Michael Logan Tierney

Manus Gerard Tolland

JAMES R. WALLACE
312 Kilmarnock Road, Newlands, Glasgow
G43 2DG
Tel: (07949) 133123
E-mail: james.robertson@wallace.ms
Categories of Work
Criminal court work
Criminal legal aid
Partner
James Robertson Wallace

WALLACE QUINN & CO LIMITED
Suite 3, 21 Glasgow Road, Glasgow G69 6JT
Tel: (0141) 7713911
Fax: (0141) 7714545
DX: 500101 BAILLIESTON
Web: www.wallacequinn.co.uk
Categories of Work
Advice the elderly & powers of attorney
Agriculture and estates
Civil court work
Commercial property
Construction
Contract & property disputes
Family and divorce
Family business advice
Landlord & tenant
Mergers and acquisitions
Residential property
SME business advice
Wills, executives and trusts
Directors
Mark Francis McBride
John Quinn
James Robert Reid
Employees
Maureen Jackson
Irene Margaret McGraw
Richard David Murray

WATERMANS SOLICITORS LIMITED
Fourth Floor, Festival House, Glasgow G2 2LB
Tel: (0141) 4307055
Fax: (0141) 2222719
DX: GW112 GLASGOW
Web: www.watermans.co.uk
Categories of Work
Civil court work
Data protection
Debt
Disability
Freedom of information
Health and safety
Medical negligence – claimant
Personal injury
Professional negligence
Road traffic
Employees
Aimee Louise Elder
Scott Callum Fulton
Susanne Marie McGraw
Ashleigh McIntyre

Lauren Mullen
Heather Isabel Mary Tierney
Darren Alexander Turnbull

WEAVER & WADDELL SOLICITORS
Suite 1/2, Spiersbridge House, 1 Spiersbridge
Way, Glasgow G46 8NG
Tel: (0141) 7396100
Fax: (0141) 620 0399
DX: www.weaverwaddellsolicitors.com
E-mail: mail@weaverwaddellsolicitors.com
Categories of Work
Advice the elderly & powers of attorney
Civil court work
Commercial property
Contract & property disputes
Debt recovery, insolvency, bankruptcy
Family and divorce
Family business advice
Landlord & tenant
Mental health
Residential property
Wills, executives and trusts
Partners
Andrea Isabella Waddell
Lucrecia Marie Weaver
Employee
Rabia Islam

WEIGHTMANS (SCOTLAND) LLP
144 West George Street, Glasgow G2 2HG
Tel: (0345) 073 9900
Fax: (0845) 0739950
DX: GW 73 GLASGOW
Web: www.weightmans.com
Categories of Work
Adoption
Agriculture, crofting and fishing
Alternative dispute resolution
Alternative investment market
Banking & finance
Charities
Children
Civil court work
Commercial litigation
Commercial property
Competition
Construction
Consumer credit
Contract & property disputes
Copyright, trade marks and design
Corporate tax
Credit brokerage
Data protection
Debt
Debt adjusting and debt counselling
Debt administration
Debt collecting
Debt recovery, insolvency, bankruptcy
Discrimination
Employment
Employment law
Environment
Environment (Business Premises)

▶ **Glasgow continued**

EU / international
Family and divorce
Family business advice
Human rights
Immigration and asylum
Insolvency & corporate recovery
Insurance
IT and intellectual property
Joint venture
Landlord & tenant
Local government
Media and entertainment
Medical negligence – defender
Mergers and acquisitions
Pensions (Company)
Personal injury
Personal injury – defender
Personal tax
Planning (Business Premises)
Power and utilities
Private equity
Professional negligence
Projects
Property litigation
Provision of credit information services
Public finance initiative
Public sector
Road traffic
SME business advice
Sport
Transport
Unit Trusts, OEICs and investment trusts
Partners
Cassandra Louise Auld
Seonaid Buchanan Busby
Noel Francis Ferry
Nicola Kay Gonnella
Claire Louise McCracken
Ingrid De Quiroz McGhee
Pamela Stevenson
Claire Elizabeth Thornber
Andrew Michael Warren
Associates
Joanne Lynsey Farrell
Steven Gerard Harte
Eleanor Zo Strong
Employees
Carolyn Bowie
Rebecca Elizabeth Ellis
Jonathan William Giblin
Ross William McIntyre
Louise Welsh

WEIR LAW LIMITED
12 Fitzroy Place, Glasgow G3 7RW
Tel: (0141) 6285544
E-mail: tim.weir@weirlaw.co.uk
Web: www.weirlaw.co.uk
Categories of Work
Advice the elderly & powers of attorney
Civil court work
Landlord & tenant

Mental health
Residential property
Wills, executries and trusts
Director
Timothy Paul Anthony Weir

WEST ANDERSON & CO.
92 Bath Street, Glasgow G2 2EJ
Tel: (0141) 3326671
Fax: (0141) 3326842
E-mail: law@westanderson.co.uk
Categories of Work
Residential property
Wills, executries and trusts
Partner
Norna Forsyth Crabbe

WEST REGENT LAW
4 Stanley Street, Glasgow G41 1JA
Tel: (07463) 660 578
E-mail: ihussain@lawyer.com
Partner
Mohammed Imran Hussain

WGM LEGAL LIMITED
17 Minard Road, Shawlands, Glasgow
G41 2HR
Tel: (0141) 6166655
Fax: (0141) 6166611
E-mail: mail@wgmlegal.co.uk
Categories of Work
Advice the elderly & powers of attorney
Commercial property
Criminal court work
Criminal legal aid
Landlord & tenant
Personal injury
Residential property
Wills, executries and trusts
Director
Jonathan Green
Consultant
John Thomson

STEWART WHYTE, SOLICITOR
26 Netherpark Avenue, Netherlee, Glasgow
G44 3XW
Tel: (0141) 2803737
E-mail: swhyte@iswlegal.co.uk
Categories of Work
Banking & finance
Charities
Copyright, trade marks and design
Data protection
Family business advice
Insolvency & corporate recovery
IT and intellectual property
Joint venture
Mergers and acquisitions
Private equity
SME business advice
Software licensing
Partner
Iain Stewart Whyte

WIGGLE LEGAL
2 West Regent Street, Glasgow G2 1RW
Tel: (0141) 5669494
Categories of Work
Advice the elderly & powers of attorney
Agriculture and estates
Agriculture, crofting and fishing
Alternative dispute resolution
Alternative investment market
Banking & finance
Benefit advice
Charities
Children
Civil court work
Civil legal aid
Commercial litigation
Commercial property
Competition
Construction
Contract & property disputes
Corporate tax
Criminal court work
Data protection
Debt
Debt adjusting and debt counselling
Debt collecting
Debt recovery, insolvency, bankruptcy
Disability
Discrimination
Employment
Employment law
Environment (Business Premises)
EU / international
Family and divorce
Family business advice
Freedom of information
Health and safety
Human rights
Immigration and asylum
Insolvency & corporate recovery
Insurance
Joint venture
Landlord & tenant
Medical negligence – defender
Medical negligence – claimant
Mental health
Mergers and acquisitions
Pensions (Company)
Personal injury
Personal injury – defender
Planning (Business Premises)
Private equity
Professional negligence
Property litigation
Provision of credit information services
Public finance initiative
Public sector
Residential property
Road traffic
SME business advice
Unit Trusts, OEICs and investment trusts
Wills, executries and trusts

WILSON & FISH SOLICITORS
Queens House, 29 St. Vincent Place, Glasgow
G1 2DT
Tel: (0141) 2227950
Categories of Work
Agriculture and estates
Banking & finance
Commercial litigation
Commercial property
Contract & property disputes
Debt recovery, insolvency, bankruptcy
Family business advice
Landlord & tenant
Property litigation
Residential property
Wills, executries and trusts

WILSON, GREEN & MORRISON
17 Minard Road, Shawlands, Glasgow
G41 2HR
Tel: (0141) 6166655
E-mail: mail@wgmlegal.co.uk
Categories of Work
Advice the elderly & powers of attorney
Commercial property
Criminal court work
Criminal legal aid
Landlord & tenant
Personal injury
Residential property
Wills, executries and trusts

WILSON MCKENDRICK SOLICITORS LIMITED
Queens House, 29 St. Vincent Place, Glasgow
G1 2DT
Tel: (0141) 2227950
E-mail: info@wilsonmckendrick.co.uk
Web: www.wilsonmckendrick.co.uk
Categories of Work
Agriculture and estates
Banking & finance
Commercial litigation
Commercial property
Contract & property disputes
Debt recovery, insolvency, bankruptcy
Family business advice
Landlord & tenant
Property litigation
Residential property
Wills, executries and trusts
Directors
Allan Timothy McKendrick
Mark Jeremy Wilson
Employees
Fiona Elizabeth Bain
Heather Alexandra Fraser
Donna Smith
David Beattie Watson

MEL WISE
3 Larchfield Avenue, Glasgow G77 5PW
Tel: (0141) 6393059
Fax: (0141) 6393059
E-mail: melwise100@hotmail.com

▶ Glasgow continued

Categories of Work
Criminal court work
Criminal legal aid
Partner
Melvyn Wise

WISHARTS LAW LLP
12 Nelson Mandela Place, Glasgow G2 1BT
Tel: (0141) 370 0342
DX: : GW548 GLASGOW
E-mail: frances.wishart@wishartslaw.co.uk
Web: www.wishartslaw.co.uk
Categories of Work
Residential property
Partners
Frances Jane Wishart
Robert Westwood Wishart

WJM DIRECTORS LIMITED
302 St. Vincent Street, Glasgow G2 5RZ
Tel: (0141) 2483434

WJM SECRETARIES LIMITED
302 St. Vincent Street, Glasgow G25RZ
Tel: (0141) 2483434

WJM SHARE NOMINEES LIMITED
302 St Vincent Street, Glasgow G2 5RZ
Tel: (0141) 2483434

WRIGHT & CRAWFORD (1906) LIMITED
110 Drymen Road, Bearsden, Glasgow
G61 3RA
Tel: (0141) 9423764
DX: 556106 BEARSDEN
Categories of Work
Adoption
Advice the elderly & powers of attorney
Alternative dispute resolution
Children
Civil court work
Commercial litigation
Commercial property
Employment law
Family and divorce
Landlord & tenant
Power and utilities
Residential property
Wills, executives and trusts

WRIGHT, JOHNSTON & MACKENZIE LLP
302 St. Vincent Street, Glasgow G2 5RZ
Tel: (0141) 2483434
Fax: (0141) 2211226
DX: GW129 GLASGOW
E-mail: enquiries@wjm.co.uk
Web: www.wjm.co.uk
Categories of Work
Adjudication
Adoption
Advice the elderly & powers of attorney
Agriculture and estates
Agriculture, crofting and fishing
Alternative dispute resolution

Alternative investment market
Banking & finance
Betting & gaming
Charities
Children
Childrens
Civil court work
Commercial litigation
Commercial property
Competition
Construction
Consumer credit
Contract & property disputes
Copyright, trade marks and design
Corporate tax
Criminal court work
Data protection
Debt
Debt collecting
Debt recovery, insolvency, bankruptcy
Disability
Discrimination
Education
Employment
Employment law
Environment
Environment (Business Premises)
EU / international
Family and divorce
Family business advice
Fishing
Freedom of information
Health and safety
Housing
Human rights
Insolvency & corporate recovery
Insurance
IT and intellectual property
Joint venture
Landlord & tenant
Liquor licensing
Local government
Media and entertainment
Medical negligence – defender
Medical negligence – claimant
Mergers and acquisitions
Mining
Oil & gas
Parliamentary
Pensions (Company)
Pensions (Employment)
Personal injury
Personal injury – defender
Personal tax
Planning
Planning (Business Premises)
Power and utilities
Private equity
Professional negligence
Projects
Property litigation
Public finance initiative
Public sector

Residential property
Road traffic
SME business advice
Software licensing
Sport
Telecoms
Transport
Unit Trusts, OEICs and investment trusts
Wills, executries and trusts
Partners
David Graham Bell
Colin John Stewart Brass
Gillian Cowie
Steven John Docherty
Rosina Marie Dolan
Iain Cameron Dunn
Liam Anthony Entwistle
Susan Jane Hoyle
William Grant Johnston
Stewart Alexander King
Ian Macdonald
Roger Lorne Mackenzie
Kathleen McArthur
Andrew Mark McFarlane
Colin John Millar
Graham Neil Murray
Martin Thomas Burnett O'Neill
Joanne Ockrim
Thomas Lloyd Quail
Martin Sutherland Stephen
Associate
John Drummond Grant
Employees
Graham Reid Adams
Kathryn Laura Davenport
Sarajane Drake
Elizabeth Alice Stewart Fleming
Leanne Follan
Stephen Ross Grant
Fiona Anne Kempsell
Emma Louise Letham
Esme Ruth Eilidh Macfarlane
Amy Jane McDougall
Alexander Bruce Mudie
Annie Elizabeth Pearson
Kathleen Docherty Proctor
Syema Raja
Nicola Claire Robertson
Iona Mary Staggs Whyte

TC YOUNG LLP
7 West George Street, Glasgow G2 1BA
Tel: (0141) 2215562
Fax: (0141) 2215024
DX: GW78 GLASGOW
E-mail: mail@tcyoung.co.uk
Web: www.tcyoung.co.uk
Categories of Work
Adjudication
Adoption
Advice the elderly & powers of attorney
Agriculture and estates
Alternative dispute resolution

Banking & finance
Charities
Children
Childrens
Civil court work
Civil legal aid
Commercial litigation
Commercial property
Construction
Consumer credit
Contract & property disputes
Credit brokerage
Criminal court work
Criminal legal aid
Data protection
Debt
Debt adjusting and debt counselling
Debt administration
Debt collecting
Debt recovery, insolvency, bankruptcy
Disability
Discrimination
Education
Employment
Employment law
Environment
Environment (Business Premises)
Family and divorce
Family business advice
Health and safety
Housing
Human rights
Insolvency & corporate recovery
Joint venture
Landlord & tenant
Mental health
Mergers and acquisitions
Pensions (Employment)
Personal tax
Planning
Planning (Business Premises)
Power and utilities
Private equity
Professional negligence
Projects
Property litigation
Public finance initiative
Public sector
Residential property
Road traffic
SME business advice
Social housing
Sport
Wills, executries and trusts
Partners
James Bauld
Alison Brynes
Douglas Collingham
Lynne Collingham
Andrew Stuart Cowan
Isabel Elder Ewing
Mark Espie Ewing
Alison Morag Hempsey

▶ *Glasgow continued*

Lauren Frances Marie Little
Consultant
Leonard Freedman
Associates
Catherine Dawn Henry
Marianne Sarah McJannett
Claire Anne Mullen
Employees
Eileen Elizabeth Barr
Kirstie Donnelly
Lynne Theresa Lind
Ainsley Paula McKinlay
John Norrie
Ross John O'Donnell
Jenna Claire McArthur Taylor
Lindsey Anne Taylor
Evelyn Anne Wallace
Amanda Jane Whillans

YOUNG & PARTNERS BUSINESS LAWYERS LIMITED
126 West Regent Street, Glasgow G2 2RQ
Tel: (0141) 428 3888
Fax: (01383) 722080
Web: www.businesslaw.co.uk
Categories of Work
Agriculture and estates
Alternative dispute resolution
Banking & finance
Charities
Civil court work
Commercial litigation
Commercial property
Construction
Consumer credit
Contract & property disputes
Credit brokerage
Debt adjusting and debt counselling
Debt administration
Debt collecting
Debt recovery, insolvency, bankruptcy
Employment law
Environment
Environment (Business Premises)
Family business advice
Housing
IT and intellectual property
Joint venture
Landlord & tenant
Liquor licensing
Mergers and acquisitions
Planning (Business Premises)
Property litigation
Provision of credit information services
Public sector
Residential property
SME business advice
Director
Ruth Waters

YUILL & KYLE LTD
Capella Building, Tenth Floor, 60 York Street,
Glasgow G2 8JX

Tel: (0141) 3327107
Fax: (0141) 3324223
DX: GW186 GLASGOW
Web: www.debtscotland.com
Categories of Work
Alternative dispute resolution
Civil court work
Commercial litigation
Consumer credit
Debt collecting
Debt recovery, insolvency, bankruptcy
Insolvency & corporate recovery
Directors
Stephen Cowan
Denise Patricia Loney

Glenrothes

BAIRD & COMPANY LAWYERS & ESTATE AGENTS LLP
North House, North Street, Glenrothes
KY7 5NA
Tel: (01592) 759555
Fax: (01592) 610414
DX: 560715 GLENROTHES
Web: www.bairdonline.co.uk
Categories of Work
Advice the elderly & powers of attorney
Agriculture and estates
Commercial property
Contract & property disputes
Employment law
Family and divorce
Family business advice
Joint venture
Landlord & tenant
Liquor licensing
Mergers and acquisitions
Planning (Business Premises)
Power and utilities
Private equity
Projects
Residential property
SME business advice
Wills, executries and trusts
Partners
Carolyn Mary Bean
John Paton McAndrew
Employee
Raymond McGurnaghan

BSW SOLICITORS LLP
5/6 Jubilee House, Pentland Park, Glenrothes
KY6 2AH
Tel: (01592) 725130
Categories of Work
Criminal court work
Criminal legal aid
Employee
Amanda Jane Sneddon

FERGUSON WALKER
5 Hanover Court, Glenrothes KY7 5SB
Tel: (01592) 759600

Fax: (01592) 756464
E-mail: fergusonwalker@btconnect.com
Categories of Work
Adoption
Children
Criminal court work
Criminal legal aid
Education
Family and divorce
Partner
Elizabeth Mary Walker

JOHN W. GILBERTSON LIMITED
16 North Street, Glenrothes KY7 5NA
Tel: (01592) 759557
Fax: (01592) 759416
DX: 560710 Glenrothes
E-mail: jwg@jwgsolicitor.co.uk
Categories of Work
Advice the elderly & powers of attorney
Commercial property
Family and divorce
Landlord & tenant
Residential property
Wills, executries and trusts
Director
Thomas John Gilbertson
Employee
Julia Barnes

GLEESON MCCAFFERTY LAW
28 North Street, Glenrothes KY7 5NA
Tel: (01592) 611660
Fax: (01592) 611810
E-mail: gleesonmccafferty@hotmail.co.uk
Categories of Work
Adoption
Advice the elderly & powers of attorney
Children
Civil court work
Civil legal aid
Criminal court work
Criminal legal aid
Debt
Employment law
Family and divorce
Human rights
Medical negligence – claimant
Mental health
Personal injury
Professional negligence
Road traffic
Wills, executries and trusts
Partners
Steven Thomas Gleeson
Iain David McCafferty
Employee
Danielle Maria Ashton Stringer

INNES JOHNSTON LLP
14 North Street, Glenrothes KY7 5NA
Tel: (01592) 757114
Fax: (01592) 765607
E-mail: glenrothes@innesjohnston.co.uk

Web: www.innesjohnston.co.uk
Categories of Work
Adoption
Advice the elderly & powers of attorney
Agriculture and estates
Agriculture, crofting and fishing
Children
Childrens
Civil court work
Civil legal aid
Commercial property
Criminal court work
Criminal legal aid
Debt
Debt collecting
Education
Family and divorce
Family business advice
Human rights
Immigration and asylum
Landlord & tenant
Liquor licensing
Local government
Mental health
Personal injury
Residential property
SME business advice
Transport
Wills, executries and trusts
Partner
Jemma Lyon Forbes
Employee
Sharron Sutherland

MCKENNAS LAW PRACTICE LIMITED
4 Heritage House, North Street, Glenrothes
KY7 5SE
Tel: (01592) 756449
Fax: (01592) 756460
E-mail: yvonnemckenna@aol.com
Categories of Work
Adoption
Children
Criminal court work
Criminal legal aid
Family and divorce
Mental health
Directors
Graham Ian Inch
Yvonne Mckenna
Employee
Lucy Anne Boylen

ORMISTONS LAW PRACTICE LIMITED
Suite 5, Unit 3, Lomond Business Park,
Glenrothes KY6 2SU
Tel: (0800) 7810413
E-mail: contact@ormistonslaw.co.uk
Web: www.ormistonslaw.co.uk
Categories of Work
Adoption
Advice the elderly & powers of attorney
Children
Civil court work

▶ **Glenrothes** *continued*

Civil legal aid
Criminal court work
Criminal legal aid
Debt
Debt collecting
Debt recovery, insolvency, bankruptcy
Employment
Employment law
Family and divorce
Health and safety
Immigration and asylum
Landlord & tenant
Medical negligence – claimant
Mental health
Personal injury
Personal injury – defender
Property litigation
Road traffic
Social housing
Director
Trevor Andrew Ormiston
Employees
Virvardhan Bansal
Vanessa Patricia Carlsson-Tait
Alison Mary Laing
Robert Christopher Alan Matthews
Sherylanne McGuinness
Kirsten McKenzie
Amy Jennifer Robertson
Kerry Christina Linda Steedman

ROLLOS LAW LLP
North House, North Street, Glenrothes
KY7 5NA
Tel: (01592) 759414
Fax: (01592) 754530
DX: 560709 GLENROTHES
E-mail: glenrothes@rollos.co.uk
Web: www.rollos.co.uk
Categories of Work
Adoption
Advice the elderly & powers of attorney
Agriculture and estates
Agriculture, crofting and fishing
Banking & finance
Children
Civil court work
Civil legal aid
Commercial property
Construction
Contract & property disputes
Criminal court work
Criminal legal aid
Debt
Disability
Discrimination
Employment
Employment law
Environment
Family and divorce
Family business advice
Fishing

Joint venture
Landlord & tenant
Mental health
Mergers and acquisitions
Personal injury
Projects
Residential property
Road traffic
SME business advice
Wills, executries and trusts
Partner
Lindsey Louise Brown
Consultant
Derek Allan Brady
Associate
Iain David Cairns Haywood

Gorebridge

ALLAN MCDOUGALL MCQUEEN LLP
26 Main Street, Gorebridge EH23 4BY
Tel: (01875) 821960
Fax: (01875) 822827
E-mail: info@mcdougallmcqueen.co.uk
Web: www.mcdougallmcqueen.co.uk
Categories of Work
Adoption
Advice the elderly & powers of attorney
Charities
Children
Childrens
Civil court work
Civil legal aid
Commercial litigation
Commercial property
Contract & property disputes
Criminal court work
Criminal legal aid
Disability
Discrimination
Employment
Employment law
Family and divorce
Health and safety
Landlord & tenant
Medical negligence – claimant
Personal injury
Personal injury – defender
Personal tax
Professional negligence
Residential property
Road traffic
Wills, executries and trusts
Employee
Alisha Malik

MCDOUGALL MCQUEEN
26 Main Street, Gorebridge EH23 4BY
Tel: (01875) 821960
E-mail: info@mcdougallmcqueen.co.uk
Web: www.mcdougallmcqueen.co.uk
Categories of Work
Adoption

Advice the elderly & powers of attorney
Charities
Children
Childrens
Civil court work
Civil legal aid
Commercial litigation
Commercial property
Contract & property disputes
Criminal court work
Criminal legal aid
Disability
Discrimination
Employment
Employment law
Family and divorce
Health and safety
Landlord & tenant
Medical negligence – claimant
Personal injury
Personal injury – defender
Personal tax
Professional negligence
Residential property
Road traffic
Wills, executries and trusts

Grangemouth

RGM SOLICITORS LIMITED
9 La Porte Precinct, Grangemouth FK3 8AZ
Tel: (01324) 482197
Fax: (01324) 482098
DX: 560720 GRANGEMOUTH
E-mail: grangemouth@rgmsolicitors.co.uk
Web: www.rgmsolicitors.co.uk
Categories of Work
Advice the elderly & powers of attorney
Commercial property
Wills, executries and trusts
Residential property
Associate
Kimberley Anne Berry
Employee
Kirsty Nona Pllu

TAIT & MACKENZIE LLP
Royal Bank Chambers, 4 La Porte Precinct,
Grangemouth FK3 8AT
Tel: (01324) 471121
Fax: (01324) 484275
DX: 560722 GRANGEMOUTH
E-mail: db@taitandmackenzie.co.uk
Categories of Work
Advice the elderly & powers of attorney
Family and divorce
Residential property
Wills, executries and trusts
Partners
Douglas Alexander Brown
Laura Elizabeth Moore

Grantown-on-Spey

COCKBURNS
21 High Street, Grantown-on-Spey PH26 3EG
Tel: (01479) 872025
E-mail: grantown@cockburns-solicitors.com
Categories of Work
Adoption
Advice the elderly & powers of attorney
Agriculture and estates
Children
Civil court work
Commercial property
Criminal court work
Criminal legal aid
Debt
Debt collecting
Debt recovery, insolvency, bankruptcy
Employment
Employment law
Family and divorce
Landlord & tenant
Medical negligence – claimant
Personal injury
Property litigation
Residential property
Road traffic
Wills, executries and trusts

MASSON CAIRNS LIMITED
Strathspey House, Grantown-on-Spey
PH26 3EQ
Tel: (01479) 874800
Fax: (01479) 874806
E-mail: ka@lawscot.com
Categories of Work
Advice the elderly & powers of attorney
Children
Contract & property disputes
Family and divorce
Family business advice
Fishing
Landlord & tenant
Residential property
Wills, executries and trusts
Director
Katharine Jennifer Anderson

Greenock

BLAIR & BRYDEN
20A Union Street, Greenock PA16 8JL
Tel: (01475) 888777
Fax: (01475) 725840
E-mail: dluke@blair-bryden.co.uk
Web: www.blairbryden.co.uk
Categories of Work
Adoption
Advice the elderly & powers of attorney
Benefit advice
Charities
Children
Civil court work

▶ **Greenock continued**

Civil legal aid
Commercial litigation
Commercial property
Consumer credit
Contract & property disputes
Criminal court work
Criminal legal aid
Debt collecting
Debt recovery, insolvency, bankruptcy
Education
Employment
Employment law
Family and divorce
Family business advice
Housing
Immigration and asylum
Landlord & tenant
Liquor licensing
Medical negligence – claimant
Personal injury
Personal injury – defender
Planning (Business Premises)
Professional negligence
Property litigation
Residential property
Road traffic
Transport
Wills, executives and trusts
Partners
Jill Elizabeth Carrick
Peter James Harvey

BLAIR & BRYDEN
4 Cathcart Square, Greenock PA15 1BS
Tel: (01475) 558420
Fax: (01475) 558425
E-mail: 27@blair-bryden.co.uk
Web: www.blairbryden.co.uk
Categories of Work
Adoption
Advice the elderly & powers of attorney
Benefit advice
Charities
Children
Civil court work
Civil legal aid
Commercial litigation
Commercial property
Consumer credit
Contract & property disputes
Criminal court work
Criminal legal aid
Debt collecting
Debt recovery, insolvency, bankruptcy
Education
Employment
Employment law
Family and divorce
Family business advice
Housing
Immigration and asylum
Landlord & tenant

Liquor licensing
Medical negligence – claimant
Personal injury
Personal injury – defender
Planning (Business Premises)
Professional negligence
Property litigation
Residential property
Road traffic
Transport
Wills, executives and trusts
Partners
Henry Harvey Gray
Duncan William Luke
Associate
Nancy Stevenson Cunningham

BROWN & CO LEGAL LLP
At Legal Services Agency, 9 Sir Michael Street,
Greenock PA15 1PQ
Tel: (01475) 553309
DX: GR3 GREENOCK
Web: www.lsa.org.uk
Categories of Work
Adoption
Advice the elderly & powers of attorney
Alternative dispute resolution
Benefit advice
Charities
Children
Childrens
Civil court work
Civil legal aid
Commercial litigation
Contract & property disputes
Criminal court work
Criminal legal aid
Debt
Debt management
Debt recovery, insolvency, bankruptcy
Disability
Discrimination
Family and divorce
Human rights
Immigration and asylum
Landlord & tenant
Medical negligence – claimant
Mental health
Personal injury
Professional negligence
Property litigation
Social housing
Wills, executives and trusts

BRADLEY CAMPBELL & CO.
8 Brougham Street, Greenock PA16 8AA
Tel: (01475) 726363
Fax: (01475) 724936
DX: GR1 GREENOCK 1
E-mail: fiona.gordon@bradleycampbell.co.uk
Web: www.bradley-campbell.co.uk
Categories of Work
Advice the elderly & powers of attorney
Children

Civil court work
Civil legal aid
Commercial property
Contract & property disputes
Criminal court work
Criminal legal aid
Family and divorce
Landlord & tenant
Medical negligence – defender
Medical negligence – claimant
Personal injury
Personal injury – defender
Professional negligence
Property litigation
Residential property
Road traffic
Wills, executives and trusts
Partners
Susan Alexandra Black
Fiona Mary Gordon
Adrian Edward McGeehan

COOK, STEVENSON & CO.
56 West Blackhall Street, Greenock PA15 1UY
Tel: (01475) 722100
Fax: (01475) 806669
E-mail: cookstevenson@gmail.com
Categories of Work
Adoption
Advice the elderly & powers of attorney
Benefit advice
Children
Childrens
Civil legal aid
Contract & property disputes
Criminal court work
Criminal legal aid
Debt
Discrimination
Education
Employment
Family and divorce
Landlord & tenant
Medical negligence – claimant
Mental health
Personal injury
Professional negligence
Residential property
Road traffic
Social housing
Wills, executives and trusts
Partners
Fiona Elspeth Cook
Claire Stevenson

FYFE & MURRAY
132 Cathcart Street, Greenock PA15 1BQ
Tel: (01475) 721251
Fax: (01475) 721937
DX: GR4 GREENOCK
E-mail: nmacloed@fyfemurray.co.uk
Categories of Work
Advice the elderly & powers of attorney
Agriculture and estates

Agriculture, crofting and fishing
Commercial property
Employment law
Family business advice
Landlord & tenant
Media and entertainment
Residential property
Wills, executives and trusts
Partner
Norman MacLeod

AIDAN GALLAGHER & COMPANY
4 Argyle Street, Greenock PA15 1XA
Tel: (01475) 726677
Fax: (01475) 729922
E-mail: aidan.gallagher1@ntlworld.com
Categories of Work
Criminal court work
Criminal legal aid
Partner
Aidan Vincent Gallagher

KEENAN SOLICITORS
2 Argyle Street, Greenock PA15 1XA
Tel: (01475) 732122
Fax: (01475) 732123
E-mail: enquiries@keenansolicitors.com
Categories of Work
Adoption
Advice the elderly & powers of attorney
Children
Childrens
Civil court work
Civil legal aid
Contract & property disputes
Criminal court work
Criminal legal aid
Debt
Debt collecting
Debt management
Employment
Family and divorce
Medical negligence – claimant
Personal injury
Professional negligence
Road traffic
Social housing
Wills, executives and trusts
Partner
Gerard Keenan
Employees
Caroline Rose Goodenough
Paul Gerard Keenan

MACPHERSON & DISSELDUFF
132 Cathcart Street, Greenock PA15 1BQ
Tel: (01475) 721251
Categories of Work
Advice the elderly & powers of attorney
Agriculture and estates
Agriculture, crofting and fishing
Commercial property
Employment law
Family business advice

▶ **Greenock continued**

Landlord & tenant
Media and entertainment
Residential property
Wills, executories and trusts

MAITLANDS
6A Brougham Street, Greenock PA16 8AA
Tel: (01475) 892131
Fax: (01475) 720713
DX: GR15 GREENOCK
E-mail: mary@maitlands.org.uk
Categories of Work
Advice the elderly & powers of attorney
Commercial property
Employment
Family business advice
Landlord & tenant
Liquor licensing
Personal injury
Residential property
Wills, executories and trusts
Partner
James MacArthur Lamb

NEILL CLERK & MURRAY
3 Ardgowan Square, Greenock PA16 8NW
Tel: (01475) 724522
Fax: (01475) 784339
DX: GR7 GREENOCK
E-mail: info@neillclerkmurray.co.uk
Categories of Work
Adjudication
Adoption
Advice the elderly & powers of attorney
Alternative dispute resolution
Charities
Children
Childrens
Civil court work
Civil legal aid
Commercial litigation
Commercial property
Contract & property disputes
Data protection
Debt
Debt collecting
Debt recovery, insolvency, bankruptcy
Employment law
Family and divorce
Family business advice
Freedom of information
Housing
Landlord & tenant
Mental health
Personal injury
Personal tax
Property litigation
Residential property
Road traffic
Wills, executories and trusts
Partners
David John Armstrong
Nicola Margaret Gillard

Alyson O'May
Pauline Isabella Ward
Employee
Charlene Elizabeth Cunningham Duncan

NEILL CLERK & MURRAY
60 West Blackhall Street, Greenock PA15 1UY
Tel: (01475) 888400
E-mail: info@neillclerkmurray.co.uk
Categories of Work
Adjudication
Adoption
Advice the elderly & powers of attorney
Alternative dispute resolution
Charities
Children
Childrens
Civil court work
Civil legal aid
Commercial litigation
Commercial property
Contract & property disputes
Data protection
Debt
Debt collecting
Debt recovery, insolvency, bankruptcy
Employment law
Family and divorce
Family business advice
Freedom of information
Housing
Landlord & tenant
Mental health
Personal injury
Personal tax
Property litigation
Residential property
Road traffic
Wills, executories and trusts

PATTEN & PRENTICE LLP
2 Ardgowan Square, Greenock PA16 8PP
Tel: (01475) 720306
Fax: (01475) 888127
DX: GR8 GREENOCK
E-mail: mail@patten.co.uk
Web: www.patten.co.uk
Categories of Work
Advice the elderly & powers of attorney
Benefit advice
Children
Civil court work
Civil legal aid
Commercial property
Construction
Consumer credit
Contract & property disputes
Criminal court work
Debt
Debt management
Debt recovery, insolvency, bankruptcy
Employment
Employment law
Family and divorce

Family business advice
Housing
Insolvency & corporate recovery
Landlord & tenant
Liquor licensing
Mergers and acquisitions
Personal injury
Personal injury – defender
Private equity
Property litigation
Public sector
Residential property
Road traffic
Social housing
Unit Trusts, OEICs and investment trusts
Wills, executives and trusts
Partners
Craig Brown
Kenneth Andrew Caldwell
Lynn Elizabeth Rayner
Consultant
William George Mitchell
Associate
Gail Docherty
Employees
Amy McNelis
Melissa Wilson

SWEENEY LAW
Roslin House, 10 Roslin Street, Greenock
PA15 1LG
Tel: (01475) 892125
Fax: (01475) 600373
E-mail: mail@sweeney-law.co.uk
Categories of Work
Criminal court work
Criminal legal aid
Partner
Edward Andrew Sweeney

THE ROBERT KERR PARTNERSHIP LIMITED
6-10 Brymner Street, Greenock PA15 1EA
Tel: (07542) 890000
DX: GR28 GREENOCK
E-mail: info@therobertkerrpartnership.com
Categories of Work
Criminal court work
Criminal legal aid
Discrimination
Human rights
Road traffic
Employee
Francis Eric Clarke

WESTCOURTS LITIGATION LTD
First Floor, 22 Westburn Street, Greenock
PA15 1JR
Tel: (01475) 601999
Fax: (01475) 600367
E-mail: info@westcourts.co.uk
Categories of Work
Adoption
Advice the elderly & powers of attorney
Benefit advice

Children
Civil court work
Civil legal aid
Contract & property disputes
Criminal court work
Criminal legal aid
Disability
Discrimination
Employment
Employment law
Family and divorce
Health and safety
Housing
Landlord & tenant
Medical negligence – claimant
Mental health
Personal injury
Road traffic
Wills, executives and trusts
Directors
Derek Henderson Buchanan
Graeme Wright
Associate
Edel Margaret McGinty

Gullane

LESLEY A. GRAY
Purvesholm, Sandy Loan, Gullane EH31 2BH
Tel: (01620) 843872
Fax: (01620) 842232
E-mail: lesley@lagray.co.uk
Categories of Work
Adjudication
Alternative dispute resolution
Civil court work
Commercial litigation
Oil & gas
Partner
Lesley Anne Gray

Haddington

ANDERSON STRATHERN LLP
14 Court Street, Haddington EH41 3JA
Tel: (01620) 822127
DX: 540736 HADDINGTON
E-mail: info@andersonstrathern.co.uk
Web: www.andersonstrathern.co.uk
Categories of Work
Adjudication
Adoption
Advice the elderly & powers of attorney
Agriculture and estates
Agriculture, crofting and fishing
Alternative dispute resolution
Banking & finance
Betting & gaming
Charities
Children
Childrens
Civil court work

▶ *Haddington continued*

Civil legal aid
Commercial litigation
Commercial property
Competition
Construction
Consumer credit
Contract & property disputes
Copyright, trade marks and design
Corporate tax
Criminal court work
Data protection
Debt
Debt administration
Debt collecting
Debt recovery, insolvency, bankruptcy
Disability
Discrimination
Education
Employment
Employment law
Environment
Environment (Business Premises)
EU / international
Family and divorce
Family business advice
Fishing
Freedom of information
Health
Health and safety
Housing
Human rights
Immigration and asylum
Insolvency & corporate recovery
IT and intellectual property
Joint venture
Landlord & tenant
Liquor licensing
Local government
Media and entertainment
Medical negligence – defender
Medical negligence – claimant
Mental health
Mergers and acquisitions
Mining
Oil & gas
Parliamentary
Pensions (Employment)
Personal injury
Personal injury – defender
Personal tax
Planning
Planning (Business Premises)
Power and utilities
Private equity
Professional negligence
Projects
Property litigation
Public finance initiative
Public sector
Residential property
Road traffic

Shipping
SME business advice
Social housing
Software licensing
Sport
Telecoms
Transport
Wills, executries and trusts

FORSYTH WS LIMITED
46 High Street, Haddington EH41 3EE
Tel: (01620) 824045
Fax: (01620) 825790
DX: 540743 HADDINGTON
E-mail: af@forsythsolicitors.co.uk
Web: www.forsythsolicitors.co.uk
Categories of Work
Adoption
Advice the elderly & powers of attorney
Children
Commercial property
Family and divorce
Residential property
Wills, executries and trusts
Director
Ellen Anne Forsyth
Consultant
Peter Madden Aitken

GARDEN STIRLING BURNET SOLICITORS LIMITED
18 Hardgate, Haddington EH41 3JS
Tel: (01620) 825368
DX: 540733 HADDINGTON
Categories of Work
Adoption
Advice the elderly & powers of attorney
Children
Commercial property
Criminal court work
Criminal legal aid
Education
Employment law
Family and divorce
Family business advice
Joint venture
Landlord & tenant
Liquor licensing
Residential property
Wills, executries and trusts

GARDEN STIRLING BURNET SOLICITORS LIMITED
22 Hardgate, Haddington EH41 3JR
Tel: (01620) 824996
Fax: (01620) 828901
DX: 540733 HADDINGTON
E-mail: haddington@gsbsolicitors.co.uk
Categories of Work
Adoption
Advice the elderly & powers of attorney
Children
Commercial property
Criminal court work

Criminal legal aid
Education
Employment law
Family and divorce
Family business advice
Joint venture
Landlord & tenant
Liquor licensing
Residential property
Wills, executives and trusts
Directors
Alan Ronald Borrowman
Angela Janet Craig
Ian William Philp
Employees
Lauren Buchanan
Callum Samuel Macleod

Hamilton

AUSTIN LAFFERTY LIMITED
84 Quarry Street, Hamilton ML3 7AX
Tel: (01698) 477614
Fax: (01698) 476 613
DX: HA9 HAMILTON
Categories of Work
Adoption
Advice the elderly & powers of attorney
Alternative dispute resolution
Banking & finance
Children
Childrens
Civil court work
Civil legal aid
Commercial property
Consumer credit
Contract & property disputes
Credit brokerage
Criminal court work
Criminal legal aid
Data protection
Debt adjusting and debt counselling
Debt administration
Debt collecting
Education
Family and divorce
Family business advice
Freedom of information
Health and safety
Human rights
Landlord & tenant
Media and entertainment
Medical negligence – claimant
Mergers and acquisitions
Personal injury
Personal tax
Professional negligence
Property litigation
Provision of credit information services
Residential property
Road traffic
SME business advice
Wills, executives and trusts

Associate
Jonathan Edward Cushley

BAKER GOSTELOW LAW
36 Cadzow Street, Hamilton ML3 6DG
Tel: 1698307170
E-mail: info@bgfamilylaw.co.uk
Web: www.bgfamilylaw.co.uk
Categories of Work
Adoption
Advice the elderly & powers of attorney
Alternative dispute resolution
Children
Childrens
Civil court work
Civil legal aid
Discrimination
Education
Family and divorce
Human rights
Landlord & tenant
Property litigation
Residential property
Wills, executives and trusts

BAKER GOSTELOW LAW LIMITED
36 Cadzow Street, Hamilton ML3 6DG
Tel: (01698) 820 700
Fax: (01698) 820 399
DX: 501905 BLANTYRE
E-mail: info@bgfamily.co.uk
Web: www.bgfamilylaw.co.uk
Categories of Work
Adoption
Advice the elderly & powers of attorney
Alternative dispute resolution
Children
Childrens
Civil court work
Civil legal aid
Discrimination
Education
Family and divorce
Human rights
Landlord & tenant
Property litigation
Residential property
Wills, executives and trusts
Director
Paul Gerard Gostelow
Employee
Rachel Helen Farrier

BLACK WOODS LEGAL LIMITED
25 Back O Barns, Hamilton ML3 6BL
Tel: (01483) 379491
Categories of Work
Commercial property
Landlord & tenant
Power and utilities
Projects
Director
Katrina McCabe

▶ **Hamilton continued**

ANDREW BROPHY
59 Skylands Rise, Hamilton ML3 8TS
Tel: (07919) 490999
E-mail: ab@andrewbrophy.co.uk
Categories of Work
Advice the elderly & powers of attorney
Children
Criminal court work
Criminal legal aid
Medical negligence – claimant
Personal injury
Residential property
Road traffic
Wills, executries and trusts
Partner
Andrew Edward Brophy

BROPHY CAREY & CO LTD
Mediacorp House, 2 Caird Park, Hamilton
ML3 0EU
Tel: (01698) 200111
DX: www.brophycareylaw.com
E-mail: info@brophycareylaw.com
Categories of Work
Adoption
Advice the elderly & powers of attorney
Alternative dispute resolution
Children
Childrens
Civil court work
Civil legal aid
Education
Family and divorce
Directors
Anne Brophy
Fiona Janet Carey
Employee
Emma Burns

CAMPBELL SIEVEWRIGHT & CO.
12 Campbell Street, Hamilton ML3 6AS
Tel: (01698) 284994
Fax: (01698) 284242
DX: HA11 HAMILTON
E-mail: ram@campbellsievewright.co.uk
Web: www.campbellsievewrightsolicitors.co.uk
Categories of Work
Commercial property
Residential property
Wills, executries and trusts
Partner
David James Sievewright

CARTYS
3 Cadzow Street, Hamilton ML3 6EE
Tel: (01698) 285432
Fax: (01698) 459208
DX: HA3 HAMILTON
E-mail: hamilton@cartylaw.co.uk
Web: www.cartylaw.co.uk
Categories of Work
Adoption
Advice the elderly & powers of attorney

Agriculture and estates
Benefit advice
Children
Civil court work
Civil legal aid
Commercial property
Consumer credit
Criminal court work
Criminal legal aid
Debt adjusting and debt counselling
Debt administration
Debt collecting
Debt management
Disability
Discrimination
Education
Family and divorce
Freedom of information
Human rights
Landlord & tenant
Mental health
Pensions (Employment)
Personal injury
Residential property
Road traffic
Social housing
Wills, executries and trusts
Partner
James Toner
Consultant
Kenneth Stewart Bonnington
Employees
Jennifer Hunter
Sean Hugh Iles
Sin ad McAleenan
Alexander Jack Morrison

CHARLES FERGUSON SOLICITOR ADVOCATE LIMITED
6 Keith Street, Hamilton ML3 7BL
Tel: (01698) 285885
Fax: (01698) 422 886
Categories of Work
Commercial property
Criminal court work
Criminal legal aid
Director
Jackson Bateman
Employee
Gregor Peter William Jarrott

ROBERT FERGUSON & SONS
7 Gateside Street, Hamilton ML3 7HT
Tel: (01698) 282551
Fax: (01698) 286438
DX: HA5 HAMILTON
E-mail: fiona@robert-ferguson-solicitors.co.uk
Categories of Work
Family and divorce
Personal injury
Residential property
Wills, executries and trusts
Partner
Fiona Margaret Lindsay Bryson

LINDA GEORGE FAMILY LAW LIMITED
Waverley House, Caird Park, Hamilton
ML3 0QA
Tel: (01698) 459200
DX: HA15 HAMILTON
E-mail: info@lgfamilylaw.co.uk
Categories of Work
Adoption
Advice the elderly & powers of attorney
Alternative dispute resolution
Children
Civil court work
Civil legal aid
Criminal court work
Criminal legal aid
Family and divorce
Mental health
Residential property
Wills, executries and trusts
Directors
Linda Elizabeth George
Rachel Elizabeth Rodgers
Consultant
Margaret Carlin

HAY CASSELS LTD
Almada Chambers, 95 Almada Street,
Hamilton ML3 0EY
Tel: (01698) 284844
Fax: (01698) 891146
E-mail: pbrown@haycassels.com
Categories of Work
Civil court work
Civil legal aid
Commercial litigation
Commercial property
Contract & property disputes
Debt
Debt collecting
Debt recovery, insolvency, bankruptcy
Disability
Discrimination
Employment
Employment law
Family business advice
Health and safety
Joint venture
Landlord & tenant
Mental health
Personal injury
Property litigation
Residential property
SME business advice
Wills, executries and trusts
Directors
Paul Daniel Brown
Raymond Leslie Brown

JOHN JACKSON & DICK LIMITED
48-50 Cadzow Street, Hamilton ML3 6DT
Tel: (01698) 281747
Fax: (01698) 891419
DX: HA18 HAMILTON
E-mail: mail@jacksondicklaw.com

Web: www.jacksondicklaw.com
Categories of Work
Advice the elderly & powers of attorney
Banking & finance
Civil court work
Civil legal aid
Commercial litigation
Commercial property
Contract & property disputes
Debt recovery, insolvency, bankruptcy
Employment
Employment law
Environment (Business Premises)
Family business advice
Housing
Insurance
IT and intellectual property
Joint venture
Landlord & tenant
Liquor licensing
Local government
Mergers and acquisitions
Parliamentary
Personal injury
Planning
Planning (Business Premises)
Power and utilities
Projects
Property litigation
Public finance initiative
Public sector
Residential property
Road traffic
SME business advice
Social housing
Software licensing
Wills, executries and trusts
Directors
Pauline Claire Milligan
Euan Campbell Stirrat
Associates
Jonathan Findlay
John Connell Gildea
Employee
Paula Agnes McCrum

LEONARDS SOLICITORS LIMITED
133 Cadzow Street, Hamilton ML3 6JG
Tel: (01698) 457313
Fax: (01698) 423683
E-mail: info@leonardslaw.com
Categories of Work
Adoption
Children
Childrens
Civil court work
Civil legal aid
Family and divorce
Directors
David Robert Lingard
Lorna Ann Turner

MCMULLEN LAW LIMITED
29 Campbell Street, Hamilton ML3 6AS

▶ *Hamilton continued*

Tel: (01698) 686110
E-mail: am@mcmullenlaw.co.uk
Categories of Work
Adoption
Advice the elderly & powers of attorney
Children
Childrens
Civil court work
Civil legal aid
Education
Family and divorce
Wills, executries and trusts
Director
Anji Frances McMullen

MCQUILLAN GLASSER & WAUGHMAN

53 Quarry Street, Hamilton ML3 7AH
Tel: (01698) 200006
Fax: (01698) 200159
E-mail: office_mcquillan@yahoo.co.uk
Categories of Work
Adoption
Benefit advice
Children
Civil court work
Civil legal aid
Consumer credit
Criminal court work
Criminal legal aid
Debt
Debt adjusting and debt counselling
Debt administration
Debt collecting
Debt management
Debt recovery, insolvency, bankruptcy
Employment
Employment law
Family and divorce
Housing
Immigration and asylum
Insurance
Mental health
Personal injury
Road traffic
Social housing
Partner
Stephen Gerard McQuillan
Employee
Mary Anne McGranaghan

D.A. MILLIGAN & CO.

104 Quarry Street, Hamilton ML3 7AX
Tel: (01698) 457733
Fax: (01698) 457733
DX: HA61 HAMILTON
E-mail: damilliganandco@gmail.com
Categories of Work
Criminal court work
Criminal legal aid
Residential property
Wills, executries and trusts
Partner
Duncan Alexander Milligan

NGL (SCOTLAND) LIMITED

62 Burnbank Road, Hamilton ML3 9AQ
Tel: (01698) 207050
Fax: (01698) 283979
E-mail: Karen.Miller@ngllawyers.com
Web: www.ngllaw.net
Categories of Work
Adoption
Alternative investment market
Children
Civil court work
Commercial litigation
Commercial property
Contract & property disputes
Criminal court work
Criminal legal aid
Debt
Debt recovery, insolvency, bankruptcy
Employment
Family and divorce
Health and safety
Housing
Insolvency & corporate recovery
Landlord & tenant
Medical negligence – claimant
Personal injury
Personal injury – defender
Property litigation
Public sector
Residential property
Road traffic
SME business advice
Wills, executries and trusts
Partner
Karen Miller

REID SOLICITORS

194 Quarry Street, Hamilton ML3 6QR
Tel: (07394) 150383
Categories of Work
Adoption
Advice the elderly & powers of attorney
Charities
Children
Civil court work
Civil legal aid
Education
Family and divorce
Medical negligence – defender
Medical negligence – claimant
Personal injury
Personal injury – defender
Professional negligence
Wills, executries and trusts
Partner
Andrew James Reid

JOHN Y. ROBERTSON

28 Gateside Street, Hamilton ML3 7JG
Tel: (01698) 282900
Fax: (01698) 283740
E-mail: patricia@jyrlaw.co.uk
Categories of Work
Advice the elderly & powers of attorney

Civil court work
Civil legal aid
Commercial litigation
Commercial property
Contract & property disputes
Criminal court work
Criminal legal aid
Debt
Debt recovery, insolvency, bankruptcy
Discrimination
Employment law
Family and divorce
Family business advice
Landlord & tenant
Medical negligence – claimant
Personal injury
Professional negligence
Residential property
Road traffic
Wills, executries and trusts
Partners
Patricia O'Neill Henderson
John Sinclair Macleod Macdonald

R R LAW
30 Nevis Avenue, Hamilton ML3 8UA
Tel: (01698) 322475
Fax: (01698) 322475
Categories of Work
Criminal court work
Criminal legal aid
Partner
Rosemary Ann Robinson

SCULLION LAW LIMITED
105 Cadzow Street, Hamilton ML3 6HG
Tel: (01698) 283265
Fax: (01698) 284 098
E-mail: info@scullionlaw.com
Web: www.scullionlaw.com
Categories of Work
Adoption
Advice the elderly & powers of attorney
Alternative dispute resolution
Children
Civil court work
Commercial property
Contract & property disputes
Criminal court work
Criminal legal aid
Data protection
Employment
Employment law
Family and divorce
Family business advice
Health and safety
Human rights
Landlord & tenant
Liquor licensing
Pensions (Employment)
Property litigation
Residential property
Road traffic
Wills, executries and trusts

Directors
Nicholas James Martin Russell Scullion
Nicholas Jonathan Scullion
Associates
Judith May Higson
Anna Ruth MacKay
Employees
Kristopher Ross Buchanan
Nicola Jean Buchanan
Urfan Hameed Dar
Nicholas John Harbison
Judith Hutchison
Farrah Mahmood
Paolo Martone
Lucy McKenna
Hope Ellen Raleigh
Emma Elizabeth Wright

STIRLING DUNLOP
36 Cadzow Street, Hamilton ML3 6DG
Tel: (01698) 820700
DX: : HA69 HAMILTON
Web: www.bgfamilylaw.co.uk
Categories of Work
Adoption
Advice the elderly & powers of attorney
Alternative dispute resolution
Children
Childrens
Civil court work
Civil legal aid
Discrimination
Education
Family and divorce
Human rights
Landlord & tenant
Property litigation
Residential property
Wills, executries and trusts

STODARTS LLP
Almada Chambers, 95 Almada Street,
Hamilton ML3 0EY
Tel: (01698) 200302
Fax: (01698) 891144
E-mail: mail@stodarts.co.uk
Web: www.stodarts.co.uk
Categories of Work
Advice the elderly & powers of attorney
Agriculture and estates
Children
Civil court work
Civil legal aid
Commercial property
Family and divorce
Family business advice
Landlord & tenant
Mental health
Residential property
Wills, executries and trusts
Partners
Alan Robert Bayley
Ruth Margaret McCall

► **Hamilton** continued

Associate
Joanne Louise Hogg
Employees
Abrarr Haq
Lyndsey Murphy

STREFFORD TULIPS LIMITED
Muirbrow Chambers, 118 Cadzow Street,
Hamilton ML3 6HP
Tel: (01698) 429428
Fax: (01698) 303020
E-mail: enquiries@strefford-tulips.co.uk
Web: www.strefford-tulips.co.uk
Categories of Work
Commercial property
Construction
Criminal court work
Criminal legal aid
Landlord & tenant
Residential property
Wills, executives and trusts
Directors
Geraldine Darroch
Lynne McDade
Lynn Pacitti
Consultants
Louise Johnstone
David Samuel Strefford
William Christopher Tulips
Associates
Lynsey Marion Anne Shearer
Sharlene Marie Wardrope
Employees
Hannah Louise Blaney
Khloe Joanne Boswell

TCH LAW
29 Brandon Street, Hamilton ML3 6DA
Tel: (01698) 312080
Fax: (01698) 312089
E-mail: tch@tchlaw.co.uk
Web: www.tchlaw.co.uk
Categories of Work
Alternative dispute resolution
Civil court work
Commercial litigation
Consumer credit
Contract & property disputes
Credit brokerage
Debt
Debt adjusting and debt counselling
Debt administration
Debt collecting
Debt recovery, insolvency, bankruptcy
Insolvency & corporate recovery
Landlord & tenant
Media and entertainment
Personal tax
Professional negligence
Property litigation
Provision of credit information services
SME business advice

Partner
Tracey Margaret Campbell-Hynd
Employee
Shabeilla Saddiq

J. WATSON SCOTT & CO LTD
Unit 3, McAdam House, Hamilton ML3 6AS
Tel: (01698) 282370
Fax: (01698) 423209
E-mail: mail@watsonscott.co.uk
Categories of Work
Advice the elderly & powers of attorney
Civil court work
Civil legal aid
Commercial property
Debt
Family and divorce
Family business advice
Landlord & tenant
Mental health
Personal injury
Residential property
Wills, executives and trusts
Director
Alison Jane Harvie

Hawick

ANDREW HADDON & CROWE
3 Oliver Place, Hawick TD9 9BG
Tel: (01450) 372738
Fax: (01450) 372786
E-mail: info@ahcsolicitors.co.uk
Categories of Work
Adoption
Advice the elderly & powers of attorney
Children
Childrens
Civil court work
Civil legal aid
Commercial litigation
Debt recovery, insolvency, bankruptcy
Education
Employment law
Family and divorce
Landlord & tenant
Personal injury
Property litigation
Residential property
Partners
Keith Robert Murray
Charles Christopher Hugh Rickett

BANNERMAN BURKE LAW
28 High Street, Hawick TD9 9BY
Tel: (01450) 372750
Fax: (01450) 378 525
DX: 580741 HAWICK
E-mail: hawick@bannermanburke.co.uk
Web: www.bannermanburke.co.uk
Categories of Work
Adoption
Advice the elderly & powers of attorney
Children

Civil court work
Civil legal aid
Commercial property
Contract & property disputes
Criminal court work
Criminal legal aid
Debt management
Debt recovery, insolvency, bankruptcy
Discrimination
Employment
Employment law
Family and divorce
Family business advice
Human rights
Liquor licensing
Local government
Mental health
Personal injury
Residential property
Road traffic
SME business advice
Wills, executries and trusts
Partners
Roderick William Alastair Bannerman
Heidi Marta Kandyba-Callis
Employee
Steven Grant Robertson

CULLEN KILSHAW
31-35 High Street, Hawick TD9 9BU
Tel: (01450) 372336
DX: 580742 HAWICK
E-mail: hawick@cullenkilshaw.com
Web: www.cullenkilshaw.com
Categories of Work
Adoption
Advice the elderly & powers of attorney
Agriculture and estates
Agriculture, crofting and fishing
Alternative dispute resolution
Children
Childrens
Civil court work
Civil legal aid
Commercial property
Contract & property disputes
Criminal court work
Criminal legal aid
Debt
Debt collecting
Debt recovery, insolvency, bankruptcy
Employment
Employment law
Environment (Business Premises)
Family and divorce
Family business advice
Fishing
Landlord & tenant
Liquor licensing
Local government
Personal injury
Planning (Business Premises)
Property litigation

Residential property
Road traffic
Wills, executries and trusts
Employee
Marinos Thomas Gladstone Calothis

GEO & JAS OLIVER WS LIMITED
13 High Street, Hawick TD9 9DH
Tel: (01450) 372791
Fax: (01450) 377654
E-mail: solicitors@gandjoliver.co.uk
Web: www.gandjoliver.co.uk
Categories of Work
Adoption
Advice the elderly & powers of attorney
Agriculture and estates
Agriculture, crofting and fishing
Betting & gaming
Children
Commercial property
Contract & property disputes
Criminal court work
Employment
Family and divorce
Health and safety
Housing
Landlord & tenant
Liquor licensing
Mental health
Personal injury
Personal injury – defender
Residential property
Road traffic
Wills, executries and trusts
Directors
Henry John Oliver
John Anthony Lindsay Oliver

Helensburgh

BRUNTON MILLER
20 Colquhoun Street, Helensburgh G84 8AJ
Tel: (01436) 675454
Fax: (01436) 678434
E-mail: info@bruntonmiller.com
Categories of Work
Advice the elderly & powers of attorney
Banking & finance
Betting & gaming
Children
Civil court work
Civil legal aid
Commercial litigation
Commercial property
Construction
Consumer credit
Contract & property disputes
Copyright, trade marks and design
Credit brokerage
Criminal court work
Criminal legal aid
Debt
Debt adjusting and debt counselling

► **Helensburgh continued**

Debt administration
Debt collecting
Debt recovery, insolvency, bankruptcy
Employment
Employment law
Family and divorce
Family business advice
Joint venture
Landlord & tenant
Liquor licensing
Local government
Mergers and acquisitions
Personal injury
Planning (Business Premises)
Provision of credit information services
Residential property
Road traffic
Wills, executries and trusts
Employee
Suzanne Gillian Falconer

MCARTHUR STANTON
15/17 Colquhoun Street, Helensburgh
G84 8AN
Tel: (01436) 678822
Categories of Work
Adoption
Advice the elderly & powers of attorney
Agriculture and estates
Children
Civil court work
Civil legal aid
Commercial property
Criminal court work
Criminal legal aid
Debt collecting
Employment law
Family and divorce
Landlord & tenant
Liquor licensing
Medical negligence – claimant
Personal injury
Personal injury – defender
Power and utilities
Residential property
Road traffic
Telecoms
Wills, executries and trusts

MCARTHUR STANTON
22-24 Colquhoun Square, Helensburgh
G84 8AG
Tel: (01436) 672212
Fax: (01436) 674411
DX: 500752 HELENSBURGH
E-mail: helensburgh@mcarthurstanton.co.uk
Web: www.mcarthurstanton.co.uk.
Categories of Work
Adoption
Advice the elderly & powers of attorney
Agriculture and estates
Children

Civil court work
Civil legal aid
Commercial property
Criminal court work
Criminal legal aid
Debt collecting
Employment law
Family and divorce
Landlord & tenant
Liquor licensing
Medical negligence – claimant
Personal injury
Personal injury – defender
Power and utilities
Residential property
Road traffic
Telecoms
Wills, executries and trusts
Partners
Nicola Bonthrone
Jonathan Charles Alexander Clinch
Employee
Linda McFarlane

BTO RAEBURN HOPE
77 Sinclair Street, Helensburgh G84 8TG
Tel: (01436) 671221
Fax: (01436) 675888
Web: www.btorh.co.uk
Categories of Work
Adjudication
Adoption
Advice the elderly & powers of attorney
Agriculture and estates
Agriculture, crofting and fishing
Alternative dispute resolution
Alternative investment market
Banking & finance
Benefit advice
Charities
Children
Childrens
Civil court work
Civil legal aid
Commercial litigation
Commercial property
Competition
Construction
Consumer credit
Contract & property disputes
Copyright, trade marks and design
Corporate tax
Criminal court work
Data protection
Debt
Debt collecting
Debt recovery, insolvency, bankruptcy
Disability
Discrimination
Employment
Employment law
Environment
Environment (Business Premises)

EU / international
Family and divorce
Family business advice
Freedom of information
Health
Health and safety
Housing
Insolvency & corporate recovery
Insurance
IT and intellectual property
Joint venture
Landlord & tenant
Liquor licensing
Media and entertainment
Medical negligence – defender
Medical negligence – claimant
Mental health
Mergers and acquisitions
Oil & gas
Pensions (Company)
Pensions (Employment)
Personal injury
Personal injury – defender
Personal tax
Planning
Planning (Business Premises)
Power and utilities
Private equity
Professional negligence
Projects
Property litigation
Provision of credit information services
Public finance initiative
Public sector
Residential property
Road traffic
Shipping
SME business advice
Social housing
Software licensing
Sport
Transport
Unit Trusts, OEICs and investment trusts
Wills, executries and trusts
Partners
Alastair John Douglas Hope
Kirstine Rose MacRae
Associate
Jennifer Deegan
Employees
Donna-Marie Brennan
Gillian Suzanne McClearn

STIRLING & GILMOUR LLP
13 West Princes Street, Helensburgh G84 8TF
Tel: (01436) 678185
Fax: (01436) 671539
DX: 500753 HELENSBURGH
E-mail: helensburgh@stirlingandgilmour.co.uk
Categories of Work
Adoption
Advice the elderly & powers of attorney
Agriculture and estates

Agriculture, crofting and fishing
Alternative dispute resolution
Charities
Children
Civil court work
Civil legal aid
Commercial litigation
Commercial property
Consumer credit
Contract & property disputes
Copyright, trade marks and design
Criminal court work
Criminal legal aid
Debt
Debt collecting
Debt recovery, insolvency, bankruptcy
Discrimination
Employment law
Family and divorce
Family business advice
Landlord & tenant
Liquor licensing
Personal injury
Personal tax
Planning (Business Premises)
Property litigation
Residential property
Road traffic
Wills, executries and trusts
Partner
William Kirkwood Loudon Brownlie
Consultant
Graham MacLellan Philips

Heriot

ANDREW T. GILBERTSON
4 Heriot House, Heriot EH38 5YB
Tel: (0131) 660 9888
Categories of Work
Criminal court work
Criminal legal aid

High Blantyre

CAREY HUGHES LIMITED
1J1, International House, Stanley Boulevard,
High Blantyre G72 0BN
Tel: (01698) 404616
Fax: (01280) 734407
E-mail: info@careyhughes.co.uk
Categories of Work
Advice the elderly & powers of attorney
Children
Civil court work
Commercial property
Family and divorce
Landlord & tenant
Liquor licensing
Residential property
Wills, executries and trusts

▶ **High Blantyre continued**

Assistant
Claire Stevenson
Directors
Martin John Carey
Patrick Eamonn Devanney
Emma Allyson Hughes
Employees
Sean Fraser
Sally Georgina Hooker
Natalie Margaret Taylor

Huntly

MURDOCH, MCMATH & MITCHELL
27/29 Duke Street, Huntly AB54 8DL
Tel: (01466) 792291
Fax: (01466) 794280
DX: 520760 HUNTLY
E-mail: christieg@btconnect.com
Categories of Work
Agriculture and estates
Agriculture, crofting and fishing
Betting & gaming
Commercial property
Employment
Family and divorce
Housing
Liquor licensing
Personal tax
Residential property
Wills, executries and trusts
Partners
Gordon John Christie
John Alexander Christie
Associate
Diane Margaret Morrison Christie
Employees
Fergus James Dow
Kirsty Marie Dunning

PETERKINS
3 The Square, Huntly AB54 8AE
Tel: (01466) 792101
Fax: (01466) 792241
Web: www.peterkins.com
Categories of Work
Advice the elderly & powers of attorney
Agriculture and estates
Agriculture, crofting and fishing
Banking & finance
Charities
Commercial property
Construction
Criminal court work
Criminal legal aid
Debt recovery, insolvency, bankruptcy
Environment (Business Premises)
Family business advice
Housing
Insolvency & corporate recovery
Landlord & tenant
Liquor licensing

Local government
Pensions (Company)
Planning
Planning (Business Premises)
Power and utilities
Residential property
SME business advice
Wills, executries and trusts
Partner
Jamie Charles Melville Craig

STEWART & WATSON
17-19 Duke Street, Huntly AB54 8DL
Tel: (01466) 792331
Fax: (01466) 794399
E-mail: info@stewartwatson.co.uk
Web: www.stewartwatson.co.uk
Categories of Work
Adoption
Advice the elderly & powers of attorney
Agriculture and estates
Agriculture, crofting and fishing
Alternative dispute resolution
Charities
Children
Civil court work
Civil legal aid
Commercial property
Contract & property disputes
Criminal court work
Criminal legal aid
Debt
Debt collecting
Debt recovery, insolvency, bankruptcy
Employment
Environment
Environment (Business Premises)
Family and divorce
Housing
Immigration and asylum
Landlord & tenant
Mental health
Personal injury
Projects
Residential property
Road traffic
Wills, executries and trusts
Partner
Michael Charles Daley

STUART TRUSTEES LIMITED
Huntly Business Centre, Gordon Street, Huntly
AB54 8FG
Tel: (01466) 792101

Innerleithen

LEYSHON WS
5 Glenormiston Steading, Glenormiston,
Innerleithen EH44 6RL
Tel: 01573-408651
Categories of Work
Agriculture and estates
Agriculture, crofting and fishing

Commercial property
Environment (Business Premises)
Family business advice
Landlord & tenant
Personal tax
Planning (Business Premises)
Power and utilities
Residential property
Wills, executries and trusts
Partner
Donald John Leyshon

Inverkeithing

WILSONS SOLICITORS
37 High Street, Inverkeithing KY11 1NT
Tel: (01383) 411533
Fax: (01383) 420005
E-mail: admin@tlwilson.co.uk
Web: www.tlwilson.co.uk
Categories of Work
Adoption
Advice the elderly & powers of attorney
Children
Civil court work
Civil legal aid
Contract & property disputes
Debt
Debt recovery, insolvency, bankruptcy
Family and divorce
Landlord & tenant
Medical negligence – defender
Medical negligence – claimant
Personal injury
Personal injury – defender
Professional negligence
Property litigation
Residential property
Road traffic
Wills, executries and trusts
Partner
Tracy Lynn Wilson

Inverness

ALEX. BROWN & CO.
Kintail House, Beechwood Business Park,
Inverness IV2 3BW
Tel: (01463) 243450
Fax: (01463) 243091
Categories of Work
Criminal court work
Criminal legal aid
Partner
William Buchanan Young

ANDERSON SHAW & GILBERT LIMITED
York House, 20 Church Street, Inverness
IV1 1ED
Tel: (01463) 236123
Fax: (01463) 711083
DX: IN6 INVERNESS
E-mail: email@solicitorsinverness.com

Web: www.propertyinverness.com
Categories of Work
Adoption
Advice the elderly & powers of attorney
Agriculture and estates
Agriculture, crofting and fishing
Alternative dispute resolution
Charities
Children
Childrens
Civil court work
Civil legal aid
Commercial property
Contract & property disputes
Debt
Education
Family and divorce
Family business advice
Landlord & tenant
Liquor licensing
Planning (Business Premises)
Public sector
Residential property
SME business advice
Wills, executries and trusts
Directors
Robert Findlay Boyd
Joseph Malcolm Leslie Duncan
Ewen Joseph Macdonald
Iain McDonald
Elizabeth Brown Thomson
Associate
Gary Munro
Employees
Sarah Helen Mary Cumming
Rachel McGillivray
Avril Gillian Spence Meighan
Daniel Gordon Stephen
Irene Walker

CHAPMAN SOLICITORS
P.O. Box 5787, Inverness IV1 9FA
Tel: (01463) 240477
E-mail: enquiries@chapmansolicitors.com
Categories of Work
Criminal court work
Criminal legal aid
Partner
Pauline Chapman
Employee
Michael Chapman

DIGBY BROWN LLP
Moray House, 16 – 18 Bank Street, Inverness
IV1 1QY
Tel: (0333) 200 5925
DX: IN7 INVERNESS
E-mail: enquiries@digbybrown.co.uk
Web: www.digbybrown.co.uk
Categories of Work
Advice the elderly & powers of attorney
Agriculture and estates
Agriculture, crofting and fishing
Alternative dispute resolution

► *Inverness continued*

Alternative investment market
Banking & finance
Benefit advice
Charities
Children
Civil court work
Civil legal aid
Commercial litigation
Commercial property
Competition
Construction
Contract & property disputes
Corporate tax
Criminal court work
Data protection
Debt
Debt adjusting and debt counselling
Debt collecting
Debt recovery, insolvency, bankruptcy
Disability
Discrimination
Employment
Employment law
Environment (Business Premises)
EU / international
Family and divorce
Family business advice
Freedom of information
Health and safety
Human rights
Immigration and asylum
Insolvency & corporate recovery
Insurance
Joint venture
Landlord & tenant
Medical negligence – defender
Medical negligence – claimant
Mental health
Mergers and acquisitions
Pensions (Company)
Personal injury
Personal injury – defender
Planning (Business Premises)
Private equity
Professional negligence
Property litigation
Provision of credit information services
Public finance initiative
Public sector
Residential property
Road traffic
SME business advice
Unit Trusts, OEICs and investment trusts
Wills, executries and trusts
Associate
Sam Rennie Cowie
Employees
Joanna Mary Corrance
Sarah Ellen Newman
Ewen Charles Reid

FERGUSON AND WILSON
Market Arcade, 24 Union Street, Inverness
IV1 1PL
Tel: (01463) 222221
E-mail: enquiries@fergusonandwilson.co.uk
Categories of Work
Criminal court work
Criminal legal aid
Partners
Kenneth Francis Ferguson
Neil Munro Wilson

FLEETWOOD & ROBB
11 Queensgate, Inverness IV1 1DF
Tel: (01463) 226232
Fax: (01463) 713447
DX: IV27 INVERNESS
E-mail: John@fleetwoodandrobb.co.uk
Categories of Work
Advice the elderly & powers of attorney
Contract & property disputes
Landlord & tenant
Residential property
Wills, executries and trusts
Partners
Michael Alec Charters
John Andrew Robb

A FRASER SOLICITORS LTD
106 Church Street, Inverness IV1 1EP
Tel: (01463) 229917
Fax: (01463) 243111
E-mail: info@afrasersolicitors.com
Categories of Work
Agriculture, crofting and fishing
Commercial property
Immigration and asylum
Landlord & tenant
Residential property
Wills, executries and trusts
Director
Alasdair Fraser
Employee
Chloe Sarah Binnie

**JACK GOWANS & MARC DICKSON
SOLICITORS LIMITED**
46 Church Street, Inverness IV1 1EH
Tel: (01463) 710677
Fax: (01463) 729251
E-mail: enquiries@gowansdickson.com
Categories of Work
Adoption
Children
Criminal court work
Criminal legal aid
Family and divorce
Directors
Marc Campbell Dickson
Joyce Denise Simpson
Employee
Cecily Clare Kingston

GREY & CO SOLICITORS LTD
46 Church Street, 1st Floor, Inverness IV1 1EH

Tel: (01463) 239011
Fax: (01463) 239055
DX: IN14 INVERNESS
E-mail: andrew@greyandcosolicitors.co.uk
Web: www.greyandcosolicitors.co.uk
Categories of Work
Children
Civil legal aid
Commercial litigation
Contract & property disputes
Debt recovery, insolvency, bankruptcy
Discrimination
Employment
Family and divorce
Housing
Medical negligence – defender
Medical negligence – claimant
Personal injury
Wills, executries and trusts
Director
Andrew Neil Grey

HARPER MACLEOD LLP

Alder House, Cradlehall Business Park,
Inverness IV2 5GH
Tel: (01463) 798777
Fax: (01463) 798787
DX: 521005 INVERNESS 3
E-mail: info@harpermacleod.co.uk
Web: www.harpermacleod.co.uk
Categories of Work
Adjudication
Adoption
Advice the elderly & powers of attorney
Agriculture and estates
Agriculture, crofting and fishing
Alternative dispute resolution
Alternative investment market
Banking & finance
Betting & gaming
Charities
Children
Childrens
Civil court work
Civil legal aid
Commercial litigation
Commercial property
Competition
Construction
Consumer credit
Contract & property disputes
Copyright, trade marks and design
Corporate tax
Criminal court work
Criminal legal aid
Data protection
Debt
Debt administration
Debt collecting
Debt recovery, insolvency, bankruptcy
Disability
Discrimination
Education
Employment
Employment law
Environment
Environment (Business Premises)
EU / international
Family and divorce
Family business advice
Fishing
Freedom of information
Health
Health and safety
Housing
Human rights
Immigration and asylum
Insolvency & corporate recovery
Insurance
IT and intellectual property
Joint venture
Landlord & tenant
Liquor licensing
Local government
Media and entertainment
Medical negligence – defender
Medical negligence – claimant
Mental health
Mergers and acquisitions
Mining
Oil & gas
Parliamentary
Pensions (Company)
Pensions (Employment)
Personal injury
Personal injury – defender
Personal tax
Planning
Planning (Business Premises)
Power and utilities
Private equity
Professional negligence
Projects
Property litigation
Public finance initiative
Public sector
Residential property
Road traffic
Shipping
SME business advice
Social housing
Software licensing
Sport
Telecoms
Transport
Unit Trusts, OEICs and investment trusts
Wills, executries and trusts
Partners
Gary Angus Campbell
Julie Doncaster
Jill Elizabeth Fryer
Calum Martin MacLeod
Fiona Elizabeth Neilson
Ross Gordon Thomson

▶ *Inverness continued*

Associates
Kenneth Campbell
Andrew John Kerr
Laura McLean
Ewan Stafford
Employees
Gilbert Angus Brown
Natalie Dawn Bruce
Grant Simon Hassan
Nicole Killman
Leanne Maitland
Marc Robert Penman
Andrea Laureen Ross

INKSTERS
Ness Horizons Business Centre, Kintail House,
Inverness IV2 3BW
Tel: (01463) 210333
Fax: (01463) 210353
E-mail: inverness@inksters.com
Web: www.inksters.com
Categories of Work
Advice the elderly & powers of attorney
Agriculture and estates
Agriculture, crofting and fishing
Alternative dispute resolution
Children
Childrens
Civil court work
Civil legal aid
Commercial property
Consumer credit
Contract & property disputes
Criminal court work
Criminal legal aid
Data protection
Debt
Debt collecting
Debt recovery, insolvency, bankruptcy
Family and divorce
Family business advice
Landlord & tenant
Personal tax
Projects
Property litigation
Residential property
Road traffic
Wills, executries and trusts
Employee
Sarah Rosalie Windsor

INNES & MACKAY LIMITED
Kintail House, Beechwood Business Park,
Inverness IV2 3BW
Tel: (01463) 232273
Fax: (01463) 243091
DX: 521008 INVERNESS 3
E-mail: info@innesmackay.com
Web: www.innesmackay.com
Categories of Work
Children
Civil court work

Family and divorce
Mental health
Personal injury
Directors
Laura Cormack
Ewan Donald
Jane Elizabeth Young
Employees
Andrew Paterson Henderson
Yve Dayna Robertson

INVERNESS LAW
Suite 1, Ground Floor East, Lyle House,
Fairways Business Park, Inverness IV2 6AA
Tel: (01463) 832818
Fax: (01463) 232889
E-mail: info@invernesslaw.co.uk
Categories of Work
Adoption
Advice the elderly & powers of attorney
Agriculture and estates
Children
Civil court work
Civil legal aid
Commercial litigation
Commercial property
Debt
Debt adjusting and debt counselling
Debt collecting
Debt recovery, insolvency, bankruptcy
Employment law
Family and divorce
Family business advice
Landlord & tenant
Mental health
Residential property
Wills, executries and trusts
Partners
Moray Macdonald
David Simpson
Consultant
James Hymers Sutherland Stewart

INVERNESS LEGAL SERVICES
33 Bellfield Park, Inverness IV2 4TA
Tel: (01463) 229981
Fax: (01463) 229 981
E-mail: inverness.legal@tiscali.co.uk
Web: www.inverness-legal.co.uk
Categories of Work
Criminal court work
Criminal legal aid
Partner
James Bryce Duncan Henderson

LEDINGHAM CHALMERS LLP
Kintail House, Beechwood Business Park,
Inverness IV2 3BW
Tel: (01463) 667400
Fax: (01463) 713755
E-mail: mail@ledinghamchalmers.com
Web: www.ledinghamchalmers.com
Categories of Work
Adjudication

Adoption
Advice the elderly & powers of attorney
Agriculture and estates
Agriculture, crofting and fishing
Alternative dispute resolution
Alternative investment market
Banking & finance
Charities
Children
Childrens
Civil court work
Civil legal aid
Commercial litigation
Commercial property
Competition
Construction
Consumer credit
Contract & property disputes
Copyright, trade marks and design
Corporate tax
Credit brokerage
Criminal court work
Criminal legal aid
Data protection
Debt
Debt adjusting and debt counselling
Debt administration
Debt collecting
Debt management
Debt recovery, insolvency, bankruptcy
Disability
Discrimination
Education
Employment
Employment law
Environment
Environment (Business Premises)
EU / international
Family and divorce
Family business advice
Fishing
Freedom of information
Health and safety
Housing
Human rights
Immigration and asylum
Insolvency & corporate recovery
Insurance
IT and intellectual property
Joint venture
Landlord & tenant
Liquor licensing
Local government
Media and entertainment
Medical negligence – defender
Medical negligence – claimant
Mental health
Mergers and acquisitions
Oil & gas
Pensions (Company)
Pensions (Employment)
Personal injury
Personal injury – defender

Personal tax
Planning
Planning (Business Premises)
Power and utilities
Private equity
Professional negligence
Projects
Property litigation
Provision of credit information services
Public finance initiative
Public sector
Residential property
Road traffic
SME business advice
Software licensing
Telecoms
Transport
Unit Trusts, OEICs and investment trusts
Wills, executives and trusts
Partners
James Peter Campbell
Victoria Jane Leslie
William Kirkwood Mackenzie Tudhope
Gary Alexander Webster
Associates
Karen Myra Shaw Cameron
Nicola Marion Grant
Graeme John Myles
Employees
Natalie Debra Thoars Coll
Sine MacConnell Mackay
Sarah McCaffery
Andrew Stott

MACANDREW & JENKINS (TRUSTEES) LIMITED

5 Drummond Street, Inverness IV1 1QF
Tel: (01463) 723500
Categories of Work
Advice the elderly & powers of attorney
Agriculture and estates
Agriculture, crofting and fishing
Alternative investment market
Betting & gaming
Commercial property
Fishing
Landlord & tenant
Liquor licensing
Oil & gas
Power and utilities
Public sector
Residential property
SME business advice
Wills, executives and trusts

MACANDREW & JENKINS, WS LIMITED

5 Drummond Street, Inverness IV1 1QF
Tel: (01463) 723500
Fax: (01463) 230743
DX: IN8 INVERNESS
E-mail: james@macandrewjenkins.co.uk
Web: www.macandrewjenkins.co.uk
Categories of Work
Advice the elderly & powers of attorney

► *Inverness continued*

Agriculture and estates
Agriculture, crofting and fishing
Banking & finance
Commercial property
Contract & property disputes
Employment
Employment law
Family business advice
Fishing
Health and safety
Insurance
Landlord & tenant
Mining
Personal tax
Residential property
Sport
Wills, executries and trusts
Directors
James Robert Edwards Wotherspoon
Jonathan Lawrence Edwards Wotherspoon

MACKENZIE LAW LTD

2nd Floor, Highland Rail House, Station
Square, Inverness IV1 1LE
Tel: (01463) 713718
Fax: (01463) 713718
E-mail: donald@mackenzie-law.co.uk
Categories of Work
Civil court work
Civil legal aid
Commercial litigation
Contract & property disputes
Criminal court work
Criminal legal aid
Debt recovery, insolvency, bankruptcy
Landlord & tenant
Medical negligence – claimant
Personal injury
Professional negligence
Property litigation
Road traffic
Director
Donald Mackay MacKenzie

MACLEOD & MACCALLUM LIMITED

28 Queensgate, Inverness IV1 1DJ
Tel: (01463) 239393
Fax: (01463) 222879
DX: IN12 INVERNESS
E-mail: mail@macandmac.co.uk
Web: www.macandmac.co.uk
Categories of Work
Adoption
Advice the elderly & powers of attorney
Agriculture and estates
Agriculture, crofting and fishing
Alternative dispute resolution
Banking & finance
Charities
Children
Childrens
Civil court work

Civil legal aid
Commercial litigation
Commercial property
Construction
Contract & property disputes
Copyright, trade marks and design
Debt recovery, insolvency, bankruptcy
Employment
Employment law
Environment (Business Premises)
Family and divorce
Family business advice
Health and safety
Housing
Insolvency & corporate recovery
IT and intellectual property
Joint venture
Landlord & tenant
Liquor licensing
Mergers and acquisitions
Personal injury
Personal injury – defender
Planning (Business Premises)
Professional negligence
Projects
Property litigation
Public sector
Residential property
Road traffic
SME business advice
Social housing
Wills, executries and trusts
Directors
Katrina Larisa Ashbolt
Lindsay Bishop
Fiona Jane Campbell
Scott Dallas
Corra Lisa Irwin
Graham Ritch Laughton
Morag Sarah MacIntosh
Alison Margaret Martin
Peter Fraser Mason
Jenna Thomson
Associates
Evelyn Ferguson Crate
Gemma Ruth McClelland
Employees
Rory Alexander Carson
Aidan Dean Grant
Gemma Mairi Johnston
Julie Theresa Kinsella
Robert Milsom
Yasmin Vanessa Myles
Tomas Michael Simpson
Stephanie Wilde

MUNRO & NOBLE

26 Church Street, Inverness IV1 1HX
Tel: (01463) 221727
Fax: (01463) 225165
DX: IN15 INVERNESS
E-mail: legal@munronoble.com
Web: www.munronoble.com

Categories of Work
Adoption
Advice the elderly & powers of attorney
Agriculture and estates
Agriculture, crofting and fishing
Alternative dispute resolution
Children
Civil court work
Civil legal aid
Commercial litigation
Commercial property
Consumer credit
Copyright, trade marks and design
Criminal court work
Criminal legal aid
Data protection
Debt
Debt adjusting and debt counselling
Debt collecting
Debt recovery, insolvency, bankruptcy
Discrimination
Education
Employment
Employment law
Family and divorce
Freedom of information
Health
Health and safety
Housing
Landlord & tenant
Liquor licensing
Local government
Medical negligence – defender
Medical negligence – claimant
Mental health
Personal injury
Personal injury – defender
Personal tax
Professional negligence
Property litigation
Residential property
Road traffic
Social housing
Wills, executories and trusts
Partners
Kay Bevans Brown
Alida Delmaestro Bryce
Deirdre Elizabeth Mary Hart
Laura Elizabeth McCarthy
Mary Nimmo
Consultant
Ian Donaldson
Associates
Susan Jane Bird
Caroline Elizabeth McIntosh
James Noone
Employees
Matthew James Albiston
Alison Foggo
Neil Brian Speight
Kathleen Joanne Sutherland

MURCHISON LAW LIMITED
5 Ardross Terrace, Inverness IV3 5NQ
Tel: (01463) 709992
Fax: (01463) 713722
E-mail: email@murchisonlaw.co.uk
Categories of Work
Agriculture and estates
Agriculture, crofting and fishing
Alternative investment market
Banking & finance
Charities
Civil court work
Commercial litigation
Commercial property
Competition
Construction
Contract & property disputes
Copyright, trade marks and design
Corporate tax
Debt
Debt collecting
Debt recovery, insolvency, bankruptcy
Employment
Employment law
Environment
Environment (Business Premises)
EU / international
Family and divorce
Family business advice
Fishing
Freedom of information
Housing
Insolvency & corporate recovery
Insurance
IT and intellectual property
Joint venture
Landlord & tenant
Medical negligence – claimant
Mergers and acquisitions
Mining
Pensions (Company)
Personal injury
Planning
Planning (Business Premises)
Power and utilities
Private equity
Professional negligence
Projects
Property litigation
Public finance initiative
Public sector
Residential property
SME business advice
Telecoms
Unit Trusts, OEICs and investment trusts
Wills, executories and trusts
Directors
Kirsten Edith Humphris
Robert Murray McCheyne
Andrew Alexander Murchison
Consultant
Alexander Arthur Duncan Keith

▶ *Inverness continued*

Employees
Stephen Robert Cranston
Sheila Fraser
Gillian Margaret Maciver
Alexandra Mary Maclean
Elizabeth Barbara Wilson

PATTERSON & PATTERSON DEFENCE LAWYERS
Highland House, 20 Longman Road, Inverness
IV1 1RY
Tel: (014) 63 418277
E-mail: office@pattersonandpaterson.com
Categories of Work
Criminal court work
Criminal legal aid
Partners
Natalie Elizabeth Paterson
David William Patterson
Employee
Josey Patricia Donachie

SAFFERY CHAMPNESS (SUISSE) S.A.
Kintail House, Beechwood Park, Inverness
IV2 3BW
Tel: (01463) 246300

SOUTH FORREST
8 Ardross Terrace, Inverness IV3 5NW
Tel: (01463) 237171
Fax: (01463) 243548
DX: IN16 INVERNESS
E-mail: email@southforrest.co.uk
Web: www.southforrest.co.uk
Categories of Work
Advice the elderly & powers of attorney
Agriculture, crofting and fishing
Commercial property
Contract & property disputes
Criminal court work
Criminal legal aid
Family business advice
Joint venture
Landlord & tenant
Liquor licensing
Mergers and acquisitions
Residential property
Wills, executries and trusts
Partners
Julia Margaret Cameron
Cristina Fraser
Rebecca Rose Fraser
Jill Elizabeth Nicholson
Marie Quickfall
Martin Alfred Smith
Employee
Dean Ross Fraser

STRONACHS LLP
Camas House, Pavilion 3, Fairways Business
Park, Inverness IV2 6AA
Tel: (01463) 713225
Fax: (01463) 238177
DX: 521002 INVERNESS 3

E-mail: info@stronachs.com
Categories of Work
Adjudication
Adoption
Advice the elderly & powers of attorney
Agriculture and estates
Agriculture, crofting and fishing
Alternative dispute resolution
Alternative investment market
Banking & finance
Benefit advice
Charities
Children
Childrens
Civil court work
Civil legal aid
Commercial litigation
Commercial property
Competition
Construction
Consumer credit
Contract & property disputes
Copyright, trade marks and design
Corporate tax
Data protection
Debt
Debt collecting
Debt management
Debt recovery, insolvency, bankruptcy
Disability
Education
Employment
Employment law
Environment
Environment (Business Premises)
EU / international
Family and divorce
Family business advice
Freedom of information
Health
Health and safety
Housing
Insolvency & corporate recovery
IT and intellectual property
Joint venture
Landlord & tenant
Media and entertainment
Medical negligence – defender
Medical negligence – claimant
Mental health
Mergers and acquisitions
Oil & gas
Pensions (Company)
Pensions (Employment)
Personal injury
Personal injury – defender
Personal tax
Planning
Planning (Business Premises)
Power and utilities
Private equity
Professional negligence
Projects

Property litigation
Public finance initiative
Public sector
Residential property
Road traffic
Shipping
SME business advice
Social housing
Software licensing
Sport
Telecoms
Transport
Wills, executives and trusts
Partners
Ross Anthony Linn
Colin Alexander Sandilands
Employees
Hazel Mary MacGregor
Karyn Anne Richmond

STUART & CO
Founders House, Charleston, Inverness IV1 3YA
Tel: (01463) 731582
Fax: (0871) 712 5865
E-mail: chris@highlandsolicitor.com
Categories of Work
Charities
Commercial property
Landlord & tenant
Residential property
Wills, executives and trusts
Partner
Christopher David Brown Stuart

SWARBRICK LAW
Ness Horizons Business Centre, Kintail House,
Inverness IV2 3BW
Tel: (01463) 732553
E-mail: duncan@swarbricklaw.co.uk
Categories of Work
Civil court work
Commercial litigation
Contract & property disputes
Debt collecting
Debt recovery, insolvency, bankruptcy
Employment
Employment law
Family and divorce
Landlord & tenant
Medical negligence – claimant
Personal injury
Professional negligence
Property litigation

THE MACKENZIE LAW PRACTICE
2nd Floor, Highland Rail House, Station
Square, Inverness IV1 1LE
Tel: (01463) 713718
Categories of Work
Civil court work
Civil legal aid
Commercial litigation
Contract & property disputes
Criminal court work

Criminal legal aid
Debt recovery, insolvency, bankruptcy
Landlord & tenant
Medical negligence – claimant
Personal injury
Professional negligence
Property litigation
Road traffic

ROGER WEBB
2 Culduthel Mains Gardens, Inverness IV2 6RD
Tel: (01463) 234036
Fax: (01463) 234036
E-mail: rogerwebbsolicitor@btinternet.com
Categories of Work
Criminal court work
Criminal legal aid
Partner
Roger Geoffrey Webb

CRAIG WOOD SOLICITORS LIMITED
23 Academy Street, Inverness IV1 1JN
Tel: (01463) 225544
E-mail: nicola@craigwood.co.uk
Categories of Work
Criminal court work
Criminal legal aid
Family and divorce
Wills, executives and trusts
Directors
Ruaridh Howard Mackinnon Gowans
Shahid Latif
John Malcolm MacColl
Employee
Clare Frances Russell

WRIGHT, JOHNSTON & MACKENZIE LLP
The Green House, Beechwood Park North,
Inverness IV2 3BL
Tel: (01463) 234445
Fax: (01463) 224995
DX: 521011 INVERNESS 3
E-mail: enquiries@wjm.co.uk
Web: www.wjm.co.uk
Categories of Work
Adjudication
Adoption
Advice the elderly & powers of attorney
Agriculture and estates
Agriculture, crofting and fishing
Alternative dispute resolution
Alternative investment market
Banking & finance
Betting & gaming
Charities
Children
Childrens
Civil court work
Commercial litigation
Commercial property
Competition
Construction
Consumer credit
Contract & property disputes

► **Inverness** continued

Copyright, trade marks and design
Corporate tax
Criminal court work
Data protection
Debt
Debt collecting
Debt recovery, insolvency, bankruptcy
Disability
Discrimination
Education
Employment
Employment law
Environment
Environment (Business Premises)
EU / international
Family and divorce
Family business advice
Fishing
Freedom of information
Health and safety
Housing
Human rights
Insolvency & corporate recovery
Insurance
IT and intellectual property
Joint venture
Landlord & tenant
Liquor licensing
Local government
Media and entertainment
Medical negligence – defender
Medical negligence – claimant
Mergers and acquisitions
Mining
Oil & gas
Parliamentary
Pensions (Company)
Pensions (Employment)
Personal injury
Personal injury – defender
Personal tax
Planning
Planning (Business Premises)
Power and utilities
Private equity
Professional negligence
Projects
Property litigation
Public finance initiative
Public sector
Residential property
Road traffic
SME business advice
Software licensing
Sport
Telecoms
Transport
Unit Trusts, OEICs and investment trusts
Wills, executries and trusts

Partners
Paul William Adams
Iain Finlay Magnus Mackay
Roderick Kenneth MacLean
Angus George MacLeod
John Douglas Smart
Associates
Roderick Stewart Cormack
Elisa Margaret Miller
Employees
Lauren Ruth Farquhar
Jenna Katrina Gallacher
Kirstin Helen MacDonald
Katie Melville
Hannah Prentice
Alison Jane Reid

Inverurie

ABERDEIN CONSIDINE AND COMPANY
43 West High Street, Inverurie AB51 3QQ
Tel: (01467) 621263
Fax: (01467) 625195
E-mail: inverurie@acandco.com
Web: www.acandco.com
Categories of Work
Adjudication
Adoption
Advice the elderly & powers of attorney
Agriculture and estates
Agriculture, crofting and fishing
Alternative dispute resolution
Alternative investment market
Banking & finance
Charities
Children
Childrens
Civil court work
Civil legal aid
Commercial litigation
Commercial property
Competition
Construction
Consumer credit
Contract & property disputes
Copyright, trade marks and design
Corporate tax
Credit brokerage
Criminal court work
Criminal legal aid
Data protection
Debt
Debt adjusting and debt counselling
Debt collecting
Debt recovery, insolvency, bankruptcy
Disability
Discrimination
Education
Employment
Employment law
Environment
Environment (Business Premises)
EU / international

Family and divorce
Family business advice
Freedom of information
Health
Health and safety
Human rights
Insolvency & corporate recovery
Insurance
Joint venture
Landlord & tenant
Liquor licensing
Local government
Media and entertainment
Mental health
Mergers and acquisitions
Pensions (Company)
Pensions (Employment)
Personal injury
Personal tax
Planning (Business Premises)
Private equity
Professional negligence
Property litigation
Public finance initiative
Public sector
Residential property
SME business advice
Social housing
Telecoms
Unit Trusts, OEICs and investment trusts
Wills, executives and trusts
Partner
Gary Francis Ross

MORTGAGE, SAVINGS AND LOAN
1 Inver House, Inverurie AB51 3SN
Tel: (01467) 672820
Categories of Work
Advice the elderly & powers of attorney
Agriculture and estates
Agriculture, crofting and fishing
Banking & finance
Charities
Commercial property
Construction
Criminal court work
Criminal legal aid
Debt recovery, insolvency, bankruptcy
Environment (Business Premises)
Family business advice
Housing
Insolvency & corporate recovery
Landlord & tenant
Liquor licensing
Local government
Pensions (Company)
Planning
Planning (Business Premises)
Power and utilities
Residential property
SME business advice
Wills, executives and trusts

PETERKINS
60 Market Place, Inverurie AB51 3XN
Tel: (01467) 672800
Fax: (01467) 672819
DX: 520772 INVERURIE
E-mail: maildesk@peterkins.com
Web: www.peterkins.com
Categories of Work
Advice the elderly & powers of attorney
Agriculture and estates
Agriculture, crofting and fishing
Banking & finance
Charities
Commercial property
Construction
Criminal court work
Criminal legal aid
Debt recovery, insolvency, bankruptcy
Environment (Business Premises)
Family business advice
Housing
Insolvency & corporate recovery
Landlord & tenant
Liquor licensing
Local government
Pensions (Company)
Planning
Planning (Business Premises)
Power and utilities
Residential property
SME business advice
Wills, executives and trusts
Partners
Paul Wilson Macallan
Linda Alison Purkis
Employee
Hannah Mackay

RAEBURN CHRISTIE CLARK & WALLACE LLP
6 North Street, Inverurie AB51 4QR
Tel: (01467) 629300
Fax: (01467) 629001
Web: www.raeburns.co.uk
Categories of Work
Adoption
Advice the elderly & powers of attorney
Agriculture and estates
Agriculture, crofting and fishing
Alternative dispute resolution
Banking & finance
Betting & gaming
Charities
Children
Civil court work
Civil legal aid
Commercial litigation
Commercial property
Competition
Construction
Contract & property disputes
Copyright, trade marks and design
Data protection
Debt

► **Inverurie continued**

Disability
Discrimination
Employment
Employment law
Environment
EU / international
Family and divorce
Family business advice
Freedom of information
Health and safety
Housing
Human rights
IT and intellectual property
Joint venture
Landlord & tenant
Liquor licensing
Media and entertainment
Medical negligence – defender
Mergers and acquisitions
Oil & gas
Personal injury
Personal injury – defender
Planning
Planning (Business Premises)
Private equity
Professional negligence
Property litigation
Residential property
Road traffic
Shipping
SME business advice
Social housing
Sport
Wills, executives and trusts
Associates
Ian Alistair Angus
Kimberley Joan Smart
Employee
Rachael Nicole Morrison

THE KELLAS PARTNERSHIP
2-6 High Street, Inverurie AB51 3XQ
Tel: (01467) 627300
Fax: (01467) 622030
DX: 520771 INVERURIE
E-mail: info@kellas.biz
Web: www.kellas.biz
Categories of Work
Advice the elderly & powers of attorney
Charities
Children
Commercial property
Employment
Employment law
Family and divorce
Landlord & tenant
Liquor licensing
Residential property
Wills, executives and trusts
Partners
Elizabeth Ann Forsyth
Stephen William Park

Louise Emily Robertson
Employees
Jennifer Louise Court
Daniel Jamie Fergusson McFarlane
Catherine Margaret McKay

Irvine

AUSTIN KELLY & CO.,
29 Bridgegate, Irvine KA12 8BJ
Tel: (01294) 275215
Fax: (01294) 272215
E-mail: mail@austinkelly.net
Categories of Work
Advice the elderly & powers of attorney
Children
Civil court work
Civil legal aid
Criminal court work
Criminal legal aid
Family and divorce
Personal injury
Residential property
Road traffic
Wills, executives and trusts
Partner
John McCaffrey
Employee
Gale McLelland Davidson

ADAM CURRIE & CO.
Galt House, 31 Bank Street, Irvine KA12 0LL
Tel: (01294) 273735
Fax: (01294) 272749
DX: IR1 IRVINE
E-mail: mail@currieirvine.co.uk
Categories of Work
Advice the elderly & powers of attorney
Commercial property
Landlord & tenant
Residential property
Wills, executives and trusts
Partner
Adam Currie

JAMES IRVINE
57 High Street, Irvine KA12 0AL
Tel: (01294) 276116
Fax: (01294) 312493
Categories of Work
Criminal court work
Criminal legal aid
Partner
Peter Murray

MCKINNON HEWITT
65 East Road, Irvine KA12 0AA
Tel: (01294) 312801
Fax: (01294) 312851
E-mail: solicitors@mckinnonhewitt.co.uk
Web: www.mckinnonhewitt.co.uk
Categories of Work
Adoption
Advice the elderly & powers of attorney

Children
Family and divorce
Personal injury
Residential property
Wills, executries and trusts
Partners
Frances Mary Hewitt
Kathleen Anne Murray

MACKINTOSH & WYLIE LLP
146 High Street, Irvine KA12 8AH
Tel: (01294) 311422
Fax: (01294) 312192
Categories of Work
Advice the elderly & powers of attorney
Agriculture and estates
Agriculture, crofting and fishing
Banking & finance
Charities
Children
Childrens
Civil court work
Civil legal aid
Commercial property
Criminal court work
Criminal legal aid
Employment
Employment law
Family and divorce
Family business advice
Landlord & tenant
Liquor licensing
Mental health
Mergers and acquisitions
Mining
Power and utilities
Residential property
Wills, executries and trusts
Consultant
Alexander Muir

MATTHEW BROWN
Eglinton House, 22 Eglinton Street, Irvine
KA12 8AS
Tel: (01294) 273721
Fax: (01294) 312199
E-mail: mail@matthewbrownsolicitors.co.uk
Categories of Work
Adoption
Advice the elderly & powers of attorney
Children
Civil court work
Civil legal aid
Construction
Criminal court work
Criminal legal aid
Education
Employment law
Environment (Business Premises)
Family and divorce
Family business advice
Housing
Human rights
Landlord & tenant

Medical negligence – claimant
Parliamentary
Personal injury
Personal injury – defender
Professional negligence
Residential property
Road traffic
SME business advice
Sport
Wills, executries and trusts
Partner
Simon David Brown
Consultant
Tracey Kathryn Elizabeth Brown
Associates
Carol McCluskey
Colin James McLaughlin

MURRAY, GILLIES & WILSON
22 Bank Street, Irvine KA12 0AG
Tel: (01294) 278355
Fax: (01294) 274202
E-mail: gr@murraygillies.co.uk
Categories of Work
Adoption
Advice the elderly & powers of attorney
Betting & gaming
Commercial litigation
Commercial property
Contract & property disputes
Copyright, trade marks and design
Employment law
Family and divorce
Family business advice
Health and safety
Human rights
Immigration and asylum
Joint venture
Landlord & tenant
Liquor licensing
Medical negligence – claimant
Personal injury
Personal tax
Planning (Business Premises)
Professional negligence
Public finance initiative
Residential property
Road traffic
SME business advice
Wills, executries and trusts
Partners
Alan William Reid
Gordon Thomas Hughes Robertson

TAYLOR & HENDERSON LLP
65 High Street, Irvine KA12 0AL
Tel: (01294) 278306
Fax: (01294) 272886
Web: www.taylorandhenderson.co.uk
Categories of Work
Adoption
Advice the elderly & powers of attorney
Agriculture and estates
Agriculture, crofting and fishing

▶ **Irvine continued**

Alternative dispute resolution
Charities
Children
Civil court work
Civil legal aid
Commercial property
Criminal court work
Criminal legal aid
Debt
Family and divorce
Landlord & tenant
Mental health
Oil & gas
Residential property
Road traffic
Wills, executries and trusts
Associates
Heather Margaret George
Jacqueline Carol Taylor
Employee
Hollie Catherine McDicken

Isle of Arran

REID BLAIR
Creag An Iar, CORRIECRAVIE, Isle of Arran
KA27 8PD
Tel: (01770) 870370
Categories of Work
Adjudication
Advice the elderly & powers of attorney
Agriculture and estates
Agriculture, crofting and fishing
Alternative dispute resolution
Alternative investment market
Benefit advice
Commercial property
Landlord & tenant
Mining
Planning
Planning (Business Premises)
Public sector
Residential property
SME business advice
Transport
Wills, executries and trusts
Partner
Elizabeth Reid Blair

Isle of Benbecula

ANDERSON BANKS
Uachdar, Isle of Benbecula HS7 5LY
Tel: (01870) 602061
E-mail: uist@andersonbanks.co.uk
Web: www.andersonbanks.co.uk
Categories of Work
Adoption
Advice the elderly & powers of attorney
Agriculture and estates
Agriculture, crofting and fishing

Children
Childrens
Civil court work
Commercial litigation
Commercial property
Contract & property disputes
Criminal court work
Criminal legal aid
Debt collecting
Debt recovery, insolvency, bankruptcy
Employment
Employment law
Family and divorce
Family business advice
Landlord & tenant
Medical negligence – claimant
Mental health
Personal injury
Personal injury – defender
Property litigation
Residential property
Road traffic
SME business advice
Wills, executries and trusts

Isle of Bute

HANNAY FRASER & CO LTD
34 Castle Street, Rothesay, Isle of Bute
PA20 9HD
Tel: (01700) 503112
Fax: (01700) 504875
E-mail: calum@hannayfraser.co.uk
Web: www.hannayfraser.freeserve.co.uk
Categories of Work
Adoption
Advice the elderly & powers of attorney
Children
Civil court work
Civil legal aid
Commercial property
Consumer credit
Contract & property disputes
Criminal court work
Criminal legal aid
Debt
Debt adjusting and debt counselling
Debt recovery, insolvency, bankruptcy
Employment law
Family and divorce
Housing
Human rights
Landlord & tenant
Medical negligence – claimant
Mental health
Personal injury
Property litigation
Residential property
Road traffic
Wills, executries and trusts
Associate
Marianne Elizabeth Hunter

Employee
Gianna Zavaroni

WM. SKELTON & CO. LIMITED
Castle Chambers, 49 High Street, Isle of Bute
PA20 9DB
Tel: (01700) 502881/504793
Fax: 1700505270
DX: 590651 ROTHESAY
E-mail: contactus@wmskelton.co.uk
Web: www.wmskelton.co.uk
Categories of Work
Adoption
Advice the elderly & powers of attorney
Children
Civil court work
Family and divorce
Liquor licensing
Residential property
Wills, executries and trusts
Director
Elaine Constance Campbell

Jedburgh

CULLEN KILSHAW
Royal Bank Buildings, 38 High Street,
Jedburgh TD8 6DQ
Tel: (01835) 863202
DX: 581220 JEDBURGH
E-mail: jedburgh@cullenkilshaw.com
Web: www.cullenkilshaw.com
Categories of Work
Adoption
Advice the elderly & powers of attorney
Agriculture and estates
Agriculture, crofting and fishing
Alternative dispute resolution
Children
Childrens
Civil court work
Civil legal aid
Commercial property
Contract & property disputes
Criminal court work
Criminal legal aid
Debt
Debt collecting
Debt recovery, insolvency, bankruptcy
Employment
Employment law
Environment (Business Premises)
Family and divorce
Family business advice
Fishing
Landlord & tenant
Liquor licensing
Local government
Personal injury
Planning (Business Premises)
Property litigation
Residential property
Road traffic

Wills, executries and trusts

TAITS
43 High Street, Jedburgh TD8 6DQ
Tel: (01835) 344911
Categories of Work
Advice the elderly & powers of attorney
Agriculture and estates
Commercial property
Landlord & tenant
Personal tax
Residential property
Wills, executries and trusts
Partner
Dorothy Janet Amos

Johnstone

EASTONS SOLICITORS LIMITED
2 Canal Street, Elderslie, Johnstone PA5 9AU
Tel: (01505) 800413
E-mail: mail@eastonssolicitors.co.uk
Categories of Work
Advice the elderly & powers of attorney
Charities
Commercial property
Family business advice
Mental health
Residential property
Wills, executries and trusts

HOLMES MACKILLOP LIMITED
35 William Street, Johnstone PA5 8DR
Tel: (01505) 328 271
Fax: (01505) 331 907
DX: 591751 JOHNSTONE
E-mail: general@homack.co.uk
Categories of Work
Adjudication
Advice the elderly & powers of attorney
Agriculture and estates
Agriculture, crofting and fishing
Alternative dispute resolution
Banking & finance
Charities
Children
Civil court work
Commercial litigation
Commercial property
Construction
Contract & property disputes
Data protection
Debt recovery, insolvency, bankruptcy
Employment
Employment law
Family and divorce
Family business advice
Freedom of information
Joint venture
Landlord & tenant
Liquor licensing
Mergers and acquisitions
Professional negligence
Property litigation

▶ **Johnstone continued**

Public sector
Residential property
SME business advice
Wills, executives and trusts
Director
Carole Margaret Johnston
Consultant
Stephen Williamson
Employees
Calum Robert Mackay
Sarah-Jane Mary Sheldon

MCCUSKER MCELROY & GALLANAGH SOLICITORS

Floor 1 & 2, 61 High Street, Johnstone
PA5 8QG
Tel: (01505) 322299
Categories of Work
Children
Civil court work
Civil legal aid
Criminal court work
Criminal legal aid
Family and divorce
Medical negligence – defender
Personal injury – defender
Professional negligence
Road traffic

STIRLING AND MAIR (HOLDINGS) LIMITED

28 High Street, Johnstone PA5 8AH
Tel: (01505) 329373

STIRLING & MAIR LIMITED

28 High Street, Johnstone PA5 8AH
Tel: (01505) 329373
Fax: (01505) 331842
DX: 591750 JOHNSTONE
E-mail: jim.black@stirlingmair.com
Web: www.stirlingmair.com
Categories of Work
Adoption
Advice the elderly & powers of attorney
Children
Civil court work
Civil legal aid
Debt
Debt recovery, insolvency, bankruptcy
Education
Employment law
Family and divorce
Landlord & tenant
Medical negligence – claimant
Mental health
Personal injury
Professional negligence
Wills, executives and trusts
Directors
James Black
Lisa Marie McLaughlan
Employee
Ashlee Waton

G. SWEENEY SOLICITORS LIMITED

7 Brierie Avenue, Crosslee, Johnstone PA6 7BQ
Tel: (01505) 615163
Categories of Work
Criminal court work
Criminal legal aid

Keith

ANTHEM LEGAL LIMITED

Clydesdale Bank Buildings, 163 Mid Street,
Keith AB55 5BL
Tel: (01542) 886267

PETERKINS

186 Mid Street, Keith AB55 5BQ
Tel: (01542) 882537
Fax: (01542) 886176
DX: 520782 KEITH
E-mail: maildesk@peterkins.com
Web: www.peterkins.com
Categories of Work
Advice the elderly & powers of attorney
Agriculture and estates
Agriculture, crofting and fishing
Banking & finance
Charities
Commercial property
Construction
Criminal court work
Criminal legal aid
Debt recovery, insolvency, bankruptcy
Environment (Business Premises)
Family business advice
Housing
Insolvency & corporate recovery
Landlord & tenant
Liquor licensing
Local government
Pensions (Company)
Planning
Planning (Business Premises)
Power and utilities
Residential property
SME business advice
Wills, executives and trusts
Employee
Debbie Maria Myron

STEPHEN & ROBB LLP

Clydesdale Bank Buildings, 163 Mid Street,
Keith AB55 5BL
Tel: (01542) 886267
Fax: (01542) 886015
DX: 520781 KEITH
E-mail: keith@stephenrobb.co.uk
Web: www.stephenrobb.co.uk
Categories of Work
Advice the elderly & powers of attorney
Landlord & tenant
Residential property
Wills, executives and trusts
Partner
Emma Joy Katherine Carle

Employee
Stacey Leigh Grubb

Kelso

BORDERS LEGAL LIMITED
15 The Square, Kelso TD5 7HH
Tel: (01573) 226999
Fax: (01573) 229219
E-mail: al@hastingslegal.co.uk
Web: www.hastingslegal.co.uk
Categories of Work
Adoption
Advice the elderly & powers of attorney
Agriculture and estates
Civil court work
Commercial property
Contract & property disputes
Copyright, trade marks and design
Debt adjusting and debt counselling
Debt administration
Debt collecting
Debt management
Debt recovery, insolvency, bankruptcy
Employment law
Environment
Family and divorce
Family business advice
Health
Health and safety
Housing
Landlord & tenant
Liquor licensing
Mental health
Personal injury
Personal tax
Planning
Planning (Business Premises)
Property litigation
Public sector
Residential property
SME business advice
Wills, executries and trusts
Directors
Ronald Andrew Hastings
Alan Livingstone
Employee
Timothy Douglas Taylor

CULLEN KILSHAW
43 The Square, Kelso TD5 7HL
Tel: (01573) 400 399
DX: 556701 Kelso
E-mail: kelso@cullenkilshaw.com
Web: www.cullenkilshaw.com
Categories of Work
Adoption
Advice the elderly & powers of attorney
Agriculture and estates
Agriculture, crofting and fishing
Alternative dispute resolution
Children
Childrens

Civil court work
Civil legal aid
Commercial property
Contract & property disputes
Criminal court work
Criminal legal aid
Debt
Debt collecting
Debt recovery, insolvency, bankruptcy
Employment
Employment law
Environment (Business Premises)
Family and divorce
Family business advice
Fishing
Landlord & tenant
Liquor licensing
Local government
Personal injury
Planning (Business Premises)
Property litigation
Residential property
Road traffic
Wills, executries and trusts

HASTINGS LEGAL
15 The Square, Kelso TD5 7HH
Tel: (01573) 226999
Web: www.hastingslegal.co.uk
Categories of Work
Adoption
Advice the elderly & powers of attorney
Agriculture and estates
Civil court work
Commercial property
Contract & property disputes
Copyright, trade marks and design
Debt adjusting and debt counselling
Debt administration
Debt collecting
Debt management
Debt recovery, insolvency, bankruptcy
Employment law
Environment
Family and divorce
Family business advice
Health
Health and safety
Housing
Landlord & tenant
Liquor licensing
Mental health
Personal injury
Personal tax
Planning
Planning (Business Premises)
Property litigation
Public sector
Residential property
SME business advice
Wills, executries and trusts

► *Kelso continued*

LEYSHON WS
11 Horsemarket Business Centre, Horsemarket,
Kelso TD5 7HE
Tel: (01573) 402520
Fax: (01573) 226084
E-mail: john.leyshon@leyshonws.co.uk
Web: www.leyshonws.co.uk
Categories of Work
Agriculture and estates
Agriculture, crofting and fishing
Commercial property
Environment (Business Premises)
Family business advice
Landlord & tenant
Personal tax
Planning (Business Premises)
Power and utilities
Residential property
Wills, executries and trusts
Partner
David Gordon Ramsay Soeder

PAUL ROPER ASSOCIATES LIMITED
47-49 The Square, Kelso TD5 7HW
Tel: (01573) 225082
Fax: (01573) 226442
E-mail: info@paulroperws.co.uk
Categories of Work
Advice the elderly & powers of attorney
Agriculture and estates
Agriculture, crofting and fishing
Commercial property
Contract & property disputes
Family business advice
Mergers and acquisitions
Residential property
Wills, executries and trusts
Director
Paul Frederick Allen Roper

TAITS
10 The Square, Kelso TD5 7HJ
Tel: (01573) 224311
Fax: (01573) 225858
E-mail: bruce.lees@taitskelso.co.uk
Categories of Work
Advice the elderly & powers of attorney
Agriculture and estates
Commercial property
Landlord & tenant
Personal tax
Residential property
Wills, executries and trusts
Partner
Bruce David Lees
Employee
Kirsty Ann Mellor

Kilbirnie

CARRICK ROBB
71 Main Street, Kilbirnie KA25 7AB

Tel: (01505) 682408
Fax: (01505) 682060
DX: 556120 BEITH
E-mail: mail@carrickrobb.co.uk
Categories of Work
Adoption
Advice the elderly & powers of attorney
Charities
Children
Childrens
Civil court work
Civil legal aid
Commercial property
Contract & property disputes
Family and divorce
Landlord & tenant
Mental health
Personal injury
Property litigation
Residential property
Road traffic
Wills, executries and trusts
Partner
Peigi Carrick Robb

Kilmacolm

AFFINITY FAMILY LAW
4 The Chalet, Broomknowe Road, Kilmacolm
PA13 4JG
Tel: (01505873751/07739) 63
E-mail: isabella@affinityfamilylaw.co.uk
Categories of Work
Adoption
Advice the elderly & powers of attorney
Alternative dispute resolution
Children
Childrens
Civil court work
Civil legal aid
Education
Family and divorce
Human rights
Medical negligence – claimant
Mental health
Personal injury
Road traffic
Wills, executries and trusts
Partner
Isabella McKerrow

KEPSTORN SOLICITORS LIMITED
7 St. James Terrace, Lochwinnoch Road,
Kilmacolm PA13 4HB
Tel: (07935) 228791
Fax: (01505) 871919
E-mail: calum.jones@kepstorn.co.uk
Categories of Work
Banking & finance
Competition
Copyright, trade marks and design
Debt recovery, insolvency, bankruptcy
Employment

Employment law
Family business advice
Insolvency & corporate recovery
IT and intellectual property
Joint venture
Media and entertainment
Mergers and acquisitions
Pensions (Employment)
Private equity
Software licensing
Telecoms
Director
Calum Symon Jones

KINGSLEY WOOD & CO SOLICITORS LIMITED
Burnside Chambers, The Cross, Kilmacolm
PA13 4ET
Tel: (01505) 874114
Fax: (01505) 874009
E-mail: mail@kingsleywood.co.uk
Categories of Work
Advice the elderly & powers of attorney
Banking & finance
Civil court work
Commercial litigation
Commercial property
Copyright, trade marks and design
Employment law
Family and divorce
Family business advice
IT and intellectual property
Landlord & tenant
Liquor licensing
Mental health
Planning
Property litigation
Residential property
SME business advice
Software licensing
Wills, executries and trusts
Director
Kingsley William Alexander Wood
Employees
Irena Janina Fabijanska
Caitlin Lynda Gillon

Kilmarnock
ALLAN KERR SOLICITORS
13 Grange Place, Kilmarnock KA1 2AB
Tel: (01563) 571571
Fax: (01563) 571571
Categories of Work
Criminal court work
Criminal legal aid
Partner
Gillian Todd Swanney

BARNETTS
7/9 Grange Place, Kilmarnock KA1 2BH
Tel: (01563) 522137
Fax: (01563) 571382
DX: KK1 KILMARNOCK
E-mail: info@barnettslaw.co.uk

Web: www.barnettslaw.co.uk
Categories of Work
Adoption
Advice the elderly & powers of attorney
Agriculture and estates
Children
Childrens
Civil court work
Civil legal aid
Commercial property
Consumer credit
Contract & property disputes
Criminal court work
Criminal legal aid
Debt
Debt recovery, insolvency, bankruptcy
Education
Employment
Employment law
Family and divorce
Insolvency & corporate recovery
Landlord & tenant
Medical negligence – claimant
Mental health
Personal injury
Professional negligence
Property litigation
Residential property
Road traffic
Wills, executries and trusts
Partners
Alastair Norman Cochrane
Mark Peter McMillan
Karen Lynn Walker
Employee
Elena-Lucia Petrescu

BELL + COMPANY SOLICITORS
12 Grange Place, Kilmarnock KA1 2AB
Tel: (01563) 535545
Categories of Work
Adoption
Advice the elderly & powers of attorney
Benefit advice
Children
Civil court work
Civil legal aid
Criminal court work
Criminal legal aid
Debt
Debt management
Family and divorce
Residential property
Wills, executries and trusts

BELL LEGAL LIMITED
12 Grange Place, Kilmarnock KA1 2AB
Tel: (01563) 535545
Fax: (01563) 535505
E-mail: susanbell@bell-co.co.uk
Categories of Work
Adoption
Advice the elderly & powers of attorney
Benefit advice

► **Kilmarnock** continued

Children
Civil court work
Civil legal aid
Criminal court work
Criminal legal aid
Debt
Debt management
Family and divorce
Residential property
Wills, executives and trusts
Director
Susan Carol Bell
Employee
Dylan William Woods

ANTHONY BONE
2nd Floor Suite, 5 St Marnock Street,
Kilmarnock KA1 1DZ
Tel: (01563) 559166
E-mail: law@tonybonelegal.com
Web: www.tonybonelegal.com
Categories of Work
Adoption
Children
Childrens
Criminal court work
Criminal legal aid
Education
Family and divorce
Road traffic
Sport
Telecoms
Partner
Anthony Francis Bone
Employee
James Robert McKay

CARRUTHERS, CURDIE, STURROCK & CO.
1 Howard Street, Kilmarnock KA1 2BW
Tel: (01563) 572727
Fax: (01563) 527901
E-mail: mail@carrutherscurdiesturrock.co.uk
Web: www.ccs-solicitors.co.uk
Categories of Work
Adoption
Advice the elderly & powers of attorney
Agriculture and estates
Agriculture, crofting and fishing
Charities
Civil court work
Commercial property
Construction
Contract & property disputes
Debt
Employment law
Family and divorce
Family business advice
Insolvency & corporate recovery
Landlord & tenant
Liquor licensing
Mental health
Personal injury

Property litigation
Residential property
SME business advice
Sport
Wills, executives and trusts
Partners
David Alan Fleming
Lauren Victoria McCall
David Alan Stewart
Consultant
Duncan McLean

DOONAN, MCCAIG & CO. LTD
1 Rowallan Drive, Kilmarnock KA3 1TW
Tel: (0141) 5526600
Fax: (0141) 5526230
DX: GW296 GLASGOW
Categories of Work
Criminal court work
Criminal legal aid
Director
David McCaig
Employees
Colleen Mary McCaig
Ashley Pollock

MARTIN DUFFY
67 Mure Avenue, Kilmarnock KA3 1TT
Tel: (01563) 528580
Categories of Work
Criminal court work
Criminal legal aid
Partner
Martin Vincent Duffy

DUNCAN MCLEAN & CO.
81 John Finnie Street, Kilmarnock KA1 1BG
Tel: (01563) 524222
Fax: (01563) 525597
DX: KK9 KILMARNOCK
E-mail:
philip.tasker@duncanmcleanandco.co.uk
Categories of Work
Commercial property
Landlord & tenant
Residential property
Wills, executives and trusts
Partner
Philip Sydney Tasker

GALLOWAY & ELSBY LEGAL LIMITED
37 Bank Street, Kilmarnock KA1 1ER
Tel: (01563) 527 564
Categories of Work
Adoption
Children
Civil court work
Civil legal aid
Debt
Education
Family and divorce
Mental health
Wills, executives and trusts
Director
Donna Margaret Elsby

GMC CRIMINAL LAWYERS
100 John Finnie Steet, Kilmarnock KA1 1BB
Tel: (01563) 533338
Fax: (01563) 524998
E-mail:
enquiries@kilmarnockcriminallawyers.co.uk
Web: www.kilmarnockcriminallawyers.co.uk
Categories of Work
Criminal court work
Criminal legal aid
Road traffic
Partner
Graeme Miller Cunningham
Employee
Nicole Frances McCondichie

JAMES GUTHRIE & COMPANY LLP
3 Portland Road, Kilmarnock KA1 2AN
Tel: (01563) 525155
Fax: (01563) 530898
E-mail: lorna@jamesguthrie.co.uk
Web: www.jamesguthrie.co.uk
Categories of Work
Adjudication
Adoption
Advice the elderly & powers of attorney
Alternative dispute resolution
Children
Childrens
Civil court work
Civil legal aid
Commercial litigation
Commercial property
Criminal court work
Criminal legal aid
Debt
Debt collecting
Education
Family and divorce
Landlord & tenant
Medical negligence – defender
Personal injury
Personal injury – defender
Residential property
Wills, executries and trusts
Partners
Jonathan Scott Elliot Gow
Alison Jean Kelly
Associate
Sarah Joanne Simpson
Employees
Emma Louise Cowie
Calum Samuel Haswell

HARRISON LEGAL LIMITED
1a Bank Place, Kilmarnock KA1 1HJ
Tel: (01563) 508114
E-mail: caroline@harrisonlaw.legal
Web: www.harrisonlaw.legal
Categories of Work
Adoption
Advice the elderly & powers of attorney
Benefit advice
Children

Civil court work
Civil legal aid
Consumer credit
Debt
Debt collecting
Debt management
Family and divorce
Medical negligence – claimant
Mental health
Personal injury
Road traffic
Social housing
Wills, executries and trusts
Director
Caroline Nicola Harrison
Employee
Holly Anne Hepburn

MCCLUSKEY BROWNE
7 Portland Road, Kilmarnock KA1 2BT
Tel: (01563) 544545
Fax: (01563) 537672
DX: KK11 KILMARNOCK
E-mail: enquiries@mccluskeybrowne.co.uk
Categories of Work
Advice the elderly & powers of attorney
Charities
Civil court work
Commercial litigation
Commercial property
Criminal court work
Criminal legal aid
Debt recovery, insolvency, bankruptcy
Employment law
Environment (Business Premises)
Family and divorce
Family business advice
Insolvency & corporate recovery
Landlord & tenant
Liquor licensing
Mergers and acquisitions
Personal injury
Professional negligence
Residential property
SME business advice
Wills, executries and trusts
Partners
Sean Thomas Lynch
Alan John Murray
Consultant
Alexander Blair Currie
Employee
Scott Kenneth McLatchie

MACKINTOSH & WYLIE LLP
23 The Foregate, Kilmarnock KA1 1LE
Tel: (01563) 525104
Fax: (01563) 537100
DX: KK7 KILMARNOCK
E-mail: amcdonald@mackwylie.com
Web: www.mackwylie.com
Categories of Work
Advice the elderly & powers of attorney
Agriculture and estates

► **Kilmarnock continued**

Agriculture, crofting and fishing
Banking & finance
Charities
Children
Childrens
Civil court work
Civil legal aid
Commercial property
Criminal court work
Criminal legal aid
Employment
Employment law
Family and divorce
Family business advice
Landlord & tenant
Liquor licensing
Mental health
Mergers and acquisitions
Mining
Power and utilities
Residential property
Wills, executries and trusts
Partners
Fiona Agnes Connolly
Lesley Dowdalls
Lynsey Carol Murray
Karen Ann Stewart
Associate
Joanna Gayle Bingham
Employee
Rosa Mhairi McKay

NEIL F. MCPHERSON
87B John Finnie Street, Kilmarnock KA1 1BG
Tel: (01563) 535363
Fax: (01563) 542998
E-mail: neil@neilmcphersonsolicitors.co.uk
Categories of Work
Criminal court work
Criminal legal aid
Partner
Neil Forsythe McPherson
Consultant
Neil Alexander Little

MCSHERRY HALLIDAY LLP
42 Bank Street, Kilmarnock KA1 1HA
Tel: (01563) 533121
Fax: (01563) 522762
Web: www.mcsherryhalliday.co.uk
Categories of Work
Adoption
Advice the elderly & powers of attorney
Agriculture and estates
Children
Childrens
Civil court work
Commercial property
Contract & property disputes
Employment law
Family and divorce
Family business advice

Insurance
Landlord & tenant
Mergers and acquisitions
Pensions (Company)
Pensions (Employment)
Planning (Business Premises)
Professional negligence
Residential property
SME business advice
Unit Trusts, OEICs and investment trusts
Wills, executries and trusts
Partners
Martha Clark
Catherine Dolan Morrow
Employee
Karen Isabella Wotherspoon

MURRAY SOLICITORS & NOTARIES
28A Nelson Street, Kilmarnock KA1 1BA
Tel: (07719) 043747
E-mail: roselyn.gallen@gmail.com
Categories of Work
Criminal court work
Criminal legal aid
Partner
Roselyn Gallen

**SCOTIA PERSONAL INJURY SOLICITORS
LIMITED**
2 Seaford Street, Kilmarnock KA1 2DA
Tel: (01563) 522433
E-mail: stuart@scotiapersonalinjury.co.uk
Categories of Work
Advice the elderly & powers of attorney
Civil court work
Civil legal aid
Debt
Employment
Employment law
Family and divorce
Medical negligence – defender
Medical negligence – claimant
Personal injury
Personal injury – defender
Professional negligence
Road traffic
Wills, executries and trusts
Director
Stuart Mackie Fraser

DOUGLAS WRIGHT
78 John Finnie Street, Kilmarnock KA1 1BS
Tel: (01563) 532177
DX: KK18 KILMARNOCK
E-mail: enquiries@douglaswrightsolicitors.com
Web: www.douglaswrightsolicitors.com
Categories of Work
Adoption
Advice the elderly & powers of attorney
Alternative dispute resolution
Children
Civil court work
Civil legal aid
Commercial litigation

Criminal court work
Criminal legal aid
Family and divorce
Partners
Brian David Holliman
Paul John McHolland
Associate
Mylene Helen Maxwell Scott

Kilsyth

DUNIPACE BROWN
Market Chambers, Market Square, Kilsyth
G65 0AZ
Tel: (01236) 826147
Fax: (01236) 826147
E-mail: enquiry@dunipacebrown.com
Categories of Work
Criminal court work
Criminal legal aid
Human rights
Partner
Ross James Elrick Brown

MATHIE, LENNOX & CO.
Market Chambers, Kilsyth G65 0AZ
Tel: (01236) 823139
Fax: (01236) 825991
E-mail: mfotheringham@mathielennox.co.uk
Categories of Work
Adoption
Advice the elderly & powers of attorney
Alternative investment market
Children
Civil legal aid
Commercial property
Consumer credit
Credit brokerage
Debt
Debt adjusting and debt counselling
Debt administration
Debt collecting
Employment
Employment law
Family and divorce
Health and safety
Insolvency & corporate recovery
Landlord & tenant
Personal injury
Personal injury – defender
Provision of credit information services
Public sector
Residential property
Road traffic
SME business advice
Wills, executries and trusts
Partners
Delanie Robyn Clarke
James Gibson

MOOREMARSHALL LIMITED
4 Market Street, Kilsyth G65 0BG
Tel: (01236) 824908
E-mail: info@mooremarshall.com

Web: www.mooremarshall.com
Categories of Work
Advice the elderly & powers of attorney
Children
Civil court work
Commercial property
Contract & property disputes
Employment law
Family and divorce
Family business advice
Landlord & tenant
Residential property
Wills, executries and trusts

Kilwinning

RUTH ANDERSON & CO.
180A Main Street, Kilwinning KA13 6EE
Tel: (01294) 551551
Fax: (01294) 556572
E-mail: ruthanderson_co@btconnect.com
Categories of Work
Adoption
Advice the elderly & powers of attorney
Benefit advice
Children
Civil court work
Civil legal aid
Criminal court work
Criminal legal aid
Debt
Education
Family and divorce
Partner
Esther May Evans

FINLAYSONS
149 Main Street, Kilwinning KA13 6EQ
Tel: (01294) 551151
Fax: (01294) 553839
E-mail: mail@finlaysonslawyers.co.uk
Categories of Work
Adoption
Advice the elderly & powers of attorney
Benefit advice
Children
Civil court work
Civil legal aid
Criminal court work
Criminal legal aid
Debt
Family and divorce
Human rights
Professional negligence
Residential property
Social housing
Wills, executries and trusts
Partner
William Alexander Finlayson

TAYLOR & HENDERSON LLP
83 Main Street, Kilwinning KA13 6AN
Tel: (01294) 557506
Web: www.taylorandhenderson.co.uk

▶ **Kilwinning continued**

Categories of Work
Adoption
Advice the elderly & powers of attorney
Agriculture and estates
Agriculture, crofting and fishing
Alternative dispute resolution
Charities
Children
Civil court work
Civil legal aid
Commercial property
Criminal court work
Criminal legal aid
Debt
Family and divorce
Landlord & tenant
Mental health
Oil & gas
Residential property
Road traffic
Wills, executries and trusts

Kinglassie

EDINBURGH CORPORATE SOLICITORS LIMITED
Whinnyhall House, Kinglassie KY5 0UB
Tel: (01592) 882205
Directors
Mairi-Claire Dougan
Martin Alexander Quinn

Kinross

ANDERSONS LLP
40 High Street, Kinross KY13 8AN
Tel: (01577) 862405
Fax: (01577) 862829
E-mail: mail@andersons-kinross.co.uk
Web: www.andersons-kinross.co.uk
Categories of Work
Advice the elderly & powers of attorney
Agriculture and estates
Agriculture, crofting and fishing
Charities
Commercial property
Consumer credit
Contract & property disputes
Copyright, trade marks and design
Debt collecting
Debt recovery, insolvency, bankruptcy
Family and divorce
Family business advice
Insolvency & corporate recovery
IT and intellectual property
Joint venture
Landlord & tenant
Medical negligence – claimant
Personal injury
Planning
Power and utilities

Professional negligence
Residential property
Road traffic
SME business advice
Sport
Wills, executries and trusts
Partners
Lorna Elizabeth Miller
Campbell Colin Watson
John Stewart Wellburn

ANDREW BAILLIE
103 High Street, Kinross KY13 8AQ
Tel: (01577) 861000
Fax: (01577) 861808
E-mail: andrewbaillie@andrewbaillie.co.uk
Web: www.andrewbaillie.co.uk
Categories of Work
Agriculture and estates
Commercial property
Contract & property disputes
Employment
Employment law
Family business advice
Joint venture
Landlord & tenant
Mergers and acquisitions
Residential property
SME business advice
Wills, executries and trusts
Partner
Andrew Baillie

COOPER JOHNSON LAW LTD
3 Waulkmill, Crook of Devon, Kinross
KY13 0UJ
Tel: (01577) 840213

JGW LEGAL SERVICES LIMITED
18 High Street, Kinross KY13 8AN
Tel: (01577) 862302
Fax: (01577) 864591
DX: 560800 KINROSS
E-mail: e.williamson@jgwilson.co.uk
Web: www.jgwilson.co.uk
Categories of Work
Advice the elderly & powers of attorney
Agriculture and estates
Agriculture, crofting and fishing
Commercial property
Contract & property disputes
Environment (Business Premises)
Family and divorce
Family business advice
Landlord & tenant
Local government
Parliamentary
Personal injury
Residential property
SME business advice
Wills, executries and trusts
Director
Eric John Williamson

Associate
Jennifer Emily Fiona Preston

MORGANS
62 High Street, Kinross KY13 8AN
Tel: (01577) 863424
Categories of Work
Adoption
Advice the elderly & powers of attorney
Children
Civil court work
Civil legal aid
Commercial litigation
Consumer credit
Contract & property disputes
Criminal court work
Criminal legal aid
Debt
Debt collecting
Debt recovery, insolvency, bankruptcy
Employment
Employment law
Family and divorce
Landlord & tenant
Medical negligence – claimant
Personal injury
Professional negligence
Residential property
Road traffic
Wills, executries and trusts

Kirkcaldy

ADAMS WHYTE
33 Whytescauseway, Kirkcaldy KY1 1XF
Tel: (01592) 267431
E-mail: kirkcaldy@adamswhyte.com
Categories of Work
Criminal court work
Criminal legal aid
Human rights
Road traffic

BOYD LEGAL LIMITED
1 Townsend Place, Kirkcaldy KY1 1HB
Tel: (01592) 264782
Fax: (01592) 641059
E-mail: newenquiries@boydlegaluk.com
Categories of Work
Advice the elderly & powers of attorney
Agriculture and estates
Charities
Commercial property
Contract & property disputes
Copyright, trade marks and design
Employment law
Family and divorce
Family business advice
Housing
Joint venture
Landlord & tenant
Mergers and acquisitions
Residential property
SME business advice

Wills, executries and trusts
Employee
Kelly Ann Matthews

W. & A.S. BRUCE
8 Hunter Street, Kirkcaldy KY1 1ED
Tel: (01592) 204774
Fax: (01592) 260748
Categories of Work
Adoption
Advice the elderly & powers of attorney
Agriculture and estates
Children
Childrens
Civil court work
Civil legal aid
Commercial property
Consumer credit
Contract & property disputes
Criminal court work
Criminal legal aid
Debt
Debt adjusting and debt counselling
Debt collecting
Debt recovery, insolvency, bankruptcy
Employment
Employment law
Family and divorce
Family business advice
Landlord & tenant
Liquor licensing
Medical negligence – claimant
Mental health
Pensions (Company)
Personal injury
Personal injury – defender
Personal tax
Professional negligence
Property litigation
Residential property
Road traffic
SME business advice
Wills, executries and trusts
Partner
Andrew Grieve
Associate
Margo Hopton

DIGBY BROWN LLP
23 Whytescauseway, Kirkcaldy KY1 1XF
Tel: (0333) 200 5925
DX: KY6 KIRKCALDY
E-mail: enquiries@digbybrown.co.uk
Web: www.digbybrown.co.uk
Categories of Work
Advice the elderly & powers of attorney
Agriculture and estates
Agriculture, crofting and fishing
Alternative dispute resolution
Alternative investment market
Banking & finance
Benefit advice
Charities
Children

▶ *Kirkcaldy continued*

Civil court work
Civil legal aid
Commercial litigation
Commercial property
Competition
Construction
Contract & property disputes
Corporate tax
Criminal court work
Data protection
Debt
Debt adjusting and debt counselling
Debt collecting
Debt recovery, insolvency, bankruptcy
Disability
Discrimination
Employment
Employment law
Environment (Business Premises)
EU / international
Family and divorce
Family business advice
Freedom of information
Health and safety
Human rights
Immigration and asylum
Insolvency & corporate recovery
Insurance
Joint venture
Landlord & tenant
Medical negligence – defender
Medical negligence – claimant
Mental health
Mergers and acquisitions
Pensions (Company)
Personal injury
Personal injury – defender
Planning (Business Premises)
Private equity
Professional negligence
Property litigation
Provision of credit information services
Public finance initiative
Public sector
Residential property
Road traffic
SME business advice
Unit Trusts, OEICs and investment trusts
Wills, executries and trusts
Partners
Lianda Jane Barnes
Innes Laing
Employees
Fiona Alison Bissett
Ryan Smith

FORDS DALY LEGAL LIMITED
Office 1, Evans Business Centre, 1 Begg Road,
Kirkcaldy KY2 6HD
Tel: (01592) 640630
Fax: (01592) 640622
E-mail: lauren@fordsdalylegal.co.uk

Web: www.fordsdalylegal.co.uk
Categories of Work
Advice the elderly & powers of attorney
Commercial property
Contract & property disputes
Disability
Discrimination
Family and divorce
Family business advice
Human rights
Landlord & tenant
Residential property
Wills, executries and trusts
Directors
Lauren Katy Paterson Daly
Fiona Agnes Ford
Scott William Ford
Consultant
Nigel William Frew Ford

INNES JOHNSTON LLP
95-99 Esplanade, Kirkcaldy KY1 1RF
Tel: (01592) 263455
Fax: (01592) 200069
DX: KY4 KIRKCALDY
E-mail: kirkcaldy@innesjohnston.co.uk
Web: www.innesjohnston.co.uk
Categories of Work
Adoption
Advice the elderly & powers of attorney
Agriculture and estates
Agriculture, crofting and fishing
Children
Childrens
Civil court work
Civil legal aid
Commercial property
Criminal court work
Criminal legal aid
Debt
Debt collecting
Education
Family and divorce
Family business advice
Human rights
Immigration and asylum
Landlord & tenant
Liquor licensing
Local government
Mental health
Personal injury
Residential property
SME business advice
Transport
Wills, executries and trusts
Partners
Stewart MacGregor
Ann Margaret Oliver
Employees
Felicity Serena Bruce
Shannon Louise Wright-Davies

JGW LEGAL SERVICES LIMITED
Evans Business Centre, John Smith Business
Park, Kirkcaldy KY2 6HD
Tel: (01592) 205000
Web: www.jgwilson.co.uk
Categories of Work
Advice the elderly & powers of attorney
Agriculture and estates
Agriculture, crofting and fishing
Commercial property
Contract & property disputes
Environment (Business Premises)
Family and divorce
Family business advice
Landlord & tenant
Local government
Parliamentary
Personal injury
Residential property
SME business advice
Wills, executries and trusts

ROBERT F MACDONALD SOLICITORS
11 Wemyssfield, Kirkcaldy KY1 1XN
Tel: (01592) 643357
Fax: (01592) 265809
E-mail: robert@robertfmacdonald.org.uk
Categories of Work
Adoption
Advice the elderly & powers of attorney
Children
Civil court work
Civil legal aid
Contract & property disputes
Criminal court work
Criminal legal aid
Debt
Debt collecting
Employment law
Family and divorce
Housing
Landlord & tenant
Mental health
Personal injury
Planning (Business Premises)
Property litigation
Residential property
Road traffic
Social housing
Wills, executries and trusts
Partners
Catherine Elizabeth Chalmers
Robert Fraser MacDonald
Kerr Malcolm Grant Sneddon

MACGREGOR LIMITED
28 Links Street, Kirkcaldy KY1 1QE
Tel: (01592) 644477
Fax: (01592) 640022
E-mail: willie@macgregorsol.com
Categories of Work
Residential property
Wills, executries and trusts

Director
William MacGregor

MCKENZIES
26 East Fergus Place, Kirkcaldy KY1 1XT
Tel: (01592) 206605
Fax: (01592) 268803
DX: KY21 KIRKCALDY
E-mail: enquiries@mckenzies-solicitors.co.uk
Web: www.mckenzies-solicitors.co.uk
Categories of Work
Adoption
Advice the elderly & powers of attorney
Alternative dispute resolution
Children
Civil court work
Commercial litigation
Contract & property disputes
Criminal court work
Criminal legal aid
Debt recovery, insolvency, bankruptcy
Employment
Employment law
Family and divorce
Family business advice
Insolvency & corporate recovery
Landlord & tenant
Liquor licensing
Medical negligence – claimant
Mental health
Personal injury
Professional negligence
Property litigation
Residential property
Road traffic
Wills, executries and trusts
Partners
Gordon Wilson Cooke
Nigel Charles Cooke
Sally Lewis Davidson McKenzie
Associate
Christine Hagan

MCLAUGHLIN & CO
Evans Business Centre, 1 Begg Road, Kirkcaldy
KY2 6HD
Tel: (01592) 645772
Fax: (0845) 2991503
E-mail: andrew@mclco.co.uk
Categories of Work
Adoption
Children
Civil court work
Civil legal aid
Commercial litigation
Criminal court work
Employment law
Family and divorce
Liquor licensing
Medical negligence – claimant
Mental health
Personal injury
Property litigation

▶ **Kirkcaldy continued**

Partner
Andrew McLaughlin
Consultant
Laura Catherine McLaughlin

MARTIN, JOHNSTON & SOCHA LIMITED
47 Whytescauseway, Kirkcaldy KY1 1XD
Tel: (01592) 640680
Fax: (01592) 640687
Categories of Work
Children
Civil court work
Civil legal aid
Criminal court work
Criminal legal aid
Data protection
Family and divorce
Human rights
Director
David Gordon Cranston
Employees
Pol Stanley Clementsmith
Calum Taylor Gordon
Eilidh Blake Grant

PATERSON BELL LIMITED
45a High Street, Kirkcaldy KY1 1LL
Tel: (01592) 646600
Fax: (01592) 646800
E-mail: crime@patersonbell.co.uk
Categories of Work
Criminal court work
Criminal legal aid
Directors
David Alan Bell
Martin McGuire
Employees
Katrina Eileen Clark
David McLaughlin
James Malcolm McMackin
Lee Qumsieh

ANDREW K. PRICE LIMITED
18 Whytescauseway, Kirkcaldy KY1 1XF
Tel: (01592) 205151
Fax: (01592) 640848
DX: KY5 KIRKCALDY
E-mail: advice@andrewkprice.co.uk
Categories of Work
Advice the elderly & powers of attorney
Agriculture and estates
Agriculture, crofting and fishing
Charities
Commercial property
Contract & property disputes
Family and divorce
Family business advice
Immigration and asylum
Joint venture
Landlord & tenant
Mental health
Personal tax
Planning (Business Premises)

Residential property
SME business advice
Unit Trusts, OEICs and investment trusts
Wills, executries and trusts
Directors
Andrew Kevin Price
Sian Price
Consultants
Alistair Lindsay Morris
Donna Marie Price
Employee
Kelsey Ann Wilson

JAMES THOMSON & SON
51a High Street, Kirkcaldy KY1 1LJ
Tel: (01592) 268575
Fax: (01592) 642082
DX: KY10 KIRKCALDY
E-mail: margaret@jamesthomsonandson.com
Categories of Work
Alternative investment market
Banking & finance
Betting & gaming
Commercial property
Consumer credit
Credit brokerage
Debt adjusting and debt counselling
Debt administration
Debt collecting
Debt recovery, insolvency, bankruptcy
Insolvency & corporate recovery
Insurance
Liquor licensing
Pensions (Company)
Personal tax
Provision of credit information services
Public sector
Residential property
SME business advice
Unit Trusts, OEICs and investment trusts
Wills, executries and trusts
Partners
Peter Frank Murray
Margaret Craig Thomson

THORNTONS LAW LLP
2 Park Place, Kirkcaldy KY1 1XL
Tel: (01592) 268608
Fax: (01592) 203369
E-mail: kirkcaldy@thorntons-law.co.uk
Categories of Work
Adjudication
Adoption
Advice the elderly & powers of attorney
Agriculture and estates
Agriculture, crofting and fishing
Alternative dispute resolution
Alternative investment market
Banking & finance
Benefit advice
Betting & gaming
Charities
Children
Childrens

Civil court work
Civil legal aid
Commercial litigation
Commercial property
Competition
Construction
Consumer credit
Contract & property disputes
Copyright, trade marks and design
Corporate tax
Credit brokerage
Criminal court work
Criminal legal aid
Data protection
Debt
Debt adjusting and debt counselling
Debt administration
Debt collecting
Debt recovery, insolvency, bankruptcy
Disability
Discrimination
Education
Employment
Employment law
Environment
Environment (Business Premises)
EU / international
Family and divorce
Family business advice
Fishing
Freedom of information
Health
Health and safety
Housing
Human rights
Immigration and asylum
Insolvency & corporate recovery
Insurance
IT and intellectual property
Joint venture
Landlord & tenant
Liquor licensing
Local government
Media and entertainment
Medical negligence – defender
Medical negligence – claimant
Mental health
Mergers and acquisitions
Oil & gas
Parliamentary
Pensions (Company)
Pensions (Employment)
Personal injury
Personal injury – defender
Personal tax
Planning
Planning (Business Premises)
Power and utilities
Private equity
Professional negligence
Projects
Property litigation
Public sector

Residential property
Road traffic
SME business advice
Social housing
Software licensing
Sport
Telecoms
Unit Trusts, OEICs and investment trusts
Wills, executries and trusts
Partner
Ronald Grant Hamilton
Associate
Zoe Pauline Stevenson

CHARLES WOOD & SON LIMITED
37 Kirk Wynd, Kirkcaldy KY1 1EN
Tel: (01592) 261621
Fax: (01592) 200663
DX: KY7 KIRKCALDY
E-mail: reception@charleswoodlaw.co.uk
Categories of Work
Advice the elderly & powers of attorney
Alternative dispute resolution
Banking & finance
Commercial litigation
Commercial property
Contract & property disputes
Employment
Employment law
Family business advice
Insolvency & corporate recovery
IT and intellectual property
Joint venture
Landlord & tenant
Mergers and acquisitions
Personal injury
Private equity
Professional negligence
Property litigation
Residential property
SME business advice
Sport
Wills, executries and trusts
Directors
Charles Thomas Cant
Colin William Cant
Employees
Thomas Graham Reid
James Hugh Durham Young

Kirkcudbright

CAVERS & CO.
40/42 St. Mary Street, Kirkcudbright
DG6 4DN
Tel: (01557) 331217
Fax: (01557) 331301
E-mail: ncavers@caversandco.com
Categories of Work
Advice the elderly & powers of attorney
Benefit advice
Criminal court work
Criminal legal aid

▶ **Kirkcudbright** continued

Debt administration
Debt collecting
Family and divorce
Residential property
Wills, executives and trusts
Partner
Paul Neil Cavers
Consultant
Neil Cavers

GILLESPIE GIFFORD & BROWN LLP
27 St. Cuthbert Street, Kirkcudbright DG6 4DJ
Tel: (01557) 330539
Fax: (01557) 331059
DX: 580817 KIRKCUDBRIGHT
E-mail: mail@ggblaw.co.uk
Categories of Work
Adoption
Advice the elderly & powers of attorney
Agriculture and estates
Agriculture, crofting and fishing
Children
Civil court work
Civil legal aid
Commercial property
Construction
Contract & property disputes
Debt
Debt collecting
Employment
Environment (Business Premises)
Family and divorce
Family business advice
Freedom of information
Landlord & tenant
Liquor licensing
Planning (Business Premises)
Residential property
Wills, executives and trusts
Partner
Adam Turnbull
Associate
Jean Louise McKnight

WILLIAMSON & HENRY LLP
3 St Cuthbert Street, Kirkcudbright DG6 4DJ
Tel: (01557) 330692
Fax: (01557) 331540
DX: 580813 KIRKCUDBRIGHT
E-mail: enquiries@williamsonandhenry.co.uk
Web: www.williamsonandhenry.co.uk
Categories of Work
Advice the elderly & powers of attorney
Family business advice
Landlord & tenant
Personal tax
Residential property
Wills, executives and trusts
Partner
Ian Murphy Rodger
Employees
Richard Lambert Thomas Arkless
Lawri James Shanks

Helen Mary Steele

WILLIAMSON & HENRY LLP
Property Office, 3 St. Cuthbert Street,
Kirkcudbright DG6 4DJ
Tel: (01557) 331049
E-mail: enquiries@williamsonandhenry.co.uk
Web: www.williamsonandhenry.co.uk
Categories of Work
Advice the elderly & powers of attorney
Family business advice
Landlord & tenant
Personal tax
Residential property
Wills, executives and trusts

WILLIAMSON & HENRY (NOMINEES) LIMITED
3 St Cuthbert Street, Kirkcudbright DG6 4DJ
Tel: (01557) 330692

Kirkintilloch

ANDERSON LEGAL LTD
16 Townhead, Kirkintilloch G66 1NL
Tel: (0141) 775 4235
Fax: (0141) 626 6996
DX: 556803 Lenzie
E-mail: ka@andersonlegal.scot
Web: www.ANDERSONLEGAL.SCOT
Categories of Work
Commercial property
Contract & property disputes
Residential property
Wills, executives and trusts
Director
Kirsten Elizabeth McDougall Anderson
Employee
Andrew Kenneth Mack

BTC (SCOT) LTD
34 Alexandra Street, Kirkintilloch G66 1HE
Tel: (0141) 7789292

DHW LEGAL LIMITED
2a Catherine Street, Kirkintilloch G66 1LJ
Tel: (0141) 7767104
Fax: (0141) 260 9092
DX: : 500821 KIRKINTILLOCH
E-mail: liz@dhwlegal.co.uk
Categories of Work
Advice the elderly & powers of attorney
Children
Childrens
Criminal court work
Criminal legal aid
Liquor licensing
Personal injury
Road traffic
Wills, executives and trusts
Director
Elizabeth Anne Dingwall

GALLACHER & CO LTD
106 Cowgate, Kirkintilloch G66 1JU
Tel: (0141) 7761111

Fax: (0141) 7777875
DX: 500828 KIRKINTILLOCH
E-mail: karen@gallachers.co.uk
Categories of Work
Adoption
Advice the elderly & powers of attorney
Children
Civil court work
Civil legal aid
Criminal court work
Criminal legal aid
Family and divorce
Road traffic
Social housing
Wills, executries and trusts
Directors
Martin Gerard Hughes
Karen McLean

INJURY CLAIMS SERVICES LTD
23 Donaldson Crescent, Kirkintilloch G66 1XF

MCGREGOR MACLEOD LTD
3 Donaldson Crescent, Southbank Business
Park, Kirkintilloch G66 1XF
Tel: (0141) 7789292
Fax: (0141) 7763914
E-mail: graememiller@mcgregormacleod.co.uk
Web: www.mcgregormacleod.co.uk
Categories of Work
Commercial property
Housing
Insolvency & corporate recovery
Landlord & tenant
Residential property
Wills, executries and trusts
Director
Graeme Crombie Miller

MCMAHON EMPLOYMENT LAW
Donaldson House, 39 Donaldson Street,
Kirkintilloch G66 1XE
Tel: (0141) 7776366
Categories of Work
Adjudication
Civil court work
Commercial litigation
Consumer credit
Data protection
Debt
Debt adjusting and debt counselling
Debt administration
Debt collecting
Debt management
Debt recovery, insolvency, bankruptcy
Employment
Employment law
Insolvency & corporate recovery
IT and intellectual property
Professional negligence
Property litigation
Road traffic

NOLANS LAW LIMITED
Donaldson House, 39 Donaldson Street,
Kirkintilloch G66 1XE

Tel: (0141) 7776366
Fax: (0141) 7778639
E-mail: mail@nolmac.co.uk
Web: www.scotdebt.co.uk
Categories of Work
Adjudication
Civil court work
Commercial litigation
Consumer credit
Data protection
Debt
Debt adjusting and debt counselling
Debt administration
Debt collecting
Debt management
Debt recovery, insolvency, bankruptcy
Employment
Employment law
Insolvency & corporate recovery
IT and intellectual property
Professional negligence
Property litigation
Road traffic
Directors
James Gerard Nolan
Simon Denis Nolan
Employee
Ahsan Mustafa

THE PRG PARTNERSHIP
111 Cowgate, Kirkintilloch G66 1JD
Tel: (0141) 7762298
Fax: (0141) 7766974
DX: 500823 Kirkintilloch
E-mail: scotslaw@prg.co.uk
Web: www.prg.co.uk
Categories of Work
Adjudication
Advice the elderly & powers of attorney
Alternative dispute resolution
Charities
Children
Civil court work
Civil legal aid
Commercial litigation
Commercial property
Competition
Contract & property disputes
Copyright, trade marks and design
Criminal court work
Criminal legal aid
Data protection
Debt
Debt collecting
Debt recovery, insolvency, bankruptcy
Disability
Discrimination
Employment
Employment law
Family and divorce
Family business advice
Health and safety
Human rights

► **Kirkintilloch** *continued*

Insolvency & corporate recovery
IT and intellectual property
Joint venture
Landlord & tenant
Media and entertainment
Medical negligence – defender
Medical negligence – claimant
Mergers and acquisitions
Pensions (Employment)
Personal injury
Personal injury – defender
Professional negligence
Property litigation
Residential property
Road traffic
SME business advice
Social housing
Software licensing
Wills, executries and trusts
Partner
John William Sullivan
Consultant
James Donald Graham

Kirkwall

DANDHLAW LIMITED
56a Albert Street, Kirkwall KW15 1HQ
Tel: (01856) 872216
Fax: (01856) 872483
E-mail: enquiries@dandhlaw.co.uk
Web: www.dreverandheddle.co.uk
Categories of Work
Agriculture and estates
Agriculture, crofting and fishing
Director
Serena Kelly Sutherland
Associate
Lauren Rose Cook

DREVER & HEDDLE TRUSTEES LIMITED
56a Albert Street, Kirkwall KW15 1HQ
Tel: (01856) 872216
E-mail: enquiries@dandhlaw.co.uk

COLIN HARCUS, SOLICITOR
13 Bridge Street, Kirkwall KW15 1HR
Tel: (01856) 878550
Categories of Work
Advice the elderly & powers of attorney
Commercial property
Family and divorce
Residential property
Wills, executries and trusts

COLIN HARCUS, SOLICITOR & NOTARY
13 Bridge Street, Kirkwall KW15 1HR
Tel: (01856) 878550
Categories of Work
Advice the elderly & powers of attorney
Commercial property
Family and divorce

Residential property
Wills, executries and trusts

LOWS ORKNEY LIMITED
5 Broad Street, Kirkwall KW15 1DH
Tel: (01856) 873151
Fax: (01856) 875450
E-mail: enquiries@lowsorkney.co.uk
Web: www.lowsorkney.co.uk
Categories of Work
Advice the elderly & powers of attorney
Agriculture and estates
Agriculture, crofting and fishing
Charities
Children
Civil court work
Civil legal aid
Commercial litigation
Commercial property
Criminal court work
Criminal legal aid
Debt
Debt recovery, insolvency, bankruptcy
Employment
Employment law
Family and divorce
Family business advice
Liquor licensing
Local government
Mental health
Planning (Business Premises)
Projects
Residential property
Wills, executries and trusts
Directors
David John Morris Fairnie
Duncan Mervin Norman Hill
Edward Thomson Cooper Nicolson
Euain James Penny
Catherine Marie Smith
Consultant
Roy John Flett
Employee
Eoin James Thomson

LOWS ORKNEY TRUSTEES LIMITED
5 Broad Street, Kirkwall KW15 1DH
Tel: (01856) 873151
Categories of Work
Advice the elderly & powers of attorney
Agriculture and estates
Charities
Children
Civil court work
Civil legal aid
Commercial litigation
Commercial property
Criminal court work
Criminal legal aid
Debt
Debt recovery, insolvency, bankruptcy
Employment
Employment law
Family and divorce

Family business advice
Liquor licensing
Local government
Mental health
Planning (Business Premises)
Projects
Residential property
SME business advice
Wills, executries and trusts

ORKNEY LAW LTD
13 Bridge Street, Kirkwall KW15 1HR
Tel: (01856) 878550
Fax: (01856) 878716
E-mail: info@orkneylaw.co.uk
Categories of Work
Advice the elderly & powers of attorney
Commercial property
Family and divorce
Residential property
Wills, executries and trusts
Director
Colin Angus Harcus

Kirriemuir

WILKIE & DUNDAS
28 Marywell Brae, Kirriemuir DD8 4BP
Tel: (01575) 572608
Fax: (01575) 574529
E-mail: wtb@wdws.co.uk
Categories of Work
Adoption
Agriculture and estates
Agriculture, crofting and fishing
Betting & gaming
Civil court work
Civil legal aid
Commercial property
Construction
Contract & property disputes
Criminal court work
Employment
Employment law
Family and divorce
Health and safety
Housing
IT and intellectual property
Landlord & tenant
Liquor licensing
Personal injury
Personal injury – defender
Personal tax
Planning
Planning (Business Premises)
Property litigation
Residential property
Road traffic
Wills, executries and trusts
Partner
William Thomson Boyd
Employee
Gordon Taylor Young

Kyle of Lochalsh

FERGUSON, MACSWEEN & STEWART
Main Street, Kyle of Lochalsh IV40 8AB
Tel: (01599) 534500
Fax: (01599) 534480
E-mail: kyle@fmslaw.co.uk
Categories of Work
Adoption
Advice the elderly & powers of attorney
Agriculture and estates
Agriculture, crofting and fishing
Alternative dispute resolution
Children
Civil court work
Civil legal aid
Commercial property
Debt
Debt collecting
Debt recovery, insolvency, bankruptcy
Education
Family and divorce
Family business advice
Landlord & tenant
Personal injury
Property litigation
Residential property
Road traffic
Wills, executries and trusts
Employee
Michael Gerard Rossi

Lanark

DAVIDSON & SHIRLEY LIMITED
11 Hope Street, Lanark ML11 7ND
Tel: (01555) 662576/7
Fax: (01555) 661904
DX: 570830 LANARK
Web: www.davidsonandshirley.co.uk
Categories of Work
Adoption
Advice the elderly & powers of attorney
Agriculture and estates
Agriculture, crofting and fishing
Banking & finance
Commercial property
Contract & property disputes
Criminal court work
Criminal legal aid
Debt
Residential property
Wills, executries and trusts
Directors
James Robertson
William Tennant
Employees
Laura Jane Frame
Lynn Murdoch

HILLAND MCNULTY LIMITED
St . Kentigern's, 15 Hope Street, Lanark
ML11 7LZ

▶ **Lanark** continued

Tel: (01555) 663020
Fax: (01555) 663025
DX: 570834 LANARK
E-mail: enquiries@hilland-mcnulty.co.uk
Categories of Work
Adoption
Advice the elderly & powers of attorney
Children
Civil court work
Civil legal aid
Commercial litigation
Contract & property disputes
Criminal court work
Criminal legal aid
Family and divorce
Family business advice
Housing
Liquor licensing
Personal injury – defender
Property litigation
Residential property
Road traffic
Wills, executries and trusts
Directors
Vincent Francis Hilland
Kathleen McNulty
Employee
Margaret Mary McNulty

HILLS SOLICITORS
74 North Vennel, Lanark ML11 7PT
Tel: (01555) 664220
E-mail: hillsolicitors@outlook.com
Categories of Work
Civil court work
Civil legal aid
Criminal court work
Criminal legal aid
Residential property
Partner
Archibald James Hill
Employee
Alanah Janna Tara Campbell

MCAFEE
74 North Vennell, Lanark ML11 7PT
Tel: (01555) 664220
Categories of Work
Adoption
Advice the elderly & powers of attorney
Children
Childrens
Civil court work
Civil legal aid
Criminal court work
Criminal legal aid
Disability
Discrimination
Education
Employment
Employment law
Family and divorce

Human rights
Immigration and asylum
Medical negligence – claimant
Mental health
Personal injury
Professional negligence
Wills, executries and trusts

MORISON & SMITH LIMITED
20 Hope Street, Lanark ML11 7NG
Tel: (01555) 662488
Fax: (01555) 664048
Web: www.morisonandsmith.com
Categories of Work
Advice the elderly & powers of attorney
Agriculture and estates
Agriculture, crofting and fishing
Charities
Children
Civil court work
Civil legal aid
Commercial property
Contract & property disputes
Debt collecting
Family and divorce
Landlord & tenant
Residential property
Wills, executries and trusts
Directors
Lisa Ann Gillespie
Leona Murphy
Employee
Emma Lawrie

MORISON & SMITH LIMITED
61 High Street, Lanark ML11 7LN
Tel: (01555) 661435
Categories of Work
Advice the elderly & powers of attorney
Agriculture and estates
Agriculture, crofting and fishing
Charities
Children
Civil court work
Civil legal aid
Commercial property
Contract & property disputes
Debt collecting
Family and divorce
Landlord & tenant
Residential property
Wills, executries and trusts

SMAIL & EWART LTD
70 High Street, Lanark ML11 7ES
Tel: (01555) 666111
Fax: (01555) 665989
E-mail: enquiry@smail-ewart.co.uk
Categories of Work
Adoption
Advice the elderly & powers of attorney
Agriculture and estates
Agriculture, crofting and fishing
Alternative investment market

Banking & finance
Benefit advice
Charities
Children
Childrens
Civil court work
Civil legal aid
Commercial litigation
Commercial property
Competition
Contract & property disputes
Corporate tax
Debt
Debt collecting
Debt recovery, insolvency, bankruptcy
Education
Employment
Environment (Business Premises)
EU / international
Family and divorce
Family business advice
Housing
Insolvency & corporate recovery
Insurance
Joint venture
Landlord & tenant
Mental health
Mergers and acquisitions
Pensions (Company)
Private equity
Public finance initiative
Public sector
Residential property
SME business advice
Social housing
Unit Trusts, OEICs and investment trusts
Wills, executries and trusts
Employee
Ailie Joanna Lothian

Langholm

JOHN RODDICK & SON (SOLICITORS) LTD
38 High Street, Langholm DG13 0JH
Tel: (01387) 380482
Web: www.roddicks.co.uk
Categories of Work
Advice the elderly & powers of attorney
Agriculture, crofting and fishing
Commercial property
Corporate tax
Family business advice
Landlord & tenant
Personal tax
Residential property
SME business advice
Wills, executries and trusts

JOHN RODDICK & SON (SOLICITORS) LTD
Eskvale House, 8 Townhead, Langholm
DG13 0JN
Tel: (01387) 380893
Web: www.roddicks.co.uk

Categories of Work
Advice the elderly & powers of attorney
Agriculture, crofting and fishing
Commercial property
Corporate tax
Family business advice
Landlord & tenant
Personal tax
Residential property
SME business advice
Wills, executries and trusts

STEVENSON & JOHNSTONE
38 High Street, Langholm DG13 0JH
Tel: (01387) 380428
Fax: (01387) 381144
E-mail: office@sandjlangholm.co.uk
Web: www.sandjlangholm.co.uk
Categories of Work
Adoption
Civil court work
Contract & property disputes
Employment
Employment law
Family and divorce
Health and safety
Personal injury
Personal injury – defender
Property litigation
Residential property
Road traffic
Wills, executries and trusts
Partner
Kenneth Macqueen Hill

Larbert

JAMES TURNBULL & CO LTD
27 King Street, Stenhousemuir, Larbert
FK5 4HD
Tel: (01324) 552456
Fax: (01324) 562394
E-mail: info@jamesturnbullandco.co.uk
Categories of Work
Residential property
Wills, executries and trusts
Director
James Scobbie Turnbull

Largs

COLVIN HOUSTON LEGAL SERVICES LTD
PO Box 3, 1Bellman's Close, Largs KA30 8AP
Tel: (01475) 672003

ROBERT F DUFF & CO LIMITED
P.O. Box 2, 30 Main Street, Largs KA30 8AB
Tel: (01475) 673663
Fax: (01475) 674 798
E-mail: tbd@rfduff.co.uk
Categories of Work
Advice the elderly & powers of attorney
Commercial property

▶ **Largs** continued

Landlord & tenant
Liquor licensing
Planning (Business Premises)
Residential property
Wills, executries and trusts
Directors
Cynthia Jamieson Duff
Alan David Hill

JAMES PATRICK & MUIR
1-3 Frazer Street, Largs KA30 9HP
Tel: (01294) 832442
E-mail: info@jpmlaw.co.uk
Categories of Work
Advice the elderly & powers of attorney
Agriculture and estates
Agriculture, crofting and fishing
Commercial property
Copyright, trade marks and design
Family and divorce
Family business advice
Liquor licensing
Personal injury
Personal tax
Residential property
SME business advice
Wills, executries and trusts

LOW BEATON RICHMOND LLP
4A Frazer Street, Largs KA30 9HP
Tel: (01475) 674576
E-mail: Largs@lbr-law.co.uk
Web: www.lbr-law.co.uk
Categories of Work
Advice the elderly & powers of attorney
Agriculture and estates
Charities
Commercial property
Contract & property disputes
Family business advice
Landlord & tenant
Mental health
Mergers and acquisitions
Personal injury
Residential property
Wills, executries and trusts

MACTAGGART & CO LIMITED
72-74 Main Street, Largs KA30 8AL
Tel: (01475) 674646
Fax: (01475) 672650
DX: 590840 LARGS
E-mail: property@mactaggarts.co.uk
Categories of Work
Advice the elderly & powers of attorney
Agriculture and estates
Agriculture, crofting and fishing
Civil court work
Commercial property
Contract & property disputes
Debt
Debt recovery, insolvency, bankruptcy
Employment

Family and divorce
Family business advice
Landlord & tenant
Planning (Business Premises)
Residential property
Wills, executries and trusts
Directors
Linda Jane Clark
Fergus Alfred Sloss Duncan
Consultant
Robert Alasdair Mactaggart

TAYLOR & HENDERSON LLP
7-9 Tron Place, Largs KA30 8AR
Tel: (01475) 670014
Web: www.taylorandhenderson.co.uk
Categories of Work
Adoption
Advice the elderly & powers of attorney
Agriculture and estates
Agriculture, crofting and fishing
Alternative dispute resolution
Charities
Children
Civil court work
Civil legal aid
Commercial property
Criminal court work
Criminal legal aid
Debt
Family and divorce
Landlord & tenant
Mental health
Oil & gas
Residential property
Road traffic
Wills, executries and trusts

Larkhall

CARTYS
14 Montgomery Street, Larkhall ML9 2AA
Tel: (01698) 885888
E-mail: larkhall@cartylaw.co.uk
Web: www.cartylaw.co.uk
Categories of Work
Adoption
Advice the elderly & powers of attorney
Agriculture and estates
Benefit advice
Children
Civil court work
Civil legal aid
Commercial property
Consumer credit
Criminal court work
Criminal legal aid
Debt adjusting and debt counselling
Debt administration
Debt collecting
Debt management
Disability
Discrimination

Education
Family and divorce
Freedom of information
Human rights
Landlord & tenant
Mental health
Pensions (Employment)
Personal injury
Residential property
Road traffic
Social housing
Wills, executries and trusts
Partner
Louise Clare Morris

JBM LAW LTD
2 Church Street, Larkhall ML9 1EU
Tel: (01698) 516999
E-mail: admin@jbmlaw.org
Categories of Work
Criminal court work
Criminal legal aid
Director
John Bunny McGeechan

Lauder

CHAMBERS LEGAL LIMITED
PO Box 9, Lauder TD2 6PR
Tel: (07921) 850565
E-mail: john.taylor@chamberslegallimited.co.uk
Categories of Work
Alternative dispute resolution
Civil court work
Commercial litigation
Debt collecting
Debt recovery, insolvency, bankruptcy
Family and divorce
Medical negligence – claimant
Personal injury
Professional negligence
Road traffic
Director
John Taylor

Laurencekirk

BECKLEY KENNY & CO
64a High Street, Laurencekirk AB30 1BJ
Tel: (01561) 377188
Fax: (01561) 318207
E-mail: mail@beckleykenny.com
Web: www.beckleykenny.com
Categories of Work
Adoption
Children
Civil court work
Civil legal aid
Commercial property
Criminal court work
Criminal legal aid
Family and divorce
Landlord & tenant

Wills, executries and trusts
Partner
Joanna Helen Kenny
Consultant
Neil Michael Wheat

GREENBERG SOLICITORS
Haughhead Farm, Laurencekirk AB30 1ED
Tel: (07415) 135957
E-mail: office@greenberg-law.co.uk
Categories of Work
Civil court work
Commercial litigation
Debt collecting
Debt recovery, insolvency, bankruptcy
EU / international
Insolvency & corporate recovery
Partner
Ferdinand Strasser

Lenzie

FINNIESTON FRANCHI & MCWILLIAMS
88-90 Kirkintilloch Road, Lenzie G66 4LQ
Categories of Work
Advice the elderly & powers of attorney
Criminal court work
Criminal legal aid
Residential property
Wills, executries and trusts

MILLER BECKETT & JACKSON LIMITED
1 Alexandra Avenue, Lenzie G66 5BE
Tel: (0141) 7767761
E-mail: mail@millerbj.co.uk
Categories of Work
Adjudication
Adoption
Advice the elderly & powers of attorney
Alternative dispute resolution
Charities
Children
Childrens
Civil court work
Commercial litigation
Commercial property
Consumer credit
Contract & property disputes
Criminal court work
Data protection
Debt
Debt collecting
Debt recovery, insolvency, bankruptcy
Employment
Employment law
Family and divorce
Family business advice
Freedom of information
Housing
Immigration and asylum
IT and intellectual property
Joint venture
Landlord & tenant
Mergers and acquisitions

▶ *Lenzie continued*

Personal injury
Professional negligence
Property litigation
Residential property
Road traffic
SME business advice
Wills, executories and trusts

PACITTI JONES LEGAL LIMITED

96 Kirkintilloch Road, Lenzie G66 4LQ
Tel: (0141) 7750005
Fax: (0141) 6480908
DX: 500826 KIRKINTILLOCH
Web: https://www.pacittijones.co.uk/
Categories of Work
Adoption
Advice the elderly & powers of attorney
Banking & finance
Children
Civil court work
Civil legal aid
Commercial property
Construction
Corporate tax
Criminal court work
Criminal legal aid
Education
Employment law
Environment
Family and divorce
Health and safety
Housing
Joint venture
Landlord & tenant
Mergers and acquisitions
Personal injury
Power and utilities
Private equity
Professional negligence
Projects
Residential property
Road traffic
SME business advice
Wills, executories and trusts
Employee
Martin McConnell

MIKE SMITH & CO.

6 Ingleside, Lenzie G66 4GN
Tel: (0141) 7762621
Fax: (0141) 7764344
E-mail: law@mike-smith.co.uk
Categories of Work
Commercial property
Landlord & tenant
Residential property
Wills, executories and trusts
Partner
Michael James Redman Smith
Consultant
Christine Anne Smith

Lerwick

ALLANS

Nordhus, North Ness Business Park, Lerwick
ZE1 0LZ
Tel: (01595) 690749
Fax: (01595) 690749
E-mail: allans1@btinternet.com
Categories of Work
Criminal court work
Criminal legal aid
Partner
Thomas Peterson Allan

ANDERSON & GOODLAD

52 Commercial Street, Lerwick ZE1 0BD
Tel: (01595) 692297
Fax: (01595) 692247
E-mail: solicitors@anderson-goodlad.co.uk
Web: www.anderson-goodlad.co.uk
Categories of Work
Adoption
Advice the elderly & powers of attorney
Agriculture, crofting and fishing
Civil court work
Commercial property
Criminal court work
Criminal legal aid
Data protection
Debt
Debt collecting
Debt recovery, insolvency, bankruptcy
Family and divorce
Freedom of information
Housing
Landlord & tenant
Liquor licensing
Residential property
Road traffic
Wills, executories and trusts
Partner
Kathryn Grace Gordon
Employee
Vaila Marie Robertson

ANDERSON STRATHERN LLP

Nordhus, North Ness Business Park, Lerwick
ZE1 0LZ
Tel: (01595) 695262
Fax: (01595) 695331
E-mail: info@andersonstrathern.co.uk
Categories of Work
Adjudication
Adoption
Advice the elderly & powers of attorney
Agriculture and estates
Agriculture, crofting and fishing
Alternative dispute resolution
Banking & finance
Betting & gaming
Charities
Children
Childrens
Civil court work

Civil legal aid
Commercial litigation
Commercial property
Competition
Construction
Consumer credit
Contract & property disputes
Copyright, trade marks and design
Corporate tax
Criminal court work
Data protection
Debt
Debt administration
Debt collecting
Debt recovery, insolvency, bankruptcy
Disability
Discrimination
Education
Employment
Employment law
Environment
Environment (Business Premises)
EU / international
Family and divorce
Family business advice
Fishing
Freedom of information
Health
Health and safety
Housing
Human rights
Immigration and asylum
Insolvency & corporate recovery
IT and intellectual property
Joint venture
Landlord & tenant
Liquor licensing
Local government
Media and entertainment
Medical negligence – defender
Medical negligence – claimant
Mental health
Mergers and acquisitions
Mining
Oil & gas
Parliamentary
Pensions (Employment)
Personal injury
Personal injury – defender
Personal tax
Planning
Planning (Business Premises)
Power and utilities
Private equity
Professional negligence
Projects
Property litigation
Public finance initiative
Public sector
Residential property
Road traffic
Shipping
SME business advice

Social housing
Software licensing
Sport
Telecoms
Transport
Wills, executries and trusts
Partner
Robert Neil Risk
Associate
Laura Ann Sinclair

HARPER MACLEOD LLP
St Olaf's Hall, Church Road, Lerwick ZE1 0FD
Tel: (01595) 695583
Fax: (01595) 695310
Categories of Work
Adjudication
Adoption
Advice the elderly & powers of attorney
Agriculture and estates
Agriculture, crofting and fishing
Alternative dispute resolution
Alternative investment market
Banking & finance
Betting & gaming
Charities
Children
Childrens
Civil court work
Civil legal aid
Commercial litigation
Commercial property
Competition
Construction
Consumer credit
Contract & property disputes
Copyright, trade marks and design
Corporate tax
Criminal court work
Criminal legal aid
Data protection
Debt
Debt administration
Debt collecting
Debt recovery, insolvency, bankruptcy
Disability
Discrimination
Education
Employment
Employment law
Environment
Environment (Business Premises)
EU / international
Family and divorce
Family business advice
Fishing
Freedom of information
Health
Health and safety
Housing
Human rights
Immigration and asylum
Insolvency & corporate recovery

▶ **Lerwick continued**

Insurance
IT and intellectual property
Joint venture
Landlord & tenant
Liquor licensing
Local government
Media and entertainment
Medical negligence – defender
Medical negligence – claimant
Mental health
Mergers and acquisitions
Mining
Oil & gas
Parliamentary
Pensions (Company)
Pensions (Employment)
Personal injury
Personal injury – defender
Personal tax
Planning
Planning (Business Premises)
Power and utilities
Private equity
Professional negligence
Projects
Property litigation
Public finance initiative
Public sector
Residential property
Road traffic
Shipping
SME business advice
Social housing
Software licensing
Sport
Telecoms
Transport
Unit Trusts, OEICs and investment trusts
Wills, executries and trusts
Partner
Paul John William Rutherford
Employee
Jennifer Morag Gear

MICHAEL INKSTER & CO.
159 Commercial Street, Lerwick ZE1 0EX
Tel: (01595) 696901
Fax: (01595) 696904
Web: www.shetlandislesproperty.co.uk
Categories of Work
Adoption
Agriculture and estates
Agriculture, crofting and fishing
Alternative investment market
Banking & finance
Betting & gaming
Children
Commercial litigation
Commercial property
Construction
Contract & property disputes
Corporate tax

Criminal court work
Employment
Family and divorce
Fishing
Housing
Insurance
Landlord & tenant
Liquor licensing
Medical negligence – defender
Medical negligence – claimant
Personal injury
Personal tax
Public sector
Residential property
Shipping
SME business advice
Wills, executries and trusts
Partner
Michael Alastair Inkster

TAIT & PETERSON
Bank of Scotland Buildings, Lerwick ZE1 0EB
Tel: (01595) 693010
Fax: (01595) 695999
E-mail: info@tait-peterson.co.uk
Web: www.tait-peterson.co.uk
Categories of Work
Advice the elderly & powers of attorney
Agriculture, crofting and fishing
Commercial property
Landlord & tenant
Residential property
Wills, executries and trusts
Partners
Eric Spence Peterson
Martin Charles Henry Taylor

Leven

DEWAR SPENCE
260 High Street, Lower Methil, Leven
KY8 3EQ
Tel: (01333) 425200
Fax: (01333) 421811
E-mail: mail@dewarspence.co.uk
Categories of Work
Adoption
Advice the elderly & powers of attorney
Children
Childrens
Civil court work
Civil legal aid
Criminal court work
Criminal legal aid
Debt
Family and divorce
Liquor licensing
Personal injury
Wills, executries and trusts
Partner
Gordon Dewar Spence

Employees
Christine Margaret Baillie
Alan Robert Davie

JAS. S. GROSSET
57 High Street, Leven KY8 4NE
Tel: (01333) 426023
Fax: (01333) 428910
DX: 560871 LEVEN
E-mail: mail@grossets.co.uk
Categories of Work
Adoption
Advice the elderly & powers of attorney
Benefit advice
Children
Consumer credit
Criminal court work
Criminal legal aid
Debt collecting
Debt management
Disability
Discrimination
Employment
Employment law
Family and divorce
Health and safety
Human rights
Landlord & tenant
Medical negligence – claimant
Mental health
Personal injury
Planning
Professional negligence
Residential property
Road traffic
Wills, executries and trusts
Partners
Keith Miller
Raymond Grant Wachtel
Employee
Margot Jardine Miller

LYNN HERBERT & CO.
82 High Street, Leven KY8 4NB
Tel: (01333) 429007
Fax: (01333) 424800
E-mail: lherbert@lynnherbert.co.uk
Web: www.lynnherbert.co.uk
Categories of Work
Adoption
Advice the elderly & powers of attorney
Agriculture and estates
Children
Childrens
Civil court work
Civil legal aid
Criminal court work
Criminal legal aid
Debt
Debt recovery, insolvency, bankruptcy
Family and divorce
Housing
Landlord & tenant
Residential property

Road traffic
Wills, executries and trusts
Partner
Lynn Kathryn Wightman Herbert
Associate
Julie Craigie

INNES JOHNSTON LLP
5/7 Commercial Road, Leven KY8 4LE
Tel: (01333) 429320
Fax: (01333) 424973
E-mail: leven@innesjohnston.co.uk
Web: www.innesjohnston.co.uk
Categories of Work
Adoption
Advice the elderly & powers of attorney
Agriculture and estates
Agriculture, crofting and fishing
Children
Childrens
Civil court work
Civil legal aid
Commercial property
Criminal court work
Criminal legal aid
Debt
Debt collecting
Education
Family and divorce
Family business advice
Human rights
Immigration and asylum
Landlord & tenant
Liquor licensing
Local government
Mental health
Personal injury
Residential property
SME business advice
Transport
Wills, executries and trusts
Partners
Mark David Alder
Claire Forbes
Jacqueline Ann Mitchell
Employee
Kirsten Elizabeth Paterson

JACKSON & CO (FIFE) LIMITED
39 High Street, Leven KY8 4NE
Tel: (01333) 422330
Fax: (01333) 422339
DX: 560868 LEVEN
E-mail: info@jacksonsolicitors.co.uk
Categories of Work
Adoption
Advice the elderly & powers of attorney
Children
Civil court work
Civil legal aid
Criminal court work
Criminal legal aid
Employment law
Family and divorce

► *Leven continued*

Medical negligence – claimant
Personal injury
Residential property
Road traffic
Wills, executries and trusts
Director
Rebecca Cross
Employee
Charles John Benjamin Jackson

MCLAUGHLIN & CO
Fife Renewables Innovation Centre, Ajax Way,
Leven KY8 3RS
Tel: (01333) 424482
Categories of Work
Adoption
Children
Civil court work
Civil legal aid
Commercial litigation
Criminal court work
Employment law
Family and divorce
Liquor licensing
Medical negligence – claimant
Mental health
Personal injury
Property litigation

SMITH & GRANT
Rathellan, High Street, Leven KY8 4PR
Tel: (01333) 423441
Fax: (01333) 427342
DX: 560872 LEVEN
Web: www.smithandgrant.com
Categories of Work
Adoption
Advice the elderly & powers of attorney
Children
Childrens
Civil court work
Civil legal aid
Commercial litigation
Commercial property
Contract & property disputes
Criminal court work
Criminal legal aid
Debt recovery, insolvency, bankruptcy
Education
Employment
Family and divorce
Family business advice
Landlord & tenant
Liquor licensing
Medical negligence – claimant
Personal injury
Professional negligence
Property litigation
Residential property
SME business advice
Wills, executries and trusts

Partners
Paul Alexander Buist
Cameron Hunter MacKenzie
Employees
Elizabeth Ann Dryburgh
Michele Louise Renton

F.T. & D.C. WALLACE
Forth House, Forth Street, Leven KY8 4PW
Tel: (01333) 423804
Fax: (01333) 428360
DX: 560873 LEVEN
E-mail: g.wood@ft-dc-wallace.co.uk
Web: www.ft-dc-wallace.co.uk
Categories of Work
Advice the elderly & powers of attorney
Commercial property
Contract & property disputes
Criminal court work
Criminal legal aid
Landlord & tenant
Personal tax
Planning (Business Premises)
Residential property
Wills, executries and trusts
Partners
David Morrice Ritchie
David Gordon Wood

Linlithgow

THOMAS DUNCAN SOLICITOR
27 Rivaldsgreen Crescent, Linlithgow
EH49 6BB
Tel: (07887) 835321
Fax: (01506) 842131
E-mail: tom@scotlandlegal.co.uk
Categories of Work
Advice the elderly & powers of attorney
Commercial property
Contract & property disputes
Landlord & tenant
Local government
Planning (Business Premises)
Public sector
Residential property
Wills, executries and trusts
Partner
Thomas Duncan

PETERKIN & KIDD
8 High Street, Linlithgow EH49 7AF
Tel: (01506) 845191
Fax: (01506) 845444
DX: 540880 LINLITHGOW
E-mail: maildesk@peterkinandkidd.co.uk
Categories of Work
Advice the elderly & powers of attorney
Civil court work
Civil legal aid
Commercial property
Family and divorce
Residential property
Wills, executries and trusts

Partners
Antonia McFarlan
Stewart Miller Robertson
David Matthew Vause
Associate
John Gerard Donnelly
Employees
Victoria Emma Harvey Taylor
Jennifer Mackintosh Wild

RGM SOLICITORS LIMITED
19-21 High Street, Linlithgow EH49 7AB
Tel: (01506) 847070
Fax: (01506) 847090
DX: 540886 LINLITHGOW
E-mail: linlithgow@rgmsolicitors.co.uk
Web: www.rgmsolicitors.co.uk
Categories of Work
Advice the elderly & powers of attorney
Commercial property
Wills, executives and trusts
Residential property

THOMAS S. VEITCH & SON
12 High Street, Linlithgow EH49 7AG
Tel: (01506) 842100
Fax: (01506) 670470
DX: 540882 LINLITHGOW
E-mail: info@tsveitch.com
Categories of Work
Advice the elderly & powers of attorney
Agriculture and estates
Charities
Civil court work
Commercial property
Employment law
Family business advice
Landlord & tenant
Personal tax
Residential property
Wills, executives and trusts
Partners
Jonathan David Blundell
Thomas Stewart Veitch
Associate
Brian James Alexander Jackson

WHOSE LAND SCOTLAND
6 Braehead Park, Linlithgow EH49 6EJ
Tel: (07867) 387591
E-mail: whoselandscotland@gmail.com
Web: www.whoselandscotland.com
Categories of Work
Agriculture and estates
Agriculture, crofting and fishing
Commercial property
Projects
Public sector
Residential property
Transport
Partner
Robin Andrew Priestley

Livingston

ADAMS WHYTE
Lennox House, Suite 3, Almondvale Boulevard,
Livingston EH54 6QP
Tel: (01506) 401999
Fax: (01506) 462909
DX: 554004 LIVINGSTON 8
E-mail: livingston@adamswhyte.com
Web: www.adamswhyte.com
Categories of Work
Criminal court work
Criminal legal aid
Human rights
Road traffic
Partners
Andrew Proven Aitken
Gerrard Bann
Kevin Anthony Dugan
Associate
Alan Jackson
Employees
Alistair John Burleigh
Kirsty Catherine Lumsden
Matthew Paul Super
James Ian Walker

AGENCY COURT INSTRUCTIONS
1/3 Market Street, Mid Calder, Livingston
EH53 0AP
Tel: (01506) 880548
E-mail: maildesk@peterkinandkidd.co.uk
Web: www.peterkinandkidd.co.uk
Categories of Work
Advice the elderly & powers of attorney
Civil court work
Civil legal aid
Commercial property
Family and divorce
Residential property
Wills, executives and trusts

AITKENS THE FAMILY LAW SOLICITORS
17 Grampian Court, Livingston EH54 6QF
Tel: (01506) 417737
Fax: (01506) 460613
Categories of Work
Adoption
Children
Family and divorce
Partners
Lynne Violet DiBiasio
David Andrew Johnstone

ALLCOURT SOLICITORS LIMITED
1 Lennox House, Almondvale Boulevard,
Livingston EH54 6QP
Tel: (01506) 443999
Fax: (01506) 443909
Categories of Work
Adoption
Children
Childrens
Civil court work

▶ **Livingston continued**

Civil legal aid
Contract & property disputes
Criminal court work
Criminal legal aid
Debt
Disability
Discrimination
Education
Employment
Employment law
Family and divorce
Human rights
Landlord & tenant
Property litigation
Directors
Desmond James Maguire
Lora Grace Meldrum
Consultant
Walter Stuart Bell Peebles

BLACK AND MCCORRY LIMITED
Ionracas House, 6 Allen Road, Livingston
EH54 6TQ
Tel: (01506) 467823
Fax: (01506) 419427
E-mail: enquiries@blackandmccorry.co.uk
Categories of Work
Advice the elderly & powers of attorney
Commercial property
Construction
Contract & property disputes
Family business advice
Landlord & tenant
Liquor licensing
Medical negligence – claimant
Personal injury
Personal injury – defender
Professional negligence
Residential property
Wills, executives and trusts
Director
Edmund Wright
Consultant
Walter Scott Sneddon

CAESAR & HOWIE
107 Almondvale South, Almondvale Centre,
Livingston EH54 6QT
Tel: (01506) 435271
Fax: (01506) 448301
DX: 540891 LIVINGSTON
E-mail: enquiries@caesar-howie.co.uk
Web: www.caesar-howie.co.uk
Categories of Work
Adoption
Advice the elderly & powers of attorney
Alternative dispute resolution
Children
Childrens
Civil court work
Civil legal aid
Commercial property

Debt
Debt collecting
Debt recovery, insolvency, bankruptcy
Disability
Education
Employment law
Family and divorce
Family business advice
Landlord & tenant
Mental health
Personal injury
Residential property
Road traffic
Wills, executives and trusts
Partner
Martin Francis Monaghan
Associate
Greg David Douglas

CENTRAL COURT LAWYERS
15 Grampian Court, Beveridge Square,
Livingston EH54 6QF
Tel: (01506) 416999
Categories of Work
Alternative dispute resolution
Civil court work
Commercial litigation
Criminal court work
Criminal legal aid
Debt collecting
Debt recovery, insolvency, bankruptcy
Human rights
Insolvency & corporate recovery
Oil & gas
Partner
Neil James Robertson
Consultants
Michael John Bell
Ian George Bryce
Employees
Louise Margaret James
Craig Colin Scott

CHRISTISON LAW PRACTICE LTD
10 Highfield, Livingston EH54 7BQ
Tel: (0800) 1588455
E-mail: christisonlaw@ymail.com
Categories of Work
Civil legal aid
Director
John Kyle Christison

CURRIE JOHNSTON & CO
18 Grampian Court, Beveridge Square,
Livingston EH54 6QF
Tel: (01506) 412377
Fax: (01506) 412315
DX: 540909 LIVINGSTON
E-mail: curriejohnston@gmail.com
Web: www.currie-johnston.co.uk
Categories of Work
Betting & gaming
Commercial property
Housing

Liquor licensing
Residential property
Wills, executries and trusts
Partner
Jacqueline Marie Johnston

FRASER & CO CRIMINAL DEFENCE LTD
Unit 2, Newyearfield Business Units, Livingston
EH54 6TW
Tel: (01506) 420532
Categories of Work
Criminal court work
Criminal legal aid
Director
Glenn James Fraser

KW LAW
Torridon House, Almondvale Boulevard,
Livingston EH54 6QY
Tel: (01506) 415333
Fax: (01506) 416116
E-mail: livingston@kwlaw.co.uk
Web: www.kwlaw.co.uk
Categories of Work
Adoption
Advice the elderly & powers of attorney
Children
Civil court work
Civil legal aid
Employment
Employment law
Family and divorce
Personal injury
Residential property
Road traffic
Wills, executries and trusts
Partners
Kirsty Elizabeth Cargill
Deborah Anne Fleming
Lilias Carol Reid
Consultants
Valerie Elizabeth Forsyth
Gillian May Knox
Associate
Gillian Sarah Reilly
Employee
Stewart Park Smith

P.C. MCFARLANE & CO
Law House, Fairbairn Place, Livingston
EH54 6TN
Tel: (01506) 497160
Categories of Work
Advice the elderly & powers of attorney
Charities
Commercial property
Contract & property disputes
Education
Employment law
Family business advice
Landlord & tenant
Liquor licensing
Mental health
Mergers and acquisitions

Residential property
Wills, executries and trusts
Partner
Jordan Valentine

PETERKIN & KIDD
1/3 Market Street, Mid Calder, Livingston
EH53 0AP
Tel: (01506) 880548
Fax: (01506) 884495
Categories of Work
Advice the elderly & powers of attorney
Civil court work
Civil legal aid
Commercial property
Family and divorce
Residential property
Wills, executries and trusts
Employee
Emma Purdie

PURDIE MACLEAN LIMITED
The Law Steading, Unit 7-8 Bloom Farm, Main
Street, Livingston EH54 7AF
Tel: (01506) 420333
Fax: (01506) 420333
E-mail: andrew@purdiemaclean.co.uk
Web: www.purdiemaclean.co.uk
Categories of Work
Advice the elderly & powers of attorney
Banking & finance
Betting & gaming
Charities
Civil court work
Civil legal aid
Commercial litigation
Commercial property
Construction
Contract & property disputes
Employment
Employment law
Family and divorce
Family business advice
Housing
Insurance
Landlord & tenant
Liquor licensing
Medical negligence – claimant
Mergers and acquisitions
Personal injury
Planning (Business Premises)
Professional negligence
Residential property
SME business advice
Sport
Wills, executries and trusts
Directors
Joy Maclean
Andrew Purdie

KEEGAN SMITH, SSC.
Cairngorm House, Almondvale Boulevard,
Livingston EH54 6QN
Tel: (01506) 497500

► **Livingston** continued

Fax: (01506) 497086
E-mail: mail@keegansmith.co.uk
Categories of Work
Criminal court work
Criminal legal aid
Partners
Darryl Lovie
Iain Henry Barclay Smith
Consultant
Gayle Jane Addison
Employee
Roisin Anne Dugan

SNEDDON MORRISON
Law House, Fairbairn Place, Livingston
EH54 6TN
Tel: (01506) 497160
Fax: (01501) 745 440
Categories of Work
Advice the elderly & powers of attorney
Charities
Commercial property
Contract & property disputes
Education
Employment law
Family business advice
Landlord & tenant
Liquor licensing
Mental health
Mergers and acquisitions
Residential property
Wills, executives and trusts
Partner
Sandra Anne Sneddon

WALLACE QUINN & CO LIMITED
Fairbairn House, Fairbairn Place, Livingston
EH54 6TN
Tel: (01506) 353400
Fax: (01506) 353419
Web: www.wallacequinn.co.uk
Categories of Work
Advice the elderly & powers of attorney
Agriculture and estates
Civil court work
Commercial property
Construction
Contract & property disputes
Family and divorce
Family business advice
Landlord & tenant
Mergers and acquisitions
Residential property
SME business advice
Wills, executives and trusts
Director
Amy Ieropoulos
Employee
Pamela Murdoch

Lochgelly

BASTEN SNEDDON COURT SOLICITORS
6 Bank Street, Lochgelly KY5 9QQ

Tel: (01592) 782194
Categories of Work
Criminal court work
Criminal legal aid

BSW SOLICITORS LLP
6 Bank Street, Lochgelly KY5 9QQ
Tel: (01592) 782194
Categories of Work
Criminal court work
Criminal legal aid

FIFE COMMUNITY LAW LIMITED
Units 4 and 5, Ore Valley Business Centre,
Lochgelly KY5 9AF
Tel: (01592) 786710
Fax: (01592) 786711
E-mail: info@fifelawcentre.co.uk
Web: www.fifelawcentre.co.uk
Categories of Work
Adoption
Advice the elderly & powers of attorney
Benefit advice
Children
Childrens
Civil court work
Criminal court work
Criminal legal aid
Employment
Employment law
Family and divorce
Health
Social housing
Director
Samuel Christopher Barr Johnston
Employees
Eilis Marion Imrie
Louise Ruth Niven Laing

Lochgilphead

JANE MACLEOD
The Rhinns, Achnaba, Lochgilphead PA31 8RY
Tel: (01546) 606666
Fax: (01546) 603789
DX: 599705 LOCHGILPHEAD
E-mail: jane@janemacleod.co.uk
Categories of Work
Adoption
Agriculture and estates
Agriculture, crofting and fishing
Betting & gaming
Children
Civil legal aid
Commercial property
Construction
Family and divorce
Housing
Liquor licensing
Mental health
Planning
Residential property
Wills, executives and trusts

Partner
Jane Margaret MacLeod

C. & D. MACTAGGART
57 Lochnell Street, Lochgilphead PA31 8JN
Tel: (01546) 602581
E-mail: mail@cdm-law.co.uk
Web: www.mactaggart-law.co.uk
Categories of Work
Adoption
Advice the elderly & powers of attorney
Agriculture and estates
Agriculture, crofting and fishing
Betting & gaming
Children
Civil court work
Civil legal aid
Commercial litigation
Commercial property
Consumer credit
Contract & property disputes
Criminal court work
Criminal legal aid
Debt
Debt collecting
Debt recovery, insolvency, bankruptcy
Disability
Discrimination
Education
Employment
Employment law
Family and divorce
Family business advice
Housing
Human rights
Insolvency & corporate recovery
Landlord & tenant
Liquor licensing
Media and entertainment
Medical negligence – defender
Medical negligence – claimant
Mental health
Personal injury
Personal injury – defender
Professional negligence
Property litigation
Residential property
Road traffic
Social housing
Transport
Wills, executries and trusts

RUBENS
77 Argyll Street, Lochgilphead PA31 8NE
Tel: (01546) 602084
Fax: (01546) 603568
E-mail: ruben.murdanaigum@live.co.uk
Categories of Work
Alternative dispute resolution
Children
Civil court work
Civil legal aid
Commercial litigation
Criminal court work
Criminal legal aid
Disability
Discrimination
Education
Employment
Employment law
EU / international
Family business advice
Fishing
Health
Housing
Human rights
Immigration and asylum
Insurance
Joint venture
Liquor licensing
Local government
Medical negligence – defender
Medical negligence – claimant
Mental health
Personal injury
Personal injury – defender
Public sector
Road traffic
Transport
Wills, executries and trusts
Partner
Ruben Valaydon Murdanaigum

STEWART BALFOUR & SUTHERLAND
7 Argyll Street, Lochgilphead PA31 8LZ
Tel: (01546) 602903
Fax: (01546) 603716
E-mail: mail@sbslaw.co.uk
Categories of Work
Advice the elderly & powers of attorney
Residential property
Wills, executries and trusts
Associate
Fiona Anne McLeod

Lockerbie

HENDERSON & MACKAY
Victoria Square, 35 High Street, Lockerbie
DG11 2JP
Tel: (01576) 202137
Fax: (01576) 203090
E-mail: info@lockerbielaw.co.uk
Web: www.hendersonandmackay.co.uk
Categories of Work
Advice the elderly & powers of attorney
Agriculture and estates
Agriculture, crofting and fishing
Charities
Commercial property
Construction
Consumer credit
Contract & property disputes
Debt
Debt collecting
Disability
Employment

▶ *Lockerbie continued*

Employment law
Environment (Business Premises)
Family and divorce
Family business advice
Housing
Landlord & tenant
Liquor licensing
Local government
Mental health
Personal injury
Planning
Planning (Business Premises)
Projects
Residential property
Wills, executries and trusts
Partners
Victor William George Clark
Karen Norman-Thorpe

MCJERROW & STEVENSON
55 High Street, Lockerbie DG11 2JJ
Tel: (01576) 202123
Fax: (01576) 202898
E-mail: mcjerrows@btconnect.com
Web: www.mcjerrowstevenson.co.uk
Categories of Work
Adoption
Advice the elderly & powers of attorney
Agriculture and estates
Alternative dispute resolution
Children
Childrens
Civil court work
Civil legal aid
Commercial litigation
Commercial property
Construction
Consumer credit
Contract & property disputes
Criminal court work
Criminal legal aid
Debt
Debt collecting
Debt recovery, insolvency, bankruptcy
Education
Employment
Employment law
Family and divorce
Family business advice
Health and safety
Human rights
Insolvency & corporate recovery
Landlord & tenant
Liquor licensing
Medical negligence – claimant
Mental health
Personal injury
Personal tax
Professional negligence
Residential property
Road traffic
SME business advice

Wills, executries and trusts
Partner
Alistair James Stevenson
Associates
Stephen Williams
Barbara Witty
Employees
Abbi Armstrong
John Euan Edment
Kara Louise MacGregor-Duke
Katie Maureen Stevenson

Macduff

WALTER GERRARD & CO.
31 Duff Street, Macduff AB44 1QL
Tel: (01261) 832491
Fax: (01261) 833444
DX: 521338 BANFF
E-mail: info@waltergerrard.co.uk
Web: www.waltergerrard.co.uk
Categories of Work
Advice the elderly & powers of attorney
Agriculture and estates
Commercial property
Family business advice
Landlord & tenant
Residential property
Wills, executries and trusts
Partner
Frances Mary McKay
Consultant
Lesley Margaret Sloan
Employee
Gemma Marie McHardy

Mauchline

D.W. SHAW
5 Kilmarnock Road, Mauchline KA5 5DB
Tel: (01290) 550249
Fax: (01290) 550972
E-mail: ayrreception@dwshaw.co.uk
Web: www.dwshaw.co.uk
Categories of Work
Adoption
Advice the elderly & powers of attorney
Agriculture and estates
Agriculture, crofting and fishing
Children
Civil court work
Civil legal aid
Commercial property
Criminal court work
Criminal legal aid
Family and divorce
Family business advice
Landlord & tenant
Medical negligence – defender
Medical negligence – claimant
Personal injury
Personal injury – defender

Power and utilities
Professional negligence
Residential property
Road traffic
SME business advice
Wills, executries and trusts
Partner
Andrew George McVean
Employee
Alastair Hamilton McIntyre

Melrose

CULLEN KILSHAW
7 Market Square, Melrose TD6 9PQ
Tel: (01896) 822 796
E-mail: melrose@cullenkilshaw.com
Categories of Work
Adoption
Advice the elderly & powers of attorney
Agriculture and estates
Agriculture, crofting and fishing
Alternative dispute resolution
Children
Childrens
Civil court work
Civil legal aid
Commercial property
Contract & property disputes
Criminal court work
Criminal legal aid
Debt
Debt collecting
Debt recovery, insolvency, bankruptcy
Employment
Employment law
Environment (Business Premises)
Family and divorce
Family business advice
Fishing
Landlord & tenant
Liquor licensing
Local government
Personal injury
Planning (Business Premises)
Property litigation
Residential property
Road traffic
Wills, executries and trusts

Methil

PATERSON BELL LIMITED
343 Methilhaven Road, Methil KY8 3HR
Tel: (01333) 427999
E-mail: crime@patersonbell.co.uk
Categories of Work
Criminal court work
Criminal legal aid

Millport

ROBERT F DUFF & CO LIMITED
38 Stuart Street, Millport KA28 0AJ
Tel: (01475) 531177
Categories of Work
Advice the elderly & powers of attorney
Commercial property
Landlord & tenant
Liquor licensing
Planning (Business Premises)
Residential property
Wills, executries and trusts

Milngavie

INTERNATIONAL & DOMESTIC LAW PRACTICE
Suites 4 & 5, 13 Main Street, Milngavie
G62 6BJ
Tel: (0141) 9424455
Fax: (0141) 956 2008
E-mail: law@idlp.co.uk
Web: www.idlp.co.uk
Categories of Work
Adjudication
Advice the elderly & powers of attorney
Alternative dispute resolution
Civil court work
Commercial litigation
Commercial property
Construction
Contract & property disputes
Employment law
Family and divorce
Family business advice
Landlord & tenant
Property litigation
Residential property
SME business advice
Wills, executries and trusts
Partner
Thomas McFarlane

KERSLAND RESIDENTIAL
4 Station Road, Milngavie G62 8AB
Tel: (0333) 6008000
Categories of Work
Advice the elderly & powers of attorney
Commercial property
Family business advice
Landlord & tenant
Mergers and acquisitions
Residential property
Wills, executries and trusts

KERSLANDS SOLICITORS LIMITED
4 Station Road, Milngavie G62 8AB
Tel: (0333) 6008000
Fax: (0333) 6008001
DX: 581605 MILNGAVIE
E-mail: enquiries@kerslands.com
Categories of Work
Advice the elderly & powers of attorney
Commercial property

▶ *Milngavie continued*

Family business advice
Landlord & tenant
Mergers and acquisitions
Residential property
Wills, executories and trusts
Directors
Alison Keith
Lesley McDermid

MACGREGOR & CO.
11 Stewart Street, Milngavie G62 6BW
Tel: (0141) 9564263
Fax: (0141) 9562696
E-mail: enquiries@macgregorandco.co.uk
Categories of Work
Advice the elderly & powers of attorney
Residential property
Wills, executories and trusts
Partner
Euan Macgregor

RENNIE MCINNES LLP
Douglas House, 42 Main Street, Milngavie
G62 6BU
Tel: (0141) 5629540
Fax: (0141) 404 8414
E-mail: stewart@renniemcinnes.co.uk
Web: www.renniemcinnes.co.uk
Categories of Work
Advice the elderly & powers of attorney
Banking & finance
Commercial property
Competition
Contract & property disputes
Copyright, trade marks and design
Debt
Debt recovery, insolvency, bankruptcy
Disability
Discrimination
Employment
Employment law
EU / international
Family business advice
Insolvency & corporate recovery
IT and intellectual property
Joint venture
Landlord & tenant
Media and entertainment
Mergers and acquisitions
Oil & gas
Residential property
SME business advice
Software licensing
Wills, executories and trusts
Partners
Aileen Jane McInnes
James Stewart Rennie
Consultant
Lucinda Jane Hunter

RUTHVEN, KEENAN, POLLOCK & CO.
18 Main Street, Milngavie G62 6BL
Tel: (0141) 9564647

DX: 581602 MILNGAVIE
Categories of Work
Adoption
Advice the elderly & powers of attorney
Children
Civil court work
Civil legal aid
Commercial property
Contract & property disputes
Criminal court work
Criminal legal aid
Debt
Employment law
Family and divorce
Landlord & tenant
Personal injury
Residential property
Road traffic
Wills, executories and trusts

Moffat

A.M. SIMPSON & SON
14 Well Street, Moffat DG10 9DP
Tel: (01683) 220118
Fax: (01683) 221162
Web: www.am-simpson.co.uk
Categories of Work
Adoption
Advice the elderly & powers of attorney
Agriculture and estates
Alternative dispute resolution
Children
Childrens
Civil court work
Civil legal aid
Commercial litigation
Commercial property
Construction
Consumer credit
Contract & property disputes
Criminal court work
Criminal legal aid
Debt
Debt collecting
Debt recovery, insolvency, bankruptcy
Education
Employment
Employment law
Family and divorce
Family business advice
Health and safety
Human rights
Insolvency & corporate recovery
Landlord & tenant
Liquor licensing
Medical negligence – claimant
Mental health
Personal injury
Personal tax
Professional negligence
Residential property
Road traffic

SME business advice
Wills, executives and trusts
Employee
Tom Stuart Pottinger

Monifieth

AEMS LIMITED
12-14 Maule Street, Monifieth DD5 4JN
Tel: (01382) 539313
Fax: (0845) 6431609
E-mail: info@legaleagles.tv
Web: www.legaleagles.tv
Categories of Work
Advice the elderly & powers of attorney
Civil legal aid
Landlord & tenant
Liquor licensing
Mental health
Residential property
Wills, executives and trusts
Employee
Zoe Allan

ALAN E. MASTERTON
12-14 Maule Street, Monifieth DD5 4JN
Tel: (01382) 539313
Fax: (0845) 6431609
E-mail: info@legaleagles.tv
Web: www.legaleagles.tv
Categories of Work
Advice the elderly & powers of attorney
Civil legal aid
Landlord & tenant
Liquor licensing
Mental health
Residential property
Wills, executives and trusts
Director
Alan Ellis Masterton

Montrose

T. DUNCAN & CO.
192 High Street, Montrose DD10 8NA
Tel: (01674) 672533
Fax: (01674) 673812
DX: 530911 Montrose
Web: www.tduncan.com
Categories of Work
Adoption
Advice the elderly & powers of attorney
Children
Childrens
Civil court work
Civil legal aid
Contract & property disputes
Criminal court work
Criminal legal aid
Debt
Education
Family and divorce
Landlord & tenant

Mental health
Personal injury
Property litigation
Residential property
Road traffic
Wills, executives and trusts
Partners
Nicholas Markowski
Julie Margaret Young
Employees
Derek Michael Devine
Norman Fraser
Sarah Jane Margaret Russo

SCOTT ALEXANDER
46 High Street, Montrose DD10 8JF
Tel: (01674) 671477
Fax: (01674) 671445
E-mail: enquiries@scottalexandersolicitors.co.uk
Web: www.scottalexandersolicitors.co.uk
Categories of Work
Advice the elderly & powers of attorney
Landlord & tenant
Residential property
Wills, executives and trusts
Partners
Elizabeth Mary Alexander
Kristin Margaret Alexander
Consultant
John Alexander Scott
Employee
Ross Francis Stirling

THORNTONS LAW LLP
55 High Street, Montrose DD10 8LR
Tel: (01674) 673 444
Fax: (01674) 673 948
E-mail: montrose@thorntons-law.co.uk
Categories of Work
Adjudication
Adoption
Advice the elderly & powers of attorney
Agriculture and estates
Agriculture, crofting and fishing
Alternative dispute resolution
Alternative investment market
Banking & finance
Benefit advice
Betting & gaming
Charities
Children
Childrens
Civil court work
Civil legal aid
Commercial litigation
Commercial property
Competition
Construction
Consumer credit
Contract & property disputes
Copyright, trade marks and design
Corporate tax
Credit brokerage
Criminal court work

► *Montrose continued*

Criminal legal aid
Data protection
Debt
Debt adjusting and debt counselling
Debt administration
Debt collecting
Debt recovery, insolvency, bankruptcy
Disability
Discrimination
Education
Employment
Employment law
Environment
Environment (Business Premises)
EU / international
Family and divorce
Family business advice
Fishing
Freedom of information
Health
Health and safety
Housing
Human rights
Immigration and asylum
Insolvency & corporate recovery
Insurance
IT and intellectual property
Joint venture
Landlord & tenant
Liquor licensing
Local government
Media and entertainment
Medical negligence – defender
Medical negligence – claimant
Mental health
Mergers and acquisitions
Oil & gas
Parliamentary
Pensions (Company)
Pensions (Employment)
Personal injury
Personal injury – defender
Personal tax
Planning
Planning (Business Premises)
Power and utilities
Private equity
Professional negligence
Projects
Property litigation
Public sector
Residential property
Road traffic
SME business advice
Social housing
Software licensing
Sport
Telecoms
Unit Trusts, OEICs and investment trusts
Wills, executries and trusts

Partner
Stuart Irvine Mackie
Employee
Graham Taylor

Motherwell

BRUCE THE LAWYERS
1 Merry Street, Motherwell ML1 1JJ
Tel: (01698) 260033
Categories of Work
Criminal court work
Criminal legal aid

FREELANDS
36 Muir Street, Motherwell ML1 1BW
Tel: (01698) 352600
Fax: (01698) 266240
DX: 570921 MOTHERWELL
E-mail: freelands@freelands.co.uk
Web: www.freelands.co.uk
Categories of Work
Adjudication
Adoption
Advice the elderly & powers of attorney
Agriculture and estates
Alternative dispute resolution
Charities
Children
Childrens
Civil court work
Civil legal aid
Commercial litigation
Commercial property
Contract & property disputes
Criminal court work
Criminal legal aid
Debt
Debt collecting
Debt recovery, insolvency, bankruptcy
Disability
Discrimination
Education
Employment
Employment law
Family and divorce
Family business advice
Health and safety
Human rights
Insolvency & corporate recovery
Joint venture
Landlord & tenant
Liquor licensing
Medical negligence – claimant
Mergers and acquisitions
Personal injury
Planning (Business Premises)
Professional negligence
Property litigation
Residential property
Road traffic
SME business advice
Wills, executries and trusts

Partners
Alistair Kilgour Buttery
Sandra Margaret Fleming
James Anderson Cowan Macdonald
Employee
Ryan Thomas Drury Bryceland

JACK GRANT & CO.
14 Hamilton Road, Motherwell ML1 1BB
Tel: (01698) 254 636
Fax: (01698) 275 121
DX: 570926 Motherwell
E-mail: jackgrant@btconnect.com
Categories of Work
Criminal court work
Criminal legal aid
Partners
Elaine Helen Grant
John Melrose Grant

HAMILTON ROSS
First Floor, The Dalziel Building, Motherwell
ML1 1PN
Tel: (01698) 337 201
E-mail: mail@hamiltonross.co.uk
Web: www.hamiltonross.co.uk
Categories of Work
Adoption
Advice the elderly & powers of attorney
Children
Childrens
Civil court work
Civil legal aid
Criminal court work
Criminal legal aid
Family and divorce
Landlord & tenant
Medical negligence – defender
Medical negligence – claimant
Personal injury
Personal injury – defender
Professional negligence
Residential property
Road traffic
Wills, executries and trusts

MICHAEL LOTT
1 Merry Street, Motherwell ML1 1JJ
Tel: (01698) 252331
Fax: (01698) 252984
E-mail: michaellott@btconnect.com
Categories of Work
Adoption
Advice the elderly & powers of attorney
Benefit advice
Children
Civil court work
Civil legal aid
Consumer credit
Criminal court work
Criminal legal aid
Debt collecting
Debt management
Debt recovery, insolvency, bankruptcy

Education
Family and divorce
Medical negligence – claimant
Mental health
Personal injury
Property litigation
Road traffic
Social housing
Wills, executries and trusts
Partner
Andrew Michael Ernest Lott
Employee
Neil Taylor

BRUCE MCCORMACK LIMITED
1 Merry Street, Motherwell ML1 1JJ
Tel: (01698) 260033
Fax: (01698) 250101
E-mail: admin@brucethelawyers.co.uk
Categories of Work
Criminal court work
Criminal legal aid
Directors
Diarmid Noel Bruce
Ian Alexander Scott
Employees
Rhonda Margaret Anderson
Simon George Gilmour
Edward Graham Robertson
Mary Ellen Scobbie

MOORE MACDONALD
2 Scott Street, Motherwell ML1 1PN
Tel: (01698) 262111
Fax: (01698) 260123
Categories of Work
Advice the elderly & powers of attorney
Civil court work
Commercial property
Contract & property disputes
Data protection
Education
Employment law
Family business advice
Landlord & tenant
Mental health
Personal injury
Property litigation
Residential property
Road traffic
Wills, executries and trusts
Partner
James Gerad Moore

NESS GALLAGHER SOLICITORS LIMITED
358 Brandon Street, Motherwell ML1 1XA
Tel: (01698) 254644
Fax: (01698) 262012
E-mail: post@nessgallagher.co.uk
Categories of Work
Adoption
Advice the elderly & powers of attorney
Benefit advice
Children

► **Motherwell continued**

Civil court work
Civil legal aid
Commercial litigation
Commercial property
Consumer credit
Criminal court work
Criminal legal aid
Debt
Debt collecting
Debt management
Education
Employment
Employment law
Family and divorce
Family business advice
Landlord & tenant
Mental health
Personal injury
Property litigation
Residential property
Road traffic
SME business advice
Social housing
Wills, executries and trusts
Consultant
Elspeth McInnes Forrest
Employee
Louise Mary Gillies

WATTERS, STEVEN & CO.
291/293 Brandon Street, Motherwell ML1 1RS
Tel: (01698) 276550
Fax: (01698) 510057
E-mail: info@watterssteven.co.uk
Categories of Work
Advice the elderly & powers of attorney
Children
Civil court work
Civil legal aid
Commercial property
Criminal court work
Criminal legal aid
Debt
Family and divorce
Liquor licensing
Personal injury
Residential property
Road traffic
Wills, executries and trusts
Partners
Andrew Gordon Steven
Thomas Martin Watters

WHYTE FRASER & CO LIMITED
Suite 1.7, Dalziel Building, Motherwell
ML1 1PN
Tel: (0141) 3785711
Fax: (0141) 4048125
E-mail: mwh@whytefraser.co.uk
Categories of Work
Adjudication
Alternative dispute resolution

Banking & finance
Civil court work
Civil legal aid
Commercial litigation
Commercial property
Construction
Contract & property disputes
Copyright, trade marks and design
Criminal court work
Data protection
Debt
Debt collecting
Debt management
Debt recovery, insolvency, bankruptcy
Employment law
Freedom of information
Housing
Insolvency & corporate recovery
Insurance
IT and intellectual property
Landlord & tenant
Local government
Media and entertainment
Power and utilities
Professional negligence
Property litigation
Residential property
Transport
Director
Marcus Fraser Whyte

WRIGHTS
70/72 Brandon Parade East, Motherwell
ML1 1LY
Tel: (01698) 267361
Fax: (01698) 264224
DX: 570924 MOTHERWELL
E-mail: info@wrightsolicitors.com
Categories of Work
Advice the elderly & powers of attorney
Agriculture and estates
Agriculture, crofting and fishing
Commercial property
Construction
Contract & property disputes
Debt
Family and divorce
Family business advice
Housing
Joint venture
Landlord & tenant
Planning
Planning (Business Premises)
Residential property
SME business advice
Wills, executries and trusts
Partners
Alan McCulloch
Gavin Hamilton Mitchell
Employees
Nevin Neil Busby
Lindsay Mairi Gilchrist

Musselburgh

DRUMMOND MILLER LLP
151 High Street, Musselburgh EH21 7DD
Tel: (0131) 6657393
Fax: (0131) 6536192
DX: 540940 MUSSELBURGH
E-mail: reception@drummondmiller.co.uk
Web: www.drummondmiller.co.uk
Categories of Work
Adjudication
Adoption
Advice the elderly & powers of attorney
Alternative dispute resolution
Charities
Children
Childrens
Civil court work
Civil legal aid
Commercial litigation
Commercial property
Contract & property disputes
Criminal court work
Data protection
Debt recovery, insolvency, bankruptcy
Discrimination
Education
Employment
Employment law
Environment
EU / international
Family and divorce
Family business advice
Health
Health and safety
Human rights
Immigration and asylum
Landlord & tenant
Medical negligence – defender
Medical negligence – claimant
Mental health
Oil & gas
Personal injury
Personal injury – defender
Personal tax
Professional negligence
Property litigation
Residential property
Road traffic
Wills, executries and trusts
Partner
Linsey Rachel Ferguson

R A LOW & COMPANY
The Drying House, Eskmills Park, Musselburgh
EH21 7AH
Tel: (0131) 6658885
Fax: (0131) 6533875
E-mail: admin@ra-low.com
Categories of Work
Adoption
Children
Criminal court work
Criminal legal aid

Family and divorce
Partner
Robert Arnott Low

SOMERVILLE & RUSSELL
39 Bridge Street, Musselburgh EH21 6AA
Tel: (0131) 6659041
Fax: (0131) 6651951
DX: ED20 EDINBURGH
E-mail: pduncan@somervilleandrussell.co.uk
Categories of Work
Adoption
Advice the elderly & powers of attorney
Children
Civil court work
Civil legal aid
Criminal court work
Criminal legal aid
Family and divorce
Human rights
Medical negligence – claimant
Residential property
Road traffic
Wills, executries and trusts
Partners
Pamela Dorothy Duncan
Andrew Patrick Dougal Mellor

Nairn

SIMON D BOOKER-MILBURN
Tarland, Albert Street, Nairn IV12 4HE
Tel: (07769) 682588
E-mail: simon@sdbmlaw.net
Categories of Work
Advice the elderly & powers of attorney
Civil legal aid
Criminal court work
Criminal legal aid
Wills, executries and trusts
Partner
Simon Donald Booker-Milburn

MONTEITH SOLICITORS LIMITED
Park Farm, Nairn IV12 5RZ
Tel: (0141) 370 0900
Web: www.monteithsolicitors.com
Categories of Work
Advice the elderly & powers of attorney
Agriculture and estates
Charities
Personal tax
Wills, executries and trusts
Director
Thomas William Monteith
Associates
Susie Kathleen Cowan
Samantha Caroline Taylor

R & R URQUHART LLP
Royal Bank of Scotland Bldgs, 20 High Street,
Nairn IV12 4AX
Tel: (01667) 453278
Fax: (01667) 453499

▶ *Nairn continued*
DX: 520950 NAIRN
E-mail: info.nairn@r-r-urquhart.com
Web: www.r-r-urquhart.com
Categories of Work
Adoption
Advice the elderly & powers of attorney
Agriculture and estates
Agriculture, crofting and fishing
Alternative dispute resolution
Banking & finance
Charities
Children
Civil court work
Commercial litigation
Commercial property
Contract & property disputes
Copyright, trade marks and design
Debt collecting
Debt recovery, insolvency, bankruptcy
Disability
Discrimination
Employment
Employment law
Environment
Environment (Business Premises)
EU / international
Family and divorce
Family business advice
Fishing
Human rights
Insolvency & corporate recovery
Joint venture
Landlord & tenant
Media and entertainment
Medical negligence – defender
Medical negligence – claimant
Pensions (Company)
Personal injury
Personal injury – defender
Planning
Planning (Business Premises)
Power and utilities
Professional negligence
Property litigation
Residential property
SME business advice
Telecoms
Unit Trusts, OEICs and investment trusts
Wills, executries and trusts
Partner
James Dunmore Hotchkis
Employee
Jade Louise Johnstone

New Galloway

WILLIAMSON & HENRY LLP
High Street, New Galloway DG7 4RN
Tel: (01644) 420440
E-mail: enquiries@williamsonandhenry.co.uk
Web: www.williamsonandhenry.co.uk

Categories of Work
Advice the elderly & powers of attorney
Family business advice
Landlord & tenant
Personal tax
Residential property
Wills, executries and trusts

Newburgh

PERFORMANCE LIVING LIMITED
The Business Suite, Barns of Woodside,
Newburgh KY14 6AD
Tel: (07714) 411415
Fax: (0808) 2800380
E-mail: neil@performanceliving.co.uk
Categories of Work
Advice the elderly & powers of attorney
Debt collecting
Environment
Environment (Business Premises)
Landlord & tenant
Mental health
Residential property
Wills, executries and trusts
Director
Neil Welch Paxton Anderson

Newmilns

MAIR MATHESON SOLICITORS LTD
53 Main Street, Newmilns KA16 9DA
Tel: (01560) 321225
Fax: (01560) 322109
DX: : KK22 KILMARNOCK
E-mail: enquiries@mairmatheson.co.uk
Web: www.mairmatheson.com
Categories of Work
Advice the elderly & powers of attorney
Commercial property
Family and divorce
Family business advice
Landlord & tenant
Residential property
Wills, executries and trusts
Directors
Lorraine Kerr
Andrew Ferrier Lister Matheson
Employee
Jacqueline Mitchell

Newton Stewart

GALLOWAY & AYRSHIRE PARTNERSHIP LLP
66 Victoria Street, Newton Stewart DG8 6DD
Tel: (01671) 402813
E-mail: mail@mccormicknicholson.co.uk
Categories of Work
Advice the elderly & powers of attorney
Agriculture and estates
Agriculture, crofting and fishing
Commercial property

Contract & property disputes
Debt collecting
Debt recovery, insolvency, bankruptcy
Employment law
Family and divorce
Family business advice
Housing
Insolvency & corporate recovery
Landlord & tenant
Liquor licensing
Personal tax
Planning
Planning (Business Premises)
Power and utilities
Residential property
SME business advice
Wills, executries and trusts

MCCORMICK & NICHOLSON
66 Victoria Street, Newton Stewart DG8 6DD
Tel: (01671) 402813
DX: 580961 NEWTON STEWART
E-mail: mail@mccormicknicholson.co.uk
Web: www.mccormicknicholson.co.uk
Categories of Work
Advice the elderly & powers of attorney
Agriculture and estates
Agriculture, crofting and fishing
Commercial property
Contract & property disputes
Debt collecting
Debt recovery, insolvency, bankruptcy
Employment law
Family and divorce
Family business advice
Housing
Insolvency & corporate recovery
Landlord & tenant
Liquor licensing
Personal tax
Planning
Planning (Business Premises)
Power and utilities
Residential property
SME business advice
Wills, executries and trusts

MATTHEWS LEGAL LIMITED
38/40 Albert Street, Newton Stewart DG8 6EJ
Tel: (01671) 404100
DX: 580962 NEWTON STEWART
E-mail: enquiries@abamatthews.com
Web: www.abamatthews.com
Categories of Work
Criminal court work
Criminal legal aid

MATTHEWS LEGAL LIMITED
Bank of Scotland Buildings, 37 Albert Street,
Newton Stewart DG8 6EG
Tel: (01671) 404100
Fax: (01671) 404140
E-mail: enquiries@abamatthews.com
Web: www.abamatthews.com

Categories of Work
Criminal court work
Criminal legal aid
Directors
Patrick Joseph Baxter
Helena Grace Fox
Peter Alexander Hope Matthews
Employee
Adam John MacCaig

SMITH & VALENTINE
66 Victoria Street, Newton Stewart DG8 6DD
Tel: (01671) 402813
Categories of Work
Advice the elderly & powers of attorney
Agriculture and estates
Agriculture, crofting and fishing
Commercial property
Contract & property disputes
Debt collecting
Debt recovery, insolvency, bankruptcy
Employment law
Family and divorce
Family business advice
Housing
Insolvency & corporate recovery
Landlord & tenant
Liquor licensing
Personal tax
Planning
Planning (Business Premises)
Power and utilities
Residential property
SME business advice
Wills, executries and trusts

North Berwick

ALSTON LAW
88 High Street, North Berwick EH39 4HE
Tel: (01620) 892000
E-mail:
eastlothianproperty@simpsonmarwick.com
Web: www.alstonlaw.co.uk
Categories of Work
Adoption
Advice the elderly & powers of attorney
Agriculture and estates
Alternative dispute resolution
Banking & finance
Children
Civil court work
Commercial litigation
Commercial property
Consumer credit
Contract & property disputes
Debt
Debt collecting
Debt recovery, insolvency, bankruptcy
Disability
Discrimination
Employment
Employment law

► **North Berwick continued**

EU / international
Family and divorce
Housing
Insolvency & corporate recovery
Insurance
Landlord & tenant
Local government
Medical negligence – claimant
Personal injury
Professional negligence
Property litigation
Public sector
Residential property
Road traffic
Wills, executries and trusts

CLYDE & CO (SCOTLAND) LLP
88 High Street, North Berwick EH39 4HE
Tel: (01620) 892000
DX: 541249 NORTH BERWICK
E-mail: Enquiries.Scotland@clydeco.com
Web: www.clydeco.com
Categories of Work
Adjudication
Adoption
Alternative dispute resolution
Banking & finance
Children
Civil court work
Civil legal aid
Commercial litigation
Commercial property
Construction
Contract & property disputes
Copyright, trade marks and design
Criminal court work
Criminal legal aid
Data protection
Disability
Discrimination
Education
Employment
Employment law
Environment
Environment (Business Premises)
EU / international
Family and divorce
Freedom of information
Health
Health and safety
Human rights
Insurance
Joint venture
Landlord & tenant
Liquor licensing
Local government
Medical negligence – defender
Medical negligence – claimant
Mental health
Oil & gas
Parliamentary
Pensions (Employment)

Personal injury
Personal injury – defender
Power and utilities
Professional negligence
Property litigation
Public sector
Road traffic
Shipping
Sport
Transport

GARDEN STIRLING BURNET (TRADING AS WALLACE & MENZIES)
8 Westgate, North Berwick EH39 4AF
Tel: (01620) 892307
DX: 54 1247 NORTH BERWICK
Categories of Work
Adoption
Advice the elderly & powers of attorney
Children
Commercial property
Criminal court work
Criminal legal aid
Education
Employment law
Family and divorce
Family business advice
Joint venture
Landlord & tenant
Liquor licensing
Residential property
Wills, executries and trusts

GILSON GRAY LLP
33 Westgate, North Berwick EH39 4AG
Tel: (01620) 893481
Fax: (01620) 894442
Web: www.gilsongray.co.uk
Categories of Work
Adjudication
Adoption
Advice the elderly & powers of attorney
Agriculture and estates
Alternative dispute resolution
Banking & finance
Betting & gaming
Charities
Children
Childrens
Civil court work
Civil legal aid
Commercial litigation
Commercial property
Competition
Construction
Consumer credit
Contract & property disputes
Copyright, trade marks and design
Data protection
Debt
Debt administration
Debt collecting
Debt recovery, insolvency, bankruptcy
Disability

Discrimination
Education
Employment
Employment law
Environment
EU / international
Family and divorce
Family business advice
Freedom of information
Health and safety
Housing
Immigration and asylum
Insolvency & corporate recovery
Insurance
IT and intellectual property
Joint venture
Landlord & tenant
Liquor licensing
Local government
Media and entertainment
Medical negligence – defender
Medical negligence – claimant
Mergers and acquisitions
Mining
Oil & gas
Pensions (Company)
Personal injury
Personal injury – defender
Personal tax
Planning
Planning (Business Premises)
Power and utilities
Private equity
Professional negligence
Projects
Property litigation
Public sector
Residential property
Road traffic
Shipping
SME business advice
Social housing
Software licensing
Sport
Telecoms
Transport
Wills, executries and trusts
Partner
Dorothy Anne Kellas
Associate
Cheryl Anne Edgar

PARIS STEELE
Clydesdale Bank Chambers, 35 Westgate,
North Berwick EH39 4AG
Tel: (01620) 892138
Fax: (01620) 895 162
DX: 541246 NORTH BERWICK
E-mail: northberwick@parissteele.com
Web: www.parissteele.com
Categories of Work
Advice the elderly & powers of attorney
Agriculture and estates

Betting & gaming
Civil court work
Civil legal aid
Commercial property
Contract & property disputes
Debt
Debt recovery, insolvency, bankruptcy
Disability
Employment
Employment law
Family and divorce
Family business advice
Human rights
Landlord & tenant
Liquor licensing
Medical negligence – claimant
Mental health
Personal injury
Personal tax
Property litigation
Residential property
Social housing
Wills, executries and trusts
Partners
Lesley Louise Anderson
Edward Andrew Danks
Employees
Rebecca Evelyn Greig
Kirsty Anne Wilson

SIMPSON & MARWICK
88 High Street, North Berwick EH39 4HE
Tel: (01620) 892000
E-mail:
eastlothianproperty@simpsonmarwick.com
Categories of Work
Adoption
Advice the elderly & powers of attorney
Agriculture and estates
Alternative dispute resolution
Banking & finance
Children
Civil court work
Commercial litigation
Commercial property
Consumer credit
Contract & property disputes
Debt
Debt collecting
Debt recovery, insolvency, bankruptcy
Disability
Discrimination
Employment
Employment law
EU / international
Family and divorce
Housing
Insolvency & corporate recovery
Insurance
Landlord & tenant
Local government
Medical negligence – claimant
Personal injury

▶ **North Berwick continued**

Professional negligence
Property litigation
Public sector
Residential property
Road traffic
Wills, executries and trusts

WALLACE & MENZIES
8 Westgate, North Berwick EH39 4AF
Tel: (01620) 892307
DX: 54 1247 NORTH BERWICK
Categories of Work
Adoption
Advice the elderly & powers of attorney
Children
Commercial property
Criminal court work
Criminal legal aid
Education
Employment law
Family and divorce
Family business advice
Joint venture
Landlord & tenant
Liquor licensing
Residential property
Wills, executries and trusts

Oban

ANDERSON BANKS
22 Argyll Square, Oban PA34 4AT
Tel: (01631) 563158
Fax: (01631) 565459
DX: OB1 OBAN
E-mail: gseaton@andersonbanks.co.uk
Web: www.andersonbanks.co.uk
Categories of Work
Adoption
Advice the elderly & powers of attorney
Agriculture and estates
Agriculture, crofting and fishing
Children
Childrens
Civil court work
Commercial litigation
Commercial property
Contract & property disputes
Criminal court work
Criminal legal aid
Debt collecting
Debt recovery, insolvency, bankruptcy
Employment
Employment law
Family and divorce
Family business advice
Landlord & tenant
Medical negligence – claimant
Mental health
Personal injury
Personal injury – defender
Property litigation

Residential property
Road traffic
SME business advice
Wills, executries and trusts
Partner
William Gordon Seaton

CURACH LIMITED
Linndhu House, 19 Stevenson Street, Oban
PA34 5NA
Tel: (01631) 562317
Fax: (01631) 566288
DX: OB6 OBAN
E-mail: mail@stevensonkennedy.co.uk
Categories of Work
Criminal court work
Criminal legal aid
Director
Gordon Goldie McNab
Employee
Kevin John McGinness

DM MACKINNON
Bank of Scotland Buildings, Oban PA34 4LN
Tel: (01631) 563014
Fax: (01631) 566463
DX: OB4 OBAN
E-mail: info@dmmk.co.uk
Web: www.dmmk.co.uk
Categories of Work
Advice the elderly & powers of attorney
Commercial property
Contract & property disputes
Debt collecting
Family business advice
Landlord & tenant
Residential property
Wills, executries and trusts
Partners
Louise Anne Fraser
Alan Andrew Manson
SallyAnn Orr
Consultant
Karen Louise MacAllister
Associate
Liam John Anthony McDermid

MACARTHUR LEGAL
Boswell House, Argyll Square, Oban PA34 4BD
Tel: (01631) 562215
Fax: (01631) 565490
E-mail: info@macarthurlegal.co.uk
Categories of Work
Advice the elderly & powers of attorney
Alternative dispute resolution
Commercial property
Family and divorce
Family business advice
Landlord & tenant
Liquor licensing
Personal injury
Personal injury – defender
Residential property
Wills, executries and trusts

Partners
Alexander Moncrieff Murray
Margaret Anne Wilson
Consultant
Terence Crawford Macnair
Associate
Robin Currie
Employee
Louise Colhoun

MACPHEE & PARTNERS LLP
First Floor, 26 George Street, Oban PA34 5SB
Tel: (01631) 562308
Fax: (01631) 358923
DX: OB10 OBAN
Web: www.macphee.co.uk
Categories of Work
Adoption
Advice the elderly & powers of attorney
Agriculture and estates
Banking & finance
Children
Childrens
Civil court work
Civil legal aid
Commercial litigation
Commercial property
Consumer credit
Contract & property disputes
Copyright, trade marks and design
Data protection
Debt
Debt management
Debt recovery, insolvency, bankruptcy
Education
Employment
Employment law
Family and divorce
Family business advice
Freedom of information
Insolvency & corporate recovery
IT and intellectual property
Joint venture
Landlord & tenant
Liquor licensing
Media and entertainment
Mental health
Mergers and acquisitions
Property litigation
Residential property
SME business advice
Software licensing
Telecoms
Wills, executries and trusts
Associates
Elizabeth Jane MacKay
Billie Smith

SHAW'S LAW LTD
Scottish Marine Institute, Oban PA37 1QA
Tel: (01631) 705007
Fax: (01631) 201324
E-mail: heather@shawslaw.co.uk
Web: www.shawslaw.co.uk

Categories of Work
Advice the elderly & powers of attorney
Commercial property
Family and divorce
Residential property
Wills, executries and trusts
Directors
Sorley Thorburn Henderson
Heather Grace Shaw

STEVENSON KENNEDY
Linndhu House, 19 Stevenson Street, Oban
PA34 5NA
Tel: (01631) 562317
E-mail: mail@stevensonkennedy.co.uk
Categories of Work
Criminal court work
Criminal legal aid

E. THORNTON & CO.
17-19 Lochside Street, Oban PA34 4HP
Tel: (01631) 566771
Fax: (01631) 564011
E-mail: info@ethornton.co.uk
Web: www.ethornton.co.uk
Categories of Work
Adoption
Advice the elderly & powers of attorney
Agriculture and estates
Agriculture, crofting and fishing
Alternative dispute resolution
Benefit advice
Betting & gaming
Charities
Children
Childrens
Civil court work
Civil legal aid
Commercial litigation
Commercial property
Construction
Consumer credit
Contract & property disputes
Criminal court work
Criminal legal aid
Data protection
Debt
Debt collecting
Debt management
Debt recovery, insolvency, bankruptcy
Disability
Discrimination
Education
Employment
Employment law
Environment
Family and divorce
Family business advice
Fishing
Freedom of information
Health and safety
Housing
Human rights
Insolvency & corporate recovery

▶ *Oban continued*

Joint venture
Landlord & tenant
Liquor licensing
Local government
Media and entertainment
Medical negligence – defender
Medical negligence – claimant
Mental health
Personal injury
Personal injury – defender
Planning
Professional negligence
Property litigation
Residential property
Road traffic
SME business advice
Social housing
Sport
Wills, executives and trusts
Partners
Donna Marie Sagewood
Edward Thornton
Employees
Jane Alice McLaren
Andrew Ross Vennard

Oldmeldrum

FALCONERS
Aird House, Urquhart Road, Oldmeldrum
AB51 0EX
Tel: (01651) 873962
Fax: (01651) 873962
E-mail: robin@falconerslaw.com
Categories of Work
Advice the elderly & powers of attorney
Disability
Discrimination
Employment
Employment law
Joint venture
Planning (Business Premises)
SME business advice
Wills, executives and trusts
Partner
Robin Andrew Falconer

STEWART & WATSON
21 Market Square, Oldmeldrum AB51 0AA
Tel: (01651) 872314
E-mail: info@stewartwatson.co.uk
Web: www.stewartwatson.co.uk
Categories of Work
Adoption
Advice the elderly & powers of attorney
Agriculture and estates
Agriculture, crofting and fishing
Alternative dispute resolution
Charities
Children
Civil court work
Civil legal aid

Commercial property
Contract & property disputes
Criminal court work
Criminal legal aid
Debt
Debt collecting
Debt recovery, insolvency, bankruptcy
Employment
Environment
Environment (Business Premises)
Family and divorce
Housing
Immigration and asylum
Landlord & tenant
Mental health
Personal injury
Projects
Residential property
Road traffic
Wills, executives and trusts

Paisley

ALEXR. MCALLISTER & MCKECHNIE
6 Moss Street, Paisley PA1 1BL
Tel: (0141) 8878961
Fax: (0141) 8872999
E-mail: property@ammlaw.co.uk
Categories of Work
Advice the elderly & powers of attorney
Alternative dispute resolution
Commercial property
Contract & property disputes
Copyright, trade marks and design
Debt collecting
Debt recovery, insolvency, bankruptcy
Employment law
Family and divorce
Family business advice
Human rights
IT and intellectual property
Landlord & tenant
Liquor licensing
Local government
Mental health
Personal injury
Residential property
Road traffic
SME business advice
Sport
Wills, executives and trusts
Partners
Douglas Jackson Currie
Fraser Macfarlane Currie
Employee
Mark Gerard O'Neill

BANKS DEVLIN & CO.
78 Causeyside Street, Paisley PA1 1YP
Tel: (0141) 8894949
Fax: (0141) 8480273
E-mail: terry.devlin@banksdevlin.com

Categories of Work
Civil court work
Civil legal aid
Criminal court work
Criminal legal aid
Personal injury
Residential property
Road traffic
Wills, executries and trusts
Partners
James Scott Banks
Terence Devlin

BUCHANAN DICKSON FRAME
Studio 3005, Mile End, Abbey Mill Business
Centre, Paisley PA1 1JS
Tel: (0141) 8480303
Fax: (0141) 8486818
E-mail: df@bdflaw.co.uk
Web: www.bdflaw.co.uk
Categories of Work
Advice the elderly & powers of attorney
Residential property
Wills, executries and trusts
Partners
David Andrew Love Frame
Allan John Swan Hutton

CAMERON PINKERTON & CO LLP
25 Gauze Street, Paisley PA1 1ES
Tel: (0141) 8875211
Fax: (0141) 8893926
DX: PA46 PAISLEY
E-mail: info@cameronpinkerton.co.uk
Categories of Work
Advice the elderly & powers of attorney
Children
Civil legal aid
Family and divorce
Residential property
Wills, executries and trusts
Partners
Roisin Mary Bonar
Sandra Love Docherty
George James Duff
Lorna McCaskill

CAMPBELL & MCCARTNEY
9c St James Street, Paisley PA3 2HL
Tel: (0141) 8899900
Categories of Work
Adoption
Advice the elderly & powers of attorney
Benefit advice
Children
Childrens
Civil court work
Civil legal aid
Consumer credit
Credit brokerage
Criminal court work
Criminal legal aid
Debt
Debt adjusting and debt counselling

Debt administration
Debt collecting
Debt management
Disability
Discrimination
Education
Employment law
Family and divorce
Human rights
Landlord & tenant
Medical negligence – claimant
Mental health
Personal injury
Personal tax
Professional negligence
Provision of credit information services
Residential property
Road traffic
Social housing
Wills, executries and trusts

COCHRAN DICKIE
21 Moss Street, Paisley PA1 1BX
Tel: (0141) 8892245
Fax: (0141) 8877769
DX: PA1 PAISLEY
E-mail: paisley@cochrandickie.co.uk
Categories of Work
Adoption
Advice the elderly & powers of attorney
Children
Civil court work
Civil legal aid
Commercial property
Contract & property disputes
Criminal court work
Criminal legal aid
Family and divorce
Family business advice
Joint venture
Landlord & tenant
Mergers and acquisitions
Personal tax
Residential property
Wills, executries and trusts
Directors
Lyndsey Adam
Jennifer May Cochran
Angus Kerr Storrie
Employees
Dale Samuel Crombie
Amy Elizabeth Docherty
Karen Watson Girvan
Hazel Alexandra Mountain Hamilton
Ewan Spence MacPhillimy
Louise Catherine McPhillimy

PAUL V COYLE SOLICITOR ADVOCATE
3005 Mile End, Abbey Mill Business Centre,
Paisley PA1 1JS
Tel: (0141) 8899546
E-mail: paul@solad.co.uk
Categories of Work
Criminal court work

► *Paisley continued*
Criminal legal aid
Residential property
Wills, executries and trusts

D AND F LAWYERS
Suite 149 St James Business Centre, 29
Linwood Road, Paisley PA3 3AT
Tel: (07736) 441238
E-mail: asim.khan@dandflawyers.com
Categories of Work
Adjudication
Alternative dispute resolution
Civil court work
Civil legal aid
Commercial litigation
Contract & property disputes
Data protection
Employment
EU / international
Family and divorce
Freedom of information
Health
Joint venture
Local government
Medical negligence – claimant
Mergers and acquisitions
Oil & gas
Professional negligence
Public sector
Partner
Asim Anwar Khan

**FRANCES EVANS COMMERCIAL LAW
PRACTICE**
26 Craw Road, Paisley PA2 6AD
Tel: (0141) 8894835
Categories of Work
Banking & finance
Commercial property
Construction
Contract & property disputes
Environment
Landlord & tenant
Oil & gas
Planning
Planning (Business Premises)
Residential property
SME business advice
Partner
Frances Bridget Geraldine Evans

JOHN GARDNER AND COMPANY
28 Moss Street, Paisley PA1 1BA
Tel: (0141) 8896458
Fax: (0141) 8898758
E-mail: jg@therobertkerrpartnership.com
Categories of Work
Criminal court work
Criminal legal aid
Partner
John Gardner

HUNTER & ROBERTSON LIMITED
35 High Street, Paisley PA1 2AG

Tel: (0141) 8893196
Fax: (0141) 8401334
DX: PA16 PAISLEY
Web: www.hunter-robertson.co.uk
Categories of Work
Adoption
Advice the elderly & powers of attorney
Agriculture and estates
Children
Civil court work
Civil legal aid
Commercial litigation
Commercial property
Contract & property disputes
Criminal court work
Criminal legal aid
Debt
Debt recovery, insolvency, bankruptcy
Disability
Discrimination
Education
Employment
Employment law
Family and divorce
Human rights
Landlord & tenant
Medical negligence – claimant
Mental health
Personal injury
Professional negligence
Property litigation
Residential property
Road traffic
Wills, executries and trusts
Directors
Robert Ferguson Dunn
Jilly-Ann Melrose
Consultant
Sheila Agnes Mechan
Associate
Terence John Docherty
Employees
Aisha Ali
James Thomas Clarke
Fiona Dalton
Lilia Muir
Hannah Elizabeth Wilson

LAM FAMILY LAW
Studio 3015, Mile End Mill, Abbey Mill
Business Centre, Paisley PA1 1JS
Tel: (0141) 8890101
Fax: (0141) 3701723
E-mail: enquiry@lamfamilylaw.co.uk
Categories of Work
Adoption
Children
Civil court work
Civil legal aid
Employment
Employment law
Family and divorce

Partner
Lindsey Ann McLachlan

MCAULEY, MCCARTHY & CO.
29 Moss Street, Paisley PA1 1DL
Tel: (0141) 5617779
Fax: (0141) 5617797
Categories of Work
Adoption
Advice the elderly & powers of attorney
Alternative dispute resolution
Children
Childrens
Civil court work
Civil legal aid
Commercial property
Environment (Business Premises)
Family and divorce
Family business advice
Landlord & tenant
Mental health
Planning (Business Premises)
Private equity
Public sector
Residential property
SME business advice
Wills, executries and trusts
Partner
Helen Hughes
Employee
Ailidh Kate O'Brien

MCCUSKER MCELROY & GALLANAGH
SOLICITORS
9 St. James Street, Paisley PA3 2HL
Tel: (0141) 5619999
Categories of Work
Children
Civil court work
Civil legal aid
Criminal court work
Criminal legal aid
Family and divorce
Medical negligence – defender
Personal injury – defender
Professional negligence
Road traffic
Employee
Michael Patrick Stewart

MACFARLANE YOUNG LIMITED
26 New Street, Paisley PA1 1YB
Tel: (0141) 8893257
Fax: (0141) 8890695
E-mail: mail@macfarlaneyoung.com
Web: www.macfarlaneyoung.com
Categories of Work
Adjudication
Adoption
Advice the elderly & powers of attorney
Agriculture and estates
Agriculture, crofting and fishing
Alternative dispute resolution
Benefit advice

Children
Childrens
Civil court work
Civil legal aid
Commercial litigation
Commercial property
Contract & property disputes
Criminal court work
Criminal legal aid
Data protection
Debt
Debt management
Debt recovery, insolvency, bankruptcy
Disability
Discrimination
Education
Employment
Employment law
Environment
Family and divorce
Family business advice
Freedom of information
Health
Health and safety
Housing
Insolvency & corporate recovery
Insurance
IT and intellectual property
Joint venture
Landlord & tenant
Liquor licensing
Media and entertainment
Medical negligence – defender
Medical negligence – claimant
Mental health
Mergers and acquisitions
Oil & gas
Pensions (Company)
Pensions (Employment)
Personal injury
Personal injury – defender
Personal tax
Planning
Professional negligence
Projects
Property litigation
Residential property
Road traffic
SME business advice
Software licensing
Sport
Wills, executries and trusts
Directors
Anne Constance Fletcher
Elizabeth Valerie O'Neil
Employees
Kirsty Docherty
Catherine Holly Johnstone

MCGEECHAN, WILLIAMSON & CO
14 St. James Street, Paisley PA3 2HT
Tel: (0141) 8899099
E-mail: tom@mcgeehanlaw.co.uk

▶ *Paisley continued*

Categories of Work
Criminal court work
Criminal legal aid

MCGEEHAN & CO LTD
14 St James Street, Paisley PA3 2HT
Tel: (0141) 8899099
Fax: (0141) 889 2262
E-mail: mcgeehan.eamonn@googlemail.com
Categories of Work
Criminal court work
Criminal legal aid
Directors
Eamonn McGeehan
Kirsty Jane McGeehan

MACNAIRS & WILSON LIMITED
9-11 New Street, Paisley PA1 1XU
Tel: (0141) 887 5181
Fax: (0141) 887 2775
DX: PA80 PAISLEY
E-mail: paisley@macnairswilson.co.uk
Categories of Work
Adoption
Advice the elderly & powers of attorney
Alternative dispute resolution
Children
Childrens
Civil court work
Civil legal aid
Commercial property
Contract & property disputes
Criminal court work
Criminal legal aid
Discrimination
Education
Employment
Employment law
Family and divorce
Housing
Human rights
Landlord & tenant
Mental health
Personal injury
Personal injury – defender
Property litigation
Residential property
Road traffic
Wills, executries and trusts
Directors
Douglas Mitchell
Stuart Fraser Wilson
Associate
Christine Anne Hirst

MJC LAW
21 Forbes Place, Paisley PA1 1UT
Tel: (0141) 849 2041
Fax: (0141) 8496231
E-mail: matthew@mjclaw.co.uk
Web: www.mjclaw.co.uk
Categories of Work
Advice the elderly & powers of attorney

Children
Childrens
Civil court work
Civil legal aid
Commercial litigation
Consumer credit
Contract & property disputes
Debt
Debt collecting
Debt recovery, insolvency, bankruptcy
Family and divorce
Family business advice
Insolvency & corporate recovery
Landlord & tenant
Property litigation
Partner
Matthew James Coffield
Employee
Karianne Falconer

MSM SOLICITORS LIMITED
51 Moss Street, Paisley PA1 1DR
Tel: (0141) 8896244
Fax: (0141) 8870964
E-mail: mail@msmlaw.co.uk
Web: www.msmlaw.co.uk
Categories of Work
Adoption
Advice the elderly & powers of attorney
Alternative dispute resolution
Benefit advice
Children
Childrens
Civil court work
Civil legal aid
Commercial litigation
Commercial property
Consumer credit
Contract & property disputes
Criminal court work
Criminal legal aid
Debt
Debt adjusting and debt counselling
Debt administration
Debt collecting
Debt management
Debt recovery, insolvency, bankruptcy
Disability
Discrimination
Education
Employment
Employment law
Family and divorce
Family business advice
Joint venture
Landlord & tenant
Liquor licensing
Medical negligence – claimant
Mental health
Personal injury
Personal injury – defender
Professional negligence
Property litigation

Residential property
Road traffic
SME business advice
Social housing
Wills, executries and trusts
Director
Graeme William McGowan
Employees
Nicola Maria McEleny
Carole Ann Thomson

PAISLEY CHILD LAW LIMITED
9 St James Street, Paisley PA3 2HL
Tel: (07896) 992200
Categories of Work
Criminal court work
Criminal legal aid
Director
David Joseph Nicholson

PAISLEY DEFENCE LAWYERS (SCOTLAND) LIMITED
9 St. James Street, Paisley PA3 2HL
Tel: (0141) 5619999
Categories of Work
Children
Civil court work
Civil legal aid
Criminal court work
Criminal legal aid
Family and divorce
Medical negligence – defender
Personal injury – defender
Professional negligence
Road traffic
Director
Terence Gallanagh
Employees
Lyndsey Heather Barber
Charles Patrick McCusker
Susan McCusker

KENNETH PATERSON
31 Wellmeadow Street, Paisley PA1 2EH
Tel: (0141) 5612215
Fax: (0141) 848 7770
E-mail: kpsols-lac@btconnect.com
Categories of Work
Adoption
Advice the elderly & powers of attorney
Alternative dispute resolution
Charities
Children
Civil court work
Civil legal aid
Commercial litigation
Education
Family and divorce
Family business advice
Personal injury
Property litigation
Road traffic
Wills, executries and trusts

Partner
Kenneth William Paterson

PATTISON & CO.
19 Glasgow Road, Paisley PA1 3QX
Tel: (0141) 8893296
Fax: (0141) 8870316
DX: PA 95 PAISLEY
E-mail:
bridget.mclaren@pattisonandcompany.com
Web: www.pattisonandcompany.com
Categories of Work
Adoption
Advice the elderly & powers of attorney
Children
Civil court work
Commercial litigation
Contract & property disputes
Criminal court work
Debt collecting
Debt recovery, insolvency, bankruptcy
Employment law
Family and divorce
Family business advice
Personal injury
Planning (Business Premises)
Professional negligence
Property litigation
Residential property
Road traffic
Wills, executries and trusts
Partner
Bridget Mary McLaren

T.F. REID & DONALDSON
48 Causeyside Street, Paisley PA1 1YH
Tel: (0141) 8897531
Fax: (0141) 8873380
DX: PA22 PAISLEY
E-mail: mail@reidlaw.co.uk
Web: www.reidlaw.co.uk
Categories of Work
Family business advice
Partners
Kenneth Gordon Macleod
David Allan Rankin
Consultant
Walter Macarthur Reid
Employee
Colette Maxwell

THE ROBERT KERR PARTNERSHIP LIMITED
28 Moss Street, Paisley PA1 1BA
Tel: (0141) 8896458
Fax: (0141) 8898758
DX: PA43 PAISLEY
E-mail: info@therobertkerrpartnership.com
Categories of Work
Criminal court work
Criminal legal aid
Discrimination
Human rights
Road traffic

► *Paisley continued*

Directors
James Edward Harris Arrol
Gemma Margaret Elder
Robert Jude Peter Kerr
Ellen MacDonald
Employee
Amy Spencer

TOD & MITCHELL
Terrace Buildings, The Cross, Paisley PA1 2YA
Tel: (0141) 8891444
Fax: (0141) 8891555
DX: PA35 PAISLEY
E-mail: enquiries@todandmitchell.co.uk
Categories of Work
Criminal court work
Criminal legal aid
Partners
Mark Allan Chambers
Paul Tierney Lynch
Rhona Marie Lynch
Robert Mitchell
Employees
Anthony Edward John Boland
Linzi Rachel Galbraith

WALKER LAIRD
7/9 Gilmour Street, Paisley PA1 1DG
Tel: (0141) 8875271
Fax: (0141) 8893268
DX: PA32 PAISLEY
E-mail: info@walkerlaird.co.uk
Categories of Work
Advice the elderly & powers of attorney
Children
Civil court work
Commercial property
Contract & property disputes
Debt
Debt collecting
Employment law
Family and divorce
Family business advice
Landlord & tenant
Medical negligence – claimant
Personal injury
Professional negligence
Residential property
Road traffic
SME business advice
Wills, executries and trusts
Partners
David Gordon Forbes
Ronald McGinlay
Associates
Barry Charles Berlow-Jackson
Kathryn Louise Gibb
Employees
Alan James McEwing
Anna Louise Miller-Brown
Alison Louise Morton

TOM WILLIAMSON LIMITED
14 St. James Street, Paisley PA3 2HT
Tel: (0141) 8899099
Fax: (0141) 8892262
E-mail: tom@mcgeehanlaw.co.uk
Categories of Work
Criminal court work
Criminal legal aid
Director
Thomas Williamson

WRIGHT & CRAWFORD (1906) LIMITED
11 Glasgow Road, Paisley PA1 3QS
Tel: (0141) 8876211
Fax: (0141) 8871122
E-mail: info@wright-crawford.co.uk
Web: www.wright-crawford.co.uk
Categories of Work
Adoption
Advice the elderly & powers of attorney
Alternative dispute resolution
Children
Civil court work
Commercial litigation
Commercial property
Employment law
Family and divorce
Landlord & tenant
Power and utilities
Residential property
Wills, executries and trusts
Directors
Denise Hooper
Colin Henry McNaught
Alan Mark Ralston
Associate
Caroline Jane Watt

Peebles

BLACKWOOD & SMITH LLP
15 Eastgate, Peebles EH45 8AD
Tel: (01721) 720131
E-mail: property@blackwoodsmith.com
Web: www.blackwoodsmith.com
Categories of Work
Adoption
Advice the elderly & powers of attorney
Alternative dispute resolution
Charities
Children
Civil court work
Commercial property
Contract & property disputes
Debt collecting
Employment law
Family and divorce
Family business advice
Landlord & tenant
Property litigation
Residential property
Wills, executries and trusts

BLACKWOOD & SMITH LLP
39 High Street, Peebles EH45 8AN
Tel: (01721) 720131
Fax: (01721) 729804
DX: 540970 PEEBLES
E-mail: office@blackwoodsmith.com
Web: www.blackwoodsmith.com
Categories of Work
Adoption
Advice the elderly & powers of attorney
Alternative dispute resolution
Charities
Children
Civil court work
Commercial property
Contract & property disputes
Debt collecting
Employment law
Family and divorce
Family business advice
Landlord & tenant
Property litigation
Residential property
Wills, executries and trusts
Partners
Struan Alexander Ferguson
Fiona Ross Fleming
Sally Ann Swinney
Employee
Carrie Wright

CULLEN KILSHAW
1 Rowan Court, Cavalry Park, Peebles
EH45 9BU
Tel: (01721) 723999
E-mail: peebles@cullenkilshaw.com
Web: www.cullenkilshaw.com
Categories of Work
Adoption
Advice the elderly & powers of attorney
Agriculture and estates
Agriculture, crofting and fishing
Alternative dispute resolution
Children
Childrens
Civil court work
Civil legal aid
Commercial property
Contract & property disputes
Criminal court work
Criminal legal aid
Debt
Debt collecting
Debt recovery, insolvency, bankruptcy
Employment
Employment law
Environment (Business Premises)
Family and divorce
Family business advice
Fishing
Landlord & tenant
Liquor licensing
Local government

Personal injury
Planning (Business Premises)
Property litigation
Residential property
Road traffic
Wills, executries and trusts

CULLEN KILSHAW
5 Northgate, Peebles EH45 8RX
Tel: (01721) 723 999
Fax: (01721) 723 888
E-mail: peebles@cullenkilshaw.com
Web: www.cullenkilshaw.com
Categories of Work
Adoption
Advice the elderly & powers of attorney
Agriculture and estates
Agriculture, crofting and fishing
Alternative dispute resolution
Children
Childrens
Civil court work
Civil legal aid
Commercial property
Contract & property disputes
Criminal court work
Criminal legal aid
Debt
Debt collecting
Debt recovery, insolvency, bankruptcy
Employment
Employment law
Environment (Business Premises)
Family and divorce
Family business advice
Fishing
Landlord & tenant
Liquor licensing
Local government
Personal injury
Planning (Business Premises)
Property litigation
Residential property
Road traffic
Wills, executries and trusts
Employee
Hannah Louise Duncan

NEIL SOLICITORS & ESTATE AGENTS
2-4 Northgate, Peebles EH45 8RS
Tel: (01721) 724199
Fax: (01721) 720869
E-mail: douglas@neilsolicitors.com
Web: www.neilsolicitors.com
Categories of Work
Advice the elderly & powers of attorney
Children
Civil court work
Commercial property
Contract & property disputes
Criminal court work
Debt
Debt management
Family and divorce

► *Peebles continued*

Family business advice
Landlord & tenant
Property litigation
Residential property
Social housing
Wills, executries and trusts
Partner
Douglas Peter Neil

ROAD TRAFFIC ACCIDENT LAW (SCOTLAND) LLP

5 Cherry Court, Cavalry Park, Peebles
EH45 9BU
Tel: (01721) 728238
Categories of Work
Civil court work
Personal injury
Professional negligence
Road traffic
Sport
Partner
Brenda Patricia Mitchell
Employees
Jodi Gordon
Zara Mary Jones
Thomas Finlay Mitchell

WRIGHTS

20 Northgate, Peebles EH45 8RS
Tel: (01721) 724172
Categories of Work
Advice the elderly & powers of attorney
Agriculture and estates
Agriculture, crofting and fishing
Commercial property
Construction
Contract & property disputes
Debt
Family and divorce
Family business advice
Housing
Joint venture
Landlord & tenant
Planning
Planning (Business Premises)
Residential property
SME business advice
Wills, executries and trusts

Penicuik

ALLAN MCDOUGALL MCQUEEN LLP

20 High Street, Penicuik EH26 8HW
Tel: (01968) 675694
Fax: (01968) 676546
DX: 551660 LIBERTON
E-mail: info@mcdougallmcqueen.co.uk
Web: www.mcdougallmcqueen.co.uk
Categories of Work
Adoption
Advice the elderly & powers of attorney
Charities

Children
Childrens
Civil court work
Civil legal aid
Commercial litigation
Commercial property
Contract & property disputes
Criminal court work
Criminal legal aid
Disability
Discrimination
Employment
Employment law
Family and divorce
Health and safety
Landlord & tenant
Medical negligence – claimant
Personal injury
Personal injury – defender
Personal tax
Professional negligence
Residential property
Road traffic
Wills, executries and trusts
Associate
Jacquelyne Pringle
Employees
Emma Margaret Jean Meechan
Donald William Towsey

MCDOUGALL MCQUEEN

20 High Street, Penicuik EH26 8HW
Tel: (01968) 676546
DX: : 551660 LIBERTON
Web: www.mcdougallmcqueen.co.uk
Categories of Work
Adoption
Advice the elderly & powers of attorney
Charities
Children
Childrens
Civil court work
Civil legal aid
Commercial litigation
Commercial property
Contract & property disputes
Criminal court work
Criminal legal aid
Disability
Discrimination
Employment
Employment law
Family and divorce
Health and safety
Landlord & tenant
Medical negligence – claimant
Personal injury
Personal injury – defender
Personal tax
Professional negligence
Residential property
Road traffic
Wills, executries and trusts

BRANDON MALONE & COMPANY LIMITED
Kirkhill House, 34 Kirkhill Road, Penicuik
EH26 8HZ
Tel: (0131) 6188868
E-mail: brandon@brandonmalone.com
Web: www.brandonmalone.com
Categories of Work
Adjudication
Alternative dispute resolution
Civil court work
Commercial litigation
Construction
Contract & property disputes
EU / international
Landlord & tenant
Oil & gas
Parliamentary
Power and utilities
Projects
Property litigation

STUART & STUART
12 John Street, Penicuik EH26 8AD
Tel: (01968) 677294
DX: 541114 PENICUIK
E-mail: penicuik@stuartandstuart.co.uk
Web: www.stuartandstuart.co.uk
Categories of Work
Advice the elderly & powers of attorney
Agriculture and estates
Alternative dispute resolution
Civil court work
Commercial property
Family and divorce
Immigration and asylum
Landlord & tenant
Liquor licensing
Mental health
Residential property
Unit Trusts, OEICs and investment trusts
Wills, executries and trusts
Partner
Andrew David John Bertram

Perth

ABERDEIN CONSIDINE AND COMPANY
72-74 High Street, Perth PH1 5TH
Tel: (01738) 450700
Fax: (01738) 450701
E-mail: ask@acandco.com
Categories of Work
Adjudication
Adoption
Advice the elderly & powers of attorney
Agriculture and estates
Agriculture, crofting and fishing
Alternative dispute resolution
Alternative investment market
Banking & finance
Charities
Children
Childrens
Civil court work
Civil legal aid
Commercial litigation
Commercial property
Competition
Construction
Consumer credit
Contract & property disputes
Copyright, trade marks and design
Corporate tax
Credit brokerage
Criminal court work
Criminal legal aid
Data protection
Debt
Debt adjusting and debt counselling
Debt collecting
Debt recovery, insolvency, bankruptcy
Disability
Discrimination
Education
Employment
Employment law
Environment
Environment (Business Premises)
EU / international
Family and divorce
Family business advice
Freedom of information
Health
Health and safety
Human rights
Insolvency & corporate recovery
Insurance
Joint venture
Landlord & tenant
Liquor licensing
Local government
Media and entertainment
Mental health
Mergers and acquisitions
Pensions (Company)
Pensions (Employment)
Personal injury
Personal tax
Planning (Business Premises)
Private equity
Professional negligence
Property litigation
Public finance initiative
Public sector
Residential property
SME business advice
Social housing
Telecoms
Unit Trusts, OEICs and investment trusts
Wills, executries and trusts
Partner
Charles William Simpson Fraser

ABL (TRUSTEES & NOMINEES) LIMITED
Bordeaux House, 31 Kinnoull Street, Perth
PH1 5EN

▶ **Perth continued**

Tel: (01738) 639999

ANDERSON BEATON LAMOND
Bordeaux House, 31 Kinnoull Street, Perth
PH1 5EN
Tel: (01738) 639999
Fax: (01738) 630063
DX: PE5 PERTH
E-mail: info@abl-law.co.uk
Categories of Work
Agriculture and estates
Agriculture, crofting and fishing
Commercial property
Construction
Contract & property disputes
Employment
Employment law
Environment
Environment (Business Premises)
Family business advice
Fishing
Health and safety
Joint venture
Landlord & tenant
Liquor licensing
Mergers and acquisitions
Oil & gas
Pensions (Employment)
Planning
Planning (Business Premises)
Power and utilities
Projects
Property litigation
Residential property
SME business advice
Wills, executries and trusts
Partners
Lydia Margaret Fotheringham
Elizabeth Marion McFadzean
Peter John Stewart
Employees
Heather Cameron
Ross Iain McNaughton

BLACKADDERS LLP
2 Tay Street, Perth PH1 5LJ
Tel: (01738) 440088
Fax: (01738) 441131
E-mail: enquiries@blackadders.co.uk
Categories of Work
Adoption
Advice the elderly & powers of attorney
Agriculture and estates
Agriculture, crofting and fishing
Alternative dispute resolution
Banking & finance
Charities
Children
Childrens
Civil court work
Civil legal aid
Commercial litigation

Commercial property
Competition
Construction
Consumer credit
Contract & property disputes
Copyright, trade marks and design
Data protection
Debt
Debt collecting
Debt recovery, insolvency, bankruptcy
Disability
Discrimination
Employment
Employment law
Environment
Environment (Business Premises)
EU / international
Family and divorce
Family business advice
Fishing
Freedom of information
Housing
Human rights
Insolvency & corporate recovery
IT and intellectual property
Joint venture
Landlord & tenant
Media and entertainment
Medical negligence – defender
Medical negligence – claimant
Mental health
Mergers and acquisitions
Pensions (Employment)
Personal injury
Personal injury – defender
Personal tax
Planning
Power and utilities
Private equity
Professional negligence
Property litigation
Public sector
Residential property
Road traffic
SME business advice
Software licensing
Sport
Telecoms
Wills, executries and trusts
Partner
Joanne Elizabeth Grimmond
Employee
Maxine Chiverton

BLACKADDERS LLP
Property Services, 77 George Street, Perth
PH1 5LB
Tel: (01738) 441124
E-mail: enquiries@blackadders.co.uk
Categories of Work
Adoption
Advice the elderly & powers of attorney
Agriculture and estates

Agriculture, crofting and fishing
Alternative dispute resolution
Banking & finance
Charities
Children
Childrens
Civil court work
Civil legal aid
Commercial litigation
Commercial property
Competition
Construction
Consumer credit
Contract & property disputes
Copyright, trade marks and design
Data protection
Debt
Debt collecting
Debt recovery, insolvency, bankruptcy
Disability
Discrimination
Employment
Employment law
Environment
Environment (Business Premises)
EU / international
Family and divorce
Family business advice
Fishing
Freedom of information
Housing
Human rights
Insolvency & corporate recovery
IT and intellectual property
Joint venture
Landlord & tenant
Media and entertainment
Medical negligence – defender
Medical negligence – claimant
Mental health
Mergers and acquisitions
Pensions (Employment)
Personal injury
Personal injury – defender
Personal tax
Planning
Power and utilities
Private equity
Professional negligence
Property litigation
Public sector
Residential property
Road traffic
SME business advice
Software licensing
Sport
Telecoms
Wills, executries and trusts

CULLEY & MCALPINE
40-42 South Street, Perth PH2 8PD
Tel: (01738) 626644
Fax: (01738) 625511

E-mail: enquiries@culleymcalpine.co.uk
Web: www.culleymcalpine.co.uk
Categories of Work
Adoption
Alternative dispute resolution
Benefit advice
Children
Civil court work
Civil legal aid
Criminal court work
Criminal legal aid
Debt
Debt adjusting and debt counselling
Debt recovery, insolvency, bankruptcy
Family and divorce
Mental health
Road traffic
Partners
Pauline Cullerton
William Warden
Consultant
John McLaughlin
Employees
Linda Elisabeth Ewing Clark
Ashleigh Jayne Falconer
Cheryl Vaughan Clark McKnight

EDEN LEGAL LIMITED
Unit E3, Inveralmond Business Centre, Perth
PH1 3FX
Tel: (01738) 310047
Categories of Work
Advice the elderly & powers of attorney
Agriculture and estates
Agriculture, crofting and fishing
Alternative dispute resolution
Commercial property
Environment
Family business advice
Landlord & tenant
Power and utilities
Residential property
Director
Craig Robert Harvie
Associates
Jennifer Isobel Douglas Davidson
Anneli Wilma Spence

ELLIOT & CO., WS
8 Charlotte Street, Perth PH1 5LL
Tel: (01738) 638246
Fax: (01738) 630527
DX: PE27 PERTH
E-mail: delliot@elliotsperth.co.uk
Categories of Work
Alternative dispute resolution
Charities
Children
Civil court work
Civil legal aid
Criminal court work
Debt
Debt collecting
Employment

► *Perth continued*

Employment law
Family and divorce
Family business advice
Medical negligence – defender
Medical negligence – claimant
Mental health
Personal injury
Personal injury – defender
Road traffic
SME business advice
Wills, executries and trusts
Partners
Catherine Mary Anne Elliot
Donald George Elliot
Associate
Hannah Martha Kennedy

GILLESPIE MACANDREW LLP
Broxden House, Lamberkine Drive, Perth
PH1 1RA
Tel: (01738) 231000
Fax: (01738) 231020
DX: PE12 PERTH
Web: www.gillespiemacandrew.co.uk
Categories of Work
Adjudication
Adoption
Advice the elderly & powers of attorney
Agriculture and estates
Agriculture, crofting and fishing
Alternative dispute resolution
Banking & finance
Benefit advice
Charities
Children
Civil court work
Civil legal aid
Commercial litigation
Commercial property
Competition
Construction
Consumer credit
Contract & property disputes
Copyright, trade marks and design
Corporate tax
Criminal court work
Data protection
Debt
Debt administration
Debt collecting
Debt recovery, insolvency, bankruptcy
Disability
Discrimination
Employment
Employment law
Environment
Environment (Business Premises)
EU / international
Family and divorce
Family business advice
Fishing
Freedom of information

Housing
Human rights
Insolvency & corporate recovery
IT and intellectual property
Joint venture
Landlord & tenant
Local government
Media and entertainment
Medical negligence – defender
Medical negligence – claimant
Mental health
Mergers and acquisitions
Mining
Parliamentary
Pensions (Employment)
Personal injury
Personal injury – defender
Personal tax
Planning
Planning (Business Premises)
Power and utilities
Private equity
Professional negligence
Projects
Property litigation
Public sector
Residential property
Road traffic
SME business advice
Software licensing
Wills, executries and trusts
Partners
Eilidh Gillian Adams
John Michael Greene Blair
Associate
Ruth Weir
Solicitor
Lindsay Davina Frances Bryce MacKay
Employees
Dionne Linda Brady
Jennifer Mary Munro

JAMESON + MACKAY LLP
1 Charlotte Street, Perth PH1 5LP
Tel: (01738) 631666
Fax: (01738) 630264
DX: PE26 PERTH
E-mail: mail@jamesonmackay.co.uk
Web: www.jamesonmackay.co.uk
Categories of Work
Advice the elderly & powers of attorney
Agriculture and estates
Civil court work
Commercial property
Family business advice
Landlord & tenant
Medical negligence – claimant
Personal injury
Residential property
Road traffic
Wills, executries and trusts

Partners
Victoria Anne Buchanan
Stephen David Inglis
Jennifer Anne Kirkwood
Alison Gail Ramsay
Consultant
Brian Marnoch
Employee
Debbie Marie Macleod

KIPPEN CAMPBELL LLP
48 Tay Street, Perth PH1 5TR
Tel: (01738) 635353
Fax: (01738) 643773
Web: www.kippencampbell.co.uk
Categories of Work
Adoption
Advice the elderly & powers of attorney
Agriculture and estates
Agriculture, crofting and fishing
Alternative dispute resolution
Charities
Children
Childrens
Civil court work
Civil legal aid
Commercial litigation
Commercial property
Contract & property disputes
Debt
Debt administration
Debt collecting
Disability
Discrimination
Employment
Employment law
Family and divorce
Family business advice
Housing
Landlord & tenant
Liquor licensing
Medical negligence – defender
Personal injury – defender
Property litigation
Residential property
SME business advice
Social housing
Sport
Wills, executries and trusts
Partners
Jacqueline Jane Dow
Robert Simon Macduff-Duncan
Sally Ann McCartney
Steven George McLaren
Susan Jane Wightman

KIPPEN CAMPBELL PROPERTY SERVICES
62 South Street, Perth PH2 8PD
Tel: (01738) 638283
Web: www.kippencampbell.co.uk
Categories of Work
Adoption
Advice the elderly & powers of attorney
Agriculture and estates

Agriculture, crofting and fishing
Alternative dispute resolution
Charities
Children
Childrens
Civil court work
Civil legal aid
Commercial litigation
Commercial property
Contract & property disputes
Debt
Debt administration
Debt collecting
Disability
Discrimination
Employment
Employment law
Family and divorce
Family business advice
Housing
Landlord & tenant
Liquor licensing
Medical negligence – defender
Personal injury – defender
Property litigation
Residential property
SME business advice
Social housing
Sport
Wills, executries and trusts

KIPPEN CAMPBELL (TRUSTEES) LIMITED
48 Tay Street, Perth PH1 5TR
Tel: (01738) 635353

KIRKLANDS LAW LIMITED
7 King Street, Perth PH2 8HR
Tel: (01738) 500 764
Fax: (01738) 443999
DX: PE 121 PERTH
E-mail: alano@orme-law.co.uk
Web: www.kirklands-law.co.uk
Categories of Work
Commercial property
Family business advice
Landlord & tenant
Mergers and acquisitions
Residential property
SME business advice
Wills, executries and trusts
Director
Graham MacFarlane Gibson

MCCASH & HUNTER LLP
25 South Methven Street, Perth PH1 5PE
Tel: (01738) 620451
Fax: (01738) 631155
DX: PE4 PERTH
E-mail: admin@mccash.co.uk
Web: www.mccash.co.uk
Categories of Work
Adoption
Advice the elderly & powers of attorney
Agriculture and estates

▶ **Perth continued**

Agriculture, crofting and fishing
Banking & finance
Benefit advice
Charities
Children
Civil court work
Civil legal aid
Commercial property
Contract & property disputes
Debt
Disability
Discrimination
Education
Employment law
Family and divorce
Family business advice
Housing
Landlord & tenant
Medical negligence – claimant
Personal injury
Personal tax
Professional negligence
Property litigation
Residential property
Social housing
Wills, executries and trusts
Partners
Alan Graham Davies
Paul Richard McGregor
Catherine Jane Newton
Associates
William Ronald Desmond Dick
Susan Jane Scott
Employees
Sophie Frances Church
Kenneth Harris McKay
Fiona Barbara McNaughton
Pamela Jean Renfrew

MCKEAN GARDNER LIMITED
E1 Inveralmond Business Centre, 6 Auld Bond
Road, Perth PH1 3FX
Tel: (01738) 700240
E-mail: craig@mckeangardner.co.uk
Categories of Work
Advice the elderly & powers of attorney
Charities
Family business advice
Wills, executries and trusts
Employee
Louise Elizabeth Wilson

MACNABS LLP
10 Barossa Place, Perth PH1 5JX
Tel: (01738) 623432
Fax: (01738) 638594
E-mail: mail@macnabs-law.co.uk
Categories of Work
Adjudication
Adoption
Advice the elderly & powers of attorney
Agriculture and estates

Agriculture, crofting and fishing
Alternative dispute resolution
Children
Childrens
Civil court work
Civil legal aid
Commercial litigation
Commercial property
Construction
Consumer credit
Contract & property disputes
Criminal court work
Criminal legal aid
Debt
Debt adjusting and debt counselling
Debt administration
Debt collecting
Debt recovery, insolvency, bankruptcy
Disability
Education
Employment
Employment law
Family and divorce
Family business advice
Health and safety
Insolvency & corporate recovery
Insurance
Landlord & tenant
Medical negligence – defender
Medical negligence – claimant
Mental health
Personal injury
Personal injury – defender
Planning
Planning (Business Premises)
Professional negligence
Property litigation
Residential property
Road traffic
Wills, executries and trusts
Partners
Stewart Alastair James Baillie
Ruth Catriona Croman
Stuart David Hunter
Rachael Hannah MacDonald
Sarah Anne Mitchell
Alan Roughead
Garry Allan Sutherland
Associate
Jane Elizabeth McNicol
Employees
Clair Margaret Helen Cranston
Valerie McDonald Gauld
Blair Ian MacDonald
Susan Mackay
Aimee Louise Young

MILLER HENDRY
10 Blackfriars Street, Perth PH1 5NS
Tel: (01738) 637311
Fax: (01738) 638685
E-mail: info@millerhendry.co.uk
Web: www.millerhendry.co.uk

Categories of Work
Adoption
Advice the elderly & powers of attorney
Agriculture and estates
Agriculture, crofting and fishing
Banking & finance
Charities
Children
Childrens
Civil court work
Civil legal aid
Commercial litigation
Commercial property
Contract & property disputes
Copyright, trade marks and design
Data protection
Debt collecting
Debt recovery, insolvency, bankruptcy
Employment
Employment law
Environment
Environment (Business Premises)
Family and divorce
Family business advice
Fishing
Housing
Immigration and asylum
Insolvency & corporate recovery
IT and intellectual property
Joint venture
Landlord & tenant
Media and entertainment
Medical negligence – claimant
Mental health
Mergers and acquisitions
Personal injury
Personal tax
Power and utilities
Professional negligence
Projects
Property litigation
Residential property
Road traffic
SME business advice
Social housing
Software licensing
Wills, executives and trusts
Partners
James Clarke Andrew
Amanda Jane Frenz
Richard Alan Frenz
Alasdair Donald Macleod
John Gibb Thom
Associate
Mhairi Lorna Cage
Employees
Samera Yasmine Ali
Emma Devaney Allan
Rebecca Carol Coltart
Michael Johnston
Alasdair Campbell Schreiber
Aileen Isobel Scott

MILLER HENDRY (TRUSTEES) LIMITED
10 Blackfriars Street, Perth PH1 5NS
Tel: (01738) 637311

A.C. MILLER & MACKAY LIMITED
63 Scott Street, Perth PH2 8JN
Tel: (01738) 620087
DX: PE15 PERTH
E-mail: ws@acmm.co.uk
Categories of Work
Criminal court work
Criminal legal aid
Directors
Frederick George Blackie
William Geddas Young Somerville

NEXT LAW (SCOTLAND) LLP
52 Kinnoull Street, Perth PH1 5EZ
Tel: (01738) 707274
Fax: (01738) 633588
Web: www.next-law.co.uk
Categories of Work
Advice the elderly & powers of attorney
Charities
Children
Civil legal aid
Commercial property
Family and divorce
Mental health
Residential property
Wills, executives and trusts
Partners
Crawford William Allan
Laura Jane Sutherland
Employee
Gemma-Grace Johnstone

THORNTONS LAW LLP
Whitefriars House, 7 Whitefriars Crescent,
Perth PH2 0PA
Tel: (01738) 621212
Fax: (01738) 444766
DX: PE 133 PERTH
E-mail: perth@thorntons-law.co.uk
Web: www.thorntons-law.co.uk
Categories of Work
Adjudication
Adoption
Advice the elderly & powers of attorney
Agriculture and estates
Agriculture, crofting and fishing
Alternative dispute resolution
Alternative investment market
Banking & finance
Benefit advice
Betting & gaming
Charities
Children
Childrens
Civil court work
Civil legal aid
Commercial litigation
Commercial property
Competition

▶ **Perth continued**

Construction
Consumer credit
Contract & property disputes
Copyright, trade marks and design
Corporate tax
Credit brokerage
Criminal court work
Criminal legal aid
Data protection
Debt
Debt adjusting and debt counselling
Debt administration
Debt collecting
Debt recovery, insolvency, bankruptcy
Disability
Discrimination
Education
Employment
Employment law
Environment
Environment (Business Premises)
EU / international
Family and divorce
Family business advice
Fishing
Freedom of information
Health
Health and safety
Housing
Human rights
Immigration and asylum
Insolvency & corporate recovery
Insurance
IT and intellectual property
Joint venture
Landlord & tenant
Liquor licensing
Local government
Media and entertainment
Medical negligence – defender
Medical negligence – claimant
Mental health
Mergers and acquisitions
Oil & gas
Parliamentary
Pensions (Company)
Pensions (Employment)
Personal injury
Personal injury – defender
Personal tax
Planning
Planning (Business Premises)
Power and utilities
Private equity
Professional negligence
Projects
Property litigation
Public sector
Residential property
Road traffic
SME business advice

Social housing
Software licensing
Sport
Telecoms
Unit Trusts, OEICs and investment trusts
Wills, executries and trusts
Partners
Katherine Muriel McGill
Anne Lesley Mearns
Bruce Norman Renfrew
Associates
Allison Elizabeth McCoo
Janice Mary Alison Napier
Rosemary Anne Scott
Angela Patricia Wipat
Employees
Deborah Campbell Dewar
Rebecca Erin Ellwood
Zoe Margaret Irving
Graham Ian Lambert

L J WADE LTD
2 Ardchoille Park, Bridgend, Perth PH2 7TL
Tel: (07310) 164305
E-mail: louisa@louisawade.co.uk
Web: www.louisawade.co.uk
Categories of Work
Adoption
Children
Childrens
Civil court work
Civil legal aid
Family and divorce
Director
Louisa Jane Wade
Employee
Michael Joseph Carroll

WARD & CO (PERTH) LTD
13 George Street, Perth PH1 5JY
Tel: (01738) 638461
Fax: (01738) 630860
DX: PE33 PERTH
E-mail: jward_wardco@yahoo.co.uk
Categories of Work
Children
Civil legal aid
Criminal court work
Criminal legal aid
Family and divorce
Mental health
Personal injury
Director
John Michael Ward
Associate
David Rennie Holmes
Employee
Susan Elizabeth Richmond

NEIL WHITTET
25 Barossa Street, Perth PH1 5NR
Tel: (01738) 628900
Fax: (01738) 621200
E-mail: hs@neilwhittet.co.uk

Categories of Work
Residential property
Partner
Neil Thomas Whittet

WYLLIE & HENDERSON SOLICITORS
Market Chambers, Caledonian Road, Perth
PH1 5NJ
Tel: (01738) 638465
Fax: (01738) 635499
E-mail: email@wyllie-henderson.co.uk
Web: www.wyllie-henderson.co.uk
Categories of Work
Advice the elderly & powers of attorney
Agriculture and estates
Agriculture, crofting and fishing
Banking & finance
Commercial property
Contract & property disputes
Family business advice
Housing
Landlord & tenant
Liquor licensing
Residential property
SME business advice
Wills, executries and trusts
Partners
Ian Kerr Lindsay
Angela Louise Scott
Employee
Grant Peter McLennan

Peterhead

ABERDEIN CONSIDINE AND COMPANY
40 & 42 Queen Street, Peterhead AB42 1TQ
Tel: (01779) 475365
DX: 521370 PETERHEAD
E-mail: peterhead@acandco.com
Web: www.acandco.com
Categories of Work
Adjudication
Adoption
Advice the elderly & powers of attorney
Agriculture and estates
Agriculture, crofting and fishing
Alternative dispute resolution
Alternative investment market
Banking & finance
Charities
Children
Childrens
Civil court work
Civil legal aid
Commercial litigation
Commercial property
Competition
Construction
Consumer credit
Contract & property disputes
Copyright, trade marks and design
Corporate tax
Credit brokerage

Criminal court work
Criminal legal aid
Data protection
Debt
Debt adjusting and debt counselling
Debt collecting
Debt recovery, insolvency, bankruptcy
Disability
Discrimination
Education
Employment
Employment law
Environment
Environment (Business Premises)
EU / international
Family and divorce
Family business advice
Freedom of information
Health
Health and safety
Human rights
Insolvency & corporate recovery
Insurance
Joint venture
Landlord & tenant
Liquor licensing
Local government
Media and entertainment
Mental health
Mergers and acquisitions
Pensions (Company)
Pensions (Employment)
Personal injury
Personal tax
Planning (Business Premises)
Private equity
Professional negligence
Property litigation
Public finance initiative
Public sector
Residential property
SME business advice
Social housing
Telecoms
Unit Trusts, OEICs and investment trusts
Wills, executries and trusts
Employee
Jordan Alexander Watt

BURKINSHAW CRIMINAL DEFENCE
60 Queen Street, Peterhead AB42 1TQ
Tel: (01779) 476453
E-mail: leonard@burkinshawdefence.com
Categories of Work
Criminal court work
Criminal legal aid
Partner
Leonard James Burkinshaw

GRAY & GRAY LLP
8/10 Queen Street, Peterhead AB42 1TS
Tel: (01779) 480 222
Fax: (01779) 470 741
DX: 521372 PETERHEAD

▶ **Peterhead** continued

E-mail: brian@graygraylaw.com
Web: www.grayandgraysolicitors.com
Categories of Work
Adjudication
Adoption
Advice the elderly & powers of attorney
Agriculture and estates
Agriculture, crofting and fishing
Alternative dispute resolution
Alternative investment market
Banking & finance
Charities
Children
Childrens
Civil court work
Civil legal aid
Commercial litigation
Commercial property
Competition
Construction
Contract & property disputes
Corporate tax
Criminal court work
Criminal legal aid
Debt
Debt recovery, insolvency, bankruptcy
Education
Environment
Environment (Business Premises)
EU / international
Family and divorce
Family business advice
Fishing
Housing
Insolvency & corporate recovery
Insurance
Joint venture
Landlord & tenant
Liquor licensing
Medical negligence – defender
Medical negligence – claimant
Mental health
Mergers and acquisitions
Mining
Oil & gas
Pensions (Company)
Personal injury
Personal injury – defender
Planning
Planning (Business Premises)
Power and utilities
Private equity
Projects
Property litigation
Public finance initiative
Public sector
Residential property
Road traffic
Shipping
SME business advice
Social housing

Transport
Unit Trusts, OEICs and investment trusts
Wills, executives and trusts
Partners
John Henry Adam
Jane Pauline Dickers
Stuart Alan Flowerdew

IAIN JANE & CO
32B Queen Street, Peterhead AB42 1TS
Tel: (01779) 477620
E-mail: iain@iainjane.co.uk
Categories of Work
Criminal court work
Criminal legal aid
Partner
Iain Andrew Jane
Employee
Declan O'Keefe

MASSON GLENNIE LLP
Broad House, Broad Street, Peterhead
AB42 1HY
Tel: (01779) 474271
Fax: (01779) 476037
DX: 521371 PETERHEAD
E-mail: mail@masson-glennie.co.uk
Web: www.masson-glennie.co.uk
Categories of Work
Adoption
Advice the elderly & powers of attorney
Children
Childrens
Civil court work
Commercial litigation
Commercial property
Contract & property disputes
Criminal court work
Debt
Debt management
Employment
Employment law
Family and divorce
Family business advice
Immigration and asylum
Landlord & tenant
Mental health
Property litigation
Residential property
Shipping
Wills, executives and trusts
Partners
Stuart John Kershaw
Victoria Louise Kershaw
Brian William McCombie
Bruce Milton
Georgina Marie Robertson
Marjorie Elizabeth Sutherland
Employees
Andrew Liam Mackey
Sarah Milton

SAM MILLIGAN & CO.
32 Back Street, Peterhead AB42 1TE

Tel: (01779) 480248
Categories of Work
Criminal court work
Criminal legal aid

STEWART & WATSON
35 Queen Street, Peterhead AB42 1TP
Tel: (01779) 476351
Fax: (01779) 478792
DX: 521373 PETERHEAD
E-mail: info@stewartwatson.co.uk
Web: www.stewartwatson.co.uk
Categories of Work
Adoption
Advice the elderly & powers of attorney
Agriculture and estates
Agriculture, crofting and fishing
Alternative dispute resolution
Charities
Children
Civil court work
Civil legal aid
Commercial property
Contract & property disputes
Criminal court work
Criminal legal aid
Debt
Debt collecting
Debt recovery, insolvency, bankruptcy
Employment
Environment
Environment (Business Premises)
Family and divorce
Housing
Immigration and asylum
Landlord & tenant
Mental health
Personal injury
Projects
Residential property
Road traffic
Wills, executries and trusts
Partners
Nicola Harvey
Simon James Carnegie Liddiard
Employee
Joanne Hunter Birnie

Pitlochry

FORSYTH EMPLOYMENT LAW
Cluain, Strathtay, Pitlochry PH9 0PJ

FORSYTH LEGAL LIMITED
Cluain, Strathtay, Pitlochry PH9 0PJ
Director
Alison Jane Forsyth

MACNABS LLP
21 Atholl Road, Pitlochry PH16 5BX
Tel: (01796) 472409
E-mail: mail@macnabs-law.co.uk
Categories of Work
Adjudication

Adoption
Advice the elderly & powers of attorney
Agriculture and estates
Agriculture, crofting and fishing
Alternative dispute resolution
Children
Childrens
Civil court work
Civil legal aid
Commercial litigation
Commercial property
Construction
Consumer credit
Contract & property disputes
Criminal court work
Criminal legal aid
Debt
Debt adjusting and debt counselling
Debt administration
Debt collecting
Debt recovery, insolvency, bankruptcy
Disability
Education
Employment
Employment law
Family and divorce
Family business advice
Health and safety
Insolvency & corporate recovery
Insurance
Landlord & tenant
Medical negligence – defender
Medical negligence – claimant
Mental health
Personal injury
Personal injury – defender
Planning
Planning (Business Premises)
Professional negligence
Property litigation
Residential property
Road traffic
Wills, executries and trusts

J & H MITCHELL LLP
51 Atholl Road, Pitlochry PH16 5BU
Tel: (01796) 472606
Fax: (01796) 473198
DX: 552040 PITLOCHRY
E-mail: j@hmitchell.co.uk
Web: www.jandhmitchell.com
Categories of Work
Advice the elderly & powers of attorney
Agriculture and estates
Agriculture, crofting and fishing
Charities
Commercial property
Contract & property disputes
Data protection
Employment
Environment
Family business advice
Housing

► *Pitlochry continued*

IT and intellectual property
Joint venture
Landlord & tenant
Liquor licensing
Mergers and acquisitions
Personal tax
Planning (Business Premises)
Private equity
Residential property
SME business advice
Wills, executries and trusts
Partners
Sarah Margaret Brown
Alan Alexander Innes
Paul Irwin Keith
Employee
Jennifer Anne Temblett

Port Glasgow

BLAIR & BRYDEN
39 Princes Street, Port Glasgow PA14 5JH
Tel: (01475) 745117
Fax: (01475) 744170
E-mail: pg@blair-bryden.co.uk
Web: www.blairbryden.co.uk
Categories of Work
Adoption
Advice the elderly & powers of attorney
Benefit advice
Charities
Children
Civil court work
Civil legal aid
Commercial litigation
Commercial property
Consumer credit
Contract & property disputes
Criminal court work
Criminal legal aid
Debt collecting
Debt recovery, insolvency, bankruptcy
Education
Employment
Employment law
Family and divorce
Family business advice
Housing
Immigration and asylum
Landlord & tenant
Liquor licensing
Medical negligence – claimant
Personal injury
Personal injury – defender
Planning (Business Premises)
Professional negligence
Property litigation
Residential property
Road traffic
Transport
Wills, executries and trusts

Partner
Alasdair William Hendry

Portlethen

ALASTAIR HART & CO.
11 The Green, Berrymuir Road, Portlethen
AB12 4UN
Tel: (01224) 784855
E-mail: info@alastairhart.co.uk
Web: www.alastairhart.co.uk
Categories of Work
Advice the elderly & powers of attorney
Childrens
Commercial litigation
Debt collecting
Family and divorce
Landlord & tenant
Residential property
Wills, executries and trusts

Portree

ANDERSON, MACARTHUR LIMITED
Unit 3, Kings House, Portree IV51 9BT
Tel: (01478) 612197
Fax: (01478) 612451
Web: www.anderson-macarthur.com
Categories of Work
Advice the elderly & powers of attorney
Agriculture and estates
Agriculture, crofting and fishing
Charities
Civil court work
Civil legal aid
Commercial property
Contract & property disputes
Criminal court work
Criminal legal aid
Employment law
Family and divorce
Family business advice
Landlord & tenant
Residential property
Wills, executries and trusts
Director
Duncan McKinnon Burd

FERGUSON, MACSWEEN & STEWART
Bridge Road, Portree IV51 9ER
Tel: (01478) 612991
Fax: (01478) 612709
E-mail: katie@fmslaw.co.uk
Categories of Work
Adoption
Advice the elderly & powers of attorney
Agriculture and estates
Agriculture, crofting and fishing
Alternative dispute resolution
Children
Civil court work
Civil legal aid
Commercial property

Debt
Debt collecting
Debt recovery, insolvency, bankruptcy
Education
Family and divorce
Family business advice
Landlord & tenant
Personal injury
Property litigation
Residential property
Road traffic
Wills, executries and trusts
Partners
Sarah Farr
Katharine Anna MacDonald

INKSTERS
1 Wentworth Street, Portree IV51 9EJ
Tel: (01478) 620 555
E-mail: portree@inksters.com
Web: www.inksters.com
Categories of Work
Advice the elderly & powers of attorney
Agriculture and estates
Agriculture, crofting and fishing
Alternative dispute resolution
Children
Childrens
Civil court work
Civil legal aid
Commercial property
Consumer credit
Contract & property disputes
Criminal court work
Criminal legal aid
Data protection
Debt
Debt collecting
Debt recovery, insolvency, bankruptcy
Family and divorce
Family business advice
Landlord & tenant
Personal tax
Projects
Property litigation
Residential property
Road traffic
Wills, executries and trusts

JOHN MACDONALD LAW
Somerled Square, Portree IV51 9EH
E-mail: office@johnmacdonaldlaw.co.uk
Web: www.johnmacdonaldlaw.co.uk
Categories of Work
Adjudication
Adoption
Advice the elderly & powers of attorney
Agriculture and estates
Agriculture, crofting and fishing
Alternative dispute resolution
Banking & finance
Charities
Children
Childrens

Civil court work
Civil legal aid
Commercial litigation
Commercial property
Construction
Contract & property disputes
Debt recovery, insolvency, bankruptcy
Education
Employment
Employment law
Environment
Environment (Business Premises)
Family and divorce
Family business advice
Fishing
Health and safety
Housing
Landlord & tenant
Medical negligence – defender
Medical negligence – claimant
Pensions (Employment)
Personal injury
Personal injury – defender
Planning (Business Premises)
Professional negligence
Property litigation
Residential property
Road traffic
SME business advice
Wills, executries and trusts
Partner
John Clarke MacDonald

MACLEOD & MACCALLUM LIMITED
Old Bank House, Somerled Square, Portree
IV51 9EH
Tel: (01478) 611336
E-mail: mail@macandmac.co.uk
Web: www.macandmac.co.uk
Categories of Work
Adoption
Advice the elderly & powers of attorney
Agriculture and estates
Agriculture, crofting and fishing
Alternative dispute resolution
Banking & finance
Charities
Children
Childrens
Civil court work
Civil legal aid
Commercial litigation
Commercial property
Construction
Contract & property disputes
Copyright, trade marks and design
Debt recovery, insolvency, bankruptcy
Employment
Employment law
Environment (Business Premises)
Family and divorce
Family business advice
Health and safety

▶ Portree continued

Housing
Insolvency & corporate recovery
IT and intellectual property
Joint venture
Landlord & tenant
Liquor licensing
Mergers and acquisitions
Personal injury
Personal injury – defender
Planning (Business Premises)
Professional negligence
Projects
Property litigation
Public sector
Residential property
Road traffic
SME business advice
Social housing
Wills, executries and trusts

Prestwick

BLACK HAY
45/47 Main Street, Prestwick KA9 1AF
Tel: (01292) 477235
Fax: (01292) 671310
Web: www.blackhay.co.uk
Categories of Work
Adoption
Advice the elderly & powers of attorney
Alternative dispute resolution
Betting & gaming
Children
Childrens
Civil court work
Civil legal aid
Commercial property
Contract & property disputes
Criminal court work
Criminal legal aid
Family and divorce
Family business advice
Human rights
Immigration and asylum
Landlord & tenant
Liquor licensing
Mental health
Personal injury
Personal injury – defender
Personal tax
Residential property
Wills, executries and trusts
Partners
Malcolm Norman MacInnes
James Ferber Picken
Consultant
Brian Hugh Dunlop

FRAZER COOGANS LTD
163 Main Street, Prestwick KA9 1LB
Tel: (01292) 478487

Categories of Work
Adoption
Advice the elderly & powers of attorney
Agriculture and estates
Agriculture, crofting and fishing
Banking & finance
Children
Childrens
Commercial property
Contract & property disputes
Criminal court work
Criminal legal aid
Family and divorce
Family business advice
Landlord & tenant
Personal injury
Personal tax
Residential property
Road traffic
SME business advice
Wills, executries and trusts

DEREK W. PETTIGREW
19 Templerigg Street, Prestwick KA9 1AZ
Tel: (01292) 475941
E-mail: derekpettigrew@hotmail.com
Categories of Work
Criminal court work
Criminal legal aid
Partner
Derek William Pettigrew

Renfrew

CALLAHAN MCKEOWN & CO LTD
54 Hairst Street, Renfrew PA4 8QY
Tel: (0141) 8851212
Fax: (0141) 885 9383
DX: 590758 RENFREW 2
E-mail: callahanmckeownandco@gmail.com
Web: www.callahanmckeown.co.uk
Categories of Work
Adoption
Alternative dispute resolution
Benefit advice
Children
Civil court work
Civil legal aid
Criminal court work
Criminal legal aid
Disability
Discrimination
Family and divorce
Human rights
Immigration and asylum
Mental health
Directors
Edward Anthony Callahan
Michael McKeown
Employees
Kevin Joseph Brady
Samantha Ruth Menzies
Lesley-Anne Mulholland

MCAULEY, MCCARTHY & CO.
58/60 High Street, Renfrew PA4 8QP
Tel: (0141) 5614449
Fax: (0141) 5614494
Categories of Work
Adoption
Advice the elderly & powers of attorney
Alternative dispute resolution
Children
Childrens
Civil court work
Civil legal aid
Commercial property
Environment (Business Premises)
Family and divorce
Family business advice
Landlord & tenant
Mental health
Planning (Business Premises)
Private equity
Public sector
Residential property
SME business advice
Wills, executries and trusts
Partners
John Hall
Linda Jane Monson
Employee
Suzanne Elizabeth Bagnall

MCCARTNEY STEWART LIMITED
1B Paisley Road, Renfrew PA4 8JH
Tel: (0141) 8851858
Fax: (0141) 8865425
E-mail: law@mccartneystewart.co.uk
Categories of Work
Advice the elderly & powers of attorney
Agriculture and estates
Commercial property
Family business advice
Landlord & tenant
Residential property
Wills, executries and trusts
Director
Ronald Alan Stewart
Employee
Laura Jane Kelly

WALKER LAIRD
10 Canal Street, Renfrew PA4 8QD
Tel: (0141) 886 5678
Fax: (0141) 886 7327
DX: 590753 RENFREW 2
E-mail: info@walkerlaird.co.uk
Categories of Work
Advice the elderly & powers of attorney
Children
Civil court work
Commercial property
Contract & property disputes
Debt
Debt collecting
Employment law
Family and divorce

Family business advice
Landlord & tenant
Medical negligence – claimant
Personal injury
Professional negligence
Residential property
Road traffic
SME business advice
Wills, executries and trusts
Partner
Ross Maxwell McGinlay
Employee
Bernadette Ann MacQueen

Rutherglen

BERMAN HOLDINGS LIMITED
90 Main Street, Rutherglen G73 2HZ
Tel: (0141) 6479851

CARR BERMAN CRICHTON LIMITED
90 Main Street, Rutherglen G73 2HZ
Tel: (0141) 6479851
Fax: (0141) 6432171
E-mail: enquiries@carrbermancrichton.co.uk
Categories of Work
Advice the elderly & powers of attorney
Landlord & tenant
Residential property
Wills, executries and trusts
Directors
Martin Berman
Samuel Robert Westwood
Employee
Jie Smitheram

ROSS ROGERS & CO LIMITED
221 Main Street, Rutherglen G73 2HH
Tel: (0141) 6479771
Fax: (0141) 6479310
DX: 501287 Rutherglen
E-mail: chris@rossrogers.co.uk
Web: www.rossrogers.co.uk
Categories of Work
Advice the elderly & powers of attorney
Civil court work
Commercial litigation
Commercial property
Contract & property disputes
Criminal court work
Criminal legal aid
Debt collecting
Debt recovery, insolvency, bankruptcy
Family and divorce
Health and safety
Landlord & tenant
Medical negligence – claimant
Personal injury
Professional negligence
Property litigation
Residential property
Wills, executries and trusts
Director
Christopher David Rogers

▶ *Rutherglen continued*

ROBERT WESTWOOD HOLDINGS LIMITED
90 Main Street, Rutherglen G73 2HZ

Saltcoats

JAS CAMPBELL & CO LTD
Bank of Scotland Buildings, 57 Dockhead
Street, Saltcoats KA21 5EH
Tel: (01294) 464301
Fax: (01294) 603023
DX: 591002 SALTCOATS
E-mail: mail@jascampbell.co.uk
Web: www.jascampbell.co.uk
Categories of Work
Adoption
Advice the elderly & powers of attorney
Agriculture and estates
Children
Civil court work
Civil legal aid
Commercial property
Construction
Contract & property disputes
Environment (Business Premises)
Family and divorce
Family business advice
Landlord & tenant
Liquor licensing
Personal injury
Planning (Business Premises)
Property litigation
Residential property
SME business advice
Wills, executives and trusts
Directors
George Ian Tolson Hunter
Ian Bruce Hunter
Jenna Catherine Merry
Associate
Alistair Fraser
Employees
Lauren Hannah Braid Smith
Peter John Walsh

JAMES IRVINE
25 Hamilton Street, Saltcoats KA21 5DT
Tel: (01294) 468027
Categories of Work
Criminal court work
Criminal legal aid

NELLANY & COMPANY LLP
35 Chapelwell Street, Saltcoats KA21 5EB
Tel: (01294) 464175
Fax: (01294) 603431
Web: www.nellanysolicitors.co.uk
Categories of Work
Adoption
Advice the elderly & powers of attorney
Children
Civil court work
Civil legal aid

Commercial litigation
Commercial property
Contract & property disputes
Criminal court work
Criminal legal aid
Debt collecting
Education
Family and divorce
Family business advice
Landlord & tenant
Mental health
Personal injury
Property litigation
Residential property
Road traffic
Wills, executives and trusts
Partners
Gordon Arnott Ghee
Michael John Nellany
Rhona Anne Nellany
Associate
Fiona Catherine McKinnon
Solicitor
Martha Louisa Christina Thomson
Employee
Laura Elizabeth Finnigan

TAYLOR & HENDERSON LLP
51 Hamilton Street, Saltcoats KA21 5DX
Tel: (01294) 464341
Fax: (01294) 464827
Web: www.taylorandhenderson.co.uk
Categories of Work
Adoption
Advice the elderly & powers of attorney
Agriculture and estates
Agriculture, crofting and fishing
Alternative dispute resolution
Charities
Children
Civil court work
Civil legal aid
Commercial property
Criminal court work
Criminal legal aid
Debt
Family and divorce
Landlord & tenant
Mental health
Oil & gas
Residential property
Road traffic
Wills, executives and trusts
Partners
Barbara-Jane Black
Emma Mackenzie Pyper
Associates
Katherine Spence Honeyman
Jessica Lindsay Hay McKee

DOUGLAS WRIGHT
20 – 22 Chapelwell Street, Saltcoats KA21 5EA
Tel: (01294) 466990
E-mail: enquiries@douglaswrightsolicitors.com

Web: www.douglaswrightsolicitors.com
Categories of Work
Adoption
Advice the elderly & powers of attorney
Alternative dispute resolution
Children
Civil court work
Civil legal aid
Commercial litigation
Criminal court work
Criminal legal aid
Family and divorce

Sanquhar

POLLOCK & MCLEAN
61 High Street, Sanquhar DG4 6DT
Tel: (01659) 50241
Fax: (01659) 50443
E-mail: mail@pollockmclean.co.uk
Web: www.pollockmclean.co.uk
Categories of Work
Adoption
Advice the elderly & powers of attorney
Children
Civil court work
Civil legal aid
Commercial litigation
Consumer credit
Contract & property disputes
Criminal court work
Criminal legal aid
Debt
Debt collecting
Debt recovery, insolvency, bankruptcy
Disability
Discrimination
Employment
Employment law
Family and divorce
Housing
Human rights
Insolvency & corporate recovery
Landlord & tenant
Liquor licensing
Property litigation
Residential property
Road traffic
Wills, executries and trusts
Partner
Kenneth McLean

ROBERT WILSON & SON
47 High Street, Sanquhar DG4 6DJ
Tel: (01659) 50251
E-mail: sanquhar@robertwilsonandson.co.uk
Web: www.robertwilsonandson.co.uk
Categories of Work
Advice the elderly & powers of attorney
Commercial property
Family business advice
Landlord & tenant
Personal tax

Residential property
Wills, executries and trusts

Selkirk

BORDERS LEGAL LIMITED
22 Market Square, Selkirk TD7 4BL
Tel: (01750) 724160
E-mail: legal@hastingslegal.co.uk
Web: www.hastingslegal.co.uk
Categories of Work
Adoption
Advice the elderly & powers of attorney
Agriculture and estates
Civil court work
Commercial property
Contract & property disputes
Copyright, trade marks and design
Debt adjusting and debt counselling
Debt administration
Debt collecting
Debt management
Debt recovery, insolvency, bankruptcy
Employment law
Environment
Family and divorce
Family business advice
Health
Health and safety
Housing
Landlord & tenant
Liquor licensing
Mental health
Personal injury
Personal tax
Planning
Planning (Business Premises)
Property litigation
Public sector
Residential property
SME business advice
Wills, executries and trusts

CULLEN KILSHAW
26 High Street, Selkirk TD7 4DD
Tel: (01750) 23868
DX: 581016 Selkirk
E-mail: selkirk@cullenkilshaw.com
Web: www.cullenkilshaw.com
Categories of Work
Adoption
Advice the elderly & powers of attorney
Agriculture and estates
Agriculture, crofting and fishing
Alternative dispute resolution
Children
Childrens
Civil court work
Civil legal aid
Commercial property
Contract & property disputes
Criminal court work
Criminal legal aid

► Selkirk continued

Debt
Debt collecting
Debt recovery, insolvency, bankruptcy
Employment
Employment law
Environment (Business Premises)
Family and divorce
Family business advice
Fishing
Landlord & tenant
Liquor licensing
Local government
Personal injury
Planning (Business Premises)
Property litigation
Residential property
Road traffic
Wills, executives and trusts

DOUGLAS GILMOUR & SON
20 Market Place, Selkirk TD7 4BL
Tel: (01750) 720271
DX: 581017 SELKIRK
E-mail: selkirk@douglasgilmour.co.uk
Categories of Work
Advice the elderly & powers of attorney
Agriculture, crofting and fishing
Charities
Commercial property
Landlord & tenant
Residential property
Wills, executives and trusts

HASTINGS LEGAL
22 Market Square, Selkirk TD7 4BL
Tel: (01750) 724160
E-mail: legal@hastingslegal.co.uk
Web: www.hastingslegal.co.uk
Categories of Work
Adoption
Advice the elderly & powers of attorney
Agriculture and estates
Civil court work
Commercial property
Contract & property disputes
Copyright, trade marks and design
Debt adjusting and debt counselling
Debt administration
Debt collecting
Debt management
Debt recovery, insolvency, bankruptcy
Employment law
Environment
Family and divorce
Family business advice
Health
Health and safety
Housing
Landlord & tenant
Liquor licensing
Mental health
Personal injury

Personal tax
Planning
Planning (Business Premises)
Property litigation
Public sector
Residential property
SME business advice
Wills, executives and trusts

PIKE & CHAPMAN
20 Market Place, Selkirk TD7 4BL
Tel: (01750) 720271
Fax: (01750) 722686
E-mail: selkirk@douglasgilmour.co.uk
Categories of Work
Advice the elderly & powers of attorney
Agriculture, crofting and fishing
Charities
Commercial property
Landlord & tenant
Residential property
Wills, executives and trusts
Partner
Stephanie Elizabeth Robertson

Skene

CONSTRUCTION LEGAL SERVICES LIMITED
The Chamber, Hillhead of Blackchambers,
Skene AB32 7BT
Tel: (07517) 994897
Categories of Work
Construction
Director
Kathleen McGrath

South Queensferry

DEANS SOLICITORS AND ESTATE AGENTS LLP
31A High Street, South Queensferry EH30 9PP
Tel: (0131) 6671900
DX: 82 Edinburgh
Categories of Work
Residential property
Wills, executives and trusts

NEILSONS
37 High Street, South Queensferry EH30 9HN
Tel: (0131) 3314009
DX: 551440 EDINBURGH 52
Categories of Work
Benefit advice
Commercial property
Debt management
Landlord & tenant
Mental health
Residential property
Wills, executives and trusts

Stewarton

FINANCIAL SERVICES ADVOCACY LTD
The Pines, 7a Loudoun Street, Stewarton
KA3 5JD

Tel: (01560) 485225
E-mail: alasdair@fsalawyer.co.uk
Categories of Work
Alternative dispute resolution
Insurance
Unit Trusts, OEICs and investment trusts
Director
Alasdair Colin Sampson

MACKINTOSH & WYLIE LLP
46 High Street, Stewarton KA3 5DB
Tel: (01560) 482 666
Fax: (01560) 484 666
Categories of Work
Advice the elderly & powers of attorney
Agriculture and estates
Agriculture, crofting and fishing
Banking & finance
Charities
Children
Childrens
Civil court work
Civil legal aid
Commercial property
Criminal court work
Criminal legal aid
Employment
Employment law
Family and divorce
Family business advice
Landlord & tenant
Liquor licensing
Mental health
Mergers and acquisitions
Mining
Power and utilities
Residential property
Wills, executries and trusts
Partner
Alastair McDonald

Stirling

ABERDEIN CONSIDINE AND COMPANY
23 Port Street, Stirling FK8 2EJ
Tel: (01786) 450944
Fax: (01786) 450229
DX: 45 STIRLING
Categories of Work
Adjudication
Adoption
Advice the elderly & powers of attorney
Agriculture and estates
Agriculture, crofting and fishing
Alternative dispute resolution
Alternative investment market
Banking & finance
Charities
Children
Childrens
Civil court work
Civil legal aid
Commercial litigation

Commercial property
Competition
Construction
Consumer credit
Contract & property disputes
Copyright, trade marks and design
Corporate tax
Credit brokerage
Criminal court work
Criminal legal aid
Data protection
Debt
Debt adjusting and debt counselling
Debt collecting
Debt recovery, insolvency, bankruptcy
Disability
Discrimination
Education
Employment
Employment law
Environment
Environment (Business Premises)
EU / international
Family and divorce
Family business advice
Freedom of information
Health
Health and safety
Human rights
Insolvency & corporate recovery
Insurance
Joint venture
Landlord & tenant
Liquor licensing
Local government
Media and entertainment
Mental health
Mergers and acquisitions
Pensions (Company)
Pensions (Employment)
Personal injury
Personal tax
Planning (Business Premises)
Private equity
Professional negligence
Property litigation
Public finance initiative
Public sector
Residential property
SME business advice
Social housing
Telecoms
Unit Trusts, OEICs and investment trusts
Wills, executries and trusts
Partner
Anthony Quin

BARTON & HENDRY
39 Murray Place, Stirling FK8 2DD
Tel: (01786) 445441
E-mail: info@bartonandhendry.co.uk
Web: www.bartonandhendry.co.uk

▶ **Stirling** *continued*

Categories of Work
Advice the elderly & powers of attorney
Children
Civil court work
Civil legal aid
Commercial property
Criminal court work
Criminal legal aid
Environment
Family and divorce
Landlord & tenant
Medical negligence – claimant
Personal injury
Power and utilities
Projects
Residential property
Wills, executries and trusts

BELL & CRAIG LIMITED
Albert House, 4 Albert Place, Dumbarton
Road, Stirling FK8 2QL
Tel: (01786) 470444
Fax: (01786) 447175
E-mail: enquiries@bellandcraig.co.uk
Web: www.bellandcraig.co.uk
Categories of Work
Advice the elderly & powers of attorney
Commercial property
Employment
Family business advice
Joint venture
Landlord & tenant
Residential property
SME business advice
Wills, executries and trusts
Director
Fergus Carson Pattison Bell
Employees
Mirren Hamilton
Abby Leigh Kemp
Aran Logan Wilson

VIRGIL M. CRAWFORD
20 Viewfield Street, Stirling FK8 1UA
Tel: (01786) 464055
Fax: (01786) 464052
E-mail: vmc@virgil-crawford.com
Categories of Work
Adoption
Advice the elderly & powers of attorney
Children
Childrens
Civil court work
Civil legal aid
Criminal court work
Criminal legal aid
Debt
Family and divorce
Medical negligence – claimant
Mental health
Personal injury
Professional negligence

Road traffic
Partner
Virgil Martin Crawford
Employees
Kenneth David Marsh
Lara Kathryn Thomson

DALLING
83 Barnton Street, Stirling FK8 1HJ
Tel: (01786) 448111
Fax: (01786) 448222
E-mail: mail@dallings.co.uk
Categories of Work
Advice the elderly & powers of attorney
Benefit advice
Children
Childrens
Civil court work
Civil legal aid
Criminal court work
Criminal legal aid
Discrimination
Family and divorce
Mental health
Road traffic
Partner
Kenneth Alexander Robertson Dalling
Employees
Ross Drummond Anderson
Jay Goodwillie

HILL & ROBB LIMITED
3 Pitt Terrace, Stirling FK8 2EY
Tel: (01786) 450985
Fax: (01786) 451360
DX: ST7 STIRLING
E-mail: info@hillandrobb.co.uk
Web: www.hillandrobb.co.uk
Categories of Work
Adoption
Advice the elderly & powers of attorney
Agriculture and estates
Agriculture, crofting and fishing
Benefit advice
Children
Childrens
Civil court work
Civil legal aid
Commercial property
Criminal court work
Criminal legal aid
Debt
Debt management
Disability
Discrimination
Education
Employment law
Family and divorce
Family business advice
Human rights
Landlord & tenant
Local government
Mental health
Parliamentary

Personal injury
Personal tax
Projects
Public sector
Residential property
Road traffic
Social housing
Wills, executives and trusts
Directors
James Valentine Davidson
Audrey Bannatyne McGhee
Anna Fleur McIntosh
Peter Gale Moffett
Alan Jamieson Rodger
Alexander Clarkson Tennant
Associate
Moira Hughes
Employees
Catherine Elizabeth Berrill
Helen McNab Davidson
Baljinder Kaur Purewal
Shiona Glen Robertson

JARDINE DONALDSON
80 Port Street, Stirling FK8 2LR
Tel: (01786) 450366
Fax: (01786) 450543
E-mail: stirling@jardinedonaldson.co.uk
Categories of Work
Adoption
Advice the elderly & powers of attorney
Agriculture and estates
Charities
Children
Civil court work
Civil legal aid
Commercial property
Debt
Family and divorce
Family business advice
Landlord & tenant
Liquor licensing
Residential property
Wills, executives and trusts
Partner
Susie Jeanne McCarron

KERR STIRLING LLP
10 Albert Place, Stirling FK8 2QL
Tel: (01786) 463414
Fax: (01786) 451395
DX: 9 STIRLING
E-mail: enquiries@kerrstirling.co.uk
Categories of Work
Advice the elderly & powers of attorney
Agriculture and estates
Agriculture, crofting and fishing
Banking & finance
Commercial property
Construction
Contract & property disputes
Debt
Debt recovery, insolvency, bankruptcy
Employment law

Family and divorce
Family business advice
Housing
Joint venture
Landlord & tenant
Liquor licensing
Mergers and acquisitions
Planning
Planning (Business Premises)
Power and utilities
Residential property
SME business advice
Wills, executives and trusts
Partners
Caroline Janet Litster
Colin James Mackenzie
Peter William David Alexan Pratt
Marc Lowson Quinn
Russell Martin Spinks
Consultant
Philip James Allison
Associate
Alison Elizabeth Neilson
Employees
Andrew James Ion
Matthew John McKeown
William Graham Sutherland

LEDINGHAM CHALMERS LLP
Unit 2B, The Paddock, Stirling Agricultural
Centre, Stirling FK9 4RN
Tel: (01786) 478100
Fax: (01786) 477 339
E-mail: mail@ledinghamchalmers.com
Web: www.ledinghamchalmers.com
Categories of Work
Adjudication
Adoption
Advice the elderly & powers of attorney
Agriculture and estates
Agriculture, crofting and fishing
Alternative dispute resolution
Alternative investment market
Banking & finance
Charities
Children
Childrens
Civil court work
Civil legal aid
Commercial litigation
Commercial property
Competition
Construction
Consumer credit
Contract & property disputes
Copyright, trade marks and design
Corporate tax
Credit brokerage
Criminal court work
Criminal legal aid
Data protection
Debt
Debt adjusting and debt counselling

► **Stirling** *continued*

Debt administration
Debt collecting
Debt management
Debt recovery, insolvency, bankruptcy
Disability
Discrimination
Education
Employment
Employment law
Environment
Environment (Business Premises)
EU / international
Family and divorce
Family business advice
Fishing
Freedom of information
Health and safety
Housing
Human rights
Immigration and asylum
Insolvency & corporate recovery
Insurance
IT and intellectual property
Joint venture
Landlord & tenant
Liquor licensing
Local government
Media and entertainment
Medical negligence – defender
Medical negligence – claimant
Mental health
Mergers and acquisitions
Oil & gas
Pensions (Company)
Pensions (Employment)
Personal injury
Personal injury – defender
Personal tax
Planning
Planning (Business Premises)
Power and utilities
Private equity
Professional negligence
Projects
Property litigation
Provision of credit information services
Public finance initiative
Public sector
Residential property
Road traffic
SME business advice
Software licensing
Telecoms
Transport
Unit Trusts, OEICs and investment trusts
Wills, executries and trusts
Partners
James Cunison Drysdale
Linda Jane Aird Tinson

Associates
Sarah Irene Kiersgaard
Lorna Agnes McKay
Employee
Susan Catherine Black

MCCREADY & CO SOLICITORS LIMITED
91 Barnton Street, Stirling FK8 1HJ
Tel: (01786) 479628
Fax: (01786) 459141
E-mail: frazer@fmccready.co.uk
Categories of Work
Criminal court work
Criminal legal aid
Director
Frazer Gordon Ewan McCready

MACGREGOR THOMSON LIMITED
Springfield House, Laurelhill Business Park,
Stirling FK7 9JQ
Tel: (01786) 406423
Fax: (01786) 406534
DX: ST37 STIRLING
E-mail: mnaismith@macgregorthomson.co.uk
Categories of Work
Banking & finance
Betting & gaming
Commercial property
Contract & property disputes
Debt
Debt recovery, insolvency, bankruptcy
Family business advice
Insolvency & corporate recovery
Joint venture
Landlord & tenant
Liquor licensing
Local government
Mergers and acquisitions
Private equity
Residential property
SME business advice
Sport
Wills, executries and trusts
Director
Andrew Michael MacGregor Thomson
Employee
Robbie David McElroy

MAILERS
2A King Street, Stirling FK8 1BA
Tel: (01786) 450555
Fax: (01786) 451353
DX: ST10 STIRLING
E-mail: Ian.mcculloch@mailers.co.uk
Categories of Work
Advice the elderly & powers of attorney
Children
Childrens
Civil court work
Civil legal aid
Commercial litigation
Commercial property
Contract & property disputes
Criminal court work

Criminal legal aid
Debt
Debt collecting
Debt recovery, insolvency, bankruptcy
Family and divorce
Family business advice
Joint venture
Landlord & tenant
Liquor licensing
Personal injury
Property litigation
Residential property
Road traffic
Wills, executries and trusts
Partner
Ian David McCulloch
Associate
Lesley Joyce Mackie

MUIRHEAD BUCHANAN
23 Port Street, Stirling FK8 2EJ
Tel: (01786) 450944
Categories of Work
Adjudication
Adoption
Advice the elderly & powers of attorney
Agriculture and estates
Agriculture, crofting and fishing
Alternative dispute resolution
Alternative investment market
Banking & finance
Charities
Children
Childrens
Civil court work
Civil legal aid
Commercial litigation
Commercial property
Competition
Construction
Consumer credit
Contract & property disputes
Copyright, trade marks and design
Corporate tax
Credit brokerage
Criminal court work
Criminal legal aid
Data protection
Debt
Debt adjusting and debt counselling
Debt collecting
Debt recovery, insolvency, bankruptcy
Disability
Discrimination
Education
Employment
Employment law
Environment
Environment (Business Premises)
EU / international
Family and divorce
Family business advice
Freedom of information

Health
Health and safety
Human rights
Insolvency & corporate recovery
Insurance
Joint venture
Landlord & tenant
Liquor licensing
Local government
Media and entertainment
Mental health
Mergers and acquisitions
Pensions (Company)
Pensions (Employment)
Personal injury
Personal tax
Planning (Business Premises)
Private equity
Professional negligence
Property litigation
Public finance initiative
Public sector
Residential property
SME business advice
Social housing
Telecoms
Unit Trusts, OEICs and investment trusts
Wills, executries and trusts

POLLOCK, ROSS & CO
18B Maxwell Place, Stirling FK8 1JU
Tel: (01786) 449933
Fax: (01786) 449777
DX: ST47 STIRLING
Categories of Work
Criminal court work
Criminal legal aid
Partners
George Edward Pollock
Alastair Crawford Ross

WATERSRULE LIMITED
1a Melville Terrace, Stirling FK8 2ND
Tel: (01786) 235 235
Fax: (01786) 235 111
E-mail: info@watersrule.co.uk
Web: www.watersrule.co.uk
Categories of Work
Advice the elderly & powers of attorney
Banking & finance
Commercial litigation
Commercial property
Contract & property disputes
Debt recovery, insolvency, bankruptcy
Family business advice
Joint venture
Landlord & tenant
Private equity
Property litigation
Residential property
SME business advice
Wills, executries and trusts

▶ **Stirling continued**

Directors
Stephen Rule
Grant James Begbie Storrar
Employee
Joanne Margaret Waters

Stonehaven

ABERDEIN CONSIDINE AND COMPANY
40 Allardice Street, Stonehaven AB39 2BU
Tel: (01569) 766166
Fax: (01569) 766110
DX: 521027 STONEHAVEN
E-mail: stonehaven@acandco.com
Web: www.acandco.com
Categories of Work
Adjudication
Adoption
Advice the elderly & powers of attorney
Agriculture and estates
Agriculture, crofting and fishing
Alternative dispute resolution
Alternative investment market
Banking & finance
Charities
Children
Childrens
Civil court work
Civil legal aid
Commercial litigation
Commercial property
Competition
Construction
Consumer credit
Contract & property disputes
Copyright, trade marks and design
Corporate tax
Credit brokerage
Criminal court work
Criminal legal aid
Data protection
Debt
Debt adjusting and debt counselling
Debt collecting
Debt recovery, insolvency, bankruptcy
Disability
Discrimination
Education
Employment
Employment law
Environment
Environment (Business Premises)
EU / international
Family and divorce
Family business advice
Freedom of information
Health
Health and safety
Human rights
Insolvency & corporate recovery
Insurance

Joint venture
Landlord & tenant
Liquor licensing
Local government
Media and entertainment
Mental health
Mergers and acquisitions
Pensions (Company)
Pensions (Employment)
Personal injury
Personal tax
Planning (Business Premises)
Private equity
Professional negligence
Property litigation
Public finance initiative
Public sector
Residential property
SME business advice
Social housing
Telecoms
Unit Trusts, OEICs and investment trusts
Wills, executries and trusts
Partners
Laura Jane Considine
Ryan Andrew Fox

KINNEAR & FALCONER
20 Ann Street, Stonehaven AB39 2EN
Tel: (01569) 690728
Fax: (01569) 766548
DX: 521022 STONEHAVEN
E-mail: law@kinnearandfalconer.co.uk
Web: www.jgcollie.co.uk
Categories of Work
Adoption
Advice the elderly & powers of attorney
Alternative dispute resolution
Banking & finance
Betting & gaming
Charities
Children
Civil court work
Civil legal aid
Commercial litigation
Commercial property
Competition
Consumer credit
Contract & property disputes
Copyright, trade marks and design
Debt collecting
Debt recovery, insolvency, bankruptcy
Employment
Employment law
Family and divorce
Family business advice
Freedom of information
Housing
Insolvency & corporate recovery
Landlord & tenant
Liquor licensing
Local government
Media and entertainment

Medical negligence – claimant
Mental health
Mergers and acquisitions
Personal injury
Professional negligence
Property litigation
Residential property
Road traffic
SME business advice
Sport
Wills, executives and trusts
Employee
Mary McLaughlin Birse

RAEBURN CHRISTIE CLARK & WALLACE LLP
1 Market Buildings, Stonehaven AB39 2BY
Tel: (01569) 762947
Fax: (01569) 766702
Web: www.raeburns.co.uk
Categories of Work
Adoption
Advice the elderly & powers of attorney
Agriculture and estates
Agriculture, crofting and fishing
Alternative dispute resolution
Banking & finance
Betting & gaming
Charities
Children
Civil court work
Civil legal aid
Commercial litigation
Commercial property
Competition
Construction
Contract & property disputes
Copyright, trade marks and design
Data protection
Debt
Disability
Discrimination
Employment
Employment law
Environment
EU / international
Family and divorce
Family business advice
Freedom of information
Health and safety
Housing
Human rights
IT and intellectual property
Joint venture
Landlord & tenant
Liquor licensing
Media and entertainment
Medical negligence – defender
Mergers and acquisitions
Oil & gas
Personal injury
Personal injury – defender
Planning
Planning (Business Premises)

Private equity
Professional negligence
Property litigation
Residential property
Road traffic
Shipping
SME business advice
Social housing
Sport
Wills, executives and trusts
Partner
Naomi Elizabeth Mearns
Employee
Laura Jean McMillan

PAT SINCLAIR & CO.
5 Westfield Avenue, Stonehaven AB39 2EU
Tel: (07483) 304780
DX: AB106 ABERDEEN
E-mail: info@patsinclair.com
Web: www.patsinclair.co.uk
Categories of Work
Advice the elderly & powers of attorney
Commercial property
Employment
Employment law
Family business advice
Health and safety
Joint venture
Landlord & tenant
Mergers and acquisitions
Planning (Business Premises)
Residential property
SME business advice
Wills, executives and trusts
Partner
Patricia Sinclair

SMITH SOLICITORS STONEHAVEN
9 Market Square, Stonehaven AB39 2BT
Tel: (01569) 767778
Fax: (01569) 766540
E-mail: ronald@smithstonehaven.com
Web: www.smithstonehaven.com
Categories of Work
Advice the elderly & powers of attorney
Commercial property
Landlord & tenant
Residential property
Wills, executives and trusts
Partner
Ronald Christopher Forbes

Stonehouse

KENNETH M. GREENER LIMITED
1 New Street, The Cross, Stonehouse ML9 3LT
Tel: (01698) 793366
Fax: (01698) 793358
E-mail: kenneth@kmglaw.co.uk
Categories of Work
Adoption
Advice the elderly & powers of attorney
Agriculture and estates

▶ **Stonehouse continued**

Alternative dispute resolution
Benefit advice
Children
Civil court work
Civil legal aid
Consumer credit
Contract & property disputes
Criminal court work
Criminal legal aid
Debt
Debt adjusting and debt counselling
Debt collecting
Debt management
Debt recovery, insolvency, bankruptcy
Disability
Employment
Employment law
Family and divorce
Landlord & tenant
Medical negligence – claimant
Mental health
Personal injury
Residential property
Road traffic
Social housing
Wills, executries and trusts
Director
Kenneth Matthew Greener

Stornoway

ANDERSON MACARTHUR LIMITED
Old Bank of Scotland Buildings, Stornoway
HS1 2BG
Tel: (01851) 703356
Fax: (01851) 702766
E-mail: lorraine@anderson-macarthur.com
Web: www.anderson-macarthur.com
Categories of Work
Advice the elderly & powers of attorney
Agriculture and estates
Agriculture, crofting and fishing
Charities
Civil court work
Civil legal aid
Commercial property
Contract & property disputes
Criminal court work
Criminal legal aid
Employment law
Family and divorce
Family business advice
Landlord & tenant
Residential property
Wills, executries and trusts
Directors
Margaret Ann Mackay
Isabel Jayne MacLeod

KEN MACDONALD & CO LIMITED
9 Kenneth Street, Stornoway HS1 2DP
Tel: (01851) 704040

Fax: (01851) 705083
E-mail: enquiries@kenmacdonaldlawyers.co.uk
Web: www.kenmacdonaldlawyers.co.uk
Categories of Work
Advice the elderly & powers of attorney
Agriculture and estates
Agriculture, crofting and fishing
Civil court work
Civil legal aid
Commercial property
Contract & property disputes
Debt recovery, insolvency, bankruptcy
Family business advice
Fishing
Housing
Landlord & tenant
Medical negligence – claimant
Personal injury
Professional negligence
Property litigation
Residential property
Road traffic
Wills, executries and trusts
Director
Kenneth Norman MacDonald
Employees
Amanda Jane Maciver
Robyn Mairi Macleod

MACDONALD, MACIVER & COMPANY LIMITED
20 Francis Street, Stornoway HS1 2NB
Tel: (01851) 704343
Fax: (01851) 706923
E-mail: enquiries@macdmac.co.uk
Categories of Work
Criminal court work
Criminal legal aid
Directors
Angus William MacDonald
Ian Maciver
Employees
Eilidh Morrison Macinnes
Jonathan Grant Maciver
Lauren Welsh

DEREK MACKENZIE & COMPANY LIMITED
20 North Beach Street, Stornoway HS1 2XQ
Tel: (01851) 702211
Fax: (01851) 709035
E-mail: derek@derek-mackenzie.com
Director
Derek Mackenzie
Employees
Joanne Elizabeth Ferguson
Christina-Jo Macleod Smith

THE MACIVER TEALE LAW PRACTICE LTD
87 Cromwell Street, Stornoway HS1 2DG
Tel: (01851) 706070
Fax: (01851) 709063
E-mail: info@maciverteale.co.uk
Web: www.maciverteale.co.uk

Categories of Work
Criminal court work
Directors
Kathleen Anne MacIver
David Sutherland Teale

Stranraer

FERGUSON & COMPANY
Clydesdale Bank Buildings, 91 Hanover Street,
Stranraer DG9 7RS
Tel: (01776) 702561
Fax: (01776) 706272
E-mail: mailbox@ferguson-company.co.uk
Web: www.mailbox@ferguson-company.co.uk
Categories of Work
Criminal court work
Criminal legal aid
Partner
Paul Feeney
Employees
Nyree Leanne Douglas
Gregor Feeney

GALLOWAY & AYRSHIRE PARTNERSHIP LLP
91 George Street, Stranraer DG9 7JP
Tel: (01776) 889293
E-mail: stranraer@smithvalentine.co.uk
Categories of Work
Advice the elderly & powers of attorney
Agriculture and estates
Agriculture, crofting and fishing
Commercial property
Contract & property disputes
Debt collecting
Debt recovery, insolvency, bankruptcy
Employment law
Family and divorce
Family business advice
Housing
Insolvency & corporate recovery
Landlord & tenant
Liquor licensing
Personal tax
Planning
Planning (Business Premises)
Power and utilities
Residential property
SME business advice
Wills, executories and trusts

HUNTER & MURRAY
25 Lewis Street, Stranraer DG9 7LA
Tel: (01776) 702581
E-mail: mail@aba-matthews.demon.co.uk
Categories of Work
Criminal court work
Criminal legal aid

MICHAEL G. KILKERR
1 Bridge Street, Stranraer DG9 7JA
Tel: (01776) 702415
Fax: (01776) 703628

Categories of Work
Adoption
Advice the elderly & powers of attorney
Children
Civil court work
Civil legal aid
Criminal court work
Criminal legal aid
Employment
Family and divorce
Residential property
Wills, executories and trusts
Partner
Michael Gerard Kilkerr

MCANDREW & RICHARDSON
44 Hanover Street, Stranraer DG9 7RP
Tel: (01776) 704324
Fax: (01776) 704329
E-mail: mail@mcandrewandrichardson.co.uk
Web: www.mcandrewandrichardson.co.uk
Categories of Work
Adoption
Advice the elderly & powers of attorney
Children
Childrens
Civil court work
Civil legal aid
Criminal court work
Criminal legal aid
Family and divorce
Landlord & tenant
Medical negligence – claimant
Personal injury
Road traffic
Social housing
Wills, executories and trusts
Partner
Amanda Frances Richardson
Employee
Hannah Rosemary McIntosh

NICOL, HARVEY & PIERCE
31 Lewis Street, Stranraer DG9 7AB
Tel: (01776) 707111
Fax: (01776) 706111
DX: 581265 STRANRAER
E-mail: mn@nhpsolicitors.co.uk
Categories of Work
Adoption
Advice the elderly & powers of attorney
Children
Childrens
Civil court work
Civil legal aid
Contract & property disputes
Criminal court work
Criminal legal aid
Debt
Debt adjusting and debt counselling
Debt collecting
Debt recovery, insolvency, bankruptcy
Education
Employment law

► **Stranraer** continued

Family and divorce
Insolvency & corporate recovery
Landlord & tenant
Medical negligence – defender
Medical negligence – claimant
Mental health
Personal injury
Personal injury – defender
Professional negligence
Property litigation
Residential property
Road traffic
Wills, executries and trusts
Partner
Margot McLeod Nicol

RANKIN & AITKEN

4/6 South Strand Street, Stranraer DG9 7JW
Tel: (01776) 702336
Fax: (01776) 706800
E-mail: enq@rankinaitken.co.uk
Web: www.rankinaitken.co.uk
Categories of Work
Advice the elderly & powers of attorney
Agriculture and estates
Agriculture, crofting and fishing
Civil court work
Commercial property
Debt recovery, insolvency, bankruptcy
Family and divorce
Housing
Landlord & tenant
Liquor licensing
Residential property
Wills, executries and trusts
Partners
Derek George Laburn
Kenneth George Paterson

SMITH & VALENTINE

91 George Street, Stranraer DG9 7JP
Tel: (01776) 889293
E-mail: stanraer@smithvalentine.co.uk
Categories of Work
Advice the elderly & powers of attorney
Agriculture and estates
Agriculture, crofting and fishing
Commercial property
Contract & property disputes
Debt collecting
Debt recovery, insolvency, bankruptcy
Employment law
Family and divorce
Family business advice
Housing
Insolvency & corporate recovery
Landlord & tenant
Liquor licensing
Personal tax
Planning
Planning (Business Premises)
Power and utilities

Residential property
SME business advice
Wills, executries and trusts

Strathaven

GEBBIE & WILSON LLP

18 Common Green, Strathaven ML10 6AG
Tel: (01357) 520082
Fax: (01357) 529477
DX: 570200 STRATHAVEN
E-mail: mail@gebbiewilson.co.uk
Web: www.gebbiewilson.co.uk
Categories of Work
Advice the elderly & powers of attorney
Agriculture and estates
Agriculture, crofting and fishing
Commercial property
Landlord & tenant
Projects
Residential property
SME business advice
Wills, executries and trusts
Partners
Jan Margaret Bayley
David Carson Murray
Employees
Louise Anne Arthur
Catherine Lorraine Black
Eva Yee Wah Kwok

JOHN JACKSON & DICK LIMITED

3 Bridge Street, Strathaven ML10 6AN
Tel: (01357) 522959
E-mail: mail@jacksondicklaw.com
Web: www.jacksondicklaw.com
Categories of Work
Advice the elderly & powers of attorney
Banking & finance
Civil court work
Civil legal aid
Commercial litigation
Commercial property
Contract & property disputes
Debt recovery, insolvency, bankruptcy
Employment
Employment law
Environment (Business Premises)
Family business advice
Housing
Insurance
IT and intellectual property
Joint venture
Landlord & tenant
Liquor licensing
Local government
Mergers and acquisitions
Parliamentary
Personal injury
Planning
Planning (Business Premises)
Power and utilities
Projects

Property litigation
Public finance initiative
Public sector
Residential property
Road traffic
SME business advice
Social housing
Software licensing
Wills, executries and trusts

VI PENSIONS LAW LIMITED
2 Lambhill Steadings, Strathaven
E-mail: enquiries@vipensionslaw.co.uk
Categories of Work
Pensions (Company)
Pensions (Employment)
Director
Vanessa Clare Ingram

Stromness

J.E.P. ROBERTSON & SON
26 Victoria Street, Stromness KW16 3AA
Tel: (01856) 850232
Fax: (01856) 851085
E-mail: enquiries@jeprobertson.co.uk
Categories of Work
Agriculture and estates
Agriculture, crofting and fishing
Banking & finance
Benefit advice
Betting & gaming
Civil legal aid
Commercial property
Debt recovery, insolvency, bankruptcy
Employment
Family and divorce
Housing
Insolvency & corporate recovery
Insurance
Landlord & tenant
Liquor licensing
Pensions (Company)
Personal tax
Planning
Residential property
Unit Trusts, OEICs and investment trusts
Wills, executries and trusts
Partner
Anne Macdonald Robertson

Tain

GEORGESONS
22 High Street, Tain IV19 1AE
Tel: (01862) 892555
Categories of Work
Advice the elderly & powers of attorney
Agriculture and estates
Agriculture, crofting and fishing
Commercial property
Contract & property disputes
Employment

Employment law
Family and divorce
Family business advice
Landlord & tenant
Residential property
SME business advice
Wills, executries and trusts

MACKENZIE & CORMACK
16-18 Tower Street, Tain IV19 1DZ
Tel: (01862) 892046
Fax: (01862) 892715
E-mail: mail@tainlaw.co.uk
Web: www.mackenzieandcormack.co.uk
Categories of Work
Advice the elderly & powers of attorney
Agriculture, crofting and fishing
Commercial property
Landlord & tenant
Residential property
Wills, executries and trusts
Partners
Nigel David Jones
Iain McIntosh
Employee
Kirsteen Margaret Louise Reekie

Tayport

DEVINE LEGAL
8 Golf Crescent, Tayport DD6 9NA
Tel: (01382) 554408
E-mail: danieldevine05@gmail.com
Categories of Work
Civil legal aid
Criminal court work
Criminal legal aid
Debt
Employment
Employment law
Medical negligence – defender
Medical negligence – claimant
Personal injury
Professional negligence
Road traffic
Partner
Daniel Devine

Thornhill

POLLOCK & MCLEAN
1 West Morton Street, Thornhill DG3 5NE
Tel: (01848) 330207
Fax: (01848) 331600
DX: 580667 DUMFRIES
E-mail: mail@pollockmclean.co.uk
Web: www.pollockmclean.co.uk
Categories of Work
Adoption
Advice the elderly & powers of attorney
Children
Civil court work
Civil legal aid

▶ **Thornhill continued**

Commercial litigation
Consumer credit
Contract & property disputes
Criminal court work
Criminal legal aid
Debt
Debt collecting
Debt recovery, insolvency, bankruptcy
Disability
Discrimination
Employment
Employment law
Family and divorce
Housing
Human rights
Insolvency & corporate recovery
Landlord & tenant
Liquor licensing
Property litigation
Residential property
Road traffic
Wills, executives and trusts
Partner
Sharon Stewart Fyall

ROBERT WILSON & SON
109 Drumlanrig Street, Thornhill DG3 5LX
Tel: (01848) 330251
Fax: (01848) 331633
E-mail: thornhill@robertwilsonandson.co.uk
Web: www.robertwilsonandson.co.uk
Categories of Work
Advice the elderly & powers of attorney
Commercial property
Family business advice
Landlord & tenant
Personal tax
Residential property
Wills, executives and trusts
Partner
Colin Bell

Thurso

DANDHLAW LIMITED
7/9 Princes Street, Thurso KW14 7BQ
Tel: (01847) 894379
Fax: (01847) 893655
E-mail: enquiries@dandhlaw.co.uk
Web: www.dreverandheddle.co.uk
Categories of Work
Agriculture and estates
Agriculture, crofting and fishing
Director
Natalie Joan Bird

INKSTERS
10 Sinclair Street, Thurso KW14 7AJ
Tel: (01847) 630 400
Fax: (0141) 229 0550
E-mail: thurso@inksters.com
Web: www.inksters.com

Categories of Work
Advice the elderly & powers of attorney
Agriculture and estates
Agriculture, crofting and fishing
Alternative dispute resolution
Children
Childrens
Civil court work
Civil legal aid
Commercial property
Consumer credit
Contract & property disputes
Criminal court work
Criminal legal aid
Data protection
Debt
Debt collecting
Debt recovery, insolvency, bankruptcy
Family and divorce
Family business advice
Landlord & tenant
Personal tax
Projects
Property litigation
Residential property
Road traffic
Wills, executives and trusts
Consultant
Charlotte Joy Platt

MACDONALD LAW
Riverside Road, Thurso KW14 8BU
Tel: (01847) 894515
Fax: (01847) 894515
E-mail: enquiries@macdonaldlaw.co.uk
Web: www.macdonaldlaw.co.uk
Partner
Fiona MacDonald

YOUNG, ROBERTSON & CO.
29 Traill Street, Thurso KW14 8EG
Tel: (01847) 893247
Fax: (01847) 896358
E-mail: donald@youngrob.co.uk
Web: www.youngrobertson.co.uk.
Categories of Work
Agriculture and estates
Residential property
Partners
Elaine Mary Robertson
Ewan John Thoms
Employee
Kerry Anne Sim

Tillicoultry

WATERSRULE LIMITED
76-78 High Street, Tillicoultry FK13 6AB
Tel: (01259) 753330
Fax: (01259) 753331
DX: 560457 ALLOA
E-mail: steven.waters@watersrule.co.uk
Web: www.watersrule.co.uk

Categories of Work
Advice the elderly & powers of attorney
Banking & finance
Commercial litigation
Commercial property
Contract & property disputes
Debt recovery, insolvency, bankruptcy
Family business advice
Joint venture
Landlord & tenant
Private equity
Property litigation
Residential property
SME business advice
Wills, executries and trusts
Director
Steven Robert Waters

Torryburn

PAUL W. RALPH
25 Adia Road, The Meadows, Torryburn
KY12 8LB
Tel: (07986) 431730
Categories of Work
Criminal court work
Criminal legal aid
Partner
Paul William Ralph

Tranent

GARDEN STIRLING BURNET SOLICITORS LIMITED
121 High Street, Tranent EH33 1LW
Tel: (01875) 611616
DX: 541033 TRANENT
Categories of Work
Adoption
Advice the elderly & powers of attorney
Children
Commercial property
Criminal court work
Criminal legal aid
Education
Employment law
Family and divorce
Family business advice
Joint venture
Landlord & tenant
Liquor licensing
Residential property
Wills, executries and trusts

ALEX LAFFERTY LTD
74 High Street, Tranent EH33 1HH
Tel: (01875) 614059
Fax: (01875) 611977
E-mail: laffertyalex@googlemail.com
Categories of Work
Criminal court work
Criminal legal aid

Director
Mary Beryl Andronika Moultrie
MCKINNON FORBES
54 High Street, Tranent EH33 1HH
Tel: (01875) 611211
Fax: (01875) 612565
DX: 541030 TRANENT
Web: www.mckinnonforbes.co.uk
Categories of Work
Adoption
Advice the elderly & powers of attorney
Alternative dispute resolution
Children
Civil court work
Civil legal aid
Commercial property
Family and divorce
Residential property
Wills, executries and trusts
Partners
Susan Jane Forbes
Yvonne Karon McKinnon
Employee
Sheila Janet Byth

Troon

MCSHERRY HALLIDAY LLP
8 Academy Street, Troon KA10 6HS
Tel: (01292) 313737
Fax: (01292) 317856
DX: 557801 TROON
E-mail: troon@mcsherryhalliday.co.uk
Web: www.mcsherryhalliday.co.uk
Categories of Work
Adoption
Advice the elderly & powers of attorney
Agriculture and estates
Children
Childrens
Civil court work
Commercial property
Contract & property disputes
Employment law
Family and divorce
Family business advice
Insurance
Landlord & tenant
Mergers and acquisitions
Pensions (Company)
Pensions (Employment)
Planning (Business Premises)
Professional negligence
Residential property
SME business advice
Unit Trusts, OEICs and investment trusts
Wills, executries and trusts
Partners
James Bone Morrison
Caroline Margaret Nisbet
Employee
Louisa Elizabeth Doole

► *Troon continued*

D.W. SHAW
8 West Portland Street, Troon KA10 6AB
Tel: (01292) 312577
DX: 557800 TROON
E-mail: ayrreception@dwshaw.co.uk
Web: www.dwshaw.co.uk
Categories of Work
Adoption
Advice the elderly & powers of attorney
Agriculture and estates
Agriculture, crofting and fishing
Children
Civil court work
Civil legal aid
Commercial property
Criminal court work
Criminal legal aid
Family and divorce
Family business advice
Landlord & tenant
Medical negligence – defender
Medical negligence – claimant
Personal injury
Personal injury – defender
Power and utilities
Professional negligence
Residential property
Road traffic
SME business advice
Wills, executries and trusts

WADDELL & MACKINTOSH SOLICITORS LTD
29 Ayr Street, Troon KA10 6EB
Tel: (01292) 314922
Categories of Work
Advice the elderly & powers of attorney
Commercial property
Contract & property disputes
Landlord & tenant
Residential property
Wills, executries and trusts
Employee
Jennifer Clare McGovern

WADDELL & MACKINTOSH SOLICITORS LTD
36 West Portland Street, Troon KA10 6AB
Tel: (01292) 312222
Fax: (01292) 318090
E-mail: rm@wmtroon.co.uk
Categories of Work
Advice the elderly & powers of attorney
Commercial property
Contract & property disputes
Landlord & tenant
Residential property
Wills, executries and trusts
Directors
Rognvald Inkster Mason
Darren Gemmell Murdoch
Employee
Andrew Gordon Stevenson

Turriff

BROWN & MCRAE LLP
10 High Street, Turriff AB53 4DS
Tel: (01888) 568950
E-mail: property@brown-mcrae.co.uk
Categories of Work
Adoption
Advice the elderly & powers of attorney
Agriculture and estates
Agriculture, crofting and fishing
Charities
Civil court work
Commercial property
Criminal court work
Criminal legal aid
Debt
Debt recovery, insolvency, bankruptcy
Family and divorce
Family business advice
Insolvency & corporate recovery
Joint venture
Landlord & tenant
Mergers and acquisitions
Public sector
Residential property
SME business advice
Wills, executries and trusts

GRANT SMITH LAW PRACTICE LIMITED
Old Bank Buildings, Balmellie Street, Turriff
AB53 4DW
Tel: (01888) 562245
Fax: (01888) 563590
DX: 521395 TURRIFF
Web: www.grantsmithlaw.co.uk
Categories of Work
Adoption
Advice the elderly & powers of attorney
Alternative dispute resolution
Children
Childrens
Civil court work
Civil legal aid
Commercial property
Contract & property disputes
Criminal court work
Criminal legal aid
Debt
Debt collecting
Debt recovery, insolvency, bankruptcy
Education
Family and divorce
Landlord & tenant
Mental health
Personal injury
Professional negligence
Property litigation
Residential property
Road traffic
Wills, executries and trusts
Director
Hilary Anne Barrowman Macandrew

STEWART & WATSON
59 High Street, Turriff AB53 4EL
Tel: (01888) 563773
Fax: (01888) 563227
E-mail: info@stewartwatson.co.uk
Web: www.stewartwatson.co.uk
Categories of Work
Adoption
Advice the elderly & powers of attorney
Agriculture and estates
Agriculture, crofting and fishing
Alternative dispute resolution
Charities
Children
Civil court work
Civil legal aid
Commercial property
Contract & property disputes
Criminal court work
Criminal legal aid
Debt
Debt collecting
Debt recovery, insolvency, bankruptcy
Employment
Environment
Environment (Business Premises)
Family and divorce
Housing
Immigration and asylum
Landlord & tenant
Mental health
Personal injury
Projects
Residential property
Road traffic
Wills, executives and trusts
Partners
Douglas David Purdie
Fiona Louise Purdie
Associate
Lindsay Ellen Anderson
Employees
Catherine Anne Bury
Hannah Louise Darnell

Uddingston

D.J. FALLS & CO.
16 Main Street, Uddingston G71 7LS
Tel: (01698) 810102
Fax: (01698) 813725
E-mail: enquiries@djfalls.co.uk
Categories of Work
Commercial property
Family and divorce
Housing
Personal injury
Residential property
Wills, executives and trusts
Partner
Daniel Joseph Falls

FRIELS SOLICITORS LIMITED
The Cross, Main Street, Uddingston G71 7ES

Tel: (01698) 815114
Fax: (01698) 810325
DX: 501050 UDDINGSTON
E-mail: frank@frielssolicitors.co.uk
Categories of Work
Adjudication
Advice the elderly & powers of attorney
Alternative dispute resolution
Banking & finance
Children
Civil court work
Civil legal aid
Commercial litigation
Commercial property
Competition
Construction
Consumer credit
Contract & property disputes
Copyright, trade marks and design
Credit brokerage
Criminal court work
Criminal legal aid
Debt
Debt adjusting and debt counselling
Debt administration
Debt collecting
Debt recovery, insolvency, bankruptcy
Disability
Discrimination
Employment
Employment law
Family and divorce
Family business advice
Housing
Human rights
Insolvency & corporate recovery
IT and intellectual property
Joint venture
Landlord & tenant
Liquor licensing
Mergers and acquisitions
Private equity
Property litigation
Provision of credit information services
Residential property
Software licensing
Wills, executives and trusts
Directors
Mark Carlin
Kathryn Devanney

KIERNAN LAW LTD
756B Old Edinburgh Road, Uddingston
G71 6LA
Tel: (01698) 844343
Fax: (01698) 846359
E-mail: kiernanlaw2012@gmail.com
Categories of Work
Criminal court work
Criminal legal aid
Director
Laura Ann Kiernan

► **Uddingston continued**

ROONEY FAMILY LAW LIMITED
52 Main Street, Uddingston G71 7LS
Tel: (01698) 815620
Fax: (01698) 313315
E-mail: info@rooneyfamilylaw.co.uk
Categories of Work
Adoption
Advice the elderly & powers of attorney
Alternative dispute resolution
Benefit advice
Charities
Children
Childrens
Civil court work
Civil legal aid
Commercial litigation
Consumer credit
Contract & property disputes
Copyright, trade marks and design
Criminal court work
Criminal legal aid
Debt
Debt collecting
Debt management
Debt recovery, insolvency, bankruptcy
Disability
Discrimination
Education
Employment law
Family and divorce
Family business advice
Human rights
Landlord & tenant
Medical negligence – claimant
Mental health
Personal injury
Private equity
Professional negligence
Property litigation
Road traffic
Social housing
Wills, executries and trusts
Director
Brian James Rooney
Associate
Julia Adrienne Harris
Employee
Ann-Marie Chalmers

Virkie

RD LAW PRACTICE
Eastbye, Exnaboe, Virkie ZE3 9JS
Tel: (01950) 310125
E-mail: info@rdlawpractice.co.uk
Web: www.rdlawpractice.co.uk
Categories of Work
Advice the elderly & powers of attorney
Agriculture, crofting and fishing
Residential property

Partner
Richard Mark Donaldson

West Calder

STEWART, WATT & CO.
42 Main Street, West Calder EH55 8DR
Tel: (01506) 872911
E-mail: law@stewartwatt.co.uk
Categories of Work
Advice the elderly & powers of attorney
Commercial property
Employment law
Personal tax
Residential property
Wills, executries and trusts

West Kilbride

JAS CAMPBELL & CO LTD
85 Main Street, West Kilbride KA23 9AP
Tel: (01294) 829599
E-mail: mail@jascampbell.co.uk
Web: www.jascampbell.co.uk
Categories of Work
Adoption
Advice the elderly & powers of attorney
Agriculture and estates
Children
Civil court work
Civil legal aid
Commercial property
Construction
Contract & property disputes
Environment (Business Premises)
Family and divorce
Family business advice
Landlord & tenant
Liquor licensing
Personal injury
Planning (Business Premises)
Property litigation
Residential property
SME business advice
Wills, executries and trusts

Wester Inch Village

LIVING LAW
346 Leyland Road, Stewart Park, Wester Inch
Village EH48 2UA
Tel: (07929) 996105
DX: DD132 DUNDEE
E-mail: susan@livinglaw.co.uk
Categories of Work
Alternative dispute resolution
Civil court work
Commercial litigation
Commercial property
Construction
Contract & property disputes
Data protection

Environment
Environment (Business Premises)
EU / international
Fishing
Freedom of information
Housing
Human rights
Local government
Mining
Oil & gas
Parliamentary
Planning
Planning (Business Premises)
Power and utilities
Projects
Partner
Susan Dorothy Shaw

Westhill

ABERDEIN CONSIDINE AND COMPANY
Unit 14, Westhill Shopping Centre, Westhill
AB32 6RL
Tel: (01224) 749444
E-mail: westhill@acandco.com
Web: www.acandco.com
Categories of Work
Adjudication
Adoption
Advice the elderly & powers of attorney
Agriculture and estates
Agriculture, crofting and fishing
Alternative dispute resolution
Alternative investment market
Banking & finance
Charities
Children
Childrens
Civil court work
Civil legal aid
Commercial litigation
Commercial property
Competition
Construction
Consumer credit
Contract & property disputes
Copyright, trade marks and design
Corporate tax
Credit brokerage
Criminal court work
Criminal legal aid
Data protection
Debt
Debt adjusting and debt counselling
Debt collecting
Debt recovery, insolvency, bankruptcy
Disability
Discrimination
Education
Employment
Employment law
Environment
Environment (Business Premises)

EU / international
Family and divorce
Family business advice
Freedom of information
Health
Health and safety
Human rights
Insolvency & corporate recovery
Insurance
Joint venture
Landlord & tenant
Liquor licensing
Local government
Media and entertainment
Mental health
Mergers and acquisitions
Pensions (Company)
Pensions (Employment)
Personal injury
Personal tax
Planning (Business Premises)
Private equity
Professional negligence
Property litigation
Public finance initiative
Public sector
Residential property
SME business advice
Social housing
Telecoms
Unit Trusts, OEICs and investment trusts
Wills, executries and trusts

STORIE, CRUDEN & SIMPSON
10 Westhill Shopping Centre, Westhill
AB32 6RL
Tel: (01224) 740718
Fax: (01224) 743986
DX: AB12 ABERDEEN
E-mail: info@storiecs.co.uk
Web: www.storiecs.co.uk
Categories of Work
Advice the elderly & powers of attorney
Agriculture and estates
Commercial property
Family and divorce
Landlord & tenant
Residential property
Wills, executries and trusts
Partner
Robert George Paterson

Whitburn

CAESAR & HOWIE
32 West Main Street, Whitburn EH47 0QZ
Tel: (01501) 741161
DX: 541065 WHITBURN
E-mail: enquiries@caesar-howie.co.uk
Web: www.caesar-howie.co.uk
Categories of Work
Adoption
Advice the elderly & powers of attorney

▶ *Whitburn continued*

Alternative dispute resolution
Children
Childrens
Civil court work
Civil legal aid
Commercial property
Debt
Debt collecting
Debt recovery, insolvency, bankruptcy
Disability
Education
Employment law
Family and divorce
Family business advice
Landlord & tenant
Mental health
Personal injury
Residential property
Road traffic
Wills, executives and trusts

FAIRFIELD FAMILY LAW

19 East Main Street, Whitburn EH47 0RA
Tel: (01501) 643999
E-mail: lesley@fairfieldfamilylaw.co.uk
Categories of Work
Adoption
Advice the elderly & powers of attorney
Children
Civil court work
Civil legal aid
Family and divorce
Partner
Lesley Fairfield

SNEDDON MORRISON

Clydesdale Bank Chambers, 16 East Main
Street, Whitburn EH47 0RB
Tel: (01501) 740345
Fax: (01501) 745 440
DX: : 541062 WHITBURN
E-mail: erl@sneddons-ssc.co.uk
Web: www.sneddonmorrison.com
Categories of Work
Advice the elderly & powers of attorney
Charities
Commercial property
Contract & property disputes
Education
Employment law
Family business advice
Landlord & tenant
Liquor licensing
Mental health
Mergers and acquisitions
Residential property
Wills, executives and trusts
Partners
Eric Robert Lumsden
James Morrison

Wick

BBM SOLICITORS LIMITED

Unit 5B, Wick Business Park, Wick KW1 4QR
Tel: (01955) 604188
Fax: (01955) 605926
E-mail: info@bbmsolicitors.co.uk
Web: www.bbmsolicitors.co.uk
Categories of Work
Adoption
Advice the elderly & powers of attorney
Agriculture and estates
Alternative dispute resolution
Charities
Children
Childrens
Civil court work
Commercial litigation
Contract & property disputes
Criminal court work
Debt collecting
Debt recovery, insolvency, bankruptcy
Employment
Family and divorce
Family business advice
Insolvency & corporate recovery
Landlord & tenant
Personal injury
Personal tax
Property litigation
Road traffic
Wills, executives and trusts
Directors
Eric Marcus Baijal
Jennifer Mairi Simpson
Employees
Vajiha Ali
Florence Catherine Fisher
Rona Dewar Plowman
Tessa Till

GEORGESONS

22 Bridge Street, Wick KW1 4NG
Tel: (01955) 606060
Fax: (01955) 603016
E-mail: bruce.de.wert@georgesons.co.uk
Web: www.georgesons.co.uk
Categories of Work
Advice the elderly & powers of attorney
Agriculture and estates
Agriculture, crofting and fishing
Commercial property
Contract & property disputes
Employment
Employment law
Family and divorce
Family business advice
Landlord & tenant
Residential property
SME business advice
Wills, executives and trusts
Partners
Bruce Gregor de Wert
Declan Francis McGinley

INKSTERS
25 Bridge Street, Wick KW1 4AJ
Tel: (01955) 950 505
Fax: (01955) 950515
E-mail: wick@inksters.com
Web: www.inksters.com
Categories of Work
Advice the elderly & powers of attorney
Agriculture and estates
Agriculture, crofting and fishing
Alternative dispute resolution
Children
Childrens
Civil court work
Civil legal aid
Commercial property
Consumer credit
Contract & property disputes
Criminal court work
Criminal legal aid
Data protection
Debt
Debt collecting
Debt recovery, insolvency, bankruptcy
Family and divorce
Family business advice
Landlord & tenant
Personal tax
Projects
Property litigation
Residential property
Road traffic
Wills, executries and trusts
Employee
Sylvia Catherine Maclennan

PATTERSON & PATERSON DEFENCE LAWYERS
13 Kirk Lane, Wick KW1 4NN
E-mail: office@pattersonandpaterson.com
Categories of Work
Criminal court work
Criminal legal aid

MYSCOTTISHDIVORCE
22 Bridge Street, Wick KW1 4NG
Tel: (01955) 606060
Web: www.MyScottishDivorce.co.uk
Categories of Work
Advice the elderly & powers of attorney
Agriculture and estates
Agriculture, crofting and fishing
Commercial property
Contract & property disputes
Employment
Employment law
Family and divorce
Family business advice
Landlord & tenant
Residential property
SME business advice
Wills, executries and trusts

Wishaw

FREELANDS
139 Main Street, Wishaw ML2 7AU
Tel: (01698) 355936
Fax: (01698) 354100
E-mail: freelands@freelands.co.uk
Web: www.freelands.co.uk
Categories of Work
Adjudication
Adoption
Advice the elderly & powers of attorney
Agriculture and estates
Alternative dispute resolution
Charities
Children
Childrens
Civil court work
Civil legal aid
Commercial litigation
Commercial property
Contract & property disputes
Criminal court work
Criminal legal aid
Debt
Debt collecting
Debt recovery, insolvency, bankruptcy
Disability
Discrimination
Education
Employment
Employment law
Family and divorce
Family business advice
Health and safety
Human rights
Insolvency & corporate recovery
Joint venture
Landlord & tenant
Liquor licensing
Medical negligence – claimant
Mergers and acquisitions
Personal injury
Planning (Business Premises)
Professional negligence
Property litigation
Residential property
Road traffic
SME business advice
Wills, executries and trusts
Partners
Craig Peter David Mackie
Stephen John Robert Wight
Consultant
Paul Santoni
Employee
Caitlin Grace Esther Gilbert

STEPHEN J. MACBRIDE & CO
17 Main Street, Wishaw ML2 7AF
Tel: (01698) 350310
Fax: (01698) 350288
Categories of Work
Criminal court work

▶ *Wishaw continued*

Criminal legal aid
Partner
Stephen James MacBride

MCGOVERN REID COURT LAWYERS
17 Caledonian Road, Wishaw ML2 8AP
Tel: (01698) 359550
Web: www.mcgoverncourtlawyers.co.uk
Categories of Work
Adoption
Alternative dispute resolution
Children
Childrens
Civil court work
Civil legal aid
Criminal court work
Criminal legal aid
Family and divorce
Health and safety
Personal injury
Personal injury – defender
Road traffic
Partner
Robert William Reid
Consultant
Vincent Gerard McGovern
Employee
Matthew McGovern

NESS GALLAGHER SOLICITORS LIMITED
95 Stewarton Street, Wishaw ML2 8AG
Tel: (01698) 355 525
Fax: (01698) 357 029
E-mail: post@nessgallagher.co.uk
Web: www.nessgallagher.co.uk
Categories of Work
Adoption
Advice the elderly & powers of attorney
Benefit advice
Children
Civil court work
Civil legal aid
Commercial litigation
Commercial property
Consumer credit
Criminal court work
Criminal legal aid
Debt
Debt collecting
Debt management
Education
Employment
Employment law
Family and divorce
Family business advice
Landlord & tenant
Mental health
Personal injury
Property litigation
Residential property
Road traffic
SME business advice

Social housing
Wills, executries and trusts
Directors
Graham David Keys
Edward John McCarron
Kevin Joseph McCarron
Consultant
Owen James Ness
Employee
Samantha Tougher

POMPHREYS
1 Kenilworth Avenue, Town Centre, Wishaw
ML2 7LP
Tel: (01698) 373365
Fax: (01698) 356409
E-mail: sl@pomphreyslaw.com
Web: www.pomphreyslaw.com
Categories of Work
Adoption
Advice the elderly & powers of attorney
Alternative dispute resolution
Children
Civil court work
Civil legal aid
Criminal court work
Criminal legal aid
Debt
Debt collecting
Debt recovery, insolvency, bankruptcy
Employment
Employment law
Family and divorce
Family business advice
Landlord & tenant
Medical negligence – claimant
Personal injury
Personal injury – defender
Residential property
Road traffic
SME business advice
Wills, executries and trusts
Partners
Robert Hugh Allan
Sarah Elizabeth Lynch
Andrew Gordon Sommerville
Iain Collier Wilson
Employee
Amy Louise Sullivan

POMPHREYS
36 Hill Street, Wishaw ML2 7AT
Tel: (01698) 373365
E-mail: sl@pomphreyslaw.com
Web: www.pomphreyslaw.com
Categories of Work
Adoption
Advice the elderly & powers of attorney
Alternative dispute resolution
Children
Civil court work
Civil legal aid
Criminal court work
Criminal legal aid

Debt
Debt collecting
Debt recovery, insolvency, bankruptcy
Employment
Employment law
Family and divorce
Family business advice
Landlord & tenant

Medical negligence – claimant
Personal injury
Personal injury – defender
Residential property
Road traffic
SME business advice
Wills, executries and trusts

Scottish Solicitors' Firms Outwith Scotland

Australia

Melbourne
PINSENT MASONS
Level 23, 360 Collins Street, 3000
Tel: (+61) 399 092 500 Fax: (+61) 399 092 501
Ewan Campbell Robertson

Perth
BLACKWALL LEGAL LLP
26/140 St Georges Terrace, 6000
Nganele Wordsworth Bhebhe
BAKER HUGHES AUSTRALIA PTY LTD
Level 14, 216 St George's Terrace, 6000
Barry Nicholas Cameron
PRICEWATERHOUSECOOPERS
Brookfield Place, 125 St Georges Terrace, 6000
Christopher McAlinden

Sydney
CBRE LTD
Level 21, 363 George Street, NSW 2000
Louisa Margaret Fitzpatrick
MINTER ELLISON
Governor Macquarie Tower, 1 Farrer Place, 2000
Kate Young Morrison
PINSENT MASONS (AUSTRALIA)
Level 32, Gateway Tower, 1 Macquarie Place, 2000
Tel: (+61) 2 8024 2808
Fraser James John McMillan
Louisa Rose Donnelly
ASHURST LLP
5 Martin Place, 2000
Tel: (+61) 2 9258 6000
Ben Judge
DLA PIPER
Level 22, No.1 Martin Place, 2001
Tel: (+61) 2 9286 8693 Fax: (+61) 2 9286 8007
Valeria Pavlovna Polovinkina

Belgium

Brussels
CMS CAMERON MCKENNA NABARRO OLSWANG LLP
85, Avenue Des Nerviens, 104
Siobhan Louise McCarville Kahmann
Kirsti Jean McKenzie
SQUIRE PATTON BOGGS (UK) LLP
Avenue Lloyd George 7, 1000
Tel: (+3202) 627 7619 Fax: (+3202) 627 1100
Robert Macdonald MacLean
WHITE & CASE
62 Rue De La Loi, B-1040
Tel: (+32) 2239 2563
Jacquelyn Freda MacLennan
DENTONS EUROPE LLP
Rue de La Regence 58 Bte 2, 1000
Tel: (+32) 2 552 2935
Mark Gerard Clough, QC
BAKER BOTTS (BELGIUM) LLP
Square De Mee s 23 – Box 11, B-1000
Tel: (+32) (0)2 891 7330 Fax: (+32) (0)2 550 3997
David Ivor William Cardwell
CLIENTEARTH BELGIUM AISBL
60 Rue Du Trone, 1050
Anne Sarah Friel
BRODIES LLP
41 Avenue Des Arts
Tel: 3228087990
Web: Brodies.com

Bruxelles
SERCO BELGIUM SA
Avenue de Cortenbergh 60, 1000
Christopher Euan Greig

Bermuda

Hamilton
CHANCERY LEGAL
52 Reid Street, HM12
Tel: (+441) 400 3884
John Grahame Blackwood

Canada

Calgary
CHEVRON CANADA RESOURCES
500 5th Avenue SW, T2P 0L7
Samantha Jane Chinn

Vancouver
WATSON ADVISORS INC.
200-2415 Columbia Street, V5Y 3E7
Stacey Leith Martin
STEWART, AULINGER & CO
1200 – 805 West Broadway, V5Z 1K1
John Andrew Kielski

Cayman Islands

Grand Cayman
MG MANAGEMENT LTD.
  2F Landmark Square, 64 Earth Close, Seven
  Mile Beach, PO Box 30116, KY1-1201
  Tel: (+1) 345 749 8181 Fax: (+1) 345 743
  6767
  Mark Victor Murray

Denmark

Copenhagen
TRUSTPILOT A/S
  Pilestraede 58, 5., 1112
  Tel: (+45) 31 676988
  Andrew Brian Farquhar
  Anoop Subhash Joshi
  Christopher Peter Knudsen
  Thomas Richard Simmons
EVERSHEDS SUTHERLAND (INTERNATIONAL) LLP
  Ostergade 27, DK-1100
  Tel: (+45) 3375 0505

England

Addlestone
DIXCART LEGAL
  Dixcart House, Addlestone Road, Bourne
  Business Park, KT15 2LE
  Tel: (0333) 1220010
  Vincent Wai Ki Chung

Altrincham
MLP LAW LTD
  7 Market Street, WA14 1QE
  Tel: (0161) 9261582
  Julie Claire Sabba

Andover
DIRECTORATE OF ARMY LEGAL SERVICES
  SO1 Resources, DALS, IDL 426, Ramillies
  Building, Marlborough Lines, Monxton Road,
  SP11 8HJ
  Tel: (01980) 615013 Fax: (01264) 381061
  John Edward Brown
  Eugene-Paul Grant
  Gavin John Law
  Chelsey Paige Mitchell
  Fiona Rennet

Bath
RENEW LEGAL LIMITED
  7-9 North Parade Buildings, BA1 1NS
  Tel: (01225) 321634
  Categories of Work
  Commercial property
  Landlord & tenant
  Residential property

Catriona Alison Murray

Bedford
ADHIBEO LIMITED
  52 Bunyan Road, Kempston, MK42 8HL
  Sylvia White

Berwick-Upon-Tweed
VIALEX LIMITED
  17a Windmill Way West, Ramparts Business
  Park, TD15 1TB

Birkenhead
CARPENTERS SCOTLAND LIMITED
  Leonard House, Scotts Quays, CH41 1FB
  Isra Jabbar Ali

Birmingham
BIG LOTTERY FUND
  Apex House, Embassy Drive, B15 1TR
  Tel: (0207) 211 3738 Fax: (0207) 2111750
  Deborah Jane Myles
PINSENT MASONS LLP
  19 Cornwall Street, B3 2DT
  Tel: (0141) 248 4858
ACCESS LEGAL FROM SHOOSMITHS
  2 Colmore Square, 38 Colmore Circus
  Queensway, B4 6SH
PINSENT MASONS LLP
  55 Colmore Row, B3 2FG
  Tel: (0121) 2001050 Fax: (0121) 6261040
  Paul Matthew Harkin
DAC BEACHCROFT CLAIMS LIMITED
  Tricorn House, 51-53 Hagley Road, Edgbaston,
  B16 8TP
  Tel: (0121) 6985200 Fax: (0121) 6985290
  Rebeccah Rachael Hamilton Jaarson
BIRMINGHAM 2022 COMMONWEALTH GAMES
  One Brindley Place, B1 2JB
  Stuart Crawford Skelly
EVERSHEDS SUTHERLAND (INTERNATIONAL) LLP
  115 Colmore Row, B3 3AL
  Tel: (0845) 4979797
THE PHARMACISTS' DEFENCE ASSOCIATION
  The Old Fire Station, 69 Albion Street, B1 3EA
  Tel: (0121) 6947000
  Baljit Kaur Bagha
GOWLING WLG (UK) LLP
  Two Snowhill, SE1 2AU
  Jamie Munro Russell
BERRYMANS LACE MAWER LLP
  63 Temple Row, B2 5LS
  Tel: (0121) 6438777
HSBC HOLDINGS PLC
  1 Centenary Square, B1 1HQ
  Tel: (020) 79925575
  Andrew Stuart McLean
DLA PIPER UK LLP
  Victoria Square House, Victoria Square, B2 4DL
  Tel: (0121) 262 5947
  Tobias Shaw Paul

HARRISON CLARK RICKERBYS LIMITED
  63 Church Street, B3 2DP
  Tel: (0121) 3124783
  Martin Ross McQueen
DEPARTMENT FOR BUSINESS, ENERGY AND
INDUSTRIAL STRATEGY
  Office For Product Safety and Standards, 4th
  Floor Cannon House, 18 The Priory
  Queensway, B4 6BS
  Elisa Ann Wamberg
SHOOSMITHS LLP
  2 Colmore Square, 38 Colmore Circus
  Queensway, B4 6SH
  Tel: (03700) 864000

Blackburn
KINETIC LAWYERS LTD
  Suite 2, Unit 2D, Phoenix Business Park,
  BB1 5RW
  Tel: (01254) 846561
BAE SYSTEMS
  Samlesbury Aerodrome, S608, 2nd Floor,
  Balderstone, BB2 7LF
  Tel: (01229) 874236
  David William Denning Graham

Bolton
KEOGHS SCOTLAND LLP
  2 The Parklands, BL6 4SE
  Tel: (01204) 677000

Bradford
SCOTIA PERSONAL INJURY SOLICITORS LIMITED
  Alpha House, 2 Coop Place, BD5 8JX

Brighton
RIVERSTONE
  Park Gate, 161-163 Preston Road, BN1 6AU
  Tel: (01273) 792411
  Ruth Lyall

Bristol
CMS CAMERON MCKENNA NABARRO
OLSWANG LLP
  2 College Square, Anchor Road, BS1 5UE
  Tel: (0207) 367 3000
OSBORNE CLARKE
  2 Temple Back East, Temple Quay, BS1 6EG
  Tel: (0117) 917 3108
  Natasha Chalaki Burbidge
TLT LLP
  One Redcliff Street, BS1 6TP
  Tel: (0333) 006 0000
  Web: www.tltsolicitors.com
  Caroline Kate Powlett Loudon
  James Arthur Johnson
FOOT ANSTEY LLP
  2 Glass Wharf, BS2 0FR
  Tel: (0117) 915 4900 Fax: (0117) 915 4999
  Mohammed Awais Anwar

LYONS DAVIDSON LTD
  43 Queen Square, BS1 4QP
  Tel: (0117) 9047740
  Michael Andrew Tait
CLIMATE TRANSITION CAPITAL LLP
  1 Redcliff Street, BS1 6TP
  Alanna Jamie Flett
WOMBLE BOND DICKINSON (UK) LLP
  3 Temple Quay, Temple Back East, BS1 6DZ
  Tel: (0345) 4150000
BERRYMANS LACE MAWER LLP
  4th Floor, St. Thomas Court, BS1 6JG
  Tel: (0117) 9337700
BURGES SALMON LLP
  One Glass Wharf, BS2 0ZX
  Tel: (0117) 9392000 Fax: (0117) 9024400
  Web: www.burges-salmon.com
  Katie Elizabeth Allen
  Julian Roderick Gerard Boswall
  Euan McIntosh Bremner
  Nicholas Stephen Churchward
  Andrew Alexander Dunlop
  Jonathan William Eves
  Ross Fairley
  Lloyd David James
  Richard John Leeming
  James Edward Phillips
  Ross Andrew Simpson
  Paul John Clark
  Christopher James Bartlett
  Alison Ann Logan
  Paula McGeady
  Kathryn Jane Smith

Bromley
LONDON BOROUGH OF BROMLEY
  Civic Centre, Stockwell Close, BR1 3UH
  Tel: (07876) 452009
  Marion Paine

Cambridge
EVERSHEDS SUTHERLAND (INTERNATIONAL) LLP
  50/60 Station Road, CB1 2JH
  Tel: (0845) 4979797
BARR ELLISON LLP
  39 Parkside, CB1 1PN
  Grant James Mathieson
AVEVA SOLUTIONS LTD
  High Cross, Madingley Road, CB3 0HB
  Sana Shahida Afzal-Ali
MILLS & REEVE LLP
  Botanic House, 100 Hills Road, CB2 1PH
  Emily Barbara Horn

Chester
LDF OPERATIONS LIMITED
  Second Floor, HQ Offices, 58 Nicholas Street,
  CH1 2NP
  Tel: (01244) 527300
  Ross Samuel Rutherford

Clitheroe
BACKHOUSE JONES
  The Printworks, Hey Road, BB7 9WD
  Tel: (0845) 0575111
  Claire Elaine McKie

Croydon
UK ANTI-DOPING
  Trafalgar House, 1 Bedford Park, CR0 2AQ
  Ailie Larissa McGowan
PENSION PROTECTION FUND
  Renaissance, 12 Dingwall Road, CR0 2NA
  Tel: (020) 8633 4957
  Laurence John Edwards
  Martha Quinn
SUPERDRUG STORES PLC, CR0 2EU
  Catherine Anna Montgomery
EDF ENERGY
  81-85 Station Road
  Tel: (07809) 593900
  Emma Brown
  Abigail Elizabeth Lloyd

Eastbourne
LSL FAMILY LAW
  8 South Lynn Drive, BN21 2JF
  Tel: (01273) 041011
  Linda Sutherland Lamb

Epsom
SARTORIUS STEDIM UK LIMITED
  Longmead Business Centre, Blenheim Road,
  KT19 9QQ
  Stacie Dawn MacIntyre

Exeter
MICHELMORES LLP
  Woodwater House, Pynes Hill, EX2 5WR
  Tel: (01392) 688 688
  Lynsey Kristen Blyth

Fareham
SHOOSMITHS LLP
  Forum 5, the Forum, Parkway, PO15 7PA
  Tel: (03700) 866800

Feltham
PERFORM GROUP
  Sussex House, 2 Plane Tree Crescent,
  TW14 7HE
  Kathleen Harriet Brocklebank Cradock

Gerrards Cross
ENERGY LAW SOLUTIONS LIMITED
  28 School Lane, Chalfont St. Peter, SL9 9BA
  Kevin Francis McGrory

Gloucester
EDF ENERGY
  Legal Affairs, Generation & Supply, Barnett
  Way, Barnwood, GL4 3RS
  Tel: (020) 3126 2208
  Susan Elizabeth Lind

Guildford
PREMIER ASSET MANAGEMENT LIMITED
  Unit 1 Eastgate Court, High Street, GU1 3DE
  Gregor Alexander Craig
STEVENS & BOLTON LLP
  Wey House, Farnham Road, GU1 4YD
  Tel: (01483) 302264
  Andrew Gabriel Steele

Harlow
TEVA UK LIMITED
  Field House, Station Approach, CM20 2FB
  Tel: (020) 75407489
  Paul Alister Gerald Taylor

Hemel Hempstead
BAM CONSTRUCT UK LTD
  Breakspear Park, Breakspear Way, HP2 4FL
  Tel: (01442) 238394
  Gillian Buchan Simpson

High Wycombe
ROYAL AIR FORCE
  Directorate of Legal Services (RAF), 3S11,
  Spitfire Block, HQ Air Command, HP14 4UE
  Stuart Charles Agnew

Hook
SERCO UK, EUROPE & SGS
  2nd Floor, Enterprise House, 11 Bartley Wood
  Business Park, RH27 9XB
  Tel: (01256) 386153
  Greg Bruce Nicoll

Horley
SCOTIA GAS NETWORKS LIMITED
  Legal Services, St Lawrence House, Station
  Approach, RH6 9JY
  Tel: (01293) 818 217
  Nicola Anne Shand

Ipswich
EVERSHEDS SUTHERLAND (INTERNATIONAL) LLP
  159 Princes Street, IP1 1QJ
  Tel: (0845) 4979797

Isleworth
SKY UK LTD
  Sky Central, Grant Way, TW7 5QD
  Tel: (020) 7032 7085
  Christina Emmeline Johnston
  Robert Marshall Jones
  Alice Jane Walton

Leeds

SHOOSMITHS LLP
Platform, New Station Street, LS1 4JB
Tel: (03700) 867300
Email: leeds@shoosmiths.co.uk

GOVERNMENT LEGAL DEPARTMENT
Lateral, 8 City Walk, LS11 9AT
Eileen Annette Waters

MEDICAL PROTECTION SOCIETY
Victoria House, 2 Victoria Place, LS11 5AE
Julia Helen Bryden
Sarah Louise Donaldson
Elizabeth Sheila Grant
Sara Lauren Macdonald Grewar
Nicola Ann Innes
Rhona Heather Keith
Gregor Alexander McPhail
Nicola Jane Paul
Karen Anne Rowney

ENGIE POWER LIMITED
No 1 Leeds, 26 Whitehall Road, LS12 1BE
Tel: (0113) 3062149 Fax: (0113) 2451515
Neil Anderson

ADDLESHAW GODDARD LLP
3 Sovereign Square, Sovereign Street, LS1 4ER
Joanna Catherine Neill Logie

ASDA STORES LTD
Legal Team, Asda House, Southbank, Great
Wilson Street, LS11 5AD
Tel: (0113) 8262272
Graeme Edward Morrison

WOMBLE BOND DICKINSON (UK) LLP
1 Whitehall Riverside, LS1 4BN
Tel: (0345) 4150000

CLARION SOLICITORS LIMITED
Elizabeth House, 13-19 Queen Street,
LS1 2TW
Tel: (0113) 2460622
Fiona Isabel Marr
Philip Morrison

PINSENT MASONS LLP
1 Park Row, LS1 5AB
Tel: (0113) 2445000

DLA PIPER UK LLP
Princes Exchange, Princes Square, LS1 4BY
Tel: (08700) 111111 Fax: (020) 77966666
Bryony Elizabeth Lunn
Ataikor Sampson Ngerebara

BERRYMANS LACE MAWER LLP
4th Floor Park Row House, 19-20 Park Row,
LS1 5JF
Tel: (0113) 2362002

EVERSHEDS SUTHERLAND (INTERNATIONAL) LLP
Bridgewater Place, Water Lane, LS11 5BZ
Tel: (0845) 4979797
Email: CatherineKnight@eversheds-sutherland.
com

Leominster

FISH LEGAL
Eastwood House, 6 Rainbow Street, HR6 8DQ
Tel: (0131) 5564462

Robert William Younger

GUY LINLEY-ADAMS SOLICITORS
Office E3, Grange Court, Pinsley Road,
HR6 8NL
Tel: (07837) 881219
Guy Edward Linley-Adams

Liverpool

LITTLEWOODS LIMITED
Skyways House, Speke Road, Speke, L70 1AB
Tel: (0844) 292 2630
Gemma Ann Gibson

HILL DICKINSON LLP
No. 1 St Paul's Square, L3 9SJ
Tricia Marianne Morrison

BERRYMANS LACE MAWER LLP
Castle Chambers, 43 Castle Street, L2 9SU
Tel: (0151) 2362002

Liversedge

QC LAW SOLICITORS LIMITED
633 Halifax Road, WF15 8HG
Tel: (01484) 818123
Rizwan Khalil Ahmed
Sophina Mehmood Ali

London

BURGES SALMON LLP
6 New Street Square, EC4A 3BF

VODAFONE GROUP SERVICES LIMITED
1 Kingdom Street, W2 6BD
Richard James Cullen

INDUCTION HEALTHCARE UK LIMITED
20 St. Dunstan's Hill, EC3R 8HL
Jemma Ann Murray
Alison Janet Talbot

SOTHEBY'S
Compliance and Busienss Integrity, 34-35
New Bond Street, W1A 2AA
Melanie Jane Allan

COUTTS & CO
440 Strand, WC2R 0QS
Fergus George Curnow Hand

GUNNERCOOKE SCO LLP
1 Cornhill, EC3V 3ND

ERNST AND YOUNG LLP
1 More London Place, SE1 2AF
Craig Forbes Stevenson

CM MURRAY LLP
First Floor, 36-38 Cornhill, EC3V 3NG
Tel: (020) 79339133 Fax: (020) 79339132
Sarah Jane Chilton

EYGS
6 More London Place, SE1 2DA
Emma Hughes

BATTERSEA POWER STATION DEVELOPMENT
COMPANY
188 Kirtling Street, SW8 5BN
Tel: (020) 7062 1912 Fax: (020) 7501 7689
Iain James Miller

AXA UK PLC
  20 Gracechurch Street, EC3V 0BG
  Hannah Jane Garrick
SHOOSMITHS LLP
  1 Bow Churchyard, EC4M 9DQ
  Tel: (03700) 863000
  Brian Thomas Morrison
PTS CONSULTING
  5 Jewry Street, EC3N 2EX
  Antonia Elizabeth Shand
TAYLOR WESSING LLP
  5 New Street Square, EC4A 3TW
  Tel: (020) 7300 4995
  Anna Patricia McCaffrey
  James Bryden
  Megan Sarah Lukins
  Ruth Marion Moffett
SAVE THE CHILDREN
  1 St John's Lane, EC1M 4AR
  Elizabeth Margaret Helen Knox
TRAVERS SMITH LLP
  10 Snow Hill, EC1A 2AL
  Tel: (0207) 2953387
  Andrew James Peter Spencer Maxwell
  Alexander John Watt
  Stuart Norman Allan
  Nicholas David Brady
  Hugh Forbes Aaron Hutchison
  Caragh Rowanne Jenkins
  Stuart Johnston MacKenzie
  Genevieve Denise Marten
  Eilidh Katherine Morrison
  Ailie Anne Murray
  Callum James O'Brien
  Leigh Alexandra Stockey
  Rachel Louise Taggart
  Silvana Giulia Van Der Velde
CLYDE & CO (SCOTLAND) LLP
  The St. Botolph Building, 138 Houndsditch,
  EC3A 7AR
  Tel: (020) 78765000
  Email: Enquiries.Scotland@clydeco.com
  Web: www.simpmar.com
NOTAMVIS LIMITED
  Unit 5 Drakes Courtyard, Kilburn High Road,
  NW6 7JR
  David Gerard Currie
KIRKLAND & ELLIS INTERNATIONAL LLP
  30 St. Mary Axe, EC3A 8AF
  Tel: (0207) 4692000 Fax: (0207) 4692001
  Euan Alston
  Annette Helen Baillie
  Adam Dennis Davies
  Latifa El-Shafei
  Jamie Peter Gordon
  Jan Maria Kapaon
  Leon Fraser MacMillan
  Alexander James Manson
  Andrew James McAlpine
  Philip Alexander McEachen
  Kirsteen Margaret Nicol
  Matthew David Pollock
  Sharon Elizabeth Skipper

  Jamie Colin Thomson
  Joanna Thomson
  Jennifer Frances Wilson
SACKER & PARTNERS LLP
  20 Gresham Street, EC2V 7JE
  Andrew Harper
  Daniel Owen Traynor
DECA MEDIA CONSULTANCY
  Tobacco Dock, E1W 2SF
  Vicki McGowan
PREMIER OIL PLC
  23 Lower Belgrave Street, SW1W 0NR
  Tel: (020) 7730 1111
  Kelly Louise Mitchell
BRACHER RAWLINS LLP
  77 Kingsway, WC2B 6SR
  Tel: (0207) 4001540
  David Roger Gerber
MAYER BROWN INTERNATIONAL LLP
  201 Bishopsgate, EC2M 3AF
  Tel: (+44) 20 3130 3033
  Duncan Forbes Watson
REED SMITH LLP
  The Broadgate Tower, 20 Primrose Street,
  EC2A 2RS
  Victoria Bryden
  Thomas Edward Gates
  Natalie Elizabeth Sharkey
GOVERNMENT LEGAL DEPARTMENT
  03-Jan, 1 Horse Guards Road, SW1A 2HQ
  Tel: (0207) 004 1293
  Jesse Clare Ambler
LEGAL & GENERAL INVESTMENT MANAGEMENT
LTD
  One Coleman Street, EC2R 5AA
  Tel: (020) 3124 3983 Fax: (020) 7634 0889
  Michael Harrats
BBC
  Wogan House, Great Portland Street,
  W1A 1AA
  Joanna Clare Elder
BARCLAYS BANK PLC
  Level 29, 1 Churchill Place, E14 5HP
  Tel: (0207) 116 1000
  Gillian Christie
  Alicia Sylvester Ebdy
  Georgina Marie Farmer
  Victoria Patricia Elizabeth Gall
  Alison Wowk
BARCLAYS BANK PLC
  Level 8, 1 Churchill Place, E14 5HP
  Jennifer Rae
PROSKAUER ROSE LLP
  110 Bishopsgate, EC2N 4AY
  Mark Williamson Hume
MITIE
  Level 12, The Shard, 32 London Bridge Street,
  SE1 9SG
  Catriona Leanne Weir
CADWALADER, WICKERSHAM & TAFT LLP
  100 Bishopsgate, EC2N 4AG
  Kerry Anne Shearer

DENTSU INTERNATIONAL LIMITED
20 Triton Street, Regents Place, NW1 3BF
Lauren Margaret Catherine Buchan

LIQUIDITY SERVICES
3rd Floor, 69 Leadenhall Street, EC3A 2BG
Tel: (020) 70983706
Jamie Paul Larkin

CHANNEL 4 TELEVISION CORPORATION
Legal & Compliance Department, 124
Horseferry Road, SW1P 2TX
Tel: (0207) 306 8119
Dominic Charles Harrison

HOGAN LOVELLS INTERNATIONAL LLP
Atlantic House, Holburn Viaduct, EC1A 2FG
Tel: (020) 7296 2861 Fax: (020) 7296 2001
Ross Kevin King
Pamela McHarg
Nicola Jane Evans
Scott Henry Gibson
Claire Elizabeth Macpherson
John Alexander Salmon

QBE MANAGEMENT SERVICES (UK) LTD
Plantation Place, 30 Fenchurch Street,
EC3M 3BD
Tel: (0207) 105 5947 Fax: (0207) 105 4070
Karen Mary Stewart

BARCLAYS EXECUTION SERVICES LIMITED
Barclays UK Legal, Level 26, 1 Churchill Place,
E14 5HP
Paul Anthony Rae

NATIONAL WESTMINSTER BANK PLC
250 Bishopsgate, Liverpool Street, EC2M 4AA
Alexander David Bicket
David John Irvine
Victoria Kate Salmon

DEBEVOISE & PLIMPTON LLP
65 Gresham Street, EC2V 7NQ
Kay Leigh Hunter

COOLEY (UK) LLP
22 Bishopsgate, EC2N 4BQ
Alexandra-Magda Mitrea

NOKIA
1 Sheldon Square, Paddington, W2 6PY
Lorna Jane Gibb

CORAM CHILDREN'S LEGAL CENTRE
Queen Elizabeth Centre, Coram Campus, 41
Brunswick Square, WC1N 1AZ
Tel: (020) 7713 2021
Stewart Bryce MacLachlan

ALDEN LEGAL LIMITED
25 Southampton Buildings, WC2A 1AL
Joanne Elizabeth Wheeler

RIDOUTS PROFESSIONAL SERVICES PLC
7-10 Chandos Street, W1G 9DG
Tel: (020) 7317 0354 Fax: (020) 7935 8310
Laura Paton Shelton

GOVERNMENT LEGAL DEPARTMENT
102 Petty France, Westminster, SW1H 9GL
Tel: (020) 7210 1476
Rebecka Buchanan
Owen Gibbons Wilton

STARLING BANK LIMITED
3rd Floor, 2 Finsbury Avenue, EC2M 2PP
Sian Elizabeth Laurie

CPFC LIMITED
Selhurst Park Stadium, SE25 6PU
Tel: (020) 8768 6000
David Gerrard Nichol

BALFOUR BEATTY INVESTMENTS LIMITED
350 Euston Road, NW1 3AX
Sandra Elizabeth Hartley

DENTONS GLOBAL SERVICES (UK) HOLDINGS
LIMITED
1 Fleet Place, EC4M 7WS
Louisa Gair Black

LINK MARKET SERVICES LIMITED
65 Gresham Street, EC2V 7NQ
Brooke Kelly Modlin

LEWIS SILKIN LLP
5 Chancery Lane, Clifford's Inn, EC4A 1BL
Tel: (0207) 0748 137
Nigel Quentin Dewar Gibb

CMS CAMERON MCKENNA NABARRO
OLSWANG LLP
Cannon Place, 78 Cannon Street, EC4N 6AF
Tel: (0207) 3673000 Fax: (0207) 3672000
Steven Francis Cochrane
Douglas Richard Land
Robert Gilmour Leckie
Iain Charles Grant Lindsay
Stephen Samuel Alexander Millar
Andrew Brian Shaw
William Graeme Simmons, WS
Alasdair Montgomerie Steele
Catherine Alice Devine
Helen Elizabeth Fyfe
Cameron Gordon Jones
Adam Michael Lovatt
Michael Jonathan Lyner
David Lorne McCallum
Konrad Pawel Rawicz
Nadia Michelle Wheeler
Charlotte Louise Bascombe
Aileen Linda Brown
Gr inne M ire Duffy
Valerie Elizabeth Fox
Sophie Jane Gallacher
Rebecca Mary Thomson

EDWARDS DUTHIE SHAMASH
12 Baylis Road, SE1 7AA
Colin Graham Davidson

TRANSPORT FOR LONDON
5 Endeavour Square, 4th Floor, Yellow Zone,
Stratford, E20 1JN
Tel: (020) 30543964 Fax: (020) 79183991
Alexandra Lyn Lavery

BANK OF NEW YORK MELLON
One Canada Square, E14 5AL
Tel: (0778) 759 5943
Euan Robert Allan Anderson

HOWARD KENNEDY LLP
No1. London Bridge, SE1 9BG
Oliver James Cormack McInnes
Marc Douglas Proudfoot

IMG (UK) LTD
  Bulding 6, 566 Chiswick High Road, W4 5HR
  Tel: (020) 8233 5300
  Dana Lesley Gibson
SQUIRE PATTON BOGGS (UK) LLP
  2 & A Half Devonshire Square, EC2M 4UJ
  Tel: (020) 7655 1000
  Donald Angus Lawrie Morrison
WESTCOR INTERNATIONAL LIMITED
  City Pavillion, Cannon Green, 27 Bush Lane,
  EC4 0AA
  Kirsty Elizabeth Noble
ACTURIS LTD
  100 Hatton Garden, EC1N 8NX
  Samantha Hastie
WIGGIN LLP
  10th Floor, Met Building, 22 Percy Street,
  W1T 2BU
  Gordon Ivor Moir
  Darren Douglas Hugh Stevenson
LAW COMMISSION
  Post Point 1.52, 1st Floor, Tower, 52 Queen
  Anne's Gate, SW1H 9AG
  Tel: (0203) 3345327
  Laura Katrina Burgoyne
DAVITT JONES BOULD LIMITED
  Level 24 The Shard, 32 London Bridge Street,
  SE1 9SG
  Gillian Sarah Lewis
FOX WILLIAMS LLP
  Ten Finsbury Square, EC2A 1AF
  Benjamin Edward Nolan
EDWIN COE LLP
  2 Stone Buildings, Lincoln's Inn, WC2A 3TH
  Tel: (020) 76914171 Fax: (020) 76914111
  Joanne McIvor
LIVINGSTONE BROWN LIMITED
  1 Fetter Lane, EC4A 1BR
  Tel: (0203) 4405865
  Email: london@livbrown.co.uk
RUSSELL-COOKE LLP
  8 Bedford Row, WC1R 4BX
  Tel: (0207) 4056566 Fax: (0207) 8312565
  Thomas Millar Ferguson
HOWDEN M&A LIMITED
  16B Wichester Walk, SE1 9AQ
  Greg David Strefford
ELLIOTT MATTHEW PROPERTY LAWYERS
  10 Margaret Street, Fitzrovia, W1W 8RL
  Sandra Rankine
LINKLATERS LLP
  One Silk Street, EC2Y 8HQ
  Tel: (0207) 4562000 Fax: (0207) 4562222
  Lizanne Blair
  Stephen John Murphy
OSBORNE CLARKE
  One London Wall, EC2Y 5EB
  Clara Hutchison
  David Andrew Charles Nisbet
  Louise Margaret Oliver
ASCENT UNDERWRITING LLP
  10th Floor, One MinsterCourt, Mincing Lane,
  Billingsgate, EC3R 7AA

Tel: (0203) 8592193
  Richard Moir
APOLLO MANAGEMENT INTERNATIONAL LLP
  25 St George Street, W1S 1FS
  Tel: (020) 3320 1562
  Christopher John Dearie
SODEXO LIMITED
  One Southampton Row, WC1B 5HA
  Tel: 7824550841
  Christopher Lindsay Lewis-Laverty
NUDE FINANCE
  C/O Cms Cameron Mckenna, Cannon Place,
  78 Cannon Street, EC4N 6AF
  Kate McKay
ACCEL PARTNERS MANAGEMENT LLP
  6th Floor, 1 New Burlington Place, W1S 2HR
  Janine Alison Suttie
REYNOLDS PORTER CHAMBERLAIN LLP
  Tower Bridge House, St Katharine's Way,
  E1W 1AA
  Heather Rachel Clark
  Leigh Gapinski
  Cheryl Davina Laird
AMBER FUND MANAGERS LTD
  3 More, Riverside, SE1 2AQ
  Tel: (0207) 939 0550
  Helen Therese Regan
MORGAN, LEWIS & BOCKIUS UK LLP
  Condor House, 5-10 St. Pauls Churchyard,
  EC4M 8AL
  Tel: (020) 3201 5000 Fax: (020) 3201 5001
  Robert Hutton
LEXIS NEXIS
  Lexis House, 30 Farringdon Street, EC4A 4HH
  Leigh Allan Monteforte
TLT LLP
  20 Gresham Street, EC2V 7JE
  Web: www.tltsolicitors.com
HELICAL PLC
  5 Hanover Square, W1S 1HQ
  Tel: (020) 7629 0113
  Eleanor Jane Gill
DENTONS UK AND MIDDLE EAST LLP
  One Fleet Place, EC4M 7WS
  Tel: (020) 7242 1212
  Email: AP.UKME@dentons.com
  Craig John Neilson
  Guy Austen Norfolk
  Alastair David MacLeod
  Ruby Megan Davies
  Matthew Thomas Gilhooly
  Charlotte Victoria Miles
AXA INVESTMENT MANAGERS
  22 Bishopsgate, EC2N 4BQ
  Tel: (07894) 942894
  Fraser Malcolm Simpson
ASHURST LLP
  1 Duval Square, London Fruit and Wool
  Exchange, E1 6PW
  Tel: (020) 7859 2145 Fax: (020) 7638 1112
  Jonathan Nicholas Byrne-Leitch
  Meela Kwok
  Callum Euan McPherson

Eilish Russell
Lauren Sinclair Morrison
Julie Marie Connolly
Annie Rose Marriner
Maria Laura McAlister
Matthew David Sharpe
PAUL HASTINGS (EUROPE) LLP
100 Bishopsgate, EC2N 4AG
Tel: (020) 3023 5100 Fax: (020) 3023 5497
Tsz Ching Li
Jordan Nathan Rhodes
Ashley Webber
MBM COMMERCIAL LLP
57 Berkeley Square, W1J 6ER
Tel: (020) 0960119
GOVERNMENT LEGAL DEPARTMENT
Caxton House, Tothill Street, Westminster,
SW1H 9NA
Tel: (0207) 4495952
Caitlin Rebecca Fitzgerald
Catriona Grace Hepburn
PETERS & PETERS SOLICITORS LLP
15 Fetter Lane, EC4A 1BW
Tel: (020) 7822 7777
David Fitzpatrick
BRITISH BUSINESS BANK
8 Salisbury Square, 2nd Floor, EC4Y 8AP
Rory Neil Swanson
CITY LAW FIRM LIMITED
T/a St John Legal, Winchester House, 19
Bedford Row, WC1R 4EB
Nils Malcolm Reid
Andrew Grant Williamson
AON UK LTD
122 Leadenhall Street, EC3V 4AB
Sophia Catherine Hytiris
UNITE THE UNION
Legal Department, Unite House, 128
Theobalds Road, WC1X 8TN
Neil Gillam
VATTENFALL WIND POWER LTD.
Legal Affairs, First Floor, 1 Tudor Street,
EC4Y 0AH
Tel: (+44) (0) 203 301 9143
Lisa Marie MacLeod
WAVEMAKER UK
Sea Containers, 18 Upper Ground, SE1 9ET
Kirsty Louisa Wilson
ATTEST TECHNOLOGIES LIMITED
25 Holywell Row, EC2A 4XE
Amy Elizabeth Andrew
MONTGOMERY SMITH SOLICITORS
7 Bell Yard, WC2A 2JR
Tel: (0203) 5822883
Email: greg@montgomerysmith.co.uk
GNEISS ENERGY LIMITED
29 Farm Street, W1J 5RL
Jonathan Scott McGlade Fitzpatrick
SIMMONS & SIMMONS
Citypoint, 1 Ropemaker Street, EC2Y 9SS
Tel: (+44) 20 7825 3740
Magdalena Lucyna Szperzynska

TEACHER STERN LLP
37-41 Bedford Row, WC1R 4JH
Tel: (020) 72423191
Lorna Anne Clarke
HOME OFFICE
2 Marsham Street, SW1P 4DF
Tel: (07778) 100 471
Robert John Home Mooney
Erin Maria Paterson
JANUS HENDERSON INVESTORS
201 Bishopsgate, EC2M 3AE
Kirsty Margaret Mary Gilmartin
Rosanna Skye Lawson
SUNNY HILL ENERGY
83 Victoria Street, Westminster, SW1H 0HW
Peter George Wilson
OSPREY CHARGING NETWORK
1st Floor, 3 More London Riverside, SE1 2RE
Tel: (0800) 0588400
Ewen Ross Cairns, WS
IRWIN MITCHELL
40 Holborn Viaduct, EC1N 2PZ
Tel: (0370) 1500100
Elzbieta Justyna Olejnik
CLYDE & CO LLP
The St Botolph Building, 138 Houndsditch,
EC3A 7AR
Tel: (020) 7876 5000 Fax: (020) 7876 5111
Stewart McNeill Healey
CAVENDISH EMPLOYMENT LAW
70 Gracechurch Street, EC3V 0HR
Shelagh Anne McKenzie
GOLDMAN SACHS
Goldman Sachs International, Plumtree Court,
25 Shoe Lane, EC4A 4AU
Tel: (+44) (0) 20 7774 1454
Ross Clements
SIMMONS & SIMMONS LLP
Citypoint, One Ropemaker Street, EC2Y 9SS
Tel: 2078253170 Fax: 2076282070
Colin John Bole
Angela-Jean Christoforou
TURCAN CONNELL
1st Floor, 12 Stanhope Gate, W1K 1AW
Tel: (0207) 4918811
Web: www.turcanconnell.com
IMPACT RADIUS LIMITED
15 Rathbone Place, W1T 1HU
Rahul Gindha
DICKSON MINTO
Broadgate Tower, Level 13, EC2A 2EW
Tel: (020) 76284455 Fax: (020) 7628 0027
Email: dicksonminto@dmws.com
Web: www.dicksonminto.co.uk
Paul Thomas Barron
Paul Andrew Buchan
Jordan Keith Simpson
Devon Clair Brewster
Daniel John Carolan
Ronan Andrew Craig
Ross Allan Cruickshanks
Alastair Ronald Dickson, WS
James Ross Duncan

Hannah Gong
Aoibheann Harkin
Robert Andrew Hay
Sophie Emma Paterson Hofford
Fraser Paul Jackson
Jennifer Jane Lynch
Drew Stewart MacDonald
Andrew John Manson
Christine Teresa McFadyen
Grant McGregor
Jennifer Barbara McLellan
Lucy Anne Reville
Katherine Sinclair
Lara Katie Watt

NORGES BANK INVESTMENT MANAGEMENT
Queensbury House, 3 Old Burlington Street, W1S 3AE
Tel: (020) 7534 9000 Fax: (020) 7534 9010
Eva Kristina Louise Sj sten

NORTON ROSE FULBRIGHT LLP
3 More London Riverside, SE1 2AQ
Barbara Kemunto Onuonga

FRIED, FRANK, HARRIS, SHRIVER & JACOBSON (LONDON) LLP
100 Bishopsgate, EC2N 4AG
Tel: (0207) 9729600 Fax: (0207) 9729602
Karen Mary Henderson
Robert Livingstone MacVicar

WHITE & CASE LLP
5 Old Broad Street, EC2N 1DW
Tel: (0207) 5321000 Fax: (0207) 532 1001
Mathew Desmond Boyle
John Bernard Timmons
Omar Anwar
Finlay Ian Fraser
Morvyn Anne Radlow

THE CHILDREN'S INVESTMENT FUND FOUNDATION (UK)
Legal Counsel, 7 Clifford Street, W1S 2FT
Gillian Margaret Fleming

HSBC HOLDINGS PLC
8 Canada Square, E14 5HQ
Tel: 2079923637
Aileen Norma Taylor

GULF KEYSTONE PETROLEUM LIMITED
6th Floor, New Fetter Place, 8-10 New Fetter Lane, EC4A 1AZ
Alasdair Nicholson Robinson

ZURICH INSURANCE PLC
11th Floor, 70 Mark Lane, EC3R 7NQ
Felix Denzil Edward Boon

IQVIA LIMITED
210 Pentonville Road, N1 9JY
Janice Kathleen Mary More

ADAPTAVIST
25 Wilton Road, Victoria, SW1V 1LW
Ava Margaret Macgregor Maitland

TRUSTPILOT LIMTED
Minster Building, 3 Minster Court, 5th Floor, EC3R 7AG
Graeme Alasdair Di Rollo

SCOTT+SCOTT UK LLP
St. Bartholomew House, 90-94 Fleet Street, EC4Y 1DH
Douglas Colin Campbell

VARDE PARTNERS EUROPE LIMITED
Level 2, 50 New Bond Street, W1S 1BJ
Tel: (020) 7078 0091 Fax: (020) 7808 3371
Bruce Alexander Hendry

ADDLESHAW GODDARD LLP
Milton Gate, 60 Chiswell Street, EC1Y 4AG
Tel: (0207) 6068855 Fax: (0207) 6064390
DX: 47 LONDON
Email: rachel.napier-williams@addleshawgoddard.com
Jaya Rajoriya Gupta
Martin Charles Stewart-Smith
Mark Eric Guttridge
Tristan Donald Johnston
Katy Anne Stevenson
Thomas William Walmsley
Katherine Ann Watson

SHELL INTERNATIONAL LIMITED
Shell Centre, SE1 7NA
Gavin John Ross

MCARTHUR GLEN GROUP
Nations House, 103 Wigmore Street, W1U 1QS
Matthew David Jamieson

ARGONON LTD
1-3 St. Peter's Street, N1 8JD
Amanda Elizabeth Goddard

SHEARMAN & STERLING (LONDON) LLP
9 Appold Street, EC2A 2AP
Gina Mugnaioni Malone
Katherine McAlinden
Jamie Douglas Turley

SLAUGHTER AND MAY
One Bunhill Row, EC1Y 8YY
Tel: (020) 7600 1200 Fax: (020) 7090 5000
Paul Ian Robert Dickson
Catriona Louise Jardine

AMAZON UK SERVICES LTD
Legal Department, 1 Principal Place, Worship Street, EC2A 2FA
Jessica Mary Campbell

STEWART TITLE LTD
11 Haymarket, SW1Y 4BP
Tel: (01698) 833308 Fax: (01698) 744111
DX: 556143 BELLSHILL
John Francis Logan

GOWLING WLG (UK) LLP
4 More London Riverside, SE1 2AU
Robert Malcolm Armour, WS

SWISS RE
30 St Mary Axe, EC3A 8EP
Tel: (020) 7933 4235
Claudia Katharina Maria Hennecke

DWF LAW LLP
20 Fenchurch Street, EC3M 3AG
Tel: (0333) 3202220 Fax: (0333) 3204440
Katie Tolmie McKernan
Michalina Pria Udhare Rebisz-Bahra

LEE & THOMPSON
80 Charlotte Street, W1T 4DF
Tel: (020) 3073 7653
Andrew Douglas Florence

THE PREMIER LEAGUE
Brunel Building, 57 North Wharf Road,
W2 1HQ
Tel: (+44) (0) 20 7864 9000
Stuart Alexander Tennant

ASSOCIATED BRITISH FOODS PLC
50-51 Russell Square, WC1B 4JA
Leanne Jane Dixon
Karen Jean Orr

BUILD HOLLYWOOD LTD
15 Duncan Terrace, N1 8BZ
Martin Campbell

BRITISH TELECOMMUNICATIONS PLC
Faraday Building, Ground Floor, 1 Knightrider
Street, EC4V 5BT
Rachel Eleanor Canham
Donald Harper Sellar

THE PENSIONS OMBUDSMAN
10 South Colonnade, Canary Wharf, E14 4PU
Robert Kenneth Alexander Palmer

ROOFOODS LTD
The River Building, 1 Cousin Lane, EC4R 3TE
Thomas Clark Hepburn

MCDERMOTT WILL & EMERY UK LLP
Heron Tower, 110 Bishopsgate, EC2N 4AY
Tel: (0207) 577 3494
Calum Blair Thom

HG CAPITAL LLP
2 More London, Riverside, SE1 2AP
Tel: (020) 70897992
Andrew David Jessop

QS QUACQUARELLI SYMONDS LIMITED
1 Tranley Mews, Fleet Road, NW3 2DG
Amy Lesley Goodbrand

FREETHS LLP
1 Vine Street, Mayfair, W1J 0AH
Ewen Alexander Lowrie

ASTON GOWMAN LIMITED
1000 Great West Road, Brentford, TW8 9DW
Tel: (0333) 3447277
Gail Margaret Millar

DLA PIPER UK LLP
160 Aldersgate Street, EC1A 4HT
Tel: (020) 77966017 Fax: (020) 77966666
Jan Claire Colhoun
Sarah Lesley Louise Crowe
Jennifer Gibbons
Fraser Mark Grant
Grant William Henderson
Sarah Grace Letson
Gregor Callum Munro
Michal Krzysztof Orzeg-Wydra
Sarah Marie Tindall

HAYNES AND BOONE CDG, LLP
2nd Floor, 1 New Fetter Lane, EC4A 1AN
Tel: (020) 8734 2807
Emma Anne Russell

WOMBLE BOND DICKINSON (UK) LLP
4 More London Riverside, SE1 2AU
Tel: (0345) 4150000 Fax: (0191) 279 9100
Iain Walter Pritty

GOOGLE UK LIMITED
Belgrave House, 76 Buckingham Palace Road,
SW1W 9TQ
Tel: (020) 7346 2927
Ruaridh Andrew Allen Goodfield
Rachael Catherine Johnston
William Malcolm
Struan James Alastair Robertson

GENERATION INVESTMENT MANAGEMENT LLP
20 Air Street, W1B 5AN
Alexander MacIntyre Marshall

IMMEDIATE MEDIA COMPANY LONDON
LIMITED
Vineyard House, 44 Brook Green,
Hammersmith, W6 7BT
Jennifer Mackay Lucas
Emily Jane McQueen

SIMPSON THACHER & BARTLETT LLP
CityPoint, One Ropemaker Street, EC2Y 9HU
Tel: (020) 7275 6500 Fax: (020) 7275 6502
Derek William Baird
Carlo Pia

MACQUARIE CORPORATE HOLDINGS PTY
LIMITED (UK BRANCH)
Ropemaker Place, 28 Ropemaker Street,
EC2Y 9HD
Nicola Hetherington
Veyoma Thushari Hevamanage

PINSENT MASONS LLP
30 Crown Place, EC2A 4ES
Tel: (020) 7418 7000 Fax: (020) 7418 7050
Kevin William Boa
Alison Margaret Ross Eckford
Murdo Maclean
Stephen Manus Tobin
Rebecca Charlotte Aspinwall
Vladim r Kucera
Sheelagh Helen MacGregor
Fiona Ross
Gabriele Ruta Geceviciute
Christina Cooke
Luke Joseph Costello
Rebecca Danielle Devaney
Helen Muriel Nicoll Gray
Priya Jhakra
Rachel Elizabeth McConnell
Mhairi Catriona Morrison
Stewart William Murphy
Angela Clare Norris
Tsvetan Kirilov Petrov
Amy Kate Stirling
Rebecca Christine Townsend

ENI UK LIMITED
10 Ebury Bridge Road, SW1W 8PZ
Tel: (0207) 3446330
Richard George Forgan

BRYAN CAVE LEIGHTON PAISNER LLP
Governor's House, 5 Laurence Pountney,
EC4R 0BR

John Thomas Conlin
Andrew David Leitch
Malcolm MacMillan Moir
SCHILLINGS
   12 Arthur Street, EC4R 9AB
   Caroline Eve Marshall
CARMICHAEL LEMAIRE LTD
   71-75 Shelton Street, Covent Garden,
   WC2H 9JQ
   Gillian Elizabeth Carmichael Lemaire
CHECKOUT.COM
   Wenlock Works, Shepherdess Walk, N1 7LH
   Joseph Paterson
GATELEY PLC
   No. 1 Paternoster Square, EC4M 7DX
   James John Hillan
   Martin John Montgomery
FINANCIAL CONDUCT AUTHORITY
   12 Endeavor Square, E20 1JN
   Kirsty Emma McLaren
   Ross Matthew Murdoch
   Charles Oliver Rogers
BANK OF AMERICA MERRILL LYNCH
   2 King Edward Street, EC1A 1HQ
   Tel: (0207) 995 0765
   Chantelle Angela Forster
BANNATYNE, KIRKWOOD, FRANCE & CO.
   76 Shoe Lane, EC4A 3JB
   Tel: (020) 73535005
   Email: lawyer@carterruck.com
OPENREACH LIMITED
   Kelvin House, 123 Judd Street, WC1H 9NP
   Tel: (0207) 8097460
   Sophie Rosalie Mary Thomson
RIDGEWALL LIMITED
   Devonshire House, 60 Goswell Road,
   EC1M 7AD
   Scott Owen Connarty
THE BUILDING SOCIETIES ASSOCIATION
   6th Floor, York House, 23 Kingsway,
   WC2B 6UJ
   Tel: (0207) 520 5915
   Julie Elaine Morton
CONDE NAST PUBLICATIONS LIMITED
   The Adelphi, 1-11 John Adam Street,
   WC2N 6HT
   Elizabeth Jane Donaldson
BARINGA PARTNERS LLP
   62 Buckingham Gate, SW1E 6AJ
   Annie Rose Carr
MLAW LLP
   3a Montagu Row, W1U 6DZ
   Neil Paterson
THE UNIVERSITY OF LAW
   3 Bunhill Row, Moorgate, EC1Y 8HQ
   Alistair David Fraser
STEPTOE & JOHNSON UK LLP
   5 Aldermanbury Square, EC2V 7HR
   Simon Andrew Tilling
AVIVA PLC
   20th Floor, St Helen's, 1 Undershaft,
   EC3P 3DQ
   Tel: (020) 7662 6646

Kirstine Ann Cooper
MANOLETE PARTNERS PLC
   21 Gloucester Place, W1U 8HR
   Rachel Mary Grant
ROTHCHILDS
   New Court, St Swithin's Lane, EC4N 8AL
   Jacob Samuel Massey
CLIFFORD CHANCE LLP
   10 Upper Bank Street, E14 5JJ
   Regan Elizabeth Turner
   Sarah-Marie Donnelly
   Robert David Edgar
   Jonathan William Forrest
   James Millar McMillan
   Struan Douglas Grant Murray
   Samuel Alexander Parry
   Chloe Louise Smith
STEPHENSON HARWOOD LLP
   1 Finsbury Circus, EC2M 7SH
   Tel: (020) 7329 4422 Fax: (020) 739 7100
   Bethany Ann Carr
   David Ross Ward Harris
OBASEKI SOLICITORS
   27 Bentley Road, Dalston, N1 4BY
   Heather Sian Hiram
JUSTICE
   Justice, 59 Carter Lane, EC4V 5AQ Fax: (0207)
   329 5055
   Andrea May Fraser
KINGSLEY NAPLEY LLP
   20 Bonhill Street, EC2A 4DN
   Tel: (0207) 8141200 Fax: (020) 73756411
   Rachel Elizabeth Ellen Cooper
   Julie Margaret Matheson
LATHAM & WATKINS (LONDON) LLP
   99 Bishopsgate, EC2M 3XF
   Tel: (020) 7710 1000 Fax: (020) 7374 4460
   Ross William David Anderson
   Douglas Alexander Abernethy
   Lewis Christopher Atherton
   Kendall Laurie Burnett
   Qi Rui Chen
   Aimee Laura Godfrey
   Fiona Margaret Maclean
   Christian Francis McDermott
   Alistair John McKechnie
   Erin Mary McKirdy
   Robert William Douglas McLaren
   Alain Michael Traill
   Danielle Van Der Merwe
OPEN SOCIETY FOUNDATION LONDON
   4th Floor Herbal House, 8 Back Hill, EC1R 5EN
   Susheela Math
ATLEU LTD
   St Saviour's House, 39-41 Union Street,
   SE1 1SD
   Tel: (0207) 7007311
   Sarah Benedicte Smith
GIBSON, DUNN & CRUTCHER LLP
   Telephone House, 2-4 Temple Avenue,
   EC4Y 0HB
   Tel: (0207) 0714249
   Robert Adam Carr

Robert Stuart Dixon
Christopher James Alexander Loudon
ASPRIS
80 Hammersmith Road, W14 8UD
Tel: (0207) 605 0922
Keir-Ewin Lynn
TOYOTA CONNECTED EUROPE LIMITED
14-18 Handyside Street, N1C 4DN
Christopher Barnaby Ivory Paton
ALLEN & OVERY LLP
One Bishops Square, E1 6AD
Tel: (020) 3088 0000 Fax: (020) 3088 0088
Stephen Ross Barclay
Arturas Jakubovskis
Gordon Bartlett
Neil Alexander Bowden
Myles Alexander Cormack
Kyle Zander Dunn
David MacGregor Early
Aisling Marie Knapton
Peter McIntyre Perry Mailer
Bruce Peter Rennie
BATES WELLS BRAITHWAITE LLP
10 Queen Street Place, EC4R 1BE
Karli Marie Hiscock
ASSURED GUARANTY
11th Floor, 6 Bevis Marks, EC3A 7BA
Tel: (020) 75628938
Tamsyn Nancy Cull McLean
FREEDMAN + HILMI LLP
101 Wigmore Street, W1U 1QU
Tel: (+44020) 7871 8600
Daniel Freedman
SENDERWOOD GROUP LIMITED
2 Brill Place, NW1 1DX
Rhian Elizabeth Saleh Al-Obaidy
MORRISON & FOERSTER
The Scalpel, 52 Lime Street, EC3M 7AF
Tel: (020) 7920 4047
Calum Mark Ablett
Stephanie Fiona Craw
HOLMAN FENWICK WILLAN LLP
Friary Court, 65 Crutched Friars, EC3N 2AE
Tel: (020) 7264 8000
Katherine Ellen Clarissa Doran
Andrew David Ross
ALDERMORE BANK PLC
5th Floor, Austin Friars House, 2-6 Austin
Friars, EC2N 2HD
Tel: (0203) 553 4236
Nicola Christine Sneddon
HERBERT SMITH FREEHILLS LLP
Exchange House, Primrose Street, EC2A 2EG
Tel: (020) 7466 2422
Lucy Clare Robson
Holly Amy Carss
Ian Andrew Mack
Jamie McLaren
Dominika Aleksandra Rogolska
TIDEWAY
Cottons Centre, Cottons Lane, SE1 2QG
Tel: (07966) 266069
Valmai Jane Barclay

CDC GROUP PLC
123 Victoria Street, SW1E 6DE
John Russell Hogg
PROVIDENCE STRATEGIC GROWTH LLP
Second Floor, 15 Sloane Square, SW1W 8ER
Fraser James Harald McLeod
PARK PLAZA HOTELS UK SERVICES LIMITED
County Hall – Riverside Building, 2nd Floor,
Belvedere Road, SE1 7PB
Andrew David Freeman
BAXENDALE EMPLOYEE OWNERSHIP LIMITED
Runway East, 20 St Thomas Street, SE1 9RS
Tel: (020) 3598 9982
Cristin Rosa Eileen Craig
Louise Fisher
Ewan Stuart Hall
VICASSET ADVISORS (UK) LIMITED
Verde, 10 Bressenden Place, SW1E 5DH
Tel: (020) 7429 2255
Neil Joseph William Sargent
BRITISH-AMERICAN TOBACCO (HOLDINGS)
LIMITED
Marketing Legal, Globe House, 4 Temple
Place, WC2R 2PG
Tel: (0207) 8452678
Alexander Juras
PRICEWATERHOUSECOOPERS LLP
7 More London Riverside, SE1 2RT
Sean Bryce Mowatt
JAMF
29 Clerkenwell Road, EC1M 5RN
Thomas Oliver Murdock, WS
LEYTON UK PARTNERS LLP
Harmsworth House, 13-15 Bouverie Street,
EC4Y 8DP
Simon Jonathan Ross Mayberry
DORSEY & WHITNEY (EUROPE) LLP
199 Bishopsgate, EC2M 3UT
Robbie Hamish Somerville
AKIN GUMP STRAUSS HAUER & FELD LLP
Eighth Floor, Ten Bishops Square, E1 6EG
Tel: (+44) 20.7012.9842 Fax: (+44)
20.7012.9601
Rebecca Mary Carwood Barron
Daniel Marcus Quinn
OFCOM
Riverside House, 2a Southwark Bridge Road,
SE1 9HA
Tel: (0207) 7834297
Philip Ian Hogg
PRICEWATERHOUSECOOPERS LLP
1 Embankment Place, WC2N 6RH
Tel: (020) 7212 1616 Fax: (020) 7212 1570
Laura Jane Freestone
Caitlin Hurst
UBS.AG
5 Broadgate, EC2M 2QS
Fiona Valansot
WSP UK LIMITED
WSP House, 70 Chancery Lane, WC2A 1AF
Tel: (0131) 344 2300
Anna Christine Savage

UNIVERSITY COLLEGE LONDON
 UCL Legal Services, Bidborough House, 38-50 Bidborough Street, WC1 9BT
 Tel: 2031088729
 Kati Johanna Kaarlehto
BRITISH TELECOMMUNICATIONS PLC
 PPA6A, BT Centre, 81 Newgate Street, EC1A 7AJ
 Tel: (0207) 356 6921
 James Alan Brockbank
FRESHFIELDS SERVICE COMPANY
 Freshfields Bruckhaus Deringer, 100 Bishopsgate, EC2P 2SR
 Tel: (020) 7936 4000 Fax: (020) 7108 7168
 Thomas James Hutchison
 James McGill Aitken
 Kenneth Baird
 Lisa Margaret Kelly
 Moray John Macdonald
ROYAL MAIL GROUP LEGAL
 185 Farringdon Road, EC1A 1AA
 Wendy Jane Sommerville
BALFOUR BEATTY GROUP
 130 Wilton Road, SW1V 1LQ
 Fiona Lesley Chambers
ACCELERANT SERVICES UK LIMITED
 One Fleet Place, EC4M 7WS
 George Francis John Peto
TULLOW OIL PLC
 9 Chiswick Park, 566 Chiswick High Road, W4 5XT
 Tel: (0203) 249 9046 Fax: (020) 8994 5421
 Adam Farquhar Holland
FARRER & CO LLP
 66 Lincoln's Inn Fields, WC2A 3LH
 Anthony Thomas McNamee
 Hayley Jane Wilson
BERRYMANS LACE MAWER LLP
 Plantation Place, 30 Fenchurch Street, EC3M 3BL
 Amelia Caitlin Catherine G. Jones
THE OFFSHORE POLLUTION LIABILITY ASSOCIATION LIMITED
 Reed Smith, Broadgate Tower, Third Floor, 20 Primrose Street, EC2A 2RS
 Jacquelynn Forsyth Craw
ARNOLD & PORTER KAYE SCHOLER LLP
 Tower 42, International Financial Centre, 25 Old Broad Street, EC2N 1HQ
 John Michael Schmidt
SANTANDER
 2 Triton Square, Regents Place, NW1 3AN
 Miriam Roncalli Hall
EVERSHEDS SUTHERLAND (INTERNATIONAL) LLP
 One Wood Street, EC2V 7WS
 Tel: (0845) 4979797 Fax: (0845) 4974919
 Ewan Panos Nelson
 Kirstin McCracken
 John Henry Morgan
ROYAL LONDON GROUP
 55 Gracechurch Street, EC3V 0RL
 Tel: (020) 75066787
 Fergus Harry Speight

LLOYDS BANKING GROUP PLC
 25 Gresham Street, EC2V 7HN
 Jennifer Jane Chambers
 Gregor John Watt
WESTFIELD EUROPE LIMITED
 6th Floor, MidCity Place, 71 High Holborn, WC1V 6EA
 Tel: (07827) 256415
 Euan Angus MacDonald
KPMG LLP
 15 Canada Square, Canary Wharf, E14 5GL
 Jennifer Eileen Phillips
FACEBOOK UK LIMITED
 10 Brock Street, NW1 3FG
 Martin Douglas Barr
 Faye Louise Govan
 Olivia Christine Alexis Roach
 Scott David Von Poulton
BLACKROCK INVESTMENT MANAGEMENT (UK) LTD
 Drapers Gardens, 12 Throgmorton Avenue, EC2N 2DL
 James Alexander Honan
 Rachel Catherine Alice McGinness
LEALT ENERGY LIMITED
 9 South Side, Stamford Brook, W6 0XY
 Tel: (020) 8563 8080
 Ian Kerr McNeill
ROONEY NIMMO LIMITED
 125 Old Broad Street, EC2N 1AR
 Tel: (0208) 6292150
 Catriona Gail Mackie Reid
WEIL, GOTSHAL & MANGES (LONDON) LLP
 110 Fetter Lane, EC4A 1AY
 Kirstin Charlotte Glen Fyffe
 Michael John Grant
 Tony Alexander Herron
UBER LONDON LIMITED
 Aldgate Tower – First Floor, 2 Leman Street, E1 8FA
 Lynn Heather Crichton
THE CRANEMERE GROUP LIMITED
 52 Brook Street, W1K 5DS
 Catriona Emma Robertson Brown
FARADAY UNDERWRITING LIMITED
 Corn Exchange, 5th Floor, 55 Mark Lane, EC3R 7NE
 Kirinjit Binning Kaur
KEYSTONE LAW LIMITED
 48 Chancery Lane, WC2A 1JF
 Tel: (020) 33193700 Fax: (0845) 4589398
 Simon John Murfitt
 Fiona Margaret McLean Nicolson
 David Thomson
BIRD & BIRD LLP
 12 New Fetter Lane, EC4A 1JP
 Tel: (0207) 415 6000
 Anna Louise Duffus
 Arif Saleem
TOTAL UK LIMITED
 183 Eversholt Street, NW1 1BU
 Tel: (0207) 3398024
 Calum James Stacey

SCHRODERS PERSONAL WEALTH
12th Floor, 1 London Wall, EC2Y 5EB
Jennifer MacDonald

ISG CENTRAL SERVICES LIMITED
Aldgate House, 33 Aldgate High Street,
EC3N 1AG
Harsharan Kaur Basrai
Visar Isaj

WILLKIE FARR & GALLAGHER (UK) LLP
CityPoint, 1 Ropemaker Street, EC2Y 9AW
Megan Jane Gairns
Andrew Michael Gray
Lindsay Claire Murray

FLO HEALTH UK LIMITED
27 Old Gloucester Street
Susanne Patricia Schumacher

ACTEON GROUP LIMITED
20 Little Britain, EC1A 7DH
Callum Rankine Scott

K&L GATES LLP
One New Change, EC4M 9AF
Tel: (0207) 360 8161 Fax: (020) 7648.9001
Andrew James Griffen Alexander
Craig Delargy Fraser
Natalie Taylor
Kevin Barry Timlin

BAKER & MCKENZIE LLP
100 New Bridge Street, EC4V 6JA
Tel: (0207) 9191000 Fax: (0207) 9191999
David Walter Duncan
Robert McKenzie Gray
Connor Alexander Lovie

BRAHAMS DUTT BADRICK FRENCH LLP
Kings House, 36 King Street, EC2V 8BB
Paula Shao Lan Chan
Hannah Anya Robertson Lynn

TELEHOUSE INTERNATIONAL CORPORATIONS
OF EUROPE LTD
Coriander Avenue, E14 2AA
Bhalindra Singh Bath

SHEPHERD AND WEDDERBURN LLP
Octagon Point, 6th Floor, EC2V 6AA
Tel: (020) 74294900 Fax: (020) 73295939
Web: www.shepwedd.co.uk
Walter Blake
Philip Craig Knowles
Matthew Robert Leslie Lamberton
Stephanie Rose Mill
Lisa Kathryn Renwick
Sarah Kate Walker

NOMURA ASSET MANAGEMENT U.K. LIMITED
1 Angel Lane, EC4R 3AB
Edward Liam Garcia
Tony Wang

SIDLEY AUSTIN LLP
70 St. Mary Axe, EC3A 8BE
Tel: 2073602040
James William Crooks
George Henry Finlay
Gregor Ross Gordon
Peter George Alexander McCorkell

DELOITTE LLP
Hill House, 1 Little New Street, EC4A 3TR
Tel: (0207) 0072147
Calum Grant Murray
Nicholas James Alexander Wowk

DECHERT LLP
160 Queen Victoria Street, EC4V 4QQ
Tel: (020) 7184 7000 Fax: (020) 7184 7001
Ann Kathryn MargaretJean Alexander
Nigel John Austin
Kevin James Gilroy
Ross Lauchlan Montgomery
Richard David Cameron Murdoch

AXIOM GLOBAL LIMITED
6th Floor, 159/173 St John Street, EC1V 4QJ
Louise Emily Duncan
Sophie Margaret Forbes

CAREY OLSEN
Forum St. Paul's, 33 Gutter Lane, EC2V 8AS
Tel: (020) 7614 5610 Fax: (020) 7628 0652
Richard Somerville Macfarlane
Colin George Masterton
Peter Gregory Stachura

MACFARLANES LLP
20 Cursitor Street, EC4A 1LT
Tel: (020) 7791 4044
Fiona Margaret Beattie
Christopher Ross Boyle
Ryan Moore
Robert Donald Oates
Brodie Campbell Thomson

EXPEDIA.COM LIMITED
Angel Building, 407 St John Street, EC1V 4EX
Tel: (0203) 1945179
Louise Anne Hopkin

BROWN RUDNICK LLP
8 Clifford Street, W1S 2LQ
Sarah Louise Melaney

FIELDFISHER LLP
Riverbank House, 2 Swan Lane, EC4R 3TT
Tel: (0207) 8614339
Anna Katharine Crosby
Murray Ronald Keir
Elora Mukherjee

MILLS & REEVE LLP
24 King William Street, EC4R 9AT
Natalie Rachael Hawes Selman
Edward Charles Paul Sloan

ACCENTURE (UK) LIMITED
30 Fenchurch Street, EC3M 3BD
Lindsey Pirelli Brown

ITV PLC
Gray's Inn Road, WC1X 8HF
Jenna Smith Alexander

FIRSTGROUP PLC
8th Floor, The Point, 37 North Wharf Road,
W2 1AF
Carol Ann McFarlane

WYELANDS CAPITAL
25 Maddox Street, W1S 2QN
Murray Lochtie Dunn

ALSTON & BIRD (LONDON) LLP
  5th Floor, Octagon Point, St. Paul's, 5
  Cheapside, EC2V 6AA
  John Alexander Stephen
TIKTOK INFORMATION TECHNOLOGIES UK
LIMITED
  One London Wall, 6th Floor, EC2Y 5EB
  Peter Eugene MacIntyre
WITHERS LLP
  20 Old Bailey, EC4M 7AN
  Tel: (0207) 5976135
  Christopher Severyn Somerville Priestley
  James Alan George Shaw
LEGAL SECRETARIAT TO THE ADVOCATE
GENERAL
  Dover House, 66 Whitehall, SW1A 2AU
  Tel: (020) 72706810 Fax: (020) 72706811
  Sarah Mary-Ann Hardie Mennie
  Lauri MacGregor Mitchell

Luton
STONEGATE PUB COMPANY
  Porter Tun House, 500 Capability Green,
  LU1 3LS
  Andrew Gerald Lingard

Manchester
GUNNERCOOKE SCO LLP
  53 King Street, M2 4LQ
HBM SAYERS
  King's House, 42 King Street West, M3 2NU
  Tel: (0161) 2362002
HORWICH FARRELLY SCOTLAND
  Alexander House, 94 Talbot Road, M16 0SP
  Tel: (03300) 240711
BRABNERS LLP
  55 King Street, M2 4LQ
  Tel: (0161) 8368800
  James Morrison Stewart
ALDERMORE BANK PLC
  4th Floor, 40 Spring Gardens, M2 1EN
  Laura C. H. Mitchell
SHOOSMITHS LLP
  The XYZ Building, 2 Hardman Boulevard,
  M3 3AZ
MANCHESTER UNITED LIMITED
  Sir Matt Busby Way, Old Trafford, M16 0RA
  Tel: (0161) 8688329
  Patrick Charles Donald Stewart
CMS CAMERON MCKENNA NABARRO
OLSWANG LLP
  1 The Avenue, Spinningfields, M3 3AP
  Tel: (0161) 3934700
LIVINGSTONE BROWN LIMITED
  St. James's Tower, 7 Charlotte Street, M1 4DZ
  Email: claims@livingstonebrownsolicitors.co.uk
TLT LLP
  3 Hardman Square, M3 3EB
  Web: www.tltsolicitors.com
  Navid Mesbah

DWF LLP
  1 Scott Place, 2 Hardman Street, M3 3AA
  Tel: (0161) 6035000 Fax: (0161) 603550
  Email: Aisha.Saeed@dwf.law
  Naomi Sarah Jane Pryde
  Hilary Anne Ross
ADDLESHAW GODDARD LLP
  One St. Peters Square, M2 3AE
  David Michael Milne
PINSENT MASONS LLP
  1 The Avenue, Spinningfields, M3 3AP
  Tel: (0161) 662 8000
PINSENT MASONS LLP
  3 Hardman Street, Spinningfields, M3 3AU
  Tel: (0161) 2348234
  Kathryn McBride
THE HUT GROUP PLC
  THG PLC, 4M Office Building, Malaga Avenue,
  M90 3RR
  Anne-Marie Bradshaw
AVENSURE LTD
  South Central, 11 Peter Street, M2 5QR
  Tel: (0330) 100 8704
  Richard John Morton
FAIRHOME GROUP
  Quays Reach, 16 Carolina Way, Salford,
  M50 2ZY
  Laura-May McMorland
GUNNERCOOKE LLP
  53 King Street, M2 4LQ
  Tel: (07775) 824295
  Christian Robert MacNachtan Hook

Milton Keynes
SHOOSMITHS LLP
  100 Avebury Boulevard, MK9 1FH
  Tel: (0370) 086 8300
  Email: accountspayablequerysection@shoosmiths.
  co.uk
DENTONS UK AND MIDDLE EAST LLP
  The Pinnacle, 170 Midsummer Boulevard,
  MK9 1FE

Newcastle Upon Tyne
JACKSON'S
  Central Square, Forth Street, NE1 3PJ
  Isabelle Anne Edmondson
SIEMENS GAMESA RENEWABLE ENERGY
  4 Quick Silver Way, Cobalt Business Park,
  NE27 0QQ
  Tel: (07917) 890322
  James Ross Everden
CLYDE & CO LLP
  Central Square South, Orchard Street,
  NE1 3AZ
  Tel: (0191) 249 5400 Fax: (0191) 230 2416
  Emily Catherine Sarah Blackett
CLIFFORD CHANCE LLP
  Partnership House, Regent Farm Road,
  NE3 3AF
  Tel: (+44) (020) 7006 3449
  Gillian Rachael Sidey

ABERDEIN CONSIDINE AND COMPANY
Merchant House, 30 Cloth Market, NE1 1EE
WOMBLE BOND DICKINSON (UK) LLP
St Ann's Wharf, 112 Quayside, NE1 3DX
Tel: (0345) 4150000 Fax: (0844) 9841501
George Lyall
David Ridley
UNIVERSITY OF NORTHUMBRIA
Room 105, Law School, City Campus East,
NE1 8ST
Tel: (0191) 3495534
Michael Peter Gordon Smith, WS
NORTH OF ENGLAND PROTECTING AND
INDEMNITY ASSOCIATION
100 Quayside, NE1 3DU
Ross David Kalusz Waddell
EVERSHEDS SUTHERLAND (INTERNATIONAL) LLP
Central Square South, Orchard Street,
NE1 3XX
Tel: (0845) 4979797
ENGIE
Engie Buildings Limited, Q3, Quorum Business
Park, Benton Lane, NE12 8EX
Sarah Mary Jane Channin

Northampton
SHOOSMITHS LLP
The Lakes, NN4 7SH
Tel: (03700) 863000

Norwich
NORWICH CITY FOOTBALL CLUB PLC
Carrow Road, NR1 1JE
Tel: (01603) 721902
Samuel Fergus Hall
BIRKETTS LLP
Kingfisher House, 1 Gilders Way, NR3 1UB
Tel: (01603) 756 477
Jan Helen Pointer
AVIVA PLC
PO Box 89, Carrara 4, Surrey Street, NR1 3DR
Tel: (01603) 683 614
Grant Ogilvie Crockart

Nottingham
SHOOSMITHS LLP
Waterfront House, Waterfront Plaza, NG2 3DQ
Tel: (03700) 865000
EXPERIAN LIMITED
Riverleen House, Electric Avenue
Ailsa Anne Gormly
EVERSHEDS SUTHERLAND (INTERNATIONAL) LLP
Water Court, 116-118 Canal Street, NG1 7HF
Tel: (0845) 4979797

Oxford
FREETHS LLP
Spire House, 5700 Oxford Business Park
South, OX4 2RW
Benjamin Philip Thomas Filmer

Peterborough
TRAVELEX CENTRAL SERVICES LIMITED
Worldwide House, Thorpe Wood, PE3 6SB
Philip David Morrison

Plymouth
WOMBLE BOND DICKINSON (UK) LLP
Ballard House, West Hoe Road, PL1 3AE
Tel: (0345) 4150000

Preston
KUDOS LEGAL LIMITED
11 Cable Court, Pittman Way, PR2 9YW
Tel: (0141) 231 2121
TURNER & WHITE LIMITED
99/101 Garstang Road, PR1 1LD
Tel: (01772) 252222
Email: info@turnerandwhite.co.uk
BAKER HARDMAN LIMITED
1A Fairways Office Park, Pittman Way, PR2 9LF

Reading
SHOOSMITHS LLP
Apex Plaza, Forbury Road, RG1 1SH
Tel: (03700) 868800
CMS CAMERON MCKENNA NABARRO
OLSWANG LLP
The Blade, Abbey Square, RG1 3BE
Tel: (0207) 0673000
THALES UK LIMITED
350 Longwater Avenue, Green Park, RG2 6GF
Tel: (01932) 824 825 Fax: (01793) 824 945
Nichola Jane McKay
ANESCO LIMITED
The Green,, Easter Park, Benyon Road,
RG7 2PQ
Donna Marie Turnbull
THE UNIVERSITY OF READING
Legal Services Department, G11 ,
Whiteknights House, PO Box 217, RG6 6AH
Tel: (0118) 378 5852
Lisa Kaplanski

Richmond
WILLIAMS MULLEN
200 South 10th Street, Suite 1600, 23219
Tel: (+001) 804 4206935
Robert Coldwell Dewar

Rochdale
KINETIC LAWYERS LTD
146 Yorkshire Street, OL16 1LD

Ruscombe
RUSCOMBE MANAGEMENT SERVICES LIMITED
33 New Road, RG10 9LN
Donald John Stewart

Salford
KIER LIMITED
 2nd Floor, Optimum House, Clippers Quay,
 M50 3XP
 Farah Mary Clark
 Neil Georg Wilson
BERRYMANS LACE MAWER LLP
 2 New Bailey, 6 Stanley Street, M3 5GS
 Tel: (0161) 2362002 Fax: (0161) 8327956
 Christopher Michael Fletcher
 Ashia Nazar
BLM
 Two New Bailey Square, 6 Stanley Street,
 M3 5GS
 Tel: (0161) 2362002
EVERSHEDS SUTHERLAND (INTERNATIONAL) LLP
 Two New Bailey, 6 Stanley Street, M3 5GX
 Tel: (0161) 831 8000 Fax: (0845) 4978888
 Morven Elizabeth Alexander
 Fiona Barker
GREENTREE LEGAL LIMITED
 HQ, Clippers Quays, Salford Quays, M50 3XP
 Tel: (0161) 7102018

Salisbury
PARKER BULLEN LLP
 45 Castle Street, SP1 3SS
 Tel: 1722412000
 Leigh Barnett

Sheffield
CMS CAMERON MCKENNA NABARRO
OLSWANG LLP
 1-3 Charter Square, S1 4HS
 Tel: (0114) 2794000
ACCELERATED DIGITAL VENTURES LTD
 Electric Works, Concourse Way, S1 2BJ
 Andrew John Sloane
DLA PIPER UK LLP
 1 St Paul's Place, S1 2JX
 Tel: (08700) 111111
 Aaron Nigel Lyons

Southampton
MARKET OPERATOR SERVICES LIMITED
 White Building, 1-4 Cumbernauld Place,
 SO15 2NP
 Jacqueline Mary Doherty
WOMBLE BOND DICKINSON (UK) LLP
 Oceana House, 39-49 Commercial Road,
 SO15 1GA
 Tel: (0345) 4150000
BERRYMANS LACE MAWER LLP
 Charlotte Place, SO14 0TB
 Tel: (023) 80236464

Sunbury-on-Thames
BP INTERNATIONAL LTD
 Chertsey Road, TW16 7LN
 Tel: (07825) 114 653
 Layla Louise Al-Hassani

Clare Campbell Haley
Yvonne Margaret McAllister
Christopher Robert Montgomery

Surrey
KELLOGG BROWN & ROOT (U.K.) LIMITED
 Hill Park Court, Springfield Drive, Leatherhead,
 KT22 7NL
 Gina Mary Wilson
BLACK & VEATCH (UK) LIMITED
 1 Farnham Road, Guildford, GU2 4RG
 Gordon James Wilson
AXA ASSISTANCE (UK) LIMITED
 The Quadrangle, 106-118 Station Road,
 RH1 1PR
 Lorraine Allison Deschildre
NOTONTHEHIGHSTREET
 63 Kew Road, Richmond, TW9 2NQ
 Tel: (0203) 318 5115
 Noor Fakhir Al Naeme

Sutton Coldfield
PORTFOLIO LEGAL LTD
 1 Coleshill Street, B72 1SD
 Robert Iain Christopher Hankin

Tavistock
CHILCOTTS
 10 Plymouth Road, PL19 8AY
 Tel: (01822) 612535
 David Michael Wilde

Telford
SCHNEIDER ELECTRIC LIMITED
 Stafford Park 5, TF3 3BL
 Rose Marie O'Donnell

Tunbridge Wells
LOCH EMPLOYMENT LAW
 Oxford House, 15-17 Mount Ephraim Road
 Pamela Ann Loch

Uxbridge
KUEHNE + NAGEL LIMITED
 1 Roundwood Avenue, Stockley Park,
 UB11 1FG
 Daniel Richard O'Brien
CNOOC PETROLEUM EUROPE LIMITED
 Prospect House, 97 Oxford Road, UB8 1LU
 Tel: (01895) 555 165
 Paul George Gunn

Warwick
WRIGHT HASSALL LLP
 Olympia House, Olympus Avenue, Royal
 Leamington Spa, CV34 6BF
 Laura Margaret Shields

Watford
DENTONS UK AND MIDDLE EAST LLP
  6th Floor, Station Road, WD18 1AF
TJX EUROPE
  73 Clarendon Road, WD17 1HE
  Ceilidh Dewar Thomson
DE LAGE LANDEN LEASING LIMITED
  Building 7, Croxley Green Business Park,
  WD18 8YN
  Bimah Khan
MEDTRONIC LIMITED
  Building 9, Croxley Park, Hatters Lane,
  WD18 8WW
  Caroline Ferrier Scott

West Drayton
TESLA MOTORS LIMITED
  197 Horton Road, UB7 8JD
  Murray Ewan Towers

Widnes
STOBART GROUP
  Viking House, Mathieson Road, WA8 0NX
  Adam Alexander Davidson

Wilmslow
CITATION LIMITED
  Kings Court, Water Lane, SK9 5AR
  Amanda Deeley

Woking
JAMES WALKER GROUP LIMITED
  Lion House, 147 Oriental Road, GU22 8AP
  Tel: (01483) 746354
  Kirstie Laura McDonald

Falkland Is (Malvinas)

Stanley
PINSENT MASONS LLP
  45 John Street, F1QQ 1ZZ
  Tel: (00500) 22690
  Alison Anne MacKenzie Inglis

France

Courbevoie
TECHNIPFMC SUBSEA FRANCE
  1 Bis Place de La Defense, Tour Trinity, 92400
  Lynne Dalrymple

La Defence Cedex
TOTAL S.A.
  Exploration & Production, Legal Dept, 2 Place
  Jean Millier, La Defense 6, 92078
  Graeme James William Hood
  Sarah Anne Vass

Paris
BNP PARIBAS
  37 Avenue de L'Opera, 75002
  Tel: (+33) 1 55 77 62 24
  Alasdair Iain MacKay
EVERSHEDS SUTHERLAND (FRANCE) LLP
  8 Place d'Iena, 75116
  Tel: (+33) 1 5573 4000
ADDLESHAW GODDARD (EUROPE) LLP
  29-31 Rue de Courcelles, 75008
  Katherine Anne Golding
NATIXIS
  68-76 Quai de La Rapee, 75012
  Gail Gwendoline Cochrane
NORTON ROSE FULBRIGHT LLP
  ParisEight, 40, Rue De Courcelles, 75008
  Tel: (00331) 53895672 Fax: (+33) (0)1
  56595001
  George Joseph Paterson
HERBERT SMITH FREEHILLS PARIS LLP
  66 Avenue Marceau, 75008
  Paul Anthony Morton
PINSENT MASONS LLP
  21-23 Rue Balzac, 75008
DWF (FRANCE) AARPI
  137 – 139 Rue de L'Universit, 75007
  Tel: (+33) 0140692650 Fax: (+33)
  0140692699
  Anne-Sylvie Vassenaix-Paxton

Suresnes Cedex
SUBSEA 7 FRANCE
  1 Quai Marcel Dassault, 92156
  Tel: (+33) 1 40 976300 Fax: (+33) 1 40
  975204
  Sarah Lorraine Bremner

Germany

Bremen
WEBER-STEINHAUS SMITH & KLEIN
  Postfach 10 72.27, 28072
  Tel: (0049) 421 639360
  Lesley Jane Smith

FRANKFURT
MOODY'S GROUP DEUTSCHLAND GMBH
  An Der Welle 5, 60322
  Tel: (+49) 69 7370 0857
  Christopher Joseph Stuart Shaw

Frankfurt am Main
NINTENDO EUROPE GMBH
  Goldsteinstrasse 235, 60528
  Calum Alexander Robertson

Guernsey

St Peter Port
MOURANT OZANNES (GUERNSEY) LLP
  Royal Chambers, St Julian's Avenue, GY1 4HP
  Greg Coburn
  Iona Kathleen Mitchell
JTC GROUP
  Ground Floor Dorey Court, Admiral Park,
  GY1 2HT
  Tel: (01481) 702 415
  Gillian Ralston Jordan
CAREY OLSEN
  Carey House, Les Banques, GY1 4BZ
  Tel: (+44) 1481 741505
  Michelle Young
  Steven Balmer
  Lois Coulter Madden
  Kirsty Elizabeth McGeough
  Kieran Patrick Ogilvie
COLLAS CRILL
  Glategny Court, PO Box 140, Glategny
  Esplanade, GY1 4EW
  Tel: (01481) 723191 Fax: (44) 1481 711880
  Quentin Murray Bregg
  Donald James Millar
VISTRA FUND SERVICES (GUERNSEY) LIMITED
  11 New Street, GY1 2JY
  Katie Adam McPherson
OGIER
  Ogier House, St Julian's Avenue, GY1 1WA
  Tel: (+44) 1481 752242
  Matthew Alexander Macfarlane
  James Matthew Walsh

Hong Kong

Hong Kong
OAKTREE CAPITAL MANAGEMENT
  20/F Champion Tower, 3 Garden Road
  Allan Clement Simpson Wardrop-Szilagyi
MOURANT OZANNES
  1002-1008, 10/F Gloucester Tower, Landmark,
  15 Queens Road Central
  Catriona MacKay Hunter
HONG KONG MONETARY AUTHORITY
  55th Floor, Two International Finance Centre,
  8 Finance Street, Central
  Tel: (+852) 28788196
  Shirley Wing Yeng Chung
DLA PIPER HONG KONG
  Floor 25, Three Exchange Square, 8
  Connaught Place, Central
  Tel: (+852) 2103 0 578
  Lauren Hurcombe
HARNEYS
  3501 The Center, 99 Queen's Road Central,
  Road Town
  Tel: (+852) 3195 7200
  Ian Clark

MAYER BROWN
  16th-19th Floors, Princes Building, 10 Chater
  Road, Central
  Tel: (+852) 28432231
  Alan Hugh Linning
SULLIVAN & CROMWELL (HONG KONG)
  20th Floor, Alexandra House, 18 Chater Road,
  Central
  Tel: (+852) 2826 8616
  Jamieson John Logie
SEYFARTH SHAW
  Unit 3701, 37/F, Edinburgh Tower, The
  Landmark, 15 Queen's Road Central
  Aimee Francine Hinksman
SHINE EFFORT INC LIMITED
  1103-1105 Saxon Tower, 7 Cheung Shun
  Street, Cheung Sha Wan
  Alexander George Kerr Grieve
EVERSHEDS SUTHERLAND (INTERNATIONAL) LLP
  21/F Gloucester Tower, The Landmark
  Tel: (+852) 2186 3200
KING & WOOD MALLESONS
  13/F Gloucester Tower, The Landmark, 15
  Queen's Road Central
  Tel: (+852) 3443 1181
  Chloe Chan
ZURICH INSURANCE (HONG KONG)
  25-26/F, One Island East, 18 Westlands Road,
  Island East
  Fiona Gai Man Cheng

Indonesia

Jakarta
HADIPUTRANTO, HADINOTO & PARTNERS
  Pacific Century Place, Level 35, Sudirman
  Central Busiess District Lot 10, Jl. Jend.
  Sudirman Kav 52-53, 12190
  Tel: (+62) 21 2960 8678 Fax: (+62) 21 2960
  8999
  Norman Shirsinger Bissett

Ireland

Dublin
POSEIDON ENHANCED TECHNOLOGIES
LIMITED
  3 Burlington Road, D04 RD68
  Jessel Nazir Shah-Gair
ARAMARK IRELAND
  Newenham House, Northern Cross, D17 AY61
  Isla Joy Stewart
ADOBE SYSTEMS SOFTWARE IRELAND
  4-6 Riverwalk Drive, Citywest Business
  Campus, Cooldown Commons, D24 DCW0
  Natasha Simmons
IRISH DISTILLERS LIMTED
  Simmonscourt House, Ballsbridge, 4
  Ailsa Mary Robertson Mapplebeck

DLA PIPER IRELAND LLP
40 Molesworth Street, DO2 YV57
Blayre Rose McBride
Scott Traynor

Leixlip
INTEL IRELAND LTD
Collinstown Industrial Park
Caroline Stakim

Isle of Man

Douglas
APPLEBY
33 Athol Street, IM1 1LB
Tel: (01624) 647 647 Fax: (01624) 620 992
Claire Catherine Milne

Japan

Tokyo
HERBERT SMITH FREEHILLS LLP
Midtown Tower, 41st Floor 9-7-1, Akasaka,
Minato-Ku, 107 6241
Paul Christopher Flynn

Jersey

St Helier
WALKERS
PO Box 72, Walker House, 28-34 Hill Street,
JE4 8PN
Tel: (01534) 700723
Louise Josephine Hamilton
Megan Rose McAuley
Jennifer Margaret Brunton
Craig MacLeod
Olivia Marie Palloch
NORDIC CAPITAL LIMITED
26 Esplanade, JE2 3QA
Jamie Michael Purdy
ROYAL BANK OF SCOTLAND INT. LTD
PO Box 64, 71 Bath Street, JE4 8BJ
Susan Purdy
HSBC BANK PLC
HSBC House, Esplanade, JE1 1HS
Benjamin Bestgen
LC INTERACTIVE LTD
3rd Floor, The Le Gallais Building, 54 Bath
Street, JE2 4SU
Euan Fraser Hutcheon
MOURANT OZANNES
22 Grenville Street, JE4 8PX
Tel: 1481731513
Sarah Elizabeth Burns
Anita Kaur Dhesi
Simone Farrer
Alana Gillies
James Paul Alexander Goddard

Paul Green
Andrew Haslett
Sean Hedges
Corrie Ann Howarth
Sarah Kerr
Fiona Christine Magee
Gemma Susan Sichi
OGIER
44 The Esplanade, JE4 9WG
Tel: (01534) 514393 Fax: (01534) 504444
Michael Shanley Anderson
Mark John Reid Watson
Chloe Lois Watson-Hill
James Henry Whiteside
STATES OF JERSEY
Law Officers' Department, Morier House,
JE1 1DD
Timothy Mark Douglas Glennie
COLLAS CRILL
Gasp House, Glategny Court, 66-72
Esplanade, JE1 4XD
Tel: (01534) 601783
Harriet Daisy Bovingdon
Lynne Anne Calder
Craig Robert Dinnett
Pamela Josephine Doherty
VIBERTS JERSEY LAWYERS
PO Box 737, Don Street, JE4 8ZQ
Tel: (+44) (0) 1534 888666
Emily Jean Paris-Hunter
BEDELL CRISTIN JERSEY PARTNERSHIP
26 New Street, JE2 3RA
Tel: (01534) 814814 Fax: (01534) 814815
Natasha Ann Kirk Bairstow
Elizabeth Shaw
CAREY OLSEN
47 Esplanade, JE1 0BD
Tel: (01534) 888900 Fax: (01534) 887744
Rachael Winifred Barber
Caitlin McNally Connor
Julie Angela Currie
Lauren Margaret Gray
Caitlin Rose Anne Hagart
Laura Elizabeth Healy
Calum Iain Hedley
Cathryn Jane Marjorie Houston
Daniel Johnstone
Steven Martin Khan
Jennifer Liss
Timothy David McAlpine-Scott
Stuart William McRobbie
Ashley Michelle Morrison
Mark Sutherland Slater
David Scott Taylor
Katherine Anne Tresca
Catriona Hazel Urquhart
APPLEBY
13 – 14 Esplanade, JE1 1BD
Tel: (01534) 888 777
Mark James Brady
Keanu Newman

COFRA JERSEY LIMITED
2nd Floor, Windward House, La Route de La Liberation, JE2 3BQ
Tel: (01534) 754 500 Fax: (01534) 754510
Colin James Dow

Kenya

Nairobi
ANJARWALLA & KHANNA LLP
The Oval, 3rd Floor, Junction of Ring Rd, Parklands & Jalaram Road, Westlands
Tel: (+254) 70 303 2000 Fax: (+254) 20 364 0201
Roderick Hugh Ross McKean

Luxembourg

Luxembourg
RAKUTEN EUROPE S. .R.L.
2 Rue Du Fosse, L-1536
Kieran Patrick Lynch

Monaco

Monaco
GROOM HILL
24, Boulevard Princesse Charlotte, 98000
Tel: (+377) 97 70 23 00
Iona Marie Doohan

Netherlands

Amsterdam
FRESHFIELDS BRUCKHAUS DERINGER
Strawinskylaan 10, 1077
Louise Jessica Bell
UBER
Mr. Treublaan 7, 3e Verdjieping, 1017 HL
Daniel Alexander Kinloch

The Hague
SHELL INTERNATIONAL B.V.
Carel Van Bylandtlaan 30, Postbus 162, 2501 AN
Karen Isobel Halliday

New Zealand

Auckland
MINTER ELLISON RUDD WATT
PwC Tower, 15 Customs Street West, 1010
Alastair Morrison Gatt

Northern Ireland

Belfast
TUGHANS
Marlborough House, 30 Victoria Street, BT1 3GG
Tel: (028) 90553330
Douglas Eric Alexander Anderson
PINSENT MASONS LLP
Soloist Building, 1 Lanyon Place, BT1 3LP
Tel: (028) 9089 4800
TLT NI LLP
29-33 Montgomery Street, BT1 4NX
Web: www.tltsolicitors.com
HERBERT SMITH FREEHILLS LLP
3 Cromac Quay, Ormeau Gasworks, BT7 2JD
Charlotte May McAfee
STRATEGIC INVESTMENT BOARD
5th Floor, 9 Lanyon Place, BT1 3LP
Tel: (028) 9090 9441
Gregor Steven Hamilton
HMRC
20-32 Chichester Street, BT1 4GF
Linda Alexandra Hamilton

Norway

Fornebu
AKER SOLUTIONS AS
Oksen yveien 8, 1360
Tel: (0047) 406 43 475
Rachel Louise Stuart

Oslo
SIEMENS ENERGY AS
LC EAF RC-SE NO, Oestre Aker Vei 88, 596
Tel: (+47) 482 67547
Jacqueline Langeroed

Oman

Ruwi
DENTONS & CO
Oman Branch, Salam Square South, 3rd Floor, Madinat Sultan Qaboos, PO Box 3552, PC 112
Tel: (+968) 2457 3000 Fax: (+968) 2457 3097
Sadaf Buchanan
AL BUSAIDY, MANSOOR JAMAL & CO.
PO Box 686, 112
Tel: (00968) 2482 9269 Fax: (00968) 2481 2256
Robert Hugh Booth

Poland

Warsaw
LINKLATERS SP.K. WISNIEWSKI I WSP LNICY
Q22, Al. Jana Pawla II 22, 00-133

Tel: (+48) 22 526 5086 Fax: (+48) 22 526 5060
Klaudia Eliza Owsianka

Qatar

Doha
PINSENT MASONS LLP
 PO Box 22758, 35th Floor, Tornado Tower
NORTH OIL COMPANY
 P.O. Box 21264, A
 Andrew Robert Russell
AL JAZEERA MEDIA NETWORK
 Television Roundabout, PO BOX 23123, 56
 Tel: 97444897643
 Barry Colin Smith
EVERSHEDS SUTHERLAND (INTERNATIONAL) LLP
 Qatar Financial Centre, PO Box 24148, Office 1101 QFC Tower

Romania

Bucharest
MCGREGOR & PARTNERS S.C.A.
 17 Porumbaru Emanoil St., Sector 1, 11421
 Tel: (+40) 21 312 24 25 Fax: (+40) 21 312 16 46
 Neil Gordon McGregor
SCHLUMBERGER OILFIELD EUROPE SRL
 1A Sergeant Constantin Ghercu Street, The Bridge 2, 6th Floor
 Tel: (07833) 465 886
 David Ian Cargill
 Emma Louise Murdoch

Saudi Arabia

Riyadh
SAUDI ARABIAN GENERAL INVESTMENT AUTHORITY
 PO Box 5927, 11432
 Ibrar Mahmood Chishti
THE SAUDI ARABIAN MINING COMPANY (MA'ADEN)
 Ma'aden Building, Abi Baker Al Siddiq Street, PO Box 68861, 11537
 James Philip More
NORTON ROSE FULBRIGHT US LLP
 Al-Nakhlah Tower, 17th Floor, King Fahad Road, As Sahafah, PO Box 52681, 11573
 David James Graham Johnston

South Doha District
THE LAW FIRM OF SALAH AL-HEJAILAN
 In Association With, Freshfields Bruckhaus Deringer LLP, Loft No.6, Alturki Business Park, PO BOX 405
 Tel: (+966) 3868 7266 Fax: (+966) 3868 7255
 Rodger Grant Murray

Singapore

Singapore
BAKER & MCKENZIE. WONG & LEOW
 8 Marina Boulevard, #05-01 Marina Bay Financial Centre, Tower 1, 18981
 Arwen Elaine Berry
ASURION SINGAPORE PTE LTD
 7 Temasek Boulevard, Suntec Tower One #09-01, 38987
 Aaron Steven Mitchell
NEURON MOBILITY PTE LTD
 37 Jalan Pemimpin, #07-17, 577177
 Tel: (+65) 82345308
 Lucy Taylor Hunter
MAPLES AND CALDER (SINGAPORE) LLP
 1 Raffles Place, #32-02A One Raffles Place, 48616
 Iain Craig Anderson
AKIN GUMP STRAUSS HAUER & FELD LLP
 2 Shenton Way, ~16-01 SGX Cente 1, 68804
 Euan Allister Strachan
DDOG SINGAPORE PTE LTD
 38 Beach Road, #29-11 South Beach Tower, 189767
 Robert Irvine
ADDLESHAW GODDARD LLP
 10 Collyer Quay, #40-00 Ocean Financial Centre, 49315
PERPETUAL
 16 Collyer Quay #07-01, 49318
 Gary McKinstray
CAREY OLSEN SINGAPORE LLP
 10 Collyer Quay #24-08, Ocean Financial Centre, 49315
 Tel: (01534) 888900 Fax: (01534) 887744
 Susan McKinstray
MAYER BROWN LLP
 6 Battery Road, #12-03, 49909
 Kieran Stephen McLaughlin
PINSENT MASONS MPILLAY LLP
 182 Cecil Street, #32-01 Frasers Tower, 69547
 Tel: (+65) 6305 8494 Fax: (+65) 65343412
 Ian Forbes Laing
CREDIT SUISSE AG
 1 Raffles Link, #03/04-01 South Lobby, 39393
 Adam Keith Dryburgh

Spain

Barcelona
ACTIVE VENTURE PARTNERS SGEIC SAU
 Av. Diagonal 401, 2 Bis, 8008
 Tel: (+34) 93 178 6868
 Blair Robert John MacLaren

Madrid
PINSENT MASONS ESPANA SLP
 Serrano 90, 28006
 Colin William McIntosh

Helen Maria Stewart

Sweden

Stockholm
NASDAQ NORDIC
    Tullvaktsv gen 15, 105 78
    Grant Alexander Morris McKelvey
MCD SPORTS & LEGAL AB
    Lundag rdsv gen 30, Sp nga, 16351
    Tel: 46736895848
    Jamie Thomas McDonald

Switzerland

Baar
TRANS ADRIATIC PIPELINE AG
    Lindenstrasse 2, 6340
    Bryan Kane

Baar-Zug
PARTNERS GROUP AG
    Zugerstrasse 57, 6341
    Tel: (+41) 41784 6376 Fax: (+41) 41768 8558
    Victoria Louise Stewart

Geneva
LALIVE
    Rue de La Mairie 35, P.O. Box 6569, 1211
    Rona Carron Ann Amigues-MacRae
G MATTHEW CONSULTANTS LLP
    2, Avenue Calas, 1206
    Tel: (+41) 22 346 12 97
    Gordon Findlay Matthew, WS

Lugano
STUDIO LEGALE DANICA M.T. GIANOLA
    Palazzo Gargantini, Via Guglielmo Marconi 4, 6900
    Tel: (+41) 91 921 24 43
    Danica Maria Teresa Gianola

Zurich
FIFA
    FIFA-Strasse 20, PO Box, 8044
    Alasdair Robert McKee Bell

Thailand

Bangkok
AGODA COMPANY PTE LTD
    999/9 The Offices At Central World 27 Fl, 10330
    Tel: (+) 6697 214 1176
    Stewart John Raeside

Turkey

Istanbul
EURASIA CONSULTANTS LTD
    CumhuriyetCad, No. 25, Cinar AptK4, TAKSIM, 34437
    Tel: (+90) 212 361 50 66 Fax: (+90) 212 361 50 67
    Jonathan William Blythe
PINSENT MASONS LLP
    Buyukdere Caddesi No 173, 1 Levent Plaza 7th Floor

United Arab Emirates

Abu Dhabi
FRESHFIELDS BRUCKHAUS DERINGER
    Level 6, Al Sila Tower, Abu Dhabi Global Market Square, Al Maryah Island, PO Box 129817
    Tel: (+) 971 2652 1706
    Cheree Flora Gemmell
BRYAN CAVE LEIGHTON PAISNER LLP
    Level 20, Al Sila Tower, Al Maryah Island, 109403
    Hazel Shakur Quinn
DENTONS & CO
    Level 4, Trade Centre – West Tower, Abu Dhabi Mall, PO Box 47656
    Tel: (+971) 2 613 1513
    Craig James Allenby Hughson
FLASH ENTERTAINMENT FZ-LLC
    Floor 3, Park Rotana Complex, TwoFour54, PO Box 77828
    Fraser Donald MacKinven
MUBADALA INVESTMENT COMPANY PJSC
    Ethics & Compliance Team, PO Box 45005
    Dominic Ciaran Sheils
    Julia Anne White Moffat
ABU DHABI NATIONAL OIL COMPANY
    Legal, Compliance and Governance, Floor 15, Al Salam Street, Sheikh Zayed Street, PO Box 4017
    Tel: 971566963496
    Alaina Ramsay
DLA PIPER MIDDLE EAST LLP
    PO Box 109950, Level 10, EIBFS Building, Muroor Road
    Tel: (+971) 2 4941500
    Nicola De Sylva
ADNOC LOGISTICS AND SERVICES
    Legal, Governance and Compliance Dept., Sheikh Khalifa Energy Complex, PO Box 61
    Tel: (+971) 2 602 8314
    Gordon Mackay Inkson
ABU DHABI NATIONAL OIL COMPANY
    Group Corporate Governance Division, PO Box 898
    Johanna Joyce Armstrong

ALDAR PROPERTIES PJSC
  Aldar HQ, Al Raha Beach, 51133
  Katy Hazel Thomson
ADNOC GLOBAL TRADING LTD
  25th Floor, Al Sarab Tower, ADGM Square, Al
  Maryah Island, PO Box 764649
  Tel: (+971) 270 66608
  Gregor John Boyd

Dubai
MCKINSEY & COMPANY INC.
  Level 4, Building 4, Dubai International
  Financial Centre, PO Box 33538
  Tel: (+971) 4 519 8073
  Patricia Frances Wardrop
WALKERS (DUBAI) LLP
  Level 14, Burj Daman, Dubai International
  Financial Centre, PO Box 506513
  Szymon Andrzej Durlo
DLA PIPER MIDDLE EAST LLP
  Level 9, Standard Chartered Tower,
  Downtown, PO BOX 121662
  Tel: (+971) (0)4 438 6315
  Richard Graham Hughes
  Iain MacLennan Skinner
  Louise Kathleen Reid
WEATHERFORD DRILLING INTERNATIONAL
  Rasis Business Centre, 5th Floor, Al Barsha 1,
  Off First Al Khail Road, PO Box 58014
  Tel: (+971) 565389910
  Alan John Alexander McGregor
INTERNATIONAL CRICKET COUNCIL
  Street 69, Dubai Sports City, PO Box 500070
  Stephanie Anne Daniel
DUBAI PROPERTIES LLC
  Vision Tower, Al Khaleej Al Tejari 1 Street,
  Business Bay, PO Box 500272, DUBAI
  Joseph Andrew Neilson
CMS CAMERON MCKENNA NABARRO
OLSWANG LLP
  Level 15, Burj Daman, Dubai International
  Finance Centre
  Tel: (+971) 4374 2813 Fax: (+971) 4374 2803
  Ashleigh Bruce
  John Smith Geddes
  Blair Grant Jones
  Greg Russell Sibbald
  Geoffrey Neilson Smith
AFRIDI & ANGELL
  PO Box 9371, Emirates Tower – Level 35,
  Sheikh Zayed Road, A
  Tel: (00971) 4330 3900
  Danielle Frances Lobo Hashmi
FRESHFIELDS BRUCKHAUS DERINGER
  20th Floor, Al Fattan Currency Tower, P.O. Box
  506 569, DIFC
  Tabasam Faqir
GIBSON, DUNN & CRUTCHER LLP
  Building 5, Level 4, Dubai International
  Financial Centre, P.O. Box 506654, A
  Tel: (+971) 4 318 4619 Fax: (+971) 4 370
  0388

Fraser Anthony Dawson
Ryan Thomas Whelan
STEPHENSON HARWOOD LLP
  Office 1302, 13th Floor, Burj Daman Bldg, Al
  Mustaqbal Street, DIFC, P.O. Box 482017
  Laura Kay Anderson
CIGNA INSURANCE MIDDLE EAST S.A.L
  Dubai World Trade Centre – One Central, The
  Offices Building 3, Level1, Office 111,
  PO 124455
  Karen Anne Duncan Gilbert
ALLEN & OVERY LLP
  11th Floor, Burj Daman Building, Al Sa'ada
  Street, DIFC, PO Box 506678
  Tel: (+971) 442 67100
  Rushal Ahmed Noor
LINKLATERS LLP
  Precinct Building 3, Dubai International
  Financial Centre, PO Box 506516
  David Anthony Hayward
BAKER MCKENZIE HABIB AL MULLA
  Level 14, O14 Tower, Al Abraj Street, Business
  Bay, PO Box 2268
  Kellie Linden Blyth
  Joanna Mary Matthews
TROWERS & HAMLINS LLP
  Office 2403, Level 24, Boulevard Plaza Tower
  2, Downtown, PO Box 23092
  Tel: (+971) (0)4 3025 137 Fax: (+971) (0)4
  3519205
  Cheryl Cairns
DENTONS & CO
  Level 18, Boulevard Plaza Tower 2, Burj Khalifa
  District, PO Box 1756, A
  Meghan Devine
VALARIS
  Al Moosa Tower 2, Suite 2601, Sheikh Zayed
  Road, PO Box 72453
  Tel: (+971) 4 403 7481
  Elaine Elizabeth Sims
DUBAI MULTI COMMODITIES CENTRE
  Almas Tower, Jumeirah Lakes Towers, P.O Box
  48800, A
  Tel: (+971) 4368 0741
  Shonagh Katherine MacVicar
LATHAM & WATKINS LLP
  Dubai International Financial Centre, ICD
  Brookfield Place, Level 16, P.O Box 506698
  Tel: +971.4.704.6385
  Alexander Gordon Hendry
ACCES LEGAL FZ LLC
  Al Saaha Office B, 404, Souk Al Bahar, Burj
  Khalifa District, P.O. Box 487177
  Kevin Cobb
SQUIRE PATTON BOGGS (MEA) LLP
  Dubai International Financial Centre, Burj
  Daman Office Tower, Level 10, P.O. Box
  111713
  Tel: (+971) 4 447 8761 Fax: (+971) 4 456
  1271
  John Christopher Skipper

PINSENT MASONS LLP
The Offices 1, One Central
Ruth Mary Stephen
Nesreen Isameldin Osman
SIMMONS & SIMMONS MIDDLE EAST LLP
PO Box 506688, Level 7, The Gate Village
Building 10
Tel: (00971) 4709 6600
Tara Sheila Jamieson
DUBAI HOLDING LLC
Umm Suqeim Street, PO Box 66000
Louise Emma Skipper
BAKER HUGHES ENERGY FZE
Baker Hughes HQ Building, National Industries
Park, PO Box 567, Jebel Ali
Tel: (+971) 4 8211650
John William Bowman
DECHERT LLP
Building 2, Level 5, Dubai International
Financial Centre, PO BOX 506675
Tel: (+971) 4 425 6346 Fax: (+971) 4 425
6301
Katrina Ann Morrison
NORTON ROSE FULBRIGHT (MIDDLE EAST) LLP
4th Floor, Gate Precinct Building 3, Dubai IFC,
PO Box 103747
Thomas James Herd
FTI CONSULTING MEDIA CENTER FZ LLC
Level 29, Media One Tower, PO Box 502428,
Dubai Internet City
David Ross Forbes
DP WORLD
5th Floor, LOB 17, Jebel Ali Free Zone, PO Box
17000
Tel: (+9714) 8080 778
Louisa Boyack
CLIFFORD CHANCE LLP
Level 15, Burj Daman, Dubai International
Financial Centre, PO Box 9380, A
Tel: (+971) 4503 2729
Daniel John Boyle
EVERSHEDS SUTHERLAND (INTERNATIONAL) LLP
Unit 804, 8th Floor, Emaar Square, Building 6
Tel: (0207) 9194500
HSBC BANK MIDDLE EAST LIMITED
Building No.5, Level 6, East Wing Emaar
Square, PO Box 502601
John Alan Tothill
CLYDE & CO LLP
PO Box 7001, Rolex Tower, Sheikh Zayed
Road
Tel: (+971) 4331 1102 Fax: (+971) 4331 9920
Adela Motyckova
ADDLESHAW GODDARD (MIDDLE EAST) LLP
Level 6, Burj Daman Tower, Dubai
International Financial Centre, PO Box 506555
Antonia Kate Grieve
Ben Thomas
DAVIDSON & CO
PO Box 34002, Suite 504, Shangri La Offices,
Sheikh Zayed Road
Tel: (+971) 4 3438897 Fax: (+971) 4 3438879
Andrew David Lyons

Joanna Jayne Stewart
INVESTMENT CORPORATION OF DUBAI
5th Floor, Building 7, Gate Village, Dubai
International Financial Centre, 333888
Tel: (+971) 04 7071539
Faris Radhwan Hadi
AL TAMIMI & COMPANY
DIFC, Building 4, 6th Floor, Sheikh Zayed
Road, PO Box 9275, A
Tel: (+971) 4 364 1641 Fax: (+971) 4 364
1777
Gordon Scott Barr
Victoria Evelyn Smylie
HERBERT SMITH FREEHILLS LLP
Dubai International Financial Centre, Gate
Village 7, Level 4
Tel: (+971) 4 428 6338
Christopher Stewart Walters
BARCLAYS BANK PLC
Dubai International Financial Centre, Gate
Village Building 10, PO BOX 506504
Tel: (+971) 04 365 0863
Fiona Critchley
EMERSON FZE
P.O. Box 17033, Jebel Ali
Catriona Jane Murray

Ras Al Khaimah
RAK GAS L.L.C.
6th Floor, RAK Gas Building, Al Jazah Road,
P.O. Box 434
Tel: (+971) 562 567 900
Philip Gordon MacLean

Sharjah
PETROFAC INTERNATIONAL LIMITED
Petrofac House, Al-Khan Road, P.O. Box 23467
Tel: (+971) 5580239 Fax: (+971) 6 5740099
Nicola Dorgham-Milne

United States

California
LATHAM & WATKINS LLP
355 South Grand Avenue, Suite 100, Los
Angeles, 90071-1560
Andrew Clark

Carlsbad
LIFE TECHNOLOGIES LIMITED
5791 Van Allen Way, 92008
Genoffir Maud MacLeod

Greensboro
VOLVO FINANCIAL SERVICES LLC
7025 Albert Pick Road, Suite 105, 27409
Tel: (+1) 336 931 3741
Alexia Jena Maas

Houston
NVENT
  7433 Harwin Dr.#2007, 77036
  Jenna Elaine McGowan

Maryland
MILES & STOCKBRIDGE P.C.
  100 Light Street, Baltimore, 21202
  Tel: (001) 4103853629 Fax: (001) 410 385 3709
  Stephen John Cullen

Milwaukee
MOLSON COORS BEVERAGE COMPANY
  VP, Ethics & Compliance, 3939 West Highland Blvd, 53208
  Tel: (+1) 414-931-2643
  Elaine Buchanan Pretorius

Minneapolis
DORSEY & WHITNEY LLP
  Suite 1500, 50 South Sixth Street, 55402
  Rhona Elizabeth Schmidt

Minnesota
UNITEDHEALTHCARE GLOBAL SOLUTIONS
  9700 Health Care Lane, Minnetonka, 55343
  Simon Hawthorne

New York
STERLING & STERLING LLC
  135 Crossways Park Drive, Woodbury, 11797
  Adrienne Rowan Shepherd
PRICEWATERHOUSECOOPERS LLP
  300 Madison Avenue, NY 10017
  Ruth MacRitchie
BANK OF AMERICA MERRILL LYNCH
  15/F Bank of America Tower, One Bryant Park, 10036
  Tel: (+1) 646 855 3672
  Niccola Luisa Russo
KIRKLAND & ELLIS LLP
  601 Lexington Avenue, 10022

Tel: (+1) 212 446 3157 Fax: (+1) 212 446 4900
Olus la Melville Paterson-Marke
WILLIAM GRANT & SONS LTD.
  300 Park Avenue South, 10010
  Tel: (+1) 212 299 9404
  William John Payne
MURRAY LLP
  305 Broadway, 7th Floor, NY 10007
  Tel: (+1) 212 729 3045
  Anthony Robert Murray

San Diego
MITCHELL INTERNATIONAL, INC
  6220 Greenwich Drive, CA 92122
  Tel: (+1) 858 368 7711
  Jana Kissel

San Francisco
SITECORE USA INC
  101 California Street, Suite 1600, 94111
  Rachael Catherine Yuille Ormiston

Texas
FLUOR CORPORATION
  6700 Las Colinas Blvd, Irving, 750+
  Tel: (+469) 3217860
  Fritha Christina Wheeler-Ozanne

Wales

Cardiff
WHICH LTD
  3 Capital Quarter, Tyndell Street, CF10 4BZ
  Benjamin Michael Rossor
EVERSHEDS SUTHERLAND (INTERNATIONAL) LLP
  1 Callaghan Square, CF10 5BT
  Tel: (0845) 4979797 Fax: (0845) 4987333
  Helen Joanne Marriott
BERRYMANS LACE MAWER LLP
  Unit 21/22, Neptune Court, CF24 5PJ
  Tel: (0292) 0447667

Commercial, Government and Other Organisations

Aberdeen

ABERDEEN CITIZENS ADVICE BUREAU
41 Union Street, AB11 5BN
Tel: (01224) 569757
Kellyann Fraser

ABERDEEN CITY COUNCIL
Legal Services, Governance, Business Hub 6,
Level 1 South, Marischal College, AB10 1AB
Tel: (01224) 522000
DX: 529452 ABERDEEN 9
Jessica Maria Anderson
Ross Grant Campbell
Graham Richard Chandler
Lisa Jane Christie
Sarah Clubley
Craig Brian Donald
Elizabeth Ann Falconer
John Simpson Forsyth
Karen Gatherum
Caragh Meriel Gilhooly
Carolyn Harrison
Steven Stewart Inglis
Vicki Johnstone
Catriona Margaret Campbell Kelly
Jennifer Louise Lawson
Gwen McEwen
Grant John Milne
Alexander Munro
Alan Douglas Thomson
Sarah Anne Walkden

ABERDEEN CITY COUNCIL
Marischal College, Broad Street, AB10 1AB
Tel: (01224) 522000
Malcolm Fraser Bell
Scott James Duncan Connor
Deirdre Anne Nicolson
Robert James Templeton
Sharon Mary Wares
Karen Wilkie

ABERDEEN CITY COUNCIL
Commercial & Procurement Services, 2nd
Floor Woodhill House, Westburn Road,
AB16 5GB
Tel: (01224) 522000
Suzanne Claire Douglas
Janey Elizabeth McFarlane
Keri Lyn Morrison
Dawn Michele Pittendreigh
Pamela Ross Wheadon

ABERDEEN CITY COUNCIL
Legal & Democratic Services, Town House,
Broad Street, AB10 1AQ
Tel: (01224) 522000
Fax: (01224) 522491
Judith Katy Forbes

ABERDEEN CORPORATE SERVICES LIMITED
10 Queen's Terrace, AB10 1XL
Tel: (01224) 631999
Fax: (01224) 647010
Jodie Elaine Chandler MacLeod

ABERDEEN FOOTBALL CLUB
Pittodrie Stadium, Pittodrie Street, AB24 5QH
Laura McCallum

ABERDEENSHIRE COUNCIL
Legal & People, Woodhill House, Westburn
Road, AB16 5GB
Tel: (0345) 608 1208
Fax: (01224) 664618
Alan Robert Adam
Leigh Anderson
Laura Jane Bremner
Lauren Jacquelene Cowie
Christopher Martin De Villiers
Donna Marie Elrick
Sheila Margaret Forbes
Geraldine Margaret Fraser
Arlene Louise Gibbs
Nicola Henderson
Tristan James Horsburgh
Martin Ingram
Patricia Jericevich
Claire Elizabeth Kent
Lynsey Jane Martin Kimmitt
John Allan Scott Mackenzie
Robert McIntosh
Jennifer Isobel Cruickshank McKearney
Catherine Rose Mullen
Ruth Elizabeth O'Hare
Sheereen Razaq
Moira Simpson Reid
Alistair James Stobie
Kirsten Frances Sutherland-George
Robin George Taylor
Laurel Ann Wheatley
Karen Frances Wiles

ABERDEENSHIRE COUNCIL
Law & Admin, Woodhill House, Westburn
Road, AB16 5GB
Tel: (01467) 530759
Fiona Margaret Binnie
Amanda Jane de Candia
Brian Holden
Anna Ziarkowska

AKER SOLUTIONS LIMITED
Buildings 1, 2 & 3, Aberdeen International
Business Park, Dyce Drive, AB21 0BR
Tel: (01224) 255000
Kristy Anne Wilson

ARCHER (UK)LTD
Main Road, Blackburn, AB21 0BP
Lyes Kennouche

▶ *Aberdeen continued*

ASCO GROUP LIMITED
ASCO Group HQ, Unit A, 11 Harvest Avenue,
D2 Business Park, Dyce, AB21 0BQ
Tel: (01224) 580396
Fax: (01224) 576172
Sara Elisabeth Duncan
Stephanie Falcus
Fraser Nicol McIntyre

BAKER HUGHES LTD.
Badentoy Avenue, Badentoy Park, Portlethen,
AB12 4YB
Tel: (01224) 401357
Neil James Adam
Heather Michelle Bricknell

BILFINGER SALAMIS UK LIMITED
4 Greenhole Place, Bridge of Don, AB23 8EU
Tel: (01224) 246311
Greig Cameron Polson Anderson

BRISTOW HELICOPTERS LIMITED
Dyce Avenue, Dyce, AB21 0LQ
Christopher George MacFarlane

CELEROS FLOW TECHNOLOGY
3 International Avenue, AB21 0BJ
Tel: (0141) 3082095
Fax: (0141) 6370215
Bruce Conroy Turner

CENTURION GROUP
Unit 6, Kirkhill Commercial Park, Dyce Avenue,
AB21 0LQ
Tel: (01224) 215 411
Gary George Chapman
Suzanne Jane Park

CHRYSAOR LIMITED
Rubislaw House, Anderson Drive, AB15 6FZ
Tel: (01224) 086203
Laura Jane Irving
Owen Gordon Paterson

CHRYSAOR PRODUCTION (U.K.) LIMITED
Legal Department, Rubislaw House, Anderson
Drive, AB15 6FZ
Tel: (01224) 205333
Fax: (01224) 205350
Harriet Clara Arnott
Victoria Margaret Helen Barnes-Insch
Michael James Hammond

CIVIL LEGAL ASSISTANCE OFFICE
353 Union Street, AB11 6BT
Tel: (01224) 402330
Fax: (01224) 968590
DX: AB153 ABERDEEN
Cara Marion Eadie
Claire Rosemary Kettlewell
Sally Hilary Jane Mair
Stephanie Lee Miller

CNR INTERNATIONAL (U.K.) LIMITED
St Magnus House, Guild Street, AB11 6NJ
Tel: (01224) 303653
Andrea Jane Bird
Nicola Corbett
Marianne Jamieson
Angela Jane MacNiven

David Stewart Ogilvie

DANA PETROLEUM LIMITED
King's Close, 62 Huntly Street, AB10 1RS
Tel: (01224) 616000
Fax: (01224) 616001
Stewart Cunningham
Kelly Deborah Thow
Grant Colin Walker

DOF SUBSEA UK LIMITED
Horizons House, 81-83 Waterloo Quay,
AB11 5DE
Tel: (01224) 614193
Graham John Ross

DRIL-QUIP (EUROPE) LIMITED
Stoneywood Park, Stoneywood Road, Dyce,
AB21 7DZ
Tel: (01224) 727000
Fax: (01224) 727075
Sonia Ann Cameron

EMERSON PROCESS MANAGEMENT
1 Harvest Avenue, D2 Business Park, Dyce,
AB21 0BQ
Tel: (01224) 776242
Neil Campbell Mackenzie

ENQUEST BRITAIN LIMITED
Annan House, Palmerston Road, AB11 5QP
Tel: (01224) 975000
Fax: (01224) 287105
Ian William Easton
Wayne Eddie
Paul Euan Massie
Rebecca Louise Young

EQUINOR PRODUCTION UK LIMITED
Prime Four Business Park, Kingswells,
AB15 8QG
Tel: (01224) 653350
Keith Alistair Angus
Adel Cruickshank
Victoria Maud Cumming

ETHOSENERGY (GBR) LIMITED
Ethos House, Craigshaw Business Park,
Craigshaw Road, AB12 3QH
Tel: (01224) 291 764
Jonathan Murray Little
Amanda Denise Ritchie
Gary Smith

GENESIS OIL & GAS CONSULTANTS LIMITED
Aspect 32, Pavilion 3, Prospect Road, Arnhall
Business Park, Westhill, AB32 6FE
Tel: (01224) 623703
Christina Isobel McKerrow

HEXAGON POSITIONING INTELLIGENCE
C/o Veripos Limited, Veripos House, 1B
Farburn Terrace, AB21 7DT
Katy Louise Patience

HFI CONSULTING INTERNATIONAL LIMITED
West Point, Prospect Road, Arnhall Business
Park, Westhill, AB32 6FJ
Tel: (01224) 766650
Hugh Fraser

HUNTING ENERGY SERVICES (UK) LIMITED
Badentoy Avenue, Badentoy Park, Portlethen,
AB12 4YB

Tel: (01224) 787000
Alison Jane Warner
HUNTING PLC (LONDON)
Bedentoy Avenue, Badentoy Park, Portlethen,
AB12 4YB
Allyson Michelle Miller
INEOS FPS LIMITED
Floor 2, Prime View, Prime Four Business Park,
Kingswells, AB15 8PU
Tel: (01224) 084429
Frances Patricia Hutchison
INOAPPS
2 Fountainhall Road, AB15 4DT
Kirsty Martie Grace Knowles
INTERNATIONAL SOS (MEDICAL SERVICES) UK
LIMITED
Forest Grove House, Foresterhill Road,
AB25 2ZP
Tel: (01224) 669000
Loren Jay Kelly
ITHACA ENERGY (UK) LIMITED
Hill of Rubislaw, AB15 6XL
Tel: (01224) 638582
Fax: (01224) 635276
Julie Elizabeth McAteer
Zoe Jane Pearson
Stephen Barclay Welsh
KELLAS MIDSTREAM LIMITED
7th Floor, The Silver Fin Building, 455 Union
Street, AB11 6DB
Ralph Leslie McIntosh
LAW AT WORK INCORPORATING EMPIRE
Empire House, 117 Grandholm Drive,
AB22 8AE
Tel: (01224) 701383
Fax: (01224) 701384
Louise Irwin
Susan Catherine Lockhart
Rebekah Anne Page
Lesley Louise Rennie
NEO ENERGY
The Silver Fin Building, 455 Union Street,
AB11 6DB
Tel: (01224) 659120
Stuart Leslie
Andrew Graham McIntosh
Victoria Katie Presly
Emily Rachel Thomson
NEPTUNE E&P UK LTD
16 North Esplanade West, AB11 5RJ
Tel: (+44) (0) 1224 281223
Megan Alice Herd
OFFSHORE HELICOPTER SERVICES UK LIMITED
Kirkhill House, Dyce Avenue, AB21 0LQ
Tel: (01224) 215186
Stuart Andrew Weir Duncan
OGUK
4th Floor, Annan House, 33-35 Palmerston
Road, AB11 5QP
Tel: (01224) 577250
Fax: (01224) 577251
Tracey Keith

OIL & GAS AUTHORITY
AB1 Building, 48 Huntly Street, AB10 1SH
Tel: (0300) 020 1068
Emma Jane Dixon
Caroline Barbara Graham
PETROFAC SERVICES LIMITED
Bridge View, 1 North Esplanade West,
AB11 5QF
Tel: (01224) 247000
Sara Clare Gordon
Joanne Marie Irvine
PREMIER OIL UK LIMITED
Upper Denburn House, Prime Four Business
Park, Kingswells Causeway, Kingswells,
AB15 8PU
Tel: (01224) 618900
Fax: (01224) 618599
Laura Anne Bisset
Ingrid Elizabeth McKay
Peter Lawrence Ripley
Gareth Peter Webster
PROCURATOR FISCAL SERVICE
AB1 Building, Crimon Place, AB10 1BJ
Tel: (0300) 0202336
DX: AB67 ABERDEEN
Ellen Jane Barr
Katy Begg
Rhea Copland
James Innes Craigen
Karen Ann Dow
Carol Elizabeth Gammie
Andrew David Hanton
Victoria Emma Kerr
Anne Macdonald
Louise Anne MacNeil
Lynne MacVicar
Alison Joan McKenzie
Felicity Margaret Merson
Dylan Rees Middleton
Kelly Marie Mitchell
Shona Nicholson
Thomas Nathan Procter
Alison Shaw
Lucy Simpson
Lynzi Johnson Souter
Lixia Sun
Rebecca Alison Thompson
Alan Cameron Townsend
Helen Jane Treharne
Christy Catherine Ward
Elaine Marie Ward
Eilidh Ann Wright
REPSOL SINOPEC RESOURCES UK LIMITED
Talisman House, 163 Holburn Street,
AB10 6BZ
Tel: (01224) 353205
Louise Anne Cowie
Adrian Matthew Gavin
John Lewis Pope
RIBNORT LIMITED
The Coach House, 29 Albyn Place, AB10 1YL
Jodi Marie Stevenson

▶ *Aberdeen continued*

ROBERT GORDON UNIVERSITY
Central Services Building, Garthdee Road,
AB10 7FY
Tel: (01224) 262021
Helen Anne Castle

SCOTTISH COURTS AND TRIBUNALS SERVICE
Legal Advisers, Aberdeen Sheriff Crt, Castle St,
AB10 1WP
Tel: (01224) 657248
Laura Bell
Nicola Faye Cunningham
James Scott McPherson
Nicola Reid
Alison Henderson Stone

SHELL INTERNATIONAL LIMITED
1 Altens Farm Road, Nigg, AB12 3FY
Tel: (01224) 882000
John Murray Stevenson Buchanan
Graeme James Hird
Neil John Roberts
Gareth Ian Rome Treharne

SHELL U.K. LTD.
1 Altens Farm Road, Nigg, AB12 3FY
Tel: (01224) 883860
Andrew Edward Brocklebank
Jillian Louise Christie
Matthew Stewart Gordon
Dorothy Catherine Hasler

SHELL U.K. LTD.
LSUI/AEGB, 1 Altens Farm Road, Nigg,
AB12 3FY
Tel: (01224) 882000
Neil Donald

SICCAR POINT ENERGY LIMITED
3rd Floor, H1, Hill of Rubislaw, Anderson
Drive, AB15 6BY
Tel: (01224) 678127
Fax: (01224) 678198
David Alexander Sheach

**SOCIAL CARE AND SOCIAL WORK
IMPROVEMENT SCOTLAND**
Ground Floor, Right Wing, AB1, 48 Huntly
Street, AB10 1SH
Tel: (01224) 793870
Alison Jean Cook

SPIRIT PRODUCTION (SERVICES) LIMITED
IQ Building, 15 Justice Mill Lane, AB11 6EQ
Tel: (01224) 411653
Fax: (01224) 415002
Natasha Anderson
Julie Joanne Hardie
David Andrew Henry
Carol Margaret Lee
Nicola Jane MacLeod
Rachel Annette Rennie
Wai-Man Shek Robertson
Scott John Smith

TAQA BRATANI LIMITED
TAQA House, Prime Four Business Park,
Kingswells, AB15 8PU
Tel: (01224) 275275

Fax: (01224) 275484
Claire Joy Anderson
Leanne Margaret Bain
Alexander Burnett Hutchison
Julie Anne Meredith Jones
Christopher Graham Ross Rettie

TAURX THERAPEUTICS LTD
395 King Street, AB24 5RP
Tel: (01224) 440911
Sara Imelda Briody-Scott
Marcus Augustine Wischik

**TRANSOCEAN ONSHORE SUPPORT SERVICES
LIMITED**
Prime View, Kingswells Causeway, Prime Four
Business Park, Kingswells, AB15 8PU
Tel: (01224) 944000
Zoe Anne Adam
Hazel Francene Stuart Meek

TRINITY KERR LIMITED
6 Oakdale Terrace, AB15 7PJ
Tel: (01224) 312767
Matthew Liam Philip Kerr

WEATHERFORD
Weatherford Centre, Souterhead Road, Altens,
AB12 3LF
Tel: (01224) 380200
Fax: (01224) 380202
Jennifer Louise Packham
Richard Khalil Strachan
Rachel Thomson

WELL-SAFE SOLUTIONS LIMITED
Site C4, Gateway Crescent, Gateway Business
Park, AB12 3GA
Tel: (01224) 548400
Graeme Scott Murray

WOOD GROUP UK LIMITED
15 Justice Mill Lane, AB11 6EQ
Tel: (01224) 851000
Andrew Peter Arnott
Natalie Ellen Fraser
Iain Angus Jones
Sarah Marion MacRury
Martin James McIntyre
Kerrie Allison McQueen
David James Paterson
Suzanne Robertson
Gavin David Barclay Thomson
Shona Eilidh van Diggelen

Airdrie

PROCURATOR FISCAL SERVICE
Procurator Fiscal's Office, 87A Graham Street,
ML6 6EE
Tel: (01236) 747027
Fax: (0844561) 3299
DX: 570417 AIRDRIE
Raeesa Ahmed
Lauren Cole
William Campbell Craig
Calum Isam Sinclair Frame
Liam Thomas Haggart
Sarah Louise Healing

Kevin Paul Jarvis
Maria McDonald Kowalczyk
Lindsay Jillian Mains
Wendy Elizabeth McAdam
Laura McGillvery
Agnes Meek
Kevin Martin Morrow
Annette Marie Ward
SCOTTISH COURTS AND TRIBUNALS SERVICE
  Sheriffdom Legal Adviser, Sheriff Court Hse,
  Graham St, ML6 6EE
  Tel: (01236) 439174
  John Gerard Donnelly
  Anne Kinsella
  Joanna Ruth Mortimer
  Meghan Kathryn Grace Neville
  Rebecca Fay Osborne

Alloa

CLACKMANNANSHIRE COUNCIL
  Kilncraigs, Greenside Street, FK10 1EB
  Tel: (01259) 450000
  DX: 560436 ALLOA
  Dale Brian Bell
  Heather Anne Buchanan
  Saul Morgan Milne
  Lee Elizabeth Robertson
  Richard John Thompson
PROCURATOR FISCAL SERVICE
  Procurator Fiscal's Office, Sheriff Court House,
  FK10 1HR
  Tel: (01259) 214561
  DX: 560437 ALLOA
  Susannah Jane Roberta Hutchison

Alyth

P3 MUSIC LIMITED
  Incheoch Cottages, PH11 8HJ
  Tel: (01828) 632133
  Alison Ruth Burns

Auchterarder

HIGHLAND SPRING
  Stirling Street, Blackford, PH4 1QA
  Tel: (01764) 660500
  Jacquiline Angela James

Ayr

PROCURATOR FISCAL SERVICE
  Procurator Fiscal's Office, 37 Carrick Street,
  KA7 1NS
  Tel: (01292) 267481
  DX: AY21 AYR
  Jason Stuart Bell
  Hayley Robertson
PUBLIC DEFENCE SOLICITORS OFFICE
  17 Wellington Square, KA7 1EZ
  Tel: (01292) 269139
  Fax: (01292) 265253
  DX: AY70 AYR
  Louise Allison Cairns Craig

Hugh Joss Duncan
James Irvine
Ashley Kane
SOUTH AYRSHIRE COUNCIL
  Legal & Licensing Services, County
  Bldgs,Wellington Square, KA7 1DR
  Tel: (01292) 612420
  Fax: (01292) 612455
  DX: AY72 AYR
  Karen Boyd Briggs
  Ruth Alexandra Burley
  Wynne Stewart Carlaw
  Catriona Jane Caves
  Morag Simpson Douglas
  Margaret Anne Horsley
  Simone Mairi Lucas-Broadley
  Deirdre Victoria Una Mackintosh
  Laura Anne McChristie
  Christine McMenamin
  Lorraine McPartlin
  Claire Helen Neillie
  Fiona Campbell Ross of Ross
  Emma Victoria Louise Stevenson
  Margaret Agnes Jamieson Vance
  Gavin Thomas Whyte

Balloch

LOCH LOMOND AND THE TROSSACHS
NATIONAL PARK AUTHORITY
  Carrochan, 20 Carrochan Road, G83 8EG
  Tel: (01389) 727745
  Yvonne Karen Christie
  Sandra Jane Dalziel
  Kenneth Clark Ross

Banff

ABERDEENSHIRE COUNCIL
  Town House, 34 Low Street, AB45 1AY
  Tel: (01261) 813200
  Fax: (01261) 815664
  DX: 521328 BANFF
  James McKay
  Fiona Mary Stewart

Bathgate

MACDONALD HOTELS LIMITED
  Whiteside House, Whiteside Industrial Estate,
  EH48 2RX
  Tel: (01506) 815115
  Stephanie Rose MacFarlane

Bellshill

HFD MANAGEMENT
  Phoenix House, Phoenix Crescent, ML4 3NJ
  Katrina Jan Ovenden
WILLIAM GRANT & SONS LTD.
  Customer Service Centre, Strathclyde Business
  Park, ML4 3AN
  Tel: (01698) 843843
  Fax: (01698) 844788
  Sabrina Rene Odile Jenquin

▶ **Bellshill** continued

Calum Stuart Daniel Johnstone
Catriona Ann Macritchie
Christie Elizabeth McCluskey
Emma Monteith
Christopher Kesson O'Donnell
David Alexander Ritchie
Shona Elizabeth Tennant

WIRELESS INFRASTRUCTURE GROUP
Braidhurst House, 2 Finch Way, Strathclyde
Business Park, ML4 3PE
Tel: (01698) 846545
Struan Barr Brock

Blairgowrie

CASTLE WATER
1 Boat Brae, Rattray, PH10 7BH
Tel: (01250) 718700
Gordon Robert Adams
Richard Davidson
Euan William Mitchell
Carrie Robertson

Brechin

JANET HOOD TRAINING AND CONSULTING
LIMITED
Kirkton of Balfour Farmhouse, Edzell,
DD9 7XU
Tel: (01356) 648 966
Janet Hebe Hood

Bridge of Don

SPARROWS OFFSHORE SERVICES LIMITED
Seton House, Murcar Industrial Estate,
AB23 8JW
Tel: (01224) 704868
Fax: (01224) 825191
Wendyanne Louise Slavan Pegler-Gault
Ruth Speedie
Claire Marie Taylor
TWMA LTD
Broadfold House, Broadfold Road, AB23 8EE
Sharon Mary Jocelyn Mackie

Crieff

STEADMAN PARTNERS
22 Drummond Terrace, PH7 4AF
Graeme Duncan Warren

Cumbernauld

A.G. BARR P.L.C
Westfield House, 4 Mollins Rd, WESTFIELD,
G68 9HD
Tel: (01236) 852400
Fax: (01236) 852477
Julie Anne Barr
Stephen David Ruairidh Taylor

Cupar

SCOTTISH SOLICITORS' DISCIPLINE TRIBUNAL
Unit 3.5, Granary Bus. Centre, Coal Road,
KY15 5YQ
Tel: (01334) 659088
DX: 560568 CUPAR
Nicola Anne Ross
Marjorie Janet Socha

Carnbroe

AD ASTRA LEGAL LIMITED
2 Brambling Road, ML5 4UP
Karima Elizabeth Higgins

Dalgety Bay

FIRST SCOTTISH GROUP
St. David's House, St. David's Drive, KY11 9NB
Tel: (01383) 826777
Fax: (01383) 826778
Stephen Mark Lock
INGENICO GROUP
17 Ridge Way, Donibristle Industrial Park,
KY11 9JU
Joanne Lauren Gray
WYNNE ASSOCIATES LIMITED
Room 18, Dalgety Bay Business Centre, Ridge
Way, KY11 9JN
Tel: (01383) 829312
Judith Wynne

Dalkeith

AMIS: ABUSED MEN IN SCOTLAND
Mayfield Farmhouse, 5 Esk View Road,
Mayfield, EH22 5EA
Tel: (0131) 4477449
Isabella Houston Quar
MIDLOTHIAN COUNCIL
Midlothian House, Buccleuch Street,
EH22 1DN
Tel: (0131) 2707500
DX: 540568 DALKEITH
Cheryl Bradley
Holly Lewis
Jane Scott McLeish
Emma Marguerite Padden
Suzanne Anderson Ross
Lindsay George Thomson
Alan Leonard Turpie
William Venters

Dingwall

BUCHANAN SHAW CONSULTING LTD
6a High Street, IV15 9HL
Gillian Shaw
HIGHLAND COUNCIL
Council Offices, High Street, IV15 9QN
Tel: (01349) 863381
Iain Paul Meredith
Shona Ann Pottinger

SCOTTISH ENVIRONMENT PROTECTION
  AGENCY
  Graesser House, Fodderty Way, IV15 9XB
  Tel: (01349) 862021
  Fax: (01349) 863987
  Emma Jane Blain
  Nicola Louise Stewart
  Jeremy Andrew Warner

Dumbarton

CHIVAS BROTHERS LIMITED
  Kilmalid, Stirling Road, G82 2SS
  Tel: (01389) 723 425
  Fax: (01389) 763 874
  Dominic Francis McLaughlin-Roberts
  Iain Robertson Wisely
PROCURATOR FISCAL SERVICE
  Procurator Fiscal's Office, St. Mary's Way,
  G82 1NL
  Tel: (0300) 020 3000
  DX: 500598 DUMBARTON
  David Joseph Gallagher
  Kenneth George Grieve
  Richard Hannay
  Martina Louise McGuigan
  Alasdair Preston Millar
  Claire Ann Lavery O'Hagan
SCOTTISH CHILDREN'S REPORTER
  ADMINISTRATION
  55 Church Court, G82 1SU
  Tel: (01389) 764268
  Kirsten Annette Ferguson
  Suzanne Quinn
WEST DUNBARTONSHIREHIRE COUNCIL
  Legal Services, Regulatory and Regeneration,
  16 Church Street, G82 1QL
  Tel: (01389) 737000
  Christopher Edward Anderson
  Alan Shaw Douglas
  Nigel William Ettles
  Maureen Teresa Hastings
  Peter David Hessett
  Valerie Love
  Raymond James Lynch
  Kimberley McCallum
  Sally Jane Michael
  Heather Lorna Campbell Milne
  John Paul Mitchell
  Gavin Walsh
WEST DUNBARTONSHIREHIRE COUNCIL
  Municipal Buildings, College Street, G82 1NR
  Clare Patricia McGinness

Dumfries

DUMFRIES & GALLOWAY COUNCIL
  Muncipal Chambers, Council Offices,
  Buccleuch Street, DG1 2AD
  Tel: (01387) 245 903
  Fax: (01387) 260034
  Vladimir Ernesto Bujanda-Valiente

DUMFRIES & GALLOWAY COUNCIL
  Council Offices, English Street, DG1 2DD
  Tel: (01387) 260000
  Fax: (01387) 260034
  DX: 580642 DUMFRIES
  Carolyn Frances Cowan
  Robin Ian Douglas Fletcher
  John Angus MacEachern
  Kirsteen Yvonne Macintyre
  Marcus Robert Parham
  Julie Shannon
  Caroline Anne Treanor
  Laura Currie Caldwell Whitelaw
DUMFRIES & GALLOWAY COUNCIL
  Council Offices, English Street, DG1 2DD
  Tel: (01387) 261234
  Lucy Wenda Irons-Young
PROCURATOR FISCAL SERVICE
  Procurator Fiscal's Office, Buccleuch Street,
  DG1 2AP
  Tel: (0300) 020 3273
  DX: 580628 DUMFRIES
  Alison Margaret Herald
  Gemma Hind
  Lyndsay Ann Hunter
  Jennifer May Templeton McGill
  Aislinn O'Donnell
  Kirsten Jennifer Ramos
  Monique Sproat
SCOTTISH COURTS AND TRIBUNALS SERVICE
  Justice of the Peace Court, Sheriff Court
  House, Buccleuch Street, DG1 2AN
  Fiona Elizabeth Ross

Dundee

ALLIANCE TRUST PLC
  River Court, 5 West Victoria Dock Road,
  DD1 3JT
  Tel: (01382) 938320
  Ian Anderson
  Lisa Brown
D C THOMSON & CO LTD
  2 Albert Square, DD1 9QJ
  Calum Alexander McKillop Hamilton
  Gemma Kelly
  Kerri Montgomery
  David Alistair Turnbull
DUNDEE CITY COUNCIL
  City Chambers, City Square, DD1 3BY
  Tel: (01382) 434209
  Fax: (01382) 434666
  DX: DD118 DUNDEE
  Aysha Anwar
  Jacqueline Bell
  Pauline Carena
  Marjory Elizabeth Geddes
  Kenneth James McKaig
  Roger William Hunter Mennie
  Gemma Elizabeth Miller
  Maureen Moran
  Mary Elizabeth Morrissey
  James Alexander Murray

▶ *Dundee continued*

Julie Ellen Murray
Sarah Jane O'Connor
Jennifer Elaine Ritchie
Karen Jane Scouller
Graeme Samuel Smillie
Brian Woodcock

EDUCATIONAL INSTITUTE OF SCOTLAND
310 Broughty Ferry Road, DD4 7NJ
Selena Graham

INSIGHTS LEARNING & DEVELOPMENT LTD
Terra Nova, 3 Explorer Road, DD2 1EG
John Alastair Beck
Robert King

PROCURATOR FISCAL SERVICE
Procurator Fiscal's Office, Westport House, 144
West Marketgait, DD1 1NJ
Tel: (01382) 342559
Fax: (01382) 202719
DX: DD35 DUNDEE 1
Carol Knox Doherty
John Paul Adams
Lora Yulianova Apostolova
Vicki Lee Bell
Gavin Gerard Burton
Gavin Thomas Robert Callaghan
Donna Grace Davidson
Stewart William Duncan
Hazel Elizabeth Edward
Emma Janet Suzanne Farmer
Nicola Gillespie
Charmaine Gilmartin
Rachel Thomson Hill
Laura Hogg
Alan William Kempton
Gavin Letford
Kirsten Watson Letford
Marie Lyons
Christopher Macintosh
Carrie-Anne Louise Mackenzie
Lynne Theresa Mannion
Larissa Jane Milligan
Saima Rasheed
John Somerville Richardson
Eilidh Lesley Robertson
Keith Coll Robertson
Muhammad Bilal Sadiq
Trina Sinclair
Isobel Vincent

PUBLIC DEFENCE SOLICITORS OFFICE
13 Cowgate, DD1 2HS
Tel: (01382) 226051
Fax: (01382) 225992
DX: DD142 DUNDEE
Nicola O'Donnell Brown
Stuart James Watson Hamilton
David Watson Sinclair

**SCOTTISH CHILDREN'S REPORTER
ADMINISTRATION**
6 Commercial Street, DD1 3EH
Nicola Lynne Fyffe

SCOTTISH COURTS AND TRIBUNALS SERVICE
Sheriff Court House, 6 West Bell Street,
DD1 9AD
Lesley Joyce Beats
Lindsay Elaine Stewart

**SCOTTISH POLICE AUTHORITY, POLICE
SCOTLAND**
Police Headquarters, P.O. Box 59, West Bell
Street, DD1 9JU
Tel: (0300) 1112222
Fax: (01382) 200449
Frances Isabel Finlay
Annice Robertson Cameron Newlands
Gillian Savage
Wendy Joan Sutherland
Erica Watson

SCOTTISH SOCIAL SERVICES COUNCIL
Compass House, Discovery Quay, 11 Riverside
Drive, DD1 4NY
Tel: (0345) 6030 891
Fax: (01382) 207215
William Watters Nelson
Susan Helen Peart
Fiona Katherine Abbott
Rachel Mary Louise Alexander
Maree Catherine Allison
Joanne Kennedy Arnot
Christopher Patrick Bailey
James Gilchrist Barrowman
Tina Boswell
Craig Brown
Stephanie Laura MacKenzie Brown
Amy Valerie Chilman
Hayley Clarkson
Charlotte Anne Cockburn
Hannah Clara Coleman
Calum McKenzie Cox
Lauren Hazel Cree
Victoria Jayne Dailly
Lisa Jane Duffy
Rachel Duffy
James Joseph Eodanable
Shona Catherine Ewen
Stephanie Aileen Gallacher
Steven Mark Gallacher
Anne Ellanor Garness
Shamielah Ghafar
Katie Jane Grant
Rachel Louise Hamilton
Jennifer Linda Graham Hannah
John Paterson Hunter
Riaz Hussein
Megan Catherine Joiner
Ashleigh Anne Kaney
Zhaira Kausar
Joan Margaret Kendall
Matthew Ian Keogh
Caitlin Alexandra Kinloch
Lauren Elizabeth Logue
Kirsten Helen Low
Kenneth Archibald Marshall
Iain David Norris Martin
Elizabeth Annie McIlmoyle

Holly Angela Jane McKie
Tonicha Louise McNab
Faye Annette McWilliam
Thomas Anthony Miller
Sheryl Moir
David John Morrison
Janice Katrina Morrison
Rebecca Elizabeth Mudie
Karen Lynsey Nicol
Gabriella Anna Notarangelo
Sarah Gyllian Prentice
Rachael Elizabeth Pryor
Laura Jane Russell
Lisa Claire Stewart
Natalie Sutherland
Paula Tomlinson
Christopher Henry Weir
Paula Barbara Wilkie
Jade Wendy Wong
THE OFFICE OF THE SCOTTISH CHARITY
  REGULATOR
  2nd Floor, Quadrant House, 9 Riverside Drive,
  DD1 4NY
  Tel: (01382) 220446
  Moira Ann Ray Cathcart
  Layla Nina Patton
UNIVERSITY OF DUNDEE
  6th Floor, Tower Building, DD1 4HN
  Tel: (44) (0)1382 385340
  Claire McGinnis
  Eloise Ann Robb
  Umran Ali Sarwar
  Jaclyn Mary Suttie

Dunfermline
CAMPION HOMES LTD
  Pitreavie Drive, Pitreavie Business Park,
  KY11 8US
  DX: 556500 DUNFERMLINE 8
  Glenn Paul Millar
PROCURATOR FISCAL SERVICE
  Sheriff Court House, Carnegie Drive,
  KY12 7HW
  Tel: (03000) 203577
  DX: DF19 DUNFERMLINE
  Dev Kapadia
  Alexandria Heather Kirk
  Mateusz Piskorz
  Azrah Yousaf
SCOTT GROUP
  Halbeath Interchange Business Park, Kingseat
  Road, Halbeath, KY11 8RY
  Tel: (01383) 627105
  Robert William Maclean
SCOTTISH WATER
  Castle House, 6 Castle Drive, Carnegie
  Campus, KY11 8GG
  Tel: (01383) 665410
  DX: 556502 DUNFERMLINE 8
  Jonathan David Robertson Bruce
  Emma Frances Campbell
  Nicola Ann Galbraith

Shavonne Grant
Susan Margaret Hill
Niall MacDonald
John Stephen Matthew
Elizabeth Christine McLaughlin
Maria Bridget McNeil
Ramsay George Robert Milne
Arlene Compton Townsend
Linda Graham Tughan
SOCIAL CARE AND SOCIAL WORK
  IMPROVEMENT SCOTLAND
  South Suite, Ground Floor, Largo House,
  Carnegie Avenue, KY11 8PE
  Lorna Melanie Henderson
STIRLING DEVELOPMENTS LIMITED
  Halbeath Interchange Business Park, Kingseat
  Road, KY11 8RY
  Tel: (01383) 720768
  Robert John Barr

Dyce
BP EXPLORATION OPERATING COMPANY LTD.
  Legal Department, 1 Wellheads Avenue,
  AB21 7PB
  Tel: (01224) 832353
  Fax: (01224) 832929
  Philip Hugh Chalmers
  Lorna Keri Dawson
  Susan Norma Gavin
  Sally Hutchison
HALLIBURTON MANAGEMENT LTD
  Halliburton House, Howe Moss Crescent,
  AB21 0GN
  Tel: (01224) 777000
  Kyla Louise Armstrong
HEXAGON POSITIONING INTELLIGENCE
  C/o Veripos Limited, Veripos House, 1B
  Farburn Terrace, AB21 7DT
  Tel: (01224) 965897
  Kenneth George Cumming
STORK TECHNICAL SERVICES UK LIMITED
  Pitmedden Road, AB21 0DP
  Tel: (01224) 722888
  Dawn Samantha Baillie
  John Findlay
  Cara Anne Miller

East Kilbride
DAVID BROWN GROUP LTD
  Orbital House, 3 Redwood Crescent, G74 5PA
  Tel: (01355) 212010
  Neil Christopher Jordan
TUV SUD SERVICES (UK) LTD
  Scottish Enterprise Technology Park, G75 0QF
  Tel: (01355) 593700
  Colin Edward Forbes

Easter Bush
ROSLIN INSTITUTE
  The University of Edinburgh, EH25 9RG
  Tel: (0131) 6519100

▶ **Easter Bush continued**
Fax: (0131) 5274499
Shereen Johnson
James Kenneth McCubbin
Clare Agnes Neilson

Edinburgh
ABERDEEN CORPORATE SERVICES LIMITED
1 George Street, EH2 2LL
Tel: (0131) 245 7508
Shona Agnes Adair
Nicola Mary Armstrong
Gayle Louise Bacchus
Ulrike Buchan
Laura Elizabeth Cameron
Jamie Donald Montgomery Campbell
Michael Brian Corr
Gavin Stewart Davis
William Archibald Drummond
David Alan Eynon
Sophie Gilmour
Jennifer Mitchell Lothian
Leila McDougall
Fiona Jean McGowan
Johanna Louise Millar
Leah Sarah Neilly
Matthew Conor Pinnons
Alison Claire Rennie
Lynsey Fiona Roy
Iain James Walker
Amanda Deborah Tracey Wright
ABERDEEN CORPORATE SERVICES LIMITED
6 St. Andrew Square, EH2 2BD
Tel: (0131) 245 7508
Jan Buchan
Scott Edward Crewes
Jozanne Kathleen Kyna Dahms
Fiona Gail Davidson
Paul Charles Evitt
Heather Catherine Hall
Maureen Kenny
Gemma Leanne McFadyen
Stewart James Gordon McLay
Victoria Barbara Mincher
Megan O'Raw
Afshan Rathore
Lauren Smith
Richard Harrison Stewart
ABERDEEN CORPORATE SERVICES LIMITED
Legal Investment Services, 1 George Street,
EH2 2LL
Tel: (0131) 245 6092
Fax: (0131) 2404669
Calum Ross McNiven
Gillian Simpson Stewart
ABRDN FINANCIAL PLANNING AND ADVICE
LIMITED
Dundas House, 20 Brandon Street, EH3 5PP
Nur Hemsi
Georgina Margaret Kathleen McBride
Anelia Stoyanova Petkova
Catriona Susan Philp

AEGON ASSET MANAGEMENT UK PLC
3 Lochside Crescent, Edinburgh Park,
EH12 9SA
Tel: (0131) 549 3062
Michael Crowe
Elizabeth Ann Moxham
Michael James O'Carroll
Arlene Patrick
Anthony David Robson
Caroline Mary Swinton
Gordon Michael Syme
AEGON UK
HR Department, 3 Lochside Crescent,
Edinburgh Park, EH12 9SE
Tel: 1315493986
Fax: (0870) 2426788
Tracy Elizabeth Marshall
Iain Fraser James Barton
Scott John Burns
Clare McMillan Donaldson
Clemency Alice Friend
Alasdair Euan Grant
Craig MacRae Hilsmith
James Kenneth MacKenzie
Iain Stuart McClay
Eloise Alexandra Natalie McGleish
Michelle Bruce Vater McNeill
John Christopher Robert Morrison
Camilla Nancy Martin Neil
Jennifer Yvonne Paton
Dervile Monica Pyper
Marion Frances Sweetland
Lynsey Susan Whelan
Lisa Jaime Wilkie
ALRUM LIMITED
Floor 3, 1-4 Atholl Crescent, EH3 8HA
Rumyana Vladimirova Anderson
AMBER INFRASTRUCTURE LIMITED
One Lochrin Square, 92 Fountainbridge,
EH3 9QA
Richard Gordon Paton
ARTEMIS INVESTMENT MANAGEMENT LLP
6th Floor, Exchange Plaza, 50 Lothian Road,
EH3 9BY
Tel: (0131) 7180517
Fax: (0131) 7180436
Michael Denis Breen
Stewart David Brown
Euan Campbell Murray
ARTISANAL SPIRITS COMPANY PLC
The Vaults, 87 Giles Street, Leith, EH6 6BZ
Douglas Henderson Aitken
BAILLIE GIFFORD & CO
Calton Square, 1 Greenside Row, EH1 3AN
Tel: (0131) 2752000
Fax: (0131) 2753979
Anne-Claire Bogle
Keith William James Borrows
David Steele Bryson
Naomi Elizabeth Ross Cherry
Emma Jane Cunningham
Ramsey Mungo Orwin Deans
Eilidh Kara Forgie

Gareth John Griffiths
Laura Lynsey Hogg
Catriona Elizabeth Hume
Caroline Jane Ironside
Michael Richard Langridge
Patricia Alexandra Law
Stephanie Jane Lynch
Alastair David Maclean
Claire Catherine MacLennan
Alexandra Macnaughton
Grant Gordon Meikle
Kerry Margaret Millar
Judith Anne Heidi Murphy
Elizabeth Robertson
Kathryn Agnes Robinson
Douglas George Selman
Emma Jennifer Shewan
Christopher Douglas Smith
Robert Stewart Swinton
Gordon Alexander Taylor
Kamila Trizuliak
Alan David Yuille
BAM CONSTRUCT UK LTD
Currie House, 597 Calder Road, EH11 4HJ
Frazer Hamilton Wardhaugh
BANK OF NEW YORK MELLON
Capital House, 2 Festival Square, EH3 9SU
Tel: (0131) 635 2612
Debbie Margaret Baird
Fraser Lamont Kane
BAXTERS FOOD GROUP
12 Charlotte Street, EH2 4DJ
Tel: (0131) 7180612
Gordon Campbell McKelvie
BAYWA R.E. UK LIMITED
Prospect House, 5 Thistle Street, EH2 1DF
Tel: (0131) 4663689
Jenny Margaret Anfield
Sarah Jo Drummond
Jennifer Helen Malcolm
Christine Alice McGregor
BLACKROCK
Exchange Place One, 1 Semple Street,
EH3 8BL
Tel: (306) 978 749 900
Scott David Birse
Lauren Greenshields
Judith Laura Joy
Rebecca Lindsay
Katherine Janet Macgregor
Konstantina Maniati
Ashleigh Moira Ovenstone
BOX MEDIA AGENCY LIMITED
7-9 North St David Street, EH2 1AW
Angus William Irvine Niven
CALA GROUP LTD
Adam House, 5 Mid New Cultins, EH11 4DU
Tel: (0131) 5355200
Fax: (0131) 5355201
DX: ED644 EDINBURHG
Katherine Anne Durie
Charlotte Emma Scott Johnson
Jennifer Marie Wylie

CALEDONIAN TRUST PLC
61A North Castle Street, EH2 3LJ
Tel: (0131) 2200416
Michael James Baynham
CAPRICORN ENERGY LTD
C/o Cairn Energy PLC, 50 Lothian Road,
EH3 9BY
Tel: (0131) 4753000
Claire Elizabeth Busby
Paul Alan Ervine
Susan Mary Gibb
Duncan Wesley Charles Holland
Susan Rose Inkson
Anne Margaret McSherry
Keir Andrew Stewart
CHILDREN & YOUNG PEOPLE'S COMMISSIONER
SCOTLAND
Bridgeside House, 99 McDonald Road,
EH7 4NS
Tel: (0131) 346 5350
Fax: (0131) 337 1275
Bruce Alan Adamson
Maria Joanna Galli
CHURCH OF SCOTLAND
121 George Street, EH2 4YN
Tel: (0131) 2255722
Fax: (0131) 240 2246
DX: ED144 EDINBURGH
Elspeth Annan
Gordon Taylor Barclay
Gregor Robert Buick
Jennifer Anne Campbell
Agnes Shirley Davidson
David John Di Paola
Susan Elizabeth Helen Killean
Mary Elizabeth Macleod
Christine Mary Paterson
Madelaine Sproule
Anne Elizabeth Steele
David Thomas Stihler
CIRRUS LOGIC INTERNATIONAL
SEMICONDUCTOR LTD
7B Nightingale Way, Quartermile, EH3 9EG
Tel: (0131) 2727000
Fax: (0131) 2727001
Mandy Deeley
Andrew Findlay Keir
Joanne Stenhouse
CITY OF EDINBURGH COUNCIL
Legal & Risk, Level 1.9, Waverley Court, 4 East
Market Street, EH8 8BG
Tel: (0131) 5294145
Fax: (0131) 529 3603
Amy Meadows Alexander
Caitlin Janina Allan
Euan George Bathgate
Matthew Robert Clarke
Morven Kirsty Coulter
Ailsa McLaren Cunningham
Margaret Catherine Deane
Abigail Laura Drummond
Alison Falconer
Shabnam Faqir

► Edinburgh continued

Charlotte Mary Todd Fleming
Charlotte Louise Flood
Nicholas Jonathan Fraser
Amy Mairead Hitchin Hood
Alexander Hugh Richard Irvine of Drum
Keith Brian Irwin
Morag Anne Leck
Sheila Jane Mackintosh
Stephen Michael McCaig
Anna Rose McKay
Kevin Joseph McKee
Margaret Jean Elizabeth McLaren
Nicola Dee McLaren
Jennifer Anne Moir
Graham Douglas Nelson
Kevin Scott Paterson
Judith Jane Peacock
Fiona Emma Ross
Hannah Beverley Ross
Craig Scott Russell
Nicholas Scott Smith
Iain David Strachan
Stefanie Thomson
Simon Daniel Todd
Julia Claire Donnetta Walker
Iain Andrew Wallace

CITYFIBRE HOLDINGS LIMITED
3 Queen Street, EH2 1JE
Domhnall McDonald Dods

CIVIL LEGAL ASSISTANCE OFFICE
Thistle House, 91 Haymarket Terrace,
EH12 5HE
Tel: (0131) 2401960
Fax: (0131) 516 3620
Hazel Bon
Jennifer Laughland
Eilidh Barbara Meikle
Siobh n Marie Ther se Murphy
Lindsay Paterson
Caitlin Alexandra Paul
Rosemary Anne Noble Pereti
Kirsty Ann Watson

COCHRAN LTD
S10, 525 Ferry Road, EH5 2FF
Tel: (01461) 200258
Fax: (01461) 205511
Andrew Boris Velichansky

COVANCE CLINICAL AND PERIAPPROVAL
SERVICES LTD
Level 5, The Stamp Office, 10 Waterloo Place,
EH1 3EG
Tel: (0131) 5507700
Janet Connerton

CREATIVE SCOTLAND
Waverley Gate, 2-4 Waterloo Place, EH1 3EG
Tel: (0330) 3332000
Fax: (0131) 5230001
David William Smith

DALMORE EXECUTIVE SERVICES LIMITED
Caledonian Exchange, 19a Canning Street,
EH3 8EG

Jennifer Alison McKay
Rachel Charlotte Tate

DENTAL PROTECTION
39 George Street, EH2 2HN
Tel: (0800) 5611010
Fax: (0131) 24001878
Helen Mary Kaney

DEVELOPMENT TRUSTS ASSOCIATION
SCOTLAND
1B Washington Lane, EH11 2HA
Tel: (0131) 225 2080
Elspeth Catherine Mathieson

DIAGEO SCOTLAND LIMITED
11 Lochside Place, EH12 9HA
Tel: (0131) 519 2261
Emma Jane Harris
Fiona Dorothy Elizabeth Rollo

DUKIC & NOVAKOVIC LLP
23 Meggetland Terrace, EH14 1AP
Saamir Kaiser Nizam

EDF ENERGY RENEWABLES
Atria One, Level 7, 144 Morrison Street,
EH3 8EX
Tel: (0131) 460 3654
Hamish Noble Blair
Kevin Bernard Cannon
Carol Cloughley
Susan Elizabeth Currie
Brian Robert Donald
Emma Victoria Fraser
Campbell William Hutcheon
Christopher Martin
Fiona Sanderson Stirling
Lucy Fiona Tait
Catherine Anne Whittaker
Suzanna Margaret Wolstenholme

EDINBURGH AIRPORT LIMITED
Legal Department, 2nd Floor Terminal,
EH12 9DN
Tel: (07901) 811 652
Aliya Habib
Stephen Andrew Swan

EDINBURGH TRAM INQUIRY
Area GC North, Victoria Quay, Leith,
EH6 6QQ
Tel: (0131) 523 0080
Gordon Leonard McNicoll

EDUCATIONAL INSTITUTE OF SCOTLAND
46 Moray Place, EH3 6BH
Tel: (0131) 225 6244
Laura Yvonne Clark
Sarah Marie Collins
Sonia Helen Campbell Kerr

EKCO GROUP INTERNATIONAL
Codebase, Argyle House, 3 Lady Lawson
Street, EH3 9DR
Sean Henry Dorian

ELEMENT MATERIALS TECHNOLOGY GROUP
Rosewell House, 2A (1F) Harvest Drive,
Newbridge, EH28 8QJ
Tel: (0131) 333 8053
Fax: (0131) 333 5082
Blair Nicholas George Carlton

Beata Katarzyna Janowska
Neil Conway MacLennan
Douglas Iain Gilmour Stewart
EMBARK CORPORATE SERVICES LIMITED
Atria One, 5th Floor, 144 Morrison Street, EH3 8EX
Tel: (0131) 603 5899
Nicola Clare Megaw
Elizabeth Maria Smith
ERG UK HOLDING LTD
4th Floor, 2 Castle Terrace, EH1 2EL
Tel: (+44) (0) 7815 513 163
Lynette Katherine Hamilton Purves
ERNST & YOUNG LLP
Atria One, 144 Morrison Street, EH3 8EX
Carolyn Fiona Thurston Smith
FINANCIAL CONDUCT AUTHORITY
Quayside House, 127 Fountainbridge, EH3 9QG
Tel: 7725552025
Andrew Michael Harkness
Katharine Anne Nicoll
FIRST SENTIER INVESTORS (UK) SERVICES LIMITED
Stewart Investors Investment Team, 23 St Andrew Square, EH2 1BB
Tel: (0131) 4732200
Fax: (0131) 4732222
Grigor Lewis Milne
FMS LEGAL AND COMPLIANCE SERVICES LIMITED
80 Argyle Crescent, EH15 2QD
Adrian Charles Newlands Smith
FNZ
Tanfield House, 1 Tanfield, EH3 5DA
Tel: (0131) 5241900
Martin John Bruce
Iain Steven Corbett
Kirstin Hilary McArthur
FORTH PORTS LIMITED
1 Prince of Wales Dock, EH6 7DX
Tel: (0131) 5558700
Fax: (0131) 5559000
Charles Graham Hammond
Emma Louise McAslan
Pamela June Smyth
FRANKLIN TEMPLETON GLOBAL INVESTORS LIMITED
Legal Department, 5 Morrison Street, EH3 8BH
Tel: (0131) 2424000
Ewan Ross Cameron
FREE CHURCH OF SCOTLAND
The Mound, EH1 2LS
Tel: (0131) 226 5286
Muriel Ann Macleod
FULL CIRCLE PARTNERS LIMITED
16 Charlotte Square, EH2 4DF
Paul Jarman-Williams
GALLIFORD TRY
Gallifordtry Construction Ltd, GT Construction Division OU, PO Box17452, 2 Lochside View, Edinburgh Park, EH12 1LB

Tel: (0131) 3386002
Ian Alexander Hughes
Suzanne Elizabeth Wilson
GNEISS ENERGY LIMITED
5A Rothesay Place, EH3 7SL
John Robert Alpine
GREYFRIARS INVESTMENTS LIMITED
56 George Street, EH2 2LR
Tel: (0131) 220 6719
Pauline Anne Bradley
H.M. COURT OF THE LORD LYON
Procurator Fiscal's Office, 8 Wellington Place, EH6 7EQ
Tel: (0131) 553 4259
Alexander Michael Stuart Green
HANDELSBANKEN
UK Legal Department, Ground Floor, 18 Charlotte Square, EH2 4DF
Tel: (0131) 225 1250
Andrea Elizabeth Fairfield
HEINEKEN UK LIMITED
3-4 Broadway Park, South Gyle Broadway, EH12 9JZ
Tel: (0131) 5281000
Fiona Clare Dickson
Jack Elliott
Ruth Carol Hunter
Claire Margaret Jackson
James Monteforte
Mairi Victoria Morgan
Lynsey Jane Nicoll
Julie McIntyre Simpson
Claudia Grace van Tooren
HERIOT-WATT UNIVERSITY
Riccarton, EH14 4AS
Tel: (0131) 4513405
Derek Gardiner Brown
Iain Jackson McClure
HGF LTD
Gordon Lamb House, 3 Jackson's Entry, EH12 5EH
Caroline Patricia Pigott
HISTORIC ENVIRONMENT SCOTLAND
Longmore House, Salisbury Place, EH9 1SH
Tel: (0131) 6688987
Susan Elizabeth Ferguson-Snedden
Karen Christine Scrymgeour
HYMANS ROBERTSON LLP
Exchange Place One, 1 Semple Street, EH3 8BL
Tel: (0131) 656 5187
Karen Gilchrist
Claire Elizabeth Hill
Jenna Hudson
Robert Craig McKinney
Brian Taylor
Charlotte Ann Louise Taylor
INTERGEN (UK) LIMITED
81 George Street, EH2 3ES
Tel: (0131) 624 7500
Diana Maria Grecu

► Edinburgh continued

JOHN MENZIES PLC
2 Lochside Avenue, EH12 9DJ
Owen Stephen Harkins
Victoria Moore
Fraser John Muego
Juliet Elspeth Thomson
Tristan George Turnbull
Catriona Louise Wolstenholme

JPIMEDIA LIMITED
Orchard Brae House, 30 Queensferry Road,
EH4 2HS
Douglas Alexander Easton
Hannah Christine Leslie

JUDICIAL OFFICE FOR SCOTLAND
Parliament House, 11 Parliament Square,
EH1 1RQ
Tel: (0131) 2406701
Fax: (0131) 2406704
Kay Roslyn McCorquodale

JUNIPER PARTNERS LIMITED
28 Walker Street, EH3 7HR
Carron Marr Dobson

LAW SOCIETY OF SCOTLAND
Atria One, 144 Morrison Street, EH3 8EX
Tel: (0131) 2267411
Fax: (0131) 2252934
Anne Hunter
Gillian Ellen Alexander
Sarah Zoe Alexander
Lisa Jane Brodie
James Patrick Campbell
Martin Donald Campbell
Morag Mary Christie
Michael Paul Clancy
Elaine Valerie Crawford
Wendy Mari Henderson
Stephanie Hendry
Samantha Mary Hollywood
Elaine Isobel Johnston
Nicola Margaret Johnstone
Lynne Kilpatrick
Helen Claire Rafferty Logan
Elaine Margaret MacGlone
Alan John McCreadie
Greg McEwen
Antony Michael McFadyen
Alison Elizabeth McNab
Tamsin Christel Nankivell
James Iain Ness
Jennifer Catherine Paton
Ian David Ritchie
Fiona A. Robb
Fiona Jane Robb
Catherine Mary Russell
Geoffrey Hugh Sanders
Brian Simpson
David John Simpson
Alan Breck Stewart
Lucy Stewart
Aidan Nicholas West
Laura Williams

Rachel Mary Wood

LEGAL SECRETARIAT TO THE LORD ADVOCATE
Lord Advocate's Chambers, 25 Chambers
Street, EH1 1LA
Tel: (0300) 020 3364
Joanne Mary Baker
Rachel Hutchinson Brubaker
Arezo Darvishzadeh-Koochesfehani
Stephen Leslie Rees
Andrew Norman Ruxton
Laurence Michael Sullivan
Colin Andrew Troup

LEONARDO UK LTD
2 Crewe Road North, EH5 2XS
Tel: (0131) 3435957
Jamie McMillan Lewis

LLOYDS BANKING GROUP
7th Floor, 69 Morrison Street, EH3 8BU
Tel: (0131) 655 7773
Jennifer Grace Angus
Gillian Elaine Dean
Andrew Richard Jordan

LLOYDS BANKING GROUP PLC
Port Hamilton, 69 Morrison Street, EH3 8BW
Tel: (0131) 442 9579
Jon Stuart Alexander
Kirsty Victoria Allen
Pamela May Atkinson
Christina Amy Barr
Ewart Leslie Baxter
Roslyn Birdsall
Caroline Brodie
Lucy Catherine Brown
Jennifer Anne Cargill
Ian Murdoch Cowan
Robert Neil Darling
Caroline Anne Douglas
Niamh Patricia Gillespie
Michelle Ann Gordon
Zoe Charlotte Hamilton
David Malcolm Harris
Esther-Nina Jack
Katie Alice Jean Lamb
Katharine Tinsley Lockhart
Isla Elaine Marwick
Donna Louise McColgan
Julie Elizabeth McCormack
Michael Paul McGrath
Sarah Louise McIvor
Greig John Millar
Kate Elisabeth Martell Mitchell
Rachel Louise Moran
Craig Kerr Nicolson
Janine Catherine Margaret Pennel
Simon Rajgopaul
Helen Mary Rice
Alistair James Scott
Rosalind Louise Scott
Kate Anne Sharp
Gavin John Simpson
Catriona Jane Smith
Jill Stevenson
Catherine Rose Stone

Natalie Aleesa Wilson

LLOYDS BANKING GROUP PLC
The Mound, EH1 1YZ
Tel: (0131) 2438625
Lysanne Jane Warren Black

LLOYDS BANKING GROUP PLC
Sighthill North, Mail Area 38, Sighthill North,
2 Bankhead Crossway North, EH11 4EF
Tel: (07824) 320663
John Francis Forsyth

LOCKTON COMPANIES LLP
40 Torphichen Street, EH3 8JB
Tel: (0131) 345 5550
Fax: (0131) 345 5566
Jennifer Margaret Cummings
Matthew Frederick John Thomson

LORD PRESIDENT'S PRIVATE OFFICE
Parliament House, 11 Parliament Square,
EH1 1RQ
Tel: (0131) 2406701
Fax: (0131) 2406704
Andrew Graeme Campbell
Sinead Garster Campbell
Darren James Cox
Mariel Louise Kaney
Katy Jane Kelman
Catriona Elizabeth Ferguson Marshall
Alannah Theresa McGinley
Edward Andrew McHugh
Ysabeau Hester Middleton
Ashleigh Lesley Pitcairn
Ian Frank Vickerstaff
Clare Whyte

LOTHIAN PENSION FUND
Atria One, 144 Morrison Street, EH3 8EX
Tel: (07395) 84879
Cathryn Rachel Bush
Struan Robertson Fairbairn
Jane Patricia Mary McKeown

LYON & TURNBULL
33 Broughton Place, EH1 3RR
Laura Anne Henderson

M&G PLC
60 South Gyle Crescent, EH12 9LD
Jennifer Anne Kantharia

MDS ESTATES LIMITED
27 Silvermills Court, Henderson Place Lane,
EH3 5DG
Elizabeth Anne Hamilton
Lyndsay Mhairi McGregor

MEDICI LEGAL ADVISERS
6a Howe Street, EH3 6TD
Scott James Moncur

MENZIES AVIATION
2 Lochside Avenue, EH12 9DJ
Tel: (0131) 459 8049
John Alasdair Frame

MENZIES DISTRIBUTION LTD
Divisional Headquarters, 2 Lochside Avenue,
Edinburgh Park, EH12 9DJ
Tel: (0131) 469 4553
Pamela Maria Abbott

MILLER HOMES LIMITED
Miller House, 2 Lochside View, Edinburgh
Park, EH12 9DH
Tel: (0870) 3365000
Julie Mansfield Jackson
Moira Jane Kinniburgh
Corinne Robertson

MODULR
80 George Street, EH2 3BU
Mark Macleod Graham

MULTREES INVESTOR SERVICES
3rd Floor, 40 Princes Street, EH2 2BY
Tel: (0131) 2473220
Fax: (0131) 2473221
Fraser Andrew Bennett
Lauren Fretwell

NATIONAL GALLERIES OF SCOTLAND
73 Belford Road, EH4 3DS
Claire Martin

NATIONAL HEALTH SERVICE SCOTLAND
Anderson House, Breadalbane St, Bonnington
Road, EH6 5JR
Tel: (0131) 2757800
Fax: (0131) 275 7993
Anthony John Allan
Laurie Anderson-Spratt
Tariq Essa Abedali Ashkanani
David George Barbour
Dianne Black
Isla Mary Bowen
Emma Christine Cormack
Elaine Rose Coull
Hazel Frances Craik
Ian Stuart Crerar
Rhidian Andrew Spencer Davies
Martin Dowds
Laura Dawn Ewart
Gregory Bennett Fletcher
Lindsay Catherine Gallagher
Ruth Helen McLaren Garrett
Kathryn Rose Gormley
Lynne Jenny Isobelle Greig
Jennifer Harding
Kirsteen Cameron Henderson
William Alexander Henderson
Judith Hetherington
Shona Nicole Swan Hewitt
Stuart Dale Holmes
Susan Anne Hopkin
Michael Joseph Hughes
Jennifer Frances Mackenzie Inglis
Robert Thomson Barr Jack
Louise Elizabeth Jardine
Michael Robert Johnston
Dianne Kane
Stuart William Kilgour
Laura-anne Langlands
Robert Duncan Loudon
Fiona Macdonald
Kathryn Anne Mackenzie
Neil Donald MacLean MacLeod
Laura Francesca Marcantonio
Hayley Jane Mayberry

► Edinburgh continued

Joanne Hunter McCabe
Lorna Jane McCall
Morag McClelland
Joanna McCormack
Lorna Elizabeth McCrae
Kathryn Therese McElroy
Natasha Alison Meikle
Susan Alexandra Murray
Julia Margaret Normand
Sandra Mary Ogg
Margaret Jane Passmore
Eleanor Mary Paton
Kay Fiona Ramachandran
Adrian Vernon Ashok Rebello
Nicola Suzanne Rinaldi
Stefano Carlo Romeo Rinaldi
Kerry Louise Ritchie
Catriona Morag Robertson
Alison Louise Sargent
Aisling Sarah Scott
Kelly Frances Service
Morag Shepherd
Katherine Mairi Shippin
Norma Anne Shippin
Caitlin McDonald Souter
Graeme David Sproule
Alison Stevenson
Michael James Stewart
Jane McNair Strathern
Elaine Tait
Tracey Amanda Turnbull
Stephen James Waclawski
Nadia Waseem
Adam Spencer Watson
Robert Kerr Wightman

NATIONAL WESTMINSTER BANK PLC
Group Legal, Business House G, P.O. Box
1000, EH12 1HQ
Tel: (0131) 626 2925
Fax: (0131) 6263325
Rachel Katherine Ellison
Michael Se n Power
Craig James Thomas Allan
Katherine Elizabeth Annand
Jennifer Beattie
Claire Rhian Bennett
Stewart Mark Bingham
Alison Lorna Blyth
Jennifer Burke
Neil John Campbell
Nikki Campbell
Scott Andrew Campbell
Margaret Elizabeth Carty
Laura Caroline Courtney
Colin Mark Cruickshank
Richard Robert Danks
Angus Robert Davidson
Alistair Thomson Devlin
Emma Louise Ann El-Alami
Hannah Claire Gardner
Philip Duncan Hall

Laura Margaret Hay
Elise Nicole Jackson
Gemma Leigh Keenan
Fergus Patrick Kildare
Leigh Kirkpatrick
Sarah Mary Lynch
Pamela Jayne Macaulay
Donald Ross Macdonald
Rachel Main
Victoria Elizabeth Marr
Euan Fraser McDougall
Ilona Whitton McGowan
Matthew Robert McIlwaine
Gary Moore
Jennifer Grace Denheen Murchison
Lisa Kathryn Parrish
Carol Anne Esther Paton
Marina Paul
Emma Ann Rees
Judith Rickerby
Kenneth Robertson
Catriona Anne Rowantree
Emily Harriette Shaw
Caroline Victoria Storrie
Mary Claire Vincent
Christopher Ross Voysey
Christine Margaret White
Elise Kirsten Whoriskey
Claire Louise Whyte
Adam John Christison Wilkie
Carol Ann Wilson
Lindsay Claire Younie

NATIONAL WESTMINSTER BANK PLC
Legal, Governance and Regulatory Affairs,
Business House G,P.O. Box 1000, EH12 1HQ
Tel: (0131) 5568555
Katherine Elizabeth Allan
Lucy Clare Burnside
Ross Douglas
Danielle Kidd
Laura Catherine Lightbody
Rebecca McIlwaine
Helen Elizabeth Miller
Jacqueline Ann Patterson
Marliese Sally Perks
Nicola Margaret Reid
Colin Scott Telford

NATIONAL WESTMINSTER BANK PLC
Business House A, Ground Floor, P.O. Box
1000, Gogarburn, EH12 1HQ
Tel: (0131) 6263433/0778830
Fiona Anne Barr
Alexandra Nichol Duff
Anna Lucy MacKenzie
Andrew John Gordon McConnell

NATIONAL WESTMINSTER BANK PLC
Ground Floor, Business House A, Gogarburn,
EH12 1HQ
Fiona Jane Boyce
Louise Manzie Davidson
John David Harrison
Kate Susan Smith

NATIONAL WESTMINSTER BANK PLC
House D Second Floor, Gogarburn House, P.O.
Box 1000, EH12 1HQ
Tel: (07711) 925720
Lisa Gillian Douglas
Rachael Emma Pocklington

NATIONAL WESTMINSTER BANK PLC
Group Legal and Secretariat, Business House
G, P.O. Box 1000, EH12 1HQ
Tel: (0131) 6264100
Justine Ann Ferguson

NATIONAL WESTMINSTER BANK PLC
Financial Crime, Risk, RBS Gogarburn, House C
Ground Floor, PO Box 1000, EH12 1HQ
Lynne Frances Mackintosh
Bruce John Daniel McCombie

NATIONAL WESTMINSTER BANK PLC
Business House C, Ground Floor, P.O. Box
1000, Gogarburn, EH12 1HQ
Tel: (0131) 5235185
Daryl Thomas Mangan
Jonathan Taylor Noble
Gemma Christine Statham

NATIONAL WESTMINSTER BANK PLC
Organisation & Performance, House A, 2nd
Floor, P.O. Box 1000, EH12 1HQ
Tel: (0131) 5568555
Alan George Nicholson

NAVIGATOR EMPLOYMENT LAW LTD
Floor 3, 1-4 Atholl Crescent, EH3 8HA
Tel: (0333) 2400308
Kelly Annmarie McManus
Natalia Anne Milne
Euan Colm Smith
Alan James Sutherland

NCM FUND SERVICES LIMITED
Fourth Floor, 7 Castle Street, EH2 3AH
Tel: (0131) 6037020
Fax: (0131) 6037035
Kathleen Moir McLeay

NUCLEUS FINANCIAL GROUP
Nucleus HQ, Greenside 12 Blenheim Place,
EH7 5JH
Tel: (0131) 2269739
Fax: (0131) 2200954
Andrew James Nicoll
Matthew Iain Orr

NURSING AND MIDWIFERY COUNCIL
2nd Floor, 10 George Street, EH2 2PF
Tel: (0131) 624 5024
Samantha Louise Forsyth
Julie Elizabeth McAra
Hazel McGuinness

OCEAN WINDS UK LIMITED
5th Floor, Atria One, 144 Morrison Street,
EH3 8EX
Tel: (0131) 5567602
Aileen Burke
Antonia Paula Pacitti
Julian Michael Poullain
Claire Allison Stewart

OFFICE OF THE ADVOCATE GENERAL
Queen Elizabeth House, 1 Sibbald Walk,
EH8 8FT
Tel: (0131) 2441635
James Peter Kelly
Claire Jayne Anderson
Kirsty Anderson
Helen Mary Bain
Shona Kirsten Robertson Bathgate
Laura Candice Begg
Andrew Roy Lazenby Brown
David Alexander Cairns
Fiona Scott Cavin
Leigh Anne Clarke
Elizabeth Sarah Connell
Victoria Fowler
Gemma Mary MacAllister
Catriona Jane Macdonald
Victoria Claire MacDonald
Ewan McCaig
Carla Melville
Eva Rebecca Milne
Sarah Mitchell
Ian Alastair McIvor Mowat
Elizabeth Ann Napier
Rebecca Anne Neilson
Alice Elizabeth Normand
Eniola Oluwadamilola Oshodi
Thomas Adam Redpath
Fiona Janet Robertson
Kirsty Anne Stead Ryan
Carol Phyllis Snow
Alison Jane Stewart
Jenny Leigh Strachan
Neil Simpson Taylor
Greg William Thomson
Raj-Kiran Kaur Uppal
Liana Esther Waclawski
Michael Gavin Wells
Anna May Wilson
Gordon Alexander Wilson

OFFICE OF THE QUEEN'S AND LORD
TREASURER'S REMEMBRANCER
Scottish Government Building, 1F North,
Victoria Quay, EH6 6QQ
Tel: (0300) 020 3512
Email: enquiries@qltr.gov.uk
Web: www.qltr.gov.uk
Catriona Ann Deans
Kyle Lawson McAra
Robert Meldrum Sandeman

PARABOLA GROUP
101 George Street, EH2 3ES
Kirsty Fraser Macgregor

POSTCODE LOTTERY LIMITED
28 Charlotte Square, EH2 4ET
Tel: (0131) 555 (ext) 9558
Fraser Keith Lovell
Gillian Catherine Rust
Stephanie Traynor

PROCURATOR FISCAL SERVICE
Crown Office, 25 Chambers Street, EH1 1LA
Tel: (0300) 0203168

▶ *Edinburgh continued*

Fax: (0844) 5614069
DX: 540311 EDINBURGH 38
Rachel Jennifer Aedy
Christine Catherine Allan
Freya Anderson-Ward
Alison Jane Atkins
Fiona Avino
Rona Baird
Valerie Janet Barber-Fleming
Wendy Ann Brown Barr
Brent Wemyss Bisset
Anthony Joseph Bonnar
Mairi Boyle
Christine Jane Brownlie
Kyrsten Leona Buist
Alan George Cameron
Erin Anderson Campbell
Ross Bradley Canning
Alice Elizabeth Anne Carey
Lynda Carnochan
Marie-Claire Elizabeth Chaffey
Anna Chisholm
Cheryl Lynne Clark
Rebecca Clark
Linda Jean Cockburn
Martin John Forrester Collins
Faye Elizabeth Cook
Rosie Cook
Katrine Shearer Craig
Mary Claire Crompton
Leanne Cross
Claire Monique Cumming
Jennifer Mary Cunningham
Honor Fiona De Gaetano
David James Dickson
Susan Dickson
Jade Nicola Doig
Catriona Margaret Dow
Hilary Susan Dyer
Jemima Elizabeth Eadie
Alasdair Graham Hood Fay
Caitlin Margaret French
Emma Lauren Gilliland
Joan Ann Gilmour
Mairi Jessica Graham
Jennifer Ann Hamilton
Juliet Claire Harkins
Kathleen Marie Harper
Darren Harty
David Bryce Harvie
Anne-Louise House
Shona Jane Howie
Erin Esther Illand
Graeme Smethurst Jessop
Jennifer Anna Johnson
Paul Stephen Kearney
Jonathan James Thomas Kemp
Jenny Louise Kilpatrick
Eileen Kirkwood
Alasdair George Knox
Emma Morna Lambie

Nicole Lee Ann Lavelle
Amber Suzanna Boyle Le Main
Alistair James Gilchrist Logan
Iain Stuart Logan
John Thomas Logue
Andrew Victor Long
Lynsay Mary Magro
Aafia Suman Majid
Mohamed Tanjeel Maleque
Gavin Marshall
Keri Maureen Marshall
Agnieszka Anna Mathieson
Flora Margaret McCamley
Carey Ann McCune
Alistair Coates McDermid
David John McDonald
Alison Anne McFadyen
Amanda McGowan
Stephen Anthony McGowan
Joseph Francis McKenna
Paul Joseph Miele
Chloe Rebecca Georgia Chirwiro Millar
Lindsey Rae Miller
Matthew Sean Miller
Peter Thomas William Motion
Kathleen Elizabeth Joyce Murray
Fiona Elizabeth Nairn
Karen Elizabeth Nicol
Mark James Nicol
Sarah Maureen Noon
Kate O'Sullivan
Emma Petterson
Vilhelmina Irene Charlotta Poppius
Alexander Prentice
Ross Eliot Price
Anna Christine Reid
Jacqualynn Margaret Reid
Pauline Mary Reid
Lynne Marie Reilly
Sheila Ann Robertson
Karon Helen Rollo
Stephanie Jayne Ross
Rebecca Julie Scott
Pauline Shade
Alasdair James Shaw
Sara Anne Shaw
Heather Jane Smith
Blair James Matthew Speed
Anthony Paul Steele
Joseph Alan Stewart
Nadya Leanne Stewart
Justine Taylor
Jennifer Irene Thomson
Peter Desmond Tierney
Baqar Saud Ul-Hassan
Joanna Page Waller
Rosslyn Walsh
Melanie Mitchell Ward
Naomei Sophia Warner
Kara Watt
Rachael Janet Weir
John William West
Alan Malachy Wickham

Colin James Wilson
Karen Wilson
Brian Alexander Young
PROCURATOR FISCAL SERVICE
Procurator Fiscal's Office, 29 Chambers Street,
EH1 1LD
Tel: (0300) 0203000
DX: 550315 EDINBURGH 37
Shaun William Alexander
Lorraine Caroline Almond
Neil Charles Dempster Almond
Iain Mark Scott Batho
Emma Bell
David Michael Bernard
Alexis Elizabeth Blake
Claire Elizabeth Bottomley
Tessa Mary Bradley
Richard Lauchlan Brown
Laura Margaret Bruce
Laura Buchan
Fiona Helen Caldwell
Ross Stewart Carvel
Rosanna Louise Chapman
Hazel Christie
Miriam Christine Clark
Kirsten Cockburn
James Lewis Crosbie
Thomas Crosbie
Jill Barbara Currie
Sean Kevin Docherty
Kenneth William Donnelly
Gerard Philip Drugan
Michael Stephen Dunlop
Jo Dunn
Stephen Douglas Ferguson
Aileen Catherine Gordon
Ann Elliot Gray
Sophie Hanlon
Aidan John Higgins
Emily Mary Hood
Sanah Anwar Idrees
Alison Margaret Innes
Clare Elizabeth Kennedy
Maria Bronislava Kicinski
Emma Alexandra Laing
Sarah Elizabeth Latta
Kirsty Louise Lyons
Diana MacDonald
Alasdair Norman MacLeod
Kerry Margaret MacLeod
Bruce Crighton Macrosson
Chelsea Catherine Martin
Malcolm David McBain
Maureen McGovern
Shona Christina McJannett
Abbie Carruthers McKerlie
Faith Roslyn Millar
Alan Morrison
Mhairi Alison Morrison
Charlene Alison Murphy
Heather Catrina Margaret Naismith
Claire Frances Nicholls
James Patrick O'Reilly

Elizabeth Anne Paton
Anthony John Quigley
Nhabeela Rahmatullah
Anna Robertson
Claire Rowan
Dawn Samson
Kim Antoinette Schofield
Arlene Martha Susan Shaw
Gulam Karima Stewart
Anne Elizabeth Sweeney
Callum MacEwan Thomson
Gertrude Elizabeth Wallace
Rachel Russell Wallace
Eilidh MacDougall Yates
Viki Louise Yuille

PROCURATOR FISCAL SERVICE
Procurator Fiscal's Office, High Court of
Justiciary, Lawnmarket, EH1 2NS
Tel: (0844) 5612000
Lindsey Maureen Armstrong

PROCURATOR FISCAL SERVICE
Procurator Fiscal's Office, 25 Chambers Street,
EH1 1LD
Fax: (0844) 5614069
Lynne Louise Barrie

PROCURATOR FISCAL SERVICE
C/o Crown Office, 25 Chambers Street,
EH1 1LA
Tel: (0844) 561 3268
Andrew Jonathan Beadsworth
Louise Catherine Beattie
Sally Margaret Clark
Lindsey K. Dalziel
Angela Jane Farrell
Kate Fleming
Jennifer Harrower
Andrew Simon Douglas Laing
Alisdair Neil Macleod
Caroline Quin MacLeod
Sarah Campbell McCall
Sharon Elizabeth Mary McCrudden
Alastair John Mitchell
Siobhan Elaine Monks
Lynsey Anne Rooney
Lesley Claire Smith

PROCURATOR FISCAL SERVICE
Civil Recovery Unit, Argyle House, Lady
Lawson Street, EH3 9SH
Julia Elizabeth Allen Bennett

PROCURATOR FISCAL SERVICE
Serious and Organised Crime Division, Crown
Office, 8th Floor, Sheriff Court, 27 Chambers
Street, EH1 1LB
Amanda Anne Bennett-Mitchell
Brian Christopher Duffy
Anne Frances Hilley

PROCURATOR FISCAL SERVICE
COVID Deaths Investigation Team, 29
Chambers Street, EH1 1LD
Nicola Irene Daly

▶ Edinburgh continued

PROCURATOR FISCAL SERVICE
Scottish Fatalities Investigation Unit,
Procurator Fiscal's Office, 29 Chambers Street,
EH1 1LA
Tel: (0844) 5612000
Jennifer Mary Graham
Rebecca Swansey

PUBLIC DEFENCE SOLICITORS OFFICE
9 York Place, EH1 3EB
Tel: (0131) 557 1222
Fax: (0131) 557 2212
DX: ED603 EDINBURGH
Paul Thomas Alexander Cannavan
Lesley Alexandra Jane Cunningham
Andrew Thomas Docherty
Paul Anthony Haran
Gillian Koren
Sean Charles Morrison
Julie Ann Torley

PULSANT LIMITED
Sirius House, Flassches Yard, South Gyle,
EH12 9LB
Tel: (0131) 514 4030
Eric Barclay McCracken

RED ROCK POWER LIMITED
5th Floor, 40 Princes Street, EH2 2BU
Tel: (0131) 5577101
Jade Lara Allali
Robert Dow McMurray
Rachel Elizabeth Williamson

REGISTERS OF SCOTLAND
Meadowbank House, 153 London Road,
EH8 7AU
Tel: 131659611
DX: 555339 EDINBURGH 15
Claire Patricia Canning
Carole Barbra Ferguson-Walker

REVENUE SCOTLAND
PO Box 24068, EH6 9BR
Mairi Anne Gibson
Kevin Graham
Caitlin Flora Kennedy Hislop
Rhona Mary McLean

ROYAL LONDON
Group Legal, St. Andrew House, 1 Thistle
Street, EH2 1DG
Tel: (0131) 4567703
Katie Marie Alden
Faisal Baig
Gayle Booth
Richard Clifford Gordon
Jennifer Hunter
Gail Louise Manchester
Rachel Kirstie Mullin
Liane Smith

ROYAL LONDON GROUP
2 Queen Street, EH2 1BG
Clare Elizabeth Moffat

SAINSBURY'S BANK PLC
3 Lochside Avenue, Edinburgh Park, EH12 9DJ
Tel: (0131) 286 0807

Lorna Burnet
Andrea Mary Louise Dow
Karen Jean Logan
Richard George Milne
Indhumathi Nilakanthi Porteous
Lauren Elizabeth Rainey
Alan John Stewart
Caroline Ann Whitten

SCHRODERS PERSONAL WEALTH
The Mound, EH1 1YZ
James Kenneth Newton

SCOTCH WHISKY ASSOCIATION
1st Floor, Quartermile Two, 2 Lister Square,
EH3 9GL
Tel: (0131) 222 9200
Fax: (0131) 777 8080
Laura Lee
Lindesay Matheson Low
Caitlin O'Donnell
James Alan Pearson Park
Andrew Gordon Swift

SCOTMID COOPERATIVE SOCIETY
Hollywood House, 2 Harvest Drive, EH28 8QJ
Margaret Anne Soderqvist Clark

SCOTTISH ARBITRATION CENTRE
Level 3, 125 Princes Street, EH2 4AD
Tel: (0131) 2264686
Fax: (0131) 2400830
Andrew Paul Mackenzie

SCOTTISH CHILD LAW CENTRE
91 George Street, EH2 3ES
Tel: (0131) 6676333
Fax: (0131) 6621713
Sadia Arshad

SCOTTISH CHILDREN'S REPORTER
ADMINISTRATION
1 Fountainhall Road, EH9 2NL
Tel: (0131) 6679431
Fax: (0131) 6624640
James Mackenzie Clark
Jennifer Elizabeth Royston
Zoe Claire Veitch

SCOTTISH COURTS AND TRIBUNAL SERVICE
Supreme Courts, Parliament House, 11
Parliament Square, EH1 1RQ
Tel: (0131) 2406886
Danielle Louise McLaughlin

SCOTTISH COURTS AND TRIBUNALS SERVICE
Edinburgh Sheriff Court, 27 Chambers Street,
EH1 1LB
Tel: (0131) 2252525
Alison Margaret Shiach Brown
Julia Ann Katherine Dunbar
Cheryl Anne Ferguson
Annie Jane MacLean Liddle
Francesca Maria Liddle
Anne Elizabeth Mainland
Deirdre Christine Morrison

SCOTTISH ENVIRONMENT PROTECTION
AGENCY
Silvan House, 3rd Floor, 231 Corstorphine
Road, EH12 7AT
Tel: (0131) 4497296

Fax: (0131) 4497277
Karen Meikle Berry
Lucy Margaret Cowan
Hannah Zoe Furness
Gillian Sandra Lock
Lauren Margaret Helen Queen
Lindsay Tolland
Duncan James Wylie
Alison Margaret York

SCOTTISH EPISCOPAL CHURCH
21 Grosvenor Crescent, EH12 5EE
Tel: (0131) 2256357
John Forester Stuart

SCOTTISH FUTURES TRUST
11-15 Thistle Street, EH2 1DF
Tel: (0131) 5100800
Fax: (0131) 5100801
Jennifer Michelle Davies
Sarah Eynon
Richard Scott Lockhart
Michael Anthony McAdam
Paul Graham Moseley
Christa Margaretha Reekie
Donna Lesley Stevenson

SCOTTISH GOVERNMENT
Legal Directorate, Victoria Quay, EH6 6QQ
Tel: (0131) 244 0815
Fax: (0131) 2447417
Ruth Elaine Lunny
Fozia Samara Ahmad
Kirsty Rosalind Aitken
Lindsay Sarah Anderson
Dawn Elizabeth Archer
Camilo Jorge Arredondo Reboa
Victoria Frances Ayre
Julie Bain
Kirsteen Baker
Afson Barekat
Janet Elizabeth Bartlett
Natalie Barton
Caroline Elizabeth Beattie
Frances Margaret Beck
Daniel Blaikie
Elizabeth Eunson Aitken Blair
Kayleigh Nicola Blair
Susan Bonellie
Sarah Francesca Booth
Carolyn Mary Linden Boyd
Magdalene Boyd
Nicola Anne Bradley
Judith Alexandra Brown
Martin Stuart Brown
Emily Rae Callaghan
Louise Ellen Rose Campbell
Michael Peter Carey
Louise Elizabeth Anne Carlin
Rona Catherine Carson
Ninian Francis Christie
Heather Kathleen Clark
James Robert Clelland
Karen Lucy Clyde
Kate Connelly
Alison Jane Coull

Rachel Jane Coutts
Sarah Jane Crawford
Andrew Wilson Crawley
Claire Frances Cullen
Felicity Rose Cullen
Stewart Duncan Cunningham
Kiera Jane Dargie
Ann Dale Davies
Joanna Ruth Dingwall
Seamus Rory McCallum Duff
Nicholas Jude Steven Duffy
Holly Dyce
Mari Jean Evans
Shirley Elizabeth Ferguson
Graham Robert Fisher
Adrienne MacKenzie Forman
Ruth Lamont Foulis
Robert Norman Karl Freeland
Michael Craig French
Lucy May Galloway
Ailsa Mary Garland
Benjamin David Gaston
Kevin Gibson
Colin Robert Gilchrist
Nicola Guild
James Robert Hamilton
Kenneth Joseph Hannaway
Redmond Porch Harris
Ailsa Elizabeth Christine Heine
Amy Jane Hogarth
Suzanne Lesley Houston
Hannah Aileen Hutchison
Johanna Vaughan Irvine
Stephen John Jackson
Kirsty Moira Jamieson
Helena Margaret Janssen
Adam Peter Robert Johnston
Isobel Sheila Joiner
Kathryn Ailna Joshi
Laura Anne Kennedy
Douglas Stewart Kerr
Lewis Neil Kerr
Caroline Mary Kubala
Brian James Lavelle
Angela Lawson
Rosemary Agnes MacLellan Lindsay
Peter Livingstone
Emma Beatrice Luton
Helen-Anne Sarah Lyle
Kathryn Elizabeth MacGregor
Caroline Ann Mackintosh
David James Maclennan
Neil Stuart MacLeod
Norman Torquil Macleod
Ruaraidh Graeme Brander Macniven
Jamie MacQueen
Rosemary Jane Sakeena MacQueen
Jennifer Carolyn Magill
Margaret Main
Inez Helen Manson
Katherine Morag Marshall
Scott Dean Matheson
Anne Louise Mathie

► Edinburgh continued

Barry Dean McCaffrey
Fiona Davidson McClean
Cecilia Ann McCullough
Katherine Stuart McGarvey
Claire Lunney McGill
Jordan McGrory
Craig Whyte McGuffie
Elise Margaret McIntyre
Denise Sarah McKay
Nico Mckenzie-Juetten
Kirstie McKerron
Clare Christina McKinlay
Grant Campbell McLarty
Rachael Frances McLean
Alison May McLeod
Lucy Jane McMichael
Katie Thomas McNair
Claire Louise Meikle
Louise Judith Miller
David James Moffat
Neel Kumar Mojee
Claire Montgomery
Francesca Louise Morton
Victoria Jane Sabine Morton
Anna Mary Munro
Norman Munro
David Bannerman Murdoch
Nadine Maria Murphy
Kate Boyer Neal
Lewis Newlands
Christopher William Nicholson
Rachel Sarah Nicholson
Thomas William Nicol
Aileen Agnes Nimmo
Megan Frances O'Brien
Carolyn Mary O'Malley
Rosemary Jean O'Neill
Lucy Avril Orren
Jacqueline Pantony
Rebecca Jane Parry
John Stephen Paterson
Rudi Alexandra Paton
Luigi Francesco Pedreschi
Marie Lorraine Penman
Emma Jean Phillips
Lori Emma Pidgeon
Christine Ann Reay
Mhairi Anne Reid
Hazel Aileen Reilly
Katherine Victoria Richards
Mark Richards
Susan Robb
Beth Saddler
Catherine Margaret Scott
Francesca Dominique Sharif
Kirsten Simonnet-Lefevre
Susan Catherine Simpson
Jennifer Trudi Singerman
Kirsten Claire Slee
David John Smith
Eilidh Catherine Smith

Magdalena Stefaniak
Kirsty Elizabeth Stevens
Emma Anne Stevenson
Natalie Stewart
Ruth Swanson
Emma Louise Thomson
John Edward Gallagher Thomson
Eileen Mary Threlfall
Jo-anne Tinto
Alison Toledo
Claire Murray Tosh
Jill Louise Turnbull
Rachel Louise Vezza
Stephanie Jane Virlogeux
Kathryn Claire Walker
Lorraine Janet Walkinshaw
Louisa-Jane Walls
Morven Smith Watson
Micheila Constance Pritchard West
Rosemary Celia Mackay Whaley
Keith Robin Hughes White
Laura Jane Wilkinson
Emily Cecilia Williams Boylston

SCOTTISH GOVERNMENT
Freedom of Information Unit, St Andrew's
House, Regent Road, EH1 3DG
Tel: (0131) 2442678
Graham William Crombie

SCOTTISH GOVERNMENT
DG Learning & Justice, St Andrews House,
Regent Road, EH1 3DG
Tel: (0131) 244 3078
Catriona Dalrymple

SCOTTISH GOVERNMENT
Scottish Government Response Unit, GB
North, Victoria Quay, EH6 6QQ
Aisha Lubna Kerr

SCOTTISH GOVERNMENT
Employee Relations, Reward & HR Policy, E1
Spur, Saughton House, Broomhouse Drive,
EH11 3XG
Tel: (0131) 2442418
Julie-Anne MacFadyen

SCOTTISH GOVERNMENT
Area 3H North, Victoria Quay, EH6 6QQ
Tel: (0131) 244 3775
Robert McAlpine Marshall

SCOTTISH GOVERNMENT
ST ANDREWS House, Regent Road, EH1 3DG
Euan Peter O'Neill
Shalani Raghavan

SCOTTISH GOVERNMENT
Victoria Quay, EH6 6QQ
Tel: (0131) 244 0815
Fax: (0131) 2447417
Jonathan Mark Stephenson

SCOTTISH GOVERNMENT CHILDREN &
FAMILIES DIRECTORATE
Area 2A- South, Victoria Quay, EH6 6QQ
Tel: (0131) 2444521
Paul Euan Beaton
Michael John Chalmers
Lisa Maisie McCloy

SCOTTISH GOVERNMENT'S PARLIAMENTARY
  COUNSEL OFFICE
  Victoria Quay/ Area 2 – J South, EH6 6QQ
  Tel: (0131) 244 6483
  Laura Elizabeth Barrie
  Andrew Watt Beattie
  Jonathan Gregor Brown
  Alison Janet Carlyle
  Christopher James Coyle
  Mark Andrew Eggeling
  Stephen Graham Feltham
  William Ferrie
  Marisa Nicole Gillick
  Fraser Norman Moore Gough
  Matthew Lynch
  Amanda Victoria Macallan
  Carla McCloy-Stevens
  Max Conrad McGill
  Annalee Jane Murphy
  Meryl Zoe Skene
  Shona Paxton White
  Heather Wortley
  Ian Brian Young
SCOTTISH HUMAN RIGHTS COMMISSION
  Bridgeside House, 99 McDonald Road,
  EH7 4NS
  Tel: (0131) 297 5759
  Catherine Ama Asante
  Eleanor Marion Deeming
  Francis Theodore Caleb Jarvis
SCOTTISH INVESTMENTS SERVICES LIMITED
  Waverly Gate, 2-4 Waterloo Place, EH1 3EG
  Victoria Allison
SCOTTISH LAW COMMISSION
  140 Causewayside, EH9 1PR
  Tel: (0131) 6682131
  Stephen Charles Crilly
  Alison Jean Fraser
  Charles Edward Birks Garland
  Graham McGlashan
  Alastair Melville John Smith
  Lorraine Stirling
SCOTTISH LEGAL AID BOARD
  Thistle House, 91 Haymarket Terrace,
  EH12 5HE
  Tel: (0131) 2267061
  DX: 555250 EDINBURGH 30
  Zahrah Mumtaz Ahmad
  Eilidh Catherine Barnes
  Helen Elizabeth Bell
  Kieran Robert Burke
  Nicola Jane Cameron
  Scott Graham Cownie
  Michael Gerard Creegan
  Elizabeth Emma Cuschieri
  Wendy Mary Dalgleish
  John Dickson
  Nerissa Louise Drennan
  Raymond Ferguson
  Gordon David Fowler
  Marie-Louise Fox
  Rosa-Maria Vittoria Gentles
  Fiona Maclachlan Glen

Alison Catherine Granger
Ross Gray
John Harper
Shona Jane Herd
Benjamin Francis Hughes
Jane Louise Joiner
Tracy Anne Kirke
Lynda Lothian
Norman Roderick MacKay
Alistair Martin Matheson
John Gerard McCafferty
James McLean
James Kinnaird Mudie
Alan Robert Muir
Donna-Marie Murphy
Leanne Murphy
John Rowan Myles
John Joseph Pearson
Kenneth Bryce Pringle
Haseeba Tariq
Gordon Cameron Tolland
SCOTTISH NATIONAL INVESTMENT BANK
  1-North, Waverley Gate, 2-4 Waterloo Place,
  EH1 3EG
  Zara Banu Margaret Diloo
  Simon Nicholas Wilson
SCOTTISH NATIONAL PARTY
  3 Jackson's Entry, EH8 8PJ
  Tel: (0131) 5258920
  Scott Martin
SCOTTISH RUGBY
  Murrayfield Stadium, EH12 5PJ
  Tel: (0131) 3465000
  Fax: (0131) 3465001
  Robert Morton Howat
  Angela Lucinda Irene McCracken
  Douglas Francis Struth
  Gillian Claire Treasurer
SCOTTISH WIDOWS LIMITED
  PO Box 17036, 69 Morrison Street, EH3 8BW
  Tel: (0131) 6557230
  Fax: (0131) 6670253
  Graham Peter Christie
  Ann Barrie Crawford
  Colin John Crocker
  Fraser Alexander Donald
  Graeme John Donaldson
  Laura Anne Forrester
  Andrew Neil Fraser
  Kenneth William Love
  Lena Elizabeth Mackay
  Heather Jane Matthew
  Jane Elizabeth Mitchell
  Christopher William Muir
  Jonathan O'Hara
  Sara Jane Oliphant
  Catherine Ann Roulston
  Victoria Marie Smithard
  Kathryn Jane Stewart-Hart
  Nicholas David Williamson
SHEKU BAYOH PUBLIC INQUIRY
  Capital House, 2 Festival Square, EH3 9WJ
  Duncan Gillies Peat

▶ **Edinburgh** continued

Sadif Ashraf
Euan Bruce
Emily Freeman
Fraser Johnston
Ciara Maria Pang
Laura Christina Wylie
SHOCKINGLY FRESH LIMITED
Gyleview House, 3 Redheughs Rigg,
EH12 9DQ
Pamela Jane Sealey
SIEMENS GAMESA RENEWABLE ENERGY
The Stamp Office, 10 Wateroo Place, EH1 3EG
Shona Mary Watson
SIGMA CAPITAL GROUP PLC
18 Alva Street, EH2 4QG
Tel: (0131) 2209444
Katy Louise Ramsey
Danielle Toal
SKYRORA LIMITED
Floor 2, 108 Princes Street, EH2 3AA
Nicholas Joseph Beach
Laura Robyn Edison
SKYSCANNER
Quartermile One, 15 Lauriston Place, EH3 9EN
Kirsteen Joanne Bell
Stuart Leslie William Davies
Iliyana Georgieva Dimitrova
Candice Elizabeth Philippa Donnelly
Thomas Anthony Jamieson
Julie Maxwell
Martin Gerard Nolan
SL CAPITAL PARTNERS LLP
1 George Street, EH2 2LL
Tel: (0131) 245 1802
Fax: (0131) 245 6105
David Ross Thompson
STANDARD LIFE ASSETS AND EMPLOYEE
SERVICES LIMITED
Group Legal Services, 6th Floor West,
Standard Life House, 30 Lothian Road,
EH1 2DH
Tel: (0131) 2457508
Heather Laura Bain
Rona Jane Cameron
Elspeth Rosemary Fairgrieve
Morag Mason Forrest
David Hoy
Lorna Kelly
Katrina Love
Radhika Sekar Natarajan
Catherine Johan Paterson
Charlotte Claire Ring-Macleod
Stephanie Reith Scrimgeour
Claire Anne Sinclair
Nicholas Stewart
Peter Trygve Tyson
STANDARD LIFE INVESTMENTS LIMITED
1 George Street, EH2 2LL
Tel: (0131) 245 4153
Tessa Maxine Allen
Claire Louise Dowle

Margot-Joy Forrest
Alison Margaret Freshwater
Hilary Sheila Neill
Mandy Louise Rawlinson
John Macdonald Fraser Smith
Lauren Aileen Smith
Fiona Gillian Struthers
STATE STREET TRUSTEES LIMITED
Quartermile 3, 10 Nightingale Way, EH3 9EG
Tel: (0131) 3155833
Gerard Paterson
SYKES GLOBAL SERVICES LIMITED
599 Calder Road, EH11 4GA
Tel: (0131) 458 6500
Graham Alexander
TESCO PERSONAL FINANCE PLC
2 South Gyle Crescent, EH12 9FQ
Tel: (0131) 274 3426
Christine Anne Barszcz
Fiona Burden
Pamela Cranston
Gerrit Johannes Henstock
Helen Elizabeth Krushave
Simon Colum Lamb
Calum Alexander Ruaridh Macnicol
Lucy Cathryn Martone
Patrick Hugh Mason
John Stephen Cunningham Murray
Michael William Mustard
Neil Brian Souness
THE COMPETITION & MARKETS AUTHORITY
Queen Elizabeth House, Sibbald Walk,
EH8 8FT
Liam Maclean
Clare Th r se Marchesi-Denham
Caitlin McLean
THE EDINBURGH PROPERTY SEARCH COMPANY
LTD
1 Lynedoch Place, EH3 7PX
Tel: 797415678
Sheona Anne Gordon
THE GENERAL TEACHING COUNCIL FOR
SCOTLAND
Clerwood House, 96 Clermiston Road,
EH12 6UT
Tel: (0131) 314 6000
Gillian Margaret Sim
Isobel Fortune Allan
Katie Anne Kearney
Jennifer Mairi Macdonald
Vivien Alexandra Whyte
THE INSTITUTE AND FACULTY OF ACTUARIES
Level 2, Exchange Crescent, 7 Conference
Square, EH3 8RA
Tel: (020) 7632 1488
Sarah Louise Drummond
Emma Louise Gilpin
Jenny Ann Higgins
Benjamin John Tizzard Kemp
Suzanne Marie Lyons
Elena McLachlan
Michael James Scott
Leisha Jayne Watson

THE INSTITUTE OF CHARTERED ACCOUNTANTS
OF SCOTLAND
CA House, 21 Haymarket Yards, EH12 5BH
Tel: (0131) 3470100
Fax: (0131) 3470105
Shuiken Nora Chan
Laura Janet Gow
Robert Huw Mudge
Michelle Rose Mullen
THE NATIONAL TRUST FOR SCOTLAND
Hermiston Quay, 5 Cultins Road, EH11 4DF
Tel: (0844) 4932100
Fax: (0131) 2439301
Sarah Margarette Ahmed
Nicola Ann Blyth
Stephen Thomas Small
THE ROYAL BANK OF SCOTLAND PLC
First Floor, 24-25 St Andrews Square, EH2 1AF
Tel: (0131) 5568555
John Gannon
THE ROYAL BANK OF SCOTLAND PLC
Trustee & Depository Services, Drummond
House, 1 Redheughs Avenue, EH12 9JN
Alan Michael Wishart
THE SCOTTISH PARLIAMENT
Solicitor's Office, EH99 1SP
Tel: (0131) 3486653
Claudia Bennett
Gillian Michelle Anne Brady
Ailidh Jean Gunn Callander
Linda Fowler
Kenneth Htet-Khin
Kirsty Moira Lauder
Cristine Ann Livingstone
Letitia Scarlette Longworth Campbell
Catriona Louise Lyle
Catriona Malcolm McCallum
Isla Isabella Gerrard McLeod
Jacqueline McRae
Judith Ann Morrison
Marian Isabel Campbell Richardson
James Duncan Shaw
Heike Stephenson
Gillian Claire Turner
Stephen Wright
TRAFFIC COMMISSIONER FOR SCOTLAND
The Stamp Office, 10 Waterloo Place,
EH1 3EG
Tel: (0131) 2004905
Fax: (0131) 2296682
Claire Marie Gilmore
TRAINLINE.COM LIMITED
1 Tanfield, EH3 5DA
Kate Elizabeth Longmuir
Katharine Laura McGregor
Jennifer Maureen McHattie
TRIP AIR TICKETING (UK) LIMITED
One Lochrin Square, 92 Fountainbridge,
EH3 9QA
Anna Maura Beale
TRUSTPILOT
9-10 St Andrews Square, EH2 2AF
Michael Andrew Cooper

TSB BANK PLC
Henry Duncan House, 120 George Street,
EH2 4LH
Tel: (0131) 260 0051
Nina Bansal
Helen Bowman
Jeremy William Fraser
Victoria Elizabeth Mullen
Kirstie Ann Ross
Paul Alexander Shearer
Martin Wilkie
Laura Fiona Wright
TV SQUARED LTD
Fifth Floor, 1 Exchange Crescent,, Conference
Square, EH3 8UL
Kathryn Claire Campbell
UNIVERSITY OF EDINBURGH
Old College, South Bridge, EH8 9YL
Tel: (0131) 651 4330
Graham Ayres
Fiona Campbell
Leigh Suzanne Chalmers
Anna Crilly
Louise Susan Cullum
Nicholas Donald Day
Esther Mary Duncan
David Louis Faith
Lindsay Hampton
Nora Alison Kellock
Joanne Christina MacConnell
David Malcolm Matheson
UNIVERSITY OF EDINBURGH
Edinburgh Research Office, Room 2.15,
Charles Stewart House, 9-16 Chambers Street,
EH1 1HT
Elizabeth Ann Greybe
David Philip Murphy
Allan David Shanks
Mar a Del Mar Val Fern ndez
UNIVERSITY OF EDINBURGH
The Data Lab, The Bayes Centre, 47
Potterrow, EH8 9BT
Kristina Elizabeth Mutch
VATTENFALL WIND POWER LTD.
The Tun, 4 Jackson's Entry, EH8 8PJ
Tel: (0131) 5263131
Sandra Leece
Nicola Mhairi MacLennan
VENTIENT ENERGY
4th Floor, 12 Blenheim Place, EH7 5JH
Anna Graham Cameron
Alasdair Hugh Lennie
VESTAS-CELTIC WIND TECHNOLOGY LTD
2nd Floor, 63A George Street, EH2 2JG
Neil John Morrison
VIALEX LIMITED
Floor 3, 1-4 Atholl Crescent, EH3 8HA
Tel: (0333) 2400127
Fax: (0333) 2400128
Christelle Olivia St phanie M. Baillie
Seona Anne Burnett
Catriona Margaret Corrigan
Elizabeth Anne Cox

► *Edinburgh continued*

Michael Christopher Drysdale
Zoe Olivia Fowlie
Louise Anne Hamilton
Catriona Seonaigh McGregor
Christina Marie Miller
Scott Callum Paterson
Allan Christopher Reid
Emma Samantha Seddon
Morag Fiona Margaret Waller
John Greig Williamson
Nicholas James Young
VIRGIN MONEY PLC
28 St Andrew Square, EH2 1AF
Tel: 1316039349
Lynsey Wilson
VISITSCOTLAND
Ocean Point One, 94 Ocean Point, EH6 6JH
Tel: (0131) 472 2382
Gayle Anne Biggart
WALTER SCOTT & PARTNERS LIMITED
One Charlotte Square, EH2 4DR
Tel: (0131) 225 1357
Fax: (0131) 225 7997
Victoria Louise Dempster
Fiona Janet Deas Ponniah
Laura Paton Ventre
WS SOCIETY
The Signet Library, Parliament Square,
EH1 1RF
Tel: (0131) 2203249
Fax: (0131) 2204016
Anna Eila Bennett
Robert Pirrie
ZONAL RETAIL DATA SYSTEMS LIMITED
1 Tanfield, EH3 5DA
Tel: (07970) 172738
Rachel Magdalene Gervaise
Jane Frances Struth

Elgin

AM EMPLOYMENT LAW LTD
Victoria House, 10 Victoria Crescent, IV30 1RQ
Tel: (01343) 569293
Adelle Morris
PROCURATOR FISCAL SERVICE
Procurator Fiscal's Office, 48 South Street,
IV30 1JX
Tel: (0844561) 2670
DX: 520661 ELGIN
Andrew William Shanks
SPRINGFIELD PROPERTIES PLC
Alexander Fleming House, 8 Southfield Drive,
IV30 6GR
Erin Louise Grant
THE MORAY COUNCIL
Council Offices, High Street, IV30 1BX
Tel: (01343) 543451
DX: 520666 ELGIN
Georgina Ann Anderson
Sean Andrew Hoath
Kathryn Lisma Violet Macpherson

Alasdair John Stewart McEachan
Neil Lachlan McGlinchey
Sana Sarwar
Aileen Scott
Jennifer Fiona Smith
Morag Jane Smith

Ellon

BREWDOG PLC
Balmacassie Commercial Park, AB41 8BX
Tel: (01358) 724 924
Richard Street

Falkirk

DIRECTORATE FOR PLANNING &
ENVIRONMENTAL APPEALS
Callendar Business Park, Callendar Road,
FK1 1XR
Tel: (0131) 244 6909
Robert Henderson Seaton
FALKIRK COUNCIL
Corporate & Housing Services-Governance,
Municipal Buildings, FK1 5RS
Tel: (01324) 506070
Fax: (01324) 506071
Wendy Margaret Barber
Douglas Blyth
Eilean Margaret Anne Duncan
Peter James Farquhar
Claire Gillan
Iain Wallace Henderson
Rose Mary Hoey
Jessica Alice Knight
Frances Mary Kobiela
Colin Douglas Moodie
Alexander Joseph Muir
Alan Peebles
Karen Anne Quin
Iona Joyce Bell Rodgers
Alistair George Steel
Julie Anne White
MCI ELECTRONICS LIMITED
27 Castle Road, Bankside Industrial Estate,
FK2 7UY
Stephanie McIntosh
PROCURATOR FISCAL SERVICE
Procurator Fiscal's Office, Mansionhouse Road,
FK1 4LW
Tel: (0300) 020 3000
Fax: (0844) 561 3106
DX: 552072 FALKIRK 4
Jane Ann Raeburn Benson
Lindsey Jane Brooks
Samantha Brown
Maire Sineidin Corrins
Katie Cunningham
Collette Louise Fallon
Catherine Margaret Fraser
Kristina Kelly
Catherine Knowles
Michael James Maguire
Sean Daniel Maher

Ann Elizabeth Orr
Tracy Ann Plant
Gail Isobel Russell
Eilidh Smith
Sarah Kate Smith
Emma Louise White
PUBLIC DEFENCE SOLICITORS OFFICE
   47-49 West Bridge Street, FK1 5AZ
   Tel: (01324) 631475
   Fax: (01324) 632389
   Nuala Ann Devlin
   Laura Anne O'Kane Jackson
   Stanley Thomas Quirk
SCOTTISH COURTS AND TRIBUNALS SERVICE
   Falkirk Sheriff Court, Main Street, Camelon,
   FK1 4AR
   Tel: (01324) 678212
   Fax: (01324) 678238
   Amanda Elizabeth Inglis

Forfar

ANGUS COUNCIL
   Legal and Democratic Services, Angus House,
   Orchardbank Business Park, DD8 1AN
   Tel: (01307) 476228
   DX: 530691 FORFAR
   Jacqueline Margaret Buchanan
   Jennifer Burns
   Marie Pauline Callander
   Lesley Law
   Elaine Longwill
   Lynsey Isabel McLeod
   John Gary Munro
   Claire Lynn Richardson
   Lewis Ian Shand
   Akemkar Singh
   David Joseph Thompson
   Ngozi Elizabeth Vincent-Eloagu
   Alison Watson
   Andrew George Wyse
GUILD HOMES (TAYSIDE) LTD
   Chapelpark House, 17 Academy Street,
   DD8 2HA
   Tel: (01307) 460011
   Peter James Farquhar
PROCURATOR FISCAL SERVICE
   Procurator Fiscal's Office, Market Street,
   DD8 3LA
   Tel: (0300) 0204048
   DX: 530681 FORFAR
   Jill Clare Drummond

Galashiels

KYOWA KIRIN INTERNATIONAL PLC
   Galabank Business Park, TD1 1QH
   Siobhan Isabella Johnstone

Giffnock

EAST RENFREWSHIRE COUNCIL
   Council Headquarters, Eastwood Park,
   G46 6UG

Tel: (0141) 5773000
DX: 501600 GIFFNOCK
Joseph George Abrami
Apryl Chalmers
Janice Mackay
Gerard James Mahon
Jacqueline McCusker
Marie Julie Paterson
Katherine Jane Robb
Siobhan Wilson

Glasgow

ABELLIO SCOTRAIL LIMITED
   Atrium Court, 50 Waterloo Street, G2 6HQ
   Samuel Andrew Price
ABRDN FINANCIAL PLANNING AND ADVICE
   LIMITED
   7th Floor, 145 St Vincent Street, G2 5JF
   Vanessa Hutchison
AGGREKO PLC
   8th Floor, Aurora, 120 Bothwell Street, G2 7JS
   Tel: (0141) 2255900
   Fax: (0141) 2255949
   Noel Thomas George Crilley
   Dawn Alison Demellweek
   Louise Margaret Harrison
   Stephanie Claire Innes
   Sean McClements
ALITER CAPITAL LLP
   21 Newton Place, G3 7PY
   Claudia Suzanne Beveridge
ARGONON LTD
   101 Portman Street, G41 1EJ
   Jennifer Leigh Whitehead
ARNOLD CLARK AUTOMOBILES LTD
   454 Hillington Road, G52 4FH
   Tel: (0141) 6481200
   Alison Fiona Keeney
   James McArthur
ARTHUR J GALLAGHER
   Spectrum Building, 7th Floor, 55 Blythswood
   Street, G2 7AT
   Tel: (0141) 285 3056
   Catherine Lindsay Faulds
   Diane Parker Harrison
   Victoria Elizabeth Scholefield
ASHURST LLP
   Clydesdale Bank Exchange, 20 Waterloo
   Street, G2 6DB
   Tel: (0141) 375 4242
   Dianne Jane Tartaglia
   Shah Zabe Ali
   Rachael Bailey
   Iain Lindsay Brown
   Kirsty Claire Cameron
   Lucy Jean Deakin
   Aimi Clare Amber Gold
   Christine Keegan Hall
   Amy Alexandra McCalmont
   Susan Alice Mairi Millar
   Michael Buchanan Polson
   Elaine Sinclair

▶ *Glasgow continued*

 Andrew Alexander Thomson
 Calum John Thornton
 Melanie Dorey Jane Todd
 Natalie Coia Wallace

AUTOREK
 The Garment Factory, 10 Montrose Street,
 G1 1RE
 Jennifer Sarah Bull-Clearie

AXLE GROUP HOLDINGS LIMITED
 26-32 Millbrae Road, Langside, G42 9TU
 Tel: (0141) 6323222
 Fax: (0141) 6495433
 Rachael Samantha Leith-Parsons

BAE SYSTEMS SURFACE SHIPS LIMITED
 Legal Department, South Street, Scotstoun,
 G14 0XN
 Tel: (07525) 391 489
 Fax: (0141) 9574027
 Laura Russell Kennedy
 Gillian Ruth Meldrum
 Graeme Robert Moffett
 Oksana Orlova-Farrelly

BANIJAY UK
 C/o IWC Media, St. Georges Studios, 93-97
 St. Georges Road, G3 6JA
 Tel: (0141) 3533222
 Fax: (0141) 3533221
 Suzanne Louise Elrick
 Leanne Irene Margaret Kyle
 Zoe Andrea Struthers

BARCLAYS EXECUTION SERVICES LIMITED
 Aurora, 120 Bothwell Street, G2 7JT
 Claire Danielle Mooney

BBC SCOTLAND
 Legal Department, 3.03, 40 Pacific Quay,
 G51 1DA
 Tel: (0141) 4226373
 Rosalind Margaret Mary McInnes
 Edward Munroe Murdoch

BBC SCOTLAND
 Commercial, Rights and Business Affairs, Zone
 1.04, 40 Pacific Quay, G51 1DA
 Tel: (0141) 4226373
 Angela Eileen Mills

BNP PARIBAS
 120 Bothwell Street, G2 7JS
 Gavin Richard Danks
 Elizabeth Muir
 Omar Adam Yassin

CAPITA BUSINESS SERVICES LIMITED
 Tannochside Park, Ellismuir Way, Uddingston,
 G71 5PW
 Tel: (07710) 378547
 Deborah Jane Le Sueur

CELEROS FLOW TECHNOLOGY
 149 Newlands Road, Cathcart, G44 4EX
 Tel: (07827) 878 267
 Fax: (0141) 6370215
 Clare-Frances Bradshaw

CELTIC PLC.
 Celtic Park, G40 3RE
 Tel: (0871) 226 1888
 Fax: (0141) 5518106
 Christopher Michael Duffy
 Michael Gordon Kenneth Nicholson

CHIVAS BROTHERS LIMITED
 2-4 Blythswood Square, G2 4AD
 Lynn Gibson McCulloch
 Kirsty Neilson
 Alexander Hugh Smiley

CIGNA INTERNATIONAL
 Grosvenor Building, 72 Gordon Street, G1 3RS
 Tel: (01475) 788679
 Scott Boyle
 Kirsten Mary Craig
 Claire Louise Kennedy
 Amy Kathleen Smith

CLYDESDALE BANK PLC
 Operations Department, 40 St. Vincent Place,
 G1 2HL
 Tel: (0141) 2232883
 Fax: (0141) 2232887
 Lorna Bennie

CLYDESDALE BANK PLC
 Legal Services, 40 St. Vincent Place, G1 2HL
 Tel: 1412423253
 Fax: (0141) 2424723
 Jill Anna Brown
 Hannah Kate Bruce
 Colin John Campbell
 Mairi Maclean Eadie-Campbell
 Fiona Alison Gray
 Andrew Roy Wilson Hinstridge
 Rachel Helen Irvine
 Joanna Louise Jennings
 Laura Kennedy
 Veronica Rachel McArthur
 Nicholas Edward McLuskey
 Mary Murison
 Laura Jane Murphy
 Caroline Mary Orr
 Nadia Rebecca Nikolaya Sirc
 Colin John Waddell
 Jennifer Ann Williams
 Jill Evelyn Wishart

COGNIZANT WORLDWIDE LIMITED
 250 West George Street, G2 4QY
 Tel: (0141) 2221561
 Debbie Joanna Griffiths
 Shona Kerrie Logie
 James Patrick McColgan

CONTRACTPOD TECHNOLOGIES LIMITED
 Savoy Tower, Floor 9, 77 Renfrew Street,
 G2 3BZ
 Tel: (0141) 280 1600
 John Crawford
 Victoria Ann Provan
 Lisa Sinclair

CORE CONSULTANTS (IMMIGRATION & STUDY
 ABROAD) LIMITED
 Suite 1, 171 Maxwell Road, G41 1TG
 Muhammad Pervez Sadiq

CREATIVE SCOTLAND
The Lighthouse, Mitchell Lane, G1 3NU
Tel: (0330) 3332000
Fax: (0141) 3021711
Mark Anthony Wilson

CREDITFIX LIMITED
4 West Regent Street, G2 1RW
Tel: (0141) 565 1300
Hannah McFarquhar

CRIMINAL INJURIES COMPENSATION
AUTHORITY
Alexander Bain House, Atlantic Quay, 15 York
Street, G2 8JQ
Tel: (0141) 2281419
Katherine Currie
Lynsey Elder
Emma Hannay
Laura Kathryn Alice Johnston
Alexander Ian MacNeil
Melanie McMaster

DEVRO PLC.
Moodiesburn, Chryston, G69 0JE
Tel: (01236) 872 261
Katherine Laura Mitchell

EDRINGTON UK DISTRIBUTION LIMITED
191 West George Street, G2 2LD
Tel: (0333) 0161910
Siobhan O'Neil

ELLIS WHITTAM LIMITED
The Beacon, 7th Floor, 176 St Vincent Street,
G2 5SG
Tel: (0345) 226 8393
Laurie Gallacher Anderson
Laura Elizabeth Auld
Craig Brown
Hussain Binn Abdul Rehman Kayani
Derick John MacLean
Holly McLean
Ruth Ying Hei Medlock
Ciaran Robertson

EPIGENETICA LIMITED
163 Bath Street, G2 4SQ
Claire Elizabeth Shepherd

EQUALITY AND HUMAN RIGHTS COMMISSION
2nd Floor, 151 West George Street, G2 2JJ
Tel: (0141) 2285966
Irene Ann Henery
Lindsey Ann Reynolds
Lynn Welsh

EQUATOR (SCOTLAND) LTD
58 Elliot Street, G3 8DZ
Caitlin Andrew O'Dowd

FIVE STAR (INTERNATIONAL) LTD
1st Floor, 299 West George Street, G2 4LF
Tel: (0141) 3397373
Shereen Shafaatulla

FORCE 9 ENERGY PARTNERS LLP
272 Bath Street, G2 4JR
Tel: (0141) 354 1410
Fax: (0141) 354 1411
Nicolas Kenneth John Mackay

FREEDOM FROM TORTURE SCOTLAND
Room 24, The Adelphi Centre, 12 Commercial
Road, G5 0PQ
Tel: (0141) 4203161
Fax: (0141) 4296578
Jennifer Aileen Todd

GLASGOW CALEDONIAN UNIVERSITY
Law Division, City Campus, Cowcaddens
Road, G4 0BA
Paul James Brown

GLASGOW CITY COUNCIL
Chief Executive's Department, 40 John Street,
G1 1JL
Tel: (0141) 2877054
Fax: (0141) 2845739
Judith Sharon Abrahamson
Shahana Andaleeb Arshad
Ikra Kausar Bhatti
Lee Cormack
Fiona Elizabeth Coulter
Ronan James Cunning
Amanda Mary Cunningham
Victoria Eve Curran
Maria-Claire Cushley
Patrick Daniel Docherty
Raymond Farrell
Jennifer Gail Forsyth
Elaine Clare Galletly
Clare Marie Gribbon
Zara Amber Heaney
Irene Kyle Hemfrey
Deborah Elise Henderson
Gillian Ingram
Yvonne Jackson
Paul Latta
Ruth Denise MacColl
Gillian Elizabeth MacEachen
Roderick William Maciver
David John Mair
Tracey Ann McAleese
Martin Fitzgerald McColgan
Kenneth McDonald
Anne Janet McFarlane
Kevin McGinnes
Louise Elizabeth McHugh
Christine Helen McInnes
Peter Grant McKechnie
Mary Josephine McKelvie
Eileen McLaughlin
Jennifer Ann McMartin
Gillian McNaught
Donald Andrew McPartlin
Kenneth Alastair Meechan
James Alexander Meneely
Mairi Davidson Millar
Iain Lindsay Miller
Michelle Murphy
Annemarie O'Donnell
Gillian O'Neil
Shirley-Ann Rhynd
Eleanor Ramage Macdonald Richards
Becky Elizabeth Robertson
Kristine Elizabeth Robinson

▶ *Glasgow continued*

Jillian Amanda Rodgers
Sanaa Shahid
Gurnish Kaur Sidhu
Fiona May Simpson
Iulia Toch
Lauren Towie
Fiona Jane Traill
Samerah Ul-Hassan
Mark Farrel Wallace
Alan Martin Wright
Andrew Wright

GLASGOW CITY COUNCIL
Corporate Property Law, City Chambers,
George Square, G2 1DU
Fax: (0141) 2845739
Pauline Marie Bradshaw
Sarah Shirley Douglas Davidson
Victoria Mary Hyndman
Lauren Margaret Anne Reid

HUTCHISON 3G UK LIMITED
123 St Vincent Street, G2 5EA
Laura Anne McAleer

HYMANS ROBERTSON LLP
20 Waterloo Street, G2 6DB
Tel: (0141) 5667777
Fax: (0141) 5667788
Rachael Elizabeth Cooke
Hayley Sherry Gibson
Natalie Greer

IDOX SOFTWARE LIMITED
First Floor, The Grosvenor Building, 72
Gordon Street, G1 3RS
Tel: (0141) 2277600
Fax: (+) 0870 333 7131
Rachel Sarah Bell
Kirsten Iona Megan Gabert
Therese Isabel Eilidh Laing
Ruth Paterson

INSPECTORATE OF PROSECUTION IN
SCOTLAND
Legal House, 2nd Floor, 101 Gorbals Street,
G5 9DW
DX: 501558 GLAS SALTMARKET
Elizabeth Joan Ross

ISG CENTRAL SERVICES LIMITED
1 Buchanan Gate, Cumbernauld Road, Stepps,
G33 6FB
Paula Lorraine Brown
Jessica Lyons

J. & J. DENHOLM LIMITED
18 Woodside Crescent, G3 7UL
Tel: (0141) 353 2090
Craig David George Daniels

J.B. BARBOUR & CO. LTD
570-572 Lawmoor Street, Dixons Blazes Ind.
Estate, G5 0TY
Tel: (0141) 4293999
Fax: (0141) 4293199
Norman Cameron Smith Barbour

JACOBS & TURNER, T/A TRESPASS
Vermont House, 149 Vermont Street, Kinning
Park, G41 1LU
Tel: (0141) 5688000
Lina Khushi

JACOBS U.K. LIMITED
95 Bothwell Street, G2 7HX
Tel: (0141) 243 8722
Fax: (0141) 2263109
Laura Catherine Allison
Laura Kilpatrick Armstrong
Yasmin Arshed
Claire Catherine Donnelly
Rhona Mary Holman
Heather Elizabeth Kemmett Maclean

JAMES FISHER AND SONS PLC
Cartside Avenue, Inchinnan Business Park,
PA4 9RW
Chloe Ashton Law

JOHNSTON CARMICHAEL LLP ACCOUNTANTS
227 West George Street, G2 2ND
Tel: (0141) 2225800
Shareen Bibi Gault

JUST EMPLOYMENT LAW LTD
City View, 6 Eagle Street, G4 9XA
Tel: (0141) 3315150
Fax: (0141) 3324716
Caroline McShane Cockbain
Gillian Emma Cumming
Fiona Louise Gorry
Pauline Anne Hughes
David Malcolm McRae
David Wilkie Reid
Angela Strzyzewska
Louise Elizabeth Walker
Lauren Wilson

KHAN ASSOCIATES IMMIGRATION LIMITED
Office 105-107, 4-10 Darnley Street, G41 2SE
Tel: (0141) 4292390
Nisar Khan

LAST MILE INFRASTRUCTURE LIMITED
Fenick House, Hamilton International Business
Park, G72 0FT
Andrew Michael McGinlay
Mark Wilburn Scott

LAW AT WORK LTD
7th Floor, The Beacon, 176 St. Vincent Street,
G2 5SG
Tel: (0141) 2715555
Fax: (0141) 2715562
Kirstie Jane Beattie
Benjamin Ian Brown
Lorna Pauline Gemmell
Daniel Stephen Gorry
Donald John MacKinnon
Sophie Rose Macphail
Gerard James O'Hare
Paman Veer Singh Sumal

LEGAL KEY CONSULTING LIMITED
Woodilee Industrial Estate, G66 3UR
Angela Jane McCallum

LEIDOS INNOVATIONS UK LIMITED
 Skypark 1, 8 Elliot Place, G3 8EP
 Tel: (0141) 8143700
 Brendan Bernard Turley
LONDON AND CAMBRIDGE PROPERTIES
 Unit 26, 6 Harmony Row, Govan, G51 3BA
 Tel: (0141) 4653391
 Robin Alastair Kennedy
MACARTHUR GREEN LTD
 93 South Woodside Road, G20 6NT
 Tel: (0141) 3425404
 Kirsty Isla MacArthur
MARY'S MEALS INTERNATIONAL
 39 Durham Street
 Marie McGovern
MAVEN CAPITAL PARTNERS UK LLP
 Kintyre House, 205 West George Street,
 G2 2LW
 Tel: (0141) 206 0124
 Miranda Anne Kelly
MAZARS LLP
 100 Queen Street, G1 3DN
 Tel: (0141) 2264924
 Paul McAllister
MCCAWLEY & CO
 30 Norwood Drive, Whitecraigs, G46 7LS
 John McCawley
MERCHANT HOMES PARTNERSHIPS LIMITED
 Merchant House, Watermark Business Park,
 365 Govan Road, G51 2SE
 Tel: (0141) 420 2026
 Alan John Minty
N4 PARTNERS LLP
 310 St Vincent Street, G2 5RG
 Shauna Margaret Powell
NETWORK RAIL INFRASTRUCTURE LTD
 151 St Vincent Street, G2 5NW
 Tel: (0141) 555 4470
 Karen Anne Gribben
 Roderick John MacDougall
 Judith Emma Morton
NHS 24
 Caledonia House, Fifty Pitches Road,
 Cardonald Park, G51 4EB
 Sarah Rebecca McConnell
OFFSHORE RENEWABLE ENERGY CATAPULT
 Inovo, 4th Floor, 121 George Street, G1 1RD
 Suzanne Margaret Hoggan
OFGEM
 Commonwealth House, 3rd Floor, 32 Albion
 Street, G1 1LH
 Tel: (0141) 354 5425
 Samantha Claire Blaikie
 Louise Marion Comiskey
 Mark John Michael Conroy
 Evan Crainie
 Ailie Elizabeth Crawford
 Carolyn Louise Dewar
 Colette Rose Heaney
 Sian Jefferies
 Andrew Daniel Jones
 Sarah Elizabeth Livingstone
 Adam Matthew McCabe

Joanne McDowall
Michelle Antoinette Graham McGowan
Martin McGuinness
James Alexander McRorie
Fiona Jane Parker
Kenzie Anne Sharkey
Hayley Stewart
Gunga Thapa-Magar
Fiona Marion Wright
PENINSULA BUSINESS SERVICES LIMITED
 Floor 4, 180 West George Street, G2 2NR
 William John McAllister Lane
POLICE SCOTLAND
 Clydegateway, 2 French Street, Dalmarnock,
 G40 4EH
 Martin Campbell Black
 Stuart John Hamilton
PORTKNOCKIE WHISKY
 23d Netherton Road, Anniesland Business
 Park, G13 1EU
 Depak Bali
PROCURATOR FISCAL SERVICE
 10 Ballater Street, G5 9PS
 Tel: (0300) 0203000
 Fax: (0844) 5614069
 DX: 501557 GLAS SALTMARKET
 Gail Cameron Adair
 Lucy Adams
 Elizabeth Ann Aitken
 Mhairi Jessica Alexander
 Amanda Louise Allan
 Mark Robert Allan
 Emma Jane Anderson
 Clare Arias
 Emma Louise Baker
 Eileen Lamont Beadsworth
 John Bedford
 Katie Margaret Bell
 Stewart John Bell
 Emma Louise Berry
 Stephanie Elizabeth Blair
 Thomas Colin Francis Bowman
 Laura Bradley
 Gillian Elizabeth Bradshaw
 Mhairi Catriona Brand
 Michelle Margaret Brannagan
 Selena Campbell Brown
 Susan Margaret Brown
 Derek John Buchanan
 Patricia Mary Callender
 Deborah Ann Carroll
 Lesley Allan Chambers
 Henna Noor Chaudry
 Julie Clark
 Ruth Lindsay Cockburn
 Annmaria Colquhoun
 Pamela-Jane Connelly
 Monique Cooney
 Henry Kevin Corrins
 Angus Crawford
 David Andrew Crawford
 Siobh n Connor Currie
 Kyle Greg Dalziel

▶ *Glasgow continued*

Deborah Rose O'Brien Demick
Aline Devaney
Tiziana Angela Maria Di Emidio
Barry Dickson
Scot James McLeod Dignan
Nicola Dodds
Kevin Doherty
Seana Doherty
Aimee Julia Doran
William Hugh Duffy
Patricia Jane Duke
Margaret Shona Dunipace
Fiona Louise Dunn
Hazel Emmerson
Karen Lesley Stuart Evans
Christopher William Farrell
Stuart John Faure
Ruaraidh Ferguson
Henry Douglas Wyllie Findlay
Lorraine Joanne Florence
Emma Elizabeth Forbes
Jennifer Forbes
Suzanne Fotheringham
Amanda Jane Gallacher
Jennifer Helen Gilmour
David Stuart Austin Green
Julie Dawn Hamilton
Jennifer Mary Harkins
Lorna Sarah Bridget Harris
Victoria Margaret Hart
Michele Harvey
Natalie Henderson
Jane Anderson Russell Hilditch
Richard Alexander Hill
Fiona Mairi Holligan
Amy Anne Hunter
Zahrah Iqbal
Elaine Love Jackson
Syeda Masooma Zainab Jaffri
Catriona Esther Jagla
Paul Alexander Jamieson
Claire Anne Johnston
Keith Eyton Gwyn Jones
Laura Mary Mathieson Knox
Zahra Marie Latif
Yolande Claire Love
Maura Anne Lynch
Cheryl Lyons
Clare Frances Macaulay
Adele Phyllis MacDonald
Graham Robert Macdonald
Lauren Anne MacDonald
Stephanie Alison MacDonald
Carrie MacFarlane
Lindsay Jean Catherine G Madden
Soraya Anne Malik
Isobel Martin
Jennifer Martinez Sillars
Alan Campbell Watt McArthur
Margaret McCallum
Marie Elizabeth McCue

Claire Ceri McEvinney
Jessica Catherine McGowan
Liam Gerald McGuigan
Jennifer Claire McKee
Alison Louisa McKenna
Graham Alexander McLachlan
Bernadette Anne McLaughlan
Charles Stewart McLean
Stuart McMillan
Lauren McRobert
Ian David Meacock
Fiona Jane Millar
Sarah Kathryn Mobsby
Alison Maria Montgomery
Jennifer Louise Morris
Flora Elizabeth Napier
Gillian Murphy Nisbet
Kathleen Anne O'Donnell
Jeremy George O'Neill
Moira Orr
Pauline Barbara Palmer
Katrina Anne Parkes
Nicola Kristina Patrick
Steven Robert Quither
Lauren Ram Sangray
Siobhan Louise Ramage
Elizabeth Lydia Ramsay
Shazia Rashid
Jennifer Kirsty Reid
Peter Michael Reid
Emma Jane Ritchie
John Paul Robertson
Ruth Ann Ross-Davie
Kavin Ryan-Hume
Cassandra Merete Scott
Elainne Lea Sibbald
Sathpal Singh
Kay Slater
John Anthony Slowey
Jacqueline Brown Hamilton Spiers
Lauren Alison Staunton
Carrie Lorraine Stevens
Hannah Ellen Sweeney
Hannah Ruth Terrance
Jacob Anthony Tomnay
Kirsty Nicola Urquhart
Claire Richmond Wallace
Wendy Wilson

PROCURATOR FISCAL SERVICE
National Forensic Gateway, Scottish Crime
Campus, Craignethan Drive, Gartcosh,
G69 8AE
Tel: (0300) 020 3000
Susan Anne Campbell
Victoria Ferguson
Sobia Hanif-Kidd
Johanne Webb

PROCURATOR FISCAL SERVICE
Scottish Prosecution College, Legal House,
101 Gorbals Street, G5 9DW
Lindsay Christina Costa
Karina Marie Duffy
Anne Marie Hicks

Jamie Paul Lipton
Anthony Martin McGeehan
Alan James Parfery
Moira Price
PROCURATOR FISCAL SERVICE
High Court West, 1 Mart Street, G1 5JT
Tel: (0300) 020 2944
Eileen Gallacher
Meghan Anne Glancey
Alan John Robert MacDonald
Emily Gail Couperthwaite Macreath
Katherine Jean McColl
Andrew John Richardson
PUBLIC DEFENCE SOLICITORS OFFICE
120-124 Saltmarket, G1 5LB
Tel: (0141) 5530794
Paul Anthony Anderson
Marco Carlo Buonaccorsi
Greg James Cunningham
Pauline Ann Mackenzie
Claire Annie McCarron
Neil Conrad Stewart
RBS AND NATWEST MENTOR
4th Floor, 110 Queen Street, G1 3BX
Tel: (0141) 227 4590
Alan Douglas Philp
Joanne Price
RENEWABLE ENERGY SYSTEMS LIMITED
Third Floor, STV, Pacific Quay, G51 1PQ
Tel: (0141) 4045591
Fax: (0141) 4045501
James Andrew Beck
Laura Margaret Blyth
Milena Kate Chetty
Andrew Stewart Fairlie
Donna Louise McFarlane
RENEWABLES UNLIMITED LLP
231 St Vincent Street, G2 5QY
Tel: (0141) 221 0276
David Robert Bowman
RTRP LIMITED
The Hub, Pacific Drive, Pacific Quay, G51 1EA
Tel: (0141) 4275880
Sarah Elizabeth Landale Lithgow
SCOTSMAN HOLDINGS PLC
Hamilton House, 70 Hamilton Drive, G12 8DR
Tel: (0141) 581 2416
David Wilson Syme
SCOTTISH CANALS
Canal House, Applecross Street, G4 9SP
Tel: (07795) 027348
Nicola Jane Christie
SCOTTISH CHILDREN'S REPORTER
ADMINISTRATION
Merchant Exchange, 10/20 Bell Street,
G1 1LG
Tel: (0300) 2001444
Fax: (0141) 5677969
Collette Gallagher
Grace Lennox
Hazel Patricia Mary McFadzean

SCOTTISH COURTS AND TRIBUNALS SERVICE
JP Legal Advisers Office For Glasgow, and
Strathkelvin, Room 2:18, 1 Carton Place,
G5 9DA
Tel: (0141) 4298888
Fax: (0141) 5488981
Rosemary Jane McLeary
Howard John Charles Rattray
SCOTTISH CRIMINAL CASES REVIEW
COMMISSION
Portland House, 17 Renfield Street, G2 5AH
Tel: (0141) 2707030
Mairi-Claire Anderson
Daniel Colin Fenn
David James Fitzpatrick
Stephen Christopher Lynn
Michael Walker
SCOTTISH ENGINEERING
105 West George Street, G2 1QL
Tel: (0141) 2213181
Kevin John Duffy
Lindsey Mary Miller
Andrew John Ross Munro
SCOTTISH ENTERPRISE
Atrium Court, 50 Waterloo Street, G2 6HQ
Tel: (0141) 2482700
Fax: (0141) 2282045
Jann Henderson Cameron
Marianne Fiona H l ne Charrier
Stuart Andrew Clarke
Catherine Mary Corr
Heather Dillon
Caitlin Ann Douglas
Jacqueline Edwards
Gail Fulton
Michelle Howell
Sarah Lucy Hume
James McRoberts
Katie O'Hara
Susannah Caroline Pencovich
Katherine Chantal Tatham Temple
Claire Sarah Thompson
Christina Jane Thorne
SCOTTISH EQUITY PARTNERS LLP
17 Blythswood Square, G2 4AD
Tel: (0141) 2734000
Fax: (0141) 2734001
Margaret Shannon Birch
Andrew John Buchan
SCOTTISH GOVERNMENT
Legal Directorate, Buchanan House, MP 13,
Port Dundas Road, G4 0HF
Tel: (0141) 2727933
Heather Elizabeth Cameron Auld
Deborah Marie Blair
Dorothy Zedzani Cohen
Joan Catherine McHutchison
Alexander Ross McNeil
SCOTTISH GOVERNMENT
Transport Scotland, Legal Directorate,
Buchanan House – MP 13, Port Dundas Road,
G4 0HF
Tel: (0141) 2727233

▶ *Glasgow continued*

Anne Frances Cairns
Susan Conroy
Anna Wiktoria Grace
Alison Kelly Martin
Jennifer Ann Spy

SCOTTISH GOVERNMENT
Advanced Learning & Science Directorate,
Higher Education & Science Division, 5
Atlantic Quay, G2 8LU
Tel: (0131) 244 0815
Fax: (0131) 2447417
Shazia Saiqa Razzaq

SCOTTISH HOSPITAL INQUIRY
PO Box 27126, G2 9NB
Judith Aileen Alcock
Lesley Ann Browne
Mawulorm Jesse Kormi Hevor
James George Logie
Mairi Claire MacNeil
John David McPhail
Kim Tamar Milligan
Umera Rashid
Samantha Mone Har Rore

SCOTTISH POLICE AUTHORITY
1 Pacific Quay, G51 1DZ
Tel: (0141) 585 8300
Robin Johnston
Eric Leggat
Susan Catherine Montgomery

SCOTTISH POLICE AUTHORITY, POLICE
SCOTLAND
Legal Services Department, Clyde Gateway, 2
French Street, G40 4EH
Tel: (01786) 895727
Fax: (01786) 895599
DX: 51200 Glasgow
Zoe Carroll Calderwood
Duncan Campbell
Helen Elizabeth Carmichael
Melanie Claire Carmichael
Johanna Helen Brechin Crowther
James Anthony Douglas
Aileen Jane Irvine
Louisa Helen Lyon
Blair Forbes Macdonald
Helen Marie Martin
Jennifer Martin
Darina Anne McAlpine
Andrew Joseph McGlone
Elizabeth Margaret McLaughlin
Tammy Alexandra McLaughlin
Elizabeth Millar
Kirsti Laura Nelson
Claire Pender
Suzanne Jane Rosenshine
Rhona Henderson Stannage

SCOTTISH POWER LIMITED
Legal Team, 320 St Vincent Street, G2 5AD
Tel: (0141) 6140000
Angus Stuart Armstrong
Andrew David Paterson Black

Helen Elizabeth Callaghan
Fiona Julie Coyle
David Lindsay Cunningham
Michael Howard Davies
Rebecca Fairley
Scott Charles Faulkiner
Lowri Clare Martin
Rachael Margaret McCready
Adam Gregor McLay
Alistair Charles Orr
Laura Pacevitch
Marc Peebles
Andrew David Pyka Philip
John Francis Reid
Marion Shepherd Venman
Anna Walker
Roddy Chun Pui Wan

SEARCH CONSULTANCY LIMITED
5th Floor, Atrium Court, 50 Waterloo Street,
G2 6HQ
Tel: (0141) 2273490
Rachel Mary Black

SERCO UK, EUROPE & SGS
3rd Floor, Tara House, 46 Bath Street, G2 1HJ
Marie Clare Gair

SKILLS DEVELOPMENT SCOTLAND
Monteith House, 11 George Square, G2 1DY
Tel: (0300) 013 2120
Louise Singleton
Aimee Watson

SMART METERING SYSTEMS PLC
2nd Floor, 48 St. Vincent Street, G2 5TS
Tel: (0141) 2493909
Lindsay Margaret Grace McCormick
Gemma Louise McDonald
Craig Alan McGinn
Lauren Jayne McLeod

SP TRANSMISSION PLC
Floor 6, ScottishPower House, 320 St. Vincent
Street, G2 5AD
Tel: (07753) 622106
Gareth David Hislop

SPORTSCOTLAND
Doges, Templeton On the Green, 62
Templeton Street, G40 1DA
Tel: (0141) 5346500
Fax: (0141) 5346501
Jennifer Jane Edmonstone
April Law-Reed

SSE PLC
1 Waterloo Street, G2 6AY
Tel: (0141) 224 7248
Jamila Ruby Louise Archibald
Michelle Baird
Ronan Sean Beale
Lesa Burns
Susan Donnachie
Paul Dynan
Lynsey Sheilagh Gilchrist
Kirsty Haxby
Kirsty Sarah Inglis
Shehzad Khalid
Stephen Anthony Maughan

Suzanne Ruth May
Katie McKenna
Emma Louise Moir
Paul Joseph Murphy
Suzanne Murphy
Jennifer Sylvia Pike
Joanne Rachel Smith
Pamela Joan Till
Dylan James Webster
Emma Marie Wills
STERLING & STERLING LLC
  Sentinel, 103 Waterloo Street, G2 7BW
  Diane Dunlop
STRATHCLYDE PARTNERSHIP FOR TRANSPORT
  131 St Vincent Street, G2 5JF
  Tel: (0141) 333 3789
  Fax: (0141) 3323076
  James Joseph Griffin
  Maegan Frances Nelson
STUDENT LOANS COMPANY LIMITED
  100 Bothwell Street, G2 7JD
  Tel: (0141) 306 2000
  Steven James Alexander Kennedy
  Shona Morag Mackay
  Andrew Adam Pattie
  Gary Stuart Womersley
STV GROUP PLC
  Pacific Quay, G51 1PQ
  Tel: (0141) 3003300
  Ross Duncan Cowan
  Jonathan Louden Tait
STV TELEVISION LIMITED
  Pacific Quay, G51 1PQ
  Tel: (0141) 3003000
  Helen Arnot
  Joan Burns Darroch
  Michael Joseph Ferrie
  Anargyros Kemerlis
  Morna Jane Macarthur
  Gemma Daniella McWatt
TEEKAY SHIPPING (GLASGOW) LIMITED
  144 Elliot Street, G3 8EX
  Tel: (0141) 222 9019
  Jennifer Helen Nicol
TERUMO AORTIC
  Newmains Ave, Inchinnan, PA4 9RR
  Lauren Louise Howe
THE EDRINGTON GROUP LIMITED
  100 Queen Street, G1 3DN
  Tel: (0141) 9404000
  Gemma May Robson
  Nicola Jane Aitchison
  Ashleigh Kay Clark
  Nicholas John McManus
  Gavin James Murray
THE MEDICAL & DENTAL DEFENCE UNION OF
  SCOTLAND
  206 St Vincent Street, G2 5SG
  Tel: (0141) 228 1228
  Fax: (0141) 2281208
  Carolyn Guild Beattie
  Joanna Frances Jervis
  Lindsey Murray McGregor

Mark Nicholas O'Reilly
Denise Kathryn Ritchie
Jane Scott
THE SCOTTISH FOOTBALL ASSOCIATION
  Hampden Park, G42 9AY
  Tel: (0141) 6166000
  Gary Alexander Booth
  Gareth David Hall
  Andrew David Phillips
THE SCOTTISH PROFESSIONAL FOOTBALL
  LEAGUE LIMITED
  Hampden Park, G42 9DE
  Tel: (07831) 859580
  Roderick Cheyne McKenzie
THE WEIR GROUP PLC
  1 West Regent Street, G2 1RW
  Claire Margaret Adams
  Jennifer Lynne Adams
  Laura Louise Howarth
  Kathryn Margaret Reid
  Graham William Corbett Vanhegan
TRANSPORT SCOTLAND
  Buchanan House, 58 Port Dundas Road,
  G4 0HF
  Tel: (0141) 2727538
  Frances Pacitti
TWO RIVERS MEDIA LTD
  1st Floor, Tontine Building, 20 Trongate,
  G1 5ES
  Murray John Buchanan
UNISON SCOTLAND
  14 West Campbell Street, G2 6RX
  Karen Louise Osborne
UNIVERSITY OF GLASGOW
  Research Support Office, Room 241, Isabella
  Elder Building, University Avenue, G12 8QQ
  Tel: (0141) 330 7725
  Louise Jane Andrew
  Claire Munro
  Alistair Wilson
UNIVERSITY OF STRATHCLYDE
  Research & Knowledge Exchange Services, 50
  George Street, G1 1QE
  Tel: (0141) 5485905
  Fax: (0141) 552 4409
  Gavin Stewart Grant
  Andrew William MacKenzie
  David Peter Robertson Reid
  Jill Gwendoline Scott
UNIVERSITY OF STRATHCLYDE LAW CLINIC
  Graham Hills Building Room 581, 40 George
  Street, G1 1QE
  Gillian Carol Melville
VINTAGE MALT WHISKY COMPANY LIMITED
  Vintage House, 21 Park Road, Milngavie,
  G62 6PJ
  Tel: (0141) 955 1700
  Fax: (0141) 955 1701
  Caroline Sanderson James
VODAFONE GROUP ENTERPRISE LIMITED
  1-2 Berkeley Square, 99 Berkeley Street,
  G3 7HR
  Tel: (0141) 3032141

▶ *Glasgow continued*

Martine Mary Burns
WHEATLEY HOUSING GROUP LIMITED
Wheatley House, 25 Cochrane Street, G1 1HL
Tel: (0845) 9001001
David Adams
Emma Grace Cameron
Heather Marion Margaret Clinton
Kathryn Faith
Katherine Sarah Graham
Michael James Kitson
Anne Mackenzie
Eilidh Louise Mowat
Roy Craig Provan
Jennifer Agnes Sharp
Gayle Louise Blaikie Turner
Jane Valentine
Stephen Stewart Wright
WHYTE & MACKAY LTD
4th Floor, St Vincent Plaza, 319 St Vincent
Street, G2 5RG
Lucy Mary McCarron
Caitlin Ann McNeish
WINDHOIST LIMITED
4th Floor, 120 Bath Street, G2 2EN
Lauren Margaret Bertram Boyle

Glenrothes
FIFE COUNCIL
Finance and Corporate Services, Fife House,
North Street, KY7 5LT
Tel: (03451) 550000
Fax: (01592) 583155
DX: 561500 GLENROTHES 3
June Anne Barrie
Lynda Anne Batchelor
Philip Robert Blair
Christopher William Glendinning
Alison Elizabeth Higgins
Rebecca Louise Jeynes
Kimberley Patricia Langley
Neil Iain Macdonald
Alison Clare Marr
William McDonald
Margaret Josephine Bannon McFadden
Kerry McLaren
Mary Elizabeth Ritchie McLean
Steven John Paterson
Ewen Graham Robertson
Sheila Rodger
Fiona Mary Stuart
Lindsay Margaret Thomson
FIFE COUNCIL
Rothesay House, Rothesay Place, KY7 5PQ
Tel: (03451) 550000
Sarah Louise Goldberg
RAYTHEON SYSTEMS LIMITED
Queensway Industrial Estate, KY7 5PY
Tel: (01592) 754311
Fax: (01592) 759775
Dylan Page Lynch
John Alan Reilly

SCOTTISH CHILDREN'S REPORTER
ADMINISTRATION
Albany House, 3 North Street, KY7 5NA
Tel: (01592) 583314
Pamela Lesley Dobson

Grangemouth
CALACHEM LIMITED
Earls Road, FK3 8XG
Tel: (01324) 498300
Carol van Beusekom

Greenock
FORSA ENERGY GAS HOLDINGS LIMITED
Clyde View (Suite F3), Riverside Business Park,
22 Pottery Street, PA15 2UZ
Tel: (01475) 749950
William Edward Henry Dunsmure
INVERCLYDE COUNCIL
Municipal Buildings, Clyde Square, PA15 1LX
Tel: (01475) 717171
Jonathan Philip Hamilton
Martin Francis Hughes
David Douglas Keenan
James Kerr
Peter John MacDonald
Siobhan MacMaster
Denese O'Donnell
Emma Peacock
Victoria Mary Pollock
Anne Margaret Sinclair
Grant Kyle Walker
PROCURATOR FISCAL SERVICE
Procurator Fiscal's Office, 1 Nelson Street,
PA15 1TR
Tel: (07752) 182 465
Hugh Anthony Brady
Pamela Brady
John Houston Penman
Lindy-Rose Scaife
RIVER CLYDE HOMES
Clyde View, 22 Pottery Street, PA15 2UZ
Tel: (01475) 788887
Marie Josephine Canning

Haddington
EAST LOTHIAN COUNCIL
John Muir House, Brewery Park, EH41 3HA
Tel: (01620) 827827
Fax: (01620) 827888
Donald Malcolm Campbell
Keren Louise Conway
Morag Ferguson
Ian Alexander Forrest
Carlo Domenico Grilli
Fariha Haque
Jacqueline Holland
Marielle Elizabeth Hunter
Catherine Mary Molloy
Louise Shearer

Hamilton

MENTAL HEALTH TRIBUNAL FOR SCOTLAND
Hamilton House, Second Floor, Hamilton Bus.
Park, Caird Park, ML3 0QA
Jennifer Pyott Whyte

PARK'S OF HAMILTON (HOLDINGS) LIMITED
Park House, 14 Bothwell Road, ML3 0AY
Craig Scott McKendrick

POLICE INVESTIGATIONS AND REVIEW
COMMISSIONER
2nd Floor, Hamilton House, Hamilton Business
Park, ML3 0QA
Tel: (01698) 542900
Michelle Robertson MacLeod
Ilya Zharov

PROCURATOR FISCAL SERVICE
Cameronian House, 3/5 Almada Street,
ML3 0HG
Tel: (0844) 5613245
Fax: (01698) 285425
DX: HA7 HAMILTON
Laura Ellen Anderson
Imran Raza Bashir
Hansa Elizabeth Brown
Leslie Armour Brown
Denise Josephine Bruce
Julie Louvain Cameron
Fiona Anne Carnan
Stuart Joseph Cassidy
John Patrick Coogan
Cecilia De Groote
Brendan Joseph Gerald Devanney
Gary Peter Dow
Alistair David Duncan
Barry Malcolm Dunne
Justin Edward Farrell
Pamela Jane Flynn
Callum Joseph Chambers Forsyth
Fraser Alexander Wright Gibson
Robert Andrew Gibson
David Christopher Glancy
Jenna Grattan
Angela Jane Gray
Jennifer Guy
Toni Hicks
Lisa Ramsay Hilton
Lynne Margaret Jamieson
Vishnu Govinda Kathuria
Scott Francis King
Fiona Anne Kirkby
Liza Claire Lann
Michael Ross Macintosh
Jennifer Ann McCabe
Linda McCaffer
Helen Sharp McCannell
Helen Margaret McFauld
Jennifer Louise McLaren
Morag Miller McLintock
Mairi-Clare McMillan
Ruth Elizabeth McQuaid
Rachael Meechan
Andrew Kerr Neilson
Scott David O'Connor

Chloe Jessica O'Hara
Julie O'Hara
Myrto Paton
Paula Louise Russell
Mohammed Hamza Sarwar
Rebecca Scully
Abby Claire Seal
Jacqueline Mary Smyth
Margaret Anne Stewart
Neil Purves Thomson

SCOTTISH CHILDREN'S REPORTER
ADMINISTRATION
Hamilton House, Hamilton Bus. Park, Caird
Park, ML3 0QA
Tel: (0131) 2448676
Melissa Sophia Christodoulou
Irzum Mahmood
Kate Smith

SCOTTISH FIRE AND RESCUE SERVICE
West Service Delivery Area HQ, 99 Bothwell
Road, ML3 0EA
Tel: (0141) 646 4699
Amanda Jane Black
Lucia Bobkova
Sharon Louise Clelland
James George Herd
Asha Surendra Narsapur

SOUTH LANARKSHIRERE COUNCIL
Administration and Legal Services, Floor 11,
Council Headquarters, Almada Street,
ML3 0AA
Michael John Barrett
Monica Eleanor Cannon
Alan Bryce Cox
Kevin John McInnes Goldie
Gillian Gray
Harry David Horsburgh
Marie Clare Lunny
Donald Patrick McLardy
Graham Stewart Murray
Sean Adam O'Neill
Jennifer Elizabeth Margaret Wallace

SOUTH LANARKSHIRERE COUNCIL
Legal Services, 11th Floor, Council Offices,
Almada Street, ML3 0AA
Tel: (01698) 454785
DX: 579641 HAMILTON 3
Susan Christie
Daryle Anne Dickson
William Alexander Dunn
Gerard Charles Mays
Elaine Alexandria Paton
Claire Margaret Rogers
Maria Therese Sharkey
Gordon John Stewart
Avril Elaine Watkins
Nicola Jane Weir
Margaret Mary Wilson

SOUTH LANARKSHIRERE COUNCIL
Floor 2, Council Offices, Almada Street,
ML3 0AA
Tel: (01698) 454658
Mary Geraldine McCann

Holytown

ENABLE GROUP
INSPIRE House, 3 Renshaw Place, Eurocentral,
ML1 4UF
Tel: (01698) 737027
Fax: (0844) 8549748
Mhairi Frances Maguire
SCOTTISH ENVIRONMENT PROTECTION
AGENCY
Angus Smith Building, 6 Parklands Avenue,
Eurocentral, ML1 4WQ
Tel: (01698) 839 000
Fax: (01698) 738 155
Josephine Vance Armstrong
Susan Catriona Cochrane
Alix Jacqueline Donaldson
Gillian Kathryn Higgins
Betheney Anne Ross
Susan Margaret Watson

Huntly

DUNCAN TAYLOR SCOTCH WHISKEY
King Street, AB54 8HP
Carol Jane Crowther

Inverness

CITIZENS ADVICE BUREAU
29-31 Union Street, IV1 1QA
Matthew Whillans
CIVIL LEGAL ASSISTANCE OFFICE
2 Castle Wynd, IV2 3EB
Tel: (01463) 641770
Rhea Frame
Angela Kathleen Graham
Simon Christopher Leigh
Ashley Martin
CROFTING COMMISSION
Great Glen House, Leachkin Road, IV3 8NW
Tel: (0143) 663 430
Fax: (01463) 725 067
David Findlay
HIGHLAND COUNCIL
Dept. of Corporate Governance, Council
Bldgs,Glenurquhart Rd, IV3 5NX
Tel: (01463) 702000
Fax: (01463) 254 915
Nicola Bain
Rhoda Nyaaba Banfro
Theresa Alison Batchelor
Jane Elizabeth Davey
Anne Fearon David
Sarah Lucia Duncan
Stewart David Fraser
Tessa Iona Arbuthnot Gall
Emma Anne Linn
Fiona Janine Malcolm
Amy Rebecca Noble
Alison Mary Scullion
Kirsty Jane Shaw
Nicola Edna Underdown

HIGHLAND COUNCIL
Town House, IV1 1JJ
Tel: (01463) 785018
David Milton Haas
HIGHLAND COUNCIL
Chief Executive's Dept, Council Bldgs,
Glenurquhart Rd, IV3 5NX
Tel: (01463) 702000
DX: IN5 INVERNESS
Karen Lyons
Jonathan Paul Harper Nevin
Calum Morrison Ross
HIGHLANDS & ISLANDS ENTERPRISE
An L chran, 10 Inverness Campus, IV2 5NA
Tel: (01463) 383010
Alison Patricia Lyner
Keir William Marshall
HIGHLANDS AND ISLANDS AIRPORTS LIMITED
Head Office, Inverness Airport, IV2 7JB
Tel: (07967) 468025
Jennifer Anne Marshall
PROCURATOR FISCAL SERVICE
Procurator Fiscal's Office, The Inverness Justice
Centre, Longman Road, IV1 1AH
Tel: (0844) 5612926
DX: IN26 INVERNESS
Karen Elizabeth Aitken
Laura Arthur
Naomi Frances Duffy-Welsh
Martina Gertrud Henrietta Eastwood
Pauline Ann Gair
Alasdair Iain Gray
Susan Thomson Love
Niall William Macdonald
Geoffrey Main
Michelle Margaret Molley
David Michael Morton
Fiona Elizabeth Murray
Karen Margaret Poke
Sharon Marie Ralph
Alexandra Eva Swain
Stella Theresa Swan
Roderick Williamson Urquhart
Robert Gray Weir
Alison Elizabeth Young
PUBLIC DEFENCE SOLICITORS OFFICE
17 Queensgate, IV1 1DF
Tel: (01463) 709680
Fax: (01463) 709682
Emma Rachel MacEwan
Laura-Jane McFarlane
Patrick William O'Dea
RUCOFIKE LIMITED
24 Broadstone Park, IV2 3LA
Euan James Donaldson

Inverurie

ABERDEENSHIRE COUNCIL
Legal & Governance, Gordon House, Blackhall
Road, AB51 3WA
Tel: (01467) 539903
Fax: (01467) 623329

Jill Maria Joss
Suzanne Victoria Ward

Irvine

NORTH AYRSHIRE COUNCIL
Corporate Services, Cunninghame House,
KA12 8EE
Tel: (01294) 310000
DX: IR11 IRVINE
Rosemary Conner
Jennifer Claire Coyne
Aileen Mary Craig
David Robert Grier
Lauren Marie Ingram
Claire Bernadette Kierney
Jean Hamilton Law
David McDowall
Kris Reid McDowall
Jennifer Linda Niven
William Henry O'Brien
Madeleine Jane Pender
Nicola Carson Shearer
Linda Joyce Taylor
Carolyn Anne Wallace
Ruth Mary Wilson

Kilmarnock

EAST AYRSHIRE COUNCIL
Council Headquarters, London Road, KA3 7BU
Tel: (01563) 576161
Fax: (01563) 576179
DX: KK23 KILMARNOCK
Gordon James Anderson
Richard Alasdair Crawford
Rosemary Dornan Duffy
Avril Agnes Elizabeth Forrest
Claire Linda Gregory
Stuart McCall
Tamara Elizabeth Mae McQuade
David John Mitchell
Michelle Audrey Mooney
Julie Anne Nicholson
Donna Ann Phelps
Sarah Leanne Thomson
Alexander Craig Young
PRA GROUP (UK) LIMITED
58 Portland Street, KA1 1JG
Tel: (07912) 467322
DX: KK2 KILMARNOCK
Catriona Sarah Borthwick
Julie Brown
PROCURATOR FISCAL SERVICE
Procurator Fiscal's Office, St. Marnock Street,
KA1 1DZ
Tel: (01563) 536211
DX: KK17 KILMARNOCK
Fraser Miller Alexander
Georgia Emma Baker
Lindzi Marion Bayne
Joanne Rachel Cunningham
Blaire Ford
Andrew Lazzarin

Mhairi Mair
Peter Duncan McClelland
Victoria McMillan
Peter Stewart William Moyes
Edwin John Sheeran
Scott Roderick Toal
Craig David Wainwright
Catherine Ann White
SCOTTISH CHILDREN'S REPORTER
ADMINISTRATION
21 West Langlands Street, (Ground Floor),
KA1 2PY
Tel: (01563) 534176
Joyce Elizabeth McCallum
SCOTTISH COURTS AND TRIBUNALS SERVICE
Kilmarnock Sheriff Court, St Marnock Street,
KA1 1ED
Angus Livingstone
Kevin Walsh

Kirkcaldy

PROCURATOR FISCAL SERVICE
Wing D, Carlyle House, Carlyle Road, KY1 1DB
Tel: (0300) 0203000
DX: Y18 KIRKCALDY
Louise Graham
Beverley Jane Adam
Claire Bremner
Fiona Margaret Eadie
Lee-Anne Moira Margaret Hannan
Ronald Andrew Hay
Jamie Vincent Hilland
Laurelle Johnstone
Laura Rose McManus
Claire Elise Millar
Isma Tahira Choudhry Mukhtar
Joanne Taylor Smith
SCOTTISH COURTS AND TRIBUNALS SERVICE
Sheriff Court House, Whytescauseway,
KY1 1XQ
Hilary Jane Stephen

Kirkintilloch

EAST DUNBARTONSHIRE COUNCIL
12 Strathkelvin Place, G66 1TJ
Tel: (0141) 5788000
DX: 500832 KIRKINTILLOCH
Thomas Bissett
Lynsey Clare Brown
Eve Marion Campbell
Mhairi Casey
Karen Marie Donnelly
Roslyn MacDonald
Eilidh MacQuarrie
Caroline Magowan
Jennifer McGrath
Andrew Kenneth McLaughlin
George McLaughlin
Cecilia Miller
Ann Marie Minty
Jane Mai O'Connell
Justine Jennifer Porter

▶ *Kirkintilloch continued*

Craig William Smith
Andrew Patrick Kearns Walker

Kirkwall

ORKNEY ISLANDS COUNCIL
Legal Services, Council Offices, School Place,
KW15 1NY
Tel: (01856) 873535
Fax: (01856) 871604
Karen Frankish Bevilacqua
Emma Louise Findlay
Georgette Herd
Paul Dominic Maxton
Katharine Elizabeth Seymour McKerrell
Gavin Rattray Mitchell
Michael Sydney William Scott
Peter Francis Trodden
Sheila Mary Tulloch
PROCURATOR FISCAL SERVICE
Procurator Fiscal's Office, Sheriff Court House,
Watergate, KW15 1PD
Tel: (0300) 020 2669
Fax: (0300) 020 2672
Susan Jane Campbell Foard
PUBLIC DEFENCE SOLICITORS OFFICE
Room 7, Scottish Government Building,
Tankerness Lane, KW15 1AQ
Tel: (01856) 870100
Cheryl Beattie

Lanark

MUIRHALL ENERGY LIMITED
Muirhall Farm, Auchengray, Carnwath,
ML11 8LL
Tel: (01501) 785604
Saroash Inam
Sarah Louise McIntosh
Derek Morrow

Larbert

ALEXANDER DENNIS LIMITED
9 Central Boulevard, Central Park, FK5 4RU
Tel: (01324) 614 720
Man Yi Cheung
Julie Thomson
SPRINGFIELD PROPERTIES PLC
Springfield House, 3 Central Park Avenue,
FK5 4RX
Tel: (01324) 555 536
Andrew Ross Todd

Largs

THE ERINBEG CONSULTANCY LLP
17 Rankin Drive, KA30 9DA
Gordon Lindsay Cunningham

Lasswade

DOBBIES GARDEN CENTRES
Melville Nurseries, EH18 1AZ
Debbie Mary Harding
Laura Naysmith Milligan

Lerwick

PROCURATOR FISCAL SERVICE
Procurator Fiscal's Office, Sheriff Court House,
ZE1 0HD
Tel: (01595) 692808
Duncan Stewart Mackenzie
SHETLAND ISLANDS COUNCIL
Governance & Law, Office Headquarters, 8
North Ness Business Park, ZE1 0LZ
Tel: (01595) 744550
Fax: (01595) 744585
David Keith Adam
Joanna Margaret Belford
Michael James Hodgson
Kristen Jane Johnston
Charlotte Stephen McAuley Jones
Caroline Margaret Laing
Jan-Robert Riise
Karen Emily Simmons
Paul John Sutherland
Paul Edward Ferguson Wishart

Livingston

IQVIA LTD
The Alba Campus, Rosebank, EH54 7EG
Tel: (01506) 814 622
Jesse Arthur Turner
PROCURATOR FISCAL SERVICE
Procurator Fiscal's Office, West Lothian Civic
Centre, Howden South Road, EH54 6FF
Tel: (0300) 020 3696
DX: 552061 LIVINGSTON 7
Louise Alma Alexander
Jack Stanley Caster
Katherine Louise Irwin
Roshni Nilesh Joshi
Fraser Murdo Matheson
Connor Ben Ronald Muir
Jane Charlotte Rennie
SCOTTISH CHILDREN'S REPORTER
ADMINISTRATION
West Lothian Civic Centre, Howden South
Road, EH54 6FF
Kirstin Elizabeth Hudson
W L GORE & ASSOCIATES
Simpson Parkway, Kirkton Campus, EH54 7BH
Tel: (01506) 678027
Fax: (01506) 420004
Linda Sneddon
WEST LOTHIAN COUNCIL
Corporate/ Support / Legal Services, West
Lothian Civic Centre, Howden South Road,
EH54 6FF
Tel: (01506) 280000
DX: 552060 LIVINGSTON 7
Eleanor Ann Campbell

Jessica Sen Tin Chan
Catherine Margaret Crowe
Eileen Cameron Grant
Nicola Marianne Hogg
Carol Grant Johnston
Sarah-Jane Kissock
Gary James McMullan
James David Millar
Lesley Mary Montague
Kerri Ann Murphy
Wendy Margaret Richardson
Audrey Frances Watson

Lochgilphead
ARGYLL & BUTE COUNCIL
   Legal and Regulatory Support, Kilmory,
   PA31 8RT
   Tel: (01546) 604164
   Fax: (01546) 604164
   Gordon Paul Dagleish
   Iain Alexander Jackson
   Emma Christina Ledsom
   David McDiarmid Logan
   Moira Catherine Logan
   Sheila Margaret MacFadyen
   Susan Catherine Mair
   Graeme James McMillan
   Annette Christiona Weaver
ARGYLL & BUTE COUNCIL
   Customer Services, Kilmory, PA31 8RT
   Tel: (01546) 604194
   DX: 599700 LOCHGILPHEAD
   Douglas MacNicol Hendry
   Anne Elizabeth MacColl-Smith
ARGYLL & BUTE COUNCIL
   DemocraticSrvs&Governance Dept, Kilmory,
   PA31 8RT
   Fiona Theresa Campbell MacDonald
ARGYLL & BUTE COUNCIL
   Procurement & Contract Management,
   Kilmory, PA31 8RT
   Tel: (01546) 604 468
   Michael John Nicol

Motherwell
APLEONA HSG LTD
   6 Crosshill Street, ML1 1RU
   Caroline Heeney
BALFOUR BEATTY REGIONAL CIVIL
   ENGINEERING
   Maxim 7, Maxim Office Park, Parklands
   Avenue, Eurocentral, ML1 4WQ
   Tel: (01698) 647 500
   Clair Catherine Crawford
   Emma Lorn Fern
   Colette McGinley
   Robert Murray Pattie
   Kirsty Santandreu
MURDOCH MACKENZIE LTD.
   39 Jerviston Street, ML1 4BL
   Tel: (01698) 265171
   Murdo MacKenzie

NORTH LANARKSHIRERE COUNCIL
   Corporate Services, Civic Centre, Windmillhill
   St., ML1 1AB
   Tel: (07939) 280102
   Fax: (01698) 302211
   DX: 571700 MOTHERWELL 2
   Archibald Henry Aitken
   Raksana Akhtar
   Gillian Emma Allan
   Rachel Elizabeth McLeod Blair
   Colette Anne Cameron
   James Paul Kennedy Corrigan
   Heather Elizabeth Cox
   Fiona Sinclair Nicolson Ekinli
   Alison Mary Gallacher
   Paul Gerard Guidi
   Mark Thomas Henderson
   Careen Margaret Hendry
   Leanne Claire Joss
   Jane Baxter Kirkhope
   Nicola Lauchlan
   Isabel Graham Lawton
   Maud Cecilia Lithgow
   John Anthony McCluskey
   Ruth Mary McCormick
   Shafana Raza
   Jill Rogerson
   Evelyn Ross
   Joanne Saunders
   Jillian Deborah Spilg
   Fiona Ann Stewart
   Caley Jane Toner

Musselburgh
QUEEN MARGARET UNIVERSITY
   Queen Margaret University Drive, EH21 6UU
   Tel: (0131) 4740000
   Lorraine Kerr
SCOTTISH LAND & ESTATES LIMITED
   Stuart House, Eskmills Business Park, EH21 7PB
   Tel: (0131) 6535400
   Fax: (0131) 6535401
   Jason Geoffrey Rust

Newtown St. Boswells
SCOTTISH BORDERS COUNCIL
   Council Headquarters, TD6 0SA
   Tel: (01835) 825 225
   Fax: (01835) 826 693
   Scott Michael Archibald
   Iain Finlay Davidson
   Christina Donald
   Ronald Adam Kirk
   Hannah Elizabeth MacLeod
   Rebecca Helen McDonald
   Nuala Bernadette McKinlay
   Lauren Margaret Mitchell
   Fraser Donald Moore Rankine
   Gillian Christine Sellar
   Sarah Marie Thompson
   Diane Margaret Jane Webster

Oban

PROCURATOR FISCAL SERVICE
Procurator Fiscal's Office, Boswell House,
Argyll Square, PA34 4BD
Tel: (01631) 64088
DX: OB9 OBAN
James Robertson Dunbar

Paisley

AGS AIRPORTS LIMITED
Glasgow Airport, Administrative Building,St
Andrews Drive, Glasgow Airport, PA3 2SW
Tel: (0141) 8484567
Christopher Gordon Simpson Allan
FIRST MILK LTD
Cirrus Hse,GlasgowAirportBusPk, Marchburn
Drive, PA3 2SJ
Tel: (0141) 8476895
Fax: (0141) 8476781
Angus John Somerville Waugh
LIFE TECHNOLOGIES LIMITED
3 Fountain Drive, Inchinnan Business Park,
PA4 9RF
Tel: (0141) 8146100
Fax: (0141) 8146260
Kathryn Mackay Barclay
Katherine Flora Barr
Michael James Byrne
Lynn Gray
Alison Ann Locke
Gordon Ross MacTavish
Chloe Anne McGuigan
Andrew James Middlecote
Mairi Mackenzie Queen
Cameron Ramage
PROCURATOR FISCAL SERVICE
Procurator Fiscal's Office, 1 Love Street,
PA3 2DA
Tel: (0141) 8497940
Fax: (0141) 8876172
DX: PA50 PAISLEY 1
Caterine Elisabet Arrabal Ward
Dana Barclay
Susan Mary Barr
Kirsten Laura Brierley
Andrew Norman Brown
Carol Ann Cameron
Claire Connachan
Michael James Cunningham
Nadine Margaret Freeman
Douglas Kennedy Hamilton
Emma Sarah Jeffrey
Jeanette Maclean
Claire Louise Rintoul Martin
Neva Alexandra McCallum
Emma McGinley
Kimberley Anne McGregor
Gemma Garrity McKechnie
Lynsey McMorran
Laura Anne Millar
Frankie Morgan
Clifford Most

Maureen Anne Mullan
Maria Candida Angela Murdoch
Paul Henry Reynolds
Mandy Jane Robertson
Kathleen Stewart
Marjory Elaine Taylor
Emma Louise Thomson
Ziad Ahmad Ullam Ul-Hassan
Laura Louise Wilcox
RENFREWSHIRE COUNCIL
Finance & Corporate Services, Renfrewshire
House, Cotton St., PA1 1TT
Tel: (0141) 6187176
Christine Murray Adam
Allison Elizabeth Black
Dorothy Anne Chalmers Briggs
Gemma Frances Cameron
Eilidh Clements
Mark John Conaghan
Amy Jane Frances Cook
Margaret Robins Craig
Lesley Ann Currie
Kenneth Andrew Graham
Ross Calum Graham
Irene Margaret Halpin
Laura-Ann Claire Michelle Lilburn
Declan MacAskill
Emma Margaret Mary McBride
Ross Kenneth McGinness
Lynn Catherine Mitchell
Bernadette O'Neill
Christine Anne Panton
Evelyn Margaret Pinkerton
Veronika Prag
Nairn Robert Young
RENFREWSHIRE COUNCIL
Finance and Resources, Renfrewshire House,
Cotton St., PA1 1TT
Tel: (0141) 6187172
Douglas John Campbell
Nina Hill
Erin Christina Leyden
Lara Macaulay Stimpson
RENFREWSHIRE COUNCIL
City Link Project – 4th Floor, Renfrewshire
House,, Cotton Street, PA1 1TT
Tel: (0141) 618 7156
Barbara Margaret Ellen Walker
RENFREWSHIRE VALUATION JOINT BOARD
16 Glasgow Road, PA1 3QF
Heather Anne Semple
**SCOTTISH CHILDREN'S REPORTER
ADMINISTRATION**
10 Glen Lane, PA3 2HU
Stacey Elizabeth O'Neill
Mairi Elizabeth O'Reilly
SCOTTISH COURTS AND TRIBUNALS SERVICE
Sheriffdom of North Strathclyde, Paisley Sheriff
and Justice of the Peace, The Court House, St
James Street, PA3 2HW
Tel: (0141) 8875291
Fax: (0141) 8876702
Eileen Burns

Angela Devine
Vivian Gay Lindsay
Julie-Marie Scott
David MacLean Watt
SOCIAL CARE AND SOCIAL WORK
IMPROVEMENT SCOTLAND
Renfrewshire House, Cotton Street, PA1 1BF
Tel: (0141) 843 6847
Kenneth William McClure
TAYLOR WIMPEY UK LIMITED
Unit C, Ground Floor, Cirrus, Glasgow Airport
Business Park, Marchburn Drive, PA3 2SJ
Tel: (0141) 849 5583
Fax: (0141) 8495548
Scott Houston Colquhoun
THE MALCOLM GROUP
Brookfield House, 2 Burnbrae Drive, Linwood,
PA3 3BU
Lucy Jill Strachan
THERMO FISHER SCIENTIFIC
3 Fountain Drive, Inchinnan Business Park,
PA4 9RF
Tel: (0141) 814 6100
Calum Whyte
UNIVERSITY OF THE WEST OF SCOTLAND
Court & Senate Office, University of the West
of Scotland, High Street, PA1 2BE
Tel: (0141) 848 3577
Fax: (0141) 848 3763
Emma Louise Cuckow
Alison Jane Niven

Perth

AVIVA
Pitheavlis, PH2 0NH
Tel: (01738) 895327
Jean Beattie Grace
Corinne Denise Ward
NEOS NETWORKS LIMITED
Inveralmond House, 200 Dunkeld Road,
PH1 3AQ
Colin Gordon Atherton
Carolyn Joy Greer
Neil John Ligertwood
Lisa MacRae
OVO (S) ELECTRICITY LTD
Grampian House, 200 Dunkeld Road,
PH1 3GH
Jennifer Susan Elizabeth Elliot
Kate Elizabeth Gibson
Rachel Audrey Margaret Gray
Laura Elizabeth McVean
PERTH & KINROSS COUNCIL
2 High Street, PH1 5PH
Tel: (01738) 475000
Fax: (01738) 475545
Lynne Sarah Clark
Lee Donald Coulter
Colin David Elliott
Geoffrey David Fogg
Adam James Heath
Helen Mary Anne Johnstone

Bernard MacFarlane
Patrick Guermont Mair
Moina Kassandra McLaren
Stuart Alan McQueen
Deborah Alison Robertson
Sarah-Louise Rodger
Lisa Simpson
Andrew William Thomson
PROCURATOR FISCAL SERVICE
Procurator Fiscal's Office, 82 Tay Street,
PH2 8NN
Tel: (01738) 637272
David Owen Currie
Catriona Janet Nisbet Dickie
Andrew Paul Harding
William Kermode
Matthew Peter Kerr
Rebecca Margaret Fairfax Kynaston
Lisa Jayne Marshall
Joanne Mary Ritchie
Michael Sweeney
Carol Georgina Whyte
SCOTTISH COURTS AND TRIBUNALS SERVICE
Sheriffdom Business Team, Sheriff Court
House, PH2 8NL
Tel: (01738) 492933
Jean Thomson Davis
Alison Rennie
SSE PLC
Inveralmond House, 200 Dunkeld Road,
PH1 3AQ
Tel: (01738) 456 000
Tarryn Bastianelli
Suzanne Borrowman
Alison Claire Broomhall
Samantha Coyne
Aoife Lynda Cuddihy
Matthew George Day
Sophie Rhiannon Dickson
Sophie Patricia Graham
Angela Michelle Gray
Andrew Roy Greer
Lesley Mhairi Halliday
Fiona Margaret Jones
Alice Margaret Leggat
Claire Violet Lennon
Johanne Sinclair Lewin
Gemma Macmillan
Angela Helen Martin
Helen Elizabeth McCombe
Finlay Alexander McCutcheon
Mark McLaughlin
Kirsty Erin McLean
William Cameron McKenzie Millar
Claire Anne Stock
Ashley Topping
Katherine Valentine
Stuart Archie Waddell
SSE PLC
Legal Services, 200 Dunkeld Road, PH1 3AQ
Tel: (01738) 453697
Laura Jane Pittam
Christina Ann Lorraine Priest

▶ **Perth continued**

Annette Hughes Roxburgh

Peterhead
PROCURATOR FISCAL SERVICE
Procurator Fiscal's Office, 70 St. Peter Street,
AB4 6QD
Tel: (01779) 476628
Ruairidh Niall McAlister
SCORE GROUP LIMITED
Ian M. Cheyne Building, Glen Test Facility,
Wellbank, AB42 3GL
Tel: (01779) 482 300
Fax: (01779) 482 345
Joanna Noble
Sonya Leigh O'Brien

Portlethen
BAKER HUGHES LTD.
Baker Hughes Building, Badentoy Avenue,
Badentoy Park Industrial Estate, AB12 4YB
Tel: (01224) 720000
Findlay Iain Anderson
Clare Swankie
KCA DEUTAG DRILLING LTD
Group Headquarters, Bankhead Drive, City
South Office Park, AB12 4XX
Tel: (01224) 987000
Anthony Joseph Byrne
Stephen John Harte
Katy Elizabeth Neill
Niall David Polson
Stuart Fraser Robson

Portree
LOCHALSH AND SKYE HOUSING ASSOCIATION
Morrison House, Bayfield, IV51 9EW
Tel: (01478) 612035
Fax: (01478) 613377
Lesley Varennes Kirkwood

Prestwick
COLLINS AEROSPACE
1 Dow Avenue, Prestwick International
Aerospace Park, KA9 2SA
Tel: (01292) 670293
Scott Barton McMaster

Renfrew
HOWDEN GROUP LIMITED
Old Govan Road, PA4 8XJ
Tel: (0141) 885 7459
Fax: (0141) 8852892
Jennifer Robertson
Lucia Giuseppa Spadaro-Dutturi
Alasdair John Swanson
Hayley Taylor

Selkirk
PROCURATOR FISCAL SERVICE
Procurator Fiscal's Office, Sheriff Court House,
TD7 4LE
Tel: (01750) 20345
DX: 581013 SELKIRK
Fiona Elspeth Hamilton

stepps
BAM CONSTRUCT UK LTD
Kelvin House, Buchanan Gate Business Park,
G33 6FB
Tel: (0141) 7798888
Fax: (0141) 7798798
Marianne Morrison
BAM PPP UK LIMITED
Kelvin House, Buchanan Gate Business Park,
G33 6FB
Tel: (0141) 7798609
Fax: (0141) 7798601
Michael John Gillespie
Laura Jane Warnock
BAM PROPERTIES LIMITED
Kelvin House, Buchanan Gate, G33 6FB
Tel: (0141) 2221020
Fax: (0141) 2221021
Euan James Miller

Stirling
FES LTD
Forth House, Pirnhall Business Park, FK7 8HW
Tel: (01786) 819600
Fax: (01786) 811456
Alison Groat
Craig Alexander Thomson
FULLBROOK ASSOCIATES
Stirling Business Centre, FK8 2DZ
Tel: (01786) 451903
Stephanie Josephine Connor
LUMIRADX UK LTD
Unit 5, Block 5, Manor Farm Business Park,
Manor Load, FK9 5QD
Jade Kennedy
NATURAL POWER CONSULTANTS LIMITED
Ochil House, Springkerse Business Park,
FK7 7XE
Tel: (01786) 542 300
Andrew Richard Jack
Janis John Miezitis
ROBERTSON CAPITAL PROJECTS LIMITED
Robertson House, Castle Business Park,
FK9 4TZ
Tel: (01786) 277865
Fax: (01786) 436090
Anne Elizabeth Gilkinson
SCOTTISH CHILDREN'S REPORTER
ADMINISTRATION
Ochil House, Springkerse Business Park,
FK7 7XE
Tel: (01786) 459500
Jenny Suzanne McCallion

SCOTTISH COURTS AND TRIBUNALS SERVICE
Sheriff Court House, Viewfield Place, FK8 1NH
Tel: (01786) 462191
Fax: (01786) 470456
Tracey Marie Scott
SCOTTISH ENVIRONMENT PROTECTION
AGENCY
Corporate Office, Strathallan House, Castle
Business Park, FK9 4TZ
Tel: (01786) 457700
Fax: (01786) 446885
Fraser Hunter Inch
Lorna Helen MacDonald
Sarah Gabrielle MacDonald
Jennifer McWhirter
STIRLING COUNCIL
Legal Services, Viewforth, FK8 2ET
Tel: (01786) 233065
Mark Alexander Easton
Claire Louise Ferguson
Graeme Bruce Forrester
Ewan Alastair Grant
Charles John Haggerty
Julia Anne McAfee
Paul McCandlish
Julia Rose Mountford
Carla Joy Roth
Lisa Taylor
STIRLING DISTRICT CITIZENS ADVICE BUREAU
LTD
The Norman MacEwan Centre, 3 Cameronian
Street
Denise Christine Borrer
WATER INDUSTRY COMMISSION FOR
SCOTLAND
First Floor, Moray House, Forthside Way,
FK8 1QZ
Tel: (01786) 430 200
Rhona Alison Harper

Stonehaven
ALBA POWER
Mill of Monquich, Netherley, AB39 3QR
Colin Carrick Watson

Stornoway
COMHAIRLE NAN EILEAN SIAR
Council Offices, Sandwick Road, HS1 2BW
Tel: (01851) 822600
Fax: (01851) 705349
Malcolm Burr
Timothy Isaac Langley
Allan Joseph MacDonald
Iain Ronald Maclean
Sheekha Saha
MG ALBA
Seaforth Road, HS1 2SD
Tel: (01851) 705550
Fax: (01851) 706432
Catriona Mairi Neally

PROCURATOR FISCAL SERVICE
Procurator Fiscal's Office, Sheriff Court House,
HS1 2JF
Karen Smith

Stranraer
PROCURATOR FISCAL SERVICE
Procurator Fiscal's Office, Sheriff Court House,
DG9 7AA
Tel: (01776) 704321
DX: 581259 STRANRAER
Paula Margaret Hamilton
Kirsty McGowan

Strathaven
J. W. MORRISON HAULAGE CONTRACTOR
Cloverhill Farm, ML10 6ST
Tel: (01357) 300414
Andrea Margaret McQuade

Westhill
ALTERA INFRASTRUCTURE
Altera House, Unit 3, Prospect Park, Prospect
Road, Arnhall Business Park, AB32 6FL
William James Duthie
ALTERA INFRASTRUCTURE
Unit 3, Prospect Park, Prospect Road, Arnhall
Business Park, AB32 6FJ
Anna Naomi Toye
ASHTEAD TECHNOLOGY
Ashtead House, Discovery Drive, AB32 6FG
Patrick Magnus Shepherd Langskog
PROSERV UK LIMITED
Proserv House, Prospect Road, AB32 6FJ
Ross Alistair MacDonald Fordyce
SUBSEA 7 (UK SERVICE COMPANY) LTD
Prospect Road, Arnhall Business Park,
AB32 6FE
Tel: (01224) 344308
Suzanne Matonti
Marie-Louise O'Hara
Kaveh Rassouli
Gary James Scott
Christopher Murray Strachan
SWELLFIX UK LIMITED
Tendeka, Vanguard House, Kingshill
Commercial Park (East), Venture Drive, Arnhall
Business Park, AB32 6FQ
Linda May Cameron
TOTALENERGIES E&P UK LIMITED
TotalEnergies House, Tarland Road, AB32 6JZ
Tel: (01224) 297818
Fax: (01224) 298999
Thomas Harry Coles
Corey Gavin Duff
Anne-Marie Fraser
Ashley Miriam Ness
Lewis Porter
Steven Andrew Shaw
Lauren Dee Stewart
Jill Fraser Turner

▶ **Westhill** continued

Jennifer Elizabeth Watt

Tel: (01955) 602197
David Alan Barclay

Wick

PROCURATOR FISCAL SERVICE
Procurator Fiscal's Office, Sheriff Court, Bridge
Street, KW1 4AJ

Scottish Solicitors Outwith Scotland

AUSTRALIA

Melbourne
PINSENT MASONS
   Level 23, 360 Collins Street 3000
   Ewan Robertson

Perth
BAKER HUGHES AUSTRALIA PTY LTD
   Level 14, 216 St George's Terrace 6000
   Barry Cameron
BLACKWALL LEGAL LLP
   26/140 St Georges Terrace 6000
   Nganele Bhebhe
PRICEWATERHOUSECOOPERS
   Brookfield Place, 125 St Georges Terrace 6000
   Christopher McAlinden

Sydney
ASHURST LLP
   5 Martin Place 2000
   Ben Judge
CBRE LTD
   Level 21, 363 George Street NSW 2000
   Louisa Fitzpatrick
DLA PIPER
   Level 22, No.1 Martin Place 2001
   Valeria Polovinkina
MINTER ELLISON
   Governor Macquarie Tower, 1 Farrer Place
   2000
   Kate Morrison
PINSENT MASONS (AUSTRALIA)
   Level 32, Gateway Tower, 1 Macquarie Place
   2000
   Louisa Donnelly
   Fraser McMillan

BELGIUM

Brussels
BAKER BOTTS (BELGIUM) LLP
   Square De Mee s 23 – Box 11 B-1000
   David Cardwell
BRODIES LLP
   41 Avenue Des Arts
CLIENTEARTH BELGIUM AISBL
   60 Rue Du Trone 1050
   Anne Friel
CMS CAMERON MCKENNA NABARRO
OLSWANG LLP
   85, Avenue Des Nerviens 104
   Siobhan Kahmann
   Kirsti McKenzie
DENTONS EUROPE LLP
   Rue de La Regence 58 Bte 2 1000

Mark Clough
SQUIRE PATTON BOGGS (UK) LLP
   Avenue Lloyd George 7 1000
   Robert MacLean
WHITE & CASE
   62 Rue De La Loi B-1040
   Jacquelyn MacLennan

Bruxelles
SERCO BELGIUM SA
   Avenue de Cortenbergh 60 1000
   Christopher Greig

BERMUDA

Hamilton
CHANCERY LEGAL
   52 Reid Street HM12
   John Blackwood

CANADA

Calgary
CHEVRON CANADA RESOURCES
   500 5th Avenue SW T2P 0L7
   Samantha Chinn

Vancouver
STEWART, AULINGER & CO
   1200 – 805 West Broadway V5Z 1K1
   John Kielski
WATSON ADVISORS INC.
   200-2415 Columbia Street V5Y 3E7
   Stacey Martin

CAYMAN ISLANDS

Grand Cayman
MG MANAGEMENT LTD.
   2F Landmark Square, 64 Earth Close, Seven
   Mile Beach, PO Box 30116 KY1-1201
   Mark Murray

DENMARK

Copenhagen
EVERSHEDS SUTHERLAND (INTERNATIONAL) LLP
   Ostergade 27 DK-1100
TRUSTPILOT A/S
   Pilestraede 58, 5. 1112
   Andrew Farquhar
   Anoop Joshi
   Christopher Knudsen
   Thomas Simmons

ENGLAND

Addlestone
DIXCART LEGAL
  Dixcart House, Addlestone Road, Bourne
  Business Park KT15 2LE
  Vincent Chung

Altrincham
MLP LAW LTD
  7 Market Street WA14 1QE
  Julie Sabba

Andover
DIRECTORATE OF ARMY LEGAL SERVICES
  SO1 Resources, DALS, IDL 426, Ramillies
  Building, Marlborough Lines, Monxton Road
  SP11 8HJ
  John Brown
  Eugene-Paul Grant
  Gavin Law
  Chelsey Mitchell
  Fiona Rennet

Bath
RENEW LEGAL LIMITED
  7-9 North Parade Buildings BA1 1NS
  Catriona Murray

Bedford
ADHIBEO LIMITED
  52 Bunyan Road, Kempston MK42 8HL
  Sylvia White

Berwick-Upon-Tweed
VIALEX LIMITED
  17a Windmill Way West, Ramparts Business
  Park TD15 1TB

Birkenhead
CARPENTERS SCOTLAND LIMITED
  Leonard House, Scotts Quays CH41 1FB
  Isra Ali

Birmingham
ACCESS LEGAL FROM SHOOSMITHS
  2 Colmore Square, 38 Colmore Circus
  Queensway B4 6SH
BERRYMANS LACE MAWER LLP
  63 Temple Row B2 5LS
BIG LOTTERY FUND
  Apex House, Embassy Drive B15 1TR
  Deborah Myles
BIRMINGHAM 2022 COMMONWEALTH GAMES
  One Brindley Place B1 2JB
  Stuart Skelly
DAC BEACHCROFT CLAIMS LIMITED
  Tricorn House, 51-53 Hagley Road, Edgbaston
  B16 8TP
  Rebeccah Jaarson

DEPARTMENT FOR BUSINESS, ENERGY AND
INDUSTRIAL STRATEGY
  Office For Product Safety and Standards, 4th
  Floor Cannon House, 18 The Priory
  Queensway B4 6BS
  Elisa Wamberg
DLA PIPER UK LLP
  Victoria Square House, Victoria Square B2 4DL
  Tobias Paul
EVERSHEDS SUTHERLAND (INTERNATIONAL) LLP
  115 Colmore Row B3 3AL
GOWLING WLG (UK) LLP
  Two Snowhill SE1 2AU
  Jamie Russell
HARRISON CLARK RICKERBYS LIMITED
  63 Church Street B3 2DP
  Martin McQueen
HSBC HOLDINGS PLC
  1 Centenary Square B1 1HQ
  Andrew McLean
PINSENT MASONS LLP
  19 Cornwall Street B3 2DT
PINSENT MASONS LLP
  55 Colmore Row B3 2FG
  Paul Harkin
SHOOSMITHS LLP
  2 Colmore Square, 38 Colmore Circus
  Queensway B4 6SH
THE PHARMACISTS' DEFENCE ASSOCIATION
  The Old Fire Station, 69 Albion Street B1 3EA
  Baljit Bagha

Blackburn
BAE SYSTEMS
  Samlesbury Aerodrome, S608, 2nd Floor,
  Balderstone BB2 7LF
  David Graham
KINETIC LAWYERS LTD
  Suite 2, Unit 2D, Phoenix Business Park BB1
  5RW

Bolton
KEOGHS SCOTLAND LLP
  2 The Parklands BL6 4SE

Bradford
SCOTIA PERSONAL INJURY SOLICITORS LIMITED
  Alpha House, 2 Coop Place BD5 8JX

Brighton
RIVERSTONE
  Park Gate, 161-163 Preston Road BN1 6AU
  Ruth Lyall

Bristol
BERRYMANS LACE MAWER LLP
  4th Floor, St. Thomas Court BS1 6JG
BURGES SALMON LLP
  One Glass Wharf BS2 0ZX
  Katie Allen
  Christopher Bartlett
  Julian Boswall

Euan Bremner
Nicholas Churchward
Paul Clark
Andrew Dunlop
Jonathan Eves
Ross Fairley
Lloyd James
Richard Leeming
Alison Logan
Paula McGeady
James Phillips
Ross Simpson
Kathryn Smith
CLIMATE TRANSITION CAPITAL LLP
   1 Redcliff Street BS1 6TP
   Alanna Flett
CMS CAMERON MCKENNA NABARRO
OLSWANG LLP
   2 College Square, Anchor Road BS1 5UE
FOOT ANSTEY LLP
   2 Glass Wharf BS2 0FR
   Mohammed Anwar
LYONS DAVIDSON LTD
   43 Queen Square BS1 4QP
   Michael Tait
OSBORNE CLARKE
   2 Temple Back East, Temple Quay BS1 6EG
   Natasha Burbidge
TLT LLP
   One Redcliff Street BS1 6TP
   James Johnson
   Caroline Loudon
WOMBLE BOND DICKINSON (UK) LLP
   3 Temple Quay, Temple Back East BS1 6DZ

Bromley
LONDON BOROUGH OF BROMLEY
   Civic Centre, Stockwell Close BR1 3UH
   Marion Paine

Cambridge
AVEVA SOLUTIONS LTD
   High Cross, Madingley Road CB3 0HB
   Sana Afzal-Ali
BARR ELLISON LLP
   39 Parkside CB1 1PN
   Grant Mathieson
EVERSHEDS SUTHERLAND (INTERNATIONAL) LLP
   50/60 Station Road CB1 2JH
MILLS & REEVE LLP
   Botanic House, 100 Hills Road CB2 1PH
   Emily Horn

Chester
LDF OPERATIONS LIMITED
   Second Floor, HQ Offices, 58 Nicholas Street
   CH1 2NP
   Ross Rutherford

Clitheroe
BACKHOUSE JONES
   The Printworks, Hey Road BB7 9WD

Claire McKie

Croydon
EDF ENERGY
   81-85 Station Road
   Emma Brown
   Abigail Lloyd
PENSION PROTECTION FUND
   Renaissance, 12 Dingwall Road CR0 2NA
   Laurence Edwards
   Martha Quinn
SUPERDRUG STORES PLC
   CR0 2EU
   Catherine Montgomery
UK ANTI-DOPING
   Trafalgar House, 1 Bedford Park CR0 2AQ
   Ailie McGowan

Eastbourne
LSL FAMILY LAW
   8 South Lynn Drive BN21 2JF
   Linda Lamb

Epsom
SARTORIUS STEDIM UK LIMITED
   Longmead Business Centre, Blenheim Road
   KT19 9QQ
   Stacie MacIntyre

Exeter
MICHELMORES LLP
   Woodwater House, Pynes Hill EX2 5WR
   Lynsey Blyth

Fareham
SHOOSMITHS LLP
   Forum 5, the Forum, Parkway PO15 7PA

Feltham
PERFORM GROUP
   Sussex House, 2 Plane Tree Crescent TW14
   7HE
   Kathleen Cradock

Gerrards Cross
ENERGY LAW SOLUTIONS LIMITED
   28 School Lane, Chalfont St. Peter SL9 9BA
   Kevin McGrory

Gloucester
EDF ENERGY
   Legal Affairs, Generation & Supply, Barnett
   Way, Barnwood GL4 3RS
   Susan Lind

Guildford
PREMIER ASSET MANAGEMENT LIMITED
   Unit 1 Eastgate Court, High Street GU1 3DE
   Gregor Craig
STEVENS & BOLTON LLP
   Wey House, Farnham Road GU1 4YD

Andrew Steele

Harlow
TEVA UK LIMITED
Field House, Station Approach CM20 2FB
Paul Taylor

Hemel Hempstead
BAM CONSTRUCT UK LTD
Breakspear Park, Breakspear Way HP2 4FL
Gillian Simpson

High Wycombe
ROYAL AIR FORCE
Directorate of Legal Services (RAF), 3S11,
Spitfire Block, HQ Air Command HP14 4UE
Stuart Agnew

Hook
SERCO UK, EUROPE & SGS
2nd Floor, Enterprise House, 11 Bartley Wood
Business Park RH27 9XB
Greg Nicoll

Horley
SCOTIA GAS NETWORKS LIMITED
Legal Services, St Lawrence House, Station
Approach RH6 9JY
Nicola Shand

Ipswich
EVERSHEDS SUTHERLAND (INTERNATIONAL) LLP
159 Princes Street IP1 1QJ

Isleworth
SKY UK LTD
Sky Central, Grant Way TW7 5QD
Christina Johnston
Robert Jones
Alice Walton

Leeds
ADDLESHAW GODDARD LLP
3 Sovereign Square, Sovereign Street LS1 4ER
Joanna Logie
ASDA STORES LTD
Legal Team, Asda House, Southbank, Great
Wilson Street LS11 5AD
Graeme Morrison
BERRYMANS LACE MAWER LLP
4th Floor Park Row House, 19-20 Park Row
LS1 5JF
CLARION SOLICITORS LIMITED
Elizabeth House, 13-19 Queen Street LS1 2TW
Fiona Marr
Philip Morrison
DLA PIPER UK LLP
Princes Exchange, Princes Square LS1 4BY
Bryony Lunn
Ataikor Ngerebara
ENGIE POWER LIMITED

No 1 Leeds, 26 Whitehall Road LS12 1BE
Neil Anderson
EVERSHEDS SUTHERLAND (INTERNATIONAL) LLP
Bridgewater Place, Water Lane LS11 5BZ
GOVERNMENT LEGAL DEPARTMENT
Lateral, 8 City Walk LS11 9AT
Eileen Waters
MEDICAL PROTECTION SOCIETY
Victoria House, 2 Victoria Place LS11 5AE
Julia Bryden
Sarah Donaldson
Elizabeth Grant
Sara Grewar
Nicola Innes
Rhona Keith
Gregor McPhail
Nicola Paul
Karen Rowney
PINSENT MASONS LLP
1 Park Row LS1 5AB
SHOOSMITHS LLP
Platform, New Station Street LS1 4JB
WOMBLE BOND DICKINSON (UK) LLP
1 Whitehall Riverside LS1 4BN

Leominster
FISH LEGAL
Eastwood House, 6 Rainbow Street HR6 8DQ
Robert Younger
GUY LINLEY-ADAMS SOLICITORS
Office E3, Grange Court, Pinsley Road HR6
8NL
Guy Linley-Adams

Liverpool
BERRYMANS LACE MAWER LLP
Castle Chambers, 43 Castle Street L2 9SU
HILL DICKINSON LLP
No. 1 St Paul's Square L3 9SJ
Tricia Morrison
LITTLEWOODS LIMITED
Skyways House, Speke Road, Speke L70 1AB
Gemma Gibson

Liversedge
QC LAW SOLICITORS LIMITED
633 Halifax Road WF15 8HG
Sophina Ali
Rizwan Khalil Ahmed

London
ACCELERANT SERVICES UK LIMITED
One Fleet Place EC4M 7WS
George Peto
ACCEL PARTNERS MANAGEMENT LLP
6th Floor, 1 New Burlington Place W1S 2HR
Janine Suttie
ACCENTURE (UK) LIMITED
30 Fenchurch Street EC3M 3BD
Lindsey Brown
ACTEON GROUP LIMITED
20 Little Britain EC1A 7DH

Callum Scott

ACTURIS LTD
100 Hatton Garden EC1N 8NX
Samantha Hastie

ADAPTAVIST
25 Wilton Road, Victoria SW1V 1LW
Ava Maitland

ADDLESHAW GODDARD LLP
Milton Gate, 60 Chiswell Street EC1Y 4AG
Jaya Gupta
Mark Guttridge
Tristan Johnston
Katy Stevenson
Martin Stewart-Smith
Thomas Walmsley
Katherine Watson

AKIN GUMP STRAUSS HAUER & FELD LLP
Eighth Floor, Ten Bishops Square E1 6EG
Rebecca Carwood Barron
Daniel Quinn

ALDEN LEGAL LIMITED
25 Southampton Buildings WC2A 1AL
Joanne Wheeler

ALDERMORE BANK PLC
5th Floor, Austin Friars House, 2-6 Austin Friars
EC2N 2HD
Nicola Sneddon

ALLEN & OVERY LLP
One Bishops Square E1 6AD
Stephen Barclay
Gordon Bartlett
Neil Bowden
Myles Cormack
Kyle Dunn
David Early
Arturas Jakubovskis
Aisling Knapton
Peter Mailer
Bruce Rennie

ALSTON & BIRD (LONDON) LLP
5th Floor, Octagon Point, St. Paul's, 5
Cheapside EC2V 6AA
John Stephen

AMAZON UK SERVICES LTD
Legal Department, 1 Principal Place, Worship
Street EC2A 2FA
Jessica Campbell

AMBER FUND MANAGERS LTD
3 More, Riverside SE1 2AQ
Helen Regan

AON UK LTD
122 Leadenhall Street EC3V 4AB
Sophia Hytiris

APOLLO MANAGEMENT INTERNATIONAL LLP
25 St George Street W1S 1FS
Christopher Dearie

ARGONON LTD
1-3 St. Peter's Street N1 8JD
Amanda Goddard

ARNOLD & PORTER KAYE SCHOLER LLP
Tower 42, International Financial Centre, 25
Old Broad Street EC2N 1HQ
John Schmidt

ASCENT UNDERWRITING LLP
10th Floor, One MinsterCourt, Mincing Lane,
Billingsgate EC3R 7AA
Richard Moir

ASHURST LLP
1 Duval Square, London Fruit and Wool
Exchange E1 6PW
Jonathan Byrne-Leitch
Julie Connolly
Meela Kwok
Annie Marriner
Maria McAlister
Callum McPherson
Lauren Morrison
Eilish Russell
Matthew Sharpe

ASPRIS
80 Hammersmith Road W14 8UD
Keir-Ewin Lynn

ASSOCIATED BRITISH FOODS PLC
50-51 Russell Square WC1B 4JA
Leanne Dixon
Karen Orr

ASSURED GUARANTY
11th Floor, 6 Bevis Marks EC3A 7BA
Tamsyn McLean

ASTON GOWMAN LIMITED
1000 Great West Road, Brentford TW8 9DW
Gail Millar

ATLEU LTD
St Saviour's House, 39-41 Union Street SE1
1SD
Sarah Smith

ATTEST TECHNOLOGIES LIMITED
25 Holywell Row EC2A 4XE
Amy Andrew

AVIVA PLC
20th Floor, St Helen's, 1 Undershaft EC3P
3DQ
Kirstine Cooper

AXA INVESTMENT MANAGERS
22 Bishopsgate EC2N 4BQ
Fraser Simpson

AXA UK PLC
20 Gracechurch Street EC3V 0BG
Hannah Garrick

AXIOM GLOBAL LIMITED
6th Floor, 159/173 St John Street EC1V 4QJ
Louise Duncan
Sophie Forbes

BAKER & MCKENZIE LLP
100 New Bridge Street EC4V 6JA
David Duncan
Robert Gray
Connor Lovie

BALFOUR BEATTY GROUP
130 Wilton Road SW1V 1LQ
Fiona Chambers

BALFOUR BEATTY INVESTMENTS LIMITED
350 Euston Road NW1 3AX
Sandra Hartley

BANK OF AMERICA MERRILL LYNCH
2 King Edward Street EC1A 1HQ

Chantelle Forster

BANK OF NEW YORK MELLON
One Canada Square E14 5AL
Euan Anderson

BANNATYNE, KIRKWOOD, FRANCE & CO.
76 Shoe Lane EC4A 3JB

BARCLAYS BANK PLC
Level 29, 1 Churchill Place E14 5HP
Gillian Christie
Alicia Ebdy
Georgina Farmer
Victoria Gall
Alison Wowk

BARCLAYS BANK PLC
Level 8, 1 Churchill Place E14 5HP
Jennifer Rae

BARCLAYS EXECUTION SERVICES LIMITED
Barclays UK Legal, Level 26, 1 Churchill Place
E14 5HP
Paul Rae

BARINGA PARTNERS LLP
62 Buckingham Gate SW1E 6AJ
Annie Carr

BATES WELLS BRAITHWAITE LLP
10 Queen Street Place EC4R 1BE
Karli Hiscock

BATTERSEA POWER STATION DEVELOPMENT COMPANY
188 Kirtling Street SW8 5BN
Iain Miller

BAXENDALE EMPLOYEE OWNERSHIP LIMITED
Runway East, 20 St Thomas Street SE1 9RS
Cristin Craig
Louise Fisher
Ewan Hall

BBC
Wogan House, Great Portland Street W1A 1AA
Joanna Elder

BERRYMANS LACE MAWER LLP
Plantation Place, 30 Fenchurch Street EC3M 3BL
Amelia Jones

BIRD & BIRD LLP
12 New Fetter Lane EC4A 1JP
Anna Duffus
Arif Saleem

BLACKROCK INVESTMENT MANAGEMENT (UK) LTD
Drapers Gardens, 12 Throgmorton Avenue EC2N 2DL
James Honan
Rachel McGinness

BRACHER RAWLINS LLP
77 Kingsway WC2B 6SR
David Gerber

BRAHAMS DUTT BADRICK FRENCH LLP
Kings House, 36 King Street EC2V 8BB
Paula Chan
Hannah Lynn

BRITISH-AMERICAN TOBACCO (HOLDINGS) LIMITED
Marketing Legal, Globe House, 4 Temple Place WC2R 2PG

Alexander Juras

BRITISH BUSINESS BANK
8 Salisbury Square, 2nd Floor EC4Y 8AP
Rory Swanson

BRITISH TELECOMMUNICATIONS PLC
PPA6A, BT Centre, 81 Newgate Street EC1A 7AJ
James Brockbank

BRITISH TELECOMMUNICATIONS PLC
Faraday Building, Ground Floor, 1 Knightrider Street EC4V 5BT
Rachel Canham
Donald Sellar

BROWN RUDNICK LLP
8 Clifford Street W1S 2LQ
Sarah Melaney

BRYAN CAVE LEIGHTON PAISNER LLP
Governor's House, 5 Laurence Pountney EC4R 0BR
John Conlin
Andrew Leitch
Malcolm Moir

BUILD HOLLYWOOD LTD
15 Duncan Terrace N1 8BZ
Martin Campbell

BURGES SALMON LLP
6 New Street Square EC4A 3BF

CADWALADER, WICKERSHAM & TAFT LLP
100 Bishopsgate EC2N 4AG
Kerry Shearer

CAREY OLSEN
Forum St. Paul's, 33 Gutter Lane EC2V 8AS
Richard Macfarlane
Colin Masterton
Peter Stachura

CARMICHAEL LEMAIRE LTD
71-75 Shelton Street, Covent Garden WC2H 9JQ
Gillian Carmichael Lemaire

CAVENDISH EMPLOYMENT LAW
70 Gracechurch Street EC3V 0HR
Shelagh McKenzie

CDC GROUP PLC
123 Victoria Street SW1E 6DE
John Hogg

CHANNEL 4 TELEVISION CORPORATION
Legal & Compliance Department, 124 Horseferry Road SW1P 2TX
Dominic Harrison

CHECKOUT.COM
Wenlock Works, Shepherdess Walk N1 7LH
Joseph Paterson

CITY LAW FIRM LIMITED
T/a St John Legal, Winchester House, 19 Bedford Row WC1R 4EB
Nils Reid
Andrew Williamson

CLIFFORD CHANCE LLP
10 Upper Bank Street E14 5JJ
Sarah-Marie Donnelly
Robert Edgar
Jonathan Forrest
James McMillan

Struan Murray
Samuel Parry
Chloe Smith
Regan Turner
CLYDE & CO LLP
The St Botolph Building, 138 Houndsditch
EC3A 7AR
Stewart Healey
CLYDE & CO (SCOTLAND) LLP
The St. Botolph Building, 138 Houndsditch
EC3A 7AR
CM MURRAY LLP
First Floor, 36-38 Cornhill EC3V 3NG
Sarah Chilton
CMS CAMERON MCKENNA NABARRO
OLSWANG LLP
Cannon Place, 78 Cannon Street EC4N 6AF
Charlotte Bascombe
Aileen Brown
Steven Cochrane
Catherine Devine
Gr inne Duffy
Valerie Fox
Helen Fyfe
Sophie Gallacher
Cameron Jones
Douglas Land
Robert Leckie
Iain Lindsay
Adam Lovatt
Michael Lyner
David McCallum
Stephen Millar
Konrad Rawicz
Andrew Shaw
William Simmons
Alasdair Steele
Rebecca Thomson
Nadia Wheeler
CONDE NAST PUBLICATIONS LIMITED
The Adelphi, 1-11 John Adam Street WC2N
6HT
Elizabeth Donaldson
COOLEY (UK) LLP
22 Bishopsgate EC2N 4BQ
Alexandra-Magda Mitrea
CORAM CHILDREN'S LEGAL CENTRE
Queen Elizabeth Centre, Coram Campus, 41
Brunswick Square WC1N 1AZ
Stewart MacLachlan
COUTTS & CO
440 Strand WC2R 0QS
Fergus Hand
CPFC LIMITED
Selhurst Park Stadium SE25 6PU
David Nichol
DAVITT JONES BOULD LIMITED
Level 24 The Shard, 32 London Bridge Street
SE1 9SG
Gillian Lewis
DEBEVOISE & PLIMPTON LLP
65 Gresham Street EC2V 7NQ
Kay Hunter

DECA MEDIA CONSULTANCY
Tobacco Dock E1W 2SF
Vicki McGowan
DECHERT LLP
160 Queen Victoria Street EC4V 4QQ
Ann Alexander
Nigel Austin
Kevin Gilroy
Ross Montgomery
Richard Murdoch
DELOITTE LLP
Hill House, 1 Little New Street EC4A 3TR
Calum Murray
Nicholas Wowk
DENTONS GLOBAL SERVICES (UK) HOLDINGS
LIMITED
1 Fleet Place EC4M 7WS
Louisa Black
DENTONS UK AND MIDDLE EAST LLP
One Fleet Place EC4M 7WS
Ruby Davies
Matthew Gilhooly
Alastair MacLeod
Charlotte Miles
Craig Neilson
Guy Norfolk
DENTSU INTERNATIONAL LIMITED
20 Triton Street, Regents Place NW1 3BF
Lauren Buchan
DICKSON MINTO
Broadgate Tower, Level 13 EC2A 2EW
Paul Barron
Devon Brewster
Paul Buchan
Daniel Carolan
Ronan Craig
Ross Cruickshanks
Alastair Dickson
James Duncan
Hannah Gong
Aoibheann Harkin
Robert Hay
Sophie Hofford
Fraser Jackson
Jennifer Lynch
Drew MacDonald
Andrew Manson
Christine McFadyen
Grant McGregor
Jennifer McLellan
Lucy Reville
Jordan Simpson
Katherine Sinclair
Lara Watt
DLA PIPER UK LLP
160 Aldersgate Street EC1A 4HT
Jan Colhoun
Sarah Crowe
Jennifer Gibbons
Fraser Grant
Grant Henderson
Sarah Letson
Gregor Munro

Michal Orzeg-Wydra
Sarah Tindall
DORSEY & WHITNEY (EUROPE) LLP
199 Bishopsgate EC2M 3UT
Robbie Somerville
DWF LAW LLP
20 Fenchurch Street EC3M 3AG
Katie McKernan
Michalina Rebisz-Bahra
EDWARDS DUTHIE SHAMASH
12 Baylis Road SE1 7AA
Colin Davidson
EDWIN COE LLP
2 Stone Buildings, Lincoln's Inn WC2A 3TH
Joanne McIvor
ELLIOTT MATTHEW PROPERTY LAWYERS
10 Margaret Street, Fitzrovia W1W 8RL
Sandra Rankine
ENI UK LIMITED
10 Ebury Bridge Road SW1W 8PZ
Richard Forgan
ERNST AND YOUNG LLP
1 More London Place SE1 2AF
Craig Stevenson
EVERSHEDS SUTHERLAND (INTERNATIONAL) LLP
One Wood Street EC2V 7WS
Kirstin McCracken
John Morgan
Ewan Nelson
EXPEDIA.COM LIMITED
Angel Building, 407 St John Street EC1V 4EX
Louise Hopkin
EYGS
6 More London Place SE1 2DA
Emma Hughes
FACEBOOK UK LIMITED
10 Brock Street NW1 3FG
Martin Barr
Faye Govan
Olivia Roach
Scott Von Poulton
FARADAY UNDERWRITING LIMITED
Corn Exchange, 5th Floor, 55 Mark Lane EC3R 7NE
Kirinjit Kaur
FARRER & CO LLP
66 Lincoln's Inn Fields WC2A 3LH
Anthony McNamee
Hayley Wilson
FIELDFISHER LLP
Riverbank House, 2 Swan Lane EC4R 3TT
Anna Crosby
Murray Keir
Elora Mukherjee
FINANCIAL CONDUCT AUTHORITY
12 Endeavor Square E20 1JN
Kirsty McLaren
Ross Murdoch
Charles Rogers
FIRSTGROUP PLC
8th Floor, The Point, 37 North Wharf Road W2 1AF
Carol McFarlane

FLO HEALTH UK LIMITED
27 Old Gloucester Street
Susanne Schumacher
FOX WILLIAMS LLP
Ten Finsbury Square EC2A 1AF
Benjamin Nolan
FREEDMAN + HILMI LLP
101 Wigmore Street W1U 1QU
Daniel Freedman
FREETHS LLP
1 Vine Street, Mayfair W1J 0AH
Ewen Lowrie
FRESHFIELDS SERVICE COMPANY
Freshfields Bruckhaus Deringer, 100 Bishopsgate EC2P 2SR
James Aitken
Kenneth Baird
Thomas Hutchison
Lisa Kelly
Moray Macdonald
FRIED, FRANK, HARRIS, SHRIVER & JACOBSON (LONDON) LLP
100 Bishopsgate EC2N 4AG
Karen Henderson
Robert MacVicar
GATELEY PLC
No. 1 Paternoster Square EC4M 7DX
James Hillan
Martin Montgomery
GENERATION INVESTMENT MANAGEMENT LLP
20 Air Street W1B 5AN
Alexander Marshall
GIBSON, DUNN & CRUTCHER LLP
Telephone House, 2-4 Temple Avenue EC4Y 0HB
Robert Carr
Robert Dixon
Christopher Loudon
GNEISS ENERGY LIMITED
29 Farm Street W1J 5RL
Jonathan Fitzpatrick
GOLDMAN SACHS
Goldman Sachs International, Plumtree Court, 25 Shoe Lane EC4A 4AU
Ross Clements
GOOGLE UK LIMITED
Belgrave House, 76 Buckingham Palace Road SW1W 9TQ
Ruaridh Goodfield
Rachael Johnston
William Malcolm
Struan Robertson
GOVERNMENT LEGAL DEPARTMENT
03-Jan, 1 Horse Guards Road SW1A 2HQ
Jesse Ambler
GOVERNMENT LEGAL DEPARTMENT
102 Petty France, Westminster SW1H 9GL
Rebecka Buchanan
Owen Wilton
GOVERNMENT LEGAL DEPARTMENT
Caxton House, Tothill Street, Westminster SW1H 9NA
Caitlin Fitzgerald

Catriona Hepburn
GOWLING WLG (UK) LLP
    4 More London Riverside SE1 2AU
    Robert Armour
GULF KEYSTONE PETROLEUM LIMITED
    6th Floor, New Fetter Place, 8-10 New Fetter
    Lane EC4A 1AZ
    Alasdair Robinson
GUNNERCOOKE SCO LLP
    1 Cornhill EC3V 3ND
HAYNES AND BOONE CDG, LLP
    2nd Floor, 1 New Fetter Lane EC4A 1AN
    Emma Russell
HELICAL PLC
    5 Hanover Square W1S 1HQ
    Eleanor Gill
HERBERT SMITH FREEHILLS LLP
    Exchange House, Primrose Street EC2A 2EG
    Holly Carss
    Ian Mack
    Jamie McLaren
    Lucy Robson
    Dominika Rogolska
HG CAPITAL LLP
    2 More London, Riverside SE1 2AP
    Andrew Jessop
HOGAN LOVELLS INTERNATIONAL LLP
    Atlantic House, Holburn Viaduct EC1A 2FG
    Nicola Evans
    Scott Gibson
    Ross King
    Claire Macpherson
    Pamela McHarg
    John Salmon
HOLMAN FENWICK WILLAN LLP
    Friary Court, 65 Crutched Friars EC3N 2AE
    Katherine Doran
    Andrew Ross
HOME OFFICE
    2 Marsham Street SW1P 4DF
    Robert Mooney
    Erin Paterson
HOWARD KENNEDY LLP
    No1. London Bridge SE1 9BG
    Oliver McInnes
    Marc Proudfoot
HOWDEN M&A LIMITED
    16B Wichester Walk SE1 9AQ
    Greg Strefford
HSBC HOLDINGS PLC
    8 Canada Square E14 5HQ
    Aileen Taylor
IMG (UK) LTD
    Bulding 6, 566 Chiswick High Road W4 5HR
    Dana Gibson
IMMEDIATE MEDIA COMPANY LONDON
LIMITED
    Vineyard House, 44 Brook Green,
    Hammersmith W6 7BT
    Jennifer Lucas
    Emily McQueen
IMPACT RADIUS LIMITED
    15 Rathbone Place W1T 1HU

Rahul Gindha
INDUCTION HEALTHCARE UK LIMITED
    20 St. Dunstan's Hill EC3R 8HL
    Jemma Murray
    Alison Talbot
IQVIA LIMITED
    210 Pentonville Road N1 9JY
    Janice More
IRWIN MITCHELL
    40 Holborn Viaduct EC1N 2PZ
    Elzbieta Olejnik
ISG CENTRAL SERVICES LIMITED
    Aldgate House, 33 Aldgate High Street EC3N
    1AG
    Harsharan Basrai
    Visar Isaj
ITV PLC
    Gray's Inn Road WC1X 8HF
    Jenna Alexander
JAMF
    29 Clerkenwell Road EC1M 5RN
    Thomas Murdock
JANUS HENDERSON INVESTORS
    201 Bishopsgate EC2M 3AE
    Kirsty Gilmartin
    Rosanna Lawson
JUSTICE
    Justice, 59 Carter Lane EC4V 5AQ
    Andrea Fraser
KEYSTONE LAW LIMITED
    48 Chancery Lane WC2A 1JF
    Simon Murfitt
    Fiona Nicolson
    David Thomson
KINGSLEY NAPLEY LLP
    20 Bonhill Street EC2A 4DN
    Rachel Cooper
    Julie Matheson
KIRKLAND & ELLIS INTERNATIONAL LLP
    30 St. Mary Axe EC3A 8AF
    Euan Alston
    Annette Baillie
    Adam Davies
    Latifa El-Shafei
    Jamie Gordon
    Jan Kapaon
    Leon MacMillan
    Alexander Manson
    Andrew McAlpine
    Philip McEachen
    Kirsteen Nicol
    Matthew Pollock
    Sharon Skipper
    Jamie Thomson
    Joanna Thomson
    Jennifer Wilson
K&L GATES LLP
    One New Change EC4M 9AF
    Andrew Alexander
    Craig Fraser
    Natalie Taylor
    Kevin Timlin
KPMG LLP

15 Canada Square, Canary Wharf E14 5GL
Jennifer Phillips
LATHAM & WATKINS (LONDON) LLP
99 Bishopsgate EC2M 3XF
Douglas Abernethy
Ross Anderson
Lewis Atherton
Kendall Burnett
Qi Chen
Aimee Godfrey
Fiona Maclean
Christian McDermott
Alistair McKechnie
Erin McKirdy
Robert McLaren
Alain Traill
Danielle Van Der Merwe
LAW COMMISSION
Post Point 1.52, 1st Floor, Tower, 52 Queen
Anne's Gate SW1H 9AG
Laura Burgoyne
LEALT ENERGY LIMITED
9 South Side, Stamford Brook W6 0XY
Ian McNeill
LEE & THOMPSON
80 Charlotte Street W1T 4DF
Andrew Florence
LEGAL & GENERAL INVESTMENT MANAGEMENT
LTD
One Coleman Street EC2R 5AA
Michael Harrats
LEGAL SECRETARIAT TO THE ADVOCATE
GENERAL
Dover House, 66 Whitehall SW1A 2AU
Sarah Mennie
Lauri Mitchell
LEWIS SILKIN LLP
5 Chancery Lane, Clifford's Inn EC4A 1BL
Nigel Gibb
LEXIS NEXIS
Lexis House, 30 Farringdon Street EC4A 4HH
Leigh Monteforte
LEYTON UK PARTNERS LLP
Harmsworth House, 13-15 Bouverie Street
EC4Y 8DP
Simon Mayberry
LINKLATERS LLP
One Silk Street EC2Y 8HQ
Lizanne Blair
Stephen Murphy
LINK MARKET SERVICES LIMITED
65 Gresham Street EC2V 7NQ
Brooke Modlin
LIQUIDITY SERVICES
3rd Floor, 69 Leadenhall Street EC3A 2BG
Jamie Larkin
LIVINGSTONE BROWN LIMITED
1 Fetter Lane EC4A 1BR
LLOYDS BANKING GROUP PLC
25 Gresham Street EC2V 7HN
Jennifer Chambers
Gregor Watt
MCARTHUR GLEN GROUP

Nations House, 103 Wigmore Street W1U 1QS
Matthew Jamieson
MCDERMOTT WILL & EMERY UK LLP
Heron Tower, 110 Bishopsgate EC2N 4AY
Calum Thom
MACFARLANES LLP
20 Cursitor Street EC4A 1LT
Fiona Beattie
Christopher Boyle
Ryan Moore
Robert Oates
Brodie Thomson
MACQUARIE CORPORATE HOLDINGS PTY
LIMITED (UK BRANCH)
Ropemaker Place, 28 Ropemaker Street EC2Y
9HD
Nicola Hetherington
Veyoma Hevamanage
MANOLETE PARTNERS PLC
21 Gloucester Place W1U 8HR
Rachel Grant
MAYER BROWN INTERNATIONAL LLP
201 Bishopsgate EC2M 3AF
Duncan Watson
MBM COMMERCIAL LLP
57 Berkeley Square W1J 6ER
MILLS & REEVE LLP
24 King William Street EC4R 9AT
Natalie Selman
Edward Sloan
MITIE
Level 12, The Shard, 32 London Bridge Street
SE1 9SG
Catriona Weir
MLAW LLP
3a Montagu Row W1U 6DZ
Neil Paterson
MONTGOMERY SMITH SOLICITORS
7 Bell Yard WC2A 2JR
MORGAN, LEWIS & BOCKIUS UK LLP
Condor House, 5-10 St. Pauls Churchyard
EC4M 8AL
Robert Hutton
MORRISON & FOERSTER
The Scalpel, 52 Lime Street EC3M 7AF
Calum Ablett
Stephanie Craw
NATIONAL WESTMINSTER BANK PLC
250 Bishopsgate, Liverpool Street EC2M 4AA
Alexander Bicket
David Irvine
Victoria Salmon
NOKIA
1 Sheldon Square, Paddington W2 6PY
Lorna Gibb
NOMURA ASSET MANAGEMENT U.K. LIMITED
1 Angel Lane EC4R 3AB
Edward Garcia
Tony Wang
NORGES BANK INVESTMENT MANAGEMENT
Queensbury House, 3 Old Burlington Street
W1S 3AE
Eva Sj sten

NORTON ROSE FULBRIGHT LLP
   3 More London Riverside SE1 2AQ
   Barbara Onuonga
NOTAMVIS LIMITED
   Unit 5 Drakes Courtyard, Kilburn High Road
   NW6 7JR
   David Currie
NUDE FINANCE
   C/O Cms Cameron Mckenna, Cannon Place,
   78 Cannon Street EC4N 6AF
   Kate McKay
OBASEKI SOLICITORS
   27 Bentley Road, Dalston N1 4BY
   Heather Hiram
OFCOM
   Riverside House, 2a Southwark Bridge Road
   SE1 9HA
   Philip Hogg
OPENREACH LIMITED
   Kelvin House, 123 Judd Street WC1H 9NP
   Sophie Thomson
OPEN SOCIETY FOUNDATION LONDON
   4th Floor Herbal House, 8 Back Hill EC1R 5EN
   Susheela Math
OSBORNE CLARKE
   One London Wall EC2Y 5EB
   Clara Hutchison
   David Nisbet
   Louise Oliver
OSPREY CHARGING NETWORK
   1st Floor, 3 More London Riverside SE1 2RE
   Ewen Cairns
PARK PLAZA HOTELS UK SERVICES LIMITED
   County Hall – Riverside Building, 2nd Floor,
   Belvedere Road SE1 7PB
   Andrew Freeman
PAUL HASTINGS (EUROPE) LLP
   100 Bishopsgate EC2N 4AG
   Tsz Li
   Jordan Rhodes
   Ashley Webber
PETERS & PETERS SOLICITORS LLP
   15 Fetter Lane EC4A 1BW
   David Fitzpatrick
PINSENT MASONS LLP
   30 Crown Place EC2A 4ES
   Rebecca Aspinwall
   Kevin Boa
   Christina Cooke
   Luke Costello
   Rebecca Devaney
   Alison Eckford
   Gabriele Geceviciute
   Helen Gray
   Priya Jhakra
   Vladim r Kucera
   Sheelagh MacGregor
   Murdo Maclean
   Rachel McConnell
   Mhairi Morrison
   Stewart Murphy
   Angela Norris
   Tsvetan Petrov

   Fiona Ross
   Amy Stirling
   Stephen Tobin
   Rebecca Townsend
PREMIER OIL PLC
   23 Lower Belgrave Street SW1W 0NR
   Kelly Mitchell
PRICEWATERHOUSECOOPERS LLP
   1 Embankment Place WC2N 6RH
   Laura Freestone
   Caitlin Hurst
PRICEWATERHOUSECOOPERS LLP
   7 More London Riverside SE1 2RT
   Sean Mowatt
PROSKAUER ROSE LLP
   110 Bishopsgate EC2N 4AY
   Mark Hume
PROVIDENCE STRATEGIC GROWTH LLP
   Second Floor, 15 Sloane Square SW1W 8ER
   Fraser McLeod
PTS CONSULTING
   5 Jewry Street EC3N 2EX
   Antonia Shand
QBE MANAGEMENT SERVICES (UK) LTD
   Plantation Place, 30 Fenchurch Street EC3M
   3BD
   Karen Stewart
QS QUACQUARELLI SYMONDS LIMITED
   1 Tranley Mews, Fleet Road NW3 2DG
   Amy Goodbrand
REED SMITH LLP
   The Broadgate Tower, 20 Primrose Street
   EC2A 2RS
   Victoria Bryden
   Thomas Gates
   Natalie Sharkey
REYNOLDS PORTER CHAMBERLAIN LLP
   Tower Bridge House, St Katharine's Way E1W
   1AA
   Heather Clark
   Leigh Gapinski
   Cheryl Laird
RIDGEWALL LIMITED
   Devonshire House, 60 Goswell Road EC1M
   7AD
   Scott Connarty
RIDOUTS PROFESSIONAL SERVICES PLC
   7-10 Chandos Street W1G 9DG
   Laura Shelton
ROOFOODS LTD
   The River Building, 1 Cousin Lane EC4R 3TE
   Thomas Hepburn
ROONEY NIMMO LIMITED
   125 Old Broad Street EC2N 1AR
   Catriona Reid
ROTHCHILDS
   New Court, St Swithin's Lane EC4N 8AL
   Jacob Massey
ROYAL LONDON GROUP
   55 Gracechurch Street EC3V 0RL
   Fergus Speight
ROYAL MAIL GROUP LEGAL
   185 Farringdon Road EC1A 1AA

Wendy Sommerville
RUSSELL-COOKE LLP
  8 Bedford Row WC1R 4BX
  Thomas Ferguson
SACKER & PARTNERS LLP
  20 Gresham Street EC2V 7JE
  Andrew Harper
  Daniel Traynor
SANTANDER
  2 Triton Square, Regents Place NW1 3AN
  Miriam Hall
SAVE THE CHILDREN
  1 St John's Lane EC1M 4AR
  Elizabeth Knox
SCHILLINGS
  12 Arthur Street EC4R 9AB
  Caroline Marshall
SCHRODERS PERSONAL WEALTH
  12th Floor, 1 London Wall EC2Y 5EB
  Jennifer MacDonald
SCOTT+SCOTT UK LLP
  St. Bartholomew House, 90-94 Fleet Street
  EC4Y 1DH
  Douglas Campbell
SENDERWOOD GROUP LIMITED
  2 Brill Place NW1 1DX
  Rhian Saleh Al-Obaidy
SHEARMAN & STERLING (LONDON) LLP
  9 Appold Street EC2A 2AP
  Gina Malone
  Katherine McAlinden
  Jamie Turley
SHELL INTERNATIONAL LIMITED
  Shell Centre SE1 7NA
  Gavin Ross
SHEPHERD AND WEDDERBURN LLP
  Octagon Point, 6th Floor EC2V 6AA
  Walter Blake
  Philip Knowles
  Matthew Lamberton
  Stephanie Mill
  Lisa Renwick
  Sarah Walker
SHOOSMITHS LLP
  1 Bow Churchyard EC4M 9DQ
  Brian Morrison
SIDLEY AUSTIN LLP
  70 St. Mary Axe EC3A 8BE
  James Crooks
  George Finlay
  Gregor Gordon
  Peter McCorkell
SIMMONS & SIMMONS
  Citypoint, 1 Ropemaker Street EC2Y 9SS
  Magdalena Szperzynska
SIMMONS & SIMMONS LLP
  Citypoint, One Ropemaker Street EC2Y 9SS
  Colin Bole
  Angela-Jean Christoforou
SIMPSON THACHER & BARTLETT LLP
  CityPoint, One Ropemaker Street EC2Y 9HU
  Derek Baird
  Carlo Pia

SLAUGHTER AND MAY
  One Bunhill Row EC1Y 8YY
  Paul Dickson
  Catriona Jardine
SODEXO LIMITED
  One Southampton Row WC1B 5HA
  Christopher Lewis-Laverty
SOTHEBY'S
  Compliance and Busienss Integrity, 34-35 New
  Bond Street W1A 2AA
  Melanie Allan
SQUIRE PATTON BOGGS (UK) LLP
  2 & A Half Devonshire Square EC2M 4UJ
  Donald Lawrie Morrison
STARLING BANK LIMITED
  3rd Floor, 2 Finsbury Avenue EC2M 2PP
  Sian Laurie
STEPHENSON HARWOOD LLP
  1 Finsbury Circus EC2M 7SH
  Bethany Carr
  David Harris
STEPTOE & JOHNSON UK LLP
  5 Aldermanbury Square EC2V 7HR
  Simon Tilling
STEWART TITLE LTD
  11 Haymarket SW1Y 4BP
  John Logan
SUNNY HILL ENERGY
  83 Victoria Street, Westminster SW1H 0HW
  Peter Wilson
SWISS RE
  30 St Mary Axe EC3A 8EP
  Claudia Hennecke
TAYLOR WESSING LLP
  5 New Street Square EC4A 3TW
  James Bryden
  Megan Lukins
  Anna McCaffrey
  Ruth Moffett
TEACHER STERN LLP
  37-41 Bedford Row WC1R 4JH
  Lorna Clarke
TELEHOUSE INTERNATIONAL CORPORATIONS
OF EUROPE LTD
  Coriander Avenue E14 2AA
  Bhalindra Bath
THE BUILDING SOCIETIES ASSOCIATION
  6th Floor, York House, 23 Kingsway WC2B 6UJ
  Julie Morton
THE CHILDREN'S INVESTMENT FUND
FOUNDATION (UK)
  Legal Counsel, 7 Clifford Street W1S 2FT
  Gillian Fleming
THE CRANEMERE GROUP LIMITED
  52 Brook Street W1K 5DS
  Catriona Brown
THE OFFSHORE POLLUTION LIABILITY
ASSOCIATION LIMITED
  Reed Smith, Broadgate Tower, Third Floor, 20
  Primrose Street EC2A 2RS
  Jacquelynn Craw
THE PENSIONS OMBUDSMAN
  10 South Colonnade, Canary Wharf E14 4PU

Robert Palmer
THE PREMIER LEAGUE
Brunel Building, 57 North Wharf Road W2 1HQ
Stuart Tennant
THE UNIVERSITY OF LAW
3 Bunhill Row, Moorgate EC1Y 8HQ
Alistair Fraser
TIDEWAY
Cottons Centre, Cottons Lane SE1 2QG
Valmai Barclay
TIKTOK INFORMATION TECHNOLOGIES UK LIMITED
One London Wall, 6th Floor EC2Y 5EB
Peter MacIntyre
TLT LLP
20 Gresham Street EC2V 7JE
TOTAL UK LIMITED
183 Eversholt Street NW1 1BU
Calum Stacey
TOYOTA CONNECTED EUROPE LIMITED
14-18 Handyside Street N1C 4DN
Christopher Paton
TRANSPORT FOR LONDON
5 Endeavour Square, 4th Floor, Yellow Zone, Stratford E20 1JN
Alexandra Lavery
TRAVERS SMITH LLP
10 Snow Hill EC1A 2AL
Stuart Allan
Nicholas Brady
Hugh Hutchison
Caragh Jenkins
Stuart MacKenzie
Genevieve Marten
Andrew Maxwell
Eilidh Morrison
Ailie Murray
Callum O'Brien
Leigh Stockey
Rachel Taggart
Silvana Van Der Velde
Alexander Watt
TRUSTPILOT LIMTED
Minster Building, 3 Minster Court, 5th Floor EC3R 7AG
Graeme Di Rollo
TULLOW OIL PLC
9 Chiswick Park, 566 Chiswick High Road W4 5XT
Adam Holland
TURCAN CONNELL
1st Floor, 12 Stanhope Gate W1K 1AW
UBER LONDON LIMITED
Aldgate Tower – First Floor, 2 Leman Street E1 8FA
Lynn Crichton
UBS.AG
5 Broadgate EC2M 2QS
Fiona Valansot
UNITE THE UNION
Legal Department, Unite House, 128 Theobalds Road WC1X 8TN

Neil Gillam
UNIVERSITY COLLEGE LONDON
UCL Legal Services, Bidborough House, 38-50 Bidborough Street WC1 9BT
Kati Kaarlehto
VARDE PARTNERS EUROPE LIMITED
Level 2, 50 New Bond Street W1S 1BJ
Bruce Hendry
VATTENFALL WIND POWER LTD.
Legal Affairs, First Floor, 1 Tudor Street EC4Y 0AH
Lisa MacLeod
VICASSET ADVISORS (UK) LIMITED
Verde, 10 Bressenden Place SW1E 5DH
Neil Sargent
VODAFONE GROUP SERVICES LIMITED
1 Kingdom Street W2 6BD
Richard Cullen
WAVEMAKER UK
Sea Containers, 18 Upper Ground SE1 9ET
Kirsty Wilson
WEIL, GOTSHAL & MANGES (LONDON) LLP
110 Fetter Lane EC4A 1AY
Kirstin Fyffe
Michael Grant
Tony Herron
WESTCOR INTERNATIONAL LIMITED
City Pavillion, Cannon Green, 27 Bush Lane EC4 0AA
Kirsty Noble
WESTFIELD EUROPE LIMITED
6th Floor, MidCity Place, 71 High Holborn WC1V 6EA
Euan MacDonald
WHITE & CASE LLP
5 Old Broad Street EC2N 1DW
Omar Anwar
Mathew Boyle
Finlay Fraser
Morvyn Radlow
John Timmons
WIGGIN LLP
10th Floor, Met Building, 22 Percy Street W1T 2BU
Gordon Moir
Darren Stevenson
WILLKIE FARR & GALLAGHER (UK) LLP
CityPoint, 1 Ropemaker Street EC2Y 9AW
Megan Gairns
Andrew Gray
Lindsay Murray
WITHERS LLP
20 Old Bailey EC4M 7AN
Christopher Priestley
James Shaw
WOMBLE BOND DICKINSON (UK) LLP
4 More London Riverside SE1 2AU
Iain Pritty
WSP UK LIMITED
WSP House, 70 Chancery Lane WC2A 1AF
Anna Savage
WYELANDS CAPITAL
25 Maddox Street W1S 2QN

Murray Dunn
ZURICH INSURANCE PLC
11th Floor, 70 Mark Lane EC3R 7NQ
Felix Boon

Luton
STONEGATE PUB COMPANY
Porter Tun House, 500 Capability Green LU1 3LS
Andrew Lingard

Manchester
ADDLESHAW GODDARD LLP
One St. Peters Square M2 3AE
David Milne
ALDERMORE BANK PLC
4th Floor, 40 Spring Gardens M2 1EN
Laura Mitchell
AVENSURE LTD
South Central, 11 Peter Street M2 5QR
Richard Morton
BRABNERS LLP
55 King Street M2 4LQ
James Stewart
CMS CAMERON MCKENNA NABARRO OLSWANG LLP
1 The Avenue, Spinningfields M3 3AP
DWF LLP
1 Scott Place, 2 Hardman Street M3 3AA
Naomi Pryde
Hilary Ross
FAIRHOME GROUP
Quays Reach, 16 Carolina Way, Salford M50 2ZY
Laura-May McMorland
GUNNERCOOKE LLP
53 King Street M2 4LQ
Christian Hook
GUNNERCOOKE SCO LLP
53 King Street M2 4LQ
HBM SAYERS
King's House, 42 King Street West M3 2NU
HORWICH FARRELLY SCOTLAND
Alexander House, 94 Talbot Road M16 0SP
LIVINGSTONE BROWN LIMITED
St. James's Tower, 7 Charlotte Street M1 4DZ
MANCHESTER UNITED LIMITED
Sir Matt Busby Way, Old Trafford M16 0RA
Patrick Stewart
PINSENT MASONS LLP
1 The Avenue, Spinningfields M3 3AP
PINSENT MASONS LLP
3 Hardman Street, Spinningfields M3 3AU
Kathryn McBride
SHOOSMITHS LLP
The XYZ Building, 2 Hardman Boulevard M3 3AZ
THE HUT GROUP PLC
THG PLC, 4M Office Building, Malaga Avenue M90 3RR
Anne-Marie Bradshaw
TLT LLP

3 Hardman Square M3 3EB
Navid Mesbah

Milton Keynes
DENTONS UK AND MIDDLE EAST LLP
The Pinnacle, 170 Midsummer Boulevard MK9 1FE
SHOOSMITHS LLP
100 Avebury Boulevard MK9 1FH

Newcastle Upon Tyne
ABERDEIN CONSIDINE AND COMPANY
Merchant House, 30 Cloth Market NE1 1EE
CLIFFORD CHANCE LLP
Partnership House, Regent Farm Road NE3 3AF
Gillian Sidey
CLYDE & CO LLP
Central Square South, Orchard Street NE1 3AZ
Emily Blackett
ENGIE
Engie Buildings Limited, Q3, Quorum Business Park, Benton Lane NE12 8EX
Sarah Channin
EVERSHEDS SUTHERLAND (INTERNATIONAL) LLP
Central Square South, Orchard Street NE1 3XX
JACKSON'S
Central Square, Forth Street NE1 3PJ
Isabelle Edmondson
NORTH OF ENGLAND PROTECTING AND INDEMNITY ASSOCIATION
100 Quayside NE1 3DU
Ross Waddell
SIEMENS GAMESA RENEWABLE ENERGY
4 Quick Silver Way, Cobalt Business Park NE27 0QQ
James Everden
UNIVERSITY OF NORTHUMBRIA
Room 105, Law School, City Campus East NE1 8ST
Michael Smith
WOMBLE BOND DICKINSON (UK) LLP
St Ann's Wharf, 112 Quayside NE1 3DX
George Lyall
David Ridley

Northampton
SHOOSMITHS LLP
The Lakes NN4 7SH

Norwich
AVIVA PLC
PO Box 89, Carrara 4, Surrey Street NR1 3DR
Grant Crockart
BIRKETTS LLP
Kingfisher House, 1 Gilders Way NR3 1UB
Jan Pointer
NORWICH CITY FOOTBALL CLUB PLC
Carrow Road NR1 1JE
Samuel Hall

Nottingham
EVERSHEDS SUTHERLAND (INTERNATIONAL) LLP
Water Court, 116-118 Canal Street NG1 7HF
EXPERIAN LIMITED
Riverleen House, Electric Avenue
Ailsa Gormly
SHOOSMITHS LLP
Waterfront House, Waterfront Plaza NG2 3DQ

Oxford
FREETHS LLP
Spire House, 5700 Oxford Business Park South
OX4 2RW
Benjamin Filmer

Peterborough
TRAVELEX CENTRAL SERVICES LIMITED
Worldwide House, Thorpe Wood PE3 6SB
Philip Morrison

Plymouth
WOMBLE BOND DICKINSON (UK) LLP
Ballard House, West Hoe Road PL1 3AE

Preston
BAKER HARDMAN LIMITED
1A Fairways Office Park, Pittman Way PR2 9LF
KUDOS LEGAL LIMITED
11 Cable Court, Pittman Way PR2 9YW
TURNER & WHITE LIMITED
99/101 Garstang Road PR1 1LD

Reading
ANESCO LIMITED
The Green,, Easter Park, Benyon Road RG7
2PQ
Donna Turnbull
CMS CAMERON MCKENNA NABARRO
OLSWANG LLP
The Blade, Abbey Square RG1 3BE
SHOOSMITHS LLP
Apex Plaza, Forbury Road RG1 1SH
THALES UK LIMITED
350 Longwater Avenue, Green Park RG2 6GF
Nichola McKay
THE UNIVERSITY OF READING
Legal Services Department, G11 ,
Whiteknights House, PO Box 217 RG6 6AH
Lisa Kaplanski

Richmond
WILLIAMS MULLEN
200 South 10th Street, Suite 1600 23219
Robert Dewar

Rochdale
KINETIC LAWYERS LTD
146 Yorkshire Street OL16 1LD

Ruscombe
RUSCOMBE MANAGEMENT SERVICES LIMITED
33 New Road RG10 9LN
Donald Stewart

Salford
BERRYMANS LACE MAWER LLP
2 New Bailey, 6 Stanley Street M3 5GS
Christopher Fletcher
Ashia Nazar
BLM
Two New Bailey Square, 6 Stanley Street M3
5GS
EVERSHEDS SUTHERLAND (INTERNATIONAL) LLP
Two New Bailey, 6 Stanley Street M3 5GX
Morven Alexander
Fiona Barker
GREENTREE LEGAL LIMITED
HQ, Clippers Quays, Salford Quays M50 3XP
KIER LIMITED
2nd Floor, Optimum House, Clippers Quay
M50 3XP
Farah Clark
Neil Wilson

Salisbury
PARKER BULLEN LLP
45 Castle Street SP1 3SS
Leigh Barnett

Sheffield
ACCELERATED DIGITAL VENTURES LTD
Electric Works, Concourse Way S1 2BJ
Andrew Sloane
CMS CAMERON MCKENNA NABARRO
OLSWANG LLP
1-3 Charter Square S1 4HS
DLA PIPER UK LLP
1 St Paul's Place S1 2JX
Aaron Lyons

Southampton
BERRYMANS LACE MAWER LLP
Charlotte Place SO14 0TB
MARKET OPERATOR SERVICES LIMITED
White Building, 1-4 Cumbernauld Place SO15
2NP
Jacqueline Doherty
WOMBLE BOND DICKINSON (UK) LLP
Oceana House, 39-49 Commercial Road SO15
1GA

Sunbury-on-Thames
BP INTERNATIONAL LTD
Chertsey Road TW16 7LN
Layla Al-Hassani
Clare Haley
Yvonne McAllister
Christopher Montgomery

Surrey
AXA ASSISTANCE (UK) LIMITED

The Quadrangle, 106-118 Station Road RH1
1PR
Lorraine Deschildre
BLACK & VEATCH (UK) LIMITED
1 Farnham Road, Guildford GU2 4RG
Gordon Wilson
KELLOGG BROWN & ROOT (U.K.) LIMITED
Hill Park Court, Springfield Drive, Leatherhead
KT22 7NL
Gina Wilson
NOTONTHEHIGHSTREET
63 Kew Road, Richmond TW9 2NQ
Noor Al Naeme

Sutton Coldfield
PORTFOLIO LEGAL LTD
1 Coleshill Street B72 1SD
Robert Hankin

Tavistock
CHILCOTTS
10 Plymouth Road PL19 8AY
David Wilde

Telford
SCHNEIDER ELECTRIC LIMITED
Stafford Park 5 TF3 3BL
Rose O'Donnell

Tunbridge Wells
LOCH EMPLOYMENT LAW
Oxford House, 15-17 Mount Ephraim Road
Pamela Loch

Uxbridge
CNOOC PETROLEUM EUROPE LIMITED
Prospect House, 97 Oxford Road UB8 1LU
Paul Gunn
KUEHNE + NAGEL LIMITED
1 Roundwood Avenue, Stockley Park UB11
1FG
Daniel O'Brien

Warwick
WRIGHT HASSALL LLP
Olympia House, Olympus Avenue, Royal
Leamington Spa CV34 6BF
Laura Shields

Watford
DE LAGE LANDEN LEASING LIMITED
Building 7, Croxley Green Business Park WD18
8YN
Bimah Khan
DENTONS UK AND MIDDLE EAST LLP
6th Floor, Station Road WD18 1AF
MEDTRONIC LIMITED
Building 9, Croxley Park, Hatters Lane WD18
8WW
Caroline Scott
TJX EUROPE
73 Clarendon Road WD17 1HE

Ceilidh Thomson

West Drayton
TESLA MOTORS LIMITED
197 Horton Road UB7 8JD
Murray Towers

Widnes
STOBART GROUP
Viking House, Mathieson Road WA8 0NX
Adam Davidson

Wilmslow
CITATION LIMITED
Kings Court, Water Lane SK9 5AR
Amanda Deeley

Woking
JAMES WALKER GROUP LIMITED
Lion House, 147 Oriental Road GU22 8AP
Kirstie McDonald

FALKLAND IS (MALVINAS)

Stanley
PINSENT MASONS LLP
45 John Street F1QQ 1ZZ
Alison Inglis

FRANCE

Courbevoie
TECHNIPFMC SUBSEA FRANCE
1 Bis Place de La Defense, Tour Trinity 92400
Lynne Dalrymple

La Defence Cedex
TOTAL S.A.
Exploration & Production, Legal Dept, 2 Place
Jean Millier, La Defense 6 92078
Graeme Hood
Sarah Vass

Paris
ADDLESHAW GODDARD (EUROPE) LLP
29-31 Rue de Courcelles 75008
Katherine Golding
BNP PARIBAS
37 Avenue de L'Opera 75002
Alasdair MacKay
DWF (FRANCE) AARPI
137 – 139 Rue de L'Universit 75007
Anne-Sylvie Vassenaix-Paxton
EVERSHEDS SUTHERLAND (FRANCE) LLP
8 Place d'Iena 75116
HERBERT SMITH FREEHILLS PARIS LLP
66 Avenue Marceau 75008
Paul Morton
NATIXIS
68-76 Quai de La Rapee 75012

Gail Cochrane
NORTON ROSE FULBRIGHT LLP
  ParisEight, 40, Rue De Courcelles 75008
  George Paterson
PINSENT MASONS LLP
  21-23 Rue Balzac 75008

Suresnes Cedex
SUBSEA 7 FRANCE
  1 Quai Marcel Dassault 92156
  Sarah Bremner

GERMANY

Bremen
WEBER-STEINHAUS SMITH & KLEIN
  Postfach 10 72.27 28072
  Lesley Smith

Frankfurt
MOODY'S GROUP DEUTSCHLAND GMBH
  An Der Welle 5 60322
  Christopher Shaw

Frankfurt Am Main
NINTENDO EUROPE GMBH
  Goldsteinstrasse 235 60528
  Calum Robertson

GUERNSEY

St Peter Port
CAREY OLSEN
  Carey House, Les Banques GY1 4BZ
  Steven Balmer
  Lois Madden
  Kirsty McGeough
  Kieran Ogilvie
  Michelle Young
COLLAS CRILL
  Glategny Court, PO Box 140, Glategny
  Esplanade GY1 4EW
  Quentin Bregg
  Donald Millar
JTC GROUP
  Ground Floor Dorey Court, Admiral Park GY1
  2HT
  Gillian Jordan
MOURANT OZANNES (GUERNSEY) LLP
  Royal Chambers, St Julian's Avenue GY1 4HP
  Greg Coburn
  Iona Mitchell
OGIER
  Ogier House, St Julian's Avenue GY1 1WA
  Matthew Macfarlane
  James Walsh
VISTRA FUND SERVICES (GUERNSEY) LIMITED
  11 New Street GY1 2JY
  Katie McPherson

HONG KONG

Hong Kong
DLA PIPER HONG KONG
  Floor 25, Three Exchange Square, 8
  Connaught Place, Central
  Lauren Hurcombe
EVERSHEDS SUTHERLAND (INTERNATIONAL) LLP
  21/F Gloucester Tower, The Landmark
HARNEYS
  3501 The Center, 99 Queen's Road Central,
  Road Town
  Ian Clark
HONG KONG MONETARY AUTHORITY
  55th Floor, Two International Finance Centre,
  8 Finance Street, Central
  Shirley Chung
KING & WOOD MALLESONS
  13/F Gloucester Tower, The Landmark, 15
  Queen's Road Central
  Chloe Chan
MAYER BROWN
  16th-19th Floors, Princes Building, 10 Chater
  Road, Central
  Alan Linning
MOURANT OZANNES
  1002-1008, 10/F Gloucester Tower, Landmark,
  15 Queens Road Central
  Catriona Hunter
OAKTREE CAPITAL MANAGEMENT
  20/F Champion Tower, 3 Garden Road
  Allan Wardrop-Szilagyi
SEYFARTH SHAW
  Unit 3701, 37/F, Edinburgh Tower, The
  Landmark, 15 Queen's Road Central
  Aimee Hinksman
SHINE EFFORT INC LIMITED
  1103-1105 Saxon Tower, 7 Cheung Shun
  Street, Cheung Sha Wan
  Alexander Grieve
SULLIVAN & CROMWELL (HONG KONG)
  20th Floor, Alexandra House, 18 Chater Road,
  Central
  Jamieson Logie
ZURICH INSURANCE (HONG KONG)
  25-26/F, One Island East, 18 Westlands Road,
  Island East
  Fiona Cheng

INDONESIA

Jakarta
HADIPUTRANTO, HADINOTO & PARTNERS
  Pacific Century Place, Level 35, Sudirman
  Central Busiess District Lot 10, Jl. Jend.
  Sudirman Kav 52-53 12190
  Norman Bissett

IRELAND

Dublin
ADOBE SYSTEMS SOFTWARE IRELAND

4-6 Riverwalk Drive, Citywest Business
Campus, Cooldown Commons D24 DCW0
Natasha Simmons
ARAMARK IRELAND
Newenham House, Northern Cross D17 AY61
Isla Stewart
DLA PIPER IRELAND LLP
40 Molesworth Street DO2 YV57
Blayre McBride
Scott Traynor
IRISH DISTILLERS LIMTED
Simmonscourt House, Ballsbridge 4
Ailsa Mapplebeck
POSEIDON ENHANCED TECHNOLOGIES
LIMITED
3 Burlington Road D04 RD68
Jessel Shah-Gair

Leixlip
INTEL IRELAND LTD
Collinstown Industrial Park
Caroline Stakim

ISLE OF MAN

Douglas
APPLEBY
33 Athol Street IM1 1LB
Claire Milne

JAPAN

Tokyo
HERBERT SMITH FREEHILLS LLP
Midtown Tower, 41st Floor 9-7-1, Akasaka,
Minato-Ku 107 6241
Paul Flynn

JERSEY

St Helier
APPLEBY
13 – 14 Esplanade JE1 1BD
Mark Brady
Keanu Newman
BEDELL CRISTIN JERSEY PARTNERSHIP
26 New Street JE2 3RA
Natasha Bairstow
Elizabeth Shaw
CAREY OLSEN
47 Esplanade JE1 0BD
Rachael Barber
Caitlin Connor
Julie Currie
Lauren Gray
Caitlin Hagart
Laura Healy
Calum Hedley
Cathryn Houston
Daniel Johnstone
Steven Khan

Jennifer Liss
Timothy McAlpine-Scott
Stuart McRobbie
Ashley Morrison
Mark Slater
David Taylor
Katherine Tresca
Catriona Urquhart
COFRA JERSEY LIMITED
2nd Floor, Windward House, La Route de La
Liberation JE2 3BQ
Colin Dow
COLLAS CRILL
Gasp House, Glategny Court, 66-72 Esplanade
JE1 4XD
Harriet Bovingdon
Lynne Calder
Craig Dinnett
Pamela Doherty
HSBC BANK PLC
HSBC House, Esplanade JE1 1HS
Benjamin Bestgen
LC INTERACTIVE LTD
3rd Floor, The Le Gallais Building, 54 Bath
Street JE2 4SU
Euan Hutcheon
MOURANT OZANNES
22 Grenville Street JE4 8PX
Sarah Burns
Anita Dhesi
Simone Farrer
Alana Gillies
James Goddard
Paul Green
Andrew Haslett
Sean Hedges
Corrie Howarth
Sarah Kerr
Fiona Magee
Gemma Sichi
NORDIC CAPITAL LIMITED
26 Esplanade JE2 3QA
Jamie Purdy
OGIER
44 The Esplanade JE4 9WG
Michael Anderson
Mark Watson
Chloe Watson-Hill
James Whiteside
ROYAL BANK OF SCOTLAND INT. LTD
PO Box 64, 71 Bath Street JE4 8BJ
Susan Purdy
STATES OF JERSEY
Law Officers' Department, Morier House JE1
1DD
Timothy Glennie
VIBERTS JERSEY LAWYERS
PO Box 737, Don Street JE4 8ZQ
Emily Paris-Hunter
WALKERS
PO Box 72, Walker House, 28-34 Hill Street
JE4 8PN
Jennifer Brunton

Louise Hamilton
Craig MacLeod
Megan McAuley
Olivia Palloch

KENYA

Nairobi
ANJARWALLA & KHANNA LLP
The Oval, 3rd Floor, Junction of Ring Rd,
Parklands & Jalaram Road, Westlands
Roderick McKean

LUXEMBOURG

Luxembourg
RAKUTEN EUROPE S. .R.L.
2 Rue Du Fosse L-1536
Kieran Lynch

MONACO

Monaco
GROOM HILL
24, Boulevard Princesse Charlotte 98000
Iona Doohan

NETHERLANDS

Amsterdam
FRESHFIELDS BRUCKHAUS DERINGER
Strawinskylaan 10 1077
Louise Bell
UBER
Mr. Treublaan 7, 3e Verdjieping, 1017 HL
Daniel Kinloch

The Hague
SHELL INTERNATIONAL B.V.
Carel Van Bylandtlaan 30, Postbus 162 2501
AN
Karen Halliday

NEW ZEALAND

Auckland
MINTER ELLISON RUDD WATT
PwC Tower, 15 Customs Street West 1010
Alastair Gatt

NORTHERN IRELAND

Belfast
HERBERT SMITH FREEHILLS LLP
3 Cromac Quay, Ormeau Gasworks BT7 2JD
Charlotte McAfee
HMRC
20-32 Chichester Street BT1 4GF
Linda Hamilton

PINSENT MASONS LLP
Soloist Building, 1 Lanyon Place BT1 3LP
STRATEGIC INVESTMENT BOARD
5th Floor, 9 Lanyon Place BT1 3LP
Gregor Hamilton
TLT NI LLP
29-33 Montgomery Street BT1 4NX
TUGHANS
Marlborough House, 30 Victoria Street BT1
3GG
Douglas Anderson

NORWAY

Fornebu
AKER SOLUTIONS AS
Oksen yveien 8 1360
Rachel Stuart

Oslo
SIEMENS ENERGY AS
LC EAF RC-SE NO, Oestre Aker Vei 88, 596
Jacqueline Langeroed

OMAN

Ruwi
AL BUSAIDY, MANSOOR JAMAL & CO.
PO Box 686 112
Robert Booth
DENTONS & CO
Oman Branch, Salam Square South, 3rd Floor,
Madinat Sultan Qaboos, PO Box 3552 PC 112
Sadaf Buchanan

POLAND

Warsaw
LINKLATERS SP.K. WISNIEWSKI I WSP LNICY
Q22, Al. Jana Pawla II 22 00-133
Klaudia Owsianka

QATAR

Doha
AL JAZEERA MEDIA NETWORK
Television Roundabout, PO BOX 23123 56
Barry Smith
EVERSHEDS SUTHERLAND (INTERNATIONAL) LLP
Qatar Financial Centre, PO Box 24148, Office
1101 QFC Tower
NORTH OIL COMPANY
P.O. Box 21264 A
Andrew Russell
PINSENT MASONS LLP
PO Box 22758, 35th Floor, Tornado Tower

ROMANIA

Bucharest
MCGREGOR & PARTNERS S.C.A.
  17 Porumbaru Emanoil St., Sector 1 11421
  Neil McGregor
SCHLUMBERGER OILFIELD EUROPE SRL
  1A Sergeant Constantin Ghercu Street, The
  Bridge 2, 6th Floor
  David Cargill
  Emma Murdoch

SAUDI ARABIA

Riyadh
NORTON ROSE FULBRIGHT US LLP
  Al-Nakhlah Tower, 17th Floor, King Fahad
  Road, As Sahafah, PO Box 52681 11573
  David Johnston
SAUDI ARABIAN GENERAL INVESTMENT
AUTHORITY
  PO Box 5927 11432
  Ibrar Chishti
THE SAUDI ARABIAN MINING COMPANY
(MA'ADEN)
  Ma'aden Building, Abi Baker Al Siddiq Street,
  PO Box 68861 11537
  James More

South Doha District
THE LAW FIRM OF SALAH AL-HEJAILAN
  In Association With, Freshfields Bruckhaus
  Deringer LLP, Loft No.6, Alturki Business Park
  PO BOX 405
  Rodger Murray

SINGAPORE

Singapore
ADDLESHAW GODDARD LLP
  10 Collyer Quay, #40-00 Ocean Financial
  Centre 49315
AKIN GUMP STRAUSS HAUER & FELD LLP
  2 Shenton Way, ~16-01 SGX Cente 1 68804
  Euan Strachan
ASURION SINGAPORE PTE LTD
  7 Temasek Boulevard, Suntec Tower One
  #09-01 38987
  Aaron Mitchell
BAKER & MCKENZIE. WONG & LEOW
  8 Marina Boulevard, #05-01 Marina Bay
  Financial Centre, Tower 1 18981
  Arwen Berry
CAREY OLSEN SINGAPORE LLP
  10 Collyer Quay #24-08, Ocean Financial
  Centre 49315
  Susan McKinstray
CREDIT SUISSE AG
  1 Raffles Link, #03/04-01 South Lobby 39393
  Adam Dryburgh
DDOG SINGAPORE PTE LTD

38 Beach Road, #29-11 South Beach Tower
189767
  Robert Irvine
MAPLES AND CALDER (SINGAPORE) LLP
  1 Raffles Place, #32-02A One Raffles Place
  48616
  Iain Anderson
MAYER BROWN LLP
  6 Battery Road, #12-03 49909
  Kieran McLaughlin
NEURON MOBILITY PTE LTD
  37 Jalan Pemimpin, #07-17 577177
  Lucy Hunter
PERPETUAL
  16 Collyer Quay #07-01 49318
  Gary McKinstray
PINSENT MASONS MPILLAY LLP
  182 Cecil Street, #32-01 Frasers Tower 69547
  Ian Laing

SPAIN

Barcelona
ACTIVE VENTURE PARTNERS SGEIC SAU
  Av. Diagonal 401, 2 Bis 8008
  Blair MacLaren

Madrid
PINSENT MASONS ESPANA SLP
  Serrano 90 28006
  Colin McIntosh
  Helen Stewart

SWEDEN

Stockholm
MCD SPORTS & LEGAL AB
  Lundag rdsv gen 30, Sp nga 16351
  Jamie McDonald
NASDAQ NORDIC
  Tullvaktsv gen 15 105 78
  Grant McKelvey

SWITZERLAND

Baar
TRANS ADRIATIC PIPELINE AG
  Lindenstrasse 2 6340
  Bryan Kane

Baar-Zug
PARTNERS GROUP AG
  Zugerstrasse 57 6341
  Victoria Stewart

Geneva
G MATTHEW CONSULTANTS LLP
  2, Avenue Calas 1206
  Gordon Matthew
LALIVE

Rue de La Mairie 35, P.O. Box 6569 1211
Rona Amigues-MacRae

Lugano
STUDIO LEGALE DANICA M.T. GIANOLA
Palazzo Gargantini, Via Guglielmo Marconi 4
6900
Danica Gianola

Zurich
FIFA
FIFA-Strasse 20, PO Box 8044
Alasdair Bell

THAILAND

Bangkok
AGODA COMPANY PTE LTD
999/9 The Offices At Central World 27 Fl
10330
Stewart Raeside

TURKEY

Istanbul
EURASIA CONSULTANTS LTD
CumhuriyetCad, No. 25, Cinar AptK4, TAKSIM
34437
Jonathan Blythe
PINSENT MASONS LLP
Buyukdere Caddesi No 173, 1 Levent Plaza
7th Floor

UNITED ARAB EMIRATES

Abu Dhabi
ABU DHABI NATIONAL OIL COMPANY
Group Corporate Governance Division, PO
Box 898
Johanna Armstrong
ABU DHABI NATIONAL OIL COMPANY
Legal, Compliance and Governance, Floor 15,
Al Salam Street, Sheikh Zayed Street, PO Box
4017
Alaina Ramsay
ADNOC GLOBAL TRADING LTD
25th Floor, Al Sarab Tower, ADGM Square, Al
Maryah Island, PO Box 764649
Gregor Boyd
ADNOC LOGISTICS AND SERVICES
Legal, Governance and Compliance Dept.,
Sheikh Khalifa Energy Complex, PO Box 61
Gordon Inkson
ALDAR PROPERTIES PJSC
Aldar HQ, Al Raha Beach 51133
Katy Thomson
BRYAN CAVE LEIGHTON PAISNER LLP
Level 20, Al Sila Tower, Al Maryah Island
109403
Hazel Quinn

DENTONS & CO
Level 4, Trade Centre – West Tower, Abu
Dhabi Mall, PO Box 47656
Craig Hughson
DLA PIPER MIDDLE EAST LLP
PO Box 109950, Level 10, EIBFS Building,
Muroor Road
Nicola De Sylva
FLASH ENTERTAINMENT FZ-LLC
Floor 3, Park Rotana Complex, TwoFour54, PO
Box 77828
Fraser MacKinven
FRESHFIELDS BRUCKHAUS DERINGER
Level 6, Al Sila Tower, Abu Dhabi Global
Market Square, Al Maryah Island, PO Box
129817
Cheree Gemmell
MUBADALA INVESTMENT COMPANY PJSC
Ethics & Compliance Team, PO Box 45005
Julia Moffat
Dominic Sheils

Dubai
ACCES LEGAL FZ LLC
Al Saaha Office B, 404, Souk Al Bahar, Burj
Khalifa District, P.O. Box 487177
Kevin Cobb
ADDLESHAW GODDARD (MIDDLE EAST) LLP
Level 6, Burj Daman Tower, Dubai
International Financial Centre, PO Box 506555
Antonia Grieve
Ben Thomas
AFRIDI & ANGELL
PO Box 9371, Emirates Tower – Level 35,
Sheikh Zayed Road A
Danielle Hashmi
ALLEN & OVERY LLP
11th Floor, Burj Daman Building, Al Sa'ada
Street, DIFC, PO Box 506678
Rushal Noor
AL TAMIMI & COMPANY
DIFC, Building 4, 6th Floor, Sheikh Zayed
Road, PO Box 9275 A
Gordon Barr
Victoria Smylie
BAKER HUGHES ENERGY FZE
Baker Hughes HQ Building, National Industries
Park, PO Box 567, Jebel Ali
John Bowman
BAKER MCKENZIE HABIB AL MULLA
Level 14, O14 Tower, Al Abraj Street, Business
Bay, PO Box 2268
Kellie Blyth
Joanna Matthews
BARCLAYS BANK PLC
Dubai International Financial Centre, Gate
Village Building 10, PO BOX 506504
Fiona Critchley
CIGNA INSURANCE MIDDLE EAST S.A.L
Dubai World Trade Centre – One Central, The
Offices Building 3, Level1, Office 111 PO
124455
Karen Gilbert

CLIFFORD CHANCE LLP
Level 15, Burj Daman, Dubai International
Financial Centre, PO Box 9380 A
Daniel Boyle
CLYDE & CO LLP
PO Box 7001, Rolex Tower, Sheikh Zayed
Road
Adela Motyckova
CMS CAMERON MCKENNA NABARRO
OLSWANG LLP
Level 15, Burj Daman, Dubai International
Finance Centre
Ashleigh Bruce
John Geddes
Blair Jones
Greg Sibbald
Geoffrey Smith
DAVIDSON & CO
PO Box 34002, Suite 504, Shangri La Offices,
Sheikh Zayed Road
Andrew Lyons
Joanna Stewart
DECHERT LLP
Building 2, Level 5, Dubai International
Financial Centre, PO BOX 506675
Katrina Morrison
DENTONS & CO
Level 18, Boulevard Plaza Tower 2, Burj Khalifa
District, PO Box 1756 A
Meghan Devine
DLA PIPER MIDDLE EAST LLP
Level 9, Standard Chartered Tower,
Downtown, PO BOX 121662
Richard Hughes
Louise Reid
Iain Skinner
DP WORLD
5th Floor, LOB 17, Jebel Ali Free Zone, PO Box
17000
Louisa Boyack
DUBAI HOLDING LLC
Umm Suqeim Street, PO Box 66000
Louise Skipper
DUBAI MULTI COMMODITIES CENTRE
Almas Tower, Jumeirah Lakes Towers, P.O Box
48800 A
Shonagh MacVicar
DUBAI PROPERTIES LLC
Vision Tower, Al Khaleej Al Tejari 1 Street,
Business Bay, PO Box 500272 DUBAI
Joseph Neilson
EMERSON FZE
P.O. Box 17033, Jebel Ali
Catriona Murray
EVERSHEDS SUTHERLAND (INTERNATIONAL) LLP
Unit 804, 8th Floor, Emaar Square, Building 6
FRESHFIELDS BRUCKHAUS DERINGER
20th Floor, Al Fattan Currency Tower, P.O. Box
506 569, DIFC
Tabasam Faqir
FTI CONSULTING MEDIA CENTER FZ LLC
Level 29, Media One Tower, PO Box 502428,
Dubai Internet City

David Forbes
GIBSON, DUNN & CRUTCHER LLP
Building 5, Level 4, Dubai International
Financial Centre, P.O. Box 506654 A
Fraser Dawson
Ryan Whelan
HERBERT SMITH FREEHILLS LLP
Dubai International Financial Centre, Gate
Village 7, Level 4
Christopher Walters
HSBC BANK MIDDLE EAST LIMITED
Building No.5, Level 6, East Wing Emaar
Square, PO Box 502601
John Tothill
INTERNATIONAL CRICKET COUNCIL
Street 69, Dubai Sports City, PO Box 500070
Stephanie Daniel
INVESTMENT CORPORATION OF DUBAI
5th Floor, Building 7, Gate Village, Dubai
International Financial Centre 333888
Faris Hadi
LATHAM & WATKINS LLP
Dubai International Financial Centre, ICD
Brookfield Place, Level 16, P.O Box 506698
Alexander Hendry
LINKLATERS LLP
Precinct Building 3, Dubai International
Financial Centre, PO Box 506516
David Hayward
MCKINSEY & COMPANY INC.
Level 4, Building 4, Dubai International
Financial Centre, PO Box 33538
Patricia Wardrop
NORTON ROSE FULBRIGHT (MIDDLE EAST) LLP
4th Floor, Gate Precinct Building 3, Dubai IFC,
PO Box 103747
Thomas Herd
PINSENT MASONS LLP
The Offices 1, One Central
Nesreen Osman
Ruth Stephen
SIMMONS & SIMMONS MIDDLE EAST LLP
PO Box 506688, Level 7, The Gate Village
Building 10
Tara Jamieson
SQUIRE PATTON BOGGS (MEA) LLP
Dubai International Financial Centre, Burj
Daman Office Tower, Level 10, P.O. Box
111713
John Skipper
STEPHENSON HARWOOD LLP
Office 1302, 13th Floor, Burj Daman Bldg, Al
Mustaqbal Street, DIFC, P.O. Box 482017
Laura Anderson
TROWERS & HAMLINS LLP
Office 2403, Level 24, Boulevard Plaza Tower
2, Downtown, PO Box 23092
Cheryl Cairns
VALARIS
Al Moosa Tower 2, Suite 2601, Sheikh Zayed
Road, PO Box 72453
Elaine Sims
WALKERS (DUBAI) LLP

Level 14, Burj Daman, Dubai International Financial Centre, PO Box 506513
Szymon Durlo
WEATHERFORD DRILLING INTERNATIONAL
Rasis Business Centre, 5th Floor, Al Barsha 1, Off First Al Khail Road, PO Box 58014
Alan McGregor

Ras Al Khaimah
RAK GAS L.L.C.
6th Floor, RAK Gas Building, Al Jazah Road, P.O. Box 434
Philip MacLean

Sharjah
PETROFAC INTERNATIONAL LIMITED
Petrofac House, Al-Khan Road, P.O. Box 23467
Nicola Dorgham-Milne

UNITED STATES

California
LATHAM & WATKINS LLP
355 South Grand Avenue, Suite 100, Los Angeles 90071-1560
Andrew Clark

Carlsbad
LIFE TECHNOLOGIES LIMITED
5791 Van Allen Way 92008
Genoffir MacLeod

Greensboro
VOLVO FINANCIAL SERVICES LLC
7025 Albert Pick Road, Suite 105 27409
Alexia Maas

Houston
NVENT
7433 Harwin Dr.#2007 77036
Jenna McGowan

Maryland
MILES & STOCKBRIDGE P.C.
100 Light Street, Baltimore 21202
Stephen Cullen

Milwaukee
MOLSON COORS BEVERAGE COMPANY
VP, Ethics & Compliance, 3939 West Highland Blvd 53208
Elaine Pretorius

Minneapolis
DORSEY & WHITNEY LLP
Suite 1500, 50 South Sixth Street 55402
Rhona Schmidt

Minnesota
UNITEDHEALTHCARE GLOBAL SOLUTIONS
9700 Health Care Lane, Minnetonka 55343
Simon Hawthorne

New York
BANK OF AMERICA MERRILL LYNCH
15/F Bank of America Tower, One Bryant Park 10036
Niccola Russo
KIRKLAND & ELLIS LLP
601 Lexington Avenue 10022
Olus la Paterson-Marke
MURRAY LLP
305 Broadway, 7th Floor NY 10007
Anthony Murray
PRICEWATERHOUSECOOPERS LLP
300 Madison Avenue NY 10017
Ruth MacRitchie
STERLING & STERLING LLC
135 Crossways Park Drive, Woodbury 11797
Adrienne Shepherd
WILLIAM GRANT & SONS LTD.
300 Park Avenue South 10010
William Payne

San Diego
MITCHELL INTERNATIONAL, INC
6220 Greenwich Drive CA 92122
Jana Kissel

San Francisco
SITECORE USA INC
101 California Street, Suite 1600 94111
Rachael Ormiston

Texas
FLUOR CORPORATION
6700 Las Colinas Blvd, Irving 750+
Fritha Wheeler-Ozanne

WALES

Cardiff
BERRYMANS LACE MAWER LLP
Unit 21/22, Neptune Court CF24 5PJ
EVERSHEDS SUTHERLAND (INTERNATIONAL) LLP
1 Callaghan Square CF10 5BT
Helen Marriott
WHICH LTD
3 Capital Quarter, Tyndell Street CF10 4BZ
Benjamin Rossor

Accountants

THE INSTITUTE OF CHARTERED ACCOUNTANTS OF SCOTLAND
(Incorporated by Royal Charter in 1854)

Edinburgh: CA House, 21 Haymarket Yards, Edinburgh EH12 5BH

Glasgow: 2nd Floor, 7 West Nile Street Glasgow G1 2PR
Tel: 0131 347 0100
Email: connect@icas.com Web: www.icas.com
Current listings of CA Firms and/or Members can be found at: https://www.icas.com/find-a-ca

ICAS (the Institute of Chartered Accountants of Scotland) is the first professional body for accountants and was created by Royal Charter in 1854. ICAS has over 24,000 students and members worldwide who work in a variety of areas such as industry, public practice and the financial sector in more than 100 countries around the world.

2021-2022
President: Bruce Pritchard BA, CA, FioD
Deputy President: Indy Hothi CA
Vice President: Clive Bellingham CA
Chief Executive: Bruce Cartwright
Executive Director, Regulation: Robert Mudge
Chief Operating Officer: Lesley Glen LLB (Hons) CPFA
Executive Director, Customer Experience: Carolyn Spencer
Executive Director, Member Engagement and Communications: Sarah Speirs

Council Members (Scotland):
Chris Campbell CA, Emily Cheyne CA, Margaret Bunyan CA, John Watson CA, Sobhan Afzal CA, Bernard Dunn CA

Open Seat Members:
Eleanor Bentley CA
David Cruickshank CA

Annie Graham CA
Louise Page CA
Jim Robertson CA
Derek Treanor CA

Co-opted Members:
Alison Cromwell CA
Robert Grome CA
Alan Horn CPA CA
Philip Johnson FCA
Tracey Rob Perera CA

Public Interest Members:
Colin McClatchie CBE FRSE
Ana Stewart
Dame Lin Homer
Dr Philip Rycroft CB

THE ASSOCIATION OF CHARTERED CERTIFIED ACCOUNTANTS *(Incorporated by Royal Charter)*

110 Queen Street, Glasgow, G1 3BX
Tel: 0141 582 2000 Fax: 020 7059 5050
Web: www.accaglobal.com
Email: scotland@accaglobal.com

An up to date reference for practicing ACCA accountants at any given time during the year can be found at
https://www.accaglobal.com/gb/en/member/find-an-accountant/directory-of-member.html
Chief Executive: Helen Brand OBE
Head ACCA Scotland: Craig Vickery FCCA
Chair: David Harris FCCA
Deputy Chair: Laura Sheilds FCCA
Vice chair: Elaine Boyd FCCA
Committee members:
Liz Blackburn FCCA (also ACCA Council)
Gillian McCreadie FCCA (also ACCA Council)
Kevin Booth FCCA
Hazel Burt FCCA
Robert Van Dijk FCCA
James Gourlay FCCA
Julie Khindria ACCA

Aberdeen and north of Scotland network:
Chair: Greg Houston ACCA
Deputy Chair: Grant Conroy FCCA
Panel Members: Suzanne Cowie ACCA, Kayleigh Milne ACCA, Natalya Naryshkina FCCA, Paul O'Donnell ACCA, Maryam Sutherland-Khan ACCA, Catherine Paterson ACCA

Edinburgh and east of Scotland network:
Chair: Andrew Blyth FCCA
Panel Members: Enoch Adeyemi FCCA, Asha Patwari ACCA, Sherisse Ennis-Thomas ACCA, Kiryl Katushkin ACCA, Chris McKeown ACCA, Kevin Ramsamy FCCA, Kayleigh Rundell ACCA

Glasgow and west of Scotland network:
Chair: Vacant
Panel Members: Tehseen Akbar ACCA, Rosslyn McMaster FCCA, Nicola Todd ACCA, Kenny Wilson FCCA, Nelum Zafar ACCA, David Nicholls ACCA

Tayside and north Fife network:
Chair: Graham Parker ACCA
Panel Members: Alison Fordyce FCCA, Katherine Thomson ACCA, Frances Maclachlan ACCA, Alan Anderson FCCA, Parminder Singh FCCA, Charlotte Rowe ACCA
Strategic Engagement Lead (Scotland): Susan Love

THE SOCIETY OF LAW ACCOUNTANTS IN SCOTLAND

THE SOCIETY provides an organisation for persons employed in accountancy work in Scottish legal offices whereby they can meet with a view to the interchange of opinion on questions of practice. Local Branch meetings afford members the opportunity of holding discussion groups and hearing talks from guest speakers. The society also aims to promote the education and advancement of persons with a view to assisting them to become proficient in all aspects of law accounting and with the Law Society of Scotland provide a three subject, one year Diploma course which commences annually in September.

Associate membership of the Society is open to those who obtain the necessary Diploma from the joint SOLAS/Law Society Examination Board and have been employed in legal accounting work for a solicitor or firm of solicitors carrying on private practice in Scotland, have been employed in legal accounting work in a court, local authority, government department or agency, or in the legal department of a bank or such other offices and in such circumstances appropriate for a continuous period of three years immediately prior to application for admission to the society. Persons accepted for associate membership are accordingly entitled to use the initials 'SLA Associate'.

The Diploma course previously covered seven subjects over a two year period. Full membership of the Society is given to those persons who completed the two year course and who fit the criteria set by the Joint SOLAS/Law Society Examination Board and are entitled to use the initials 'SLA'.

Office Bearers
President: Lynne Alexander, Dundee (Tel: 01382 200055)
Vice-President: Natalie Cooke, Edinburgh (Tel: 0131 226 7411)
General Treasurer: Gillian Gray, Glasgow (Tel: 0131 4768121)
General Secretary: Lindsay Murray, Edinburgh (Tel: 0131 6560018)
Education Treasurer: Gillian Forsyth, Edinburgh (Tel: 0131 225 1200)

Council Members
Aberdeen:
Jenny Hiscox, Andersonbain
Joyce Forbes, The Law Practice
Blair Chalmers, Andersonbain
Dundee:
Heather Davidson, Rollos Law LLP
Nikki Scott, Blackadders LLP
Edinburgh:
Paul McRobb, Your Cashier
Glasgow:
Carrie McQueen
Noreen Hope, Milne Craig
David Hamilton, Hamilton Mullen Law Accountants Ltd

Administrator
Dorothy Nicholson, Kirkcaldy (Tel: 01592 260021 Email: dorothy.nicholson@solas.org.uk)

Local Branch Secretaries
ABERDEEN: Joyce Forbes, The Law Practice Tel: 01224 593100
DUNDEE: Nikki Scott, Blackadders Tel: 01382 229222
EDINBURGH: Tracey O'Brien, Anderson Strathern Tel: 0131 2707700
GLASGOW: Kirsteen Conway, Clyde Offices Tel: 0141 2260271

Actuaries

INSTITUTE AND FACULTY OF ACTUARIES
Level 2, Exchange Crescent, 7 Conference Square, Edinburgh EH3 8RA Tel: (020) 7632 2100
Fax: (0131) 240 1313 Website: www.actuaries.org.uk

The Scottish Board was established in 2010 and consists of members elected to Council by the Scottish Constituency and members who join the Board through a selection process.

The remit of the Board is:
a) to encourage and develop the actuarial community in Scotland
b) to raise the profile of actuaries and the profession in Scotland, and
c) to encourage and advance actuarial academic developments in Scotland.

The Scottish Board is currently made up of eight Council members and other members of the Scottish Constituency who are not on Council.

The Scottish Board
Leader: Mark Chadwick (RBS)
Deputy Leader: Caitlin Stronach (Royal London)
Contact the Scottish Board: Engagement.team@actuaries.org.uk
*Members:*Members: Chris Anderson, Nicholas Chadha, Philip Darke, Dermot Grenham, Jane Hamilton, Graeme Jones, Alison Kearns, Patrick Kelliher, Nitesh Khyami, Mark Laidlaw, Andrew Murphy, Sarah Neil, Anne-Marie Pettie, Alan Rae, Andy Rear, Craig Ritchie, Ian Sharpe, Claire Yule, Saoriath O'Neill, Ben Bailey-Conlon

Arbitrators

The Chartered Institute of Arbitrators (ARBITERS)
Scottish Branch
12 Bloomsbury Square, London WC1A 2LP Tel: (020) 7421 7447 Website:
www.ciarb.org/our-network/great-britain/scotland/
The CIArb Scotland Branch aims to promote the use of arbitration, mediation, adjudication and other alternative means of dispute resolution in Scotland.
President: Jane Gunn CIArb
Scottish Branch Chair: Torquil Murray FCIArb
Honorary Secretary Scotland: Alyson Shaw Email: CIARBS@shepwedd.com

Family Law Arbitration Group Scotland Website: www.flagsarb.com/
FLAGS is a group of nearly 50 solicitors, counsel and former members of the judiciary who have undergone training to act as family law arbitrators under the FLAGS scheme.
FLAGS offers arbitration services in relation to any disputes arising from personal relationships where the parties agree that they want Scots Law to apply to the subject of the dispute.
All arbitrators have undergone training to arbitrate disputes under the FLAGS (Family Law Arbitration Group Scotland) scheme. You can search for an arbitrator by reference to their professional training – some are solicitors, some counsel and some former members of the judiciary. Alternatively you can search by geographic area if you are looking to instruct an arbitrator local to you.
Honorary President: Lady Wise
Chair: Alasdair Loudon
Secretary: Lesley Gordon
Treasurer: Rachael Kelsey
Committee members: Sheriff Wendy Sheehan, Kirsty Malcolm, Ashley Simpson, Ruth Croman, Lynda Brabender QC

RICS Dispute Resolution Service (DRS)
Property & Construction Industries
Level 3, 125 Princes Street, Edinburgh EH2 4AD Tel: (0131) 240 0832 Email: drsscotland@rics.org
Website: www.rics.org
RICS in Scotland works closely with the Scottish Government on matters relating to land, property and construction.
Regional Director – Scotland: Gail Hunter

Scottish Arbitration Centre
Floor 3, 125 Princes Street, Edinburgh EH2 4AD Tel: (07827) 232 494 Website:
www.scottisharbitrationcentre.org
The Scottish Arbitration Centre was opened in March 2011. It promotes arbitration to the Scottish business community as an alternative to litigation, and Scotland to the world as a place to conduct international arbitration. The Centre is a non-profit company limited by guarantee, made up of the Law Society of Scotland, the Faculty of Advocates, the Chartered Institute of Arbitrators, the Royal Institute of Chartered Surveyors, and the Scottish Ministers.
Chairman of the Board: Brandon Malone
Chief Executive: Andrew Mackenzie
Directors:
Brandon Malone
Angus Glennie, Lord Glennie
Janey Milligan
Ysella Jago
Brandon Nolan
Gillian Carmichael Lemaire
Mary Thomson
Peter Scott Caldwell

Banks and Building Societies

THE BUILDING SOCIETIES ASSOCIATION
6th Floor, York House, 23 Kingsway, London WC2B 6UJ
Tel: 020 7520 5900 Fax: 020 7240 5290 Web: www.bsa.org.uk Email: simon.rex@bsa.org.uk
The Building Societies Association or BSA is the voice for building societies and for some other mutual financial service providers.
Chief Executive: Robin Fieth
Chairman: Mark Bogard
Head of Legal Conduct Risk and Compliance: Elaine Morton
Head of External Affairs: Hilary McVitty
Chief Economist: Andrew Gail
Head of Financial Policy: Jeremy Palmer

CHARTERED BANKER INSTITUTE

2nd Floor, 39 George Street, Edinburgh EH2 2HN

Tel: +44 (0)131 473 7777 Email: info@charteredbanker.com Web: www.charteredbanker.com

The CHARTERED BANKER INSTITUTE is the largest professional body for bankers in the UK, with more than 30,000 members.

To mark its centenary in 1975, it received Royal Charter and became the Chartered Institute of Bankers in Scotland.
Chief Executive: Simon Thompson
President: Steve Pateman
Vice President: David May

THE COMMITTEE OF SCOTTISH BANKERS
39/2 George Street, Edinburgh EH2 2HN
Tel: 0131 473 7770 Fax: 0131 473 7799 Email: info@scotbanks.org.uk Web: www.scotbanks.org.uk

Composition of the Committee
Member banks are the Bank of Scotland, the Royal Bank of Scotland plc, the Clydesdale Bank, TSB Scotland plc, Tesco Bank, HSBC and Sainsbury's Bank.

History of the Committee
The Committee acts as a representative body of its members and provides a forum through which its member organisations can discuss and debate matters of mutual interest or concern that are non-competitive in nature and that are of significant relevance to the operation of banking in Scotland. Regular contact is maintained with the Bank of England, the Scottish Government, financial regulators, relevant trade associations and professional bodies, economic development organisations and other key stakeholders. A dialogue is maintained with these bodies in order to provide advice, information and assistance and a channel of communication on matters significant to the operation of banking in Scotland.

UK FINANCE
1 Angel Court, London, EC2R 7HJ
Web: www.ukfinance.org.uk
From 1 July 2017 the Council of Mortgage Lenders was integrated into a new trade association, UK Finance. UK Finance represents around 300 firms in the UK providing credit, banking, markets and payment-related services.
CEO: David Postings
Managing Director, Chief Operating Officer: Alastair Gilmartin Smith
UK Finance Chair: Bob Wigley

ADAM & COMPANY PLC
40 Princes Street, Edinburgh EH2 2BY
Tel: 0131 380 9500
Web: www.adamandcompany.co.uk
Email: enquiries@adamandcompany.co.uk

Head: Graham Storrie
Investment Directors: Susan Boyd, Stuart Dickson, Mark Ivory
Senior Wealth Advisor: Colin Mann

A Connacord Genuity Group Company

SCOTTISH BUILDING SOCIETY

Head Office and Edinburgh & East Area Office, SBS House, 193 Dalry Road, Edinburgh EH11 2EF
Tel: 0333 207 4007
Website: www.scottishbs.co.uk

Chief Executive: Paul Denton
Finance Director: Neil Easson
Chair: Raymond Abbott
Vice Chair: John (Jack) Ogston

Branches:
BORDERS AREA OFFICE, 48 Bank Street,
Galashiels TD1 1EP Tel: 0333 207 4007

GLASGOW & WEST AREA OFFICE, 78 Queen
Street, Glasgow G1 3DN Tel: 0333 207 4007
INVERNESS & NORTH AREA OFFICE, 71
Queensgate, Inverness IV1 1DG Tel: 0333 207
4007
TROON & SOUTH WEST AREA OFFICE, 27 Ayr
Street, Troon KA10 6EB Tel: 0333 207 4007
ABERDEEN AREA OFFICE, 6 Alford Place,
Aberdeen AB10 1YD Tel: 0333 207 4007

BANK OF SCOTLAND

(Constituted by Act of Parliament, 1695)
(Part of Lloyds Banking Group)
The Mound, Edinburgh EH1 1YZ Tel: 0345 711 1111
Website: www.bankofscotland.co.uk

Head of Mid Corporate, Scotland: Ewan Kinnear
Regional Director, SME Banking, Bank of Scotland:
Fraser Sime
*Managing Director, Head of Consumer and
Technology:* Zahra Sadry
*Managing Director, Head of Real Estate and
Housing:* Madeleine McDougall

Managing Director, Head of Financial Services:
Adrian Walkling

Branches
All enquiries to Tel: 0345 721 3141

CLYDESDALE BANK PLC

Head Office:
40 St Vincent Place, Glasgow G1 2HL Tel: 0800 345 7365 DX: GW188 Website: www.cbonline.co.uk

Nature of Business
The Clydesdale Bank, the only clearing bank in the United Kingdom with its Head Office in Glasgow, became a member of the National Australia Bank Limited in 1987. It was established in 1838 and has 153 retail branches in Scotland together with offices in London.

Executive Leadership Team
Chief Executive Officer: David Duffy
Chief Financial Officer: Clifford Abrahams
General Counsel and Purpose Officer: James Peirson

Parent Organisation:
Virgin Money UK PLC

Branches

When sending mail via the DX Business Mail Service each individual Clydesdale Bank location, the branch name, sort code and Head Office DX number should be included in the address.

Example:

Clydesdale Bank plc, Aberdeen, Bridge of Don (82-69-23) DX: 500500 CLYDEBANK

THE ROYAL BANK OF SCOTLAND
36 St Andrews Square, Edinburgh EH2 2YB
Tel: 0345 600 2230
Website: www.rbs.co.uk

RBS International Executive Management Team
CEO: Andrew McLaughlin
CFO: Lynn Cleary
Interim CRO: Ian Gannon
HR Director: Fiona Levy
Head of Legal, Governance, Data Protection and Financial Crime: Stephanie Duke

Branches

When sending mail via the DX Business Mail Service each individual Royal Bank of Scotland location, the branch name, sort code and Head Office DX number should be included in the address.

Example:
The Royal Bank of Scotland, Aberdeen, Bridge of Don (83-28-42), DX: 551727, DRUMMOND HOUSE
(Subsidiary of NatWest Group).

HAMPDEN & CO
9 Charlotte Square, Edinburgh EH2 4DR
Tel: 0131 226 7300 Email: contact@hampdenandco.com
Web: www.hampdenandco.com
Head of Banking – Scotland: Mark Prentice
Banking Directors: David Bell, Duncan Buchanan, George Grierson, Graeme Morris, Clare Ansell, Ian Gibson, Ryan Beattie, Gillian Dobson, Linda Duthie

NOBLE & CO
Noble & Co is a Scottish Investment Bank
Noble & Company (UK) Limited, 95A George Street, Edinburgh EH2 3ES
Tel: +44 (0) 131 603 7680 Email: contactus@nobleandcompany.com
Web: www.nobleandcompany.com
CEO: Angus Macpherson
Managing Director, Head of Power and Energy: Gillian Watson
Managing Director, Head of Infrastructure: Jonathan Hunt
Managing Director, Head of Food and Drink: Duncan McFadzean
Managing Director, Head of Sustainable Finance: Kal Sangha
Managing Director, Head of Corporate Finance: Susi Crawford

NOBLE GROSSART
Noble Grossart Limited is a merchant bank formed in 1969. It provides corporate advice and investment banking support.
48 Queen Street, Edinburgh EH2 3NR
Tel: 0131 226 7011 Email: mail@noblegrossart.co.uk
Web: http://www.noblegrossart.co.uk/
Senior Executives: Sir Angus Grossart (Chairman), Todd Nugent, Roger Brown, David Harraghy, Dave Ward

SAINSBURY'S BANK
3 Lochside Avenue, Edinburgh Park, Edinburgh EH12 9DJ
Tel: 08085 40 50 60
Web: www.sainsburysbank.co.uk

Chairman: Lesley Jones
Chief Executive Officer: Jim Brown
Chief Financial Officer: Michael Larkin
Independent Non-Executive Directors: Guy Thomas, Michael Ross, Carole Butler, Peter Clarke
Retail and Digital Director: Clodagh Moriarty

TESCO BANK

EHQ, 2 South Gyle Crescent, Edinburgh EH12 9FQ Tel: 0131 203 5000
Customer Service Centre, Broadway One, 199 Renfield Street, Glasgow G2 3AX Tel: 0345 678 5678
Website: www.tescobank.com
Parent organisation: Tesco PLC

Executive Committee:
Chief Executive: Gerry Mallon
Chief Financial Officer: Richard Henderson

Chief Risk Officer: Debbie Walker
Chairman: Sir John Kingman

TSB BANK PLC

Henry Duncan House, 120 George Street, Edinburgh EH2 4LH
Tel: 03459 758 758
Website: www.tsb.co.uk

Leadership Team:
Interim Chief Executive Officer: Robin Bulloch
Chief Financial Officer: Declan Hourican
TSB General Counsel: Guy Dunlop
Chief Operating Officer: Suresh Viswanathan
Interim Chief Risk Officer: Richard Bowles
Communications and Corporate Affairs Director:
George Gordon
Human Resources Director: Liz Ashford
Interim Customer Banking Director: Mark Curran

Chief Audit Officer: Vanessa Swanton
Customer Delivery Director: Gary Jones

Branches
When sending mail via the DX Business Mail
Service each individual TSB location, the branch
name, sort code and Head Office DX number
should be included in the address.

(Parent organisation is Sabadell Group)

Financial Services

BANK OF SCOTLAND WEALTH MANAGEMENT
The Mound, Edinburgh EH1 1YZ
Tel: 0131 376 1815
Web: http://www.bankofscotland.co.uk/privatebanking/wealth-management/

ABDRN PLC
abrdn plc, 1 George Street, Edinburgh EH2 2LL
Tel: 0371 384 2464
Web: www.abrdn.com
Email: questions@abdrnshares.com
Chairman: Sir Douglas Flint CBE
Chief Executive: Stephen Bird
Chief Financial Officer: Stephanie Bruce
General Counsel: Rushad Abadan
Global Chief Operating Officer: Mike Tumilty
Chief People Officer: Tracey Hahn
Chief Risk Officer: Gareth Murphy

ALLIANCE TRUST PLC
DUNDEE, River Court, 5 West Victoria Dock Road, Dundee DD1 3JT Tel: 01382 938 320 Email: investor@alliancetrust.co.uk
Computershare Investor Services PLC, EDINBURGH, Edinburgh House, 4 North St Andrew Street, Edinburgh EH2 1HJ Tel: 03708 893 187
Web: www.alliancetrust.co.uk
Chairman: Gregor Stewart
Senior Independent Director: Sarah Bates
Non-Executive Directors: Anthony Brooke, Clare Dobie, Chris Samuel, Jo Dixon, Dean Buckley

BAILLIE GIFFORD
Baillie Gifford & Co, Calton Square, 1 Greenside Row, Edinburgh EH1 3AN
Tel: 0131 275 2000 Fax: 0131 275 3999
Web: www.bailliegifford.com
Senior Partners: Andrew Telfer, Malcolm MacColl

EDINBURGH INVESTMENT TRUST PLC
Quartermile One, 15 Lauriston Place, Edinburgh EH3 9EP
Web: www.majedie.com/fund/edinburgh-investment-trust
Fund Manager: James de Uphaugh
Deputy Fund Manager: Chris Field

MARTIN CURRIE INVESTMENT MANAGEMENT LIMITED
Head office, Saltire Court, 20 Castle Terrace, Edinburgh EH1 2ES
Tel: +44 (0) 131 229 5252
Web: www.martincurrie.com Email: enquiries@martincurrie.com
Chief Executive Officer: Julian Ide
Chief Operating Officer: Jennifer Mair
Chief Operations Officer: Megan Scott

SCOTTISH DEVELOPMENT INTERNATIONAL
UK Head Office, Atrium Court, 50 Waterloo Street, Glasgow G2 6HQ Tel: 0300 013 2734
Web: www.sdi.co.uk

SCOTTISH FINANCIAL ENTERPRISE
Scottish Financial Enterprise is the industry trade group that represents and promotes the interests of Scotland's international financial services industry.
24 Melville Street, Edinburgh EH3 7NS
Tel: 0131 247 7700

Web: www.sfe.org.uk
Chairman: Philip Grant
Chief Executive: Sandy Begbie CBE
Chairman, Scotland and Managing Director for Corporate & Commercial Banking: Malcolm Buchanan
Head of Financial Services, Scotland for EY LLP Sue Dawe

Debt Collection Agencies

Chamberlain McBain
CBC House, 24 Canning Street, Edinburgh
EH3 8EG Tel: (0131) 272 2799
Fax: (0131) 272 2883 DX: 550862 Email:
info@cmcb.co.uk Website: www.cmcb.co.uk

Debt Collect UK
Centrum House, 38 Queen Street, Glasgow
G1 3DX Tel: (020) 3389 6205
Fax: (0333) 800 8929 Email:
enquiries@debtcollectuk.com Website:
www.debtcollectuk.com

Fox Investigations
Fox House, 1 Glasgow Road, Kirkintilloch,
Glasgow G66 1AG Tel: (0141) 7760072
Fax: (0141) 7764769 Email:
info@foxdetectives.co.uk Website:
www.foxinvestigation.co.uk

Shoosmiths LLP
Saltire Court, 20 Castle Terrace, Edinburgh
EH1 2EN Tel: (03700) 863000
Fax: (03700) 868008 DX: 553051 Edinburgh 18
Email: generalenquiries@shoosmiths.co.uk
Website: www.shoosmiths.co.uk

Shoosmiths LLP
Garment Factory, 5th Floor, 10 Montrose Street,
Glasgow G1 1RE Tel: (03700) 863 000
Fax: (03700) 868 008 DX: GW 504 Glasgow
Email: generalenquiries@shoosmiths.co.uk

Website: www.shoosmiths.co.uk

Stirling Park LLP
Enforcement Service Centre, 24 Blythswood
Square, Glasgow G2 4BG Tel: (0141) 565 5765
Fax: (0141) 565 5764 DX: 512051 GLASGOW
CENTRAL Email: officers@stirlingpark.co.uk
Website: www.stirlingpark.co.uk

Walker Love
16 Royal Exchange Square, Glasgow G1 3AB
Tel: (0141) 248 8224
Fax: (0141) 221 7944 DX: GW 98 Email:
Corrdept@walkerlove.com Website:
www.walkerlove.com

Walker Love
17 Hart Street, Edinburgh EH1 3RN Tel: (0131)
557 0100
Fax: (0131) 557 0200 DX: 551052 EDINBURGH
6 Email: Corrdept@walkerlove.com Website:
www.walkerlove.com

Yuill & Kyle Ltd
Capella, 60 York Street, Glasgow G2 8JX
Tel: (0141) 331 2332 Email:
info@debtscotland.com Website:
www.debtscotland.com

Yuill & Kyle Ltd
10 George Street, Edinburgh EH2 2PF Email:
info@debtscotland.com Website:
www.debtscotland.com

Expert Witnesses

Expert Witnesses

NOTE: For future editions the publishers would be pleased to receive from professional bodies the names, addresses and qualifications of persons who are able to act as expert witnesses in any field. For a full list of expert witnesses in Scotland visit the Scottish Law Society's Expert Witness Directory at: www.lawscot.org.uk/wcm/lssservices/Member_Services/Expert_Witness/Search_Expert_Witness.aspx

Architect
Prof Tim Sharpe
27 Alder Road, Glasgow G43 2UU Tel: (0141) 5894272 Email: timsharpe@me.com

Chartered Accountant
Mr Jeffrey A C Meek
Birns Farm Cottage, Ladybank, Cupar KY15 7UL Tel: (01337) 832501 Email: jacmeek@me.com Website: www.jeffreyacmeek.co.uk

Chartered Construction Manager/Chartered Surveyor
Mr Donald Mackinnon
1 George Square, Glasgow G2 1AL Tel: (07771) 928144 Email: donny@mackinnonconsult.com Website: www.mackinnonconsult.com

Clinical Biochemist and Consultant Toxicologist
Mr Janusz Knepil
Toxicology Consultants, 23 McConnell Road, Lochwinnoch PA12 3EB Tel: (01505) 842253 Email: jknepil@btinternet.com

Clinical Forensic/General Medical Practitioner
Dr Katherine M. Morrison
Ballochmyle Medical Group, The Loan, Mauchline KA5 6AJ Tel: (07737) 113629 Email: katherine.morrison@btinternet.com

Construction Dispute Resolution
Ms Janey Milligan
1 George Square, Glasgow G2 1AL Tel: (0141) 773 3377 Email: jlm@cdr.uk.com Website: www.cdr.uk.com

Consultant in Accident and Emergency Medicine and Surgery
Mr Rudy Crawford
Crawford Medical Legal Services Ltd, PO Box 10092, Glasgow G71 9DA Tel: (07795) 295 115 Email: crawford@ardmhor.com

Consultant Metallurgist
METTEK Limited
3 Howard Court, Nerston Industrial Estate, East Kilbride G74 4QZ Tel: (01355) 220990 Email: jamie.pollock@mettek.co.uk Website: www.mettek.co.uk

Consultant Neurologist
Dr Colin J. Mumford
Department of Clinical Neurosciences, Royal Infirmary of Edinburgh, 50 Little France Crescent, Edinburgh EH16 4TJ Tel: (0131) 552 4244 Email: colin.mumford@ed.ac.uk

Employment Consultant and Careers Adviser
Keith Careers Ltd
50 Oakbank Crescent, Perth PH1 1DF Tel: (01738) 631200 Email: niall@briankeith.co.uk

Engineering
Consultant Engineer
Dr Calvert Stinton, Lower Inchlumpie, Strathrusdale, Alness IV17 0YQ Tel: (01349) 884 410 Email: calvert.stinton@outlook.com Website: www.calvertstinton.co.uk

Forensic Accountants
Adamson Forensic Accounting Ltd
14 Rutland Square, Edinburgh EH1 2BD Tel: (07914) 070741 Email: info@adamsonforensics.co.uk Website: www.adamsonforensicaccounting.com

Forensic Clinical Psychologists
City Clinics
93 George Street, Edinburgh EH2 3ES Tel: (0333) 8002909 Email: info@cityclinics.org Website: www.cityclinics.org

Forensic pharmacologists
Glasgow Expert Witness Service Ltd
Dr Stephanie Sharp, 11 Wyvill Avenue, Glasgow G13 2PE Tel: (07734) 865349 Email: steph@gews.org.uk

Forensic Road Traffic Consultant
George Gilfillan
64 Greenoakhill Crescent, Uddingston G71 7PW Tel: (07841) 129690 Email: georgegilfillan@btinternet.com Website: www.road-traffic-investigation.co.uk

General Practitioner
Dr Norman W. Wallace
20 Craigs Bank, Edinburgh EH12 8HD
Tel: (07800) 634733 Email:
normanwallace@btopenworld.com

Image Processing
Prof Stephen Marshall
Dept of Electronic and Electrical Engineering,
University of Strathclyde, 204 George Street,

Glasgow G1 1XW Tel: (0141) 5482199 Email:
smcs_ltd@yahoo.co.uk Website:
www.strath.ac.uk/staff/marshallstephenprof

Solicitor
Professor Stewart Brymer OBE
Brymer Legal Limited, 8b Rutland Square,
Edinburgh EH1 2AS Tel: (07801) 034530 Email:
stewart@brymerlegal.co.uk Website:
www.brymerlegal.co.uk

The Royal College of Midwives
RCM Scotland, 37 Frederick Street, Edinburgh EH2 1EP Tel: (0300) 303 0444 Website:
www.rcm.org.uk
Chief Executive: Gill Walton
President: Rebeccah Davies
Chair: Giuseppe Labriola

Vehicle Examiner/Road Transport Consultant
Mr Allan Campbell
47a Craw Road, Paisley PA2 6AE Tel: (07493) 135819 Email: allan@roadtransportsolutions.co.uk
Website: www.roadtransportsolutions.co.uk

Insurance Companies

The Association Of British Insurers

One America Square, 17 Crosswall, London EC3N 2LB Tel: (0207) 600 3333 Email: info@abi.org.uk
Website: www.abi.org.uk
Director General: Hannah Gurga
Chair: Rt Hon Baroness Nicky Morgan
President: Barry O'Dwyer
Deputy President: Cristina Nestares
Director, General Insurance Policy: James Dalton
Director of Policy, Long-Term Savings and Protection: Yvonne Braun
Director and General Counsel: Philippa Handyside
Director of Corporate Affairs and Climate Change: Ben Wilson
Director of Regulation: Charlotte Clark CBE

Aegon UK

Edinburgh EH12 9SE
Tel: 03456 10 00 10
Web: www.aegon.co.uk
Chief Executive Officer: Mike Holliday-Williams
Chief Financial Officer: Jim Ewing
Chief Risk Officer: Colin Black
General Counsel and Company Secretary: James Mackenzie

Scottish Friendly

16 Blythswood Square, Glasgow G2 4HJ
Tel: 0333 323 5433
Web: www.scottishfriendly.co.uk
Acting Chief Executive: Martin Pringle BSc FCA
Commercial Director: Neil Lovatt ACII, BA (Hons), MSc

Scottish Widows

Part of Lloyds Banking Group
69 Morrison Street, Edinburgh EH3 8BW
Tel: 0345 716 6777
Web: www.scottishwidows.co.uk
Chairman (Independant Governance Committee): Mark Stewart
Chief Executive: Antonio Lorenzo

AIG

2nd Floor, Sutherland House, 149 St Vincent Street, Glasgow G2 5NW
Tel: 0141 303 4400
Fax: 0141 303 4441
Email: AIGDirect.Queries@aig.com
Web: www.aig.co.uk
President & Chief Executive Officer: Peter Zaffino
EVP and Chief Financial Officer: Shane Fitzsimons
EVP, General Counsel & Global Head of Communications and Government Affairs: Lucy Fato
EVP and Chief Risk Officer: Sabra Purtill

General Accident

General Accident is a trading name of Aviva UK Digital Limited
Registered Office, Pitheavlis, Perth PH2 0NH
Web: www.generalaccident.com

SCOTTISH TECHNOLOGY COMPANIES

SkyScanner
Skyscanner Ltd, Quartermile One, 15 Lauriston Place, Edinburgh EH3 9EN Web: www.skyscanner.net
CEO: John Mangelaars
General Counsel: Martin Nolan
Chief Financial Officer: Laurence Tracol

Ice Robotics
IceRobotics Ltd, Suite 2, Ground Floor, Orchard Brae House, 30 Queensferry Road, Edinburgh EH4
   2HS Tel: 0131 541 2010 Email: info@icerobotics.com Web: www.icerobotics.com

Rockstar North
Barclay House, 108 Holyrood Rd, Edinburgh EH8 8AS Web: www.rockstarnorth.com
Founder: David Jones
Studio Director: Andrew Semple

4J Studios
Blackadders, 30-34 Reform Street, Dundee DD1 1RJ
Web: www.4jstudios.com/ Email: enquiries@4jstudios.com
Chair: Chris Van der Kuyl CBE
CEO: Paddy Burns

Agenor Technology
Floor 2, The Bonnington Bond, 2 Anderson Place, Edinburgh EH6 5NP Tel: 0131 297 2270 Email:
   enquiries@agenor.co.uk
CEO: Gary Montgomery
Head of Finance & Business Services: Eilidh Young
Head of Business Operations: Tony Smith

Mediators

CALM Scotland
51 Moss Street, Paisley PA1 1DR Tel: (0141) 889 6244 Email: ns@msmlaw.co.uk Website: www.calmscotland.co.uk

CALM Scotland was established in 1993 by a group of family lawyers keen to provide an alternative process for sorting out disputes arising from family breakdowns.

Core Solutions Group Limited
10 South St Andrews Street, Edinburgh EH2 2AZ Tel: (0131) 524 8188 Email: info@core-solutions.com Website: www.core-solutions.com

Core helps people in business, organisations and the public sector to find solutions to disputes and other difficult situations.
Founder, CEO, Senior Mediator: John Sturrock QC
Executive Assistant and Business Manager: Paula Cumming
Senior Associate and Mediator: Charlie Woods
Mediators: Louise Dunlop, Liz Rivers

Family Mediation West
19 Woodside Place, Glasgow G3 7QL Tel: (0141) 332 2731 Email: info@fmwest.org.uk Website: www.familymediationwest.scot
Kilmarnock Centre: 28-30 Grange Street, Kilmarnock KA1 2DD Tel: 01563 572 429 Email: ayrshiremediation@outlook.org

Relationships Scotland
18 York Place, Edinburgh EH1 3EP Tel: (0345) 119 2020
Fax: (0845) 119 6089 Email: enquiries@relationship-scotland.org.uk Website: www.relationships-scotland.org.uk

Relationships Scotland's network provide relationship counselling, family mediation, child contact centres and other family support services across all of mainland and island Scotland.
Chief Executive: Stuart Valentine
Head of Practice for Family Mediation and Relationship Counselling: Rosanne Cubitt
Head of Corporate Services: Mike Reid
Head of Network Services: Heather Lickley
Chair: Dr Kirsty A Darwent
Vice Chair: Jim Stephen
Treasurer: Iain Grimmond

Scottish Community Mediation Centre
29 Albany Street, Edinburgh EH3 6QN Tel: (0131) 624 7263
Fax: (0131) 624 7269 Website: www.scmc.sacro.org.uk
Administrator: Robert Lambden

Scottish Mediation
18 York Place, Edinburgh EH1 3EP Tel: (0131) 556 8118 Email: admin@scottishmediation.org.uk
Website: www.scottishmediation.org.uk

Scottish Mediation seeks to:
Promote a wider understanding of the appropriate use of mediation in conflict management and prevention
Support and promote education, training and research in skills and best practice
Create and encourage links between mediators and Scottish public, private, voluntary and community organisations
Promote and organise standards of professional conduct and training
Director: Graham Boyack
Chair: Alun Thomas
Vice Chair: Linn Phipps

Workplace Mediation Scotland
Standard Buildings, 94 Hope Street, Glasgow G2 6PH Tel: (0141) 221 4488 Email: giles@workplacemediation-scotland.com Website: www.workplacemediation-scotland.com

Workplace Mediation Scotland provides a specialist workplace mediation service for organisations who have employees in Scotland.
Workplace Mediator: Giles Woolfson

Registers of Scotland

REGISTERS OF SCOTLAND

Registers of Scotland (RoS) keeps public registers of land, property and other legal documents in Scotland.

What we do

The Keeper of the Registers of Scotland is directly accountable to the Scottish Parliament.

Every year we publish a corporate plan for the coming five years.

Our Registers

We are responsible for public records, including the Land Register of Scotland and the General Register of Sasines.

Status and Funding

We are part funded by the Scottish Government from the consolidated budget.

Why land registration matters

A land register is a publicly accessible register of property rights. Most, like ours, are underpinned by state guarantee.

It is considered beneficial to government, citizens and the economy.

Land registration offers certainty of title to property owners, potential purchasers and lenders.

With a land register, you can prove ownership of what you are selling or borrowing against.

Our land register:

- is easy to search
- identifies property on the Ordnance Survey Map
- gives clarity of what rights benefit and burdens affect properties
- gives businesses confidence to lend against or invest in property

Our Registers

We hold and maintain 21 public registers relating to land and property ownership in Scotland.

- Land register of Scotland
- General Register of Sasines
- Crofting Register
- Register of Sites of Special Scientific Interest
- Register of Community Interests in land
- Register of Applications by Community Bodies to Buy Land
- Scottish Landlord Register
- Scottish Letting Agent Register
- Register of Inhibitions
- Register of Judgements
- Register of Deeds
- Register of Protests
- Register of the Great Seal
- Register of the Quarter Seal
- Register of the Cachet Seal

- Register of Sheriff's Commissions
- Register of Crown grants
- Register of Service of Heirs
- Register of Prince's Seal
- Register of Hornings
- Register of Persons Holding a Controlled Interest in Land

Our Board

Keeper of the Registers of Scotland (Chief Executive): Jennifer Henderson

Accountable Officer: Janet Egdell

Corporate Director: Billy Harkness

Business Development Director: Kenny Crawford

Registration and Policy Director: Chris Kerr

Non-Executive Directors:

Andrew Harvey

Andrew Miller

Mhairi Kennedy

Asim Muhammad

Elaine Melrose

Contact us

Our specialist teams are available for a wide range of enquiries.

Call us – Customer Services 0800 169 9391

If you are a British Sign Language (BSL) user, you can contact us via our national BSL video relay service – contactscotland-bsl.org

Office locations
Coronavirus (COVID-19)

Our offices in Glasgow and Edinburgh have temporarily closed but we're still open for business.

You can access our services online or contact customer services if you have an enquiry.

Edinburgh Office – Meadowbank House, 153 London Road, Edinburgh EH8 7AU

Glasgow Office – St Vincent Plaza, 319 St Vincent Street, Glasgow G2 5LP

Both offices have hearing loops and wheelchair access.

DX post

We have opened a dedicated DX and PO box address for Register of Deeds submissions.

While our offices remain closed all other post is being returned to sender.

Services

- Search land and property information
- Order deeds
- Order a copy of a will
- Search as a business user
- Update the land register
- Discharge a mortgage deed
- Register land and property (RLP)
- Access business services
- Digital discharges

- Legal and plans reports
- Development plan approval
- Plan assistance
- Advance notices
- Voluntary registration
- Keeper-induced registration
- Application checking service
- Land register API

Publications

Search our website for a comprehensive database of publications.

More information on the types of information we publish and how to access it can be found on our website, under freedom of information.

Registration fees

This guidance contains information about the fees associated with land and property registration.

Land Register of Scotland

Deeds transferring the ownership of a property

Where the deed being registered transfers the ownership of a property, or is evidential to the transfer, then the fee that is payable is based on the consideration narrated in the deed or the value of the property (whichever is greater). The fee is calculated using the rates in the table below. These rates will apply to applications to register the following deeds:

- disposition
- notice of title
- general vesting declaration
- statutory conveyance

Where an application for Voluntary Registration is submitted using the VR application type the fees specified in column 3 will apply.

Consideration paid or value	Fee (£)	Voluntary registration fee (£)
0–50, 000	£80.00	£60.00
50,001–100,000	£140.00	£110.00
100,001–150,000	£260.00	£200.00
150,001–200,000	£400.00	£300.00
200,001–300,000	£530.00	£400.00
300,001–500,000	£660.00	£500.00
500,001–700,000	£800.00	£600.00
700,001–1,000,000	£930.00	£700.00
100,001–2,000,000	£1,100.00	£830.00
2,000,001–3,000,000	£3,300.00	£2,480.00
300,001–5,000,000	£5,500.00	£4,130.00
5,000,000 or more	£8,250.00	£6,190.00

Where the deed transferring land affects more than one title sheet, in addition to the fee specified in table 1, a fee of £80 is payable for each title sheet affected other than the first. This additional fee does not apply to shared plot title sheets or shared lease title sheets where the deed affects the sharing plot title sheet.

Where the consideration consists of a yearly or periodical payment, the consideration is calculated at 10 years purchase.

General Register of Sasines

Completion of title

Where the recording of a completion of title by decree or a notice of title is made, the fee is calculated on the value of the property to which the recording is made. The fee that is payable is calculated on the rates specified in column 1 of the table below.

Value	Fee (£)
0–50,000	£80.00
50,001–100,000	£140.00
100,001–150,000	£260.00
150,001–200,000	£400.00
200,001–300,000	£530.00
300,001–500,000	£660.00
500,001–700,000	£800.00
700,001–1,000,000	£930.00
1,000,001–2,000,000	£1,100,00
2,000,001–3,000,000	£3,300.00
3,000,001–5,000,000	£5,500.00
5,000,001 or more	£8,250.00

Advance Notices

The fee payable for an application for recording an advance notice for first registration is £20.

The fee payable for an application recording a discharge of an advance notice in the Register of Sasines is £20.

Other deeds

The fee for recording any other deed in the Register of Sasines is £80 (other than a receipt under the Industrial and Provident Societies Act 1965 where no fee is payable).

Recording by memorandum

Where any deed is presented in the Register of Sasines for recording by memorandum in more than one county, a fee of £80 for each memorandum is payable.

Additional extract or plain copy

Where a deed is being recorded, in respect of an additional extract or plain copy requested at the date of the application for recording, the fee is £20 plus VAT.

Chancery and Judicial Registers

The fees payable in relation to registering a document in the Chancery and Judicial Registers are specified below.

Chancery and Judicial Registers

Register	Product/service	Fee (£)
Register of Inhibitions	For each document	£25.00

Register of Deeds and Probative Writs in the Books of Council and Session	For each document (including first extract)	£20.00
Register of Protest	For each document (including first extract)	£20.00
Register of Judgements	For each document (including first extract	£20.00
Register of the Great Seal	For a Charter of Incorporation	£260.00
Register of the Great Seal	For a Commission	£640.00
Register of the Cachet Seal	For each impression	£40.00
Register of the Quarter Seal	For each gift of ultimus haeres or bona vacantia	£140.00

When a document is being registered in any of the Chancery and Judicial Registers, you can request an additional extract or plain copy at the date of registration for £20 plus VAT.

The Rules of the Court of Session provide for the keeper to issue certain types of certificate. The fee payable for each certificate issued in terms of these rules is £40.

Crofting Register

Applications for registration and updating a registration schedule	Fee (£)
Registration of a croft under section 4(1) or (2) of the Crofting Reform (Scotland) Act 2010 ('the 2010 Act')	£90.00
Updating the registration schedule of a registered croft following an event under section 5(1) of the 2010 Act	£90.00
Registration of a common grazing under section 24(1)(a) or (b) of the 2010 Act	£90.00
Updating the registration schedule of a registered common grazing under section 25(1) of the 2010 Act	£90.00
Registration of land held runrig under section 32(1) of the 2010 Act	£90.00
Updating the registration schedule of registered land held runrig following an event under section 32(5) of the 2010 Act	£90.00
Registration of a croft under section 4(1) or (2) of the Crofting Reform (Scotland) Act 2010 ('the 2010 Act')	£90.00
Requests for Searches, reports, copies of documents or information	**Fee (£)**
Copy registration schedule of a croft, common grazing or land held runrig	£25.00 plus VAT
Office Copy of a registration schedule of a croft, common grazing or land held runrig	£35.00 plus VAT
Copy of an Ordnance Survey map supplied for the purpose of registration	£25.00 plus VAT
Information provided by the Keeper regarding the suitability of an applicant's map for registration purposes	£35.00 plus VAT

Register of Community Interests in Land

The fees payable in relation to registering a tenant's interest in acquiring land in the Register of Community Interests in Land for the purposes of the Agricultural Holdings (Scotland) Act 2003 are specified in the table below.

Product/service	Fee (£)
Initial registration of tenant's interest	£40.00
Subsequent registration of an existing or previously registered interest	£25.00

Legislation

The fees referred to in this guidance are provided for in The Registers of Scotland (Fees) Order 2014 (as amended by the Registers of Scotland (Fees) Amendment Order 2021) and The Registers of Scotland (Voluntary Registration, Amendment of Fees etc) Order 2015 made under the powers in section 110 of the Land Registration etc (Scotland) Act 2012.

Searching the registers

You can search the land register for free via www.scotlis.ros.gov.uk to:

- find property prices
- view property boundaries on a map
- check if a property is on the land register

If you can't find your property on the land register, you can ask us to conduct a search via a form on our website.

We charge an initial fee of £30.00 plus VAT per request to include one plain copy deed, or nil return.

The initial fee applies only where there is a full postal address, including postcode.

Should you wish to order any additional copy deeds identified, you can order these at a cost of £25.00 plus VAT each.

We'll let you know the cost of all identified deeds before we complete your search.

Register	Online form, email or letter	In person	Using ScotLIS
Land Register of Scotland	£20.00 plus VAT	£30.00 plus VAT	£3.00 plus VAT
General Register of Sasines	£20.00 plus VAT	£30.00 plus VAT	£3.00 plus VAT*
Books of Council and Session	£20.00 plus VAT	£30.00 plus VAT	N/A
Register of Inhibitions	£20.00 plus VAT	£30.00 plus VAT	£1.00 plus VAT*

*Business users only

Ownership search for an area of land

We charge an initial fee of £20 plus VAT per area. If your search covers more than one title we'll charge £16 plus VAT for plain copies for each additional title.

We'll let you know if your search covers several titles before we send you any plain copies.

You can search the following registers for free:

- Crofting Register
- Register of Community Interests in Land
- Sites of Special Scientific Interest
- Scottish Landlord Register
- Copies of documents

You can order documents from our registers via our website.

Find out more about extracts, certified copies and plain copies of documents in our register.

Plain copies

A plain copy is a copy of any document within our registers. It does not carry the evidential status required for court purposes.

Register	Online form, email or letter
Land Register of Scotland	£25.00 plus VAT
General Register of Sasines.	£25.00 plus VAT
Books of Council of Session	£25.00 plus VAT
Register of Inhibitions	£25.00 plus VAT

Certified Copies

You can request certified copies of documents in the Land Register of Scotland when the deed requested is still undergoing the process of registration. These copies also have evidential status.

Certified copies cost £35 plus VAT.

Extracts

Extracts are copies of documents from our registers that carry evidential status for court purposes.

Register	Fee
Land Register of Scotland	£35.00 plus VAT
General Register of Sasines	£35.00 plus VAT
Register of Deeds, Judgements and Protests	£35.00 plus VAT

Duplicate Plans

If you are ordering a duplicate plan, there is no extra charge if the plan is held within RoS.

If the plan is held by a third party, there may be an additional charge of £10 or £15+VAT.

The charge is per plan and will depend on size.

Reports

You will need to register for access to our online services via our website to purchase a report.

Report Type	Fee
PRR01: legal report unregistered subjects	£95.00 plus VAT
PRR02: legal report registered subjects	£85.00 plus VAT
PRR03: legal continuation report	First is free for a period of 6 months from the date of the original report
	Subsequent reports £50.00 plus VAT
PRR06: plans report, level 1	£65.00 plus VAT
PRR04: plans report, level 2	£80.00 plus VAT
PRR05: plans report, level 3	£95.00 plus VAT
PRR07: plans continuation report	Free
PRR10: combined plans and legal report, level 1	£140.00 plus VAT
PRR08: combined plans and legal report, level 2	£155.00 plus VAT
PRR09: combined plans and legal report, level 3	£160.00 plus VAT

Application form guide – Land Register

This guidance provides step-by-step information to help you fill out the land register application form.

It takes account of amendments RoS has made to the application form, brought about by legislation change that allows RoS to amend and respond to changing customer, business and technological needs and developments.

Use this guidance when you're filling in the land register application form. It applies to both paper and electronic application forms.

Sasine Application Forms (SAFs) are unaffected by the legislative changes and still require to be signed.

Under the one-shot rule, we reject applications with errors or omissions, so it's important to make sure your application satisfies the requirements.

You can find the electronic application form at our online services portal via our website.

You need to register to access our online services. Find information on how to register via our website www.ros.gov.uk.

This guidance should be used in conjunction with:

The application checklist, which will help you make sure you include everything you need with your application

The land registration process guide, which lists the checks we make at each step of the registration process

View an example application form via our Knowledge Base at www.kb.ros.gov.uk to use as reference: (https://kb.ros.gov.uk/__data/assets/pdf_file/0007/87928/Application_for_Registration_v10–1_example.pdf).

Unless the context states otherwise, any reference to a section of an Act in this guidance refers to a section of the 2012 Act.

Sasine Application form guide

This guidance provides step-by-step instructions on how to complete each part of the sasine application form.

Use of the sasine application form is a statutory requirement. You must complete a separate form for each deed to be recorded in the sasine register, and each must be completed fully and accurately.

Don't staple or pin any documents to the application form. You should ensure the form is not torn, crumpled or excessively folded.

If you have access to our online services, you'll find an electronic version of the sasine application form in the online services portal. Enquire about signing up for our online services.

For help with registering a plot of land, see the separate guidance for registration in Land Register of Scotland.

Further information is contained on at Knowledge Base website at www.kb.ros.gov.uk.

Scottish Legal Aid Board (SLAB)

SCOTTISH LEGAL AID BOARD (SLAB)

Office: 91 Haymarket Terrace, Edinburgh EH12 5HE
Tel: 0131 226 7061 (all departments) Website: www.slab.org.uk

Information for the public about:

Financial Eligibility Tel: 0131 560216; Legal merits of your civil case Tel: 0131 240200

(open Monday to Friday 8.30am to 4.30pm)

SLAB was established by the Legal Aid (Scotland) Act 1986. It is a non-departmental public body sponsored by the Scottish Government.
Chairman of SLAB: Ray Macfarlane
Chief Executive: Colin Lancaster
Director of Corporate Services and Accounts: TBC
Director of Operations: TBC
Director of Strategic Development: Marie-Louise Fox
Principal Legal Adviser: Ian Dickson

Contact Names:
Civil and Children's legal assistance
Head of Legal Services, Civil and Children's: Wendy Dalgleish
Civil Finance Manager: Cindy Morrice

Criminal legal assistance
Head of Criminal Legal Assistance: Kingsley Thomas

Finance and Accounts
Finance Controller: Vince Simmons
Accounts Assistant Managers: Karen Shaw, Eileen Grant

Legal Services

Any queries concerning the operation of the Legal Aid (Scotland) Act or the regulations or other legal issues.
Principal Legal Advisor: Ian Dickson

Legal Aid Registers
Compliance & Investigations Manager: Brian Millar

Legal Aid Online
Helpline: 0131 240 2037 or online@slab.org.uk

Communications
Media and Communications Manager: David Montgomery

Mail

For general mail SLAB's mailing addresses are:

DX 555250 Edinburgh 30
Post: Thistle House, 91 Haymarket Terrace, Edinburgh EH12 5HE

Legal Intimations

All formal written intimations of motions or orders relating to matters in which the SLAB has an interest whether as a party or otherwise should be marked for the attention of the Director of

Operations and be accompanied by sufficient explanatory material to facilitate identification of the case involved, the nature of SLAB's interest in it, and the date and location of any court hearing.

Forms

The following legal aid forms are available from SLAB's website: https://www.slab.org.uk/solicitors/forms-and-declarations/.

Information about Legal Aid Online services is available on SLAB's website https://www.slab.org.uk/solicitors/training-e-learning-and-laol/

Civil legal assistance application forms and online declarations

CIV/FIN/2	Financial Eligibility Form 2 – for applicants not in receipt of the benefits listed above for Form 1	
CIV/FIN/2 – Gaelic	Financial Eligibility Form 2 – translated into Gaelic	
CIV/FIN/3	Financial Eligibility Form 3 – earnings statement by applicant's employer	
CIV/FIN/4	Financial Eligibility Form 4 – financial eligibility for self employed	
CIV/FIN/5	Financial Eligibility Form 5 – service personnel	

Criminal legal assistance application forms and online declarations

AA/LAO/CRIM	Criminal advice and assistance/ABWOR declaration	
LAO/CRIM	Summary criminal legal aid declaration	
LAO/SOL	Solemn criminal legal aid declaration	
LAO/CRIMTR	Criminal legal aid transfer declaration	
LAO/APP/1	Criminal legal aid appeal declaration (where legal aid granted in first instance)	
LAO/APP/2	Criminal legal aid appeal declaration (where legal aid NOT granted in first instance)	
(Reg15 D-C)	Reg 15 Special Urgency for Criminal Appeals data capture form	

Children's legal assistance application forms and online declarations

CHLA/LAO – 2011 Act	Children's Legal Aid – Legal Aid Online client declaration	
CHILDTR/LAO	Children's legal aid online transfer declaration	
AA/VERF/MAND	Advice and Assistance/ABWOR financial verification mandate	
AA/FIN/CIV	Advice and Assistance – capital declaration	
CHILD/APP	Application to court	

Account forms – all legal assistance types

AA/HARDSHIP/1	Applicant grave hardship or distress	
AA/HARDSHIP/2	Solicitor's application where payments will be delayed or difficult	

SLA/ROL/5	Request for reimbursement of outlays where there is no potential for any financial recovery	
CH/DUP/SYN	Children's Legal Assistance – Duplicate Account Synopsis	
CIV/ACC/CONC	Civil account synopsis and conclusion of proceedings	
SLA/ROL/1	Application for reimbursement of outlays	
SLA/POA/3	Payment on account of fees	
SLA/ROL/6	Request for reimbursement of outlays or interim payment of fees under criminal legal aid (in solemn and appeals cases) and children's legal aid	
CRIM/ACCTS/SUPP	Criminal legal assistance supplementary account synopsis – Use this form for supplementary accounts in criminal and ABWOR fixed fee matters only	
CRIM/SUPP/AB	Criminal ABWOR supplementary account synopsis – Use this form for supplementary accounts for ABWOR detailed time and line accounts only	
CRIM/ACCTS/TRAN	Criminal legal assistance transfer accounts synopsis – Use this form for criminal/ABWOR cases for transfer accounts only	
ABWOR/EXCEPTIONAL	Criminal ABWOR exceptional payments application – Use this form to apply to SLAB for exceptional payment status for a criminal ABWOR fixed payments case	
CRIM/ACCTS/DSF	Criminal legal assistance account synopsis duty follow up proceedings	
Duty limit increase E-form	Increase in duty capped limit/duty sanction	
ACC/CRIM/DET/SHER/SUP	Summary criminal proceedings: sheriff court – detailed fees – supplementary account – *in use from 1 April 2008 to 29 June 2008*	
ACC/CRIM/DET/SOLM/SUP	Solemn, appeals and automatic: detailed fees – supplementary account	
ACC/ROAS/1	Claim for payment by rights of audience solicitors	

Other materials for use by the legal profession

Keycards are only available via website for download at www.slab.org.uk	
Category codes card (advice and assistance/ABWOR) are only available via website for download at www.slab.org.uk	
Equality card is only available via website for download at https://www.slab.org.uk/solicitors/forms-and-declarations/legal-aid-online-declarations/#equalitiescard	

Legal aid leaflets for the public

Access to information	Each
1 Guidance for opponents in civil legal aid cases	Each
2 Children's legal assistance – information for children	Each
3 Children's legal assistance – information for adults and young people	Each

| 4 Civil legal aid – information for applicants | Each |
| Complaints and comments about SLAB | Each |

Scottish Legal Assistance Guidance

SLAB's Legal Assistance Guidance can be found online:

https://www.slab.org.uk/solicitors/legal-aid-guidance

Messengers-at-Arms and Sheriff Officers

SOCIETY OF MESSENGERS-AT-ARMS AND SHERIFF OFFICERS
Forth House, 28 Rutland Square, Edinburgh EH1 2BW
Tel: (0131) 292 0321 DX: ED 575 Edinburgh Email: admin@smaso.org.uk Website: www.smaso.org
Administrative Secretary: Ian Munro

Objects of the Society

Objects of the Society:
(I) The promotion of the interests of the profession of Messengers-at-Arms and Sheriff Officers; and
(II) The promotion of the interests of the public in relation to that profession.
(III) The enforcement of strict adherence to –
(a) the duties owed by Officers of Court by virtue of their legal powers.
(b) the scale of remuneration as may be fixed by Act of Sederunt or otherwise.
(c) the completion of compulsory continuing professional development.
(d) the Code of Practice.
(e) the duty of Officers of Court to serve the public and to handle complaints about them impartially and transparently.
(IV) These objects include –
(a) the provision of a curriculum and standards of qualification for Officers of Court.
(b) the improvement, through compulsory continuous professional development, of the status of Officers of Court.
(c) the promotion of conferences, meetings, discussions and lectures which provide information that assists Officers of Court in their work.
(d) the co-operation of the Society with any associated or kindred society and the doing of anything incidental to fulfilling the objects of the Society.

Editor's note

As of 2015, the following Members Directory of Sheriff Officers and Messengers-at-Arms is obtained from the Society of Messengers at Arms and Sheriff Officers (SMASO). The Members Directory is dated March 2022. At the time of going to press various appointments were in the offering but not confirmed and have therefore not been included. Any inaccuracies in the following list should be updated with SMASO to ensure such changes are reflected in future editions of the Scottish Law Directory. It should also be noted that the list is now contained within one section – Sheriff Officers and Messengers-at-Arms, as opposed to two separate sections.

Aberdeen

NELSON JAMES
9A Bon Accord Crescent, Aberdeen AB11 6DN
Tel: (01224) 337454 DX: AB60 Aberdeen Email:
enquiries@nelsonjames.co.uk Website:
www.nelsonjames.co.uk

Sheriff Officers:
Nicola Gallagher
Grant Lumsden
Steven Morris
Dean Crane

Messenger-at-Arms and Sheriff Officer:
Michael Gallagher
Ryan Morris

SCOTT & CO
16 Queens Road, Aberdeen AB15 4ZT
Tel: (01224) 627170 Email:
diligence@scottandco.uk.com Website:
www.scottandco.uk.com

Sheriff Officers:
Alistair Hogg
Carol Nicol
Fraser Reid
Fraser Shaw
Graham Anderson
Graham Baird
Hugh Davies
Kenneth Hutt
Laura Michie
Lauren Scott
Robin Gilchrist
Walter McGill
Hugh Edwards
Raymond Geddes
Paul Heron

Messenger-at-Arms and Sheriff Officers:
Adam Armstrong
Alan Black
Alan Davie
Alexander Horne
Christopher McEwan
Duncan Clark
Eleanor Cameron
Fraser Shaw
Gary McLean
John Smart
Louise Mackland
Mark McMurdo
Sheilagh Scott
Vivienne Johnston
William Cameron
Andrew Carmichael
Richard Rance

WALKER LOVE
Skene Business Centre, 96 Rosemount Viaduct,
Aberdeen AB25 1NX
Tel: (01224) 635771 Email:
edinburgh.diligence@walkerlove.com Website:
www.walkerlove.com

Sheriff Officers:
Alan McLaughlin
Andrew McKelvie
Brian Walker
Colin Gowrie
Dale Barret
Dorothy Lowe
Gordon Glen
James A. Walker
James B. Booth
Jamie Barr
Julie Swan
Julie Weir
Stephen McCallum
Stewart Maclaren
Steven Murray
Chelsea Murray

Messenger-at-Arms and Sheriff Officers:
Andrew McLean
Bryan McNamara
Christopher Andrew
Christopher W.G. Bell
Colin Gowrie
David Hynd
David Walker
Douglas Barr
John Scott
Paul A. Cameron
Robert Quinn
Robert Weir
Robert White
Roderick Stevenson
Stuart Sinclair
Thomas S. Davidson
William Wywalec
William P. Dollier
Matthew Cameron

Airdrie

MALCOLM J BOYD
Room31, Business Centre, 1 Chapel Lane, Airdrie
ML6 6GX
Tel: (01236) 763289 DX: 570424 Email:
mjboyd@btconnect.com

Sheriff Officer:
Malcolm J. Boyd

Dumfries

CLARKS
Tigh-Bainne, Wallacetown, Dumfries DG2 0TG
Tel: (01387) 820 702 DX: 580604 Dumfries
Email: mikeclark.clarks@btinternet.com

Messenger-at-Arms and Sheriff Officer:
Mike Clark

Dunbar

LLEWELLYN & COMPANY
The Annexe, East Links Road, Dunbar EH42 1LT
Tel: (0131) 665 5429 DX: 541198 Email:
mail@sheriffofficer.com Website:
sheriffofficer.com/

Messenger-at-Arms and Sheriff Officers:
Douglas Llewellyn
Keith Morrison

Dundee

A.A. HUTTON
2nd Floor, 31 Albert Square, Dundee DD1 1DJ
Tel: (01382) 227573 DX: DD47 Dundee Email:
diligence@aahutton.co.uk Website:
www.aahutton.co.uk/

Messenger-at-Arms and Sheriff Officers:
Andrew Carmichael
Richard Rance

KILLEAN & CO
27 Crichton Street, Dundee DD1 3AS
Tel: (01382) 221093 DX: DD25 Dundee Email:
killean_co@hotmail.com

Messenger-at-Arms and Sheriff Officers:
Alistair Moulds
Alan Moulds

SCOTT & CO
31 Albert Square, Dundee DD1 1DJ
Tel: (01382) 227573 Email:
diligence@scottandco.uk.com Website:
www.scottandco.uk.com

Sheriff Officers:
Alistair Hogg
Carol Nicol
Fraser Reid
Fraser Shaw
Graham Anderson
Graham Baird
Hugh Davies
Kenneth Hutt
Laura Michie
Lauren Scott
Robin Gilchrist
Walter McGill
Hugh Edwards
Raymond Geddes
Paul Heron

Messenger-at-Arms and Sheriff Officers:
Adam Armstrong
Alan Black
Alan Davie
Alexander Horne
Christopher McEwan
Duncan Clark
Eleanor Cameron
Fraser Shaw
Gary McLean
John Smart
Louise Mackland
Mark McMurdo
Sheilagh Scott
Vivienne Johnston
William Cameron
Andrew Carmichael
Richard Rance

Dunfermline

SCOTT & CO
22A East Port, Dunfermline KY12 7JB
Tel: (01383) 721439 Email:
diligence@scottandco.uk.com Website:
https://www.scottandco.uk.com/

Sheriff Officers:
Alistair Hogg
Carol Nicol
Fraser Reid
Fraser Shaw
Graham Anderson
Graham Baird
Hugh Davies
Kenneth Hutt
Laura Michie
Lauren Scott
Robin Gilchrist
Walter McGill
Hugh Edwards
Raymond Geddes
Paul Heron

Messenger-at-Arms and Sheriff Officers:
Adam Armstrong
Alan Black
Alan Davie
Alexander Horne
Christopher McEwan
Duncan Clark
Eleanor Cameron
Fraser Shaw
Gary McLean
John Smart
Louise Mackland
Mark McMurdo
Sheilagh Scott
Vivienne Johnston
William Cameron
Andrew Carmichael
Richard Rance

Edinburgh

ALEX M ADAMSON LLP
9-10 St.Andrew Square, Edinburgh EH2 2AF
Tel: (01324) 634229 DX: 551108, Edinburgh-3

Email: officers@alex-m-adamson.co.uk Website: www.alex-m-adamson.co.uk/

Sheriff Officers:
Andrew Harrison
Michael Schofield
Alan Buchan
Stuart P. Hunter
Richard Harrison
Allan Hamilton
Graeme MacDonald

Messenger-at-Arms and Sheriff Officers:
Stephen Rowe
Kevin Mackay

FRASER IRVINE SHERIFF OFFICERS
22 Constitution Street, Edinburgh EH6 7BT
Tel: (0141) 588 0388 Email:
enquiries@fraserirvine.co.uk Website:
www.fraserirvine.co.uk

Sheriff Officers:
Andrew Fraser
Joy McLaughlin
Alistair Hogg

Messenger-at-Arms and Sheriff Officer:
Alexander Irvine
Douglas Bruce
Melissa Rigby

THOMAS HANNAH & CO
9 Mansfield Place, Edinburgh EH3 6NB
Tel: (0131) 556 8601 DX: ED127 Email:
enquiries@thomashannah.co.uk Website:
www.thomashannah.co.uk/

Sheriff Officer:
Patrick Dooley

Messenger-at-Arms and Sheriff Officer:
Ian Runciman

NELSON JAMES
12 South Charlotte Street, Edinburgh EH2 4AX
Tel: (0131) 202 1159 DX: 554 000 Livingston 8
Email: enquiries@nelsonjames.co.uk Website:
www.nelsonjames.co.uk

Sheriff Officers:
Nicola Gallagher
Grant Lumsden
Steven Morris
Dean Crane

Messenger-at-Arms and Sheriff Officer:
Michael Gallagher
Ryan Morris

SCOTT & CO
9 Melville Crescent, Edinburgh EH3 7LZ
Tel: (0131) 272 7220 DX: ED88 Edinburgh
Email: diligence@scottandco.uk.com Website:
www.scottandco.uk.com

Sheriff Officers:
Alistair Hogg
Carol Nicol
Fraser Reid
Fraser Shaw
Graham Anderson
Graham Baird
Hugh Davies
Kenneth Hutt
Laura Michie
Lauren Scott
Robin Gilchrist
Walter McGill
Hugh Edwards
Raymond Geddes
Paul Heron

Messenger-at-Arms and Sheriff Officers:
Adam Armstrong
Alan Black
Alan Davie
Alexander Horne
Christopher McEwan
Duncan Clark
Eleanor Cameron
Fraser Shaw
Gary McLean
John Smart
Louise Mackland
Mark McMurdo
Sheilagh Scott
Vivienne Johnston
William Cameron
Andrew Carmichael
Richard Rance

WALKER LOVE
17 Hart Street, Edinburgh EH1 3RN
Tel: (0131) 557 0100 DX: ED173 Email:
edinburgh.diligence@walkerlove.com Website:
www.walkerlove.com/

Sheriff Officers:
Alan McLaughlin
Andrew McKelvie
Brian Walker
Colin Gowrie
Dale Barret
Dorothy Lowe
Gordon Glen
James A. Walker
James B. Booth
Jamie Barr
Julie Swan
Julie Weir
Stephen McCallum
Stewart Maclaren

Steven Murray
Chelsea Murray

Messenger-at-Arms and Sheriff Officers:
Andrew McLean
Bryan McNamara
Christopher Andrew
Christopher W.G. Bell
Colin Gowrie
David Hynd
David Walker
Douglas Barr
John Scott
Paul A. Cameron
Robert Quinn
Robert Weir
Robert White
Roderick Stevenson
Stuart Sinclair
Thomas S. Davidson
William Wywalec
William P. Dollier
Matthew Cameron

Falkirk

ALEX M ADAMSON LLP
7 Park Street, Falkirk FK1 1RE
Tel: (01324) 634229 DX: FA1 Falkirk Email:
officers@alex-m-adamson.co.uk Website:
www.alex-m-adamson.co.uk/

Sheriff Officers:
Andrew Harrison
Michael Schofield
Alan Buchan
Stuart P. Hunter
Richard Harrison
Allan Hamilton
Graeme MacDonald

Messenger-at-Arms and Sheriff Officers:
Stephen Rowe
Kevin Mackay

Galashiels

SCOTT & CO
50-52 High Street, Galashiels TD1 1SE
Tel: (01896) 757782 Email:
diligence@scottandco.uk.com Website:
www.scottandco.uk.com

Sheriff Officers:
Alistair Hogg
Carol Nicol
Fraser Reid
Fraser Shaw
Graham Anderson
Graham Baird
Hugh Davies
Kenneth Hutt

Laura Michie
Lauren Scott
Robin Gilchrist
Walter McGill
Hugh Edwards
Raymond Geddes
Paul Heron

Messenger-at-Arms and Sheriff Officers:
Adam Armstrong
Alan Black
Alan Davie
Alexander Horne
Christopher McEwan
Duncan Clark
Eleanor Cameron
Fraser Shaw
Gary McLean
John Smart
Louise Mackland
Mark McMurdo
Sheilagh Scott
Vivienne Johnston
William Cameron
Andrew Carmichael
Richard Rance

Glasgow

DAVIDSON DEMPSTER LLP
219 Paisley Road West, Glasgow G51 1NE
Tel: (0141) 473 1711 DX: GW110 Email:
diligence@ddllp.co.uk Website: www.ddllp.co.uk

Messenger-at-Arms and Sheriff Officer:
David Dempster

FRASER IRVINE SHERIFF OFFICERS
Park Lane House, 47 Broad Street, Glasgow
G40 2QW
Tel: (0141) 588 0388 DX: 500414 Dennistoun 2
Email: enquiries@fraserirvine.co.uk Website:
www.fraserirvine.co.uk

Sheriff Officers:
Andrew Fraser
Joy McLaughlin
Alistair Hogg

Messenger-at-Arms and Sheriff Officer:
Alexander Irvine
Douglas Bruce
Melissa Rigby

GORDON & NOBLE
Suite No 3, Building 1,, Spiersbridge Business
Park,, Thornliebank, Glasgow G46 8NG
Tel: (0141) 221 8615 DX: 556322 Clarkston
Email: clientservices@gordonnoble.co.uk Website:
www.gordonnoble.com/

Messenger-at-Arms and Sheriff Officer:
Mark Fishman

GRAHAM STEWART & CO. LLP
272 Bath Street, Glasgow G2 4JR
Tel: (0141) 354 1555 DX: DX:561485, Glasgow
16 Email: info@graham-stewart.co.uk Website:
www.graham-stewart.co.uk

Messenger-at-Arms and Sheriff Officers:
Ian Wylie
Stuart Miller

HANNAHS
Suite 335, 337 Baltic Chambers, 50 Wellington
Street, Glasgow G2 6UJ
Tel: (0141) 221 9111 DX: GW364 Email:
instructions@hannahs.org.uk Website:
www.hannahs.org.uk/

Sheriff Officers:
Colin Miller
Derek Miller

Messenger-at-Arms and Sheriff Officers:
Alexander Jack
Gary Stewart

GRAHAM LOWRIE
50 Brook Street, Glasgow G40 2AB
Tel: (0141) 550 8868 Email:
graham@lowriesheriffofficers.scot

Messenger-at-Arms and Sheriff Officer:
Graham Lowrie

MILLER MCKENNA
87 Carlton Place, Glasgow G5 9TD
Tel: (0141) 429 4903 DX: DX 513208 Glas
Carlton Place Email:
millermckenna@btconnect.com

Messenger-at-Arms and Sheriff Officer:
Paul Miller

NELSON JAMES
38 Queen Street, Glasgow G1 3DX
Tel: (0141) 212 0337 DX: 554000 Livingston 8
Email: enquiries@nelsonjames.co.uk Website:
www.nelsonjames.co.uk

Sheriff Officers:
Nicola Gallagher
Grant Lumsden
Steven Morris
Dean Crane

Messenger-at-Arms and Sheriff Officer:
Michael Gallagher
Ryan Morris

RUTHERFORD & MACPHERSON
102 Bath Street, Glasgow G2 2EP
Tel: (0141) 332 3223 DX: 561470 Glasgow 16
Email: ram@arandem.co.uk Website:
www.arandem.co.uk

Messengers-at-Arms and Sheriff Officers:
Ian C. Lamont
R. A. Macpherson
John Ross

SCOTT & CO
279 Bath Street, Glasgow G2 4JL
Tel: (0141) 565 4000 Email:
diligence@scottandco.uk.com Website:
www.scottandco.uk.com

Sheriff Officers:
Alistair Hogg
Carol Nicol
Fraser Reid
Fraser Shaw
Graham Anderson
Graham Baird
Hugh Davies
Kenneth Hutt
Laura Michie
Lauren Scott
Robin Gilchrist
Walter McGill
Hugh Edwards
Raymond Geddes
Paul Heron

Messenger-at-Arms and Sheriff Officers:
Adam Armstrong
Alan Black
Alan Davie
Alexander Horne
Christopher McEwan
Duncan Clark
Eleanor Cameron
Fraser Shaw
Gary McLean
John Smart
Louise Mackland
Mark McMurdo
Sheilagh Scott
Vivienne Johnston
William Cameron
Andrew Carmichael
Richard Rance

STIRLING PARK LLP
Enforcement Service Centre, 24 Blythswood
Square, Glasgow G2 4BG
Tel: (0141) 565 5767
Fax: (0141) 565 5764 DX: 512051 GLASGOW
CENTRAL Email: officers@stirlingpark.co.uk
Website: www.stirlingpark.co.uk/

Sheriff Officers:
Ronald J Murison
Debbie Mulligan
Stacey Mulligan
Derek P Hamilton
Scott Fenwick
Craig Stuart
Kenneth Gillies
Graeme Scott
William Sweeting
Euan McLaughlin
Steven Gray
Liam MacGillivray
Bryan McLaughlin
David Buchan
Allan Bryson
Scott Livingstone
Sam Mitchell
Grant Moore
David Orr
Alastair Monteith
Ian Smith
Ryan Morris
Cameron Sutherland
Grant Campbell
Iain Elliot
James Smith
Derek Brown
Michael Farquhar
Sarah Louise Fergusson
David Scarth
Steven Cameron
Laura Boyle
Christopher McEwan

Messenger-At-Arms and Sheriff Officers:
Ronald J Murison
Derek P Hamilton
Grant Moore
David Orr
Alastair Monteith
Craig Stuart
Ian Smith
Stacey Mulligan
Kenneth Gillies
Steven Cameron
James Smith
Ryan Morris
David Scarth
Scott Fenwick
Cameron Sutherland
Grant Campbell
Euan McLaughlin
Steven Gray

WALKER LOVE
16 Royal Exchange Square, Glasgow G1 3AB
Tel: (0141) 248 8224 Email:
edinburgh.diligence@walkerlove.com Website:
www.walkerlove.com

Sheriff Officers:
Alan McLaughlin
Andrew McKelvie

Brian Walker
Colin Gowrie
Dale Barret
Dorothy Lowe
Gordon Glen
James A. Walker
James B. Booth
Jamie Barr
Julie Swan
Julie Weir
Stephen McCallum
Stewart Maclaren
Steven Murray
Chelsea Murray

Messenger-at-Arms and Sheriff Officers:
Andrew McLean
Bryan McNamara
Christopher Andrew
Christopher W.G. Bell
Colin Gowrie
David Hynd
David Walker
Douglas Barr
John Scott
Paul A. Cameron
Robert Quinn
Robert Weir
Robert White
Roderick Stevenson
Stuart Sinclair
Thomas S. Davidson
William Wywalec
William P. Dollier
Matthew Cameron

Glenrothes

MCKENZIE & CO
7 Cowal Crescent, Glenrothes KY6 3PS
Tel: (01592) 743913 Email:
h.mckenzie284@btinternet.com

Messenger-at-Arms and Sheriff Officer:
Henry McKenzie

Greenock

ALEX M ADAMSON LLP
63 Cathcart Street, Greenock PA15 1DE
Tel: (01324) 634229 DX: 556621 Greenock
Email: officers@alex-m-adamson.co.uk Website:
www.alex-m-adamson.co.uk/

Sheriff Officers:
Andrew Harrison
Michael Schofield
Alan Buchan
Stuart P. Hunter
Richard Harrison
Allan Hamilton
Graeme MacDonald

Messenger-at-Arms and Sheriff Officers:
Stephen Rowe
Kevin Mackay

KIRK & CO
6 Brougham Street, Greenock PA16 8AA
Tel: (01475) 732200 DX: GR14 Greenock Email:
enquiries@kirkandcompany.co.uk Website:
www.kirkandcompany.co.uk

Messenger-at-Arms and Sheriff Officer:
Graeme Kirk

Hamilton

JOHN CAMPBELL LLP
Diligence House, 61 & 63 Clydesdale Street,
Hamilton ML3 0DD
Tel: (01698) 420160 DX: HA21 Email:
info@jcllp.co.uk Website: www.jcllp.co.uk/

Sheriff Officers:
Mark Finnigan

Messenger-at-Arms and Sheriff Officer:
John Campbell

KIERNAN OLIVER
Sheriff Officers Unit 17A, 69 Bothwell Road,
Hamilton ML3 0DW
Tel: (01698) 285 386 Email:
info@kiernanoliver.co.uk Website:
www.kiernanoliver.co.uk/

Sheriff Officer:
Damian Cusick

Inverness

SCOTT & CO
29 Innes Street, Inverness IV1 1NP
Tel: (01463) 236048 Email:
diligence@scottandco.uk.com Website:
www.scottandco.uk.com

Sheriff Officers:
Alistair Hogg
Carol Nicol
Fraser Reid
Fraser Shaw
Graham Anderson
Graham Baird
Hugh Davies
Kenneth Hutt
Laura Michie
Lauren Scott
Robin Gilchrist
Walter McGill
Hugh Edwards
Raymond Geddes
Paul Heron

Messenger-at-Arms and Sheriff Officers:
Adam Armstrong
Alan Black
Alan Davie
Alexander Horne
Christopher McEwan
Duncan Clark
Eleanor Cameron
Fraser Shaw
Gary McLean
John Smart
Louise Mackland
Mark McMurdo
Sheilagh Scott
Vivienne Johnston
William Cameron
Andrew Carmichael
Richard Rance

WALKER LOVE
Suite 2B1, 2nd Floor, Metropolitan House, 31-33
High Street, Inverness 1V1 1HT
Tel: (01463) 236203 Email:
edinburgh.diligence@walkerlove.com Website:
www.walkerlove.com/

Sheriff Officers:
Alan McLaughlin
Andrew McKelvie
Brian Walker
Colin Gowrie
Dale Barret
Dorothy Lowe
Gordon Glen
James A. Walker
James B. Booth
Jamie Barr
Julie Swan
Julie Weir
Stephen McCallum
Stewart Maclaren
Steven Murray
Chelsea Murray

Messenger-at-Arms and Sheriff Officers:
Andrew McLean
Bryan McNamara
Christopher Andrew
Christopher W.G. Bell
Colin Gowrie
David Hynd
David Walker
Douglas Barr
John Scott
Paul A. Cameron
Robert Quinn
Robert Weir
Robert White
Roderick Stevenson
Stuart Sinclair
Thomas S. Davidson
William Wywalec
William P. Dollier
Matthew Cameron

Kilmarnock

COLIN R. WILKS
39 Irvine Road, Kilmaurs, Kilmarnock KA3 2TF
Tel: (01563) 527 871 DX: KK3, Kilmarnock Email:
colin@colinrwilks.co.uk

Messenger-at-Arms and Sheriff Officer:
Colin R. Wilks

STIRLING PARK LLP
25 Bank Street, Kilmarnock KA1 1ER
Tel: (0141) 565 5767
Fax: (0141) 565 5764 DX: 512051 GLASGOW
CENTRAL Email: officers@stirlingpark.co.uk
Website: www.stirlingpark.co.uk/

Sheriff Officers:
Ronald J Murison
Debbie Mulligan
Stacey Mulligan
Derek P Hamilton
Scott Fenwick
Craig Stuart
Kenneth Gillies
Graeme Scott
William Sweeting
Euan McLaughlin
Steven Gray
Liam MacGillivray
Bryan McLaughlin
David Buchan
Allan Bryson
Scott Livingstone
Sam Mitchell
Grant Moore
David Orr
Alastair Monteith
Ian Smith
Ryan Morris
Cameron Sutherland
Grant Campbell
Iain Elliot
James Smith
Derek Brown
Michael Farquhar
Sarah Louise Fergusson
David Scarth
Steven Cameron
Laura Boyle
Christopher McEwan

Messenger-At-Arms and Sheriff Officers:
Ronald J Murison
Derek P Hamilton
Grant Moore
David Orr
Alastair Monteith
Craig Stuart
Ian Smith
Stacey Mulligan
Kenneth Gillies
Steven Cameron
James Smith

Ryan Morris
David Scarth
Scott Fenwick
Cameron Sutherland
Grant Campbell
Euan McLaughlin
Steven Gray

WALKER LOVE
15 Portland Road, Kilmarnock KA1 2BT
Tel: (01563) 572410 Email:
edinburgh.diligence@walkerlove.com Website:
www.walkerlove.com

Sheriff Officers:
Alan McLaughlin
Andrew McKelvie
Brian Walker
Colin Gowrie
Dale Barret
Dorothy Lowe
Gordon Glen
James A. Walker
James B. Booth
Jamie Barr
Julie Swan
Julie Weir
Stephen McCallum
Stewart Maclaren
Steven Murray
Chelsea Murray

Messenger-at-Arms and Sheriff Officers:
Andrew McLean
Bryan McNamara
Christopher Andrew
Christopher W.G. Bell
Colin Gowrie
David Hynd
David Walker
Douglas Barr
John Scott
Paul A. Cameron
Robert Quinn
Robert Weir
Robert White
Roderick Stevenson
Stuart Sinclair
Thomas S. Davidson
William Wywalec
William P. Dollier
Matthew Cameron

Kirkcaldy

ALEX M ADAMSON LLP
25 High Street, Kirkcaldy KY1 1LQ
Tel: (01324) 634 229 DX: KY2, Kirkcaldy Email:
officers@alex-m-adamson.co.uk Website:
www.alex-m-adamson.co.uk/

Sheriff Officers:
Andrew Harrison
Michael Schofield

Alan Buchan
Stuart P. Hunter
Richard Harrison
Allan Hamilton
Graeme MacDonald

Messenger-at-Arms and Sheriff Officers:
Stephen Rowe
Kevin Mackay

WALKER LOVE
5 South Fergus Place, Kirkcaldy KY1 1YA
Tel: (01592) 200184 Email:
edinburgh.diligence@walkerlove.com Website:
www.walkerlove.com/

Sheriff Officers:
Alan McLaughlin
Andrew McKelvie
Brian Walker
Colin Gowrie
Dale Barret
Dorothy Lowe
Gordon Glen
James A. Walker
James B. Booth
Jamie Barr
Julie Swan
Julie Weir
Stephen McCallum
Stewart Maclaren
Steven Murray
Chelsea Murray

Messenger-at-Arms and Sheriff Officers:
Andrew McLean
Bryan McNamara
Christopher Andrew
Christopher W.G. Bell
Colin Gowrie
David Hynd
David Walker
Douglas Barr
John Scott
Paul A. Cameron
Robert Quinn
Robert Weir
Robert White
Roderick Stevenson
Stuart Sinclair
Thomas S. Davidson
William Wywalec
William P. Dollier
Matthew Cameron

Livingston

ALEX M ADAMSON LLP
Unit 3, Grampian Court, Grampian Square,
Livingston EH54 6QF
Tel: (01324) 634229 DX: 540894 Email:
officers@alex-m-adamson.co.uk Website:
www.alex-m-adamson.co.uk/

Sheriff Officers:
Andrew Harrison
Michael Schofield
Alan Buchan
Stuart P. Hunter
Richard Harrison
Allan Hamilton
Graeme MacDonald

Messenger-at-Arms and Sheriff Officers:
Stephen Rowe
Kevin Mackay

NELSON JAMES
Suite 3 Ochil House, Beveridge Square,
Livingston EH54 6QF
Tel: (01506) 429988 DX: 554000, Livingston 8
Email: enquiries@nelsonjames.co.uk Website:
www.nelsonjames.co.uk

Sheriff Officers:
Nicola Gallagher
Grant Lumsden
Steven Morris
Dean Crane

Messenger-at-Arms and Sheriff Officer:
Michael Gallagher
Ryan Morris

Motherwell

JAMES S ORR
Room 3.13, Dalziel Building, Scott Street,
Motherwell ML1 1PN
Tel: (01698) 267408/259567 DX: 570932 Email:
mail@jsorr.co.uk Website: www.jsorr.co.uk/

Messenger-at-Arms and Sheriff Officer:
David A. Orr

Paisley

ROBERTSON THOMSON
Unit 2018 Mile End, Abbeymill Business Centre,
Seedhill Road, Paisley PA1 1JS
Tel: (0141) 887 4495 Email:
enquiries@robertsonthomson.co.uk Website:
www.robertsonthomson.co.uk

Messenger-at-Arms and Sheriff Officer:
Stephen Thomson

WALKER LOVE
3rd Floor, 1 Smithhills Street, Paisley PA1 1EB
Tel: (0141) 212 6767 Email:
edinburgh.centre@walkerlove.com Website:
www.walkerlove.com/

Sheriff Officers:
Alan McLaughlin
Andrew McKelvie

Brian Walker
Colin Gowrie
Dale Barret
Dorothy Lowe
Gordon Glen
James A. Walker
James B. Booth
Jamie Barr
Julie Swan
Julie Weir
Stephen McCallum
Stewart Maclaren
Steven Murray
Chelsea Murray

Messenger-at-Arms and Sheriff Officers:
Andrew McLean
Bryan McNamara
Christopher Andrew
Christopher W.G. Bell
Colin Gowrie
David Hynd
David Walker
Douglas Barr
John Scott
Paul A. Cameron
Robert Quinn
Robert Weir
Robert White
Roderick Stevenson
Stuart Sinclair
Thomas S. Davidson
William Wywalec
William P. Dollier
Matthew Cameron

Perth

SUTHERLANDS
King James VI Business Centre, Friarton Road, Perth PH2 8DY
Tel: (01738) 622292 DX: PE132 Email: admin@sutherlandsperth.com Website: sutherlandsperth.com

Messenger-at-Arms and Sheriff Officer:
Robert Sutherland

Stirling

ALEX M ADAMSON LLP
77 Port Street, Stirling FK8 2ER
Tel: (01324) 634229 DX: ST24 Email: officers@alex-m-adamson.co.uk Website: www.alex-m-adamson.co.uk/

Sheriff Officers:
Andrew Harrison
Michael Schofield
Alan Buchan
Stuart P. Hunter
Richard Harrison
Allan Hamilton
Graeme MacDonald

Messenger-at-Arms and Sheriff Officers:
Stephen Rowe
Kevin Mackay

SCOTT & CO
Viewfield Chambers, Viewfield Place, Stirling FK8 1NQ
Tel: (01786) 450938/471512 Email: diligence@scottandco.uk.com Website: www.scottandco.uk.com

Sheriff Officers:
Alistair Hogg
Carol Nicol
Fraser Reid
Fraser Shaw
Graham Anderson
Graham Baird
Hugh Davies
Kenneth Hutt
Laura Michie
Lauren Scott
Robin Gilchrist
Walter McGill
Hugh Edwards
Raymond Geddes
Paul Heron

Messenger-at-Arms and Sheriff Officers:
Adam Armstrong
Alan Black
Alan Davie
Alexander Horne
Christopher McEwan
Duncan Clark
Eleanor Cameron
Fraser Shaw
Gary McLean
John Smart
Louise Mackland
Mark McMurdo
Sheilagh Scott
Vivienne Johnston
William Cameron
Andrew Carmichael
Richard Rance

Patent and Trade Mark Attorneys

The Chartered Institute of Patent Attorneys
(Founded 1882, Incorporated by Royal Charter 1891)
2nd Floor, Halton House, 20-23 Holborn, London EC1N 2JD Tel: (020) 7405 9450
Fax: (020) 7430 0471 Email: mail@cipa.org.uk Website: www.cipa.org.uk
Chief Executive: Lee Davies
Deputy Chief Executive: Neil Lampert
President: Alasdair Poore
Vice President: Daniel Chew
Honorary Secretary: Gwilym Roberts

Aberdeen

HGF Limited
   1 Marischal Square, Broad Street, Aberdeen
   AB10 1BL Tel: (01224) 258510
   Fax: (01224) 258511 Email:
   hgf-aberdeen@hgf.com Website:
   www.hgf.com

Lincoln IP
Intellectual Property Services
   4 Rubislaw Place, Aberdeen AB10 1XN
   Tel: (01224) 433123 Email:
   info@lincoln-ip.com Website:
   www.lincoln-ip.com

Marks & Clerk
Patent & Trade Mark Attorneys
   9 Abercrombie Court, Prospect Road, Arnhall
   Business Park, Aberdeen AB32 6FE
   Tel: (01224) 957100
   Fax: (01224) 957119 Email:
   aberdeen@marks-clerk.com Website:
   www.marks-clerk.com

Murgitroyd & Co
   The Enterprise Centre, Exploration Drive,
   Aberdeen AB23 8GX Tel: (01224) 706616
   Fax: (01224) 706617 Email:
   james.brown@murgitroyd.com Website:
   www.murgitroyd.com

S. William Wallace & Company
UK & European Patent and Trade Mark
Attorneys
   12b Carden Place, Aberdeen AB10 1UR
   Tel: (01224) 900746 Email:
   stuart@sww-ip.com Website: www.sww-ip.com

Edinburgh

HGF Limited
   Gordon Lamb House, Jackson's Entry,
   Edinburgh EH8 8PJ Tel: (0131) 220 7500
   Fax: (0131) 229 5801 Email:

hgf-edinburgh@hgf.com Website:
www.hgf.com

Hindles Ltd
Patent and Trade Mark Attorneys
   2nd Floor, Clarence House, 131-135 George
   Street, Edinburgh EH2 4JS Tel: (0131) 243
   0660
   Fax: (0131) 243 0661 Email:
   mail@hindles.co.uk Website:
   www.hindles.co.uk

Johnsons
Patent & Trade Mark Attorneys
   8 Stafford Street, Edinburgh EH3 7AU
   Tel: (0131) 226 5918
   Fax: (0131) 225 1116 Email:
   mail@johnsons.attorney Website:
   www.johnsons.attorney

Marks & Clerk
Patent & Trade Mark Attorneys
   40 Torphicen Street, Edinburgh EH3 8JB
   Tel: (0131) 2217000
   Fax: (0131) 2217010 Email:
   edinburgh@marks-clerk.com Website:
   www.marks-clerk.com

Marks & Clerk
   40 Torphichen Street, Edinburgh EH3 8JB
   Tel: (0131) 2217000
   Fax: (0131) 2217010 Email:
   edinburgh@marks-clerk.com Website:
   www.marks-clerk.com

Glasgow

Creation IP Ltd
   Hillington Park, Innovation Centre, 1 Ainslie
   Road, Glasgow G52 4RU Tel: (0141) 5856472
   Fax: (0141) 8465399 Email:
   mailbox@creationip.com Website:
   www.creationip.com

Harrison IP Ltd
UK Patent & Trade Mark Attorneys
4 Lynedoch Place, Glasgow G3 6AB
Tel: (0141) 3314478
Fax: (01904) 795382 Website:
www.harrisonip.com

HGF Limited
50 West Nile Street, Glasgow G1 2NP
Tel: (0141) 2295800
Fax: (0141) 2295801 Email:
hgf-glasgow@hgf.com Website: www.hgf.com

Lawrie IP
European Patent & Trade Mark Attorneys
310 St Vincent Street, Glasgow G2 5RG
Tel: (0141) 2127070
Fax: (0141) 4276299 Email:
mail@lawrie-ip.com Website:
www.lawrie-ip.com

Lincoln IP
Intellectual Property Services
150 West Regent Street, Glasgow G2 2RQ
Tel: (0141) 2993123 Email:
info@lincoln-ip.com Website:
www.lincoln-ip.com

Marks & Clerk LLP
Patent & Trade Mark Attorneys
Aurora, 120 Bothwell Street, Glasgow G2 7JS
Tel: (0141) 221 5767

Fax: (0141) 221 7739 Email:
glasgow@marks-clerk.com Website:
www.marks-clerk.com

Murgitroyd & Co
Murgitroyd House, 165-169 Scotland Street,
Glasgow G5 8PL Tel: (0141) 307 8400
Fax: (0141) 307 8401 Email:
jacqueline.mckay@murgitroyd.com Website:
www.murgitroyd.com

S. William Wallace & Company
European & UK Patent & Trade Mark
Attorneys
The Centrum Building, 38 Queen Street,
Glasgow G1 3DX Tel: (0141) 3781070 Email:
stuart@sww-ip.com Website: www.sww-ip.com

Scintilla IP LLP
Patent & Trade Mark Attorneys
The Centrum Building, 38 Queen Street,
Glasgow G1 3DX Tel: (0141) 255 0295
Fax: (0141) 255 0296 Email:
mail@scintilla-ip.com Website:
www.scintilla-ip.com

Inverness

Capella IP Ltd
Suite 5 Nexus, Solastas House, 8 Inverness
Campus, Inverness IV2 5NA Tel: (01463) 225
749 Email: email@capellaip.com Website:
www.capellaip.com

Professional Investigators and Enquiry Agents

The Association of British Investigators Ltd
Brentano Suite, Catalyst House, Centennial Park, Elstree, Hertford WD6 3SY Tel: (020) 81917500
Email: Secretariat@theABI.org.uk Website: www.theabi.org.uk
President: Ron Harrison
Vice President & Treasurer: Kevin Howard
Chairman: Vince Butler
Discipline Chairman Compliance, Enforcement & Byelaws: Paul Moores
Membership: Sam Cooper

The Institute of Professional Investigators
5 Westcott, Welwyn Garden City, Hertford AL7 2PP Tel: (01707) 371144 Email: admin@ipi.org.uk
Website: www.ipi.org.uk

The objectives of the Institute are:
To provide an organisation to assist, regulate or control those engaged in investigation
To assist participants to improve their academic and business knowledge in investigation by provision
   of categories of participation based upon an approved examination structure
To provide a system of regulation of the conduct of participants to ensure that they operate within
   such principles and Code of Ethics as the Institute may prescribe
To ensure persons engaged in their investigative profession achieve internationally recognised
   professional academic and vocational standards and distinctions and to improve their technical
   expertise by promoting, organising and recommending courses, including correspondence courses,
   seminars, lectures and by other education means and to recommend examination structures for
   the purpose of enabling participants to carry out Object 2
To promote the recognition of professional investigation as a profession by government, law and
   public Members are required to adhere to the Institute's code of ethics.

The management of the Institue is vested in a Board of Governors consisting of elected participants.
Principal: Richard Cumming FIPI
Board Members: John Bateman MIPI, Brian Collins MIPI, Steve Smith MIPI
Secretary General: Glyn Evans MIPI

Edinburgh

Grant & McMurtrie
Grant House, 7 Palmerston Place Lane,
Edinburgh EH12 5AE Tel: (0131) 220 6660
DX: ED75 Edinburgh Email:
enquiries@grantec.co.uk Website:
www.grantec.co.uk

Pegasus Investigations Ltd
CBC House, 24 Canning Street, Edinburgh
EH3 8EG Tel: (0131) 272 2766 Email:
admin@pegasus-investigations.co.uk Website:
www.pegasus-investigations.co.uk

Glasgow

Athena Intelligence
272 Bath Street, Glasgow G2 4JR Tel: (0141) 354
8880 Email: enquiries@athenaintelligence.co.uk
Website: www.athenaintelligence.co.uk

Boothroyds
Centrum House, 38 Queen Street, Glasgow
G1 3DX Tel: (0141) 548 8055 Website:
www.boothroydassociates.co.uk

Fox Investigations Ltd
Fox House, 1 Glasgow Road, Kirkintilloch,
Glasgow G66 1AG Tel: (0141) 776 0072
Fax: (0141) 776 4769 Email:
info@foxdetectives.co.uk Website:
www.foxinvestigation.co.uk

Grant & McMurtrie
10 Newton Place, Glasgow G3 7PR Tel: (0141)
229 1166 Email: enquiries@grantec.co.uk
Website: www.grantec.co.uk

ID Inquiries Ltd
High Dundas House, 29 Eagle Street, Craighall
Business Park, Glasgow G4 9XA Tel: (0141) 333
9656
Fax: (0141) 333 9643 Email:

info@idinquiries.com Website:
www.idinquiries.com

Walker Love
16 Royal Exchange Square, Glasgow G1 3AB
Tel: (0141) 248 8224
Fax: (0141) 221 7944 DX: GW98 Glasgow
Website: www.walkerlove.com

Key contact – Professional Investigations:
Brian Walker, Partner

Strathaven

DPB Tracing Services Ltd
53 Glasgow Road, Strathaven ML10 6LZ Email:
mail@dpbtracing.co.uk Website:
www.dpbtracing.co.uk

Surveyors, Estate Agents and Property Managers

Aberdeen

F G Burnett Limited
Property Consultants
33 Albyn Place, Aberdeen, AB10 1YL
Tel: (01224) 572661 Fax: (01224) 593496
Email: richard.noble@fgburnett.co.uk
Web: www.fgburnett.co.uk
Richard J Noble, BSc MRICS MCIArb
Graeme P Watt, MRICS MCIArb
Jonathan Nesbitt, LLB(Hons) MLE MRICS
FCIArb
C N Yannaghas, BSc MRICS
Jim Johnstone, BSc MRICS
G A Nisbet, BLE (Hons), MRICS
M Gordon, MSc MRICS
I M Gove, MRICS BLE(Hons)

David Adamson + Partners LTD
Chartered Surveyors
7 Queen's Gardens, Aberdeen, AB15 4YD
Tel: (01224) 586795 Fax: (01224) 586801
Email: aberdeen@davidadamsongroup.com
Web: www.davidadamsongroup.com

Allied Surveyors Scotland PLC
Chartered Surveyors
Marywell House, 29-31 Marywell Street,
Aberdeen, AB11 6JE
Tel: (01224) 571163
Email: aberdeen@alliedsurveyorsscotland.com
Web: www.alliedsurveyorsscotland.com
A Clouston, MRICS
G D Gibb, BLE MRICS
G S MacDonald, FRICS
D Murray, MRICS

Balfour Beatty
Building Contractors
Mindmull Business Park, Tumulus Way,
Aberdeen, AB51 0TG
Tel: (0800) 121 4444
Email: help@balfourbeatty.com
Web: www.balfourbeatty.com/

Baxter Dunn & Gray
Chartered Quantity Surveyors
Chattan Mews Offices, 18 Chattan Place,
Aberdeen, AB10 6RD
Tel: (01224) 210422
Email: office@bdgthomsongray.co.uk
Web: www.bdgthomsongray.co.uk
Douglas Fiddes, LL.M., Dip. Q.S., F.R.I.C.S.,
F.C.I.Arb
Shirley Thomson, B.Sc., F.R.I.C.S., M.C.I.Arb.,
R.M.a.P.S.

Beedie Mitchell
Quantity Surveyors
136 Hutcheon Street, Aberdeen, AB25 3RU
Tel: (01224) 623166 Fax: (01224) 633122
Email: beedie.mitchell@btclick.com
I W Mitchell, BSc FRICS

Bell Ingram LLP
Chartered Surveyors
2 Albert Street, Aberdeen, AB25 1XQ
Tel: (01224) 621300 Fax: (01224) 634666
Email: aberdeen@bellingram.co.uk
Web: www.bellingram.co.uk
James I Petty, MRICS

Belvoir
Letting Agents
24 Rosemount Place, Aberdeen, AB25 2XU
Tel: (01224) 645 707
Email: aberdeen@belvoirlettings.co.uk
Web: www.belvoir.co.uk
Lewis Stuart

Bill BT Ltd
4 Coull Green, Kingswells, Aberdeen,
AB15 8TR
Tel: (01224) 741686
Email: bill.beattie@outlook.com
W Beattie, FRICS FASI FCIOB

CBRE
1 Albyn Terrace, Aberdeen, AB10 1YP
Tel: (01224) 219 000
Web: www.cbre.co.uk
Derren McRae, BLE MRICS
Iain Landsman

CKD Galbraith
Property Consultants
337 North Deeside Road, Cults, Aberdeen,
AB15 9SP
Tel: (01224) 860710
Email: aberdeen@galbraithgroup.com
Web: https://www.galbraithgroup.com
Hannah Christiansen, MNAEA
Tom S Stewart, MRCIS ACI Arb

Alan Crichton
Chartered Quantity Surveyors
30 Kinmundy Avenue, Westhill, Aberdeen,
AB32 6TG
Tel: (01224) 746605
Email: alan@alancrichton.co.uk
Web: www.alancrichton.co.uk
A Crichton, MRICS

DM Hall
Chartered Surveyors
4-5 Union Terrace, Aberdeen, AB10 1NJ

▶ **Aberdeen continued**
Tel: (01224) 594172 Fax: (01224) 574615
Email: aberdeen@dmhall.co.uk
Web: www.dmhall.co.uk
Shaun H Peddie, MRICS
Kyle Mutch
Laurence F Neil, MRICS
Paul Delaney
Philip Rhind
Staurt Johnston

Faithful+Gould
Project Managers and Cost Consultants
Kirkgate House St. Nicholas Centre,
Upperkirkgate, Aberdeen, AB10 1HW
Tel: (0 1224) 620 202
Email: info@fgould.com
Web: www.fgould.com
Jon Sealy
Chris Taylor

Fugro Subsea Services Limited
Hydrographic Surveying
Fugro House, Denmore Road, Bridge of Don,
Aberdeen, AB23 8JW
Tel: (01224) 257600
Web: www.fugro.com

Hardies Property & Construction Consultants
35 Queens Road, Aberdeen, AB15 4ZN
Tel: (01224) 202 800
Email: aberdeen@hardies.co.uk
Web: www.hardies.co.uk
David Vince, BSc MRICS
Gary Ovenstone, MRICS
Murray Warner, BA MSc LLM MRICS MAPM
MCIArb
Martin McConnell, BSc(Hons) MRICS

Harvey Donaldson & Gibson
Chartered Surveyors
23 Rubislaw Den North, Aberdeen, AB15 4AL
Tel: (01224) 516 207
Web: www.hdg.co.uk

J & E Shepherd
35 Queens Road, Aberdeen, AB15 4ZN
Tel: (01224) 202800
Email: aberdeen@shepherd.co.uk
Web: www.shepherd.co.uk
Kevin I Angus, MRICS
Christopher J Grinyer, MRICS
James Richardson, MRICS
Stuart Dunne, MRICS BSc (Hons)
Jason W Begg, MRICS

James Gibb
Residential Factors
2 Thistle Street, Aberdeen, AB10 1XZ
Tel: (0333) 240 8325 Fax: (01224) 650 602
Email: enquiries@jamesgibb.co.uk
Web: jamesgibb.co.uk

McCue & Porter
Chartered Quantity Surveyors
41 Queens Road, Aberdeen, AB15 4ZN

Tel: (01224) 326122 Fax: (01224) 312193
Email: dgc@mccueporter.com
Web: www.mccueandporter.co.uk/
David G Cobban, BSc MRICS

McLeod & Aitken
Quantity Surveying Project Management
30 Queens Road, Aberdeen, AB15 4YF
Tel: (01224) 313900
Email: admin@mcleod-aitken.com
Web: www.mcleod-aitken.com
Duncan Moir, BSc MRICS
G R Cantlay, BSc FRICS
P W Hennigan, BSc MRICS
G Jessiman, BSc MRICS
M H Shirreffs, LLM FRICS FCIArb
M M MacVicar, BSc FRICS

Morgan Munro
Chartered Quantity Surveyors
4 Waverley Lane, Aberdeen, AB10 1XG
Tel: (01224) 648 004
Email: aberdeen@morganmunro.com
Web: morganmunro.com

Rubislaw Surveying Services Ltd
Chartered Surveyors
18 Northburn Avenue, Rubislaw, Aberdeen,
AB15 6AH
Tel: (07710) 456373
Email: nmclennan@rubislaw-ssl.co.uk
Web: www.rubislaw-ssl.co.uk
N K McLennan, BSc MBA FRICS MAPM
MACostE MCIPS

Squire Associates
Chartered Building Surveyors
430 Clifton Road, Aberdeen, AB24 4EJ
Tel: (01224) 663838
Email: info@squire-associates.co.uk
Web: www.squire-associates.co.uk
K M Moir, BSc FRICS

W.I. Talbot LLP
Chartered Quantity Surveyors
8 Albert Street, Aberdeen, AB25 1XQ
Tel: (01224) 643516
Email: iain@witalbot.co.uk
Web: www.witalbot.co.uk/
I M Chalmers, BSc MRICS
G B Still, MRICS

Trinity Factoring Services Ltd
1 South Mount Street, Aberdeen, AB25 2TN
Tel: (01224) 641010
Email: admin@trinityfactors.co.uk
Web: www.trinityfactors.co.uk

Aboyne

Andrew Nicol
Chartered Forester
Deeside Activity Park, Dess, Aboyne,
AB34 5BD
Tel: (013398) 85335 Fax: (013398) 83312

Email: info-enq@andrewnicol.com
Web: www.andrewnicol.com

Airdrie

Countrywide North Ltd
Estate Agents
33 Stirling Street, Airdrie, ML6 0AH
Tel: (01236) 490 146
Email: airdrie@countrywidenorth.co.uk
Web: www.countrywidescotland.co.uk

Annan

Butler Land Management Ltd
Chartered Surveyors
Beckfoot, Annan, DG12 6SN
Tel: (01461) 201200
Email: david.butler@butlerlm.co.uk
Web: www.butlerlm.co.uk
D E Butler, FRICS FIA

Arbroath

Thorntons Property Services
165 High Street, Arbroath, DD11 1DR
Tel: (1241) 876633 Fax: (1241) 871688
Email: arbroath@thorntons-law.co.uk
Web: www.thorntons-law.co.uk
David Mathieson
Sandra Sutherland

Ayr

Donald Ross Residential
1 Beresford Terrace, Ayr, KA7 2ER
Tel: (01292) 288222 Fax: (01292) 280083
Email: office@donaldross.co.uk
Web: www.donaldross.co.uk
Jacqueline Miller
Fraser Stewart

Allen & Harris
Estate Agents
18 Parkhouse Street, Ayr, KA7 2HH
Tel: (01292) 267248 Fax: (01292) 611901
Email: ayr@allenandharris.co.uk
Web: www.allenandharris.co.uk

Allied Surveyors Scotland PLC
Chartered Surveyors
3 Alloway Street, Ayr, KA7 1SP
Tel: (01292) 260509
Email: ayr@alliedsurveyorsscotland.com
Web: www.alliedsurveyorsscotland.com
K S Hay, BSc MRICS
D C Wooley, MRICS

ARP Lorimer & Associates
11 Wellington Square, Ayr, KA7 1EN
Tel: (01292) 289777 Fax: (01292) 288896
Email: office@arpl.co.uk
Web: www.arpl.co.uk
Gordon Fleming, BArch DipArch RIAS RIBA

Rebecca Cadie, BArch DipArch ARIAS RIBA
Robert Gilliland, HNC

Bell Ingram LLP
Chartered Surveyors
33 Sandgate, Ayr, KA7 1BG
Tel: (01292) 886 544 Fax: (01292) 284 428
Email: ayr@bellingram.co.uk
Web: www.bellingram.co.uk
Geoff Brown, MRICS

CKD Galbraith
Chartered Surveyors & Estate Agents
7 Killoch Place, Ayr, KA7 2EA
Tel: (01292) 268181
Email: ayr@galbraithgroup.com
Web: https://www.galbraithgroup.com

Clyde Property
Estate Agents
9 Beresford Terrace, Ayr, KA7 2ER
Tel: (01292) 262777 Fax: (01292) 267781
Email: ayr@clydeproperty.co.uk
Web: https://www.clydeproperty.co.uk
Andrew Bryden

DM Hall LLP
Chartered Surveyors
15 Miller Road, Ayr, KA7 2AX
Tel: (01292) 286974
Email: ayr@dmhall.co.uk
Web: www.dmhall.co.uk
Robert Murdoch, FRICS
M Rutherford, MRICS

Martin & Co
24 Parkhouse Street, Ayr, KA7 2HH
Tel: (01292) 619539
Email: ayrandkilmarnock@martinco.com
Web: https://www.martinco.com

Shepherd
22 Miller Road, Ayr, KA7 2AY
Tel: (01292) 267987
Email: ayr@shepherd.co.uk
Web: www.shepherd.co.uk
Graeme F Stewart, MRICS
Liam Loudon, MRICS

Slater Hogg & Howison
Estate Agents
4 Parkhouse Street, Ayr, KA7 2HH
Tel: (01292) 400 184
Web: www.slaterhogg.co.uk

Banchory

Strutt & Parker
Chartered Surveyors
Burnett House, Burn O'Bennie Road,
Banchory, AB31 5ZU
Tel: (01330) 558778 Fax: (01330) 822637
Email: banchory@struttandparker.com
Web: www.struttandparker.com
David Smart, MRICS
Matthew Havers

► *Banchory continued*

Larry Irwin
Andrew Duncan
Dan Newcombe

Bathgate

Allied Surveyors Scotland PLC
Chartered Surveyors
66 South Bridge Street, Bathgate, EH48 1TL
Tel: (01506) 631717
Email: bathgate@alliedsurveyorsscotland.com
Web: www.alliedsurveyorsscotland.com

Martin & Co
49a Hopetoun Street, Bathgate, EH48 4PB
Tel: (01506) 676306
Email: bathgate@martinco.com
Web: www.martinco.com

Bearsden

Allied Surveyors Scotland PLC
Chartered Surveyors
132 Drymen Road, Bearsden, G61 3RB
Tel: (0141) 942 9666
Email: bearsden@alliedsurveyorsscotland.com
Web: www.alliedsurveyorsscotland.com
M P Forsyth, MRICS

Berwick-Upon-Tweed

Edwin Thompson LLP
44-48 Hide Hill, Berwick-Upon-Tweed,
TD15 1AB
Tel: (01289) 304432 Fax: (01289) 302027
Email: berwick@edwin-thompson.co.uk
Web: edwin-thompson.co.uk/
N H Parmenter, BA BSc MRICS
A R Hamilton, MRICS

Birichen

Ruth Brown & Co Ltd
Chartered Surveyors
New Office, Whisperdale, Birichen, IV25 3NE
Tel: (01862) 811248
Email: ruthbrownandcoltd@outlook.com
Web: www.ruthbrowncoltd.co.uk
R Brown, MRICS

Blairgowrie

Irving Associates
Chartered Quantity and Building Surveyors
11 Grampian View, Coupar Angus,
Blairgowrie, PH13 9EW
Tel: (01828) 627731
Email: sd1vng@gmail.com
S D Irving, MRICS

Bonar Bridge

Bell Ingram LLP
Chartered Surveyors
Old Bank Buildings, Lairg Road, Bonar Bridge,
IV24 3EA
Tel: (01863) 766 683 Fax: (01863) 766 736
Email: bonarbridge@bellingram.co.uk
Web: https://bellingram.co.uk
Rob S Whitson, BSc(Hons) MRICS

Bothwell

Clyde Property
Estate Agents
47 Main Street, Bothwell, G71 8ER
Tel: (01698) 338 777 Fax: (01698) 477 119
Email: bothwell@clydeproperty.co.uk
Web: www.clydeproperty.co.uk

Brechin

Dalhousie Estates
Chartered Surveyors
Estates Office, Brechin, DD9 6SG
Tel: (0 1356) 624566 Fax: (0 1356) 623725
Email: enquiries@dalhousieestates.co.uk
Web: www.dalhousieestates.co.uk

Savills (UK) Ltd
Chartered Surveyors
12 Clerk Street, Brechin, DD9 6AE
Tel: (01356) 628600
Email: Brechin@savills.com
Web: www.savills.co.uk
R J Stirling-Aird, BSc FRICS

Bridge of Weir

Allen & Harris
Estate Agents
Neva Place Main Street, Bridge of Weir,
PA11 3PN
Tel: (01505) 612114
Email: BridgeofWeir@allenandharris.co.uk
Web: www.allenandharris.co.uk

Slater Hogg & Howison
Estate Agents
1 Windsor Place, Bridge of Weir, PA11 3AF
Tel: (01505) 630 122
Web: www.slaterhogg.co.uk

Brodick

Arran Estate Agents
Estate Agents
Invercloy House, ISLE OF ARRAN, Brodick,
KA27 8AJ
Tel: (01770) 302 310 Fax: (01770) 302 713
Email: sales@arranestateagents.co.uk
Web: www.arranestateagents.co.uk

Carlisle

Edwin Thompson LLP
Fifteen, Montgomery Way, Rosehill Industrial
Estate, Carlisle, CA1 2RW
Tel: (01228) 548385 Fax: (01228) 511042
Email: carlisle@edwin-thompson.co.uk
Web: edwin-thompson.co.uk/
Christopher R Gray, BSc BA MRICS FAAV
John Haley, BSc (Hons) MRICS
John G Raven, FRICS

Castle Douglas

Allied Surveyors Scotland PLC
Chartered Surveyors
27 King Street, Castle Douglas, DG7 1AB
Tel: (01556) 505020
Email:
castle.douglas@alliedsurveyorsscotland.com
Web: www.alliedsurveyorsscotland.com
J R Stalker, BSc FRICS ACIArb

CKD Galbraith
Chartered Surveyors & Estate Agents
93 King Street, Castle Douglas, DG7 1AE
Tel: (01556) 505346 Fax: (01556) 503729
Email: castledouglas@galbraithgroup.com
Web: https://www.galbraithgroup.com
David Corrie, MA Hons Dipsurv MRICS
Marion Currie, AssocRICS MNAEA
Aaron Edgar, MNAEA
Joyce Chapman, MNAEA
S D Brown, MRICS FAAV

Clydebank

Mchugh Estate Agents
Estate Agents
576 Kilbowie Road, Hardgate Cross,
Clydebank, G81 6QU
Tel: (01389) 879941 Fax: (01389) 879822
Email: info@mchughestateagents.co.uk
Web: https://www.mchughestateagents.co.uk/

Coatbridge

Shepherd
Coatbridge Business Centre, Unit 27, 204
Main Street, Coatbridge, ML5 3RB
Tel: (01236) 436561
Email: coatbridge@shepherd.co.uk
Web: www.shepherd.co.uk
Neil M Thomson, BSc MRICS

Crieff

Morris Property Tax
Chartered Surveyors
Halleys Yard, Earnbank Road, Crieff, PH7 3HL
Tel: (01764) 650919
Email: scott@morrispropertytax.co.uk
Web: www.morrispropertytax.co.uk/

Cumbernauld

DM Hall
Chartered Surveyors
Suite 9, Muirfield Centre, South Muirhead
Road, Cumbernauld, G67 1AA
Tel: (01236) 618900
Email: cumbernauld@dmhall.co.uk
Web: www.dmhall.co.uk
Derek Anderson, MRICS
Douglas Thomson, MRICS

The Rennie Partnership
Chartered Quantity Surveyors
22 Locksley Crescent, Cumbernauld, G67 4EL
Tel: (01236) 720144
Email:
angus.rennie@therenniepartnership.co.uk
Web: www.therenniepartnership.co.uk
R A Rennie, FRICS
C A Brodie, FRICS

Shepherd
2 The Wynd, Cumbernauld, G67 2SU
Tel: (01236) 780000
Email: cumbernauld@shepherd.co.uk
Web: www.shepherd.co.uk/
Neil Thomson

Slater Hogg & Howison
Estate Agents
11 Tay Walk, Cumbernauld, G67 1BU
Tel: (01236) 490 147
Web: www.slaterhogg.co.uk

Cupar

CKD Galbraith
Chartered Surveyors & Estate Agents
16 Catherine Street, Cupar, KY15 4HH
Tel: (01334) 659980
Email: cupar@galbraithgroup.com
Web: https://www.galbraithgroup.com
Dominic Wedderburn, MA (Hons) MLE
Mike J Reid, BSc (Hons) MRICS FAAV

DM Hall
Chartered Surveyors
25 Crossgate, Cupar, KY15 5HA
Tel: (01334) 844826
Email: cupar@dmhall.co.uk
Web: www.dmhall.co.uk

Martin & Co
27 Bonnygate, Cupar, KY15 4BU
Tel: (01334) 657219
Email: cupar@martinco.com
Web: www.martinco.com

Currie

Davidson & Robertson Ltd
Chartered Surveyors
Riccarton Mains, Currie, EH14 4AR
Tel: (0131) 449 6212 Fax: (0131) 449 5249

▶ *Currie continued*

Email: office@drrural.co.uk
Web: www.drrural.co.uk
Martin Hall, FRICS, FAAV, ACIArb, ARAgS, FRAgS
Charles Reid-Thomas, BA, MSc, MLE, MRICS
Niall Milner, BLE (Hons), MRICS, FAAV
George Hipwell
Ian Austin
Derek Bathgate
Chris Edmunds

Dalkeith

Legge Associates Ltd
Quantity Surveyors, Project Mgt., CDM Co-ordination
1 Eskbank Toll, Dalkeith, EH22 3DY
Tel: (0131) 654 9596
Email: s.legge@leggeassociates-cqs.co.uk
S B Legge, BSc MRICS

Your Move
Property and Estate Agents
51 High Street, Dalkeith, EH22 1JA
Tel: (0131) 660 3033
Email: dalkeith@your-move.co.uk
Web: www.your-move.co.uk

Dingwall

Allied Souter & Jaffrey
Chartered Surveyors
Suite 1, Mayfield, High Street, Dingwall, IV15 9ST
Tel: (01349) 862237 Fax: (01349) 865061
Email: dingwall@alliedsurveyorsscotland.com
Web: www.asandj.co.uk

Your Move
Property and Estate Agents
59 High Street, Dingwall, IV15 9HL
Tel: (01349) 864 848
Email: dingwall@your-move.co.uk
Web: www.your-move.co.uk

Dumbarton

Allen & Harris
Estate Agents
163 High Street, Dumbarton, G82 1NZ
Tel: (01389) 731314
Email: dumbarton@allenandharris.co.uk
Web: www.allenandharris.co.uk

The Hay Lough Davis Partnership
Chartered Architects and Surveyors
Glenfield House, 69 Glasgow Road, Dumbarton, G82 1RE

Shepherd
130 High Street, Dumbarton, G82 1PQ
Tel: (01389) 731682
Email: dumbarton@shepherd.co.uk

Web: www.shepherd.co.uk/

Dumfries

Allied Surveyors Scotland PLC
Chartered Surveyors
35 Buccleuch Street, Dumfries, DG1 2AB
Tel: (01387) 254425
Email: dumfries@alliedsurveyorsscotland.com
Web: www.alliedsurveyorsscotland.com
D B Telford, BSc MRICS
J Kempsell, BSc(Hons) MRICS

A.H.R. Crossan & Co
Chartered Quantity Surveyors
2 Irving Street, Dumfries, DG1 1EL
Tel: (01387) 264 569
Email: andrew@ahrcrossan.co.uk
A H Crossan, FRICS

DM Hall LLP
Chartered Surveyors
17 Buccleuch Street, Dumfries, DG1 2AT
Tel: (01387) 254318
Email: dumfries@dmhall.co.uk
Web: https://www.dmhall.co.uk

G.M. Thomson & Co
Chartered Surveyors
35 Buccleuch Street, Dumfries, DG1 2AB
Tel: (01387) 254424 Fax: (01387) 257266
Email: dfs@gmthomson.co.uk
Web: https://www.gmthomson.co.uk
David B Telford, BSc MRICS
Simon J Allen, BSc MRICS
J A McMillan, BSc MRICS
J R Stalker, BSc FRICS ACIArb

Hardies Property & Construction Consultants
18 Castle Street, Dumfries, DG1 1DR
Tel: (01387) 264 333
Email: dumfries@hardies.co.uk
Web: www.hardies.co.uk
David Vince, BSc MRICS
Gary Ovenstone, MRICS
Murray Warner, BA MSc LLM MRICS MAPM MCIArb
Martin McConnell, BSc(Hons) MRICS

J & E Shepherd
Chartered Surveyors
18 Castle Street, Dumfries, DG1 1DR
Tel: (01387) 264333 Fax: (01387) 250450
Email: dumfries@shepherd.co.uk
Web: www.shepherd.co.uk
J Malcolm Hunter, MRICS

McGowan Miller Construction Consultants
Incorporating M R Rodger & Partners
Chartered Surveyors
36 George Street, Dumfries, DG1 1EH
Tel: (01387) 254283 Fax: (01387) 263471
Email: info@mcgowanmiller.co.uk
Web: www.mcgowanmiller.co.uk
Stuart Callander, MRICS

J Cameron Graham, MRICS
J S Cowan, MRICS
R D Richmond, BSc FRICS

Savills (UK) Ltd
Chartered Surveyors
28 Castle Street, Dumfries, DG1 1DG
Tel: (01387) 263066
Email: mfogden@savills.com
Web: smithsgore.co.uk
A M Fogden, MRICS
G Kerr, BSc(Hons) MLE MRICS
R A Henderson, BSc MRICS
K Paton, MRICS

Thomson Roddick Scottish Auctions Ltd
Chartered Surveyors
The Auction Centre, Irongray Road, Dumfries,
DG2 0JE
Tel: (01387) 721635
Email: dumfries@thomsonroddick.com
Web: www.thomsonroddick.com
Sybelle Thomson

Your Move
Property & Estate Agents
2 Queensberry Street, Dumfries, DG1 1EX
Tel: (01387) 257 666
Email: dumfries@your-move.co.uk
Web: www.your-move.co.uk

Dunbar

Richard Amos Ltd
Chartered Building Surveyors
& Chartered Architect
138 High Street, Dunbar, EH42 1JJ
Tel: (01368) 863255
Email: ra@richardamosltd.co.uk
Web: www.richardamosltd.co.uk

Dunblane

Keynorth UK Ltd
Chartered Building Surveyors
1 Wedderburn Road, Dunblane, FK15 0FN
Tel: (07712) 668838
Email: mt@keynorth.co.uk
Web: www.keynorth.co.uk
M D Totten, MRICS

Dundee

Allied Surveyors Scotland PLC
Chartered Surveyors
8 Whitehall Crescent, Angus, Dundee,
DD1 4AU
Tel: (01382) 349930
Email: dundee@alliedsurveyorsscotland.com
Web: www.alliedsurveyorsscotland.com
G Black, MRICS

Belvoir
Letting Agents

21a Camperdown Street, City Quays, Angus,
Dundee, DD1 3JA
Tel: (01382) 843 933
Email: dundee.admin@belvoirlettings.com
Web: www.belvoir.co.uk
Nick Horan

Brownriggs
Incorporating Flemings
Chartered Quantity Surveyors
1/7 Discovery House, Gemini Crescent,
Dundee Technology Park, Dundee, DD2 1SW
Tel: (01382) 802572
Email: mail@brownriggs.co.uk
Web: www.brownriggs.co.uk
J Milne, MRICS

Christie & Partners
Chartered Quantity Surveyors
Whitehall House, 35 Yeaman Shore, Dundee,
DD1 4BU
Tel: (01382) 220 699 Fax: (01382) 220 640
Email: admin@christie-partners.co.uk
Web: www.christie-partners.co.uk
D R McKay, DipSurv MRICS

DM Hall
Chartered Surveyors
Unit 34 City Quay, Camperdown St, Dundee,
DD1 3JA
Tel: (01382) 873100
Email: dundee@dmhall.co.uk
Web: www.dmhall.co.uk
Joe Dowie, MRICS
J G Honeyman, MRICS
Robert T Fraser, MRICS

John Duguid Partnership
Chartered Quantity Surveyors
18 South Tay Street, Dundee, DD1 1PD
Tel: (01382) 225674 Fax: (01382) 202721
Email: admin@jduguid.co.uk
Web: www.jduguid.co.uk
Graham S Kerr, BSc MRICS
Robert B Muir, MRICS

Graham & Sibbald
Chartered Surveyors
Endeavour House, 1 Greenmarket, Dundee,
DD1 4QB
Tel: (01382) 200 064 Fax: (01382) 229 773
Email: dundee@g-s.co.uk
Web: www.g-s.co.uk
Andrew W Dandie, MRICS
Graham Tonner, MRICS

Harvey Donaldson & Gibson
14 Tom Jonston Road, Dundee, DD4 8XD
Tel: (0138) 259 7568
Web: https://www.hdg.co.uk

J & E Shepherd
Chartered Surveyors
13 Albert Square, Angus, Dundee, DD1 1XA
Tel: (01382) 200454
Email: dundee@shepherd.co.uk

► *Dundee continued*

Web: www.shepherd.co.uk
Paul Taylor, MRICS
Gerry McCluskey, MRICS

K.L.M. Partnership
Chartered Surveyors
The Red House, St. Vincent Street, Broughty
Ferry, Dundee, DD5 2BB
Tel: (01382) 739511 Fax: (01382) 480240
Email: alastairnicoll@klmp.co.uk
Web: www.klmp.co.uk
R Connor, BSc (Hons) MRICS

Lickley Proctor
Chartered Surveyors and Property Consultants
58 Bell Street, Dundee, DD1 1HF
Tel: (01382) 207790 Fax: (01382) 207799
Email: property@lickleyproctor.co.uk
Web: www.lickleyproctor.co.uk
R W Murray, FRICS

Martin & Co
33 Albert Square, Meadowside, Dundee,
DD1 1DJ
Tel: (01382) 313580
Email: dundee@martinco.com
Web: www.martinco.com

Graham Sinclair Associates
Construction Consultants
291 Brook Street, Broughty Ferry, Dundee,
DD5 2DS
Tel: (01382) 527272
Email: gsinclair@gsassociates.org.uk
G F Sinclair, FRICS

Your Move
Property and Estate Agents
22 Whitehall Crescent, Dundee, DD1 4AU
Tel: (01382) 224 333
Email: dundee@your-move.co.uk
Web: www.your-move.co.uk

Dunfermline

Allied Surveyors Scotland PLC
Chartered Surveyors
18A Dickson Street, Dunfermline, KY12 7SL
Tel: (01383) 728833
Email:
dunfermline@alliedsurveyorsscotland.com
Web: www.alliedsurveyorsscotland.com
P J Bennet, BSc MRICS
R R Peters, FRICS

CQS Consultants Ltd
Chartered Quantity Surveyors
44 Cameron Street, Dunfermline, KY12 8DP
Tel: (0775) 285 4028
Email: cw@cqs.org.uk
Web: www.cqs.org.uk/
Chris M Ward, MRICS

DM Hall
Chartered Surveyors
27 Canmore Street, Dunfermline, KY12 7NU
Tel: (01383) 621262 Fax: (01383) 621282
Email: dunfermline@dmhall.co.uk
Web: www.dmhall.co.uk
Michael M Court, MRICS
Alan Jeffrey
Alasdair E Seaton, BSc MRICS
Iain Swayne
Peter McLavin
Amanda Cameron
Paul Hope
Jane Brockie

Hardies Property & Construction Consultants
Unit 8, Pitreavie Court, Pitreavie Business Park
Queensferry Road, Dunfermline, KY11 8UU
Tel: (01383) 731841 Fax: (01383) 739714
Email: dunfermline@hardies.co.uk
Web: www.hardies.co.uk
C R Gilmour, BSc MRICS
D McArthur, BSc(Hons) MRICS
M F McConnell, BSc(Hons) MRICS

Martin & Co
32 Chalmers Street, Dunfermline, KY12 8DF
Tel: (01383) 737243
Email: dunfermline@martinco.com
Web: www.martinco.com

Mason Surveys Ltd
Chartered Land Surveyors
1C Dickson Court, Dickson Street,
Dunfermline, KY12 7SG
Tel: (01383) 623112
Email: info@masonsurveys.co.uk
Web: www.masonsurveys.co.uk/

Mccrae & Mccrae Ltd
Chartered Surveyors
12 Abbey Park Place, Dunfermline, KY12 7PD
Tel: (01383) 722454 Fax: (01383) 621180
Email: info@mccraemccrae.co.uk
Web: mccraemccrae.co.uk
R J McCrae, BLE MRICS

Moore Ross Limited
Chartered Surveyors & Construction
Consultants
7 Broomhead Drive, Dunfermline, KY12 9DT
Tel: (01383) 620088
Email: mail@mooreross.co.uk
Web: www.mooreross.co.uk
B J Moore, MRICS

Bruce Shaw Property Consultants Limited
Chartered Building Surveyors
6 Forth Reach, Dalgety Bay, Dunfermline,
KY11 9FF
Tel: (01383) 824450 Fax: (01383) 823197
Email: colin.bruce@bruce-shaw.co.uk
Web: bruce-shaw.co.uk
Brian W Shaw, BS MRICS
Colin Bruce, MRICS MICS

Shepherd
8 Pitreavie Court, Dunfermline, KY11 8UU
Tel: (01383) 722337
Email: dunfermline@shepherd.co.uk
Web: www.shepherd.co.uk/
Bilal Ashraf

Wilkinson & Lowe
Chartered Surveyors
22 Viewfield Terrace, Dunfermline, KY12 7HZ
Tel: (01383) 721158
Email: admin@wilkinsonandlowe.com
Web: wilkinsonandlowe.com
B J Kinnell, MRICS

Your Move
Property and Estate Agents
11 Regents Way, The Bay Centre, Dalgety Bay,
Dunfermline, KY11 9YD
Tel: (01383) 824 242
Email: dalgetybay@your-move.co.uk
Web: https://www.your-move.co.uk

Your Move
Property and Estate Agents
11 New Row, Dunfermline, KY12 7EA
Tel: (01383) 739 729
Email: dunfermline@your-move.co.uk
Web: www.your-move.co.uk

Dunkeld

Preston Tait
Chartered Surveyors
Craigbeithe, Birnam, Dunkeld, PH8 0BW
Tel: (01350) 727750 Fax: (01350) 728752
Email: prestontait@o2.co.uk
Web: businessrates2000.com
R J Preston, FRICS

Dunoon

Allied Surveyors Scotland PLC
Chartered Surveyors
160 Argyll Street, Dunoon, PA23 7NA
Tel: (01369) 705 000
Email: dunoon@alliedsurveyorsscotland.com
Web: www.alliedsurveyorsscotland.com

Stewart & Williamson
160 Argyll Street, Dunoon, PA23 7NA
Tel: (01369) 705000
Web: www.alliedscotland.com
K A Noakes, BSc MRICS

Duns

Richard Amos Ltd
Chartered Building Surveyors
& Chartered Architect
2 Golden Square, Duns, TD11 3AW
Tel: (01361) 882599 Fax: (01361) 882577
Email: ra@richardamosltd.co.uk
Web: www.richardamosltd.co.uk

D Burgon, AssocRICS MCIAT IMaPS

East Calder

McLeman QS Network
Chartered Quantity Surveyors
Unit 2, Overshiel Farm, East Calder, EH53 0HT
Tel: (01506) 880 260 Fax: (8708) 555 608
Email: qs@mcleman.net
Web: www.mcleman.net
Andrew A McLeman, FRICS IMaPS

East Kilbride

Shepherd
Chartered Surveyors
Suite 7, Jacobean House, Glebe Street, East
Kilbride, G74 4LY
Tel: (01355) 248535
Email: eastkilbride@shepherd.co.uk
Web: www.shepherd.co.uk/

Slater Hogg & Howison
Estate Agents
10 Brouster Gate, East Kilbride, G74 1LD
Tel: (01355) 530 152
Web: www.slaterhogg.co.uk

Edinburgh

David Adamson & Partners
Chartered Surveyors
32 Rutland Square, Edinburgh, EH1 2BW
Tel: (0131) 229 7351 Fax: (0131) 228 4523
Email: edinburgh@davidadamsongroup.com
Web: www.davidadamsongroup.com/
G D Miller, MRICS
K M Milne, FRICS
N J Smith, FRICS

Murning Associates
Chartered Surveyors
21 Redhall House Avenue, Edinburgh,
EH14 1JJ
Tel: (0131) 443 8839
Email: edinburgh@murningassociates.com
Web: murningassociates.com

Allied Surveyors Scotland PLC
Chartered Surveyors
22-24 Walker Street, Edinburgh, EH3 7HR
Tel: (0131) 226 6518
Email: edinburgh@alliedsurveyorsscotland.com
Web: www.alliedsurveyorsscotland.com
J Harold, MRICS
C J Highton, DipSurv FRICS
M P Paul, BSc MRICS
R R Peters, FRICS
A Leask, BSc MRICS
A Hutchison, MA MRICS

Arcadis
Built Asset Consultants

▶ **Edinburgh continued**

Part Ground Floor Apex 3, 95 Haymarket
Terrace, Edinburgh, EH12 5HD
Tel: (0131) 347 3800
Email: UKenquiries@arcadis.com
Web: www.echarris.com
Edel Christie
Mac Alghita
Tom Morgan

Armour Construction Consultants
83 Princes Street, Edinburgh, EH2 2ER
Tel: (0131) 357 4618
Email: edinburgh@armour.co.uk
Web: https://www.armour.co.uk
Hunter D Kirkpatrick, BSc MRICS
Colin Watt, BSc MRICS
Malcolm W Carrick, BSc(Hons) FRICS
Kenny K Barclay, BSc MRICS

Avison Young
Property Consultants
6th Floor, 40 Torphichen Street, Edinburgh,
EH3 8JB
Tel: (0131) 255 8000
Email: getintouch.uk@avisonyoung.com
Web: www.avisonyoung.co.uk
Stuart Agnew, BSc FRICS

Baird Lumsden
17 Corstorphine Road, Edinburgh, EH12 6DD
Tel: (0131) 477 6001 Fax: (0131) 477 6016
Email: info@dmhbl.co.uk
Web: www.bairdlumsden.co.uk
Donald Yellowley, BSc (Hons) MRICS
Gordon King, BSc FRICS

Ballantynes
Chartered Surveyors
30 Stafford Street, Edinburgh, EH3 7BD
Tel: (0131) 459 2222
Email: rory@ballantynes.uk.com
Web: www.ballantynes.uk.com
Rory Ballantyne, FRICS

Belvoir
Letting Agents
28-28a Dundas Street, Edinburgh, EH3 6JN
Tel: (0131) 226 2545
Email: edinburgh@belvoir.co.uk
Web: www.belvoir.co.uk

Bruce Rae
Property Management
110b St Stephen Street, Edinburgh, EH3 5AQ
Tel: (0131) 220 0303 Fax: (0131) 220 0440
Web: www.brucerae.co.uk

Building Surveying Partnership
Chartered Building Surveyors
36 Barnton Avenue West, Edinburgh, EH4 6DE
Tel: (0131) 336 1098
Email: mgraham@bspartners.co.uk

CBA QS Limited
115 George Street, Edinburgh, EH2 4JN

Tel: (0131) 226 5791
Email: stuart.robinson@cba-qs.com
Web: cba-qs.com
W Bruce Cargill, MRICS
Stuart Robinson, MRICS
R B Adam, FRICS

CBRE
Chartered Surveyors
7 Castle Street, Edinburgh, EH2 3AH
Tel: (0131) 469 7666 Fax: (0131) 469 0131
Email: miller.mathieson@cbre.com
Web: www.cbre.co.uk
Steven C Hirst, BSc(Hons) MRICS
Mark A Little, MRICS
M S Mathieson, BLE MRICS
A Lowe, MRICS
Stewart Taylor
Callum Mortimer

Chandlerkbs
Chartered Quantity Surveyors
61 Dublin Street, Edinburgh, EH3 6NL
Tel: (0131) 523 1930 Fax: (0130) 221 7101
Email: edinburgh@chandlerkbs.com
Web: chandlerkbs.com
Craig J Garvey, BSc MRICS

CKD Galbraith
Chartered Surveyors & Estate Agents
59 George Street, Edinburgh, EH2 2JG
Tel: (0131) 240 6960
Email: edinburgh@galbraithgroup.com
Web: https://www.galbraithgroup.com
Peter R Scott Aiton, MRICS
Pam J Over, BSc (Hons) MRICS
Richard J Higgins, BA Dip.LE FRICS
Pamela H Gray, MA Dip.LE FRICS
James M Galbraith, MRICS
Martin A Cassels, BSc (Hons) MRICS
J Thain, BLE MRICS

Cobb Mccallum & Company UK Ltd
Chartered Quantity Surveyors
35 Clark Avenue, Edinburgh, EH5 3AY
Tel: (0131) 662 8562 Fax: (0131) 662 8563
Email: admin@cobbmccallum.co.uk
B D Souness, MRICS

Colliers International Property Advisers UK
LLP
Chartered Building Surveyors
1c Exchange Crescent (Level 2), 1 Conference
Square, Edinburgh, EH3 8UL
Tel: (0131) 240 7500
Email: uk.property@colliers.com
Web: www.colliers.com
A G Clark, DipSurv MRICS
Andrew J McFarlane, BSc MRICS
I Prentice, BSc(Hons) MRICS
H Ounsley, BSc MRICS
I D Boxall, BSc MRICS

Culverwell
Property Consultants
68-70 George Street, Edinburgh, EH2 2LT

Tel: (0131) 226 6611 Fax: (0131) 226 6622
Email: edinburgh@culverwell.co.uk
Web: culverwell.co.uk
Alex Culverwell, FRICS
James N Godfrey, BSc MRICS

Currie & Brown
Apex 1, Fourth Floor, 99 Haymarket Terrace,
Edinburgh, EH12 5HD
Tel: (0131) 313 7810
Web: www.curriebrown.com
William Allan
Russell Frame

Cushman & Wakefield
Chartered Surveyors
1 Edinburgh Quay, 133 Fountain Bridge,
Edinburgh, EH3 9QG
Tel: (0131) 222 4545
Web: www.cushmanwakefield.com
James Thomson

Richard De Klee & Co
Chartered Surveyors
23 Stafford Street, Edinburgh, EH3 7BJ
Tel: (0131) 226 7744
R A de Klee, MRICS

DHKK
Chartered Valuation Surveyors
54 Corstorphine Road, Edinburgh, EH12 6JQ
Tel: (0131) 313 0444
Email: survey@dhkk.co.uk
Web: www.dhkk.co.uk
Philip Lovegrove

DM Hall
Chartered Surveyors
17 Corstorphine Road, Edinburgh, EH12 6DD
Tel: (0131) 477 6000 Fax: (0131) 624 6188
Email: edinburgh@dmhall.co.uk
Web: www.dmhall.co.uk
Andrew H Milne, MRICS
Eric Andrew
Nicholas Hancock
Alan Patrick
Gordon C King, BSc(Hons) FRICS
Michael M Court, MRICS
Roddy Macdonald, BLE FRICS
Graeme Pollock
Roy Hudghton

Doig & Smith
**Quantity Surveyors, Project Managers,
Building Surveyors**
Unit 1, 2 Canning Street, Edinburgh, EH3 8EG
Tel: (0131) 656 5820
Email: enquiries@doigandsmith.co.uk
Web: https://www.doigandsmith.co.uk
Ian H Jamieson, FRICS

Dove Davies & Partners
Chartered Surveyors
9-11 Atholl Place, Edinburgh, EH3 8HP
Tel: (0131) 228 3999 Fax: (0131) 228 4999
Email: enquiries@dovedavies.com

Web: https://www.dovedavies.com
Colin G Dove, BSc MRICS
Fraser G Crichton, MRICS

Faithful+Gould
Project Managers and Cost Consultants
Canning Exchange, 10 Canning Street,
Edinburgh, EH3 8EG
Tel: (01312) 215 600
Email: info@fgould.com
Web: https://www.fgould.com

G L M
Chartered Building Surveyors and Architects
20 Torphichen Street, Edinburgh, EH3 8JB
Tel: (0131) 225 4235
Email: enquiries@weareglm.com
Web: www.weareglm.com
Ian F McKee, BSC (HONS) FRICS FCABE
David Gibbon, MRICS MCABE
David Johnson, RIAS RIBA

Graham & Sibbald
Chartered Surveyors
40 Torphichen Street, Edinburgh, EH3 8JB
Tel: (0131) 225 1559 Fax: (0131) 226 3754
Email: edinburgh@g-s.co.uk
Web: www.g-s.co.uk
Les McAndrew, BLE MRICS
Kevin A Murchie, BLE MRICS
Donald C Cameron, BSc(Hons) MRICS
Keith Watters, BSc(Hons) MRICS
Paul E Docherty, MRICS

Hacking & Paterson
103 East London Street, Edinburgh, EH7 4BF
Tel: (0131) 523 1575
Email: edinburgh@hackingandpaterson.co.uk
Web: www.hackingandpaterson.co.uk
Neil Watt
David Doran
Alastair Leitch
Alan Gifford
Colin Devon
Gordon Douglas
Emma Blair
Gordon Hay
Graham Hay
Chris Graham
Gordon Buchanan
George Watson

Hardies Property & Construction Consultants,
20-22 East London Street, Edinburgh,
EH7 4BQ
Tel: (0131) 557 9300 Fax: (0131) 557 3520
Email: standrews@hardies.co.uk
Web: www.hardies.co.uk
Derek M Ferrier, BSc MRICS
G Brewster, FRICS
D I Vince, BSc MRICS

Harvey Donaldson & Gibson
33 Castle Street, Edinburgh, EH2 3DN
Tel: (0131) 278 3405
Web: www.hdg.co.uk

▶ *Edinburgh continued*

Henderson Surveying Ltd
Chartered Surveyors
1 St Colme Street, Edinburgh, EH3 6AA
Tel: (0131) 220 5840
Email: enquiries@hendersonsurveying.com
Web: www.hendersonsurveying.com
Ian A Henderson, MRICSDipBS MRICS MCIArb

James Gibb
Residential factors
4 Atholl Place, Edinburgh, EH3 8HT
Tel: (0333) 240 8325 Fax: (0131) 229 3771
Email: edinburgh@jamesgibb.co.uk
Web: www.jamesgibb.co.uk/
Angela Kirkwood, MIRPM

JLL
Chartered Valuation and Estate Agents
7 Exchange Crescent, Conference Square,
Edinburgh, EH3 8LL
Tel: (0131) 225 8344 Fax: (0131) 225 2147
Email: alasdair.humphery@eu.jll.com
Web: https://www.jll.co.uk/en/cities/edinburgh
Alasdair N Humphery, FRICS
M Clements, MSc MRICS
C Finlayson, BLE MRICS
A R Gray, BLE FRICS MCIArb
J M Hogg, MRICS
C L Macfarlane, BSc MRICS
D A Pestell, BSc MRICS
B D Reed, MRICS
E A Stevens, MRICS
K W Waitt, MA MRICS
A S Bennett, BSc(Hons) MRICS
A Briggs, BSc(Hons) MRICS
S M Cusiter, MRICS
K J Frew, MRICS
R A Mackie, BLE MRICS
K A Myles, BSc MRICS
G Quigley, MRICS
C C Stott, BSc MRICS
C I Watson, MRICS

JSM Development Consultants
Chartered Valuation & Estate Agents
10 Strathalmond Green, Edinburgh, EH4 8AQ
Tel: (0131) 339 7577 Fax: (0131) 339 7577
Email: jim@jsmdevelopments.co.uk
Web: www.jsmdevelopments.co.uk
J S MacDonald, FRICS IRRV

K.L.M. Partnership
Chartered Surveyors
Stanhope House, 12 Stanhope Place,
Edinburgh, EH12 5HH
Tel: (0131) 221 9464
Email: bobconnor@klmp.co.uk
Web: www.klmp.co.uk
B Connor, BSc MRICS IMaPS

Knight Frank
Chartered Surveyors
80 Queen Street, Edinburgh, EH2 4NF
Tel: (131) 516 9698

Email: edres@knightfrank.com
Web: www.knightfrank.co.uk
Edward Douglas-Home

Know Edge Ltd
Chartered Land Surveyors
33 Lockharton Avenue, Edinburgh, EH14 1AY
Tel: (0131) 443 1872
Email: robin.mclaren@knowedge.com
Web: www.knowedge.com
R A McLaren, BSc(Hons) MSc FRICS MBCS

Longworth Consulting Worldwide Ltd
Chartered Quantity Surveyors/Legal Advisors
Celect House, 12 Fairbairn Road, Livingston,
Edinburgh, EH54 6TS
Tel: (01506) 414167
Email: nick@longworthconsulting.co.uk
Web: www.longworthconsulting.co.uk
Nick Longworth, LLM, FRICS, FCIOB, FInstCES,
FCMI, FAPM, FACostE, FInstPet, MCIPS,MAICA,
MAE, FCIArb
Caroline Longworth

Malcolm Hollis
63a George Street, Edinburgh, EH2 2JG
Tel: (0131) 240 2800 Fax: (0131) 240 2801
Email: edinburgh@hollisglobal.com
Web: https://www.hollisglobal.com/
Ben Mack, MRICS

Matheson
Chartered Surveyors
22 Forth Street, Edinburgh, EH1 3LH
Tel: (0131) 623 2320 Fax: (0131) 623 2330
Email: mathesoncs@aol.com
Web: www.mathesoncs.co.uk
I H Matheson, MRICS MCIArb

MONTAGU EVANS LLP
Chartered Surveyors
Exchange Tower, 19 Canning Street,
Edinburgh, EH3 8EG
Tel: (0131) 229 3800 Fax: (0131) 229 2588
Web: www.montagu-evans.co.uk
Ross A Burnett, BSc(Hons) FRICS
Andrew D Munnis, MRICS MRTPI
Andrew M Walker, BSc MRICS
Peter B Grant, BLE MRICS
K Hutchison, MRICS
S J Kay, BLE MRICS
A Veitch, MRICS

Morham & Brotchie Limited
Chartered Quantity Surveyors
126 Calton Road, Edinburgh, EH8 8JQ
Tel: (0131) 556 2556
Email: admin@mb-qs.com
Web: www.mb-qs.com
Alan S Harper, BSc MRICS
Ewan B Slight, BSc MRICS
E R Watson, MRICS

Packer Associates Ltd
Quantity Surveyors

1 Exchange Crescent, Conference Square,
Edinburgh, EH3 8AN
Tel: (0131) 226 4555
J F G Packer

Pottie Wilson
Chartered Quantity Surveyors
19b Graham Street, Edinburgh, EH6 5QN
Tel: (0131) 555 3030
Email: mail@pottie-wilson.co.uk
Web: pottie-wilson.co.uk/
Mike R Armstrong, BSc FRICS
Alan J Smith, BSc MRICS

Redpath Bruce
18 Walker Street, Edinburgh, EH3 7LP
Tel: (0131) 297 7560
Email: mail@redpathbruce.co.uk
Web: https://www.redpathbruce.co.uk

Rettie & Co
Chartered Surveyors
11 Wemyss Place, Edinburgh, EH3 6DH
Tel: (0131) 220 4160
Email: lettings@rettie.co.uk
Web: https://www.rettie.co.uk
John Boyle, MRICS
Simon J Rettie, FRICS
Alastair Houlden, BSc MRICS
Chris R Hall, MRICS
A H Perriam, MRICS
A G Smith, MRICS

Savills (UK) Ltd
Chartered Surveyors
22 Young Street, Edinburgh, EH2 4JB
Tel: (0131) 3440888
Email: Edinburgh@savills.com
Web: smithsgore.co.uk/

Savills (UK) Ltd
Property & Estate Agents
8 Wemyss Place, Edinburgh, EH3 6DH
Tel: (0131) 2473700
Email: cdudgeon@savills.com
Web: www.savills.co.uk
J M Adamson, BSc(Hons) MRICS
A Briggs, BSc(Hons) MRICS
B Brough, BSc(Hons) MRICS
A E Bryen, BSc MRICS
I Buchan, BLE MRICS
I E Channing, BSc MRICS
M A Collings, MRICS
C L Dudgeon, FRICS
P Durnan, MRICS
M R Fleming, MRICS
B Fox, MRICS
S A Jackson, MRICS
R D Leslie, BSc(Hons) MRICS
R D Leslie, BSc(Hons) MRICS
J W Macnab, MRICS
H R Maitland, MRICS
R D McArthur, MRICS
S A Moncur, BLE MRICS
K M Munn, MRICS

N J Penny, BSc(Hons) MRICS
D M Spens, BSc MRICS
R W Thompson, FRICS
C Timney, MRICS

Shepherd
12 Atholl Crescent, Edinburgh, EH3 8HA
Tel: (0131) 225 1234
Email: edinburgh@shepherd.co.uk
Web: www.shepherd.co.uk
George Brewster, FRICS
D Niall Gunn, BSc MRICS
Ian F Hannon, MRICS
Michael W Horne, BSc MRICS
Darren Lewis, BSc MRICS
Anthony Bennett
Donal Henretty, MRICS
John Paul Bennett

Stewart Anderson Associates
Chartered Quantity Surveyor
124 Morningside Drive, Edinburgh, EH10 5NS
Tel: (0774) 841 5830
Email: stewart@anderson-associates.co.uk
S Anderson, BSc FRICS

Strutt & Parker
Chartered Surveyors
76 George Street, Edinburgh, EH2 3BU
Tel: (131) 226 2500
Web: www.struttandparker.com
Malcolm Leslie
Robert A McCulloch
Andrew Riddell
Joanna Lindsay
Jonathan Lambert

Summers Inman Construction & Property Consultants
Chartered Surveyors
Suite 4, Pavilion 1, The Quadrant, 14 New
Mart Road, Edinburgh, EH14 1RL
Tel: (0131) 455 9700 Fax: (0131) 557 6534
Email: edinburgh@summers-inman.co.uk
Web: www.summers-inman.co.uk
Aynsley Cheatley, BSc(Hons) MRICS

Surveying Solutions Limited
Chartered Building Surveyors
34-36 Rose Street North Lane, Edinburgh,
EH2 2NP
Tel: (0131) 225 1212
Email: edin@surveying-solutions.co.uk
Web: www.surveying-solutions.co.uk
Douglas McDonald, MRICS
Colin J Sutherland, BSc MRICS
I Adam Monteith, BSc(Hons) MRICS
M F Skinner, BSc MRICS
K W Lang, DipBS MRICS MaPS

Thomas & Adamson
Chartered Quantity Surveyors
10 Wemyss Place, Edinburgh, EH3 6DL
Tel: (0131) 225 4072
Email:
elaine.gilhooley@thomasandadamson.com

▶ **Edinburgh continued**
Web: www.thomasandadamson.com
Brian Donaldson, BSc MRICS
Les Banks, BSc FRICS
Alastair J Wallace, BSc FRICS
N P Lyus, BSc(Hons) MRICS

Thomson Bethune Ltd
Chartered Quantity Surveyors
6 Forres Street, Edinburgh, EH3 6BJ
Tel: (0131) 220 1828
Email: edinburgh@thomsonbethune.co.uk
Web: thomsonbethune.co.uk/
David N Kirkwood, BSc MRICS
Iain Logan, BSc MRICS
A Patton, BSc MRICS

Thomson Roddick Scottish Auctions Ltd
Auctioneers and Valuers
The Auction Centre, 118 Carnethie Street,
Rosewell, Edinburgh, EH24 9AL
Tel: (0131) 440 2448
Email: edinburgh@thomsonroddick.com
Web: www.thomsonroddick.com
Sybelle Thomson

Trinity Factoring Services Ltd
Block, Flat & Estates Managers
Retirement Home Managers, Residential
Lettings and Timeshare Resales
209 – 211 Bruntsfield Place,, Edinburgh,
EH10 4DH
Tel: (0131) 447 9911
Email: admin@trinityfactors.co.uk
Web: www.trinityfactors.co.uk

Turner & Townsend
Chartered Quantity Surveyors
Osborne House, 1 Osborne Terrace,
Edinburgh, EH12 5HG
Tel: (0131) 347 3400
Web: www.turnerandtownsend.com
G J Easton, BSc MRICS
J Eckersall, DipSurv MA(Hons) MRICS
A A Findlay, MRICS
M J Bruce, BSc(Hons) MSc MRICS
S Jackson, BSc(Hons) MRICS
K Jones, BSc(Hons) MRICS
P A Reilly, BSc(Hons) MRICS
A M Smith, BSc(Hons) MSc FRICS

Wardell Armstrong LLP
Chartered Minerals Surveyor, Environmental &
Mining Engineering Consultants
Great Michael House, 14 Links Place,
Edinburgh, EH6 7EZ
Tel: (0131) 555 3311
Web: www.wardell-armstrong.com
Neil Sutherland

Wise Property Care
Property Preservation
53 Easthouses Road, Dalkeith, Edinburgh,
EH22 4EB
Tel: (0131) 516 0590

Email: edinburgh@wisepropertycare.com
Web: https://www.wisepropertycare.com
Brian Reid

Eric Young & Co
Chartered Surveyors
Atholl Exchange, 6 Canning Street, Edinburgh,
EH3 8EG
Tel: (0131) 226 2641 Fax: (0131) 558 5101
Email: reception@eyco.co.uk
Web: www.eyco.co.uk
Andrew J Bain, BSc MRICS
Douglas R Curley, FRICS MCIArb
Robert J Farmer, BSc MRICS
D N Gordon, MRICS
Duart C Keith, BSc MRICS
Ian G Whelan, BSc MRICS
Craig M Wilson, BSc MRICS
E J Lindgren, BSc MRICS
K Hughes, MRICS
G L Martin, MRICS
N McConnachie, MRICS
S R Bashford, MSc MRICS

Your Move
Property and Estate Agents
295 Leith Walk, Edinburgh, EH6 8PD
Tel: (0131) 554 6222
Email: edinburgh@your-move.co.uk
Web: www.your-move.co.uk

Elgin

Allied Souter & Jaffrey Limited
209 High Street, Elgin, IV30 1DJ
Tel: (01343) 547481 Fax: (01463) 711061
Email: elgin@alliedsurveyorsscotland.com
Web: www.asandj.co.uk
Angus F Gunn, BSc MRICS

Allied Surveyors Scotland PLC
Chartered Surveyors
209 High Street, Elgin, IV30 1DJ
Tel: (01343) 547481
Email: elgin@alliedsurveyorsscotland.com
Web: www.alliedsurveyorsscotland.com
A F Gunn, BSc MRICS

CKD Galbraith
Chartered Surveyors and Estate Agents
5 Commerce Street, Elgin, IV30 1BS
Tel: (01343) 546362
Email: elgin@galbraithgroup.com
Web: https://www.galbraithgroup.com

DM Hall LLP
Chartered Surveyors
27 High Street, Elgin, IV30 1EE
Tel: (01343) 548501
Email: elgin@dmhall.co.uk
Web: www.dmhall.co.uk
Michael G McDonald, MRICS

Mcleod & Aitken
21 Reidhaven Street, Elgin, IV30 1QG

Tel: (01343) 546 444
Email: john_mackay52@hotmail.com
Web: www.mcleodaitken.net/

Shepherd
Park House, South Street, Elgin, IV10 1JB
Tel: (01343) 559 939
Email: elgin@shepherd.co.uk
Web: www.shepherd.co.uk

Your Move
Property and Estate Agents
75 High Street, Elgin, IV30 1EE
Tel: (01343) 548 861
Email: elgin@your-move.co.uk
Web: www.your-move.co.uk

Ellon

Haddo Estate
Chartered Surveyor
Estate Office, Mains of Haddo, Tarves, Ellon,
AB41 7LD
Tel: (01651) 851664 Mob: 0779 933 4973
Email: info@haddoestate.com
Web: www.haddoestate.com

Falkirk

Allied Surveyors Scotland PLC
Chartered Surveyors
1st Floor, 22 Newmarket Street, Falkirk,
FK1 1JQ
Tel: (01324) 629329
Email: falkirk@alliedsurveyorsscotland.com
Web: www.alliedsurveyorsscotland.com
R Hyslop, BSc(Hons) MLE MRICS

Campbell & Dean Ltd
12 Meadow Street, Falkirk, FK1 1RP
Tel: (01324) 578 304 Fax: (01324) 918 304
Email: hello@campbellanddean.com
Web: campbellanddean.com
James Redfern, BSc MSc MRICS

Clyde Property
24 Newmarket Street, Stirlingshire, Falkirk,
FK1 1JH
Tel: (01324) 881777
Tel: (01324) 467300 Fax: (01324) 898777
Email: falkirk@clydeproperty.co.uk
Web: https://www.clydeproperty.co.uk
Clark Gillespie

DM Hall
Chartered Surveyors
Unit 6a, The Courtyard, Callendar Business
Park, Falkirk, FK1 1XR
Tel: (01324) 628321
Email: falkirk@dmhall.co.uk
Web: www.dmhall.co.uk
David Telford
Michael McIntyre

Graham & Sibbald
Chartered Surveyors
Suite 1/10A, Falkirk Business Hub, 45 Vicar
Street, Falkirk, FK1 1LL
Tel: (01324) 638377
Email: falkirk@g-s.co.uk
Web: www.g-s.co.uk

Shepherd
Chartered Surveyors
23A Wellside Place, Falkirk, FK1 5RL
Tel: (01324) 635999
Email: falkirk@shepherd.co.uk
Web: www.shepherd.co.uk

Slater Hogg & Howison
Estate Agents
50 Newmarket Street, Falkirk, FK1 1JQ
Tel: (01324) 910 179
Web: www.slaterhogg.co.uk

Your Move
Property and Estate Agents
4 Bank Street, Falkirk, FK1 1NB
Tel: (01324) 632 266
Email: falkirk@your-move.co.uk
Web: www.your-move.co.uk

Fochabers

Savills (UK) Ltd
Chartered Surveyors
7 The Square, Fochabers, IV32 7DG
Tel: (01343) 823000
Email: fgonzalez@savills.com
Web: smithsgore.co.uk/
R J Bromby, MA MSc MRICS FAAV
J E Evans-Freke, BSc MRICS
F Gonzalez, MRICS
W J Hawes, MRICS

Forfar

Bell Ingram LLP
Chartered Surveyors
Manor Street, Forfar, DD8 1EX
Tel: (01307) 462 516 Fax: (01307) 466 920
Email: forfar@bellingram.co.uk
Web: https://bellingram.co.uk
Malcolm J Taylor, TD MA FRICS

Fort William

Allied Souter & Jaffrey Limited
Commercial House, 20 High Street, Fort
William, PH33 6AT
Tel: (01397) 705541
Email: fortwilliam@alliedsurveyorsscotland.com
Web: http:www.asandj.co.uk

Allied Surveyors Scotland PLC
Chartered Surveyors
Commercial House, 20 High Street, Fort
William, PH33 6AT

▶ **Fort William continued**

Tel: (01397) 705541 Fax: (01463) 711061
Email:
fort.william@alliedsurveyorsscotland.com
Web: www.alliedsurveyorsscotland.com

Bidwells LLP
Property Consultants

Carn Dearg House, North Road, Fort William,
PH33 6PP
Tel: (01397) 702433
Email: finlay.clark@bidwells.co.uk
Web: www.bidwells.co.uk
Finlay C Clark, BSc(Hons) FRICS
Graeme Ferguson, BSc(Hons) MRICS

Samuel & Partners
Chartered Surveyors

20 High Street, Fort William, PH33 6AT
Tel: (01397) 702686
Email: info@samuelandpartners.co.uk
Web: https://www.samuelandpartners.co.uk
J R Strachan, DipBS MRICS

Fraserburgh

J & E Shepherd
Chartered Surveyors

11 Dalrymple Street, Fraserburgh, AB43 9BH
Tel: (01346) 517456
Email: fraserburgh@shepherd.co.uk
Web: www.shepherd.co.uk
M Waite, MRICS

Galashiels

CKD Galbraith
Chartered Surveyors and Estate Agents

7 Bank Street, Galashiels, TD1 1EN
Tel: (07867) 977633
Email: polly.cregan@galbraithgroup.com
Web: https://www.galbraithgroup.com
Mike Thompson, BSc (Hons) MRICS
James Galbraith, MRICS
Harry Lukas, MRICS

DM Hall
Chartered Surveyors

38 Island Street, Galashiels, TD1 1NU
Tel: (01896) 752009
Email: galashiels@dmhall.co.uk
Web: www.dmhall.co.uk
Richard A Clowes, BSc MRICS

Edwin Thompson LLP

76 Overhaugh Street, Galashiels, TD1 1DP
Tel: (01896) 751300 Fax: (01896) 758883
Email: galashiels@edwin-thompson.co.uk
Web: edwin-thompson.co.uk/
Simon J Sanderson, MRICS

Shepherd

70 High Street, Galashiels, TD1 1SQ
Tel: (01896) 750 150

Email: galashiels@shepherd.co.uk
Web: www.shepherd.co.uk/
William Laidlaw, MRICS (Resident Associates)

Glasgow

Gordon Adams (G & S Properties)
Estate Agents

50 Drymen Road, Glasgow, G61 2RH
Tel: (0141) 942 9090 Fax: (0141) 942 0775
Email: info@gsproperties.co.uk
Web: www.gsproperties.com
Gordon Adams
Sandra Adams
Mark Adams
Jamie Adams

Allen & Harris
Estate Agents

240 Stonelaw Road, Glasgow, G73 3SA
Tel: (0141) 613 3992
Email: Burnside@allenandharris.co.uk
Web: www.allenandharris.co.uk

Allen & Harris
Estate Agents

183 Kilmarnock Road, Glasgow, G41 3JE
Tel: (0141) 649 9011
Email: Shawlands@allenandharris.co.uk
Web: https://www.allenandharris.co.uk

Allen & Harris
Estate Agents

560 Alexandra Parade, Glasgow, G31 3BP
Tel: (0141) 556 7661
Email: dennistoun@allenandharris.co.uk
Web: www.allenandharris.co.uk

Allied Surveyors Scotland PLC
Chartered Surveyors

Herbert House, 30 Herbert Street, Glasgow,
G20 6NB
Tel: (0141) 337 1133
Email:
glasgow.north@alliedsurveyorsscotland.com
Web: www.alliedsurveyorsscotland.com
H G Campbell, BSc FRICS
J K Denholm, FRICS
S J Hamilton, BSc(Hons) MRICS
F R Malcolm, BSc(Hons) MRICS
G Robertson, FRICS
R J Smith, MA MRICS
P R Fraser, MRICS
A E MacDonald, BSc(Hons) MRICS
G J Hinks, MRICS

Allied Surveyors Scotland PLC
Chartered Surveyors

246 Kilmarnock Road, Shawlands, Glasgow,
G43 1TT
Tel: (0141) 636 5345
Email:
glasgow.south@alliedsurveyorsscotland.com
Web: www.alliedsurveyorsscotland.com
G Firth, DipSurv MRICS

D A Ross, BLE MRICS
D Gibson, MRICS

Arcadis
180 West George Street, Glasgow, G2 2NR
Tel: (0141) 343 9000
Email: UKenquiries@arcadis.com
Web: www.arcadis.com

Armour Construction Consultants
Chartered Quantity Surveyors
111 Bell Street, Glasgow, G3 7LW
Tel: (0141) 332 4311 Fax: (0141) 332 5311
Email: glasgow@armour.co.uk
Web: https://www.armour.co.uk
Kenny M Barclay, BSc MRICS
Malcolm W Carrick, BSc(Hons) FRICS
Hunter D Kirkpatrick, BSc MRICS
Colin J Watt, BSc MRICS

Avison Young
Chartered Surveyors
Sutherland House, 149 St Vincent Street,
Glasgow, G2 5NW
Tel: (0141) 300 8000
Email: getintouch.uk@avisonyoung.com
Web: www.avisonyoung.co.uk
Alison Taylor

Belvoir
Letting Agents
563 Dumbarton Road, Glasgow, G11 6HU
Tel: (0141) 337 3395
Email: glasgownorth@belvoirlettings.com
Web: www.belvoir.co.uk
Sharon Walker

Binnie Murray & Hutton
Chartered Quantity Surveyors
1/1, 15 North Claremont Street, Glasgow,
G3 7NR
Tel: (0141) 889 8833 Fax: (0141) 848 1286
Email: info@binniemurrayhutton.co.uk
B J Horsburgh, BSc DipProjMan FRICS

BNP Paribas Real Estate
Chartered Surveyors
First Floor (Suite 1), Glasgow, G1 3AN
Tel: (0141) 4730842
Web: https://www.realestate.bnpparibas.co.uk

C. R. Broadley
Chartered Quantity Surveyors
Wright Business Center, 1 Lonmay Road,
Glasgow, G33 4EL
Tel: (0141) 773 6243
Email: crbroadley@btinternet.com
C R Broadley, MRICS

Brown & Wallace
Chartered Quantity Surveyors
22 James Morrison Street, Glasgow, G1 5PE
Tel: (0141) 552 8881
Email: admin@brownandwallace.co.uk
Web: www.brownandwallace.co.uk
Craig Macdonald

Greg McCallum
Ian Macleod
Gordon S Brown, FRICS
Craig M McKenzie, MRICS
Steven J Stewart, MRICS
Gordon Wallace, BSc MRICS

Capita Symonds
Project Managers, Building & Quantity
Surveyors
4th Floor, 7 West Nile Street, Glasgow,
G1 2PR
Tel: (141) 285 3600
Web: https://www.capitaproperty.co.uk

CBRE
Chartered Surveyors
Pacific House, 70 Wellington Street, Glasgow,
G2 6UA
Tel: (0141) 204 7666 Fax: (0141) 228 7299
Email: jean.brines@cbre.com
Web: www.cbre.co.uk
Brian Rogan, MRICS
M Brown, BSc MRICS
M Galbraith, MRICS
D McRae, BLE MRICS

CBRE
7th Floor, Sutherland House, 149 St Vincent
Street, Glasgow, G2 5NW
Tel: (0141) 204 7666 Fax: (0141) 204 7677
Web: www.cbre.co.uk
Iain King
Aileen Knox, BSc MRICS
Craig I McDonald, BSc MRICS MCIArb
Kevin J Sims, MRICS
Douglas Smith
Teri Porter

Leslie Clark Construction Consultants
Chartered Quantity Surveyors, 30 Gordon
Street, Glasgow, G1 3PU
Tel: (0141) 248 3888
Email: office@lclark.com
Web: www.lclark.com

Clyde Property
Estate Agents
68 Drymen Road, Bearsden, Glasgow,
G61 2RH
Tel: (0141) 570 0777 Fax: (0141) 570 0123
Email: bearsden@clydeproperty.co.uk
Web: https://www.clydeproperty.co.uk
Mike Bottomley

Clyde Property
Estate Agents
226 Kilmarnock Road, Shawlands, Glasgow,
G43 1TY
Tel: (0141) 571 3777 Fax: (0141) 571 0071
Email: shawlands@clydeproperty.co.uk
Web: https://www.clydeproperty.co.uk
Gavin Hunter

▶ *Glasgow continued*

Clyde Property
Estate Agents
    145 Byres Road, West End, Glasgow, G12 8TT
    Tel: (0141) 576 1777 Fax: (0141) 576 0123
    Email: westend@clydeproperty.co.uk
    Web: https://www.clydeproperty.co.uk
    Lewis Gilmore

Clyde Property
    8 Busby Road, Clarkston, Glasgow, G76 7XL
    Tel: (0141) 534 3777
    Tel: (0141) 212 7033 Fax: (0141) 638 7530
    Email: clarkston@clydeproperty.co.uk
    Web: https://www.clydeproperty.co.uk
    Greg Wilkinson

Colliers International Property Advisers UK
LLP
Chartered Surveyors
    6/1, 2 West Regent Stree, Glasgow, G2 1RW
    Tel: (0141) 226 1000
    Email: uk.property@colliers.com
    Web: www.colliers.com/en-gb/uk
    I D Boxall, BSc MRICS
    I M Davidson, MRICS
    J Duffy, BSc MRICS
    C McManus, MRICS
    D J McPhail, BSc MRICS
    P J Shiells, BSc MRICS
    R T Wilkie, BLE MRICS

Construction Dispute Resolution
Quantity Surveyors & Dispute Advisers
    291 Springhill Parkway, Baillieston, Glasgow
    Business Park, Glasgow, G69 6GA
    Tel: (0141) 773 3377 Fax: (0141) 773 3311
    Email: jlm@cdr.uk.com
    Web: www.cdr.uk.com
    J L Milligan, LLM FRICS FCIArb
    E H Cattanach, BSc LLM FRICS

Cooper Cromar
Chartered Quantity Surveyors
    The Eagle Building, 215 Bothwell Street,
    Glasgow, G2 7EZ
    Tel: (0141) 332 2570 Fax: (0141) 332 2570
    Email: info@coopercromar.com
    Web: www.coopercromar.com
    Graham Connor, MCIAT
    Jon Scordia, RIBA RIAS
    Steven Carroll, RIBA RIAS
    Graham Forsyth, RIBA RIAS
    Simon Walsh, RIBA RIAS
    Tom A Cromar, BSc FRICS
    David Dool, RIBA FRIAS
    Jeff Howe, RIBA RIAS

Countrywide
Estate Agents
    71 Candleriggs, Glasgow, G1 1NP
    Tel: (01414) 321 085
    Email: cityliving@countrywidenorth.co.uk
    Web: www.countrywidescotland.co.uk

Countrywide North Ltd
Estate Agents
    202 Kilmarnock Road, Glasgow, G41 3PG
    Tel: (01414) 321 089
    Email: shawlands@countrywidenorth.co.uk
    Web: www.countrywidescotland.co.uk

Countrywide North Ltd
Estate Agents
    214 Eastwoodmains Road, Clarkston, East
    Renfrewshire, Glasgow, G76 7HA
    Tel: (01414) 321 082
    Email: clarkston@countrywidenorth.co.uk
    Web: www.countrywidescotland.co.uk

Countrywide North Ltd
Estate Agents
    612 -614 Alexandra Parade,, Dennistoun,,
    Lanarkshire,, Glasgow, G31 3BT
    Tel: (01414) 321 086
    Email: dennistoun@countrywidenorth.co.uk
    Web: www.countrywidescotland.co.uk

Countrywide North Ltd
Estate Agents
    107-111 Byres Road, Glasgow, G11 5HW
    Tel: (01414) 321 091
    Email: westend@countrywidenorth.co.uk
    Web: www.countrywidescotland.co.uk

Countrywide North Ltd
Estate Agents
    1 Barrachnie Road, Baillieston, Lanarkshire,
    Glasgow, G69 6HB
    Tel: (01414) 321 083
    Email: baillieston@countrywidenorth.co.uk
    Web: www.countrywidescotland.co.uk

Countrywide North Ltd
Estate Agents
    71 Candleriggs, Lanarkshire, Glasgow, G1 1NP
    Tel: (01414) 321 085
    Email: cityliving@countrywidenorth.co.uk
    Web: www.countrywidescotland.co.uk

Countrywide North Ltd
Estate Agents
    43 Townhead, Kirkintilloch, Glasgow,
    G66 1NG
    Tel: (01414) 321 087
    Email: kirkintilloch@countrywidenorth.co.uk
    Web: www.countrywidescotland.co.uk

CPC Project Services LLP
    69 Buchanan Street, Glasgow, G1 3HL
    Tel: (0141) 248 9635
    Email: glasgow@cpcprojectservices.com
    Web: www.cpcprojectservices.com
    Brandon Stringer
    Andy Norris
    Graham Hastie, MRICS
    Tim Barber
    Steve Mole

CRGP Limited
Architects, Building and Quantity Surveyors,
    26 Herbert Street, Glasgow, G20 6NB

Tel: (0141) 337 2255 Fax: (0141) 337 7500
Email: glasgow@crgp.co.uk
Web: www.crgp.co.uk
Kenneth Veitch
Richard Walker, B.Sc (Hons), BArch, Arb, RIBA,
RIAS
Derek Brown, BSc, MSc, MAPM
Colin Dair, FRICS

Culverwell
Property Consultants
46 Gordon Street, Glasgow, G1 3PU
Tel: (0141) 248 6611 Fax: (0141) 248 6612
Email: glasgow@culverwell.co.uk
Web: https://www.culverwell.co.uk
Alex Culverwell, FRICS
Andrew A Britton, MRICS

Cushman & Wakefield
0/1 Troon House, 199 St. Vincent Street,
Glasgow, G2 5QD
Tel: (0141) 226 5241
Web: www.dtz.com/
S I Dorward, BSc MRICS
A Hare, MRICS
C Hutchinson, MRICS
C R MacKenzie, BSc MRICS
K W Miller, BSc MRICS
S F Spalding, BSc MRICS
P D Balnave, FRICS MCIArb
C Lygate, BSc(Hons) MRICS

Cushman & Wakefield
Chartered Surveyors
199 St Vincent Street, Glasgow, G2 5QD
Tel: (0141) 304 3280
Web: www.cushmanwakefield.com
Stuart Dorward

Derek Paterson Limited
Chartered Surveyors
11 Elmbank Street, Glasgow, G2 4PB
Tel: (0141) 229 5393
Email: derek@g-pltd.co.uk
D Paterson, BSc MRICS

Devers Boyle
Chartered Quantity Surveyors
Suite 8, Enterprise House, Strathkelvin Place
Kirkintilloch, Glasgow, G66 1XQ
Tel: (0141) 578 2280
Email: mail@deversboyle.co.uk
James F MacBeth, MRICS

DM Hall
Chartered Surveyors
220 St Vincent Street, Glasgow, G2 5SG
Tel: (0141) 332 8615
Email: GlasgowCommercial@dmhall.co.uk
Web: www.dmhall.co.uk
Alan Cunningham, BSc MRICS
Paul Reilly, MRICS
Kenny Geddes
Graeme Todd, MRICS
Alan Gordon, MRICS
Alan McGregor

Mark O'Neill
Adam Jennings
Eric Curran, FRICS

DM Hall LLP
Chartered Surveyors
151-153 Kilmarnock Road, Lanarkshire,
Glasgow, G41 3JE
Tel: (0141) 636 4141
Email: glasgowsouth@dmhall.co.uk
Web: www.dmhall.co.uk
Steven W Graham, BSc MRICS
David Cree, BSc MRICS

Doig + Smith
Chartered Surveyors
Kintyre House, 209 West George Street,
Glasgow, G2 2LW
Tel: (0141) 241 4600
Email: enquiries@doigandsmith.co.uk
Web: https://www.doigandsmith.co.uk
Gordon McLintock, BSc MRICS
William Bowie, BSc(Hons) MRICS
Gillian S Kirkness, FRICS
Fraser McQuarrie, BSc(Hons) MRICS

Driver Trett
Construction Consultants
Queens House, 19 St Vincent Place, Glasgow,
G1 2DT
Tel: (0141) 442 0300
Email: uk@driver-group.com
Web: www.driver-group.com
Michael King
Mike Noteyoung
Keith Strutt
Alistair Cull
Antoine Clouet
Kirsteen Cacchioli
Geraldine Fleming
Michael Foster
Pat Fox
Carl Morris
Marine Maffre Maucourt
Nicola Huxtable
David Palentine
Javier Sanchez Llopes
David Wileman
Tom Comerford
Hugo-Frans Bol
Helen Bentley
Mark Wheeler

Colin Ely & Company
Chartered Surveyors
3/4, 40 St. Enoch Square, Glasgow, G1 4DH
Tel: (0141) 221 5233 Fax: (0141) 221 4911
Email: colin.ely@btconnect.com
C P Ely, MRICS

Ewing Somerville Partnership Limited
40C Speirs Wharf, Port Dundas, Glasgow,
G4 9TH
Tel: (0141) 353 3531 Fax: (0141) 353 1155
Email: info@ewing-somerville.com

▶ *Glasgow continued*

Web: www.ewingsomerville.com
Geraldine McCann, MRICS
B Farrell, MRICS

Faithful+Gould
Project Managers and Cost Consultants
200 Broomielaw, Glasgow, G1 4RU
Tel: (0 1412) 202 200
Web: https://www.fgould.com/uk-europe
Jon Sealy

Fitzsimons
Chartered Quantity Surveyors
5 Park Terrace, Basement, Glasgow, G3 6BY
Tel: (0141) 332 4200 Fax: (0141) 332 4211
Email: glasgow@fitzsimons.co.uk
Web: www.fitzsimons.co.uk
Alan Garrick
Stephanie McQuilter
Greig Hanley
Kevin Murray

G & S Properties
Estate Agents
50 Drymen Road, Bearsden, Glasgow,
G61 2RH
Tel: (0141) 942 9090 Fax: (0141) 942 0775
Email: info@gsproperties.co.uk
Web: www.gsproperties.com
Gordon Adams
Sandra Adams
Mark Adams
Jamie Adams

G2 Property Ltd
Chartered Surveyors
South Craighall Lodge, Jackton Road, Jackton,
Glasgow, G75 8RR
Tel: (01355) 301392
Email: rkg@g2property.com
Web: www.g2property.com
R K Gilchrist, BSc MRICS

Gardiner & Co
Chartered Surveyors
21 West Nile Street, Glasgow, G1 2PS
Tel: (01899) 220590
Email: alan@gardco.co.uk
Web: www.gardco.co.uk
Alan Gardiner, FRICS MCIArb

Gardiner & Theobald LLP
Chartered Quantity Surveyors
G1 Building, 5 George Square, Glasgow,
G2 1DY
Tel: (0141) 568 7300
Email: g&tglasgow@gardiner.com
Web: www.gardiner.com
Kenneth E Deans, MRICS BSc (Distinction)
Kevin Bryson
Mark Gilluley, BSc(Hons) MRICS
Colin Mackillop
Grant Sim
Graham Speirs

Max Graham, BSc MRICS
David Logue
John McGee
Garrie Renucci
Gordon Ritchie

Gerald Eve
Chartered Surveyors
140 West George Street, Glasgow, G2 2HG
Tel: (0141) 221 6397 Fax: (0141) 204 2226
Email: info@geraldeve.com
Web: https://www.geraldeve.com
Ken R Thurtell, FRICS IRRV MCIArb
M J Clarkson, BSc MRICS
G R Howarth, MRICS
S A Macaulay, BSc MRICS
M J Forbes, MRICS
B J McEwan, BSc MRICS

Gleeds
Chartered Quantity Surveyors
163 West George Street, Glasgow, G2 2JJ
Tel: (0141) 204 6100 Fax: (0141) 204 6101
Email: glasgow@gleeds.co.uk
Web: https://www.gleeds.com
A Dickson, BSc FRICS
D W Miller, BSc MRICS
Brian Stevenson, MRICS
S M Ewing, BSc MRICS

Graham & Sibbald
Chartered Surveyors
233 St. Vincent Street, Glasgow, G2 5NY
Tel: (0141) 332 1194 Fax: (0141) 332 5914
Email: glasgow@g-s.co.uk
Web: www.g-s.co.uk
Ian C Gillies, FRICS MCIArb
Calum Campbell, BSc MRICS
Neil MacFarlane, MRICS
P E Docherty, MRICS
S W McGarva, BSc(Hons) MRICS

Greenbelt Holdings Limited Ltd
McCafferty House, 99 Firhill Road, Glasgow,
G20 7BE
Tel: 08450 940 940 Fax: 08450 940 941
Email: mail@greenbelt.co.uk
Web: https://www.greenbelt.co.uk

Griffin Webster Ltd
Chartered Surveyors
First Floor, 95 West Regent Street, Glasgow,
G2 2BA
Tel: (0141) 248 7808
Email: david@griffinwebster.co.uk
Web: www.griffinwebster.com
David Griffin, BSc (Land Economics)

Hacking & Paterson Management Services
Property Managers/Surveyors
1 Newton Terrace, Charing Cross, Glasgow,
G3 7PL
Tel: (0141) 248 5693
Email: info@hackingandpaterson.co.uk
Web: www.hackingandpaterson.co.uk
David Doran

Neil Watt
John MacLeod
Colin Devon
Alan Gifford
Chris Graham
Gordon Hay
Graham Hay
Alastair Leitch
Gordon Buchanan
Emma Blair
Gordon Douglas

Hardies Property & Construction Consultants
5th Floor, 80 St Vincent Street, Glasgow,
G2 5UB
Tel: (0141) 331 2807
Email: glasgow@hardies.co.uk
Web: www.hardies.co.uk
David Vince, BSc MRICS
Gary Ovenstone, MRICS
Murray Warner, BA MSc LLM MRICS MAPM
MCIArb
Martin McConnell, BSc(Hons) MRICS

Harvey, Donaldson & Gibson
Chartered Surveyors
3/7 The Standard Building, 94 Hope Street,
Glasgow, G2 6PH
Tel: (0141) 204 0808
Email: andrew.scrimgeour@hdg.co.uk
Web: https://www.hdg.co.uk
J M Gibson, BSc FRICS
A G Scrimgeour, BSc MRICS
J R Annan, MRICS
G Haggarty, MRICS
J Shaw, BSc(Hons) MRICS

G.L. Hearn
Chartered Surveyors
7 West Nile Street, Glasgow, G1 2PR
Tel: (0141) 226 8200 Fax: (0141) 221 7703
Email: info@glhearn.com
Web: www.glhearn.com
Alistair S Ferrier, BSc FRICS
A Blair, BSc MRICS
P J Lejkowski, MRICS

Hogg Eadie Partnership
Chartered Quantity Surveyors
2 Lowther Terrace, Glasgow, G12 0RN
Tel: (0141) 07836 312 556
Email: rbeadie@btconnect.com
R B Eadie, FRICS

Hollis
Chartered Building Surveyors
0/1, 18 Blythswood Square, Glasgow, G2 4BG
Tel: (0141) 331 4030
Email: glasgow@hollisglobal.com
Web: www.malcolmhollis.com
Peter Martin, BSc MRICS
Robert Ballantyne, BSc(Hons) MRICS
C D Munro, BSc(Hons) MRICS

Intl Fire Investigators & Consultants
Chartered Surveyors

Rushbrook House, 220 Ayr Road, Glasgow,
G77 6DR
Tel: (0141) 639 6611
Email: instructus@ific.co.uk
Web: www.ific.co.uk
James F Lygate, BSc MRICS CEng

J & E Shepherd
31 Byres Road, Lanarkshire, Glasgow,
G11 5RD
Tel: (0141) 353 2080
Email: glasgow@shepherd.co.uk
Web: www.shepherd.co.uk/
I W Cameron, MRICS
A Fleming, MRICS

J C & P
Property and Construction Consultants
216 St. Vincent Street, Glasgow, G2 5SG
Tel: (0141) 221 6607 Fax: (0141) 221 3031
Email: david.macdonald@jcandp.co.uk
Web: www.jcandp.co.uk
David J MacDonald, BSc FRICS
Chris P Ross, DipBS MRICS

James Gibb
Residential Factors
65 Greendyke Street, Glasgow, G1 5PX
Tel: (0333) 240 8325 Fax: (0141) 552 2646
Email: enquiries@jamesgibb.co.uk
Web: jamesgibb.co.uk
Debbie Rummens, MIRPM

John Britton Associates
Building Surveyors
69 Buchanan Street, Glasgow, G1 3HL
Tel: (0141) 314 3701
Email: brittonltd@aol.com
J A Britton, FRICS

Brian Johnstone Associates
Chartered Quantity Surveyors
36 Park Way, Cumbernauld, Glasgow,
G67 2BU
Tel: (01236) 728978
Email: bjaqs@btconnect.com
B A Johnstone, BSc MBA FRICS

Jones Lang LaSalle
Chartered Valuation and Estate Agents
1/1, 150 St. Vincent Street, Glasgow, G2 5ND
Tel: (0141) 248 6040 Fax: (0141) 221 9032
Email: mike.buchan@eu.jll.com
Web: https://www.jll.co.uk/en/cities/glasgow
N M Bryers, BSc MRICS
M J Buchan, MRICS
A C Creevy, BSc FRICS MCIArb
C Di Mambro, MRICS
J MacBean, BSc MRICS
N D Macdonald, MRICS
S A Malone, MRICS
N S Robertson, BSc MRICS
A E White, MRICS
A D Crosbie, BLE MRICS
S Lockhart, BSc MRICS
A D McCracken, MRICS

▶ *Glasgow continued*

N M Stobie, MRICS
A Reid, MRICS
N E Rankin, MRICS

Knight Frank
Chartered Surveyors
1st Floor, 25 Bothwell Street, Glasgow,
G2 6NL
Tel: (0141) 221 9191
Web: www.knightfrank.com
J Gallagher, BSc MRICS
John P Rae, MRICS
A McCoan, BSc(Hons) MRICS
I W McGhee, MRICS

Macfie & Co
Property Managers
5 Cathkinview Road, Mount Florida, Glasgow,
G42 9EA
Tel: (0141) 632 5588 Fax: (0141) 636 6775
Email: manager@macfie.com
Web: https://www.macfie.com
John Walker
Mary Forbes
Michael Tarelli
Leigh McCartney
Callum Bruce
Joanne Graham

Mackinnon & Co
Chartered Building Surveyors
208 West George Street, Glasgow, G2 2PQ
Tel: (0141) 204 3311
Email: sean@mackco.co.uk
Web:
www.mackinnon-building-surveyors.co.uk
S D Docherty, DipBS MRICS
C D MacKinnon, MRICS
D G Simms, MRICS

Martin & Co
Property Letting & Sales
186 Kilmarnock Road, Glasgow, G41 3PG
Tel: (0141) 649 5848
Email: glasgowshawlands@martinco.com
Web: https://www.martinco.com

Martin & Co
172 Woodlands Road, Glasgow, G3 6LL
Tel: (0141) 3529988
Email: westend.enquiries@martinco.com
Web: www.martinco.com

Mason Evans Partnership
Geotehnical Mining & Environment
Consultants
The Piazza, 95 Morrison Street, Glasgow,
G5 8BE
Tel: (0141) 420 2025
Email: mail@masonevans.co.uk
Web: www.masonevans.co.uk
David D A Mason, BSc (Hons) CEng CGeol
MIMMM FGS

Niall Lawless, BSc (Hons) MSc CEng CGeol
MIMMM FGS
Patrick Barry, BSc (Hons) MSc CGeol MIMMM
FGS
Neil M Thomson, BSc (Hons) FGS

McKenzie Pollock Ltd
Commercial Property Consultants
69 Buchanan Street, Glasgow, G1 3HL
Tel: (0141) 314 3703 Fax: (0141) 314 3803
Email: vmaclean@mckenziepollock.co.uk
Web: www.mckenziepollock.co.uk
James Pollock, FRICS
Vivienne A Maclean, MRICS

MONTAGU EVANS LLP
Chartered Surveyors
Ravenseft House, 302 St. Vincent Street,
Glasgow, G2 5RU
Tel: (0141) 204 2090 Fax: (0141) 221 8441
Email: enquiries@montagu-evans.co.uk
Web: www.montagu-evans.co.uk
Barry J Finlayson, BSc MRICS
Marie Brown, BA BSc MRICS
S J Dalton, BSc (Distinction) DipRating FRICS
M Hewines, BLE MRICS
N D Dryburgh, BSc MRICS
S M McDonald, BSc MRICS

Neil Munro Property Consultancy Limited
Chartered Surveyors, 10 Bulloch Avenue,
Giffnock, Glasgow, G46 6NF
Tel: (0141) 248 4447
Email: neil@neilmunroproperty.co.uk
Web: neilmunroproperty.co.uk
N C Munro, FRICS

NBM Construction Cost Consultants Limited
9 Woodside Crescent, Glasgow, G3 7UL
Tel: (0141) 333 1836
Email: glas@nbm.bz
Web: www.nbm.bz
Steve R Pollock, MRICS
K G Robertson, BSc MRICS
S Bradshaw, BSc(Hons) MRICS
H C MacAnespie, MRICS

Neilson Partnership
Chartered Quantity Surveyors
Jacobean House, Glebe Street, East Kilbride,
Glasgow, G74 4LY
Tel: (01355) 268266 Fax: (01355) 265276
Email: admin@neilsons.biz
Web: www.neilsons.biz
David J Neilson, MSc FRICS MAPM
Gordon J Campbell, FRICS RMaPS

Pick Everard
Chartered Surveyors
The Beacon, 176 St Vincent Street, Glasgow,
G2 5SG
Tel: (0141) 204 2044
Email: Glasgow@pickeverard.co.uk
Web: https://www.pickeverard.co.uk
Trevor Graham, BSc, CEng, MICE, MCIWEM

Prime Land Consultants
Chartered Surveyors
38 Falkland Street, Glasgow, G12 9QY
Tel: (0141) 334 3303
Email: tomrankin@landrequired.co.uk
Web: www.landrequired.co.uk
Tom F Rankin, BSc MRICS

Redpath Bruce LLP
Chartered Surveyors
152 West Regent Street, Glasgow, G2 2RQ
Tel: (0141) 332 9041 Fax: (0141) 333 0848
Email: mail@redpathbruce.co.uk
Web: https://www.redpathbruce.co.uk
C K Bruce, PgDip MA(Hons) MRICS
R M McCall-Smith, BLE MRICS

Reid Associates
Chartered Quantity Surveyors
13 Sandyford Place, Glasgow, G3 7NB
Tel: (0141) 248 6545 Fax: (0141) 248 6480
Email: admin@reids.uk.com
Web: www.reids.uk.com
Alistair D McCracken, BSc FRICS
Russell J Miller, BSc MRICS
Iain M Drummond, BSc Hons MRICS

Riddell Thoms & Company LLP
Chartered Surveyors
21 West Nile Street, Glasgow, G1 2PS
Tel: (0141) 226 2284
Email: fwc@riddellthoms.co.uk
Web: www.riddellthoms.co.uk/
Fraser W Clearie, BSc FRICS MCIArb

Robinson Low Francis LLP
Construction and Property Consultants
29 St Vincent Place, Glasgow, G1 2DT
Tel: (0141) 332 5034
Email: glasgow@rlf.co.uk
Web: www.rlf.co.uk/
David Thomson, BSc MRICS
Chris S McLagan, BSc(Hons) MRICS
Dorothy H Robertson, BSc MRICS
David Harris, MRICS
Sean Clemons, BSc(Hons) MRICS
Paul Anderson, BSc FRICS MaPS FFOB
Christopher Barker, BSc (Hons) MSc MRICS
Kevin Campbell, BSc MRICS
Tony Milward, DipSurv MRICS
Mark Newberry, BSc(Hons) MRICS MAPM
Neville Onan-Read, FRICS

J.W.H. Ross & Co Ltd
Chartered Mineral Surveyors
225 Bath Street, Glasgow, G2 4GZ
Tel: (0141) 204 8800
Email: glasgow@fairhurst.co.uk
Web: www.jwhross.co.uk

Sanders Cartwright Limited
Chartered Surveyors
95 West Regent Street, Glasgow, G2 2BA
Tel: (0141) 221 9399
Email: graham@sanderscartwright.co.uk
Web: www.sanderscartwright.co.uk

G J Sanders, BSc FRICS

Savills (UK) Ltd
Chartered Surveyors
163 West George Street, Unit 0/1, Glasgow, G2 2JJ
Tel: (0141) 248 7342
Email: bpatrick@savills.com
Web: www.savills.co.uk
Mark R Fleming, MRICS
Martin J Wallace, BA(Hons) MSc MRICS
Alastair R Wood, MRICS
John Gallagher, BSc MRICS
Suzanne Taggart, BSc MRICS
Hugo C Struthers, MRICS
J G Clark, MRICS
D J Cobban, BSc MRICS
M A Collings, MRICS
R J Dunn, MRICS
R Fairbanks, BSc MRICS
G R Fraser, BSc MBA MRICS
L J Heron, MRICS
C MacKie, FRICS
K A McGuire, MRICS
S J Orr, MRICS
J B Patrick, BSc MRICS
R C Sinclair, MRICS
A Wedderspoon, MRICS
J S Menzies, BSc MRICS

Sharp & Fairlie
Chartered Surveyors
103 Douglas Street, Glasgow, G2 4HA
Tel: (0141) 221 2011 Fax: (0141) 204 2022
Email: sharpandfairlie@btconnect.com
Web: www.letting-in-scotland.co.uk

Shepherd
31 Byres Road, Lanarkshire, Glasgow, G11 5RD
Tel: (01413) 532 080
Email: glasgow@shepherd.co.uk
Web: www.shepherd.co.uk
Alan Fleming, MRICS
I W Cameron, MRICS

Shepherd
269 Kilmarnock Road, Glasgow, G43 1TX
Tel: (01416) 498 020
Email: glasgowsouth@shepherd.co.uk
Web: www.shepherd.co.uk
Martin Waite, MRICS

Slater Hogg & Howison
Estate Agents
102 Drymen Road, Glasgow, G61 3RA
Tel: (01414) 321 094
Web: www.slaterhogg.co.uk

Slater Hogg & Howison
Estate Agents
214 Eastwoodmains Road, Clarkston, Glasgow, G76 7HA
Tel: (01414) 321 099
Web: www.slaterhogg.co.uk

▶ Glasgow continued

Slater Hogg & Howison
Estate Agents
234 Stonelaw Road, Burnside, Lanarkshire,
Glasgow, G73 3SA
Tel: (01414) 321 095
Web: www.slaterhogg.co.uk

Slater Hogg & Howison
Estate Agents
123 Candleriggs, Glasgow, G1 1NP
Tel: (01414) 321 098
Web: www.slaterhogg.co.uk

Slater Hogg & Howison
Estate Agents
564 Alexandra Parade, Dennistoun, Glasgow,
G31 3BP
Tel: (01414) 321 201
Web: www.slaterhogg.co.uk

Slater Hogg & Howison
Estate Agents
255-257 Kilmarnock Road, Shawlands,
Glasgow, G41 3JE
Tel: (01414) 321 204
Web: www.slaterhogg.co.uk

Slater Hogg & Howison
Estate Agents
146 Byres Road, West End, Glasgow, G12 8TD
Tel: (01414) 321 205
Web: www.slaterhogg.co.uk

Slater Hogg & Howison
Estate Agents
153 Kirkintilloch Road, Bishopbriggs, Glasgow,
G64 2LS
Tel: (01414) 321 097
Web: www.slaterhogg.co.uk

Speirs Gumley
Chartered Surveyors
Red Tree Magenta, 270 Glasgow Road,
Glasgow, G73 1UZ
Tel: (0141) 332 9225 Fax: (0141) 332 7899
Email: glasgow@speirsgumley.com
Web: www.speirsgumley.com
Iain Friel
Bryan McManus
Tom McKie

Stirling Fleming
Chartered Building Surveyors
19C Montgomery Street, East Kilbride,
Glasgow, G74 4JS
Tel: (01355) 279472
Email: stirlingfleming@btconnect.com
R S Fleming, MRICS

Storrier & Donaldson Ltd
Chartered Quantity Surveyors
33A Gordon Street, Glasgow, G1 3PF
Tel: (0141) 272 2500 Fax: (0141) 272 2550
Email: sanddltd@btconnect.com
Web: storrieranddonaldson.com

R I Currie, FRICS
D O McKinney, BSc MRICS

Surveying Solutions Limited
Chartered Building Surveyors
97-99 West Regent Street, Glasgow, G2 2BA
Tel: (0141) 353 3939
Email: glas@surveying-solutions.co.uk
Web: www.surveying-solutions.co.uk

Walker Fraser & Steele
Chartered Surveyors
First Floor Suite 1/3 Cadell House, 27
Waterloo Street, Glasgow, G2 6BZ
Tel: (0141) 221 0442 Fax: (0141) 258 5976
Email: enquiries@walkerfrasersteele.co.uk
Web: www.walkerfrasersteele.co.uk
Richard Sexton

Watts Group Limited
Chartered Building Surveyors
177 West George Street, Glasgow, G2 2LB
Tel: (0141) 353 2211 Fax: (0141) 353 2277
Email: glasgow@watts.co.uk
Web: www.watts-international.com

Westwater
Chartered Quantity Surveyors
10 – 46 Speirs Wharf, Glasgow, G4 9TH
Tel: 7968 985018
Email: gregor@westwaterscotland.co.uk
G F Westwater, BSc MRICS

Whitelaw Baikie Figes
Chartered Surveyors
3/1, 81 St. Vincent Street, Glasgow, G2 5TF
Tel: (0141) 221 6161 Fax: (0141) 204 3335
Email: graham@wbf.co.uk
Web: www.wbf.co.uk
Gavin Anderson, BSc MRICS
Graham R Figes, BSc FRICS MCIArb

Whyte & Barrie
Chartered Valuation & Estate Agent
65-67 Strathmore House, East Kilbride,
Glasgow, G74 1LF
Tel: (01355) 229 317
Web: www.wbcs.co.uk
Alan R Crooks, MRICS

Whyte & Barrie
Chartered Valuation & Property Services
Suite 5, Legal House, 101 Gorbals Street,
Glasgow, G5 9DW
Tel: (0141) 404 6364
Web: www.wbcs.co.uk

William M McVicar
Chartered Surveyors
2/3, 132 West Nile Street, Glasgow, G1 2RQ
Tel: (0141) 331 1003
Email: mcvicarsurveyors@hotmail.com
W M McVicar, FRICS

Wiseman Associates Ltd
Chartered Building Surveyors

Douglas House, 9 Parkhall Street, East Kilbride,
Glasgow, G74 4JT
Tel: (01355) 233499
Email: info@wiseman-associates.co.uk
Web: www.wisemanassociates.co.uk
Greig A Douglas, BSc(Hons) MRICS

Glenrothes

Allied Surveyors Scotland PLC
Chartered Surveyors
14 Edison House, Glenrothes, KY7 5QR
Tel: (01592) 611149
Email: glenrothes@alliedsurveyorsscotland.com
Web: www.alliedsurveyorsscotland.com
R R Peters, FRICS

Slater Hogg & Howison
Estate Agents
1 Heritage House, North Street, Glenrothes,
KY7 5NA
Tel: (01592) 730 142
Web: www.slaterhogg.co.uk

Your Move
Property and Estate Agents, 26 North Street,
Glenrothes, KY7 5NA
Tel: (01592) 759653
Email: glenrothes@your-move.co.uk
Web: https://www.your-move.co.uk

Greenock

Allied Surveyors Scotland PLC
Chartered Surveyors
35A Union Street, Greenock, PA16 8DN
Tel: (01475) 723254
Email: greenock@alliedsurveyorsscotland.com
Web: www.alliedsurveyorsscotland.com
C Hotchkiss, BSc MRICS

Shepherd
28 Westburn Street, Greenock, PA15 1RY
Tel: (01475) 730717
Email: greenock@shepherd.co.uk
Web: www.shepherd.co.uk/
Michael McDade

Slater Hogg & Howison
Estate Agents
55 West Blackhall Street, Greenock, PA15 1UT
Tel: (01475) 430 152
Web: www.slaterhogg.co.uk

Haddington

Allied Surveyors Scotland PLC
Chartered Surveyors
21 Church Street, Haddington, EH41 3EX
Tel: (01620) 825585
Email:
haddington@alliedsurveyorsscotland.com
Web: www.alliedsurveyorsscotland.com
S D Breeze, MSc MA(Hons) MRICS

Chalmers & Co
Chartered Surveyors
Ogilvy Chalmers, 48 High Street, Haddington,
EH41 3EF
Tel: (01620) 824000 Fax: (01620) 824040
Email: enquiries@ogilvychalmers.com
Web: www.ogilvychalmers.com

Hamilton

Allied Surveyors Scotland PLC
Chartered Surveyors
14 Clydesdale Street, Hamilton, ML3 0DP
Tel: (01698) 421361
Email: hamilton@alliedsurveyorsscotland.com
Web: www.alliedsurveyorsscotland.com
Donald R Watt, BSc MRICS

Countrywide North Ltd
Estate Agents
29 Cadzow Street, Hamilton, ML3 6EE
Tel: (01698) 225 187
Email: hamilton@countrywidenorth.co.uk
Web: www.countrywidescotland.co.uk

DM Hall
Chartered Surveyors
Unit 3, Cadzow Park, 82 Muir Street,
Hamilton, ML3 6BJ
Tel: (01698) 284939
Email: hamilton@dmhall.co.uk
Web: www.dmhall.co.uk
Mark H Williams, MRICS
Stephen Thomson
Bill Lauder
Ian A Woods, BSc MRICS
Ken Topping
Jacqueline King
Keith Craig

Graham & Sibbald
Chartered Surveyors
29 Campbell Street, Hamilton, ML3 6AS
Tel: (01698) 422500 Fax: (01698) 458800
Email: hamilton@g-s.co.uk
Web: www.g-s.co.uk
Dominic McCormick

Robert C Brown Ltd
Part of Riley Consulting
Waverley House, Hamilton Business Park, Caird
Park, Hamilton, ML3 0QA
Tel: (01698) 286060
Email: leslie@robertcbrown.co.uk
Web: www.robertcbrown.co.uk/
Leslie P Fraser, DipSurv MRICS

Shepherd
32 Campbell Street, Hamilton, ML3 6AF
Tel: (01698) 897548
Email: hamilton@shepherd.co.uk
Web: www.shepherd.co.uk
Norman Robb, BSc MRICS (Resident
Associates)

▶ *Hamilton continued*

Slater Hogg & Howison
Estate Agents
43 Cadzow Street, Hamilton, ML3 6EE
Tel: (01698) 225 188
Web: www.slaterhogg.co.uk

Whyte & Barrie
Chartered Surveyors
Suites 7 & 8 Waverley House, Caird Park,
Hamilton, ML3 0QA
Tel: (01698) 891 400 Fax: (01698) 284 516
Email: hamilton@wbcs.co.uk
Web: www.wbcs.co.uk
A R Crooks, MRICS
J Leighton, MRICS
A D MacFarlane, BSc MRICS

Your Move
Property and Estate Agents
31 Cadzow Street, Hamilton, ML3 6EE
Tel: (01698) 891 799
Email: hamilton@your-move.co.uk
Web: https://www.your-move.co.uk

Helensburgh

Allied Surveyors Scotland PLC
Chartered Surveyors
13 Colquhoun Street, Helensburgh, G84 8AN
Tel: (01436) 674976
Email: helensburgh@alliedsurveyors.com
Web: www.alliedsurveyorsscotland.com
J P Aitkenhead, MRICS
Armour Robert Graeme, BSc MRICS

Clyde Property
22 West Princes Street, Helensburgh, G84 8TD
Tel: (01436) 670780 Fax: (01436) 675548
Email: helensburgh@clydeproperty.co.uk
Web: https://www.clydeproperty.co.uk

Slater Hogg & Howison
Estate Agents
6 East Princes Street, Helensburgh, G84 7QA
Tel: (01436) 460 125
Web: www.slaterhogg.co.uk

Invergordon

Torrance Partnership LLP
Chartered Surveyors
165 High Street, Invergordon, IV18 0AL
Tel: (01349) 853151 Fax: (01349) 853878
Email: invergordon@torrance-partnership.co.uk
Web: www.torrance-partnership.co.uk/
Nick E Lawton, BSc MRICS
Angus J MacAulay, BSc MRICS
D S Gordon, BSc(Hons) MRICS

Inverness

Allied Souter & Jaffrey Limited
Chartered Surveyors

Lyle House, Pavilion 1, Fairway Business Park
Castle Heather, Inverness, IV2 6AA
Tel: (01463) 239494 Fax: (01463) 711061
Email: inverness@alliedsurveyorsscotland.com
Web: www.asandj.co.uk
K D Campbell, AssocRICS
A D Gray, MA(Hons) MRICS

Allied Surveyors Scotland PLC
Chartered Surveyors
Lyle House, Pavillion 1, Fairways Business Park,
Castle Heather, Inverness, IV2 6AA
Tel: (01463) 239494
Email: inverness@alliedsurveyorsscotland.com
Web: www.alliedsurveyorsscotland.com
K L Hutchison, BSc MRICS
K D Campbell, AssocRICS
A D Gray, MA(Hons) MRICS
J Burns, BSc MRICS

Bidwells LLP
Property Consultants
Elm House, Cradlehall Business Park, Inverness,
IV2 5GH
Tel: (01463) 796050 Fax: (01463) 798246
Email: alastair.campbell@bidwells.co.uk
Web: www.bidwells.co.uk
Clive W Meikle, MRICS

CKD Galbraith
Chartered Surveyors & Estate Agents
Reay House, 17 Old Edinburgh Road,
Inverness, IV2 3HF
Tel: (01463) 224343 Fax: (01463) 243234
Email: inverness@galbraithgroup.com
Web: https://www.galbraithgroup.com
John R Bound, FRICS
Phiddy Robertson, AssocRICS
Dougal J Lindsay, BSc (Hons) MRICS
T J Kirkwood, BSc MRICS

DM Hall LLP
Chartered Surveyors
Ardross House, 3 Ardross Terrace, Inverness,
IV3 5NQ
Tel: (01463) 241077
Email: inverness@dmhall.co.uk
Web: www.dmhall.co.uk
Graham Forbes, MRICS

Graham & Sibbald
Chartered Surveyors
4 Ardross Street, Inverness, IV3 5NN
Tel: (01463) 236977 Fax: (01463) 224886
Email: inverness@g-s.co.uk
Web: www.g-s.co.uk
John MacBean, BSc MRICS
Charlie Lawrence, BSc(Hons) MRICS

Grant Stewart Chartered Surveyors Ltd
Ness Mews, Ardross Place, Inverness, IV3 5BY
Tel: (01463) 718719 Fax: (01463) 710712
Email: gs@gs-cs.co.uk
Web: gs-cs.co.uk
Grant Stewart, MRICS

Hardies Property & Construction Consultants
Mulberry House, 39-41 Harbour Road,
Inverness, IV1 1UA
Tel: (01463) 712 239
Email: inverness@hardies.co.uk
Web: www.hardies.co.uk
David Vince, BSc MRICS
Gary Ovenstone, MRICS
Murray Warner, BA MSc LLM MRICS MAPM MCIArb
Martin McConnell, BSc(Hons) MRICS

Harvey Donaldson & Gibson
Duncan House, Wester Inshes Place, Inverness,
IV2 5HZ
Tel: (0146) 364 1245
Web: www.hdg.co.uk

K.L.M. Partnership
Chartered Surveyors
24 Union Street, Inverness, IV1 1PL
Tel: (01463) 230804 Fax: (01463) 710336
Email: billhamilton@klmp.co.uk
Web: www.klmp.co.uk
William A Hamilton, BSc MBA FRICS MCIArb

McLeod & Aitken
Chartered Quantity Surveyors
5 Drummond Street, Inverness, IV1 1QD
Tel: (01463) 239 444
Email: admin@mcleodaitken.net

Pick Everard
38 Longman Drive, Inverness, IV1 1SU
Tel: (0345) 045 0050
Email: Inverness@pickeverard.co.uk
Web: https://www.pickeverard.co.uk
Duncan Green, BSc(Hons), CEng, MICE, MCIWEM
Andrew Almond, DipArch, RIBA, ARB
Mark Colby, BSc(Hons), CEng, MICE, MCIWEM, C.WEM
Alastair Hamilton, BSc, MRICS
David Nisbet, BA (Hons) Dip Arch, RIBA
Doug Soutar, IEng, MIET, ACIBSE

Shepherd
Mulberry House First Floor, 39-41 Harbour
Road, Inverness, IV1 1UA
Tel: (01463) 712239
Email: inverness@shepherd.co.uk
Web: www.shepherd.co.uk
Gregor J Simpson, MRICS
Neil Calder

Strutt & Parker
Chartered Surveyors
The Courier Building, 9-11 Bank Lane,
Inverness, IV1 1WA
Tel: (1463) 896845
Email: inverness@struttandparker.com
Web: www.struttandparker.com
Kevin Maley
Suzanne Moss
Euan MacCrimmon

Torrance Partnership LLP
Chartered Surveyors
1st Floor, Larkfield, 23 Southside Road,
Inverness, IV2 3BG
Tel: (01463) 237999
Email: inverness@torrance-partnership.co.uk
Web: www.torrance-partnership.co.uk
Mark J Stevenson, BSc(Hons) MSc MRICS

WSD Scotland Ltd
Chartered Quantity Surveyors
Duncan House, Wester Inshes Place, Inverness,
IV2 5HZ
Tel: (01463) 717345
Email: info@wsd-inverness.co.uk
Web: www.wsd-scotland.co.uk
G R Wilson, BSc MRICS

Your Move
Property and Estate Agents
58-60 Academy Street, Inverness, IV1 1LP
Tel: (01463) 234 743
Email: inverness@your-move.co.uk
Web: https://www.your-move.co.uk

Inverurie

Aberdeen & Northern Estates Ltd
Thainstone Agricultural Centre, Inverurie,
Inverurie, AB51 5XZ
Tel: (01467) 623800 Fax: (01467) 623809
Email: estates@anmgroup.co.uk
Web: www.anestates.co.uk
James C Presly, MRICS

DM Hall LLP
Chartered Surveyors
64 Market Place, Inverurie, AB51 3XN
Tel: (01467) 624393
Email: inverurie@dmhall.co.uk
Web: www.dmhall.co.uk
Colin F Hepburn, MRICS
Greig G Baxter, BSc(Hons) MRICS

Irvine

Allen & Harris
Estate Agents
31 Bank Street, Irvine, KA12 0LL
Tel: (01294) 271151
Email: Irvine@allenandharris.co.uk
Web: https://www.allenandharris.co.uk

Countrywide North Ltd
Estate Agents
19 Bank Street, Irvine, KA12 0AJ
Tel: (01294) 340 128
Email: irvine@countrywidenorth.co.uk
Web: www.countrywidescotland.co.uk

DM Hall LLP
Chartered Surveyors
45 Bank Street, Irvine, KA12 0LL
Tel: (01294) 311070
Email: irvine@dmhall.co.uk

► **Irvine** continued
Web: www.dmhall.co.uk
John G McHugh, MRICS

Kelso

CKD Galbraith
Chartered Surveyors and Estate Agents
21 Woodmarket, Kelso, TD5 7HL
Tel: (01573) 224244
Email: kelso@galbraithgroup.com
Web: https://www.galbraithgroup.com
Alex Inglis, BA (Hons) MRICS FNAEA
Kathleen McIntee
Jackie Tait
Frances Sheehan

FBR Ltd
Rural Surveyors
Abbey Row, Kelso, TD5 7JF
Tel: (01573) 224381 Fax: (01573) 227389
Email: admin@fbr.co.uk
Web: www.fbr.co.uk
Andrew Wemyss
Richard Armitage
Stuart Buchanan
David Nairn
Rob Forrest

Keswick

Edwin Thompson
28 St. Johns Street,, Keswick, CA12 5AF
Tel: (017687) 72988 Fax: (017687) 71949
Email: keswick@edwin-thompson.co.uk
Web: edwin-thompson.co.uk/
M R Bell, MRICS

Kilmarnock

Allied Surveyors Scotland PLC
Chartered Surveyors
91 John Finnie Street, Kilmarnock, KA1 1BG
Tel: (01563) 572341
Email: kilmarnock@alliedsurveyorsscotland.com
Web: www.alliedsurveyorsscotland.com

Armour Construction Consultants
Chartered Quantity Surveyors
65 King Street, Kilmarnock, KA1 1PT
Tel: (01563) 522223
Email: kilmarnock@armour.co.uk
Web: www.armour.co.uk
Hunter Kirkpatrick, MRICS
Colin J Watt, Bsc MRICS
Malcolm W Carrick, BSc (HONS) MRICS
Kenny M Barclay, BSc MRICS

Countrywide North Ltd
Estate Agents
45 John Finnie Street, East Ayrshire,
Kilmarnock, KA1 1BL
Tel: (01563) 528 165

Email: kilmarnock@countrywidenorth.co.uk
Web: www.countrywidescotland.co.uk

Graham & Sibbald
Chartered Surveyors
5 St. Marnock Place, Kilmarnock, KA1 1DU
Tel: (01563) 528000 Fax: (01563) 537764
Email: kilmarnock@g-s.co.uk
Web: www.g-s.co.uk
Fraser H Lang, BSc MRICS

Shepherd
24 Portland Road, Kilmarnock, KA1 2BS
Tel: (01563) 520318
Email: kilmarnock@shepherd.co.uk
Web: www.shepherd.co.uk

Slater Hogg & Howison
Estate Agents
31-33 John Finnie Street, Kilmarnock, KA1 1BL
Tel: (01563) 760 172
Web: www.slaterhogg.co.uk

Kinross

Langley-Taylor
Chartered Surveyors
Middleton, Fossoway, Kinross, KY13 0PB
Tel: (01577) 840907
Email: enquiries@langley-taylor.co.uk
Web: www.langley-taylor.co.uk

Kirkcaldy

David Adamson + Partners LTD
Chartered Surveyors
Carlyle House, Carlyle Road, Kirkcaldy,
KY1 1DB
Tel: (01592) 268 689 Fax: (01592) 641 488
Email: kirkcaldy@davidadamsongroup.com
Web: www.davidadamsongroup.com
Blair Martin, BSc MRICS
Paul Kennedy, BSc
Christopher Smith, BSc(Hons), MRICS
Andrew Mitchell, BSc (Hons) MAPM FCIOB
Rohit Chavan, MRICS, BE (Civil)
Vishal Patange, MRICS, BE (Civil), MBA
Sandesh Pangerkar, FRICS, MCIArb, MCIOB,
RICS Accredited Civil Commercial Mediator,
AMIE

DM Hall
Chartered Surveyors
13 Wemyssfield, Kirkcaldy, KY1 1XN
Tel: (01592) 598200
Email: kirkcaldy@dmhall.co.uk
Web: www.dmhall.co.uk
Steven D Buist, BSc(Hons) MRICS

Graham & Sibbald
Chartered Surveyors
Evans Business Centre, 1 Begg Road,
Kirkcaldy, KY2 6HD
Tel: (01592) 266211 Fax: (01592) 200732
Email: kirkcaldy@g-s.co.uk

Web: www.g-s.co.uk

Martin & Co
93 St. Clair Street, Kirkcaldy, KY1 2BS
Tel: (01592) 651495
Email: kirkcaldy@martinco.com
Web: www.martinco.com

Shepherd
Chartered Surveyors
11 Wemyssfield, Kirkcaldy, KY1 1XN
Tel: (01592) 205442
Email: kirkcaldy@shepherd.co.uk
Web: www.shepherd.co.uk
Jonathan Reid

Slater Hogg & Howison
Estate Agents
27 Whytescauseway, Kirkcaldy, KY1 1XF
Tel: (01592) 730 143
Web: www.slaterhogg.co.uk

Your Move
Property and Estate Agents
87 High Street, Kirkcaldy, KY1 1LN
Tel: (01592) 205 432
Email: kirkcaldy@your-move.co.uk
Web: https://www.your-move.co.uk

Kirkwall

N J Coward
Chartered Valuation Surveyors
Grainshore Road, Hatston, Kirkwall, KW15 1FL
Tel: (01856) 873342 Fax: (01856) 875712
Email: nick@njcoward.co.uk
Web: www.njcoward.co.uk
N J Coward, MRICS

S. J. Omand
Chartered Valuation Surveyor
14 Victoria Street, Kirkwall, KW15 1DN
Tel: (01856) 876215 Fax: (01856) 876199
Email: info@sjomand.co.uk
Web: www.sjomand.co.uk
Stephen J Omand, FRICS
Christopher J Omand, BSc(Hons) MRICS

Lanark

Cass Property Consultants Ltd
Chartered Surveyors
6 Wheatpark, Wheatpark Road, Lanark,
ML11 7QA
Tel: (01555) 660206
Email: enquiries@cassproperty.co.uk
Web: www.cassproperty.co.uk
K A Sergeant, DipSurv MRICS

Whyte & Barrie
Chartered Valuation & Estate Agent
50 Bannatyne Street, Lanark, ML11 7JS
Tel: (01698) 891400
Email: lanark@wbcs.co.uk
Web: www.wbcs.co.uk

Larbert

Andrew Simpson Associates Limited
Chartered Quantity Surveyors
33 Rowantree Walk, Stirlingshire, Larbert,
FK5 4FT

Stark Associates
Chartered Quantity Surveyors
Glenbervie Business Centre, Glenbervie
Business Park, Larbert, FK5 4RB
Tel: (01324) 682066
Email: stark.org@btconnect.com
Web: www.starkqs.co.uk
John Stark, MRICS

Largs

Douglas H Dickie
Chartered Quantity Surveyors
2 Tron Place, Largs, KA30 8AR
Tel: (01555) 661115
D H Dickie, BSc MRICS

Slater Hogg & Howison
Estate Agents
94-96 Main Street, Largs, KA30 8AN
Tel: (01475) 430 166
Web: www.slaterhogg.co.uk

Lerwick

David Adamson & Partners
Chartered Surveyors
4A North Ness, Lerwick, ZE1 0LZ
Tel: (0 1595) 696 788 Fax: (0 1595) 694 522
Email: lerwick@davidadamsongroup.com
Web: www.davidadamsongroup.com
Greig D D Miller, MRICS

Livingston

DM Hall
Chartered Surveyors
Unit 12, Grampian Court,, Beveridge Square,
Livingston, EH54 6QF
Tel: (01506) 490404
Email: livingston@dmhall.co.uk
Web: www.dmhall.co.uk

J & E Shepherd
Unit 4, Grampian Court, Beveridge Square,
Livingston, EH54 6QF
Tel: (01506) 416777
Email: livingston@shepherd.co.uk
Web: www.shepherd.co.uk
Craig J Brown, BSc MRICS

Slater Hogg & Howison
Estate Agents
Unit 102, Livingston, EH54 6HS
Tel: (01506) 260 142
Web: www.slaterhogg.co.uk

▶ **Livingston** continued

Your Move
Property and Estate Agents
17 Almondvale Centre, Almondvale South,
Livingston, EH54 6NB
Tel: (01506) 440 440
Email: livingston@your-move.co.uk
Web: https://www.your-move.co.uk

Longridge

M. Hislop
Chartered Surveyors
Staff Cottage, 6 Fauldhouse Road, Longridge,
EH47 8AQ
Tel: (01501) 770986
Email: marc@mhislop.com
Web: www.mhislop.com
M Hislop, AssocRICS

Montrose

J & E Shepherd
11 High Street, Montrose, DD10 8LU
Tel: (01674) 676768
Email: montrose@shepherd.co.uk
Web: www.shepherd.co.uk

Your Move
Property and Estate Agents
51 Murray Street, Montrose, DD10 8JZ
Tel: (01674) 672979
Email: montrose@your-move.co.uk
Web: https://www.your-move.co.uk

Motherwell

J & E Shepherd
64 Windmillhill Street, Motherwell, ML1 1TA
Tel: (01698) 252229
Email: motherwell@shepherd.co.uk
Web: www.shepherd.co.uk
Lachlan G Macfarlane, BSc MRICS

Musselburgh

DM Hall LLP
Chartered Surveyors
35 Bridge Street, Musselburgh, EH21 6AA
Tel: (0131) 665 6782
Email: musselburgh@dmhall.co.uk
Web: www.dmhall.co.uk
J Hunter, MSc MRICS

Shepherd
Chartered Surveyors
187 North High Street, Musselburgh,
EH21 6AN
Tel: (0131) 653 3456
Email: musselburgh@shepherd.co.uk
Web: www.shepherd.co.uk
Adrian Stott, BA(Hons) DipSurv FRICS

Newton Stewart

Allied Surveyors Scotland PLC
Chartered Surveyors
10 Victoria Street, Newton Stewart, DG8 6BT
Tel: (01671) 404335
Email:
newton.stewart@alliedsurveyorsscotland.com
Web: www.alliedsurveyorsscotland.com
J A McMillan, BSc MRICS

G.M. Thomson & Co
Chartered Surveyors
10 Victoria Street, Wigtownshire, Newton
Stewart, DG8 6BT
Tel: (01671) 402 887 Fax: (01671) 402 650
Email: ns@gmthomson.co.uk
Web: www.gmthomson.co.uk/
Dougal F Evans, FRICS
David Telford, BSc MRICS
Allan McMillan, BSc MRICS
Jim Stalker, BSc FRICS AClarb
Simon Allen, BSc MRICS

North Berwick

Alan Craig Associates
Chartered Quantity Surveyors
Home House, Athelstaneford, North Berwick,
EH39 5BE
Tel: (01620) 880288 Fax: (01620) 880235
Email: alan-craig@btconnect.com
A Craig, FRICS

Oban

Bell Ingram LLP
5 Albany Street, Oban, PA34 4AR
Tel: (01631) 566 122 Fax: (01631) 566 908
Email: oban@bellingram.co.uk
Web: https://bellingram.co.uk

Dawsons Estate Agents
Alliance House, 1 George Street, Argyll, Oban,
PA34 5RX
Tel: (01631) 563901
Web: www.dawsonsestateagents.co.uk
Amanda (Mandy) Carmichael

DM Hall LLP
Chartered Surveyors
Oban Times Buildings, Corran Esplanade,
Oban, PA34 5PX
Tel: (01631) 564225
Email: oban@dmhall.co.uk
Web: www.dmhall.co.uk
Gary P Duff, MRICS

Morham & Brotchie
Chartered Quantity Surveyors
5 Stafford Street, Oban, PA34 5NJ
Tel: (01631) 563721
Email: admin@morhambro.co.uk
McQuade Thomas, BSc(Hons) MRICS

Paisley

ADA Construction Consultants Ltd
Quantity Surveyors
Pavilion 3, St James Business Park, Linwood
Road, Paisley, PA3 3BB
Tel: (0141) 816 0184
Email: alan.shanks@ada-cc.co.uk
Web: www.ada-cc.co.uk
A Shanks, BSc(Hons) MRICS

Ian Allan Associates (UK) Limited
Chartered Quantity Surveyor
Mirren Court (One), 119 Renfrew Road,
Paisley, PA3 4EA
Tel: (0141) 848 7470 Fax: (0141) 889 3117
Email: mail@ianallanassociates.co.uk
Web: www.ianallanassociates.co.uk
A Bain, MRICS
R L David, BSc MRICS
T Kerrigan, MRICS
R J McGhee, BSc(Hons) MRICS

Allen & Harris
Estate Agents
16 Causeyside Street, Paisley, PA1 1UN
Tel: (0141) 889 7222
Email: paisley@allenandharris.co.uk
Web: www.allenandharris.co.uk

Allied Surveyors Scotland PLC
Chartered Surveyors
43 Gauze Street, Paisley, PA1 1EX
Tel: (0141) 889 4105 Fax: (0141) 848 1706
Email: paisley@alliedsurveyorsscotland.com
Web: www.alliedsurveyorsscotland.com
Douglas Hyde, MRICS

Countrywide North Ltd
Estate Agents
5 Causeyside Street, Renfrewshire, Paisley,
PA1 1UW
Tel: (01414) 321 088
Email: paisley@countrywidenorth.co.uk
Web: www.countrywidescotland.co.uk

DM Hall LLP
Chartered Surveyors
1 Glasgow Road, Paisley, PA1 3PX
Tel: (0141) 887 7700
Email: paisley@dmhall.co.uk
Web: www.dmhall.co.uk
Lesley A Gardner, BSc MRICS

Graham & Sibbald
Chartered Surveyors
76 Causeyside Street, Paisley, PA1 1YP
Tel: (0141) 889 3251 Fax: (0141) 887 3713
Email: paisley@g-s.co.uk
Web: www.g-s.co.uk

J & E Shepherd
Unit 1A-1B, 41 Gauze Street, Renfrewshire,
Paisley, PA1 1EX
Tel: (0141) 889 8334
Email: paisley@shepherd.co.uk

Web: www.shepherd.co.uk
Andrew Neil, MRICS

Martin & Co
21 Underwood Road, Paisley, PA3 1TH
Tel: (0141) 8870080
Email: paisley@martinco.com
Web: www.martinco.com
Joseph Quaradeghini

Slater Hogg & Howison
Estate Agents
17-19 Gauze Street, Paisley, PA1 1ES
Tel: (01414) 321 203
Web: www.slaterhogg.co.uk

Peebles

Allied Surveyors Scotland PLC
Chartered Surveyors
Unit 2, Silver birch Studios, Cavalry Park,
Peebles, EH45 9BU
Tel: (01721) 722728
Email: peebles@alliedsurveyorsscotland.com
Web: www.alliedsurveyorsscotland.com
K J Hughes, MRICS

Perth

Allied Surveyors Scotland PLC
Chartered Surveyors
10 Charlotte Street, Perth, PH1 5LL
Tel: (01738) 444 414 Fax: (01738) 447 627
Email: perth@alliedsurveyorsscotland.com
Web: www.alliedsurveyorsscotland.com

Hamish Bell Associates
Chartered Quantity Surveyors
36 George Street, Perth, PH1 5JR
Tel: 07711255982 Fax: (01738) 440360
Email: enquiries@hbaperth.co.uk
Web: hbaperth.co.uk
J Bell, MRICS

Bell Ingram LLP
Chartered Surveyors
Durn, Isla Road, Perth, PH2 7HF
Tel: (01738) 621121 Fax: (01738) 630904
Email: enquiries@bellingram.co.uk
Web: https://bellingram.co.uk
J G Lumby, FRICS
Mark A Mitchell, FRICS
Sarah C Tyson, BSc FRICS FAAV
M Thompson, MRICS

Bidwells
Property Consultants
Broxden House, Lamberkine Drive, Perth,
PH1 1RA
Tel: (01738) 630666 Fax: (01738) 627264
Email: andrew.wood@bidwells.co.uk
Web: www.bidwells.co.uk/
Rosalind A Clifford, MRICS
Raymond Henderson, MRICS
Andrew T Wood, FRICS

▶ *Perth continued*

CKD Galbraith
Chartered Surveyors & Estate Agents
Lynedoch House, Barossa Place, Perth,
PH1 5EP
Tel: (01738) 451111
Email: perth@galbraithgroup.com
Web: https://www.galbraithgroup.com
Emma J Chalmers, BSc (Hons) DipSurv MRICS
Scott Holley
Wattie H Barbour, BLE FRICS
Ian Hope, BSc PGDip MRICS
Calum J Innes, BLE FRICS
Robert Rattray, BSc (Hons) MRICS
Colin W Stewart, BSc (Hons) MRICS
Jay Burden, MARLA
Laura Ellis, AssocRICS
Lucie Howatson, BSc (Hons) MLE MRICS
Mungo Ingleby, MA MSc MRICS
William Jackson, BLE FRICS
Nick Morgan, MA (Hons) MRICS
Hamish Robertson, MICFor CEnv
Paul Schofield, HND MIC For
Richard Stewart

Clyde Property
26 George Street, Perth, PH1 5JR
Tel: (01738) 507070 Fax: (01738) 629439
Email: perth@clydeproperty.co.uk
Web: https://www.clydeproperty.co.uk
Derek Hughes

DM Hall LLP
Chartered Surveyors
52 Tay Street, Perth, PH1 5TR
Tel: (01738) 562100
Email: perth@dmhall.co.uk
Web: www.dmhall.co.uk
Tom J Laurie, BSc MRICS

Graham & Sibbald
Chartered Surveyors
3 Charlotte Street, Perth, PH1 5LW
Tel: (01738) 445733 Fax: (01738) 445833
Email: perth@g-s.co.uk
Web: www.g-s.co.uk
Keith M Scobbie, BSc MRICS
Greg Davidson, MRICS

Hardies Property & Construction Consultants
Old Academy Buildings, 7 Rose Terrace, Perth,
PH1 5HA
Tel: (01738) 631631
Email: perth@hardies.co.uk
Web: www.hardies.co.uk

J & E Shepherd
2 Whitefriars Crescent, Perth, PH2 0PA
Tel: (01738) 638188
Email: perth@shepherd.co.uk
Web: www.shepherd.co.uk
C S McLagan, BSc(Hons) MRICS
D H Robertson, BSc MRICS

Ralph A. Ogg & Partners
Chartered Quantity Surveyors
2 King James Place, Perth, PH2 8AE
Tel: (01738) 625619
Tel: (01738) 638666 Fax: (01738) 643529
Email: enquiries@raogg.com
Web: www.raogg.com
M Jarmuszewski, BSc(Hons) MRICS
Angus Simpson, BSc MRICS

Savills (UK) Ltd
Chartered Surveyors
Earn House, Lamberkine Drive, Perth, PH1 1RA
Tel: (01738) 445588
Email: Perthshire@savills.com
Web: www.savills.co.uk
Jonathan R Henson, MBA MRICS
Nick Green, MRICS BLE(Hons)
Alastair Gemmell, MRICS
M E Robertson, MRICS

Peterhead

DM Hall LLP
Chartered Surveyors
7 Chapel Street, Peterhead, AB42 1TH
Tel: (01779) 470220
Email: peterhead@dmhall.co.uk
Web: www.dmhall.co.uk

John Pascoe
Chartered Quantity Surveyors
2 Armoury Lane, Longside, Peterhead,
AB42 4TR
Tel: (01779) 821351
Email: john@johnpascoe-cqs.co.uk
J S Pascoe, BSc MRICS

Shepherd
5 Chapel Street, Peterhead, AB42 1TH
Tel: (01779) 470766
Email: peterhead@shepherd.co.uk
Web: www.shepherd.co.uk
A D Sykes, BLE MRICS

Portree

Torrance Partnership
Chartered Surveyors, Portree
Tel: (01478) 612659
Email: admin@torrance-partnership.co.uk
Web: www.torrance-partnership.co.uk
Andrew Turley
Keith Bowman
Angus MacAulay
Douglas Gordon

Redditch

Derek Young & Company
Chartered Surveyors
Estate House, 144 Evesham Street, Redditch,
B97 4HP
Tel: (01527) 62124

Tel: (01527) 63547 Fax: (01527) 584502
Email: info@derekyoung.co.uk
Web: www.derekyoung.co.uk
Steve Young, BSc FCA
Mike Taylor, FCCA

Rutherglen

Countrywide North Ltd
Estate Agents
230 Stonelaw Road, Rutherglen, G73 3SA
Tel: (01414) 321 081
Email: burnside@countrywidenorth.co.uk
Web: www.countrywidescotland.co.uk

Saltcoats

Allied Surveyors Scotland PLC
Chartered Surveyors
24 Chapelwell Street, Saltcoats, KA21 5EA
Tel: (01294) 602292
Email: saltcoats@alliedsurveyorsscotland.com
Web: www.alliedsurveyorsscotland.com
Craig Millar

Shepherd
31 Hamilton Street, Saltcoats, KA21 5DT
Tel: (01294) 464228
Email: saltcoats@shepherd.co.uk
Web: www.shepherd.co.uk
David Breingan, MRICS (Resident Associates)

Selkirk

Allan Associates
Chartered Quantity Surveyors
Building 4 – Unit 12, Dunsdale Mill, Dunsdale
Haugh, Selkirk, TD7 5EF
Tel: (01750) 725675
Email: ken.allan@btconnect.com
K L Allan, MRICS

Allied Surveyors Scotland PLC
Chartered Surveyors
The Hermitage, 101 High Street, Selkirk,
TD7 4JX
Tel: (01750) 724170
Email: selkirk@alliedsurveyorsscotland.com
Web: www.alliedsurveyorsscotland.com
J Harold, MRICS
E Henderson, BSc(Hons) MRICS

St Andrews

Hardies Property & Construction
Consultants
Swilken House, 35 Largo Road, St Andrews,
KY16 8NJ
Tel: (01334) 476 469
Email: standrews@hardies.co.uk
Web: www.hardies.co.uk
David Vince, BSc MRICS
Gary Ovenstone, MRICS

Murray Warner, BA MSc LLM MRICS MAPM
MCIArb
Martin McConnell, BSc(Hons) MRICS

J & E Shepherd
Swilken House, 35 Largo Road, St Andrews,
KY16 8NJ
Tel: (01334) 477773
Email: standrews@shepherd.co.uk
Web: www.shepherd.co.uk

Stirling

Allen & Harris
Estate Agents
1C Pitt Terrace, Stirling, FK8 2EY
Tel: (01786) 445011
Email: stirling@allenandharris.co.uk
Web: https://www.allenandharris.co.uk

Allied Surveyors Scotland PLC
Chartered Surveyors
13 Allan Park, Stirling, FK8 2QG
Tel: (01786) 450291
Email: stirling@alliedsurveyorsscotland.com
Web: www.alliedsurveyorsscotland.com
A M Imrie, BSc MRICS

CKD Galbraith
Chartered Surveyors & Estate Agents
Stirling Agricultural Centre, Stirling, FK9 4RN
Tel: (01786) 434600
Email: stirling@galbraithgroup.com
Web: https://www.galbraithgroup.com
Simon Brown, MRICS FAAV
Chris B Addison-Scott, MRICS
Richard Higgins, BA Dip.LE FRICS
Ian Hope, BSc PGDip MRICS
Duncan Barrie, MRICS

DM Hall
Chartered Surveyors
Suite 2c, 1 Pitt Terrace, Stirling, FK8 2NQ
Tel: (01786) 475785
Email: stirling@dmhall.co.uk
Web: www.dmhall.co.uk
Gordon McCulloch, DipSurv MRICS
Michael McIntyre

DMH Baird Lumsden
Chartered Surveyors
The Mill, Bridge of Allan, Stirling, FK9 4JS
Tel: (01786) 833 800 Fax: (01786) 834382
Email: info@dmhbl.co.uk
Web: https://bairdlumsden.co.uk/
Donald H Yellowley, BSc MRICS

Graham & Sibbald
Chartered Surveyors
22 Allan Park, Stirling, FK8 2QG
Tel: (01786) 463 111 Fax: (01786) 450 281
Email: stirling@g-s.co.uk
Web: www.g-s.co.uk

Hardies Property & Construction Consultants
11 Gladstone Place, Stirling, FK8 2NN

► **Stirling** continued

Tel: (01786) 474 476
Email: stirling@hardies.co.uk
Web: www.hardies.co.uk
David Vince, BSc MRICS
Danny McArthur, BSc MSc MRICS MaPS
Gary Ovenstone, MRICS
Murray Warner, BA MSc LLM MRICS MAPM
MCIArb
Darron McKay, CEM DipSurv, MRICS
Kate Bilbrough, DipBS, MRICS
Martin McConnell, BSc(Hons) MRICS

Martin & Co
14 King Street, Stirling, FK8 1AY
Tel: (01786) 448812
Email: stirling@martinco.com
Web: www.martinco.com

A. D. Norman Ltd
Chartered Quantity Surveyors
12 Pitt Terrace, Stirling, FK8 2EZ
Tel: (01786) 880650 Fax: (08707) 620169
Email: a.norman@adnorman.com
Web: www.adnorman.com
A D Norman, BSc LLM FRICS FCIArb

Seymour & Co (Scotland) Ltd
Specialist Estate Agents
Thorntree, Arnprior, Kippen, Stirling, FK8 3EY
Tel: (01786) 870 555
Peter Seymour

Shepherd
11 Gladstone Place, Stirling, FK8 2NN
Tel: (01786) 450438
Email: stirling@shepherd.co.uk
Web: www.shepherd.co.uk
Ian J Fergusson, BSc FRICS

Slater Hogg & Howison
Estate Agents
44-46 Port Street, Stirling, FK8 2LJ
Tel: (01786) 340 173
Web: www.slaterhogg.co.uk

Your Move
Property and Estate Agents
55 Port Street, Stirling, FK8 2EW
Tel: (01786) 451555
Email: stirling@your-move.co.uk
Web: https://www.your-move.co.uk

Stornoway

Torrance Partnership LLP
Chartered Surveyors
6 Garden Road, Stornoway, HS1 2QJ
Tel: (01851) 702185 Fax: (01851) 702617
Email: stornoway@torrance-partnership.co.uk
Web: www.torrance-partnership.co.uk

Uddingston

Stewart Milne Group
Chartered Surveyors
Kestrel House, 3 Kilmartin Place, Tannochside
Business Park, Uddingston, G71 5PH
Tel: (0845) 009 2878 Fax: (01224) 747 499
Web: www.stewartmilnetimbersystems.com

Wemyss Bay

James McGee
Chartered Surveyors
Kilblain, Cliff Terrace Road, Wemyss Bay,
PA18 6AP
Tel: (01475) 522100
Email: james@jamesmcgee.com
Web: www.jamesmcgee.com/
J C McGee, FRICS

West Linton

Mick McWilliam Chartered Land Surveyors
Rosbeg, Main Street, West Linton, EH46 7EE
Tel: (01968) 660 304
Email: mick@mickmcwilliam.co.uk
Web: www.mickmcwilliam.co.uk
Mick McWilliam, MRICS

Weybridge

Graham & Sibbald
Wey House Suite 12, 15 Church Street,
Weybridge, KT13 8NA
Tel: (07831) 353 572 Fax: (01932) 842 848
Web: www.g-s.co.uk
Calum Campbell
John Docherty

Wick

Baxter Dunn & Gray
Chartered Quantity Surveyors
15 MacLeay Street, Wick, KW1 5AE
Tel: (01955) 602 970
Email: office@bdgthomsongray.co.uk
Web: www.bdgthomsongray.co.uk
A I Scott, BSc MRICS RMaPS

Windermere

Edwin Thompson
23 Church Street, Windermere, LA23 1AQ
Tel: (01539) 448811 Fax: (015394) 48916
Email: windermere@edwin-thompson.co.uk
Web: edwin-thompson.co.uk/

Property Managers

Property Managers Association Scotland Ltd
Scott Moncrieff, Allan House, 25 Bothwell Street, Glasgow G2 6NL Tel: (0141) 567 4500 Email:
info@pmas.org.uk Website: www.pmas.org.uk
President: Nic Mayall
Vice President: Neale Bisset
Immediate Past President: David Reid
Representative Consultant: Alison McDiarmid
Council: Adele Mclaughlin, Jacqueline Borthwick, George Mcguire, Derek Macdonald, Ross Watt

SPC Scotland

SPC Scotland (Solicitors' Property Centres)

SPC Scotland comprises the following Solicitors' Property Centres (SPC)

Centres:

ABERDEEN SPC: 40 Chapel Street Aberdeen AB10 1SP Tel: 01224 632949 Email: centre@aspc.co.uk Website: www.aspc.co.uk

BORDERS SPC: Border Marketing Company, First Floor, Horsemarket Business Centre, 11 Horsemarket, Kelso TD5 7HE Tel: 01573 408590 Email: bspc@bordermc.com Website: www.bspc.com

EDINBURGH SPC: 107 George Street, Edinburgh EH2 3ES Tel: 0131 624 8000 Website: www.espc.com

FIFE SPC: 67 Crossgate, Cupar, Fife KY15 5AS Web: www.fifespc.co.uk

HIGHLAND SPC: 30 Queensgate, Inverness IV1 1DJ Tel: 01463 231173 Email: info@hspc.co.uk Website: www.hspc.co.uk

PERTHSHIRE SPC: 6 South St., John's Place, Perth PH1 5SU Tel: 01738 635301 Email: moving@pspc.co.uk Website: www.pspc.co.uk

TAYSIDE SPC: 9-11 Whitehall Crescent, Dundee DD1 4AR Tel: 01382 228770 Email: admin@tspc.co.uk Website: www.tspc.co.uk